9
11
9
2
10
13

McGAA ST.

WITHDRAWN

6
15

FIFTEENTH ST.

PHOTOGRAPH BY BILL PEERY

1. City Hall.
2. Wootton's attic: birthplace of the *News*.
3. Second home of the *News*.
4. Third home of the *News*.
5. The Rocky Mountain News Building washed away in the flood of 1864.
6. The Apollo Theater.
7. Tremont House

8. The Rocky Mountain Herald.
9. Elephant Corral.
10. Denver House.
11. Arapaho Indian Village.
12. Louisiana Saloon.
13. The first hospital.
14. The first school.
15. Criterion Saloon.

EX LIBRIS

STELLA F. COON

THE FIRST HUNDRED YEARS

THE FIRST HUNDRED YEARS

An Informal History of Denver
and the

Rocky Mountain News

by

ROBERT L. PERKIN

With a Foreword by
GENE FOWLER

Garden City, New York
DOUBLEDAY & COMPANY, INC.
1959

To the Men and Women of the
ROCKY MOUNTAIN NEWS,
Past and Present, and Especially to the Memory of
WILLIAM NEWTON BYERS:
". . . pass-crosser of a pure American breed . . ."

Foreword

WHEN in the early morning I put aside this book by Robert L. Perkin, I felt as though I had been reading a love letter to two of my old sweethearts: the City of Denver, and the *Rocky Mountain News*. The city and the newspaper had to wait one hundred years for someone capable of seeing the spiritual as well as the physical bond between the newspaper and the city which is its twin sister.

These fair sisters were born the same year; together they have shared a noteworthy heritage. Their lives, as Mr. Perkin so ably demonstrates, have been and are concurrent, inseparable one from the other in aspiration; filled with historic significance; flooded with the colors of Western romance; touched by the ups and downs of fate. The long recital by the teller of the tale is a most rewarding pleasure.

As one born in the Queen City of the Plains almost seventy years ago (how young we both were when we fell in love!) and as one who worked on the *News* early in this century, perhaps I may be forgiven when I take on the airs of an eyewitness to many of the events, and a crony of not a few persons portrayed in the pages of this book. As a professional writer I am amazed that *anyone* could manage the prodigious research; or put together the ragtag bits of almost lost traditions; sort out the facts; and make hitherto hidden or neglected data serve the demands of this authentic history—and *still* avoid the tedium which follows when most of the "documented" chronicles appear between boards. The non-scholar feels like taking leave of the whole work and mailing the author a get-well card.

Historian Perkin has told his story with skill; brightening it with rare anecdotes; and making his characters speak, live, and behave in true relation to their respective times. Not only has he blended the dual theme of Denver and its great newspaper, and with the insight of a virtuoso, but his contrapuntal notes also are superb.

Indeed, he has supplied us with sprightly excursions into the careers of several great editors, reporters, politicians, miners, pioneers, and other earth-shakers of the era. His story of the earliest Denver editor, William N. Byers, is the first comprehensive and informative appraisal of that man. Until now the Byers legend, told piecemeal up and down the city-room and Press Club reaches for many years past, lacked a co-ordinator. Byers belatedly has found a Boswell.

The fabulous names are many in this book. They appear in good perspective, from the far-off Byers down to the dynamic Roy Howard, and to the present-day editor of the *News*, Jack Foster, one of America's brightest journalistic stars.

If the University of Colorado does not award Mr. Perkin a degree, and if Roy Howard does not give him a medal in recognition of this warm, vital, important tribute to a city and to its oldest newspaper, then I shall tear up my birth certificate. Whatever else happens, or does not happen, an ancient suitor thanks Bob Perkin for having written a love letter to two of that ex-Lochinvar's old sweethearts.

GENE FOWLER

PROLOGUE

Something of a Saga

THIS is the joint history of a city and a newspaper.

The city is Denver, and the newspaper is the *Rocky Mountain News*. The commingling of their biographies is no arch trick of historical sleight of hand. They were born together one hundred years ago, and the life they have shared every day since then has been a robust one.

Denver came into being as a side issue to the Pike's Peak or Bust! gold rush of 1859. It is now one of America's major cities. The transformation was not without the trying of souls.

The *Rocky Mountain News*, a journal of some little durability, has survived flood, fire, starvation, and mounted desperadoes with nervous trigger fingers. It has come through half a dozen wars, including the Indian. It has stood off plagues of grasshoppers and, narrowly, two gentlemen of exquisite rapacity named Bonfils and Tammen. Drouths, panics, and the Ku Klux Klan have done their worst. Repeal of the Sherman Silver Purchase Act left a deep wound, and the *News* also has lived out the boycotts of corporations, the ink-tipped lances of Eugene Field, and the hyperbole of flatterers.

Editors of the *Rocky Mountain News* have been kidnaped, shot at, caned, pistol-whipped, hanged in effigy, and immortalized in stained glass. They have chased redskins, built commonwealths, founded universities, climbed mountains, and been clouted from the rear while walking to work. On one day of scandalous memory an editor was the target of an unrequited mistress armed, naturally, with a pearl-handled pistol. In varied local catalogues the editors appear as pioneers, builders of city and state and star-guided Western empire, as public benefactors, history makers, grand gladiators, forces for the right, and champions of the people. The editor also has been typed as pinhead, Bub, Buster, wildcat, slinking dog, moral leper, cutthroat, low vagabond, and "the grandest liar and most infamous rascal out of hell alive."

An early contemporary summed it up. The *Colorado Iris* said in May of 1891:

The *Rocky Mountain News* was 32 years old last month. It is the oldest continuously published paper in this portion of the great West. . . . The wild Indians have held high carnival around its cabin and the coyotes have scratched its roof off. Rattlesnake Pete, Bronco Bill and other Western "terrors" have each in turn demanded "satisfaction," and generally went away with more than they wanted. It has been drowned, burned, scalped and boycotted and it is still there, the leading newspaper of the greatest country out of doors.

Rhetoric and circumstance have been hectic, but neither has prevailed. A generation or two ago this would have been attributed to something called grit, but that word now is long out of fashion and its alternative offends sensitive ears.

Only yesterday, as time runs for Denver and the *News*, there was gravel in the gold pan and painted savages lurking. Today Denver is a large city, growing larger at a dizzying pace, and the *News* is its oldest institution. A little older, in fact, than the city itself. The printing press preceded school, church, court, and permanent municipal government into the Pike's Peak wilderness. A newspaper was on the scene, a going proposition, when the news events began to happen, which is possibly the ideal "scoop" situation. It is also an occurrence without precedent in American journalism.

There are many centenarians among the daily newspapers of the United States. A compilation by the American Newspaper Publishers Association lists 277 of them. The nation's first newspaper, the Boston *News-Letter*, began its reporting in 1704 and stood for fifteen years as the only news press in America, but it has not survived. The Boston of the *News-Letter*'s day was the colonial metropolis, with a population of 7000. Hartford, too, was an established colonial city of note with a proud New England culture more than a century old when the *Courant*, America's senior living newspaper, made its bow in 1764. New Yorkers in frock coats and fastidious mutton chops already were discussing earnestly in 1851 whether a wasteland of civic rubbish far uptown should be converted into a central park. In the midst of this debate on the high and advanced level of urban renewal, Henry Jarvis Raymond brought forth his *Times* by candlelight in a half-completed building for a population nearly as large as Denver's today. Both the *Times* and the *Courant* are pioneers and pillars of the American press, but their cities were built, ready and waiting for them when they appeared.

In the mountain West two notable newspapers predate the *Rocky Mountain News*. Salt Lake City's *Deseret News* began publication in 1850, and the Santa Fe *New Mexican* a year earlier. Again, these papers were created to serve the news hunger of communities already substantial and flourishing, even if far distant from centers of civilization back in "the States." In Utah, Brigham Young's buffeted church came first, and then a press was established to advance the aspirations of the hardy, self-reliant Mormon way of life. In New Mexico, Santa Fe had been a colonial capital long before tea was dumped in Boston Harbor, and a news press actually was laggard in arriving, probably because a dominant church amply met the needs of the community for public instruction and guidance.

But Denver and the *News* started from scratch and hardscrabble together.

One year there was a waste of prairie and mountain, crisscrossed by the trails of Indians, fur traders, and explorers and passed by and through, leaped over, by the argonauts of the original gold rush to California. Flip the calendar, and there is a newspaper in business, informing, counseling, cajoling, bullying, and boosting a ragtag town in the midst of a brawling tidal wave of immigration which was being denounced by most of the country, and many of the participants, as a humbug.

It happened that fast.

An avaricious dream of overnight fortune was the touchstone. "By God, now my wife can be a lady!" That shout bounced out of a rocky gulch when one gold hunter struck it rich. The decency implicit in the cry assures him a place in the Colorado legend. But there would be no brownstone mansions for most of the pilgrims, no carriages or soirees with potted palm and violin, no mulberry moiré gowns or lady-hoods for their wives. A few made it; most didn't. And air castles were converted into a city and state by historical processes more laborious and mundane, including a newspaper's urgings of horny-handed agriculture on bonanza chasers too much in a hurry to wait upon the cyclic bounties of the seasons.

The *News* arrived in April of 1859, along with thousands of other immigrants. They found a gaggle of contentious settlements rough-built out of those materials which came most quickly to the hands of men more interested in panning for gold dust. Mostly the materials were cottonwood logs, mud, and prairie sod. The settlements were named Montana, Auraria, St. Charles, and, with almost comic civic patriotism, "Denver City."

Of these, Montana had come first. It had been laid out, off to the south, in September 1858, and ten or twelve cabins built for the winter. The settlers of Montana had crossed the plains on the strength of persistent rumors, dating back to 1852 and beyond, that there was gold to be had in the streams which drained the farthest high prairies at the foot of the Rockies.

Montana lasted less than a year. Its cabins were torn down and the building materials moved a few miles north to the spot where the proponents of Auraria, St. Charles, and Denver City had been noisily contending their rights to townsites in the late summer and fall of 1858. Auraria was established in August and named for a Georgia gold-mining town. St. Charles was blocked out in September only to have its 640-acre claim jumped unceremoniously in November by the sponsors of Denver City, who named their hopeful village for the then governor of Kansas Territory, James William Denver.

Although the plurality of "towns" might imply otherwise, the area was not much congested in 1858. The towns and city were largely on paper or in the dreams of visionaries. The combined population of all four would not have exceeded a few score men and a half dozen women, and many of these journeyed back home for the winter. "Pike's Peak fever" had not yet become pandemic.

During the summer a few dollars' worth of elusive gold flakes had been sluiced or panned from the creeks of the vicinity, and some of the magic dust in goose or turkey quills—"Cherry Creek safes"—was carried back to the Missouri River towns which formed the westernmost fringe of civilization. The growing nation still lingered there, close to navigable waters it had come to understand and command, and hesitated to make the plunge out into the high, dry, lonely plains where Comanche and Pawnee roamed with scalp knife and yet more nameless terrors persisted out of travelers' tales a century old. Out there beyond Westport Landing, west of Leavenworth and Omaha and St. Joseph, lay the formidable Great American Desert of the explorers Pike and Long and all the school geographies. This was the wasteland the great and eloquent Daniel Webster had denounced from the floor of the United States Senate in 1838:

> What do we want with this vast worthless area, this region of savages and wild beasts, of deserts, shifting sands and whirlwinds of dust, of cactus and prairie dogs? To what use could we ever hope to put these great deserts or those endless mountain ranges, impregnable and covered to their very base with eternal snow? What use have we for such a country?
>
> Mr. President, I shall never vote one cent from the public treasury to place the Pacific Coast one inch nearer Boston than it is now.

Aside from a few adventurous souls of the sort to whom horizons always sing a siren song, most of the population of the Missouri River towns felt in 1858 about the way Webster had in 1838. Let the crazy mountain men with their dirty beards and greasy fringed jackets go out to the "Shining Mountains" if they wished. They seemed to have a passion for loneliness anyway. They could roam and hunt out there if they wanted to, and bring back the beaver skins and other furs. That was all there was out there: just beavers and grizzly bears, with a few sleepy Mexicans down on the southern border of nowhere. And between the steamboat landing and nowhere was nothing but dust and rattlesnakes and mean Indians. Maybe the critics were right in insisting President

Jefferson had been stung when he laid out fifteen million good American dollars for Louisiana. This damp black earth of the river valleys was fine for raising corn, but that was a big gap on the map between here and California, whence had come stories so wild and fabulous as hardly to be credited by any hardheaded, right-living man. The star of empire of Bishop Berkeley and John Quincy Adams was temporarily stalled in its westward course.

The panic of 1857, however, had spread gloom like a river-bottom fog up and down the Missouri. Everyone was hard up, and there was precious little market in town for the small surpluses of grain and produce the good black earth yielded. Money was tight, of a sudden debts were mountainous and crushing, and there were patches on homespun britches frugally dyed with the juice of the butternut. Young men, particularly, dreamed of a place to strike out anew.

Into this atmosphere came a few quills of gold dust from the far Pike's Peak country. The value of the dust was nominal, but no one was in much of a mood to quibble about quantity when quality was there plain to see. And the hopeful stories told by the sunburned Pike's Peakers were Midas-touched. Word spread up and down the river like prairie fire in a high wind, the story growing more wonderful, more detailed, and more inaccurate as each person or journal added just a mite from imagination to the retelling. In no time at all it came to be asserted and believed that Pike's Peak itself was absolutely and entirely pure, glorious, solid yellow gold, and the whole peak could be carried away, piece by piece, for the taking.

One account had it that the way to gather gold at Pike's Peak was to build oneself a framework of heavy timber, like a stone boat, a vehicle familiar to every industrious Missouri valley farmer. The bottom should be constructed of heavy rasps. One then hoisted this cumbersome device to the summit of the peak, embarked in it, and slid down the precipitous slopes as a child rides a bobsled down a pasture hill. The rasps on the bottom would scrape off the solid gold in great, heavy shavings and these would curl up and back into the machine. By the time the gold boat and its pilot reached the foot of the peak something approximating a ton of the metal would be on board. This, the story went, was "the common manner of gathering" gold in the Far West. It was obvious that one easily could become a millionaire, richer than Croesus, richer even than the town banker.

Or there was the "Wheelbarrow Man," who had a different formula for striking it rich. He swore that when he arrived in the Pike's Peak country he ran the wheel of his barrow into the waters of Cherry Creek. The waters were so auriferous that when he withdrew the wheel it had turned to gold by a wondrous process of conversion unknown to metallurgists then or since. Everything about the Pike's Peak country was "auriferous" in those days: creek, mountain and sky, language and literature, intent and expectation. The region, in fact, was so drippingly gold-bearing that one was advised not to take pack mules along: the long-eared beasts would not be able to bring back loads as heavy as oxen could.

Fed on such tall tales and other reports scarcely milder, the Missouri Valley simmered and seethed and built up steam. Some of the border newspapers fanned the flames, cannily reasoning that if a full-fledged rush should be whipped up their towns would profit by the added commerce as jumping-off places for the diggings. Guidebooks were rushed into print to offer a dozen "best" routes to Pike's Peak and detailed inventories of what the well-supplied gold seeker would take along as outfit.

One of these guides was prepared by a young Omaha man, William N. Byers, who soon would follow his own route west to become the founding editor of the *Rocky Mountain News*. Byers earlier had traveled the Oregon Trail and knew whereof he spoke. He suggested these items, among others, for a party of four planning six months of prospecting:

3 yoke of oxen, at $75 per yoke	$225.00
1 wagon (wooden or wrought iron axle)	85.00
1 Tent and poles—the latter ironed	15.00
1 Dutch oven, for baking bread	1.25
1 wooden bucket	.25
4 steel picks, best quality, with handles	9.50
4 steel shovels, best quality, Ames' make	6.00
5 Gold pans, largest size	4.00
Sheet iron for Long Tom	.75
Pair of gold scales	2.00
3 gallons Brandy	12.00
Gunpowder, 8 pounds	3.20
Lead, 25 pounds	2.50
Shot, 10 pounds	1.00
2000 Gun Caps	1.20
10 yards drilling, for sluice	1.25

"Your ruffled shirts, standing collars and all kinds of fine clothing had better be left in your trunk, or wardrobe at home," Byers advised; "discard *all* cotton or linen clothing; adapt yourself at once to woolen and leather; provide yourself with woolen underclothes; woolen overshirts, thick and strong; woolen pants. . . . You may also leave your razor, for you won't use it. Pack all your baggage in a carpet or canvass sack; carry no trunks or boxes, if you can avoid it. . . ."

Byers was a temperate man throughout a life that extended into the present century. He probably thought a word of caution in order about all that brandy. "Brandy is intended for medicine," he lectured pro-

spective pilgrims, "rainy days and Fourth of July, and should always be
used *very* sparingly."

He also counseled temperance in travel, that reins be put to haste
in getting to Pike's Peak to pick up nuggets:

> About twenty miles each day is as far as cattle should be driven. This
> will occupy about ten hours, the balance of the day they should have
> to feed, so that they may rest at night.
>
> The day's travel should commence from six to seven o'clock A.M.,
> continue five hours, rest two, again travel five hours, and camp for the
> night. Of course this rule cannot always be adhered to, but it should
> be so far as practicable. Don't travel Sundays. Your cattle need rest,
> and so do you.

And he had a final word of moral advice:

> In conclusion, we would say to all who go to the mines, especially
> to the young, *Yield not to temptation.* Carry your principles with you;
> leave not your character at home, nor your Bible; you will need them
> both, and even *grace* from above, to protect you in a community whose
> god is Mammon, who are wild with excitement [sic], and free from
> family restraints.

The city of Mammon soon was to become Byers' own. Before the
year was out he would be babying, boosting, and scolding it and jealously
protecting it from all slanders. During the winter of 1858–59, however,
the Cherry Creek diggings were not a settlement in terms of geography,
but a myth, a great pot of gold just over the horizon, and the Missouri
River border towns could scarcely contain themselves in their eagerness
to send deputations out to partake of the riches. A few parties started
that winter, and some of them made it through. But when spring came
the frontier exploded, shooting out filaments of migration which carried
thousands westward along trails black with men and animals and
luminous with hope.

The *Rocky Mountain News* was born of this explosion which burst
the barrier that had held the nation so long at the banks of the Missouri.
As he had announced in his guide book, Byers himself took to the Platte
River trail in March at the head of an outfit which included a printing
press along with, presumably, the specified three gallons of brandy. By
the end of April he had launched his newspaper—and had time for a
little personal prospecting on the side.

Though he never stopped trying, Byers failed to find his own El
Dorado of gold or silver, but he quickly became conscious that he and
his *News* were making history. Out of rough materials, and in the midst
of a half-mad tumult, a city was being fashioned at his doorstep. He
and his paper pitched in to help.

It wasn't easy work. Most of the immigrants arrived in a euphoria of rosy optimism. This was not going to be rough pioneering but a jubilation, a get-rich-quick lark of an outing. Few came prepared, in psyche or pocketbook, for the rough business of mining or the equally stern task of mere survival five hundred long, slow miles from civilization. One fifty-niner later confessed he had set out from the Missouri with total fluid assets of twenty-five cents, and had squandered ten cents along the way.

The disillusionment was brutal. No gold sleds. Cherry Creek did not flow in a gold-lined channel. The Rockies were not, as advertised, lined, plated, or even uniformly veined with gold. A muttering, angry despondency mounted as each band of arrivals learned the worst. A few miners with experience gained in California or Georgia were making wages with their pans, Long Toms, and sluices, but no one was getting rich. Pike's Peak was a humbug, a cruel hoax. Thousands had come, and thousands headed back in a reverse migration of dejected and angry men vowing "Death & Vengeance!" on those who had lured them so far from home with golden promises.

The *News* helped stem the tide of "gobacks" with authoritative reports of actual and substantial strikes. It heaped editorial scorn on the fatuous and the foolhardy and never ceased to admonish all who would travel west to see the elephant that they should arrive well capitalized, prepared for work, and with their heads screwed on tight. Pike's Peak was no country, the *News* warned, for tenderfeet, greenhorns, tail-turners, and other "creatures who should never have been unloosed from their mothers' apron strings." Of these days of trial and gloom the press historian and bibliographer Douglas C. McMurtrie has written:

> From the beginning, the *Rocky Mountain News* made itself felt as a commanding influence in the life and activities of the new settlements. It was ably and fearlessly edited, and more than ordinary care and effort was expended upon procuring accurate and reliable information about conditions in the mines. In fact, accuracy and truthfulness in its reports was the all-embracing policy of the paper. Nevertheless, such was the skepticism in the eastern states about everything connected with Colorado that the editor of the *News* was widely regarded by his eastern contemporaries as one of the most capable and dangerous liars in the country. . . .

It was a busy but disheartening summer for the *News* and its editor. Prospective subscribers were leaving the country in droves, but there was at least one cause for some rejoicing. The paper was winning its campaign for peace and unity between the rival villages of Auraria and Denver City, which had been glaring across Cherry Creek at each other like schoolboys.

Rivalries bristled, and civic pride was a point of jealous honor. Aurarians

and Denver Citians hotly contested each other's claims to population
supremacy, to first painted house, first birth of a "white child" (Indians
and half-breeds didn't count in the tabulation), first bank, first school—
to the first of anything that was or seemed to be what a proper town
ought to have. Any new enterprise persuaded to locate east or west
of the creek became a prize—ammunition for a new salvo in the intercity wars. The *News* was a civic trophy of first order, since any
town worthy the name had to have a newspaper. Auraria had the
News, Denver City didn't, and nothing so rankled in the patriotic
breasts of the Denver City fathers. There were blandishments and
courtings. In October, Byers was offered twenty-four city lots if he would
move his press a hundred yards or so northeast across the sandy bottoms
of the dividing creek. In June town company officials had made a similar
offer to Albert D. Richardson if he would establish a weekly "equal in
size to the *Rocky Mountain News*" in their newsless town. Within a
few years Richardson was to become the famous Civil War correspondent
of the New York *Tribune*, noted for his feat of running the blockade
at Vicksburg by floating down the river on a bale of hay. After the war
Richardson wrote his *Beyond the Mississippi*, a classic of early Western
travel, but in 1859 he was covering the Pike's Peak rush for the *Tribune*
and the Boston *Journal*. For a time in 1859–60 he helped edit the lively
little *Western Mountaineer* in Golden City, a dozen miles west of
Cherry Creek in the foothills, and he was briefly a member of the *Rocky
Mountain News* editorial staff in 1860.

Eventually Denver City got not one but several newspapers, and in
good time the *News* picked up its types and moved across the creek,
never to return to the "West Side." Civic jealousies cooled under the
necessity of presenting a common front to late-arriving and irreverent
detractors, and a movement for consolidation gained ground. Neither
settlement was much by itself, it had to be candidly admitted, but perhaps putting the two together would make a presentable village to serve
as capital of the new-won empire. By December the legislature of the
provisional, and entirely illegal, territory of Jefferson was in a mood of
conciliation sufficiently mellow to adopt an act providing for the consolidation of Auraria, Denver City, and Highland, which had been
platted on the slopes across the river by a group of optimistic promoters
including editor Byers.

An election was held December 19, a mayor chosen for the consolidated towns, and the present city of Denver dates from these beginnings: an illegal act by a legislature of no authority and an election of
dubious validity. The tainted status of their united town apparently
troubled the Denverites all winter. So a mass meeting was held in March
to give the consolidation decision a second round of public approval.
Then in the moonlit night of April 6, 1860, the populace met on the
newly completed bridge across Cherry Creek at Larimer Street to "rejoice

over the marriage, and to listen to the inevitable speeches." The *News* reported the historic occasion from its new building a block downstream. In those days, everything happened within a stone's throw of the *News*.

The paper had reported on December 8: "A meeting of citizens was held at Jumps' Hall on Tuesday evening for the purpose of nominating candidates for the municipal offices, under the charter recently granted by the legislative assembly, to incorporate Denver, Auraria and Highland, under one municipal government. . . ." The following week the text of the consolidation act appeared on page one, and on December 21 the vote was in for the first municipal election of the consolidated city. John C. Moore had won handily in an election which had brought out, the *News* reported, a grand total of 690 voters, 342 of them in Denver, 348 in Auraria.

Denver had arrived as a going concern. Within a very short time she would be loudly demanding a place in the sun among American cities, devil take the hindmost and no holds barred. Her newspaper champion was ready to bet its boots or eat its hat that she was the finest baby, for her weight, in all the land. Bubbled the *News* on May 28, 1863:

> We will wager an iron clad to a dugout that no city in the world less than four years old can boast as handsome women, as fast horses, as busy streets, as many churches, and as much genuine prosperity, as Denver. Who wants to bet?

So runs the background to the story of a frontier journal and a mile-high city on the eve of their joint centennial.

Denver today is a city of about 830,000 persons and growing so rapidly toward the million mark that all but her most confirmed boosters long since have abandoned the view that bigness is a civic virtue. The altitude is precisely 5280 feet at the sixteenth step of the granite flight leading up to the west portico of the Colorado statehouse, which imitates the national Capitol in architecture and has pure gold leaf from Colorado mines covering its dome.

The city sits, rather handsomely most visitors and all residents think, on a dozen gentle hills that slope down to the confluence of Cherry Creek and the South Platte River. Neither stream is navigable by any vessel of deeper draft than a canoe, although the *News* once sought to remedy this situation by sheer force of language. Early in its career the paper inaugurated with a straight face a shipping news department to report on dockings and sailings of river-borne traffic. The department soon was discontinued. Most of the scows and rafts which had been christened with pleasantly nautical names—possibly by the *News*— came to early grief on the sand bars of the Platte, since known as "the river that flows upside down." The *News* diverted its promotional instincts to matters of artificial irrigation, a system to which Denver owes most of its beauty and Colorado much of its economic base.

Denver lies at the far western edge of the arid Great Plains. The upslope of the Rocky Mountains, where the water comes from, begins a few miles farther west. The Denver rainfall sustains a natural vegetation which browns off rapidly as dry summer days advance. So Denver has imported her own greenery. Except for a few hoary cottonwoods and evergreen conifers, the trees which make an oasis of the city are imports; they and the lawns are kept alive only by faithful and ritualistic irrigation. The garden hose and the lawn sprinkler deserve a place on the city seal along with mountain sky line and soaring eagle.

The jagged western sky line is, of course, the dominant landscape feature. The Rockies in their changing moods of sun and cloud form a rampart behind the Mile-High City. Snow fields of dazzling white high up along the Continental Divide are visible from Denver doorsteps around the year, and "the hills," as Denver calls them, are a constant in the city's ethos. The peak which looks directly down on Denver from the middle distance is Mount Evans (14,264 feet). Off to the south is Pike's Peak (14,110), which once lent its name to the whole region. To the north is Long's Peak (14,255), first climbed in 1868 by editor Byers of the *News*—a busy man—in company with the one-armed explorer of the Colorado River, Major John Wesley Powell. Between the extremes of Pike's and Long's peaks lies a panorama a hundred and ten miles in scope which is Denver's daily portion of natural grandeur.

Denver is the capital of her state, and she proclaims that, as the largest city, she is also the capital of an area extending from border to border and from Kansas City to—well, at least to Salt Lake (overlapping spheres of influence allowed for, naturally). The Chamber of Commerce is at some pains to keep alive the statistic that the Denver population is, and has been for a long time, greater than that of any city between the Missouri River and the Pacific coast, an area comprising about half the nation. This sort of bold geographical quartering once was part of the standard repertoire of any Denverite of decent civic pride, but of late long-timers who knew a quieter, less exuberant city with no one-way streets can be heard grousing, "Yes, and why don't they go back where they came from?"

The economic underpinning includes commerce, service industry, finance—Denver's Seventeenth Street likes to think of itself as "the West's Wall Street", a designation the *News* sometimes irreverently edits into "Scratch Lane"—agriculture, mining, and tourists. Other factors: federal employees, railroads, air travel, sugar beets, cattle and sheep and meat packing, oil exploration, refining and marketing, a spanking new guided missiles plant with its cluster of satellite industries, uranium, and a top-secret Atomic Energy Commission installation, skiing, light industry, Fitzsimmons Army Hospital (on which the eyes of the world centered when a President suffered a heart attack), the Rocky Mountain Arsenal, Buckley Field Naval Air Station, and Lowry Air Force Base. At the turn of the century, when fresh air and climate cures for tuberculosis were in vogue, scores of sanitariums were built in Denver and filled with an army of health-seekers, some later to become prominent leaders in business and the professions. The TB germ accounts for the beginning of Denver's growth as a health and medical center.

This is also the town where the "damn Yankees" trained their young ballplayers, farmed out to the Denver Bears, and it's the city where a shavetail Ike wooed and won Mamie, the belle of Lafayette Street.

So much in the way of profile of the current setting.

The role of the *Rocky Mountain News* in all of this has been a lusty and sinewy one, and it doesn't fit the standard script. This can be no onward and upward tale of corporate enterprise vaulting sure-footedly to successively higher and higher pinnacles of achievement. Beloved as that sort of legend is in the folklore of American initiative, it won't do in this case. The *News* has picked itself up off the canvas too often, and too bloody, to be shaped into the image of all-conquering hero. For most of its years the *News* has been lean, hungry, and uncomplacent. It has enjoyed high moments of success, dominance, and triumph. It also has known defeat and despair. If there was a day when the city fondly named it "Old Reliable," there also was another day when there was not enough cash in the till to pay off the help and lock the doors. The story of the *News* illustrates with an uncommon clarity just how organic a newspaper can be. There's something human in its instinct to live, its will to persist and endure through natural catastrophe or economic prostration. The heart of the matter may lie in the close involvement of newspaper with community, an intimacy necessarily nearer than that of any other institution. A hot commerce of all things transient and timeless, grubby and exalted, runs in the columns of a newspaper, which is discarded daily as garbage wrapper yet lives a hundred years.

The *News* is more than just the oldest settler at the junction of Cherry Creek with the Platte. It has been committed. It helped create city and state, and found lost dogs. It published daily lessons when a coal strike closed down the schools, and it told of the legal and social difficulties of Gilda Gray, the "shimmy queen." It has offered counsel to the lovelorn and hounded municipal corruption from office. And the record starts at the very beginning. Perhaps no other newspaper in America has a history which so exactly parallels that of the community it lives with and serves.

The story of the *News* cannot be told in the notable headlines it has published. This will be no methodical analysis of how the *News* covered the assassination of Lincoln, Custer's last fight, the sinking of the Maine, the betrayal of Woodrow Wilson, or the Normandy landings. These were events of great moment to all those who, like the *News,* lived through them, but the way the *News* handled their presentation to its readers was not substantially different from that of any other ably edited newspaper. Nor will this be a maudlin, righteous catalogue of acts of nobility, of crusades for the right and good with banners flying and the *News* armored as avenging knight with flaming sword. The *News* has crusaded on occasion, but so has every other newspaper worthy of its salt. These things are not *sui generis.* The *News* has its own personality, and the intent in these pages is to probe more intimately. The red-blooded and the antic will not be passed over here in order to elaborate the obvious.

President Franklin D. Roosevelt saluted the *News* on its eightieth birthday and commented, "What a rich mine of history the files of your paper must be with their continuous chronicle of the life of the community and the state through all the changes and chances of eighty years." The historian Hubert H. Bancroft set it down thus: "The *Rocky Mountain News* must ever constitute the corner-stone of Colorado History." And Jerome C. Smiley, author of the standard history of Denver, wrote of the history recorder as history maker: ". . . no other single agency did so much to hearten the people, to uphold the right and to lead the way through the many difficulties that beset the paths of those who founded Colorado and its queen city. . . . It was a valiant champion of the new country under oft discouraging conditions; and the defender of faith in the ultimate triumph that would come to those who were steadfast. It rose above the trials and disappointments of the day and pointed with what would now seem the gift of prophecy to that which the future held for the town and country."

The whole of the west-running time of a city, a state, and a region lies preserved in the columns of the *Rocky Mountain News.* A newspaper which has sold its individual copies for hay, shingles, cabbage, gold dust, and specie has become invaluable to the historian, and it is cited somewhere among the footnotes of any scholarly treatment of the Rocky Mountain West which presumes to go to original sources.

When it began its labors pioneering still was a matter of "a rifle, an axe, and a bag of corn." During its years a continent filled up and rounded out and a modern city rose from huts of logs and mud. The *Rocky Mountain News* can say—as Aeneas said to Dido—"All of which I saw, part of which I was."

Contents

THE FIRST HUNDRED YEARS

CHAPTER ONE

Baptized in Snow Water

A LATE-SEASON snow, heavy and wet, fell on Auraria, Kansas Territory, throughout the day and into the night of April 22, 1859. Big puffs of clustered flakes drifted down on the mud roofs of cabins and on the conical tipis pitched among the trees along the river. It wasn't really cold: just chill, sodden, and dispiriting, were it not for the hints of laggard spring. The cottonwoods were beginning to leaf out, sticky green.

Auraria was not much of a town. Nothing to write home about, even if there had been a mail service. A raw little settlement far out in Indian country. An orphan huddle of cabins and nondescript shacks in the wilderness.

But it was a busy and noisy wilderness.

Thousands of men were on the move, going and coming. Draft oxen bawled their discomfort. Wagon wheels strained and creaked, and the long bull whips cracked. Over the whole turmoil a tumult of shouting, much of it profane.

Members of the Arapaho band, silent in damp blankets, stood beside their lodges to watch the wild traffic through the storm. Scouts from down the Platte reported many more white men headed up the trail. Here beside Cherry Creek they were everywhere underfoot, like dogs in a hunting camp. They jostled each other, seeking spots to put up tents or spread out bedrolls. They seemed to be able to talk only in shouts, except that they fell silent and moved their hands uneasily toward rifle, pistol, or belt knife when an Indian moved by. The wheels of their wagons had churned the sandy bottom of the creek into a quagmire, and sometimes a wagon would founder hub deep. The hoofs of their oxen, mules, and horses already had pounded the nearby prairie as bare of grass as a buffalo wallow. The animals themselves, lean and galled from forty days of hard travel and scant pasturage, were so trail-poor as to be scarcely worth stealing. The men were strange ones: tense, jumpy, loud, possessed by evil spirits which would not let them be still.

The white men were trespassing again, and their noisy coming frightened away the game. The soldiers had promised that this country where the Rockies rise from the high plains would remain forever a hunting preserve for the Arapahoes and Cheyennes. There had been a pipe and presents to seal the bargain, and the chiefs had pledged their braves to good behavior. For the most part the pledge had been kept—if one didn't count a little honest thievery of casually guarded ponies. Yet now the country swarmed with white men who had come so swiftly and in such great numbers that protest was impossible. No one had time or inclination, obviously, to hold council on legal title to this muddy, churned-up land. The Sioux and Pawnees said it had happened like this before. Now it was happening again, and this time in a swooping flood of men and animals that darkened the prairie.

This was the Pike's Peak gold rush, last of the nation's abrupt westerings, and the objective was this crude place called Auraria, where, in all the town, there was only one building with glass windowpanes. In beyond the windows, one particular bunch of the newcomers was behaving more oddly than all the rest.

In the first place they had pitched their square tipi *inside* the house. They had lighted candles and lanterns because the day was snowy and dark. In the flickering light some of the strangers were making erratic, magical movements of their hands over flat boxes tipped up at an angle. Their fingers moved as rapidly as those of a squaw picking lice from a buffalo robe.

The building with the windows was "Uncle Dick's" saloon, and what was happening there was the birth of printing in the Rocky Mountains. As the damp evening passed, the first sheet of the *Rocky Mountain News* was peeled from the form of a Washington hand press.

In distant Manhattan the next morning, warm and well-fed New Yorkers stretched their legs expansively before glazed tile hearths and read in their elegantly refined *Ledger:*

THE FIRST MORNING HOUR

Nature tells us what it should be. Not ushered in with din and strife, and the trumpet-call to battle; but stealing softly, quietly, serenely over the senses, with song of birds and scent of myriad flowers. Just so should the spirit be in its waking hours, buoyant, hopeful, bright, soaring, rejoicing. . . . Oh mothers, fathers, guard your first *waking* thoughts! . . . Look to the *first* morning hours of each day, for, like the little stone which you idly throw into the lake, careless where it sinks, it leaves a ripple that shall widen till it reach the shore of eternity.[1]

Out on the frontier, fevered and unserene Pike's Peakers, well beyond the scent of potted begonias, read in *their* ink-fresh newspaper:

CHEERING.

Mr. R. P. Smith, formerly of Plattsmouth, N. T., has just called at our office and shown us a package of Gold dust weighing a few cents

[1] New York *Ledger*, April 23, 1859.

over forty two dollars. Mr. S. informs us that this is the result of three days labor by three men, working with the common rocker, and that in a new claim. This claim is on what is known as Dry Creek, three miles above its junction with the Platte, and eight miles west of Cherry Creek. . . .

This gold is all scale, or wash gold of the finest quality, perfectly clean and pure.

Other reports in similar vein had come in during the day before to "Uncle Dick" Wootton's store-saloon-meeting hall-printing office. They were rushed into type as fast as the thin light of a dark and stormy day would permit, and they became parts of the content of the new newspaper sputtering into being as a pinpoint of light in the wilderness.

A home for the newspaper, a partial shelter from inclement and inauspicious weather, had been provided by the doughty old frontiersman, Richens Lacy ("Uncle Dick") Wootton, a renowned mountain man who had known a wilder but more placid West for nearly two decades. It was an inadvertent providing. "Uncle Dick" really had been headed home to Kentucky. He never got there.

On my way, I intended to make one more trade with the Indians, and that was to wind-up my affairs in the Rocky Mountain region. [Wootton told Howard Louis Conard.] I loaded several wagons with goods, pocketed the drafts on St. Louis, in which the bulk of my fortune had been invested, and early in October, found myself again on the road, but with a different object in view from what I had had, when setting out on my former trips. . . . My first objective point was the upper Platte River, where I knew I should find the Arapahoe and Cheyenne Indians, and it was with them that I proposed to trade.

I followed what is now the line of the Santa Fe Railroad from Fort Union to Trinidad, and from there went due north by way of the Pueblo, to where Denver is now. There I came to a stop, and all my plans and I suppose the whole course of my after life was changed.

There wasn't much of Denver at that time, and I don't think anybody ever dreamed that any such city as we find there to-day would grow up inside of a hundred years. . . .[2]

Wootton found the first gold seekers beginning to settle at Cherry Creek, and they were eager for his New Mexican trading goods. He arrived on Christmas Eve of 1858, and a part of the cargo in the Wootton "train" consisted of several kegs of Taos lightnin', a virulent, corrosive 40-rod whiskey warranted to curl hair and cross eyes. "Uncle Dick" generously knocked in the heads of a couple kegs, hung out a tin cup, and invited all of his prospective customers to help themselves. The

[2]Howard Louis Conard, "Uncle Dick" Wootton: The Pioneer Frontiersman of the Rocky Mountain Region (Chicago, 1890), p. 372.

entire population gladly obliged, and Denver's first Christmas was merry with wild carouse and friendly skull-thumping disputation.

Such hearty celebrations were much to Wootton's robust taste. He decided to locate permanently. The town fathers of Auraria subsidized him with a hundred and sixty acres of land—which they didn't own— and "Uncle Dick" put up the settlement's first "business block" with hewn pine logs, a few whipsawed planks, a shake roof and—*mirabile dictu!*—the only glass windows within five hundred miles. The precious panes had been hauled to New Mexico on the Santa Fe Trail, and Wootton either brought them with him when he came or sent down to Santa Fe or Taos for them.

The Wootton "block" was not an imposing structure. Stark, bare, and plain, it stood one and a half stories in height on the flat Cherry Creek bottoms, southwest of the stream, at what became Fourth and Ferry streets when Auraria got around to platting and naming its thorough-fares. The present-day equivalent would be about 1413–15 Eleventh Street, in the heart of one of Denver's busy produce markets. Unfortu-nately no good picture of the Wootton building is available. An artist's conception in wood-block engraving appears in *Frank Leslie's Illustrated Newspaper* for August 20, 1859, and this drawing later was copied with slight changes in both Albert D. Richardson's *Beyond the Mississippi* (Hartford, 1867) and Jerome C. Smiley's *History of Denver* (Denver, 1901), and subsequently in many places. It is probably, however, that the *Leslie's* artist had not seen his subject and was working from descriptions; for he shows a two-story structure with several upper windows. The best contemporary accounts tell of a one-story building with a little slope-roofed attic lighted by a single four-pane window.[3] It was in this dark and cramped attic that the first *News* was printed.

Downstairs, the Wootton building was somewhat more commodious. It measured 30 by 22 feet, and it served Auraria as saloon, trading post, and public auditorium. Wootton had rolled some of his kegs into line to form a counter, and across them he did business. He told Conard that he found it impossible to resist "the importunities of the pioneer settlers" that he open a store, but profits probably played a greater part than sentiment in the decision of the old trader. Measured by modern standards, the profits were handsome if not usurious.

"There was not much money in the town, or the camp, as we called it, but I got the most of what there was," Wootton candidly admitted, "and when the miners didn't have money, they generally had something to barter, and so we managed to keep business moving. . . .

"They would reach Denver 'broke,' and the first thing to do of course

[3]*Rocky Mountain News*, Jan. 18, 1860, and Feb. 1, 1860; Arthur E. Pierce, "The First Two Years," *The Trail*, June 1912; Jerome C. Smiley, *History of Denver* (Denver, 1901), p. 248, quoting William N. Byers; William N. Byers, "History of Colorado," in *Encyclopedia of Biography of Colorado* (Chicago, 1901), p. 39.

was to 'make a raise.' They nearly all came through with ox-teams, and they would come to me and leave a good yoke of cattle, as security for a loan of twenty-five dollars. On the day following they would bring back thirty dollars or forfeit the cattle. This was a matter of such frequent occurrence that loaning money in this way became a part of my business. . . ."[4]

Sale of the Taos tanglefoot from the counter kegs constituted, along with sharp monylending practices, a major part of Wootton's custom, and his patrons were inclined to become boisterous and reckless with their weapons. Discussions were likely to be punctuated, for emphasis, with a pistol shot into the ceiling. Inasmuch as all men went armed, and it was often a long time between drinks with accompanying high-level debate, the Wootton ceiling frequently was peppered. This was scarcely conducive to serene slumbers, as recommended by the New York *Ledger*, for *Rocky Mountain News* staff members sleeping on the plank floor directly overhead. They solved the problem by hauling up an extra layer of protective planking, rearranging their blankets, and going back to sleep. Subsequently, when the *News* had vacated for a less hazardous location, the attic became a noted gambling room and the store downstairs was converted to the Young America saloon, a place described as "low."[5]

Earlier, the Wootton store, being the largest structure in the ragtag settlement, had been used as the site of public gatherings. Meetings of the members of the Auraria Town Company were held there, the first efforts at municipal government in the Cherry Creek diggings. It also was the scene of the first proposals for a state government. Presumably the multipurpose kegs served as speakers' rostrum for these sessions of citizens assembled.

Outside the building a rude stairway led to the upper loft. Effective space up under the eaves has been variously estimated. One account says it was 14 by 20 feet. Another reports 16 by 18 feet. In any event it was scarcely spacious, and it was called upon to serve as editor's sanctum, composing room, business office, kitchen, and sleeping apartment. On top of everything else, the roof leaked.

William N. Byers, the young editor who was to occupy these quarters with his pioneer press, arrived at Cherry Creek on horseback on April 17. He did a little prospecting up the South Platte and was shown some encouraging "colors" taken from the placers. One miner gave him twenty-two cents worth of dust washed out of a single pan of gravel. Then he discovered he was not alone in his ambition to found a gazette to serve the mines and miners of Cherry Creek. John L. Merrick had put in an appearance from St. Joseph, Missouri, four days earlier. Merrick had

[4]Conard, op. cit., pp. 376–77.

[5]*Rocky Mountain News*, Feb. 1, 1860.

brought with him a shirttail full of types and a little "cap" size lever press which had once belonged to the harassed Mormons. The press had been tossed into the Missouri River at Independence in 1833 in one of the periodic outbursts of mob violence against the Saints, and years later it was fished out, cleaned up, and used in printing the St. Joseph *Gazette*.[6] With this equipment and no capital, Merrick leisurely was preparing to issue the first number of the *Cherry Creek Pioneer*.

Once the rival publishers became aware of each other's presence and intent, a lively contest developed to see who would be first on the streets. The race aroused the intense interest of the population, and since this consisted, "Uncle Dick" computed, of about nine tenths gamblers, there was spirited wagering on the outcome. Merrick got busy with two helpers in his rented cabin on the northeast side of the creek at what would now be Sixteenth and Larimer streets. Byers dispatched a hurry-up message to his party, which had stopped at Fort St. Vrain to the north to prospect the Cache la Poudre River. Meanwhile Byers had become acquainted with Wootton, who offered use of the attic room as a printing office.

Word that the *Rocky Mountain News*, already named, was headed out from Omaha had preceded Byers into town, and the Byers & Company party had heard vaguely at Fort Kearney that another printer, who proved to be Merrick, was headed west. The rival settlements at Cherry Creek—Auraria and Denver City—were developing civic pretensions despite their appearance and youth, and the westward course of the presses was watched with anticipation. Soon they would have what any proper town should have: a newspaper. Maybe even two.

The wagons containing the *News* press and other equipment creaked into the settlements on the evening of April 20, but one of them, heavy-laden, got stuck in the soft, sandy bed of Cherry Creek in fording the stream to the Auraria side at present-day Blake Street. It was late night before it could be lightened and pulled loose. The weary printers, however, carried their cargo up the stairs to Wootton's attic, opened and tipped up the type cases, and assembled the press to be ready for business the following morning. On the twenty-first type clicked into composing sticks and a newspaper began to take shape.

Who the printers were on that first issue is not a matter of firm record. Byers was there, and Thomas Gibson of Fontanelle, Nebraska Territory, and John L. Dailey, an experienced printer who had worked for half a dozen frontier journals in Iowa and Nebraska. Byers was neither printer nor newspaperman; this was his maiden voyage at the rudder of a public press. Gibson was both, and he was one of the partners in Wm. N. Byers & Company. Dailey came out as printing foreman, and though he later picked up skills as a paragrapher and correspondent,

[6]Douglas C. McMurtrie and Albert H. Allen, *Early Printing in Colorado* (Denver, 1935), p. 19.

he remained for many years the hardheaded, practical member of the business. So the major task of supervising typesetting for the first edition of the *News* fell to Dailey and Gibson. Varied accounts of the founding also agree on a fourth man as being present. He was Charles S. Semper, a young printer who, the following year, was instrumental in organizing Colorado's first union, Denver Typographical Union No. 49, among his fellow typos on the *News* and the papers which followed it. Others who have been listed as being connected with the *News* at its founding include Copeland Rabe, Irwin Sansom, P. W. Case, Jack Smith, L. A. and W. J. Curtice, James and Harry Creighton, W. W. Whipple, H. E. Turner, "Pap" Hoyt, Henry Gibson, and Robert L., Edward Charles, Will and Jack Sumner, Byers' brothers-in-law.

Editorial chores for the first issue were accomplished, it is assumed, by editor Byers, probably with the assistance of Thomas Gibson. But it is by no means certain that all of the articles and editorials then and later which have been freely attributed to the editor actually were written by him. Manuscript material in Byers' handwriting indicates that to the day of his death in the following century his literary style remained undistinguished and his grammar and spelling eccentric. Byers was a self-educated man and, though his output was prolific, he at no time regarded himself as a writer. Presumably John Dailey and his fellow printers—as members of their craft sometimes do—undertook considerable editing of the editor as they stood at their cases.

It is probable that Byers did most of the reporting for the first issue. If so, the editor's pen charged merrily along on April 21 and 22 as the *News* raced the *Pioneer* to press. Not much "leg work" outside the office was required, however. Byers remembered later that all the local news in the first issue was brought into the office by interested volunteer reporters anxious to be helpful.

The snowstorm hit on the night of the twenty-first and continued intermittently throughout the twenty-second. The task of the printers in hand-setting Brevier and Nonpareil type must have been a difficult one by the light of candles and whatever illumination a leaden, snow-filled sky permitted to enter through the single window. Moreover, as the heavy snow piled up on the shakes overhead, the roof began to leak. The icy melt dripped down in streams into the cases, over the press, and on the paper stocks under tarpaulins. When the time came to begin the presswork it was necessary to rig up a tent over the press so that the sheets would not be spoiled before they could be printed. The *News* was born to a baptism of snow water.

The attic editorial room, small enough to begin with, grew crowded with spectators, well-wishers, and betters as the race grew hotter on the twenty-second. The population "vibrated" between the offices of the *News* and the *Pioneer* to observe progress and protect their bets with body English and moral support. What with the storm, it wasn't a good day for gold hunting anyway, and a steady stream of citizens sloshed back and forth across the creek between Merrick in Denver City and Byers in Auraria, watching with relish Denver's first newspaper "war."

Long after night had fallen the slow, meticulous handwork at the cases went on. At last the forms were locked up. Byers gave a moment of glory to one of the onlookers, little O. P. ("Old Scout") Wiggins, mountain man, hunter, trapper, who never before had seen a printing press. He had hung around all day bugeyed with fascination. Byers let Wiggins run the ink roller over the type forms fixed in the bed of the press. Wiggins lived a long time, but he never forgot the rare honor and privilege he had been accorded. It remained in his memory as bright as his friendship with Kit Carson, his days as guide to the "Great Path-finder," John Charles Frémont, on the 1842 and 1843 expeditions to the Rockies, or his experiences as a forty-niner in California. Later "Old Scout" twice would seek to show his gratitude for being tapped as a printer's devil. He would name a town on the eastern Colorado plains for Byers, and he would thrust Scripture aside to make room for paper supplies for the *News*. During Civil War days Wiggins was given command of a detachment of fifty Omaha and Winnebago Indians and detailed to escort stages and wagon trains as protection against hostile tribes on the prairie. Wiggins and his Indians had their headquarters at Alkali, fifty miles southeast of Julesburg, so that they might scout both the Platte River and the Smoky Hill trails for the war-thinned cavalry. On one occasion Wiggins discovered a stagecoach was departing with a heavy load of Mormon Bibles consigned to Salt Lake City. A stock of sorely needed paper for the *News* in Denver was being left behind. These were trying times for an isolated journal. Wagon trains weren't getting through regularly, and the *News* was printing on any paper it could find, wall, wrapping, or tissue. "Old Scout" was aware of the situation. He threw out the Mormon Bibles, crammed the coach with paper for the *News*, and sped it on its way.[7]

In the Wootton attic on Friday night, April 22, 1859, the beaming little frontiersman worked happily with his ink roller for more than an hour. About 10 P.M. the outside sheets had been printed and the newly set inside pages were put on the press. Jack Smith, a "huge Negro," bent his two-hundred-pound bulk to the lever, and Byers emerged from the indoor tent with the first complete issue of the *Rocky Mountain News* in his hands. It was dated Saturday, April 23. Twenty minutes later by the watches of a dozen unofficial timekeepers, Jack Merrick handed out the first number of his *Cherry Creek Pioneer*, also dated April 23. He had lost the race. The first issue of the *Pioneer* would be its last.

Jack Merrick either was a good loser or he wanted to hunt gold more

[7]*Rocky Mountain News*, Apr. 23, 1897; Eugene Parsons, " 'Old Scout' Wiggins," *The Trail*, Dec. 1910, pp. 5ff.

than he wanted to be a journalist. Next day he traded off the entire *Pioneer* outfit for twenty-five dollars in flour and bacon and headed for the hills to find an auriferous fortune.[8] Gibson of the *News* "gathered the *Pioneer* establishment into his arms" and carried it across the creek to Auraria.[9] It consisted of a "bee gum" full of types and a little press capable of printing a 7- by 10-inch paper one page at a time. Merrick never did hit his strike as a gold miner, though he tried, and he would drop down from the mountains from time to time to work as a printer for the *News* until he accumulated a grubstake for a new try.

Relations apparently remained amicable both during the "war" and after. Because Merrick had been on the ground first, though he had lost the publishing race by twenty minutes, Byers later would salute him as a "jolly, wide-awake printer" and the "real pioneer" of Colorado journalism:

At the first alarm of war, he hurried to the States and enlisted in one of the earliest volunteer regiments organized in Illinois. He served his term with credit and gained promotion. When mustered out he returned to his former home, Leavenworth, Kansas, and secured a commission in a Kansas veteran regiment. About the close of the war he was provost marshal in Leavenworth, where, whilst in the active discharge of his duty, he was killed in a street riot. Poor Jack, he was one of the most generous, big-hearted men that ever lived, and the real pioneer of our craft in Colorado.[10]

Actually it hadn't been an entirely fair-and-square contest. Merrick's *Pioneer* was smaller—three columns wide against the *News'* six—but he was working with two assistants against probably a half dozen experienced men in the Wootton loft. Moreover, the *News* cold-decked him. The entire two outside pages of the paper had been set in type before the expedition ever left Omaha. The type had been brought across the plains locked in the form and ready to print. All that remained was to gather, write, and set enough news and advertisements to fill up the two inner pages.

The striking contrast in content between the inside and the outside pages often has puzzled persons who have examined one of the rare surviving copies of the first *News*. The disparity is readily understandable when one considers that part of the paper was prepared nearly two months earlier in Omaha and the balance rushed together in two days at Auraria, five hundred miles away. It sometimes has been recorded by

[8]William N. Byers, ms., Bancroft Library Pac Ms.L6, n.d. [1884].

[9]William N. Byers, "Early Journalism in Colorado," *Magazine of Western History*, April 1889, p. 692.

[10]Idem.

reputable historians that half the first *News* actually was printed in Omaha before the Byers & Company two-wagon train left for the Rockies. An examination of what a bibliographer would call internal evidence shows this to be impossible. The date April 23, 1859, appears in the masthead on page one, which otherwise had been put together at Omaha. Considering the hazards and uncertainties of plains travel in the midst of a gold rush, Byers could not have been certain what day he would issue his prospective journal, and it would have been rash beyond credibility to have dated it that far in advance. Nor was he exactly sure *where* he would publish, except that it would be somewhere in the Pike's Peak gold regions of the Rocky Mountains. Yet the page-one masthead also carries the dateline "Cherry Creek, K.T.," in an obvious bid for neutrality amid the inter-settlement rivalries of Auraria and Denver City. Merrick was committed; his *Pioneer* boldly declared its location in Denver City. The masthead of the first *News* also stipulates that it was being published for "The Mines and Miners of Kansas and Nebraska." At this time the 40th parallel was the dividing line between Kansas and Nebraska territories, both of which extended far west of present state boundaries. The 40th parallel cuts through Colorado just a few miles north of Denver, and Byers, a surveyor by trade, must have known that he might locate either north or south of the line. His several reminiscences of the founding show clearly that he did not know precisely where he was going and that he planned to pick whatever location seemed most auspicious. Under other circumstances the *Rocky Mountain News* might have been published in Golden City or Boulder City, both struggling into existence at this time, or at the old fur-trade post of Fort St. Vrain or at Arapahoe, a ghost town several miles west of Denver of which nothing now remains but a historical marker.

The manuscript diary of John L. Dailey for 1859 shows that he was at work in Omaha from February 28 through March 4 "fixing up the material for the 'Rocky Mountain News'. . . ."[11] At another point Dailey states specifically: "We had the first half of the first edition of The News in type and locked in the forms when we arrived. We prepared the first half of the sheet in Omaha before we left. . . ."[12] It must be assumed, then, that the form for the outer sheet of the first *News* was unlocked after the expedition found haven in Auraria, the dateline inserted, and the first and fourth pages run off while the subsequent form for the second and third pages was being prepared.

The press which accomplished this historic printing was a used Washington hand press, and it already had something of a pedigree in pioneering. It was an "Imperial," six-column folio in size, capable of printing two six-column pages 13¾ by 19 inches at one impression. To obtain an

[11]These diaries are in the Western History Collection, Denver Public Library.

[12]Undated clipping. Dailey scrapbook, Denver Public Library.

imprint, the form of type, lying flat in the hip-high bed, was inked with a hand roller and a sheet of paper laid upon it. The bed of the press then was cranked by hand into position under the platen and the latter levered down to make the imprint. Then the process was reversed to remove the printed sheet and begin another. A slow and laborious process by modern standards, yet a practical, efficient one which turned out good printing. In fact this same model of the Washington press sometimes still is used today for ultra-fine, damp-paper hand printing.

The Washington which printed the *News* was obtained by Byers from Bellevue, Nebraska Territory, where it was "the relict of a starved-to-death newspaper." The Missouri River town of Bellevue, half a dozen miles south of Omaha, was then larger than Omaha and viewed itself as a candidate for the territorial capital. Today Bellevue is a pleasant little suburban town of 6000 inhabitants and lies well within the shadow of Nebraska's first city. In early 1859 it long had been important as fur-trade post and outfitting point for plains travel and expeditions of exploration.[13]

Although Bellevue was a frontier village of fur-trade fame and an antiquity stretching back to 1810, it had let two newspapers starve to death in the four years prior to 1859, when Byers began shopping for a press to print his prospective *Rocky Mountain News*. It is probable that the first press to print a newspaper in Nebraska also printed the first one in Colorado.

The *Nebraska Palladium and Platte Valley Advocate*, first paper printed in the Cornhusker state, began publication in Bellevue on November 15, 1854, with H. (or D.) E. Reed as editor and Thomas Morton, Dan Carpenter, and A. D. Long as printers. It managed to collect 500 subscribers but died with the issue of April 11, 1855. The press, however, remained in Bellevue, possibly in the hands of the settlement's leading merchant, as security for bills covering provisions which had sustained the editor and his printers in their struggle with bankruptcy.

Using this same press, the Bellevue *Gazette* now made its hopeful bow on October 23, 1856, under the editorship of R. S. McEwen, but it too was short-lived.[14] The *Nebraska Advertiser* (Brownville) noted in its October 14, 1858, issue that the *Gazette* had suspended publication and gone over to the Great Majority. This was about the time William N. Byers was coming down with an attack of printer's ink in nearby Omaha.

Early in 1859 a Bellevue missioner, Rev. C. Chaucer Goss, published

[13]James C. Olson, *History of Nebraska* (Lincoln, 1955), pp. 50–51.

[14]*Proceedings and Collections of the Nebraska State Historical Society*, Second series, Vol. V (Lincoln, 1902), pp. 15–16; J. Sterling Morton and others, *Illustrated History of Nebraska* (Lincoln, 1906), Vol. II, pp. 368–69; A. T. Andreas, pub., *History of the State of Nebraska* (Chicago, 1882), pp. 1366–67.

a pamphlet history of the settlement, and he mentions that the *Gazette* was "a company affair."[15] One of the leading members of the Bellevue Town Company, organized in 1854, was a hard-bitten little man, Peter A. Sarpy, whose exploits and adventures crowd through the chronicles of the fur-trade era in the American West. A noted and inveterate frontiersman and horizon-chaser, Sarpy had been factor for the American Fur Company when the settlement was young, and he was one of the leading promoters of Bellevue, the town, as distinguished from Bellevue, his old trading post. He also was the town's leading merchant and owned the ferry to St. Mary on the Iowa side of the river. It can be supposed that any bankrupt newspaper in his precinct well might have deposited its tangible assets with him in payment of debts, and the supposition has some confirmation in the record.

In a letter to the Nebraska State Historical Society from Salt Lake City dated December 31, 1897, Hadley D. Johnson mentions the Bellevue presses.[16] Johnson had been elected territorial printer for the second session of the Nebraska Territory legislature in 1855–56. He wrote that the political plum which fell to his lot found him with no outfit to accomplish his duties in the "art preservative," as printing was designated (mostly by printers) in those days. So he "purchased from Col. Peter A. Sarpy, the Indian trader at Bellevue, the press and other material upon which the *Palladium* and the *Gazette* had been printed."

In the Beatrice, Nebraska, *Express* for May 14, 1874, appears a further note about the *Gazette* by a reporter who apparently had firsthand knowledge of the situation:

> The *Gazette*, Bellevue, was first issued October 23, 1856; Strickland (Silas A.) Burt & Co.—L. L. Bowen, P. A. Sarpy, Fenner Fergusen [Ferguson] and J. T. Allen [Allan] the company. Henry M. Burt afterwards became the sole proprietor. Mr. B. is now editor and publisher of the New England Homestead and Sunday Telegraph, Springfield, Mass., and visited Nebraska the past summer. The Gazette was continued until September, 1859 [obviously an error of a year], and then sold to Wm. V. Byers and J. L. Daily [Dailey], and by them taken by ox-teams to Denver, Col., and there published as the Rocky Mountain News, the first paper in Colorado, and yet published by Mr. Byers.
>
> Parenthetically and digressively I state that the movement of Mr. Byers at the time of purchasing the Bellevue Gazette was a "forestaller" by which the writer with the Nebraska Advertiser office "did not go" to Denver, arrangements having been made to that effect, and abandoned because of the "claim" being "jumped."

[15]C. Chaucer Goss, *Bellevue, Larimer & Saint Mary: Their History, Location, Description and Advantages* (Bellevue, 1859); reprint edition (Bank of Bellevue, 1957), p. 11.

[16]*Proceedings and Collections*, etc., pp. 51–52.

The Hadley Johnson letter goes on to say that he hauled the Bellevue press and type to Omaha to carry out his legislative printing and also to publish the *Nebraska Democrat*. Subsequently, he says, the press was sold to S. M. Owens and taken to Florence—now a part of Omaha but then a separate village, also contending for the Nebraska capital—and used to print the *Courier* there for a short time. Johnson continues: "The plant, I think, was removed elsewhere and some other newspaper born, to bloom for a day and then to die,—'unwept, unhonored, and unsung.'" The record of the movements of this active little hand press is by no means conclusive, but if Johnson intended to refer to the *Rocky Mountain News* his lamentations were premature.

If the *Palladium* press was indeed the *News* press, as seems highly likely, its frontier adventures were not completed when the labors were done on the night of April 22, 1859, in Auraria. The old "Imperial" remained a part of *News* equipment for more than five years, and a caprice of nature was its final undoing. Along with all the rest of the *News* chattel and plant, the press was swept away in Denver's memorable Cherry Creek flood of May 19, 1864. Years later, in 1899, excavators uncovered pieces of the press, its lever and some types, in the Cherry Creek sands far downstream. Portions were given as keepsakes to Byers and Dailey, and the balance of the relics went into custody of the Colorado State Historical Society for preservation in the State Museum. Hadley Johnson had suggested to the Nebraska Historical Society that it hunt up the old press as a museum piece; his suggestion was carried out, all unknowing, in another state.

But the old Washington was not yet an exhibit on the snowy April night in '59. It was a working press, and it was taking up the task of observing a nation's westward march. The Pike's Peak gold rush now had a recorder. History could get on with its processes.

The first completed copy of the *News* which Byers brought out from under the protective tent was retained by him. Later he would print on the margin of page one:

This is the first sheet ever printed in the Pike
Country, at 10 P.M., April 22d, 1859.
Wm. N. Byers

At the top of the second page he printed the legend: "Second page of first paper ever printed in what is now the Territory of Colorado, April 22, 1859, at 10 o'clock, P.M." This officially attested copy now is a part of the Western History Collection of the Denver Public Library.

Having established his claim to being "first," Byers completed only two or three copies of the paper that night to pass around among the jostling well-wishers in the attic.[17] One of these copies was presented to Arthur E. Pierce, who lived to become the last of the pioneers who were "among those present."[18] Pierce was a close friend of Dailey's and became proprietor of Denver's first book, magazine, and "news depot," headquarters for daily gatherings of the press gang.

The following day, April 23, the balance of the first edition was struck off, some 500 to 800 copies by varying accounts. Dailey noted in his diary that the *News* "goes like hot cakes" at twenty-five cents a copy, in coin or gold dust. The amount of dust a seller could pinch from a buyer's buckskin pouch between thumb and forefinger passed for twenty-five cents. No allowance made for ham-handed dust pinchers. Byers also had brought along a pair of gold scales and, presumably, the small square of Brussels carpet which every alert Pike's Peak merchant kept on his counter beneath his scales. Any gold flakes dropped during weighing of a payment fell into the nap of the carpet, and at the end of the day's business the carpet was shaken out to add accidentals to receipts.

A preliminary effort has been made to locate surviving copies of the scarce, gold-bought Volume 1, Number 1, of the *News*. Nine only can be definitely placed. One hangs framed on the wall of the office of Jack Foster, present editor of the *News*. Another is preserved in the journalism room of Denver's Byers Junior High School, named for the founder and occupying the site of the home in which he died. Copies are owned privately by Ted Morris and Nolie Mumey of Denver. The *Union List of Newspapers* locates copies—which have been confirmed—in the Denver Public Library; Western Americana Collection, Yale University Library (two copies); Colorado State Historical Society, Denver; and Norlin Library, University of Colorado, Boulder; and a facsimile in the Library of Congress. Facsimiles also are held by the Nebraska State Historical Society, Lincoln, and the New York State Library, Albany. Unconfirmed reports have located copies in the ownership of John Evans of Denver, the Shaw family of Grand Junction, Colorado, and J. D. Bayard of Honolulu. In 1919 a copy was reported (*The Trail*, Vol. XI, No. 11, p. 12) in the possession of Senator Scott of West Virginia. Experts in the field of rare ephemera estimate the value of a copy at upwards of five hundred dollars. Another piece of Rocky Mountain incunabula, if a copy ever were found and authenticated, might be equally interesting to collectors and scholars of the history of American printing.

Printing in the shadow of the Rockies did not begin with that first complete copy of the *News* which Byers so carefully designated for posterity, but with a lowly lost-and-found handbill. So far as is known, Jack Merrick printed nothing on his press until he published the *Pioneer*. But Byers, in an address to a meeting of Colorado pioneers in 1899, told of a job his press turned out ahead of the *News*:

[17]*Rocky Mountain News*, Feb. 1, 1860.

[18]Ibid., Apr. 23, 1921.

. . . Before the first issue of the paper was made a little dodger was struck off for a man who had lost a horse and a dog. This was the first printing done in this territory.[19]

Douglas C. McMurtrie, the authority on early printing in Colorado, made an unsuccessful effort to trace down this dodger and reported: "No copy of it is known to exist, nor is it known for whom it was printed."[20] Undoubtedly it was a minor effort, and certainly evanescent, but it can be hoped that it was effective and that the man got his horse and dog back. He needed the horse badly in the Pike's Peak country of 1859, and his concern for his dog seems to suggest that he deserves a kind thought a century later.

The *News* proved somewhat less transitory than this first fruit of its press, and over the years it has found many lost dogs. One of the fondest traditions of Denver journalism—which has a host of eccentricities less savory—is that the columns of its newspapers always have been open to appeals—free of charge—for the return of strayed or stolen dogs. In one of the recent gridiron shows of the Denver Newspaper Guild a city-room scene opened with a reporter on the telephone. "Okay, lady," the resigned newsman said. "What's the dog's name?" The scarcely hilarious allusion brought an instant, knowing laugh from the audience and indicates how deeply the lost-dog tradition is entrenched in the *mores* of the city and its press. Of late, however, the practice of dog watching seems to be withering in the hot blast of big-city ways, and there are those who mourn its passing.

Some have said that the tradition had its start in the uncharacteristic affection for dogs of the late Frederick G. Bonfils, famous publisher of the Denver *Post* and a man of such steely power of will as to have evoked few warm and tender sentiments in Denver breasts. Unfortunately this pleasant version of the custom's origin does not square with historical fact. Lost-dog stories in Denver have a pedigree much more antique. The *News* was printing them regularly and ritually before Bonfils was born. The lineage of dog journalism runs, clear and true, straight back to an ephemeral handbill which, somehow, got published amid the rush of setting up news about the "physical certainty that gold in lump must be found in the mountain from whence these sands are washed" and the demanding business of seducing the muse:

> Hurrah for the land where the moor and the mountain
> Are sparkling with treasures no language hath told,
> Where the wave of the river and the spray of the fountain
> Are bright with the glitter of genuine gold.

[19]Smiley, op. cit., pp. 248–49; Wilbur Fisk Stone, *History of Colorado* (Chicago, 1918), p. 782.

[20]McMurtrie and Allen, op. cit., p. 24fn.

Both the poesy and the prophetic declaration of greater things to come from the mountains are from the pages of the first issue of the *News*. The inside pages. The outer, Omaha-composed pages, were both less ebullient and less timely. Nearly a full column of page one was given over to a borrowed report from the *American Messenger* on the opening of Japan, an item of intelligence which was then about three years old. "Cape Horn to Be Avoided," the front page of the *News* informed any landlocked mariners who might be interested, and "Crime in New York City and Vicinity" regrettably had reached a level of 60,865 arrests in a single year, 30,065 of them involving persons of Irish persuasion.

Dr. A. F. Peck, who will be met again later in this story, advertised on the cover page that as a physician and surgeon he had established offices at Cache-a-la-Poudre, Nebraska Territory, "where he may at all times be found when not professionally engaged or digging gold." The Cache la Poudre River flows into the South Platte about fifty miles northeast of Denver, and it was the first likely-looking stream the gold rushers hit.

Wm. N. Byers & Co., editors, publishers, and proprietors, announced on the front page that they would accept subscriptions at five dollars per annum in advance, that they were prepared to do job printing of all kinds, and that you could have a full column of advertising space in the *News* every week for a year at a cost of a hundred and fifty dollars. Your business card, assuming a business, would be published (five lines or less) for twelve dollars a year.

The rest of page one, with a notable exception, was composed of news which bore almost no relation to conditions or events indigenous to Cherry Creek and environs. There was speculation about what the world would be like without a Sabbath—in a country which had no churches. A Yankee's visit to the great Carlyle was commented upon, and the New York *Tribune* was quoted as warning against feeding cattle on sugar cane—in a land where it sometimes snows in June. A moral preachment concerning the use of tobacco (in England) filled the bottom of one column, and at the foot of another was a two-line riddle of the sort much beloved by compositors in the day, not too far past, when "fillers" often were employed in newspapers. "What key is that that opens the gate of misery? Whis-key." Shortly before World War II another such space killer rendered *News* readers similarly nauseous for several months. The filler was a scientific note and ran to the effect that the emu lays four eggs and plucks down from her breast to make the nest. It began appearing frequently and regularly. Denver became the best-informed city in the world on the nesting habits and parturition of the emu. The managing editor's unsuccessful efforts to locate and dispose of the offending bit of type drove him frantic. It seemed to be immune to mandatory kills sent down from the editorial room upstairs. Finally it was discovered that one of the make-up men was carrying the two lines around in the pocket of his printer's apron and using them whenever a column came up short.

For weeks he had been thriftily retrieving the filler when the pages were broken down each day in order that he might be instantly equipped for two-line emergencies at press time.

The one exception to the reign of whis-keys and statistics on shoe consumption on page one of the first *News* was an item which cast a long shadow ahead. It appeared under the headline "Farming vs. Gold Digging."

> From present appearance, our citizens are likely to all be taken off with the Cherry Creek Yellow Fever, inasmuch that the farming interest of our Territory is likely to suffer materially, and the miners will also have to suffer for want of supplies.
>
> This is all wrong; and our opinion is that farmers who stay at home, and spend as much money to improve and cultivate their farms, will realize more clear profit by so doing, than they will to go to the mines.
>
> There will be enough to go to dig all the gold the Union will need, and those who raise stock and produce for miners will get their equal share of the gold in exchange for their produce. . . .

This was the *News'* first brief in a long-continued pleading that agriculture not be neglected. Again, the young but bearded Byers was speaking in the voice of a prophet. For although gold and silver were to provide a foundation for Colorado's early growth, the dominance of mining would be relatively short-lived. The wealth of the mines would produce cloud cities and millionaires like Tabor, Stratton, McLean, and Penrose, but it also would yield ghost towns and shattered hopes. In pursuit of the magic metals men soon would string a network of narrow-gauge railroad lines over, under, and around the Colorado peaks in fantastic feats of dauntless engineering. Yet these would pass and become mere souvenirs of an era. Within a few decades the Colorado mines were to give up wealth far in excess of that which the California forty-niners found, but great as the riches were in millions and billions they would not approach the secure return won by tilling the good earth. In the twentieth century mining still is a major industry in the wide, far spaces the *Rocky Mountain News* serves, and the nation finds it advantageous to maintain its major coinage mint in Denver. The firm growth came, however, from grass and grain and the annual increase nature works by casting sunlight on the factories of a green leaf.

It came from cattle and wheat and sugar beets, fruits from the orchard, timber from the hills, alfalfa hay and sheep, potatoes and melons and the tender produce of intensively cultivated bottomland gardens to which water was brought at some cost in sweat and dollars. Novice editor Byers at twenty-eight, son of two generations of frontier farmers, caught a glimpse of what was to come, and he lent himself and his newspaper, from the beginning, to every movement aimed at the development of

Colorado agriculture. He himself planted some of the first ears of experimental wheat. He was the godfather of Colorado's huge sugar-beet industry. On his own farm, now well within the city limits, he set out the first fruit trees and grapevines. His alert reportorial eye, encompassing everything about this new country, did not fail to note that trail-thin oxen, turned out to die during the first winter, unaccountably showed up again in the spring fatter than ever. Even the dry, brown prairie grass of winter was nutritious. Byers planted trees and dug ditches. He experimented with nut culture (a failure) and with watermelons (a success), and he became a founder of the first agricultural society, the first forestry association. And he used his *News* to foster all his schemes and visions for a land of plenty in the "Great American Desert."

Considering the tenor of the times in '59 and the perfervid mood of the newly arrived population, it is not strange that the early pleadings of the *News* for the hoe and plow as against the rocker and Long Tom should have fallen on ears made deaf by siren songs. Most of the arrivals had come from farms in Nebraska, Kansas, Iowa, and Missouri, and they knew *that* life and its calluses all too well. In fact they had come here precisely to escape the drudgery of following the plow. They would, instead, pick up nuggets the size of hen's eggs. Not many of them were thinking in terms of agriculture, though a few were. Rufus Clark was one fifty-niner who saw from the start that there were more ways of getting gold than scrabbling among the rocks with a sluice. He earned himself a fortune and a lifetime nickname by raising potatoes in soil more easily worked than gravel or granite. One of his smaller crops sold for thirty thousand dollars, and "Potato" Clark wound up a philanthropist with forty-five hundred pieces of property occupying twelve consecutive pages in the county assessor's books.

Byers demonstrated his own belief in the future of agriculture by many activities, but he also was an experienced real estate promoter. He had been involved in one or more of the "paper city" promotions which sprang up in eastern Nebraska Territory during the flush of optimism which followed the Kansas-Nebraska Act of 1854. As a surveyor, he was half of the land and law firm of Poppleton & Byers in Omaha. On the possibility that the Pike's Peak country might not yet be ready for enlightenment, he had prudently retained his real estate office in the Missouri River town when he struck out west with his press. So he hedged a little at the end of his first apotheosis of agriculture:

. . . Those who wish to get real estate will never be able to purchase it as cheap, nor on as good terms again, as the gold mines has [sic] turned the heads of all those who have bought property in the [Nebraska] Territory, and all they think of is to dig gold and wash gold.

It is our candid opinion that those who have a few dollars to spare, will make more by buying property in eastern Nebraska at present, while the excitement is so high, than they will to go to the mines.

He didn't quite say that the firm of Poppleton & Byers was "at your service," but he came as close to it as he probably felt he dared.

Nor was Byers immune to his own "Cherry Creek Yellow Fever," and the inside pages of his first newspaper sang of gold. He personally raced to the scene of each new discovery in the mountains, and he staked claims at all of them. Throughout his active life he pursued the golden will-o'-the-wisp on countless excursions which took him into every gulch and cañon across the breadth and depth of the state, and he was the personification of the eternal sucker for boom-and-bust mining investments. He held claims or interests in mines in nearly every gold- or silver-bearing district of the Rockies. He explored, prospected, and invested, and he was never so busy at the editorial desk that he couldn't take off on a moment's notice when word of some new strike trickled in. The chores of weekly, and then daily, newspapering apparently were detailed to faithful John Dailey or to other partners or subordinates. It was not Byers' lot ever to hit it rich, and though no good record exists among his surviving accounts it is highly probable that his fliers in mining were in part responsible for the many years he spent flirting with bankruptcy or in high-interest hock to moneylenders.

Page two of the first *News* drips gold from every pore. There are reports of success from O. P. Goodwin at Boulder City, B. F. Langley on St. Vrain's Fork, W. M. Slaughter on Dry Creek. An article headed "Mining Intelligence" says:

It is not to be expected that the "Rocky Mountain News" will contain much mining or local information in the first number, published as it is within 3 days of our arrival. No reliable particulars could be gathered in a few days, we have seen the region, however, and have seen many of the men engaged here; some of them are old California miners; some of them are fresh from the nearest settlements; some have wintered here in order to be on the spot at the first opening of the season; others have travelled through the mud and frost of early spring, and the united testimony of all who have investigated for themselves is that gold exists, in greater or less quantities, over a large tract of country, extending from Cherry creek on the south to far above Ft. Laramie on the north. Many concur in saying that most of these deposits are richer than similar ones in California, and that there is not a reasonable doubt but that as soon as the gulches of the mountains can be explored, lump and quartz gold will be found in large quantities. It would seem to be a geological impossibility that gold in scale could be widely diffused as this is, all along the rivers running from the mountains, and not find the source of this supply.

If we credit individual stories we could relate marvels equal to the Arabian Nights for wealth. One has heard of great deposits on the head waters of the Missouri and Yellowstone; another has understood the secret signs of the mountain Indian, explaining the secret of the treasure.

But from the mass of marvel we can glean this truth. Gold, in scale, exists in sufficient quantity to reward the working miner, over a large surface of the plain on the eastern slope of the mountain, and in the sands of nearly all the rivers yet prospected, and which rise in the Rocky mountains. Where this state of things exists in a country upheaved by volcanic eruptions, it is almost a physical certainty that gold in lump must be found in the mountain from whence these sands are washed. By next week we hope to make a beginning at least for precise information.

And so, in the main, would events prove out. The lode and vein gold *was* found a few weeks later, and it *was* in the mountains whence washed the sands.

In a day when reckless optimism alternated with deepest despair the early *News* succeeded rather admirably in keeping its head. The prospectus, appearing on page three of the first number, stated: "We hope by conducting the paper honestly and fairly, to obtain for it a wide circulation in all the Eastern states, as well as at the Mines, and by carefully see[k]ing correct information, render our statements perfectly reliable." Later writers, seeking to weigh the influence of the early *News*, have concluded that the paper lived up remarkably to its promises, that it promoted without fanning wildfires, that it was "ably and fearlessly edited, and more than ordinary care and effort was expended upon procuring accurate and reliable information about conditions in the mines. In fact accuracy and truthfulness in its reports was the all-embracing policy of the paper. . . ."[21]

The first *News* declared on page three:

Our aim is to locate permanently at a point which will be nearly central to the whole mining region and at the same time most accessible to the great eastern cities. By this we hope to obtain the eastern news as speedily as possible for the miners and collect information from all the prominent mines for the east. We will have reliable correspondents in different mining regions, and will not knowingly admit any correspondence unless we are satisfied of its truth. We cannot however undertake to vouch for correspondents, but no statements will be made editorially in regard to the mines or any other matter in this region unless we know it to be true. Politically, this paper will be independent; there is neither time or place for those discussions which interest older and organized communities. The local matters of the mining regions will be abundantly sufficient, and we

[21]Ibid., p. 34.

think, by a straight forward truthful course, and a steady devotion to the interest of the Rocky Mountain settlement to receive and deserve a general support, and respect for the "Rocky Mountain News."

"Yes," the new journal announced, "NEWS from the Rocky Mountains, NEWS from the Desert Plain!" There were new eras fermenting in at least a few brains, and new empires definitely were in prospect if not clearly in purpose.

> . . . The hum of busy men is heared in the mountains so lately rising lonely in majestic silence; the cheerful tones of a multitude fill the air that but lately echoed only the occasional voice of a weary wanderer; the Buffalo and Deer that but yesterday scarcely feared the form of man, are already driven by the presence of men, from the boundless plains where they had roamed almost undisturbed for a thousand years; the wandering savages, often an object of fear to the pilgrim travellers, are themselves, in the twinkling of an eye, trembling before the coming wave of a countless emigration. The poor Indian, heretofore quietly displaced by treaty, is now pushed rudely on by the resistless rush of Yankee enterprise; and ere the year shall close, the Indians of Kansas and Nebraska will have closed by a leap, almost the last space between them and their mournful destiny. Men are rapidly gathering together, towns are built, cities are in embryo formation, and all the paraphernalia of busy life are seen and heard 500 miles west of last years outposts of civilization. The Missouri River is no longer the "farther west" to the ambitious emigrant but leaping at a bound over 500 miles of solitude, the emigrant now settles at the base of the Rocky Mountains, and here, even in mid winter, has formed the nucleus of a future State. Spring has scarcely dissipated the dangers of winter travel, and yet thousands are here, many thousands on their way, and even now men ask with avidity for "News" from the Mountain Mines. If the richness and extent of the Gold Regions realize their present promise, a new State will be organized west of Kansas and Nebraska ere this year is closed, with a hundred thousand inhabitants. . . .

The *News* continued with a frank statement of the reasons behind its founding;

> The proprietors of this paper have, until within a month past, lived at Omaha, within 500 miles of the Gold Regions, and have had abundant opportunity of judging the truth or falsity of the testimony daily presented in regard to the Gold Mines. We think there is more evidence of a reliable character of the richness and extent of these mines, and obtained under far more unfavorable circumstances, than was offered from California. The geological structure is the same as the gold regions of California, and men, who are familiar with mining in California, have examined these mines west of Kansas and Nebraska,

as far as the season would admit, and pronounce these of greater promise than any heretofore known. The testimony is absolute as to the gold, though it is not absolute as to the extent and richness of the deposit. We know enough, however, to believe that a large population will settle here at once, and prosper, and we believe that this will be a reading and intelligent population. Believing this we have at great trouble brought a printing press and all necessary fixtures over 500 miles, at an inclement season, and over roads freezing at night and thawing by day. We have done this because we wished to collect and send forth reliable information, because we wished to help mould and organize the new population, and because we thought it would pay. . . .

Page two gives an apologetic explanation for the lack of timely news "from the States." There was no telegraph, of course, and no mail service except irregularly and by courtesy of travelers from Fort Laramie on the Overland Trail two hundred and twenty miles to the north.

. . . Owing to the fact that our exchanges and eastern letters are all addressed to Fort Laramie—the nearest post office—and we have had no opportunity of getting them since our arrival, we are unable to give our readers any news whatever from the States this week; but we hope before our next issue to have full files, when we will give a faithful digest of the news of the world.

On the following page the *News* goes on to complain further that of mail "We have none, but we hope soon to hear the postman's horn and see Uncle Sam's letter bags. Certainly we should have some kind of postal favors. Five thousand people have each left friends in 'America,' from whom they wish to hear occasionally, and who wish to hear from them and the gold mines. Give us post offices and mails, and we will patronize the institution as much [as] any community of the same number in the United States."

In such an isolated situation it obviously was a part of prudence and foresight to establish and maintain good relations with the postmaster at Fort Laramie.

Fort Laramie P.O.—We are gratified to hear the ecomiums [sic] bestowed upon the Post Master of the above office for the many favors he has shown to the citizens of the mining regions for some months past. May we always be as well served.

Page three also carries a bit of apology about the paper's appearance, although an effort had been made to dress up the inside with two illustrations. One is a rudely carved woodcut which shows a Pike's Peaker striding off toward the mines in hussar's boots and smoking a long clay churchwarden pipe. Over his shoulder is slung a pick and a musket.

The second illustration is the same map of the gold regions which had appeared earlier that year in Byers' guidebook for prospective pilgrims.

But the inside pages of the first *News* bear full testimony to haste and difficulty of preparation. Typographical errors are numerous. Italic characters appear at random in words otherwise Roman in style. Letters are inverted and omitted. Words have been skipped over by the compositors, and John Dailey and Charlie Semper apparently exhausted their supply of periods and lower-case *k*'s. So they used commas for periods and for the *k*'s ran in other letters upside down, leaving the divided "feet" of the types to print in vertical pairs of smudgy blocks.

> OUR APPEARANCE THIS WEEK is not all we hope and expect to make it. Our readers will bear in mind that we have not been three days upon the ground—that we are setting up and arranging a new office in a new country, remote from many of the conveniences of civilization, and therefore overlook the shortcomings of this our first issue. When once our office is arranged, and everything has found its proper place, we hope to present as fair a sheet as is often seen in older lands.

The initial *News* carries word that the first wagonload of sawmill lumber had arrived in town and the first murderer been executed. The boards came in from the Cherry Creek pineries, courtesy of Messrs. Cooper and Wyatt; but the *News* neglected to obtain, or at least to give, the name of the murderer.

> MURDER AND EXECUTION—On the 7th inst. four Germans—an old man, two sons and a son-in-law—set out from their camp on Vasquer's fork [Vasquez Fork, now Clear Creek] to look for cattle. But one—the son-in-law—returned. After returning he acted so strangely as to arouse suspicion that all was not right, and he was arrested, when he confessed that he murdered his brother-in-law. A search was instituted, and the body of the murdered man found, shot through the head. The murderer was put upon his trial, before Judge Smith found guilty on his own confession, and forthwith executed by hanging to a tree.

The killer was John Stoefel,[22] and the details of his taking off are supplied by "Uncle Dick" Wootton, to whom he sold a buckskin bag of gold dust taken from his victim:

> . . . three men got into a two horse wagon, and were driven under a cottonwood tree on the bank of Cherry Creek. These three men were the prisoner, the executioner, and a minister, who had found his way out from the east along with the great crowd of gold seekers.
>
> A rope was placed around the murderer's neck and thrown over a limb of the tree. Then the minister, a good Christian man, kneeled

[22]Smiley, op. cit., p. 339.

down in the wagon to offer up a prayer, and the executioner also got down on his knees. The fellow who was to be hanged didn't follow their example, but stood up, until the executioner poked him in the ribs, and asked him if he didn't know better than to act like a heathen.

After prayer the wagon was driven out from under the tree, and the man who had murdered his friend to get possession of a few dollars worth of gold dust was left dangling from the Cottonwood limb until he was pronounced dead and cut down. It was as neat and orderly an execution as ever took place anywhere, and was the first of a series which revolutionized Denver society. . . .[23]

The "society" of Auraria-Denver, to which the *Rocky Mountain News* now had come as the first ornament of civilization and culture, stood badly in need of revolutionizing in the spring of 1859, by Wootton's testimony. And the old trapper and Indian trader could scarcely have held other than liberal views on behavior. He was used to men with the bark on. Nonetheless, he pronounced a large part of the first Denver population "utterly lawless." Murders, he said, were "almost everyday occurrences" and "stealing was the only occupation" of a considerable section of the populace. The thieves "seemed to steal for the love of it, and would take anything from a pet calf or a counterfeit gold dollar, up to a saw mill." Wootton asserted it for "actual fact" that the first steam sawmill set up in Denver had been stolen from a boat on the river at St. Joseph and spirited across the plains in a ponderous getaway at ox-team speed.

Other observers of the Cherry Creek settlements in 1859 confirm, in essence if not degree, Wootton's estimate that about nine out of ten residents were gamblers. "Gaming was universal," Albert D. Richardson wrote, and he paused to listen to the pitch of a three-card monte dealer in the luxurious Denver House (canvas roof, dirt floor):

"Here you are, gentlemen; this ace of hearts is the winning card. Watch it closely. Follow it with your eye as I shuffle. Here it is, and now here, now here and now," (laying the three on the table with faces down)—"where? If you point it out the first time you win; but if you miss you lose. Here it is you see," (turning it up;) "now watch it again," (shuffling.) "This ace of hearts gentlemen is the winning card. I take no bets from paupers, cripples or orphan children. The ace of hearts. It is my regular trade, gentlemen—to move my hands quicker than your eyes. I always have two chances to your one. The ace of hearts. If your sight is quick enough, you beat me and I pay; if not, I beat you and take your money. The ace of hearts; who will go me twenty?"[24]

[23]Conard, op. cit., pp. 380–81.

[24]Albert D. Richardson, *Beyond the Mississippi* (Hartford, 1867), p. 187.

The Denver House, Richardson observed, was "always crowded with swarthy men armed and in rough costumes." The bar retailed "enormous quantities of cigars and liquors" and at half a dozen gaming tables gamblers were busy day and night. "I saw the probate judge of the county lose thirty Denver lots in less than ten minutes, at cards, in this public saloon on Sunday morning; and afterward observed the county sheriff pawning his revolver for twenty dollars to spend in betting at faro."

Other elements of the sporting world also made their appearance early in the village. In a recently discovered, unpublished letter a Pike's Peaker who signed himself "Pink S.," wrote to his sweetheart back in Cherry Fork, Adams County, Ohio, on February 26, 1859, and gave an inventory of the town's physical progress:

> The Emigration is comeing in continually, and our town is building almost like a 2d sanfrancisco. . . . it all ready contains . . . one theater, one oppera or ball room, any amt. of Liquor and gambling saloons and one or two *H Hs* or *assignation houses* [the emphasis is Pink's] are to be supplied from Mexico and Saint louis & Cincin. . . .[25]

Although Denver still had no school, church, court or government, and almost no homes, the brides of the multitude already were congregating to provide their professional solace to lonely men with gold dust in their pokes.

A. K. McClure, Pennsylvania newspaperman, made a tour of the West a few years later and reported his findings in letters to the New York *Tribune* and *Franklin Repository* of Chambersburg, Pennsylvania, which subsequently were gathered into a book. McClure also gave a low opinion of Denver yeomanry: ". . . nine tenths of those who came at first were either fugitives or adventurers. In one mingled mass came the honest bankrupt, the fugitive from justice, the gambler and the loafer."[26]

This was not so, insists Jerome Smiley, ever the patriotic historian and booster. In a way everyone at Cherry Creek in '59 was an adventurer, he concedes, "but to assert or imply that as a whole the mass was composed of bankrupts, criminals, gamblers, and loafers, is stupid, ignorant nonsense, formulated from the stories it was once common to relate of many places in the west."[27] He goes on:

> . . . There were gamblers and other criminals a-plenty; but as to loafers, this country was probably the most uninviting region in the

[25]Pink S. to Miss Maggie S. Kirk, ms. letter, collection of Mose Iacino, Denver; photostatic copy courtesy Daniel A. Stone, Denver.

[26]A. K. McClure, *Three Thousand Miles through the Rocky Mountains* (Philadelphia, 1869), p. 124.

[27]Smiley, op. cit., p. 242.

world for them. The truth is that while many had been bankrupted,
and many others impoverished by the collapse in 1857, in the main
the men who came here in the pioneer times were of average honesty,
and of more than average enthusiasm and heedlessness. They were
inspired by no worse motive than one to better their worldly condition,
and to do it in one or two summer seasons. . . .

The appearance of the Pike's Peakers, Smiley continues, lent some
credence to reports of criminality and bloodthirsty barbarity. They were,
he says, "hideously hairy and unkempt, sun-browned, recklessly ragged,
some of them bare-footed, and all dust-covered and begrimed. The
addition of goggles, worn to protect their eyes from the glare of the
prairie sun, gave to many a mild-mannered and peaceful man a dangerous and, to some individuals, a ferocious, aspect."

A picture of Denver and her people at the height of the influx of such
strange travelers is further filled out by the observant Richardson, who
found the settlement a "most forlorn and desolate-looking metropolis."
He arrived on the morning of June 6, in company with the famous
Horace Greeley of the *Tribune*, aboard one of the first stagecoaches to
reach Cherry Creek.

. . . If my memory is faithful, there were five women in the whole
gold region; and the appearance of a bonnet in the street was the
signal for the entire population to rush to the cabin doors and gaze
upon its wearer as at any other natural curiosity. The men who
gathered about our coach on its arrival were attired in slouched hats,
tattered woolen shirts, buckskin pantaloons and moccasins; and had
knives and revolvers suspended from their belts. . . .

Denver society was a strange medley. There were Americans from
every quarter of the Union, Mexicans, Indians, half-breeds, trappers,
speculators, gamblers, desperadoes, broken-down politicians and honest
men. Almost every day was enlivened by its little shooting match.
While the great gaming saloon [the Denver House] was crowded with
people, drunken ruffians sometimes fired five or six shots from their
revolvers, frightening everybody pell-mell out of the room, but seldom
wounding any one. One day I heard the bar-keeper politely ask a man
lying upon a bench to remove. The recumbent replied to the request
with his revolver. Indeed firing at this bar-tender was a common
amusement among the guests. At first he bore it laughingly, but one
day a shot grazed his ear, whereupon, remarking that there was such
a thing as carrying a joke too far and that *this* was "about played out,"
he buckled on two revolvers and swore he would kill the next man who
took aim at him. He was not troubled afterward. . . .

. . . Denver and Auraria, (now West Denver,) contained about one
thousand people, with three hundred buildings, nearly all of hewn
pine logs. One third were unfinished and roofless, having been erected
the previous winter for speculative purposes. There were very few glass

windows or doors and but two or three board floors. The nearest saw-mill was forty miles away, and the occupants of the cabins lived upon the native earth, hard, smooth and clean-swept. One lady, by sewing together corn-sacks for a carpet and covering her log walls with sheets and table cloths, gave to her mansion an appearance of rare luxury. Chairs were glories yet to come. Stools, tables and pole-bedsteads were the staple furniture, while rough boxes did duty as bureaus and cupboards. Hearths and fire-places were of adobe, as in Utah, California and Mexico. Chimneys were of sticks of wood piled up like children's cob-houses and plastered with mud. A few roofs were covered with shingles split by hand, but most were of logs spread with prairie grass and covered with earth. . . .

Between my cabin and the Denver House were a dozen Indian lodges, enlivened by squaws dressing the skins of wild animals or cooking puppies for dinner. . . .[28]

Into this scene the inquiring, observing, admonishing press now thrust itself. When William N. Byers rode his horse down over the hill where the Colorado Capitol now stands, he looked down, perhaps with some misgivings, on a busy but unpromising settlement of a few straggling tents and rude log huts. Oxen bawled or slept stoically in the middle of the roadway, still yoked to covered wagons whose owners were off somewhere inquiring the way to the gold of other men who were asking the same question. A pall of dust churned up by the hoofs of mules and horses hung like smoke in the bottomlands. A long line of vehicles— prairie schooners, buckboards, open wagons, handcarts, even wheelbarrows—waited in line at the ferry on the far side of Cherry Creek for transportation across the spring-swollen Platte. A village of Arapaho tipis was scattered among the cottonwoods, then just coming into new leaf.

On April 17 the rush was at its peak. Or just past it. A day or so earlier a reverse migration of angry, disappointed men, their visions dashed, had begun. The gobacks spread wrathful tales of the Pike's Peak humbug along the line of incoming pilgrims. The line, stretching unbroken to the horizon, slowed and wavered. Many turned and headed home. Many kept coming in one of the major tides of American migration.

During the previous December there had been perhaps two or three hundred men and four or five women wintering through at Cherry Creek. Now in April new arrivals numbered a hundred or more every day. An election for officials of Arapahoe County, Kansas Territory, had been held March 28. In Auraria, 231 votes were cast, and over in Denver City, 144. But the indicated population of something over 375 persons was swollen by many hundreds of newcomers who had little interest in the tenuous affairs of a county government irregular to the point of myth. By late spring, it was estimated, Denver had a highly

[28]Richardson, op. cit., pp. 177-78, 186.

fluid population of 1000 or more, and other thousands had passed on through to the mountains.

"When I arrived here there was a camp of perhaps 1000 or 1200 people," Byers told the historian Hubert Bancroft in 1884.[29] Some were living in tents, some in cabins. Most of them were on the Auraria side of the creek, and Denver City could count perhaps a dozen completed cabins. Byers estimated 150,000 persons were on the plains that year bound for Pike's Peak. Of these, perhaps a third turned back as the cry of hoax passed eastward along the trails. "I think over 100,000 of them reached here," Byers said, "and about 35,000 remained at the end of the season. . . . Things were very lively on the route."

The young editor had camped with Indians at Henderson's Island, twelve miles out, on the night of April 16, and he rode into Cherry Creek settlement about eleven next morning. The first thing he saw, he recalled later, was a cabin with a white canvas roof "where City Hall now stands."[30] (Today the City Hall Byers spoke of has come and gone. The site is now a parking lot, with only the big bell from the tower, preserved on a monument, to mark the former seat of municipal government on the shore of Cherry Creek at Fourteenth and Larimer streets.) Otherwise, Denver was largely a shanty town of log huts roofed with slabs of prairie sod, grass side down. Byers' *News* would make considerable point of it as a milestone in civic progress when the first paint was used in town the following December.

To this unpainted and unprepossessing community his *Rocky Mountain News* hopefully—and perhaps a touch unrealistically—addressed the prospectus on page three of its maiden issue. The *k*'s now have been restored to remedy the shortage experienced by compositors Dailey and Semper a hundred years ago.

PROSPECTUS
of the
ROCKY MOUNTAIN NEWS

The News is the first journal established in the Gold mining region of Kansas and Nebraska, at the east foot and under the very shadow of the great Rocky Mountains chain, in the center of what will ere many months be a great community [k]noc[k]ing at the door of the Union for admission as a sovereign State,

The character of this important region will depend much upon the influence brought to bear upon its early settlement, and no influence is as powerful to dissuade from disorder, or assist to organize with dignity and order as a Free Press.

The editorial department will be conducted with entire independence

[29]Byers, Bancroft ms.

[30]*Rocky Mountain News*, Apr. 23, 1897.

of all partizens or pecuniary considerations; and while free from all undue sectional influence, will be devoted thoroughly to western interests and especially the central west, Reliable correspondents will be secured in every important Mining Region and information collected with care, as to their extent and richness, and also their Agricultural and commercial resources. Special attention will be paid to ascertaining the result of reliable surveys for roads through the mountains and particularly for the Main Central Trac[k] of a Pacific Rail Road, In a word, all that will be useful to the stranger in forming a correct estimate of the Mining Region and its prospects: either for Mining, Farming or Trading, will be faithfully communicated in the ROCKY MOUNTAIN NEWS,

At the same time private arrangements will be made until the Mail or Express is regularly established, to obtain the earliest Eastern News for the Miners, We hope by conducting the paper honestly and fairly, to obtain for it a wide circulation in all the Eastern States, as well as at the Mines, and by carefully see[k]ing correct information, render our statements perfectly reliable, Wholesale dealers wishing to deal with the mining region will find it to their interest to advertise in the MOUNTAIN NEWS as being the first newspaper established it will be read by all the Miners.

Being the first it is the intention to ma[k]e the NEWS the best Newspaper in the country, It is printed upon an Imperial press, with new type and furnished with a most complete Office in all its appointments, the first establishment of the [k]ind ever set up within the borders of the great plains west of the Missouri River, The NEWS will publish no mining reports, or rich discoveries upon mere rumor, but only upon the best authenticated accounts of [k]nown correspondents, or the personal [k]nowledge of the Proprietors, so that its reports may be fully relied upon.

For Terms, see first page,

W, N, BYERS & CO,

Other of the hopes and aspirations of a fledgling editor and his newborn journal are set forth in the traditional "salutatory" at the head of the editorial column on the opposite page.

With our hat in our hand and our best bow we this week make our first appearance upon the stage in the capacity of Editor.

We make our debut in the far west, where the snowy mountains look down upon us in the hottest summer day as well as in the winters cold; here where a few months ago the wild beasts and wilder Indians held undisturbed possession—where now surges the advancing wave of Anglo Saxon enterprise and civilization, where soon we fondly hope will be erected a great and powerful state, another empire in the sisterhood of empires.

Our course is marked out; we will adhere to it with stedfast and fixed determination, to speak, write and publish the truth and nothing but the truth, let it work us weal or woe.

Fondly looking forward to a long and pleasant acquaintance with our readers, hoping well to act our part, we send forth to the world the first number of the *Rocky Mountain News*.

CHAPTER TWO

West to the Rockies

T HE expedition which toiled across the plains to found the *Rocky Mountain News* was financed, in part, by three hundred dollars found on the cadaver of a horse thief. Some of the other parties on the trail were less generously capitalized.

The dollars were acquired in the pursuit of his professional duties, or education, by Dr. A. F. Peck, who has been met earlier in the pages of this narrative as the medic who confidently advertised in the first *News* that he would alternate his time between surgery and digging gold on the Cache la Poudre. The ad was one of those which had been collected and set into type before Byers & Company struck out from Omaha. There the good doctor had acquired some measure of distinction for his height and had won the nickname of "Long" Dr. Peck. Shortly before the press party left Omaha he had been engaged in dissecting the body of a man lynched for horse stealing and had made his first—perhaps his only— lucky strike in the deceased's pockets, a small bonanza which must have caused some self-castigation among the righteous vigilantes for not ascertaining more carefully their victim's assets.

Although he was not a part of the *News* enterprise itself, Dr. Peck was signed on as a fully participating member of the expedition and served, at least on one occasion, as its chaplain. It may be assumed that some of the windfall three hundred dollars went into the outfitting of the two wagons with flour, bacon, coffee, dried apples, saleratus, and other necessaries, including brandy and gold pans.

An effort has been made, with indifferent success, to document the case of the wealthy horse thief and his unintended contribution to the founding of the *News*. The story has its basis in a *post hoc* report some thirteen years late, plus a little substantiation by coincidence. The *News* of December 31, 1873, told of Dr. Peck's membership in the party and went on to quote (without a date) from "Dr. Miller's 'Home Gossip'" column in the Omaha *Herald*:

. . . The doctor had just become wealthy by finding $300 on the person of a gentleman who swung off into eternity for horse stealing here at about that time, whose body he had been engaged in dissecting. $300 was a large amount of money in those days of impecuniosity and is said to have added considerably to the fearful natural length of the lofty doctor. . . .

There would seem to have been little occasion for an autopsy on a strung-up horse thief, even if Nebraska Territorial justice had advanced at that date to the point of holding inquests, which it hadn't. So apparently Dr. Peck had seized upon macabre opportunity for the perfection of his anatomical and surgical knowledge by an exercise in dissection. This was a day when cadavers were hard come by, and the good doctor probably would have considered himself fortunate even if the horse fancier had not been carrying a bankroll.

Dr. Peck is something of an elusive figure. The Nebraska State Historical Society made a preliminary try at locating him in early Omaha records but nothing was found. He cannot have had much success finding gold in the Cache la Poudre, since he was in Denver practicing medicine early in the fall of 1859. A local item in the *News* for October 13 describes the paper's companion-of-the-trail as "a graduate of one of the best New York medical colleges" and says he "also attended medical lectures in New Orleans, and served with distinction as a Surgeon in Gen. Walker's Nicaraguan army." Aside from this, little more is known about the background and attainments of the lanky, far-wandering medic who helped pioneer his profession in Colorado under somewhat unusual circumstances. The *News* of October 27 reports that he was one of the seconds to R. E. Whitsitt in a duel—Navy Colts at ten paces—with William Park McClure, the "Little Thunderer," on October 19. McClure was hit in the groin but recovered. Whitsitt, one of the most prominent of Denver's early settlers, escaped injury and had no need for the ministrations of his professional second. Dr. Peck's name appears among the eight physicians and surgeons listed in the city's first directory,[1] but he was gone by the time D. O. Wilhelm compiled the second directory in 1866.

It is not difficult to establish a probable identity for the horse thief who contributed toward Dr. Peck's excursion to the gold regions. The case was a celebrated one in the early annals of Omaha, and the doctor had a choice of two anatomical specimens. Harvey Braden and John Daley had been picked up on a charge of pilfering horses and were thrown into the Omaha jail. A band of outraged horse owners spirited them from the jail on January 8, 1859, and hanged them from a tree two miles north of nearby Florence.[2] Some of the lynchers were arrested, but the prosecution dwindled off as such prosecutions often did in an era sensitive about horse ownership. Alfred Sorensen tells substantially the same story in his *The Early History of Omaha*, though he gives

[1] *Denver City and Auraria, The Commercial Emporium of the Pike's Peak Gold Regions,* which is dated 1859 but appeared sometime after Jan. 1, 1860.

[2] Andreas, op. cit., p. 698.

the month of the lynching as March. The *Nebraska Advertiser* for February 10, however, carries a report on the trial of the vigilantes. The record shows no other lynchings in the vicinity at this time. So if the gossip reported by Dr. George L. Miller, founding editor of the *Herald*, was faithfully relayed, it must have been either Braden or Daley who helped with the outfitting of the *Rocky Mountain News* for the voyage across the plains.

A trip westward across the treeless prairies in 1859 was a voyage, not into the unknown, but into a vacuum. Too often in the stories of the Rocky Mountain West it is suggested that the region was *terra incognita* before the fifty-niners came. Actually the Rockies had been rather thoroughly explored and considerably traveled before Cherry Creek got into the news of the day. It was just that the explorers and travelers— except for the fur brigades of mountain men and the Indian traders— found little to detain them in the mountain fastnesses except scenery and good hunting.

Three historic migrations—the Oregon pioneers, the forty-niners to California, and the Mormons to Utah—already had passed through years before the Pike's Peak rush. The Overland Trail up the Platte and over South Pass was a well-established roadway, a broad avenue for westering. But even before these mass movements the Rockies were crisscrossed by the trails of conquistadores, official explorers, trappers, cavalrymen, dragoons, diarists, and even gentleman hunters over from England for an outing.

Spanish soldiers as far back as Coronado in 1541 had been in the area. Juan de Oñate possibly had penetrated as far northward as the site of Denver in 1601, and in the year of the nation's independence the hardy friars Silvestre Vélez de Escalante and Francisco A. Domínguez traversed much of the western slope of the Rockies in what is now Colorado. Juan de Uribarri was on the eastern Colorado plains in 1706, and there were others who came, seeking the gold-paved streets of fabled Quivira or pursuing Indian slaves who had the pagan impertinence to run off from the Christian settlements in New Mexico.

Meanwhile French traders were coming up the rivers from the east. They had reached the foothills of the Rockies in 1706, and the Mallet brothers traversed Colorado from north to south as early as 1739. The ruggedly glamorous fur-trade era, which would reach its height in the 1820s and 1830s, had begun. How much of Colorado was trod by the moccasins of these *voyageurs* will never be known precisely, but they went where the beaver and the buffalo were. Most of them were unlettered men, and they left little record. Others who began the written record later practiced a precious discrimination. The Anglo-Saxon historians who started to write things down only a century or so ago made great point of "first white explorer," "first white settler," "first white baby." The bold Spanish and Mexicans, who actually had plunged into an unknown country, were not white by these writers' standards, and the mountain men, since they freely and frequently took squaws to wife, didn't qualify either.

One who did qualify, by any count, was Lieutenant Zebulon Montgomery Pike, the first official explorer of the Colorado plains and Rockies. Pike was sent out in 1806 to take a look at the farther reaches of newly purchased Louisiana, and he either was a part of the Aaron Burr conspiracy to establish an independent empire in the West or he got lost. Probably the latter, though it's a harsh thing to say about a pathfinder. But he did establish a major landmark in the West which would perpetuate his name and become a lodestone and a catchword. His significant report gave the nation its first reliable estimates of the nature of the Rocky Mountain West. He didn't succeed in his effort to climb his "Grand Peak" in the "Mexican Mountains"; in fact he believed "no human being could have ascended to its pinnacle." Time would place both a cog railroad and an automobile highway on the summit of Pike's Peak.

In 1820, Major Stephen H. Long was dispatched to explore the boundries of the Louisiana Purchase, and the historian-naturalist of his expedition, Dr. Edwin James, led the first recorded ascent of Pike's Peak. The Long party made its way up the Platte (Pike had used the Arkansas River as his roadway), and in the accounts of his tour are the first detailed descriptions of the site which the city of Denver would occupy. Dr. James called Cherry Creek "Vermilion Creek," and Captain John R. Bell, in his recently rediscovered journal, tells of a pleasant camp that was made:

Wednesday, July 5th. Proceeded at 20 minutes before 5 oclock A.M. Major Long & Lieut. Swift in advance of the party again, to select a suitable place for encamping & to take observations—passed two buffalo at a distance, and on the opposite side of the river three creeks that have their source in the mountains—the largest is called Cannon ball creek [present Clear Creek] from the size & form of the stone in its bed—came up with the Major at ½ past 7 oclock halted and encamped for the remainder of the day and night. Dr. James and Mr. Peale with two men, set out on foot to go to the base of the mountains. The Major & Lieut. Swift engaged in taking astronomical observations for determining the latitude & longitude of the place. Dr. Say was quite indisposed, he was in bad health when we left the Engineer cantonment and has not bettered any on the march, but he seldom complains—the hunters killed a deer & an antelope—our camp is beautifully situated on the bank of the river, which is here about 100 yards wide—our tents pitched in grove of cotton wood trees [Denver], that shade us from the scorching rays of the sun—the altitude of the mercury at 91°. About 6 P.M. Dr. James, Mr. Peale & the two men returned, having experienced a hard days travel, without reaching the base of the mountains—the distance [about fifteen miles] was greater than they anticipated—as far as they did progress the[y] followed the course of the cannon ball creek—which they represent as abounding with fish & a beautiful stream of clear water. . . .[3]

Throughout the period of exploration the mountain men ranged everywhere ahead of the official parties, always another horizon farther on into the wildernesses. Pike met one of them when the Spanish captured him and took him into Santa Fe, and the trapper showed him some gold he had picked up in the Rockies. Fur-trade forts were built on the Arkansas and Gunnison rivers and on the South Platte at several points north from present Denver. Lonely, strange, self-sufficient men the trappers were. Men who bore famous names bright with romance: Jim Bridger, Kit Carson, Céran St. Vrain, Jim Beckwourth, the mulatto war chief of the Crows, Ezekiel Williams, "Uncle Dick" Wootton, old Jim Baker, Louis Vasquez, Tom ("Broken Hand") Fitzpatrick, Andrew and Milton Sublette, and many others. They ranged the Indian game trails as if the Rockies were their own private hunting park. Most of them were squawmen, and they knew, accepted, and adopted Indian ways. With little equipment other than a "possibles bag," a rifle, and a knife they could live, even prosper, in the virgin forests and among the peaks and crags for a year or more at a time. Then, like as not, they would blow the value of a season's peltries in an orgy of strychnine whiskey and wild fellowship at a rendezvous on the Green River or in a few nights of fandango at Taos. At one time or another many of the mountain men served as trail-knowing, Indian-wise guides to expeditions of exploration, and they taught the newcomers all they knew about the red man's savage but plastic ways. The lessons didn't take very well. Had those who came later been better scholars, had they heeded the trappers' advice about fair dealing and understanding, been less self-righteous in their protestations of "destiny" or their evangelism of strange customs, the West might have been spared decades of bloody Indian wars.

During the 1820s, '30s, and '40s a dozen or more trading posts, bastions of adobe and logs, were built along the rivers of Colorado wherever Indians would come to trade or beaver plews could be gathered. The largest and most famous of these was Bent's Fort on the Arkansas, a stopping place on the Santa Fe Trail, about which much has been written early and late. Little is known about another fur-trade fort which probably was the first settlement at the present site of Denver.

Sketchy accounts occur in several places[4] of a cottonwood log

[3]Harlin M. Fuller and LeRoy R. Hafen, eds., *The Journal of Captain John R. Bell* (Glendale, 1957), pp. 146–47.

[4]Smiley, op. cit., p. 152; *Rocky Mountain News*, Feb. 1, 1860; Nolie Mumey, *History of the Early Settlements of Denver* (Glendale, 1942), pp. 29–30; Jerome C. Smiley, *Semi-Centennial History of the State of Colorado* (Chicago, 1913),

stockade apparently built in 1832 by Louis Vasquez on the bank of the South Platte opposite the mouth of the creek once named for him but now called Clear—the Cannon Ball Creek of the Long expedition. This would be at the northern outskirts of modern Denver. Louis—the "Vaskiss" of Francis Parkman's works—was a French-Canadian and a veritable captain among the mountain men. His brother, Antoine François ("Baroney") Vasquez, had been interpreter on the Pike sortie, and a nephew, A. Pike Vasquez, would become a freighter and a businessman in pioneer Denver. During his later years Louis Vasquez was a partner of Jim Bridger, the famed "Old Gabe."

Smiley's history of Denver, published in 1901, reports that the stockade opposite the mouth of Vasquez Fork "remained there many years," but by the time Smiley compiled his semicentennial history of Colorado in 1913 he had decided it was a "temporary establishment" and wrote that no remains of it were discovered when "the foundations of Denver were laid." Smiley's Denver history connects Jim Beckwourth with the Vasquez stockade, but since he confuses Jim with Pike Vasquez as a nephew of Louis, he probably has his mountain men mixed. All of the accounts agree that the post was a small one.

Some further confirmation of its existence as Denver's first settlement is found in an unpublished manuscript editor Byers of the *News* gave in 1884 to the historian Hubert Howe Bancroft and which now is preserved in the Bancroft Library, University of California. Byers told Bancroft:

> . . . The first Trading Post established in the valley of the South Platte was built in 1832 by Louis Vasquez about 5 miles northeast of the present site of Denver at the junction of Vasquez Fork with the Platte River. . . . A nephew of Louis Vasquez known as "Pike" Vasquez was a clerk in that Trading Post from 1832 to 1836. He was also a citizen of Denver in its early days & I was very intimately acquainted with him. He told me that they frequently purchased gold from trappers & hunters with whom they carried on trade & who informed them that they procured it in the mountains, but he had no knowledge of where in the mountains & seemed to take no interest. In answer to inquiries he said the employes of the Fur Company employed about the Post took no interest in learning where the gold came from or how it was procured & in fact knew very little about anything outside the Post. . . .[5]

The dates Byers gives would fit. For it is known that Louis Vasquez joined with Andrew Sublette in 1837 to build another post subsequently known as Fort Vasquez farther down the Platte. This later fort, a rather

Vol. I, pp. 181–82; Frank Hall, *History of the State of Colorado* (Chicago, 1889), Vol. I, p. 169.

[5]Byers, Bancroft ms., op. cit.

elaborate adobe affair, was in ruins when Francis Parkman came by in 1846, but remnants still remained into the twentieth century. In recent years the fort has been restored as a historical monument and stands beside the paved highway just south of Platteville, thirty-seven miles north of Denver.

The stories of the *News* and of another obscure trading post in the Denver vicinity also intersect. Fort Jackson was built, also in 1837, by Henry Fraeb and Peter A. Sarpy as a close neighbor to Vasquez and Sublette only four miles to the south of Fort Vasquez near the present town of Ione. Sarpy was a "squat, volatile, bushy-bearded Frenchman" whose name punctuates the annals of fur-trade days. He appears to have been everywhere the trapper-hunter brigades went throughout all the time beaver pelts and buffalo robes and tongues were currency. Here, in 1837, he is on the remote South Platte at the foot of the Rockies. Twenty-one years later he is factor at Bellevue on the Missouri south of Omaha, trading with the Omaha Indians. As has been noted, he may have been the person who sold Byers the old hand press of the Bellevue *Gazette* on which the first *Rocky Mountain News* was printed. Byers wrote that he met him in Bellevue in 1858, "living with the Omaha Indians, among whom he was known as 'The Stud-Horse on the Sand Bar.' "[6] Smiley describes Sarpy as an "irascible man" who "got along much better with the red men than he did with the white ones."[7]

If Smiley's estimate of Sarpy is accurate it would be only typical. Most of the mountain men were much more at home in a tipi than at a booster meeting or a political rally, and there is ample evidence that the self-consciously pioneering settlers who came later, buoyant with local patriotism and gregariously political by instinct, distrusted these shaggy firstcomers of wild habits and no fixed residence. And the decline of the fur-trade era saw an abrupt and fundamental change in the relationships between "new" Westerners and the old and native ones. The mountain man was the last American who could get along with the Indian. Although he could fight the red man ferociously on occasion, trading savagery for savagery in highly personalized combat, he could understand, accept, and live with Indian ways and possessed the dignity of an almost infinite patience. But by 1859 he was growing old and garrulous of past exploits, and dying off. A new breed of Westerner was moving in. Henceforth the plains and mountains would fill with impatient empire-builders whose first reaction to the word "Indian" was to twitch toward a rifle.

In the van of the new movement rode the United States Dragoons, resplendent in colorful uniforms with crossed shoulder belts. Through June, July, and August of 1835, Colonel Henry Dodge led the hundred

[6]Byers, *History of Colorado*, p. 21.

[7]Smiley, *History of Denver*, p. 152.

and twenty men of his 1st Dragoons on a long, looping march to the Rockies, sixteen hundred miles up the Platte, and home to Fort Gibson by way of the Arkansas. They were out to "show the flag," to council with the Indians and demonstrate to them that their Great White Father, possessed of swivel howitzers and many troopers, would brook no foolishnesses. Significantly, the dragoons found no occasion to fire a shot in anger, though they met with parties and villages of Pawnees, Arapahoes, Comanches, and other tribes.

On July 22 the tour of the dragoons brought them to the forking of the Platte and Cherry Creek, and one of their number, young Captain Lemuel Ford, set down in his journal another brief description of the site which would become Denver:

Monday July 20th 1835

The command Marched S 20 West about ten miles & S 10 West 10 Miles with the Rocky Mountains covered with Snow on our right presenting a most magnificent appearance The Buffalowe Still more abundant fat & fine we encampted on the Second Bank of the river fine timbered Bottom with good grass

Tuesday July 21st 1835

remained in camp to day to rest & graize our horses (I was officer of the day)

Wednesday July 22nd 1835

command marched South 22 Miles Country about Same as passed Several days Back Bottom covered with timber Cotton wood & Willow grass good [Denver]. We encampted for the evening on the Plt [Platte][8]

Other cavalrymen followed the dragoons on missions military or exploratory. In 1845, Colonel Stephen Watts Kearny rode west along the Oregon Trail to remind hostile tribes not to molest the emigrants. He, too, returned through Colorado and down the Arkansas. A year later Kearny led his Army of the West out the Santa Fe Trail to the conquest of New Mexico, stirring up the tribes as he went. Lieutenant Colonel William Gilpin had to come back in 1857 on a punitive expedition to relieve Indian plundering of traffic along the trail.

During this same period the Great Pathfinder, John C. Frémont, was trying on five expeditions—1842, 1843, 1845, 1848, and 1853—to find an easy way through the escarpment of the Colorado Rockies. At least three of these probing explorations brought him close to the future site of Denver. The last, privately financed to seek a transcontinental railroad route and advance presidential aspirations, followed the route taken

[8]Nolie Mumey, *March of the First Dragoons to the Rocky Mountains in 1835: The Diaries and Maps of Lemuel Ford* (Denver, 1957), pp. 62–63.

earlier in the year by Captain John W. Gunnison from Bent's Fort over Cochetopa Pass to the river of deep cañons and big trout which now bears Gunnison's name.

The scene of Denver before its gold rush also is interestingly described by two notable diarists. Rufus B. Sage, newspaperman, trapper, and naturalist, spent much of the period 1842-44 roaming the Colorado Rockies, and several times he made his campfire where a busy city's traffic now hums. In the autumn of 1842 he left Fort Lancaster, on the Platte north of Denver near present Fort Lupton, bound for Taos. He followed what was by now a well-established trappers' and traders' trail linking the fur forts of the South Platte with Bent's Fort down on the Arkansas and with the New Mexican settlements. Thirty-five miles upstream, at Cherry Creek, he found the increasingly popular stopping place among the cottonwoods and willows already was populated by "a camp of free traders and hunters."

Sage describes the scene, and incidentally explains why the name of the creek has by now been changed from Vermilion to Cherry.

> This stream is an affluent of the Platte, from the southeast, heading in a broad ridge of pine hills and rocks, known as the "Divide" [separating the watersheds of the Platte and the Arkansas]. It pursues its course for nearly sixty miles, through a broad valley of rich soil, tolerably well timbered, and shut in for the most part by high plats of table land,—at intervals thickly studded with lateral pines, cedars, oaks, and shrubs of various kinds,—gradually expanding its banks as it proceeds, and exchanging a bed of rock and pebbles for one of quicksand and gravel, till it finally attains a width of nearly two hundred yards, and in places is almost lost in the sand. The stream derives its name from the abundance of cherry [chokecherries] found upon it. . . .
>
> Our route bore nearly due south for twenty miles following the Platte bottom to the mouth of Cherry creek. . . . The Platte presented heavy groves of timber upon both banks, as did also its islands, while its bottoms appeared fertile.
>
> The mountains, some fifteen miles to our right, towering aloft with their snow-capped summits and dark frowning sides, looked like vast piles of clouds, big with storm and heaped upon the lap of the earth; while the vaporscuds that flitted around them, seemed as the ministers of pent up wrath, in readiness to pour forth their torrents and deluge the surrounding plains, or let loose the fierce tornado and strew its path with desolation.
>
> Three or four miles before reaching our present camp, we passed a village of Arapahos on its way to the mountains, in pursuit of game.[9]

[9]Rufus B. Sage, Scenes in the Rocky Mountains (Philadelphia, 1846), quoted in LeRoy R. and Ann W. Hafen, Rufus B. Sage: His Letters and Papers (Glendale, 1956), Vol. II, pp. 65-66.

Sage goes on to tell about the camp of free trappers he found at Cherry Creek. There were, he writes, four lodges, three of whites and one of Blackfoot Indians. "Each of the whites has his squaw wife, and the usual accompaniment of ruddy faced children. In regard to the latter, I must say they were more beautiful, interesting, and intelligent than the same number of full-bloods,—either of whites or Indians."

LeRoy R. Hafen, dean of Rocky Mountain historians, speculates that one of the squawmen was "Uncle John" Smith, who had a Blackfoot wife, and a few years later became one of the founding fathers of the Denver City Town Company. Hafen also believes "Uncle John," a seasoned veteran of the Rockies since 1826, may have been the historical person who served as model for the character Killbuck in George Frederick Ruxton's *Life in the Far West,* one of the most authentic accounts of the era of the mountain men.

Sage returned to Cherry Creek, this time down out of a winter hunt in the peak-rimmed parks of the central Rockies, on December 19 and found a land flowing with milk and honey:

> Our horses being quite enfeebled from the fatigue of travel, we gladly availed ourselves of the presence of buffalo to prolong our stay at Cherry creek some ten days, and meanwhile found no difficulty in procuring a continued feast of good things from the dense herds that thronged the country upon every side.
>
> The severe weather and frequent snows of the past two months, had driven these animals from the open prairie into the creek bottoms and mountains, whose vicinities were completely blackened with their countless thousands.
>
> The antelope, too, seemed to have congregated from all parts, and covered the country in one almost unbroken band. Their numbers exceeded anything of the kind I ever witnessed before or since. . . .[10]

But there were wolves there, too, attracted by the plenitude of game, and Sage tells of a unique council of war which a pack conducted on hills now well within the Denver city limits:

> Upon a neighboring eminence some fifty or a hundred of these insatiate marauders were congregated, as if for consultation. Adjoining this, two parallel lines of low hills led out from the river bottom into the prairie, for five or six miles, defining a narrow valley, at the extremity of which a large band of antelope were quietly grazing.
>
> The chief topic of the wolfine conference seemed to have particular reference to this circumstance; for, in a very short time, the council dispersed, and its members betook to the hills skirting the valley before described, and, stationing themselves upon both lines at regular intervals, two of them commenced the attack by leisurely approaching

[10]Ibid., p. 191.

their destined prey from opposite directions, in such a manner as to drive the whole band between the defile of hungry expectants. This done, the chase began without further preliminary.

Each wolf performed his part by pursuing the terrified antelope till relieved by his next companion, and he by the succeeding one; and so on, alternately; taking care to reverse their course at either extremity of the defile—again and again to run the death-race, until, exhausted by the incessant effort and crazed with terror, the agile animals, that were wont to bid defiance to the swiftest steed, and rival the storm-wind in fleetness, fell easy victims to the sagacity of their enemies.[11]

Only four years after Sage had watched with fascination this seemingly planned attack of the wolf pack, another and even more famous diarist visited Cherry Creek. He was Francis Parkman, whose *The Oregon Trail* is part and parcel of every literate boy's knowledge of the Old West. Parkman came in 1846 and on August 15

> . . . A long morning's march brought us to Cherry Creek, over a very hot and dry prairie. Weather too smoky to see the mts. Creek dry—camp of Mormon emigrants, who passed this way with Richard a few week[s] ago. Cherries—plums—black currents–and gooseberries. No water in creek—dug holes and got some. Camped at night on the creek.[12]

It is interesting to watch this brief sketch of Denver in the dry season become a graphic, colorful description in *The Oregon Trail*:

> About noon the next day we reached Cherry Creek. Here was a great abundance of wild cherries, plums, gooseberries, and currants. The stream, however, like most of the others which we passed, was dried up with the heat, and we had to dig holes in the sand to find water for ourselves and our horses. Here we found traces of the camp of some Mormon emigrants, who had passed this way with Richard some weeks ago. The following day we left the banks of the creek, which we had been following for some time, and began to cross the high dividing ridge which separates the waters of the Platte from those of Arkansas. The scenery was altogether changed. In place of the burning plains, we passed through rough and savage glens, and among hills crowned with a dreary growth of pines. We encamped among these solitudes on the night of the sixteenth of August. A tempest was threatening. The sun went down among volumes of jet-black cloud edged with a bloody red. But in spite of these portentous signs, we neglected to put up the tent, and being extremely fatigued, lay down on the ground and fell asleep. The storm broke about midnight, and we pitched the

[11]Ibid., p. 192.

[12]Mason Wade, ed., *The Journals of Francis Parkman* (New York, 1947), Vol. II, p. 472.

tent amid darkness and confusion. In the morning all was fair again, and Pike's Peak, white with snow, was towering above the wilderness afar off.[13]

Parkman's trip through Colorado was a leisurely one, essentially a sight-seeing excursion, but the most luxurious of the early Colorado "tourists" undoubtedly was the Irish baronet, Sir George Gore of Sligo, whose name has been left behind on a range of mountains in memory of his spectacular visit. Sir George came to Colorado in 1855 strictly *pour le sport*. He brought with him a retinue of fifty servants, secretaries, stewards, cooks, fly makers, and dog tenders, and an outfit which consisted of a hundred and twelve horses, twelve yoke of oxen, six wagons, twenty-one carts, fourteen hunting dogs, an arsenal of firearms, and bundles of fishing rods. The blueblood hunting party remained in the wilderness two years. Its kill was totted up at forty grizzlies, nearly three thousand buffaloes, and uncounted thousands of antelope and deer. During about half his hunt Sir George was guided by "Old Gabe," Jim Bridger himself. Jim told later how it was his noble client's habit to sleep until about 10 or 11 A.M. in his well-furnished pavilion, rise, bathe, break his fast, and then set out for a day of hunting which often extended into the night. Late supper included the proper wine, and then Sir George often would read aloud to Bridger by the light of the campfire. The sporting peer was an admirer of Shakespeare, but "Old Gabe" allowed the Bard "was a leetle too highfalutin'" and moreover he "rayther calculated that thar big Dutchman, Mr. Full-stuff, was a leetle too fond of lager beer." The same amount of alcohol, Jim felt, might better be infused in the medium of good old bourbon whiskey.[14]

So Shakespeare, too, had been in the Colorado wilds before the peopling started. The era of exploration, fur trade, and mere visiting, casual or purposeful, was drawing to a close. A good military road now followed the old trappers' trail up the South Platte, linking Fort Laramie in present Wyoming with the new American territory of New Mexico to the south and fording the river at the point where a city would be born.

It was not that the charms, hazards, and possible riches of the Rockies were unknown in 1858. Copious reports, both official and literary, had been turned in. The difficulty was that a formidable country stretched between the Missouri River frontier and those far and shining mountains. Treeless, waterless, barren, the Great Plains stretched westward for five hundred miles or more as a sea of grass and sand on which only the most adventurous embarked.

[13]Francis Parkman, *The Oregon Trail* (Heritage Press ed., New York, 1943), p. 235.

[14]J. Cecil Alter, *James Bridger: A Historical Narrative* (reprint ed., Columbus, 1951), pp. 264ff.

Pike had reported on his return to civilization in 1808 that the plains should be written off as uninhabitable. "But from these immense prairies may arise one great advantage to the United States, viz., the restriction of our population to some certain limits, and thereby a continuation of the union. Our citizens being so prone to rambling, and extending themselves on the frontiers, will, through necessity, be constrained to limit their extent on the west to the borders of the Missouri and Mississippi, while they leave the prairies, incapable of cultivation, to the wandering and uncivilized Aborigines of the country."

Long echoed Pike's sentiments, saw the plains as a buffer against enemy action by the Spanish, and labeled them on his map the "Great American Desert." This section of America was "almost wholly unfit for cultivation, and of course uninhabitable by a people depending upon agriculture for their subsistence."

Even a half century later another military man, General William Tecumseh Sherman, would look out across the ocean of grass and write to his friend, Admiral David Dixon Porter: "Our Plains resemble your seas."[15] And though he would change his mind later, Sherman then believed that "In general terms, the settlements of Kansas, Dacotah, and Iowa have nearly or quite reached the Western limit of land fit for cultivation, Parallel 99° of West Longitude. Then begin the Great Plains 600 miles wide, fit only for Nomadic tribes of Indians, Tartars, or Buffaloes. . . ."[16]

But Pike and Long reckoned without a powerful stimulus which would act upon the westbound instincts of a naturally rambling people, and it fell to the lot of Sherman to protect the ramblers from the savages when they refused to be constrained by the Missouri River. The stimulus, of course, was gold.

Reports of gold in the Colorado Rockies had been received by Pike, and Sage relates the story that a war party of Arapahoes once used solid gold bullets against the Pawnees, "every bullet discharged killing an enemy." There had been many other scattered and more or less vague reports. While Sir George Gore was cruising the Colorado parks, legend insists, a member of his party discovered gold in a stream. Sir George immediately packed up his wine cellar and trophies, broke camp, and moved on lest gold fever spoil his hunt. The mountain men knew there was gold about, but they were disinterested. Editor Byers of the *News* was not the only one who would record, incredulously, that these wild roamers "took no interest" in something so patently the goal of all rational mankind. Pike had expressed similar amazement when James

[15]Sherman to Porter, Nov. 24, 1865, Library of Congress; quoted in Robert G. Athearn, *William Tecumseh Sherman and the Settlement of the West*, (Norman, 1956), p. 13.

[16]Sherman to John A. Rawlins, March 6, 1866, National Archives; Athearn, op. cit., p. 36.

Pursley, or Purcell, told him in Santa Fe in 1807 that he had found gold at the head of La Platte and had carried some of it in his shot pouch for months. But "losing in his mind all the IDEAL VALUE which mankind have stamped on that metal, he threw the sample away." The capital letters are Pike's.

A party of Cherokees, passing through en route to California in 1850, found a little gold in Ralston Creek, a tributary of Vasquez Fork. This was the first discovery firmly placed in the vicinity of future Denver. The Cherokees, however, went on to California seeking bigger bonanzas, which they didn't find. Other reported strikes in the Cherry Creek area dotted the next decade. Byers, in his *History of Colorado*, said General Thomas Taylor of Kentucky told him in later years that he had washed some dust out of the Cherry Creek sands in 1852 while he was on a campaign to "chastise the Comanches."

Numerous other passers-by, prospecting parties, and cavalry missions produced additional stories of precious metal in the Pike's Peak region. The reports, printed with some embellishments in border newspapers and then copied by the press throughout the East, built up increasing interest in the craggy country beyond the hazardous plains. Slowly the reports of gold began to firm up, although no one yet had recovered enough dust to make the trip worth while.

A little real Pike's Peak gold actually began to show up in the frontier villages to bolster the newspaper accounts, which became increasingly glowing. A Delaware Indian named Fall Leaf went out in 1857 as scout and hunter for Major John Sedgwick in a punitive campaign against the Cheyennes. Fall Leaf found some dust in one of the streams near Cherry Creek, and when he returned to his home in eastern Kansas he showed it off around the town of Lawrence. The following May, Captain Randolph B. Marcy was leading a supply party from New Mexico to General A. S. Johnson's army, then at Fort Bridger beyond South Pass in Wyoming. The supply train paused at the mouth of Cherry Creek to build a ferryboat. The Platte, swollen by the spring runoff, could not be forded by the mules and wagons. While the boat was being constructed one of Marcy's civilian teamsters, George S. Simpson, washed out a few flecks of gold from the sands of the creek. Simpson passed on his gold to an eastbound friend at Fort Bridger, and it made its way to Westport, Missouri, to add to the fulminating excitement. John Cantrell, or Cantrill, of Westport, heading a party of traders States-bound from Salt Lake, stopped by Cherry Creek and took home both some dust and a sackful of sand and gravel from the stream. This he panned out publicly in the streets of Kansas City in the fall of 1858 for a demonstrated yield of twenty-five cents in gold to the panful. The Missouri River country quickly calculated how many panfuls of pay dirt could be handled in a single day and went wild.

Meanwhile, during the summer, the first serious prospecting parties had arrived at Cherry Creek and the settlement of future Denver began. The Great American Desert with its alkali wastes and its Indians held no insurmountable terrors if gold could be picked up at twenty-five cents a grab on its farther shore.

One of the principal parties of fifty-eighters was led by William Green Russell and his brothers, Dr. Levi J. and J. Oliver, all from the Lumpkin County gold region of northern Georgia.[17] Green Russell, as he was known, was married to a Cherokee, and from his wife's relatives out in Indian Territory he learned of the discoveries made in 1850. Ever since then the Cherokees had wanted to go back to Pike's Peak to follow up on their original strike. The Russell brothers, experienced with gold, were interested too, and they agreed to head the expedition.

The Russell-Cherokee party set out in May and was joined on the trail by two groups of Missourians, so that on June 24, 1858, a band of a hundred and four eager prospectors arrived at the mouth of Cherry Creek. Gold was found, but not much, and the eagerness wilted. By July 2 some of the wagons already were headed back eastward. Green Russell—who wore his beard plaited into two long braids that could be tucked into his shirt front—and thirteen others stayed on. Later in the summer they began to find gold in paying quantities at Little Dry Creek, some eight miles farther up the Platte, and by October they had accumulated five hundred dollars worth.

Other parties were joining the Cherokees and Georgians in the field. Out from Lawrence, Kansas, came forty-nine men, two women, and a child, led by John Easter. They had seen Fall Leaf's nuggets, tied up in a rag. The Indian had agreed, and then refused, to accompany them as a guide, but the thirteen wagons struck out on May 24 anyway, taking along Sharps rifles and bowie knives for protection and a guitar and violin as cultural necessaries. The Lawrence gold seekers did not come immediately to Cherry Creek but headed straight for Pike's Peak, the one landmark everyone was sure of. During the summer months they prospected the streams around the foot of the peak with no success. A passing Mexican packer—whose language they couldn't understand—offered to show them where the gold was, and units of Lawrence men followed him on two wild-goose chases through the hills and down toward New Mexico. They returned with a handful of yellow iron pyrites—"fool's gold."

The women of the Lawrence party—Mrs. James H. Holmes and Mrs. Robert Middleton—left their mark on time by bringing paleface femininity, with some forcefulness, into the rough and masculine wastelands. Pert little Julia Holmes, in particular, will be remembered. She was a twenty-year-old bride, and her slight figure was highly charged

[17]Mrs. Richard French Spencer of San Antonio, granddaughter of Oliver Russell, says the full names were William Greeneberry Russell and Levi Jasper (rather than James, as it sometimes appears) Russell.

with moral conviction and physical endurance. One of her fellow travelers said of her:

> She is a regular woman's righter, wears the bloomer, and was quite indignant when informed that she was not allowed to stand on guard. She is young, handsome, and intelligent.[18]

Tiny Julia, clothed in her scandalous bloomers and armored with her convictions about the natural superiority of women, accomplished what Zebulon Pike said couldn't be done. She climbed Pike's Peak.[19] She was the first woman to do it. Her group made the third recorded ascent of what is probably America's most famous mountain. From the summit on August 5, 1858, Julia wrote home to mother:

> . . . I have accomplished the task which I marked out for myself, and now I feel amply repaid for all my toil and fatigue. Nearly every one tried to discourage me from attempting it, but I believed that I should succeed, and now, here I am, and I feel I would not have missed this glorious sight for anything at all.
> In all probability, I am the first woman who has stood upon the the summit of this mountain, and gazed upon this wondrous scene which my eyes now behold. How I sigh for a poet's power of description, so that I might give you some faint idea of the grandeur and beauty of this scene. Extending as far as the eye can reach, lie the great level plains, stretched out in all their verdure and beauty, while the winding of the grand Arkansas is visible for many miles. We can also see distinctly where many of the smaller tributaries unite with it. Then the rugged rocks all around, and the almost endless succession of mountains and rocks below, the broad blue sky over our heads, and seemingly so very near—all, and everything, on which the eye can rest, fills the mind with infinitude, and sends the soul to God.[20]

Julia never got to the Denver settlements. She and her husband and some others of the Lawrence party tired of questing gold and made their way south to the comparatively civilized adobe villages of New Mexico, where she became tutor to the children of a wealthy family. Word of the greater success of the Russells at Little Dry Creek now reached the remnants of the Lawrence party, and they moved north to arrive at Cherry Creek on September 6.

Meanwhile the first of several unenduring settlements had been started.

[18]Lawrence *Republican*, July 15, 1858.

[19]An engaging story of Julia Holmes and her climb is told in Agnes Wright Spring, *A Bloomer Girl on Pike's Peak* (Denver, 1949).

[20]*Daily Missouri Republican*, Oct. 17, 1858. The same scene which so enraptured Julia would prove the inspiration, in 1893, for Katharine Lee Bates' patriotic hymn, "America the Beautiful."

The first to bear a name was Placer Camp, which is what the Russell-Cherokee prospectors called their clutch of huts built at the mouth of Little Dry Creek in midsummer of 1858. A bronze tablet on the bridge which carries present South Santa Fe Drive across the creek bed near West Dartmouth Avenue now marks the approximate location of Placer Camp.

The second and more substantial settlement was called Montana or Montana City. It was established in September and represented the first effort of the newly arrived Lawrence party to provide winter quarters for itself. A formal "Montana Town Company" was organized with Josiah Hinman as president and W. J. Boyer as secretary. William Hartley, a civil engineer, surveyed and staked out a town with blocks, lots, streets, and alleys. Fifteen or twenty cabins were built, fronting on the streets in an orderly fashion. Montana City came into being a short distance north of Placer Camp, and its site also is marked with a present-day tablet. A marker at South Huron Street and West Evans Avenue perpetuates the memory of Montana City as the first organized town and "the beginning of Denver." It was a short-lived beginning.

Dissension had broken out. Montana had been located where it was in order to be close to the Little Dry Creek diggings, the only placer that had produced anything even vaguely auspicious in the way of flour gold. Some in the Lawrence party didn't like that location. They felt their town should have been closer to the spot where the regular military road from Fort Bridger to New Mexico crossed the Platte in the shoal water formed by the entry of Cherry Creek into the larger stream. The dissenters argued that a new town ought always to be established on a major traffic artery. This country had only one such—the military trail which followed the old trappers' trace laid out on an Indian pathway nobody knew how ancient.

Moreover blandishments in chamber-of-commerce style already were appearing. John S. ("Uncle John") Smith, trapper and squawman, had a wickiup in the cottonwood bottoms at Cherry Creek. He also had, it was charged, a barrel of whiskey with which he was proselytizing prospective settlers.

For one reason or another a second town company was formed before the month of September was out. Six men of the Lawrence party (John A. Churchill, Frank M. Cobb, Adnah French, William Hartley, Charles Nichols, and William M. Smith) picked up T. C. Dickson, originally one of the Russell boys, and moved north down the river. They took in "Uncle John" and his partner, William McGaa, who, the folklore of Denver insists, was the son of a Lord Mayor of London and had been educated for the clergy but had forsworn English comforts to become a trapper in the American wilds and take an Arapaho squaw. This group organized on September 24 as the St. Charles Town Association.

For the site of their city they chose what is now the downtown business section of Denver. St. Charles was staked off on land lying northeast of Cherry Creek and east of the Platte. It was a paper town. Having established their claim, the St. Charles men set out for home on October 1, planning to winter in eastern Kansas and return in the spring with an official charter from the Kansas Territory legislature for their town.

Throughout this three- or four-month flurry of town founding, additional expeditions of gold hunters were creaking into the area behind their oxen or mules, and real estate promotion cannot have been far from the minds of some of the founders. Gold was hard come by, they had discovered, but a lot of men who didn't know that already were arriving, and more would come. The newcomers probably could be sold town property at tidy profits. With a duly embossed go-ahead from the Kansas legislature, the St. Charles town proprietors might do a lot better as town promoters than they had as prospectors.

As they moved down the Platte toward home the St. Charles men met the first gold-seekers moving toward Pike's Peak after seeing Cantrell's twenty-five-cents-a-pan demonstration in the streets of Kansas City and Westport. Here was a threat that the St. Charles townsite might be jumped. Charles Nichols was dispatched back to the mouth of Cherry Creek to winter through and guard the claim. The fears of jumping were amply justified.

For at the head of one of the westbound parties rode "General" William Larimer, a shrewd, forceful, and experienced leader of men and an accomplished town boomer. He had been active in the early affairs of Nebraska Territory, had organized the town of Larimer[21] overlooking the junction of the Platte and Missouri rivers, and subsequently moved on to Leavenworth in Kansas. The Larimer party was en route from Leavenworth and Lecompton to the gold fields. It arrived November 16 and, despite the patrol of Charles Nichols, unceremoniously jumped the St. Charles claim and took over. On November 22 officers were elected and a constitution adopted for the Denver City Company. The town was named for James W. Denver, who had been governor of Kansas Territory when the Leavenworth party left home but by now already had resigned that strife-plagued post. The name of Denver thus appeared in the new land under auspices which, before and since, subjected less adroit men to neck-stretching.

Before Denver City engineered its coup, however, Auraria had come into being across on the southwest side of the creek, east of the Platte. Like St. Charles, Auraria owed its beginning to remnants of the Russell and Lawrence parties. Green and Oliver Russell and others had left for home on October 1, taking "a few hundred weights" of gold of "a light chaffy character." On October 28, Dr. Levi Russell, R. J. Pierce, William McFadding, William McKimens, and Luke Tierney arrived back from

[21]Goss, op. cit., p. 17.

the military and trading post at Fort Garland in the San Luis Valley of southern Colorado with provisions for the winter. They joined with "Uncle John" Smith in erecting a double cabin far down on the point of land later claimed by Auraria. The cabin was the start of "Indian Row," a déclassé neighborhood which came to be sniffingly regarded as a sort of early slum.

The Russell-Smith cabin also has been considered the first more or less permanent structure on the site of Denver. The first Denver historians consistently withheld this designation from Smith's earlier shanty. They were acutely conscious of such distinctions and made it plain that a hut built by a low trapper could not qualify in their catalogues of civic progress. The Russell-Smith cabin, on the other hand, was at least half free from the taint of squawman origins, and so it could be counted as a "first." Similarly, Smith, William McGaa, and others of their redolent crew—they undoubtedly smelled ripely of beaver oil and rancid skins—never were able to make the grade as Denver's "first settlers," although they were there first and had been stopping at Cherry Creek for years.

As more and more new arrivals camped around the Russell-Smith cabin the notion of another town company inevitably bubbled up. And so a public meeting was called on October 30. Committees were formed in the best American tradition, a site chosen, and on November 1 the constitution of the Auraria Town Company was adopted. The name came from Auraria, Georgia, home of the Russell boys. William A. McFadding was elected president of the company, Judson H. Dudley vice-president, Dr. Russell secretary, and "Uncle John" treasurer, which seems to indicate that, although the old trapper may have smelled bad and been otherwise held in disrepute, he was recognized as having integrity enough to be trusted with the municipal coffers. Smith and McGaa happily and diplomatically changed sides with complete freedom during these days of intertown contests which tried the souls of less pliable men. Both had been founding fathers of the ill-fated St. Charles enterprise, McGaa as vice-president and Smith as treasurer. Now both were members of the Auraria company, with "Uncle John" again in a post of public trust. A few weeks later, not wishing to offend any of their newly arrived friends, both were pleased to join up in the Denver City company too. This refusal to stand hitched still greatly vexed historian Jerome Smiley a half century later; he regarded it as evidence of unreliability and scandalous want of civic patriotism. He summarily denied to the pleasant joiners—and their squaws, of course—all distinction as "first settlers." Social snobbery has deep roots in Denver.

CHAPTER THREE

Pike's Peak or Bust!

I T WAS coming up winter now, and the "Pike's Peak or Bust!" commotion was approaching full cry.

Of those who remained behind to brave it out in the contentious settlements at Cherry Creek, few had much of an idea what a winter in the Far West might be like. They expected the worst. Many of them knew the damp, marrow-numbing cold of Missouri Valley winters, and the craggy mountains which here seemed to lean over and peer down into the lonely cabins foretold a violent season. Surely the wind would rip down from those peaks and, as in Iowa, a man's breath would stand frozen before his face. The few score settlers and hardy ones who elected to essay a Rocky Mountain winter knew very well that they were far from home. Comforts of hearth and wife, of parson, Saturday night sociable, village pump and town saloon—all these were on the far, left-behind side of the desolate prairie.

They knew, too, that they were illegal squatters in a distant land which rightly belonged to red men about whose intentions one never could be quite sure.

The several town companies were bold intruders, trespassers. The treaty of Fort Laramie back in 1851 had guaranteed all this land east of the Rockies between the Platte and the Arkansas rivers to the Arapaho and Cheyenne Indians. The tribes had been promised their sway over the prairies, rich in the all-important buffalo herds, and the Great White Father further had pledged fifty thousand dollars a year in benefits to the Indians. The solemn chiefs had agreed to the bargain, and the federal government had paid *some* of the annuities provided for in the treaty. Technicalities in Washington had prevented formal ratification of the treaty. Washington had other things on its mind—including preservation of the Union—at the time, and the troubles of a few thousand savages on a remote frontier were only minor annoyances. But as far as the Arapahoes and Cheyennes were concerned, the treaty was in full force and binding. By and large they faithfully observed its provisions. Only when obstreperous and trigger-happy white men fecklessly invaded their guaranteed preserve, or when the annual presents failed to come through, did the braves of the warrior clans thrust aside the counsel of their chiefs and take to the warpath. The provocations were many. It is hardly surprising that young braves, their manhood still to be proved by tribal standards, should have become impatient with casual treaty breaking and answered, now and again, with violence.

Thoughts of bloodshed rested uneasily beneath the scalps of the trespassers wintering at Cherry Creek, exposed, uncomfortable, isolated. Although it would be another six years before Indian patience was finally exhausted by the constant faithlessness of his white brother, it can well be imagined that the Cherry Creekers in the winter of 1858–59 created Indian raids out of every chance sound which disturbed the prairie night or stirred in the brush along the river. Not only was the Laramie Treaty in effect so far as the Arapahoes and Cheyennes were concerned, but the Kansas-Nebraska Act of 1854 also had solemnly repromised that the Indian hunting grounds were not subject to entry "until said tribe shall signify their assent to the President of the United States. . . ." By 1861 the Arapahoes and Cheyennes had been persuaded to cede their title to lands "in the Pike's Peak region" with a new treaty signed at Bent's Fort, but it was not until May 28, 1864, that a congressional act finally confirmed white men's title to the land on which Denver meanwhile had grown up. Until then, and especially in the winter of 1858–59, this was Indian country: by treaty, by law, by prior possession, by every standard except the "destiny" in Fourth of July speeches. And especially, the settlers must have reflected queasily, by the sheer ease of dominance and control.

But neither red savage nor Rocky Mountain winter measured up to the fears.

Indians did not attack the defenseless Cherry Creek outpost. In fact a village of Arapahoes spent most of the season camped in the bottoms in full view of the interlopers.

Nor was the winter a harsh one. It turned out to be mild, dry, and open, as many Denver winters are. The peaks to the west shielded, rather than threatened, the settlements. Game was plentiful, and the weather so nice that two outdoor Christmas parties could be held.

One of them has been mentioned. Dick Wootton was host. He had rolled in from the south with several wagons of trading goods on Christmas Eve. Part of his cargo consisted of barrels of Taos lightning and another high-powered whiskey called Wallipete. Dick's fellow trader and mountain man, Céran St. Vrain, had retired as the trapping days waned and gone into business down in New Mexico. One of his enterprises was a small distillery at the Wallipete pueblo which turned out a wheat liquor "clear as spring water and very fierce." Wootton rolled out a keg of his friend's distillate, bashed in the head, hung a tin cup on a cottonwood limb, and told the community: "Be my guest." The town of Auraria accepted as a man, and the word of free whiskey quickly crossed the creek to bring Denver City to the party.

A slightly more decorous celebration was taking place at the "ranche" of Captain R. A. Spooner on the Platte three miles below Denver City. It was complete down to bill of fare, toasts, formal resolutions, and high poetry. An account of the feast was sent east by A. O. McGrew, Pennsylvania printer and newspaperman who had trundled a wheelbarrow across the plains that autumn to become *a* if not *the* "Wheelbarrow Man." McGrew later became city editor of the New York *Evening News*.

Some of the items on the menu he reported were: oyster and oxtail soups, salmon trout, corned beef, buffalo tongue, elk tongue, venison à la mode, antelope, grizzly bear, mountain pig, pheasant, rabbit, turkey, duck, sage hen, prairie chicken, squirrel, prairie dog, snipe, mountain rats, white swans, quails, sand-hill crane, prickly pear, and dried mountain plums. The wine list embraced madeira, champagne, golden sherry, cherry bounce, hock, Monongahela whiskey, claret, brandy, scotch whiskey, jam rum, bourbon whiskey, and Taos lightning.[1] How much of this menu was window dressing for the folks down east in Nebraska probably can be judged from the fact that the "Wheelbarrow Man" later earned fame as a notorious hoaxer. But considering the plenitude of game that season, the Christmas guests of Captain Spooner had little occasion, in contrast with a later prominent pioneer, to "damn a country where dried apple pies are a luxury."

The toasts were mellow, the songs hearty, and the after-dinner speech by "General" Larimer magniloquent. One of the offerings of the Resolutions Committee resolved that

> Although there are good things come up from Old Taos,
> Its Whisky ain't worth three skips of a Louse.

The convivial banqueteers, ranged along outdoor tables of whipsawed planking, also paid their respects to "Eve's fair daughters," much missed in their absence, and their disrespects to those men who cursed the country and departed because they were unable to achieve a fortune in a day. "Let them go; we have no use for them here; they are much better at home, where they can have someone to wash their faces every morning, and see that they do not stray too far from home." A formal salute was made to "The Press," which was not yet among those present:

> That mighty engine which controls Powers and Principalities, converts howling wilderness into smiling fields and busy marts of commerce, sheds its blessing alike upon the rich and poor, the great and the small, the lowly and the exalted; the lever which moves the world. May its influence never be perverted to serve base purposes; may our case not be to copy after others, but may we make it rule to stick to our sheets (when we get one) as long as there are quoins (coins) in the bank,

[1] Omaha *Times*, Feb. 17, 1859; quoted by Dolores C. Renze, "Not So Rugged at All," in *Denver Westerners' Brand Book: 1952* (Denver, 1933), pp. 157-58.

after which we will down with the dust, even though imposing stones rear themselves before our forms in our arduous chase after the precious metal.

All in a spirit of innocent merriment, to which correspondent McGrew went on to contribute epic poetry:

Way out upon the Platte, near Pike's Peak we were told
There by a little digging, we could get a pile of gold,
So we bundled up our duds, resolved at least to try
And tempt old Madam Fortune, root, hog, or die. . . .

Speculation is the fashion even at this early stage,
And corner lots and big hotels appear to be the rage,
The emigration's bound to come, and to greet them we will try
Big pig, little pig, root, hog, or die. . . .[2]

When bellies were round and verse had run its course, the Spooner ranch party adjourned to "town" full in a holiday mood. Dick Wootton's guests were similarly situated, and apparently less critical of the merits of Taos lightning. McGrew wrote:

. . . we found the town alive with an influx of miners. . . . In a short time an immense fire was blazing in the public square, and Terpsichore answered to the voice of Orpheus. Light hearts, merry countenances, and active feet were soon in motion, and the dance continued until midnight. . . . Groups of Indians, with their squaws and papooses, filled up the background. It was a picture that Rembrandt would have contemplated with delight. . . .

Although the dances must have been largely male caperings, goat-footed and tap-lush, the Spooner camp's mournful love songs to absent woman did not state the situation with entire accuracy. Paleface woman had made her entry into the Pike's Peak country but was doubly precious by her rarity. According to Smiley, the first non-Indian females to settle in Denver were Mrs. S. M. Rooker and her daughter, name unrecorded, who arrived August 30, 1858, stopped first at Placer Camp, and then moved into Auraria. At Christmas there were five women in camp, not counting squaws: Mrs. Rooker and daughter; "Countess" Katrina Murat, who is supposed to have made the community's first American flag from her red petticoat; Mrs. David Smoke, whose cabin became, in February, the El Dorado Hotel; and Wootton's second wife, a dark-eyed Taos girl who had arrived just the day before.

The refining and gentling influence had been supplied, though it

[2]Omaha *Times,* ibid.; quoted in LeRoy R. Hafen, *Colorado and Its People* (New York, 1948), Vol. I, p. 263.

would require several years really to assert itself, and the country was slowly coming up to the mark. Obstetrically, too, progress was being made. On March 8 the first native son was born and named, appropriately, William Denver McGaa. His mother was omitted by the early record-keepers from their census of "first" ladies; she was a half-breed Sioux. Her son, however, was permitted to make the grade as a "first." The father, William McGaa, already has figured in the chronicles. McGaa named his son for Denver, and Denver, briefly, named one of its streets for McGaa. Present Market Street originally was platted as McGaa, but the "better element" in town saw to it that the honor was taken away a little later when the street's namesake took to frequenting low dives and perambulating the avenues with a skinful.

Meanwhile other settlements were coming into being as a population straggled in. During the winter of '58-'59 there were camps at half a dozen points in addition to the several clusters of huts at the junction of Cherry Creek with the Platte. There were a few cabins at Plum Creek, farther up the river. Six miles west up Clear Creek was Arapahoe City and beyond that Mountainvale against the foothills. Off to the southeast at the headwaters of Cherry Creek, Russellville had been started. Thirty miles to the northwest Red Rock Camp or "Eleven Cabins" occupied the site of the present university town of Boulder. Spooner's Ranche— Westerners added an e to "ranch" for many years—has been mentioned; facing it from the opposite bank of the Platte was Curtis' Ranche, and downstream from these points were Chat D'Aubrey's trading post, Sander's Ranche, and remnant settlements clinging to the sites of the old Platte Valley fur-trade forts.

As 1858 drew to a close Auraria had about fifty cabins and Denver City some twenty-five, and Yankee commercial genius was asserting itself. The first Denver business was the mercantile firm of Blake & Williams. Charles H. Blake and Andrew J. Williams arrived from Crescent City, Iowa, at the close of October and established themselves with a stock of general merchandise in Auraria. A week later Kinna & Nye brought in a supply of hardware, sheet iron, and tinner's goods. J. D. Ramage, an itinerant jeweler and repairer of watches, established himself early in December, also in Auraria, and at Christmas Wootton set up his shop and public house. Thomas Pollock arrived on December 29 and opened the first smithy.

The pioneers now could get a watch repaired or a worn wagon wheel retired, but the sorry little "cities" still formed only a forlorn outpost. The boom town was shaping up back along the Missouri River, and it required spring weather to start rolling westward.

All through the fall and winter months small samples of gold had been reaching the Missouri Valley towns. Some of the early Pike's Peakers folded a pinch of dust into the letters they sent home. Quills filled with specks of float gold appeared on the streets and in the saloons of

Nebraska, Kansas, and Missouri villages. Pink S., whose roving eye spotted the beginnings of Denver's *demimonde*, sent his sweetheart in Ohio a specimen of dust, enough to plate a child's finger ring. "Just one dol worth I took it from a few pans dirt a few days ago while trying my hand washing," he wrote.[3]

From his winter-quarters ranch on the Platte, Sam S. Curtis sent thirty-seven and a half cents worth of Cherry Creek gold "in its native purity" to his brother, S. R. Curtis, then representing Iowa in Congress. The Council Bluffs *Bugle* reported that it had seen twenty dollars in dust brought back by a Mr. Ritchman, and W. R. Reed sent a twelve-fifty sample home with a friend. Both reports were republished in William N. Byers' guidebook for prospective emigrants, whose numbers grew as the season advanced.[4] William McKimens dispatched a small sample to the editor of the Leavenworth *Times* down in Kansas,[5] and the *Times* also reported a fifty-dollar nugget. All of these accounts found their way into Byers' guide, along with an even more auspicious finding of quartz gold and articles at varying degrees of rising pitch from the Omaha *Republican*, Omaha *Times*, *Missouri Democrat*, *Kansas Weekly Press* (which heralded a kettle of dust valued at seven thousand dollars), Council Bluffs *Nonpareil*, St. Louis *Democrat*, *Nebraska News* and other papers.

The excitement in the Western press reached such a level that in New York the *Ledger* felt called upon to admonish its readers on January 1:

> We see many innocent-looking paragraphs in the newspapers now-a-days, which inform the public that a new gold mine has just been discovered here, or there, or elsewhere, from which the finder took ever so many dollars' worth of ore in a few days. These are simply preparatory baits wherewith sharpers hope to catch gudgeons. Our readers must be careful how they embark in gold-mining-company speculations.

The gold-rush handbook published by Byers with Jno. H. Kellom, superintendent of public instruction for Nebraska Territory, was only one of fifteen sped into print during the winter.[6] The Byers and Kellom book, printed in Chicago, was calmer than most of the others and, since it drew on Byers' personal experience over the road to Oregon,

[3]Pink S. to Maggie Kirk, ms. letter.

[4]Byers and Kellom, *Hand Book to the Gold Fields of Nebraska and Kansas* (Denver, 1949 facsimile), pp. 97, 103, 104.

[5]Leavenworth *Times*, Dec. 18, 1858.

[6]A full account of the guidebooks is given in LeRoy R. Hafen, *Pike's Peak Gold Rush Guidebooks of 1859* (Glendale, 1941).

more trail-wise. Some of the guidebooks boldly fanned the flames; Byers and Kellom opened theirs with a disclaimer:

To The Reader

It is not the object of this work to persuade you to go to the recently discovered Nebraska and Kansas Gold Mines, but to lay before you a mass of testimony and information whereby you may be able to make a judicious decision. . . .

But they went on to mention the *Kansas Weekly Press's* kettle of gold and a nugget *"nearly as big as his fist"* which a man had picked up on the Frémont expedition in 1842.

Under such ministrations the mania grew. Thousands of impatient gold miners were poised along the Missouri at Omaha, Plattsmouth, Nebraska City, St. Joseph, Leavenworth, Lawrence, and Westport. January dawdled into February, and February perversely lingered. In March, despite a late and unusually wet season which left the plains a bogland, human patience could no longer endure delay. The floodgates burst. The stampede to Pike's Peak was on.

The expedition to found the *Rocky Mountain News* might have taken to the field even earlier had it not been for an accident. In September, Byers' lifelong talent for getting himself mixed up in shootings nearly cost his life. He had been passing through Omaha's "Irish Town" on a Sunday afternoon. A German immigrant had just located there and was being initiated with a thrashing by a mob of about a hundred bully boys. Byers and David H. Moffat, Jr., later to become one of Denver's wealthiest men and leave his name behind on a railroad tunnel piercing the Continental Divide, tried to break up the party and harvested rue for their pains. The German sought refuge in his shanty, and Moffat and Byers were standing by its door, the future editor holding a saber he had seized from one of the Irishmen. Suddenly the door swung open. A shotgun was discharged at the crowd. The buckshot ripped into Byers' right shoulder. He went down with a wound thought at the time to be fatal. He recovered, but his plans for the *News* were delayed.

Chauncey Thomas, Byers' nephew, wrote in 1934 that the shotgun blast "tore out Byers' collarbone" and left him severely incapacitated for many months. "In fact," Thomas said, "for the rest of his life he would not use suspenders, always used a belt." If the wound permanently handicapped Byers, he did not let it interfere with a full and active life which included mountain climbing, Indian chasing, lumbering, and other rigorous pursuits.

As he recovered from the injury Byers gathered together his press outfit and made ready to join the spring rush. The decision to move on west from Omaha was Mrs. Byers', according to Chauncey Thomas, who unfortunately romanticized the Colorado pioneers elaborately and is not

an altogether reliable source. Thomas also gives the only account which
has been located of the naming of the *News*. Again he credited his aunt
Elizabeth:

> . . . The founders wanted to call it either the Cherry Creek Express
> or the Pikes Peak Herald because in those days there was no such
> thing as Denver and no such thing as Colorado. The names hadn't
> been heard of yet. The people who were interested in founding the
> newspaper were discussing the name and Mrs. Byers suggested, "Let's
> name it the Rocky Mountain News." Her suggestion was adopted and
> so the paper got its name.[7]

So far as is known, Byers himself never explained the name choice, but it
is well established that the paper had its name before it left Omaha.

Associated with Byers in the publishing venture were Thomas Gibson
of Fontanelle, Nebraska Territory, a "somewhat cranky cockney Englishman" who had published the Quincy *Whig* in southern Illinois, and Dr.
Gilbert C. Monell of Omaha, owner-editor of the *Nebraska Republican*
there and later candidate for territorial representative in Congress.
Together they formed Wm. N. Byers & Company, a three-way partnership. John L. Dailey, a skilled printer with a wealth of experience on
frontier papers in Iowa and Nebraska, joined the group as printing foreman. Dailey had quit a job and come down to Omaha in response to a
letter from Byers and apparently was under the impression he was to be a
partner in the enterprise. When he got there, however, he found the
company already formed, and he did not achieve partnership status with
Byers until later.

Byers & Company had something lacked by most of the tramp-printer
outfits of the day with their highly portable presses and their aprons of
types. The partners had capital. Not much, but enough to meet the
initial costs with a little margin to finance the first few issues. How much
money they had, and where it came from, is not clear. None of the
three men had much to spare; all three were hopeful frontier followers.
They had sold considerable advertising in advance to Omaha merchants
who were doing a lively business as outfitters of parties bound for the
new El Dorado, and they probably pooled their own resources. Some
help may have come from the family of Mrs. Byers. She was a granddaughter of Robert Lucas, who had been governor of Ohio and later
the first territorial governor of Iowa. Her father, Colonel Horatio N.
Sumner of West Liberty, Iowa, was a man of means.

Whether or not Colonel Sumner backed the expedition out of pocket,
he did supply some of the motive power. He sent two teams of horses
to help draw the press wagons across the prairie. He also dispatched four
of his sons from West Liberty to Omaha. Edward C., usually known as

[7]*Rocky Mountain News*, Aug. 1, 1926.

Charles, remained with his sister Elizabeth in Omaha. Jack, Will, and Robert became members of the party and put their strong young shoulders to the wheel to help empire along on its westward course.

On March 8, 1859, the *Rocky Mountain News* hoisted sail for Pike's Peak.

The departure was not unobserved. The partners were men of prominence in Omaha, the formation of their company was common knowledge, and the Missouri River frontier was watching with interest to see if they could make good on their declared intention of taking a public press to the far Rockies. The Omaha newspapers gave their prospective colleague a send-off with notices on March 9.

Said the *Nebraskian:*

Rocky Mt. News:

The press, type and other "fixings" pertaining to the above-named establishment, started for Fort Laramie yesterday, accompanied by several gentlemen from this city, under the charge and command of Capt. W. N. Byers—Success to the enterprise.

The *Republican* headlined its item "A Pikes Peak Paper":

A train of wagons, taking out the press, etc. of The Rocky Mountain News, left town yesterday for the gold regions, with a large party, all in the best of spirits, with banners flying, W. N. Byers in command.

"There goes Westward the March of Empire!" We shall soon gladly welcome The News to our exchange list. Success to the enterprise, for it is deserved.

Even the distant New York *Tribune* took note, little anticipating that within a few months the big boss himself, Horace Greeley, would be making news by way of the infant *Rocky Mountain News*. On March 19 the *Tribune* published a letter from Omaha City dated February 28:

A company of persons from this city will start this week with a press and materials for printing a newspaper to be called the Rocky Mountain News at Fort Laramie or some other suitable point in or near the mining region. The first number is expected to be issued about the first of April.

The Chicago *Press and Tribune* copied on March 21 the item from the Omaha *Republican* of March 9. Few unpublished weekly newspapers have received so lavish a coverage of their good intentions. But if the "press" was good, other omens didn't measure up. The *News* was having trouble before it had traveled a quarter of a mile.

The spring was a wet one, and the thaw had turned the black gumbo of eastern Nebraska into a sea of tar. The *News* wagon promptly bogged down in the muddy streets of Omaha. "Twice before we got well out of Omaha we had to unload part of the heavier pieces, such as the press and stones, to give the oxen a chance to pull out," John Dailey recalled. For nearly half the journey ahead the party would battle mud and high water.

When Alfred Sorensen wrote his *Early History of Omaha* some years later he remembered the inauspicious departure. "On the side of his wagon he [Byers] had printed the name of his contemplated newspaper, 'The Rocky Mountain News'. . . ."[8] So there actually was a banner flying, though it may have been somewhat spattered with mud.

The press wagon was not alone in its struggle with mushy roads and trails, late snows and sheets of icy rain. Not even the weather slowed the rush, and the trails bore a heavy traffic. Travelers at that season have recorded that they made the entire trip from the Missouri to Cherry Creek without once being out of sight of fellow pilgrims. The argonauts traveled on foot and by horseback, in wagons, buggies, and sulkies, or trudged along pushing handcarts or wheelbarrows. One outfit moved westward with the multitude behind a small cart drawn by a team of dogs. Another, having lost one ox to Indian thieves or exhaustion, yoked the remaining animal with a mule for the rest of a journey, which must have been a difficult one for the teamster. The *Daily Missouri Republican* for April 20, 1859, reports an even more exotic mode of transportation:

> The affair is on wheels which are mammoth concerns, about twenty feet in circumference, and the arrangement for passengers is built somewhat after the style of an omnibus-body. It is to be propelled by the wind, through the means of sails. As to the wheels, it looks like an overgrown omnibus; and as to the spars and sails, it looks like a diminutive schooner. It will seat about twenty-four passengers . . . the Prairie Ship, or wind wagon, is to ply between Westport and Pike's Peak as a regular passenger vessel. The inventor [a Mr. Thomas] proposes to make the trip to Pike's Peak and back in twelve days and travel an average of over 100 miles per day.

The Prairie Ship came to early grief in an eastern Kansas gully, although one of less ambitious dimensions later made it through. The *News* reported on April 18, 1860, the arrival "from the States" of a "combined wind wagon and hand car." Three men had piloted the craft from the Missouri in twenty days, "equalling the speed of horse teams with but a tithe part of the expense."

Still later another fantastic vessel which embarked on the Great American Desert sought to harness steam for the crossing. The "Prairie Motor" consisted of a large boiler which was to power enormous iron-cleated

[8]Alfred Sorensen, *The Early History of Omaha* (Omaha, 1876), p. 97.

wheels and drag behind it a whole train of emigrant wagons. It made nine miles in 1862 and then mired down of its own weight, and the boiler ended its days providing steam for a small Nebraska village.

The standard outfit was one or more yokes of oxen. They were slow but rugged, better even than mules and much more durable than draft horses. Behind the oxen rolled the much-pictured prairie schooner, familiar symbol of American pioneering. A full-rigged schooner carried a cover of white canvas or drill stretched over supporting bows, and on this cover many others besides the News chalked ebullient notices or bold advertisements.

The standard wagon slogan, of course, was "Pike's Peak or Bust!" But some of the emigrants rang changes on this theme. One determined man with an artistic flair painted a sharp peak piercing the clouds and labeled it "I'll Get There." An Ohio wagon picked up words from a song popular in the panic of '57, "Root, Hog, or Die." A schooner drawn by six milch cows was on a pay-as-you-go basis: "Family Express— Milk for Sale." Several wagons announced: "Old Bourbon Whiskey Sold Here." Some of the other recorded slogans: "This out Fitt for sail," "Good-bye, Friends, I am Bound for the Peak," "I Am Off for the Peak— Are You?" "Jordan Am a Hard Road to Travel," and a belligerent "The Eleventh Commandment—Mind Your Own Business."

All the nautical language and imagery was particularly appropriate for the emigrants who, like the News, began their trip in spring-flooded eastern Nebraska. The News outfit made only eight miles through the mud on its first day, and editor Byers later set down some of the difficulties encountered:

> On the third day after crossing Elkhorn River on a military bridge we broke the ice and traversed for two miles a sheet of water from one to four feet deep. Streams were all flooded, and mud bottomless, snow and rain storms frequent, and it was the last day of March when the caravan reached Fort Kearney, one hundred and eighty-five miles from Omaha. . . .[9]

The News expedition was divided, military style, into two platoons. There were two wagons. One, drawn by the Sumner horses, Byers in command, led the way. John Dailey brought up the rear in charge of four plodding oxen dragging the second wagon, which carried the heavier items of printing equipment. Along with Byers in the lead party traveled his brother-in-law, Robert Sumner, and Copeland Rabe, Irwin Sansom, and the lanky Dr. A. F. Peck with his grisly bankroll, or what was left of it after the outfitting. Gibson, Will and Jack Sumner, and others traveled with Dailey. Dr. Monell remained behind to obtain additional paper supplies and follow later.

[9]Byers, "Early Journalism in Colorado," Magazine of Western History, p. 692.

Byers kept a sketchy diary—principally concerned with the weather and daily expenditures—during most of his adult life, but the small vest-pocket books for the interesting years 1855 to 1863 have been lost. Accounts of the trip survive in Byers' reminiscent writings, statements by Copeland Rabe, and the Dailey diaries and other papers.

Rabe, a twenty-two-year-old Iowan, provided fresh meat for the party as its principal hunter of buffalo, antelope, and deer. He lived until 1927 and was the last survivor of the expedition. Rabe remembered in 1902 that "hundreds of wagons, handcarts and horsemen were in sight almost every day, and good camping places were hard to find."[10] So heavy was the noisy emigration that game was scarce within range of the trail, and the prairie grass was trampled down by the passing of thousands of hoofs. "Miles of the country were dismal stretches of mud," Dailey recalled.

> . . . We had no end of trouble with the mud until after we passed Fort Kearney. We were six weeks on the way. When we reached Elkhorn creek we found ourselves contending with troublesome high waters. All the creek's bottoms were overflowing. We traveled watery ways for many miles. Finally, we came to a gulch we could not ford. Felling trees across it where we could, we used these improvised bridges for carrying over every light thing in our outfit.
>
> After that we made our oxen swim across the swelling torrent, and attaching our wagons, stones and press, together with all the heavier articles of our outfit, to ropes to which we hitched our oxen, we dragged them across the flood. Of course many of our chattels were wet. I think our printing press particularly resented the bath, for it accumulated considerable rust as a result of the experience. However, it was that method or wait several days, and neither Byers nor myself cared to sit in a drowning wilderness to wait for an uncertain turn of the flood. . . .
>
> Our press worked all right after all and both Byers and myself have always kept pieces of it as souvenirs. . . .[11]

Dailey's diary for 1859 contains brief day-by-day notes of the crossing. On March 12 he recorded that the water had been "knee deep over a large portion" of the day's travel to reach Elkhorn River. On the thirteenth it snowed. By the seventeenth the wagons were at Columbus on the Loup Fork, where the spring floods had washed out the derrick of the ferry, delaying the party for several days. On Sunday, March 20, Dailey notes that he "Attended religious services at Mr. Case's tent. Discourse read by Dr. Peck."

The press got its bath at Prairie Creek on March 22, and two days later the wagons had to be unloaded again to get through a slough. Four yoke of oxen strayed off, and the Dailey wagon again was delayed.

[10]*Rocky Mountain News*, Sept. 21, 1902.

[11]Undated clipping [1903], Dailey scrapbook, Denver Public Library.

Byers and the rest pushed on to Woodriver Camp. Other excerpts from the Dailey diary:

March 30—Following most of the way the old California trail. Marks of which are plainly seen.

April 2—Met a train of 20 wagons from Santa Fe via the gold mines, which had brought out provisions from New Mexico to the mines and were on their way to St. Louis for goods. Teamsters mostly Mexicans. (More snow today.)

April 3—Baked up a mess of bread for the next 200 miles of our journey which is represented to be utterly destitute of timber.

April 8—Passed 2 lodges of Cheyenne Indians in the afternoon, the first we have seen. They were very hungry and willingly exchanged a pair of moccasins for a couple of cups of meal.

April 10—It was discovered that the prairie was on fire above us and the fire fast coming down upon us, and orders were given to pull up stakes and leave, which was done with dispatch.

April 11—A mule, horse & hand cart train passed us this morning.

April 14—Today we had the first sight of the Rocky mountains, which now loom up magnificently before us. Gibsons off ox gave out today.

Beyond Fort Kearney, as Dailey's journal indicates, the party's troubles changed from wet to dry ones. Rabe mentions that buffalo chips were the only fuel to be found, dust "blew in clouds," and alkali filled the throats of the travelers. Forage for the horses and oxen was scarce, and good water a problem. Byers' earlier overland diary of 1852 indicates he had an antidote for bad alkali water. He noted: "A little acetic, nitric or tartaric acid destroys the poisonous qualities of alkaline water and renders it wholesome."

At Fort Kearney, established on the lower Platte in 1848 to protect the Oregon, Mormon, and California migrations, the commanding officer turned out the garrison on March 30 in salute to the westbound printing press. Editor Byers returned the courtesy in the first issue of his *News:*

THANKS.—It is with feelings of pleasure we acknowledge our obligations to the army officers stationed at Fort Kearney for the many courtesies shown us upon the occasion of the general drill and inspection at that post on the last day of March.

Every thing was in apple pie order and neat as a pin as it always is at that post.

Neither the press nor any of the other emigrants along the Platte Valley route had need for the protection of the Kearney troopers. Indians were encountered but they were by no means as hostile as their fearsome reputations. Later, pioneer gaffers would spin the wildest sorts of bloody scalping yarns until it would seem that the gold rush had made its way west on trails paved with the bodies of dead redskins. There were a few depredations, savage and nasty, along the Smoky Hill Trail, which struck out across western Kansas approximately midway between the Platte and the Santa Fe Trail, but the northern route that season was quiet so far as Indians were concerned. As was their custom, they did a little thieving of livestock, and they annoyed many pilgrims with their begging and the hangdog way they would linger, silent and impassive, in the outer shadows of a campfire's ring of light. They had also complicated the forage problem by burning off large areas of grass west of Fort Kearney in their efforts to scare up game.

If the Indians caused little trouble, there were other hazards which did not depend on a lively imagination: distance, drouth, starvation. A passage of five to six hundred miles measured up to exhaustion for men and animals at the slow pace of eight, ten, fifteen miles a day. Potable water was scarce through at least the western half of the journey, and the shortage was particularly acute on the Smoky Hill route. Along that roadway a wagon might travel a week or more between "sweetwater" holes.

For many of the ill-financed, ill-equipped parties starvation was a daily threat. The rush brought all kinds of people out onto the trails. Most of them were tenderfeet, and nearly all of them had suffered privations when the state banks crashed and carried the nation's economy down with them in the depression of 1857. Whether through ignorance, reckless buoyancy, or simple lack of funds, many of the Pike's Peakers headed west with insufficient provisions to carry them through forty days or more of rigorous travel in an inhospitable land. Friendly Indians found and fed some of the starving argonauts. Others were sustained by trains better supplied with corn meal, flour, and salt pork. Still others had it rougher.

One woman, who was back home in Elkhorn City, Nebraska Territory, by May, told of what she had seen in a letter to her sister:

. . . Oh Ann you [have] no idea what I have suffered—I was taken with the Ague before we [left] Columbus had to be carried on a bed six days—sleeping on the ground—rained in on to us—cold—snowed— besides almost starved to death—the meanest company I ever was in— Oh the suffering that I have seen—men starving—one man that went out with Capt. Parks son from Omaha went eight [days] without eating anything but a snake that he killed and cooked—Walker killed a buf- falo—no one else killed anything—so we had some meat to eat. We camped among the Cheyane Indians four days and the Sioux—they are very tall. Tried to steal the baby—one of their chiefs offered any amount of gold for her. I never left the tent—he came after dark—Walker was away to their war dance—they killed fifteen pawnees the day before and had their scalps hanging on their beld—fresh from their heads— they were fasened on a little hoop to dry—one walked into my tent held one up before my face—as I was saying he came to my tent after

dark—I called the guard—the next morning he came with his squaw—
she had lost her Pappoose—he wanted I should let her nurse the baby
—wanted to take her—I let him—he turned around and walked out of
the tent away on to the bluffs—20 rods off—with her in his arms—I
screamed—he finally brot her back . . . we met one thousand people
in one day coming back and hundreds of beggars—hundreds starved
to death—22 in one spot laid by the road side dead on the Smoky hill
route. . . . All our furniture is gone. . . . I (and all the rest) went a
great many days without anything but a little piece of bread made of
flour and oatmeal mixed together. . . .[12]

Early in May a haggard man stumbled into Russellville at the head of
Cherry Creek and reported that his nine starving companions had given
up and stretched themselves out on the prairie, not far away, to die. A
relief party was sent out and found one man dead and two others so far
gone they died after they were brought in. A few days later thirteen men
arrived over the Smoky Hill Trail carrying their goods on their backs;
they had eaten their pack horse. Two other footmen came in after
subsisting for nine days on prickly pears and a hawk. Another report
told of nine "tottering skeletons" who reached Fort St. Vrain. "They
stated they had not tasted bread for more than 10 days, part of which
time they had lived upon the flesh of a dead ox, which they found upon
the prairie, but partially devoured by wolves, and for 4 days they had
nothing but roots. They stated they had traveled more than 100 miles
without finding water, and must have perished of thirst but for some
snow squalls that occurred."[13]

There were many more such accounts, but the story which chilled all
spines told of the fate of the Blue brothers. One of them was found
wandering the plains hollow-eyed and raving. The third issue of the
News, May 14, 1859, told why:

Mr. Williams, Conductor of the Express, informs us that he picked
up on the plains, a man in the last stages of exhaustion, who had sub-
sisted upon the remains of his two brothers, who had died of starvation.
Three brothers set out from Illinois for the Gold regions. From Kansas
City they took the Smoky Hill Route—found the distance much greater
than represented, ate up their provisions, and when near to death, one
of them sinking more rapidly than the others, requested them to live
upon his flesh, and try to get through. He died and they commenced
their horrible feast—ate the body and again braved starvation—another
died and the survivor lived upon his remains, but the same fate had
almost reached him, when he was found by an Indian—carried to his
lodge and fed, the next day the Express came along and took him in

[12]Amalia Simons Nichols to Ann Kilbourne, May 1859; quoted in Philip W.
Whiteley, "A Pioneer Story in Western Cover," Denver Westerners' Brand Book:
1956 (Denver, 1955), pp. 294–96.

[13]Rocky Mountain News, May 7, 1859.

and brought him part way through but was obliged to leave him because of his feebleness and delirium. He will be brought up by the next coach and probably arrive today.

Mr. Williams, after learning the man's story from himself and the Indian, searched for, and found the bones of the second one who died, and interred them.

This we fear is one of a hundred tales of horror, yet to be told of the Smoky Hill Route—which will bring sorrow to many a hearthstone.

Emigrants who started too early in the year froze hands and feet along the way. Those who set out too late found grass and water gone, and some wagons creaked into the Cherry Creek settlements behind gaunt oxen which had been fed on flour for the last three hundred miles. "Getting to the gold" was no lark, and the company one met on the trail wasn't very good, either. Others shared Amalia Nichols' opinion that some of the Pike's Peakers were about the "meanest" men ever encountered. Copeland Rabe of the *News* party did, for one. He said the press expedition sometimes camped at night with other emigrants, but

. . . There were times, however, when the Byers party preferred to take chances against redskin raids rather than camp with some of the white travelers they met. Some of the pioneers were of the hardboiled variety, it seems, and suspected of being not above a bit of brigandage to fatten their lean pocketbooks.[14]

Amid these companions and scenes the press ground out slow miles toward its promised land. West of Fort Kearney, in drier climate and sandier soil, the road got better and progress was faster. Spirits revived when, at last, the Rocky Mountains could be seen, as Zebulon Pike had seen them, like clouds on the far horizon. The wagons forded the Platte and followed up its south fork, bearing off toward the southwest with the Rockies now constantly in view on the right hand. The Platte was a clearer, colder stream now, and had dwindled in size.

On April 17 the party came finally to Fort St. Vrain, which Dailey described as "the ruins of an adobe building about 100 feet long & 80 wide." The expedition paused here where there was good water and wood to regroup and replenish—and to begin the hunt for gold. Dailey's diary reports for the eighteenth: "A party from our company are making preparations to start on a prospecting tour up the Cache a la Poudre river & Thompson's Fork tomorrow. Saw returning gold seekers today who give very discouraging reports. Byers started on horseback for Cherry Creek to make arrangements to establish his press."

Some of the men remained behind to continue their prospecting when Byers' message arrived two days later ordering that the press be brought

14*Rocky Mountain News*, June 5, 1927.

on as fast as the oxen could travel. The end of the long road was in sight. Teams were hitched, and after dark on April 20 they plodded into the Cherry Creek settlements. Byers met his crew and directed them to the Wootton building on the Auraria side. But in fording the sandy trickle of a creek the heavy press wagon ended its trip as it had started it— bogged down. The equipment was unloaded and carried several hundred yards to the Wootton attic. It was late night when at last the durable old Imperial was assembled and set in its place. The Rockies now had their first printing press, and Dailey's diary for the next day says:

"Went to work early on the 'Rocky Mountain News.'"

CHAPTER FOUR

Gobacks and Greeley

THE round little German scurried about Council Bluffs picking up empty meal bags from millers, stores, and housewives. He had more than twenty of them, each large enough to hold a hundred pounds or more of corn meal, stacked neatly in a tired cart drawn by a pair of venerable, sag-eared mules.

"What're you going to do with all them bags?" he was asked.

"Take 'em to Pike's Peak and fill 'em with gold," he replied.

"Ha," said the skeptics.

"Oh yes, I will," the German insisted, "even if I have to stay there till *fall*."

The incident is somewhat typical.[1]

Many, if not most, of the argonauts of '59 were about like the sanguine German in Council Bluffs. Their hopes were towering, and they weren't quite sure about gold except that it was yellow, desirable, and to be had at Pike's Peak. The consequences were about as could be expected.

Of the 150,000 persons who, with the *News*, swept out on the plains that spring and summer, at least a third didn't reach the spot where the end of the rainbow was guaranteed to be. They were turned back along the way by the angry words "Hoax!" and "Humbug!" The road home was strewn with abandoned mining equipment and bitter with remnants of shattered dream castles. The shining mountains took on a tarnish.

The whole of the expansive new population of the Pike's Peak country might have left as abruptly as it came, had it not been for three things: palpable gold in coinable quantity, the high regard in which the name Horace Greeley was held, and a four-column newspaper printed on one side of scraps of brown wrapping paper.

As the flood of emigration swept up to Cherry Creek, wavered, and began to ebb, authentic bonanzas were shaping up in the mountains thirty miles to the west. And down in eastern Kansas the white linen duster of Horace Greeley had been seen passing through on a westbound

[1]It is told by Ovando J. Hollister in *The Mines of Colorado* (Springfield,1867), p. 9fn.

heading. The press was on the ground, ready to bring the two—gold and Greeley—together. With his fussily flapping coattails, under-the-chin whiskers, and oval spectacles, Greeley didn't much look the part, but he was riding into the West as the savior of a municipal infant in distress. Had he known it, he would have relished the role even more than he did later in retrospect.

After all, he had an almost paternal interest in this country he was seeing for the first time. He and his New York *Tribune* for years had been counseling young men to leave the growing cities of the eastern seaboard and seek opportunity in the fresh and open agricultural lands of the West. Out there, the famous editor assured ambitious youth, a man could win his way by temperance and hard work and be his own master. Born on a New Hampshire farm rich in gravel and granite, Greeley always mistrusted cities, and his own New York more than any. At the height of his power and prestige as oracle of the *Tribune*, when "Greeley says——" was enough to end any argument, the great man was slipping off in spare moments to his waterlogged farm in Westchester County outside Chappaqua to drop seeds in the ground and marvel at their growth. At the New York State Fair of 1854 he proudly claimed second honors, and two dollars, for prize turnips grown in "Greeley's Bog."[2] Chappaqua cost him a small fortune, but he never relaxed his dogged insistence that farming was man's only true way of life. There was farm land to be claimed out west; *ergo*, young men should go there.

Greeley, however, did not invent the admonition, "Go west, young man," although nearly everyone has credited it to him. The sentence first was used by John Babsone Lane Soule in the Terre Haute, Indiana, *Express* in 1851. Greeley's *Tribune* reprinted Soule's article with full credit, and the editor found its agrarian sentiments much to his liking. He wrote an editorial about it and later retailed the advice widely to all who would listen. Now, in the spring of 1859, Greeley was following his own advice and touring out to see how an even triter phrase—"manifest destiny"—was getting on with the job of filling up the continent.

It was nip and tuck in the case of newborn Denver. In the rutted lanes, alternately muddy or dusty, between the sod-roofed cabins, newly arrived men and animals brawled and seethed. But the reverse tide already had set in, and though the settlement floundered in a Rotarian's dream of new-won population, the future hung poised in the angry uncertainties of men who were not finding what they came for. Few had come in the poetic spirit of the bounteous earth that Greeley hymned. Most of them knew more than he did about the fickle tantrums Mother Nature sometimes threw, and how it cost brow sweat and calluses to win from her a few bushels of oats and a little corn that wasn't worth much

[2]William Harlan Hale, *Horace Greeley: Voice of the People* (New York, 1950), pp. 177-78.

when hauled into town. It was precisely that sort of honest, God-fearing toil they had sought to escape by becoming rich on Pike's Peak gold. Only now they discovered that shoveling gravel into a sluice box was just as hard work as pitching hay, and no more profitable. Moreover, all the likely-looking placers already were claimed by men who carried rifles as well as picks. So what now? Brand the whole thing a hoax and head home to the I-told-you-so's of less adventurous neighbors? Or push on up into the hills and see if day wages could be dug?

The atmosphere was tense with indecision and disillusionment, and in such a climate the new journal of the Pike's Peak region tried to hold to a calm and sober middle course. The *Rocky Mountain News* was dedicated to "The Mines and Miners of Kansas and Nebraska," and it reported and speculated on all the new strikes. But it also extolled the virtues, moral and material, of agriculture in terms which could have come right out of Greeley's *Tribune*. It offered garden seeds at twenty-five cents a packet to a country where there were few plows and almost no dedicated plow hands. The editor—after prudently staking out a farm in the Platte bottoms a few miles upstream, about where West Alameda Avenue now crosses the river—was himself making prospecting forays into the mountains between editions. He was reporting on the mining camps for the paper, but he also was courting his own yellow witch. Even hard-working John Dailey deserted his cases and press for short-term flings at fortune hunting.

During April and most of May the outlook was bleak. Despite the massive emigration the prospect seemed to be excellent that Denver would have fewer inhabitants by the end of the summer than it had had a year earlier. When the *News* arrived the rush was just past its crest. Something had to be done or the new "empire in the sisterhood of empires" wouldn't survive its birth. Byers got out his plain-talking pen:

THE RETURNING EMIGRATION.

Recent arrivals from the East report a larger travel toward the States than in this direction.

All this has been brought about by the action of a few restless spirits who are of no advantage to any country. They arrive in the vicinity of the mining region, stop a few hours or a day or two, perhaps prospect a little in places the most unlikely in the world for finding gold, and, because they cannot shovel out nuggets like they have been accustomed to dig potatoes, they raise the cry that it is all a humbug, that there is no gold in the country, and take the back track for home where it is to be hoped they will ever after remain . . . the contagion spreads as it travels, each man tells the worst story he can and it gains strength as it passes from mouth to mouth until the column of emigrants which a few days since was moving so steadily towards the west, wavers in its march, then falters, and hundreds turn their faces toward the east, to travel over again the same weary road without having reached the land of their hopes and bright dreams. . . .

We do not wish our readers to think that we endorse all the extravagant stories that have been written respecting the gold mines of this region, many we admit are much over-colored, but that does not palliate in any degree the great harm which is now being done by the class of persons of whom we now write. We have in our mind one particular individual who left Cherry Creek just one week ago. At Fort St. Vrain he told that he had prospected for three days and that the mines were a perfect humbug, that in three days these flourishing towns would be heaps of smoking ruins, that the old settlers would be hung, that some had already fled to save their lives. This story he repeated to every train he met each time increasing the horrors and his lies, which from the first were as false as his own black heart. . . .

. . . And we predict that before six months have passed away hundreds who are wending their way towards the states will be again as anxious as ever before to visit the Gold mines of the South Platte.

We have but just arrived, three days ago we were wending our way over the dusty road bound for Cherry Creek; we became imbued with the same feeling which seemed to pervade the whole emigration on the latter part of the route, we had met the croaking birds of evil omen, and acknowledge that their stories had their intended effect to a certain extent, but we had set out determined to see for ourself, and see we did —upon our arrival we accompanied a friend to prospect on our own account—our first effort was less than half a mile from where we now sit, the result was over twenty cents to two pans of earth. We proceeded some two miles further up the Platte and prospected in various places, finding gold in *every* pan, varying in amount from one and a half to ten cents to the pan. . . . Miners are at work all along and making about two dollars per day to the man. . . .[3]

Byers went on to caution emigrants to bring their own tools and provisions for at least three months. Picks and shovels and gold pans were "scarce and difficult to obtain," and food supplies were not available for "fifty or even ten thousand people."

When Byers arrived in advance of his press on April 17, the first major movement in the reverse rush was one day old. He wrote later that the turnabout may have been triggered by Denver's second killing (the victim of the first was only nine days in his grave). On the sixteenth John Scudder had killed Captain P. T. Bassett, who, it was alleged, sought to use a pick handle to enforce his position in an argument over town lots. Bassett was a member of the Denver City Town Company, and Scudder had succeeded "Uncle John" Smith as its treasurer. The initial number of the *News* told of the homicide under the headline "Shooting Affair." The report said Scudder "immediately gave himself up to the authorities and a man named Carroll Wood was arrested as an accomplice, but

[3]*Rocky Mountain News,* Apr. 23, 1859.

through the connivance of some of their friends, they succeeded in making their escape before any examination could be held, and escaped the country." Carroll Wood will re-enter this story later. Scudder returned to Denver in 1860, demanded a trial, and was acquitted by a "People's Court." He became a substantial citizen and survived into the twentieth century.

Byers felt the Scudder-Bassett affair might have contributed to the exodus, but the real cause was "disappointment in not finding gold here." "If that killing had any effect," he wrote, ". . . it was simply to dissatisfy those who saw it. . . . They thought there might be a series of outlawry & became panicky." The comments are part of the recollections Byers set down in 1884 for Hubert H. Bancroft:

. . . What we called a stampede took place. The first who reached here in the spring were disappointed. There had been no discovery of gold to amount to anything. No gold had been discovered in the mountains, & only experienced miners were satisfied there was gold in the mountains reasoning from the fact that there was gold in the alluvial deposits along the streams. The great majority of people having had no experience were easily discouraged. They found nothing to do, had no possible resource to rely upon & as is very often the case among large numbers of people they became infected with a kind of panic . . . they started back across the plains & turned back all they could on the plains. It started from here on the 16th of April 1859 . . . the first crowd were on foot having no teams or means of transportation.

Probably 60 or 70 started out on the 16th down the Road & turned back every one they could. They told very exaggerated stories about the conditions of things here & what was going to be done. They became very much embittered against a few men who had spoken well of the country & who they charged had induced people to come here without good reason for doing so.

The man they abused most was Henry Allen [a leader in the Auraria Town Company], the next most prominent perhaps was General William Larimer [of the Denver City Town Company], & I suppose I came in for the next share of abuse. . . . I had incurred ill will because I had published in the winter of 1858 a Guide Book for emigrants crossing the Plains. . . . It had no exaggerated stories though some were bright perhaps. . . .[4]

Byers soon had reports from down the road that he and other authors of the gold-rush guidebooks were being hanged in effigy by the disappointed men now back-trailing home with empty pockets. At one place along the South Platte road his name was inscribed on the buffalo-skull tombstone of a freshly mounded grave, and a popular couplet among the humbuggers was:

[4]Byers, Bancroft ms.

Hang Byers and D. C. Oakes[5]
For starting this damned Pike's Peak hoax.

A letter written in 1859 by a Nebraska woman who was on the plains in the midst of the rush, both ways, indicates clearly both the mood of violent despondency and the pitiful condition of many of the emigrants:

> . . . their is nobody in Cherry Creek—we met one thousand people in one day coming back and hundreds of beggars—hundreds starved to death—22 in one spot laid by the road side dead on the Smoky hill route. They shot Bassed one of their leaders that reported the stories about the gold—the rest fled—Dr. Peck and all of his company have returned—Byers is hid. We met one day over two hundred men heard that Steinberger was behind us—said they should hang him—They had him hid in one of the waygons—In regard to gold there is gold there but not in large quantities—very small particles—may be discovered in the mountains in larger quantities. This excitement was gotten up by these men that were speculating in town property—thousands ruined —you can have no idea of the immense emigration. . . .[6]

Slogans on the covered wagons, so proudly flaunted a few weeks earlier, now sang a sadder tune. To "Pike's Peak or Bust" was added "Busted by Thunder!" Another wagon rolled back through Jefferson, Missouri, bearing the legend, "Oh Yes! Pike's Peak in H—l and D—mnation!" A third, possibly driven by the same artistic fellow who had drawn the peak on his wagon cover for the outbound trip, reached the Missouri bearing a sketch of an elephant and the caption, "What We Saw at Pike's Peak."

The Missouri border newspapers reported the daily arrival of down-hearted and starving "Pikers." The papers now picked up the "humbug" refrain as loudly as they had sung the "Ho! for Pike's Peak" marching music during the winter. Taking a deep breath, the Hannibal *Messenger* said on June 9:

> This has been, not inaptly styled, the age of humbugs, and Pike's Peak has indeed proven the humbug of humbugs. It has no parallel in the history of civilized nations. . . . The spectacle of 100,000 people simultaneously abandoning all the comforts, conveniences and endearments of home, and setting out, many of them on foot, and without a dollar in their pockets, and with barely provisions to last them a week, upon a journey from five hundred to a thousand miles, over a wild and

[5]Oakes had co-authored with H. J. Graham and George Pancoast for the Chicago, Burlington & Quincy Railroad the 16-page *Traveler's Guide to the New Gold Mines in Kansas and Nebraska* (New York, 1859), and with S. W. Smith had published *History of the Gold Discoveries on the South Platte River* by Luke Tierney (Pacific City, 1859).

[6]Amalia Simons Nichols to Ann Kilbourne; quoted in Whiteley, op. cit., p. 295.

inhospitable region, all animated and almost run-mad with gold greed; and then, after a lapse of a few weeks, coming back, begging, starving, cursing, and many of them hopelessly ruined, is one never before witnessed, and one that teaches such a lesson as in our opinion, will prevent repetition of a similar act of folly for a long time to come.

As far away as New York the press was watching the flow and ebb of the Pike's Peak rush with great interest. The significant shifting back and forth of a major block of population seems to have escaped the big-city papers, as it did the border journals, which were too close to the dust to see clearly. But on their lofty plane of disengagement the New York papers were fascinated by the horror of it all. Even so genteel and other-worldly a journal as the weekly *Ledger* carefully paragraphed the wild events of the Far West through 1859. The *Ledger* was primarily concerned with moral elevation, literary nicety, and the evils of drink and tobacco. It published, however, a column of "Current Items" as exotic and bloodthirsty as anything that has appeared in the sensational press of the "yellow" era or since. Most of the *Ledger's* Pike's Peak news was carried under "Current Items."

The *Ledger* on June 11 scrambled its report on the hanging of Byers and Oakes:

A Western Editor who went to Pike's Peak a few months ago, writes home to his paper that it is the greatest humbug of the day, and that thousands of men now in that region are suffering indescribably from destitution. A mob of the victims lately hung two men who had been engaged for some months previous in writing glowing accounts of the "diggings" to eastern papers, for which letters they were paid by heartless speculators.

As early as March 5 the *Ledger* had reported that "last news from Pike's Peak is rather disheartening. . . ." By April 9 the existence of "fool's gold" was made known to *Ledger* readers: "A man at Pike's Peak not long since found a large mass of shining stuff which he supposed to be gold, and thereupon put on most consequential airs; but the next day he discovered that it was nothing but a yellow and glittering kind of stone, and humbly went to work again." On April 16 the "rush for Pike's Peak" was "almost beyond belief." "All the river towns of Kansas and Nebraska, and the road from Fort Leavenworth to the 'diggings,' are reported as being full of men on their way to the new 'El Dorado'; and hundreds are said to be literally perishing from hardship and destitution."

On April 23, the same day that the *Rocky Mountain News* appeared, the *Ledger* found that "Many persons who have been to Pike's Peak are declaring in the papers that 'it is one of the most shameful humbugs of the day.' Let everybody with the 'gold fever' take warning."

The same issue tells of a young man named Gadsden, "destitute and disheartened," who blew his brains out with a revolver bullet. The *Ledger* was much concerned about Pike's Peakers who destroyed themselves. On July 9 a man named Wilbrum had taken off by pulling the trigger of his rifle with his toe. On September 17, Theodore Kaughney, "having been ten days without decent sustenance," used a pistol. In each case the same phrase: "blew his brains out."

The violence of these primitive Westerners was fascinating too. The *Ledger* asserted on July 2 that they had lynched the Denver City postmaster for opening letters. (This was the first appearance of the name of the town in the *Ledger* and was a garbled version of a public controversy—no blood let—over handling of mail by the stage company.) Equally titillating to refined Eastern sensibilities was the report on November 12 that

> A couple of gamesters at Pike's Peak got into a fight a short time since about the division of their spoil, and drawing their bowie-knives, mangled each other horribly. One had his left eye cut out and his stomach ripped open, and the other's head was nearly severed from his shoulders. Both of them were killed.

Starvation and suffering had "increased to frightful degree" by June 25, and word reached the *Ledger* of September 10 that the Utes were killing miners in the mountains.

In the midst of its reports of "wrecked constitutions" at the diggings the *Ledger* came up with a unique solution to New York's juvenile-delinquency problem. Orphaned and homeless children, an editorial of July 9 suggested, should be deported to the West, which by now must have assumed fearsome proportions indeed in the minds of New Yorkers. "Western hearts are kind and warm," the *Ledger* argued in the face of much evidence to the contrary in its own columns, ". . . and labor, even juvenile labor, is at least worth food and clothing. . . . Necessity cannot tempt to crime in that region of Nature's affluence, and other temptations to transgress the laws are fewer than in the Elder States. . . . Providence seems to smile upon this scheme of providing homes and moral culture in the West, for the uncared-for children of the East. . . . They [children already transported] have found a purer moral atmosphere, and more physical comfort, than they ever experienced before. . . . Push forward the column! Let all who love to aid a holy mission . . . put their shoulders to the wheel. There are multitudes of children this day roaming our streets whose moral salvation depends upon their rescue from the life they are now leading. Transplant them to the West. Here their moral nature is crushed down. There it would have room and opportunity to grow." In an adjoining column one of the *Ledger's* uplifting maxims for the week was: "No day without one act of love."

But if the *Ledger* as an act of love would have banished New York street urchins to a country of bowie knives, suicides, and lynchings, it voiced other sentiments less tender than rational in a May 21 editorial addressed to the Pike's Peak problem. Horace Greeley must have approved as he read:

> Probably a hundred thousand would-be Croesuses will be congregated at the new Dorado before midsummer, and it is equally probable that of that number full fifty thousand will devoutly wish they had never heard of it. Fortunes will be made, but not by the gleaners of the gold fields. The bulk of their hard-earned gains will be *sharked* out of them by speculators. But no amount of sad experience seems to damp the enthusiasm of your gold hunter. . . . They will find a tolerably healthy climate[7] there [at the Nebraskan placers] and *some* gold; but we will venture to say that the average daily earnings of the entire crowd will not be equal to the wages of the same number of ordinary mechanics in any of the Atlantic States, while their expenses will be much heavier. Young men who have been smitten with the Pike's Peak fever, cannot be restrained, we suppose, from rushing in pursuit of this new *mirage*. But we earnestly advise those who are not entirely demented, and have any certain means of support at home, to pause and reflect before they resolve to take the "Kansas-Nebraska slide." Next to war, gold-hunting is the most hazardous of human pursuits, and a large majority of those who embark in it, return like disbanded soldiers from a long campaign, with broken constitutions, ragged wardrobes and empty purses. . . . The moral of the tale is that good husbandry pays better than gold-hunting—that the scythe and cradle is a more remunerative implement than the "cradle" that has no scythe. Young farmers who are anxious to start for Pike's Peak will please for their own sakes, "make a note of this."

Newspapers nearer the frontier used more direct, and sometimes abusive, language. The *Rocky Mountain News* lost patience steadily as the cries of humbug grew more shrill and the exaggerations piled up. After all, the *News* had given in its first issue much the same sort of advice the *Ledger* now was peddling. It had warned constantly of the dangers of crossing the plains ill equipped or euphoric. Editor Byers began dipping his pen in caustic.

When the Franklin, Indiana, *Democrat*—which was in the wrong party anyway—announced that "the Pike's Peak humbug is about exploded once more," the *News* bit back:

> "About exploded" is it, Mr. Democrat; well, that is news to us, how did you learn it? or is it only your opinion given to the public for fact?

[7]The *Ledger* noted, apparently with equal lack of firsthand knowledge, on Sept. 3: "There are reported to be over two thousand persons ill with fever and other diseases, in the vicinity of Pike's Peak, and great numbers die every week."

Toot away, blow your horn, show your long ears and see how long you can make the people believe it is a "humbug"—(Ed.)[8]

The Davenport, Iowa, *Gazette* charged that the editor of the *News* "lied his paper black in the face." Byers snapped:

We defy the world to point to one single editorial statement in the News which we are unable to substantiate literally as set forth. So pitch in, gentlemen, your abuse is powerless to harm us. . . .

The papers denounce the "Pike's Peak humbug," as they are pleased to call it, basing their opinions in the main upon the lying reports of men who have never seen this region of country—men who have turned back and made their way home howling like whipped curs—creatures who should never have been unloosed from their mothers' apron strings. . . .[9]

Very early in the turnabout migration, on May 14, the *News* sought to scotch some of the reports which later were printed for fact by Midwestern and Eastern papers:

FALSE RUMORS.

We are informed that the returning emigration are giving currency to many absurd and false stories, as they wend their way towards the States; such for instance as that "Denver and Auraria were burned—that all the old citizens were hung or fled the country—that a vigilance committee guarded the road, and whenever an emigrant-wagon approached, it was surrounded and plundered, the cattle or horses killed and the owners compelled to flee for their lives—" all of which are so monstrously and outrageously false, we wonder that people can be found who will believe them.

A month later, on June 18, the *News* boiled over into a short editorial which added a word to the American language.[10]

GOBACKS.

We hope that this class are all again safely at home with their Pa's and Ma's, their sweethearts, or "Nancy and the babies"; there they may dwell in sweet seclusion, retirement, and repose, and whilst they sit around the chimney corner they can fight their battles again. . . . Farewell to these "gobacks." They have had their day and soon will be forgotten.

[8]*Rocky Mountain News*, Sept. 10, 1859.

[9]Ibid., Aug. 20, 1859.

[10]Mitford M. Mathews, ed., A *Dictionary of Americanisms on Historical Principles* (Chicago, 1951), p. 704.

Although the *News* and its country had some reason to feel put upon by public comment and sentiment in the spring and summer of 1859, the paper managed to keep its sense of humor. There's a wry sort of honest levity in an item which appeared on August 27:

INFIT FROM PIKE'S PEAK.

Some time since we were giving tables showing items to constitute a complete outfit to Pike's Peak. We are now able to give a schedule of an infit as we saw exemplified yesterday by one who has been there and got back:

1 ragged coat with collar and tail torn off.
1 pair pants, hanging together by shreds.
1 old black hat, barrin' the brim.
1½ shoes, looking like fried bacon.
¼ lb. raw beans.
½ pint parched corn.
00,000 oz. of gold dust and nuggets.
specie, nary red.

In answer to my interrogatory whether he designed returning to Pike's Peak shortly, our traveler responded, "not by a jug full."

Not all the gobacks walked home in one and a half shoes. Some decided to make a water passage, down the Platte. This was a difficult undertaking. For the Platte is not a navigable stream. Not then, and particularly not now with the intensive irrigation of the rich Platte Valley lands northeast from Denver. (For many years irrigated Weld County, once part of the Great American Desert, has ranked among the half dozen top agricultural counties of the nation in cash value of crops.) Sometimes, when the season has been long and dry and the irrigation demands heavy, the Platte entirely disappears as a stream of water, leaving long stretches of dry bottom exposed to the sun. The trickles of affluents farther down slowly rebuild a river.

Frémont tried boating the Platte on one of his expeditions and gave it up. Some of the fur traders had used the uncertain stream, in proper seasons, to float bales of skins down to Missouri River trading posts like Peter Sarpy's at Bellevue. But no one, least of all the Plains Indians, counted on the Platte as a reliable waterway. This fact was just one of many the gobacks didn't know about the country they had visited briefly and were now fleeing; they went blithely ahead and built scows and rafts.

The season was with them. Perhaps the wet spring had kept the river flowing steady and deep over the endless shoals and sand bars. At any rate some of the river runners made relatively quick trips home to the Missouri, and there was enough water in the stream that some of them drowned. A lot more swamped in the swift, erratic currents immediately

below Denver or grew tired of poling and dragging their vessels through
the shallows where the river spreads out to flow down across Nebraska
in great broad loops. William and Charles Fry, experienced Missouri
rivermen, were two of the successful ones. They built a flatboat 11
feet long by 3½ wide, drawing only four inches, and set out from
Denver on May 4. They made it to St. Joseph in twenty days, compared
with the thirty to forty days required for an overland crossing. The
Chicago Academy of Science was a loser on one of the unsuccessful
voyages. The *News* of May 14 regretted "to learn of the wreck of Mr.
C. Davisson's boat on the Platte, on his second day's sail, with the loss
of his provisions, books, notes, clothing, etc., to the value of about $1000.
Mr. D. had a fine collection of botanical and geological specimens, &c,
which he intended as a present to the Chicago Academy of Science.
Mr. D. describes the shores of the Platte along which he sailed as most
beautiful and abounding in wild game but he will try a safer method
hereafter."

While the gobacks streamed home by land or by water, events were
shaping up in the hills to bring some of them scampering back again for
three crossings of the formidable plains in a single season. Actually one
of the events had occurred in January but was held as a tight-lipped
secret until April.

George A. Jackson was among the few score men who had elected to
winter through in the new country. He and two or three companions
made a camp on Vasquez Fork in the lateral valley behind the first foothills of the Rockies about where the town of Golden now is situated.
Jackson was a California forty-niner and knew how to go about the
grubby business of prospecting. When the winter turned out to be an
open one he pushed up into the mountains with his dogs, Drum and Kit,
to see if he could find colors in the half-frozen creek. So far as is known,
Jackson was the first prospector purposefully to seek gold in the Colorado
Rockies; the others on the scene still were trying the Platte, Cherry,
Ralston, Little Dry, and other creeks and dry washes down on the plains.

On New Year's Day of 1859 Jackson was startled to see smoke rising
from a mountain valley. He feared Utes but scouted ahead through the
snow, which at this elevation lay deep on the hills. Instead of Indians, he
discovered the warm mineral waters at what is now Idaho Springs. The
springs were sending clouds of steam up into the frosty air, and gathered
about the warm-water pools were large flocks of mountain sheep. Jackson
moved down and made the sheep his larder.

Jackson kept a diary, and in it he tells of his troubles with mountain
lions and his success with gold. The lions—*carcajous* to the early
trappers—were attracted to the spot, as Jackson was, by the plentiful
supply of fat mutton, and the prospector had to kill three of them in less
than a week. Excerpts from his diary give the story:

Jan. 2—"Drum" and "Kit" woke me by low growls at daylight; sheep all gone; mountain lion within twenty steps; pulled gun from under blanket and shot too quick; broke his shoulder, but followed up and killed him. Clear, high wind, and very cold. In camp all day; built bough house, and ate fat sheep all day; bread all gone; plenty fat meat; "no wantum bread."

Jan. 3—Still clear and cold. Sheep came down again; are very tame; walk up to within one hundred yards of camp and stand and stamp at me and the dogs; mountain lion killed one within 300 yards of camp to-day, and scattered the whole band again; went up the main creek to another tributary coming in from the south, a little larger than this one.

Jan. 5—Up before day; killed a fat sheep and wounded a mountain lion before sunrise; ate ribs for breakfast; drank last of my coffee; after breakfast moved up half mile to next creek on south side; made new camp under big fir tree; good gravel here; looks like it carries gold; wind has blown snow off the rim, but gravel is hard frozen; panned out two cups; no gold in either.

Jan. 6—Pleasant day; built big fire on rim-rock to thaw the gravel; kept it up all day; carcajou came into camp while I was at fire; dogs killed him after I broke his neck with belt-axe; hell of a fight.

Jan. 7—Clear day; removed fire embers and dug into rim on bedrock, panned out eight treaty cups[11] of dirt and found nothing but fine colors; ninth cup I got one nugget of coarse gold; feel good to-night; dogs don't. "Drum" is lame all over; sewed up gash in his leg to-night; carcajou no good for dog.

Jan. 8—Pleasant day. . . . I've got the diggings at last . . . dogs can't travel; damn a carcajou. Dug and panned to-day until my belt-knife was worn out, so I will have to quit, or use my skinning knife. I have about a half-ounce of gold, so will quit and try and get back in the spring.

Jackson had dug out with his sheath knife only about nine dollars worth of gold at prices then current, but his experience in California told him there was more to be had. He went back down to the plains, kept his counsel, and waited for the thaw. He was back in the spring as guide and leader of a party of prospectors known as the Chicago Company. On April 17 they met together at the mouth of the stream since known as Chicago Creek and formally organized the first mining district in Colorado. Then they knocked the box beds of their wagons apart for lumber to make sluices and went to work in what became known as

[11]Iron drinking cup, holding about a pint, of a type furnished by the federal government to the Indians with their treaty goods.

Jackson's Diggings or Chicago Bar. Within seven days they had nineteen hundred dollars in gold.

The first of the two bonanzas which were to save Denver now had been hit.

Word of the strike trickled down to the Cherry Creek settlements, thirty miles away, early in May, and editor Byers of the *News* bounced right up to take a look—and stake a claim. He was not alone. Smiley says there was a "headlong stampede for Clear creek, and real estate in Auraria and Denver rose in value by leaps and bounds a hundred percent at a jump." Byers reported in the May 28 *News* that he found three hundred men already at work on May 14 when he got there, and he had not dallied along the way.

The Jackson Diggings, like most of the other early Colorado "mines," were placers. The gold they produced was float gold—small flakes or grains of the yellow metal which because of their weight could be washed free of earth and sand in a pan. Now and then nuggets were found in placer mining, but mostly the recovery was in "dust" or "flour" gold. The gold pan was the basic tool, at least for prospecting. This was and is a shallow basin with straight-sloping sides in which a miner swirls water in a circular movement over a few handfuls of likely-looking gravel. As the soil and sand are swept over the brim the heavier gold is left in the bottom of the pan. Panning gold still is practiced, professionally and by amateurs, along Colorado streams, and during the great depression of the 1930s Denver's Opportunity School for adults taught the process to classes which met in the bed of Cherry Creek where it passes through the downtown district. Some of the unemployed took a dollar or two in gold daily from the stream which had so frustrated the fifty-niners.

The refinements of panning for gold involved the cradle or rocker, the Long Tom, and the sluice. The cradle was a small box of wood or sheet iron on rockers. A few shovelfuls of pay dirt would be scooped into the box, water added, and the whole machine then rocked until the gold had settled and the dross was slopped over the sides. In some cases a cradle had two bottoms, an upper one of coarse screen to catch rocks and larger bits of gravel and a lower, watertight basin to catch the gold. A Long Tom was a larger cradle, often requiring several strong men at its upright handles to provide the rocking motion. Sluices were U-shaped troughs of boards—the longer and larger the better—in which a stream of water was kept flowing by gravity. Dirt was shoveled into the sluice all along the way and any gold which was washed free was captured by small cleats nailed transversely at intervals along the bottom of the trough. Sometimes bits of carpet were used in place of the cleats, the nap catching the gold. A supply of quicksilver greatly helped in gold recovery, if the miner was well financed enough to have it on hand. A little mercury could be placed behind the cleats of a sluice or in the bottom basin of a rocker and by its affinity for gold would pick up and hold any passing particles. The quicksilver then could be retorted off over a campfire, leaving the gold behind.

Placer mining was backbreaking labor, an item which contributed to its unpopularity among the greenhorns and tenderfeet of '59, and it was slow. Hard-rock mining in tunnels and shafts required capital and machines and yielded larger returns. It sent men burrowing into the mountains themselves to seek out the veins of ore and the "mother lodes" which had cast the small particles and nuggets of gold into the streams. It would come later.

The next discovery, which became known in May of 1859, was a placer too, but it pointed the way toward a hard-rock mining operation which would boast that it sat upon "the richest square mile on earth."

The discoverer's name was Gregory, John H., and he was "poor white trash" from Georgia. The spot was just over a high ridge on the north fork of Clear Creek, less than ten miles from Jackson's Diggings. The date has been forgotten, but it was sometime in February. Like Jackson, Gregory was winter prospecting, and he stumbled onto the outcroppings of a lode which would make fortunes for hundreds of men.

On his winter tramp Gregory washed out a small amount of gold in the gulch which now carries his name, but he was forced to retreat to the plains for provisions. The showing hadn't been much, and he was discouraged. He didn't like hard work very much anyway, his associates later said. But he told of his findings to a party of South Bend, Indiana, men, and they persuaded him to lead them back up into the hills in May. In the group were David K. Wall, the Defrees brothers, William Ziegler, William Fouts from Missouri, and a man named Kendall from Iowa.

Gregory and his associates held their tongues through March and April as they laid quiet plans. On May 6 they reached the steep gulch where Gregory had found colors. Climbing up the slope, they began prospecting with pick and shovel, with Gregory, by virtue of his rank as discoverer, in the role of straw boss.

"Here's a likely-looking spot," he told Defrees. "Stick your shovel in there, Wilk.

"Now give me some in the pan," he directed.

The half peck of dirt washed out in a nearby stream to $4.00 in gold. Succeeding pans were almost equally rich; forty of them produced $40. Here was a bonanza at last. Gregory put aside his pan and built a sluice. In a week he had taken out $972, and this was only a beginning. Before long many claims in Gregory Gulch and nearby Russell Gulch were yielding $3000 to $4000 a day. In the years ahead, when hard-rock mining began and refining problems were solved, the nearby hills would give up millions and create mining kings and smelting magnates in dazzling numbers.

Those who wrote about it later said John Gregory seemed dazed at first by what he had wrought.

"By God, now my wife can be a lady!" he shouted. "My children will be schooled!"

Then, according to those who were there, he worked hard for a week or two, began muttering to himself, and finally came loose at the hinges. In a transaction which demonstrates his shaken condition, he sold out his two choice claims for $22,000 to two men without capital, loaning them $200 for tools and taking as payment $500 a week in the proceeds from his own pay dirt. His successors washed out $607 in their first day of operations. Gregory became a this-pan-for-hire prospector for other parties at a fee of $200 a day, and in September he went home to Georgia with $30,000. He came back the next year, bought a quartz mill for $7000, operated it several weeks at a profit of $200 a day, and sold it for six times its cost. Then, mysteriously, John Gregory disappears from the Colorado story. No one ever bothered to find out whether Mrs. Gregory became a lady or the Gregory children got to Harvard.

News of Gregory's bonanza couldn't be kept secret long. Word sped into Denver and up the south fork of Clear Creek to Jackson's Diggings on May 17. There were at that time seventeen persons working in Gregory Gulch and environs; by June 5 there were thirty thousand.

The discovery "set the country wild, not only this country, but the whole country," editor Byers of the News wrote. Byers himself learned about it at Jackson's Diggings and two days later was on the scene in Gregory Gulch, again alternating his time between reporting for his newspaper and staking claims. He told his readers he personally had washed out one four-dollar pan. Byers held part ownership in a Gregory district mine for the rest of his life, but he missed the wealth that came to others in that rich cañon. His accounts indicate that his interest in the Great Mammoth mine earned him nothing but a long series of assessments.

Between the two of them Gregory and Jackson had vindicated the editorial position of the News. There was gold at Pike's Peak, after all. At first the newspapers on the other side of the plains scoffed at the discovery reports in the News, branded the paper the "Rocky Mountain Liar," and consigned Byers to flames. Later they were forced to abandon the humbug vogue and republish the News' accounts of what was going on in Rocky Mountain gulches and valleys. Byers continued to bound happily from strike to strike, and his reports bear scrutiny in terms of modern standards of newspaper objectivity. He was eternally confident and buoyant, but he also was diligently factual and he never ceased to point out that most of the men who were hitting it were experienced or well capitalized or both.

In the first real gold discoveries, as in nearly everything else of the pioneer period, Byers was involved intimately from the beginning. He was on the ground almost before Gregory had straightened up to examine the findings in his pan. He wrote:

. . . When I reached the . . . diggings on the 19th of May, Gregory had two lengths of sluices started and had been sluicing a part of three days with one man helping him and he had taken out about $1000 in gold. He quit work then. When I went there he was living under a little shelter of pine boughs on the side of the hill. . . . I was gathering news for the newspaper and thought I would at once see him. . . . I went down the gulch, climbed up the hillside to his camp and he was muttering to himself about his good fortune. He seemed like a man half witted and the burden of his thoughts seemed to be the advantage it would be to his family, it would make gentlemen and ladies of his children. He belonged to the class of poor whites in Georgia, and thought it would make a new man of him, give him wealth and position and admit him to society. . . . He had the habit of talking to himself. I went to him and began talking to him, told him who I was and that I represented a paper. That seemed to arouse some interest in his mind. I told him I would like to know what he was doing, what he had found, he leaned back and turned over the frying pan turned upside down on the ground and there lay three chunks of retorted gold, the result of his three days work. He had gathered the gold with quicksilver in his sluice and had retorted it, had squeezed it out in a buckskin as dry as he could and had retorted it in a common little iron retort and it had left three irregular pieces of gold something like brick bats, that laid there under the frying pan . . . worth $300 to $400 each. . . .[12]

A few days later Byers was part of a bit of political sleight of hand which probably averted revolution in the now populous gulch. The first regulations drawn up for the district had followed California custom and specified that claims should be 50 by 150 feet in size. The multitudes of newcomers, who were stepping on each other's heels, thought this too much. They wanted the claims cut down to 25 feet in width. So they called a meeting. The thousands who attended covered both slopes of the gulch and looked, Byers wrote, "like a flock of blackbirds."

The firstcomers, now old settlers of some three weeks' duration, mingled with the crowd. First they arranged to have Gregory's companion, Wilkes Defrees, appointed chairman. Then Wilkes rose to his responsibility and appointed a twelve-man committee—all old-timers—to take up the matter of amending the district regulations. Byers was one of the appointees. He recalled the moment as "the most dramatic scene I ever had part in." The committee withdrew into the woods to deliberate, emerged to return a report sustaining the original claim measurements. The mass meeting, unaware it had been outwitted, grudgingly gave its assent and dispersed. Byers later justified the bit of jobbery on grounds that the original dimensions were established mining practice. It was, he said, "an instance where a minority of certainly not five percent, I do not know whether it exceeded one percent of the people actually

[12]Byers, Bancroft ms.

present . . . carried the voice of the meeting with it because the opposition had no organization. . . ."

The stampede to Gregory Gulch drew all sorts of people and spawned a thousand legends. There was, for example, the hard-shell preacher from Wisconsin. On the first Sabbath after his arrival he preached from a point of rocks overlooking the gulch. With great eloquence the reverend exhorted his congregation to follow paths of righteousness and avoid the sins which new-found gold must surely encourage. He ended his pleading with an invitation to any who wished to come to his tent that evening for another meeting. The evening sermon turned out to be a social game of twenty-one, from the proceeds of which the reverend next day purchased a rich claim. Jerome Smiley asserts it for historical fact that the adroit dominie later sold his mine for a hundred thousand dollars.

There was also "Mountain Charley" Forest, the "veritable and notorious Charley, smoking, drinking, swearing," as the News put it. Charley wore pants and cussed, but the real name was Eliza Jane Forest. In her autobiography she claims that she donned men's clothing to track down the murderer of her husband. She became a cabin boy on Mississippi boats, worked as a brakeman for the Illinois Central Railroad, engaged in business as a mule skinner in California, came to Colorado and held her own in a man's country both as prospector and saloonkeeper. It was "Mountain Charley" who opened up the Mountain Boys Saloon in Auraria. It was a dive of ill repute, the bluenoses said, and catered exclusively to a clientele given to settling arguments with bowie knives. Eliza said she twice cornered the man responsible for her widowhood—once in St. Louis and once in Denver—and shot him both times. In neither case, however, was the revenge complete, and Eliza finally consoled herself by marrying her barkeep.

"Mountain Charley" and the ordained twenty-one dealer were only two of many who beat their ways up through the roadless mountains to the fabulous gulch. A blacksmith arrived and promptly became a man of means by sharpening picks at fifty cents each. A butcher shop set up to convert worn-out yoke oxen into steaks. Mountain City came into being at the foot of the cliff below Gregory's lode. Within a month it had given way to Black Hawk and Central City. The latter became one of Colorado's major towns and threatened for a time to overshadow Denver in population and importance. Central City built itself a stone opera house to which came Edwin Booth, Emma Abbott, and the "divine" Fanny Barlow in Mazeppa. The same opera house today presents a summer opera and drama festival featuring stars of the Metropolitan and such players as Helen Hayes, Maurice Evans, Katharine Cornell, and Shirley Booth. The present atmosphere of haut culture and formal-dress openings, Lucius Beebe in attendance, represents a wild and improbable contrast with the Gregory Gulch of 1859.

Then, the mountains around about literally were being turned inside out in the scramble for gold. The scars remain. And the hills are treeless. It was not always so. Some of the pines gave way to the ax in a frenzy of cabin building which saw more than two hundred rough houses built in less than two weeks in May of 1859, and some fell in flames as the richest square mile on earth caught the brunt of manifest destiny in full cry. Perhaps by design in order to clear land for their placers, perhaps accidentally in the insatiable hunger for lumber to build houses and sluices, one way or the other the miners casually put fire to the primeval forests around them. At least three of the argonauts, with their pony and dog, were caught in the backlash of the flames and perished. It was weeks before the fires burned themselves out to leave a blackened landscape which has not recovered in the century since.

The first instances of Indian savagery also were stirred into the cauldron of flame, tumult, and avaricious scramble. A small party of the mountain-roaming Utes, perhaps attracted by the forest fires and possibly resentful of their effect on future hunting, ambushed three miners, killed one, mortally wounded another, and sent the third fleeing. "Trouble with the Indians. Our Miners Shot and Scalped without Provocation," the *News* headlined. A little later the Utes struck again in the Taylor Park country to the south. Six bodies, scalped and mutilated, were found in a place since known as Dead Men's Gulch. Kit Carson, then agent to the Utes at Taos, had warned of just such tragedies in a report to the Bureau of Indian Affairs that spring:

I have been informed that in the Belle Solado [Bayou Salade, or South Park] gold has been discovered, and that large parties of miners are on their way thither. If such is the case the Utahs will be dissatisfied. The Belle is the only place in their country where game of any consequence can be found, and if the miners and Indians come in contact I fear there will be trouble. The Indians will object to their being in their country and, if able, will drive them thence. . . .

In spite of Utes, however, and in the face of mounting doubts and shrill cries of hoax, gold now had been discovered in the Rocky Mountains in quantities somewhat approaching the advance billing.

Out on the plains the backwash of gobacks wavered as word of the discoveries passed down the line. Many reversed their courses again and headed back toward Pike's Peak. Many more, still muttering their disappointments, rejected the news as merely a new variation on a cruel scheme.

The *Rocky Mountain News* now had reported the bonanzas simply, directly, factually, with on-the-scene coverage by the editor. But the Missouri border journals wouldn't believe. They preferred to regard Byers as a scoundrel and his paper as a liar. A more disinterested vindication was needed, and it was on the way. Horace Greeley was headed west.

"We see a note in the N. Y. Tribune, from Horace Greeley," the News told its readers on May 28, "announcing his intention of making a western tour, extending his visit to the gold mines of this country, and hence to Salt Lake City, thence to California, and return to New York by the Isthmus. He may be expected in a few days. We hope a hearty welcome may greet him."

The co-founder of the Republican party—probably the only Republican editor ever to employ Karl Marx as a foreign correspondent—at the moment was jolting through eastern Kansas in a Concord coach of the Leavenworth and Pike's Peak Express Company. Two of the company's coaches earlier had made their way to Denver in nineteen days, breaking a new trail on the way. They had arrived at Cherry Creek on May 7, giving the settlements their first transportation link with civilization. Meanwhile the express company had established twenty-six relay stations along the route and now two coaches daily were started from each end of the line with fair irregularity. The charge was a hundred dollars one way.

Greeley boarded his coach at Manhattan, Kansas, on May 27. Already aboard was Albert D. Richardson, then a correspondent for the Boston Journal. Later, as a result of this trip, Richardson became the ace member of Greeley's Tribune staff and was about to be made managing editor when a love rival shot him to death in a scandal which left the New York of 1869 gasping.

Greeley and Richardson apparently hit it off well together from the start, and away they rocked, adventurous companion scribblers, across the endless Kansas prairie. The tour of the famous Tribune editor was being watched with great interest not only by his own readers but also by all who learned that the great man was passing through. His white slouch hat and bleached-out linen duster were trade marks familiar to all. Even the aborigines were awed. An Indian girl commented in Richardson's hearing: "Horace Greeley in his old white coat is sitting in that coach."

The dispatches the two men sent back to their papers from points along the 650-mile route carried parallel comments on three items of interest: the bone-shaking jolts of stage travel, the enormous migration on the plains, and the endless herds of buffalo. For miles the prairie would be black with the ponderous, shaggy animals. They looked "like wood-land afar off." The two travelers, along with all their fellow voyagers of the desert, dined on the meat of the humpbacked beast. Greeley didn't care for what he ate: "I do not like the flesh of this wild ox. It is tough and not juicy." Richardson said the meat "tastes like ordinary beef though of coarser fiber, and sometimes with a strong, unpleasant flavor. When cut from calves or young cows it is tender and toothsome."

Plains traffic of Pike's Peakers coming and going amazed both men. Richardson estimated their coach passed ten thousand migrants en route to the mines, and Greeley noted that they were arriving at Cherry Creek at a rate of one hundred a day. "Six weeks ago not a track had been made upon this route," the *Journal* correspondent wrote. "Now it resembles a long-used turnpike. We meet many returning emigrants, who declare the mines a humbug; but pass hundreds of undismayed gold-seekers still pressing on."

All day on May 27, Greeley wrote, the coach met eastbound ox wagons loaded with disheartened men who told tales of disillusion. Greeley's dispatch said:

> . . . Those whom we met . . . coming down confirm the worst news we have had from the Peak. There is scarcely any gold there; those who dig cannot average two shillings per day; all who can get away are leaving; Denver and Auraria are nearly deserted; terrible sufferings have been endured on the Plains, and more must yet be encountered; hundreds would gladly work for their board, but cannot find employment— in short, Pike's Peak is an exploded bubble, which thousands must bitterly rue to the end of their days. Such is the tenor of our latest advices. I have received none this side of Leavenworth that contradict them. My informant says all are getting away who can, and that we shall find the region nearly deserted. That is likely, but we shall see.[13]

As to the personal discomforts of traveling journalists, Greeley and Richardson agreed that a Concord coach represented a threat to one's molars. Nearing Station Seventeen, they fell into a jocular discussion of the precipitous descents their coach made into the many arroyos, gullies, and dry washes that intersected the road.

"It is some consolation," Richardson suggested, "that the sides of these gullies cannot be worse than perpendicular."

"They could be and are," his older and more vulnerable companion insisted. "Some of them not only have perpendicular sides but also an inclination of forty-five degrees to one side of the track." Within a few minutes Greeley would accumulate the scars to prove it.

As the coach descended one of the abrupt hills the mules were spooked by an approaching band of Indians. Richardson got out of the coach to take the lead team by the head. The driver pulled up with all his weight, and the left rein to the leaders parted. The mules, Greeley recalled later, "sheared out of the road and ran diagonally down the pitch. In a second, the wagon went over, hitting the ground a most spiteful blow. I of course went over with it, and when I rose to my feet as soon as possible, considerable bewildered and disheveled, the mules had been disengaged by the upset and were making good time across the

[13]Horace Greeley, *An Overland Journey from New York to San Francisco* (New York, 1860), p. 85. The book collects Greeley's dispatches to the *Tribune*.

prairie, while the driver, considerably hurt, was getting out from under the carriage to limp after them. I had a slight cut on my left cheek and a deep gouge from the sharp corner of a seat in my left leg below the knee, with a pretty smart concussion generally, but not a bone started nor a tendon strained, and I walked away to the station as firmly as ever. . . ." Greeley would spend nearly a month in Denver recuperating from his injuries and walked with a limp for a year later.

The rest of the journey was comparatively uneventful, Indians peaceful and landscape dreary in its flat, dry monotony. On the morning of June 6, after rolling all night, the stage arrived in Denver City. Editor Byers of the *News*, fresh down from the excitement in Gregory Gulch, was on hand to greet the arrivals. Richardson said the other men who gathered about the coach "were attired in slouched hats, tattered woolen shirts, buckskin pantaloons and moccasins; and had knives and revolvers suspended from their belts." The *News* gave notice of the presence of the eminent visitor:

HON. HORACE GREELEY

This distinguished gentleman arrived in our city on Monday morning last, by Leavenworth coach, and is spending a few days in this region for the purpose of investigating and reporting upon the true conditions of the mines and agricultural resources of the country. On Monday evening he delivered a short address to an assemblage of our citizens, giving much wholesome advice and recommending a state form of government, independent of all political influences.

He reported himself as being perfectly astounded with the reported gold discoveries and only hoped he might find them as rich upon investigation. The agricultural resources are even better than he hoped. On Tuesday morning he set out for the mines to spend a few days rambling among the Rocky Mountains.[14]

Denver was afire with the recent revelations of the Jackson and Gregory strikes, and Greeley's first Colorado letter to the *Tribune*, dated June 6, caught the spirit of the day:

. . . As to gold, Denver is crazy. She has been low in the valley of humiliation, and is suddenly exalted to the summit of glory. The stories of days' works, and rich leads that have been told me to-day—by grave, intelligent men—are absolutely bewildering. I do not discredit them, but I shall state nothing at second hand where I may know if I will. I have come here to lay my hand on the naked, indisputable facts, and I mean to do it. Though unfit for travel, I start for the great diggings (fifty miles hence nearly due west in the glens of the Rocky Mountains) to-morrow morning.[15]

[14]*Rocky Mountain News*, June 11, 1859.

[15]Greeley, op. cit., p. 114.

Greeley and Richardson were taken to the Denver House for lodging. This "Astor of the Rockies" was a long, low log building, about 130 feet in length by 36 in width. It had a roof of white canvas and windows of the same stuff. The earthen floor was sprinkled regularly to keep down the dust kicked up by traffic to and from the bar and a half dozen gaming tables. Although one end of the building was curtained by sheeting into several "rooms" for guests, the Denver House was much more a saloon and gambling hall than a hotel.

Guests of the house demanded that Greeley favor them with an address, and Horace never was known to refuse a platform. Byers said he talked about politics and gave wholesome advice, for both of which the man in the white linen duster was noted. Richardson goes on to supply the details of a strange and wonderful meeting. In the veritable presence of Demon Rum and Goddess Chance, the doughty Greeley reared back and delivered himself of a rouser on temperance and the evils of gambling. "On one side the tipplers at the bar silently sipped their grog," Richardson noted; "on the other the gamblers respectfully suspended the shuffling of cards and the counting of money from their huge piles of coin. . . ." The dissertation, he said, "was received with perfect good humor."

Next morning Byers collected the celebrated visitors and escorted them off to see the golden wonders at Gregory's Diggings. They were joined by Henry Villard, then roving Rocky Mountain correspondent for the Cincinnati *Commercial* and later the builder of the Northern Pacific Railroad. Villard had arrived in Denver City by an earlier coach.

They crossed the Platte via the rope ferry, and Greeley took note of the long line of wagons waiting at the landing. The ferryman, he concluded, was "making his pile out of the diggings" if no one else was. He saw that two or three farms had been established on the west side of the river. In the foothills, where Clear Creek tumbles out of the Rockies at the present site of suburban Golden, the party abandoned its wagon and took to muleback. Very gingerly, in the case of the wounded and sore Greeley. All along the steep trail the party of journalists traveled in company with a steady stream of gold-seekers. The previous week Byers had met more than a thousand in the fifteen miles or so from Gregory Gulch to the edge of the plains. Even now they still were moving up the trail at the rate of five hundred a day—and departing, Greeley reported, in daily batches of a hundred.

In crossing one mountain creek Greeley's mule stumbled on the rocky bottom and nearly pitched him into the icy waters. "Had she done it," he confessed, "I am sure I had not the strength left to rise and remount." But the determined editor pushed on. When the expedition stopped for the night he had to be "tenderly lifted from my saddle and laid on a blanket." He was too tired and stiff to eat or sleep, and he spent his first night in the Rocky Mountain wilderness massaging his sore and chafed body.

The following day the party pushed through to tumultuous Gregory Gulch, where twenty sluices now were in operation and speculation in claims had shot prices as high as $6000. One miner demonstrated panning for the reporters, and they saw him take out $2.50 in gold. Another prospector hit $17.87—Richardson recorded the decimals—from a single pan. For two days the newspapermen moved from camp to camp in the gulches centered about Mountain City, observing the frenzied operations and taking notes.

The occasion, of course, called for speeches. Greeley had the rhetoric in stock and talked at length to fifteen hundred to two thousand men sprawled among the boulders on the two sides of the cañon. His opening and his close each received "three rousing cheers," the *News* reported. He talked of a vast future for the region and advocated immediate statehood, and he urged the miners to eschew drinking, gaming, and other unspecified temptations to which he felt they were peculiarly exposed. They should, he counseled, "live as the loved ones they left at home—the brothers and sisters, fathers and mothers, wives and children—would wish." He advocated that any gambler who came among them should be put on a mule and asked if he would not like to take a ride. (Laughter and applause.) He was going on, he said, to California, and the main purpose of his overland journey was "to hasten the construction of the Pacific Railroad, which ought to have been built long ago." (Loud applause.)

At last the reporters decided they had seen their fill of gold being wrung from the earth. They sat down to collaborate on a report to the waiting world. Greeley conceded that he had touched the nude facts he had come after, but he reserved some doubts on moral, aesthetic, and conservational grounds. He asked himself "will disemboweling these mountains in quest of gold *pay?*" and judged that it was "a very pregnant question." An ascending scale of pregnancy established, he was ready to join Richardson and Villard in proclaiming the truth about Pike's Peak madness. They handed their dispatch to the express company for delivery to Byers, who had gone back to his paper in Auraria.

Byers and Gibson were standing by, anxiously awaiting the verdict of writers, particularly Greeley, whose names were known and would carry weight in the East. They were short on paper. Dr. Gilbert C. Monell, third partner in the *News* enterprise, had left Omaha a month after the advance party and was supposed to bring out a stock of newsprint. He got as far as Julesburg in northeastern Colorado and then was caught in the goback throng and swept home to Omaha. He never came to Denver. But John Dailey had on hand in Wootton's attic a supply of thin brown wrapping paper, and it was made ready for the press.

The coach from the mountains rolled into town on June 11, and a few hours later the *Rocky Mountain News* appeared on the streets with its first extra: four columns of hastily set type imprinted on one side of small squares of grocer's wrapper.

"Extra—Greeley's Report," the headline proclaimed.

> We are indebted to the kindness of Mr. Williams, of the Leavenworth & Pike's Peak Express, for the following report from Messrs. Greeley, Richardson and Villard, which will give satisfaction to the public mind, and at once set at rest the cry of "humbug" reiterated by the returning emigration from this region. The names of the gentlemen signed to this report are sufficient to give it credence without further comment from us; and the indefatigable exertions of Mr. Williams to get it before the public are commendable.

Greeley, Richardson, and Villard wrote that they had "seen the gold plainly visible in the riffles of nearly every sluice, and in nearly every pan of rotten quartz washed in our presence." They had also "seen gold, (but rarely), visible to the naked eye, in pieces of the quartz not yet fully decomposed. . . ." They went on to give the names of miners, their home towns, and the results of their labors to date. Ziegler, Spain & Co. of South Bend, Indiana, had $3000; Sopris, Henderson & Co. of Farmington, Indiana, took $607 in four days; Foote & Simmons from Chicago, $40; Shorts & Collier had been offered $10,000 for their claim.

They warned that "many persons who have come here without provisions or money, are compelled to work as common laborers at from $1 to $3 per day and board," and they could not "conclude this statement without protesting most earnestly against a renewal of the infatuation which impelled thousands to rush to this region a month or two since, only to turn back before reaching it, or to hurry away immediately after, more hastily than they came. Gold-mining is a business which eminently requires of its votaries, capital, experience, energy, endurance, and in which the highest qualities do not always command success. . . ."

The words were like a melody to Byers. This was what he had been saying all along, only to see his paper described as the "*Rocky Mountain Liar.*" Now, at last, he had distinguished confirmation. Denver would not be abandoned after all.

The *News* extra sped eastward along the lines of returning emigrants, and the name Greeley was magic. The great *Tribune* crusader—even if he *had* gone off his rocker on that Brook Farm utopia—was a solid man and would never lend himself to a hoax. The report, Richardson wrote, "was widely copied throughout the country as the first specific, disinterested and trustworthy account of the newly-discovered placers." The brown-paper broadside, an ugly little sheet, had changed the prospects of an infant city from dismal to bright.

The tide has turned, Byers soon would write. Events and Horace Greeley himself now sustained his earlier rhapsody:

Let us then rejoice that the demand has equalled the supply, and now that a brighter day is dawning and the mountains are seen to blossom with gold-bearing quartz; strain every nerve to make the best use of our time to reap the golden harvest, which seems at every hill and glade to meet our pathway ere we reach the snowclad mountains of the Rocky Mountain Range. Let notices be prevalent on the saloon doors—"gone to the mountains." There is room for all and thousands more, who will prospect and faint not until their hopes are realized.

"But mark in conclusion," the editor scolded, "gold is not bought without labor."

CHAPTER FIVE

The Inky Pioneers

VINDICATION for the soaring optimism of Byers and his *News*, although it was on the way, took time. The Greeley extra, since it appeared suspiciously on wrapping paper, was denounced as a forgery by many Eastern papers. Temporarily, some of the editors back in "the States" continued to hoot their derision in the direction of Pike's Peak and its journal. It was at this point that the Davenport, Iowa, *Gazette* cued in on the unlikely newsprint:

> The Cherry Creek Rocky Mountain News comes to us printed on brown wrapping paper. The editor has evidently lied his paper black in the face. This number teems with glorious news about new discoveries of gold, and says the town is half deserted. So we heard, but not from that cause. . . .[1]

The *Gazette* conveniently overlooked the Greeley by-line and invented the part about Denver being deserted, but with gold now coming down from the mountains in quantities which soon would require the establishment of a mint, Byers could reply with all the complacence of a poker player with four aces. This was grand and glorious country, and no less an oracle than Horace Greeley confirmed it—in the face of some rather compelling reasons for distaste.

His trip to the Rockies was proving to be considerably more than a placid rural jaunt. The Greeley-Richardson-Villard expedition tottered down out of the hills bruised and battered. Villard's mule snapped a saddle girth, pitched the future railroad magnate headfirst into a rock, then dragged him down the trail with his foot caught in the stirrup. Villard "declared himself the victim of misplaced confidence," Richardson said. Greeley, still recovering from injuries suffered in the stage upset, now also had to contend with saddle soreness. He was "so lame he could barely hobble." One might have supposed he would have returned to Denver with a profound aversion to both mules and mountain grandeurs. But though soul and body were sorely tried, there still was starch in the Greeley shirt, and he wrote:

[1]Quoted in Smiley, *History of Denver*, p. 294.

The Rocky Mountains, with their grand, aromatic forests, their glassy glades, their frequent springs and dancing streams of the brightest, sweetest water, their pure, elastic atmosphere and their unequaled game and fish, are destined to be the favorite resort of civilized man. I never visited a region where physical life could be more surely prolonged or fully enjoyed.[2]

Some Rocky Mountain tourists assert the "elastic atmosphere" leaves them a little giddy at first, but if this was the explanation in Greeley's case the euphoria did not extend to the ganglia controlling his oratorical reflexes. He had been back in the Cherry Creek settlements only overnight when he again was invited to say a few words to the assemblage in the Denver House. This time it was Byers who preserved the scene and the utterances of the *Tribune* editor to "red-shirted, bearded-faced adventurers":

> . . . He stood behind a gambling table, accommodatingly deserted for the occasion by the owner, a scienced dealer of French or three card monte. The white-coated philosopher gave much good and fatherly advice to a mixed audience of some two or three hundred persons, and wound up with a recommendation to early test the agricultural resources of the country. As he stepped from the table, it was again occupied by its industrious owner, who opened with, "Come down! come down! gentlemen; who goes $40 on the ace?—Come, gentlemen, rull up, and down your dust; you'll find this don't much resemble agriculture, but it's mightily like mining" were the words that greeted the renowned Horace as he made his exit from the room.[3]

This sort of thing had been interesting and lively the first time around. But now the busy attractions of Rocky Mountain inns were palling on the battered Greeley, whose admiration, in any case, was for rural quiet rather than rustic gaming. Although it was he who christened the Denver House the Astor of the Pike's Peak country, he cannot have cherished a very high opinion of hotel keeping, mountain style. Up in the Gregory Diggings he, Richardson, and Villard, along with three others, had been crammed into a little tent ambitiously named the Mountain City Hotel. They slept on the ground, "lying so close," Richardson said, "that none of us could turn over separately." The noisy Denver House, with the constant clamor of pitchmen urging victims to buck the tiger, now was too much; it "proved unfavorable to literary pursuits."

So Greeley and his future star reporter checked out and jumped a cabin. They chose the best empty one they could find, moved in, and took possession. A few days later the owner came down from the mines and looked in on them. Richardson remembered that "he apologized

[2]*Rocky Mountain News*, Aug. 27, 1859.

[3]Ibid., Feb. 15, 1860.

humbly for his intrusion, (most obsequious and marvelous of landlords!) begged us to make ourselves entirely at home, and then withdrew, to jump the best vacant cabin *he* could find, until the departure of his non-paying tenants. We design exhibiting him at the next world's fair as the best specimen of the Polite Gentleman on the terrestrial globe."

Greeley and Richardson continued their squatter life together for ten days, until June 21, while the *Tribune* editor mended from his wounds and exposures to mountain mules. During the time one of their visitors was Little Raven, a chief of the band of nearly a thousand Arapahoes then camped in the cottonwood bottoms. Richardson felt Little Raven was "the nearest approximation I ever met to the Ideal Indian," with a "fine manly form and a human, trustworthy face." On one of his calls the Arapaho indicated the lame Greeley lying on the bunk and wanted to know who he was.

"I reply," Richardson wrote, "that he is a great chief and named the 'Goose Quill,' endeavoring to explain that his realm and authority are purely intellectual, but giving up in despair when the Raven interrupts me to ask how many horses he owns!"

Toward the end of his stay "Goose Quill" dispatched to the *Tribune* his candid analysis of newborn Denver:

> . . . I apprehend that there have been, during my two weeks sojourn, more brawls, more fights, more pistol-shots with criminal intent in this log city of one hundred and fifty dwellings, not three-fourths completed nor two-thirds inhabited, nor one-third fit to be, than in any community of no greater numbers on earth. This will be changed in time—I trust within a year, for the empty houses are steadily finding tenants from the two streams of emigration rolling in daily up the Platte on the one hand, down Cherry Creek on the other, including some scores of women and children, who generally stop here, as all of them should; for life in the mountains is yet horribly rough. Public religious worship, a regular mail and other civilizing influences, are being established; there is a gleam of hope that the Arapahoes—who have made the last two or three nights indescribably hideous by their infernal war-whoops, songs and dances—will at last clear out on the foray against the Utes they have so long threatened, diminishing largely the aggregate of drunkenness and riot, and justifying expectations of comparative peace. . . .[4]

As his visit to Denver drew to a close Greeley's regular visitors, along with Little Raven, must have included the men of the *News*: the omnipresent Byers, who certainly would not have left the distinguished visitor unattended; Byers' cantankerous partner, Thomas Gibson; John L. Dailey, who, like Richardson, was a friend and admirer of Little Raven. Dailey had buttonholed Greeley up in Gregory Gulch on June 9 and sold him a subscription to the *News*. It was characteristic of the man.

[4]Greeley, op. cit., p. 159.

While everyone else was going half mad over gold in terms of thousands and tens of thousands of dollars, or spouting purple oratory about the future of a new Western empire, Dailey was willing to devote a few down-to-earth minutes to the matter of a five-dollar subscription for a newspaper badly in need of subscribers. Byers forever was the high-level thinker, the visionary, the head dreamer in councils of dreamers; he was the man who served on committees, drafted memorials to Congress, commanded guards of honor, and greeted visiting dignitaries. The practical Dailey never lost sight of the fact that someone had to keep shop and get the paper out, although he, too, tried his luck at mining on the side.

Probably some of the callers at the Greeley-Richardson cabin also were *News* printers—men like W. W. Whipple or young Charlie Semper. In that day the line of legitimate birth was less sharply drawn between the back shop and the editorial room than it came to be later. Printers— "typos," they called themselves—were Fourth Estaters too; they were conceded membership in the human race and were admitted to the exalted presence of the scribbling colleagues whose spelling they regularly corrected. As a typo who, at least for a few grand hours, had elevated himself to the choirs of editors, "Jolly Jack" Merrick surely must have dropped in to pay his respects to the convalescent *Tribune* chief. Ever since the brief moment of his *Cherry Creek Pioneer,* Jack had fluctuated between gold chasing in the hills and picking type for the *News.* He was one of many whom fortune eluded, but he was a good printer, and John Dailey always had an opening for him. Merrick had a prominent place in the early days of the *News;* he was rated a good shot with a rifle, and when the chips were down he proved himself a handy man to have around. He became the first president of Denver Typographical Union No. 49, the city's second oldest surviving institution, and served as one of several vice-presidents of the initial people's convention—in session concurrent with Greeley's visit—to demand statehood for the Pike's Peak territory. On October 24, 1859, he was elected marshal of the provisional territory of Jefferson. When, a few months later, a bloody business began at Fort Sumter, Merrick trekked back across the plains to enlist in an Illinois regiment of volunteers. He never returned to Colorado.

One of Jack Merrick's closest friends—both are described as "convivial" in the annals—was George West. Like Merrick, West became a leading figure in the early affairs of Denver and the region and a pioneer of Colorado journalism. He was one of the printers called upon to set into type the history-hinging words of Greeley, Richardson, and Villard for the brown-paper extra. Many years later, as the twentieth century dawned, West gave his version of the occasion to the curator of the Colorado State Historical Society:

According to my recollection it was the 10th of June [Friday], 1859, that it was printed, but it might have been dated the next day [it was]. My party had just arrived from across the plains and about noon were pulling through the sand of Cherry Creek at the Blake street crossing, twenty or thirty teams of us, when we heard a shout from a man standing on a little foot bridge which crossed the creek at that point. It proved to be old man Gibson of The News.

"Hey there!" he ejaculated, "are there any printers in this crowd?"

I told him there were two or three of us. He then asked us to go into camp and come up and set up an extra for him. As we were uncertain about what we were going to do even now that we had reached "Pike's peak," we concluded to do as he requested. Bill Summers, Mark Blunt, late of Pueblo, and I went to the office, then located in a one-and-a-half-story log cabin on Ferry street, now Eleventh street, where we found Horace Greeley, A. D. Richardson and Henry Villard, who had just returned from the mountains, and the News wanted to publish their report in an extra. We then buckled to, set it up and worked off, I believe, 500 copies on the old Washington hand press, the handle of which you have in your collection. For this we received five pennyweight of gold dust.

Now old man Gibson is dead, Horace Greeley is dead, A. D. Richardson is dead, Bill Summers and Mark Blunt are dead, leaving only Mr. Byers, Mr. Villard and myself as survivors of that wonderful coterie to whom the world owes so much for the production of that celebrated extra.[5]

Like many another aging fifty-niner, George West by 1900 was taking his pioneerhood very seriously, but if he overestimated the importance of events in which he had a hand, the local record speaks well and often of him without need of a glossing. After a few months on the *News*, West moved out to Golden in the foothills and on December 4, 1859, published the *Western Mountaineer*, Colorado's third newspaper if Merrick's short-lived *Pioneer* is not reckoned in the tally. Sponsor of the *Mountaineer* was the Boston Company, founders of Golden in the picture-postcard valley formed between flat-topped Table Mountain and the first upslope of the Rockies. Located on Clear Creek and some fifteen miles nearer than Denver to the riches of Gregory Gulch and Jackson's Diggings, Golden at the time was heralded as a rival to Auraria-Denver City in metropolitan importance, and it later would be, briefly, the capital of Colorado Territory. It was not named for its proximity to mineral wealth but for Thomas Golden, a friend of George A. Jackson, who had made the placer strike upstream at present Idaho Springs.

West suspended his *Mountaineer* early in 1860 in order to make a trip east to buy more printing equipment, but he was back in business at Golden on June 28 with a pair of distinguished editorial associates. One was Albert Deane Richardson, now back in the Rockies as a full-

[5]Smiley, *History of Denver*, p. 280.

fledged New York *Tribune* correspondent (thanks probably to his intimate association with Greeley the previous summer). The other was Thomas Wallace Knox, then writing for the Boston *Atlas and Bee*. Like Richardson, Knox soon would become one of the most famous of Civil War reporters. He would be court-martialed for writing in the New York *Herald* that General Sherman was insane during the affair at Chickasaw Bayou. It would require the intercession of President Lincoln for him to get his credentials back from the indignant, press-hating Union Army.[6]

Although they held themselves high as "specials" for big Eastern newspapers, Knox and Richardson were happy to pick up odd change by helping West fill the columns of his lively little *Mountaineer*. Politics was crowding their dispatches out of the papers in Boston and New York anyway. The Lincoln-Douglas-Breckinridge-Bell contest was requiring a lot of journalistic supervision, as was the mounting storm over slavery. The *Tribune's* Charles A. Dana wrote Richardson that his Western stuff was piling up in the overset and he wanted no more "leisurely accounts of travel or buffalo hunting or mining camp brawls." The gold rush was "played out" as news, Dana said, "unless there is some really big bonanza discovery." Knox received similar down-play orders from his managing editor at the *Atlas and Bee*. In this situation West's revived *Mountaineer* offered a handy outlet for two of the most restless pens of the era. Moreover, if Golden City prospered, as nearly everyone—particularly members of the Boston Company—predicted, perhaps they could help build the *Mountaineer* into a challenger of the *Rocky Mountain News* for newspaper supremacy in the Rockies.

Editor Byers, in Denver, did not appear to be worried by the threat. Richardson and Knox were his friends; he admired them and probably envied their distinction as big-time journalists from back east. West, too, was a friend and had been a good and faithful employee. So Byers gave the *Mountaineer* a generous send-off in the *News* of July 4, 1860:

> The first number of the second volume of our sprightly contemporary at Golden City, reached our table on Friday last. It is out in a span new dress, worked on a new press, and in every respect a model newspaper. Our Golden City friends and the public generally should bestow on it a liberal patronage, for which they will richly receive their money's worth. Geo. West, editor and proprietor. Terms five dollars per year.

Despite the *News'* good wishes and a highly talented staff, the *Mountaineer* weakened and died with its December 20, 1860, issue. Several months earlier both Knox and Richardson had left Golden and served briefly in Denver on the staff of the *News* before the big story of the rebellion called them east to fame and glory as war reporters. George West also faced east, but as a soldier rather than a newspaperman.

[6]Emmet Crozier, *Yankee Reporters: 1861–65* (New York, 1956), pp. 297–305.

He became a captain in the 2nd Colorado Infantry. When the war ended, West returned to Denver and in August 1865 joined the staff of the *News* as "local" or city editor. In September 1866 he withdrew from the *News* and founded in Golden the *Colorado Transcript,* a weekly which is still being published. For about nine months in 1875 West printed a daily edition of the *Transcript* for circulation in Denver. Later he served a two-year term as adjutant general of Colorado, led an expedition against marauding Utes, and always thereafter was known as "General" West. He survived, full of years and honors as soldier and editor, well into the twentieth century.

His distinguished early associate, Richardson, who was strongly drawn to the West and its rough ways, made still another trip to Denver after the Civil War was over in company with Schuyler Colfax, then Speaker of the House of Representatives (for whom a principal Denver street was named), William Bross of the Chicago *Tribune,* and Samuel Bowles of the Springfield, Massachusetts, *Republican.* In the latter pages of *Beyond the Mississippi* Richardson expressed his amazement at the changes which had come to the squalid settlements and wild country he had known five years earlier. Denver had "grown up through great tribulation," he wrote. Seventy thousand acres of farm land were under cultivation, and the Colorado mines had deposited twelve and a half millions in gold with the mint.

At my last visit, five years before, Civilization had barely extended to these wilds the tips of her gracious fingers. Now Denver boasted a population of five thousand, and many imposing buildings. The hotel bills-of-fare did not differ materially from those in New York or Chicago. Single building lots had commanded twelve thousand dollars. One firm had sold half a million dollars worth of goods in eight months.

With fresh memories of the log-cabins, plank tables, tin cups and plates, and the fatal whisky of 1859, I did not readily recover from my surprise on seeing libraries and pictures, rich carpets and pianos, silver and wine—on meeting families with the habits, dress and surroundings of the older States. Keenly we enjoyed the pleasant hospitalities of society among the quickened intelligences and warmed hearts of the frontier. Western emigration makes men larger and riper, more liberal and more fraternal.

The mountain view from the city impressed me as more grand and beautiful than ever. . . .[7]

Richardson noted that there were now "six or seven daily newspapers" being published for the 5000 people of Denver and the 30,000 permanent residents of the new Colorado Territory. The *Rocky Mountain News* had acquired competition. It began with "old man Gibson" and the

[7]Richardson, op. cit., p. 333.

almost toy-size *Cherry Creek Pioneer* press acquired from Jack Merrick in the swap for a grubstake.

Thomas Gibson came west from Fontanelle, Nebraska, as a partner in the *News* venture with some background in newspapering.[8] He was a printer-editor and for a time had published the Quincy, Illinois, *Whig,* described as "a notable political sheet." Nearly everyone who remembers Gibson in contemporary memoirs describes him as a difficult man. Before the *News* was a month old he and Byers were quarreling violently. In a huff, Gibson stalked off to the Gregory Diggings on May 17, 1859, with John Dailey, P. W. Case, and "Pap" Hoyt of the *News* staff. He and Dailey and others commuted back and forth between the gulch and Auraria, alternating between chasing gold and getting out the *News,* for the next two months, but relations between the cranky Englishman and the often bullheaded Byers did not improve. The July 13 entry in John Dailey's diary says:

> Gibson staid with us tonight [at Mountain City] & he proposed to sell his interest in the printing office to me for $500, $250 to be paid when possession is given and the balance in 6 mo from that time. I studied over it & by morning concluded to accept his offer.

Next day Dailey and Gibson went down to Denver "& we drew writings of the agreement between us & I went on down to work. The $250 is to be paid down about the 8th of August, and I to take his place in the office." It was Gibson's contention that Dr. Gilbert Monell, third partner in the *News,* had forfeited his interest by failing to come through to Pike's Peak with the paper supplies. Gibson was offering Dailey a half interest, and thereby was placing a valuation of a thousand dollars on the total assets, good will, and hopes of future glory of the struggling little hand-printed newspaper.

Hitches developed in the deal, however. Byers had made a quick trip back to Omaha in July to bring out his wife and their two children. While in Omaha he withdrew from the real estate firm of Poppleton & Byers and bought out Dr. Monell's third interest in the *News.* He had confidence in the future of his paper, if Gibson didn't. Arriving back in Auraria on August 7, he discovered that instead of the two-thirds interest he thought he had acquired he was faced with a contract which would leave him with only half. The already strained relationship with Gibson was not improved. Gibson trotted up to Mountain City, where Dailey was hitting as high as seventy-two dollars a day in his sluices, and the printer-prospector noted in his journal: "He said that the arrangement between him and myself was not altogether agreeable to Mr. Byers, and that it would be necessary for me to go with him to town on Saturday."

[8]Morton, op. cit., Vol. I, p. 277.

Back in Denver, Dailey found that "G. was anxious to have our bargain concluded tonight & wanted me to go over & have the papers made out before I saw Byers, which I objected to & went over to the Potluck house to see him. He didn't talk to suit me in regard to the difference between he & G & I concluded to have no more to do with it." Next day, while Dailey was working in the printing office, "B & G had a little spat . . . but arrived at no conclusions." "I told G today," Dailey says in his diary, "that as the thing stood between him and B I could have nothing more to do with it. So it stood till in the evening, when B spoke to me alone proposing certain things to G in the morning & if he was agreeable to buy him out. So it rested till morning." The diary entry for August 15 says:

> Made proposition to G, he accepted & we immediately proceeded to have writings drawn, which was hurriedly done by Gen. Larimer in order that G. might be prepared to start on the stage at 6: for the States.

The "certain things" that Byers proposed to Dailey as a means of hastening Gibson on his way are not of record, but henceforth the two men were associated as principal owners of the *News* for eleven years. The change of ownership notices appeared in the *News* for August 20:

NOTICE OF DISSOLUTION.

The co-partnership heretofore existing between Wm. N. Byers, G. C. Monell and Thomas Gibson, in the publication of the Rocky Mountain News, is this day dissolved by mutual consent.

Auraria, K.T.   August 15, 1859   Wm. N. Byers & Company

NOTICE OF COPARTNERSHIP.

We have this day entered into copartnership, under the name and style of Wm. N. Byers & Co. for the purpose of carrying on the publication of the Rocky Mountain News.

Wm. N. Byers
Auraria, K.T.   August 15, 1859   Jno. L. Dailey

In the midst of squabbling with Byers and dickering with Dailey, Gibson had established Colorado's second newspaper. He and his son took Merrick's miniature *Pioneer* press up to Mountain City on July 28, and on August 6 they issued from George Aux's half-completed log cabin the first number of the *Rocky Mountain Gold Reporter and Mountain City Herald.* The paper's tenure was scarcely longer than its name. It lasted until October, when Gibson returned to Omaha, announcing he would be back to resume the *Reporter* in the spring. On his way down from the mountains he sold the much-traveled Mormon press to George

West, who used it to start his *Western Mountaineer* at Golden in December.

Gibson returned in 1860 but not to Mountain City, and the *Reporter* did not report again. Instead Gibson remained in Denver and conjured up even rougher competition for his onetime partner, Bill Byers. He had brought with him a new and extensive printing plant, and on May 1 he came forth with the *Daily Herald and Rocky Mountain Advertiser*, Colorado's first daily newspaper, followed on May 5 by the weekly *Rocky Mountain Herald*. Gibson had as silent partner in his enterprise none other than William Gilpin, frontiersman of high standing, a potent leader in civic affairs, and the man who would be chosen the following year as the first territorial governor of Colorado.

The combination of high-placed connections and a daily rate of issue made the *Herald* formidable opposition. It was the first of many threats to the supremacy and continued life of the *News*. In good time Byers would take full measure of the *Herald*, but in the summer of 1860 he had to reckon with Gibson's new sheet as a lively foe. The prior bitterness between the ex-partners did little to keep the competition on a high plane of journalistic endeavor. They jabbed each other with editorial barbs, indulged freely in personalities, trotted out adjectives smelling of brimstone. The two editors brawled over a public printing contract in a battle which echoed into the halls of Congress. Gibson delighted in solemnly announcing that the venerable *News* had grown old and tired and would give up its ghost with the next succeeding issue. The tactic left Byers fuming.

The newspaper business was getting brisk at Cherry Creek. Something had to be done.

Fortunately Byers and Dailey were in a position to do it. Their paper had gained modestly in strength during the past year, and there had even been an infusion of new money and talent. Two Chicago newspapermen, Horace E. ("Hod") Rounds and Edward Bliss, arrived in town at midsummer intending to start a newspaper. Bliss was the founder in 1844 of the *Genesee Courier* of Leroy, New York, and later had worked as a printer in Racine, Wisconsin, before becoming managing editor in 1857 of the Chicago *Sunday Leader*, owned by "Hod" Rounds' brother Sterling.

After surveying the situation, Bliss and Rounds abandoned their plans for another paper and joined with Byers and Dailey to form the News Printing Company. They continued as part of the *News* staff and management until the spring of 1863. Subsequently Bliss ranged far and colorfully in a notable journalistic career. He published papers in Africa, South America, and Australia.

After quitting the press in Colorado, he went to England, and there for a time held a position on the London *World*. Many years prior to this he accompanied Bayard Taylor through Lapland, Labrador and the frozen North in search of knowledge for the New York *Tribune,* and had twice made the circuit of the earth. As a correspondent for the New York *Herald* he had traveled on foot the Russian possessions [Alaska] and British North America. He had lived on crackers and cheese in a New York garret while writing squibs at a penny a line, and again had dined with Washington Irving on the Hudson, and with Mr. Thackeray in the London club rooms. . . . He went out to the Crimean War with the British troops and witnessed the fall of Balaklava; was with the same army in the campaign in China. He had written several small volumes in his day, but invariably let the publishers get away with the profits.[9]

Bliss and Rounds brought an outfit with them from Chicago. Byers and Dailey ordered more equipment. Then, with six presses in the plant, the *News* became a daily on August 27, 1860. The weekly also was continued, and in fact more care apparently was lavished on its preparation than on the daily edition. But the paper now was "metropolitan" in stature. Let Gibson and his *Herald* fire away; the *News* could reply, salvo for salvo. The situation was back in hand—except that it had grown more complex. The *News* had missed by two days becoming Denver's second daily. For a ragtag bobtail boom town with a highly fluid population of a few thousand persons, Denver was getting the saturation treatment from the press.

On August 25, John C. Moore, then mayor of Denver City, and James T. Coleman brought out the *Daily Mountaineer* (not to be confused with George West's hapless *Western Mountaineer* out in Golden), which also had a weekly edition. Although the town by then was a consolidated city, the old Auraria-Denver City rivalry died hard, and the *Daily Mountaineer* had its origin in the lingering bitterness between what now were officially West Denver and East Denver. Byers had located his *News* on the Auraria side of the creek, although he now occupied a new plant built on stilts in the very bed of the stream. This was billed as "neutral ground," although it actually was southwest of the dividing line and still in what had been Auraria. Gibson's *Herald* also was being published on the Auraria side. East Denver still didn't really have its own newspaper. As has been noted, the Denver City Town Company had offered Byers twenty-four city lots if he would move across Cherry Creek, and then dangled ten lots before Albert D. Richardson in an unsuccessful effort to bait him into bucking the *News.* The line dividing the settlements now was a myth, except in the patriotic breasts of the East Denver town fathers. They offered the ten lots again, and Coleman and Moore accepted.

The *Daily Mountaineer* started out as a Democratic paper in a country

[9]Denver *Republican*, Sept. 13, 1883; quoted in McMurtrie and Allen, op. cit., p. 29fn.

which was swarming with Lincoln Republicans. As events moved toward cannon fire at Fort Sumter it became an out-and-out secession journal. It did not prosper; the bulk of the Pike's Peakers were Midwesterners or Yankees. In May of 1861, Coleman, then its remaining publisher, sold the *Mountaineer* to Byers. Both Coleman and Moore became officers in the Confederate Army. Byers has left a record of the closing of the transaction:

> . . . When we agreed upon the terms of the purchase the editor of the Mountaineer took a rebel flag that was sticking in his desk and another one that was in the office and said "I suppose you don't want this" and I said "I haven't any use for that" and so he took them down. . . .[10]

With the *Mountaineer* disposed of, the *News* could give its undivided attention to trading adjectives with Gibson's *Herald*. One of the bitterest of the fights arose over the contract for public printing let by the new territory of Colorado. Bliss was the standard-bearer for the *News*.

When the first territorial legislature met in 1861 it was dominated by Republicans. Byers was a party stalwart. Bliss promptly was elected public printer. But Gibson got the ear of the new territorial secretary, Lewis Ledyard Weld, and the printing contract was given to the *Herald* office. The contract was important in both money and prestige to the two journals, and they fought for it. The *News* had strongly supported Hiram P. Bennet as unofficial delegate to Congress from the provisional Jefferson Territory. Bennet was in Washington; the *News* demanded he see to it that the federal government make good on the Colorado legislature's selection of Bliss as public printer. Secretary of State William H. Seward—who, in view of other things on his mind at the time, must have been mightily annoyed by the picayune squabble—came to a Solomon's decision and ordered Weld to divide the printing between the *News* and the *Herald*. Distances and distractions being what they were, Weld cheerfully ignored the order and continued to use only the *Herald* plant. The *News* dispatched Bliss to Washington, where he swore out an affidavit against Weld, and the plagued Seward this time ordered Weld to turn over the printing to the *News*. Seeking to justify his disobedience, Weld adopted a tactic which has had some polished applications in modern times; he impugned the loyalty of his opponent. The *News*, he wrote Seward, was

> not a sheet reputable in this community either for honesty of purpose or loyalty to the government. Under an outside garb of devotion to the Union, there is very strong reason to believe that it is venal to the last degree—and it has always been, as it now is, the open apologist

[10]Byers, Bancroft ms., Pac ms L8.

for the worst and most dangerous class of people in our midst. Its columns daily abound in the most virulent personal abuse of the Federal officers of this Territory—and one of the most prominent writers for its pages is a man who was driven from the City of St. Joseph, Missouri, as a rebel & a traitor. . . .

The charges were wholly without foundation. Byers was a Lincoln man from the beginning, and the Johnny Reb on the staff is unidentifiable. True, the *News* had been attacking Weld vigorously in the fashion of the day, which was scarcely impersonal, and it had opposed the financial policies of Governor Gilpin. The *Herald*, of course, was supporting Gilpin, who a few months later was removed from office by Lincoln for some of the same actions the *News* had been labeling "ruinous."

Weld, however, resigned his post a month after his smear, and his successor, Samuel H. Elbert, at last gave the printing to the *News*.[11] The fight had been won, and in the course of it the *News* picked up more ammunition for its campaign, begun in the first issue, demanding statehood for Colorado. Carpetbagging federal appointees like Weld should never again be allowed to override so callously the will of the sovereign people as expressed through the noble organ of their elected legislature.

Gibson's *Herald* did not long survive the defeat. He had taken O. McCraney, a Republican leader, into the firm and changed the name on May 25, 1861, to the *Colorado Republican and Rocky Mountain Herald*, but McCraney withdrew a few months later. Gibson held out alone until July 10, 1862, when he again changed the name of his paper, this time to the *Commonwealth and Republican*, daily and weekly, with O. J. Hollister and Lew Weld, ally in the printing squabble, as editors. At the end of December 1863, Gibson sold out to Simeon Whiteley, who, it was understood, had the backing of the second territorial governor, John Evans, a close friend of Byers'. Gibson returned to Omaha and figured no more in the newspaper annals of Denver. He had helped start three Colorado newspapers, and the only one to endure was the one he deserted.

Of the original *News* pioneers, only Byers and Dailey now were left to fight new battles with drouth and deadbeats, grasshoppers, Indians, and competitors in the years ahead.

Although they did not always agree, Byers and Dailey complemented each other admirably. Dailey was a gangling six-footer, Byers shorter and inclined to portliness, particularly as the years advanced. Dailey had an enormous capacity for loyalty and diligence. He sometimes worked all day and then through until dawn getting the paper out. He kept tab

[11]The *News-Herald* printing controversy is documented in William Hanchett, *Politics and Patronage in Territorial Colorado*, unpublished doctoral dissertation, Colorado State University, Fort Collins, 1955.

on the printers' lost time, baby-sat the Byers children, dipped often into his own pocket for small loans to his partner, who was continually caught short. Byers needed someone exactly like Dailey. The editor was gone from Denver much of the time. When he was in town he was too busy at high-level politicking, attending public functions, and empire building to be bothered with the day-to-day practicalities of printing a newspaper. He was a policy maker. Byers, of course, became the prominent one, and in the Dailey diaries there are traces of envy of his partner's many distinctions and of annoyance with his ceaseless perambulations. But between the two of them—one faithfully tending shop; one dreaming no dreams that were small-sized—the *News* appeared regularly and grew steadily in stature and solvency.

When Jerome Smiley described Byers as "our ranking pioneer" he was granting the distinction with more than usual precision. William Newton Byers was born a pioneer, and he lived most of his life as a frontiersman in seven states. The only city he knew, aside from those he visited on his travels, was the one he built.

His father, Moses Watson Byers, son of one veteran of the Revolution and grandson of another, was among the first settlers to put the plow to the Darby plains in Ohio. Moses Byers was of Scotch-Presbyterian ancestry. His wife, Mary Ann Brandenburg, came of a German family who also arrived early in Ohio and took up land in the Miami Valley. The Byerses originally stopped at Circleville in Pickaway County, but Moses moved on to Madison County, near West Jefferson, where he claimed and developed three hundred acres. William Newton Byers was born on February 22, 1831, the first of six children. He lived the life of a fringe-land farm boy, with almost no opportunity for schooling. But he was a reader, and most of the education he acquired was worked out laboriously from the pages of books he borrowed or begged. When the farm work was completed late in the autumn of 1848, Bill was given the rare opportunity of a short semester in the new academy at West Jefferson. Along with the rudiments of a few basic subjects he picked up a working knowledge of practical surveying. It would become his trade, although at seventeen he was helping his father fill a contract for ties for the Cleveland, Columbus & Cincinnati Railroad.

In 1850, Ohio had become too congested for Moses Byers, and he took his family west to Muscatine on the Mississippi in the newly admitted state of Iowa. The next year his son pushed even farther west, joining a federal survey party as chainman and compassman. Although he was not yet twenty-one, Byers was named deputy United States surveyor for Iowa and assisted in the running of many of the original section lines in the western part of the state. Early in 1852 he was back in Muscatine, helping his father with slaughtering and lumbering. The earliest of his surviving pocket diaries is for this year, and it pictures a young man highly competent in the wide variety of skills which frontier life demanded. He could build a gristmill and grind meal, tap trees and make sugar, construct a log sled or a wheelbarrow, put up a house for a neighbor. In April he was back at his surveying near Kanesville, working for a Mr. Bumgardner. The memo pages at the end of Byers' diaries often carry bits of poetry he liked and lists of books he wanted to buy when the cash was available. In the 1852 journal he jots down the following desired volumes: *Stoddard's Complete Ready Reckoner, The Philopene Cong-ster, Forget Me Not, True Love Knots,* and *Paper Bullets from Love's Pocket Pistol,* which treatise was available for twelve and a half cents from Stearns & Company, booksellers, at 202 Williams Street, New York City. He also notes, with a little uncertainty, a bit of Pope he wanted to remember:

Health $\left\{ \begin{array}{c} \text{exists} \\ \text{consists} \end{array} \right\}$ of with Temperance alone
And Peace, O virtue is
all thine one.

Byers was now twenty-one, the mysteries of love were beginning to trouble him, and, like many another idealistic and perfectionist young man his age, he had firmly committed his conscience to temperance, truth, and high moral living.

Byers did not return home from Kanesville. Instead he signed on with Messrs. Donnellan and Cannon of Dubuque for overland passage to Oregon and California. The party set out May 5 and on May 9 crossed the Missouri at the old Mormon "Winter Quarters," later Florence, Nebraska, and that night was visited by friendly Pawnees. Traveling behind ox teams, Byers and his companions toiled up the Platte Valley. On May 25 they began to encounter emigrant trains from St. Joseph and Independence, coming up the southern route and reporting cholera back down the trail. On June 6 they had reached Scotts Bluff, where Byers heard how the landmark was named: "A party of mountaineers were returning to the states, their provisions were exhausted; they were nearly starving. One named Scott was taken sick and begged his comrades to leave him and take care of themselves. They did so. Afterwards a human skeleton was found here, supposed to be Scott." The expedition passed Fort Laramie in present Wyoming on June 9 and on July 1 was at South Pass, ready to drop down into the Pacific watershed. Byers wrote in his diary:

. . . Craggy precipices, rocky steeps, mountain gorges and everything awful as connected with the South Pass in the minds of emigrants, are all humbug; gentle rolling prairie surrounded it on every side; in short it seems nature intended this as the gateway of the great highway of nations. . . . Commencing the descent four miles brought us to Pacific

Springs, the first water flowing to the west and one of the sources of
Green River, the great Colorado of the west. . . . Here we camped;
grass scarce; plenty of sage. . . .

The Byers party took the Sublette cutoff, passed by Fort Hall in
present Idaho, and after a hundred and forty-five days of travel reached
Oregon.[12] By October, Byers was cutting, rafting, and milling logs
up the river from Portland, but in December returned to surveying as
an employee of Joseph Hunt, deputy U.S. surveyor, in the area around
La Fayette. Again he was involved in the laying out of the first section
lines in a Western state. His diary for December 28 records: "Started
up the second tier of sections." Within a few months he was running
the first township boundaries in what would become the state of Washington. The diary for 1853 carries traces of a young man's homesickness,
and it dreamily remembers in verse a girl back home in Iowa:

> I think of thee
> When through the trees
> Sound symphonies
> Of nightingales.
> When dost thou think of me?
>
> I think of thee
> At Evening's blink
> Beside the brink
> Of Shady well.
> Where dost thou think of me?
>
> I think of thee
>   with anguish sweet
> With longing fears
>   and ardent tears.
> How dost thou think of me?
>
> O think of one
> Until beneath
> A better star
> We meet. Though far
> I think alone of thee.

The book list for the year includes: A Complete Dictionary of Poetical
Quotations, History of the World by Henry Bill, Wilson's Ornithology.
He reminds himself to look up the words to "Old Folks at Home" and
"Home, Home" at first opportunity.

[12]Byers' journal of his trip has recently been republished by Byron G. Hooper,
Jr., in his Overland News (Denver), Vol. 1, Nos. 10, 11, and 12 (May, June, and
July–Aug. 1958).

By November of 1853 the survey work was completed, or Byers had had enough of it. He settled up with Hunt for a $250 compass, $550 in cash, and "balance on account." Then he sailed from St. Helena on November 15 for San Francisco. "Farewell to Oregon. Thy lofty mountains. Thy noble rivers & magnificent waterfalls. Thy green & pleasant plains & flowering hillsides. I bid you all adieu." But next day: "'A life on the ocean wave' how I detest it, this horrible seasickness." Two days later the ship, the *Columbia*, was off the Golden Gate but "shut out by fog." On the nineteenth: "Beat about all day in the fog without knowing where." Byers landed in San Francisco on the twentieth, and the next day's entry reads: "Looking around over the city, with which I was agreeably disappointed. In the evening went to the San Francisco Theater." The diarist spent the most of the rest of the month on a side excursion to the California gold country. He visited "Sackramento"—"a brisk pleasant place and a beautiful situation"—and "Colomo," where he saw Sutter's Mill, scene of the first gold discovery. Back in San Francisco, he attended the theater again, and on December 1 set sail abroad the *Sierra Nevada* for Acapulco, the bay of San Juan del Sud, and a muleback trip across Nicaragua to the Caribbean. He arrived in New York on Christmas Eve aboard the steamer *Northern Light* and calculated the passage at "2100 ms. in 8 days & 2 hours." The boy who knew three different frontiers at the age of twenty-three opened his eyes wide to the gaslit wonder-world of the big city. He visited the Crystal Palace, went to a "Georama of the Holy Land"— "a very interesting exhibition"—and looked in on P. T. Barnum's Museum, where they were playing *Hot Corn*. But he didn't tarry long, and as the year ended he was home in Muscatine. Four days later he was helping slaughter hogs.

Through the winter, spring, and summer Byers helped out around the farm. He heard the prairie chickens drumming on February 21, built a chimney, planted fruit trees and an Osage orange hedge, shingled the smokehouse, and whitewashed the Byers home. He cut wheat, cradled oats, and went fishing. For entertainment there were always two meetings at church each Sunday, morning and evening, and someone came to town to deliver lectures on the new science of phrenology. Byers attended twice. But there were other developments, too, and the strictly high-minded level on which they unfolded is perhaps suggested by the clipping of a poem tucked in the 1854 diary opposite the page for March 15: "What a lovely morning," Byers exulted. "Robbins, Doves, Larks, Bluebirds, Blackbirds & Jays and the Chickens keep up their 'Boo hoo.'" The poem reads:

> Something in every part of thee
> To praise, to love, I find;

But dear as is thy form to me,
Still dearer is thy mind.

On May 7, Byers rented a carriage and went to a meeting at the High Prairie schoolhouse. Miss Sumner was beside him, and Mr. and Mrs. E. M. Kessinger went along as chaperones. A week later Byers again was a customer at the livery stable: "Took the girls to the country and returned to town with Miss Sumner. Spent a *very* pleasant evening." He underscored the "very." There were other bosky idyls, and apparently an understanding of intentions had been reached when Byers left on September 5 for Nebraska Territory. He crossed over the Missouri to Omaha City, "a pretty place," on September 15, found employment as a surveyor, and built a house. He also took out land claims in the area and on September 22 participated in a council with Chiefs Standing Hawk, Yellow Smoke, and White Cow. On September 23 he helped organize and was elected secretary of the Papao Claim Association.[13] In his free time he hung out at the Big Six, a popular eating house and saloon owned by William Clancy, who, like Byers, later would go to Pike's Peak and for whom a downtown Denver street was named briefly (it is now Tremont Place).[14]

Byers quickly made his mark in Omaha, and he became as prominently identified with its early affairs as he became later in the building of another city farther west. The Omaha *Arrow* for September 22, 1854, gave notice of the arrival of

. . . W. N. Byers, formerly of Muscatine, Iowa, an old [Byers was now twenty-three] stager on the Oregon frontier, who brings with him one of the best solar compasses for field surveying in the west. He purposes making our soil his home. . . .[15]

On October 27 all the foundations were in place and Byers was ready to make a quick trip back to Muscatine. There on November 16 he was married to Miss Elizabeth Minerva Sumner of nearby West Liberty. The young couple set out the same day for their new home in Omaha, but the honeymoon trip was clouded by at least one untoward incident. They encountered a severe wind storm on November 24, and in the middle of the night the gale ripped off the roof of the house in which they were stopping.

The young transitman helped plat the city of Omaha, drew its first map, laid out its Jeffer's addition, and once again became a deputy U.S. surveyor for a new state. Moreover, on December 12, the happy

[13]Omaha *Arrow*, Oct. 6, 1854.

[14]Arthur C. Wakeley, *Omaha: The Gate City, and Douglas County* (Chicago, 1917), Vol. 1, p. 91; Alfred Sorensen, *The Story of Omaha* (Omaha, 1923), p. 72.

[15]Quoted in Sorensen, op. cit., p. 73.

bridegroom was elected a member of the first Nebraska Territory legislature. His cup of happiness was brimful. The diary entry for December 25 says: "Christmas and so nice & pleasant."

The Omaha *Arrow* having expired, Byers took a card in the *Nebraska Palladium* at Bellevue on January 31, 1855, to advertise his availability:

> W. N. Byers
> Land Surveyor-Omaha City, Nebraska Territory
> Friends, I am again in the field, and at your
> service, better supplied with instruments than
> formerly.

The following year he joined with his fellow legislator, Andrew J. Poppleton, later a prominent attorney for the Union Pacific Railroad, in a real estate and law partnership. Their ad in the *Nebraska Advertiser* for June 14, 1856, said:

A. J. Poppleton   Wm. N. Byers

> Poppleton & Byers
> ATTORNEYS AT LAW
> And General Land Agents,
> Omaha, Nebraska
>
> Land Warrants Bought and Sold
> Land Entered on Time
>
> Special attention given to the selection and entry of
> Lands of Settlers, and all others desiring choice
> locations.
> Land Claims, Town Lots and all kinds of Real
> estate, bought and sold and investments made for
> distant dealers.

Byers and his bride lived for two or three years in the fifth house to be erected in Omaha. It stood on Tenth Street at Farnham, had been built in 1854 by the first sheriff, P. G. Peterson, and it already had acquired a history. Dr. Charles A. Henry had been chained to the floor of the building after his arrest for the killing of George Hollister at Bellevue in an altercation over town lots.[16]

At the first town election in March 1857, Byers was chosen as an alderman. Presumably he had a voice in the first ordinance the new city council passed on March 5. The law was aimed at tidying up the town, and it specified that swine no longer would be permitted to run at large.[17]

[16]Sorensen, *The Early History of Omaha*, p. 202.

[17]Ibid., p. 94.

During the following year fevered reports of gold in the Rockies began to make their way east to Omaha. Byers was in a mood to listen to them. The panic had hit. Several of his townsite promotions had collapsed. Why not try his luck farther west, particularly since he already knew the way out there? Byers organized his *Rocky Mountain News* and turned his hopes toward the shining mountains.

Although he had yet to mark his thirtieth birthday, Byers by now had enough of a taste of public prominence and policy making so that henceforth he would take the large and long view of affairs. It was not so much that he felt the nagging, day-to-day details of business were beneath his dignity as that it just didn't seem to occur to him that they required attention and solutions. Fortunately he had the practical-minded John Dailey at his side as the *News* began to make its way. When Byers' one-time associate Thomas Gibson wanted to complain about undercutting of prices on job printing—the *News* and the *Herald* were bitter enemies on everything else, but they had an agreement to hold the line on printers' charges—he knew where to address his ire. On June 7, 1860, Gibson wrote Dailey:

> *Dear Sir*—Your being the practical partner in the firm of W. N. Byers & Co., I address this to you on a subject of vital importance to the profession. Some time since we had an understanding not to run prices of job work down. I have invariably adhered to the prices—$8 for a 4th sheet etc etc—for 100. Now I have sufficient evidence in two instances that you have fell [sic] considerably from the price. If this is your intention . . . I am fully satisfied I am in a position to do work in my office, with the assistance of my family, at less than you *possibly* can. I am not to be deceived more than once again. If you think this deserving of attention, I shall be glad to hear from you.
>
> Yours in haste
Thos Gibson[18]

Dailey took time that night to note calmly in his diary: "Received an epistle from Father Gibson relative to prices of job work."

The anchor man of the Byers and Dailey team shared Ohio birth with his partner, though they apparently had not met until both reached Omaha. John Dailey was born in Tiffin, Seneca County, on November 19, 1833, the fifth child of a pioneer who had cleared eighty acres of forest and swamp for a farm. At seventeen John became an apprentice printer at Fort Wayne, Indiana, in the office of Thomas Cook, publisher of the *Laurel Wreath of Fort Wayne*, a literary paper which lasted only a year. He completed his apprenticeship under John W. Dawson at the Fort Wayne *Times*, and then at twenty-one struck out further west. In Des Moines he helped issue the first number of the *Iowa Citizen*,

[18]Ms. letter in Dailey scrapbook, Denver Public Library.

forebear of the Des Moines *Register*.[19] By 1855 he was on the fringe of
civilization in Nebraska Territory, where he lost his savings in a farm
and timber claim near Cuming City. His able fingers burned at speculation, he returned them to his trade.

During the winter of 1856–57 he and Henry M. Burt, later the Springfield, Massachusetts, publisher and author, entered into a contract
with an Omaha real estate promoter named William N. Byers to go to
the proposed new town of Central City, Nebraska Territory, and start
a newspaper to be called the *Times*. The panic pulled the rug out
from under Byers' project and Central City became a paper town.
Everyone left but Dailey, who couldn't. He had cut his foot with an
ax while working on a survey party. When he recovered he moved on
to Dakota City on the Missouri opposite Sioux City and printed the
first issue of the *Herald* there. It also lasted a single year. By that time
the *Rocky Mountain News* was being conceived, and Byers wrote him
to come down and join in. Dailey was delayed in winding up his affairs,
and when he reached Omaha the management interest he had expected
was gone, split two ways between Dr. Monell and Thomas Gibson. So
he came west as printing foreman and bided his time for the partnership
that finally fell to him.

Dailey's activities with the *News* are detailed through many of these
pages. In 1864 he interrupted his newspaper labors to enlist in the
3rd Colorado Cavalry, and he was present at the Sand Creek Massacre.
He served Bill Byers long and faithfully, and then in October 1870 sold
out to him to start his own job-printing business. Retiring in 1874,
Dailey dabbled in real estate, served three terms as treasurer of Arapahoe
County, gave a quarter century as a member of the school board, and
was president in 1893 of the city's first park board. Both he and Byers
long had been interested in civic beautification. Together they planted
trees along both sides of Broadway from Fifth to Jewell avenues, some
of which survived until a few years ago. A brother of Dailey's, William
M., also was a Colorado pioneer and an early rancher in Wyoming.[20]

Dailey was married twice. His first wife, Melissa Rounds of Chicago,
died in childbirth less than a year after he brought her to Denver as
a bride in 1866. Later he married Helen Emelia Manley, a young widow
who was a friend of his first wife and had taught school with her in
Chicago. Nellie Dailey was diminutive: five feet, eighty pounds. She
also was a very proper person, and didn't like her given name of Helen
because there was a "Hel" in it. Four children were born to the Daileys:
Anne, Lissie, Grace, and John L., Jr.

John Dailey died in Denver at seventy-four on January 3, 1908, a

[19]*The Palimpsest*, State Historical Society of Iowa, Iowa City, Vol. XXX, No. 9
(Sept. 1949), p. 284.

[20]L. G. Flannery, ed., *John Hunton's Diary: 1873–'75* (Lingle, Wyo., 1956),
p. 110.

quiet, conscientious man to the end.[21] Dailey Park at West Ellsworth Avenue and Cherokee Street is named for him. His son and his daughter Grace still live in Denver, and the old Dailey mansion at West Fourth Avenue and Broadway stands with some time-scarred dignity in a jungle of used-car lots.

[21]Biographical sketches occur in *Rocky Mountain News*, Jan. 4, 1908; Smiley, *History of Denver*, p. 659; Hall, op. cit., Vol. II, pp. 482–83, Vol. III, p. 137; Chapman Publishing Company, *Portrait and Biographical Record of Denver and Vicinity* (Chicago, 1898), pp. 296–97; Century Publishing and Engraving Company, *Encyclopedia of Biography of Colorado* (Chicago, 1901), pp. 437–38; Grace Dailey, typescript, Western Collection, Denver Public Library.

CHAPTER SIX

Boar Fights, Culture, and Bootblacks

J AMES TRUSLOW ADAMS has written that one of the negative contributions of the frontier to the American character was the loss of qualitative values in the quantitative. Size came to be the principal measure of success. "Bigger" was equated so directly with "better" that the popular catch phrase "bigger and better" became redundant.[1] The philosophy lingers in the credos of "service" clubs in every village that wants to be a town, every town on the way to becoming a city. "Boost, don't kick." Boosting is virtue, and criticism—since kickers and gobacks are a threat to physical growth—a sin. This overlay of moral and evaluative judgments on the dynamics of growth Adams saw as a legacy of the frontier; not just of the Rocky Mountain West, of course, but of the successive Wests, each in its turn a little farther out from tidewater than the West was yesterday. Pioneering was hard and often grubby work, and in the materialization of values to the lowest common denominator of growth-serving utility, culture "came to be considered [a] foolish ornament for those who were effeminate in taste and not up to a real man's work." Thus the frontier made leisure a sin also. With some assistance, Adams might have added, from the flinty New England Puritan conscience.

The distinguished historian asks his readers to observe that the first years of any new settlement are years of harsh toil, and historical perspective is achieved only at a cost of distance and disinterest. Growth and the winning of farms, mines, and cities from the wilderness represented the setting of a foundation upon which, eventually, a civilized life could rest. They also represented, in practical terms, survival. It could not often have crossed the minds of men actively engaged in the business of surviving that they might be debasing cultural values or erecting a structure of false virtues. *They* thought they were winning the West, a good and noble thing to do. (And they paused every now and then to preen themselves on it.)

The West's gunplay and violence, the reckless Indian wars, the greed, the pompous empire building, the mining kings romping with their whores, the sometimes pathetic strainings for culture and gentility, the

[1]*The Epic of America* (Boston, 1931), pp. 216ff.

moments of elegance rendered all the more striking by contrast and rarity—these things, in the long view, are not important. But they were important to the gun slingers and their victims, to the harried Arapahoes, the soiled doves and their diamond-bearing escorts, to tired, red-handed women who could remember how Sundays were in parlors "back home" on the other side of the Missouri. And certainly to a newspaper, which, above all else, must be contemporary.

The first years are harsh. They were for the *Rocky Mountain News*. They were also violent, scrabbling, vulgar, and touched with glory.

On October 6, 1859, for example, it was a matter of some importance to the *News* that a boar fight, with one hundred spectators, had occurred in the streets. In New York the *Ledger*—again to call into testimony that fascinating journal so unexplainably neglected by social historians —at about the same time was giving publication to the first story written for an American periodical by a promising English writer named Charles Dickens.[2]

Denver was not entirely a cultural desert of boar fights and three-card monte, however. The same issue of the *News* offered a critique on the town's first theatrical performance, October 3 in Apollo Hall. On the whole, it was stated, the performance was "excellent and unexceptionable." Had it not been for the miner in the back row who got roostered and interpolated a running commentary, the affair would have been entirely *recherché*. The *News* ended its theatrical review with a public spanking for the drunk: "We are sorry to say that the audience was somewhat disturbed . . . by a drunken man, who is hereby notified that a rigid police is established, and he and all such will be summarily ejected if good order is not kept."

The show offered Colonel C. B. Thorne, late of Leavenworth, and his company in the two-act play, *Cross of Gold; Or, The Maid of Croisay*. This was followed by *Maggie's by My Side*, described as a "favorite ballade" and sung by Miss Flora Wakely (local talent). "M'lle Haydee" then performed a "favorable dance," and the evening was rounded out with a "laughable farce" entitled *Two Gregories; Or, Luck in a Name*, the colonel himself in the role of John Bull. Tickets $1. Doors open 7 P.M., performance at 7:30. "Front seats reserved for the ladies."

The critic for the *News*—probably editor Byers—was rather more than kind. "Col. Thorne can hardly be excelled in any country and he is most ably supported by his company." Miss Wakely's singing was "excellent." Mlle. Haydee had "no superior" as a danseuse. "Our people," the *News* said, "are most fortunate in the establishment of a theatre at this time . . . to help the long winter months to pass pleasantly. We hope they will see to it that he [Colonel Thorne] receives the patronage he deserves. Performance every evening."

[2]The story was "Hunted Down." It began in the *Ledger* on Aug. 20, 1859.

Deplorable disturbances such as the *News* castigated apparently were not uncommon. Richardson tells in *Beyond the Mississippi* about attending the Apollo one night to see *La Tour de Nesle,* which he said was "performed not much worse than at our ordinary metropolitan theaters."

> . . . But the auditors were the real attraction. The entrance fee was a very moderate price for the amusement they afforded. Gaultier agonizingly asked concerning his murdered relative:
> "Where, O where is my brother?"
> A sepulchral voice from the midst of the house, answered:
> "I am thy brother!"
> The spectators supposed it a part of the play, but discovering that the response came from a favorite candidate for Congress greeted it with cheer after cheer.
> Queen Marguerite with due horror gave the exclamation:
> "Then I am lost indeed!"
> A miner, directly in front of the stage, responded emphatically:
> "You bet."
> The tragic death of Marigny, elicited from another spectator:
> "Well old fellow, so *you* are gone up too."
> And at the tragic close Gaultier, Marguerite and Buridan were greeted with:
> "Bound to have a big funeral, aren't you?"[3]

Apollo Hall had been built during the summer by the Barney brothers on the north side of Larimer Street between what are now Fourteenth and Fifteenth streets. It was a two-story frame building with the theater on the second floor. The ground floor was occupied by Harry Gunnell's billiard parlor and saloon, and the sound of clicking billiard balls, clinking glasses, and stag-at-eve songs floated unobstructed up an open stairway to compete with the dramatic presentations. The house accommodated three hundred and fifty persons on rough board benches, and a dozen candles did duty as footlights.

Whatever niceties of fixtures or deportment the Apollo lacked, it was a joy to editor Byers. Throughout his life he was an avid theatergoer. His diaries reveal that on his trips to New York he haunted the playhouses, often attending five plays on as many nights in orgies of drama not unlike those some Colorado tourists indulge in today when they visit Manhattan. (One of the most popular promotions of the contemporary *News* is the "Show Plane," a chartered air liner which whisks parties into New York for a week on Broadway.) Touring dramatic companies which came to Denver's early theaters nearly always could count on support from the *News,* and Byers had even proposed to open his own theater as a side line to his newspaper. The original minutes of the Auraria

[3]Richardson, op. cit., pp. 306–7.

Town Company in the archives of the Colorado State Historical Society show that on January 9, 1860, the "board received proposition from Byers & Co. to build a theatre building and asking for a donation." On January 16, Byers was given eight town lots "with the condition that Byers & Co. erect a theatre in Auraria." Byers did not build his theater, and presumably the lots were forfeited, but he never lost his enthusiasm for the drama. The theaters of Denver progressed in a few years from board benches and candle footlights to opera houses of onyx, mahogany, and plush, and a first night was not official unless Billy Byers sat in the dress circle.

A rustic theater was not the only indication that a foot-shuffling, self-conscious gentility was developing in the Denver of 1859–60. Woman was becoming less and less a natural curiosity, and with the calico and crinoline came the gentling harness for the basic unwashed instincts of the male. A party was held to open the Pollock House on July 9, 1859, and there were twenty-two ladies present, virtually the entire feminine population. "Social parties," the *News* commented on October 20, "are getting very frequent, and in fashionable display, sumptuous fare and unexceptionable [Byers was fond of the word] character, they cannot be excelled 'away down East.'" Taking advantage of the upsurge in high life, a pioneer merchant advertised in the paper that he had for sale collars and cuffs of enameled steel for more or less formal occasions when pistols were to be checked at the door and cut plug resolutely forsworn. A fancy autumn ball was held, and another on January 2 to greet the New Year 1860. The latter was, again, "unexceptionable." It was a "complete success" with "a large number of ladies" in attendance, "and the merry dance was prolonged until a late hour." The *News*—its editors were not yet out of their twenties—luxuriated in the new opportunities for feminine companionship and urged blissfully: "O ladies, do your d—ivinest."

The city's first wedding was given public notice in the *News* for October 20, 1859:

> MARRIED. In Auraria, K.T., on Sunday, the 16th inst., by Rev. G. W. Fisher, John B. Atkins, of Mt. Clemens, Mich., to Lydia B., eldest daughter of Col. Henry Allen.
>
> "The boys" acknowledge the receipt of a generous supply of cake, the handwork of the fair young bride, and the whole office join in best wishes for long life to the happy couple.
>
> This is the first marriage notice ever published in the Terr. of Jefferson.

Mrs. Byers founded a Ladies' Union Aid Society, and her husband was elected president of a chess club. A. E. Pierce, the city's first news dealer, started a circulating library with a ten-dollar packet of paper-bound books and on February 10, 1860, organized a public library, the

Denver City and Auraria Reading Room and Library Association. A levy of twenty-five cents a month was made on the one hundred members.

Meanwhile, during the summer, a major force toward the taming of the settlements arrived in town wearing a glossy plug hat, a broadcloth Prince Albert, and boiled shirt but driving an ox team with a regulation bull whip. Lavender gloves of fine kid protected his delicate white hands. A favorite local legend insists he was cussing his teams in Latin. The story is unverifiable but likely. Professor Owen J. Goldrick of County Sligo was a scholar of Latin, Greek, orthography, philosophy ("intellectual, moral and natural"), English grammar and composition, trigonometry, both plain and spherical, chemistry, physiology, astronomy and, the pecksniffs added regretfully, of good old Magnolia whiskey. He also was an exponent of literature on its loftiest and most empurpled planes. One of the most colorful figures in the story of early Denver, Owen Goldrick became the town's first schoolmaster, an editor of the *News*, and an unforgettable character. As a young man he wore his whiskers mutton-chop style, joined by a bushy mustache, and his erudition made a profound impression on the rough community. He was promptly awarded the affectionate and respectful lifelong title of "The Professor."

Despite the swath he cut and the debt owed to him by a village wholly untutored until he came, Goldrick has remained a shadowy if prominent figure in Denver history. In recent years an elementary school has been named for him, but the honors due him have been in large part denied. It is apparent that the dissipations of his youth—he was thirty when he made his spectacular entrance into Denver—offended the postured Victorian sensibilities of the late nineteenth century, when the city was selecting pioneers to be canonized as civic heroes. Denver was considerably awed by her "Professor" but also a little shocked by his eccentricities, and no one bothered to find out much about him.

It is not known, for example, where he acquired the learning which dazzled the settlements. For many years it was casually repeated that he was a graduate of Trinity College, Dublin, and later had studied at Columbia University. Neither institution, it finally was discovered, has any record that Goldrick was a student.[4] His birth date usually is given as 1833, but a letter written from Ireland by his father, Owen, Sr., on December 17, 1848, gives the date as March 31, 1829, and says the baptism occurred April 9.[5] The younger Owen probably came to America in the early 1840s, although one of his father's letters indicates the boy

[4]Harry M. Barrett, "Early Schools and Teachers," *University of Colorado Bulletin*, Vol. XXXV, No. 11 (Apr. 26, 1935), p. 38.

[5]Much new information on Goldrick has come to light in a collection of family letters of scattered dates now in the possession of his grand-niece, Mrs. L. G. Johnson of Hickory, North Carolina.

may have been shipped to this country in the custody of two older brothers as a lad of five or younger to escape the Irish famines and religious persecution. The elder Owen, a court functionary of some standing, boasted that he could "Talk with Judges with my Hat on after Salutation." Owen, Sr., had led his family into apostasy early in the century and suffered for it. He wrote a friend in America in 1834: ". . . My wife and I are of Roman Catholick Families, and about 30 years ago I met with a Bible by Stealth and saw nothing there for most of popish absurdities. I promulgated my Doubts. The priests attacked me as a Heretick from their Altars and said I went Contrary to 'The Council of Trent which ordained that no Laic should open a Bible' much worse Luthers . . . Bible—Sir I then protested openly against popery and 'all my House'—then we were much persecuted and most of all by our own friends and connections. Then I sent Wm. [the eldest son] to Explore America, and we all intended to follow after him. . . . Sir I beg to refer you to my sons, as to what popery in Ireland is."

Young Owen inherited much of his father's pride and bristling independence, along with a thirst for knowledge. Somehow he acquired at least the rudiments of a classical education, and both he and his brother James became schoolmasters. William was a physician in Reynoldsburgh, Ohio, where he early was hampered in his practice by strong feelings against Irish immigrants, particularly Protestant Irishmen, and often sought to persuade his brothers to go into the grocery business with him. A fourth brother, Patrick, apparently skidded into a life of drink and vice, went off to the Civil War, and never was heard from again.

The desire to teach runs deep in the Goldrick family. Relatives and collateral descendants—Owen, Jr., had no children—have served on the faculties of Ohio State, Illinois, and Hawaii universities and St. John's College in China, and in the public schools of Columbus, Ohio, and Indianapolis. Owen and James opened a "select school" in Middletown, Pennsylvania, in April 1848, and in 1850 Owen was teaching in Dodgeville, Wisconsin. There a delegation of Cornish roughs, suspicious of high-toned eggheads on principle, waited upon him one afternoon and beat him up. Three years later Owen was working as second bookkeeper and salesman in Cincinnati for the publishing and book wholesaling house of Moore, Anderson, Wilstach & Keys. Possibly remembering Cornishmen with sticks and fists, he wrote to James that he would "rather have my place here than 1000 $ at school teaching, by a long splice!" He was still in Cincinnati in 1855, but he went back to teaching.

Owen drifted on down the Ohio to St. Louis, where he met Joseph B. Doyle, a prosperous plains freighter who had a ranch and trading post on the Santa Fe Trail at Hermosilla in what is now Huerfano County, Colorado. Doyle persuaded the handsome and talented young Irishman to come west as private tutor to the Doyle children on the isolated ranch. S. T. Sopris, who knew Goldrick, wrote that the tutor soon "tired of the lack of excitement that prevailed in and around Hermosilla, and made his getaway via one of Doyle's ox trains. . . ."[6] J. B. Doyle & Company had opened a large storehouse in the summer of 1859 at Fifth and Ferry streets (now Eleventh and Larimer streets) in Auraria, and Goldrick came north as one of the bullwhackers in charge of a trainload of goods.

Goldrick's entry into Denver, sun glistening on the silk of his top hat, left a lasting impression, as did the cultural excitement he immediately began to stir up. In September he circulated a petition for a school in the two towns and obtained subscriptions of two hundred and fifty dollars in a few days. Then he put his card in the *Rocky Mountain News*, announcing that he would open a "Union School" on October 3. The *News* lent its weight to the enterprise under a headline, "Westward the Star of Education—as of Empire, Takes its Way."

> We hail it as another significant sign of our times and of our future, that a first class school under the charge of a competent professional teacher is already established among us. It is a maxim which for ages has stood the test of time, that popular education is the surest hand-maid to a people's welfare, and the cheapest safeguard of its society and liberty, coincident to a healthy civilization. Next to the Church of God, the school is the most useful institution, and the best wealth in any community, and particularly so in this country of ours.
>
> Please notice Card of Professor Goldrick in another column. We have read flattering notices of him as a gentleman and teacher.[7]

As a "local item", the *News* went on to comment: "Professor Goldrick is prepared to 'teach the young idea how to shoot.' Send your children to school."

The Union School opened with thirteen pupils—nine "whites," two Mexicans, and two Indian half-breeds. Professor Goldrick wrote to John D. Philbrick, superintendent of the Boston schools, asking his advice on textbooks. The noted educator was pleased to oblige and also extended fraternal greetings: "And now, imagine my arm extended with the speed of thought from the cradle of the free school on the Atlantic shores, over the Alleghanies, over the 'Father of Waters,' to give you a cordial greeting in your 'Union School' on the frontier of civilization at the foot of the Rocky Mountains." Goldrick was elected in 1861 to a two-year term as the first superintendent of schools in Arapahoe County. He also served as superintendent of schools for Boulder County, 1871–73.

There's a familiar, present-day ring to the *News'* "A Word to Parents" which appeared October 13 in further support of the new school:

[6] S. T. Sopris, "Some Early-Day Reminiscences," *Trail*, Vol. VII, No. 2 (July 1914), p. 5.

[7] *Rocky Mountain News*, Sept. 29, 1859.

Now that we have a good school in operation among us, with suitable furniture, black boards, etc., for the convenience of all grades of pupils, and gotten up by the teacher, individually, regardless of expense, we ask the special attention of parents to encourage the enterprise with their timely patronage. A school is not like a watch or clock, which you can start and then leave it, to go of itself. It is an organized living body. It has sensibilities and expenses, and it craves sympathy and support. Of all human institutions it is at once, the most useful, the most responsible, the most difficult, and the most delicate. It is a principle, that in judiciously educating the young; you serve them the most effectually possible not by what you do for them only, but by what you teach them and discipline them to do for themselves.

Founding Colorado's first school was not the only contribution of Professor Goldrick to the civilizing of the Far West. Denver in 1859 had a newspaper, several "hotels," a variety of business houses and was liberally supplied with brothels, saloons, and gambling hells, but it still had no church. So Goldrick pitched in with the Methodist missioners, the Rev. Jacob Adriance and the Rev. George W. Fisher, to start the first Sunday school in November. The professor also was a founding member of A. E. Pierce's subscription library and was in demand as a public orator on patriotic or cultural topics. He went on from there to become a newspaperman.

Late in the fall the professor was installed as the *News'* first reporter. His maiden writings appear in the paper dated November 17, and for the next five years he was the principal ornament of the staff, dividing his time between journalism and teaching. He also contributed frontier correspondence to the St. Louis *Democrat* under the *nom de plume* of "Observer." Not all of the items he sent east pleased the home folks, and specifically one dispatch offended the first Denver postmaster, W. P. McClure, a Southern duelist with a sensitive honor, who admired being called the "Little Thunderer" when he was in his cups. Richardson supplies the details:

> . . . The correspondent of the St. Louis *Democrat* excited the ire of one of Buchanan's shining appointees, the Denver postmaster. . . . One evening this functionary lured the journalist into the post-office; then closing the doors, with a cocked revolver at the head of the luckless scribe, he compelled him to write and sign a statement that he knew his published allegations to be false and slanderous when he made them.
>
> Under that influence which knows no law, the correspondent made this voluntary retraction. But the people took the matter in hand and after a fierce struggle, the postmaster, who was a man of wealth, and sustained by all the leading desperadoes, as his only means of escape from the gibbet, succumbed to the city government, and gave bonds to keep the peace.[8]

[8]Richardson, op. cit., pp. 305-6.

Smiley says McClure armed and entrenched himself in the post office and defied the authorities who went to arrest him on a charge of assaulting Goldrick with intent to kill. But the postmaster was "prominent and influential in the community" and he "practically dictated terms for settling the matter."[9] As will subsequently appear, the "Little Thunderer" met a fate at least proportionate to his arrogant affront to freedom of the press.

Goldrick was made city editor and finally associate editor of the *News* in 1864, but a year later he went to Salt Lake City to help edit the *Daily Union Vidette*, an experiment at gentile journalism in Brigham Young's stronghold. The Mormons, however, were less than receptive to such missionary work, and the *Vidette* folded in 1866, apparently with some bitter feelings. Byers wrote later that he understood that his former associate "was given a limited time to leave the territory." Returning to Colorado, the professor became co-editor with Henry Garbanati of the *Daily Colorado Times*, which made its bow December 1, 1866, in Black Hawk, one of the successor towns to Mountain City at the Gregory Diggings. The following April the *Times* moved a half mile up the cañon to Central City, where it expired in January 1868. Goldrick had withdrawn from the mountain daily in September 1867 and returned to Denver. On February 1, 1868, he established the second *Rocky Mountain Herald*, arbitrarily numbering it back to the founding of Thomas Gibson's *Herald* of 1860 although that paper had passed out of existence in 1864. The professor continued to edit his weekly *Herald* for the rest of his life, and for a short time in July and August of 1870 he attempted a daily edition. This proved too much, however, for a one-man operation, even when that man had the professor's flair for language. His *Herald* still is published regularly every Thursday in Denver, and it has become a unique sort of journal. Its interior is jammed with legal advertising and cuts of whalebone corsets or fire engines culled from ancient boiler-plate services. The front page is given over to the graceful and brilliant personal essays of Thomas Hornsby Ferril, the West's leading poet, some of which were gathered into the book *I Hate Thursday*. Tom's wife, Hellie, author of *The Indoor Bird-Watcher's Manual*, is editor of the *Herald*. She conducts a "Dumb Friend's League" with the aid of distinguished authors and industrialists as First, Second and Third Assistant Sea Serpent Editors and a noted educator as Limerick Editor. Regular correspondents of the modern *Herald* have included the late Bernard DeVoto, Robert Frost, and Carl Sandburg.

Although publishing a daily singlehanded taxed Goldrick's capacities, his production of longhand copy was prodigious even by comparison with the rapid work of typewriter-equipped rewrite men of the present day. A contemporary remembered him thus:

[9]Smiley, *History of Denver*, p. 348.

While on the News, Goldrick became sadly dissipated, seldom going to bed sober, or for that matter, seldom "hitting the hay" twice in the same room. He was known by everyone, and usually had no trouble in finding shelter any hour of the night. It became the regular thing in the office, when the city editor failed to show up by noon, for the boss to say "who will go and find Goldrick?" The News then was an evening paper, went to press at five o'clock, and Goldrick could output enough "copy" to fill his page in two or three hours, if he could be found in time.

Going to Chicago to secure material for the Herald, he met a middle-aged widow, a fine woman, and after a brief acquaintance, they were married, and now comes the surprising part of the story. From the time he met her until after her death, five or more years, Goldrick did not touch or taste liquor, and was one of the best behaved and best dressed men in Denver. It was one instance where a woman reformed a man by marrying him. As I remember it, he drank more or less after her death, and did not long survive her. . . .[10]

Denver's distinguished but dissipated professor died of pneumonia in a lonely rented room on November 25, 1882. Both in spite of and because of his handicap he left his mark on the city.

The town eventually got around to replacing his Sunday school with churches. The Methodists built one in the summer of 1860, and the Catholics completed theirs a few months later in time for a Christmas service conducted by the Rev. J. P. Machebeuf, the pioneer priest on whose life story Willa Cather drew for her *Death Comes for the Archbishop*. Professor Goldrick's Union School was the forerunner of the first public schools of 1862, though it was not until 1872 that Denver built its first schoolhouse, and the entire school system was suspended for a time in 1864 during the lean days of isolation brought about by the Civil War and Indian troubles on the plains. The war, however, was not permitted to impede planning for higher education. The *News* in May 1863 announced that proposals for a seminary were being considered. Among the twenty-six founding trustees, was, of course, editor Byers. Governor John Evans was elected president of the trustees, and Byers secretary and head of the building committee. Byers apparently handled his assignment with dispatch; for the *News* could report on September 10 that "the University building is being pushed forward rapidly and when finished will compare most favorably with any similar structure west of St. Louis." By Christmas a new bell was hung in the tower of the completed Colorado Seminary, now the University of Denver, at Fourteenth and Arapahoe streets across from the mansion of Governor Evans. The completion must have been a peculiar satisfaction for an editor who had received almost no formal schooling himself and was watching his town grow rapidly toward appointments and luxuries he had never

[10]Sopris, op. cit., pp. 6–7.

known. At thirty-two Byers, who had taught himself to read and write, was a founding father of a university.

But the task of city building was far from complete for Byers, and life in Denver fell a long way short of polish and grace, even allowing for the treble enthusiasms of seminarians. Three years later William Hepworth Dixon, an English cleric, paid the city a visit on his American grand tour. In his *New America*, Dixon is aghast at the murders, hangings, and gunplay. He found Denver a "wifeless town" and the men "swearing, fighting, drinking, like old Norse gods."

> Denver is a city of four thousand people, with ten or twelve streets laid out; with two hotels, a bank, a theatre, half a dozen chapels, fifty gambling houses and a hundred grog-shops. As you wander about these hot and dirty streets you seem to be walking in a city of demons. Every fifth house appears to be a bar, a whisky-shop, a lager-beer saloon; every tenth house appears to be either a brothel or a gambling house; very often both in one. In these horrible dens a man's life is of no more worth than a dog's. . . .[11]

Dixon's statistics may have been off—the very proper Jerome Smiley complained that the British visitor was a badly misguided observer as a consequence of falling in with the "wrong people"—but the over-all impression he conveys cannot have been too much exaggerated. The comforts and conveniences of life came slowly to Denver.

One of the first campaigns of the *News* was for so simple an asset as a bridge across Cherry Creek. Only a rickety footbridge spanned the stream, and wagon traffic was forced to wallow through a hundred yards of loose sand. "Cherry Creek needs a bridge," the *News* insisted on September 10, 1859, and "a few days work will build it." In a gross misestimate of the innocent-appearing rivulet which he may have remembered ruefully a few years later, Byers went on to advocate that a causeway of willows covered with stone and earth be laid down across the sandy bottoms and the few feet of meandering water. It was a successful campaign. Two months later, on November 17, the paper could report the bridge under construction, but it prodded the community onward in the realm of bridge building. "Why not the same at Blake and McGaw streets?"

Then there was the matter of mail service. In the beginning the nearest post office was at Fort Laramie, two hundred and twenty miles to the north, and the Pike's Peakers felt acutely their isolation in a wilderness not even the U.S. mails penetrated. Later, when the stage line started, there were loud complaints against the twenty-five-cents-a-letter charge for ferrying mail from the end of the federal postal lines in Leavenworth to the mouth of Cherry Creek. Moreover, some of the letters were

[11] William Hepworth Dixon, *New America* (Philadelphia, 1867), pp. 92, 96, 97.

tampered with and opened while in the hands of the express agents. A clamor, to which the *News* added its trumpets, went up for a genuine post office.

Cherry Creek had a nominal post office beginning in May of 1859. To complicate matters, it was named Coraville, although there was no settlement by that name in the Pike's Peak country. The *News* on May 7 reported that Washington had established Coraville post office and installed Mathias Snyder of Virginia as postmaster. There is no record of the source of the name Coraville, although a local legend says postmaster Snyder named it for his wife. A contract for a daily post to and from Coraville was announced, but it was never carried out, and the post office lasted only about two months. On June 9 the *News* carried a story of the appointment of Henry Allen as postmaster of Auraria, and a canceling device was immediately fashioned for him from *News* back-shop types. Allen made a contract with a Mr. Willis to carry mails to and from the Missouri River. Again the contractor failed to deliver, leaving the Auraria post office as stranded as Coraville had been.

Mail had been coming through since May 7, however, as private express matter on stages of the Leavenworth & Pike's Peak Company, which added a charge of twenty-five cents for each letter and ten cents for each newspaper. The Cherry Creek pioneers, who earlier in the year had been happy to pay a dollar a letter for mail brought down from Fort Laramie, soon decided the stage company's charges were exorbitant, and indignant letters filled the *News*. Denver City finally got its own post office in February 1860, and the "Little Thunderer," as has been noted, used it as fort and private jail for the squaring of personal scores with newspapermen. Denver remained a stagecoach town until the coming of the railroads in 1870, and although the various express companies eventually received government contracts which reduced postage rates to normal levels, the service often was disrupted by bad weather, Indians, or bankruptcy of the stage lines.

When editorial tirades failed to produce results William Byers tried his hand at improving mail service from the inside. He stepped in as postmaster for the consolidated towns late in 1864 and held the office, in addition to his many other duties and activities, until 1866. Later, when he had retired from his editorial career with the *News*, he began a second term as postmaster in 1879 and put into effect the first free home delivery of mail with a force of six carriers.

Byers' concern with the early mails was not, of course, unalloyed civic altruism. As publisher of probably the most remote newspaper in America he had a big stake in postal frequency and regularity. There was no telegraph line west of Fort Kearney in Nebraska, and the *News* depended upon Eastern exchanges for latest word about one of the key political campaigns in American history and the ominous rumblings of approaching war. Without Eastern papers to clip and copy, news coverage could not extend much beyond boar fights, chess clubs, and Sunday school sociables. The uncertainty of the mails forced the *News* into the very channels which make its old files an inexhaustible source of the important minutiae of local history, but the isolation rankled the news judgments of keen young men like Byers, Dailey, and Goldrick, who were acutely aware that they lived in exciting, newsworthy times.

Denver and its *News* also were wholly dependent on the long, exposed lines of plodding oxen which freighted supplies across the interminable plains. Rugged Murphy wagons, specially built in St. Louis for the prairie traffic, carried most of the essentials out to the new country. If, now and then, one of the wagons carried a piano or a box of books, the bulk of the cargo ran to the staples, the flour and the nails, needed by a town that was growing and building. Plains freighting reached enormous proportions in the boom days of 1859 and 1860. Trains of fifty wagons or more, one after another, came creaking up the Arkansas, the Platte, or the waterless Smoky Hill central route. The draft animals, between trips, grazed the prairie brown and bare in a huge circle around Denver. Slowly the nature of the things they brought assumed variety: window glass, steam boilers, tinned oysters, French champagnes and Havana cigars, lace parasols and New York frocks. The luxuries commanded almost any price sellers demanded, and they were beyond the means of most Pike's Peakers. For them, dress was plain and diet plainer. The average table was set with beans, bacon, and biscuits, wild game, tough beef slaughtered from worn-out oxen, a few home-grown vegetables in season, melons from the Arkansas Valley, and dried fruit. The *News* tried to be helpful with what today would be called kitchen hints. On September 3, 1859: "A small portion of sassafras bark mixed with dried fruit will keep it free from worms for years." On May 30, 1860, somewhat insistently: "Molasses made from the box elder trees on Clear Creek is fully equal to the product of the sugar maple."

Ox freight arrived slow and cost dear. Normally a train consisted of twenty-six wagons. Twenty-five of them carried three to four tons of cargo apiece; the twenty-sixth was loaded with camp equipment and in-transit supplies for the teamsters. Five or six yokes of oxen were assigned to each wagon. Such trains made the trip through from the Missouri in forty to sixty days, and it was no catch-as-catch-can business. Freighting lines were well-organized enterprises, trains departed on schedule, followed closely mapped routes, unloaded at specific terminal warehouses and, for a time, turned handsome profits for investors in the companies. One major line, Russell, Majors & Waddell, not only demanded strict obedience from its employees but also supervised their morals. Each man was required to swear a pledge: "While in the employ of Russell, Majors & Waddell, I agree not to use profane language, not to get drunk, not to treat animals cruelly, and not to do anything incompatible with the conduct of a gentleman." The vow must have been a sore trial to the innocent souls of mule skinners and bullwhackers.

Freight rates generally were six to ten cents a pound, although they sometimes soared to twenty, twenty-five, and forty cents. Moreover, the trains didn't always get through on schedule in times of bad roads, storms, or Indian wars, and the *News*, which depended upon them for supplies of newsprint, often was caught short. Some issues of the paper had to appear as half sheets, or smaller. An edition on brown wrapping paper already has been mentioned, and the *News* also used tissue paper and writing paper. Contemporary sources tell of issues on wallpaper, but none of these are known to have survived. Byers recalled one paper emergency during the Indian wars when he was forced to bring in newsprint by stagecoach express at a charge of a dollar a pound. Small wonder, then, that the *News* was beating the drum early for the transcontinental railroad and urging that it be routed through Colorado. A rail line up the Platte "would pay better than two-thirds of the roads in the States," the paper declared on November 24, 1859, and suddenly the rugged peaks, whose precipitous grandeurs the *News* on all other occasions extolled, flattened out and became no barrier at all to railroad construction. The paper hovered paternally over the several visits of old Jim Bridger as guide to survey crews seeking a slot in the mountains through which rails could be laid, but this was a campaign that failed. The railroad took the easy grade through Wyoming, and Denver and the *News* remained dependent on mule coaches and ox wagons.

The paper also was viewing with great interest any other means of transportation that presented itself.

Camels, for example. The *News* was hot on the story May 30, 1860, when word came from San Francisco that thirty dromedaries would arrive about midsummer to be used instead of oxen or mules for mountain express and freight commerce between California and Denver. The camels never reached the Rockies, though they did get a tryout in the desert Southwest.

Or boats. And here was another *News* campaign that failed. Nature refused to co-operate with Byers' determination to convert the Platte into a navigable stream and Denver into a river port. He began the campaign by starting to print "Shipping News," surely one of the most cheerful anomalies in American journalism. On September 10, 1859:

BOAT DEPARTURES. On Wednesday afternoon Scows "Ute" and "Cheyenne" for mouth of Platte. Scow "Arapahoe" for New Orleans. All ladened with passengers and freight.

On September 17:

BOAT DEPARTURE. Sailed, on the 14th, clipper "Pittsburg," Capt. J. Steiner, for Pittsburg, Pa.; eight passengers and their baggage. At St. Louis, boat and passengers will take steamer for final destination. Capt. Steiner thinks he will put a steamer on the Platte the coming season. Success attend him.

On October 6:

Boat "Empire State" sailed on Tuesday last for St. Joseph, Mo., with G. H. Washburn and N. C. Bartholomew as passengers, and their baggage, bound for Tompkins county, N. Y.

A month later, on November 3, Byers was still hammering away—and the Platte hadn't deepened by an inch. He reprinted, almost plaintively, an item from the St. Joseph *Journal* about the *Colona*, a "little Platte river steamer" which had arrived at the levee there. "She is the most complete little steamboat that has yet visited our wharf," the *Journal* said. "She is 100 feet long, about 25 feet wide, has one boiler, two engines and two shells and draws but 18 inches light. . . ." Out on the upper reaches of the South Platte, where shoal water is likely to be closer to eight than eighteen inches and the banks often have less than twenty-five feet between them, editor Byers insisted:

Should the spring and summer of 1860 prove as favorable for navigation on the Platte as has been the past, we shall expect to see, not only the "Colona," but half a dozen other steamboats as high up the Platte as this city. We have frequently traveled on steamers that could navigate the Platte, clear to the mountains, with ease.

No steamboat ever whistled for a landing at the Denver docks. Byers at last bowed to hydrology and shifted his promotional energies elsewhere.

On April 18, 1860, it already has been noted, the *News* told how three men had arrived from the States in a "combined wind wagon and hand car," a light wagon fitted out with sails to catch prairie breezes. There is no indication, however, that the *News* thought the device had practical large-scale application.

Byers was more convinced by the new overland steam machines, and urged on February 27, 1860, that they be employed to help bring out the seasonal emigration during the approaching spring. One of these already has been touched upon. A veritable behemoth among motorcars, it was built in eastern Nebraska by J. R. Brown at a cost of twelve thousand dollars. It had drive wheels ten feet tall with rims two feet wide, and it weighed twelve tons, about one fifth the weight of the locomotive of the day. Plans called for the "Prairie Motor" to haul a string of wagons behind it. It set out in July of 1862, made nine miles, and broke a vital crank. Brown died, Congress voted the Pacific Railroad, and the "Prairie

Motor" gathered dust on the Morton ranch. Its boiler eventually was put to use in the gas works at Nebraska City.[12]

Another hope exploded. Back to the mules and oxen—and attendant high cost of living. The *News* for August 20, 1859, listed the following current prices: flour from the States $14 to $15 per 100 pounds, Mexican flour $10 to $14, corn meal $12 per 100, bacon 30 cents a pound, sugar 25 cents, coffee 25 cents, salt 15 cents, beans 15 cents, onions 25 cents, potatoes 25 cents, rice 20 cents, butter 75 cents, cheese 35 to 50 cents, lard 50 cents, crackers 30 cents, bread 15 cents, fresh beef 10 cents, venison $1.00 per quarter, milk 10 to 15 cents a quart, molasses $3.00 a gallon, whiskey $3.00 a gallon, lumber $70 per 1000 feet, nails $20 per 100 pounds, window glass $10 to $12 a box. All these in the 1859 dollar, which commanded a value roughly three times that of the 1958 dollar. By autumn of 1859 flour was up to $40 a barrel, beans had gone to 75 cents a quart, coffee to 90 cents a pound, and eggs to $2.00 a dozen.

Somehow Denver settlers paid the prices or tightened their belts another notch and roughed it through. Or went home. Both in 1859 and 1860 countermigration in the fall and winter months carried the bulk of Colorado's highly mobile population back to the States. The general superintendent of the Hannibal & St. Joseph Railroad estimated that his line alone carried fifteen thousand Pike's Peakers on the first leg of their journeys west in 1859 and 1860, but on December 21, 1859, the *News* reported homeward-bound miners tumbling out of the hills at a rate of fifty to a hundred a day. The population of Denver dropped to not more than three thousand during the cold and cheerless winter of '59–'60. Only 690 men turned out to cast votes in the first city election, but the *News* said this was "not more than one-third of those in the corporate limits." Some heart could be taken, however, in the announcement Russell, Majors & Waddell gave to the New York *Tribune* that they were expecting to transport eighty thousand emigrants to Pike's Peak next season. The *News* on January 11 forecast the new rush for March but held its estimate of prospective arrivals to between ten and thirty thousand. It cautioned those planning to move west to "come prepared and not until April or May," and it warned: "So sure as there is such a rush, at such a season as was the last, we will again see a backward rush, and the old cry of 'humbug' will again ring in our ears." Still, it was "Ho for Pike's Peak!" in the *News* of January 25, and "the exodus from the States the coming spring will exceed anything of the kind ever before known in the world's history." By February 15 the new rush already had started, and the paper again cautioned the eager pilgrims to wait for better weather later. "We can only urge, as before, upon our readers in the States, to delay their departure until the season is more advanced; then come with a determination to remain and *work*, and they

[12]*Colorado Magazine*, Colorado State Historical Society, Denver, Vol. VIII, No. 1 (Jan. 1931), pp. 4 et seq.

will be abundantly repaid for their industry." Thomas W. Knox, who visited Denver later in 1860, estimated that there were seventy thousand arrivals in that year and placed Denver at 5000 inhabitants.[13] But the first territorial census of June 1861 found only 25,329 persons—not counting Indians—in the whole territory and 3500 in Denver. The census broke down to 18,136 males over twenty-one, 2622 males under twenty-one, 4484 females, all ages, and 89 Negroes. The News pronounced the census "incomplete" on July 17, 1861, and said there were a lot of people scattered around in the hills that the census takers hadn't caught up with. Nevertheless, nine years later the federal census of 1870 was unable to do much better and could locate only 4759 residents in Denver. The city's major growth would not begin until the railroads arrived.

If the Denver of 1859–60 was neither so large nor so grand as the News would have liked to make it appear, the town still was building at what seemed to be a furious pace. By December 28, 1859, the paper reported there was a great shortage of nails and glass, even at the fancy prices, and "paints are getting to be generally used." Many people went back east for the winters, some returned to their former homes so they could vote in the 1860 election, and patriots of both North and South marched across the plains to take up arms in the rebellion. During the Civil War years the nation almost forgot about the little city which had been hailed as the newest child of manifest destiny. But through the time when the nation's attention was diverted to its own survival Denver managed to eke out a slow and painful progress.

E. B. Sutherland opened the first drugstore; "a desideratum long wanted in this country," applauded the News on October 13, 1859. "Noisy Tom" Pollock, village blacksmith-hangman-marshal, found coal out near the foothills and began mining it for sale at a dollar a bushel. Down near Cañon City an "oil spring" was discovered and developed as the nation's second producing oil field. In its issue of February 26, 1863, the News acknowledged receipt of a sample of the oil. "It burns with a beautiful clear red flame and we inaugurate its use in Denver in writing this notice by its light." Arrival of another fluid, even earlier, also did much to cheer the office of the News. In November of 1859 Messrs. Solomon and Tascher opened their Rocky Mountain Brewery in Auraria, and the News on November 24 gave as its considered opinion that "this teutonic beverage will materially decrease the present consumption of strychnine whisky and Taos lightning."

Photographers were busy in and around Denver from the start, although far too few of their plates have survived. John Dailey's diary for September 20, 1859, records that a "picture taker [was] around taking a view of the office." The man under the black hood probably was James M. Burdick, Leavenworth ambrotypist, who was shooting scenes of the

[13]The Knickerbocker or New-York Monthly Magazine, Vol. LVIII, No. 2 (Aug. 1861), pp. 126, 128.

new country for exhibit in the States during the winter, according to the September 22 *News*. The first resident photographer was George Wakely—"a talented artist from Chicago," the *News* said October 20, 1859—who opened an ambrotype gallery on Larimer Street opposite Apollo Hall, where his wife and three daughters were performers.

Over on the west side of the Platte, still another town, Highland, was laid out in the late summer of 1859 on the bluffs overlooking the river. Secretary of the town company—William N. Byers. He published in the October 13 *News* a notice of a fifteen-dollar assessment on stockholders. There was horse racing as early as 1858 and a short-lived Jockey Club in 1861.[14] For pioneers with more conservative ideas about where their money should go, there were banks. In June 1860, George W. and Samuel Brown opened the first, and later the same month Turner & Hobbs started the second.[15] Neither survived. In the *News* of November 29, 1862, a notice appeared that Luther Kountze, a friend of Byers' in his Nebraska days, had arrived in town to open a branch of the Omaha banking firm of Kountze & Brothers. The Kountze bank on August 1, 1866, became the Colorado National Bank, still in business on "Scratch Lane" in Denver today.

Another bank and a mercantile firm, both pioneers of the sixties, also have lived to help Denver observe its centennial. The First National Bank had its beginnings on July 20, 1860, as Clark, Gruber & Company, bankers and minters of Pike's Peak gold into coins. Editor Byers of the *News* was invited to be present for the striking off of the first gold pieces.

> . . . In compliance with which invitation, we forthwith repaired to the elegant banking house of the above firm on the corner of McGaa [Market] and G [Sixteenth] streets, and were admitted to their coining room in the basement, where we found preparations almost complete for the issue of Pike's Peak coin. At four o'clock the machinery was put in motion, and "mint drops" of the value of $10 each began dropping into a tin pail with a most musical "chink." About a thousand dollars were turned out, at the rate of fifteen or twenty coins a minute, which was deemed satisfactory for the first experiment. . . .
>
> On the face [of the coins] is a representation of the Peak, its base surrounded by a forest of timber, and "Pike's Peak Gold" encircled the summit. Immediately under its face is the word "Denver" and beneath it "Ten D." On the reverse is the American Eagle, encircled by the name of the firm, "Clark, Gruber & Co.," and beneath it the date 1860.[16]

14Byers, Bancroft ms. L8 op. cit.

15Alonzo E. Ellsworth, "Early Denver Business," *The Denver Westerners' Brand Book: 1950* (Denver, 1951), p. 253.

16*Rocky Mountain News*, July 25, 1860.

The Clark, Gruber ten-dollar piece actually was some seventeen grains richer in gold than the federal coin of the same denomination. Later the private mint turned out twenty-, five-, and two-and-a-half-dollar coins, all now highly prized by numismatists. The Clark, Gruber mint was taken over in April 1863 by the federal government and became the Denver branch of the United States Mint, which today turns out nearly seventy-five per cent of the nation's coinage. The banking part of the firm continued as Clark & Company, which on May 10, 1865, evolved into the First National Bank of Denver, now resident of the city's newest and tallest building at Seventeenth and Welton streets. Two of Byers' personal friends were closely identified with the First National over the years: Dr. John Evans, second territorial governor, and David H. Moffat, Jr., who was present in 1858 when Byers received a load of buckshot in the shoulder for his pains as peacemaker in Omaha's shanty town.

The mercantile pioneer dates to October 6, 1864, when W. B. Daniels of Leavenworth walked into town beside an ox wagon loaded with dry goods and notions. It ended its independent life last year (1958) when it merged with the May Company, national department store chain which had its origins in a tent in early-day Leadville, Colorado. In the interval the Daniels & Fisher Stores Company was Denver's leading department store and gave the city its most striking landmark—a 330-foot replica, once cream-colored but now dingy with soot, of the sixteenth-century Campanile of St. Mark's in Venice. The famous Venetian bell tower has been remodeled considerably in restoration efforts of recent years, and travelers say the Denver building now remains a more faithful model of the original than the present remodeled Campanile itself. The tower at Sixteenth and Arapahoe streets was built in 1910–12, and for nearly half a century it dominated the relatively squat Denver sky line. It has now been topped by the 28-story, 365-foot First National Bank building. (The Statue of Liberty stands 152 feet, the Washington Monument 555, and the Empire State building 1250.) The store was "D&F's" to three generations of Denver residents, and its tower marked the hours with bell and clock, flashed news of the election of Taft, mounted Denver's first airport beacon, tempted numerous suicides from its observation deck, and wafted Christmas music over the downtown district. A *Rocky Mountain News* reporter of the 1890s, Charles MacAllister Willcox, was president of D&F's for thirty years until his retirement in 1929. When he became a merchant prince Willcox loved to tell the story of how, as a *News* police reporter, he invented the civic crisis of a woman who had swallowed a fistful of dynamite caps and was wandering about the city subject to explosion at the slightest jar. "Dynamite Dolly" had the town edgy for more than a week.

When Daniels & Fisher's was merged last year with the May Company deference was paid to honorable antiquity by giving the store which has become the center of the new Courthouse Square development the hyphenated name of "May-D&F." The May Company itself is a Colorado mercantile pioneer. David May, one of the thousands who came west seeking health, founded the firm in September 1877 in a tentlike shack in boomtown Leadville with a stock heavy on long red woolen underwear and miners' overalls.[17] The May Company moved to Denver in 1880 and since has grown into a nationwide operation with thirty-five stores in eight major cities from Baltimore to Los Angeles. The vacated D&F campanile has been renamed the Allen Tower and is being converted into a merchandise mart for wholesalers and brokers.

In the year of D&F's founding Denver was still wild enough that an antelope could be shot on Larimer Street well within the corporation limits. But the wilderness was giving way. The *News* found it necessary to editorialize at an early date on the subjects "Don't Kill the Birds" and "Save the Trees." Denver soon became far too citified for Jim Beckwourth, the mulatto mountain man and honorary chief of the Crows. Jim stopped by for the winter of 1859–60 and told the *News* he felt like prosecuting the settlers for "building cities on his old hunting grounds."[18] Byers was responsive to the protest, even though he was con-ductor of the chorus which called for a bigger and better town, more and more settlers and miners. He, too, had known the West when it was un-spoiled and lonely, and there was much of the nature lover in him. Pleas for songbirds and against wanton destruction of forests were in character. Between the pages of his pocket diaries he often pressed mountain wild flowers, and they can be found there today, fragile, brown, and telling of the man.

Byers had his farm a few miles up the Platte. He planted fruit trees and grapevines there, the first to be brought into the country. Byers organized the Colorado State Forestry Association, and around the "Kenneth Square" mansion he later built at 171 South Washington Street, he planted thirty-five species of trees not native to Colorado. Some of them survive and are used by nature-study classes of Byers Junior High School, which now occupies the site. The young editor was a founder of Colorado's first agriculture society and served as its secre-tary.[19] His *News* consistently lent its support to every movement for agricultural development by crop diversification, irrigation, experi-mental work, or the training of young farmers and foresters in the agricultural college to be established at Fort Collins. Alvin T. Steinel, the historian of Colorado agriculture, credits an editorial in the *News*

[17]Ida Libert Uchill, *Pioneers, Peddlers and Tsadikim* (Denver, 1957), pp. 98–99.

[18]*Rocky Mountain News*, Dec. 1, 1859.

[19]Ibid., Apr. 2, 1860.

for November 3, 1866, with setting in motion the idea of raising sugar beets, now one of the state's major cash crops, on the desert.[20] Byers also was in on the beginning of wheat farming in Colorado. The *News* of October 27, 1859, told of what happened to a single grain accidentally seeded in the corn plot of a Denver garden:

> Mr. McClure has shown us one hundred and forty-eight grains of wheat, the yield of two heads, grown in the gardens of the Messrs. Parkison, in Denver City. The grains are very large, fully one-third larger than the best we ever saw in the eastern states, and fully equal in size and weight to the famous wheat of California and Oregon. We have not a doubt that millions of acres of our plains and mountain valleys will produce wheat that for quantity and quality, the world cannot excel.

The questing eye of the busy editor watched field and garden as well as mountain and mine. Up in the hills the miners were running into difficulties. Placer mining passed its peak by 1860. The gold seekers turned to tunnel and drift mining, which was slower and required a heavier investment in machinery for refining and milling the ores. Moreover, the ores themselves were beginning to prove refractory in yielding up their treasure. Assays proved the gold was there, but the refining methods then in use were not recovering it in full measure. During the years 1858–70 the Colorado mines produced more than thirty-three million dollars in gold, but production dropped in the following decade to twenty-eight million. Finally smelting methods were developed for the complex Colorado ores, which usually contained silver, copper, lead, and zinc in addition to gold. Gold production then climbed steadily to hit its high mark of two hundred and thirty-five million in the first decade of the twentieth century.

Meantime, however, a new bonanza was hit. The white metal, silver, had been principally an annoyance to the gold miners because it complicated refining. Now it was being sought for its own sake. The *News* reported the first major silver discovery, the Belmont Lode, in September 1864. Within a few years silver produced the new towns of Georgetown, Silver Plume (where the first power rock drill was developed in 1869), Creede, Aspen, Leadville, and Caribou (producer of the silver bricks over which President Grant walked to the Teller House in Central City on his 1880 visit). For thirty years Colorado silver was more lucrative than Colorado gold. It created many of the rich-overnight mining kings. Silver, probably more than any other single factor, finally brought wealth to Denver, glistening carriages to her tree-lined avenues, and many-

[20]Alvin T. Steinel, *History of Agriculture in Colorado* (Fort Collins, 1926) pp. 281–84, 288, 292.

gabled mansions to Brown's Bluff overlooking what had been a sordid, dusty frontier village.

But the reign of the silver kings was still in the future when Byers sang out in the *News* of June 27, 1864, to herald another rung gained in the climb up the ladder of municipal advancement:

> A shoe blacking shop was started here on Saturday. The city is finished and the country is safe!

CHAPTER SEVEN

The Editor Is Kidnaped

I T WAS still a rough country: new, brash, ungentled. Perils of man and nature lay in wait, and a high-pitched note of primal violence carries through accounts of the early years like the sound of a file grating on saw teeth.

A man's body had been found on the west side of South Park, the *News* said. His left leg was "broken below the knee, by a pistol shot, evidently his own, as a pistol lay by his side with one barrel bursted. The broken leg had been bound up and put in a box, which had been taken off, and he had commenced cutting off the leg with a razor, which still remained in the wound. . . ."[1]

Some of the names on the land are eloquent. Dead Men's Gulch and Skull Creek. Troublesome. Stringtown. Greenhorn. Cripple, Disappointment, and Mad creeks. Gouge Eye Gulch. River of the Lost Souls. Cannibal Plateau and Last Chance.[2]

In Denver there was a breed of men to whom knives in the dark represented a proper answer to insults. John Rooker arrived in '58. He built one of the first houses in Auraria, and his mother was one of the town's first white women. Jack O'Neill came a little later. Byers says he was a sporting man and came from Utah with a woman named Salt Lake Kate. Probably O'Neill was Kate's fancy man, since Jerome Smiley concedes he was "somewhat notorious" and "very conspicuous." Difficulties arose between Rooker and O'Neill, and Jack proposed they settle them with bowie knives, locked together in a dark room, only the winner to come out. Rooker declined. O'Neill denounced him for a coward, appending comments on his parentage and the virtue of his mother and sister. So Rooker went home, got his rifle, and shot O'Neill dead in the streets of Auraria on March 30, 1860. In his account of the affair Byers adds that "no notice was taken of the murder." Killings, too, were at times "unexceptionable."

Knives, rifles, pistols, and also scalp dances. Fresh scalps, they were, and proudly shown with war paint and whooping in the streets at the doorstep of the *News*. In May of 1860 an Arapaho war party returned to

[1] *Rocky Mountain News*, Sept. 29, 1859.

[2] See J. Frank Dawson, *Place Names in Colorado* (Denver, 1954).

Denver with four Ute scalps and fifty horses. The warriors staged a big victory scalp dance in the western hills, now North Denver, where a thousand of the tribesmen under Chief Little Raven were camped. Several times the Indians proudly brought their trophies down into the principal streets of the settlement and danced before hundreds of curious spectators.

A month later, however, there was a turn in the tide of the savage wars. On June 10 a large number of Arapahoes, some Sioux, and other Plains Indians (Byers says there were Apaches present, but it seems scarcely likely) assembled at Denver and again organized an expedition against the mountain-dwelling Utes. Jim Beckwourth and Kit Carson, in town as agent for the Utes, sought to dissuade them, but the braves set out anyway. They found a Ute village in South Park, the beautiful Bayou Salade of the fur traders, and attacked it. But the Utes followed up with a counterattack, disastrously defeated the invaders from the prairies, and sent them retreating back to Denver. The crestfallen war party returned with five dead and thirty-two wounded. A few days later another party made a foray into the mountains, found Utes, and stampeded back to camp on Blake Street in the heart of town. There were Utes behind every rock and bush, they said. Great numbers of them, and carrying the war pipe. Denver had the jitters for a week.

As late as 1873 and 1874, Denver was still being treated to scalp dancing, and on these occasions it was the Utes who wanted to show off *coups* to the white man. A special Ute agency had been established in Denver in 1871 with James B. Thompson as agent. Thompson was well liked by his charges, but he stoutly disapproved of their plans for a scalp dance on July 12, 1873, through the now much more metropolitan Denver streets. The Utes went ahead with their plans anyway. It didn't rate as much of a celebration; there was just one lone scalp to be hymned. It had been lifted two days earlier from an Arapaho in a clash on the Denver outskirts which was really more a gang fight than a battle. But by this time wild Indians were beginning to be a civic attraction. They could be shown off profitably to Eastern visitors. U. M. Curtis, agency interpreter, seized upon the incident to line his pockets. He put up a big circus tent and planned to charge admission to see the "scalp dance." Piah's band of Utes was persuaded to stalk the streets daily for a week in war attire to advertise the show, and a brass band was added as a touch of promotional genius. Thompson met the first parade in the street in front of his office and broke it up in a sulphurous exchange of profanity with Curtis. The *News* spent two and a quarter columns telling about it on July 16 under the headline, "The Ute Circus; Thompson Checkmates Curtis' Indian Menagerie," and Thompson fired off a report to the Commissioner of Indian Affairs bragging that he had acted "firmly and fearlessly" in putting down "what I think would have been for this enlightened age and community a disgusting spectacle, and what

I feared most of all, might have fostered enmity between the tribes: resulted in serious disturbances in our streets and increased the chances of visits to our settlements from war parties of Plains Indians."[3]

In the summer of the following year, however, about two hundred Utes were back in Denver with three fresh scalps which they said they had taken on a raid against Sioux and Cheyennes out on the plains. Plans were announced for several nights of celebration, spectators welcome, no charge. More than a thousand persons journeyed out to Sloan's Lake, now a municipal sailboating center, to see the show. Among the ladies present were Mrs. William N. Byers and her sister, wife of W. R. Thomas, then associate editor of the *News*. Chauncey Thomas wrote later of what his mother told him:

> . . . She says they [the Utes] had a rope circle, perhaps seventy-five to one hundred feet in diameter, the Indians standing outside of it, each holding the rope with both hands, waving it up and down, hopping up and down themselves, grunting, and sometimes yelling, but not circling; perhaps two hundred of them, both male and female, but no children holding the rope.
>
> Inside this rope circle were three very old squaws, dirty, repulsive old hags, each holding aloft a long pole, and on the tip of each pole was a fresh scalp, stretched to about the size of a dinner plate, and these old women were crow-hopping in characteristic fashion around inside the rope circle, chanting gutterally [sic]. . . .[4]

Next day, the Utes becoming more and more frantic, the mayor stepped in and ended the ceremony.

Although their wives had been in the gaping audience the editors of the *News* voiced disapproval. On July 15 the paper said:

> The Utes, with the pious Piah at their head, held a scalp dance, last evening, near Sloan's Lake, over three bloody Cheyenne topknots, which dangled from three poles. The barbarous scene was witnessed by a crowd of at least five hundred people, many of them ladies. The dance opened at 5 o'clock and was kept up until far into the night.

The following day the *News* continued:

> The Utes resumed their hilarious scalp dance at early candle light last evening. Rolling carriages raised a dust between the city and the camp from five to ten o'clock. The crowd was large and heterogeneous— which is a big word. It was disgusting to notice, among the spectators, lots of ladies, prominent in church and society circles, straining for a

[3]James W. Covington, "Ute Scalp Dance in Denver," *Colorado Magazine*, Vol. XXX, No. 2 (Apr. 1953), pp. 119–24.

[4]Chauncey Thomas, "Last Scalp Dance in Denver," ms., 1936, Colorado State Historical Society.

sight of the reeking scalps, which they scanned as eagerly as if they had been new bonnets. Next Sunday these ladies will be railing at THE NEWS for disseminating reading matter that is calculated to vitiate the public taste.

Throughout the early years, and particularly in 1859 and 1860, Indian lodges were a familiar sight on the fringes of the town. The bottoms had been a favored stopping place for a long time, and the Arapahoes and Utes, at least to this point, saw no reason to avoid them now that they contained a paleface settlement. In fact there was a special appeal about this civilization being thrust upon them. It came in bottles. Both the *News* and some of the Indians early recognized a peril. The paper was less than two months old on June 18 when it sounded out a

> CAUTION. On Wednesday night last, two individuals, who are well known, busied themselves by furnishing whisky to some of the Indians camped in town. We give them notice that there is a Vigilance Committee of long standing, still in existence here, which is pledged to lynch any man found engaged in giving or selling liquor to the Indians, and thus endangering the safety of the settlers. Once more, gents, and you will see the operation of the people's prohibitory law.

Richardson remembered that the Arapahoes visiting Denver were ordinarily peaceful but could be dangerous when drunk. "One evening," he writes, "I saw a brawny brave, with a club thwack two of his drunken brethren upon their heads, so lustily that the blows were heard a quarter of a mile away. Then musing for some minutes, he solemnly ejaculated: 'Whisky—bad! Make Indian bad.' After which bit of wisdom he walked thoughtfully away. In ten minutes however, he returned with a bottle and a silver dollar and begged me to buy whisky for *him*. Like Hosea Bigelow he was 'in favor of the Maine Law, but agin' its enforcement.'"[5]

The pages of the *News* through the first years fail to record, however, a single instance in which the Indian, drunken or not, lived up to his dangerous reputation around town. Denver, although it titillated itself with numerous scares, never suffered an Indian attack, exposed as it was in its youth. In town the red man might put on fascinatingly barbaric ceremonials such as scalp dances, and he could be a nuisance with his drinking, begging, and thieving, but he quite evidently comported himself better than some of the whites. And he did not escape their tender mercies. The *News* for April 18, 1860, carried an indignant letter from Jim Beckwourth:

> Editor News.—Justice to the Indian—an article they seldom obtain— and security to my fellow citizens, compel me to seek your columns to redress one of the grossest outrages ever perpetrated in this, or any

[5]Richardson, op. cit., p. 189.

other country; and I am charitable enough to believe that a majority of the whites would assist in punishing severely the perpetrators were they known.

On Saturday last [April 14] a band of Cheyenne and Appache Indians visited our city, in compliance with a promise made to me in January last. . . .

On their arrival they called upon me in a body, requesting me to show them a camping place—I done so. After dark a lot of *drunken devils* and "bummers" went to the lodges, took the Indian women and girls forcibly out, committing acts of violence, which in any other country would condemn the perpetrators to ignominy and shame; age was not respected—the gray hairs of John Poisel's old Indian wife could not protect her; she was taken from her husband's side in bed; but before they succeeded in their hellish work, crippled as he is, [he] compelled them, by threats with his pistol, to release her. The same night three mules were stolen from the Indians, taken off some ten miles and fettered; but the thieves could not *steal the trail*; the red man found his mules, and on Sunday morning came to me with their complaints. . . .

They left here on Sunday morning to deliberate in council, as to the course they ought to pursue. I asked them to make no definite conclusion until I had a talk with the whites, when I am to meet them in council and report, if the white men of Denver tolerate such inhuman and ungrateful conduct.

The Indians are as keenly sensible to acts of injustice, as they are tenacious of revenge, and it is more humiliating to them to be the recipients of such treatment *upon their own lands*, which they have been deprived of, their game driven off and they made to suffer by hunger, and when they pay us a visit, abused more than dogs. My advice is, that municipal regulations be made, preventing the sale of intoxicating drinks to them, with such penalties as would make the law respected. And all emigrants who are on their way here, ought to, most religiously, refrain from giving Indians whisky, or trading it to them for their horses, for if he sells his pony, he will steal one from the next white man that comes along. All our Indian troubles are produced by the imprudent acts of unprincipled white men. . . .

Jim was in a position to give advice. He had lived with the Indians for more than forty years, was an adopted brother of the Crows, and as their honorary war chief had led them in battles with the Blackfeet.

In the same issue the *News* took up the cry with an editorial entitled "Lo the Poor Indian" (using the phrase, for once, without ironical inflection):

We earnestly invite the attention of our citizens to the communication, to be found in our columns, from Capt. Beckwourth, in reference to the outrage committed upon the Indians lately encamped in our city for the purpose of peaceful trade. . . .

We hope the suggestions contained in the Capt.'s letter will be heeded. . . . Cannot some public expression of our municipal authorities or of the people be had, condemning the outrage, so that Capt. Beckwourth may bear to them such redress as it is in our power to make? . . .

A public meeting was called for Apollo Hall on April 20, and, Yankee fashion, it selected a five-man investigation committee. The committee left the matter in the hands of Beckwourth, who reported to a second meeting on April 27 that he had been able to identify only one of the rapists, Phil Gardner. This was probably the ne'er-do-well known generally, without explanation, as "Big Phil the Cannibal." Gardner once had brought the mail in from Fort Laramie at a dollar a letter before stage service started. Otherwise there seems to be no record that he was distinguished for civic benefactions. Smiley characterizes him as "a low character and loafer" and dismisses him as "of no particular value." Phil departed Denver abruptly a little after the Indian outrage, dodging two pot shots from a drunken friend.

No action was taken against Gardner, but the second indignation meeting drew up two resolutions. It was unanimously resolved "that we condemn the outrages lately perpetrated upon our Indian brethren, and pledge ourselves to bring to punishment the guilty parties if any further insults are offered them of that character" and "that the citizens of Denver entertain the Indian hospitably upon their visits to our city for purpose of trade." The *News* published the resolutions and a report of the meeting and, like the rest of Denver, promptly forgot about the whole affair.

Jim Beckwourth lived in and around Denver for about seven years, beginning in 1859, and he and Byers became well acquainted. The young editor, when he met the celebrated mountain man, had expected a "rough, illiterate back-woodsman" but found him "a polished gentleman, possessing a fund of general information which few can boast."[6] During 1859-60, Beckwourth was employed as a storekeeper by A. P. Vasquez, nephew of Louis Vasquez, an old friend of the fur trails. Later Jim took up a ranch on the South Platte, south of the Byers place. There he built a cabin which became headquarters for visiting Indian friends and the few aging mountain men who still passed by. Byers' attorney, Lewis B. France, defended Beckwourth when he killed William ("Nigger Bill") Payne in 1864 for attempting to steal a ring from the finger of Mrs. Beckwourth, always referred to by the old trapper as "my wife, Lady Beckwourth."[7]

[6]*Rocky Mountain News*, Dec. 1, 1859.

[7]For a full account of Beckwourth's Denver years see Nolie Mumey, *James Pierson Beckwourth: An Enigmatic Figure of the West* (Denver, 1957).

As a neighbor, Beckwourth paid frequent calls on the Byers family, and the first of these caused some flutters for Elizabeth Byers. Jim was a mulatto, and dark. Mrs. Byers came from Iowa but there was Virginia in her background, she insisted.

Elizabeth M. Byers was the spunky duchess type, and the personality revealed by her surviving letters and papers is not an attractive one at this distance. She had to have a proper carriage when she paraded to the fair and threw a pet when the one the livery sent was not up to her station. She flounced around a great deal. The low quality and bad habits of maids and cooks gave her much trouble, and none of them stayed long in the Byers household. When her daughter Mollie lost a baby Mrs. Byers sought to cheer her by lugubrious warnings that she would "go insane of morbid grief" if she didn't straighten up. Then, for years, she would remind Mollie in letters of how sweet the child had been and how, just that day, she had been to the cemetery to strew flowers on "the dear little grave." Mrs. Byers enjoyed a poor health which required protracted journeys back home to Iowa, and later to Cape Cod, Pasadena, or Florida. She outlived her husband by nearly twenty years. Like many another Victorian wife with a busy and prominent husband, Elizabeth Byers flung herself, clucking, into good works and affairs of her church, but always self-consciously and always with a careful appraisal of honors and prerogatives due. As she grew older her role as a Denver pioneer noticeably enlarged, a circumstance not rare among first settlers. She began to describe herself as the eighth white woman in town, a calculation which was off by several score petticoats. But by her own standards, and perhaps by the standards of her day, Elizabeth Byers was a good woman. She founded and endowed the Byers Home for Boys, gave liberally to the Methodist Church, and always attended funerals punctually. She had a far better business head than her often financially embarrassed husband, and she stood by him through a scandal that would have sent most wives packing off home to mother permanently.

Elizabeth gushed a lot about her "nice silver" and "nappery" and how she "never lived a pioneer life without having artistic things about me," and she left this record of how it was when a mulatto mountain man in fringed buckskins came to call:

> . . . But when our guests arrived and I found that one of them, Jim Beckwith, was a colored man, my aristocratic Virginia blood rather boiled, because I hadn't been used to sitting at a table with a colored man, and I hardly knew what to do, but almost instantly decided that there was but one thing to do and that was to ignore it altogether and treat them all alike, which I did.[8]

[8]Typescript, Byers papers, Western History Collection, Denver Public Library.

Elizabeth Byers survived her social crisis as Denver survived its mis-treatment of Jim Beckwourth's friends the Indians. The Arapahoes and Utes drifted back to be cheated again by Denver traders and primed again with rotgut whiskey. They pilfered the clotheslines of unwary housewives and appeared suddenly, and frighteningly, at back doors to demand biscuits and sugar. The years when, finally, they would kill and plunder were still ahead.

Nor were the Indians the only ones who indulged in petty thievery. It became a popular art, and the *News*, struggling along on short rations, was among the victims. During the fall of 1859 the two Cherry Creek villages experienced a crime wave. Cattle were stolen and butchered. Someone tapped the till at Reed's saloon for six hundred dollars in gold and silver. Two yokes of oxen and a wagon were stolen in Boulder City, brought to Denver, posted as gambling collateral, and lost. The *News* gave warning on September 17 that "the light fingered gentry had better look out, or some of them will be suddenly called upon to perform upon a tight rope in a style differing essentially from the celebrated Blondin. 'Honesty is the best policy'—gentlemen—a timely precaution may save your lives. . . ." The good advice came to nought, however, and the *News* itself was hit where it hurt most, in the larder. Byers unlimbered on December 21:

> Some unprincipled scamp, not having the fear of our devil,[9] and the city dads before his eyes, has got in the habit of milking our cow—that same old brindle one, whose milk we depend upon to lubricate our mush and flavor our coffee. The thief perhaps does not know how near starvation this brings us, and we would like to have him call and talk the matter over.
>
> That same fellow, or his brother, has been stealing our wood from the door, after it was cut and prepared for the stove. Our devil, we notice, has for a few days been experimenting with gunpowder to see just how much, inserted carefully in a stick of wood, will be necessary to elevate a medium sized shanty. We assure you his experiments are very interesting, and, if carried into practical effect, must tell on the prospects of somebody's wood pile.

The situation had deteriorated by January 18:

SPECIAL NOTICE.

To the semblance of a man who stole our venison hams:

You miserable, mean, contemptible, thieving scoundrel, you are hereby notified that on Saturday morning last—the morning succeed-ing the disappearance of our last venison ham—we said to our devil, "prepare for war!"—an order which was music to his ear; and such a

[9]The *News'* first printers' devil was George Collier.

war, too: just equal to his former experience; he having maintained, for over two years, a war of extermination against wolves, skunks, prairie-dogs, rattle-snakes and long-tailed swifts, that inhabit the sandhills just below Fremont's Orchard. . . .

Advertising and subscription revenues apparently were as slim as the editor's diet. On October 27, 1859, Byers made a bold editorial demand for advertising support. He pointed out that there were "now a number of houses doing business exceeding $50,000 a year and several of them more than three times that amount." They were not supporting the *News* with advertising to match. "Our subscription list, too, is exceedingly small for a community of 4000 persons; it should be increased at least 300 immediately." In another column Byers issued a flat "Last Call" and, "in view of the circumstances, and our urgent necessity for money," published the names of nine men who owed two dollars to two-fifty for subscriptions. "[To be continued Semi-Occasionally]" the list concluded in fair warning to those who didn't want to be posted for bad debts.

A week later, on November 3, there was an editorial entitled ominously, "Debtors":

We have done a large amount of work since we set up our press here, for which we have received no pay. A considerable number of our friends owe us for job-work; which should have been paid long ago. In May last, we printed an "Address to the people of Jefferson", to gratify the ambition of certain political aspirants. We did the work for less than half the price, we took a due bill for the amount which was promised to be paid in two or three days. Not a dime of it has ever blessed our sight, yet it is less than one dollar for each signer of the note. Practically the same thing happened in printing the "Constitution."

Recently a County ticket (20,000 Election Tickets) was wanted, in rushed two gentlemen and ordered two thousand tickets printed immediately. "Well, what about the pay?" we ventured to ask. "Oh, we will collect it tomorrow, or if we do not, we will pay it ourselves."

We done the work; but the first cent of pay has yet to greet our eyes.

Now, gentlemen, one and all, who are indebted to us on old scores, with all due deference to your feelings, we want our pay.

We cannot afford to haul our press and office here, pay freight bills ranging from ten to sixty cents a pound for paper and ink; pay office rent, compositors; work for nothing and board ourselves: just to tickle your vanity, to display your name in print, to help you to a fat office, to enhance your property in value, nor to furnish you a paper just for the honor of doing it.

We want each and all of you to call on us without delay, settle up your accounts—pay us money if you can—some thing else, if you cannot pay money—or if you can do neither, let us know when you can pay, so that we may know what to depend on.

We want to pay our debts, and to do so we must collect our dues; peac[e]ably if we can, forcibly if we must.

The plain talk seems reasonable enough. But all it brought Byers was a challenge to pistols for two.

Denver had in these days a number of Southerners who carried themselves as gentlemen and boasted of a taste for cold bourbon, hot blood, and jealous honor. The McClure-Whitsitt duel has been mentioned. Byers had denounced it as "another stain cast upon the name of our fair young city, to be taken up and enlarged upon by the correspondents of the Eastern press."

Among the names of the delinquent debtors the News now published was that of a friend of Thomas Warren, pioneer ferryman and brickmaker, and a Southerner. Warren took offense and sent a challenge to Byers. The editor replied in the News for November 24:

> . . . To any who may feel like calling us out, we have only to remark that you will only waste your time in inditing and sending us challenges, or other belligerant espistoles. You may murder us, but never on the so-called field of honor under the dignified name of a duel. . . .
>
> While we do live and conduct a public press, it shall be free and unfettered, fearless to rebuke the wrong and uphold the right. . . .

Duels, Byers said, were a "relict of barbarism which has descended to us from the dark ages." Moreover, and getting very practical about the matter, he admitted that "our right arm is almost powerless from the effect of an unfortunate gun-shot" (the shotgun blast he had received in Omaha a year earlier).

Byers does not seem to have educated his community out of its barbarous ways, however. The following March prides again became ruffled, this time fatally. L. W. Bliss, secretary of the Territory of Jefferson, was an ardent anti-slavery man. In a patriotic toast at an assemblage of leading citizens in the Pacific House he dropped some remarks which Dr. J. S. Stone, Dixie-born judge of the miners' court at Mountain City, construed to be both personal and offensive. They wrangled, and a glass of wine was dashed in Dr. Stone's face. This was too much. The doctor challenged on the spot. The duel was fought March 7. Bliss chose shotguns loaded with ball at a distance of thirty paces. Dr. Stone fell mortally wounded with the first shot.

Denver was less than two years old and had a population certainly not exceeding 4000 persons. But the 4000, plus itinerants, had managed to chalk up the rather startling record of fifteen murders (one by ax, another by butcher knife, and the remainder prosaic shootings), two duels (plus one that misfired), innumerable acts of mayhem of ingenious variety (one man had his ear bitten off in a catch-as-catch-can competition, another lost the tip of his nose), and assorted thievery which carried off everything that could be lifted. For some reason armed robbery does not seem to have been a problem. At that, the secret vigilantes—Denver called hers the Committee of Safety—were kept busy enough. Byers appears to have been a member of the committee, possibly even one of its organizers; his moral code outlawed duels as barbaric, but a little indignant lynching was no more than the duty of any right-minded and public-spirited citizen.

Much has been made of the West's vigilantes as inevitable improvisations in the absence of other means to law and order and as effective deterrents to homicide and horse stealing. Inevitable they certainly proved to be; for they appeared in one form or another in nearly every frontier community which was west of the law. A town would stand for just so much before it struck back in defense of homes, businesses, and tranquillity with impromptu justice and hemp. But deterrents they certainly were not, if the Denver record is typical. Western violence appears to have been a public mood, and it fed upon lynching as easily as upon quick-tempered murder. Denver's murder-a-month pace in a population of hamlet proportions continued unabated throughout the campaign of the Committee of Safety, and it ended only when the laggard law arrived with full-time sheriffs to enforce it even-handedly.

Denver, to be sure, sought to give her hanging-tree justice the trappings of a legal procedure. In most, not all, of the executions in 1859 and 1860 a "People's Court" sat upon the case, sometimes in a saloon, sometimes in the street. A judge and two associates were chosen by acclamation, prosecuting and defense attorneys by the same means, and a jury selected from among the bystanders, who already had made up their minds about both the guilt and the fate of the culprit. The formalities of a trial then were run through. The jury's verdict, once arrived at, was submitted to the crowd for confirmation by voice vote. There were few acquittals in cases involving capital offenses, and he would have been a brave and rash man indeed who voted "No" when all about him were yelling "Aye." Nonetheless, it occurred—once. On June 24, 1860, in the trial of William T. Hadley for the fatal carving of J. B. Card with a butcher knife, a single negative response was heard when Judge William Person asked the crowd of four hundred if the verdict was just. The name of the dissident, obviously a scalawag and probably drunk, has not been preserved.

It can be said in behalf of the People's Courts that the men they condemned to dance from cottonwood limbs appear to have been villains of the deepest dye and guilty as sin, but then, of course, the record has been in the hands of the aye-voters and the same prominent and outraged men who served anonymously on the Committee of Safety. In later years Byers said of the summary methods:

We never hanged on circumstantial evidence. I have known a great many such executions, but I don't believe one of them was ever unjust. But when they were proved guilty, they were always hanged. There was no getting out of it. No, there were no appeals in those days; no writs of errors; no attorneys' fees; no pardon in six months. Punishment was swift, sure and certain. Murderers almost always confessed their crimes.[10]

In the midst of the lawlessness, however, the *News* questioned the value of the People's Courts even while left-handedly endorsing the vigilantes. Following one of the hangings, the paper editorialized on September 5, 1860:

> Much as we deprecate mob violence, or the working of Lynch law,—and no one can be more conscientiously or sincerely opposed to it—we can in the present juncture see no other alternative than to resort to the extreme measures that have been adopted. Our "people's court" has become little better than a farce, and, no other is recognized. If we gather the right inference from what we have been able to learn, every movement of the Vigilance Committee—or whatever it may be called, has been taken with calm deliberation; evidence has been amassed extending back for many months, and in cases only where it has been most conclusive has action been taken.

When Patrick Waters was called up to answer for the killing of Thomas R. Freeman on November 30, 1860, the indictment accused him not only of a slaying but also of offenses against "all the laws of God and man."[11] Waters confessed to the inclusive specifications anyway and was hanged December 21 from a gallows set up on the banks of the Platte at the far end of the Fifteenth Street bridge. It was the last execution by a People's Court. The courts were born of grim necessity, perhaps, and no reliable protests against their verdicts have come down through the years, but they were hardly the noble instruments of a stern and temperate justice into which they have been romanced by their apologists. Jerome Smiley wrote of "the majesty of aroused, outraged public sentiment; the quiet, awful determination of those Courts of the People," and said that "the swift, terrible and unrelenting execution of their irrevocable decrees, appalled the more wanton ruffians and brought to their brutal minds a shivering conviction that they could not successfully defy the whole community." The rhetoric is impressive, but the conclusion is fiction. The ruffians remained unappalled and undeterred, and the community was defied almost daily in the wave of lawlessness which mounted straight through the era of the People's Courts.

It was the reign of the self-styled "Bummers," and it began with the

[10]Smiley, *History of Denver*, p. 349.

[11]Byers, Bancroft ms. L6; *Rocky Mountain News*, Dec. 20, 1860.

famous "Turkey War" of January 30, 1860. The *News* heralded the affair with an extra, a three-column sheet printed on one side, on February 3. The headline was a crescendo of exclamatory type: "Exciting Times! Citizens in Arms! War Against Claim Jumpers and Thieves! Order vs. 'Bummers' Misrule! The 'Turkey War' of 1860."

The hostilities involved two matters which became thoroughly intermingled in the confusion. In Denver City late-comers jumped several town lots and began building cabins in defiance of the town company. In Auraria the Bummers stole a load of plump turkeys, strong-arming the little Mexican rancher who had brought them up from the southern part of the territory in the hope of profits in the Denver market.

How much duplication of personnel there was between the forces of the Claim-Jumpers and the Bummers is not clear, but there was shooting on both sides of the creek. The Jumpers manned forty loaded rifles when a delegation from the Arapahoe County Claim Club appeared to tear down the offending cabins. The law-and-order platoon made a dignified withdrawal. Then, during the night, someone threw down and chopped up the Jumpers' house logs anyway. They blamed Richard E. Whitsitt, secretary of the town company, and armed patrols took to the streets seeking him. Whitsitt fled over into Auraria.

On *that* side of the creek the aroused citizenry was taking up arms against the Bummers, a gang of low-livers and cutthroats who made the Criterion saloon their headquarters, in the matter of the turkey thefts. The inoffensive *ranchero* had loudly denounced a community which would stand by and permit him to be despoiled of his gobblers. The inevitable public meeting was called and in due course a committee appointed. The investigators reported back that the thievery was the work of Bummers Thomas Clemo, William ("Chuck-a-Luck") Todd, William Harvey, William McCarty, and William ("Buckskin Bill") Karl. There were no recognized police authorities. So the women barred their cabin doors and the men armed themselves and stewed around in the streets waiting for targets of opportunity. The Bummers also were parading the streets, and sooner or later the two forces had to meet.

After dark the Bummers took to stopping all pedestrians. At nine o'clock a shot fired by McCarty grazed the head of W. H. Middaugh as he stood in front of the Vasquez House. Middaugh ducked inside, only to have Harvey shoot at him again through the window. The country's first militia, the Jefferson Rangers (William N. Byers, major), marched in force to the seat of the disturbance but found the Bummers had departed, hurling back threats to fire the town. Thomas Pollock, blacksmith and hangman, encountered McCarty, who displayed unfriendliness and a large bowie knife. Pollock lowered the barrel of his heavy Hawken's rifle on the Bummer's skull. One down. A few minutes later Harvey drew a six-shooter on Pollock, who now had supporting troops. "The clear click, click, click of cocking pistols didn't suit him [Harvey], and he beat a hasty retreat," the *News* reported.

The outcome of the comic-opera Turkey War is anticlimactic. It ended, without further casualties, with the cracking of McCarty's pate. The Claim-Jumpers agreed to vacate the lots they had invaded, and Todd, Harvey, Clemo, and Karl were run out of town. McCarty is not mentioned in the banishment proceedings; possibly he took his aching head and departed of his own volition. Smiley says: "Several months afterward two or three of the leaders sneaked back but, as they behaved conservatively, they were not hanged." The Turkey War has all the elements of a Keystone-cop comedy, but it cannot have been much of a farce to those who were trying to live peaceably in Denver in 1860. These were indeed, as headlined, "Exciting Times!" A month later there was another murder—buckshot at a range of twenty feet.

The shotgun artist was duly strung up by a People's Court, and the subsequent record is as follows: March had two killings, April one, June two more, and July another pair plus a horsewhipping. Which brings accounts down to the notorious Gordon case and the kidnaping of an editor.

Twenty-three-year-old James A. Gordon was, when sober, an intelligent and well-behaved young man and, it was said, exceptionally kind to his aged mother and father. When drunk, he was a holy terror. On the night of July 18 he took on a load of popskull, shot down the barkeep in a bordello on Arapahoe Street, tottered over to the Denver Hall, and—his aim now was deteriorating—missed in two attempts to shoot another man. He moved on to the Louisiana saloon, where he encountered and took a dislike to John Gantz, an innocent stranger in town from Leavenworth. Gordon knocked Gantz down, chased him into the street, dragged him back, sat on him, held him by the hair and, after four times snapping the trigger on empty chambers, shot him through the head.

Gordon fled town in a shower of bullets. A posse headed by W. H. Middaugh finally ran him to earth in southeastern Kansas Territory. He had to be three times rescued from lynch mobs in Leavenworth, where Gantz had been well and favorably known. Eventually Gordon was returned to Denver, convicted, and hanged in the Cherry Creek bottoms with Middaugh as executioner at the prisoner's request.

Meantime Charley Harrison was adding to his fearsome reputation. Harrison was proprietor of the Criterion saloon and boasted that he planned to kill twelve white men so that he would have a jury of his peers in hell. He said he wouldn't count the eleven "Mexicans and niggers" he had slain.

On July 12, Harrison was gambling in Cibola Hall when a Negro called "Professor" Stark came in and offered to join the game. Stark was a former slave who had purchased his freedom from a Missouri master and now worked in Denver as a freeman and a blacksmith. How he got the nickname "Professor" is not explained, but apparently Stark was a man of intelligence and some spirit.

Harrison, a tall, suave, and handsome Southerner, was insulted by Stark's proposal to sit down with a white gentleman. He demanded a retraction of the offer and an apology. Stark replied that he was as good as any white man. There are at least two versions of what happened next. One is that Charley simply drew his Colt's and put three bullets into Stark.[12]

The *News* said on July 18 that Stark was a "Mexican Negro" and that he actually had been involved in the game. There was a charge of a "foul hand." Stark said it was a "d——d lie." Harrison countered with choice phrases, and Stark "rejoindered even more insultingly." By the following week the paper had reached its verdict on the affair:

DEATH OF STARK.

Prof. Stark, the Mexican Negro, who was shot on the 12th inst. by the gambler, Charley Harrison, died on the night of the 21st, from the effect of his wounds. From the facts that have transpired since the shooting, we are led to think that the act was wanton and unprovoked; in short a cold blooded murder—if called by its right name—scarcely less enormous than the several others that have occurred recently.

The man who has shot down an unarmed man, and then repeats his shots, while his victim writhes at his feet, until the charges of his pistol are exhausted—even if justified in the first act, is unfit to live in, and an unsafe member of a civilized community. Six shots were fired into Stark, five of them after he had fallen from the effect of the first, which passed completely under the breast bone, from side to side.

Murder is murder, whether committed on the body of an unknown and unsuspected human being, or on that of the highest citizen of the land, although our citizens still persist in making a distinction between the killing of a Wm. West or a Jack O'Neil.

The paper went on to editorialize:

WORDS OF CAUTION.

The rowdies, ruffians, shoulder-hitters and bullies generally, that infest our city had better be warned in time, and at once desist from their outrages upon the people. Although our community has borne their lawless acts with a fortitude, very nearly akin to indifference, we believe that forebearance has ceased to be a virtue, and that the very next outrage will call down the venegeance of an outraged people, in a wave that will engulf not only the actors, but their aiders, abettors and sympathisers

[12]William MacLeod Raine, "The Gordon Case," in Lee Casey, ed., *Denver Murders* (New York, 1946); Raine also reviews the Gordon-Gantz killing and the Turkey War.

whoever they may be. One more act of violence will at once precipitate the inevitable fate; and the terrors that swept over the fields of California at various times, and first purified its society, will be re-enacted here with terrible results to outlaws and villains, or else we are no judge of the determined countenances, compressed lips and flashing eyes that we have so frequently met in the last few days.

At any rate Stark was dead, and no one did anything about Charley Harrison except a mild-mannered scribbler with one ineffective wing who picked wild flowers and presided over the exciting contests at the Chess Club.

The *News* had been scolding about the lawlessness and violence all spring. It was unconvinced that the spur-of-the-moment People's Courts did much to diminish crime. Look at what was happening. But the main point the editor wanted to get across to his readers was that this country needed an effective government, statehood preferably, and municipal officers with a budget to hire a sheriff and town marshals. Byers had managed to get the two jealous villages to consolidate on April 3, but that was about as far as it had gone. The elected officials were figureheads, fussed importantly with papers and meetings, and accomplished almost nothing in the way of orderly city government. The town didn't even have a jail in case anyone took a wild notion to lock up some desperado who was hurrahing the streets.

Along with the demands for civic order and organization, the *News* had been giving the back of its hand on every likely occasion to the thimbleriggers, cutthroats, and hard-bitten loafers who hung out at the Criterion, the Louisiana, and Cibola Hall. It's hard to say whether Byers actually was as fearless as he seems or merely was carried away in his stubborn determination to convert a sow's-ear village into a silk-purse city. Either way, the *News* got out its indignation type when Gantz was murdered before Stark was dead of his wounds. In the issue of July 25 the paper catalogued and indexed the bloody record, named the Criterion specifically as the poisonous wellspring of contagion and Harrison personally as a blackhearted murderer.

The bully boys in the back room at the Criterion were incensed, in their fashion. The *News* had slandered them, they decided. Harrison, who was canny as well as vicious, appears not to have been unduly disturbed on his own account, but he let his associates build up a head of steam with dark broodings and vows of vengeance. Charley had been denounced by experts, and he probably realized that direct action against the editor would be more likely to raise the town against him than any amount of editorial inkslinging. So he tended his bar and hole card and let his cronies do the fuming. A crowd of them, led by Carroll Wood and George Steele, finally decided on July 31 to carry out their threats to put an end to the nosy editor and his eloquence. They tossed off another round of drinks and headed for the *News* office.

The delegation burst in on Byers and his force of printers, Wood flourishing a pistol and uttering what are described for posterity as "vile oaths." The desperado grabbed Byers by the collar and thrust a pistol in his face, demanding that he accompany the crowd to the Criterion. One of the printers, George L. Sanborn, had run upstairs into the attic with a rifle, which he now aimed down between the joists. He threatened to shoot if Byers would give the word. Byers told him to hold his fire, that he would go along peacefully.

When the editor and his kidnapers arrived at the Criterion, Harrison was behind the bar. His handsome face darkened with anger when he saw what his troops were up to. Byers was somewhat more precise, granting ellipsis, than the other historians in describing the conversation that followed. He says Harrison grabbed Wood by the arm and demanded, "What in h—l do you mean by this?"

"We brought Byers here for you to settle with," the baffled Wood replied. He had expected approval, not anger. "He called you a murderer."

Harrison thrust Wood aside and led Byers through the gambling hall to a back room. He pressed a pistol into the editor's hand and showed him a rear door. Go back to the *News*, he said, arm your force and "be ready for the s—s of b—s." (The quotation, again, as Byers recorded it.)

Byers took the advice. Windows and doors were barricaded and preparations made to resist siege. With Byers and Sanborn in the building were John Dailey, Jack Merrick of the *Pioneer*, Joseph Wolff, a man named Clark, and possibly others, including young George Collier, the printers' devil. Shortly the attack began. Steele rode up on horseback, wheeled, passed by at a gallop, and fired in through a window. The shot whistled past the editor's table. Steele made "indecent gestures" and fired again into the office. Merrick replied with a shotgun and caught Steele in the back and hip. Then Merrick traded ineffective shots with Wood, who was sheltered behind a neighboring cabin. The wounded Steele slumped in his saddle but managed to ride off.

The shots roused the town. Word was passed that Byers had been killed. Crowds began to gather in the streets, and Tom Pollock emerged from his smithy with his shotgun. About the same time Steele rode back up the street. He and Pollock fired at the same time, but the smith's aim was better. Steele toppled to the ground with a charge of buckshot in his head. He died that afternoon.

Wood was seized and placed on trial next day. The sentence was banishment. He and several of his fellows moved out about six miles and camped, and John Dailey's diary for August 3 says Wood "sent word back to Byers in the evening that he had no ill feelings against Byers and if it was ever in his power to befriend him he would do it." Wood later became a leader of Confederate bushwhackers in Missouri and was killed in a drunken brawl in Texas in 1865.

Wood's departure did not entirely restore peace. There were other threats against Byers' life and rumors of violent plans for the entire *News* establishment. The office became for a time an arsenal. A contemporary illustration shows rifles standing at the ready beside printers at their cases. Mrs. Byers said later: "I experienced the horror of seeing desperate men hiding behind a low shed waiting to shoot my husband as he came from the office. Nothing but a disguise changed every night prevented his assassination."[13]

Less than a month after the kidnaping someone tried to burn down the *News* plant. The paper of September 25 gives the story:

Incendiary.—An attempt was made last Monday night 17th inst., to burn the NEWS office by firing some shavings and refuse lumber in the basement. Fortunately a light shower dampened the air, so that the fire went out before extending beyond the material used for its kindling. It will be remembered that a severe gale blew for several hours that night, and every citizen can imagine what would have been the result if the fire had once got under way. A large portion of our inflammable city would have been swept away like chaff before the wind. We have not alluded to the fact, because we deemed silence best to enable us to detect the perpetrator in which we have succeeded to our full satisfaction, though the proof is not such as would secure conviction. We warn our citizens to be careful and watchful for incendiaries. It is certain that we have such in our midst, and the man who will voluntarily fire a building, thereby endangering the whole city, and scores of human lives will not scruple to take life singly for spite or for spoil.—We would expect him to waylay and stab in the dark. And he who will incite the act by promise of reward is if any odds the worst man of the two.

Charley Harrison smoked his angular cheroots, fingered his brocaded vest, and maintained an air of calm superiority through the whole affair, and no one molested him. He began to profess friendship and high regard for the editor who had called him a wanton murderer. For his part Byers was grateful and always credited the gambler with having saved his life in the Criterion that day. Charley had a large ring made of native gold and mounted with a Masonic emblem—both he and Byers were Masons—and presented it to the editor as a token of esteem. Byers kept the ring the rest of his life, and on the wall of his office hung the shotgun that killed Steele. In the midst of this season of good feeling Harrison moved ahead toward his declared objective of a jury of victims

[13]Ralph L. Crosman, "Early Colorado Newspapers and Editors," *University of Colorado Bulletin*, Vol. XXV, No. 11 (April 1935), p. 35.

to judge him in the after world. On December 2 he killed James Hill while pretending to embrace him. The jury said it was self-defense. Not long thereafter the notorious Charley left Denver never to return. His end belongs in another part of the story.

Two disinterested and non-combatant witnesses can be called upon for testimony about these days of bloodletting. Albert Richardson and Thomas Knox were sojourning at Denver and Golden City. Their brief affiliations with the *News* did not come until later in the fall of 1860, but they were on the scene and they knew all the principals. Reported Richardson:

> It was a fascinating country for a journalist. Over his devoted head daily and nightly hung the sword of Damocles. An indignant aspirant for Congress meeting the editor of the Denver *Herald* in the street spat in his face. Mr. Byers of the *News*, whose establishment after the first murderous assault was a well stocked armory, had his office fired and his dwelling burned, but by taking a bold stand verified the proverb that threatened men live long.[14]

Knox offered a brief critique on the *News* and its editors in addition to a report on their joint perils:

> . . . It is now by far the best daily and the most attractive weekly newspaper west of St. Louis. Its editors are human curiosities, and worthy of niches at Barnum's. The senior was "raised" in Ohio. He has been a pioneer settler in Iowa, Nebraska, Oregon and Pike's Peak; has acted as Government surveyor in all those territories, excepting the last; has been four times over the plains; was once shot and badly wounded in an attempt to quell a riot; and on numerous occasions has listened to the pleasing whistle of a bullet in close proximity to his head. The junior [Bliss], an ardent admirer of a huge meerschaum, is by birth a New-Yorker. He has published papers in Buffalo, Chicago, Melbourne, New-Zealand, Peru and California. Australia and adjacent lands, many isles of the Pacific, South America, and all parts of the United States, have received the impress of his restless foot, and where next he may turn up, it is difficult to imagine. A novelist might make a fine two-volume romance from the history of these two men. If he had, in addition, the career of each of the workmen in the composing and press-rooms—no less than four of whom have been editors of daily papers in various parts of the Union—the "Scottish Chiefs" would be a mere nothing.
>
> Journalism at Pike's Peak, like the course of true love, does not run smooth. Repeated shots have been fired at the *News* office by indignant "roughs"; the editors have been assaulted at various times, and on a few occasions their lives have been in great jeopardy. . . . Every few weeks a threat of cleaning out the *News* office was made by its enemies,

14Richardson, op. cit., p. 305.

and the whole corps, from the "devil" upward, is prepared to resist such a purifying process. The sanctum abounds in guns and revolvers, always at hand; and in squally times each man in the composing-room has a "six-shooter" by the side of his copy. The foreman [Dailey] sports a huge "navy" at his belt, and the roller-boy is ready to support the honor of the establishment with the weapon of his branch of trade. Pleasant business, publishing newspapers at Pike's Peak.[15]

[15]Knox, *The Knickerbocker*, ibid.

CHAPTER EIGHT

The News Becomes a Daily

T HE ROCKY MOUNTAIN NEWS was being published with "tolerable
regularity," come hellions and, a little later, high water.

Circumstances considered, the regularity was a small monument to
rugged determination, perhaps even rash stubbornness. Only bullheaded-
ness or a vision could have kept Byers and Dailey at work. Probably they
foresaw that this unlikely and uncomely village of theirs eventually
would become a town in which it would be worth while to publish a
newspaper, but if so it was a dogged prescience and entirely unjustified
on the surface. Denver was dirty, ugly, and hazardous. The newspaper
was doing no more than paying day wages, at best. The year 1860 brought
another large wave of emigration, but again only a small fraction of it
stayed on; in 1861 there was almost no emigration, and the News
watched the roads from the East wistfully all spring to no avail. With
the outbreak of war the rest of the country forgot all about Denver.
The Pike's Peak country was abandoned to isolation. Yet Byers and
Dailey clung on.

After the initial effort on April 23, 1859, the News skipped the April
30 issue. Everyone was up at the Gregory Diggings trying his hand at
prospecting. The next three issues were dated May 7, 14, and 28, missing
the twenty-first. There was also no paper on June 4, and Nos. 5 and 6
of Vol. 1 both are dated June 11. No. 8 (June 25) was a four-column
extra about mining progress and the Gregory Gulch forest fires printed
on one side of brown paper. Only two issues appeared in July, on the
ninth and twenty-third. Byers left Denver on June 25 to return to Omaha
for his family. He displayed genuine Pike's Peak gold in his real estate
office there and made a speech extolling the grandeurs and rich prospects
of the new country whose herald-voice he was determined to be. When
he returned to Cherry Creek the News settled into a consistent pattern
through the fall and winter. From August 6 through December 28 it
appeared each week on schedule. The schedule was shifted around
somewhat to confirm to arrivals and departures of stages and to fit in
with other publishing ventures. The day of issue shifted on September
22 from Saturday to Thursday, and on December 14 was advanced again
to Wednesday. For some reason not now apparent the issue of January
4, 1860, is numbered as 34, although the December 28 issue was No.

32. Possibly an extra was printed which has not survived, but there is no evidence in either the December 28 or January 4 issues that this was the case. Byers did number his extras serially with the regular editions. His paper now was coming out on time and faithfully, although it was not always what he would like to have it be. It was only a half sheet on November 24, for example, and Byers apologized to his readers, explaining that his stocks of paper had run low awaiting arrival of an ox freight. "Yesterday we received an eight months' supply of paper and ink, and we do not expect to again be under the necessity of making a similar apology." There were also other occupational hazards. The issue for July 25, 1864, pleads in extenuation that "in putting the form upon the press this afternoon, the first page of the paper was pied, in consequence of which we necessarily issue a half sheet." Extras sometimes were broadsides of three or four columns, printed on one side of the sheet, and when paper supply was short the regular issues often shrank in size to five columns.

As the first anniversary approached in April of 1860, it was a time of stocktaking and pride for editors of the *News*. On April 18 they boldly announced plans for a triweekly or, perchance, a daily edition (if advertisers and subscribers would just fall in step with the march of progress) and called attention to

THE END OF THE VOLUME.

. . . How could we print and publish a newspaper unless there existed a community to sustain it? . . . The enterprise of publishing the ROCKY MOUNTAIN NEWS, once so problematical, is a success, fixed and certain. . . .

As far as our own course is concerned we have only a word to say. We have been, and trust we ever shall be, as free as the wind that bloweth where it listeth. We have stood up for what we believed to be the right, regardless of consequences. If we have done any one an injury, it was unintentional; if we have erred, it has been a fault of the head, not of the heart. . . .

On the following Wednesday the *News* entered upon its second year with:

NEW VOLUME.

The second volume of the *Rocky Mountain News* commences with the issue of April 25th, 1860. Over a year has passed since its establishment in this city, in the darkest days the country has ever seen, and notwithstanding the cautions that have been tendered, and the many threats made against us, if we *dared* to publish the truth respecting this country, the *News* has gone steadily forward in its proposed course, speaking plainly the truth, without fear or favor, and the result is that it stands to day, the most widely known and universally quoted, of any newspaper of its age, ever before published in the United States. And now we have the satisfaction of looking back, and seeing that every report we have published, has been confirmed and every prediction fully verified.

What the *News* has been it shall continue to be, fearless and free as the mountain air we breathe; and in its improvements and additional attractions from time to time; shall fully keep pace with the progress of the country.

The *News* has already a circulation in every State of the Union, save two—all the Territories and both the Canadas.—It is forwarded by express every Thursday morning, and received by its subscribers everywhere with the utmost regularity.

Byers, however, still was receiving poison-pen letters to the editor from persons who didn't agree that everything about the Pike's Peak wonderland was now confirmed and verified. W. G. George of Rockport, Missouri, for one, took his pen in hand. His felicitations appeared in the issue of February 8, 1860:

After viewing your past life in connection with the low dirty infamous sheet you publish I am forced to say you are the grandest Liar and most infamous rascal out of hell alive. Should I speak comparatively of you I would crave the pardon of all devils you are prostituting your calling by base lies to fill your pockets & your intimate Friends cut Throats & low Vagabonds.

I have seen your Mountain Liar filled with two thirds of lies that I know to be such while I was in your Territory. By these tissues of falsehoods you have deceived thousands. But sir Justice is fast on your tracks & ere another six months rolls round you will be paid the penalty with your worthless life of your base deceptions. Men of worth and character have staked their all upon your word & now are left penniless & now have swor a fearful vengeance upon the author of all their miseries you are now organizing a Ter. be careful the next Territory you will occupy will be foreign and called Hell Hell. I don't conceal my name or purpose. Death & vengeance.

The *News'* postscript commented:

Whew! isn't that refreshing? How we trembled when we read it. Who wouldn't be an editor? Let us see, we were given six months from the 30th of August to prepare for a final reckoning—five months used—time nearly gone—we must cast about. Who wants to be remembered in our will? . . .

Mr. George wrote under date of August 30, the *News* explained, but his letter was delayed in the mails.

Although some of the gobacks remained obstinately unconvinced, enough gold was coming in and enough growth occurring to permit the "Mountain Liar" a reasonable expansion. The News even branched out into a modest "chain" operation.

During the campaign leading to the first territorial election in 1861, a campaign which decided whether Colorado would go Union or Confederate, the News published the Miner's Record at Tarryall in South Park some seventy miles southwest of Denver. Tarryall, located about four miles northwest of the present hamlet of Como, got its name because it was rated a "good spot to stay awhile." Nothing remains of Tarryall today, although in the summer and fall of 1859 it had boomed briefly on the basis of rich placer sands. The story is told that the original prospectors who clung on through the winter to hold their claims appropriated one of the richest pits in the diggings and used it as a "bank." The man who had discovered the pit went back home for the winter months, and while he was gone the other miners drew upon his unexploited wealth when thirst was compelling. The pit became known as the "Whisky Hole."[1] Late arrivals found all the likely claims taken at Tarryall, and they asserted the settlement was misnamed. They called it Grab-All and named *their* nearby town Fair Play.

The Miner's Record was started July 4 and had a brief existence. Only eleven issues appeared before the paper suspended on September 14. The Record probably was printed on News presses in Denver and hauled to South Park by stage or wagon for distribution. During its short span the Record had the distinguished Professor Goldrick as its traveling agent, and John Dailey went up to supervise the operation and serve as reporter and editor-on-the-scene. His diaries show the notes upon which the "locals" were built. Though it didn't last long, the Record apparently accomplished its main purpose. Election returns from Tarryall gave 158 votes for Congress to the News' candidate, Republican Hiram P. Bennet, and cut off Beverly D. Williams with 46.

Earlier the News had experimented, also briefly, with another sister paper. During the high tide of the 1860 emigration Byers and Dailey began publishing the Denver Bulletin and Supplement to the Rocky Mountain News. The project was announced in the News of April 18:

[Figure of pointing hand] "Bulletin."—Merchants, Hotel Keepers, Expressmen, Ranch Keepers and all other advertisers are respectfully notified that we will early in the coming week, commence the publication of the BULLETIN, for gratuitous distribution among the emigrants on the road out. It will be published weekly, semi-weekly or daily, as occasion may require, and the pay justify, and it is the very best advertising medium that can offer.

Send in advertisements by Saturday evening 21st inst., earlier if possible.

[1]Norma L. Flynn, "Early Mining Camps of South Park," Denver Westerners' Monthly Brand Book, Vol. 7, No. 11 (Nov. 1951), p. 6.

Some hitch must have developed; for the first number of the *Bulletin* did not appear until May 2 as a six-column half sheet printed on both sides.

The giveaway continued as a single broadside sheet of varying size with its editorial content picked up from previous or current issues of the *News*. As a means of extending the power of the *News*, or fattening its owners' lean purses, the *Bulletin* was a rather baffling little enterprise. For while Byers and Dailey exalted it above the *News* as an advertising medium, its space rates were half those of the regular paper and thus must have cut into the principal revenues. The supplement was dated on Wednesdays, the same day as the *News*, but pay did not justify—or the owners became aware that they were undercutting themselves. Only six *Bulletins* appeared—May 2, 9, 16, 23, and 30 and June 6—and it finally dwindled off with a four-column sheet headed merely *Supplement to the Rocky Mountain News*, undated but apparently released during the week of June 18. A similar supplement appeared irregularly without serial numbering between January 25 and July 5 of 1862.

As the *Bulletin* expired Byers and Dailey already were looking forward to even larger undertakings, and new blood was about to enter the firm. Horace E. ("Hod") Rounds, brother of the Chicago publisher and manufacturer of type and printing machinery, Sterling P. Rounds, came to town on the June 13 stage. Edward Bliss, who had been managing editor of Sterling Rounds' *Sunday Leader*, arrived on July 4. Rounds and Bliss planned to give Denver another newspaper, and they had equipment for a printing office on the way. After surveying the field, however, they decided to join forces with Byers and Dailey. Dailey's diary says a consolidation agreement was worked out on July 11, although he gives no details. The new partnership under the name of the News Printing Company went into effect July 19. The *News* of the previous day had announced the company and said additions to the plant in the value of three thousand dollars would be made through the consolidation. The Dailey diary shows that the Rounds and Bliss equipment arrived July 22 by wagon and was unloaded into the *News* plant. Mastheads of the paper beginning July 25 list Bliss and Byers as joint editors. Rounds apparently went into the business end of the operation.

With new equipment in the composing and press rooms, new talent in the editorial office and, presumably, new financing, the *News* now was at last ready to launch into the long-promised daily publication. Plans for a daily had been announced as early as April. The June 13 paper said the daily would start in July, and a month later this was amended to "by Aug. 1." On that date the weekly *News* came out in an enlarged seven-column format, but the start of the daily was being held up pending arrival of paper. Meantime, on May 1, Thomas Gibson had come out with his *Daily Herald and Rocky Mountain Advertiser*. Then, on August 25, James T. Coleman, with the backing of Mayor John C. Moore, brought out his Democratic sheet, the Denver *Daily Mountaineer*, although it was able to issue only fifteen numbers in its first month of operation.

At last the *Daily Rocky Mountain News* appeared on August 27 as the third daily newspaper in a town hardly big enough to support one weekly. Like the enlarged weekly, the daily edition was printed in seven columns on four folio-sized pages. Damp printing methods on a good, rag-made paper were used, and the sheet presented a fair typographical appearance which commanded twenty-five cents a copy or twenty-four dollars a year. The masthead on page two called the paper the Denver *Evening News*, and the objective was to hit the streets between 4 and 5 P.M. As a milestone in the paper's career, the "Salutatory" of the new daily deserves reproduction at some length:

> The impatience manifested on the part of our patrons in this city, as well as the interest expressed in the enterprise by our friends in the mountains, has induced us to commence the publication of the DAILY ROCKY MOUNTAIN NEWS a week or two earlier than our preparations seemed to warrant. The arrival by express of a small supply of paper, and the confidence that a large invoice now far on the Plains, will soon follow, prompts us to send forth the initial number.
>
> Of its appearance typographically we have no inclination to speak, further than that it is the best we can do until after the arrival of a large amount of new material, which is coming with the paper. It is hardly necessary to promise that our daily and weekly issues, in one month from now, will compare favorably in appearance with any papers published in the western cities of the States.
>
> We do not expect to be able to give that daily variety of news, or invest our paper with the same general interest possessed by our eastern contemporaries. The facilities afforded by a score of telegraph lines, which throw their iron net-work over a region of many thousand square miles, gathering in the pulsations of the great public heart, are not only here wanting, but even our postal arrangements are yet in their infancy, and consequently very imperfect. But in this mountain region we hope to garner sufficient items of local interest to make the DAILY NEWS a welcome visitor in the counting rooms and offices of our business men; in the cabins of the hardy miner, and in the open field tents of the daring prospector, in his toil. . . .
>
> It is not our purpose to make the NEWS the organ or mouthpiece of any party, sect or organization. The editors entertain political opinions, but the expression of them here, where none have a voice in the selection of rulers, seems to us supererogatory. In a new country like this, where no good can possibly result from distinct political organization, it appears to be a waste of time and space to devote the same to political discussions. The development of the resources of this wonderful region, and the promotion of the best interests of those who are identified

with its growth and prosperity—seems to us to offer the most useful and most welcome field for journalistic effort. We do not wish to be misunderstood in reference to this matter.—The great struggle now going forward at the East, between the mighty political parties, has awakened in us a deep interest, and we shall watch the result with intense solicitude. But our preferences and predilections will not be made public through these columns.

Having a numerous corps of talented and spicy correspondents in the various mining districts—most of them daily devotees of the rocker, the tom and the more formidable crusher—our columns will contain a daily reflex of the experiences, the success and the prospects of the different localities. We shall aim to give truthful, reliable reports of the results of mining operations in every gulch or ravine where the stalwart arm of industry is delving in the earth, and to this end we enjoin upon our correspondents great care in the collection of statistics and figures upon this subject. The truth is what will redoun[d] most to the credit and prosperity of this region, and let it be told under all circumstances.

In our intercourse with our contemporaries we shall always aim to be courteous, manly and just; ever holding ourselves in readiness to make ample amends for all wrongs or injuries we may unwittingly commit. It is our earnest wish to maintain with them personal relations of the most friendly character.

As public journalists we shall endeavor to mete out even and exact justice to all. Depending for much that will appear in our columns upon rumors—not always well authenticated—it is not unlikely that we may at times do injustice to individuals. It shall be our greatest pleasure, under such circumstances, to make complete and honorable reparation for the offence.

To set forth at greater length the course we intend to pursue, seems unnecessary. Our former efforts as conductors of a weekly journal, have generally met the approval of the public, and we do not propose now that we are at the helm of a daily craft, to adopt a new system of reckoning, or venture over an untried track. We shall do the best we can, and do it often.

Thus the *News* declared itself out of the great political battles then raging on the eve of the Civil War, at the same time taking a slap at the new *Daily Mountaineer* for its open Democratic leanings. Byers was a Republican and boasted of it, but the *News* had been campaigning for territorial, state, and municipal governments and, as he explained later, he felt the situation was complex enough and the local rivalries already sufficiently bitter without the admixture of Democratic-Republican divisions on national issues. Putting itself on the side lines politically also was the better part of valor for the *News*; there still was a considerable Southern element in the town, and some of the men from Dixie held the more important positions in business and civic leadership.

The salutatory also outlines a course of conduct vis-à-vis the other papers which, in the case of Gibson's *Herald,* was abandoned almost immediately. No file of the *Herald* survives, and so it is not known precisely what the provocations were, but the *News* took after Gibson and his paper with vehemence and personal jibes. The *Herald* commented on one of Byers' frequent chasings-off to the mountains and suggested he was fleeing threats. The *News* jibed back on September 10:

> "The Editor of the *Herald* has not gone to the mountains because he is *afraid* to stay in Denver."—*Herald.*
> He that knows nothing fears nothing.

Earlier the *Herald* seems to have taken some glee in the attack of the Bummers on the *News* office and the kidnapping of Byers, perhaps even suggesting the whole affair was justified. An editorial in the *News* for August 8 concludes: "We only hope that GIBSON's bones may never have a similar cause for becoming an involuntary rattle-box." The newspaper quarrel grew more and more bitter and personal. Said the *News* on September 17:

> WANTED.—At the *Herald* office, a small boy who has advanced at least twenty pages in Sander's First Reader, to read proof and correct the 'orrid orthography of some of the *Herald* correspondents. Such a lad who will take coffee mills in weekly payments, can secure a permanent situation.

This was followed up September 19 with

> —An apology is due to our readers for the space devoted to the *Herald* in the letter of our Mountain City correspondent. It is not our design to cumber our space, or disgust their taste by any reference whatever to that scurrilous lying sheet, or its imbecile editor.

The *News* took a malicious delight in Gibson's cockney *h*-dropping, and brought illustrations into the fight. On October 8:

> "No Proscription."—A life-like portrait of the sensation editor of the *Herald*. Copyright secured:
> [Figure of an ass]

On August 29:

> [Figure of pointing hand] The spirit of this morning's *Herald:*
> [A bottle]

And on May 11, 1861:

Accurate Likeness
of the

[Figure of man with bellows for head]

Blower of the 'Erald

[Taken by a Denver white-washer, with one hand tied behind him.]

The whole squabble must have become tiresome after the first few exchanges to readers of both the *Herald* and the *News*, but it continued unremittingly until Gibson sold out his paper, by then renamed the *Commonwealth and Republican*, on January 1, 1864, and went back to Omaha.

By contrast, relationships between the *News* and the *Daily Mountaineer*, despite its secession sympathies, were on a neighborly basis of over-the-back-fence borrowings. The *News* made a polite bow to its Democratic contemporary on September 11, 1860:

> We are under obligation to friend Coleman of the *Denver Mountaineer*, for a supply of paper on which to print our to-morrow's Weekly. Such favors are highly appreciated, and we shall not be backward to reciprocate them, when occasion offers.

John Dailey's journal for 1860 shows that he loaned Coleman a half bundle of paper not long thereafter, and a few weeks later "two shts colored card board."

George West watched the situation gleefully from his post, out of line of fire, on the *Western Mountaineer* in Golden. He commented pungently:

> THREE DAILY PAPERS.—Denver is probably the only city in the world of less than five thousand inhabitants in which three daily papers are issued. Of course, the business is greatly overdone, and some of them must die out one of these fine mornings. It is impossible, however, to predict the time with exact precision, for newspapers, like toads shut up in a dark cellar, are characterized by a wonderful amount of vitality, and live upon nothing for an almost incredible period.

The *News*, which knew all about living on next to nothing, was amused by the item and republished it on September 20.

Coleman's *Daily Mountaineer* was the first to succumb. It was sold to the *News* in May 1861, and publication ceased. By that time Colorado Territory was definitely in the Union camp, and there was little comfort or profit in publishing a Democratic journal in Denver. Byers told H. H. Bancroft: "The editors and proprietors of the Mountaineer went south within a few days after sale of the paper, and one of them [Coleman], in trying to get through the Union lines was shot by a picket and had one of his arms shattered from the wrist to the elbow. The other publisher [Moore] of the Mountaineer went south and became chief quarter-master of Hood's division of the Confederate army and served during the war and afterwards started a paper in Kansas City."[2] Moore later returned to Pueblo, Colorado, where he became a prominent citizen.

The time would come when the News also would swallow up the descendant of Gibson's irksome Herald.

Through these days of consolidations and expansions the News did not remain static physically, either. The attic room of Dick Wootton's pioneer skyscraper in Auraria did not long meet the needs of frontier newspaper publishing. Moreover, the paper wished its custom to embrace both of the jealous villages and could not therefore become solely identified with either. So it bounced back and forth across Cherry Creek seeking to establish a neutrality.

On the southwest end of the bridge which today carries Market Street across Cherry Creek is a bronze plaque, placed there by the Colorado State Historical Society in 1934, marking the approximate location of the newspaper's birth. The News gratefully participated in the unveiling of the plaque on its seventy-fifth anniversary, but the bronze words perpetuate several errors in addition to saying nice things about the city's pioneer journal. The legend reads: "On this site stood the original home of the Rocky Mountain News, first newspaper established in the 'Pike's Peak Gold Region.' Founded by William N. Byers April 23, 1859. Champion of law and order in 'Jefferson Territory'; advocate of faith in emerging Colorado. Located on neutral ground between pioneer towns, Denver and Auraria. Building and press lost in great Cherry Creek flood, May 19, 1864."

The bronze plaque comes closer to marking the site of the fourth than the first home of the News. Dick Wootton's leaky attic, in which the paper received its baptism of melted snow water, was several blocks away as Denver now is laid out, at what would be about 1413–15 Eleventh Street in the present Wazee produce market. On the first map of the Cherry Creek towns the location would have been near the corner of Fourth and Ferry streets, Auraria. The News was issued from the attic through the summer and into the fall of 1859. Byers and Dailey talked about building but between publishing a newspaper and rushing off to hunt gold didn't get around to it. In September, "Uncle Dick" decided to sell his pioneer storehouse-saloon-meeting hall. Byers made an offer, but it was sold to an earlier bidder. So on October 15 the presses and type cases were moved across the creek into Denver City to a temporary location in the log cabin of Sam Kime.[3] The cabin perched on the edge of the creek bottoms at the southeast corner of McGaa (present Market)

[2]Typescript, Bancroft Library Pac Ms. L8, op. cit.

[3]John L. Dailey diaries, Western History Collection, Denver Public Library.

Street and E (Fourteenth) Street. Kime's cabin later housed the Denver and Auraria Reading Room, the city's first library, and the school of Lydia Marie Ring. "Old" City Hall was built on the site in 1882–83, facing on the next street above Market, Larimer. It lasted as the seat of municipal government until 1932, when the new City and County Building was completed at Civic Center. For another eight years the old building with its bell and clock tower saw service as police head-quarters before it finally was abandoned in May 1940. Shortly there-after it was torn down, and the site now is a municipal parking lot with the bell from the tower preserved as a monument about where Sam Kime's log shanty once stood.

The cabin in Denver City was a get-by for Byers and Dailey. They were building their own log printing office about a block away to the southwest—across the creek in Auraria again. They moved in late in December during a cold snap, which, Dailey says, sent the thermometer down to 39 below and froze the mercury in the tube. This building, the first actually built as a printing plant, was near the intersection of Front (Thirteenth) and Fourth (Walnut) streets, about the same distance south of the creek as Sam Kime's place was north. The present location would be approximately 1301 Walnut Street. Byers and his family temporarily occupied the rear of the story-and-a-half building as their home, and the printers, who boarded at the Byers table, lived in another cabin next door to the north. A photograph of the third News building, taken in 1900 during its last, sway-backed days, survives. After the paper left it the structure became a guardhouse during the Civil War, the city jail, and finally a city stables and hangout for tramps. When it was dismantled there was some talk of re-erecting it in City Park as a pioneer museum. John Dailey had the logs hauled to the yard of his home. But the proposal came to naught, and the square-hewn timbers gradually disappeared as firewood. A section of one of them is preserved as a memento in the office of the editor of the News.

By June of 1860 business had expanded sufficiently that the News was ready to move again. It built for itself a new frame building about a hundred feet to the north on Fourth Street, and it is this building that the bronze plaque marks.

It was an odd sort of house. The dimensions were 24 by 47 feet, and it rose on pilings from a triangular plot of "worthless" land, mostly sand, in the very bed of Cherry Creek. Byers said he chose the spot because it was "neutral ground" between the two cities, now consolidated but still not entirely happy about the wedding. The site frequently has been described as the "middle of Cherry Creek." It wasn't, quite, nor was it no man's land between the two towns. The Fosdick and Tappan map of 1859 shows that the site was in Block 241, Auraria, and at least one building, the Earl Brothers Music Hall, soon was built between the News and the trickle of water which divided Auraria and Denver.

With plenty of flat and higher ground to build on, both the cities crowded close to the meandering bed of the presumably innocent stream. Rough streets were graded up to a level perhaps six feet above the sands, and the new *News* building had to have a bridgelike walk to carry traffic from Fourth Street to its front doors. The street-level main floor had the editorial and press rooms. There was an attic in which the printers lived, and with further expansion of business Dailey walled in the pilings below to form a basement storeroom and job-printing department. On the roof was a large sign which proclaimed the home of the *Rocky Mountain News* to all comers. A tall lodgepole pine was trimmed into a flagstaff to stand by the front walk. Dailey records that he slept in the new office for the first time on May 18, helped build the walk on May 25, and moved the printing equipment in on June 2. The paper dated June 6 announced:

A recent removal of our office has prevented our giving this week's issue as much attention as we could wish; particularly to the "Bulletin" for distribution among the emigrants.

Our office is in the large frame building in the middle of Cherry creek, under the sign of the American flag, at which place emigrants are invited to call and register their names.

It was from this building that Byers was kidnaped, and in it the *News* became a daily. Out of its windows one could look down, a hundred feet or so, on the little creek which carried hardly enough water to wet a whistle. Dailey's diary tells of how he would take a clean shirt and hike over to the Platte, perhaps half a mile away, for a bath.

The much-traveled Imperial and Double Medium Washington hand presses were installed in the stilted building, but before long they were joined by the first power press to cross the plains to Pike's Peak, a steam-driven Guernsey. It arrived July 7, and Dailey reports it in operation on July 15. Soon thereafter, probably as a result of the entry of Bliss and Rounds into the firm, another power press, a clumsy Northrup cylinder "threshing machine," went into the plant.

With these presses the *News* was turning out 1600 to 2000 copies of the weekly paper and much of the commercial and governmental printing of the town. It printed the shares of the consolidated Denver City company, and earlier had put on paper the "Laws and Regulations of the Miners of the Gregory Diggings District," the first attempt at a local legal code in a country where other laws were inoperative and little recognized. A pamphlet of standing rules for the House of Representatives of the Territory of Jefferson came from the *News'* presses, along with tickets for balls, community sociables, and the Cibola Minstrels. Business cards cost twenty dollars a thousand at the *News* in 1861, handbills five dollars a hundred and ball tickets ten dollars a hundred. When the *News* "went daily" in August 1860 the paper claimed a circulation which began at 500 copies and climbed slowly to perhaps 700 the following year.

In addition to John Dailey, the printers who manned the cases and presses included, at various times, Charles S. Semper, George L. Sanborn, W. W. Whipple, Bill Summers, Mark Blunt, Nathan A. Baker, Frank Roff, Harry Stafford, James P. Oliver, Copeland Rabe, and Byers' brothers-in-law, the Sumner boys, Robert, Charles, John, and Will. Jack Sumner and Oramel G. Howland, another *News* printer, were with John Wesley Powell in 1868 on the expedition which first explored the Colorado River. Howland was killed by the Shivwits Indians in Utah; Howland Butte in the Grand Canyon is named for him, and Sumner Point for the other *News* member of the expedition.[4] One of Howland's fellow workers in the *News* print shop was Albert Auer, later foreman of the Government Printing Office in Washington. Jack Merrick was in and out of the plant and, after the Carroll Wood-George Steele affair, was rated "a good shot with a rifle." Until his father, the irascible Thomas, pulled out, young Henry Gibson was a *News* printer. Others mentioned at various points in the record include Irwin Sansom, P. W. Case, T. C. Brown, Thomas S. Tucken, L. A. and W. J. Curtice, James and Harry Creighton, H. E. Turner, "Pap" Hoyt, Joseph Wolff, and Richard Sherriff. One of the force, James L. Lee, became president of the Challenge Machinery Company in Chicago. The devil, George M. Collier, learned his trade and set himself up as printer-editor in his own right. He founded the daily and weekly Black Hawk *Journal* in 1872.

Dailey noted down the arrivals and departures of his highly fluid force of printers in his pocket journals, and kept accounts on their lost time in the memoranda pages. The names Merrick, Stone, J. R. Devor, Semper, Ruff, Tucken, Sanborn, Martin, Chet Langdon [or Sangdon], Sam Bolster, Cummings, and Robert Anes [or Aner] appear in the 1859 and 1860 diaries.

Bolster "lost a day and a half from the 12th," the careful foreman recorded, and Anes "one day from the 12th." On June 11, 1860, "Martin got his back up in the evening and concluded to leave. Settled off with him & let him slide." Dailey also notes the signing on of the *News'* first female employee but fails to give her name. March 29, 1860: "Hired a girl this evening."

Merrick, it appears, not only was "jolly" and a marksman but also somewhat irregular in showing up for work. Dailey charges him frequently with lost time and records that on June 31, 1860, "Jolly Jack" was missing from the shop "from 10 till night." Conviviality may be an explanation; for the pioneer fraternity of printer's ink apparently enjoyed a close fellowship which now and then bubbled up into elaborate town-

[4] See Wallace Stegner, *Beyond the Hundredth Meridian* (Boston, 1954).

painting. Dailey says that on July 3 he and his men were "Busy at work to get the paper up. Got to work at it in the evening. Worked at it until late at night and devoured several bottles of choice fluid, the effects of which were to exhilerate [sic] the company." On July 14 the new typographical union held forth: "Typo meeting in the evening, generally attended. Golden City boys down. Had a spree after meeting and all next day."

Charlie Semper, who had set type for the first issue, offered to quit the paper in December 1859, when his pay was cut to twenty dollars a week, but he stayed on to work out a balance due the office and Byers and Dailey decided to keep him at twenty-five dollars a week. The matter of wages came to issue in the spring of 1860. Dailey "sent the printers a note this evening [April 21] cutting down their wages." The result was Denver's first strike—on the day of the paper's first anniversary.

"Boys struck this morning," Dailey's diary for April 23 says, "and declined going to work at the rates we proposed. The day disagreeable, they took it pretty hard—That is, loafing."

Tucken, although he was an officer of the union, went back to work the next day, and by the twenty-sixth "the boys begin to feel like compromising matters, and Jack [Merrick] appoints a printers' meeting for tonight at the News office. We met in the evening, the meeting composed of all the jours [journeymen] and Mr. G [Gibson] and myself and the jours reconsidered the bill of prices and came down to ours." Sanborn and Merrick were on the job next day, but Charlie Semper was bitter and switched allegiance to Gibson's Herald temporarily. Exactly what the wages were at this point is not in the record, although Dailey records that beginning February 12, 1865, the scale was seventy-three cents an hour for the evening (daily) paper and eighty cents an hour for night work (usually on the weekly or commercial printing), twenty-seven dollars by the week with a three-dollar differential for the foreman.

The pay scale certainly fell short of providing the means for high living, oyster suppers with scarlet ladies on the "row," or bucking the gambling hells. A young News bookkeeper, reputedly a member of a prominent Pennsylvania family, had tastes along those lines, and he accomplished what probably has occurred to every person with normal criminal instincts: he robbed the United States Mint.

Twenty-one-year-old James D. Clarke, a little man with a "genteel address," quit his job of grubbing over the News account books and on December 30, 1863, was appointed pay clerk of the Denver mint. He carried with him high recommendations from Hiram P. Bennet, Colorado territorial delegate to Congress, and Mayor Amos Steck. A few weeks later, however, the News was carrying announcement of a thousand-dollar reward for the capture of its former accountant.

Clarke had filched $36,817.05 from the mint on February 13, 1864, and "absconded on horseback," riding a one-eyed livery-stable sorrel with a tolerably long tail and saddle galls. He had paused only long enough to settle up a few gambling debts and buy himself a brace of handsome and costly Navy Colts. Then he lit out for Mexico. The *News* described the case as "one of the most serious, strange events that have occured [sic] in our country's history." The little bookkeeper was "galloping into the grim abyss of infamy eternal."

He didn't get away with it, although there is no record that he ever did time for his almost successful peculations. He was captured near Pueblo and all but $4419 of the swag recovered. Clarke escaped from jail once, but hung around Denver sleeping on a couch in the shadows under the stage of the Denver Theater and hiding in the groves near Jim Beckwourth's ranch up the Platte. He was recaptured. It has not been determined that he ever was tried or sentenced. The embezzlement charge against him was dropped in 1867.

How he turned the robbery is detailed on the rice-paper sheets of the Denver mint's ninety-three-year-old letter books, made public recently by Mrs. Alma K. Schneider, current superintendent. The superintendent in 1864, George W. Lane, reported to Treasury Secretary Salmon P. Chase that his young pay clerk propped the window of his office open with a pencil at quitting time, put the money on the sill, and said good night pleasantly to everyone. Then he went outside and reached in through the window to pick up the stack of treasury notes, gold dollars, and small bar of gold bullion. The bar, cut in two, presumably still lies in the ravine somewhere between Denver and Pueblo where it was secreted and later could not be located.

Lane reported that he and all other officers and employees of the mint, being men of great probity, never frequented the horrible gaming dens, and so they were unaware that their pay clerk had been hitting a streak of bad luck (or marked cards) and was deep in hock. The superintendent apologetically defended himself in each of his dispatches to Washington: "That I have been deceived in Mr. Clarke is true, but the recommendations I received from men worthy of confidence whose advice I felt it a duty to respect, his well established character for morality and integrity, his superior qualifications and his pride of character induced me to give him the appointment. . . ." "And whether I do or do not remain as Superintendent of this Mint I wish here to say that it was with pride and satisfaction that I reflected over the names of those I had appointed and called to my aid in the management of this institution. . . ." "If I am censurable after a fair hearing and a full knowledge of all the facts, it must be so. . . ." As Lane nervously anticipated, he was held personally accountable for the $4419 deficit.[5]

[5]Forbes Parkhill documents the Clarke case in "Pioneer Denver Mint Robbery," *The Denver Westerners' Monthly Roundup*, Vol. XIII, Nos. 7 and 8 (July, Aug. 1957).

The Clarke effort has been one of several attempts, indifferently successful, to rob the Denver mint, which today is the well-heeled next-door neighbor of the *Rocky Mountain News*, sitting across Delaware Street from the newspaper plant on underground vaults containing undisclosed billions in gold bricks.

The gold, along with other baser but negotiable currencies, has proved consistently tempting. In 1921 peg-legged Orville Harrington came under suspicion, although he had been a good and faithful mint employee, quiet, meek, and diligent. Then he was arrested for having taken ninety-thousand dollars in gold bars home with him to his modest South Denver bungalow. A favorite Denver legend has been that Orville had his peg leg hollowed out and stomped out the gate each night with, in effect, a gold-lined prosthesis. Actually it wasn't quite that colorful. One of his fellow employees had noticed him fingering a bar and then wrapping it in a bit of cloth. A secret service agent was set to watching Orville and soon found that he was tucking wrapped bars of gold into his clothing when he checked out at night. Agents went out to the Harrington home and dug up the ninety-thousand dollars which the squirrel-like Orville had buried in his basement and back yard. For several years sanguine Denver citizens used to drive by the Harrington home with active little speculations about the possibility there might still be some bars under the garden. The mint said no, that it recovered every ounce of gold that was missing, and it now keeps records to a tolerance of four ten-millionths of an ounce on scales that can weigh a covetous glance.

The next notable mint robbery occurred less than a year later, on December 18, 1922. Lee Casey, for many years Denver's favorite columnist, covered the story for the *News*. He summarized his experience in the preface to a book, *Denver Murders*, which he edited in 1946:

> On that morning I was attending a session of the Colorado Supreme Court, pretending, along with seven justices, to listen to soggy arguments about a writ certiorari. Not because he had more confidence in my knowledge of crime than in my acquaintance with judicial procedure, but simply because I was closer to the spot than anyone else on the staff, the city editor directed me through the bailiff to chase myself three blocks west to the mint, which was then being robbed to the accompaniment of considerable gunfire.
>
> I obeyed, of course—I have always wondered how that writ of certiorari came out—and found the situation, as usual, exaggerated. On the lawn in front of the mint was the body of a guard, killed either by a stray shot by the infantry on his side or by a bullet from the enemy. Nobody ever found out which. The robbers had withdrawn and by the curb was a Reserve Bank truck from which $200,000 in nice, new, passable five-dollar bills was missing, and is missing yet. Scattered about were the sort of people who spring out of the ground

at times like that and get in a reporter's way. Within the building, guarded by steel doors, a platoon of guards directed by Robert J. Grant, superintendent, was firing in the general direction of the gilt on the Capitol dome.

I telephoned a summary of the situation and went to the office to write new leads, precedes, last adds and inserts for every edition through twenty-four hours. If reporters on a morning-and-evening combination dropped dead in those days, as they sometimes did, it seldom was from atrophy.

Promptly, federal, state, county and municipal authorities held a multitude of conferences, offered $5000 of the taxpayers' money for "information leading to, etc.," and a blatant afternoon newspaper published, with somewhat less than its usual assurance, a tagline that Crime Does Not Pay. Conditions soon became normal and Christmas arrived, the Legislature met, and other topics began to occupy public interest. Then, a month after the robbery, a neighborhood plumber went into a a garage he had rented and on which payment was overdue. He found therein a stolen Rickenbacker and a body that was identified as that of one of the mint bandits.

The plumber got $5000 of the taxpayers' money and officials started issuing more statements. They also urged that newspapers quit referring to "The Mint Robbery" and mention instead "The Robbery of a Federal Reserve Bank Truck in Front of the U. S. Mint," just as though that would fit in a two-column head. The people, instead of being out $200,000, were $205,000 shy.

A. A. McVittie, an enterprising restaurateur, attracted business by posting on his window bills whose serial numbers proved they were part of the loot. The $200,000, it developed, had been peddled in St. Paul at a fifty percent discount, which local experts considered extortionate.

As for arrests, there never was one. . . .

Since then the Denver branch of the United States Mint has enjoyed immunity to unauthorized withdrawals. The guards say that among the thousands of tourists who visit the solid gray building each year the inevitable jocularity is, "Are you giving out samples today?"

Very early in the game, when the mint was still a private enterprise of Clark, Gruber & Company, it and the other pioneer Denver banks had to step lively to keep ahead of con artists with calculations on how gold could be won without digging it. There were some inspired counterfeiting attempts that didn't involve crude coinage.

About the middle of June 1861 bogus gold bricks began to show up in Denver countinghouses. One banker bought twenty thousand dollars worth before he got wise. The counterfeiter was aware that bankers customarily took a penknife shaving off the corner of a gold brick or bar for testing in *aqua regia* before purchase. So he built his dross bricks with genuine gold corners that could pass muster. Then, counting on the cupidity of the human race, including bankers, he would offer a brick at a discount, pleading the need for quick cash. The frock-coated financiers, quickly calculating the markup and profit, fell for the deal. It worked— for a while—and the red-faced bankers had to explain how they had come to buy what seemed to be gold so cheaply and with so few questions about its shadowy origins. Some of them even were taken in by false gold dust carefully confected of a small portion of silver filings, particles of glistening quartz, and limestone with coloring matter added. The *News* of March 1, 1862, reported the imitation dust was in circulation and cautioned the unwary and avaricious.

Busy minds also figured out ways to cheat the smelters on gold ore. These usually involved tampering with the assay sample upon which payment for the gross ore tonnage was based. Smelter assayers, frequently with the assistance of the miner bringing in the ore, would drop a small portion of the native ore into a bin to be tested. One enterprising miner discovered that while bending over the sampling bin he could dribble into it from his sleeve a small quantity of finely powered gold and thereby convert country rock into high-grade ore. He boasted following his arrest that he became so adept he could prearrange the assay value of his "ore" to the second decimal point.

Some of the early Denver bunco schemes were scarcely less imaginative than the tall tales and hoaxes which delighted nineteenth-century newspapers, including the *Rocky Mountain News*. Joseph E. Hood, who became an associate editor of the *News*, whipped up one which was republished throughout the country as a fabulous advance in geologic and geographic knowledge. Hood had been with Samuel Bowles' Springfield, Massachusetts, *Republican* before he came west with his Jules Verne fantasies.

With a perfectly straight face he told of an interview with a man who had made an underground voyage from the Great Salt Lake to southern Colorado. Salt Lake, he pointed out, has no known outlet. In southern Colorado there was a lake with no known inlet. The mystery of how this could be now was solved. Hood's voyager had been boating on Salt Lake and was caught in a whirlpool which bore him straight downward into the earth to a great underground river flowing in a tunnellike cavern hung with varicolored stalactites of great beauty. The man's boat was whipped along this nether-world river for a distance of something over six hundred miles at breath-taking speed. Finally he shot upward and popped out on the surface of the Colorado lake. Hood, by virtue of the great and cost-scorning enterprise of the *News*, had obtained an exclusive interview.

S. T. Sopris, later night telegraph editor for the paper, said Hood's story "was copied from the *News* by many papers, East and West, and a goodly number of people swallowed it whole. It was the sensation of the day."[6]

[6]"Early Day Reminiscences," *Trail*, Vol. VII, No. 7 (Dec. 1914).

Everything was bigger and better in the Rockies. Even the mosquitoes. The *News* of August 27, 1859, told of a group of men who were traveling by stage through the pineries and saw in the distance what they supposed to be the frame of a log house under construction in a lonely glen. On approaching they found it was just the skeleton of a mosquito which had starved to death.

Such "news" helped keep the ads apart in a paper which had no telegraphic service. But as the *News* moved toward a daily edition a substitute for the talking wires was being fashioned out of horseflesh. In the spring months of 1860 the paper began to talk of news "by pony."

Looming large in the foreground of nearly everyone's image of the old West is the dashing figure of a small, wiry man on a galloping horse with saddlebags labeled, inaccurately, "U. S. Mail." The Pony Express was a glorious adventure which thrilled a nation. It also was a financial flop. During the eighteen months of its service from April 1860 to October 1861 the express lost $200,000 on a $700,000 operation, and it carried its sponsors, the freighting firm of Russell, Majors & Waddell, into bankruptcy. But the fleet ponies and their nervy riders fired the imagination, and Americans of 1860 shook their heads over a shrinking world. Eight days from the Missouri to San Francisco! "The race is to the swift!" the *Gazette* exulted in St. Joseph, starting point of the pony line. "We are eight days from New York, eighteen days from London!"

The Pony Express spanned half the continent, two thousand miles of prairie, mountain, and desert from St. Joe to Sacramento, with relay points ten to twenty miles apart. Mounts were changed at each station, riders at every third. The mail charge was five dollars for two ounces, and some Eastern newspapers published tissue-paper editions for dispatch by pony. The first run left St. Joseph at 4 P.M. on April 3, 1860, and reached San Francisco at 1 A.M., April 14, for an average speed of about ten miles an hour. The time was better than many railroads of the day maintained, and over a longer distance.

The audacious enterprise had been announced late in March with ads in the New York *Herald* and the Washington *Star*, the latter then owned by W. H. Russell of Russell, Majors & Waddell. Plans specified once-a-week service in each direction on schedules which called upon the riders to hold an average pace of eight miles an hour. Later in the summer this was advanced to twice-weekly service and the speed set at ten miles an hour, or eight days from the Missouri to Sacramento. The riders, sixty of them, were hand-picked for light weight, courage, and general fitness. Their assignment demanded that they ride about seventy-five miles with only two brief stops to switch horses, but sometimes they were required to double back and ride a second course without rest. Smiley records the feat of one pony rider who in an emergency covered 384 miles with time out only for hasty meals and mount changes.

Denver was off the main route of the Pony Express, which came up the Platte, crossed the South Platte near Julesburg in northeastern Colorado, and then swung through Wyoming to cross the Continental Divide on the easier grade later followed by the Pacific Railroad. A branch line was established, however, between Denver and Julesburg over which lathered horses began to bring the *News* phenomenally "hot" dispatches only four or five days old. In the autumn of 1860 the News Printing Company contracted with the Pony Express for the regular delivery of telegraphic news from St. Joseph, 660 miles away as the ponies ran.

One of the first items of news "by pony" appeared in the paper dated May 30, 1860. It was datelined Chicago, and it brought a new name into prominence in Denver.

> On the 18th inst. Hon. A. Lincoln of Illinois was nominated for president, received 354 votes, Seward on the same ballot receiving 110½ votes, Dayton one, McLean one-half. His nomination was received with immense applause, and guns were fired throughout the city.

A few weeks later, on June 27, the *News* still was amazed by the rapid communication of modern times. The headlines read:

LATEST NEWS

BY THE PONY EXPRESS!

FASTEST TIME ON RECORD!!

HURRA FOR THE PONY!!!

> By the coach that arrived yesterday morning we received dispatches from our St. Joseph correspondent, to the morning of the 22d, forwarded by Pony Express to the South Platte crossing, and from there by the C. O. C. & P. P. Express Company's coach, reaching us in the unprecedented short time of four days and six hours. . . .

The dispatches didn't amount to much; the big news was the pony itself.

By November, when the nation went to the polls in one of the key elections of American history, the *News* was publishing daily and Pony Express news was highly important to the operation. When the express left St. Joseph on November 8 it carried a special envelope addressed to A. Benham Esq. in Julesburg for forwarding to the *Rocky Mountain News*. On the outside of the envelope someone wrote what it contained: "Election News. Lincoln Elected." The pony riders also shouted out the news like prairie Paul Reveres to passers-by along the trail. Albert Richardson had left the *News* staff a day or two earlier and was headed east to join the New York *Tribune*. He wrote that the first word he had of Lincoln's election came in the middle of the night as his coach rocked eastward. A Pony Expressman rode past in the opposite direction and sang out the word to the coach passengers.

The important envelope arrived in Denver four days after it left the end of the telegraph wires on the Missouri, and the *News* published the details of Lincoln's victory in an extra on November 12. The story was pirated immediately by the *Herald*, with which the *News* still was feuding bitterly and interminably. The theft was denounced with some vigor in the *News* for November 14:

> We have in our day seen many newspapers of all kinds of principles, and of no principles at all, but never have we known one, no matter how low its pretentions or groveling its nature, that was conducted with such utter disregard of truth, honesty and common decency as the *Rocky Mountain Herald* of this city.
>
> Monday morning it pretends to publish election returns "by Pony Express especially for the *Herald*"—a statement as false as the general principles of that foul, dirty sheet. It never received ANY dispatches by Pony, but steals them from the *News* and palms them off upon its readers as legitimately belonging to itself.

As the divided nation moved closer and closer to war Lincoln's inaugural message was awaited, east and west as well as north and south, with anxiety and intense interest. Except for the fragile line of pony relays, California's news was twenty-one days coming by steamship via Panama, and the new territory of Colorado was scarcely less isolated. Yet both wanted to know at the earliest possible moment what the lanky new President would say. The Pony Express made special arrangements to speed the news. Relay points were moved closer together. Time allotted for change-overs was cut. When the message came on March 4 (". . . there needs to be no bloodshed or violence, and there shall be none unless it be forced upon the national authority . . ."), the words were sped from St. Joseph to Sacramento in seven days and seventeen hours, and to Denver in two days and twenty-one hours. The pony making the final run into Denver with dispatches for the *News* covered ten miles in thirty-one minutes. (The full text of Lincoln's message came more slowly by coach. The *News* published some three columns of it on March 11 and ended abruptly with: "[Here the coach came along, and the report was stopped.]")

Despite its heroic swiftness, the system of tough little men and fast horses was doomed. Congress had passed an act providing for the Pacific Telegraph, and the wires were inching westward from Omaha. By April they had reached Fort Kearney in western Nebraska, and in October the eastward- and westward-advancing lines would meet at Salt Lake City. Until then the Pony Express filled in the steadily diminishing gap. When the express at last gave way to a completed strand of wire the *News* established its own pony relays to bring news from the telegraph offices in, first, Fort Kearney and then Julesburg. At what must have been ruinous expense for the times the paper maintained its private express for another two years until a branch telegraph line was strung into Denver from Julesburg. Both the *News* and the *Herald* also maintained pony express lines to Black Hawk, Central City, Nevada, and Missouri City, towns which had come into being in and about the Gregory Diggings. The papers had offices in Central, and there was brisk competition to see who could get there first with the latest edition. The racing ponies pounded into the mountain towns with papers only three to four hours off the presses, and this was regarded as high journalistic enterprise in 1861.

Dispatches received by the *News* via combined telegraph and pony express were brief and undetailed. Although "Reported from the Associated Press" appears for the first time December 10, 1860, the great national and international news-gathering agencies of the present day were unknown. Special correspondents had to be hired to forward telegraphic news borrowed freely from distant newspapers and other sources. Remote editors like Byers begged, copied, or stole their national and overseas news, and were grateful for what they could get.

Speed of news handling was stepped up when the telegraph line finally got to Denver in September of 1863. The city, pushed along by *News* editorials, subscribed thirty-five thousand dollars to string the wire down from Julesburg. But when the civic dignitaries gathered in a little office over the Warren Hussey & Company bank at Fifteenth and Market streets on October 1 to dispatch the historic first message, the key was dead. A storm had severed the line even before it could be placed in operation. Ten days later repairs had been completed, and Mayor Amos Steck exchanged congratulatory messages with the mayor of Omaha. Denver at last was in communication with the outside world at a pace faster than a horse's. For another decade or more, however, the linkage with civilization would be a tenuous one. Indians would tear down the wires for ornaments, or war parties would cut them to hamper cavalry pursuit. Trigger-happy cowboys would use the insulators to sharpen their aim. And the great, shaggy buffalo used the poles as scatching posts. A big bull luxuriously massaging his tough hide could easily topple a pole, and as it went down the brittle iron wire would snap. Denver again was plunged back into isolation, and the *News* would have to apologize to its readers because "the line is down somewhere east." No news today.

Telegraph tolls were high—nearly a dollar a word to New York—and news was skeletonized to the barest minimum. Fifty or a hundred words would come in, virtually in code, and it was the task of the *News* telegraph editor, a post of new and shining eminence, to expand this into more extensive reports in approximate English. S. T. Sopris, who held the job in the sixties, recalled that he "had to keep well informed as to names of places, generals, rivers and the like, in order to give the readers a clear understanding of what was going on. . . . Every page of the reports was a 'missing word' contest and a producer of headaches." The night telegraph editor had other difficulties too. Sopris described them thus:

> . . . The last report for the day reached the Denver office about midnight, and it was part of my day's work to walk down there, wait for "30" and then hike back to the office. There were no street lamps and for much of the way wooden "awnings", mere sheds they were, extended the full width of the sidewalk, intensifying, if possible, the Cimmerian darkness usual at that hour. At and around the north corner of Larimer and Fifteenth streets were a cluster of Grocery stores: Davis & Clarke, L. D. Reithmann, Isaac Underwood and Mitchell & Sons.
>
> Along about 10 o'clock P.M. Johnnie Murphy's cows would meander down from Curtis street to forage along the fronts of the grocery shops for such stray cabbage leaves, potatoes and other vegetables as might have been left outside after closing time. Having made a clean-up, the blamed cows would lie down on the sidewalk, to await the coming of "Aurora, the goddess of morn, with rosy fingers dripping gentle dews," and then hie themselves homeward. After sprawling over a few of them, I adopted the plan of taking to the middle of the street, greatly to the relief of the cows, who seemed to object to my intrusions upon their privacy. . . .

The active Byers, of course, was not content merely to be a passive recipient of news dispatches by wire. He had to get into the game itself. He was one of the organizers in 1866 of the United States & Mexico Telegraph Company, a director and vice-president of the firm. He surveyed and personally supervised construction of the first telegraph line south from Denver to New Mexico, completed in 1868. His diary for March of that year tells of setting poles through a storm which left three feet of snow on the ground.

With the completion of the original line in 1863, his newspaper began to take form which would be recognizable by present-day readers of the daily press. The News was no longer exclusively an insular recorder of boar fights in the street or saloon rumpuses. The pulse of the world, however attenuated by high telegraph tolls, was beginning to flow in its veins. Fire, flood, and Confederate raiders still had to be contended with, and wild Indians yet would be troublesome to press and city, but modern times were arriving.

CHAPTER NINE

Fire, Flood, and Recognition

D ENVER in the early 1860s was a tinderbox town waiting for a spark. Most of the flimsy buildings which clustered around the Larimer, McGaa (Market), and Blake street crossings of the creek were built of logs or rough, unmilled clapboards sawed from pitch-filled native pine. Wooden awnings, arcades, and balconies extended over plank sidewalks where loose or missing boards were traps for the unwary of foot. A few of the "business blocks" towered to two stories. A lot more pretended to such architectural glory with false fronts. In the commercial district the structures stood cheek by jowl without room for a yellow cat to squeeze between them. Most of the homes still were log cabins. A few were frame, and some of these were prettied up with wooden fretwork lace at the eaves. As gestures to gentility the interior walls and ceilings of more pretentious homes often were hung with cheesecloth or sheeting in lieu of wallpaper. Roofs were of wooden shingles or rough-split shakes. Nearly everything was inflammable.

And the pioneers, whatever other virtues they possessed of close husbandry and vigilance, were careless with fire. They had casually burned off the forests around the Gregory Diggings. Their campfires were left to smolder for days or weeks. They set prairie fires, stored powder in wooden shanties, and, as has been related, tried to burn down the offices of offensive newspapermen.

With a population of cheerful arsonists and a ready supply of fuel, an incendiary future might have been predicted.

The Byers family had an advance sample, very nearly disastrous, of what was in store for the city. Their house burned down on the evening of October 12, 1860. They had moved in June from the two rooms at the rear of the printing office to a frame house luxuriously lined with muslin. The flames can be imagined. Mrs. Byers and the older children, Frank and Mollie, got out safely, but the baby, born earlier that year, had to be grabbed from a blazing crib. The infant survived the close brush only to die a few months later of natural causes. (The Byerses had four children, two of whom lived to adulthood.) Neighbors and printers from the office pitched in to fight the fire, but the house was a total loss. Elizabeth Byers wrote that she lost "all my pretty homelike things," and the family had to start over again with only the few household items saved from the flames. A card of thanks was published in the *News*, expressing gratitude to "those neighbors and citizens, who so kindly and promptly lent the aid of their hands last night" and voicing "the wish that they may never be like sufferers."

On July 15, 1862, an uneasy City Council finally decided to remedy the total lack of fire-fighting facilities. A resolution was adopted providing for the organizing and equipping of a volunteer hook-and-ladder company and two bucket brigades. But the cart and buckets still were on order and the fire department only on paper when the night of April 19, 1863, arrived.

The spring had been a dry one, and high winds had lashed plains and town. One was blowing in fitful, compass-boxing gusts between 2 and 3 A.M. on April 19 when flames burst through the roof at the rear of the Cherokee House on the southwest corner of Fifteenth and Blake streets, less than three blocks away from the *News* office. The shifting wind spread the fire in all directions, hurling it across streets and from roof to roof of the dry, resinous buildings. Every man in town was called out as a fire fighter. Buildings were torn down to halt spread of the fire, but two or three hours later at dawn the heart of the city was a black, smoking waste. Heaps of char marked the locations of many of the most substantial businesses. The total loss was estimated at three hundred and fifty thousand dollars, a stiff blow for a four-year-old town.

The *News* itself, perched on its stilts in Cherry Creek, escaped the flames, although the trickle of a stream would have interposed no barrier had the chances of the wind's turning been otherwise. But the paper had lost some of its best advertisers and customers: Broadwell & Cook, the Cherokee House, W. S. Cheesman, the City Bakery, Daniels & Brown, Tritch Hardware, the Elephant Corral, Nye & Co. Prices of provisions doubled within a few days, and times were lean until new ox trains of supplies came through.

Rebuilding started almost immediately, however, and the fire proved a bonanza for small boys. They poked about in the charred ruins and picked up nails. The *News* of May 7 said some of them were finding a hundred to two hundred pounds a day and netting five to ten dollars for their efforts. The secondhand nails went into the new buildings, but the construction was different. Denver rebuilt largely with brick, and the "Great Fire of '63" became the dividing line between architectural eras.

The *News* lived through Denver's first major disaster with only secondary damages, but it would not be twice lucky. The paper would pay a total penalty for disregarding nature's laws and an Indian's warning.

Cherry Creek carried so little water, even during the spring runoff, that the town straddling it came to regard it as a dry stream. Originally the small flowing rivulet wandered amiably down a bed of white sand one hundred yards or more in width. The bottoms of fine sand and occasional seeps were only an annoyance; heavy wagons would now and then get stuck in them. So they were bridged, after a fashion, at several busy points. Dikes were graded out from the slightly higher ground on either bank to carry roadways to short bridges just high enough to let spring waters pass beneath. Then the town itself crowded in on both sides with City Hall, Methodist Church, printing office, banks, saloons, and homes. It is not clear why the pioneers went to the added expense of putting down pilings to get firm foundations when good, flat town lots were available for a few dollars or a horse, but they did. It is also not clear why some of them, nature-wise as pioneers are supposed to be, did not read in the white, clean-washed sands of the channel testimony of occasional high water. But they didn't.

As they rebuilt after the fire they encroached farther and farther into the stream bed. The *News* already had taken its position there and was merrily turning out its daily and weekly editions with exclamatory promises that soon it would be forced to print "800 copies!" every day. Bliss and Rounds retired from the News Printing Company in 1863, and now it was once more "Byers & Dailey, props."

The *News* appears to have had a premonition that its "neutral ground" position may have been a wise political move in the intracity squabbles but that topography might be no respecter of the subtle arts of diplomacy. Back in 1860 there had been a heavy rain to the southeast and the creek had risen moderately. Byers commented on August 1: "Cherry Creek appears to present a rather serious problem, for we have had a demonstration of what may be expected from a heavy rainfall on the Divide, though we are not yet inclined to believe the Indian claims that the whole settlement is subject to flood." (The editor was not referring to the Continental Divide in the mountains; "the Divide" to the early settlers was the high ground at the headwaters of Cherry Creek which separates the drainage basins of the South Platte and Arkansas rivers.)

Some time later, with rueful afterthought, Byers would recall what a deep-lined old Arapaho had said as he watched the town building. He didn't understand, the patriarch told the young editor, why the white men were building their village in the creek bottom. That was where the floods came down. He and his people had seen "big water" to a depth, "so," and he held his hands high above his head. Plainsmen and mountaineers also had warned of a prairie phenomenon later to be known as a "flash flood," but then of course everyone knew those old gaffers as yarn spinners of rare ability.

The flood hit a year, a month and a day after the fire.

During the week before May 19, 1864, there had been heavy rains over the headwaters of Cherry Creek, soaking the high plains to saturation. Wild, black thunderheads hung over the area. A pleasant shower laid the dust in Denver on May 19, but a rainbow appeared at dusk, and after dark the moon shone brightly. The creek had risen some, but the town paid it no mind and went to bed contentedly.

Suddenly, sometime after midnight, the placid little brook changed its disposition.

For an account of what happened that night there is no more inspired a witness than Professor O. J. Goldrick, journalist, pedagogue, and stylist. His lyric essay on the memorable flood has become the most famous news article in the annals of Denver journalism. It deserves full reproduction here. The headline went: "Sketch of the Great Deluge in Denver."

About the midnight hour of Thursday, the nineteenth instant, when almost all in town were knotted in the peace of sleep, deaf to all noise and blind to all danger, snoring in calm security, and seeing visions of remoteness radiant with the rainbow hues of past associations, or roseate with the gilded hopes of the fanciful future—while the full-faced queen of night shed showers of fertility, garnishing and suffusing sleeping nature with her balmy brightness, fringing the feathery cottonwoods with lustre, enameling the housetops with coats of pearl, bridging the erst placid Platte with beams of radiance, and bathing the arid sands of Cherry creek with dewy beauty—a frightful phenomenon sounded in the distance, and a shocking calamity presently charged upon us. The few who had not retired to bed, broke from their buildings to see what was coming. Hark! what and where is this? A torrent or a tornado? And where can it be coming from, and whither going? These were the questions soliloquized and spoken, one to the other. Has creation's God forsaken us, and has chaos come again? Our eyes might bewilder and our ears deceive, but our hearts, all trembling, and our sacred souls soon whispered what it was—the thunders of omnipotence warning us "there's danger on the wing," with death himself seeming to prompt our preparation for the terrible alternative of destruction or defence; Presently the great noise of mighty waters, like the roaring of Niagara, or the rumbling of an enraged Etna, burst upon us, distinctly and regularly in its sounding steps as the approach of a tremendous train of locomotives. There was soon a hurrying to and fro in terror, trying to wake up one's relatives and neighbors, while some favored few who were already dressed, darted out of doors, and clamorously called their friends to climb the adjacent bluffs and see with certainty for themselves. Alas, and wonderful to behold! it was the water engine of death dragging its destroying train of maddened waves, that defied the eye to number them, which was rushing down upon us, now following its former channel, and now tunneling direct through banks and bottoms a new channel of its own. Alarm flew around, and all alike were ignorant of what to think, or say, or do, much less of knowing where to go with safety, or to save others. A thousand thoughts flitted o'er us, and a thousand terrors thrilled us through. What does this mean? where has this tremendous flood or freshet, this terrific torrent come from? Has the Platte switched off from its time-worn trace and turned its treasure down to deluge us? Have the wild waterspouts from all the clouds at once conspired to drain their upper cisterns, and thus drench us here in death? Have the firm foundations of the great deep burst forth on fallen men, regardless of that rainbow covenant which spanned in splendor yon arc of sky last evening? Is the world coming to an end, or special wreck of matter impending? These, and thoughts like these, troubled the most fearless souls.

Its Progress of Destruction.

Now the torrent, swelled and thickened, showed itself in sight, sweeping tremendous trees and dwelling houses before it—a mighty volume of impetuous water, wall-like in its advancing front, as was the old Red Sea when the Israelites walked through it and volcano-like in its floods of foaming, living lava, as it rolled with maddened momentum directly towards the Larimer street bridge and gorged, afterwards rebounding with impetuous rage and striking the large Methodist church and the adjoining buildings, all of which it wrested from their foundations and engulphed in the yawn of bellowing billows as they broke over the McGaa street bridge. Like death, leveling all things in its march, the now overwhelming flood upheaved the bridge and the two buildings by it, Messrs. Charles & Hunt's law offices, in the latter of which C. Bruce Haynes was sleeping, whom, with the volocity of a cataract, it launched asleep and naked on the watery ocean of eternity, to find his final, fatal refuge only in the flood-gate port of death! Poor Haynes! Your summons came, but 'twas short and sudden, after and not before you had "wrapped the drapery" of your humble couch about you, and had lain down to "pleasant dreams." Precipitately and in paroxysms the tempestuous torrent swept along, now twenty feet in the channel's bed, and bridging bank to bank with billows high as hills piled upon hills —with broken buildings, tables, bedsteads, baggage, boulders, mammoth trees, leviathan logs and human beings buffeted with the billowcrests, and beckoning us to save them. But there we stood, and there the new made banks and distant bluffs were dotted with men and families, but poorly and partly dressed, deploring with dumb amazement the catastrophe in sight. The waters like a pall were spreading over all the inhabited lower parts of town and townsite. Nature shook about us. The azure meads of heaven were darkened as in death, and the fair Diana with her starry train, though defended by the majesty of darkness all around her, and by batteries of thick clouds in front, looked down on shuddering silence dimly, as if lost in the labyrinth of wonder and amazement at the volume and vast abyss into which we all expected to be overwhelmed. Next reeled the dear old office of the *Rocky Mountain News*, that pioneer of hardship and of honor, which here nobly braved the battle and the breeze for five full years and a month, regularly without intermission or intimidation, and down it sank, with its union flag staff, into the maelstrom of the surging waters, soon to appear and disappear, between the waves, as, wild with starts, in mountains high, they rose and rolled, as if endeavoring to form a dread alliance with the clouds, and thus consumate our general wreck.

Before this a few moments, one of the proprietors, Mr. J. L. Dailey, and four of the young gentlemen employees, who had been asleep in the building, awoke to realize the peril of their critical situation, and without time to save anything at all in the whole establishment, not even their trunks at their bedsides, or watches on the table-stands, they fortunately escaped, by jumping out of a side window, down into the eddy water caused by a drift which had formed against the building, and thence by the aid of ropes and swimming, struck the shore, on the instant of time to see the sorrowful sight of their building, stock, material, money, all, even to the lot on which it stood (for which all $12,000 would have been refused a few hours previously), uptorn, and yet scattered to the four winds of heaven, or sunk, shattered in sand banks between here and the States.

Higher, broader, deeper, and swifter boiled the waves of water, as the mass of flood, freighted with treasure, trees and live stock, leaped towards the Blake street bridge, prancing with the violence of a fiery steed stark mad:

"Fierce as ten furies, terrible as hell."

Great God! and are we all "gone up," and is there no power to stem the tide was asked all round. But no; as if that nature demanded it, or there was need of the severe lesson it teacheth to the citizens of town, the waves dashed higher still, and the volume of water kept on eroding bluffs and bank, and undermining all the stone and foundations in its rapid course.

The inundation of the Nile, the Noachian deluge, and that of Prometheus' son, Deucalien, the Noah of the Greeks, were now in danger of being out-deluged by this great phenomenon of '64.

Oh! it was indescribably and inconceivably awful to behold that spectacle of terrible grandeur, as the moon would occasionally shed her rays on the surges of the muddy waves, whose angry thundering drowned all other noise, and to hear the swooping of the death angel as he flew o'er the troubled surface, suggesting the idea of death and destruction in the wild tumults of the torrent!

Previous to this had gone towards the ocean-like delta of the creek and Platte, the Blake street bridge, General Bowen's law office, Metz's saddlery shop, F. A. Clark's and Mr. McKee's stores, the City Hall buildings and jail, together with Cass & Co.'s old Bank, Stickney's brick, and Tilton & Co.'s adjoining brick emporium, all with a crash and speedy disappearance in the current stateward bound, and with not a few people as passengers aboard. Now we see a youth, white with wan despair, and a child stiff in the cramps of death, popping his head up stories high on the river's surface, only to be struck senseless by an overtaking tree or solid sheet of water, thereafter thence, when the roaring of the raging elements, exemplification of the Almighty's voice and power, will tell their only funeral knell as calamity's sad corpse on sorrow's hearse is carried to its watery grave, with a watery winding-sheet and melancholy moonlight for its shroud! Verily, "the Lord giveth and taketh away," yet "shall mortal man be more just than his maker?"

More About the Freshet.

For about five hours, up to daylight, the floods in Cherry creek and in the Platte were growing gradually, spreading over West Denver and the Platte bottoms in the eastern and western wards of town, divided by Cherry creek, and bounded westerly by the then booming Platte. For squares up Cherry creek, on either side of its old channel, and along to its entrance into the Platte, the adjoining flats were inundated, and the buildings thereon made uncomfortable if not unsafe by the amount of water carpeting their floors to a depth of from one to five feet deep. Blake street was covered to a foot in depth in water with mire, and the basements of many of its stores were solid cisterns of muddy water. From the Buffalo House to the site of F street bridge, on the East Denver flats, was one shining sea of water. Most of the settlers had to leave their homes and household goods, and made up town to escape the inundation. The same was the case with the majority of the citizens on the west side also. There it was still deeper and more dangerous, and there, too, it proved more destructive to the residents and residences.

Scores and scores of the families from Camp Weld, along down to the foot of Ferry street and thence southwesterly to the old site of Chubbuck's bridge, were surprised in their sleep, and surrounded by an oceanic expanse of water from the overflowing Platte. Many found their floors flooded from three to six feet deep with water before they knew it, or had waking warning to escape for their lives, and gladly leave the frame structures and their furniture and fixtures to float down with the flood. 'Twas here that the most severe and serious losses and privations were encountered. 'Twas here, West Denver, along Front street, Fifth street, Cherry street, and Ferry, as well as all over the streets of the southwestern bottoms, that the gallant officers and men of the Colorado First, together with several of the citizens, showed their timely presence and their truly great assistance, rescuing families from their flooded homes, and removing them on horseback and otherwise, to distant dwellings high and dry.

During this time, which lasted a few hours, commencing about daylight's dawn, the scenes of sorrow and of suffering should have been seen to be appreciated, to draw forth due gratitude to the rescuers for the self-sacrifice they showed. Many of the families, women and children, had to flee in their sleeping habiliments, having neither time nor inclination to squander in search of their "good clothes." Thanks and remembrances eternal to all of those active, noble souls on the several sides of town who worked from the noon of night to next noonday assisting the sufferers and aiding the citizens in all good efforts and good works.

'Twas not till daylight that the chocked up Cherry creek completely spread itself and formed independent confederations, one stream running down Front street, deep and impetuous enough to launch a good-sized building from its foundations; another down Cherry street, conclusively gutting the street and blockading the dwellings' doors with "wood and water" up almost to their very lintels. On Ferry a lively river flowed, five or more feet deep, with a current strong enough to make a Hudson river steamer hop along its waves. The Ferry street and F street bridges fell early in the flood, and the erosions in the estuary at the latter entirely changed the river's bed, forming a new cycloidal channel nearly an eighth of a mile to the westward. The same freaks were exhibited by Cherry creek during its twelve hour lunacy, leaving the old time bed, and breaking another farther north, by undermining the bluffs, and excavating and upheaving old alluvial mounds without ceremony. Now this celebrated creek resembles a respectable river, with a prospect of a perpetual, flowing stream throughout the year, instead of selfishly sinking in the sands some miles above, as heretofore. Its having defined its position and established its base for future operations, will prove a good thing to the town eventually, notwithstanding it falls heavily on hundreds for the present.

Origin of the Flood.

For a few days previous, there was an abnormal amount of rain at the heads of Cherry creek and Plum creek, along the water-shed range of the divide, so much so that it terrified tillers of the soil, and threatened their cultivated fields with failure. On Thursday afternoon it rained there incessantly, so that the natives knew not whether the cistern clouds had lost their bottoms, or had burst asunder altogether. It would shower hail-stones as large as hen's eggs one hour, and during the next hour it would literally pour down waterspout sheets of rain from reservoirs not over two hundred feet above, while a few minutes more would wash the hail away, and leave four feet of water on the level fields. And this ponderous downpouring was so terrible that it instantly inundated and killed several thousand sheep and some cattle that were corraled at ranches in that region. This phenomenon will plausibly prepare us to believe that the "dry cimarron" beyond Bent's Fort, the Ocate, the Pecos, and large but partially dry *aroyas* of New Mexico were formerly what the "exaggerating" mountaineers have heretofore assured our infidel minds were but stubborn matters of facts. Even at this present writing, and in our own immediate neighborhood, it will not be believed what startling changes have been made by the alluvial developments of last Friday, unless you have your auditors accompany you to the theatre of the tempestuous flood, on Cherry creek and elsewhere, so that seeing becomes believing.

Items and Incidents.

The spirit of departed day had joined communion with the myriad ghosts of centuries, and four full hours fled into eternity before the citizens of many parts of town found out there was a freshet here at all!

Denver in 1859. A wood engraving of Larimer Street, looking northeastward from Cherry Creek, as pictured by an artist for *Frank Leslie's Illustrated Newspaper*, Aug. 20, 1859.

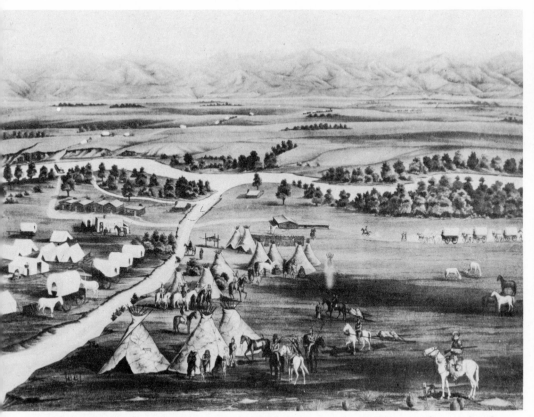

Auraria, left, and Denver City, right, in 1859. From a painting by an unknown hand in the Western Collection, Denver Public Library. Cherry Creek at left. South Platte River across the middle distance.

Before the flood. A photo from the early 1860s showing the *News* office built on stilts in the bed of Cherry Creek. The deluge of May 20, 1864, swept it away.

Auraria viewed across Cherry Creek from Denver City on the morning after the memorable flood of '64. At upper left is the printing office of the *Commonwealth*, purchased by the drowned-out *News*.

O pioneers! The *News* moved into this log cabin in Auraria in December 1859. Photo was taken shortly before it was dismantled in 1900. The cabin also saw duty as jail, guardhouse, and stable.

A night view of the present *Rocky Mountain News* building, occupied in 1952.

The *News* office when it occupied the ground floor of the Markham Hotel, 17th and Lawrence streets, 1897-1901. Horse-and-wagon delivery.

(Above) The Patterson & Thomas Block, later the Quincy Building, at 17th and Curtis streets, home of the *News* from 1887 to 1897. *News* office can be seen faintly at right of main entrance. Site is now a parking lot. *(Below)* The *News* building at 1720 Welton Street, 1901 to 1952. The site is now a parking lot.

Western Collection, Denver Public Library

(Above) Editorial room of the *News* as seen by an artist for *Beadle's Monthly,* June 1866. Note the armaments. *(Below)* The *News* shared its proud "brick block" with the stage-coach office. Building was completed in 1866. It stood at 389 (now 1547) Larimer Street.

Western Collection, Denver Public Library

At home with the editor's family, 1862. Byers, his wife and children on their Platte River ranch at Denver's outskirts. They were rescued by boat from this house in the flood of 1864.

A volu
News
Mississi

The *News'* birthplace: "Uncle Dick" Wootton's saloon and store in pioneer Auraria, 1859. The first edition came out of the attic. The Wootton building as conceived by an artist for *Frank Leslie's Illustrated Newspaper*, Aug. 20, 1859.

Word of Lincoln's election reached the *News* via Pony Express.

Argonaut on the rocks. A woodcut illustration from Albert D. Richardson's *Beyond the Mississippi,* 1867.

Pike's Peaker in full regalia. This crude woodcut was the first illustration to appear in the *News*.

Armed neutrality. The *News* office about the time of the editor's kidnaping, as depicted in Albert D. Richardson's *Beyond the Mississippi*. The bearded scrivener at right presumably represents Edward Bliss.

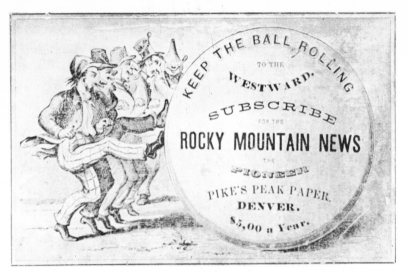

Manifest Destiny in action. An early promotion piece for the *News*.

A long-continued *Rocky Mountain News* campaign finally pays off:
Statehood for Colorado, 1876. Jerome B. Chaffee, territorial delegate
to Congress, presents the maiden Miss Colorado to Columbia. In
the group of Colorado leaders at left, Editor Byers is the dark-
bearded one whose head appears immediately to the left of Miss
Colorado. Profile of John Evans, second territorial governor, at
left foreground. Governor's Guard at right. From a contemporary
newspaper drawing.

One of the causes of the commotion. Title page from the rare Pike's Peak guidebook issued by Byers in the winter of 1859. Reproduced from the facsimile edited by Nolie Mumey and LeRoy R. Hafen.

Rocky Mountain News

A Scripps-Howard Newspaper

Colorado's First Newspaper—Founded in 1859

100TH YEAR, NO. 174

Published every morning by Denver Publishing Co.
Entered as second class matter, postoffice, Denver.

DENVER 1, COLO., MONDAY, OCT. 13, 1958

HOME
FINAL
★ ★ ★ ★
FORECAST:
Fair
PRICE 5 CENTS
76 PAGES

ROCKET DIVES BACK TO EARTH

Cherry Hills Mother Saves Baby
—STORY ON PAGE 5

Heidi Ann Henkel smiles in play after her narrow scrape with death Sunday. The 8-month-old infant toppled into a fish pond in the rear yard of her home at 4500 S. Lafayette st., Cherry Hills, and was rescued by her mother, Mrs. Denny Henkel. Mrs. Henkel saved the tot's life by applying artificial respiration she learned in a first aid class. Beau, the family French poodle and Heidi Ann's playmate, takes it easy after the harrowing experience.

—Rocky Mountain News Photo by Bob Talkin.

79,120 Mi. Altitude Reached by Pioneer; End Is Blaze of Glory

Compiled from UPI and AP Dispatches

WASHINGTON, Oct. 12—Pioneer, America's moon rocket, plunged back to earth at about 9 p.m. Denver time Sunday and disintegrated in a blaze of glory.

After soaring 79,120 miles into outer space—farther than any man-made object ever has gone before—the Pioneer lost its thrust at 5:42 a.m. Denver time Sunday and began hurtling back to earth.

The Air Force said it is assumed the missile burned up upon re-entering the earth's atmosphere at a point estimated to be over the South Pacific Ocean.

No reports of visual observation of re-entry were received.

Tracking Station Loses Contact

The Air Force issued an announcement that said:

"The Hawaiian tracking station lost contact with the U.S. Pioneer lunar probe vehicle at 11:46 p.m. EDT (8:46 p.m. Denver time).

"It was the last tracking station in the lunar probe tracking and communications network to receive signals.

"Analysis of the data received by the Hawaiian station indicates that the Pioneer re-entered the earth's atmosphere at approximately midnight (9 p.m. Denver time) and is assumed to have burned up upon re-entry.

"The re-entry point was estimated to be over the South Pacific, latitude about 20 degrees south, longitude about 106 degrees west."

During the last two hours of the historic flight, the Air Force said repeated efforts were made to fire the retro rocket on Pioneer, but no confirmation of successful firing was received.

Attempt at Orbit of Earth

Attempts to fire the retro or terminal rocket in the nose of the satellite's payload were made in an effort to divert the Pioneer into orbit around the earth.

The final velocity was estimated at 34,425 feet per second, the same speed attained shortly after liftoff at Cape Canaveral, Fla., early Saturday.

In New York, President Eisenhower congratulated all those responsible for launching Pioneer into space.

"Already it is clear," the President said, "that it will yield knowledge of great benefit to mankind." He added that this flight is a tremendous achievement which has "truly pioneered in deep penetration into outer space."

(Concluded on Page 3)

The *Rocky Mountain News* as it appears today.

ROCKY MOUNTAIN NEWS.

THE MINES AND MINERS OF KANSAS AND NEBRASKA.

VOL. 1.   CHERRY CREEK, K. T., SATURDAY, APRIL 23. 1859.   NO. 1.

Rocky Mountain News.

WM. N. BYERS & CO.,
Editors, Publishers and Proprietors.
CHERRY CREEK, K. T.

Terms—Five Dollars per annum in advance.
Single Copies for Mail, 25 cents.

RATES OF ADVERTISING:
Business Cards, (3 lines or less) 1 year, $12.00

JOB PRINTING,

In a dispatch, in the best manner, and on reasonable terms.

BUSINESS CARDS.

A. F. PECK, M. D.
PHYSICIAN AND SURGEON,
Cache-a-La-Poudre, Nebraska.

HERNDON HOUSE.
Omaha City, Nebraska.

MILLER & RICHARDSON,
PROPRIETORS.

SAHLER & CO.,
BANKERS, COLLECTORS, LAND
AND GENERAL AGENTS,
A3A CITY, NEBRASKA.

CASADY & TEST,
Attorneys & Counsellors at Law
AND
GENERAL LAND AGENTS,
Council Bluffs, Iowa.

BALDWIN & DODGE,
BANKERS & DEALERS IN EXCHANGE,
Council Bluffs, Iowa.

FRANK STREET,
ATTORNEY AT LAW,
Land Agent and Conveyancer,
Council Bluffs, Iowa.

A. COCHRAN,
—DEALER IN—
LANDS, LOTS & LAND WARRANTS,
COUNCIL BLUFFS, IOWA.

B. R. PEGRAM,
No. 1 Broadway, Council Bluffs, Iowa.
Wholesale and Retail dealer in Dry Goods, Groceries, Boots and Shoes, Provisions, Outfitting goods, &c., &c.

THE OPENING OF JAPAN.

The present age is signalized by the rapid succession of striking events in the history of divine providence. Nations and continents which had maintained a rigid exclusiveness, or had been enveloped in unbroken obscurity, are now brought into friendly communication with the rest of mankind...

ALPHABETICAL CONUNDRUMS.

Why is the letter A, like a cow idiot? Because it is in the middle of day.

Why is the letter B, like a hot fire? Because it makes oil hot.

THE WORLD WITHOUT A SABBATH.

What would it be? Labor without rest; care without solace; probation without preparation; a night without day...

COMMUNICATIONS RECEIVED BY THE NEBRASKA IMMIGRATION SOCIETY.

MONROE, N. T. Nov. 30, 1858.

DEAR SIR: The Circular of the Nebraska Immigration Society of which you are Secretary has been received, and I will cheerfully give any information that I can, at any and all times. In regard to...

L. GERARD.

YANKEE VISIT TO CARLYLE.

The Rev. Theodore Clapp, of New Orleans, in an autobiography, gives the following account of his introduction to the "Great Censor of the Age," Thomas Carlyle...

FARMING VS. GOLD DIGGING.

The First Edition of the *Rocky Mountain News.*

BRASS-KNUCK BONFILS
JUST EATS 'EM ALIVE

SENATOR THOS. M. PATTERSON, SLUGGED FROM BEHIND ON A VACANT LOT IN BROAD DAYLIGHT

THOS. J. O'DONNELL, AMBUSHED AND SLUGGED IN DENVER COURTHOUSE IN BROAD DAYLIGHT

WHO'S NEXT?

THIS BLANK SPACE MAY BE FILLED WITH SOMEBODY'S PICTURE SOON; **YOURS?**

The war with the *Post* gets personal with fists. A clipping from the *News* of 1914 makes capital of Fred Bonfils' attack on Senator Patterson.

Whether it was caused by "deep sleep falling upon men," or by the concentrated essence of constitutional laziness, there were many made aware of the awful risk they ran by sleeping sluggard-like, after frequent rousings, not only later than the hour of dying twilight after the advent of the goddess of the morning, but even after Sol's bright beams had dispelled the dark and shown the awful escapes that all had run from the delugic danger. Some sons of men and women will not be made to move unless folks, Gabriel-like, will blow a trumpet through and through their ears, bedress them in their beds, and bewilder them into the belief that an ocean of old rectified poison will encircle them if they don't start!

To show how prolific they are of prophets, it is only necessary to cite the hundredth part of the number of those people who volunteered to inform the public the day after the flood, that they had prognosticated a few days previously, every particle of the things that happened; full well knowing, as they generously informed us, that there was a freshet coming just about the time it did! Prophetic souls, how envious you do make us, and how fortunate you were in not building your new houses "on the sand!" Were it not that knowing this aforetime, you probably have pre-empted them ahead of us, we would immediately take up a mill site and go ground-sluicing on the creek, considering you are all "in with us" in the "dividends!"

Of the thousand and one incidents, actual and exaggerated, that have been borne on the breeze of rumor since the flood, we shall mention here but few, since they would not prove of any special interest to our readers at a distance, for whose satisfaction this cursory sketch was scribbled. The fortunate finding alive of the young man Schell after buffeting the billows for three miles, the heroic and happy escape of Martin Wall, after encountering the distress of a deck passage on the jail roof for an equal distance, and the remarkable presence of mind and power of perseverance shown by the colored woman, Mrs. Smith, while tossed on the waters with her family of five children for a couple of miles, afterwards effecting a safe landing place for them and her till morning, are deserving the pen of an Irving to only do them justice. The perilous condition of Mr. Wm. N. Byers and family, also, together with the considerate coolness displayed by them while dangerously surrounded, would deserve no less congratulatory mention than the kind efforts of Gov. Evans, Col. Chivington, and those skiff-constructing soldiers would demand a corresponding complimentary one. Of the various persons who proved themselves kind and humane to assist, it would be invidious to individualize, where each did all he could.

Death and Damages.

The number of persons drowned, as well as the amount of property, real and personal, that was lost and damaged has been variously estimated by varying approximations. Some think there has been about a million dollars worth of goods and property laid waste and lost, in the city and the country surrounding, and between fifteen and twenty lives lost, or at least that many persons started Statesward *via* the Platte. Our opinion inclines us to the belief that the total amount of pecuniary loss will leave a very big breach in a million dollars.

Not knowing for certain the number of transient folks in the town, or those in the upper ranches, who are missing, we will waive expressing an opinion at present on the latter, but doubt not for a moment that a few hundred thousands worth of loss and damage was sustained by our merchants and citizens of town and country. The following are the fatal effects, as far as heard from up to date:

C. Bruce Haynes, late of the Quartermaster's office, Gumble Rosebaum, clothier, Otto Fisher, (four years old), Henry Williamson, who herded stock for General Patterson down the Platte, a woman and two children from up Cherry creek, a woman and two children from Plum creek, and a Mr. and Mrs. I. R. Tyson and two children. August Metz, of Blake street bridge, who was carried along with the torrent eighteen miles to Henderson's Island, is the only person found whom we have yet heard of. Among the heavy sufferers in property are Byers & Dailey, publishers and proprietors of the *Rocky Mountain News*, who lost their entire all, with the building and the *lot it stood on*, A. E. & C. E. Tilton, house, lot, and $6,000 worth of goods damaged; also, F. A. Clark, Gen. Bowen, Wm. McKee, Mr. Charles, Messrs. Hunt, Metz and others, lost all they had in store or office, together with the buildings, and sand substracted lots on which they stood. Esquires Hall & Kent lost nearly all their office books and papers. The probate records, city records, commissioner's records, Judge Odell's old dockets, Judge Wilcox's dockets, and the city safe itself, all, all are gone, and whither the deponent saith not.

In the country, Messrs. Gibson Arnold, Schleier, Lloyd and Stoner, ranchmen, and scores of others, lost stock, and had their well-trimmed farms desolated into wastes of sand and gravel. D. C. Oakes lost his saw mill, part of which was impelled down the current for a few miles. Messrs. Reed, Palmer and Barnes lost, collectively, over four thousand sheep off their ranches up Cherry Creek.

Several sacks of flour which floated down the Platte have been discovered lying high and dry on sand bars, four to six miles from the city; also, many things that were given up as lost, were yesterday found, and free from damage by the action of the waterly element or by the (far worse) action of the wandering thieves that practiced prowling around for days past, seeking what they might pick up and pilfer. In some of the storages of town there was an amount of clothing and dry goods drenched, so that the owners might materially make more money selling it by the pound avoirdupois, than by the yard-stick lineal measure. But we must beg an apology of our distant readers, for our tediousness this time, and will conclude this column with the following, as

The Lesson It Teaches.

Men are mere cyphers in creation; at least, the chattels of the elements, and the creatures of circumstances and caprice. While worldly fortune favors, they think of nought but self, care little for the laws of nature, and care less for nature's God! Providential warning will alone affect them, when their well-being and their wealth are affected at the same time. As "the uses of adversity are sweet," so the interpositions of the Almighty are found eventually salutary and gracious. That the great clouds and eternal fountains are the Lord's, and will obey his fixed laws forevermore. That his kind purposes are as high above our selfish comprehensions, as are those of the physician above the understanding of the infant he inoculates. Had we continued thickly settling Cherry creek as we commenced, and thoughtless of the future, see what terrible destruction would have been our doom, in a few years more, when the waters of heaven, obeying the fixed laws, would rush down upon us, and slay thousands instead of tens!

The people of Denver felt the professor's cursory sketch treated their flood with a proper flair. If his Irish eloquence flagged somewhat in the middle distances, he still finished strong on a ringing note of moral philosophy. Both the eloquence and the metaphysics were commented upon favorably, and when the *News* resumed publication the professor was elevated to the post of associate editor.

"Professor Goldrick's Flood Story," as it has been known these ninety-odd years since, appeared in the *Daily Commonwealth and Republican* for May 24, 1864.[1] The *Commonwealth's* two-story frame building, prudently located a little distance from the creek on the southeast corner of Front (Thirteenth) and Fifth (Larimer) streets, got its feet wet when the floodwaters spread through the West Denver bottoms, but it escaped major damage and was able to get back into operation on May 23. The rival paper hospitably opened its columns to the stricken Byers.

Simeon Whiteley, who presumably had the financial backing of John Evans, second territorial governor, had taken over the *Commonwealth* with its issue dated January 1, 1864, and was in a position to offer editorial haven to the drowned-out proprietors of the *News*.

Deeply sympathizing with our neighbors of the Rocky Mountain News in the calamity which has fallen upon them (more heavily, perhaps, than any other of our citizens) we have placed the Commonwealth office at their disposal, until the arrival of their new printing office, which will be ordered forthwith. The plan determined upon is at present to issue but one paper, the Daily Commonwealth, with which the subscribers of the News will be furnished. During this arrangement the paper will be published in the evening instead of the morning.[2]

Byers and Dailey had indeed lost "their entire all." Not a trace remained of the *News* building. Its site stood under five feet of muddy

[1]The present copying is from the 1909 facsimile of J. E. Wharton, *History of the City of Denver* (Denver, 1866), pp. 121–43.

[2]*Weekly Commonwealth*, May 25, 1864.

water. The presses, type, and machinery were scattered downstream by the force of the flood and battered beyond salvage. Portions of the power press came to rest in the bed of the Platte. In 1899, when excavations were under way at the foot of Fifteenth Street for a waterworks, workmen uncovered at a depth of twelve feet the lever and other parts of the Washington hand press which had printed the first issue. Bits of type and other relics from the *News* office would be found in the sands of the creek well into the next century. The press lever was presented to the Colorado State Museum for preservation, and other souvenirs of destruction went as mementos to Byers and Dailey. Some of the building's hardwood timbering, hand-hewn in eastern Nebraska and freighted across the plains, was fished from the flotsam and survives as beams in a barn on the Albert N. Williams farm near suburban Littleton.

Contemporary observers were beguiled by the force of the flood and particularly by the ease with which it had moved the *News'* 3000-pound steam press. They thought the iron mass had been floated away, and they sought to explain this by the nature of the floodwaters. The current carried so much swept-up sand and earth, they decided, that its "specific gravity" exceeded that of iron. The press thus became buoyant and was wafted away like a cork. Byers said that a tin cup filled with floodwater settled out to half sand.

Toll of the flood finally was set at twelve lives and between half a million and a million dollars in property damage. Financial loss to the *News* partners came to $19,200. The sum was fixed in a later court suit in which Byers and Dailey sought to quit title to the soggy real estate their plant had once occupied.[3] Their brief estimated value of the building at $6000 and itemized $13,000 worth of equipment and a $200 stable.

The *News* came close to contributing to the death toll as well as the property damage. Asleep in the upper half story of the building when the flood descended were John Dailey and four of his employees: Nathan A. Baker, Frank Roff, Harry Stafford, and James P. Oliver. Baker, then twenty-one, had been successively bookkeeper, pony express rider, and printer for the paper. Later he would be the founder of three pioneer Wyoming newspapers, the Cheyenne *Leader*, South Pass *News*, and Laramie *Standard*. In 1927, at the age of eighty-four, Baker recalled his night of terror for the *News* writer Milus Gay. The five men, he said, were awakened by "a roaring noise."

> . . . I looked out of the window and saw a wall of water six feet high rushing down the dry creek bed at terrific speed. Before we could escape from the building, the flood waters had reached an embankment connecting the plant with the high shores of the creek. In a few seconds

[3] Case No. 1326, First District, Colorado Territorial Court; cited in Forbes Parkhill, *The Law Goes West* (Denver, 1956), p. 134.

we were completely isolated, with raging water surrounding the building. The Methodist church was located on the creek bank at Larimer st. The flood washed out its foundations and the building toppled into the stream. Its roof lodged on the bank at Market st. That was our salvation. A crowd gathered on the church roof, from which ropes were thrown to us. We escaped in the nick of time, going hand over hand along the ropes to shore.[4]

The perils of the Byers family alluded to by Professor Goldrick involved the concurrent rampage of the Platte. The Byerses already had moved out for the summer to their riverside ranch above town. Like his friend Horace Greeley, Byers espoused the agricultural life and always did a little farming on the side. His diary shows that he had just sold a calf for $6.90 and picked the first lettuce of the season from his garden when the Platte rose up in the night and snatched a good part of his bottomland farm away. The Byers ranch house had been on the east bank. The river cut a new channel, putting the house on the west bank. Meantime water spread out over the Byers farm and flowed in at the doorway.

Mrs. Byers has left a picture of her marooned family's plight. As the water rose in the house they climbed up and sat on tables, "telling funny stories" as they awaited rescue. Her husband, she remembered, wrote a note stating that his wife and babies were clinging to treetops, sealed it in a bottle, and cast it adrift. Finally soldiers from Camp Weld arrived with a hastily constructed skiff in a military wagon and the Byerses were rowed to safety.[5] Leader of the rescue expedition was a great, black-bearded bull of a man, John M. Chivington, who could thunder equally well as the Methodists' presiding elder or as colonel of volunteers. His work on that wet night probably sealed a friendship which would determine the editorial course of the News later in the year when an authentic mititary hero plunged to disgrace as a bloody butcher.

The homeless Byers family was taken in that night and sheltered for several days by territorial Governor John Evans, thereby cementing another friendship which would be long and loyal. Byers moved his wife and children back out to his silt-covered farm, but recurrent floods on May 27 and June 10 drove them into town again for temporary lodging in the Colorado Seminary building, which had been completed but not yet occupied by its first class of students.

When he wasn't shuttling his family to safety from floods Byers was trying to get his newspaper back into operation. Possibly he had the silent financial backing of Governor Evans, but at any rate his multiple losses had not eroded his determination to continue as publisher of the

---

[4]*Rocky Mountain News*, March 13, 1927.

[5]"The Experiences of One Pioneer Woman," typescript in Western History Department, Denver Public Library.

town's leading newspaper. On the day after the flood he sat down and penned a notice which Simeon Whiteley published for him in the *Daily Commonwealth* of May 23:

To Subscribers to the News——

In the destruction of our office, our subscription books shared the common fate, so that we are without a list of subscribers anywhere. It is not our intention that any subscriber shall miss a single number of his paper and to avoid their doing so, we hope that each will give us his address, and, as near as possible, the length of time for which their subscription is paid. When desired, the Commonwealth will be supplied to subscribers who have paid for the News, or, the News will be furnished from the time of its resumption for the full time for which it is paid. Send your lists at once. Will Postmasters oblige us by aiding in the matter?

Byers & Dailey

Then the partners began dickering with Whiteley for purchase of the *Commonwealth*. They concluded the deal on June 24, paying four thousand dollars, and took possession of the plant next day. Two days later the daily *Rocky Mountain News* reappeared.

The first post-deluge issue contains a statement which illustrates Byers' stubborn insistence that his paper should live. It also demonstrates the frank style with which he sometimes dealt with the customers and reveals how unprofitable frontier journalism was. Byers headed his editorial "Plain Talk":

In resuming the publication of the Rocky Mountain News, it will doubtless be excusable for us to indulge in a little plain talk to its friends, patrons and the public generally.

It is a little more than a month since our old office was swept away. In the building itself, and its contents, for carrying on the business, we had invested over $12,000 in cash, all of which was a total loss. With it we lost all our files and many of our books—in the latter of which were unpaid accounts amounting to many more thousands of dollars— together with notes, due-bills, county warrants, packages of letters, legal papers, and many other articles, the monetary loss of which we cannot estimate. Many of these things we valued far more than money, and their loss is irreparable. In addition to these absolute losses, we had devoted more than five years to building up a business, which thus far had given but little satisfaction and allowed but little enjoyment in its pursuit. Of this, we expect yet to reap some return, since we have again resumed it; otherwise, that labor, too, would have been a dead loss, and it may even prove so yet, though we have a strong hope to the contrary. At any rate, we believe Colorado has been benefited by our labors, which is a consolation, even though the pecuniary loss has been ruinous to ourselves.

A few days after the destruction of our office, we published an address, in which we proposed to resume the News, upon certain conditions. We regret to say that those conditions were not complied with, except to a limited extent. Only about one-half the subscriptions asked were secured, and we did think, in their failure, we would absolutely give it up. But, the necessity of supplying our old subscribers with the papers they have paid for, the want of something to do, and the importunities of our friends, have induced us to again "put in an appearance" before the public. Having done so, the News is again, and will remain, one of the permanent institutions of the country. In other words, *we expect to stay with you!* Though unable to start in with a good office, and all the conveniences we could desire—though necessarily burthened somewhat with debt, and the tenant of "my landlord," we shall strive to do the best we can, and labor zealously to make the News, at least acceptable, until we can do better.

To make up for the deficiency in the subscription list we asked, we shall expect a liberal patronage from the businessmen of Denver. Seeing the paper re-established, we hope that many will increase the subscriptions already made, and that others who have stood back, will now step forward and lend a helping hand. Remember, we ask no gratuity, but will give full value for every dollar received.

One other vital point, and then we are done with this personal article, already spun out too long. We shall be compelled to advance prices in some branches of our business. Our rates are not in proportion with others. Since they were established, four years ago, paper and all other printer's stock has advanced more than 100 per cent. Type, and other office material, have gone up in almost the same proportion, and the price of labor has increased nearly as much. To illustrate plainly how much printer's prices have fallen below the true proportion, compared with other branches of business, we will state that for the first quarter's business of the current year, our balance sheet showed a margin of profit of only $142.63. This is all we had to pay for the labor of two proprietors—for interest upon the money invested—the wear and tear of material—and the risk, *for three months.* Out of that would probably have to be deducted some bad debts—accounts that could never be collected; for it is notoriously and lamentably true that *some people* consider the printer a legitimate subject to victimize.

Whilst everything else has been crawling up, following gold in its airy flight, our prices have not materially changed, and many customers would always higgle and beat down at that. Flour and meat, sugar and coffee, may turn into jumping jacks, bob up and down a dozen times a week, and the dear public will stand it without a murmur; but if the printer advances his rates 10 per cent., to keep partial pace with his type founder, his paper dealer and his grocer, he is at once looked upon and pronounced an extortioner.

Who is there in Denver, or elsewhere, we ask, that would invest the money we individually have, do the work that we have done, and receive the curses and abuses that have been heaped upon us, for the pitiful sum of $71.31½ per quarter?

We will have many things to buy, to make our office complete; therefore, we desire a prompt and liberal response in the way of subscriptions. We must forward immediate orders to the type founder, and they must be accompanied with money; therefore, we want it now, as we start out. The current expenses of our office will not fall below $70 per day; therefore, our prices must be advanced; but the increase will be made as slight as possible, whilst some things will not be affected at all. The new schedule will be announced on the first proximo, and when published, it will be strictly adhered to.

The same issue of the paper paused to note: "That spasmodic stream called Cherry Creek is now entirely dry, and its broad channel's sands are once more glistening in the sunshine."

Today the creek has been tamed. It flows between concrete retaining walls ten feet deep as it curves down through the city. Speer Boulevard follows much of the course, a pleasant parkway planted with trees, shrubs, and grass. Every so often prisoners from the county jail are brought out to cut and burn the weedy, brushy growth in the bottom of the channel. Kids use park department sprinkling hoses as ropes to descend the retaining walls and splash about in the infrequent ponds. Now and then a berserk auto plunges over the banks to wind up with its nose buried in the sands whose mythical gold brought ox teams rolling across the continent.

The taming of Cherry Creek was not accomplished with any unseemly haste. Despite '64, Denver required several more convincings that the kitten could be a tiger. Floods of almost equal violence hit on July 25, 1875, May 22, 1878, July 14, 1912, and, even with the retaining walls, August 3, 1933. This last flood soaked much of the lower downtown business district and filled up the subway ramps under the train sheds at Union Station. But it was turn about this time for the *News*; it set type to keep the Denver *Post* going through a couple of days when gas and power supplies were cut off in that part of town. To insure that the creek would not again jump out of its confined channel, the army's Corps of Engineers completed in 1950 the three-mile-long, fifteen-million-dollar Cherry Creek Dam southeast of the city. It is now judged that Denver is secure from the havoc which can be brewed up by cloudbursts over a small, normally arid drainage basin only 414 square miles in extent.

The concrete walls which help restrain Cherry Creek's aberrant excesses were built between 1907 and 1911 by Mayor Robert W. Speer, for whom the paralleling boulevard is named. Speer the Builder, they called him, for this and other public works including the development of Civic Center. He was no friend of the *News*, which campaigned against him rigorously, but he acquired a loyal following who regarded him as the personification of Good Government, the veritable apex of all the forces for municipal betterment that were set in motion on April 6, 1860, when the populations of Auraria and Denver met in the moonlight on the Larimer Street bridge and voted to unite.

City government dates from that moonlight meeting, and the *News* amended the dateline of its masthead from the fence-straddling "Auraria and Denver, J.T." to "Denver, Jefferson." The paper had been demanding consolidation through the autumn months of 1859, and several preliminary moves led up to the April 6 gathering. The legislature of the provisional territory of Jefferson, as one of its first acts, approved joint incorporation for Auraria, Denver City, and Highland on December 3. Full text of the act was printed on page one of the *News* for December 14. The legislators begged the issue of what the town should be called by granting their charter to the "City of Denver, Auraria and Highland," which was given powers, among others, to "restrain, suppress, and prohibit tippling shops, billiard tables, tenpin alleys, houses of prostitution and all disorderly houses and restrain gaming and gambling houses, and all kinds of public indecencies." The provision could have been a stiff blow to a large portion of the constituency, but fortunately the language was permissive.

Under this charter an election was held December 19, and the amiable Southerner, John C. Moore, later to edit the *Mountaineer*, was elected mayor. He called a first session of the City Council for January 21, but in the meantime a mass meeting of citizens on December 26 voted to override the statute and shorten the name of their town to "Denver City." Mayor Moore's government appears not to have been entirely convincing. The Aurarians held out but finally called an election on April 3 to vote on the question of joining with Denver City. Consolidation carried 146 to 39, and the moonlight meeting completed the wedding.

This first city government, however, dwindled away before the year was out and gave almost no account of itself during the era of the Turkey War, the rule of the Bummers, the Byers kidnaping, and the People's Courts. In September another meeting was called to consider a new civic constitution for "The People's Government of the City of Denver." The constitution was adopted, *viva voce*, on September 21 in Apollo Hall, and another election called for October 1. The new rules did not provide for a mayor but placed authority in the hands of a six-man "Legislative Council" to which D. C. Oakes, J. M. Taylor, William Dunn, C. A. Cook, L. N. Tappan, and J. M. Broadwell were elected. This council on October 24 designated the *News* as "official paper" of the city. It then gave way to a new slate chosen the following April 6.

By that time a legal territory of Colorado had come into being. At last, on November 7, 1861, the territorial legislature gave Denver its first legitimate existence as a civic entity squaring with all the laws of the land. An election was hastily contrived for November 18. Denver's first legal officers were: C. A. Cook, Mayor; P. P. Wilcox, police magistrate; W. M. Keith, city marshal; J. Bright Smith, city clerk and attorney; E. D. Boyd, city surveyor; Joseph B. Cass, city treasurer; George W. Brown, city collector; D. D. Palmer, street commissioner; and H. J. Brendlinger,

John Nye, L. Mayer, W. W. Barlow, J. E. Vawter, and L. Buttrick, aldermen. George E. Thornton was appointed chief of police.

No less devious was the struggle toward the territorial status and the statehood the *News* insistently demanded for its orphan Pike's Peak country. The rending noises of disunion were so loud in Washington that Congress almost couldn't hear the complaints of a few thousand gold rushers that they were without effective government.

Denver began as an unwilling resident of Kansas Territory, and Kansas didn't much care whether or not the settlement recognized its authority. It was otherwise occupied. John Brown was kicking up a fuss, and the border ruffians were on the prod. The first Kansas territorial legislature designated the whole nebulous western end of its jurisdiction as Arapahoe County in 1855. The county embraced most of what is now the eastern half of Colorado, right up to the Continental Divide. County officials were appointed, but they never bothered to take up residence in their assigned territory. Kansas granted charters to the St. Charles and Denver City town companies, and in 1858 Governor James Denver sent H. P. A. Smith, Hickory Rogers, and E. W. Wynkoop forth to Pike's Peak to constitute a county government. Their authority never was recognized by the Pike's Peakers, although they did get together on November 6, 1858, and elect A. J. Smith as their representative in the Kansas legislature.

By February 1859 the gold rush was on, and Kansas, anticipating a large new population on its western reaches, abolished Arapahoe County by splitting it up into Montana, El Paso, Oro, Broderick, and Frémont counties. In Denver, preoccupied with gold dust and nuggets, the first-comers met on March 28, elected a complement of officers for Montana County, and promptly forgot all about them in the confusion. When William Byers arrived with his press a few weeks later he found no one paying any attention to the officials and the whole affair so uncertain the general impression was that they had been elected for Arapahoe County. Montana County withered away for want of recognition.

The Pike's Peak country was busy seceding from Kansas and setting up its own "State of Jefferson."

One of the leaders of the secessionists was the newly arrived editor. In the first issue of the *News* Byers reported on a public meeting lately held on "the 11th inst." in the room now immediately below his busy press. Dr. Levi Russell had been called to the chair in Wootton's saloon— the *News* dignified it for the occasion as "Wootton's Hall"—and the company present had highly resolved "that the different precincts be requested to appoint delegates to meet in convention on the 15th inst. to take into consideration the propriety of organizing a new State or Territory." The meeting calmly took over from the distant Kansas legislature the responsibility for governing the region and as a condescending gesture seated the recently elected county officers: ". . . on account of our distance from, and the difficulty of communicating with, the proper authorities, we the people who are the power here, authorize the late county officers-elect to enter at once upon the discharge of their respective duties." It was audacious, but it was democracy in action.

The April 15 convention wound up

Resolved—That the discussions of this convention shall have but one object, viz.: The formation of a new and independent State of the Union

and fixing June 6 as the date for a constitutional convention. By that time Byers had his *News* in operation and was a figure of prominence in the community. He was chosen as one of Auraria's delegates to the convention, and when the body convened in the Denver House he was chosen as its president. His partner, Thomas Gibson, was named secretary, and Byers & Gibson were appointed public printers.

This convention was in session two days, despite the fever generated by the successes up at Jackson's Bar and Gregory's Gulch, which badly cut into attendance and seemed to distract the founding fathers from business at hand. They managed to confirm choice of the name "Jefferson," Byers appointed drafting committees (he put himself on the one to consider boundaries and Bill of Rights), and then they adjourned until August 1, hopeful of a larger roll call.

When the convention resumed on that date Byers passed the presidency on to Captain A. F. Garrison. Gibson remained as secretary to keep the *News* on the inside, and George West, who had helped print the Greeley extra, was designated sergeant at arms. By this time views of moderationists were prevailing, and it was decided to start by seeking only a territory rather than a state. Byers' committee was not modest, however, in setting boundaries. It calculated the territory of Jefferson should embrace all of what is now Colorado, plus most of southern Wyoming, the Nebraska panhandle, and a slice of eastern Utah. The convention remained in session for a week, and it drafted a memorial to Congress demanding "immediate" organization of a territorial government.

The proposition was submitted to the electorate on September 5, giving the voters a choice between a state and a territory. If there were, as claimed, 30,000 persons in the region, not very many of them interrupted their prospecting and sluicing to cast ballots. The vote was 2007 for a territory, 649 for a state. Without waiting for Congress to act on, or even receive, their memorial, the Pike's Peakers immediately began organizing their provisional territory. An election was set for October 3 to choose delegates to still another convention called for October 10. In this round of balloting Beverly D. Williams was elected Jefferson's delegate to Congress, and he set off for Washington clutching the memorial. Congress refused to give him standing as a delegate but admitted him to the lobby of the House of Representatives as a measure of left-handed recognition of the provisional people's government at Pike's Peak.

There was a minority of citizens, however, which had doubts about the legality of all this extemporaneous politicking. They recognized the jurisdiction of Kansas. So for the October 3 election they got together a full ticket of officials for Arapahoe County, Kansas Territory. These were elected by a fraction of the 4386 citizens who cast ballots for congressional delegate, the hot contest of the day. Thus the governmental confusion was compounded, and the *News* was moved to comment editorially on October 6:

> So it goes; one day we understand that we are cut off from Kansas; the next, we have cut ourselves off, and will pay no regard to Kansas Legislation, but have an independent provisional government of our own; and the very next, when there is a chance for a petty office under Kansas laws, there are hundreds ready to enter the lists, and before their certificates of election are dry in their pockets you will hear them lustily advocating "independent government," and "let Kansas go to the dogs." When this county scheme was started, why was it not carried out, and members of the Kansas Legislative Assembly elected, also? Nobody seems to have thought of that except two or three shrewd ones who, we learn, received a few votes for Representative, and under them will claim seats in the next Kansas legislature, not the representatives of the people, but of a few of their friends.
>
> Here we go, a regular triple-headed government machine. South of 40 [degrees latitude] we hang on the skirts of Kansas; north of 40 on those of Nebraska. Straddling the line, we have just elected a Delegate to Congress from the Territory of Jefferson; and ere long we shall have in full blast a Provisional Government of Rocky Mountain growth and manufacture. This last we hope may succeed, and swallow up the delectable uncertainty of law now existing; when one man claims that he lives in Arapahoe county, while his neighbor asserts that he is in Montana [county]—where one man acknowledges Kansas laws, and another says he is on Indian land where no law can reach. A compact of the people under any name, state, territory, or provisional government, if either can be effected, is better than the present, and if some such is not soon adopted, with a determination to abide by, and respect it, we bid fair to out-Kansas Kansas herself.

The efforts of Pike's Peak to secede and establish its own government were being watched with some interest and no little venom on the other side of the Great Plains. The *Missouri Republican* came forth with the helpful suggestion that Jefferson and any other territory seeking recognition should be administered by a federal governor and two appointed judges. The *News* gave this idea its scorn on September 17:

. . . It is simply a preposterous idea in this day and age that 20,000, or any other number of intelligent American citizens, as are the citizens of Jefferson, will submit to be "well-governed" by three of those "demagogues and place-hunters" or that laws for their government can be enacted without their having a voice therein.

Advocates of grass-roots democracy through a new territory pressed right ahead with their plans, and the *News* gave its full support both editorially and in the frontier counterparts of smoke-filled rooms, where Byers was an active and respected figure. His experience as a member of the first Nebraska territorial legislature presumably lent added weight to his words. One of the delegates to the new convention denounced the entire proposition as a "gigantic Vigilance Committee," but he was given no heed. The territorial constitution was worked over again, and Jefferson trudged back to the polls on October 24. The constitution was ratified, 1852 to 280. Robert W. Steele was elected governor.

To aid the voters in making up their minds the *News* had published on October 20 the entire proposed Jefferson constitution, word for legalistic word, column upon column. And when the returns were in the paper immediately banished "Kansas Territory" from its masthead and substituted "Jefferson Territory." Said an editorial on November 10:

. . . We hope and expect to see it [Jefferson] stand until we can boast of a million of people, and look upon a city of a hundred thousand souls, having all the comforts and luxuries of the most favored. Then we will hear the whistle of the locomotive and the rattle of trains to and from the Atlantic and Pacific. . . . The future of Jefferson Territory— soon to be a sovereign State—is glorious with promise.

Governor Steele, an Ohio-Iowa lawyer who had served with Byers in the Nebraska legislature, called the assembly of Jefferson Territory into its first session on November 7 in Denver, using the second floor of a building which had been the stage office of the Leavenworth & Pike's Peak Express. Between them, Steele and the Jefferson legislature held dominion until Colorado Territory was established in 1861, but it was a regime of steadily diminishing authority. Debility set in before it was six months old, and there was difficulty mustering a quorum for the second general assembly on November 12, 1860. This body soon adjourned to Golden City and set up shop there, making the foothills town temporarily the territorial capital. The move was made, said the *News* in a huff, only because "board is offered at six dollars a week— wood, lights, and hall rent free." The sovereign territory of Jefferson slowly faded away, but it had more or less bridged the gap between the indifference of Kansas and the creation by Congress of Colorado Territory.

Byers recalled these days of toddling efforts at self-government for Hubert Bancroft in 1884. Only a little had been done toward Anglo-Saxon law and order before the young editor's arrival in April of 1859.

> . . . In the winter of 1858 & 1859 the people informally chose a delegate to Congress, in fact they chose 2, at least 2 went from here to Washington & endeavor[ed] to get some kind of an organization or provision for the government of the country through Congress. They did not accomplish anything. In the spring of 1859 soon after I came here there was a movement to organise a State Government. There was such an immense migration of people across the plains, so many coming in, that the sanguine people believed that we would have people enough before the end of the season to form a State. Elections were held about the first of May in the various camps here for delegates to attend a convention to assemble in Denver to organise a State Government. That was what was talked about at the time. That convention assembled on the 22nd of June, held a brief session, concluded that the time had not arrived for organising a State Government & adjourned to assemble again in August. In August they re-assembled & again concluded it was not best to make any effort to organise a State Government, but took preliminary steps toward the organisation of a Provisional Government & that was done in the fall of that year. A Governor & full list of State officers were elected & a Legislative Assembly without any authority of Congress & entirely founded upon the will of the people. That Provisional Government enacted Laws & enforced them as far as it could & continued to act & be partially recognized until Congress passed the act for the organisation of the Territory. . . .[6]

A little later the editor of the *News* gave Jerome Smiley an explanation of the choice of the name "Jefferson":

> We wanted our territory named Jefferson. Why? Because it was part of the great Louisiana purchase, effected by Jefferson in 1803; and not only did President Jefferson purchase this country, but he sent out the early exploration parties into it, like the Lewis and Clark, and others. This country was ever the object of his fondest hopes and confidence, and this State might with propriety and justice have been named after him. But Congress would not have it so. They said no State should be named after a man, Washington alone excepted. They didn't consult us as to our wishes, but finally chose the name Colorado, the others under discussion having been Jefferson, Idaho and Montana. Colorado is a more euphonious and romantic name than Jefferson would have made, and none of us objected to it. But I have always thought that one State carved out of the great Louisiana purchase should have been named after Jefferson. When we started the movement for a State in 1859, and were discussing a name, one delegate from the mountains rose in the argument, and made an impassioned appeal in favor of calling the

[6]Bancroft ms., Pac Ms L6.

State "Bill Williams." Bill Williams was one of the earliest of the mountaineers. He seemed to be ubiquitous, for there were all sorts of places all over the mountains named after him. He seemed to be worshipped by the mountaineers, and this admirer of his could not be comforted when the convention unkindly laughed at the idea of calling the new State "Bill Williams."[7]

As the year 1860 ran out the territory of Jefferson was tottering but not quite defunct and Delegate Williams at last was meeting with some success in Washington. He had obtained introduction of bills for a new territory into both houses of Congress in January 1860. The Senate bill carried the name Idaho; the House version preferred Tahosa—supposedly an Indian word meaning "dweller of the mountain tops." These bills, however, fell into limbo in the great division over whether Kansas and Nebraska were to be admitted as free or slave states.

In February of 1861, Williams pressed his suit again. The Senate bill, with the substitution of "Colorado" for "Idaho" at Williams' insistence, was passed on February 2. The House agreed with some changes on February 6, and the Senate concurred February 26. President Buchanan signed the act creating Colorado Territory on February 28, but in recognition of his lame-duck position deferred to his successor on the appointment of territorial officials.

There had been other names suggested for the newest territory. Governor Denver of Kansas had wanted the region called Shoshone. Proposals at the various Jefferson conventions had included Cibola (Spanish for "buffalo"), Platte, Lula, Arapahoe, Nemara, San Juan, Tampa, Wapola, Lafayette, Colona, Columbus, Franklin, and simply Pike's Peak (citing the precedent of Rhode Island). It has not been established how or why Colorado (Spanish for "red") entered the picture and won Delegate Williams' favor, but the name is not inappropriate. Large areas of Colorado soil on both its eastern and western slopes have been colored by the decomposition of red sandstone formations which once, before the upthrust of the Rockies, overlaid the entire region.

News of the admission of Colorado Territory was six days coming by telegraph, Pony Express, and stage, but when the *News* published the dispatch on March 4 there was rejoicing in the dusty streets.

The paper of that day immediately adds "C.T." after "Denver" in the masthead, but its comment on the grand occasion is a little gem of left-handedness:

COLORADO.

We are enabled to day to convey to our readers the welcome intelligence of the passage of the bill of the organization of our Territory. There may be an error in this conclusion, but we think not. . . .

[7]Smiley, *History of Denver*, pp. 317–18.

This is a consummation long desired, and there is now an assurance of established law and order, which will send a thrill of joy to every city, village and hamlet throughout the Rocky Mountains.

Full text of the act establishing the territory appeared March 16.

One of the early acts of Abraham Lincoln's administration was to supply the new territory of Colorado with its first legal officials. For governor he chose a picturesque West Pointer, William Gilpin of Missouri, Pennsylvania, and Oregon. The other appointees were: Lewis L. Weld, secretary; William L. Stoughton, attorney general; Francis M. Case, surveyor general; Copeland Townsend, marshal; and B. F. Hall, S. N. Pettis, and Charles L. Armour, judges of the supreme court. The *News* reported the appointments on March 27.

Gilpin was a man of dash and eloquence. He had been educated in a private school in England and at the University of Pennsylvania before going to West Point. As a second lieutenant of dragoons he served through the Seminole War and then went west to take up law and politics and to sing a booming bass in the manifest-destiny choir. He practiced law in Independence, Missouri, and was elected to the state legislature. The plains and the Rockies were not unknown country to Gilpin. He went with Frémont to Oregon in 1843 and there drafted the memorial to Congress asking for admission of that territory. He claimed he was one of the founders of Portland. During the Mexican War he saw service with Doniphan as a cavalry major, and later, now a colonel, led a force of twelve hundred men out onto the prairie to pacify hostile Indians. He had wintered in the Pike's Peak country in 1847-48, and so he knew where he was going when Lincoln dispatched him west again in 1861.

A friend and protégé of Andrew Jackson, Gilpin had traveled in high circles ever since Old Hickory appointed him to West Point. A brother was attorney general under Van Buren. Frémont was a friend and companion of the trail. Gilpin had been an adviser to Senator Thomas Benton of Missouri, and when Lincoln went to Washington, Gilpin went along with him. The Missourian was a member of the personal bodyguard of one hundred picked men who slept in the White House as the gaunt man from Springfield entered upon the duties which brought him martyrdom.

Even before he became Colorado's first territorial governor Gilpin was the leather-lunged, jewel-worded apostle of the West. He was the devoted enemy of everything represented by the phrase "Great American Desert." So much so that in his writings he pivoted the world on a Rocky Mountain axis. The West's climate was incomparably salubrious; its soils so fertile the farmer didn't even need a plow. On one of his high flights Gilpin drew a direct-ratio comparison between the Rockies and what he decided were the mountains of the Holy Land, and what the one had accomplished for mankind, he implied, the other could top:

What cardinal element have we, in the immense mental system of our civilization, which has not come to us and with us from thence? Hence (from this Plateau of Syria) have resounded through all time and into every heart, the direct oral teachings of Jehovah and of Jesus: hence have issued forth the miraculous alphabet and the numerals: hence have come the cereals and animals of our agriculture, wine, and fruits: hence our religion, law, social manners, history, music, poetry, and arts: from hence, as from the cradle of nativity, have issued forth for our inheritance, to abide with us forever, "the unconquerable mind and freedom's holy flame!"[8]

The West, Gilpin would like to point out to everyone, had mountains, too, and moreover it was smack on the *isothermal axis* of the universe, along which for fifty centuries had flowed

the immortal fire of civilization revealed to man. This central current has reached the Plateau of America, up which it will ascend to plant the sacred fires over its expanse and shine upon the world with renewed effulgence. Such is the resplendent era and the gorgeous promise unveiled to humanity. . . .[9]

Editor Byers, a little dazed, concluded that William Gilpin was "a very peculiar man," and the *News* eyed his administration carefully, particularly where hardheaded matters of public finance were concerned. Bernard DeVoto since has commented that everything Gilpin dreamed up "is and always was nonsense," and Wallace Stegner has written:

. . . The Manifest Destiny which he had learned from Benton, and which was a creed and a policy of his generation, was a passionate vision to Gilpin. He saw the West through a blaze of mystical fervor, as part of a grand geopolitical design, the overture to global harmony; and his conception of its resources and its future as a home for millions was as grandiose as his rhetoric, as unlimited as his faith, as splendid as his capacity for inaccuracy.[10]

The visionary Gilpin, who awed and puzzled his constituents but was much honored and loved by them, arrived in his shabby little capital on May 27, 1861. There was cannon firing in honor of his arrival, the

[8]William Gilpin, *Mission of the North American People* (Philadelphia, 1874), p. 53.

[9]Ibid.

[10]Stegner, op. cit., p. 2.

News records, and a grand levee and assembly ball was appointed for the Tremont House at "7½ P.M." Gilpin cast down to the multitude from the hotel's balcony a few of his radiant words. "A large number of Denver's fairest ladies were . . . present," the inspired *News* reporter said, "and, like nature's flowers on our mountains' brow, beautified the balcony, creating an ornament and an interest to the lookers up from below."

The years immediately ahead would be difficult ones for Gilpin, but he never lost his verve or his eloquence. He died in Denver on January 19, 1894, "a man," Jerome Smiley said, "of no ordinary type, brave, generous, enthusiastic, impractical in some things, and of winning ways in his intercourse with his fellow-man." One of his successors as governor of Colorado, Frederick W. Pitkin, retold to Hubert Bancroft a popular anecdote which purported to illustrate Gilpin's enthusiasm for the castles words can build.

In his later years, the story went, Gilpin became a great street-corner conversationalist who, quite literally, buttonholed his acquaintances. He would reach out, grasp a vest button of his friend, and twist it idly while, with eyes closed, he let his words and visions soar. One busy man, Pitkin asserted, took out his penknife, cut off the button Gilpin was holding, and hurried on to tend to a matter of urgent moment. He returned a half hour later and Gilpin, eyes still closed, was at the same spot. Still talking, still holding the button in front of him.[11]

This eccentric man bequeathed to American history a substantial part of what DeVoto and others have denounced as the "Western myth," and it also fell to his lot to have to cope with treason and insurrection on the Far Western border. Here, too, his efforts would be disavowed.

Lincoln's first annual message to Congress on December 3, 1861, gives hints of what his appointee was facing:

> The Territories of Colorado, Dakota, and Nevada, created by the last Congress, have been organized, and civil administration has been inaugurated therein under auspices especially gratifying when it is considered that the leaven of treason was found existing in some of these new countries when the Federal officers arrived there. . . . I submit the resolutions of the legislature of Colorado, which evidence the patriotic spirit of the people of the Territory. So far the authority of the United States has been upheld in all the Territories, as it is hoped it will be in the future. I commend their interests and defense to the enlightened and generous care of Congress.

[11]Bancroft ms., Pac Ms. L44.

CHAPTER TEN

A Place Called Gloriéta

THE Civil War in the West, as a phrase, usually doesn't mean what the words imply. When generals and historians speak of "the Wilderness," "the Army of the Frontier," or "the battles of the West" they are talking about scenes and events eight hundred miles or more to the eastward of the thinly scattered, then forgotten outposts in the Rockies. During the war years the concept of the West moved back again to the east to where there were towns and river ports, railroads and populations worth battling over. The surge of a nation's westering, which had been so imagination-filling a few years earlier, so proudly to be hailed in Fourth of July orations, would have to wait while armies ground out a bitter decision: one nation or two? And by the time the last gun spoke before Appomattox, westering would have changed its nature. It would be a matter no longer of fierce, lonely trail blazing but of development and utilization: a process of filling up the empty places, of dispossessing Indians who thought the empty places already more than filled, a great thrusting out of railroads and telegraph lines, and the plowing of virgin sod.

Considering the number and magnitude of urgencies near at hand, it is not a little surprising that the riven government of the United States should have found time to create a territory of Colorado for a few thousand distant gold miners, that the heartsick Lincoln could have found, in the midst of dismemberment, the boldness to send out a new government to a new people. Denver and the *Rocky Mountain News* thought differently, of course. The action had been scandalously, shamefully delayed, and the officials were all too slow in coming. Yet how near Richmond must have seemed to Washington in those days, and how remote, in space and time and importance, the village of Denver, not yet two years old. Far more men soon would meet in battle at a little creek called Bull Run than there were in all the Western country five hundred miles in any direction from the importunate new capital of Colorado Territory.

The West was in the far backwaters of the rebellion, and it would have been strange indeed had the situation been otherwise. But the deep division which split friend from friend reached the frontier too. Here also there was arming, drilling, marching, and some blood spilled. Most histories of the war ignore the minor maneuverings and skirmishings in the Far West, or dismiss them with a paragraph, a page or two at most.

Yet in New Mexico there is a place called La Gloriéta. As Western distances run, it is not too far from Denver, not so far that it couldn't be reached afoot, in forced marches, by a regiment of Union volunteers.

What happened at La Gloriéta on March 26 and 28 of 1862 can be made the basis of very large speculations. There, among the rocks and adobe walls, a force of eleven hundred men, mostly Colorado volunteers with a few regulars, met the Texans of General Henry H. Sibley's invading brigade in a battle which, at minimum, determined the destiny of the entire West for the next three years.

The Battle of Gloriéta Pass has been called the "Gettysburg of the West"—and the losses on both sides were proportionately greater. Gloriéta "saved the West for the Union." The wild Pike's Peakers, so the Texas Rebels said, fought with subhuman viciousness and a violent, exultant abandon. They were "devils" and "regular demons, upon whom iron and lead had no effect." In the end Sibley retreated from New Mexico with fewer than two thousand of his original force of thirty-seven hundred men, and the Confederacy gave up its plans for conquest of the Rockies and their gold mines.

Sibley's invasion of New Mexico was frontal assault, and as the most notable action of the Western war it will be discussed more fully presently; but there also had been subversion to contend with.

When William Gilpin arrived in Denver City on May 27, 1861, to establish his territorial government the town was split in sentiment. The first substantial gold discoveries had been made by Georgians. There had been but recently a newspaper openly "secesh" in sympathies. Many of the leading citizens, including the first mayor, were Southerners.

Perhaps a majority of the Peakers were Midwesterners and loyalists, although the *News* assayed North-South feelings as "about evenly divided."[1] Until the first political campaign was over, and the territory safely in the Republican fold, the paper adopted for itself and urged upon others a policy of avoiding sharp party lines "for the good of the Union."[2] But the loyalties boiled up in hot words, fist fights, and occasional pot shots about the streets. Tension increased as the *News* headlined on April 18: "Most Exciting News! Commencement of Hostilities! Batteries Open on Sumpter!" When word of the fall of Sumter reached Denver the Southerners were jubilant and the Stars and Bars flew briefly over the city.

On the morning of April 24 the Confederate flag was seen billowing from a staff on top of Wallingford & Murphy's general store near what is now Sixteenth and Larimer streets. The store stood next door to

[1]*Rocky Mountain News*, May 1, 1861.

[2]Ibid., July 17, 1861.

Criterion Hall, where the polished, handsome Charley Harrison held forth, his pearl-handled Colt's on each hip, as one of the acknowledged leaders of the Southern element. An angry, turbulent crowd soon gathered in the rutted street in front of Wallingford & Murphy's. There were shouted demands that the flag be hauled down and equally belligerent refusals. Finally Samuel M. Logan, soon to become a captain of the 1st Regiment of Colorado Volunteers, elbowed his way through the fuming but indecisive mob, climbed to the top of the building, and ran down the Rebel ensign.

The Confederate coup failed. On the following night the Unionists countered with a bonfire rally complete with brass band and patriotic speeches. And resolutions. The mass meeting resolved

> That, as for Colorado, she, with willing hearts and ready feet, will follow the flag and keep step to the music of the Union.
> That the government of Washington is good enough for us—that it is the best government the world ever saw—that we will sustain it. . . .
> That the flag of Colorado Territory is the STAR SPANGLED BANNER.
> That we desire peace in our midst, and that each one of us will exert himself to preserve peace and harmony in this Territory, among our fellow-citizens, because we love peace, and lest we may have need of all for common defense against the Indian tribes around us.[3]

It was further "the sentiment of the committee" that a note of support be dispatched to President Lincoln.

To the President of the United States:
> The eyes of the whole world are upon you—the sympathies of the American People are with you—and may the God of Battles sustain the *Stars and Stripes.*
>
> R. Sopris, President
> Scott J. Anthony, Secretary

There were in Denver at this point no federal forces of any kind, military or civil; Gilpin still was en route to his post. On hand, however, were two militia companies, and they existed, characteristically, on either side of Cherry Creek and on either side of the secession issue. Auraria had the Jefferson Rangers, a veteran outfit with service honors for its duties in the Turkey War of the previous year. The Rangers were commanded by Captain H. H. C. Harrison—no kin to Charley—and were Union men. On the other side of the creek a mounted company of Denver Guards paraded now and then on dress occasions. Their commanding officer was the "Little Thunderer," W. Park McClure, lawyer, duelist, and sometime postmaster. McClure was an ardent secessionist. Fortunately both outfits were dying on the vine, drill nights had become

[3]Ibid., April 26, 1861.

highly irregular and informal, and the opposing forces made no attempt
to convert Cherry Creek into a Bull Run.

Festivities upon the arrival of Governor Gilpin served both to promote
a truce in squabblings and to lend support to the Union faction. The
assembly in front of the Tremont House to greet the new executive was
patriotically "grand and glorious," the *News* reported. Gilpin was
introduced by Hiram P. Bennet, soon to become territorial delegate to
Congress, who made a "polished and patriotic little speech." Then,
the *News* reporter continued:

> . . . Gov. Gilpin responded in a somewhat lengthy speech, and in
> a style and manner which seemed to suit and satisfy all parties present.
> His remarks were clearly and cautiously composed, not committing him-
> self on anything, yet assuring and inspiring the hearers with the feeling
> of being interested and impartially devoted towards all the sections and
> the citizens of our Territory; and of being loyal and sound toward the
> Union and the Constitution.
>
> His appearance is pleasing and dignified, and his manner as a speaker
> betrays the scholar, the thinker and man of calm judgment and deep
> discrimination. . . . He alluded briefly to the troubled conditions of
> the Union, and seemed to be confident that the great battle of patriotism
> versus treason would be amicably adjusted. . . .
>
> He closed with the following beautiful apostrophe, as near as we
> could get it:
> "Hail to America! Land of our birth.
> "Hail to her magnificent continental domain.
> "Hail to her liberty-loving sons, and her matrons and maidens.
> "Hail to her, as she is! May she never become divided or her glory
> less dim."[4]

As the Gilpin regime began to organize itself, virtually as a military
government, the old territory of Jefferson gave its last gasp. On June 6,
"Governor" Steele abdicated in a formal proclamation to the people:

> By virtue of the authority in me vested, I, R. W. Steele, Governor of
> the Territory of Jefferson under the Provisional Government, and in and
> by virtue of my election by a majority of the People of the then called
> government of the People of the Mining Region, unrecognized by the
> General Government, at the base of the Rocky Mountains, on the East
> and at the center thereof, and placing our confidence in that "Over-
> ruling Providence" that has for a long period of time, steadied us as an
> American People, through so many difficulties, by foes seen and unseen,
> I therefore issue this my proclamation in view of the arrival of Governor
> Wm. Gilpin, and other officers of the United States, whom I recognize
> as being duly in authority. I deem it but obligatory upon me, by virtue
> of my office, to yield unto "Caesar the things that are Caesar's" and I

4Ibid., May 28, 1861.

hereby command and direct that all officers holding commissions under
me, especially all Judges, Justices of the Peace, &c., shall surrender the
same and from this date shall abstain from exercising the duties of all
offices they may have held under me by virtue of said commissions, and
further I advise and recommend to all law and order loving citizens to
submit to the laws of the United States and restrain themselves from
deeds of violence which so long have made our peculiar position almost
a bye word in the eyes of the civilized world. Again I advise my fellow
citizens who know me "so long and so well," to yield obedience to the
Laws of the United States, and do it by attending to your proper and
legitimate avocations whether Agricultural or Mining.

Gilpin had a system of courts functioning by July 10, and on September
9 the first lawful general assembly convened in Denver. The legislature
enacted a civil and criminal code, established counties, made the penalty
for counterfeiting gold dust or coins one to fourteen years, and also, by
joint resolution, proclaimed Colorado's fealty to the Union.

Although he had no funds—the territorial treasury "was like the bed of
Cherry creek in drouthy midsummer," Smiley says—Gilpin began to gird
for war. He ordered the recruiting of two companies and then of the 1st
Regiment of Colorado Volunteer Infantry. To arm his troops, Gilpin
sent his military staff around to buy up any serviceable firearm the people
could be persuaded to sell. Nearly every Coloradan of the times had a
gun of some kind, and soon a weird arsenal of ill-matched arms—shotguns, rifles, derringers, pistols of all models and calibers—was accumulated. The Denver insurgents also were trying to buy weapons to send to
the South or to arm themselves for possible domestic rebellion. They
published small handbills listing the types of guns they would buy and
the prices they would pay.

Through the summer of 1861 North-South skirmishing continued in
the streets and saloons. It was largely a vocal warfare, but sometimes
there was a shot. Late in August a bunch of the boys from the 1st
Colorado, spreeing it in full military tradition, started a handsome fight
in a brothel operated by a lady friend of Charley Harrison. The sports
and blacklegs from the Criterion took offense at this unchivalrous
deportment in a public boudoir and set out in a body to teach the
ruffian Yanks a lesson in Southern manners. But they were outnumbered
and got the worst of it.

The same night another task force from the Criterion beat up a sentry
guarding the building used as a barracks by the 1st Colorados. Harrison
and John Cody, uncle of "Buffalo Bill," were arrested but released under
bond. Then came a Saturday night, August 24. A group of soldiers took
umbrage at being denied entrance to the Criterion and started a free-
for-all that wrecked the establishment. The rumor got out that Harrison
and his gang had received reinforcements from southern Colorado
insurgents and that they planned to raid banks and business establish-

ments and put Denver to the torch. Military guards were doubled, and soldiers in pairs patrolled the streets.

The inevitable gunfire began sometime after midnight, and it was asserted that the first shots issued from the Criterion. Private George McCullought was hit in the ankle. Another soldier took a ball through his left ear lobe. Bugles sounded, and a company marched up in close order to place a cannon with its muzzle peering straight into the Criterion at point-blank range. Two hours later Harrison was arrested and placed in chains. He was put on trial before territorial Chief Justice Benjamin F. Hall on September 3, was fined five thousand dollars, but escaped imprisonment on his promise to quit the territory. The handsome Charley, sauve, debonair, a ladies' man and a killer, sold out the Criterion and departed. He did not return, though he tried.[5]

Meanwhile Governor Gilpin was stepping up recruitment of his 1st Regiment, boldly meeting expenses with scrip in the form of unauthorized drafts on the United States Treasury. John P. Slough, politically wrong but a "War Democrat" who rated as "unflinching," was commissioned as the regiment's colonel. Samuel F. Tappan was appointed lieutenant colonel, and the post of major went to John M. Chivington, presiding elder of the Methodist Episcopal Church for the Rocky Mountain district, the man who would rescue the flood-stranded Byers family the following spring. Chivington first was offered the regimental chaplaincy, which he declined, asking for a fighting assignment.

Thirty acres of Platte bottomland about two miles up the river near the Byers ranch was selected as a training ground and named Camp Weld in honor of territorial Secretary Lewis L. Weld. By October 24 the *News* could report that the camp had a headquarters building, barracks, mess rooms, guardhouse, and hospital built in a hollow square around the parade grounds. Denver citizens took to driving out from town to watch the evening drill. The paper listed the official blueprint for the life of a soldier:

> Order of Camp duty. Reveille at daylight, and breakfast call at 7 o'clock. Guard mount at 8, and company drill at 9 A.M. Battalion drill at 2½ P.M., and Dress Parade a half hour before sundown. Tattoo at 8½ P.M., and at 9, lights are extinguished and all visitors withdraw from camp.

All regular and rigorous enough to be standard soldiering. But the 1st Colorados were highly irregular troopers.

They deserted at will, cussed out their officers with impunity, jayhawked the countryside for food to supplement army rations, and

[5]A full story of Harrison and his lurid involvements with Denver's past is told by Stanley Zamonski in "Colorado Gold and the Confederacy," *The Denver Westerners' Brand Book: 1956* (Denver, 1957), pp. 87ff.

generally raised hell. Taps was merely a signal to head for the fleshpots in town. A supply sergeant sold off company property in his care, including several hundred bushels of grain, and lost the whole stake at monte. He was secesh anyway and deserted a few days later. Company F was sent to Fort Laramie to pick up arms and hurrahed the countryside going and coming on a whiskey diet. Private Ovando J. Hollister, Company F, who would become an associate editor of the *News* in 1868, tells of a passing captain who chanced to drop an ill-timed remark about the "common soldier" in the hearing of one of the volunteers. The private sounded off:

> "G——d d——d old white livered whiskey-tub! If you don't eat them words in three winks of a louse's tail, we'll tear you limb from gut! By G—d! you'll find we're uncommon soldiers, first you know. We don't 'low no such things as you to insult us, if you do wear shoulder-straps."[6]

One regimental unit discovered there was a standing order to detail the guard from men in the left of the ranks. So they began falling in, Hollister says, "crowded together like a flock of sheep worried by dogs"—"there *was* no left." One morning they formed ranks in three circles. Another company, enlisted as mounted rifles, refused to take the oath when it was decided they would have to serve as foot soldiers. Still another unit, deprived of its whiskey ration by the commander, marched to his quarters and "gave him three groans." He slapped the whole outfit in the guardhouse. Arrest in Denver City didn't mean much, however. Any misbehaving soldier who was picked up by the city police was promptly delivered by comrades who battered the jail door off its hinges. On the trail the 1st Colorados supplied themselves with horses, wagons, and food by seizure from any ranch or farm unlucky enough to be in their line of march.

The candid Hollister gives a riotous picture of the carousing Firsters as they waited, bored and devilish, at Camp Weld for their hour of glory to come:

> Near the 1st of December the good people of Denver, alarmed at the growing insolence of the soldiers among whom no one seem[ed] disposed or was able to maintain much discipline, organized a police to preserve order in town. Henceforth it became the object of many to create and foment variance with these minions of the city. I never *loved* fighting and disturbances for their own sake, and hence could not countenance acts of aggression in any party because it was able to back them. But there are always enough who will, regardless of consequences, as they are of governing principles of right and wrong. This

6William J. Barker, ed., *Boldly They Rode* (Lakewood, 1949), a republication of Ovando J. Hollister, *History of the First Regiment of Colorado Volunteers* (Denver, 1863), p. 24.

was too much the case with us at the time and such demonstrations of
hostility to the town and to good order as were occasionally made under
the *nom de plume* of company Q, calling for interference not only from
the police but from our brother cohorts of the barracks, did no credit to
our sense or courage.

As the holidays approached the boys began to "scour the country
round" to get forage for a big time. On Christmas eve parties might
have been seen wending their noiseless way through back alleys, whispering ominously on street corners, or carefully reconnitering out-houses.
One party worked anxiously and assiduously a long time to pick the
lock of a hen-roost door that was hung on leather hinges. Another, with
great labor and no little risk of detection, carried a forty-gallon barrel of
vinegar to the quarters, supposing it to be "rot." Pigs were coaxed and
driven to the cook-house door. A pistol would appear at a knot-hole
and piggy would disappear at a trap-hole. Eggs, hams, oysters, champagne, cheese and vegetables were the results of the night's foraging.
It was rough on the town, but we had been dogs now four months
without pay. No money in the company. We couldn't live over Christmas on bread and beef. It already stunk in our nostrils like quails in
those of Israel.

Christmas dawned. By breakfast half a dozen were drunk. Mart
was caving. The side-walk was altogether too small for him. He transferred the billingsgate of the "hells" to the street. Police appeared on
the corners; Mart became more scurrilous than ever; we tried to get
him to quarters—no use; word was sent for a patrol. . . .

A little sparring was exchanged, and the citizens gave it up and kindly
allowed us to manage our own affairs. The city was lawful "loot," the
rest of the week. Everything was gobbled. Beef, mutton, vegetables,
wine, cheese and clothing. Loads of hay were sold while the owner was
"smiling" with a confederate. The city complained, and no wonder!

We were removed to the barracks. . . . We jayhawked pork, beef
and mutton wherever we could successfully. If the company was moved
to the barracks to rid the town of it, the action failed of the object. As
Major Chivington said, "They only came to camp to get their meals."
Whoever failed to get out on the regular pass, failed none the less to pass
the sentinels guarding the fold, and proceeding to town, failed not again
to take vengence on their supposed enemies in every way they could
think of. . . .

. . . It is over now, and there is no use in hard feelings, but we were
not disposed to submit to what we considered the insults of the Denver
people. . . .[7]

Slowly events were shaping up which would provide an outlet for the
unused energies of the unruly 1st. Meanwhile they occupied themselves
by working up resentment against Gibson's *Herald* for an editorial
commenting, rather mildly considering the circumstances, on the
conduct of the Camp Weld soldiers and some of their officers. A landing

[7]Ibid., pp. 33–36.

squad broke into the *Herald* office, seized the entire stock of newsprint, and happily distributed it to the winds around town. By some quirk of liquored logic the *News* escaped a similar fate even though it was saying things scarcely less uncomplimentary about the regiment.

But there was some action, and many alarms. Hollister says the troops were alerted several times to meet rumors that invading Texans were at the gates of the city. On one occasion the scouting party returned sheepishly to report the invading force was a drove of cattle kicking up a dust on the southern horizon. A Captain McKee, described as an old Texas Indian fighter, was picked up and thrown in the city jail on the charge that he had organized a force of forty partisans and was about to move south with it to join Sibley's army in New Mexico. But the "Secesh party" in Denver was petering out. Mayor Moore, Park McClure, and Charley Harrison all had left. A. B. Miller sought to get out with a wagon train of supplies for the Confederates. The wagons were captured on the plains. The *News* of November 23, 1861, reported that a Rebel supply train and twenty-one men had been seized November 18 near Fort Wise (now Fort Lyon) in the Arkansas Valley. A unit of the 1st was dispatched to bring the prisoners into Denver whence, in due time, they escaped without much difficulty.

The geostrategists of the South had not been idle during these times. They had designed a whole new geography for the North American continent, and it involved lands well above and beyond Mason and Dixon's line.

Colorado mines were producing nearly seven million dollars in new gold for the Philadelphia mint during 1861, even though many of the miners had deserted the placers and shafts to try the roistering army life. The Confederate planners, moreover, were well informed on the divided loyalties in Colorado Territory. Out in California there was gold, too, and a large and influential element, particularly in the southern part of the state, who favored dismemberment of the old Union, which was being run, they said, for the bankers in Boston, New York, and Philadelphia with precious little concern for the needs of a far-distant commonwealth. In New Mexico sentiment was both divided and apathetic. The western end of the territory, present Arizona, had the same complaints of neglect that rankled California and actually set itself up as a secessionist Confederate territory. In New Mexico proper, oriented toward Mexico as it had been for centuries, many citizens took little interest in federal affairs, North or South. The Mormons of Utah Territory, then including present Nevada, had been embittered by several decades of what they considered rough handling by federal authorities. Their empire of Deseret had been invaded and occupied by United States troops, and the Saints had long memories for the religious persecutions which had driven them west from New York to Utah seeking peace, freedom of conscience, and a promised land where they would be let alone. Even as far north as Oregon there was feeling for secession, though less in sympathy with the Rebel cause than in the conviction that an independent government was needed for the development of the Pacific Slope.

Viewed from the South, all of this added up to strategic opportunity. The entire West with its dazzling new gold and its ports opening on the riches of the China trade could easily be won, it appeared, for the Confederate States. Alternatively, the plans called for sponsorship of an independent Confederacy of the West which would deny to the Union the gold and other Western resources.

Mexico was not omitted from the grand design. The unsettled, financially embarrassed, and volatile state of politics in that young republic seemed to make available, by easy conquest or purchase, the states of Chihuahua, Sonora, and Baja California.

Moreover, there is some evidence that this sort of continental planning was under way long before Beauregard fired on Fort Sumter. During 1860, John B. Floyd, Buchanan's Southern Secretary of War, had moved large stores of arms and other military supplies to small, exposed forts and posts in the Southwest. One major cache was deposited at little Fort Union in northeastern New Mexico. Then Floyd resigned from the cabinet on December 29 in a cloud of treason.

Confirmation of the outlines of the whole plan came in the 1880s when Major Trevanion T. Teel, C.S.A., one of Sibley's officers, wrote his memoirs of the march to the West. If the New Mexico campaign proved successful, he wrote,

. . . negotiations to secure Chihuahua, Sonora and Lower California, either by purchase or by conquest, would be opened; the state of affairs in Mexico made it an easy thing to take those States, and the Mexican President would be glad to get rid of them and at the same time improve his exchequer. In addition to all this, General Sibley intimated that there was a secret understanding between the Mexican and Confederate authorities, and that, as soon as our occupation of the said States was assured, a transfer of those States would be made to the Confederacy. Juarez, the President of the Republic (so called), was then in the City of Mexico with a small army under his command, hardly sufficient to keep him in his position. That date [1862] was the darkest hour in the annals of our sister republic, but it was the brightest of the Confederacy, and General Sibley thought that he would have little difficulty in consummating the ends so devoutly wished by the Confederate Government.

Then, Major Teel went on,

. . . with the enlistment of men from New Mexico, California, Arizona and Colorado, [Sibley would] form an army which would effect the ultimate aim of the campaign, for there were scattered all over the

Western States and Territories Southern men who were anxiously awaiting an opportunity to join the Confederate army; . . . an army of
advance would be organized, and "On to San Francisco" would be the
watchword. . . .[8]

Up in Denver City rumors about the Confederate designs for the
West kept the town tense and jittery. Any day now an advancing horde
of murderous Texans might come marching down Cherry Creek.
Governor Gilpin, still without funds but still convinced he was doing
what had to be done, redoubled his efforts to recruit and equip his 1st
Colorados. His "Pet Lambs," he called them, in spite of the street
brawling and plundering. Gilpin wrung an authorization out of Washington to dispatch his regiment beyond the territorial boundaries if
necessary. It was well known in Denver that the West Pointer Sibley
was organizing an army at San Antonio, Texas, for an invasion of the
West, and Gilpin wanted Colorado to help counter the move.

Finally word came that Sibley had left San Antonio with a force of
thirty-seven hundred rugged Texans. In less than a month he marched
his "Army of New Mexico," more generally known as "Sibley's Brigade,"
nearly a thousand miles across the breadth of Texas. On December 14
he was at Fort Bliss on the Rio Grande near El Paso.

Gilpin hastily organized two independent companies under Captains
James H. Ford and Theodore H. Dodd, dispatched them to Fort Garland
in southern Colorado's San Luis Valley and then on to New Mexico
to reinforce Colonel Edward R. S. Canby, Union commander in the
territory.

Sibley moved up New Mexico's Rio Grande Valley in January. Forts
Fillmore and Thorn fell to him without opposition. At Valverde, near
Fort Craig, on February 21, Canby attempted to meet and halt the
invasion with a force of thirty-eight hundred troops and militiamen,
including Dodd's company of Coloradans. They were defeated, and
Sibley moved north and occupied Albuquerque and Santa Fe, territorial
capital.

The rebellion was going well on the faraway left flank of the Confederacy. Canby's forces were now scattered and demoralized. There
appeared to be nothing to bar Sibley's way to the Colorado gold fields.
Canby sent urgent pleas to Denver City for help as Sibley dispatched a
force to the northeast to claim the stores Secretary Floyd had thoughtfully
cached at Fort Union, a post Sibley had built not many years before.

In Denver the News reported early in January that Sibley was on the
move up the Rio Grande, and efforts were made to obtain orders from
Fort Leavenworth, Kansas, for the 1st Colorado to move to Canby's
assistance. Nearly a month later, February 10, the order finally reached

[8]Quoted in William Clarke Whitford, Colorado Volunteers in the Civil War
(Denver, 1906), pp. 12–13.

Acting Governor Weld (Gilpin had been called to Washington to explain why he was issuing drafts on the Treasury without authorization):

> Send all available forces you can possibly spare to reinforce Colonel Canby, commanding Department of New Mexico, and to keep open his communication through Fort Wise. Act promptly and with all the discretion of your latest information as to what may be necessary and where the troops of Colorado can do most service.
>
> D. [David] Hunter
Major-General, Commanding[9]

The restive 1st now entered upon its day, and, moralists notwithstanding, the months of training in Denver City saloons, the high living on stolen pork, had not sapped the troopers' vitality. Colonel Slough marched south on February 22. A portion of his command, detailed to Fort Wise, set out March 3 to join him. The columns united near present Trinidad on the headwaters of the Purgatoire (which some Coloradans, unable to bend their tongues around the Spanish, have called "Picket-wire" for a century or longer). The full regiment now toiled up the mountain branch of the Santa Fe Trail and over Raton Pass.

It was the same old outfit. The main column helped itself to horses and wagons as it moved down from Denver, and Hollister says his unit from Fort Wise made a commissary of any herd of cattle encountered along the way. But they marched—thirty, forty, or more miles a day at a pace that killed their draft animals. Horses and mules began to drop dead in the harness. On the drag into Maxwell's ranch on the Cimarron the regiment was on the road from sunup to sunup and made sixty-seven miles, for a total of ninety-two in thirty-six hours. Major Chivington's "big grays" were left where they fell, dead.

The 1st reached Fort Union on March 11. It found there a force of about four hundred regulars, many of them survivors of the Valverde disaster. The Coloradans remained at the fort ten days for re-outfitting and daily drilling, and the boys made a merry time of it. A drunken sergeant shot a lieutenant in the face, and a cadre broke into the sutler's cellar to carry off a supply of whiskey, wine, canned fruit, and oysters. On the twenty-second Slough moved on toward Santa Fe by way of Las Vegas and Gloriéta Pass, and Hollister says:

> About noon we succeeded in getting under way. A party started ahead early to secure the plunder stolen from the sutler last night. A squad of regulars were sent after them, but they had no inclination to interfere with the volunteers and took care to discover nothing. The boys concealed some, drank more, lost and sold the balance. What was drunk immediately under the eyes of the sutler was about all the good

[9] Ibid., p. 75.

they got of it; a doubtful good certainly, for the command was scattered from Dan to Beersheba, burying plunder, drinking, fighting and carousing with Mexican women at the Lome, a small "Sodom" five or six miles from Union. There were a dozen of us too drunk to know friends from foes, consequently most provokingly troublesome. Many came in during the night with rough usage painted on their faces in unmistakable colors. . . .

All the sutlers in New Mexico are traitors at heart. Still they meanly fatten on the government they would destroy. Their property is lawful "loot" to Union soldiers, in my way of thinking.[10]

At Las Vegas, temporary seat of the territorial government since Sibley had driven it from Santa Fe, the Firsters scattered through town looking for women and loot. Both were scarce, Hollister reports. The sight of the women, he said, "was more sedative than stimulating," and "if there chanced to be one that by any possible stretch of courtesy could be termed decent, there were enough [soldiers] around her to eat her and then go off with empty stomachs."

Slough's force as he moved down from Fort Union numbered 1342 men. Opposing him were 1100 Texans under Colonel W. R. Scurry, ordered from Santa Fe for what was planned as an easy conquest of Fort Union. Unknown to each other, the two armies marched toward a head-on meeting as they rounded the spur of mountains which separates Santa Fe from the Fort Union country.

On the morning of March 25, Major Chivington was given four hundred men and detailed as advance party to probe ahead. He was to scout and raid, possibly even as far as Santa Fe itself, but he was under strict orders not to precipitate a general engagement. The following day Chivington reached Pigeon's Ranch, so called, according to Whitford, because of its owner's "peculiar style of dancing at parties." A scouting force of twenty Texans was captured and sent to the rear, and then Chivington, although he had now learned that the main enemy force was entering the far end of Gloriéta Pass, pushed on during the afternoon into Apache Cañon.

There, suddenly, he encountered Scurry's advance force of five hundred men under Major Charles L. Pyron. Disregarding his orders to avoid a general action, Chivington attacked. In a fierce three-hour battle of howitzers, cavalry charges, and hand-to-hand fighting, he won the day. Dressed in full regimentals and making a conspicuous target, Chivington rode about the battlefield "with a pistol in each hand and one or two under his arms." One of the Texas officers, taken prisoner, said he emptied his revolver three times at the big major and had his company fire a volley at him. But Chivington galloped unhurt through the bullets.

Pyron fell back toward his main body, then sixteen miles to the rear.

[10]Barker, op. cit., pp. 55–56.

He sent a flag of truce to Chivington and an armistice was arranged until 8 A.M. next day to give time for burying the dead and removing the wounded from the field. The Colorados also moved back to water at Pigeon's Ranch. The first engagement of the Battle of La Gloriéta had gone to the untested irregulars from Pike's Peak.

Later the *News* would publish a letter written by one of the captured Texans to his wife:

> . . . On the twenty-sixth, we got word that the enemy were coming down the canon, in the shape of two hundred Mexicans and about two hundred regulars. Out we marched with two cannon, expecting an easy victory, but what a mistake. Instead of Mexicans and regulars, they were regular demons, that iron and lead had no effect upon, in the shape of Pike's Peakers from the Denver City Gold mines . . . before we could form in line of battle, their infantry were upon the hills, on both sides of us, shooting us down like sheep. . . . They had no sooner got within shooting distance of us, than up came a company of cavalry at full charge, with swords and revolvers drawn, looking like so many flying devils. On they came to what I supposed certain destruction, but nothing like lead or iron seemed to stop them, for we were pouring it into them from every side like hail in a storm. In a moment these devils had run the gauntlet for a half mile, and were fighting hand to hand with our men in the road . . . some of them turned their horses, jumped the ditch, and like demons, came charging on us. It looked as if their horses' feet never touched the ground. . . . Had it not been for the devils from Pike's Peak, this country would have been ours. . . .[11]

On the twenty-seventh both sides waited tensely for the other to attack, and neither moved from defensive positions. Slough came up with seven hundred men to reinforce Chivington. Scurry had joined Pyron to give the Texans an effective force of about eleven hundred men.

The forces thus would have been approximately equal for the next day's battle had not Slough again decided to divide his command. He ordered Chivington and his four hundred to cross the mountains and attack the enemy's rear. The Colorado commander with his seven hundred then prepared to bear the frontal assault of Scurry's eleven hundred. The battleground was Pigeon's Ranch, at the eastern end of the pass.

The Coloradans and Texans met late in the morning of the twenty-eighth and fought for six or seven hours. Slowly Slough retreated before the superior force, but at 5 P.M. Scurry sent a flag of truce. He had just learned that his supply train had been burned.

Chivington again was the hero of the day. He and his flanking party had made it through the mountains, had fallen upon the lightly guarded

[11]Ibid., pp. 166–70.

supply train, burned eighty wagons of supplies, bayoneted five hundred horses and mules, and made prisoners of the guard detail.

It had been a bloody day's work for both sides. Nearly one fourth of all the men engaged were casualties.

The Confederates were demoralized. Under cover of the armistice Scurry withdrew.

It was, he reported to Sibley's headquarters, "the hardest contested fight it had ever been my lot to witness." His dispatch continued:

> . . . Our brave soldiers, heedless of the storm, pressed on, deter-mined, if possible, to take their battery. A heavy body of infantry, twice our number, interposed to save their guns. Here the conflict was terrible. . . . Inch by inch was the ground disputed, until the artillery of the enemy had time to escape with a number of their wagons. . . . The pursuit was kept up until forced to halt from the extreme exhaustion of the men. . . . [There were] two acts which the most barbarous savage of the plains would blush to own. One was the shooting and dangerously wounding the Rev. L. H. Jones, chaplain of the 4th regi-ment, with a white flag in his hand; the other an order that the prisoners they had taken be shot in case they were attacked on their retreat. These instances go to prove that they have lost all sense of humanity, in the insane hatred they bear to the citizens of the Confederacy, who have the manliness to arm in defence of their country's independence.[12]

Sibley's retreat from New Mexico began immediately. He withdrew down the Rio Grande, burning his wagons and supplies as he went. The West had been saved for the Union.

Slough and his demonic Pike's Peakers wanted to pursue, but General Canby sent him specific orders to return to Fort Union. The Colorado commander resigned in disgust, and Chivington, hero of Gloriéta, was advanced to the colonelcy in his place. The regiment remained on duty in New Mexico through the rest of the year.

The 1st Colorados cannot be left in New Mexico without a final frank note on their conduct from the future associate editor of the News, Ovando Hollister. Camp life became dull. Two of the officers got into a brawl, from which one emerged with a pocketful of the other's whiskers as a souvenir.

Although the Colorado troops stayed on to help chase Sibley back to Texas and then to guard the frontier against possible future attack, the grandiose Confederate plan for the West crashed in ruins on those two March days at Apache Cañon and Pigeon's Ranch. Gone was the hope for a Confederacy that would stretch from sea to shining sea. Shattered the dreams of Colorado and California gold, which Jefferson Davis had seen both as direct support for his shaky economy and as enticement

[12]Colonel W. R. Scurry to Major A. M. Jackson, Mar. 31, 1862; quoted in Henry Steele Commager, The Blue and the Gray (one-volume ed., Indianapolis-New York, 1950), pp. 404–6.

for foreign loans. And there would be no Pacific ports to help ease the tightening Union naval blockade.

Large speculative structures can be raised, and have been, on the premise that the relatively small, far-isolated engagement at La Gloriéta was a key battle in the nation's tragic division. The speculations rest entirely on ifs. But opportunity was there when Sibley marched west, and it ended among the rocks, piñons, and scrub cedars of a shallow cañon on the old trail to Santa Fe. The South attempted no further operations of a regular nature in the Far West.

There were a couple of irregular ones still to come, and both have juncture with the story of Denver and the *News*. One was a mixture of banditry and Southern patriotism, with probably more of the one than the other, and the second involves as barbaric an episode as ever gave the Great Plains a dark name for violence.

Jim Reynolds and his eight raiders may have been Confederate guerrillas, but larceny seems to have been the principal sentiment in their hearts as they came up the Arkansas Valley and into South Park late in July of 1864. They claimed they were out to raid gold for the South and that they had got sixty-three thousand dollars of it from a wagon train in New Mexico. The flyleaf of Reynolds' pocket diary did carry an oath which the gang presumably had sworn to:

> I do solemnly swear or affirm that I will bear true allegiance to the Confederate States of America and the President and all officers appointed over me, so help me God. I further swear that I will aid or assist all true southern men and their families wherever they may be at a reasonable risk of my life whether in the army or out of it. I furthermore swear that I will not reveal, divulge or cause to be divulged any of the grips, signs, passwords or proceedings of the order, except to those who have been regularly initiated or to whom it may by right belong, and if I should be so vile as to violate this my solemn oath or obligation I shall be taken and hung by the neck until I am dead, dead, dead, and my bones left on the plains to bleach as unworthy of burial.[13]

The Reynolds gang started its Colorado operations by robbing a lonely traveler in South Park of a hundred dollars and the stagecoach, near Hamilton, of some three thousand dollars. Kenneth Englert, authority on the notorious "Reynolds Raid", believes this was the total extent of the gang's "take," at least in Colorado, but rumors that the sixty-three thousand dollars is buried somewhere in the mountains touched off a long-time treasure hunt which still sends some people searching the forests and glens around the headwaters of the South Platte.

A Paul Revere in the form of William H. Berry, traveling subscription

[13]*Rocky Mountain News*, Aug. 13, 1864.

agent in South Park for the *Rocky Mountain News*, raced through the mountains and then on down to Denver to spread the alarm that Colorado had been invaded by Rebel guerrillas. Berry dashed ahead of the gang for a time, then stalked them, finally got himself captured. He was released in time to speed on into Denver a little after noon on July 26. He made the deadline for the afternoon edition, and the *News* sounded the alarm.

Several civilian posses and two cavalry companies hit the trail to track down the guerrillas, who were boasting at roadhouses that they had served with Quantrill and that they had in mind sweeping down on Denver, robbing the banks, and setting fire to the town. Denver was going to get what Lawrence, Kansas, got, they said.

Finally one of the gang was shot dead from ambush, a posseman got an accidental rifle bullet through both thighs, and another of the raiders was captured alive. On threat of peremptory lynching, he led the pursuers to a rendezvous where five of the band, including Jim Reynolds, were captured. Three got away and were chased two hundred and twenty miles in two days into the mountains of New Mexico, where the trail was lost. The five captives were taken to Denver and, a secret military "trial" and ordered moved to Fort Wise. A company of the 3rd Colorado Cavalry started south with them, but on upper Cherry Creek near the old gold-rush town of Russellville all five prisoners were shot "trying to escape." Dick Wootton happened by the spot later and said he found three skeletons lashed upright against trees with bullet holes in their skulls.[14]

The only other known Confederate guerrilla pass at Colorado Territory didn't reach the border, but it had some distinguished personnel: W. Park McClure and the banished Charley Harrison. After he left Denver, McClure became a captain in the Confederate Army and served with General Sterling Price on his raids through Missouri. Charley Harrison became one of the ranking leaders of bushwhacker bands in southern Kansas, Missouri, Arkansas, and Indian Territory. He carried the rank of lieutenant colonel in Colonel Emmett MacDonald's Confederate 4th Missouri Cavalry, and reports praise him for fearlessness and gallantry in action.

Harrison persuaded his superiors that a long-distance raid into Colorado Territory would be feasible and profitable. The raiders could capture arms, mules, wagons, federal mail, maybe some gold. There was also a possibility of recruits from among Southern sympathizers still in the West. At minimum, such a raid would cause confusion and strike fear in the hearts of Union forces. Moreover there was nothing to obstruct the raiders between the Missouri and Denver City but a few Plains Indians.

[14]For a full account of the affair see Kenneth E. Englert, "Raids by Reynolds," *The Denver Westerners' Brand Book: 1956*, pp. 151ff.

The ex-gambler organized his force at Center Creek, Missouri, and one of the first volunteers turned out to be his old friend Park McClure. The party of twenty picked raiders, many of them cavalry officers with Western experience, set out on May 16.

The Osage Indians at this time had been driven north into Kansas by Texas and Arkansas guerrillas, and their resentment of such treatment took the form of loyalty to the Union. They assigned themselves the task of intercepting Confederate efforts to rouse the Plains Indians against Union settlements. Some of the Osages enlisted for scouting duty. One of the Osage bands under Little Bear was on the Verdigris River near Humboldt in southeastern Kansas. Little Bear and his braves met the Harrison party at Lightning Creek with rifles, tomahawks, lances, and arrows.

Park McClure went down with the war hatchet of an eighteen-year-old brave, Gra-tah-more, embedded in his skull to the haft. Harrison was shot in the face and rolled to the ground from his saddle. On his knees, still firing, he shot a charging Indian through the chest. Then he was overwhelmed in a wave of naked red bodies, and razor-sharp skinning knives flashed. Only two of the Confederate band got away, and the Osages left no wounded survivors on the field.

The eighteen bodies were mutilated. The heads of some were chopped off. Others were scalped. Charley Harrison's dark hair by this time was thinning on top, and the Osages instead counted *coup* on his handsome black beard. Investigating troopers from Humboldt a few days later saw the beard-scalp hanging as a totem on a lance in front of an Osage lodge. They also found Harrison's body, but it had no face.[15]

So ends the story of Denver's most glamorous badman. And Charley had his jury waiting for him; he had killed the twelfth man in Leavenworth before he took up authorized killing as a soldier.

[15]William L. Bartles and Thomas Moshier, "Massacre of Confederates by the Osages," *The Osage Magazine*, Feb. and May 1910; quoted by Zamonski, op. cit., pp. 103–14.

CHAPTER ELEVEN

Massacre at Sand Creek

WILLIAM GILPIN was sure the war in the Far West had vital bearing on the fate of the Union. So much so that he felt he had direct access to the United States Treasury in financing his efforts to defend his new territory and keep Colorado gold out of Dixie. No one had given him the slightest encouragement in the belief, but it was characteristic of the man that this was no impediment. With sweeping executive vigor he undertook what is probably the most casual, and impersonal, raid ever made on federal funds. There was no thought of private gain. He was striking a blow for the Union when he issued, in mounting numbers, his personally autographed drafts on the Treasury Department. Money was needed to recruit and equip men for the service of their country, *ergo*, their country should provide the cash. Gilpin, as territorial governor, represented the might of the nation over all these plains and mountains. So he signed the chits. It was as simple as that.

When Gilpin arrived the territorial treasury was as barren as the prairies he had crossed by coach. In fact there *was* no treasury; Coloradans had not been introduced to the privilege of paying taxes on a regular basis. Gilpin had to start from zero, with a war on, with all the disquieting rumors drifting in more and more frequently that the Johnny Rebs were about to sally north from Texas in force. So the "Gilpin drafts" became legal tender, temporarily, in Denver stores, warehouses, and banks, and the roistering 1st Colorado was born. Not everyone conceded that the silver-tongued new governor was morally justified in reaching into the country's pocket this way, though no one had any doubt of its illegality. The *News* eyed the process with a good deal of conservative reservation and promptly got to trading blows with Gibson's *Herald* on the issue. The *Herald* went all the way with the governor. The financing, instead of being "impractical" as the *News* said it was, actually was the soul of practicality. What else could the poor man do? the *Herald* argued. He had been given Denver and the West to defend; he had to have funds.

The first territorial legislators were not much help. Individually and collectively they were as broke as Gilpin was. The general assembly was likely to meet wherever lodging was cheapest and board most generous and inexpensive. Moreover, then as now, there was resentment by the country legislators of Denver's size and status as regional metropolis.

So the legislature became, by its own fiat, a migratory body. The first territorial assembly met in Denver beginning September 9, 1861, but it voted on November 5 to designate Colorado City as capital and site of its next session. Colorado City was at the very foot of Pike's Peak and long since has been swallowed up by Colorado Springs. When time came for the second meeting, however, the legislators decided they couldn't meet: no cash in the till for salaries. It could have appropriated its own pay, but there was nothing to appropriate from. The session was postponed until July 7, 1862, when the legislators finally gathered at their own expense in Colorado City. A trial of four days was enough for that rustic little log-cabin town; facilities were inadequate. The assemblymen adjourned to meet in Denver City on July 11. Subsequently, beginning in 1864, the capital shuttled back and forth between Golden City and Denver, and it was not until December 9, 1867, that a decree permanently designating Denver as the capital was adopted. Strangely, the one town in the territory which rivaled Denver in size and importance, Central City, never made a successful bid for capital honors. Along the way the legislature-on-horseback paused long enough to designate the *News* as its official paper. Column upon column of proceedings, minutes, and verbatim bills and acts appear during these years. Tastes in political reporting in those days ran to the precise text, however ponderous and interminable. The electorate apparently was impressed by and demanded to see all the whereases and now-therefore-let-it-be-resolveds.

Gilpin appears to have been not much concerned about the comings and goings of his general assembly, nor overly interested in what it did. He viewed his task as primarily military, and set up his government on that basis. He was busy recruiting his "Pet Lambs," finagling arms for them, and studying reports on Sibley's well-known hostile intentions. His drafts on the treasury were willingly accepted by Denver merchants and suppliers during the summer of 1861, and Denver felt very much a part of the Union as it girded. The *News* began to run a woodcut of the Star-Spangled Banner at the head of its editorial column.

By fall, however, the first of the drafts had reached Washington, and eyebrows in the hard-pressed Treasury Department bounced off the ceiling. Payment of the scrip was instantly refused. Dispatches came through inquiring of Gilpin, in effect but in politer language, whatinhell he thought he was up to.

Dishonoring of the drafts was a stiff blow to the entire Denver economy. They were circulating freely as currency, each holder endorsing the paper on to the next. A financial pyramid had been built on confidence that Gilpin knew what he was doing and would be sustained. The town had a population, according to an enumeration by Deputy Marshal N. Otis, of only 2477 persons.[1] The *News* patriotically

[1]*Rocky Mountain News*, June 24, 1861.

claimed this was short by at least two thirds, but if the truth of the matter lay somewhere in between, Denver still was scarcely more than a crossroads village. Into this village Gilpin had poured, within the space of a few months, some $375,000 worth of scrip.

When the first drafts began arriving back from Washington marked "worthless," chaos took over. Scarcely a business in town was untouched. The collapse was total, and Denver plunged into a winter of depression, hardship, and want. Gilpin, who had been so proudly welcomed with flying flags and booming cannon, now was bitterly denounced. He was summoned to Washington to account for his blithe ways with the public treasury, and Lincoln's cabinet, faced with a thousand matters more pressing, had to take time out to inquire into the bursting of a bubble far out beyond the western horizon. Gilpin was removed, effective April 19, 1862. Eventually a small portion of his drafts was honored. A paymaster was sent out, and any original draft-holder who could prepare an itemized and verified bill for his goods or services got paid. The drafts themselves, however, never were recognized, and since many of them had passed through a number of hands by endorsement and could not be thrown back to the original holders, most banks, businessmen, and private citizens were left holding an empty bag. Smiley says:

> . . . Public feeling against him [Gilpin] here became of extreme bitterness and he was assailed upon every hand by the exasperated and impoverished holders of his drafts. As an old army officer he was held to have known the government's rigid financial methods, and it was principally because of his assumed authority that the people had unquestioningly accepted his irregular and unauthorized drafts. . . . But, through all the trouble no one questioned Governor Gilpin's integrity, the purity of his purpose, the loftiness of his patriotism, or the sincerity of his zeal to protect the people from invasion, and to serve them to the best of his ability. He was in many ways a visionary man whose mind and thoughts were often far above the practical affairs of every-day life; and when that emergency came his enthusiasm for the Union overshadowed all other things. Notwithstanding the unfortunate results that grew out of his methods of financing his military preparations, the people of Denver and of Colorado were immeasurably indebted to him for the promptness, vigor and earnestness with which he prepared for war.[2]

To succeed Gilpin, Lincoln chose another of his close friends, John Evans of Illinois. Evans, a physician-financier, was a man of prominence in the Midwest. He had been one of the organizers of the Republican party in Illinois and had helped win the nomination for the man from Springfield. He was founder of Chicago's suburban Evanston and of Northwestern University there. As a physician he was a pioneer in

[2]Smiley, *History of Denver*, pp. 379–80.

humanizing care of the mentally ill, occupied a professorship for eleven years in the old Rush Medical College at Chicago, and was the first to demonstrate the contagious nature of cholera. As a financier he made a fortune building and dealing in Midwestern railroads. Lincoln had wanted him to take the governorship of Washington Territory in 1861 but he had declined.

Evans came to Denver in the spring of 1862 as a man of great wealth and a figure of towering prestige and authority. For the rest of his life, which ended in 1897, he dominated Denver and Colorado affairs. With Byers, he was one of the founders of the University of Denver, and he built railroads, ran banks, joined the *News* editor in mining ventures, owned traction firms, real estate, and a wide variety of businesses. Always a devout Methodist, he poured much of his great and growing wealth into the pioneer churches of Denver. Financier, statesman, and philanthropist, Evans was one of the chief architects of Colorado's development. A son-in-law, Samuel H. Elbert, also became a Colorado governor, and Evans's descendants remain today one of Denver's most wealthy and influential families, the pivot of "old guard" maneuvers on Seventeenth Street.

John Evans was not a man to be opposed or thwarted, and he seldom was. But his one conspicuous failure was to win a seat in the U. S. Senate. The name of the dominant peak looking down on Denver was changed in his honor. Streets, chapels, and towns were named for him, and in the era of rich men which would come to Denver he would be one of the richest. Only the Senate escaped him, and it was not because his reverent fellow citizens denied him the distinction. Evans resigned from the governor's chair in 1865 to run for the senatorship after Colorado voters had narrowly ratified a proposed state constitution. He was elected. But President Johnson decided there were not yet enough people in Colorado to form a new state, and he vetoed the enabling act.

The Trinidad *News* once contrasted the personal appearance and demeanor of Evans with those of another prominent Denver resident:

> Governor Evans owns the South Park railroad—is worth a million dollars in Colorado and a quarter of a million in Chicago, and yet Professor Goldrick, the Adonis of the Rocky Mountain Herald, wears the best clothes, smokes the finest cigars, looks the most like a million-aire on the street, and enjoys what there is in life. Stocks may go up; Evans may go down, but Goldrick goes on forever.[3]

Smiley passed judgment in comparing Evans with Gilpin:

> . . . Governor Gilpin was an honest, brilliant man, but his tastes, inclinations and life-training unfitted him to deal with the political

[3]Undated clipping, Denver Public Library.

and other conditions he found here; and the kind of executive ability he possessed was that of a military commander and not that of the successful head of a civil government. His personal character was far beyond reproach. Governor Evans was a different type of man—one of the great Captains in civil life, a projector, an organizer, a man with the ability to conceive and execute great undertakings among the people. But his administration was subordinated to political ends. His ambitions were divided between two great purposes; one was to quickly develop Colorado resources by railroads, wagon roads, irrigation and other internal improvements; the other was to enter the United States Senate from the new State he had in view when he came here. Therefore, his administration was bent, swayed and influenced by his political aims. In fulfilling his other purpose, the efforts of no other man produced results comparable with those growing out of his energy, farsightedness and remarkable ability for organizing and carrying forward great enterprises. . . .[4]

Hubert Bancroft, as he organized his notes for his *History of Nevada, Colorado and Wyoming* in 1884, was specifically uncomplimentary:

> . . . About ex-Governor Evans and his son-in-law Judge Elbert there is much humbug. They are cold-blooded mercenary men, ready to praise themselves and each other profusely, but who have in reality but little patriotism. I never met a railroad man who was not the quintessence of meanness in more particulars than one. . . .[5]

Whatever the verdict, John Evans rapidly became one of Colorado's most prominent and forceful leaders. There is very little in the nineteenth-century progress of the state which does not have his name attached to it in some way.

Editor Byers and the new governor soon were intimates. They shared the same political convictions. Both had visions of what Denver and Colorado might become. One had and the other aspired to wealth and distinction, and both were in positions of leadership. Evans became a partner with Byers and Dailey in numerous mining enterprises. As has been noted, the flooded-out Byers family was taken in by the Evanses and sheltered following the Great Deluge in the ugly, boxlike house which was the gubernatorial mansion of 1864. There is circumstantial evidence to indicate that Evans generously dipped into his well-lined pockets to help his young editor friend get back on his feet after the flood.

Evans bought one of the Byers homes and lived in it for the rest of his life. (A previous Byers house had stood atop the bluff on the site at East Colfax Avenue and Sherman Street where a third annex to the

[4] Smiley, *History of Denver*, pp. 493-94.

[5] Bancroft ms. L-13.

Colorado Capitol currently is being completed. Byers had wanted a house placed where he could see the mountains from every window.) The Byers-Evans mansion, quaint and blocky and with a cast-iron widow's walk, still stands at West Thirteenth Avenue and Bannock Street. When Governor Evans died there, Mrs. Byers was one of those in attendance. It was typical of Lib Byers to write that she "never saw a more beautiful death."

As Evans came to power in Denver the *News* was going through its hectic era of kidnap, fire, and flood, somehow landing right side up after each. Byers soon put his paper as staunchly behind the Evans administration as the *Herald* had been behind Gilpin's. Following the flood, Byers did not long remain in the plant of the old *Commonwealth*, which Evans may have helped him purchase. Byers and Dailey took over the *Commonwealth* late in June of 1864. A month later, on July 26, they were in Murdock's frame building on Larimer Street in Denver City. The site was on the west side of the block two doors north from F (now Fifteenth) Street, a location today occupied by the soiled old Railroad Building and numbered 1515 Larimer.

Larimer had become the main street of the town, and the *News* now was in the center of civic bustle. Byers, as usual, was a busy man. He took over the postmastership on November 7, 1864, and held office for two years. He also was searching the mountains for likely claims, climbing peaks, fishing for trout, berrying and raising experimental crops on his river ranch. The telegraph line had arrived, and the *News* was publishing in the modern manner.

But Denver still was an outpost, an island village totally surrounded by prodigious distances and savage Indians.

The fast-flying rumors of imminent Confederate invasion and, finally, the turned-back attempt excited the town and gave its citizens a sense of participation in the great events which were wrenching the nation. The *News* published numerous extras when word got through, days late, of the great battles and maneuvers of the war.

But Denver really was less worried about distant Rebels than nearby Indians, and where redskins were concerned, the town, viewed from the safe distance of a century, seems to have been positively paranoid. It is easy to shrug off other men's perils, but pioneer Denver, on the record, reacted to Indians like a troop of Boy Scouts scaring themselves with scalping stories around a campfire. The town jumped at every shadow, indulged itself frequently in high moments of wild alarm, shocked itself into delicious terrors with unverified reports of bloody outrages—some of them as far away as Minnesota and Nevada. Any killing, no matter how distant, was a "massacre," and represented an immediate threat to Denver's continued existence.

The story of the Indian troubles of the early sixties makes a dark chapter in the history of Denver and the *Rocky Mountain News*, and both share a large measure of responsibility for precipitating the actual Indian wars which followed in the late sixties and seventies. Then, indeed, the plains ran with blood—mostly Indian—and the hard-pressed, much-maligned United States Cavalry would have to fight more than two hundred engagements to force the tribes into submission. They were not always honorable fights—and neither was Sand Creek, which started it all.

Probably the wars would have had to come anyway, sooner or later. The trail of broken promises, mistreatment, and systematic debasement was too long, with too many malignantly twisted turnings, to be retraced. There is scarcely a clean page in the whole record of white dealings with the American red man, and it fell to Denver's lot to come into existence at that historical moment when the pent-up forces of retribution reached a crisis. The little capital of Colorado Territory, self-important and self-indulgent as cities always are, arrived just in time to tamp in the wadding and light the fuse. It was not only that the Indian was being encircled, displaced, and starved to death, but he also was being consistently and uniformly cheated at every step of the way by Christian gentlemen with fiercely moral philosophies of private gain.

The Indian need not be idealized as a "noble savage." His traditions often were cruel and sanguine. It was his practice to mutilate the fallen foeman, and he tortured both himself, in ritual dances and ceremonials, and any captive enemy. Captured women, white or bronze of skin, often became community property. Neither Indian male nor female understood such stubborn moral sophistications as are clothed in the phrase "death before dishonor." And the rape sometimes was accomplished by spread-eagling the victim, naked and bound, to pegs driven into prairie sod. White men on occasion were similarly picketed in anthills and abandoned to go blind under the powerful sun, or mad, or both, before merciful death arrived. There is at least one record of the building of a fire over the genitals of a spread-eagled victim. The Plains Indian could be a formidable and terrifying enemy.

Yet his patience in the face of decades of provocation seems now to have been as superhuman as his cruelties were subhuman. Certainly the forbearance and wisdom exhibited by the "peace chiefs," who saw the shape of things to come, towers in retrospect over that of the white men from Denver who slaughtered them and their bands with a blood-thirstiness which would have awed a Comanche. Yet the chieftains were savages, and the leader of the whites a Methodist elder.

Denver saw little Indian barbarity during its first years, although it heard much and imagined worse. Arapahoes, Cheyennes, and Utes camped often in the Platte bottoms or passed through to wage their wars against each other at a distance. Denver never was subjected to Indian attack, but its citizens proclaimed often and noisily that a raid was imminent. The red men who visited town came to trade, see the strange sights, get drunk, or beg, and in the latter two activities they frequently must have been confounded nuisances. They also were light-fingered, and to a culture which justified the lynch noose for horse stealing, this was cardinal sinning. It did not matter that the Indians had an ignorant custom by which a brave won honor and dignity in proportion to his skill at acquiring other men's ponies. Moreover one Indian was about as bad as another; though of course it was white "Bummers" who maltreated the Indians and always "good" whites who were massacred by them in retaliation.

The Indian also was being casually debauched with firewater. His rapidly acquired taste for whiskey made him an easy mark at trading sessions, and full advantage was taken of the weakness. The *News* early had hurled a vigilante threat at those who traded or sold liquor to Indians, and later a reporter tells, with what seems to be genuine compassion, of seeing a drunken brave sloshing and stumbling up a Denver street clutching his stark naked, starving, but unwhimpering son by the hand. There is no evidence that either the paper's thundering or its pity was effective. The *News* also seems to have partaken somewhat of Jim Beckwourth's ire at the rape of the Indian women in their lodges beside the Platte by drunken whites but, like the rest of Denver, it dropped the issue once things calmed down again. The frontier and its press had a double standard on such matters. The violation of squaws was unfortunate, of course, but, well, boys will be boys when they're in their cups. Rape as applied by red men to white women, however, was intolerable.

There seems to have been a lot of inexpensive pride involved in some of the noisiest of the outrages. An examination of contemporary reports discloses that, besides thievery, the item of Indian misconduct which most frequently offended the settlers was bronze boldness and a want of deference to those whose skin was obviously of a superior hue. And the Indian's arrogance in begging and stealing almost matched that of the white men who had established themselves and built their settlements, wholly in violation of treaty, on tribal lands.

As an example, there is the case of Denton Shook, who got hit on the head.[6] A party of a hundred Cheyennes were camped in South Park near Hamilton, and some of them went begging for food at the ranch of Robert Stubbs. The rancher and Denton and Peter Shook gave them some, but they wanted more and began to take it. In a struggle over a side of bacon Denton took a blow on the head and hit back. The foraging Indians then departed but returned with a force of sixty braves who began shooting arrows into the Stubbs cabin. Then they invaded the house. The seven women present saved Peter Shook from being dragged off "by encircling his body with their arms. (Who wouldn't be the young man? Ed. News.)" The feminine phalanx turned the trick, and the

[6]*Rocky Mountain News*, July 22 and 23, 1862.

Cheyennes moved on to scenes where begging was less complex and women didn't interfere in man's work.

The *News*, however, demanded blood for the incident. "Such outrages," it commented, "have gone quite far enough; it is time the redskins learned to behave themselves; they are paving the way for extermination faster than nature requires, and need another General Harney to 'regulate' them. . . ." (Colonel William S. Harney in 1855 had attacked a Sioux village at Ash Hollow near the forks of the Platte and slaughtered men, women, and children.)

A year earlier the *News* had approached the matter more calmly:

THE INDIANS.

It is sincerely to be hoped that our citizens, in all their intercourse with the Indians, will be guided by that prudence and discretion which promotes friendly and peaceful relations. A civilized and enlightened people can well afford to remember that the tribes by which we are surrounded are our inferiors physically, morally, mentally, and that the commission of what we call crimes, assumes with them the merit of bravery and manly action. In all our dealings with these untutored barbarians, we should be governed by the greatest caution—avoiding in all cases a disposition to overreach and deceive them. They are naturally, and not without reason, suspicious of their white brethren. They feel that their rights have been invaded, their hunting grounds taken possession of, and their possessions appropriated without adequate remuneration. It should be the aim of every good citizen to conciliate the Indians, and show them by a peaceful policy, that we are not committed to an aggressive and tyrranous [sic] course.

But at the same time, when the necessity arises, they should be taught the importance of maintaining an orderly and quiet bearing, and if needs be, convinced that the whites have the will and the power to punish those who commit outrages upon us. When that necessity arises, we should proceed moderately, and yet firmly. Rash and intemperate and ill-directed attack upon the Indians, would involve us in difficulties and dangers, from which it might be impossible to extricate ourselves. We must not forget that the whites are in a measure responsible for the commission of Indian outrages. Liquor has been furnished contrary to law not only, but in defiance of the inevitable consequences which always follow the use of "firewater" by these savage tribes. Under its influence we have no doubt acts of violence have been committed, which otherwise never would have been committed. Let an effort be made to suppress the liquor traffic with the Indians. There is a stringent United States law against it, and we hope our citizens will aid and cooperate with Col. [A. G.] Boone [son of Daniel Boone and then Indian agent for the Denver area], in his efforts to enforce that law. In this way we are confident troubles may be avoided which otherwise will assume a serious and formidable shape.

In this connection we take occasion to enter our formal protest against recent efforts in certain quarters to influence the public mind against the Indians. The peace of our community should not be jeopardized in order that a few indiscreet and turbulent spirits may gain a little notoriety. We have an Indian agent in our midst, whose advice and warning will have ten-fold more effect than the frothy declamation of a few who are "spoiling for a muss" with the Indians.[7]

In an adjacent column the News further indicated its displeasure by putting the caption "White Barbarians" over a letter to the editor complaining of an "element whose chief ambition seems to be to debauch the squaws, and sell or swop" whiskey to the braves.

Within the next four years, however, the News would abandon nearly every item of its own sensible advice. These were the last words of "prudence and discretion" it would address to the "Indian question."

The News moved full circle and went clamoring into the camp of those who were "spoiling for a muss." And Byers knew better. As a trailsman to Oregon in '52, when the West was much more trackless than it now was, he had acquired experience with Indians, and it had been peaceful experience. During his years in Omaha he had participated in treaty councils with the eastern Nebraska tribes. He had seen how Indians had rescued and fed starving fifty-niners who struck out across the plains to Pike's Peak with sails full of hope and no cargo of either knowledge or provisions. Byers knew that the Indian was, or could have been, tractable. But politics, personalities, and community emotional jags robbed him of his judgment, and he and his paper embarked on a shameless course of pandering to alarms from which there was no retreat.

There was provocation, too, of course. The Indians were raiding, scalping, and killing. They at last had understood that they were being hemmed in, driven, and harried toward extermination, and they were fighting back. Word of barbaric raids on exposed outposts not too distant must have been a disquieting experience for even the most levelheaded Denver citizen of the sixties. The course the News took, if it cannot be justified in the long view, nonetheless can be readily understood. Nor was its attitude unique; newspapers everywhere on the fringes of the plains were demanding punishment of the Indians. For better or worse, the journals spoke for their orphan communities, even if they failed to guide them through the strong currents of fear and anger as an idealized press is supposed to do.

The sporadic raiding and pillaging began to reach serious proportions in the summer of 1862. It mounted in 1863 as Governor Evans arrived to take his post, and by 1865 the prairie was aflame, touched off by the success of a wild pack of Colorado volunteers in outdoing the Indian

[7]Ibid., Apr. 23, 1861.

in vicious savagery. These were Civil War years, of course, and nine-teenth-century writers, seeking any explanation other than that the Indian finally was reacting to being dispossessed of his homeland, tried to attribute the growing tribal restiveness to a vast plot hatched to take advantage of the nation's preoccupation with its fraternal war. The effort doesn't come off. It doesn't square with Indian ways. Those who knew the red warrior best—seasoned cavalry officers among them—conceded that he could be an excellent tactician in battle, but there is no hint he was a strategist in the grand manner. Had he been, the history of the whole North American continent might have been written much differently.

There is some evidence that Confederate agents sent Southern Indians up from Arkansas and Indian Territory to stir up the plains tribes, but their influence was minor if effective at all. The grievances and pressures were so great that *provocateurs* were unnecessary. Moreover the tribes, at this time, were not waging that kind of organized warfare. Small bands and warrior clans such as the Cheyennes' implacable "Dog Soldiers" were ranging about hitting at targets of opportunity: isolated ranches, lightly guarded wagon trains, and the coveted horse and mule strings at stage relay stations.

Denver felt itself much exposed to such maraudings. The 1st Colorado Regiment was still in New Mexico and would not have its triumphant homecoming until January 1863. The 2nd Colorado Regiment was organized in the summer of 1862, but in August moved down to Fort Lyon and then on to Indian Territory and Kansas, not to return to Denver until it had helped run Sterling Price's sixteen thousand Rebels out of Missouri in 1864. The city now sorely missed the ribald rioters from Camp Weld; it had no force to send against the pillagers on the plains. The Indians had not begun to kill yet, but as early as June 16, 1862, the *News* was getting nervous:

PROSPECT OF INDIAN TROUBLES.

Indian affairs in our Territory are in anything else but a desirable state, just at this time. A growing animosity to the white settlers is mani-fest in the disposition of our immediate neighbors, the Arapahoes and Cheyennes. . . .

Governor Evans arrived May 16 and in July obtained from the legislature a law authorizing the enrollment of militiamen. The militia was not organized immediately, but the army designated Colorado a military district and placed Colonel Chivington in charge of it. Chiving-ton had resigned his command with the 1st in New Mexico and returned home to receive adulation as the "Hero of Gloriéta." On the strength of his popularity he was preparing to run for Congress.

The Indians in October ran off the horses and mules at several stage stations on the Santa Fe Trail and then remained quiet until the following March, when they made a similar raid on settlements along the Cache la Poudre north of Denver. No blood was spilled in either encounter. To that point, there had been more men killed in Denver City saloons than in Indian warfare, but the citizens were jittery. During 1863, Governor Evans kept the mails busy and the new telegraph line hot in a voluminous correspondence with Washington complaining of the tribal "uprising" and warning of worse to come. In October, however, he conceded that while there had been some depredations by scattered bands, acting independently, the tribes to the north and east of Denver now were quiet and there was no talk of war.[8] Denver continued to talk of a vast confederation of savages being organized to wipe out the white man in the West.

The following spring real trouble actually began. A detachment of the 1st Colorado, now a cavalry regiment, went out on the plains east of Denver looking for cattle reported stolen but possibly strayed. The troop was spoiling for a fight and, when it didn't get one, plundered and burned the lodges of two small Cheyenne villages from which the Indians had fled before them.[9]

About the same time another unit of the 1st was scouting down the South Platte and got into a fight with a small band of fifteen Southern Cheyenne warriors at Frémont's Orchard over possession of four mules. Two troopers were fatally wounded. Shortly thereafter, late in April, a rancher was killed. A detachment under Major Jacob Downing took to the road to avenge the deaths. He found a camp of Cheyennes in Cedar Cañon, a hundred and forty miles down the Platte, and attacked at sunrise. George Bird Grinnell, who knew the Cheyennes probably better than any other white man, says it was a friendly village. "These people did not know that there had been any trouble with whites; the men were away and only old women and children were in the camp."[10] Downing claimed twenty-six Indians were killed and thirty wounded, but didn't mention age or sex. He lost one man. Years later he told the News he had located the "hostile" camp by capturing a passing Indian and "toasting his shins" over a small fire.

By June, Denver had worked itself into full-blown hysteria. Reports came that masses of Indians were advancing on the city from the east and north. Denver was to be sacked and burned. Governor Evans slapped a 6:30 P.M. curfew on all business houses and ordered every able-bodied man to assemble daily for drill. Blockhouses and log fortifications were thrown up at the fringes of the town. On June 15

[8]*Report of the Commissioner of Indian Affairs* (Washington, 1863), p. 129.

[9]George Bird Grinnell, *The Fighting Cheyennes* (Norman, 1956), pp. 138–40.

[10]Ibid., p. 143.

the supposed horde was firmly declared to be just a few miles from the city, and women and children were gathered into the brick business houses in the central district for protection. Next day it was all over. Someone bothered to ascertain that there was no huge force of redskins just over the horizon.

There *was* a small band of angry Cheyennes buzzing about nearby. They ran off some stock on Coal Creek, ten miles to the northwest, then looped around the city and paid a bloody visit to the lonely ranch of Isaac P. Van Wormer, twenty-five miles east on Running Creek. Van Wormer's tenant, Nathan P. Hungate, and a hired man named Miller were out caring for their stock on June 18 when they saw the ranch buildings in flames. Miller set out immediately for Denver, and Hungate headed for the ranch house, where his wife, Ellen, and two blonde daughters, Florence, six, and Laura, three, had been left alone.

In Denver, Miller notified Van Wormer of the raid, and the ranch owner, unable to persuade any volunteers to go with him, set out by himself in a buckboard. He found Hungate's mutilated body, eighty bullets in it, some distance from the charred house. The bodies of the wife and children, also mutilated, had been stuffed into a shallow well. Roman Nose, a Northern Cheyenne chief who had been regarded as friendly, was blamed.

Bodies of the Hungate family were brought to Denver and placed on public exhibition in a downtown store. Everyone in town crowded around to see the grisly display.[11] From that day forward Denver was of one mind: exterminate all Indians.

Governor Evans sent a circular to the Indians, calling upon those who wished to be regarded as friendly to come in and camp near military posts where they could be watched. The Cheyennes and Arapahoes were to go to Fort Lyon in the Arkansas Valley, the Kiowas and Comanches to Fort Larned, farther down the river in Kansas.

Then, on August 10, the *News* carried his proclamation calling all Colorado Territory to arms:

APPEAL TO THE PEOPLE.

Patriotic citizens of Colorado:—

I again appeal to you to organize for the defense of your homes and families against the merciless savages. . . .

Let every settlement organize its volunteer militia company for its defense. . . .

Any man who kills a hostile Indian is a patriot; but there are Indians who are friendly, and to kill one of these will involve us in greater difficulty. . . .

Jno. Evans

[11]Elmer R. Burkey, "The Hungate Massacre," *Colorado Magazine*, Vol. XII, No. 4 (July 1935).

Three days later the governor announced he had won permission from the Secretary of War for enlistment of a volunteer cavalry regiment for one hundred days to fight the Indians. The 3rd Colorado Regiment came into being.

Denver was under martial law all summer. Twelve of the *News* printers, including John Dailey, joined the 3rd, so decimating the staff that Byers persuaded the regimental officers to detail a squad of compositors back to him in order to get the paper out. Some issues contained little but military orders and reports, with some Civil War news thrown in whenever the telegraph line was open.

Indian raiding continued at widely separated points, and although there were no real battles it was enough to slow plains travel virtually to a standstill. Supply trains came through on the Platte road only at irregular and widely spaced intervals. The telegraph line was frequently cut. Mail arrived by way of Panama and California.

Supplies of staples in Denver grew short and advanced to high prices. At one point the town was entirely out of coal oil and had to return to candles. A group of leading businessmen and officials seized opportunity by the forelock. They bought up all the flour and boosted the price to thirty-two dollars a hundred pounds.

The *News* had great difficulty obtaining paper to print on. With Dailey in the army, Byers was going it alone now. Bliss had withdrawn in September 1863 and Rounds shortly thereafter. The paper of September 24 announced dryly that the "junior [Bliss] retires to engage in other, and we hope more lucrative business, than the publication of a newspaper." During the grim days of 1864, Byers doggedly got out his sheet on whatever paper he could find. Sometimes it was only a dodger, printed in two or three columns of type on scraps of paper six or eight inches deep. He used brown wrapping paper, pink and white tissue paper, and there are reports of wallpaper and foolscap issues, though none of these has been located. On September 13, Byers printed a four-column handbill on bright orange cartridge paper and explained: "We used the last of our white paper yesterday for the Daily. For a few days we will be obliged to issue only a slip containing the telegraphic news and such items of local news as may be of importance."

The issue of October 1 is on a slick, yellow paper, possibly butcher's wrapping, and complains: "Every paper we issue now costs us more money than we receive for it." Byers managed a bit of grim humor out of the situation in his white tissue edition of October 5:

> Wanted.—Three thousand shingles to be immediately delivered in lots of one thousand each, respectively, at the offices of the three newspapers of this territory, to be used for printing purposes, instead of the cartridge and tissue paper now employed.

The daily *News,* however, came through without missing an issue, although the weekly for November 5 was dropped. "Utterly unable to obtain paper."

Finally, on November 14 a wagon train with the *News'* paper stocks got through. It had been four months on the road. Byers resumed a full six-column folio format, but then on December 2 announced he was reducing the paper's size to five columns "simply to keep it, if possible, on a paying basis." He explained that paper was costing him sixty-five cents a pound delivered, compared with sixteen cents in the pioneer days of '59. Some, brought in by express coach, cost a dollar a pound. The paper remained small until April 1, 1865.

Much of the news in these starveling, get-by issues consists of reports and rumors of new Indian outrages. There are meager dispatches on the progress of the Civil War and one gallant comment on a turn for the better in women's fashions:

> The ladies, according to the August magazines, have adopted a mode of gathering their garments in festoons by an elastic cord, which not only relieves them of dragging their skirts over the dusty pavements, but introduces to mankind one of the most attractive fashions extant. The American ladies have the handsomest feet of any in the world, and, having deprived us of the sight of them through an absurd fashion, we naturally welcome the return with joy.[12]

There was also politics to be watched and played. The *News* was beating its biggest drum for statehood, although by the most optimistic count there were fewer than thirty thousand residents in the whole territory. It also was trying to get Byers' friend Chivington elected to Congress. The big colonel had become a close personal and political friend of the editor as a result of the rescue on the night of the flood, and they also were associated in mining ventures.

The election to which the citizens were called on September 11 was an odd one. A proposed state constitution was before them for ratification or rejection, along with a slate of state officials. But at the same time they were asked to ballot on a territorial delegate to Congress. Chivington was a candidate both for member of and delegate to Congress. The *News* was whipped on its man and its issue. The nine thousand voters who turned out defeated the state constitution and thus the proposed new bid for statehood. Chivington was beaten by Allen A. Bradford as territorial delegate to Congress but outpolled Bradford for a seat in the House of Representatives which could not exist because the statehood move had gone down. The campaign had been a bitter one, and the lines drawn in it would bring sordid political cliques into the acrimonious debate over Indian policy.

[12]*Rocky Mountain News,* Aug. 3, 1864.

The *News* of this period often used an oblique reference to current news as a lead-in to a promotional or advertising paragraph in its "Locals" column. One effort to combine Indian outrages, politics, and printing turned up this ludicrous item:

> Indian Murders.—The most revolting, shocking cases of assassination, arson, murder and manslaughter that have crimsoned the page of time have been done by Indians, in former days and recently,—but nevertheless we hold ourselves hourly prepared to strike you off from one to twenty thousand election tickets at lowest panic prices, and in the type of the art, that's sure to make you win.[13]

The first part of the paragraph is a fair sample of the attitude toward the Indians to which the *News* had now moved. When some of the Cheyenne and Arapaho chiefs came to Denver on September 28 to parley with Governor Evans there was talk of a new peace treaty. The *News* commented on the night before the council: ". . . we are opposed to anything which looks like a treaty of peace with the Indians who have been actively engaged in the recent hostilities. The season is near at hand when they can be chastised and it should be done with no gentle hand instead of patching up another compromise to be broken by them again next spring or summer when grass is good and their food plenty. . . ."

Cheyenne chiefs at the Denver council were Black Kettle, who for years had ignored the scorn of his young men and sought peaceful compromises with the whites; Bull Bear, chief of the Dog Soldiers; and old White Antelope, once a fierce Dog Soldier but now snowy-haired. White Antelope had been to Washington to talk peace with the Great White Father, and he wore on his breast a large medal given him in token of his promise to break his war arrows. Also present were Neva, No-ta-ne, Boisse, and Heap Buffalo, representing Left Hand of the Arapahoes. Left Hand, whose name remains on a creek and a foothills cañon north of Boulder, had visited Denver often and was well known as a friendly.

Governor Evans told the chiefs he had no power to conclude a peace treaty with them, that their fate was now in the hands of the military. He advised them to go back to Fort Lyon, as he had suggested in his earlier message to them, and to remain there out of harm's way. Colonel Chivington thundered threats and warnings at them, and then the parley broke up. The Indians accepted Evans' advice, and some of them said later they understood from his letter and his speech that if they complied they would be regarded as friendly Indians and would not come under attack by the cavalry troops now ranging the plains.

The chiefs led their bands back to Fort Lyon, where they turned in

[13]Ibid., Sept. 7, 1864.

their arms and were given food. A few days later the rifles were returned to them for hunting use. Officers at the fort said the guns were so old as to be almost worthless. The authorities at Lyon also told the Indians to move out away from the fort. So Black Kettle moved his mixed village up to the open prairie of the Arapaho-Cheyenne reservation and camped about forty miles north of the fort on the big bend of Sand Creek. He assumed he was still complying with Governor Evans' order to remain where he could be watched.

In Denver, meanwhile, the 3rd Colorado had been filled. The "100 Dazers" were eager for action and rankled under the taunt of "Bloodless Third." Their colonel was George L. Shoup, who had served with the 1st Colorados in New Mexico. Horses, arms and other equipment arrived at Camp Weld early in October, and the regiment of six hundred and fifty men sallied out into the Bijou basin east of Denver.

Chivington assumed personal command, outranking Shoup by virtue of his position as commander of the Colorado Military District. The big, black-bearded colonel, described by Jerome Smiley as "a fine example of the preacher militant," was determined to lead his troops to glory— and vault himself into Congress—by hitting the Indians a blow which would be hailed by everyone as decisive. Late in August he had delivered an address, either as a sermon or a campaign speech, in which he declared his policy was to "kill and scalp all, little and big," because "nits make lice." He was warmly applauded, and the phrase became a fighting slogan for the 3rd. "Nits make lice."[14]

In November, through two feet of snow, Chivington led his "Bloodless Third" southward. Units of the veteran 1st, now a cavalry regiment, what was left of it, joined him. As the column jogged down into the Arkansas Valley the ground cleared and the cold eased, but there were still white patches of snow out among the yucca clumps on the gray-brown prairie. The troopers huddled down in their new army-issue overcoats and cursed the maggoty hardtack given them for breakfast. They were saddle-sore, cold, and already sick of soldiering, with the first hostile redskin yet to be encountered.

There had not been a depredation within two hundred miles for two months, and the settlers were beginning to move back to their farms and ranches to harvest corn and try to round up scattered stock. John Dailey's Company A had been on a detached mission to Fort Garland, in the San Luis Valley, where he found the colonel in charge "d–k all day, as usual." Company A moved up to join the main column and lingered pleasantly and informally at Pueblo, where, Dailey's diary indicates, the "100 Dazers" faithfully observed the riotous traditions of the 1st Colorados. He records a wild and wonderful account of chicken and melon stealing, casual AWOLs, late sleeping, trout fishing, bitching, drunken officers, saloon fights, and tumbles in the hay with country

[14]Senate Report No. 156, 39th Congress, 2nd Session (Washington, 1867), p. 71.

maidens much impressed by new blue cavalry uniforms. Hangovers considered, it must have been rigorous duty for the officers. No one wanted to drill, guard duty was ignored, and none of the volunteers, apparently, obeyed any order unless the mood was on him and the tone of the command suitably civil.

Company A joined the main column, which then swung east down the river.

Chivington was getting the scent, and his tense excitement mounted. Two hundred and fifty pounds of six-foot fighting man, he forked his beautiful black horse like an emperor on parade. Imperiously he halted the United States mails. No one must know he was coming. In sudden, slashing movement to left and right he dispatched squadrons to nearby ranches to place occupants under house arrest until the command had moved far down the road beyond danger that word of its coming would pass on ahead. Out in advance of the spearpoint of the force rode Jim Beckwourth, the old mountain man, pressed into service as guide and scout. Poker-faced and stoic, Jim rode with his rifle cradled across his arms and one leg hooked up over the saddle for comfort. His passive brown eyes took in everything and seemed to see nothing.

The column surprised the small garrison of 1st Regiment troops and New Mexico volunteers at Fort Lyon. The black-bearded colonel was pleased when the garrison officers told him they had not known the 3rd had left the Bijou. He was more than life-sized. "Hero of Gloriéta," congressional candidate, and now author of a model cavalry maneuver across two hundred and fifty miles of open plains with a large body of troops in complete secrecy. Surely Washington could not long withhold his brigadier's stars.

Chivington routed out his men before dawn on November 28, and they had trotted into Fort Lyon at 9 A.M. They went into camp, but not before the colonel had circled the fort with a strong line of pickets. No one was to leave. Colonel's orders.

It now became apparent what was afoot. Some of Chivington's officers said later that they remonstrated with him against the plan, but their claims well may have been self-serving, as was so much of the testimony that would be given. Even if they did protest, it was of no consequence one way or the other. Chivington's mind, the mind of a popular hero and an ambitious man, was set. As leader of the "First Indian Expedition," he knew precisely what he was doing. As commanding officer of the Colorado Military District, he also knew, as well as any man could, where the Indians were. Any Christian scruples he may have felt had long since been conquered.

He knew where Black Kettle's village was. He and Evans had sent them there. He knew about what Indians he would find; they had been to visit him and hear his blusterings. He knew they were friendly. Or, at minimum, they professed friendship, had sought out, made themselves subject to, and now relied upon the protection of the Fort Lyon troops. They would not suspect a thing.

Chivington also knew the work ahead would be bloody and easy. His force was far larger, better armed, better equipped than anything he would meet, and perhaps he had planned it that way a long time ago. Just when his design was laid can only be conjecture, but possibly it had been fermenting in his mind in September when he had told these chiefs exactly where to go and what to do to put themselves under the eye and command of his forces at Fort Lyon. Yet none of this need appear in public accounts. Chivington obviously was confident he could make it all seem to be a fiercely fought and glorious victory. The hysterical town of Denver, whipped up by the dispatches and editorials in the *News*, would support him in anything he did so long as Indians were killed. He could count on that.

By nightfall of November 28 all was in readiness. Three days' cooked rations in each man's saddlebags. Horses rested and fed. The bulk of the Fort Lyon garrison added to the force. At 8 P.M., under cover of darkness, Chivington moved out. All told, he had at his command about nine hundred and fifty mostly raw but well-equipped and emotionally aroused men, along with a battery of four 12-pounder mountain howitzers armed with grape and canister. The men were not told where they were going, except that there would be an Indian fight at the end of the march. Only the officers knew Chivington's secret.

Jim Beckwourth guided the long column of fours off to the north through the frosty night. Although Jim once was confused briefly by a low pool of fog lying in a swale like a lake, the course was straight and true. He brought the command to the top of a rise just as the eastern sky began to pale off to grays and yellows. There in the wide bottoms of white sand was Black Kettle's village, a few over a hundred lodges, most of them Cheyenne, eight or ten of them occupied by Left Hand's Arapahoes. The first morning smoke was just beginning to curl out of the wings of the tipis.

Chivington halted his column and rode back down the line.

"Off with your coats, men," the commander ordered. "You can fight better without them. Take no prisoners. Remember the slaughtered white women and children! Remember the Hungates!"

Beckwourth said he heard it this way: "I don't tell you to kill all ages and sex, but look back on the plains of the Platte, where your mothers, fathers, brothers, sisters have been slain, and their blood saturating the sands on the Platte."

According to his aide, Captain A. J. Gill, Chivington said: "Now boys, I shan't say who you shall kill, but remember our murdered women and children."

Then, at sunrise, the attack began.

It lasted eight hours or longer, and it presents as brain-splitting a picture of fiendish savagery as exists in the records of the human race. The day of November 29, 1864, ran deep with blood and rocked the heavens with insanity.

The village was totally surprised and wholly confused by the treachery. If reliable estimates can be found in the tangle of perjured testimony which came later, the lodges contained between five and six hundred Indians. At least two thirds of these were women and small children. Many of the others were old men, like Black Kettle and White Antelope themselves. Altogether there were perhaps a hundred warriors, armed with bows and arrows, lances and guns which had been turned back to them as worthless.

Other considerations aside for the moment, the battle was a horrible botch as a military operation. Those hundred ill-armed warriors kept nearly a thousand soldiers, mounted and supported by artillery, busy until midafternoon. Meanwhile nearly five hundred Indians escaped across the prairie, most of them on foot, through lines which supposedly encircled the camp. The "enemy" commander, Black Kettle, was among those who got away. Fighting was confused, disordered, entirely undisciplined. Command was lost early in the day and never recovered until after the last shot was fired. Soldiers caught each other in their own cross fire. Some of the eight killed and forty wounded were not victims of the Indians. Orders were lost, countermanded, or frankly disobeyed. If Chivington had displayed any military aptitude at Apache Cañon, he showed not a glimmer at Sand Creek.

Those of the Indians who could not flee died on the spot. The most credible estimates place the number at something under two hundred, though Chivington would claim five to six hundred killed out of a "hostile" force of nine hundred to a thousand. Two thirds of the bodies counted later were women and children.

White Antelope was among the first to go down. Soon after the firing began he advanced from his lodge toward the troopers with both hands upraised, palms forward, in the traditional sign of peace. Shots kicked up sand around him. He stopped, folded his arms, and began to chant his death song:

> "Nothing lives long,
>   Except the earth and the mountains . . ."[15]

At last the excited volunteers found the range. The Lincoln peace medal on the old warrior's chest bounced and he pitched face forward to the ground.

As he had been instructed to do, Black Kettle flew the Stars and Stripes on a pole over his lodge. The flag had been given to him by

15Grinnell, op. cit., p. 178.

an Indian commissioner some years earlier. Under it he flew a white flag. Neither was recognized. The chief took his wife and began to flee. She was shot and went down. Troopers rode over her, putting eight more bullets in her body. But she was still alive, and Black Kettle, far past his prime as a brave, put her over his shoulder and ran. They got through the lines.

A three-year-old Indian child, perfectly naked, toddled out on the sands of the dry creek bed. Three troopers dismounted seventy yards away and assumed the position shown in the cavalry manual for kneeling fire. One carbine cracked and sand spurted at the child's heels. "Let me try the little son of a bitch," the second trooper demanded. He, too, fired and missed. "Hell," spat the third soldier, "you boys couldn't hit the side of a mountain." He took aim and squeezed. The baby dropped. One nit that would never make a louse.

Out of one of the lodges came running ole "Uncle John" Smith, one of the founders of Denver, the squawman who had helped build the city's first house. He had been sent to the Indian camp a few days earlier to trade and report on what the savages were doing. His orders had come from Major Scott J. Anthony, who now led a portion of the attack.

Smith ran out toward the troops and was greeted by fire. He was recognized. "Shoot the old son of a bitch," someone shouted; "he's no better than an Indian." Bullets spattered around him. The gray-haired man hesitated and then scuttled back toward his lodge. "Run here, Uncle John," Chivington himself called. "You are all right." Smith cast a glance back at the lodges, turned, and scampered toward the troops. He climbed on the caisson of one of the howitzers and was safe. So low had one of the founding fathers fallen for running with the redskin.

Smith's half-breed son Jack didn't fare as well. He was captured, held prisoner for twenty-four hours in a lodge, and then killed by a shot from a pistol thrust through a cut in the stretched buffalo hide of the tipi. Officers reported they were unable to ascertain who fired the shot. Chivington had been told that his troopers planned to kill Jack Smith. He had shrugged. His orders, he said, had been to take no prisoners; he couldn't change them now.

As the fight progressed madness seized the battlefield. The troopers had knives out and were scalping everything that fell, "one week to 80 years" of age. Children were shot at their mothers' breasts. The victims of the scalping were not always quite dead. One old squaw wandered sightless through the carnage. Her entire scalp had been taken, and the skin of her forehead fell down over her eyes to blind her. Several troopers got into a quarrel over who should have the honor of scalping one body. The issue could not be decided; so all took scalps from the same carcass.

Nor was the scalping the worst of it. The "Bloodless Thirdsters" would show the Indians a thing or two about barbarity and the finer points of mutilation.

A group of soldiers paused amid the firing to take turns profaning the body of a comely young squaw, very dead. The nose and ears, as well as the scalp, of White Antelope were cut off. Indians' fingers were hacked away to get their rings as souvenirs. One soldier trotted about with a heart impaled on a stick. Others carried off the genitals of braves. Someone had the notion that it would be artistic work to slice away the breasts of the Indian women. One breast was worn as a cap, another was seen stretched over the bow of a saddle. In Denver, many years later, there was a persistent rumor that one of the surviving Thirdsters had a tanned Indian breast that he carried in his pocket as a coin purse.

The catalogue of atrocities could go on and on. All except the ghoulish purse and the blinded squaw are from the sworn testimony presented to the two investigations into the affair ordered by Congress. The record of those proceedings form what is possibly the most shocking document in the American archives.[16] How much of the testimony is truth and how much lie, no one can say; for it is obvious that otherwise honorable men, on both sides, perjured themselves repeatedly under oath. Partisanship was at white heat, and neither investigation was unprejudiced against Chivington. It is unlikely that he could have received a calm hearing, in Colorado or elsewhere, for a quarter century after that November day of 1864. Nearly halfway into the twentieth century Denver still remembered Sand Creek with shame. When someone, thinking of the valiant fight at La Gloriéta, proposed that a street be named Chivington, a storm of protest blew up and the boulevard got another designation. (Hale Parkway, for a Spanish-American War hero.)

Testimony at the hearings indicates that Chivington said he was out "after scalps," that he would give the Indians "a lively buffalo hunt," and that he "longed to be wading in gore." Others testified he "issued an order that he would hang any 'son of a bitch' who would bury the bodies or bones" of prisoners who were killed and that he asserted "he believed it right or honorable to use any means under God's heaven to kill Indians that would kill women and children, and 'damn any man that was in sympathy with Indians.'" It is probable the big colonel said these, or similar, things. Before Sand Creek, Denver was clamoring in almost one voice for extermination of the Indians, good or bad, and Chivington knew he had the city behind him.

When word of his victory reached Denver on December 7 the News carried a bulletin:

[16]Executive Document No. 26, Senate, 39th Congress, 2nd Session (Washington, 1867) and Massacre of Cheyenne Indians, report of the Joint Committee on the Conduct of the War, House of Representatives, 38th Congress, 2nd Session (Washington, 1865).

Big Indian Fight.

The First and Third Regiments have had a battle with the Indians on Sand Creek, a short distance northeast of Fort Lyon. Five hundred Indians are reported killed and six hundred horses captured. Captain Baxter and Lieutenant Pierce are reported killed. No further particulars. A messager is hourly expected with full details. *Bully for the Colorado boys.*

Next day the official report to Major General S. R. Curtis, commanding the Department of Kansas at Fort Leavenworth and Chivington's superior, was in. For the second time the colonel deliberately had disobeyed the orders of his commanding officer; Curtis in a general order had instructed all troops under his command to spare Indian women and children. Chivington did not admit his disobedience, however. He reported to Curtis:

Headquarters District of Colorado
In the field, on Big Bend of Sandy Creek, Col. Ter., Nov. 29, 1864

Sir: I have not the time to give you a detailed history of our engagement to-day, or to mention those officers and men who distinguished themselves in one of the most bloody Indian battles ever fought on these plains. You will find enclosed the report of my surgeon in charge, which will bring to many anxious friends the sad fate of loved ones who are and have been risking everything to avenge the horrid deeds of those savages we have so severely handled. We made a forced march of forty miles, and surprised, at break of day, one of the most powerful villages of the Cheyenne nation, and captured over five hundred animals; killing the celebrated chiefs One Eye, White Antelope, Knock Kno [Knee], Black Kettle, and Little Robe, with about five hundred of their people, destroying all their lodges and equipage, making almost an annihilation of the entire tribe.

I shall leave here, as soon as I can see our wounded safely on the way to the hospital at Fort Lyon, for the villages of the Sioux, which are reported about eighty miles from here, on the Smoky Hill, and three thousand strong; so look out for more fighting. I will state, for the consideration of gentlemen who are opposed to fighting these red scoundrels, that I was shown, by my chief surgeon, the scalp of a white man taken from the lodge of one of the chiefs, which could not have been more than two or three days taken; and I could mention many more things to show how these Indians, who have been drawing government rations at Fort Lyon, are and have been acting.

Very respectfully, your obedient servant,

J. M. Chivington
Col. Comd'g. Colorado Expedition against Indians on Plains

The *News* published the text of the report on December 8 and went on editorially:

This noted, needed whipping of the "red skins" by our "First Indian Expedition," particulars of which appear elsewhere, was the chief subject of comment and glorification through town today. The members of the Third, and First, and the First New Mexico, who collectively "cleaned out" the confederated savages on Sand Creek, have won for themselves and their commanders, from Colonel down to corporal, the eternal gratitude of dwellers of these plains. This brave beginning will bring down the *hauteur* of the treacherous tribes, all round, so that, should there not be even another similar defeat enacted on them through this season, our people may rest easy in the belief that outrages by small bands are at an end, on routes where troops are stationed. Having tasted of the "bitter end," the news of which will quickly be dispatched among the others, the supremacy of our power will be seriously considered, and a surrender or a sueing for peace be perhaps very soon proclaimed. This plan of attacking them in their villages is the only one available, while it is certainly as advantageous to the Indians as they justly dare desire, if they're in for a fair fight.

Despite his brave declarations to General Curtis, Chivington moved his command not an inch nearer the big camp of hostile Cheyennes and Sioux eighty miles away on the headwaters of the Smoky Hill River. Instead he boldly scouted back in the direction of Fort Lyon and then east down the Arkansas. He reported he found no hostiles in that quarter. Along the way, he neglected to report, the Indian baby that had been thrown into the feed box of one of the wagons was abandoned on the prairie.

The hundred-day enlistments of his Thirdsters were now about to expire; so the colonel wheeled his column to the homeward road. They arrived in Denver December 22, and the *News* of that date tells of a big parade and a glorious homecoming. The "Bloodless Third" boasted that it was the "Bloody Third," and the whole town smiled proudly and applauded the boast.

The boys brought along "hundreds" of Cheyenne scalps, and the *News* confessed itself somewhat confused by the trophies. Every soldier, it said, "gives a different version" and "each has the scalp of the chiefs." The "local" editor commented: "Cheyenne scalps are getting as thick here now as toads in Egypt. Everybody has got one, and is anxious to get another to send east."

In addition to the scalps, the 3rd had brought home other spoils: three small Cheyenne children, two girls and a boy. The children were shoved out onto the stage of the Denver Theatre between acts to be exhibited as curiosities along with a rope of a hundred scalps. The captives shared the bill with "Seignor Franco, the great stoneeater, and Mons. Malakoff, the celebrated sword swallower,"[17] and big posters printed by the *News* were plastered up around town.

[17]*Rocky Mountain News*, Dec. 24, 1864.

As late as December 16, Chivington was still contending in his official messages that he had attacked a hostile camp of nine hundred to a thousand Indians and killed five to six hundred of them. And on December 17 the *News* was still standing staunchly behind him:

> Among the brilliant feats of arms in Indian warfare, the recent campaign of our Colorado volunteers will stand in history with few rivals, and none to exceed it in final results. . . .
>
> Whether viewed as a march or as a battle, the exploit has few, if any, parallels. A march of 260 miles in but a fraction more than five days, with deep snow, scanty forage, and no road, is a remarkable feat, whilst the utter surprise of a large Indian village is unprecedented. In no single battle in North America, we believe, have so many Indians been slain. . . .
>
> A thousand incidents of individual daring and the passing events of the day might be told, but space forbids. We leave the task for eyewitnesses to chronicle. All acquitted themselves well, and Colorado soldiers have again covered themselves with glory.

Space also prevented mention of the fact that Indian women and children were killed, although the paper admitted "there were neither wounded nor prisoners."

Other and differing reports were being made, however, and the aroused Eastern press was demanding facts about the "massacre." Pressure was put on Congress to investigate. On December 30 the *News* printed a Washington dispatch saying that an investigation would be conducted on the strength of "letters received from high officials in Colorado" reporting that "the Indians were killed after surrendering, and that a large proportion of them were women and children." In the space immediately below the Washington dispatch the paper loosed its best irony on the "high officials":

> Indignation was loudly and unequivocally expressed, and some less considerate of the boys were very persistent in their inquiries as to who those "high officials" were, with a mild intimation that they had half a mind to "go for them." This talk about "friendly Indians" and a "surrendered" village will do to "tell to marines," but to us out here it is all bosh.
>
> The *confessed* murderers of the Hungate family—a man and wife and their two little babies, whose scalped and mutilated remains were seen by all our citizens—were "friendly Indians," we suppose, in the eyes of these "high officials." *They* fell in the Sand creek battle.
>
> The confessed participants in a score of other murders of peaceful settlers and inoffensive travellers upon our borders and along our roads in the past six months must have been *friendly*, or else the "high officials" wouldn't say so. . . .

Possibly those scalps of white men, women and children, *one of them fresh, not three days taken*, found drying in their lodges, were taken in a *friendly*, playful manner; or possibly those Indian saddle-blankets trimmed with the scalps of white women, and with braids and fringes of their hair, were kept simply as mementoes of their owners' high affection for the pale face. At any rate, these delicate and tasteful ornaments could not have been taken from the heads of the wives, sisters or daughters of these "high officials." . . .

The House of Representatives went ahead anyway and on January 10, 1865, ordered an investigation which began in March. Clippings from the *News* were read into the record as comments from "the organ of Governor Evans." Governor Evans himself was called as a witness and masterfully side-stepped questions to the great annoyance of committee members. At the conclusion of its hearings the committee issued a blistering report.[18] It said in part:

> . . . From the suckling babe to the old warrior, all who were overtaken were deliberately murdered. Not content with killing women and children, who were incapable of offering any resistance, the soldiers indulged in acts of barbarity of the most revolting character; such, it is to be hoped, as never before disgraced the acts of men claiming to be civilized. . . .
>
> It is difficult to believe that beings in the form of men, and disgracing the uniform of United States soldiers and officers, could commit or countenance the commission of such acts of cruelty and barbarity. . . .
>
> His [Governor Evans'] testimony before your committee was characterized by such prevarication and shuffling as has been shown by no witness they have examined during the four years they have been engaged in their investigations [of the conduct of the Civil War]; and for the evident purpose of avoiding the admission that he was fully aware that the Indians massacred so brutally at Sand creek, were then, and had been, actuated by the most friendly feelings towards the whites, and had done all in their power to restrain those less friendly disposed. . . .
>
> As to Colonel Chivington, your committee can hardly find fitting terms to describe his conduct . . . he deliberately planned and executed a foul and dastardly massacre which would have disgraced the veriest savage among those who were the victims of his cruelty. . . .

Almost concurrently with the Washington investigation a three-man military commission met for seventy-six days in Denver and at Fort Lyon to hear duplicating but more extensive testimony. Chivington, now a civilian, appeared before the commission with attorneys in an effort to defend his actions. The commission made no finding, but the evidence

[18]*Massacre of Cheyenne Indians.*

it heard was damning. During the course of its inquiry one of the principal witnesses against Chivington, Captain Silas S. Soule, was assassinated in the streets of Denver. His killer, a soldier of the 2nd Colorado Cavalry named Squires, admitted the slaying, then was reported to have escaped. Squires was not seen in Denver again.

Byers lost the fight to save his friend Chivington. The Methodist Church forced his resignation as presiding elder, and the big man left town stripped of honor, his political dreams shattered. He returned to Denver years later to die.

Nor was time kind to the predictions of the *News* that the affair at Sand Creek would bring peace to the plains. Outrages did not come to an end. Hauteur was not decreased. There was no surrender or suing for peace. Instead of striking terror, the "bully" work of the "Bloody Third" kindled a towering anger that scorched the prairies from Montana to Texas for twenty years to come. When Custer and his men went down on the Little Big Horn in 1876, Cheyenne and Arapaho warriors were leading the charges.

Fugitives from Sand Creek had scarcely been sheltered in the Cheyenne-Sioux camp at the head of the Smoky Hill before the war pipe was making its rounds. Cheyenne pipe bearers fanned out to the northern tribes, and all the chiefs they visited smoked.

On January 6, little more than a month after Sand Creek, the Indians hit Julesburg with a force of one thousand warriors. The *News* reported the attack on January 7 and offered:

A SUGGESTION.

Since it is a settled fact that the friendly—peaceable—surrendered—hightoned—gentle-minded—quiet—inoffensive savages are again "on it" down the Platte, we respectfully suggest that a small select battalion of "high officials" be permitted to go down instanter to pacify the devils, receive their arms and negotiate a treaty by which they will bind themselves not to massacre any but the outside settlements this winter, and also to let an occasional train come through with bread and meat. We have no doubt that the gentlemen are ready, willing and waiting to enter upon the pleasant duty of proceeding under the protection of a white flag, with olive branches in their hands, to the country residences of Messrs. Black Kettle, White Antelope & Co., where it will be their pleasure to fix things to suit them.

Three days later another Indian force struck on the Arkansas, and so it went through the 1860s and into the '70s. Exposed settlers, wagon freighters, fort garrisons, railroad builders, and cavalrymen paid the price for Chivington's moment of glory. Jim Beckwourth told the military inquiry that he made a private attempt in January of 1865 to mediate.

Jim, known to the Cheyennes as "Medicine Calf," set out alone from Denver and rode boldly into a camp on White Man's Fork. He told the commission:

> I went into the lodge of Leg-in-the-Water. When I went in he raised up and he said, "Medicine Calf, what have you come here for; have you fetched the white man to finish killing our families again?" I told him I had come to talk to him; call in your council. They came in a short time afterwards, and wanted to know what I had come for. I told them I had come to persuade them to make peace with the whites, as there was not enough of them to fight the whites, as they were as numerous as the leaves of the trees. "We know it," was the general response of the council. But what do we want to live for? The white man has taken our country, killed all of our game; was not satisfied with that, but killed our wives and children. Now no peace. We want to go and meet our families in the spirit land. We loved the whites until we found out they lied to us, and robbed us of what we had. We have raised the battle-axe until death. . . .[19]

In October of 1865 two men who should have been listened to backed off and took a long-range view of the flaming plains. Their summary and suggestions, ranged against the violent temper of the times, stand out as singularly wise and prescient. Both knew what they were talking about, if any men in the West did. They were Colonel Christopher (Kit) Carson and Colonel William W. Bent of Bent's Fort, whose 'breed son, incidentally, had been among the Indians wounded at Sand Creek. In a letter to Major General John Pope, Carson and Bent wrote:

> . . . For a number of years the policy of our Government has been to remove our Indians Westward, before the steady advancing tide of Eastern progress, but now emigration leaps forward from the West itself, swarming over the Eastern slope of the Sierra Nevada, and will probably soon make the Rocky Mountains resound throughout its entire length to the hum of busy life . . . gradually encircling them [the Indians] with its ever advancing stride, civilization presses them on all sides, their ancient homes forcibly abandoned, their old hunting grounds destroyed by the requirements of industrious and civilized life, how pitiable a prospect is presented for the preservation of any portion of those vast numbers of aboriginals that swarmed through the interior of our continent the happy possessors of a country full of game, and replete with everything that tended to realize their ignorant ideas of happiness and comfort. The cruel or the thoughtless, might leave to this steady advance of a superior race, the ultimate destruction of the various Indian tribes, that it would occur from this cause alone is certain, but humanity shudders at the picture presented by the destruction of hundreds of thousands of our fellow creatures, until every effort shall

[19]Senate Executive Document No. 26, pp. 71–72.

have been tried for their redemption and found useless, by dispossessing them of their country, we have assumed their stewardship, and the manner in which this duty is performed will add a glorious record to all American history, or a damning blot and reproach for all future time. . . .[20]

In oblique reference to Chivington's raid, Carson and Bent urged that the army garrison the Indian country with "Regular troops, and officers of known discretion and judgment . . . (who would) not rashly place the country in danger of an Indian war in consequence of any slight provocation on the part of the Indians."

The Civil War was over, and William Tecumseh Sherman had come west from his march to the sea in Georgia to take over the nasty, thankless task of cleaning up the plains after Chivington. Sherman saw the Carson-Bent letter and passed it on to U. S. Grant with the comment: "Probably no two men exist better acquainted with the Indians than Carson & Bent and their judgment is entitled to great weight."[21]

The *News* was only one of a number of Western journals which kept up a steady, sniping fire on Sherman and his policies. The army was not prosecuting the Indian wars vigorously enough. Sherman's thinly spread cavalrymen never seemed to be at the right place at the right time. The papers wrote of "Poor Lo" with heavy-handed sarcasm, and the *News* branded treaties as farcical. Extermination was the only thing that would satisfy the West, and it was proceeding.

The last chapter in the sordid, bitter tragedy was written in September 1879 high in the Colorado Rockies on the White River at a place called Milk Creek. Byers had a role to play in it too.

An active, restless, questing man, Byers never was too busy editing his *News*, supervising Indian wars, or searching for mine bonanzas, to take time to range his beloved mountains. He explored them on foot and horseback from the San Juans to the Yampa River country, from the Spanish Peaks to the Laramie Plains. He prospected as he went, collected wild flowers and geological specimens, scaled peaks to see the view, and always wet a line in any likely trout water.

In 1867, on a fishing and tramping outing with Bayard Taylor of the New York *Tribune*, Byers visited mountain-girt Middle Park. He was entranced by its lush beauty, the green meadows and clear, sparkling streams where the mighty cañon-carving Colorado River has its origins, the spectacular peaks which surround the protected valley. Middle Park became his personal Shangri-La. (Many years later, when the weariness of age and many responsibilities was on him, he wrote plaintively to his

[20]Carson and Bent to Pope, Oct. 26, 1865, War Department Records, National Archives, File C–201–1865.

[21]Sherman to Grant, Nov. 6, 1865, William T. Sherman Papers, Vol. 17, Library of Congress; quoted in Athearn, op. cit., p. 26.

son that he wished he could sell everything he had in Denver and "go
to the woods" in Middle Park "*and stay*.")

Byers homesteaded one of the first ranches in Middle Park and ceaselessly experimented there with nut culture, forestry, and the growing of
grains, vegetables, and fruits never before seen in a high mountain
valley of the Rockies. Later he divided a portion of the ranch into lots
and founded the town of Hot Sulphur Springs. The town takes
its name from warm springs, within the original Byers homestead, which
in the early days flowed in a six-foot cascade into a basin of rock. The
Utes of the mountains had known the springs from time beyond memory,
and they came there to cure wounds and rheumatism in the hot mineral
waters.

Byers became well acquainted with many of the passing Utes and
achieved a measure of standing among them, even though he was an
illegal squatter and they had better title to the springs than he did. The
country still was treaty land for the Utes, and Byers would not hold true
title to his lands and hot waters until he acquired them later by pre-
emption. Nevertheless, at least some of the Utes respected him. At one
council following a brush between braves and settlers the Indians told
all the other whites to shut up and let Byers do their talking for them.

The editor of the *News* knew both the country and its natives, and
thus he was the logical man to lead the counterattack when, as Marshall
Sprague puts it, Denver "braced itself against invasion by eighteen Ute
lodges" in 1878. The small band had committed minor depredations
and then killed a settler to avenge, they said, the prior killing of one
of their clan by a Hot Sulphur Springs posse which included Byers'
son Frank. When the word of the "uprising" reached Denver, Sheriff
Dave Cook and Byers got together twenty-six hardies and rushed up to
Middle Park.

After only five days of roughing it Cook and fifteen others turned
back. Byers took the remaining squad and pushed over the Roan Plateau
and on to the White River Ute Agency. There he learned that his quarry
had flown long since in entirely the opposite direction and by now was
far away to the south in the Uncompahgres. Byers also met a remarkable
English-speaking Ute woman named Jane, who spunkily told him he was
on the reservation with armed men and had better get out immediately.
The expedition left by way of Milk Creek, where Byers had heard there
were some trout he ought to try.

The man in charge at the White River Ute Agency was Nathan C.
Meeker, who was probably the least qualified man in the West to be
an Indian agent. It was not that he was evil. Quite the contrary. It was
just that the sight of evil hurt him so that he couldn't bear not reforming
evildoers. Throughout his life, which would end soon, Nathan Meeker
was shocked, appalled, and saddened by the base instincts of his fellow
man as demonstrated by cursing, waltzing with women, and lack of thrift

and industry. And now he was in charge of the White River Utes, who worshiped nature and spent their lives doing what came naturally.

Meeker had been a Greenwich Village poet, a Fourierist Phalangist, then Civil War correspondent and, later, agricultural editor—an important post, considering the boss's inclinations—of Horace Greeley's *Tribune*. Through Greeley he became acquainted with Byers, and when the *Tribune* editor decided to sponsor a "union colony" agricultural experiment in the West, Byers just happened to have on hand the ideal spot for it. Byers, as has been noted, wore many hats. One of them was that of Colorado agent for the National Land Company, an organization established to dispose of the public lands granted to the Denver Pacific Railroad for pushing its rails across the plains to Denver.

Byers sold Meeker twelve thousand acres of northern Colorado land, much of it useless without water and six hundred and forty acres, it developed, not even owned by the National Land Company. The site was near the railroad stop of Evans, and it became the city of Greeley. The colony was limited to "temperance people of good moral character," and to this day ardent spirits cannot be vended in Greeley.

Meeker became president of the colony and a prompt failure, though much loved and respected by the "Saints," as the old settlers called them. He couldn't balance the books. His irrigation project flopped. The Colorado climate, despite his determination and good works, would not grow walnut and hickory trees. The grasshoppers ate up the crops planted according to scripture as found in Horace Greeley's book *What I Know about Farming*.

Despite the land deal, Meeker and Byers became close friends. When the hard-driving Utopian found himself in need of a job the *News* editor helped pull political strings in Washington to get him appointed agent of the White River Ute Agency in northwest Colorado. Meeker took the post with characteristic zeal. Here was man's work and God's. He would bring his innocent, ignorant charges up from savagery to civilization. Moreover he would do it before the year was out. The mission was a challenge, an inspiration.

Meeker began by plowing up the Utes' racecourse in the meadows to show them how to plant crops and to discourage immoral idleness, sporting, and gambling. Things went from bad to worse. The Utes willfully refused to be civilized on Meeker's crash time schedule, and the good but foolish man's heart was slowly broken. He became distant and disinterested, petulant and arbitrary in his orders, and finally vindictive, growling about chains and hangings for his disobedient red children.

Violence came, and finally Meeker telegraphed for troops. It was too late. On September 29, 1879, the Utes ambushed Major Thomas T. Thornburgh and his command on Milk Creek and attacked the agency, near the present town of Meeker. They killed Thornburgh and a number of his troopers. They killed Meeker and all of his white male employees at the agency. Meeker's stripped body was found with a log chain around his neck. He had been dragged around the corral behind one of the Indian ponies. Then a barrel stave had been pushed down his throat.

The agency buildings were burned, and the three white women present—Meeker's wife Arvilla, his grown daughter Josie, and Flora Price—kidnaped. They were carried away on a long trail with rape at every night's stop. The women eventually were given up when the Southern Ute chief, Ouray, intervened and put an end to the rampage of his White River cousins.

The "Meeker Massacre" was an ugly, brutal, and tragic affair, and it also was the last major uprising of the American Indian. He had escaped extermination, narrowly, but he now could be shoved entirely out of the way of the white man's civilization.

In his masterful history of the barbaric last stand on White River, Marshall Sprague summarizes:

> All told, this small Ute band killed thirty white men and wounded forty-four more. Their punishment was the usual. They and their neighbors, the Uncompahgre Utes, who had nothing to do with either the ambush or the massacre, were branded as criminals without trial by commissions of doubtful legality. Their treaty rights which had been guaranteed them by the United States Senate were canceled. Their rights to be American citizens as described in the Fourteenth Amendment were ignored. Title to their twelve-million-acre Colorado homeland, which they had owned exclusively since pre-Columbian times, was extinguished. They were moved at gunpoint to barren lands in Utah. By these means, the last and largest chunk of desirable Indian real estate in the nation, the Western Slope of Colorado, was thrown open to white settlement.[22]

The Denver papers, along with nearly every other journal in the nation, burst into flame over the massacre. Byers was hard hit by the slaughter of his friend; why, it had been only a short time ago that Elizabeth Byers had received a note from Arvilla Meeker thanking her for the gift of a dress to an Indian girl, the daughter of Jane, who had been so saucy the year before. Byers now was no longer editor and publisher of the *Rocky Mountain News*, but surely this last and final outrage vindicated, once more, the harsh and flaming words he had published in the dark days of '64 and '65 when the whole inexorable process began.

[22]Marshall Sprague, *Massacre: The Tragedy at White River* (Boston, 1957), p. ix.

CHAPTER TWELVE

Iron Horses and a Scandal

BACK on the shores of the Missouri brawny gangs of brawling men were shaping a final answer to the West's ever explosive "Indian question." Many of them were Irish emigrants, refugees from potato famine in the homeland. The "terriers," as they chose to call themselves, were iron men—muscle, stomach, and disposition.

They could riot most of the night in some tent saloon, perhaps sleep it off under the stars in a prairie slough, and be ready at dawn for a long day of brute labor under a pitiless sun. A little cabbage-stack locomotive would come wheezing out, pushing a flatcar loaded with rails before it. The rails were transferred to a smaller, horse-drawn car and pulled forward to where the newly graded roadbed waited. A dozen men then would take their places on each side of the car. On signal of the foreman—"Hup!"—two heavy rails of iron would go up on shoulders. In lock-step cadence the rails were marched to position. "Halt! Down! On with another, me boys! Drill, ye terriers!" A rhythmic clang of sledges on spikes, and "end of track"—manifest destiny's newest catch phrase—would be a few feet farther west on the Nebraska sod than it had been minutes before. The horses pulling the car would have farther to go next trip, and the end of the Plains Indian's wild ways was closer by measurable inches and feet of adamant iron.

"End of Track" became a dateline, like "With the Troops" or "On the High Seas," for newspaper dispatches which told an exciting story of a continent being spanned. In the East newspaper readers thrilled with national pride at the steady march of civilization. In Denver the approaching rails meant an end to isolation, a chance to arrive, to be, to bloom in the full tradition of expansive American progress.

The Pacific railroad had been a continental dream since early in the 1850s. It had been the subject of much talk, huge visions, and a lot of sordid politicking. Numerous expeditions had fanned out to seek and survey the several "best ways" to and through the West. Finally, on December 2, 1863, the first spade of dirt was turned at Omaha for a mile-long grade which since has disappeared into the bed of the shifting Missouri. The Union Pacific was on its way. The troubles of war and finance, however, put a blight to the auspicious beginning, and it was not until July 10, 1865, that the first spike was driven and the track laying started. The peace of Appomattox was only two months new.

Within a few months more the "hero of Atlanta" would be waging an exasperating war over tens of thousands of square miles with a copper-colored enemy, often half naked and yelling, who could and would teach his cavalry lessons in hit-and-run tactics. Sherman quickly saw in the railroad a solution to the now necessarily forcible pacification of the Indian. Railways through the West would make it possible for him quickly to move his troops, steadily diminishing as American armies always do immediately after a war, over great distances to seek out and punish marauding bands. As a mounted warrior the Indian has few equals in the long history of warfare, and Sherman's cavalry was finding him hard to catch. The Indian refused to be maneuvered into large and formal battles. Small war parties, often fewer than a hundred braves, would pounce suddenly out of nowhere and then disappear into the trackless void of the plains. By the time a company of cavalry could ride out from the nearest post the war party would be long gone and in a direction no man could tell. Railroads, Sherman saw, would greatly increase the maneuverability of his thinly spread army. Moreover, the rails would bring more and more settlers to maintain a steady pressure on the tribes, forcing them into smaller and smaller ranges where they might be cornered, whipped, and brought to terms.

So Sherman did everything he could, short of dismounting his troopers and putting them in the terrier gangs, to speed the rails westward. He detailed units to guard the track-laying crews, and the surveying parties far out in advance usually worked under protection of squadrons of cavalry. The protection was not always perfect. Irish scalps were taken, and the railroads began to arm their construction gangs, berating Sherman for not keeping the Indians away. But the track was getting laid, often at record-breaking speeds, and straight across the buffalo runs and the hunting trails. It was coming on toward sundown for a free, nomadic, nature-following way of life centuries old.

As the rails reached and spread out through Colorado's mountains and plains they became a factor in the last brushes between an ebullient new commonwealth and the hated red savages it always contended were about to swallow it alive. When the ambush came on Milk Creek, soldiers were moved by Union Pacific to Rawlins, Wyoming, to ride south to the rescue of Thornburgh's survivors.

By June of 1867 the transcontinental line had reached the extreme northeast corner of Colorado Territory, and the man who had marched through Georgia came west on iron wheels for an inspection tour. From Julesburg on June 6 he telegraphed Governor Alexander C. Hunt in Denver:

I am here now and General Augur is across the Platte on the line
of the Union Pacific Railway. The Indians are everywhere. Ranchers
should gather at stage stations. Stages should bunch up and travel
together at irregular times. I have six companies of Cavalry and General
Custer is coming up from the Smoky Hill Route.

General W. T. Sherman[1]

The Indians were not blind to what was happening to them. In 1868
the Union Pacific had climbed to the Continental Divide at Jim Bridger's
Pass in Wyoming, and the Kansas Pacific was slashing west through
Kansas and the heart of the great buffalo range which lay between the
Platte and the Arkansas rivers. The restlessness of the tribes grew, and
they hit at any target which exposed itself to their raids. During August
a band of Arapahoes estimated at two hundred initially, and at six
hundred as fevers rose, began hitting at Colorado settlements, some of
them within sixty miles of Denver. Their attacks precipitated what has
been called "Hall's War" in memory of Acting Governor Frank Hall,
later one of the state's historians.

Governor Hunt was up at Byers' hot springs in Middle Park. He was
one of a party of high-ranking dudes the editor of the *News* was entertaining with a taste of roughing it in the Rockies. Also in the group
were Schuyler Colfax, Speaker of the House of Representatives and soon
to become Grant's boodling Vice-President; William Bross, the powerful
Midwestern politician from Illinois and part owner of the Chicago
Tribune; Samuel Bowles, editor of the Springfield *Republican*; and John
Wesley Powell, professor, naturalist, and future explorer of the Grand
Canyon. The party arrived at Hot Sulphur Springs on August 14, just two
days after Byers recorded in his diary that he had caught forty-two pounds
of trout on the Williams Fork. The editor guided his guests up the same
fishing waters, and presumably all came back with filled creels.

Back in Denver, Acting Governor Frank Hall was having no carefree
outing. His people were jumping sideways at the mere mention of
Indians, and they demanded that he take action to defend them. Hall
began firing telegrams in all directions. Speaker Colfax and his party, he
wired Sherman, were in imminent danger of being captured or massacred.
"For God's sake give me authority to take your men," Hall said in a
telegram to General Phil Sheridan, demanding use of federal troops at
Fort Reynolds near Pueblo. Sherman authorized him to call up a militia,
and by the last of August Hall was insisting that the army supply rifles:
"My men are fighting the Indians every day at Latham & I am compelled
to keep them supplied." Pressure was brought on Colfax to use his
considerable influence in Washington to see that the army didn't let
the Indians wipe Colorado off the map. The crusty Sherman, now

[1]E. O. Davis, *The First Five Years of the Railroad Era in Colorado* (Denver,
1948), p. 3.

increasingly testy under the cross fire of Indian lovers in the East and Indian haters in the West, told everyone to keep his pants on, that he was doing the best he could. Certainly he wasn't going to send a full regiment of cavalry to Denver, as requested by Hall, when he had only four regiments to cover the entire plains.

There was much panic and a little fighting. A few men, red and white, were killed, and as usual Indian casualties far outnumbered white. Eventually "Hall's War" dwindled away and the telegraph wires had a chance to cool off. By October, Sherman had moved enough men by railroad into the high prairie country to restore a measure of peace and quiet.[2]

Not, however, before the Cheyennes and Sioux under Roman Nose staged another "massacre" on the Colorado plains very near to Sherman's wonderful railroad at Julesburg. In the Battle of Beecher Island some six hundred Indians cornered a cavalry force of fifty-one men under Major George A. Forsyth, one of Phil Sheridan's staff, on a sandy island in the Arickaree Fork of the Republican River. The battle site is close to the Colorado-Kansas line about seventeen miles south of Wray.

Forsyth's troopers were trapped and besieged on September 17, 1868, and they were held under attack by circling warriors until a rescue force reached them on the twenty-fifth. The soldiers ran out of food during the siege. They caught and ate a coyote, pronouncing it "very good." They ate prickly pears and their own horses. A soup was made from putrid horse meat salted with gunpowder. When units of the 10th and 2nd Cavalry Regiments arrived to end the battle, Forsyth, himself wounded, counted five of his men killed, including Lieutenant Frederick W. Beecher, for whom the island and the battle were named. Grinnell says Indians who were there told him the Cheyennes and Sioux lost seven of their number. But one of them was the great Roman Nose. He had gone into the battle convinced he would die. A squaw had lifted food for him with an iron fork. "That breaks my medicine," Roman Nose said. "I'll be killed today." He was right.[3]

The Beecher Island battle with its heroic stand by a small, badly outnumbered cavalry force is the stuff of Indian war legend. The last great countermarching by the habitually beleaguered Colorado whites, "Colorow's War" of 1887, was strictly comic opera. The railroads played a part in it, and naturally William N. Byers was there.

Colorow was a Comanche who early had adopted himself into the Utes and attained a measure of standing as leader of one band of the White River branch of the mountain tribe. With the others he had

[2]Robert G. Athearn, "Colorado and the Indian War of 1868," *Colorado Magazine*, Vol. XXXIII, No. 1 (Jan. 1956), pp. 42ff.

[3]Grinnell, op. cit., pp. 277ff.; see also Merrill J. Mattes, "The Beecher Island Battlefield: Diary of Sigmund Schlesinger," *Colorado Magazine*, Vol. XXIX, No. 3 (July 1952), pp. 161ff.

been banished to Utah following the Meeker Massacre in 1879. But the White River country still had game and was filling up slowly with settlers, and the Utes sometimes came back to their old homeland for hunts.

In August of 1887 a report reached Denver that Colorow had invaded Colorado. The fat old chief, who earlier had been a familiar beggar at ranch houses in the Denver area, had brought a band of some twelve braves and enough old men, women, and children to make up a force of between forty and fifty persons, and had come into Colorado seeking game. Along the way they had stolen two horses at Rangely and sold them at Meeker. Garfield County had been newly organized in the White River country, and it had an energetic sheriff named Jim Kendall who was anxious to prove to his scattered constituents that they had picked the right man for the job. He mounted a posse of seventy-two men to turn back Colorow's invasion and telegraphed word to Denver that northwestern Colorado was under attack.

Governor Alva Adams called out seven brigades of the Colorado National Guard, some thousand guardsmen, and for their transport in this hour of Colorado's peril seized every available car of the Denver & Rio Grande Railway. By this date the narrow-gauge lines were climbing through the Colorado Rockies like mountain goats. No mine was so high on any peak that the "little iron" couldn't get there to haul its ores away. The Denver & Rio Grande had pushed its line down the Colorado River as far as Gypsum. The guardsmen were dispatched thence as fast as the diminutive engines could pull them up and over the steep grades.

At a more leisurely pace Governor Adams assembled a command force, Byers in charge because of his knowledge of the Middle Park country and the Utes. The gubernatorial brass chugged over to Glenwood Springs, and Byers led them north to the threatened village of Meeker. They encountered no hostiles.

Meanwhile Colorow's band had accidentally run into Sheriff Kendall's men and there had been a loud argument broken off by gunfire from the posse. Colorow gathered his berry-picking squaws together and started his bunch ambling back toward the reservation. Kendall and the guardsmen finally caught up with them just two miles short of the Utah border and forced a fight. Three white men and eight Utes died. It also cost the now sovereign state of Colorado $80,314.72, and untallied wear and tear on nerves, to turn back an old biscuit-beggar and his band of reservation-jumpers. Moreover the Utes kept right on hunting for years thereafter in the high and lonely White River wilds.[4]

As the West moved into the railroad era and Indian alarms dwindled away into busynesses, Denver began its first period of solid growth. The

[4]Sprague, op. cit., pp. 326–28.

key date is June 24, 1870, and the expansion, long delayed, was an explosive release of pent-up forces.

The Civil War and the Indian troubles had been powerful deterrents to civic progress on the frontier. Denver and her boosters, Byers and his *News* in the front rank, could chalk up few really substantial gains during the first decade. At least they would have been hampered in their patriotism had they been candid about it, which of course they weren't. A town had been started under rather hectic circumstances, and it had acquired at some cost in pain and pelf a few of the accouterments of nineteenth-century American civilization. But Denver was far from the city it pretended to be. The population, which had dropped to around 2000 during the rebellion, climbed slowly to about 3000 in 1864, but this was still short of the peak reached in the heyday of the gold rush in 1860. A census ordered by the territorial legislature in the summer of 1866 could find only 3500 residents in town, and the first official federal census in 1870 counted 4759 souls, a net gain of fewer than 1000 persons in four trying years.

Antelope still could be hunted within the city limits in 1864, and the *News* announced on April 23 of that year that the streets were so muddy a theatrical performance had to be canceled. So far as the streets were concerned, things weren't much better seven years later. The Central City *Register* jibed down from its rocky perch in the mountains in April 1871: "The streets of Denver were reported to be navigable for the largest type of flat boats."

Settlers weren't arriving in very large numbers but grasshoppers did. Colorado was visited by plagues of locusts in 1864, 1865, and 1867, and the insects contributed heavily to the woes of the despondent years. Great swarms of Rocky Mountain locusts, commonly called grasshoppers, descended on the state and devoured everything in sight. The *Register* said of one invasion:

> As the sun reached the meridian today, countless millions of grasshoppers were seen in the air while the atmosphere for miles high was literally crammed with them. They sailed by under the pressure of a light east wind in vast billowy clouds, the lower strata falling in a ceaseless shower on the ground, covering the streets, sidewalks, the exterior of buildings, jumping, crawling, crushed by every passing foot, filling the eyes and ears, and covering the garments of pedestrians, swarming everywhere in irrepressible currents.

Crops were ruined and prices of foodstuffs soared. The *News* for October 9, 1865, said that had it not been for the 'hoppers "the territory would this year have produced its own supply of breadstuffs, vegetables, and feed for stock. They destroyed the crop totally in many places and injured it in all." War, Indians, mud, high prices, drouth, and disaster. What next in this dismal decade?

But many churches and a few schools had been built, and General U. S. Grant came visiting in July 1868. He was given a memorable public reception in the Masonic hall on the third floor—the sky line was mounting—of the Tappan Building on Fifteenth Street. Grant returned again in 1873 as President and on a visit to Central City alighted from his carriage to walk over a pavement of solid silver ingots into the Teller House, quaint old mountain hostelry still in use today, self-consciously restored to Victorian charms.

The antimacassars and onyx statuary in the Teller House weren't the only indications that a veneer of gentility was being applied to rude frontier mores. Pump organs were appearing in parlors, and lawns and shrubbery at doorsteps. There was a great "sanitary festival" in Denver on Febraury 28, 1864, to raise money for care of the ill. The new delicacy, ice cream, could be purchased. Editor Byers, a moderate man where potables were concerned, was developing a taste for sherry. And although his *News* snarled ferociously at the Indians, he was an advocate of conservation for all other forms of wild life. The *News* of May 20, 1864, addressed a strong plea to trigger-happy pioneers to stop killing the songbirds.

Byers and Dailey apparently were not long in winning their way back from the financial disaster of the '64 flood. They were renters when they moved to the Murdock building on Larimer Street in July of that year. Two years later they were putting up their own masonry building down the street a few doors in the same block.

Somewhere along the way, possibly in payment for a job-printing bill, the *News* partners acquired the lots at 389 Larimer (now numbered about 1547). Business must have been good for them in spite of war, Indian-enforced isolation, and a grasshopper plague. They had recouped their nineteen-thousand-dollar flood loss and the four thousand dollars laid out for the *Commonwealth*. Now they were ready once again to put up their own building. Although he never managed to stay very far out of debt, Byers abhorred being anyone's tenant.

The lots owned by the paper were still unoccupied in 1866 despite the growing importance of Larimer Street. They were situated just south of the corner of G (Sixteenth) Street on the west side of the block. Byers' diary for May 23, 1866, notes that he "contracted with Kinney for first and second story walls of printing office—first of stone at $8.00 a perch, 2nd of grout at 15 cts. per foot." Next day he concluded an agreement with Flaherty & Hays for excavation at sixty cents a yard and for a well "at $1.75 per foot to be walled with brick or $1.50 per foot if curbed with wood." By July 30, Byers had the satisfaction of watching the joists go up, and the grout for the second story was under way on August 2.

When completed, the building was pronounced an ornament to the city. Large letters across the front proclaimed it the "News Block." It was a two-and-a-half-story structure with a brick front fancily cut up into five arched doorways. The building extended sixty feet toward the rear of the lot, and it had a deep basement for the steam-powered Campbell cylinder press capable of turning out twelve hundred newspapers an hour. The editorial and counting rooms occupied the south part of the ground floor and the north half was rented to the United States Express Company, the stage line which operated the Overland Express. The composing room was on the second floor, except for job work, which was handled in the basement. A couple of rented law offices were squeezed into the second floor, too, just to help meet overhead. The half-story garret was a book bindery.

On September 19, 1866, the paper proudly announced:

> The *News* building, near the corner of Larimer and G streets, is rapidly approaching completion. We shall soon be permanently, we trust, established within its walls. Living beneath one's own vine and fig tree, with no rents to pay, is a rather enjoyable thing these tight times.

The move was made October 5, and the paper craved the indulgence of its subscribers in the necessity of skipping an issue. "Our patrons will please bear with us and we will try to make amends for this deficiency in the superior facilities afforded us for making a good newspaper, in our new and permanent quarters."

The vacated Murdock building down the street was taken over by Count Henri Murat, Horace Greeley's whilom barber, as a saloon and poolroom. It was remodeled into "one of the finest frame structures in the city" and subsequently became known as the Mozart Billiard Hall.

The *News* might be able to build itself a new block and install new machinery, but Byers didn't want anyone to get the wrong impression. He brought out his "plain talk" manner again for the issue of October 25:

> There are men in this city who have an idea that the publishing of a newspaper in Denver is an immensely lucrative business. . . . There never was a greater error, as there is not a daily paper out of a thousand that has not been a struggling starveling during the first year or years of its existence. Count up the number of dailies that have sprung up in Denver since its first settlement, only seven years ago, and flickered out for want of support. But one of that number yet remains, and that one has met with reverses that would have made 99 of every 100 men quit the business in disgust. . . . It costs here about $1200 per week to run a daily newspaper. The voting population of Denver is about 1200. Of these about two-thirds take and pay for a daily paper. . . . Did the News depend only on its subscription for support, it could not live a week. To meet current expenses the advertising

patrons must make up the sum which the subscription fails to pay—about $650. The average number of advertisers in this community is not over 100. These 100 advertisers must pay weekly, to sustain the paper, $6.50 each, in order to meet the mechanical and professional labor required in its columns. . . . The great majority are below that sum. When business is flush the paper makes a fair profit; when it is dull no firm quicker feels the pressure than the newspaper . . . The News is barely established on a paying basis, after seven years of struggle. . . .

Professor Goldrick now had departed Denver and the *News* staff on his temporary editorial mission to the Mormons, and Simpson T. Sopris had joined the Byers and Dailey forces. The name of George West, who helped print the Greeley extra and later published the *Western Mountaineer* in Golden, appears beginning August 14, 1865, as "local" editor of the *News*. He held the post into the next year. Dr. Junius E. Wharton joined the staff May 1 as associate editor, replacing Goldrick, who resigned the same day. Wharton in 1866 wrote and published the first history of Denver, printed for him in the *News* job shop.

Sopris later set down his recollections of Denver newspapering in the late sixties:

> Mr. Byers was often in "hot water" because of his nerve in showing up certain of the residents, principally of the sporting element, and had some narrow escapes. I have been in the office with him when men ready and seemingly quite willing to kill him entered and endeavored to provoke a quarrel, but he managed to avoid a shooting affray by keeping his head and standing for all the indignant visitor had to say. Having relieved themselves of a lot of mean words, his callers usually retired and left him with a whole skin.
>
> I had one experience with an indignant citizen that cured me of any further desire to provoke hostilities. Across the street from the News office, on Larimer street, was some vacant ground, part of which was used as a wood yard. The wood was delivered to purchasers in a wagon drawn by one horse and that horse was the thinnest animal I had ever seen. Standing in the sun he wouldn't throw a shadow, and no X-ray was needed to show what was inside his hide. That horse got on my nerves. Sitting at the "local" desk, facing the front of the office, every time I looked up and out I could see the poor beast, and the sight unfitted me for the work I had to do, which was inventing items for the local column.
>
> Finally one day I perpetrated the following brief reference to the unfortunate horse: "There is a man in this town who drives a horse that is so poor the owner has to tie a knot in his, the horse's, tail to keep the animal from slipping through the collar." That was all, but it proved amply sufficient. Any elaboration would have been a waste of printer's ink. The item appeared in the morning issue the following day. In the afternoon of that day, while at my desk, I happened to

look out on the street and noticed the owner of the aforesaid horse coming toward the office. In his right hand was a gun, one that seemed to me to be unnecessarily large, and the manner in which he swung the gun, and the more or less uncertainty of his steps, indicated that he had taken aboard a full cargo of "pizen," which happened to be the case. Mr. Dailey was in the front of the office working on the books, and it suddenly occurred to me that two of us were not needed in the office just then, so, grabbing my hat, I slipped quietly out the back door. Returning an hour or so later, I learned from my friend Dailey that he had had a lot of trouble quieting the excited visitor, who had been induced to depart after promising to shoot me full of holes the first time he caught me on the street. And I was admonished to let up on such "personal" items, or else stick around and fight my own battles. . . .[5]

Sopris left the *News* in 1871 to join Clarence E. Hagar, a former compositor for Byers and Dailey, in the publication of the *Daily City Item*, later to become the *Daily Times*, a pillar of Denver journalism for a half century.

When Dr. Wharton resigned from the *News* in May of 1867 to become one of the founders of the *Colorado Miner* in the new silver camp of Georgetown, his post as associate editor was filled by William Russell Thomas, a young reporter fresh from the Chicago *Tribune*. Thomas was a nephew of William Bross, one of the *Tribune* proprietors, who gave him a letter of introduction to Byers. He soon cemented the relationship and became the editor's brother-in-law by marrying Elizabeth Byers' sister Flora. Thomas remained with the *News*, off and on, until 1904, when he became a history professor at Colorado A&M College in Fort Collins.

Byers, Sopris, and Thomas all helped entertain Bayard Taylor, the New York *Tribune's* crack travel reporter, when he visited Colorado in 1866. Sopris showed him the agricultural progress in the Denver area, Byers guided him over Berthoud Pass and through Middle Park to Breckenridge, where their host was a Mr. Sutherland, a peripatetic bugler who claimed to have sounded the signal for the charge of the light brigade at Balaklava. Mr. Sutherland favored the travelers with a rendition of "Peas upon a trencher," Taylor wrote.[6] The trumpeter also set a good table, including oyster soup. The *Tribune* writer described Byers as "an accomplished mountaineer, to whom much of the ground is familiar, and I preferred taking his advice to that of others who spoke from hearsay rather than experience." He also commented that the *News* editor's "love of trout would lead him to fish even in Bitter Creek." After a month's adventuring in the wilds Byers escorted Taylor back through South Park to Denver. Thomas then took him up to Boulder

[5] *Trail*, Vol. VII, No. 7 (Dec. 1914), pp. 20–21.

[6] Bayard Taylor, *Colorado: A Summer Trip* (New York, 1867), p. 112.

Valley, where Taylor lectured in the since disappeared town of Valmont.

Others on the *News* editorial staff in this era included Ovando J. Hollister, author of the bold history of the 1st Colorado Regiment, who joined the force in 1866 and became associate editor in 1868 and 1869; Joseph E. Hood, the imaginative inventor of the underground-river sensation, 1869–70; "Deacon" John Walker, city editor in 1867; Marcus E. Ward; and Charles E. Harrington, city editor 1870–74 and author of *Summering in Colorado*.

Following purchase of the *Commonwealth* in 1864, the *News* had the Denver newspaper field to itself for nearly a year until the closing days of the Civil War. With no local papers to quarrel with, it had to reach up into the mountains to the Black Hawk *Journal* for an adversary in the bellicose tradition which was ritual with nineteenth-century editors. The two papers spent a happy season exchanging insults on the calling out of a militia and the statehood campaign of 1864, the *Journal* allied with the antis and not at all sure Colorado was ready to govern herself, and the *News* strongly committed to the pros, the Evans-Chivington-Byers crowd. But somehow the scrap lacked the full-bodied flavor which had characterized the pleasantries between the *News* and Gibson's 'Erald.

On May 13, 1865, however, Frederick J. Stanton came forth with the first number of the *Daily Denver Gazette*. Byers and Dailey sold Stanton the equipment he needed to get started and even furnished him paper on credit. It was good again to have a contemporary near at hand for sparring purposes. What was even better, the *Gazette* announced itself as a Democratic sheet. The *News* pushed its hat over one eye, hitched up its britches, and slapped a chip on its shoulder. The *Gazette* promptly became "the morning Pollywog of this city," and Stanton was a Copperhead.

Byers got more than he bargained for this time. Fred Stanton came up behind him in the street one morning and clipped him on the head with a stout hickory cane.

The *News* for September 15 and 16, 1865, gives details of the dirty deed. No effort was spared to martyr the fallen editor.

> . . . The spirit that animated the cowardly brute who made this dastardly attack is the same that animated John Wilkes Booth in his attack that made desolate the hearts of the American people, only that the would be assassin in this instance, lacks the courage of his teacher (Booth) in copperheadism. . . .

The *News* had been attacking the *Gazette* for its politics and its not entirely enthusiastic attitude toward the heroes of Sand Creek, but the precipitating factor appears to have been a charge that Stanton had lifted mail from Postmaster Byers' post office. On the morning of September

15, Byers was bidding farewell to a group of friends about to depart by coach for the States. The *News* that afternoon reported that Stanton, "coming up behind him, dealt him a heavy blow with a hickory cane, severing the left temporal artery, and inflicting a severe and dangerous wound." As Byers went down the enraged *Gazette* proprietor laid on with several more blows. The article continued with a review of Stanton's despicable ingratitude in the matter of the sale to him of former *News* equipment and paper supplies. Moreover the paper was "in part unpaid for and the bill uncollectable."

Byers noted in his diary: "Was attacked by Stanton this A.M. & badly hurt." Next day, however, he was "able to get to the P.O." He also was able to write a lengthy personal version of the affair for his paper, thanking the many friends who rallied to his support and explaining that he never carried a gun because he was not proficient in the use of firearms. He had not been able to hit back, he went on, because he was "incapacitated for fist fighting by a wound received years ago."

Stanton soon learned that it was perilous to let editorial forensics become physical violence—particularly if a pioneer and first citizen were the victim. One didn't play the newspaper game by those rules. The town rallied immediately to Byers' side. Advertisers withdrew their support of the *Gazette*. The City Council, which in a moment of misplaced generosity had made Stanton's journal the official city paper, pulled back all municipal printing from the *Gazette* job shop. And the crowning blow fell when Typographical Union No. 49 expelled Stanton from his honorary membership.

The *Gazette* died a lingering death in May of 1869, given away free at the end.

Life was not all attacks and attacking for Byers. (In fact, considering the vehemence of some of the items his paper published, it's amazing that he was not more frequently caned.) There were also mountaineering and distinguished visitors to be entertained, and often the two could be combined. The visit of Bayard Taylor has been mentioned. His *Tribune* colleague, Albert D. Richardson, came back again and was struck by the changes in the town. The postwar railroad expansion and the peace which now lay upon the land greatly encouraged writers and adventurous spirits to journey out to see what the wild West was like.

One such was Henry M. Stanley, the English orphan-wanderer who had served on both sides in the American Civil War and would win a knighthood for finding Livingstone in darkest Africa. Stanley came to Denver in 1866 as a space-rate correspondent for the St. Louis *Missouri Republican*. He was one of the few men in Western history to make the Platte a navigable waterway. When his lifelong wanderlust seized him again and it was time to leave Denver, he and W. H. Cook built themselves a flat-bottomed skiff, loaded it with provisions and arms to fight off hostiles, and pushed it into the South Platte at the height of its May run. They made it through to Omaha with no trouble from the red man, although their boat twice capsized on the voyage. The following year—he had been to Turkey and been captured by brigands in the meantime—Stanley was back in the American West as special writer at fifteen dollars a week for the St. Louis *Democrat*, attached to General Winfield Scott Hancock's expedition against the Indians.

Stanley saw little military action against the tribes but participated in many councils and much treaty making. In his reminiscences he records the speech of one chieftain in answer to the general's plea that the Indian should settle down to agricultural calm:

> I love the land and the buffalo, and will not part with them. I don't want any of those medicine houses [schools] built in the country; I want the papooses brought up exactly as I am. I have word that you intend to settle us on a reservation near the mountains. I don't want to settle there. I love to roam over the wide prairie, and, when I do it, I feel free and happy; but, when we settle down, we grow pale and die.[7]

Stanley met and interviewed Wild Bill Hickok, who said he had already killed over a hundred men, all for good cause. Also attached to the Hancock expedition was a five-year-old Indian boy, orphaned at Sand Creek. The child had been exhibited with the Wilson & Graham circus and may have been one of the forlorn young captives brought to Denver after the battle and placed on show in the Denver Theater. As a result of his circus connections the boy had been named Wilson Graham, and Stanley found him "a boy of extraordinary intelligence . . . [who]shows the true spirit of the savage by drawing his jack-knife on anyone who attempts to correct him."

When Hancock's mission ended Stanley stayed on in the West to report the activities of William Tecumseh Sherman's peace commission for the New York *Herald*. Later in 1867 he again visited Denver and toured the mining regions. He apparently was caught up in the fever of the day and went off to scratch in the streams for gold of his own. He returned to his hotel with his carpetbag full of shining particles. One of his pieces of treasure he showed to a bearded miner in the bar. The man rolled the nugget over in his fingers. "Pretty nice specimen of iron pyrites you got there."

Another visitor to Denver was the German-born landscape artist, Albert Bierstadt, who had created a stir in art circles by selling a painting for twenty-five thousand dollars. Editor Byers of the *News* helped him find the scenic subject for a 12-by-7-foot canvas that later went for thirty-five thousand dollars: *Storm in the Rocky Mountains—Mount Rosalie.*

[7]Quoted by Byron Farwell, *The Man Who Presumed* (New York, 1957), p. 32.

Byers told of how the artist got his picture on a pack trip south from the present town of Idaho Springs:

> . . . He came to Denver in search of a subject for a great Rocky Mountain picture, and was referred to me—probably because I had the reputation of being something of a mountain tramp. . . . It was a gloomy day in the dense forest. I was ahead, the pack animals following. . . . At a certain point the trail emerged from the timber and all the beauty, the grandeur and sublimity of the great gorge and the rugged amphitheatre and its head would open to view in an instant, like the rolling up of a curtain. . . . When I rode out into the flower-decked meadow I turned aside so as to be out of the line of vision. . . . Bierstadt emerged leisurely. His enthusiasm had been badly dampened; but when he caught the view fatigue and hunger were forgotten. His face became a picture of intense excitement. . . . He slid off his mule, glanced quickly to see where the jack was that carried his paint outfit, walked sideways to it and began fumbling at the lash-ropes, all the time keeping his eyes on the scene up the valley. "I must get a study in colors; it will only take me fifteen minutes!" He said nothing more . . . and at length the sketch was finished. "There—was I more than fifteen minutes?" I answered: "Yes—you were at work forty-five minutes, by my watch."[8]

The peak Bierstadt painted was named Mount Rosalie for his wife, but the name didn't stick. It is now Mount Evans. The 14,260-foot eminence on Denver's immediate western horizon was renamed for Byers' friend and patron, Governor John Evans. The name "Rosalie" was transferred to a lesser (13,575-foot) mountain to the southeast, and the name "Bierstadt" was given to a 14,046-foot summit to the southwest, connected with Mount Evans by a ridge above a glacial cirque which holds Lake Abyss.

Before leaving Denver, Bierstadt presented his hostess with one of his paintings of the Mohawk Valley, and for years thereafter Lib Byers was telling Denver women's clubs how the great artist had insisted she "criticize" his work and how he was her "intimate friend."

After the color sketch was made Byers and Bierstadt climbed to the top of Mount Rosalie. It was only one such ascent for the far-ranging *News* editor. He was more than just a "mountain tramp" or a guide for tourists. He was the Rockies' original alpinist, the first specimen of that hardy breed of men who toil to the summits of peaks in order, as one of them explains, "to get to the top," or, as another says, "because they're there."

In the summer of 1864, Byers set out with an ornithologist friend, Dr. Jacob W. Velie, to challenge 14,255-foot Long's Peak, the northern-

[8]William N. Byers, "Bierstadt's Visit to Colorado," *Magazine of Western History,* Jan. 1890; quoted by Harold McCracken, *Portrait of the Old West* (New York, 1952), p. 141.

most high pinnacle on the Denver sky line. Although it had stood as a guidepost for explorers and fur traders for a half century or longer, Long's had never been climbed and was popularly regarded as unscalable. Byers was the type of man who had to find out for himself. He and Dr. Velie reached Estes Park on August 17 and spent the next night high above timberline on the north side of the peak.

The following day they set out to climb what Byers incorrectly regarded as the highest mountain in the United States. The mountain turned them back. They made it to the top of the "east peak"—possibly Mount Meeker or a 13,456-foot summit later named Velie's Peak and now known as Storm Peak—and Byers told his diary the main summit was "inaccessible."

Byers gave readers of the *News* a report on the expedition in the September 22 issue:

> . . . Having failed to find a route of ascent from the northwest, we had agreed this morning [August 20] to strike for the southeastern foot and ascend the eastern peak, hoping thereby to reach the main peak, though all had failed who went that way before us. When seemingly almost to the immediate point of ascent, Mr. Nichols and the writer, who were in advance, came suddenly upon the brink of a stupendous chasm, half a mile in width and fully as much in depth, which ran plump up against the vertical face of the main Peak,—its source or head abuting square up against or into the very heart of the loftiest mountain in the United States; in its stupendous proportions and sublime grandeur, it can hardly be equalled and certainly not excelled. . . . But by halfpast 9 o'clock we were on the summit of the east peak as high as anyone has ever gone. We added our names to the five registered before, and upon a careful survey concluded that we were as far as man can go. Another point three or four hundred feet distant was even inaccessible, whilst the main or west peak still towered hundreds of feet above our heads presenting sheer precipitous sides, and a smooth rounded summit upon which it looked as though a man must be tied to remain, if ever by any miracle he could reach it. . . .

Four years later to the day another party set out from Grand Lake to the west of the mountain to try it from an unexplored direction. Byers tells the story in the *News* of September 1, 1868:

> . . . *August* 20. The party destined for the ascent of Long's Peak, consisting of Major J. W. Powell [soon to explore the Grand Canyon], W. H. Powell [a brother], L. W. Keplinger, Sam'l Garman [later a Harvard professor and assistant to the great Alexander Agassiz], Ned E. Farrell, John C. Sumner [Byers' brother-in-law] and the writer, left camp at the west side of Grand Lake, each mounted, and with one pack mule for the party. . . . Each man carried his bedding under

or behind his saddle, a pistol in his belt, and those not encumbered with instruments, took their guns. We had two barometers and two sets of thermometers.

Crossing the Grand [River] where it leaves the lake, we made one half its circuit, around the northern shore, through a dense mass of brush and fallen timber, and at a point directly opposite our camp on the eastern shore, began the ascent of the mountains. . . .

Turning away from the lake at right angles, we followed up a sharp, narrow ridge, very steep, rocky and almost impassable on account of the fallen timber. Progress was necessarily slow, and we were full three hours making the first four miles. Then we entered green timber and got along much faster. In about seven miles from the starting point we reached the limit of timber growth and wound along the crest of the sharp, rocky ridge which forms the divide between before mentioned [affluents of Grand Lake]. The route is very rough and tortuous. On either side, thousands of feet below, are chains of little lakes, dark and solitary-looking in their inaccessibility. About five miles from the timber line we camped for the night, turning down, for that purpose to the edge of the timber on our right. The barometer showed an altitude of about 11,500 feet, and the frost was quite sharp.

August 21. Our start was over much the same kind of country traversed in the afternoon yesterday; skirting around the side of a very lofty mountain; clambering over broken rocks, or climbing up or down to get around impassable ledges. In some places we pass over great snow banks, which are really the best traveling we find. At the end of a mile we came to an impassable precipice which subsequent exploration proved to extend from the summit of the mountain on the left down to the stream on our right, and thence down parallel with it. We spent the day in searching for a place to get down or around it, but without success, and were compelled to go into camp, like the night before, at the timber line. We had proved one thing, that horses and mules could go no further, and we made preparations for proceeding on foot. The animals were turned loose to feed on the short, young grass of the mountain side; the trail by which we came down being barricaded by a few loose stones and a pole or two to prevent their going back. Escape in any other direction was impossible.

August 22. We were off at 7 o'clock; each man with biscuit and bacon in his pockets for two day's rations. One or two carried blankets, but most preferred doing without carrying them. Arms were also left behind. After some search a place was found where we descended the precipice—not without risk—then crossed a little valley, just at the timber line, and began the ascent over the range directly over a huge mountain which had the appearance of extending quite to Long's Peak. Gaining its summit, we found ourselves still further from our destination than we supposed we were the day before. Descending its precipitous northern face—which upon looking back appeared utterly impassable—we followed for a mile along a very low ridge, which is the real dividing range—then turned eastward along a similar ridge, which

connects Long's Peak with the range. It has been generally supposed
that great mountain was a part of the range, though occupying an
acute angle in it, but such is not the case. It is not less than two miles
from the range, and all its waters flow toward the Atlantic. Following
up this ridge, it soon culminated in a very lofty mountain [Chief's
Head, visible from Denver], only a few hundred feet lower than Long's
but with a crest so narrow that some of the party became dizzy in
traveling along it. This, we supposed would lead to the great mountain,
but found the route cut off by impassable chasms.

There remained but one route—to descend to the valley and climb
again all that we had already twice made. Turning to the right, we
clambered down with infinite labor to the valley of a branch of [the]
St. Vrain, where we went into camp at the extreme timber line [in
Wild Basin]. Some explorations were made, however, preparatory to
the morrow's labor; the most important by Mr. Keplinger, who ascended
to within about eight hundred feet of the summit, and did not return
until after dark. We became very uneasy about him, fearing that he
would be unable to make his way down in safety. A man was sent
to meet him, and bonfires kindled on some high rocks near us. An
hour after they came in; Mr. K. with the report that the ascent might
be possible, but he was not very sanguine. The night was a most cheerless
one, with gusts of wind and sprinkles of rain; our only shelter under
the side of an immense boulder, where we shivered the long hours
through.

August 23. Unexpectedly the day dawned fair, and at six o'clock
we were facing the mountain. Approaching from the south our course
was over a great rockslide and then up a steep gorge down which the
broken stone had come. In many places it required the assistance of
hands as well as feet to get along, and the ascent at best was very
laborious. There was no extraordinary obstacle until within seven or
eight hundred feet of the summit. Above that point the mountain
presents the appearance, in every direction, of being a great block of
granite, perfectly smooth and unbroken. Close examination, however,
removed this delusion in some degree, and we were most agreeably
surprised to find a passable way, though it required great caution, coolness, and infinite labor to make headway; life often depending upon
a grasp of the fingers in a crevice that would hardly admit them. Before
ten o'clock the entire party stood upon the extreme summit without
accident or mishap of any kind. The Peak is a nearly level surface,
paved with irregular blocks of granite, and without vegetation of any
kind, except a little gray lichen. The outline is nearly a parallelogram
—east and west—widening a little toward the western extremity, and
five or six acres in extent. . . .

Barometric and thermometric observations were taken to determine
altitude, and a monument erected to commemorate our visit. A record
of the event with notes of the instrumental readings was deposited in
the monument, and from a flag-staff on its summit a flag was unfurled
and left floating in the breeze. . . .

Today Long's Peak is climbed each summer by thousands of mountaineers, expert and inexpert, of all ages and sexes, by a route which virtually circles the top of the mountain to reach the couloir Byers' party climbed. Long's today is a popular mountain with both tourists and natives. But in 1868 its first ascent was a mountaineering victory of classic proportions. The Swiss Matterhorn had been climbed only three years earlier.

Wallace Stegner, in his valuable analysis of John Wesley Powell's role in the winning of the West, appends a few additional details on the climb. It was the frontiersman, John Sumner, who got dizzy on the ridge, Stegner discovered, while the tenderfeet of Powell's scientific party clambered merrily on and up. Sumner at one point sat down, spat into space, and declared: "By God, I haven't lost any mountain." He was persuaded to go on, but he "got down and cooned it."

Sober-sided Sam Garman, a Quaker, wrote back to his girl friend in Bloomington, Indiana:

> After a pretty hard climb we did it, built a monument on the top, raised a flag, threw some wine on the monument & the little that remained in the bottle was drank by 5 of the party. 2 of us withstanding all entreaties did not drink on Long's peak, whatever the papers may say to the contrary.

Stegner comments: "Garman does not name his fellow abstainer, nor say who took the trouble (it could only have been Byers) to carry a bottle of wine through two strenuous days of scrambling over cliffs and ridges."[9]

Stegner also offers his slant on Byers as a man and personality: "Energetic, literate, sanguine, Byers was an ardent sportsman, a keen fisherman. While Durley and Allen and others of Powell's party threshed the waters of Grand River and a dozen creeks in vain, Byers caught all the fish he could carry. . . . Byers was a pioneer, an opener, a pass-crosser of a pure American breed, one for whom an untrodden peak was a rebuke and a shame to an energetic people. . . ."

The Byers-Powell victory is hailed as the first conquest of Long's, although there is some indication, almost in the realm of legend, that the Indians got there earlier. The Arapahoes told Oliver W. Toll in 1913 that one of their elders, named Gun, maintained an eagle trap atop the peak as early as 1858. Gun, they said, dug a hole up there and would lie in wait, baiting for the eagles with a stuffed coyote scented with tallow. When an eagle descended to strike the coyote old Gun

[9]Stegner, op. cit., pp. 26–29; for other accounts see also William N. Byers, "First Ascent of Long's Peak", Trail, Vol. VII, No. 5 (Oct. 1914), pp. 21ff; William Culp Darrah, Powell of the Colorado (Princeton, 1951), pp. 97–102; John L. Jerome Hart, Fourteen Thousand Feet (Denver, 1931) pp. 32–34; and Levette J. Davidson, "The Letters of William N. Byers," Denver Westerners Brand Book: 1952 (Denver, 1953), pp. 212–16.

would reach out of his hole and grab the bird by the legs. Griswold, Gun's son, said his father also had a magic herb no one else knew anything about. Applied to a captive eagle, it would cause the bird to have a fit and become helpless. Gun used the eagle feathers to make war bonnets. Byers reported his expedition found no evidence of any such trap.

The victory over Long's Peak was by no means Byers' last mountain-climbing jaunt. Throughout his life he was always ready to head for the top of the nearest hill on the slightest provocation, even though hampered by a rupture which forced him to wear a truss from young manhood. On August 14, 1901, at the age of seventy, he was suffering from rheumatism and sciatica and was drenching himself with such medicaments as Honyadi water, Bishop's citrate of magnesia, malt whiskey, and belladonna, and he had but two more years to live; but he was still able to climb up and unfurl another flag on the top of the 13,000-foot peak named for him.

Byers Peak is a noble and picturesque mountain to the southeast of Middle Park, beyond Berthoud Pass. Bierstadt painted his Mount Rosalie, and Byers Peak has been captured in oils by another notable artist, Dwight David Eisenhower. President Eisenhower painted the mountain in 1953 when he maintained his "summer White House" in Denver. The peak looks down a high green valley directly on the Fraser ranch of Denver banker Aksel Nielsen, where Ike fished for trout and took recreation from his box of colors.

As a "pass-crosser" Byers was particularly interested in the lofty gap bearing the name "Berthoud," over which President Eisenhower shuttled in 1953 on a fine paved highway and through which Bayard Taylor toiled in June 1866, fighting snow up to his horse's belly. The pass crosses the Continental Divide at an elevation of 11,316 feet, close to timberline, and it has become a favorite skiing area for thousands of winter-sports enthusiasts each season.

In the 1860s the *News* editor was morally and intellectually convinced to the very heart of his large booster instincts that Berthoud Pass offered *the* route for the transcontinental railroad. He had a mass of figures on grades and elevations to prove that—with the little matter of a three-mile tunnel under the apex of the pass—palace cars soon could roll from coast to coast through his city of Denver and also, conveniently, through his private Elysium, Middle Park.

Byers built large-sized dreams for his park, once he got control of the Utes' warm medicinal springs. An era of spas and fashionable watering places was developing, and he pictured a great tourist center rising from his ranch with its fortunate pools of steaming water. Byers was genuinely in love with the almost heartbreaking beauty of his peak-ringed mountain paradise, and he saw no reason why many others shouldn't be similarly impressed. He had scientific analyses made of the mineral content of the hot spring waters. Once the Civil War was over he joined the enormous pilgrimage of tourists to the principal battlefields and historic places, but he also took time to visit the spas of the South, closely observing how they had been built and how they were operated. He brought back volumes of literature and comparative mineral-content analyses which showed that his springs were the equal of any, and better than most, in chemical capacity to provide salubrious benison for a long list of socially acceptable illnesses. He put up a sawmill, personally surveyed and staked out the town of Hot Sulphur Springs, erected a small log hotel as a starter and a concrete bathhouse beside the pools. He was in business. Season passes for healing baths were issued to Colorado notables and fellow editors who might plug the project in their columns. For many years Byers' pocket diaries carry a meticulous accounting of "bath money" income ranging from a few cents to forty or fifty dollars a day during the "season." But Hot Sulphur Springs never developed quite the way Byers planned that it should, though he stubbornly clung to his spa—to the great exasperation of his financially acute wife—through a series of five-figure offers for the property.

So Byers was not entirely disinterested in his efforts, backed by the full editorial might of his *News*, to drag a railroad over the awesome Berthoud Pass heights. The pass was the one feasible gateway to Hot Sulphur Springs. Yet his interest was not entirely a selfish one either. His town of Denver desperately wanted and needed a railroad, and the only chance that the city could be put on the main line lay in selection of the Berthoud route.

Trail-blazing Jim Bridger had come down from Wyoming in 1861 to help E. L. Berthoud, a Golden City civil engineer, survey a stage road west from Denver for the Central Overland California & Pike's Peak Express Company (sometimes irreverently referred to by the pioneers as the Clear Out of Cash & Poor Pay). Berthoud found his pass, and a rough road was laid out extending through some four hundred miles of wilderness to Provo, Utah.

By 1862 talk of the Pacific railroad was growing. Denver raised a fund by popular subscription to try to find a way that would route the railroad through the Rockies instead of around them. Byers and F. M. Case, another engineer, were sent out in June on a preliminary reconnaissance. They probed up and along Berthoud's route and returned with a report that, while the grade was a bit steep in spots, it was a practicable proposition. Case was sent back to the mountains on July 24, the day Congress passed the Pacific railroad bill, to gather the statistics to support Denver's case.

The Union Pacific wanted to build through Denver. It was the only sizable town between Omaha and Salt Lake, and its prospects seemed good, now that war was over. Careful consideration was given to Case's report. But the logical decision was made: the transcontinental line would go over 7534-foot Bridger's Pass in Wyoming.

When General Grenville M. Dodge, chief engineer of the Union Pacific, announced the decision, Denver was plunged into gloom and despair. Within a short time Cheyenne, which would be on the main line, boomed to a city of 2000 to 3000 persons. Many Denver businesses pulled up stakes and moved north. The railroad town obviously would become the new metropolis of the Rocky Mountain West. Cheyenne's sponsors offered Byers a substantial inducement to move his paper to the future Wyoming capital. He refused, and sent a correspondent instead. The *News*, smarting under the Union Pacific's highhanded rebuke to its city, was infuriated by a taunt from a Cheyenne gazette that "Denver now is too dead to bury."

Dodge's report choosing the Bridger's Pass route recommended that a branch line be built a hundred miles south to Denver from Cheyenne, and the hint was that the Union Pacific would build it. But, watching the furore kicked up by the decision in railroad-eager Denver, the financiers decided on another course. They gauged the city's desire for a rail line, which was enormous, and weighed this against the probable financial resources of the village, which were rather more than might have been expected. Then they began shuffling their feet. It was going to be impossible, after all, for the Union Pacific to build the branch line. But if Denver could acquire and grade the line and put down the ties, perhaps they would be able to find the rails and then would co-operate by taking over the branch and running it. The maneuver was only the first of many by which railroad builders, foreign and domestic, would milk the little town of Denver, hurt in pride and prestige and now sure that everything it hoped to be was bound up in the immediate acquisition of a railroad. The coolheaded railroad financiers, free of emotional entanglements of the "our fair city" order, sat back and watched. It worked.

Denver held a couple of mass meetings in the fall of 1867 and subscribed five hundred thousand dollars for the grading, bridging, and tie laying. Byers' friend, Governor John Evans, was the prime mover, and the *News* editor was dealt into the inner circle on his value as promoter and booster. Byers whooped into the build-up with characteristic vigor and civic patriotism, not seeming to notice things were so arranged that he would not participate with the others in the probable profits of future railroading. The *News* spared no adjectives in its promotion of the Denver Pacific bond issue, and the city voted it by a large majority in January 1868.

No delay was permitted to dim the bright plans for the Denver Pacific. Ties began floating down the Platte to be caught in a boom rigged across the river at the foot of F (Fifteenth) Street. The Union Pacific then discovered conveniently that it could supply forty thousand ties at a dollar each, the *News* reported with naïve jubilation on April 27, 1868.

On May 18, 1868, ground was broken. The scene was about three miles northeast of the main business section, and the town turned out. "This auspicious event, the most important in its bearings on the future of Colorado of any that ever transpired in her history, took place today with appropriate ceremonies," the *News* heralded that afternoon.

At 11:15 A.M. the Denver Band struck up "The St. Louis Quickstep" and two teams began plowing a pair of furrows. Lyman Cole and Thomas G. Anderson achieved local immortality by handling the reins of the teams. In a gesture to the fair sex, Miss Nettie Clark and Mrs. F. G. Stanton were permitted to tuck up their voluminous skirts ever so slightly and guide the plows for a few symbolic feet. General John Pierce, president of the Denver Pacific, proposed three cheers for the ladies, and the response, the *News* said gallantly, was deafening.

Billy Marchant opened a keg of lager beer, which soon disappeared. Then, as the band played "The Philadelphia March", John W. Smith, first president of the new Denver Board of Trade, threw precisely nine shovelfuls of earth on the grade. Former Governor Gilpin climbed up in a wagon and delivered himself of "one of his remarkable speeches", Byers says in his history of Colorado. General Pierce also spoke, and the band closed the proceedings with a lively reading of "The Railroad Gallop", which everyone thought was *so* appropriate. By nightfall a mile of the grading had been finished.

The *News* was sure this would be a model railroad in every respect. "A map of the grade line can hardly be distinguished from the ground line, there is so little variation. It is said to be better than the route from St. Petersburg to Moscow, so famous for its natural grade line."

Work went merrily along, and the Union Pacific concluded it had gravely underestimated the down which could be plucked from the goose. Suddenly, in July 1869, it developed that the UP would be unable to iron the road or supply the rolling stock it had promised. Perhaps Denver could help out again? A great new era was being fashioned, and Denver certainly wouldn't want to be shut out of its rightful place in the sun. No, indeed, Denver agreed, and dug down for another million dollars in bonds.

Denver might have kept its shirt on. There was traffic to be had in the Colorado capital and its tributary mining regions, and the railroads wanted it. The Kansas Pacific, cousin germane of the big main line, was building rapidly across the Kansas plains, headed straight for Denver, although it feinted toward Golden City and the Arkansas Valley in an effort to tap the community support the UP had found so generous. The Kansas Pacific tried to get two million dollars out of Denver, but the effort failed. The KP was too closely linked with the railroad manipulators up in Golden, which at this time also fancied itself as a rail center.

Denver had just won the territorial capital back from Golden in 1867, and it did not propose to give the rival foothills city anything but the back of its hand.

The Union Pacific's Irish terriers met the Central Pacific's imported Chinese tracklayers at Promontory Point in Utah, and on May 10, 1869, the gold spike supplied by Leland Stanford was tapped down to complete the first coast-to-coast rail network. A race meanwhile had developed between the Denver and Kansas Pacific lines to see who could get the first rail into Denver. Prodigious feats of track construction were chalked up, a mile and more in a day, under conditions scarcely conducive to undistracted labors.

On May 14, 1870, the News reported, Indians in small bands of five to ten braves struck simultaneously at ten different points along the Kansas Pacific near Kit Carson, killed eleven graders, wounded nineteen, and herded four hundred head of stock ahead of them when they rode off. General Custer was dispatched from Fort Wallace to chase them. Cavalry and infantry were detailed to patrol the construction area.

Up in Nebraska an Indian tried to rope a Union Pacific locomotive, passing at forty miles an hour. The brave made the mistake of tying one end of his lariat around his waist. He managed to get a loop over the smokestack. "All that was left to bury was a small piece of copper-colored flesh tied to the rope."[10]

On the Kansas Pacific, now just east of Denver, it was found necessary to carry a dog on each engine and send him ahead to drive the "wild Texas cattle" off the track.[11] The longhorns were moving north; the age of the cowboy and the open range was starting.

The Denver Pacific won the race. On June 17, 1870, the construction locomotive was "in plain sight . . . from the roof of the News Block." A last-minute shortage of track developed, but the News said on June 20: "Tomorrow brings it into the city if the iron holds out. Then three times three and a Tiger!" On the twenty-second, the first locomotive, garlanded with streamers and flags, entered the town. It was named the General D. H. Moffat, Jr., for the man who had been Byers' companion on the day of the shooting in Omaha. Moffat had followed Byers out to Denver, began business as a stationer and bookseller, and went on to great wealth in mining, real estate, banking, and railroad building.

June 24 was appointed as a day of ceremony and celebration. The miners up in the "Silver Queen" city of Georgetown sent word they would supply a silver spike to complete the railroad.

The News of that date required four front-page columns to do the great event justice. There was a mounted parade through town by the

[10]Rocky Mountain News, Nov. 8, 1870.

[11]Ibid., June 7, 1870.

Masons. Episcopal Bishop George W. Randall laid the cornerstone for a depot. After the orations Governor Evans descended from the pilot of the *D. H. Moffat, Jr.*, and drove the last spike. A last-moment substitution had been necessary.

Billy Barton, proprietor of the Barton House in Georgetown, had brought the silver spike down to Denver but the night before had been overwhelmed by the spirit of the occasion. He got drunk, pawned the spike, and still was sleeping it off when the ceremony was under way at noon. When he failed to show up Sam E. Browne, territorial attorney general, picked up an iron spike, wrapped a piece of white paper around it, and handed it to Evans: "Here's the silver spike from Georgetown, with the compliments of the people of Clear Creek County." The happy crowd apparently didn't notice the sleight of hand, or didn't care. Later Evans retrieved the silver spike from the pawnshop, and it now rests in the Colorado State Museum.

The Kansas Pacific, building from both east and west, completed its line on August 15 near the present town of Strasburg, thirty-eight miles east of Denver. The two construction gangs laid down ten and a quarter miles of track in nine hours. Denver now had two railroads; the cup of civic pride ran over at the brim.

With everything up to date in Denver, the *News* could afford a little nostalgia. On the night of August 18 a stagecoach swayed into town behind two spans of mules, Steve Harmon at the reins. It was the last of the overland stages from the East, and the *News* sang its swan song next day:

> . . . We wish to bear witness to the amount of capital required, and the pluck, energy and enterprise displayed in the running and management of these lines of travel which the railroads now unceremoniously shove off the theater of the present into the dead past. For eleven years these coaches have been running with a regularity unparalleled. They were our only means of public transportation.
>
> While we yield full praise to the companies, there is another group of men to whom greater credit is due, still higher respect for services performed: the stagecoach employees who took the risks of heat, cold and Indians—road agents who, by the power of their endurance, made the overland stages a success.
>
> As the traveler glides over the iron rails in the luxurious palace cars he sees where many a brave fellow met his fate from the bullet or arrow of a foe and fell true to duty with a death-grip on his reins. It was he who braved and dared so much on the lonely plains of Kansas and Colorado in pioneering the way for the trains in which we now ride.
>
> Their occupation is gone. The bright stages will soon be dusty, the shining harness rusty, the handsome, prancing four-in-hands descended to the position of farmhorses or drafthorses. The overland boys will be scattered. . . .

. . . An all-Pullman palace-car excursion train will leave St. Louis for Denver on Aug. 30. . . . On and after Sept. 1 trains of the Kansas Pacific will arrive in Denver at 5:00 o'clock in the morning and depart at 9:00 o'clock at night. . . .

Denver now began to grow as never before. It had a population of 4759 in 1870 as the railroads were putting down their last spikes. By 1880 the census stood at 35,629. In its first full month of operation the Denver Pacific brought 1067 passengers to Denver and carried thirteen million pounds of freight.

The Colorado Central Railroad was built down Clear Creek from Golden, and William Jackson Palmer, one of the promoters of the Kansas Pacific, started south with his narrow-gauge Denver & Rio Grande Railroad. Soon Governor Evans would begin sending his Denver, South Park & Pacific up, over, and through the mountains. Byers was fascinated by the light but serviceable narrow-gauge equipment, and he judged it exactly the thing for the mountain country he knew so well. In the *News* for February 5, 1871, he said: "We believe that the Union Pacific, Kansas Pacific and all their tributary lines would be better roads for the country and for their owners if they were narrow gauge 30 inches instead of 56½ inches. They can be built for one-half cost and handle all traffic developed. The D&RG is right in adopting the narrow gauge exclusively for their projected lines." (The gauge actually was thirty-six rather than thirty inches.) In the next couple of decades a score of short-lived railroad companies would drape the little iron around the Colorado peaks. Today a single short stretch of the yard-wide track remains in operation: excursion trains of the miniature cars run each summer between Durango and Silverton in the extreme southwestern corner of the state to carry tourists and a steady stream of rail fans on devout pilgrimage to the scenes of little engines and big men.

It took Denver citizens a while to find out what time it was in the railroad era. The Denver Pacific ran its trains on a schedule thirty-five minutes faster than Denver time. The KP ran fifty-five minutes ahead. On February 16, 1871, the *News* confessed it was confused:

> Jewelers in this city have decided to adopt a system of time that will approach uniformity. They will get Chicago Meridian Time each day by telegraph and regulate their time pieces accordingly. As it is now, every man has his own time and will swear by it. Each watchmaker has his own time and each of the three railroads has its own time. It is enough to puzzle and perplex a saint. Chicago time will be a little fast, but we will get used to it. . . .

The railroad brought Susan B. Anthony for a call and a stirring address to an overflow audience which was "mostly women," the *News* said on June 24, 1871, though "there were a few brutes in attendance."

The reporter wrote that the petticoat crusader confidently predicted "wars would practically be eliminated as soon as women could vote."

But despite time confusion and fluttering suffragettes, Denver was making rapid progress. A gas works was built, and Denver was illuminated for the first time on the night of January 21, 1871. By April of the same year water mains were being laid and fire hydrants installed. Work had begun in December 1870 on a two-mile street railway system of horsecars, though the cars didn't begin running until a year later. The *News* was agitating on April 20, 1871, for street signs and a uniform system of house numbering. City Council voted not to levy a city tax for 1871 but still was able to grade the town's first boulevard, a hundred-foot roadway west from the Platte and up onto the bluff where Highland perched. The *News* of May 23, 1871, was ecstatic over the view Boulevard F afforded of both mountains and city. "It is estimated that 300 carriages passed over it last Sunday."

The luxury and leisure of the new era also produced a boom in sports. The Kansas Pacific brought the Kit Carson baseball team to town on April 26, 1871, to play the Denver "McCooks" (named for territorial Governor Edward McCook). Denver won 66 to 31, and the *News* sports writer said "the Kit Carson boys threw in the sponge in the ninth inning when Denver had completed 12 runs with no outs." The Central City team was unimpressed. It sent down a challenge backed by a five-hundred-dollar wager.

Along with the city, the *News* was expanding. With completion of the Denver Pacific and accompanying improvement in telegraphic services, the paper found it convenient to switch to morning publication on July 2, 1870. The issue of December 20, 1870, announces expansion to a nine-column format. New equipment and new type were put into the plant.

Yet in spite of all the progress toward a future which looked bright with promise, John Dailey decided to pull out. Possibly he was tired of doing most of the day-to-day work while Byers took the bows and glory, chased off to climb mountains, and dabbled in a dozen enterprises which had nothing to do with meeting daily deadlines and weekly payrolls. At any rate Dailey sold his half interest to his partner. The bill of sale, preserved among the Dailey papers in the Denver Public Library, indicates he took for his half of the *News* the sum of six hundred dollars plus "one bay horse called 'Prince' and one California saddle." The date is October 31, 1870.

Even if Prince were a thoroughbred and the saddle silver-mounted, the low valuation placed on the paper would be hard to understand. Possibly Byers had paid Dailey other sums earlier. Quite probably the presses and other fixtures were heavily encumbered with debt. No mention is made of Dailey having an interest in the News Block as a property, and perhaps Byers had built it with his own funds separately from the partnership. Whatever the explanation, Dailey retired from the *News* with precious little to show for eleven years of faithful service and hard work.

John Dailey was a quiet, unostentatious man, not given much to talking unless spoken to. He was as content to remain in the background as Byers was determined to cut a swath. His name appeared at the head of no civic committees, he is listed on no boards of directors, and he mingled silently if at all with bankers, railroad builders, governors, and financiers. Perhaps he didn't have time for such things; every indication is that Byers kept him busy running the business and supervising the printing plant.

Dailey had built up an operation which, in addition to handling daily and weekly newspapers, could do five-color printing in Indian country in the 1860s. When he left the *News* he stayed with his printing trade. In partnership with Nathan Baker, who had returned to Denver after founding three Wyoming newspapers, and a man named Smart,[12] he operated the job-printing firm of Dailey, Baker & Smart from 1871 to 1873. The firm became Dailey & Smart in 1873 and finally went broke. For a short time in 1872, Dailey and Baker were part owners of the Denver *Daily Times*, having purchased the interest of Andrew J. Boyer for five hundred dollars. At one point or another in the early seventies, four Denver newspapers issued from the Dailey printing office, among them the *Lorgnette*, a theatrical sheet which became the *Daily City Item* and then the *Times*, and the *Colorado Courier*, a semiweekly in German. When Dailey left the *News*, S. T. Sopris took over as Byers' business manager before becoming a partner in the publication of the *Item* and its successor, the *Times*. After Dailey & Smart went on the rocks in 1875—the firm's assets going to Frederick J. Stanton, he of the *Gazette* and the hickory cane—Dailey became briefly the business manager of the Denver *Tribune* beginning in March of that year.

The birth rate of Denver newspapers was high in the glad new age of the Iron Horse, and the death rate was not much lower. Daily and weekly papers and the dates of their appearance were: *Daily Colorado Tribune*, 1867; weekly *Colorado Tribune*, 1867; Goldrick's *Rocky Mountain Herald*, 1868; *Colorado Democrat*, 1868; *Daily Denver Times*, 1868; *Lorgnette*, 1870; *Tribune*, 1871; weekly *Tribune*, 1871; *Daily City Item*, 1871; Denver *Daily Times* (a different outfit entirely from the *Daily Denver Times*), 1872; weekly *Times*, 1873; *Colorado Journal*, 1872; *Western Miner and Engineer*, 1872; weekly *Coloradian*, 1872; *Rocky Mountain Leader*, 1872; *Colorado Real Estate and Mining Review*, 1873; *Colorado Courier*, 1873; Denver *Mirror*; 1873; *Daily Programme*, 1873; *Colorado Agriculturist and Stock Journal*, 1873; *Commercial Advertiser*, 1873; *Colorado Farmer*, 1873; Denver *Com-*

[12]Probably Charles Willard Smart; see *Colorado Magazine*, Vol. XVI, No. 4 (July 1939), p. 158.

mercial, 1873; Denver *Daily World*, 1873; Denver *Mining Journal*, 1874; *Journal of Commerce*, 1874; daily *Colorado Democrat*, 1874; *Daily Colorado Transcript*, 1875; *Daily Colorado Sentinel*, 1875; weekly *Colorado Sentinel*, 1875; biweekly *Colorado Mining Review*, 1875; *Daily Democrat*, 1876.[13]

Out of all this flurry of energetic publishing, only the *Rocky Mountain News* and Goldrick's weekly *Herald* have survived. During one press-busy period eight daily newspapers were hopefully being printed for the edification of a city under 30,000 in population. Among them, only the *Times*, the *Tribune*, and the *Democrat*—which metamorphosed rather startlingly into the *Republican* in June 1879—showed any staying power, and all of them were eventually purchased by the *News*.

By the winter of 1875–76 the Denver press was in a frenzy reporting preparations for Colorado's statehood. William H. Vischer, late of the Louisville, Kentucky, *Journal*, was city editor of the *News*. One of his reporters was Tom Cannon, the veritable personification of the old-time boomer journalist. Cannon had come West a couple of years earlier as correspondent for the St. Louis *Globe-Democrat* and had helped found the Lake City *Silver World* in June 1875 down in Alfred Packer's Hinsdale County. He moved on up to Denver in the winter and signed on with the *News*.

Cannon covered the constitutional convention which met from December into March of 1876, and when the convention's efforts were overwhelmingly approved by the voters in a July 1 election, Colorado went wild with pride and joy over becoming the thirty-third state. Bonfires were built at street corners in Denver and everyone got howling drunk. A party of enthusiasts set out on July 3 for the top of Pike's Peak with nearly a ton of fireworks, and Tom Cannon went along to give the *News* a firsthand account of the pyrotechnics. It was planned to set off the display at midnight, as the centennial of American independence arrived, but just as it grew dark a rain began to fall on the peak. The rain turned to sleet and then to snow. Cannon wrote later:

> We were obliged to walk around in circles to keep from freezing. After two hours of torture we abandoned the program and heaped the fireworks on the summit of the peak. We laid a train of powder and lighted it with matches. Then we fled down the mountain. There was a rush and a roar and a blinding sheet of flame. All our fireworks had gone off at once. But the people of the plains saw nothing of the display.
> We groped our way down to where the pack train had camped and spent a most uncomfortable night. Next morning we returned to Colorado Springs, most of us lamenting that we had not voted against the constitution. My newspaper story was highly decorated, but not with flags.[14]

[13]McMurtrie and Allen, op. cit., pp. 250–66.

[14]Gary, Indiana, *Post-Tribune*, Dec. 2, 1956.

Cannon remained on the *News* staff until November 1879 and was on the scene at Cañon City for the bloodless "Royal Gorge War" in which the Rio Grande and Santa Fe railroads contended with mercenaries and armed survey crews for the route to booming Leadville up through the Royal Gorge of the Arkansas, a defile so narrow and tortuous that it could carry only one set of tracks. The Rio Grande finally won the "war" in the courts after Cannon had departed for other less robust climes. He worked on papers in Kansas City, Arkansas, and Texas, returned to the *News* in 1887–88, went on to Chicago, and finally, in 1909, became editor of the Gary, Indiana, *Evening Post*. His reminiscences appeared serially in the Gary *Post-Tribune* August 19, 1956, to September 1, 1957, following his death in 1936. Cannon remembered Denver journalism during one of its liveliest and most competitive eras.

As the competition grew keener in the early seventies Byers, alone now that Dailey had left, put more money from some of his ancillary enterprises into the *News*. He installed a new steam press, a Taylor pattern, single-cylinder model, into the basement pressroom of the News Block to turn out the daily and weekly paper and for poster work. He put up a three-story and basement addition, 65 by 22 feet, at the rear of the block. When the addition was complete on November 1, 1873, he had going, in addition to the Taylor, several Hoe presses capable of printing a sheet 19 by 24 inches at a rate of 2700 impressions an hour. There were also job presses—Gordon jobbers.

Busy as he was with printing and publishing, Byers as usual was neck deep in other activities. As Colorado agent for the National Land Company, he had gone to New York to help get the Union Colony organized and then had sold it the present site of the abstemious city of Greeley. (Meeker's Unionists meant it when they said they wanted their town dry; the *News* reported on October 2, 1870, that a "committee" had burned down on the night of October 22 the first saloon which attempted to open its doors. Ralph Meeker, Nathan's son, was charged with rioting and a Mr. Norcross with arson, but *that* didn't get far in the arid climate.)

The colonization business was good. Once Byers had Greeley well established he journeyed to Chicago and sold fifty-five thousand acres to another group of men who moved west in March 1871 and founded the town of Longmont. The dynamic Byers thus was involved, directly or indirectly, in the establishment of at least five Colorado towns: Denver, Greeley, Longmont, Meeker, and Hot Sulphur Springs. And it was he who gave Central City its name.

A Board of Trade was organized as Denver sought to arrange financing for the Denver Pacific, and this became in 1884 the Denver Chamber of Commerce—with Byers as its president for 1900, his last public post. In 1871 the Board of Trade was busy organizing and promoting the many new businesses which had come to town on the railroad. But it was decided that even more commercial ventures should be encouraged to make the trip, along with more settlers to buy their wares. A Board of Immigration was set up, and William N. Byers became its head. His correspondence with interested persons in the States was heavy, but one letter in particular cast a long shadow across his life.

It came from a Mrs. Hattie E. Sancomb of Lawrence, Kansas. Mrs. Sancomb was a milliner. She inquired respectfully about opportunities for her trade in the territory of Colorado. Byers made her the standard reply: excellent opportunities, the sky's the limit, watch Denver grow, everything's modern, and the horsecars will be in operation very soon. Come on out.

Mrs. Sancomb took the advice, stopped briefly in Denver to thank Mr. Byers for his many courtesies, then established residence in a little house at Golden City. She immediately acquired, it was alleged, a number of very loyal male friends. But the good-looking, nobly bearded Byers had caught her eye. She wrote him a note or two intimating that their brief acquaintance was too beautiful a thing not to last. Byers said later that her professions of desire for a closer friendship were "ardent." He had just entered the roaring forties of his life, an age when men sometimes make a last rebellion against time and yearn nostalgically for young goathood. Lib Byers had developed into something of a shrew and a scold, purse-mouthed, pretentiously pious, busy as a hen with her "club work." Moreover she was away much of the time on grand tours with social-climbing overtones to Cape Cod, Florida, Pasadena, and Europe. Byers was at minimum vulnerable; he wrote to Golden City that it would indeed be charming to have so handsome a young lady as a close friend.

The friendship ripened through 1872 and 1873, and then, on April 5, 1876, it burst into passionate flower. Hattie, it developed, had brought along from Lawrence not only her millinery needles but also a pearl-handled pistol. She hadn't learned to use it very well.

She shot once at close range and missed. She tried to shoot again, at even closer range, and was so weak from anger and nervous tension that she couldn't pull the trigger.

The whole affair took place in the street not over a block from Byers' home. Mrs. Byers was watching the encounter from behind the lace curtains of her parlor window. She got into her buggy, drove down, and rescued her errant husband.

A messenger was sent for Officer Sanders, who slapped Hattie in jail to reflect on the impropriety of shooting at a leading citizen.

The scandal had nothing but the highest-quality ingredients. A pioneer and civic dignitary, strictly top of the heap, respected, envied by many, probably maliciously and privately disliked by some for his prominence and many honors. A beautiful young woman, a divorcee (practically scandalous in itself), and the rumors were that she was "pretty fast." And then, on the other side, the wronged wife: pillar of the Methodist

Church, gentle, charming, a lady bountiful to the poor, leading club-woman, and . . . well, how could he! Poor, *poor* Libbie. Female friends beat a path to her side with covered dishes and comfort.

And to top it all the whole disgraceful affair had been acted out right there in the street, practically at Libbie's doorstep. Imagine!

Fellow editors in Denver, who constituted a rather considerable platoon at the time, forgot any lumps the *News* might have given them in the past and tried to suppress the story. It didn't work, of course. The whole town buzzed deliciously, and the story got better with each retelling. In one version Lib Byers had stood her ground and traded shots with the hussy home wrecker. It is just possible that some of Byers' male friends eyed him with new interest and revised estimates; he always had seemed *so* proper, fussy even.

Then, on April 15, George West—Byers' onetime employee and erst-while friend—blew the lid off in his Golden *Transcript*. (West had also become a close friend of the lovely but erratic milliner.) The Golden *Globe* followed the *Transcript's* lead, and both began publishing Byers' letters to Hattie, as foolish as love letters nearly always are out of context. There had been a mutual return of correspondence during a split-up in 1874, but Hattie had prudently retained copies for her files. The *Globe* didn't rush into the scandal rashly. Word was sent to Byers that five hundred dollars, in cash, might cause the paper to pass over its journalistic responsibilities and forget about the scoop. Byers didn't reply.

Hattie had promised him the attack for more than a year. He had seen it coming, though probably he clung to hope right up to the moment the pearl-handled pistol cracked. Afterward he must have sagged some under the lash of his conscience and the weight of his dishonor; but then he took a deep breath, squared his shoulders, and opened his purse to pay the piper.

The *News* on April 1, was the first Denver paper to comment on its editor's descent into sin. Byers at no point denied his culpability; he only wanted to make it clear that if he had submitted to blackmail—five thousand dollars was the sum mentioned—he might have avoided be-coming the public target of a young lady whose act of injured innocence was, after all, a trifle overdone. He could also have escaped trouble by acceding to her demands that he abandon home and family for her love nest, and, besides, he wasn't at all sure her heart was really broken. If it were true, she had been generous with the pitiful fragments to several other men whose names could be supplied if occasion warranted.

The *News* said it had become necessary to make the matter public in order to clear up the "distorted and false" statements of the Golden *Transcript*. Mrs. Sancomb, divorced in Lawrence on a charge of adultery with one Colonel Burns, had "for nearly a year past kept up a series of attacks and a round of persecution upon Mr. Byers. . . . The causes were of her own seeking, and the various alleged provocations entirely pretended."

On the fifth instant she had sought to gain entrance to Byers' office and failed. She waited in the streets, and when he took the horsecar at 12:20 P.M. to go home for lunch she ran alongside and tried several times to jump on. The driver finally slowed the car, Hattie climbed aboard and flounced herself down on Byers' lap. "I pushed her one side to a seat." They got off together near his home, still arguing. At last she drew the pistol from her handbag. Byers pinioned her arms. Mrs. Byers saw the struggle from her window and flew to the corner in her buggy. Byers released his embrace and jumped in. As he did Hattie shot. The bullet passed behind the seat and nearly struck a child playing down the block. In her excitement Libbie Byers dropped the reins. The confused horse made a U-turn in the roadway and returned to give Hattie a second chance. But she couldn't pull the trigger.

She did, however, follow the buggy home. Frank Byers, the editor's son, armed himself and met her at the gate. Hattie waved her pistol under his nose but finally left. Officer Sanders picked her up three blocks away.

On April 16 the *News* devoted more than two columns of space to a select anthology of Hattie's threatening letters with the preface: "On reviewing the ground, the incidents and her many letters, it becomes very evident that Mrs. H. E. Sancomb became satisfied, about a year ago, that her game was safely trapped, and that she might proceed with her 'bear-baiting' in her own way, and at her own time, doubtless expecting the offer of a large amount of 'hush money.' . . ."

Hattie had written on June 3, 1875: "I have dedicated the rest of my life to your misery. . . . You are only dear to me as an object of revenge. . . . Send me a letter, I say, or I will one day pierce *her* heart with a dozen bullets. . . . Oh infernal villain, if I had you here I'd plant my fingers in your eyes and tear them from their sockets. . . ."

Another note complained: "During all these letters you have not so much as said you even cared the least for me. There has been no word of love and but few of sympathy. Then I *know* you hate me. . . . You have angered me through all our relations. You have paid me little attention, though knowing well that you were toying with a sensitive heart. . . ."

On July 3, 1875: ". . . You can do nothing now to save you or your family. . . . Ah, my friend, such letters as the one this morning will not do for me. A letter with kisses quiets me in a measure. Without them all is lost but my thirst for revenge. . . ."

On Jan. 15, 1876: ". . . I will take you on the street—anywhere. All I ask is a glimpse of you, and my bullet will be aimed. . . ."

Another January letter said: ". . . You had ought not to make confession of anything to anyone. You have done no wrong. We have done nothing wrong. As I remember it now, I do not regard it as such a terrible affair. I have but made a hero of you, though I have yet to make a heroine of myself. . . . I fancy your gentlemen friends will envy you. . . . Yes, your own life will satisfy me after I have given *her* the heartache. . . . You show a wonderful love for wife and children by offering to give up your own life to save theirs. Such a love as you never had for me. . . . I asked you which you would rather lose your wife or myself, and you were brave enough and honest enough to make answer that you would rather lose me. . . ."

In March, Byers had received from one of Hattie's more current admirers a note which informed him the distraught milliner had prepared "an auto-biography of Colorado experience, containing a minute account of the 'ills of life that flesh is heir to' . . . embellished with engravings of the principal characters, and the voluminous correspondence on both sides *verbatim*. . . ." Publication of the opus, it was suggested, might be suppressed by prompt action.

Byers made no effort in that direction, and events progressed to the sunny noonday of April 5.

Once the story was out Denver shook its head sadly over the weakness of mortal men, including civic dignitaries, but in general stood with Byers. The eloquent Professor Goldrick, in particular, loosed his vocabulary in scolding but defending his friend. The *Herald* was of the opinion that the sensational versions of the affair only showed the *"animus* of the *expose* against the editor and owner of the *News,* as an available piece of property for plucking, on the plea of 'injured innocence,' chaste-ned 'heart-aches,' virgin virtues, tender throbbings, Kansas blue-grass, spring-chickens, and 'sich.'" Goldrick continued:

> Understand us now definitely. We don't palliate the defendant, or defend the plaintiff, in this much mixed and melancholy case. We consider that Mr. Byers was a big fool to allow himself to become attached, intrigued or inveigled into any such entangling alliances with any divorced woman, when he knew that *she* knew he wasn't a single man, but was, on the contrary, "just the oyster" for baiting or beating into blackmail or blacker misfortune. Nor do we desire to impugn or question the privilege of any editor to pile it on, for glory or gain, against Mr. Byers, if they so elect, on the plea of espousing the woman's side, for "popularity's" sake. "Free trade and sailors' rights" is the right motto in matters of news, notions and ideas. Ours is the independent one, as we here give it, under all the circumstances of the scandalous case. And it is this: That the whole thing was a well laid plan, to play the Laura Fair, and "rule or ruin" one of the most prominent pioneer citizens of Colorado—whose services have been worth more to this Territory than a thousand little milliners, fresh from the courts of

"Bleeding Kansas." Aye, and a damaged article at that (as per Lawrence letter below,)

—"Whose tongue
Outvenoms all the worms of Nile"

(as per scores of her chaste "cusses" in letters below.)

. . . Then, we say treat them as they deserve. Fight the devils with fire. Prevent the killing of a good, useful man, even though it chagrined and showed up the schemes of every dangerous damsel or dame in Denver and Golden combined. "Them's our sentiments" on the subject, and we'll stick to them, for a friend who is otherwise worthy, while there's a toe to our boot or a type in our office. . . .[15]

The Lawrence letter Goldrick refers to was a communication from the town marshal of that city containing the information that Hattie's reputation there was not entirely a chaste one, that in fact she had been taken in adultery with the dashing Colonel Burns of Fort Leavenworth. The *Herald* also made up a bouquet of Hattie's letters to Byers. A couple of samples:

. . . Answer my question, or damn your soul I'll cut you into inch pieces. . . . Now your suffering has commenced. I want to see you, to rip your heart out. O, God have mercy. This is terrible. Am I in hell? Where am I? . . .

. . . You've made me hate you again with all the deadly hatred a woman can have for a man, and you have always lied like hell to me, expecting to "put me off." . . . Damn again and G–d damn you. I will kill you. . . . If you go to the Boulder parade I'll be likely to meet you at the Junction, and wouldn't it be fun to put a few bullets, four, just four, through your heart. When and where I can have the pleasure of killing you cold and lifeless in your regalia. For pleasure it will be to me G–d damn you, damn you, damn you, damn you. . . .

When Hattie appeared in court to answer for her gunplay one of the reporters offered a tone poem to her charms. She sat demurely in the harsh glare of the courtroom "with eyes of coal gray tint, regular features, dazzling teeth, penciled eyebrows, small poised head and wavy auburn hair. Her voice was soft and her manner caressing." The case was permitted to die on the docket without decision. No one seems to have recorded what later became of the gray-eyed milliner.

All of this in April, and the Republican party had summoned its stalwarts to assemble on June 14 to nominate candidates for the first offices of the newly created state of Colorado. Byers had been mentioned prominently as the ideal and logical candidate for governor.

[15]*Rocky Mountain Herald,* Apr. 15, 1876.

Congress on February 25, 1875, had passed an enabling act for the admission of the thirty-eighth state. A constitution had been drawn and approved. The goal for which Byers and his *News* had campaigned ceaselessly for so long now was reached.

The Republicans held their convention but, discreetly, there was no presentation of Byers' name. When Colorado voters trooped happily to the poles on October 3, 1876, first-class citizens of the United States at last, they elected a Republican, John L. Routt, to be the state's first governor.

CHAPTER THIRTEEN

Byers Bows Out

S O OPEN and lush a scandal as the case of the popular milliner might have wrecked the life of a lesser man. The fall was from the heights, and the descent abrupt. William N. Byers paid bitterly for his sinning, but he faced up to it in as public a penance as might have been contrived by the most saber-toothed moralist. And he lived it down. Probably he never carried his head quite so high again on the bustling streets of growing Denver, but he was undefeated. At the end he had won back the respect of the town which he, more than any other single man, created.

Byers had been one of the founders of the Republican party in Colorado. His career as a political power ceased with finality. He never permitted his name to be mentioned again for high public office, and he did not seek to resume his place in the inner circles of his party. It is apparent that he felt his shame closed the book firmly on that chapter of his life. Although he still moved in the select group of men who controlled Colorado politics, there is no indication that he made any effort to make his voice heard except through the impersonal columns of his *News*. And that chapter of his life soon was to end too.

There is some evidence that the scandal brought Byers business reverses, principally in his many side-line enterprises, though at a distance of many years it is difficult to say whether these came because he had been placed in Coventry or arose out of his own largehearted, soft-headed way with the business world. When he was flush Byers was always good for a touch, a grubstake, a contribution. He would go any friend's bond, Lib Byers complained. He invested enthusiastically in many schemes only to discover later that they were retroactively assessable. He was never out of debt, and nineteenth-century interest rates were merciless.

The daily record of receipts and expenditures in his pocket diaries is fascinatingly meticulous. Entries carefully note a nickel given to a beggar boy, a dollar-and-a-half hat for an Indian friend, twenty-five cents in the collection plate at church, ten cents spent for grapes or forty cents for beer. But they give only a confused picture of Byers' volatile business affairs. He is maintaining an account with Brooks Brothers on Broadway in New York and at the same time paying a fee in bankruptcy. He loans four hundred dollars to a friend, and pays nine hundred dollars interest on an overdue note. He juggles one note against another, and meantime is investing in half a dozen mining, real estate, commercial, and railroad ventures. Through all the ups and downs, however, tidy sums of money passed through his hands, sums which loom larger when considered in relation to the scarce dollar of his place and time. At the close of his diary for 1866 he entered a record of how things went in 1864, a year of Indian war, isolation, and depressed conditions in Denver. He shows income of $33,933.59 and expenses of $24,116.98, for a "nett" of $9,876.61. It is not indicated whether this is a personal accounting or includes the operations of the *News*, for which no early financial records exist. On an adjoining page in the 1866 journal there is an account for 1865 which shows income of $4932.52, with no entries of receipts from the *News*, and expenditures of $13,898.87.

Running deep in the red or riding high as a man of means, Byers by 1876 had brought his territory of Jefferson to statehood, his town up from border ruffianism, and his little newspaper to a position of respect and dominance. Gold and silver mines were pouring wealth through Denver's funnel. Each train arriving on the new tracks brought more settlers, and the tourists and sight-seers were beginning to arrive in the golden stream which ever since has been a major renewable resource to the Mile-High City. The town called the *News* "Old Reliable" and studied its pronouncements on all matters foreign and domestic. The other newspapers lambasted the *News* with an intensity and consistency which attest to its position of strength, or they deferred to it as to an unchallengeable leader. It must have seemed to Byers that all his labors were being crowned, all his bright visions for the new land fulfilled. Then Hattie Sancomb made the trip in from Golden with her pistol.

The advertising columns of the *News* through 1876 and 1877 indicate no substantial loss of patronage, but it is possible the blow was felt in the job department, and commercial printing often has been the margin of solvency for a small-city newspaper. In May 1876, Byers was forced to borrow twelve thousand dollars on the News Block site and building and his ranch up the river. The newspaper was reorganized as the Rocky Mountain News Printing Company later that year. Initially Byers held all the stock in the firm, but gradually he took in other investors. An enterprise which had always been a highly personal one moved toward corporate anonymity, and Byers must have suffered further loss of heart as he watched this final penalty being levied. Toward the end of the unhappy year prospects apparently improved. The scandal was simmering down and it became possible for Byers to get away from it all without giving the appearance of fleeing public scorn. He left Denver in February for a two-month vacation in Florida. He camped, loafed, fished, and shot an eight-foot ten-inch alligator. The beginnings of the citrus-fruit industry were observed with interest, and the jottings in his diary indicate he toyed with the idea of throwing it all over in Denver and making a fresh start raising oranges. But he didn't, and he came home in April. Shortly thereafter it was announced that associates in the News Printing Company now included Kemp G. Cooper, W. B. Vickers, and Byers' future son-in-law, William F. Robinson.[1]

During 1877 the News led a campaign for smallpox vaccination when an epidemic threatened the city, and it reached eastward across the continent to vent its ire on New York sweatshop operators who were oppressing the "sewing girls." Byers plunged into new business and mining ventures, began collecting native gem stones on his mountain rambles and sending them off to lapidaries for polishing. He experimented with a trout bait consisting of beef soaked in whiskey and port wine. At the end of the year his diary carries a brief note which is the only recognition he gave to his journal that he had been through the fires of scandal:

D. McC knew H. S. as Hattie Russell at Lawrence in 1868—Character bad. Lived alone—Usher, Ballene, Barkalow & Mc next knew her in Denver in 1870 as Mrs. Chichester. She took in Rube Chichester & pretended to have married him.

On May 4, 1878, the pioneer editor of the Rockies withdrew from his Rocky Mountain News. Possibly the financial condition of the company made it impossible or inadvisable for him to continue. Perhaps he was weary of carrying a public load, though he was only forty-seven. Certainly he wanted to spend more time in his beloved mountains. His plans for Hot Sulphur Springs were growing taller and wider in direct proportion to his restored spirits.

At any rate the paper announced on May 5 that there had been a meeting of the stockholders on the previous day. Byers was out. The "trustees elected to manage the company for the ensuing year" were K. G. Cooper, W. B. Vickers, W. F. Robinson, L. B. France, and Gus Alden. Cooper was chosen president, Vickers vice-president, and Robinson secretary-treasurer. Cooper was an aggressive young business-man who was moving into new prominence in the affairs of the city. France was Byers' personal attorney and real estate associate; he had seen the retiring editor through the Sancomb affair. Vickers, later one of Denver's historians, was the journalist in the firm.

In the same issue Byers sang his swan song as a newspaper publisher. He had started his career as an editor with "hat in hand," and he ended it with equal humility:

[1]Rocky Mountain News, May 16, 1877.

Good Bye

With this issue my pecuniary interest in and editorial control of The Rocky Mountain News ceases. The News Printing Company continues with but a single change in its directory, and will conduct the publication of the News, as well as all the varied branches of the business that have grown up with and around it. I apprehend there will be no material change in its course, but of its plans the new management will probably speak in its next issue. This assurance, however, I can give: that it is backed by plenty of capital to keep it at the front. Friends who have feared its failure may dismiss their alarm. Enemies who have hoped for its downfall may possess their souls in peace. It will continue as it always has been in Colorado—"a power in the land."

It is impossible after more than nineteen years of daily repeated tasks; of constant solicitude and anxiety, how best to perform a great duty to the public; of intimate association with all the newspapers that have ever risen, lived and died, or that yet live, in Colorado; of personal acquaintance with so many—it seems to me with all—of the people of the state, to lay down the editorial pen without sad and strange emotions. These years have compassed a larger part of my life than can be given to any other undertaking, and they were of what should be its best for work. Undertaken by accident, the newspaper business has had for me a strange fascination. Not educated as a journalist, I have not been confined to the straight and narrow path of the profession. My feelings have been those of personal championship for a state in which I have felt a deep personal interest; of neighborly feeling for every person who has become a citizen of the state. I know that my work has been roughly done and that I have made many mistakes. If I have seemed too earnest it was not with malice, and I crave the pardon of each and every one whom I may have unintentionally offended. Toward my brethren of the press I have none but the kindest feelings. All differences are forgotten and only pleasant recollections of them shall dwell in my memory.

Wm. N. Byers

The news of Byers' retirement was made public on Sunday. No Monday edition was being published at this time. The next issue of the paper, on Tuesday, May 7, 1878, carried the declaration of the new management:

A New Departure

In assuming entire instead of partial control of the columns and business of the News, the new managers will make no parade of their purposes beyond a few simple announcements. First, there will be no change in the politics of the paper. Secondly, we have bought the good will alone and not the quarrels of the News. We do not enter at all into the question whether the News has been right or wrong in regard to its differences, and above all we do not wish to reflect upon Mr. Byers, from whom we part company with unfeigned regret. But we do say that wrangling is an unprofitable business for a newspaper, and henceforth it will be eschewed as much as possible by us, though in making this statement we do not wish to be understood as resigning the right to repel attacks upon ourselves or on our paper. Finally, the News modestly aspires to be a paper for the whole state, and not for the north or south or for Denver alone. Our ambition is to overcome every prejudice against the paper in every portion of Colorado, and to increase its widespread popularity by a liberal, straight forward, consistent course in politics and in business. We have no friends to reward nor enemies to punish. We neither seek nor expect anything for ourselves in the way of political preferment. The News stands to-day "free and untrameled for the public good," backed by sufficient capital to make it entirely independent and ready to follow the dictates of its own conscience in regard to public affairs. We intend to print a newspaper second to none in the state of Colorado, and will try to please as many of our subscribers as possible. We will extend the utmost editorial and business courtesy to everybody, and trust that our feelings of friendly interest in all the people and towns and mining camps of the state will be reciprocated elsewhere, and that the News will always be considered the people's paper—the personal organ of every citizen who has the good of the state at heart.

Byers' brothers of the press gave him a good sendoff, and he remained for the rest of his life an emeritus member of the Denver newspaper fraternity. He continued to be active in the Colorado Press Association and was retained in the councils of the Press Club. His rival editors forgot the many bitter quarrels and the acid words that had been exchanged on matters which were as often picayune as momentous. Nearly every newspaper in the state took note of Byers' departure, all of them with words of praise. The tribute of the Denver *Tribune* was typical:

The News of Sunday morning contained the valedictory of its founder and builder, William N. Byers. Mr. Byers established the Rocky Mountain News nineteen years ago, in the very beginning of the history of Colorado. He has given to that paper the best years of his life, and the result of his work may well be to him just cause of pride and self-congratulation. The News has ever been, alike in its origin, its traditions, its associations, its characteristics and its daily work and accomplishments, a part of Colorado. Its growth has marked and reflected the growth of the great country whose advancement it has promoted. The paper has been, in a peculiar and preeminent sense, William N. Byers, and he has been in the same sense the paper. It has reflected and embodied his pluck and energy and will and faith, and has been the instrumentality for the exercise of those qualities. And who can deny that the sum of the results of their exercise has been greatly for the good of Colorado. The influence of the News in giving direction to the energies of the young, vigorous and grasping commonwealth at the foot of the Rocky Mountains, and in giving form and character to the new civilization, cannot be over-rated. And that influence none can deny was Mr. Byers. In this early and great work of direction and formation and right starting the News has no rival. And only feelings of regret will be experienced at the retirement from the active work of journalism of the man who did that work so well—a work that was necessarily, in some respects, a rough work. Our contemporary will, however, be continued by able hands. Mr. Cooper is a fine businessman, and Mr. Vickers an experienced and capable journalist.[2]

Byers retained ownership of his mortaged News Block and rented it to the printing company. Occasionally, in the years ahead, he would write accounts of his mountain rambles and experiences for the paper, but his days as a newspaperman were over.

He returned briefly during the summer and autumn of 1878 to his original trade. A survey was made for a road near 8369-foot Grand Lake, which today claims the world's highest yacht club, and then he lugged his transit and chains over Gore Pass into Egeria Park and ran lines down the Yampa River as far north as present Steamboat Springs. Early the following year he was up at the new boom town of Leadville, looking for likely mining properties in the two-mile-high silver camp. It is probable that some of his highly placed friends used their influence in Washington and, in March 1879, Byers accepted his second appointment as postmaster of Denver. He took over the post office on April 12, and held the $250-a-month position to April 14, 1883. During this period he inaugurated Denver's first carrier delivery of mail with six men.

Meantime he was branching out into real estate and other fields. He developed two subdivisions and saw them added to the city of Denver, and he held downtown property and lots in several other areas of town. Nor were his landholdings confined to Denver. At one point he was paying taxes in eleven counties of the state, still owned lots in Omaha and inherited farm land in Iowa. The real estate operations apparently provided the sizable sums which were dissipated in a variety of other undertakings.

In an era when the Colorado mines were producing many silver kings and Midases, Byers missed his lucky strike, although he was on the scene early in each new camp, was the intimate associate of many of the men who did hit, and was deep in the speculations. He made several trips to New York during the mine boom times, and he wrote home on February 27, 1880, that Eastern investors "take mines like trout take flies." Some of his virtually fruitless mining ventures included the Iron Mask, Great Mammoth Lode, and Phil Sheridan No. 2 mines and the

[2]Reprinted in the *Rocky Mountain News*, May 8, 1878.

Swan River Mining Company. He was heavily in the game in Boulder, Gilpin, Clear Creek, Pitkin, Lake, and Summit counties, and at Twin Lakes south of Leadville he at one time held extensive mining, water, and property rights in an area now receiving extensive preliminary development for the rare alloy metal molybdenum. Like the rest of the mining men of his day, Byers was after gold and silver, but he never found them.

Few of his early contemporaries took much interest in water, even though they saw the city of Denver growing and knew that the prairie sweeping up to the foot of the Rockies was thirsty land subject to vicious drouth. Byers, with some foresight, was an exception. As early as the late 1870s he was looking ahead and exploring for water rights, now more precious than most of the mines ever discovered in Colorado. In the summer of 1880 he secretly incorporated with his attorney, L. B. France, and the future silver king, H. A. W. Tabor, as the Denver Water Supply Company. He had made reconnaissance on foot and horseback to the summit of Mount Rosalie, and the company laid claim to a lake at the head of Bear Creek which Byers was convinced would meet demands "until Denver grows to 500,000 people."

Up in his Middle Park in 1883 he opened a sawmill near the town of Hot Sulphur Springs, which he had platted, and operated it at a profit for several years while the town was building. His dreams of a fashionable spa never got beyond an income of a few hundred dollars a week from fees for healing baths, but in 1899 the Byers family—which owned the hot springs property jointly—received sixty thousand dollars for the undeveloped fountains of health. Byers had wanted to hold out for more, which exasperated his business-wise wife. He was, as usual, heavily in debt, and Lib Byers wrote to her son:

. . . Frank I want to say *one* thing and I say it with all the force I am worth. You must give up your idea that your father is to have all he put in there. Such a thing is most unjust and is not to be thought of and I will *never* sign the deeds if that is to be the outcome. He is not entitled to it. He has squandered more money in the loss of *other* property than he ever put in the Springs and I—me—had our interest in that property. Has he ever thought of making that good to us? *Never.* And would anyone else give him the lions share after he had given up all claims to it through his own mismanagement. No Sir. We will do what is right and just but he shall not claim and certainly does not expect to have more than anyone else. *Yours* is much the larger part and I intend to see that you have it. . . . If he had every dollar the Springs would bring he would be signing somebody's *Bond.* He would soon bankrupt us all if we could furnish him with all the money he wanted. I want him to be comfortable *all* his days but he will not be if he has the handling of means. He has never been out of debt since

I have known him, and you *know* there has been no excuse for it. It is 45 years tomorrow since I started out on lifes long journey and *I* know what I am talking about. . . .[3]

Frank Byers lived and ranched at Hot Sulphur Springs for many years and served as a sort of resident manager for the family's Middle Park properties.

A few days later Mrs. Byers wrote Frank she was "in favor of selling the Springs for anything like their value. We can't hope to get what Father *thinks* they are *worth*. So we will not consider that at all. You know he would rather loose a property by mortgage than sell it any time."

As Denver shot up from a frontier settlement to a modern small city through the seventies and eighties street railways became a necessity and a profitable business. In 1870 the population had been 4759 persons. A sixfold growth occurred by 1880 to put the census at 36,629, and by 1890 there were 106,713 persons who needed a means of getting around town more conveniently than by foot, horseback, or buggy. Horsecars began trundling through the streets in 1871 and served the city's traction needs for nearly fifteen years. But in the mid-eighties science was advancing into new fields. Byers and his friend John Evans, as pillars of the University of Denver, were in a particularly favorable position to learn of the developments.

On their faculty was a physics professor named Sidney H. Short. Professor Short, watching experiments in his field then under way in the East and in England and Germany, became convinced he could make a streetcar go by means of electric power. He built a little four-hundred-foot circle of track on the university's grounds and proved his case by taking curiosity-seekers for rides on a car which drew its power from runners following a mid-track slot containing a charged cable.

Byers, Evans, and others were convinced they glimpsed the future in Professor Short's invention. They incorporated in 1885 the Denver Electric and Cable Railway Company, converted the following year into the Denver Tramway Company, the firm which still operates Denver's mass transit system. Tracks and underground power conduits were laid, and in the winter of 1885–86 one of the first electric street railway systems in America began operating through Denver streets. The United States Electric Company, with Byers as its president, was organized to exploit the system in other cities.

Unfortunately Professor Short's invention didn't work too well. Pedestrians complained that they suffered a severe shock if they happened to make simultaneous contact with the mid-track slotway and one of the rails in crossing the street. Horses, particularly, objected. Their rearings

[3]Elizabeth Byers to Frank Byers, Nov. 5, 1899, Byers papers, Western History Collection, Denver Public Library.

and boltings as they felt the shock created a major traffic hazard in the increasingly busy streets. The Short system was abandoned in 1887, and the Tramway Company went back to four-legged power.

Underground cable traction meantime had been perfected in other cities, and the system was installed in Denver in 1888, though late in 1889 the first overhead trolley electric cars began experimental operations. Byers was a Tramway director from the beginning, and later he became the operating vice-president. He kept a close eye on the lines, noting down in his pocket diary the number of passengers carried and reminding himself that reprimands were called for when he saw a motorman let a patron escape fare payment.

But even running a streetcar system on such a highly personal basis failed to keep Byers fully occupied. His abundant energies were poured into a bewildering variety of other concurrent activities. He was "in" intercity railroads too. His part as one of the organizers of the Denver Pacific already has been mentioned. As the railroad era progressed he also became involved in Evans' Denver, South Park & Pacific, the Denver & Rio Grande, the Utah & Pacific, and the Mexican National railroads. In 1896 he was Colorado chairman for the Deep Water Utilization Committee, a device established to win traffic for lines to Gulf coast ports in Texas and thereby apply pressure on the Union Pacific monopoly for freight rate reductions.

All along the way Byers continued to dabble in mining and agriculture and also found time to become a pioneer oil-well investor, rear and breed a Kentucky thoroughbred, and promote a fish hatchery for Grand County. He even had a nasty little brush with banking in the depths of the panic of 1893.

Byers emerged from the Union National Bank with his wings neatly clipped. He went into the financial adventure with his friend and former colleague, "General" Roger W. Woodbury, Civil War hero, onetime compositor, and later owner-editor of the Denver *Times*.[4] Woodbury became president of the bank and Byers a vice-president. But the institution was carried under in the panic which shook silver-rich Colorado when the Sherman Silver Purchase Act was repealed by President Cleveland. The Union Bank closed its doors on July 18, 1893, reopened August 21, and finally went under July 29, 1895. Byers had invested ten thousand dollars and then dug down for a matching sum as he and the other directors sought to save their institution. Endorsements on his stock certificates, preserved among his papers in the Denver Public Library, show that when the receiver finished sorting through the debris Byers salvaged five hundred dollars of his twenty thousand.

His financial relationships with friend Woodbury seem to have been star-crossed. Concurrently with the bank failure Byers lost $9308.20 in

4Woodbury scrapbook, collection of the author.

going the bond of Woodbury for a Nevada Southern Railroad deal with the Newport Wharf & Lumber Company of Los Angeles in June 1895. This was one of the experiences which led Libbie Byers to complain of her husband's incautious way with a signature. Mrs. Byers wrote to her daughter: "Of course you know we have been lifted high and dry by the old Union Bank—If I can just prevent your old dad from signing any more Bonds, I guess we are safe."[5]

Byers' last connection with the *Rocky Mountain News* was severed on October 1, 1888, when he sold the News Block on Larimer Street, which he had been renting to the publishing company for ten years. Meantime, during 1888, he had constructed the Byers Building, a two-story structure uptown at Fifteenth and Champa streets. This was a flier in investment for rentals and had a number of offices over several small ground-floor stores. The building apparently returned Byers a modest income for ten years or more, and he clung to it with characteristic doggedness long after its site became far more valuable as downtown real estate than as a rental property, a shift in values which did not escape the attention of his wife.

"I wrote Pa last week," Mrs. Byers said in an April 5, 1898, letter to Frank, "just begging him to sell his Block, as that is the only property big enough to get him out of debt. I suppose he will be very angry, as he *cannot* or *will* not *see* that he is sinking deeper and deeper every day, or that $100,000 or even $75,000 today would be worth twice that later on. As things are *now* I don't see the slightest chance for him to save anything. Oh *why* will he be so stubborn. I believe he hopes that I will encumber all I have to save him from going to the wall. But I *cannot* do it. I have already loaded myself down to help him (and no thanks either). I am awfully sorry."

The matter came up again in another letter to Frank on March 27, 1899: "An eastern man wanted to buy your father's block but the Pater scared him off by asking $150,000. Then of course he got *mad* when I said that was entirely too high. . . . Frank it is no use—I don't think it ever enters his head that he is getting old, that but ten or twelve years is probably the extent of his life. . . ."

Despite the debts and the note-juggling they required, Byers and his family were leading a good life. There was money enough for frequent trips to New York, Florida, California, and back to visit the scenes of Byers' early surveying in Oregon. There was a Caribbean cruise and a tour to Europe. In 1891 they moved into a large and lavishly appointed new home at 171 South Washington Street. It was named Kenneth Square, apparently after Bayard Taylor's home town in Pennsylvania. The location was part of one of Byers' subdivisions, and the mansion sprawled over a full square block of grounds which he planted to gardens

[5]Elizabeth Byers to Mary E. Robinson, Aug. 4, 1895, Byers papers, Denver Public Library.

and landscaped with an arboretum of imported trees and shrubs. The interior of the house was fitted out in mahogany, oak, and walnut, and soft ivory damask covered some of the walls.

The Denver School Board acquired the north half of the Kenneth Square block in 1904 and leased the Byers mansion in 1918 or 1919 for use as Logan Junior High School. Later in 1919 the entire property was purchased for forty-five thousand dollars, and in 1920–21 Byers Junior High School was built. For a time the old mansion was occupied as an annex to the new school, but eventually it was torn down.[6] The junior high school is the second Denver school to be named for the *News'* founder. The present Alameda Elementary School had been called Byers until the junior high was completed, when the name was shifted by the school board.[7] Damask from the walls of the old Byers home was taken down, laundered and dyed, and cut into costumes to add splendor to school dramatics, and some of the mahogany woodwork and mirrors from the house are still preserved in the school. The tombstone of one of Byers' dogs remains in place on the school grounds, along with part of the ornate iron fence which once surrounded Kenneth Square. A few of the exotic trees the nature-loving Byers planted continue to cast shade on the junior high school lawns.

The dignity of his big house on its hill and the green beauty of the grounds must have been sources of comfort to Byers as he struggled with his debts and many responsibilities in the declining years of his life. A hint of the expansive but nip-and-tuck struggle he waged with fortune shows in an annual accounting at the end of his 1901 diary. The notation specifies receipts totaling $51,324.62, but expenses of $50,186.10.

To the year of his death, however, Byers remained active and prominent in city life and gave generously of his time to a wide assortment of community projects. He served three terms—1893, 1894, and 1900— as president of the Denver Chamber of Commerce. In 1884 he was the founder and first president of the Colorado State Forestry Association. He had been a founding member of the Colorado Pioneer Society, was its president and its secretary. For six years he also was president of the Colorado State Historical Society. He was a founder and longtime director of the Colorado Humane Society. He stood high in the Masonic fraternity, serving as the head of two Denver orders and as "grand high priest" for the state.

When Denver sought to inaugurate an annual civic carnival on the pattern of New Orleans' Mardis Gras, Byers was called upon. For four years he was president and guiding spirit of the Festival of Mountain

[6]Alice L. Moore, *Early History of Byers Junior High School, 1919–1940*, typescript, Department of Information Services, Denver Public Schools.

[7]Minutes, Denver Board of Education, Feb. 11, 1920, and Sept. 14, 1921.

and Plain, staged annually from 1895 through 1899 and revived in 1901 and 1912. The festival was a three-day celebration involving elaborate parades, outdoor balls, fireworks, exhibits, trolley-car serenading, fire-truck runs, rock-drilling contests, and what may have been the West's first public rodeo of "world champion rough-riders." Elite of the festival were the "Slaves of the Silver Serpent," and a blocks-long reptile was the feature of the illuminated night parade.[8]

Early in the 1890s, Byers began conserving his energies with long weekends of rest at the mountain cabin he built at Ferndale in Platte Cañon, but in general his health remained good and he was still vigorous enough to climb mountains. His wife wrote Mollie at the end of 1901 that "of course we all see changes in your father but nothing alarming yet. I should not be surprised if he were to have the same troubles as Gov. Evans had. Either that or he may go very suddenly someday. However, I think he is safe for many months yet. I notice these sudden deaths that seem so common these days affect him deeply but in his case I fear softening of the brain most of all. Indeed, I can see symptoms of it now."[9] Later, a month before Byers' death, she voiced from Pasadena her opinion that "surely father must be dissipating."[10]

Byers' diaries show that toward the end of his life he was taking a nip now and then of Swamp Root, Red Raven Spirits, and Duffy's malt whiskey to keep the chill from his bones. The last entry in his pocket journal, December 31, 1902, is: "Bottle whiskey 1.75." The diaries indicate that he was in failing health during his last year, and the alcoholic tonics probably were taken with medicinal intent rather than in abandonment of lifelong habits of moderation. He was also consuming quantities of Carlsbad, Honyadi, and Piperazine waters, and during the latter part of 1902 he received almost daily medical treatments for unindicated ailments.

At last death came to Byers in his bed at Kenneth Square on March 25, 1903, at the age of seventy-two. It was the end of a long, active, and useful life. There was almost nothing in the affairs of his city which he had not influenced in some way at some time.

The city, in its turn, mourned its pioneer. Byers was buried in Fairmount Cemetery following a funeral attended by all the leading citizens, nearly every one of them a personal friend. The honorary pallbearers were the faithful John L. Dailey; D. H. Moffat, Jr., the railroad and banking millionaire; Rodney Curtis, president of the Denver Tramway Company; Andrew Sagendorf, pioneer of '59; Lewis B. France, Byers'

[8]Levette J. Davidson, "The Festival of Mountain and Plain," *Colorado Magazine*, Vol. XXV, Nos. 4 and 5 (July, Sept. 1948), pp. 145ff. and 203ff.

[9]Elizabeth Byers to Mary E. Robinson, Dec. 3, 1901, Byers papers, Denver Public Library.

[10]Elizabeth Byers to Frank Byers, Feb. 6, 1903, Byers papers, Denver Public Library.

attorney and long-time business associate; Alfred Butters, L. C. Ellsworth, and E. T. Wells. Active pallbearers were the son of Governor Evans, William G. Evans, Charles H. Reynolds, Charles Kibler, John J. Berkey, A. D. Wilson, Arthur Williams, C. C. Gird, and Aaron Gove, later to become a famous American educator.[11]

The obituaries in the newspapers were flowery and lengthy, and many of the organizations to which Byers had given his abundant energies worked up memorial volumes for presentation to the family. Some of them are hand-bound with burnt or tooled leather covers. They are illustrated, illuminated, and soar into calligraphic flourishes. The homage was elaborate, in the fashion of the day, and probably sincere.

All the proper things were said, the words of tribute and veneration which take so much from a man by making him more than mortal. The hand-lettered, water-colored memorial of the Chamber of Commerce saluted its former president as builder and pioneer and spoke of his "unselfish devotion to public interest." Byers was, the Chamber said, "Denver's most loyal and best beloved citizen." He was "faithful, sincere," with "dignity, courtesy, modesty, affability," the State Historical and Natural History Society of Colorado said. Denver Lodge No.5, AF & AM, called him a "leader, builder and force for the right." His "massive character" was noted in a letter of condolence from a leading law firm, which described him as "a great man," a "man in every fiber of his being," whose "fortitude, foresight and unwavering faith, underly the foundation of things in this state as granite underlies our hills." Byers was "the recognized chief architect" of a "great and prosperous Commonwealth," the Society of Colorado Pioneers said. He had "high ideals and aspirations" and "honesty, constructive genius, unswerving determination."[12]

The local historians have been equally respectful. Wilbur Fisk Stone says: "Not seeking honor, honors were yet multiplied unto him because of his recognized ability and his devotion to the general good. His name and record have been indelibly impressed upon the history of Colorado, for he was one of those who aided in laying broad and deep the foundation upon which the present progress and prosperity, the political, legal and moral status of the state have been builded." Joseph G. Brown wrote for the biographical section of Byers *History of Colorado*: "Among the men of distinguished and unusual note in Colorado, there is none whose name will be longer treasured in history than that of William N. Byers. There is none whose works for public benefit will be longer remembered with gratitude by a people. So closely has his private life and public service been identified with the progress of the State that they become an essential part of its history."

[11]*Rocky Mountain News*, Mar. 27, 1903.

[12]The memorials are preserved among the Byers papers in the Denver Public Library.

Jerome Smiley, Denver's most meticulous and voluminous historian, found that very little he wrote about in his thousand-page chronicle of the city did not in some way involve Byers: "As will have been seen by the reader, his name is encountered almost everywhere in the Story of Denver, in the preparation of which it became to the writer a matter of much personal interest to ascertain whether anything of commanding importance in the city's history had been consummated without Mr. Byers' personal participation. The reader who follows the Story to its close will not need to be told that the exceptions to the rule are very few, and that even in most of the exceptions the indirect influence of this eminent figure in the annals of Denver is apparent. . . . He has seen the majestic panorama of civilization unroll from the Mississippi River to the Pacific Ocean over the plains and mountains he traversed as a pioneer in the vast domain; and it would seem, than he, no man bore a nobler, more unselfishly useful, part in preparing the way for it."[13]

All of the kind and praising words of obituaries, memorials, and history books, or most of them, speak in true approximations of Byers. But they create an austere image; they do not give back a living man. No one remembered, in public, that he had once erred with a beautiful woman. Or that he had lived to pay for and then to triumph over his error. No one mentioned that his sometimes imperious wife, despite her carping, remained by his side while the forked tongue of scandal darted. Probably only Libbie Byers remembered that in his age he became so attached to a calf he named Trilby that his heart would have broken if she had been sold. "He is a queer old chap," she wrote with affection. Little note was taken of his deep love for the mountains and high, far places, or that on his hikes he stuffed bits of rock, pine cones, and samples of mosses into his pockets. No point was made of his affection for the theater or of the voluminous reading by which he educated himself. It would have occurred to no one at the turn of the century to mention, as part of the man, that he had a sweet tooth and was more likely to indulge himself on rock candy than on whiskey. Or that another of his private passions was fresh fruit. Only readers of the sketchy, routine, and generally uninformative jottings in his diaries know that Byers faithfully recorded each year the first bluebird and crocuses, noted the wild birds singing and the greenup. Aspirations and spring always were closer to his being than autumn and harvests.

Somehow, though he sowed with a generous hand and in many seasons, the great reapings which came to many of his associates never

[13]No full-length biography exists, but there are numerous biographical sketches. See Smiley, *History of Denver*, pp. 654–56; Wilbur Fisk Stone, op. cit., Vol. III, pp. 499–503; James H. Baker and LeRoy R. Hafen, *History of Colorado* (Denver, 1927), Vol. V, pp. 571–73; Frank Hall, op. cit., Vol. III, pp. 136–37, and Vol. IV, pp. 368–69; Will C. Ferril, *Sketches of Colorado* (Denver, 1911), Vol. I, pp. 368–69; Byers "History of Colorado," in *Encyclopedia of Biography of Colorado*, pp. 187–90; and *Portrait and Biographical Record of Denver and Vicinity*, pp. 145–47.

came to him. His will was filed for probate in the county court of Judge Ben B. Lindsey, who later would found in Denver the nation's first juvenile court. Everything went to Elizabeth, Mollie, and Frank. The executors—widow, son, and son-in-law, William F. Robinson—reported on April 25, 1903, that the estate could be closed. They had received and disbursed $7286.46.

Elizabeth Byers survived her husband until January 6, 1920, when she died of pneumonia in California. Four children had been born to them, but only two came through the harsh treatment the frontier gave to infants. Charles Fred and James Byers both died before they were two. Frank Sumner Byers lived until November 4, 1937, and his sister, Mary Elizabeth (Mollie) Byers Robinson, died December 28, 1940.

When the Board of Managers of the Colorado State Capitol decided to create a "Hall of Fame" to the memory of builders and founders, the editor of the News was one of their first selections. The gallery consists of sixteen stained-glass portraits occupying circular windows high in the bell-shaped dome of the Capitol. The faces of fifteen men and one woman, wreathed in imperishable columbines, look down from their heights into the statehouse rotunda. With Byers in the group are William Gilpin, John Evans, Bela M. Hughes, Nathaniel P. Hill, Alexander Majors, Christopher (Kit) Carson, John L. Dyer, Chief Ouray, Jim Baker, J. W. Denver, William J. Palmer, Mrs. Frances Wisebart Jacobs, Casimiro Barela, R. G. Buckingham, and Benjamin H. Eaton.[14]

[14]Levette J. Davidson, "Colorado's Hall of Fame," Colorado Magazine, Vol. XXVII, No. 1 (Jan. 1950), pp. 23ff.

CHAPTER FOURTEEN

A Democrat Buys the News

THE regime of Kemp Cooper and associates which took over the *News* when Byers bowed out in May 1878 didn't last long. Its interregnum was so short, in fact, that one is led to suspect a setup. Possibly one of the motives in establishing the printing company was to spare Byers further political embarrassment. As a loyal Republican he would have suffered much additional loss of face had he been a party to what happened to his newspaper two months after his retirement.

On July 16 the paper was sold to a Democrat.

William Austin Hamilton Loveland wore his whiskers mutton-chop style, and he not only was the state's leading Democrat but in other matters, too, he was the veritable antithesis of nearly everything the *News* had stood for. He was, moreover, one of the few men in America who ever bested Jay Gould in a railroad manipulation. Loveland beat the master at his own game with a maneuver which was Western and direct: a train was stopped and a federal judge kidnaped at gunpoint by masked men.

Loveland laid down thirty thousand dollars for the *News* and its facilities, exclusive of the News Block. He became president of the Rocky Mountain News Printing Company, which was reorganized on the basis of 400 shares of ownership at forty thousand dollars capitalization. James T. Smith was elected vice-president, and W. F. Robinson carried over temporarily as secretary-treasurer. Loveland held 396 shares of the stock, and one share went to Smith, Robinson, Gus Alden, and James F. Wellborn, who replaced France as the company attorney. Smith was made editor with M. J. Gavisk as city editor. William Vickers left to take over editorship of the *Tribune*, which now became the city's principal Republican organ. W. R. Thomas also departed the *News* staff to return later after serving for a spell as editorial writer for Woodbury's *Times*.

In announcing the new ownership on July 17, the *News* said that politico-economic pressures forced the change. There were two strong Republican papers in town—the *News* and the *Tribune*—and "the republican party of Colorado cannot support two." The previous proprietors had "preferred a profitable sale to the possibility of losing money by continuing the publication of the paper." All of this may have been merely a dig at the Republicans, since the *News* had been that party's chief spokesman, but at any rate "Old Reliable" henceforth would be reliable from a Democratic point of view.

Loveland declared himself in the same issue:

To the Public.

With this issue of The News the undersigned assumes the varied responsibilities of proprietor—responsibilities that concern himself, the democratic party and the public at large, and which, as soon as the necessary details can be arranged, he hopes to share with citizens of the state, located permanently here and permanently identified with the growth and prosperity of the commonwealth.

Speaking of the policy of The News, it is hardly necessary to say that the interest of Colorado, material and social, will continue to engage the best efforts of its circulation, to the end that The News may assist all parts of the state, and all classes of people, without injuring any. In other words, the state first, last and all the time, will be the burden of our labors, even when party, locality, or corporate interests, might seem to otherwise demand. Upon this broad policy we look for success. Upon a policy less broad, comparative failure would be invited from the start. A residence of nineteen years in Colorado, during which period my time has largely been given to enterprises of a public nature, is the best pledge that can be offered in support of the general policy herein set forth.

Keeping in view the general and prevalent policy of the pioneer journal of the Rocky Mountain slope, The News will be democratic in politics, and will aim to set forth and sustain the recognized teachings of the party, so far as the same do not conflict with the local interests of the state. When conflict of that nature arises, The News will array itself upon the side of Colorado, and will seek, with all the means and influence it can command, to secure the needed reform within the party. Recognizing this commonwealth as in the infancy of a prosperous career, and as at the foundation of its building-up period, it follows that our material interests may rightfully claim the encouragement and protection of favoring legislation to a larger degree than those of older and more fully developed states.

The News has no enemies to punish, no friends to reward, and asks from the public, what it fully means to extend and merit, a helping hand in every effort that is right, proper, and calculated for the best good of the greatest number.

Captain James T. Smith will have editorial charge of The News, assisted by a corps of experienced writers, well qualified to gather *all* the news and present it in reliable and proper form.

W. A. H. Loveland

"Cap" Smith did not remain long with the *News* at this point. John M. Barret took over as editor in December, and the "Cap" apparently joined the staff of the *Transcript* in Golden.[1] But he returned to the

[1]*Rocky Mountain News*, Aug. 24, 1879.

News later to occupy the chair of mining editor for nearly forty years. He became a living legend in Denver journalism and model for the principal character in Gene Fowler's novel, *Salute to Yesterday.* "Cap" affected a dark slouch hat, an Inverness cape, and a sword-cane, and his handwriting was such that there was never more than one printer in the composing room who could decipher the runic script with which he reported a never ending series of bonanzas in the Colorado hills.

Fowler asserts that Smith won his captaincy on an early morning when Cherry Creek, not yet corseted in concrete, went into one of its periodic spring floods. The waters swept up and carried away a square frame palace of pleasure in which Smith had sought shelter from the chills of the night.

> Bellowing "All hands on deck!" the veteran of Hampton Roads assisted the screaming ladies and their confused admirers to the roof. Fascinated spectators on high ground watched the captain-to-be minister to the hysteria of lovely women and at the same time apply the science of navigation to the swaying house of social charms.
>
> Eye-witnesses commented upon the technical idiom of the skipper. His baritone—lately exercised in wassail—now outroared the waters. He was heard to command "Trim ship!" as the houseboat listed to port, and "Man the funnel!" when bricks from the chimney promised to maim the madam's personnel. . . .
>
> At length the veteran of Hampton Roads maneuvered his listing craft toward the lee of a dismantled bridge. The warping of this ark to an emergency dock was a demonstration of maritime finesse. The master, roaring the while, made fast to a bulkhead, then halted a stampede of absent-minded males with the admonition:
>
> "Women first, you foul weasels!"
>
> He saw the ladies down a gangplank—in more congenial times the door of Madam Cunningham's bathroom. He permitted the cowed gentlemen to follow. Then, with a fine blue eye for saltwater etiquette . . . saluted and was the last to leave his sinking ship. He dived overboard and swam ashore.[2]

Some of the more enthusiastic admirers of this feat of gallant seamanship elevated Smith to the rank of "Admiral," but generally the nickname was "Cap," and it stuck for the rest of his life. Beyond, in fact. Nearly every newspaperman in Denver today knows of "Cap" Smith, but not one in a hundred knows his first name was James. No one knows what the "T." stood for; Fowler called him Trolley, and perhaps that's good enough.

In 1878, "Cap" was called from the staff of the poverty-stricken Denver *Democrat* to assist in the political conversion of "Old Reliable." The about-face created a sensation. Predictions were offered freely that

[2]Gene Fowler, *Salute to Yesterday* (New York, 1937), pp. 13–14.

the *News* was a stranded investment and would go under. Aside from Loveland and a young man named Tom Patterson, almost no one of consequence in Denver would admit to voting Democratic. One scandalized Republican took up his pen and indited a letter to the editor of the *Tribune*:

> . . . Now, sir; this thing is an outrage on Denver. It is an outrage on the Republican party of the whole State. It is an outrage upon the commercial interests of Colorado because it [the *News*] passes into the hands of a great railroad monopoly. It is an outrage on subscribers because it proposes to give Democracy when Republicanism was contracted for. Because it proposes the advocacy of Golden City against Denver, when the promotion of Denver interest was subscribed for. It is a gross outrage because it proposes the advocacy of the railroad monopoly, when the advocacy and defense of the rights and interests of the people were subscribed for.
>
> In fact a purchase for money, of the interests of peoples, parties and communities, without their knowledge and consent is beyond compare an attempt at the greatest possible tyranny. And no adequate rebuke would be possible, but for the righteous indignation it will arouse among Republicans all over the State, and among all the people of Denver without distinction of party. . . .
>
> Every true Republican, I believe, will let the old paper lie in the bed its present sole proprietor is making for it. Every friend of Denver will rally to the support of papers owned by Denver men. . . .[3]

The *Times* forecast doom and debt for the Democratic *News*:

> In purchasing the *News* Mr. Loveland has cabbaged a sort of white elephant. He has assumed the indebtedness of a $20,000 mortgage held by a Republican, and has spent for it, besides that raised by his party supporters, as much as he would derive in the way of salary from a term of office as governor of the state; viz: five thousand dollars. All may go well during the heat and excitement of the campaign, but when the winter of discontent shall break o'er the *News*, and that mortgage shall come due next May, election times will then be gone, the good old Republican support gone, we predict the said paper will no longer be of use to the immortal Wm. A. H., and he will let her go back to her first love through the means of the mortgage held by that Arapahoe county Republican.

The *Times'* jab brought to light further details about the purchase transaction. Loveland, it developed, had put $5000 of his own into the deal along with $5000 from party angels, and he had assumed the $20,000 mortgage on the publishing firm held by Byers' old Omaha friend, David H. Moffat, Jr., now a rising Denver banker and railroad financier. The

[3]Denver *Tribune*, July 17, 1878.

dire predictions, however, were not borne out. On May 11, 1879, the *News* was cleared of the mortgage, and within a few years a leading Republican politician would offer $250,000 for the paper.

The new proprietor was, like Byers, a pioneer. But he had cast his lot initially with Golden City, and intertown rivalries died hard. Byers and Loveland were acquainted through the frontier years, but they traveled in different circles and seldom saw eye to eye, although the *News*, recognizing Loveland's leadership in the foothills city, had endorsed him for the state House of Representatives in 1861. It was Loveland more than any other man who had been responsible for the temporary location of the territorial capital in Golden. Moreover he was on the other side of the fence from the Evans-Moffat-Byers crowd on the matter of bringing the iron horse to Colorado. He was the organizer and president of the Colorado Central Railroad, and had proposed to bring the main line down along the foothills to Golden. Denver would be served by a spur. Denver remembered and never forgave the effrontery.

Loveland was born May 30, 1826, in Chatham, Massachusetts, the son of a Yankee sailor who was captured by the British in the War of 1812. The father, Leonard, was an early settler in the Ohio Valley, and the town of Loveland, Ohio, is named for him. William was reared in frontier Illinois. As a young man he became a wagon master in the Mexican War. He was along on the campaign from Vera Cruz to Mexico City, and in the assault on Chapultepec Heights in September 1847 was wounded in the leg by an artillery shell fragment. Invalided home to Illinois, he had just established himself in the mercantile business when the rush to the California gold fields began.

He packed up and set out across the plains in May of 1849 and reputedly built the first house in Grass Valley, California. Success escaped him as a gold miner, however, and he was back in Brighton, Illinois, in 1851. But his restless feet responded again when word came that gold had been found at Pike's Peak. He struck west in the great wave of the fifty-niners, but this time as a merchant rather than a miner. He brought with him a wagon train of merchandise, and in June he built the first store in Golden, hard by the swarming trail to the Gregory Diggings.

Henceforth Loveland was Golden's first citizen. He opened the first coal mine and started a brick and pottery works, drawing on the clays which since have made Golden world-famous for scientific ceramics. Soon after he built the first wagon road up Clear Creek Cañon he became interested in the possibilities of a railroad over the mountains to Salt Lake City. He financed a survey and as early as 1866 had a charter from the territorial legislature for his Colorado Central & Pacific Railroad.[4]

In the scramble of railroad construction during the late sixties and

[4]Biographical data from Loveland family papers, courtesy Hobart Loveland of Nanuet, New York, grandson of W. A. H., and Harold M. Dunning, Loveland, Colorado; see also Ferril, op. cit., pp. 278–79.

early seventies Loveland built his Colorado Central as a broad-gauge line between Golden and Denver and through northern Colorado, and as a narrow-gauge track up Clear Creek Cañon to Black Hawk and the mines of the Little Kingdom of Gilpin. He played the Union Pacific and the Kansas Pacific against each other, accepting support from the two giants alternately. In the process he kept the Denver Pacific crowd stewing lest Golden instead of Denver become the major rail center of Colorado. During the manipulations Loveland was temporarily forced out of the presidency of the Colorado Central but remained in close touch as vice-president. In the early seventies Jay Gould had entered the Colorado railroad wars. He gained control of the Kansas Pacific and was plotting toward the forced consolidation with the Union Pacific which came in 1880.

Gould seized the Denver Pacific from the Evans group in Denver, and the plan was to consolidate the KP and the Colorado Central, which was in financial trouble, into one line. But this would have firmed up Denver's position as rail center and left Golden only a way station en route to the mining country. Meanwhile the Union Pacific played into Gould's hands by taking the Colorado Central into court and forcing receivership on a $1,500,000 bill for materials and rolling stock.

Loveland acted with vigor and directness against the double threat to his railroad and his town. He took the chair at the Colorado Central's annual meeting May 18 and 19, 1876, in Golden, summarily threw out the proxy votes which would have approved consolidation with the Kansas Pacific, and then seized control of the Central's property. His men "slept on their guns" in the roundhouse and shops.[5]

The immediate threat of forced consolidation disposed of, Loveland had to do something about the threatened receivership, which would have resulted in the same undesirable wedding by only slightly slower means.

Circuit Judge Amherst W. Stone was scheduled to hold court in Boulder, north of Golden, on August 15, 1876, and it was common knowledge that he would appoint David H. Moffat, Jr., as receiver for the Colorado Central. Moffat held an interest in Gould's Kansas Pacific, and the foothill and mountain counties, which were with Loveland in the fight, denounced his impending appointment as a cold-deck deal.

But Judge Stone didn't reach Boulder that day. The Denver–Boulder train on which he was riding was stopped by a barricade of ties on the tracks at Kenneer's Lake, midway on the journey. A band of masked men boarded the train, and one of them waved a big gun under the judicial nose.

"My God!" said the judge.

"Never mind," replied the masked man. "Come on."

[5]M. C. Poor, *Denver, South Park & Pacific* (Denver, 1949), pp. 10, 23, 26, 63ff.

Sam Browne, onetime territorial attorney general and then counsel for the petitioners in the receivership, arose from a nearby seat and sought to enter a demurrer.

"I protest against this indignity——"

A hog leg was waved in his direction. "Sit down." Browne sat.

The judge was assisted from the train, placed in a waiting carriage, and under escort of armed and masked riders was driven to the mouth of Coal Creek Cañon. The judge was treated with firmness but courtesy. He was told that from this point the rest of the journey would be on horseback.

"I can't ride," he protested; "I don't know anything about riding a horse."

"You are safe; get on and we'll have a man lead the horse. No trouble. No danger."

The jurist was led to a high point at the base of a cliff in the foothills, from which the prairie could be scanned with field glasses for many miles. A lazy day was spent lolling in the shade of the pines. After dark Judge Stone was brought down to the plains again, and at eleven-thirty placed in a closed carriage driven by two of his captors. Sometime after midnight he was deposited in front of the Alvord House in Denver and bade good night.

The bold raid had Denver on edge through the day. The *News* and the other papers got out extras. There was a rumor Judge Stone had been lynched in Golden Gate Cañon. Governor Routt called out the militia and dispatched a unit by special train, with a brass cannon on a flatcar, to Boulder.

There was no doubt in anyone's mind about who was behind the sally, but the identity of the masked abductors remained a secret for sixty years. In 1936, Carlos W. Lake, by then president of the Colorado Pioneer Society, addressed a meeting of the bar association in Denver and told the whole story. He said he and Mott Johnson, afterward a noted sheriff of Jefferson County, had been detailed by the board of directors of the Colorado Central to organize a fourteen-man party and rob the train of its judicial cargo. Lake confessed it was he who applied the .45-caliber persuader to Judge Stone aboard the train.[6]

Strangely enough the Colorado Central's strong-arm tactics worked—in combination with some further stubbornness and a lot of legal obfuscation and delay. Judge Stone, of course, got to Boulder next day (under military guard) and placed receiver Moffat in office. The Colorado Central then simply refused to grant him possession and ignored a supporting writ issued by Judge Stone a few days later.

Loveland managed to retain his hold. He kept the issue seesawing in the courts for more than a year, parried another Union Pacific suit for

[6]Carlos W. Lake, "The Kidnaping of Judge A. W. Stone," *Colorado Magazine*, Vol. XVII, No. 1 (Jan. 1940), pp. 19ff.

two million dollars, and finally won a capitulation in which he was to be retained at the head of the Colorado Central and all litigation would be dropped. Loveland wound up a director of the Union Pacific, and the construction of his railroad was pushed forward through northern Colorado. In 1877 the town of Loveland was laid out in Larimer County fifty miles north of Denver and named for him. An automobile road, one of the highest year-round routes in America, now carries transcontinental Highway 6 across the Continental Divide through 11,992-foot Loveland Pass at the head of the south fork of Clear Creek. Loveland once visioned a railroad over the same route.

The audacious maneuverings of the mutton-chopped hero of Chapultepec apparently won the admiration of Jay Gould, although the tactics delayed his conquest of the Colorado railroads for several years. They became good friends, visited each other in New York and Golden, and corresponded intimately on railroad affairs. The intimacy did not help Loveland's political aspirations; Denver and most of Colorado bitterly resented the rail monopoly Gould soon established. Loveland's *News* was nicknamed "The Tow Line" by the opposition papers, which charged that Gould led Loveland around on a leash.

Like many another magnate of his time and since, Loveland in buying the *News* was less interested in the practice of journalism than in the political power of the press. He had been active in Colorado politics ever since the constitutional convention for Jefferson Territory in 1859. In 1861 he was chairman of the convention called to set up a provisional government for the territory of Colorado, and in 1864 of a statehood convention. He served for nine years in the territorial Senate. He also accomplished the multiple feat of serving simultaneously on the boards of county commissioners of five counties—Gilpin, Clear Creek, Jefferson, Boulder, and Larimer—contrary residence requirements notwithstanding.

Loveland wanted to be governor of Colorado. The purchase of the *News* and its abrupt political metamorphosis were intended to realize that ambition. On the same day, July 17, 1878, that Loveland was declaring his editorial policies for the *News*, the Democrats were holding their convention in Pueblo. Loveland was nominated.

The campaign was a rigorous one. Loveland was denounced as a railroad monopolist and the tool of Gould. The Democratic papers, including the *News*, hung the tag of "carpetbagger" on his opponent, Frederick W. Pitkin of Ouray, newly a resident of the state. But in the election on October 2, Pitkin won, 14,308 votes to 11,535. The Republicans also swept the state legislature, and it was with less hope than courtesy to a defeated standard-bearer that the Democrats presented Loveland's name as a candidate for the United States Senate when the legislators gathered in Walhalla Hall in January 1879. The Republicans in the legislature, which then elected senators, passed blithely over the minority nomination and chose Nathaniel P. Hill, the professor-chemistsmelterman who had grown rich on his process for the extraction of metals from Colorado ores.

Loveland remained an active Democratic leader for many years. Never successful as a candidate, his political career's high point probably came in June 1880 at the Democratic National Convention in Cincinnati. He was one of Colorado's six delegates, and he received five favorite-son votes for President on the first ballot.

Things were tough all over for Colorado Democrats in the early days.

Down in the remote high country of the southwestern part of the state a renegade Republican of odd appetites ate five of the seven Democrats in Hinsdale County, according to a favorite legend.[7]

The political affiliations are myth; the cannibalism is not. Alfred Packer had engaged to lead a party of prospectors from Provo, Utah, to a new strike in the Colorado mountains. Sometime between February 9 and April 16 of 1874 the six men became trapped in a snowstorm and lost their way high in the rugged San Juans. On the latter date Packer walked into the Los Pinos Indian Agency carrying live coals in a coffeepot. He had run out of matches, he explained, and had to carry his campfire with him.

Packer appeared to be very sleek and well fed for a man lost sixty days in wild, unnourishing country. Under questioning he broke down and confessed that his five companions had died or killed each other, or he had killed them, and he had been living off portions of their bodies. The man-eater escaped jail in Saguache but was recaptured in 1883 in Wyoming and brought to trial at Lake City. Folklore insists that Judge Melville B. Gerry, an old-school Southern gentleman from Georgia, meted out the death sentence in this fashion:

"Stan' up, yah voracious man eating son of a bitch, stand up!

"They was sivin Dimmicrats in Hinsdale County, and ye eat five of thim, God damn ye!

"I sintins ye t'be hanged by the neck until ye're dead, dead, DEAD, as a warnin' ag'in reducin' the Dimmycratic population of th' state."[8]

Another version of the sentencing has Judge Gerry saying: "Alfred Packer, you voracious Republican cannibal, I would sentence you to hell but the statutes forbid it."[9]

Actually Gerry lectured Packer with "awful solemnity" and reviewed his crime with a good deal of compassion:

. . . To other sickening details of your crime I will not refer. Silence is kindness. I do not say things to harrow your soul, for I know you have drunk the cup of bitterness to its very dregs, and wherever you

[7]Rocky Mountain News, Mar. 13, 1883.

[8]Lake City Silver World, Nov. 1930.

[9]Rocky Mountain Herald, June 13, 1942.

have gone the sting of your conscience and the goadings of remorse have been an avenging Nemesis which have followed your every turn in life and painted afresh for your contemplation the picture of the past. . . . Be not deceived, God is not mocked, for whatsoever a man soweth, that shall he also reap. You, Alfred Packer, sowed the wind; you must now reap the whirlwind. . . . Prepare to meet thy God; prepare to meet the spirits of thy murdered victims. . . . For nine long years you have been a wanderer, upon the face of the earth, bowed and broken in spirit; no home, no loves, no ties to bind you to earth. You have been, indeed, a poor, pitiable waif of humanity. I hope and pray that in the spirit land to which you are so fast and surely drifting, you will find that peace and rest for your weary spirit which this world cannot give. . . .

Then, his voice failing for a time, the judge pronounced sentence, firmly and with triple emphasis:

. . . on said 19th day of May, A.D., 1883 . . . you, then and there, by said Sheriff, be hung by the neck until you are dead, dead, dead, and may God have mercy upon your soul.[10]

Packer won a Supreme Court reversal of the death sentence and was given a second trial in Gunnison. This time he was sentenced to forty years in the state prison for manslaughter. He was paroled on January 8, 1901, and came to live in a little shack near the Denver suburb of Littleton, a quiet, retiring old man loved by the children of the neighborhood. Packer died April 23, 1907, and was buried in the Littleton cemetery. There, on September 22, 1940, Bishop Frank Hamilton Rice of the Liberal Church Inc., the friend and champion of Denver's skid-row bums, officially laid the ghost of Packer the Man-Eater.

Six of Bishop Rice's followers, wearing monkish robes and masks and chained together, filed to the grave leading Angelica, a white angora nanny goat. One of the robed figures was barefoot, representing Packer. The others were the ghosts of his victims. Goat milk was poured on the modest tombstone. Then Bishop Rice read a ceremony which transferred Packer's sins to the scapegoat. He cited Scripture—Leviticus 26:29, Deuteronomy 28:53-57, Jeremiah and Ezekiel—which he said looked with compassion on cannibalism. "Therefore, Alfred Packer," he concluded, "we won't hold that against you." It was reported that Angelica accepted her burden meekly.[11]

During their dismal misfortunes of the New Deal days Colorado Republicans organized a Packer Club. Members carried cards bearing a picture of Packer and the pledge: "I agrees to eliminat five Nu Deal

[10]Rocky Mountain News, Apr. 14, 1883; quoted in Paul H. Gantt, The Case of Alfred Packer the Man-Eater (Denver, 1952), pp. 73-75.

[11]Gantt, op. cit., pp. 111-14.

Dimmycrats witch makes me a mimber of th' Packer Club of Colorado."
Charter members were Ralph L. Carr, later governor of Colorado; writer
Gene Fowler, who told Packer's story in his *Timber Line*; and Denver
attorneys Fred M. Mazzulla and H. Dick Davis.

If Packer was a trifle ardent as a Republican, W. A. H. Loveland was
ahead of his time as a Democrat. Colorado was a solidly Republican
state from the beginning. It did not elect a Democratic governor until
1883, and then only because the dominant party got to squabbling
within itself. There wouldn't be a Colorado Democrat in the Senate
until after the turn of the century, when Populism and the issue of free
coinage of silver blew party lines sky high in the West.

During Loveland's political-minded ownership the *News* became for
the third time a member of a "family" of newspapers. On January 1, 1880,
Loveland founded the Leadville *Democrat*, the fifth daily paper in the
then new and booming silver camp two miles high in the Rockies. The
News of January 4 hailed the first number of "our young brother" and
said it was patterned, politically and typographically, on "Old Reliable."
The Rocky Mountain News Printing Company also had begun publication on July 16, 1879, of the semiweekly *Colorado Post*, a German-
language paper.

In spite of defeats at the polls the *News* clung faithfully to its party.
When the Denver *Democrat* finally gave up in June 1879 and became
overnight the *Republican*, Senator Hill's organ, the *News'* funnybone
was tickled by the three-pronged Republican opposition:

> Now pitch in. We will cheer the victor, nurse the wounded and
> bury the slain. Let the Tribune pour a broadside into the Republican
> and show it up to be a fraud, and while the Times exposes the cussedness
> of the Tribune the Republican can strike hands with the latter and
> crush the Times. The very breeze smells of sulphur.[12]

Denver, meanwhile, was enjoying a rapid growth. Settlers were arriving
at the rate of a hundred a day, the *News* estimated on July 8, 1879. The
new silver strikes, smelting, and the proliferation of railroads all contributed to the boom times. Loveland was deep in railroading and smelting. He could afford to dabble in newspapering and politics. Then, to
relieve still further the smarts of his defeats, he hit it rich with his Fanny
Barret silver mine in the Mosquito Range. The Fanny and other
ventures made him a notable silver king in an era of much conspicuous
wealth.

Denver at this time also was entering upon a long-lasting vogue as a
health resort. The "climate cure" was being prescribed for tuberculosis,
and the new railroads brought thousands of sufferers to Colorado's high,
dry sunshine. Many of them remained to become leading citizens in

[12]*Rocky Mountain News*, June 5, 1879.

business, the professions, and the arts. P. T. Barnum commented on one of his visits that Coloradans were the most disappointed people he ever saw. "Two-thirds of them came here to die," he said, "and they can't do it. The wonderful air brings them back from the verge of the tomb." (Barnum's puff was not entirely a disinterested one. He had purchased an area still named for him and was in the business of selling town lots for a subdivision.)

Hundreds of sanatoria were built. Tent colonies for open-air living dotted the suburban fringe. The tide of health seekers lasted fifty years or more, and the tubercle bacillus has always been credited as a factor in Denver's growth. The fresh-air treatment and the rest homes it brought into being also supplied the impetus which carried the city into front rank as a center for medical education and research.

As Pullman's "palace cars" came into service fashionable tourists began flocking to Denver too. One of the distinguished sight-seers of the time was Joaquin Miller, who described Denver admiringly as "Queen of the Tawny Desert." The *News* of May 25, 1879, wasn't exactly sure the California poet's nickname was wholly flattering. Colorado was being boomed as a lush land of milk and honey, and any hint of aridity was not appreciated.

Another visitor was Miss Emily Faithful, an Englishwoman of delicate airs and elegant tastes. She liked what she saw in the little city only twenty years away from log cabins. In her travel book, *Three Trips to America*, published in 1884, she commented:

> The Tabor Opera House justly ranks as one of the finest theatres in America. . . . I not only heard Gerster sing but saw the rank, fashion and beauty of the city assembled to welcome her. Patti received an immense ovation the next day. . . .
>
> The streets are full of activity; there are fine houses and fast horses; carriages are to be seen with heraldic crests familiar to Europeans but somewhat out of place in this land of equality. . . . Considerable extravagance is also to be seen—gorgeous clothes and pretentious entertainments; but at the same time there is energy and liberality—schools have been built, an excellent university opened and, if Denver has the faults, she also has the virtues of a new wealthy Western city. . . .

Walt Whitman also came west. Crossing the plains from Topeka to Denver, he saw "a variety of country, but all unmistakably prolific, western, American, and on the largest scale." The *News* of September 20, 1879, reported his arrival: "Walt Whitman, the venerable poet, in company with a party of friends is in the city." But Jay Gould had arrived at the same time, and he took all the play in the papers. Railroads were far more important than poetry to a town which was in a hurry to grow up.

Whitman roamed the streets and visited the smelters, where he saw

$20,000 silver bricks in casual piles of twenty each. Unbashfully he submitted a written interview with himself to the *Tribune*, speaking of a great affection for a city of "climatic magnetism" and "delicious air." Denver, he said, was a town one "suddenly loves and hardly knows why."[13]

He made the narrow-gauge tour up to Leadville, and in the gorge of Platte Cañon he found the natural model for the formless, "heaven-ambitious" style and spirit of his own verse. " 'I have found the law of my own poems,' was the unspoken but more-and-more decided feeling that came to me," he wrote in *Specimen Days*.[14] Here was "grim yet joyous elemental abandon . . . plenitude of material . . . entire absence of art . . . untrammel'd play of primitive Nature. . . ." The cañon of the Platte appears in *Leaves of Grass* as

> Spirit that form'd this scene,
> These tumbled rock-piles grim and red,
> These reckless heaven-ambitious peaks,
> These gorges, turbulent-clear streams, this naked freshness,
> These formless wild arrays, for reasons of their own,
> I know thee, savage spirit—we have communed together,
> Mine too such wild arrays, for reasons of their own. . . .

"Yes," Whitman wrote as he headed back toward St. Louis, "I fell in love with Denver, and even felt a wish to spend my declining and dying days there."

By 1880, Denver's population had jumped to 35,600, and that figure would be tripled to 106,700 in the 1890 census. A bustling town, and everything was proudly modern. In 1879, only a year after the first switchboard had gone into operation with twenty-one subscribers at New Haven, Connecticut, Denver had not one but two telephone systems. F. O. Vaille began preparations for a network using Bell's device in the fall of 1878 and by February 20, 1879, he was open for service to two hundred patrons. Six months later a competing system using the Edison telephone was introduced by the Western Union Telegraph Company. The disadvantages of two conflicting services became immediately apparent, however, and in 1880 there was a merger to the Bell system.

The *News* greeted the telephone as the "galvanic muttering machine" and took note that patrons could not restrain themselves from shouting into the mouthpiece. The advantages of the apparatus to the gathering of news were quickly recognized, however, and in 1880 the paper installed a set of phones, each with bell crank and individually equipped with a mass of wires and storage batteries.

[13]Rollo G. Silver, "Whitman Interviews Himself," *American Literature*, Vol. X, No. 1 (Mar. 1938), p. 84.

[14]*Complete Prose Works of Walt Whitman* (New York, 1914), p. 136.

Concurrently the electric lights were going on in Denver. Paris had been the first city to use electric street lighting during the Universal Exposition of 1878, and in this country Cleveland followed with arc lamps the next year. Early in 1880, Denver began turning out the gas lamps on her streets and replacing them with electric lights. Smiley says his home town was "probably the third—certainly the fourth—city in the world" to use incandescent lamps for street illumination. After some experimentation with small, individual lights at street corners, Denver adopted a novel system for piercing the gloom of its downtown district. In 1883 fifteen steel towers one hundred and fifty feet high were erected at strategic points. From the top of each tower six 3000-candlepower Brush arc lights poured illumination over the surrounding streets. The towers, which dominated the city's squat sky line, remained in use for about ten years.

Denver was a proud, even vainglorious, little city. She preened herself on her alertness in being among the municipal pioneers of streetcars, telephones, and electric lighting. But she also pleased herself with her own brand of superior insularity. The *News* of March 24, 1880, noted that "Denver is like Paris in this respect, that its own affairs interest its people more than distant events do. We have a little world of our own."

The city advanced and strutted, and the *News* expanded with it. Much of the journalistic progress can be attributed to the talents of John M. Barret, installed by Loveland as his editor in December 1878. Barret was a Kentuckian, a law graduate of Center College, and he served with the Rebel army in the Civil War. When the war was over he became an editor of the New Orleans *Picayune* and then edited both the *Times* and the *Republican* in St. Louis and the Sedalia, Missouri, *Democrat* before Loveland brought him to Denver.

Barret became "the chief of the *News*" and the best-known news-paperman of his day in Colorado. Within a few months, despite espousal of the minority political cause, Barret raised the circulation of the *News* from 2300 to 5000. William Vickers, his predecessor as chief editor of the *News*, wrote:

> The News, losing the patronage that had clung to it through Re-publican ownership, was regarded as a stranded investment. The sub-scription list had dwindled to a beggarly edition, and old publishers predicted its suspension at the close of the campaign. But with the indomitable energy that has since characterized his management, Mr. Barret took the News, infused life into its editorial pages, and made its news columns bristle with fresh and sparkling intelligence that gave the paper a strong foothold which has since been fostered and strength-ened, until today it is regarded as a most important factor in educating public opinion in Colorado.[15]

15William B. Vickers, *History of Denver* (Chicago, 1880), pp. 319–20.

The paper was now selling for five cents a copy, six days a week. There was no Monday edition. By carrier or mail, subscribers could have the *News* for twenty-five cents a week, $1.00 a month, $2.50 for three months, $5.00 for six, or $10 a year. The weekly paper went for $2.00 a year.

On July 4, 1879, Barret enlarged and changed the format of his paper. It had been appearing for years as a nine-column "blanket" folio of four pages. Now it came forth in a six-column quarto of eight pages as a result, it was stated, of "constantly increasing advertising patronage." Moreover the Sunday issue became a mammoth twelve-page edition filled with social, literary, and sporting news along with the hammer-and-tongs politics. "On top as usual," the paper boasted, "and we propose to stay there. . . . Pretty as a school girl, The News comes out in its best bib and tucker."

Nine days later, on July 13, the *News* announced it had a remedy for the late appearance of the paper on the streets. The expanded size had made the press runs longer, it was explained, but now a new Cottrell & Babcock press had been constructed for the *News* in the East. It would be able to turn out "3000 IMPRESSIONS AN HOUR!" The new press was in operation on July 27, and the plant also added a quarto medium Gordon job press. There were now five presses in the office, and James Beattie was the press foreman.

A book review column was added, and illustrations now began to appear occasionally. One of the first had been printed on January 19 and amounted to a generous salute to the political victor by the vanquished. It was a wood engraving of Senator Nathaniel P. Hill, the man who got the post Loveland had wanted. Woodcuts had been common in the advertising columns of the paper for several years, but only rarely did it occur to the editors that news stories could be illustrated. A two-column woodcut of the first building at the new state agricultural college in Fort Collins was printed on July 27, but the next notable feat of illustrated journalism did not come until January 1, 1880, when the *News* sent to the Photo-Electro Company of Boston to have a four-and-a-half-column cut made of a view of the new town of Leadville. This twenty-eight-page New Year edition also contained a number of two- and one-column woodcuts of stores and buildings, many of them probably engraved in Denver by J. M. Bagley, who had done the portrait of Senator Hill. On June 17, 1881, the *News* put its first picture on page one—a likeness of James Moon, desperado, who on the day previous had received a fatal dose of lead in the Arcade Saloon on Larimer Street. The illustration was a "kaolotype"—a chalk, scratch-block technique— by the Mills Engr. Company, a resident of the News Block but apparently an independent organization. The picture didn't print very well. Stereotyping was not yet in use, and the fragile, gouged-out lines on the chalk surface couldn't stand the poundings of the giant Cottrell & Bab-cock at its mad pace.

The Press Club met on July 5, 1879, at the home of Wolfe Londoner, a rotund grocer who later was elected mayor and who enjoyed great popularity among the newspapermen because of his well-stocked cellar. The name of J. E. Leet of the *News* was proposed to the meeting for membership. In a few years Leet would become one of the festive circle of antic journalists which centered on Eugene Field. Another addition to the *News* editorial staff in 1879 was J. S. Dickerson, late of the Indianapolis *Sentinel*. Other members of Barret's staff included "Cap" Smith and John McKenna, and there were occasional contributions from John McCarthy, who wrote under the nom de plume of Fitz-Mac, and William F. Stapleton, later managing editor.

Promotional and special-edition journalism was beginning in Denver at this time. The *News* began publishing elaborate New Year editions, and on April 23, 1879, it marked its twentieth anniversary with some prominence. An illustrated annual of the history of Colorado was offered to subscribers on January 1, 1882. By April 7 the bait was George A. Crofutt's *Grip-Sack Guide of Colorado,* "a complete encyclopedia of the state; resources and condensed authentic descriptions of every city, town, village, station, post office and important mining camp . . . where to hunt, fish and view the most magnificent scenery in the world. . . ." The following year the *News* prepared its own *Colorado Condensed* pamphlet, partly for the tourist trade and partly to boost circulation. Calcium lights were brought out into Larimer Street to whoop it up for the election returns on the night of November 2, 1880.

Editorially the paper boasted that it was "not a corporation sheet," and proved it by coming out strongly for the income tax and the labor-ing man. It also was campaigning at white heat for free coinage of silver and at somewhat more reasonable temperature for a sanitary sewer system.

In its Democratic affection for the workingman and his vote the *News* fanned the flames of public violence in these years with as dishonorable a result, in retrospective view, as the bloodthirstiness with which it had promoted and justified the Sand Creek Massacre.

Thousands of Chinese laborers had been imported as railroad track laborers, particularly by the Central Pacific, in the building of the transcontinental line. Some of them came on to Denver after the Denver Pacific was completed in 1870, and slowly a small Chinatown grew up in the lower downtown area bounded by Sixteenth, Eighteenth, Blake, and Wazee streets. The census for 1880 shows that 238 Chinese, most of the men still wearing pigtails, were living in Denver.

The *News* contended that the Chinese worked for nothing and ate mice. Their undercutting effect on wage rates was such that the American workman couldn't compete. The Chinaman, like the Ute, would have to go. A reporter was sent down to Chinatown for an on-the-scene report. He discovered for the paper of March 28, 1880, a scandalous nest of opium dens and about a hundred and fifty residents, most of them washermen. Of the population, only thirteen were women, and of these, three were the wives of gainfully employed (if mouse-eating) husbands. The other ten were ladies "of easy virtue or no virtue."

The Chinese became a major political issue in the West during the 1880 campaign of James A. Garfield, and the *News* contributed its share to the angry emotions. As election day approached, the fever grew. The riot came on October 31.

Several railroad toughs under a head of payday steam entered a saloon on Wazee Street near Sixteenth and found two Chinese there. They hit one of them over the head with a billiard cue. The other drew a pistol and took a badly aimed shot at his tormentors. Within a few minutes word had spread through town that a Chinaman had killed a white man. A mob formed and began to ransack Chinatown, seeking victims. Windows were broken, doors pushed in, and shanties pulled down. The Chinese were beaten, hounded, and their pigtails tied together. Before the twenty-five-man police force and a volunteer fire company with hoses could break up the riot one inoffensive old man had been hanged from a lamppost opposite the Markham Hotel.

In a few days the excitement died away. The Chinese colony, as time went on, grew slightly and continued to hold a modest place in the community. Its few score wage earners did not noticeably subvert Anglo-Saxon civilization or undermine prosperity. They moved quietly through the city's streets and customs with a profound Eastern courtesy and dignity, accepting their lot and improving it. But it would be decades after the 1880 riot before Denver would remember it with any uneasy feeling that decency had been violated. In the seventies and eighties the days were too golden, abundant destiny too glorious, to permit such gloomy philosophies.

Something of the spirit of the times is captured in a bit of doggerel which was warmly applauded by civic nabobs gathered for a meeting of the Manufacturers' Exchange:

Ode to Denver
All hail to thee, City of Denver!
  Bright gem of the Centennial State.
Thy history is brief, yet as brilliant
  As the gold from thy mountains so great.
The range of the Rockies engird thee,
  Their snow peaks like sentinels stand.
The breath from their pinnacles nerve thee
  To a destiny lofty and grand.

Chorus——
Our song then for Denver the Peerless,
    Shall roll down from Mountain to Sea;
As leaps through the Canon the Cascade,
    So our hearts leap at mention of thee.
San Francisco and New York, our gateways,
    Through which come all lands east and west;
Chicago, the lap of our riches,
    Kansas City and St. Louis fair breasts.
But Denver still shines as the Jewel
    Aloft on Columbia's brow,
Her diadem rich Colorado,
    Crown of glory and always as now.

With health for the sick and wealth for the poor,
    And a tree shaded homestead for all;
Sparkling rivulets flowing past every door.
    Gardens echoing turtledove's call.
Surely this was the vision across the wide plains,
    Weary Pike's Peak pilgrims saw
A city where Liberty equally reigns,
    The home of Virtue and Law.[16]

The "ode" was not merely read to the meeting, nor printed offhand in the program. It was set to music and sung by a male quartet.

As Denver moved into the 1880s hymning herself such music, a new name entered into the continuing story of the *Rocky Mountain News.* The paper announced on June 15, 1880, that John Arkins had purchased a part interest from Loveland and henceforth would direct the general management. John Barret would continue as editor in chief, and there would be no change in politics. Arkins had bought a quarter interest, and in the reorganization of the company Loveland continued as president, Arkins became vice-president, Gus Alden secretary, and Frank W. Loveland, son of the principal owner, treasurer.

Arkins was Irish, dashing, and handsome. He became the "glamorous gladiator" of Denver journalism, and his wit gave the nation a widely reported anecdote to chuckle over. On a visit to New York, Arkins was interviewed by a big-time reporter much concerned over the burning issue of a site for the forthcoming World's Fair.

"Colonel Arkins," the newsman asked, "where do you think the World's Fair should be held?"

"Around the waist," Arkins answered.

[16]Programme, Manufacturers' Exchange, Oct. 3, 1885; Woodbury scrapbook.

CHAPTER FIFTEEN

Eugene Field in Denver

OUR ESTEEMED CONTEMPORY

This Awkward sheet is our Esteemed Contemporary. It is Run by an Unhung Felon. We would not Give him a Glass of Water to Save his Life, but we would Take a Beer with him if we were Properly Approached. Our esteemed Contemporary has no Circulation and its influence is Correspondingly Small. It cuts Advertising Rates and is So Mean it would Skin a Skunk to Save a Scent. If we had Our Way, we would Suspend our Esteemed Contemporary and Put its Editors and Reporters in Jail where they belong.

THE sketch is from *The Tribune Primer* by Eugene Field, who was managing editor of the Denver *Tribune* from 1881 to August 1883, and who is best remembered in Denver, not for the boozily sentimental children's verse which charmed the contentedly teary American *fin de siècle*, but for his practical jokes. These were sometimes as crude as putting a cannon cracker in a roast turkey at a banquet, or as inspired as impersonating Oscar Wilde.

The "esteemed contemporary" of Field's portrait can only have been Arkins' *Rocky Mountain News*. For while the *Tribune* often squabbled with or sniped at the other Republican dailies—the *Times* and the *Republican*—all three of them reserved their best insults for the Democratic *News*. As the dominant paper, the venerable pioneer, it was the No. 1 bear for their baiting. Moreover its political creed was popular with no one in an era when wealth gushed from the mountains endlessly and anyone who was anybody was either a millionaire or about to be. Popular with no one, apparently, except the man in the street who bought a daily paper, owned no silver mines, and was yet to make his voice heard at the Colorado polls in the face of skillful ballot-box stuffing and voting of gravestones. The Republicans were pious, rich, and determined to keep on winning, and three fourths of the Denver press served their intentions.

When Arkins took over operating control of the *News* the little city of Denver was entering upon a silver-lined decade of showy affluence. Gold had created the town, but it was the white metal which put Tiffany doorknobs in the brownstone mansions on newly aristocratic Capitol Hill, popped the corks on an ocean of Mumm's, and blazoned sometimes questionable heraldic crests on the glistening broughams. There wasn't a native son in town old enough to grow a beard, but Denver was acquiring the airs of London and the manners of Pompeii.

Much of the wealth was rolling down from Leadville, ten thousand feet in the clouds on the other side of the Mosquito Range from South Park. There, at the foot of Colorado's loftiest peaks, the silver lodes were discovered in 1878. Within two years the town had a 15,000 population and four daily newspapers. Soon it blossomed out with an opera house and a theater seating five thousand in four tiers of gilt boxes. In the space of ten years Leadville showered more than a hundred million dollars down on Denver.

Two of America's most famous fortunes got their start in the Leadville mines. Marshall Field took a gamble on the Chrysolite mine, hit the jackpot, and compounded his immense profits as Chicago's merchant prince. Meyer Guggenheim and his seven sons built their world-wide financial empire on a watered Leadville mine and Colorado smelters which later swallowed up the giant American Smelting & Refining Company.

The same Chrysolite mine which gave its blessings to Marshall Field also was one of the sources of the H. A. W. Tabor fortune. Tabor, an indigent Vermont stonecutter, became Colorado's most fabled silver king. His personal income in 1882 was estimated at four million dollars. Most of it came from the Little Pittsburgh and the Matchless mines, but the Chrysolite contributed its share. And the Chrysolite was supposed to be a hoax. Legend insists that "Chicken Bill" Lovell salted the Chrysolite when he sold it to Tabor for nine hundred dollars—and moreover got the high-grade ore for the salting from Tabor's own Little Pittsburgh. Tabor sank the shaft another ten feet and hit a lode which produced three millions. The Tabor lucky streak began one May morning in 1878 when he grubstaked two prospectors to about seventeen dollars in groceries in return for a third interest in anything they found. They found the Little Pittsburgh, incorporated that fall at twenty million.

Tabor built Leadville its opera house and then moved down to Denver to look after his growing interests, which included half the First National Bank. He put up a sixty-thousand-dollar mansion for his faithful, strait-laced wife Augusta, who wore a pince-nez and a green-persimmon expression. With stone imported from Ohio he constructed the towering, six-story Tabor Block, still standing at Sixteenth and Larimer streets. He became part owner of the plush Windsor Hotel, which also survives on now tawdry Larimer Street but recently had to be rescued as a historical landmark.

Finally, to crown his civic glory, Tabor opened on September 5, 1881, the Tabor Grand Opera House (now a movie house) with Emma Abbott singing *Lucia* to the most *recherché* audience Denver had produced to date. The opera house was fitted out with carpets from Brussels, French brocades and tapestries, Japanese cherry wood, mahogany from Honduras, and a painting of H.A.W. The story goes that the niche had been intended for the Bard. Tabor, who supervised every detail, had happened by while the artist was at work on the portrait. He wanted to know who was being painted. His comment has become part of the enduring folklore of Denver:

"Willum Shakespeare? Who's Willum Shakespeare and what in hell did he ever do fer Colorado? Paint him out and put me up thar."

Tabor's millions got him into a lively scandal and the United States Senate (for thirty days, on a vacancy appointment). Flitting around Denver at the time, and hailed as the most beautiful woman in Colorado, was a blonde divorcee with a creamy expression and tiptilted nose. Her name was Elizabeth Bonduel McCourt, but everyone called her "Baby Doe." She had just won a divorce from her husband, Harvey Doe, by personally leading a raid on a popular bagnio and dragging him away from his scarlet diversions practically by the ear. Tabor reportedly paid a thousand dollars for an introduction to Baby Doe and soon she was installed as his mistress in a luxurious suite at the Clarendon Hotel in Leadville. Their affair was common gossip, and tongues flapped. Old-line society—anyone in Denver whose wealth and social standing dated back in excess of two years—looked down its nose at the coarse *parvenu* from the Little Pittsburgh and gave its support to Augusta, who didn't hold at all with the high life her once poor husband now was leading.

There was a callous divorce, and Tabor married his Baby Doe in the Willard Hotel in Washington with President Chester A. Arthur among those present. The bride wore a seventy-five-hundred-dollar gown and a ninety-thousand-dollar diamond necklace, but the Colorado delegation in Washington snubbed the wedding. Denver never accepted the alliance. The Republican party, though it enjoyed his lavish contributions, withheld further political honors from Tabor. The silver king had bought his election to a term as lieutenant governor in 1878, and in 1883 when President Arthur appointed Senator Henry M. Teller Secretary of the Interior, Tabor was presented with the thirty-day remainder of Teller's term as a pat on the head for his campaign-fund generosities.[1]

The appointment caused criticism, but the *News* argued candidly (from the Democratic side of the fence and comfortably uninvolved): "There are twenty-six men in the United States Senate because they are millionaires. Why should Tabor be barred on account of his millions?"

The Tabor story ends in pathos. He lost everything except the Matchless mine in the panic of 1893 when the price of silver dropped below production costs. His fall was as abrupt as his rise had been. Suddenly he was poor again, and an old man. Friends obtained his appointment

[1] R. G. Dill, *The Political Campaigns of Colorado* (Denver, 1895), pp. 29ff. and 62ff.

as Denver postmaster to spare him from his three-dollar-a-day job wheeling slag in a Leadville smelter. He died in 1899, and his last words to his still young and pretty wife were: "Hold onto the Matchless." Baby Doe accepted the charge. She moved into the shaft house of the Matchless, long since water-filled and derelict. She died there in 1935, starved and frozen. Her feet were wrapped in gunny sacks.

On the curtain of the Tabor Grand Opera House there had been painted, in the fashion of the day, a scene of decadent and noble Old World ruins. Beneath the picture are two lines from Charles Kingsley's poem "Old and New":

> So fleet the works of men, back to the earth again;
> Ancient and holy things fade like a dream.

The words were of Tabor's own selection. Canon Kingsley had visited Colorado in 1874 and for a time occupied the pulpit of Grace Episcopal Church in Colorado Springs. Tabor heard one of his sermons, met the visiting English cleric, and was presented with a thin volume of his poems. Years later, when the opera house was being finished, Tabor designated the soothsaying two lines: "I want these on the curtain."

The motion picture *Silver Dollar* based on Tabor's rise and fall has him die brokenhearted beneath the Kingsley lines on the stage of the deserted opera house. Actually he died of a ruptured appendix in a cheap Denver rooming house. The legend-inspiring Tabor story also has been told in the folk opera, *The Ballad of Baby Doe*, by Douglas Moore and John LaTouche, presented originally with a Metropolitan cast at the 1956 Opera Festival in Central City, where Tabor met Baby Doe, then to critical acclaim on Broadway and, more recently, at the Brussels International Exposition.

But the Tabor story was only one of many in Denver of the 1880s, more glamorous than most perhaps, and if in it nature outdid art in melodrama there were dozens of other men who also rode an incomparable boom to insuperable heights. Few rose so fast or plunged so sharply, but the Midas-men and their ladies set the pace, and they turned a town into a city. Some of the other mining and smelting kings of the era included Byers' old friend, David H. Moffat, Jr., Nathaniel P. Hill, Ed Wolcott, Tom Bowen, James B. Grant, J. J. Brown, and John F. Campion.

Nor was Leadville the only camp which rained riches on Denver. Just west over the mountains from Tabor's town was Aspen with the Smuggler, the Mollie Gibson, the Midnight, and the Tam-O-Shanter, all producing ore faster than the pack trains of jacks or the narrow-gauge railroads could haul it away. From Aspen would come the "world's biggest" silver nugget—1840 pounds and 93 per cent pure. Ore and bullion also poured in from the San Juans, Ouray, Telluride, Silverton, and Durango; from the upper reaches of Clear Creek Valley, George-town, and Silver Plume; from Nederland and Caribou in the high country west of Boulder.

Along with silver, one of the products of boom-time Leadville was John Arkins. Arkins went to the Cloud City as a printer, a compositor. He returned in slightly over a year to become one of the most capable and successful editor-publishers in the record of Denver journalism.

Arkins was born in Fayette County, Pennsylvania, and learned his trade in the office of the *Goodhue County Republican* at Red Wing, Minnesota, and on the St. Louis *Globe*. He served with the 5th Minnesota through the Civil War, lugging around a volume of the complete plays of Shakespeare while fellow soldiers were sifting gun-powder from their cartridges to make the belts lighter. Later Arkins said he always planned to write a book of his war experiences to be called *Three Years under a Musket: The Plain Story of a Private*. Unfortu-nately, he said, he had been mustered out a corporal and thus was shut out from authorship. Military titles were long-lived and frequently spurious in Arkins' day, and he was generally called "colonel." He jeered at the unearned title, which was given him by Colorado Governor James B. Grant and afterward by other governors who enjoyed decorative staffs.[2]

Arkins came west to Denver in 1873 and started as a printer for Stanley G. Fowler's *Sunday Mirror*. By 1878 he was foreman of the composing room of the *Tribune*. When word of the Leadville strikes reached town he and two fellow *Tribune* compositors, Carlyle Channing Davis and James M. Burnell, decided to try a paper of their own in the new camp. They borrowed every penny anyone would lend them, invested in a press, type, and other equipment, and sent their "office" up into the mountains by pack train. The three partners followed by stage and on January 29, 1879, a crowd waited in the muddy streets of Leadville from 3 until 9 P.M. for the maiden issue of their Leadville *Chronicle*, the camp's first daily paper. Arkins was the editor, "Cad" Davis gathered news as the leg man, and Burnell was business manager.

The *Chronicle* was a small silver mine in itself. By early the following year Arkins and Burnell had made so much and learned so much that they felt ready to buck the big time in Denver. Davis stayed on and subsequently changed the name of the paper to the *Herald-Democrat*. It is still being published under that name.

Arkins invested his share of the *Chronicle* earnings in a quarter interest in Loveland's *Rocky Mountain News* and took over editorial control on June 15, 1880. He had learned a lot in Leadville. Under Arkins the *News* matured, converted petty bickerings with the other

2Ellis Meredith, "Three Distinguished Figures of the Early Rocky Mountain News," *Colorado Magazine*, Vol. XXVII, No. 1 (Jan. 1950), pp. 34ff.

papers into a hammer-and-tongs style of aggressiveness, and solidly underscored its leadership.

Those who have written of Arkins speak in almost one voice of a ready wit, Irish charm and gallantry, a level and modest head in times of much foolish pretense, of flashing blue eyes and a shock of black curly hair. Surviving pictures show a handsome man.

Frank Hall, who was a contemporary and knew him, wrote:

> That Mr. Arkins is a man of acute perceptions, of quick nervous energy and indomitable perseverance, is manifest to all who know him; that he is capable of producing excellent editorial matter when moved to it, is a part of his record; that he is a steadfast, helpful friend to his friends, is proverbial; that he is almost extravagantly generous, kind hearted, sympathetic and charitable, hundreds will attest; that he is always just or intensely scrupulous in politics, will not be claimed; that he is prone to lash his enemies with ships of scorpions, and exalt his adherents, is the natural outgrowth of an ardent, impulsive temperament [Hall was one of the leading opposition editorial writers, a Republican true blue, and earlier acting governor]. Strong, impetuous, bold and daring, he is fond of leading, directing, dominating, yet he is one of the most captivating and companionable of comrades in social intercourse, known and admired throughout the broad field of journalism from the Atlantic to the Pacific coast. His capabilities as a manager are seen in the phenomenal augmentation of value in the "News" property from $150,000 in March, 1886, to nearly $400,000 in 1890. As the successor of Mr. Byers in the "New Era," he became the potential force of the paper. From the poor and humble printer of 1879, he has risen to affluence, and to a conspicuous position among the strong influences of his time.[3]

Arkins was not long in making his strong influence felt when he joined Loveland as junior but managing partner in 1880. Within a few weeks the *News* was beginning to use page one for news matter instead of advertising. Headlines ceased to be labels or captions and began to tell the story, although in the style of the times they frequently were nearly as long as the articles they headed. Some of them ran thirteen "decks" or more in an elegant variety of types, caps, lower case, and italics. There was more experimenting with illustration. The paper expanded to ten pages, and soon a Monday edition was added to put publication on the seven-day basis which has continued since.

In November additional fonts of type were added to the cases, and Arkins brought in a new press. Richard M. Hoe had been working since 1845 to perfect a rotary, type-revolving press to replace the flat-bed models which had been in use ever since Gutenberg.[4] Into the News Block came

[3]Frank Hall, op. cit., Vol. III, pp. 138–39.

[4]Thomas MacKellar, *The American Printer* (Philadelphia, 1889), pp. 239–40.

one of Hoe's latest efforts: a double-cylinder press capable of pounding out 4500 impressions in an hour. The new Hoe probably succeeded the Cottrell & Babcock, although Frank Hall mentions that a single-cylinder Potter had been in use.[5]

On January 1, 1881, the *News* again reviewed its ancient history, making point of the perfect parallels in the annals and growth of newspaper and city. To the discomfort of its smaller competitors, the paper boasted that a payroll of seventy-five to a hundred persons now was required to meet demand for its superior product, and a staff of eight constantly alert editors and reporters bent to their literary labors on a we-never-sleep basis to supply Denver's needs for immediate intelligences of city, state, nation, and world. When the *Republican* bought a new press the *News* fired a hot shot about "a Bullock press in the basement and bullock brains in the editorial rooms."

With its own new Hoe press in position and operating, the *News* announced on November 23, 1880, that hereafter it would devote part of its Saturday editions to coverage of sporting news. The result was Denver's first sports page, and very partisan to the Denver Browns. The ball park was on Glency Street (originally Clancy, then Glancy and Glency, and now Tremont Place) between Fifteenth and Sixteenth streets, about where a skyscraper hotel is currently rising under auspices of William Zeckendorf, the New York real estate wonder boy Denver irreverently calls "Wild Bill."

The *News* staff of the day was headed by William F. Stapleton, one-time associate editor and later Washington correspondent for the St. Louis *Globe-Democrat,* who took over from Barret in 1882 or 1883. Other staff members included Richard Stapleton, William's brother, as city editor, John Shepherd, Charles M. Thompson, C. G. Noble, Ralph Bayard, J. Gordon Temple, Clint Snowden, Ben Zalinger, Mrs. C. M. Hampson, the *News'* first woman writer and possibly the first in the West. "Cap" Smith was back after a term as city clerk. W. R. Thomas returned to the staff in 1886. Will C. Ferril was city editor in 1887–88. Another city editor of the day was named Henry James and became a Hearst pillar in San Francisco.

James Burnell returned from a season of prospecting Battle Mountain and in September 1881 rejoined Arkins. He was given charge of the *News'* mechanical departments. Later he became business manager. One of his chief assistants was Frederick A. Meredith, appointed composing-room foreman in 1885, later proofreader and then managing editor. Meredith had worked beside Arkins at the cases of the *Goodhue County Republican* in Minnesota and subsequently on the *Globe* in St. Louis, and he is the man credited with the novel notion of Monday paydays for printers. When he became composing-room foreman of the *Globe-*

[5]Hall, op. cit., p. 138.

Democrat he found he was having difficulty getting the Sunday edition out on Saturday nights. Printers of the day were at least as bibulous as the modern variety, and the Saturday payday created lush patronage for adjacent saloons and five-thumbed typesetting in the composing room. Meredith announced that henceforth salaries would accrue on Mondays, a practice soon adopted throughout the newspaper publishing business. There was some grumbling among the *Globe* compositors, but none from *Globe* compositors' wives, who began getting first cut at the pay envelopes, and the Sunday edition had fewer "bulls" to annoy readers sensitive to typographical error. Meredith's daughter Ellis did a turn in the *News* proofroom and then became one of the most prominent of Denver's early newspaperwomen at the turn of the century. She went on to Washington as a correspondent and for many years was a prominent member of the capital press corps.

The *News* got out a rash of special editions in 1883 for the national encampment of the Grand Army of the Republic, a gathering which launched Denver's career as a convention city. The year 1883 also saw the first of a series of reprints of the first issue of the *News*, facsimile duplicates which ever since have been confused with authentic copies of the valuable maiden edition.

William B. Thom, a *News* compositor in the eighties, has left some reminiscent sketches of the period:

> Those were the days of handset type, the installation of the linotype machine in the News office taking place several years later. The night force worked under gaslight. At midnight an old man whose name I regret to have forgotten brought to us in a pushcart an excellent luncheon; and such was his opinion of the integrity of the News printers that he took the word of each customer as to the amount due for food consumed. . . .
>
> If a printer had a timepiece that he desired to pawn for a few dollars until the next pay day, he found accommodation at the watch-repairing shop of General Don Carlos Hasselteno, next door to the News office, the rate of interest being, as I remember it, 25 percent per month. . . .[6]

Thom also ticked off a partial roster of his colleagues in the composing room: David W. Phillips, H. M. Green, C. H. Poole, Al C. Holt, O. L. Smith, Oscar L. Smallwood, W. H. Dedrick, John W. Hastie, Horace Haines, Oliver App, Henry Lees, James Young, Charles L. Merritt, Angelo Noce, Joseph Utter, Harry Buchanan, Willis A. Brainard, Charles F. Coffin, C. M. Kimball, Schuyler C. Killen, James Egan, Walter Shissler, James Salisbury, James Laughlin, James F. Boyne, George T. McFall, A. G. Anderson, David W. Phillips, Charles J. Spencer, Thomas

[6]William B. Thom, "As It Was in the '80s," *The Trail*, Vol. XX, No. 2 (July 1927), p. 3.

J. Morris, Horace Duff, Charles Boughton, Buff Corwin, and Andrew McNassor. Many of these men left descendants who still pursue the printing trades in Denver.

With more than fifty columns of type to set for each daily edition, the *News* required a proportionately large staff of printers. A handful of scribblers and editors could take care of what news coverage was necessary and defend institutional honor from the slings and arrows of Eugene Field.

The *News* as the dominant paper and Arkins as its editor became the puckish Field's targets-of-choice, though he didn't spare his contemporaries on the *Times* and *Republican*. Field already had something of a reputation as jackanapes and pungent paragrapher before he came to the Denver *Tribune*. He had been managing editor of the Kansas City *Times* for about a year in 1881 when O. H. Rothacker, *Tribune* editor, heard about him and made a journey east to lure him to Denver at the princely wage of forty dollars a week. In Denver he made legend as managing editor of the *Tribune*, although he stayed less than three years.

Anticipating Don Marquis, Field seized upon the lowly cockroach as a literary device. He did not develop a rationale by which an insect could write lower-case sentences on a typewriter, but he let it be known that he was the cockroach's friend and could speak the language.

In this fashion, Field asserted in his column, "The Nonpareil," he had learned that when Arkins became the chief of the *News* he had instituted such a penurious system of economy in regard to editorial-room paste that he starved out half a million dependent roaches. The report had come to him first hand. A poor, weak, emaciated cockroach had crept over to the *Tribune* from the *News* and had become Field's confidant. The bug now was sleek and fat and prosperous because in the *Tribune* office there was plenty of paste, as well as dirty towels and crumbs from the printers' lunch table, all evidence of "the superior management of the *Tribune* and the humane principles and generosity of its editors."

The "Colorado Roach" became a fixture. Field transcribed roach dialogues to needle Arkins and the *News*, and composed an essay entitled "To Improve the Literary Style of the Rocky Mountain News." No opportunity was lost to send a barbed dart at Arkins and the *News*, but they were not the only victims. Field also took on the rest of the local press, politicians of both stripes, and any likely businessman. One of his hoaxes helped elect a mayor, though that wasn't the intention, and the Georgetown *Courier* complained that Field finally had gone too far and "should be muzzled" when he made sport of Colorado's first congressman.

Judge James B. Belford was known as the "Red Rooster of the Rockies" because of his flaming hair and magnificently roseate beard. The Field report which roused the *Courier's* ire ran like this:

Congressman Belford has suddenly developed into a great social belle at Washington. Young ladies from every part of the republic are besieging him for strands of his beautiful red hair for their crazy quilts. One fair female from the Sunny South has completed a lovely quilt, the centerpiece of which is a most unique design composed entirely of hair from the Colorado congressman's head and beard. It represents a big juicy strawberry on a terracotta-colored plaque.

Kemp G. Cooper, once president of the News Printing Company, was reserved and aloof, a man of much chill dignity. By this time Cooper was managing director of the *Republican* and Field wrote: "Colonel K. G. Cooper went swimming in the hot water pool at Manitou last Sunday afternoon, and the place was used as a skating rink in the evening."

Grocer Wolfe Londoner was Field's good friend, in fact, as generous and perennial host to the Press Club, the good friend of every newspaperman in town. The *Tribune's* practical joke on him had unexpected consequences. Field inserted an advertisement in his paper to the effect that "in appreciation of our colored citizens, of whom he is a great admirer, Wolfe Londoner invites every member of that race in Denver to come to his store at 4 o'clock this afternoon, where each will receive a present of a fine watermelon." Londoner bought up three carloads of melons and was ready. The gratitude of a sizable bloc of voters did him no harm in his then current job as Republican campaign manager, and he went on to election as mayor.

The paragraphs which later were gathered into *The Tribune Primer*, a rare little book today much prized as a collector's item by persons who scorn Field's more famous children's verse, originally appeared in his day-to-day column during 1881 and 1882. Several of them deal with the Denver newspaper scene.

The Bottle

This is a Bottle. What is in the Bottle? Very bad Whisky. It has been Sent to the Local Editor. He did not Buy it. If he had Bought it the Whisky would have been Poorer than it is. Little Children, you Must never Drink Bad Whisky.

The City Editor

Here we Have a City Editor. He is Talking with the Foreman. He is saying he will have a Full Paper in the Morning. The Foreman is Smiling Sadly. Maybe he is Thinking the Paper will have a Full City Editor before Morning.

The Editor's Home

Here is a Castle. It is the Home of an Editor. It has stained Glass windows and Mahogany stairways. In front of the Castle is a Park. Is it not Sweet? The lady in the Park is the editor's wife. She wears a Costly robe of Velvet trimmed with Gold Lace, and there are Pearls and Rubies in her hair. The editor sits on the front Stoop smoking a Havana Cigar. His little Children are playing with diamond Marbles on the Tesselated Floor. The editor can afford to Live in Style. He gets Seventy-Five Dollars a month Wages.

THE BUSINESS MANAGER

Here we Have a Business Manager. He is Blowing about the Circulation of the Paper. He is Saying the Paper has Entered upon an Era of Unprecedented Prosperity. In a Minute he will Go up Stairs and Chide the Editor for leaving his Gas Burning while he Went out for a Drink of Water, and he will dock a Reporter Four Dollars because a Subscriber has Licked him and he cannot Work. Little Children, if we Believed Business Managers went to Heaven, we would Give up our Pew in Church.

THE REPORTER

What is That I see? That, my Child, is the *News* Interviewer, and he is now Interviewing a Man. But where is the Man? I can see no Man. The Man, My Child, is in his Mind.

The "local editor" of the *Tribune* in these days was E. D. Cowen, who became city editor of the *News* in 1902 following a stint in Europe in charge of the London and Paris editions of Bennett's *Herald*. In a memoir Cowen recalled the black walnut chair in Field's office. The chair had no bottom, but its seatlessness was concealed by a casually thrown newspaper. Purpose of the device was to discourage libel and damage suits, which, in view of Field's methods, must have been often threatened. Unwary callers would drop into the chair and plunge through to an undignified and awkward position. "When the victim chanced to be an irate complainant," Cowen wrote, "Field would make profuse apologies for the scant furnishings of the office, owing to the poverty of the publishing company, and tender his own chair as some small compensation for the mishap."[7]

There is good reason to believe that Field never took seriously the weepy nursery verse he began writing during his Denver years. It brought him a sort of fame, which he always discounted, and he himself described it as "popular but rotten." It must have shocked the thousands who dabbled at their eyes over "Little Boy Blue" and his faithful toy soldier when Field declared flatly in his foreword to the 1901 Boston edition of *The Complete Tribune Primer*: "I do not love all children."

One of his vernacular poems tells a newspaper story of Denver:

[7]Charles A. Murray and others, *Newspaper Career of E. D. Cowen* (Seattle, 1930), pp. 129–30.

Mr. Dana, of the New York Sun

Thar showed up out'n Denver in the spring uv '81
A man who'd worked with Dana on the Noo York Sun.
His name wuz Cantell Whoppers, 'nd he wuz a sight ter view
Ez he walked inter the orfice 'nd inquired fer work to do.
Thar warn't no places vacant then,—fer be it understood,
That wuz the time when talent flourished at that altitood;
But thar the stranger lingered, tellin' Raymond 'nd the rest
Uv what perdigious wonders he could do when at his best,
'Til finally he stated (quite by chance) that he hed done
A heap uv work with Dana on the Noo York Sun.

Wall, that wuz quite another thing; we owned that ary cuss
Who'd worked f'r Mr. Dana *must* be good enough fer *us!*
And so we tuk the stranger's word 'nd nipped him while we could,
For if *we didn't* take him we knew John Arkins *would;*
And Cooper, too, wuz mouzin' round fer enterprise 'nd brains,
Whenever them commodities blew in across the plains.
At any rate we nailed him, which made ol' Cooper swear
And Arkins tear out handfuls uv his copious curly hair;
But *we* set back and cackled, 'nd hed a power uv fun
With our man who'd worked with Dana on the Noo York Sun.

It made our eyes hang on our cheeks, 'nd lower jaws ter drop
Ter hear that feller tellin' how ol' Dana run his shop;
It seems that Dana wuz the biggest man you ever saw,—
He lived on human bein's, 'nd preferred to eat 'em raw!
If he hed democratic drugs ter take, before he took 'em,
As good old allopathic laws prescribe, he allus shook 'em.
The man that could set down 'nd write like Dany never grew,
And the sum of human knowledge wuzn't half what Dana knew;
The consequences appeared to be that nearly every one
Concurred with Mr. Dana of the Noo York Sun.

This feller, Cantell Whoppers, never brought an item in,—
He spent his time at Perrin's shakin' poker dice f'r gin.
Whatever the assignment he wuz allus sure to shirk,
He wuz very long on likker and all-fired short on work!
If any other cuss had played the tricks he dared ter play,
The daisies would be bloomin' over his remains to-day;
But somehow folks respected him and stood him to the last,
Considerin' his superior connections in the past.
So, when he bilked at poker, not a sucker drew a gun
On the man who'd worked with Dana on the Noo York Sun.

Wall, Dana came ter Denver in the fall uv '83,
A very different party from the man we thought ter see,—
A nice 'nd clean old gentleman, so dignerfied 'nd calm,
You bet yer life he never did no human bein' harm!
A certain hearty manner 'nd a fulness uv the vest
Betokened that his sperrits 'nd his victuals wuz the best;

His face was so benevolent, his smile so sweet 'nd kind,
That they seemed to be the reflex uv an honest, healthy mind;
And God had set upon his head a crown uv silver hair
In promise uv the golden crown He meaneth him to wear.
So, uv us boys that met him out'n Denver, there was none
But fell in love with Dana uv the Noo York Sun.

But when he came to Denver in that fall uv '83,
His old friend Cantell Whoppers disappeared upon a spree;
The very thought uv seein' Dana worked upon him so
(They hadn't been together fer a year or two, you know),
That he borrered all the stuff he could and started on a bat,
And, strange as it may seem, we didn't see him after that.
So, when ol' Dana hove in sight, we couldn't understand
Why he didn't seem to notice that his crony wa'n't on hand;
No casual allusion, not a question, no, not one,
For the man who'd "worked with Dana on the Noo York Sun!"

We broke it gently to him, but he didn't seem surprised,
Thar wuz no big burst uv passion as we fellers had surmised.
He said that Whoppers wuz a man he'd never heerd about,
But he mought have carried papers on a Jersey City route;
And then he recollected hearin' Mr. Laffan say
That he'd fired a man named Whoppers fur bein' drunk one day,
Which, with more likker *underneath* than money *in* his vest,
Had started on a freight train fur the great 'nd boundin' West,
But further information or statistics he had none
Uv the man who'd "worked with Dana on the Noo York Sun."

We dropped the matter quietly 'nd never made no fuss,—
When we get played for suckers, why, that's a horse on us!—
But every now 'nd then we Denver fellers have to laff
To hear some other paper boast uv havin' on its staff
A man who's "worked with Dana," 'nd then we fellers wink
And pull our hats down on our eyes 'nd set around 'nd think.
It seems like Dana couldn't be as smart as people say,
If he educates so many folks 'nd lets 'em get away;
And, as for us, in future we'll be very apt to shun
The man who "worked with Dana on the Noo York Sun."[8]

Arkins may have failed to bag the *Sun* man for the *News*, but he picked up some equally picaresque characters during the period. One of them, Ralph Bayard, came west out of New York with a reputation as a "chain-lightning man." Bayard gave the *News* a brief sample of his rapidity, turned around and went back to New York, and made a fortune as a bookmaker, withdrawing to genteel retirement during one of Tammany's reform waves.

The *News* chief, a diligent reader of exchanges, watched with interest

[8]Eugene Field, *A Little Book of Western Verse* (New York, 1895), pp. 96–102.

how the big-city papers in New York handled these periodic outbursts of civic morality. He observed that, quite aside from certain positive results in the way of municipal elevation, newspaper crusades against sin and corruption were popular with subscribers and led to increases in circulation. If it worked in New York it ought to work in Denver, which had at least its fair share of gaudy wrongdoing. So Arkins, although not notably a pecksniff, opened up on rampant vice in his prosperous and booming little city.

The saloons, many of which had side entrances for the ladies and secluded "private dining rooms" with horsehair sofas, ran seven days a week. Some of them threw away the key ceremonially at the grand opening and never closed their doors, day or night. The *News* began a campaign for a Sunday closing law. Arkins told his staff: "Any man that can't go from midnight Saturday night to six Monday morning can take a bottle home, or maybe wake up to the fact that he needs a spell without the Demon Rum. Anyhow, it's good stuff to make talk and bring in subscribers. If we succeed in getting a Sunday closing ordinance it's a victory for the paper and if we don't—well, I had three years losing battles now and then, but we won the war."[9]

The crusade made no particular dent on Denver's hard-drinking habits, and a Sunday blue law did not come until many years later, but the clergy applauded as a man, and one temperance meeting filled the Tabor Opera House to the gold-leaf rafters. As Arkins had predicted, the campaign made talk, was popular, and boosted circulation. Strangely enough, it was even popular with the bartenders, who thought it might be nice to have a day off once in a while.

Denver still was a wide-open town on gambling. Three-card monte had been banned early on the reasonable grounds that it was sleight of hand, not gambling; but the rest of the games flourished. There were numerous gaming parlors and variety halls in which a happy sucker could have his choice, or a mixture, of twenty-one, entertainment, liquor, and feminine companionship. In one of the popular resorts "Big Ed" Chase, later the city's political boss, sat on a high stool and observed all with a cold eye. Across his lap he held a shotgun to enforce decorum and discourage protests from poor losers about fast shuffles or wallets which disappeared from pants pockets in upstairs dressing rooms while the pants were temporarily unoccupied.

Another palace of chance was owned by one Jefferson Randolph ("Soapy") Smith, who earned his nickname (and the money to open his lavish graduate school for unconvinced dreamers) by operating on Leadville and Denver streets a pitch which employed a variation on the shell game. Forbes Parkhill, author of the definitive work on Denver's scarlet times, tells how it went:

[9]Ellis Meredith, op. cit., pp. 41–42.

"Use this soap and wash your sins away!" twenty-eight-year-old Soapy would call, spilling a handful of loose banknotes beside the pile of soap. "Cleanliness is next to godliness, but the feel of good, crisp greenbacks in the pocket is paradise itself. Step up, friends, and watch me closely."

He would then offer to sell those interested in cleanliness alone a soap cube for twenty-five cents. As this was some five times the market price, there would be few takers. So he would hold up a hundred-dollar bill from the pile before him.

"But if you want to take a chance on winning one of these little green papers with the big numbers on them, I'll sell you a wrapped bar at the ridiculous price of five dollars."

The watchers saw him apparently twist the hundred-dollar bill around a cube of soap and then wrap it in a square of blue paper, tossing it carelessly alongside the unwrapped pile. Swiftly his dextrous fingers would wrap additional cubes, apparently enclosing one-, ten-, or twenty-dollar bills with each.

Someone would step up, pay his five dollars, and carefully select a wrapped cube. Unwrapping it, he would shout gleefully as he displayed the hundred-dollar bill he found inside. The first buyer was, of course, Doc Baggs or another capper.

Eagerly the suckers would swarm in to take advantage of this get-rich-quick offer. But surprisingly they would find no banknotes wrapped with their soap. When business slackened off then another capper "found" a hundred-dollar bill.[10]

"Soapy" did well, but as time went on bunco games and gambling became nominally illegal. Every so often the gamblers would be hailed into court to explain their suddenly discovered flaunting of Denver's decency and to pay wrist-slap fines. So when the prospering "Soapy" prepared to open a legitimate gambling house he decided he required a dodge which would take the heat off. He employed a lawyer to help him think one up, and counsel came up with an idea. When "Soapy's" elaborate and luxurious Tivoli Club opened there was a large sign, *Caveat Emptor*, over the entrance.[11]

It was in character. Hauled in during one of the recurrent cleanups, "Soapy" blandly explained that the Tivoli was an educational institution and that he operated a cure for the soul-destroying gambling habit. The press called him "the hayseed-educator of 17th Street."

"I am conducting a fair, legitimate business," "Soapy" told the *News* reporter. "My mission is to skin suckers. I defy the newspapers to put their hands on a single man I ever beat that was not financially able to stand it.

"I am emotionally insane. When I see anyone looking in a jewelry

[10]Forbes Parkhill, *The Wildest of the West* (New York, 1951), pp. 87-88.

[11]William Ross Collier and Edwin Victor Westrate, *The Reign of Soapy Smith* (New York, 1935), p. 139.

store window thinking how they would like to get away with the diamonds, an irresistible desire comes over me to skin them. I don't drink, smoke, chew, or cheat poor people. I pay my debts."

"Soapy" also carried a pistol, and he used it on John Arkins. The *News* participated enthusiastically in, if it did not inspire, several of the anti-gambling drives. At one point the paper became so tiresomely specific on the matter that it was more than a libeled humanist and educator could bear. "Soapy" waylaid Arkins in the street one day and pistol-whipped him to the sidewalk. The *News* editor carried a scar for the rest of his days, and normally smooth and mild-mannered "Soapy" regretted his violence immediately. He sent Arkins a handsome easy chair for his office the next day. Arkins sent it back.[12]

"Soapy" also threatened Loveland, warning that he would kill the *News* owner on sight. Loveland for a time had to employ a bodyguard, F. D. (Bill) Weeks, later one of the West's most prominent metal-lurgists.[13]

The *News'* campaignings against gambling were, again, popular with the "better element" but foredoomed. In an era when the corner news-boy was taking a flier in silver-mine stocks and skyrocketing Denver real estate, no one could work up much real indignation against penny-ante stuff across green baize. Anyway, most of the natives knew enough to stay away from the luck emporiums; they were for tourists, tinhorns, and the incorrigibly hopeful.

Another of the *News'* moral-uplift projects also came to nought in the enervating climate of public unconcern. Denver in the eighties and nineties had a tenderloin second only to San Francisco's Barbary Coast or New Orleans' Storyville. The cribs and sumptuous parlor houses centered on Holladay Street, and the section became so notorious that the heirs of Ben Holladay, the stagecoach king for whom the thorough-fare had been named, petitioned City Council for relief from their shame. The street is now called Market.

The *News* alternately professed shock over the scandalous things that happened on "the Row" and chuckled archly in print with the rest of the town over the racy doings. Commercial love had progressed a long way from the crude "hog ranches" of the pioneer days. Some of the pleasure palaces were the *dernier cri* in luxury. Appointments were voluptuous, the merchandise handsome, and the madams insisted on a level of deportment which would have done credit to a countess' tea party. Loud, obscene, or profane language was strictly prohibited, and one resort entertained its clientele with Beethoven symphonies on the gramophone.

Secretly Denver was rather proud of her wickedness, and none of the periodic surges of moral redemption got much beyond fuss and feathers.

[12]Letter from W. M. Arkins, a nephew, to the author, Aug. 5, 1952.
[13]Letter from F. P. Loveland, a grandson, to the author, Mar. 10, 1958.

On one occasion the City Council decreed that each "public woman" would have to wear a yellow ribbon on her arm to designate her profession and distinguish her from chaste wives and daughters, who often were less well dressed. The *filles de joie* blossomed out in yellow gowns, saffron parasols, and gold slippers, paraded the streets, and sashayed into restaurants and the opera house. The unhappy aldermen repealed the ordinance. The *News* for August 21, 1880, reported that the Council had been unable to hold its session for lack of a quorum. Most of the councilmen were attending a ball arranged for the opening of "a newer and fashionable den of prostitution on Holladay Street."

When Belle Jones, Daisy Smith, and Annie Griffin were overtaken with youthful high spirits and danced birthday-nude at Nineteenth and Larimer streets, they of course were detained by police and fined. The charge was "naughty capers."

For the benefit of tourists and visiting firemen a directory of the city's illicit charms, the Denver Red Book, was published and freely distributed. The edition for 1892 carried the subtitle: "A Reliable Directory of the Pleasure Resorts of Denver." Blanche Brown advertised that she had "lots of boarders" who offered "all the comforts of home." Belle Birnard's notice urged male visitors to make her establishment a home away from home: "Strangers Cordially Welcomed." She had "14 Rooms, 5 Parlors" and "12 Boarders" along with "Music and Dance Halls" and "Choice Wines, Liquors and Cigars." Prospective patrons were assured that all was "Strictly First-Class in Every Respect." The card of Minnie A. Hall boasted of thirty rooms, twenty boarders, and five lounges, including the "Mikado Parlor."

On April 16, 1883, the *News* interrupted a routine report on a meeting of the board of aldermen to interject:

> The clerk read a petition from one Mattie Silks requesting the change of a liquor license. He began, "A petition from Mattie Silks——" Alderman Armstrong, who was busily employed fixing up some papers, raised his head when the name was read and exclaimed, "What?" Everybody laughed while the mayor pounded with his gavel and Alderman Armstrong bent to his work on the papers with an energy both surprising and praiseworthy. But he blushed.

Mattie was Denver's most famous madam, and she had a ne'er-do-well fancy man named Cort Thomson, a swaggering gambler (with Mattie's coin), a fleet foot racer, a former Quantrill guerrilla. But Mattie loved him, and she had proved it with a gun. She had thrown a party for the elite of the sporting world at the Denver Gardens, a pleasant outdoor variety theater on the west bank of the Platte River. The guest list included nearly every thimblerigger, faro dealer, rounder, and rake in town, along with most of the frail sisterhood and their madams. Mattie bought the champagne. As the evening wore on toward morning and the eastern sky was growing light Mattie decided that a rival chatelaine was paying entirely too much attention to her handsome Cort. Then and there she challenged Katie Fulton to a duel, pistols at thirty paces. One version of the affair says the ladies stripped to the waist for their encounter. Mattie chose Cort for her second, and Katie selected a gambler named Sam Thatcher. The thirty paces were stepped off in a grove of cottonwoods, and on the count of three the ladies turned and fired. Cort Thomson went down, a bullet through the back of his neck. Mattie flung herself beside him and stanched the flesh wound with her lace handkerchief. There were some who said the jealous Katie had deliberately shot at Cort. Others blamed the champagne.

The News of August 26, 1877, was irate. A scandalous going on. An affront to civic dignity. Couldn't the authorities prevent such wild and sybaritic revels?

A few years later, in 1882, the doves of Holladay Street, who perhaps hadn't got the word, were as excited as everyone else in Denver about the forthcoming visit of Oscar Wilde. The American tour of the English aesthete had been widely publicized. His affection for Japanese paper fans, sunflowers, and lilies had been well established through reports in the papers of interviews in other cities. The girls in the cribs and parlor houses chattered gaily about sunflowers and silk knee breeches, and at the maison of Rosa Lovejoy Japanese fans were added to the standard equipment of enticement. Wilde's jargon was on every boarder's lips: things were just "too too" or "too utterly utter."[13]

On April 5, a few days before Wilde's arrival, Minnie Clifford and Emma Nelson sallied forth in the full regalia of aestheticism. Minnie, the News said, had "placed upon her hat, between the port gangway and the rudder chains, an immense sunflower fully a foot in diameter." Emma was decorated with an "immense lily." The girls encountered Officer James Connor on his beat and minced up to him with praise for his "too, too divine" new helmet. "I know what makes the wildcat wild, but who makes Oscar?" the lusty Minnie chortled to the intense delight of onlookers. Officer Connor, being an Irishman and faithful to his duty, was a troubled man. He appealed to Police Chief James J. Lomery for advice on how to proceed. The chief suggested that he book the girls for "meretricious display." Then he issued an order calling for the arrest of any notorious woman unusually attired.

Next day the Tribune urged Wilde to "hurry up and deliver your disciples from the oppression of the tyrant", and the News headline read: "Arrested for Estheticism." An anonymous poet in the News of April 9 celebrated the case in verse entitled "Ascerbated Esthetics" which wound up:

[13]Lloyd Lewis and Henry Justin Smith, "Oscar Wilde in Denver," Harper's, Vol. 171 (Nov. 1935), p. 48.

Oh, Oscar! Oh, Oscar!
Pray take a hoss car
And hasten to aid us;
Aid or we're busted.
No daffydowndilly
No sunflower or lily
In Denver is trusted!

A few days later the *News* again hailed Wilde with poesy:

We hail thee as the most successful humbug of the age,
    If thou dost boast of being too
We will produce Charles Baggs, M.D.,
    Who is as too as thou art, and a durned sight tooer.

The reference is to "Doc" Baggs, sometime capper for "Soapy" Smith and a notorious local con artist who at one point operated the Commercial Bank of Denver with facilities which included a huge and impressive safe. Public confidence in the Commercial Bank was shaken when it was disclosed that the safe could be folded up to fit into a suitcase. The *News* at this point was on Chief Lomery's back for not arresting Baggs, and the paper said that in view of the civic commotion the chief planned to escort Wilde straight from the train to jail. "If the old vigilance committee were only in existence now," the item continued, "the reign of the aesthetic pestilence would be very brief."

Nonetheless the *News* and the *Republican* both dispatched reporters north to meet the Wilde train. The interviewers found him gracious and friendly, but critical of the country, "so brown, bare, and disconsolate." Wilde possessed, the *News* reporter observed, "a complexion . . . so clear and beautiful, that the maidens may well grow green with envy, for no balm or powder can give to their cheeks the peculiar beauty of the esthete's complexion."

On the eve of Wilde's arrival Gene Field announced solemnly in the *Tribune:*

It is said that Colonel Arkins will introduce Oscar Wilde to the Denver public tomorrow night. He will wear a breech-clout and a sunflower.

Wilde lectured that night to a good house in the Tabor Grand on "Interior and Exterior House Decoration", and the *News* said there was only slight "merry decorous laughter from the parquette." The customary fee had been raised from a dollar to a dollar and a half in recognition of the Colorado bonanzas, and the stage carpenters had provided a tasteful drawing-room set with a single lily on a round center table. Wilde entered "languidly and dreamily" and paused now and again during his lecture to touch his lips daintily with a snowy handkerchief. He stopped at the Windsor, where a suite had been prepared for him papered in pink "with lily design and storks in the sunflowers."

The following day he took the narrow-gauge to Leadville for an appearance there. In his lectures when he returned to England, Wilde ignored his rude reception in Denver, but recorded his impressions of the Cloud City. Leadville, he told his countrymen, was

> . . . the richest city in the world. It has also got the reputation of being the roughest, and every man carries a revolver. I was told that if I went there they would be sure to shoot me or my travelling manager [D'Oyly Carte]. I wrote and told them that nothing that they could do to my travelling manager would intimidate me. They are miners —men working in metals, so I lectured to them on the Ethics of Art. I read them passages from the autobiography of Benvenuto Cellini and they seemed much delighted. I was reproved by my hearers for not having brought him with me. I explained that he had been dead for some little time which elicited the enquiry, "Who shot him?" They afterwards took me to a dancing saloon where I saw the only rational method of art criticism I have ever come across. Over the piano was printed a notice:—

> Please do not Shoot the
> PIANIST
> He is doing His Best

> The mortality among pianists in that place is marvelous. Then they asked me to supper, and having accepted, I had to descend a mine in a rickety bucket in which it was impossible to be graceful. Having got into the heart of the mountain I had supper, the first course being whisky, the second whisky and the third whisky.
> I went to the Theatre to lecture and I was informed that just before I went there two men had been seized for committing a murder, and in that theatre they had been brought on to the stage at eight o'clock in the evening, and then and there tried and executed before a crowded audience. But I found these miners very charming and not at all rough.[14]

The mine of the whiskey supper was H. A. W. Tabor's Matchless, and for the descent into its damp depths Wilde wore Tabor's own India-

[14]Oscar Wilde, *Impressions of America*, Stuart Mason, ed. (Sunderland, 1906), pp. 30–32.

rubber suit. Wilde said the suit kept him dry and warm but complained that it should have had a purple satin lining, storks embroidered on the flaps, and fern around the edges.[15] If Leadville was somewhat less rugged than he had anticipated, it still was rough enough. A few days before Wilde's arrival Judge A. W. Stone—the jurist kidnaped in the railroad wars—had been cowhided through the streets by a local matron.

Two days later, on April 15, Denver was braced for the second coming of Oscar. Gene Field had been something of a disappointment to the town. He had not lived up to his reputation for practical jokes—and with an ideal butt in town, too. Instead Field had written generously and seriously in the *Tribune* about the visitor's literary fame and artistic philosophies. He had sheathed the pen which sometimes nicked sharply in his theatrical reviews. One of them had consisted of three lines of type: "The Rev. George W. Miln played 'Hamlet' at the Opera House last night. He played it until 11 o'clock." On another occasion he had observed that an actor "played the king as though he expected someone else to play the ace." But Wilde had received no such treatment from Field.

The *Tribune* wit and jokester was waiting at the station for the Leadville train on the night of April 15. His boss, O. H. Rothacker, was standing by with an elegant team and an English drag. He planned to take Wilde on a ride about the city before his evening lecture, and later there would be a select party at the Denver Club. But a late snowstorm delayed the train, and the welcoming committee recessed to a saloon.

Wilde's advance man, Charles E. Locke, suggested that someone be fixed up to represent his Irish poet in order not to disappoint the waiting throngs. Field jumped at the opportunity. He was fitted out in a fur-trimmed overcoat, a long-haired wig, and a wide-brimmed hat. Then the party drove through the streets, Field with his limp head resting on one hand and a book in the other. He wore a "pathetic and dreamy expression" and fluttered his fingertips at the crowds. As they passed one corner a newsboy shouted, "Shoot Oscar!"

The tallyho proceeded to the *Tribune* office, where the dignified business manager, Fred J. V. Skiff, later director of the Field Museum in Chicago, was waiting at the door. Skiff recognized Field and shied a broom at him.

The hoax was exposed in the *Republican* two days later. Field, that paper felt, had "played it pretty low-down on the people of Denver." The dead-pan Field shot right back in that afternoon's *Tribune:*

> The *Republican* is getting more and more unreliable every day. Its statement that gentlemen connected with the *Tribune* imposed a bogus Oscar Wilde upon the people of Denver last Saturday afternoon is not

[15]Lloyd Lewis and Henry Justin Smith, *Oscar Wilde Discovers America 1882* (New York, 1936), p. 316.

only a gross misrepresentation of fact but an unprofessional snub of Mr. W. H. Stapleton of the *News*, who perpetrated the practical joke. Mr. Stapleton will probably take up the cudgel in his own behalf through the columns of the *News* this morning.

The innocent managing editor of the *News* didn't. He had eccentrics on his own staff to deal with. One of them was Orth Stein. He had recently joined the staff after a period as city editor of the *Chronicle* in Leadville. The quality of his japeries is indicated by the "exclusives" he invented about the finding of a derelict battleship on top of Battle Mountain and an amphibious monster in Twin Lakes. He also had decided, on his way from the railway station to the *Chronicle* office, that all Leadville doctors were quacks. So he published an exposé which resulted in a legislative investigation.

In honor of Wilde's visit Stein had composed for the *News* a parting shot:

> Long and thin is the form within
> That rests in the easy chair
> And he counts his pelf, while high on the shelf
> Is a wig of flowing hair.
> No cut-off pants adorn his leg,
> But hang on the wall on a humble peg.
>
> A dressing gown warm encircles his form,
> He holds a pipe in his hand;
> Softly, says he, "What fools they be,
> In this semi-civilized land.
> They think that I live on sunflower seed—
> An Irish stew is more what I need."

Wilde escaped Denver on the ten-thirty train following his final lecture. An hour later Orth Stein was felled at Fifteenth and Blake streets by a party unknown wearing brass knucks. The attack bore no relation either to his verse or to Wilde's visit, but Officer Jim Connor again was on the scene. In fact, Stein complained to Chief Lomery, Officer Connor had stood by and let the assailant beat him up. Conner replied that he didn't intend to get mixed up in any family quarrels. Stein, the patrolman said, was out with a lady trapeze performer from the Tivoli Theater and had been waylaid by her husband.

The *News* reporter apparently had a peculiar talent for getting himself in trouble. When he died later in New Orleans he was wanted in several states for forgery, and he had been the victim in another brawl with apparent tragic results before he left Denver. E. D. Cowen wrote of him:

> . . . He disappeared in a Southern prison for a while only to reappear in an Alabama shooting scrape, after which he moved to

Louisiana. It may be questioned whether Stein was sane during the years after he had been set upon by some unknown person and beaten almost to death with a bludgeon one night in 1883 near the old Palace Theatre. Until that assault occurred, both at Leadville and Denver, he seemed to have as keen moral perceptions as anyone. Shortly afterward he assassinated a variety theatre keeper named Fredericks at Kansas City, in a petty quarrel over a Ganymede of the boxes. From the penalty for this crime, he was rescued by his mother, who spent a small fortune in his deliverance. His father had died from a broken heart at the disgrace in which the son had involved the family. When liberated, Stein embarked on an adventurer's career, which was punctuated at intervals by brilliant work in the Eastern cities. Confidence operations of a peculiarly daring and unscrupulous nature finally outlawed him in the North.[16]

Denver journalism calmed down somewhat with the departure in 1883 of Stein and Eugene Field. Field's health had broken, and after a slow recovery during which he was tormented with melancholia he moved on the *Daily News* in Chicago.[17] His popularity as a children's poet began shortly thereafter. The small frame house he occupied in Denver was moved many years later to Washington Park, where it now is used as the Eugene Field Branch of the Denver Public Library. In the same park there is a fountain and statue of his "Wynken, Blynken and Nod," who sailed off in a wooden shoe.

Another Denver newspaperman of the late eighties lived a forlorn and blighted life, haunted by the ghosts of legions of suffering boys. He was the original Little Lord Fauntleroy. His name was Henry Burnett, and his novelist mother, Frances Eliza Hodgson Burnett, was the author of *Little Lord Fauntleroy*, a precious book which sold more than a half million copies and then, to compound the offense, was dramatized. Mrs. Burnett let it be known that she had used her son as model for the proper little priss in curls and lace collar who was dearly beloved by all late nineteenth-century mothers and detested by their sons. Henry came to Denver fleeing his reputation and joined the staff of the *Republican*. It is said that he was a good reporter and handy with his fists, which he was forced to employ when taunts became unbearable. He covered "the lowers"—the hotel beat along Larimer Street and on down to the railroad station—and did the best he could. But he had to keep on fighting, and the label stuck. Henry held out for about a year and then wearily shouldered his burden and trudged off into the mists, a pathetic and doomed figure.[18]

[16]Murray, op. cit., p. 29.

[17]For an account of Field's Denver years see Slason Thompson, *Eugene Field: A Study in Heredity and Contradictions* (New York, 1901), Vol. I, pp. 143ff.

[18]*Rocky Mountain News*, Dec. 28, 1950.

The talent-laden *Tribune* of Rothacker, Skiff, Cowen, and Field did not long survive the prankster's going. In 1884 it was near collapse and was merged with Kemp Cooper's *Republican*, the morning rival of the *News*, which had now built itself up to a 2200 circulation as the property of Senator Hill. For a time the paper was published as the *Tribune-Republican*, but the joint title was dropped January 1, 1887.

On March 2 of the previous year there had been another change in the ownership of the *News*. Arkins with his brother Maurice and James Burnell formed a partnership and bought out the three-quarter interest still held by W. A. H. Loveland.

Toward the end of the partnership there were strained relationships. The junior partner, Arkins, began to dip into the cash drawer for small sums without checking with the firm's treasurer and cashier, F. W. Loveland, the senior partner's son. Arkins kept promising to repay the till but never got around to it. The younger Loveland took the matter into court on a garnishment and got an okay from his father to change the combination on the safe.

Arkins walked in while the cashier was jiggling the combination, grabbed his personal box out of the safe, and checked its contents insultingly. Then he picked up part of the notes on the new combination and one of the nuts which held the locking machinery together. The Lovelands, father and son, sent for a locksmith, but Arkins, who had been drinking, pulled a gun. Loveland faced him down, and a few days later the unpleasantries were ended by sale of the *News*.[19]

The pioneer Democrat withdrew to devote himself to his mining, railroad, and other business ventures. Along with hundreds of other mining kings, he was caught in the panic of '93 and lost most of his sizable fortune. He held onto his big house in suburban Lakewood, and he died there December 17, 1894, a much-honored pioneer and state builder. His family could remember that among his many activities and distinctions he was one of the founders of Colorado School of Mines, a technical school in Golden which earned a world-wide reputation and draws students of engineering, metallurgy, geology, and related fields from scores of far lands.

The Arkins brothers and Burnell had scarcely settled into their ownership before bad luck hit. On the morning of July 6, 1886, the Denver Academy of Music next door to the News Block burned down in a $125,000 fire. The blaze spread to the *News* building to damage office and pressroom. When the smoke had cleared the paper had suffered a $35,000 loss, more than Loveland had paid for the entire establishment. The weekly *Colorado Topics* at Hyde, Weld County, boasted for the *News* that "with an enterprise that is one of the prominent characteristics

19Diary of F. W. Loveland, Jan. 23 to Mar. 2, 1886, courtesy of his son, F. P. Loveland of Colorado Springs.

of all Western newspapers in general and of Colorado in particular, they never missed an issue."

Arkins had to go shopping for more new presses, however. On October 3 the paper was printed from a Hoe web "presto-perfecting" press, the first News press to employ a continuous roll of paper instead of hand-fed sheets. Capacity: a fabulous 10,000 newspapers an hour, cut, folded, and ready for delivery. With the new press, the stereotyping process—printing by page-size plates cast in a mold from the type—came to Denver for the first time. The News, of course, was not bashful in announcing its enterprise.

By 1889 illustrations were becoming more common. Half-tone photo-engraving was added to the facilities in 1898, permitting the reproduction of pictures without first tracing or hand-engraving them. A daily cartoon became a feature in 1891, and one of the early staff cartoonists was Wilbur Steele, nephew of Fred Meredith.

Another major technical advance came on February 24, 1890—a leased wire for telegraphic news. The paper announced: "This morning The News takes another great stride in advance of its contemporaries. The columns of telegraphic news from every part of the earth which appear in this paper this morning were received direct in this office over four wires, which were put in place on Saturday, and are handled by The News operators." The wires were leased from Western Union, which had stretched an independent press wire between Kansas City and Denver. Up to this time the News had been receiving a condensed report of about 29,000 words of wire news weekly. Now it could receive that much and more in a single day. Stagecoach mail, Pony Express, the first tele-graphic dispatches received in Denver, and now its own leased wire to meet the insatiable news hungers of a booming town. The News crowed in triumph.

In the midst of these improvements and advances the paper found it was outgrowing the venerable, fire-singed News Block on Larimer Street. On December 27, 1887, it moved uptown to rented quarters in the Patterson & Thomas Block at Seventeenth and Curtis streets. The red sandstone building, towering five stories in the center of the growing financial center of the city, later was renamed the Quincy. Recently it was wrecked to make way for a parking lot.

The move and continued progress again required new printing equipment. This time it was two Goss perfecting presses. They were installed in 1888 and raised production speed to 12,000 copies an hour.

It was an Arkins family paper through and through in these days. John was the boss, Edwin G. dramatic editor, Frank J. telegraph editor and Tom proofreader, but Maurice, partner with John and Jim Burnell in the firm, died in 1887. His death led soon to the introduction of a new blood line into the News genealogy.

An aggressive, and prospering Democratic attorney—one of the owners of the building in which the paper was being published—bought up for a never disclosed price on August 9, 1890, Maurice Arkins' one-third interest. Tom Patterson, as Colorado Territory's non-voting delegate to Congress, had been the man who did the log-rolling which won statehood. Later he would be a United States senator. With Loveland, he was one of Colorado's most forceful and powerful Democratic leaders. There was no middle ground so far as Tom Patterson was concerned. One loved or hated or feared him. And he was a fighter who could sass the Supreme Court to its face.

CHAPTER SIXTEEN

Tom Patterson Takes Over

Thomas MacDonald Patterson was a Black Irishman, a Presbyterian from County Carlow, and he was Colorado's first successful Democrat. A contemporary who knew him well described him as "a reserved, rather silent personage" and insisted that "personage" was the right word. His dignity was accompanied, as often seems to be the case, by a somewhat underdeveloped sense of humor. He was never "one of the boys." But he was a persuasive orator, a bold and driving politician, and a dramatic courtroom lawyer who never would admit defeat.

A long-time political enemy, Judge Belford the Red Rooster, once scolded a critic: "But for Tom Patterson, folks like you and me couldn't live in this city. He is the one man who has put up a continuous fight for the rights of common people, and kept it up, year after year. You can be thankful that he is a fighting man with the courage of his convictions."

Patterson was born November 4, 1840. His family emigrated to America when he was nine, and he was reared on Long Island and in Crawfordsville, Indiana, where he learned the printer's trade on the *Review*. After a hitch in the Union Army under Colonel Lew Wallace of the 11th Indiana Volunteers, he educated himself as a lawyer. In 1872, about the time his colonel was writing *Ben Hur*, young Patterson struck out for the West to hang up his shingle. He lit in Denver in December and almost simultaneously became a candidate.

Eighteen months after he arrived he was elected city attorney. Three months later he was the Democratic candidate for territorial delegate to Congress, and he went in with a smart majority. It was the first major post Colorado had given a Democrat.[1]

In Washington, though hampered by the non-voting status of a territorial delegate, Patterson won passage of several key pieces of legislation paving the way for transition to statehood. Edward Keating, Patterson's employee as newspaperman and one of his successors as congressman, had from his mentor a firsthand account of the infighting

[1]Biographical data may be found in Byers, "History of Colorado," pp. 213–16; Smiley, *Semi-Centennial History of the State of Colorado*, Vol. II, pp. 1–3; Ferril, op. cit., pp. 110–11; Stone, op. cit., Vol. II, pp. 16–19; and F. Edward Little, "Thomas M. Patterson: The Game-Cock of the Colorado Courts," *Rocky Mountain Law Review*, Vol. XI, No. 3 (Apr. 1939), pp. 149ff.

which led to the enabling act for Colorado's admittance to the Union in March of 1875. Patterson teamed with Stephen B. Elkins, later a rich West Virginia coal operator but then Republican delegate from the territory of New Mexico. Elkins also was out after statehood for his territory, much older in terms of settlement than Colorado. Patterson worked the Democratic side of the House, Elkins the Republican, and together they pushed the two enabling bills to the floor for action.

But the "Southern Brigadiers" were beginning to return to Congress in force at this time and already had become decisive powers in both House and Senate. As the Colorado and New Mexico bills neared action Representative Julius Caesar Burrows of Michigan, a Union Army veteran, launched into an eloquent attack on the Southern Democrats, reopening all the old, nearly healed Civil War wounds, twisting the knife in them and waving the bloody shirt. The Republicans cheered lustily, and Elkins could not restrain his enthusiasm. He rushed down the aisle and was the first to shake Burrows' hand. The "Southern Brigadiers" raged. "Look at that damn Yankee from New Mexico," they told each other.

The Southerners held the balance of power, and they decided to kill both statehood bills. Patterson, who had remained conspicuously neutral in the flare-up over Burrows' speech, argued with them, promising that the new state of Colorado would give up its errant Republican habits and swing into the Democratic column. The Southerners were impressed by Patterson's deportment and words; they okayed his bill and killed Elkins'.

"So it was that Colorado came into the Union as the Centennial State on the hundredth anniversary of the Declaration of Independence," Keating says. "New Mexico remained on the outside for over 35 years— all because its hot-blooded young delegate could not refrain from shaking hands with a gentleman who knew how to wave the bloody shirt."

Patterson returned to Denver in triumph. But he couldn't deliver on his pledge to reform Colorado's politics. Judge Belford trounced him roundly when they stood against each other for election as Colorado's first United States representative, 1876–77. The state went Republican all the way, as usual, and cost Samuel Tilden the presidency. In the famous and heated contest which followed the election Rutherford B. Hayes went to the White House by the margin of one electoral vote— Colorado's.

After some shrewd legalistic maneuvering—and bungling by the Republicans, who permitted two elections to be held—Patterson unseated Belford in the next go-round and went back to Washington as Colorado's first Democratic congressman, 1877–79. Nearly a quarter century later Patterson paired his victory by winning election as the first Democratic senator from Colorado, 1901–7, although Henry M. Teller, a Republican, had been elected on a bipartisan ticket in 1896 in the blowup over silver coinage. Patterson was defeated for governor in 1888, but his law partner and fellow Democrat, Charles S. Thomas, became both a governor and a senator.

Patterson remained in politics—partisan, non-partisan, municipal, and corporate—all his life, and the *News* became his most potent weapon. Its columns carried his lashing, often brilliant statements, and he threw the paper headlong into every fight.

The *News* had progressed mightily under Arkins. Circulation was booming. *Pettingill's Newspaper Directory* for 1877 says the paper then had 1920 daily and 1800 weekly subscribers. By 1891 the totals were up to 15,600 daily, 5500 weekly, and 23,800 Sunday, according to *Dauchey & Co.'s Newspaper Catalogue* for that year. When the Arkins-Burnell partnership took over from Loveland in 1886 the property had been valued at a hundred and fifty thousand dollars. Four years later, when Patterson moved in, it was worth nearly four hundred thousand dollars.[2]

In 1892, Patterson picked up, again for an undisclosed price, the one-third interest of James M. Burnell. The brief, early taste of printer's ink on the little Crawfordsville *Review* had left a permanent appetite. The lawyer-politico now was firmly in the newspaper business. He owned two thirds of the *News*, John Arkins the other third, and the silent partnership which started in 1890 now began to become vocal. Arkins remained in day-to-day management of the paper, but his health was failing.

In the summer of 1894 the "glamorous gladiator" took a leave from the paper and went to Excelsior Springs in Missouri to see if he could recapture his health. It was no good. He returned a pain-haunted skeleton, and died August 19. The funeral was an occasion of civic mourning. Hothouses and floral shops were swept clean of flowers for wreaths. Everyone in town recalled some personal instance of the Irish charm, generosity, and wit. Rev. Myron Reed in his sermon said: "When I came down the street this morning, I felt as if the world was mighty thinly populated." Newsboys and bootblacks remembered the Thanksgiving and Christmas dinners Arkins gave them each year. The colored janitor at the *News* told how the boss had sent him to Tortoni's for a chicken breast to feed a stray cur which had wandered into the office— "de boosum ob a chicken!"

One of Arkins' last acts was to stave off—probably with Patterson money in the background—an attempted Republican recapture of the paper. Years later William M. Arkins, nephew of the *News* editor, told Edwin A. Bemis, manager of the Colorado Press Association, how it happened:

I have forgotten the year, but it was when certain persons representing the Republican Party secured an option on the *Rocky Mountain News*

[2]Hall, op. cit., Vol. III, p. 139.

for $400,000. The sum of $10,000 was paid down and the option read that the balance had to be paid in cash.

The night the option was expiring I sat with my Uncle and A. M. Stevenson on the Stout Street side of the Albany Hotel bar room. A. M. Stevenson had a certified check for $390,000 and wanted Uncle John to take it and close the deal. Just before the clock struck twelve, Stevenson asked Uncle John to take the check but he refused. He said he didn't know of an easier way of making $10,000. As the clock struck twelve Uncle John said: "Well, I'll buy a drink." The option had expired because they had not lived up to the terms—cash. Stevenson told me some years later that he was of the opinion that T. M. Patterson had talked Col. Arkins out of selling. At that time, Col. Arkins had an option on the old *Chicago Times*.[3]

The certain persons were associates of Edward O. Wolcott, the Republican Tom Patterson eventually would succeed in the Senate. Wolcott was a wealthy lawyer and financier of New England origins, and he lived high. During his terms in Washington he was known as the ablest poker player, most compelling orator, and best-dressed man in the Senate. He wore striped trousers, a fawn waistcoat and, always, a boutonniere. In the $100,000-a-night games at Chamberlin's Restaurant, Ed Wolcott, son of a clergyman, drew shrewdly and bet tough. On trips to New York he became one of the plungers at Richard Canfield's famous gambling establishment. Herbert Asbury in his book, *Sucker's Progress*, says Wolcott's special limit on faro at Canfield's was $2000 on cases and $4000 on doubles—only slightly under the $2500 and $5000 limits of John W. ("Bet-A-Million") Gates. Wolcott sometimes bucked the games at Canfield's for two days and nights at a sitting. Although he was representing Colorado, Wolcott lived so much of the time at the family home in Woodlawn that he became known as the "third senator from Massachusetts." He did build a big country home, Wolhurst, on the Platte south of Denver, and there he entertained his friends from the East on a manorial scale. (Wolhurst, after a recent career as a roadhouse gambling den, now is a private country club.) When Wolcott died, at Monte Carlo, he left behind a $60,000 IOU at Canfield's. It was settled, a hundred cents on the dollar.

But Wolcott came a cropper in his brief fling in the direction of the newspaper game. He was up against a determined opponent who took his politics seriously, and he lost. Tom Patterson, although he became a wealthy man and died leaving a four-million-dollar estate, never was interested in the Senate as a rich man's club. His political and economic sympathies were always with the man in the street, and though he belonged to the archly exclusive Denver Club he was seen there only once. "Its snobbishness almost suffocated me." His personal life was one

[3]Edwin A. Bemis, "Journalism in Colorado," in LeRoy R. Hafen, *Colorado and Its People*, Vol. II, pp. 271-72.

of simplicity, thrift, and rigid routine. Work possessed him. A busy and growing criminal and mining law practice claimed his days, and he was at the *News* half the night. He never learned to enjoy the wealth which came to him.

When Arkins died his widow and son Edwin inherited his remaining third interest in the *News*. Then Edwin died, leaving Mrs. Arkins and Patterson as owners. Patterson bought up the widow's share, and the *News* became his personal property thenceforth to 1914. His son-in-law, Richard C. Campbell, was made business manager and acted for the publisher in his frequent absences on legal and political errands.

Patterson assumed control of the *News* as the nation was slipping into an economic trough. Colorado was hurting more than most areas. Its economy was based largely on the money metals, gold and silver, and the "sound money" men of Wall Street and Washington had turned their backs on "hard money"—the kind that clinked when you tossed it on the bar. Loveland's *News* had helped make silver a burning political issue in Colorado, and Patterson's *News* hammered the same anvil. Free coinage of silver was the cry in Colorado for more than twenty years, and until very recently a leading Denver department store, the Denver Dry Goods Company, urged its customers to accept silver dollars in change "to help the mining industry."

The price of silver had dropped to a 20-to-1 ratio with gold when Congress voted the Sherman Silver Purchase Act of 1890. By this act the treasury was required to purchase four and a half million ounces of silver monthly at the prevailing prices. The buying helped a little in Western mining states, but it further weakened the nation's precarious gold reserves. Moreover the West wanted free and unlimited coinage of silver.

Grover Cleveland won the 1888 election at the polls only to lose it in the electoral college to Benjamin Harrison. As the Democratic National Convention of 1892 approached it became obvious that Cleveland would be the choice again. And Cleveland had declared in 1891 that the Sherman Act was a "dangerous and reckless experiment in free, unlimited and independent coinage." Colorado fumed and fulminated.

In June 1892, Tom Patterson packed his bags to go to the convention in Chicago on a trip he knew was a hopeless one. He took along his star woman reporter, Ellis Meredith, to cover the proceedings for the *News*. The convention met in the Wigwam, where Lincoln had been nominated in 1860, and the roof of the old building leaked dismal rain on the delegates. Patterson delivered an hour-long minority report on the monetary plank in his party's platform, and then he walked out of the convention taking a queue of Western Democrats with him. As expected, the anti-silver plank was adopted and Cleveland nominated. Ellis Meredith wrote her story for the *News* and handed it to the telegraph operator.

In the morning she and her boss read in the Chicago press that "Patterson's Paper Bolts Democratic Ticket." Patterson had not wanted to go that far that fast, but John Arkins, back in Denver, had seized the initiative. Frank Arkins later sketched that convention-night scene in the *News* city room for Miss Meredith:

Times had been getting steadily worse, politically and every way. In our part of the country nobody wanted Cleveland, but there was no other candidate of the same importance in the party. He got the nomination on a platter. As I recall it, the Republicans were not specially joyous over the renomination of Harrison. As for Weaver, nobody thought he had a chance except the lunatic fringe of his party, who could believe anything. Nobody goes crazy working for a man they think can't win.

So, it was a grim party that met in the telegraph room that night. You know Uncle John. He stormed up and down and said, over and over: "This paper is never going to support Cleveland. I don't care if Patterson is a delegate to that convention. He'll probably get howled down when he brings in that minority report. . . ."

Then the wires began their clickety-click, Seaman taking it down, and I copying. Patterson was telling what had happened, and advising that the paper take a wait and see attitude. Uncle John broke in with words you could put on a wire but not over a telephone . . . he said a daily paper would never get anywhere waiting for whatever is going to happen next. Making things happen is the newspaper job.

Then Patterson made a mistake. He was "Cold Irish" all right, but the other two [Arkins and Fred Meredith, managing editor] were the red-hot fighting type, that don't take anything that looks like an order. He demanded that nothing be done until he got home—some thirty-six hours off, according to train schedules. . . . Uncle John burned up the wires. The printable part of what he said was something like this:

"You don't understand the situation here. I do and now is the time to act. You know this paper could never support Cleveland and our people wouldn't support it, if it did. The Omaha platform [Populist] may be wild-eyed in spots, but folks know what it means, and they like it. As for Weaver, he served in the Union Army, that ought to give him the G.A.R. vote, and he was in Congress. This paper will announce tomorrow morning that it will support Weaver. Release your editorial, Fred, and tell 'em to spread our turn to Weaver all over the front page. Shut off the wire, Frank. We've just got time to make the mail."

So, Seaman shut down the key, with Patterson still protesting and begging for time and sending wires over the Western Union. . . .[4]

Thus Tom Patterson, who had borne the heat of the day as one of the fathers of Colorado Democracy, found himself supporting James B. Weaver and leading the Populist revolt. When he got back to Denver he discovered that Arkins' gauging of public sentiment once again had

[4]Ellis Meredith, op. cit., pp. 45–46.

been a sure one. Even with extra help in the *News* business office there was a string of men waiting to subscribe that reached down into the next block. Colorado was one of four states Weaver carried, and the Populists swept to local power with the election of a governor and two congressmen. Only the terms of the two senators—Henry M. Teller and Edward O. Wolcott—spared them in the rebellion. Party lines had been thoroughly scrambled. Splinter groups which called themselves Silver Democrats and Silver Republicans held conventions, entered the campaign, and helped split the vote. It was the first time Colorado had been out of the Republican column in a presidential year.

The following year, 1893, was the bleakest Colorado had known. Cleveland—described by Arkins as "that man of all belly and neck"— signed the bill repealing the Sherman Purchase Act. Panic hit. In three days twelve Denver banks failed. The smelters closed, and then the silver mines which had gushed wealth in the eighties. Thousands of men were thrown out of work. Bread lines and a relief camp appeared in Denver, where a unit of Jacob Coxey's army formed and laid plans to sail on Washington down the Platte in a fleet of scows made from scrap lumber and unguarded outhouses. The little silver city of Georgetown formally seceded from the Union by vote of its board of selectmen. The *News*, though its circulation boomed, shared the common fate. Its advertising revenues were suddenly halved.

In the midst of the panic Populist Governor Davis H. ("Bloody Bridles") Waite was having his troubles. Waite was a benign old gentleman from Aspen, firm in his principles, sympathetic and well meaning in his efforts to aid the suffering wage earners of the state, but totally untalented in public administration. His deficiencies had been recognized by the Populists themselves during the campaign, but he had refused a five-thousand-dollar bribe to withdraw from the ticket to which he was morally committed. Waite won his ferocious, and entirely uncharacteristic, nickname by a phrase in a speech. When Cleveland called the special session of Congress to repeal the Sherman Act a large and boisterous rally was held in Denver's Coliseum Hall. In the main address Governor Waite warned Wall Street, which was being blamed for the monetary disasters, that the people would rise up and fight and that "it is better, infinitely better, that blood should flow to the horses' bridles rather than our national liberties should be destroyed." The press of the nation seized upon the statement as evidence that wild-eyed Colorado was headed toward repudiation and revolution.

Now that he was in the governor's chair Waite found that the road to reform has chuckholes. His attorney general got himself tarred and feathered in Colorado Springs. The legislature revolted against some of his more exotic notions. And he had to mount a military operation to get rid of one set of his appointees.

The "City Hall War" made him the butt of every joke and helped limit the Populist regime to one sitting. At this time, by a patronage-hungry act of the previous legislature, some of Denver's municipal officials were appointed by the governor and subject to his control. Waite's appointees to the police and fire board failed to carry out to his satisfaction orders for a cleanup of gambling hells, the red-light district, and law-violating saloons. He dismissed the board and appointed a new one, but the incumbents refused to budge. They had been confirmed by the state Senate, they said, and could be impeached only by act of the legislature.

Waite called out the state militia and marched three hundred of them down to the City Hall at Fourteenth and Larimer streets. Artillery was trained on the building. The rebellious board concentrated the entire police force in the hall, and the policemen called upon their friends and associates of the underworld for reinforcements. "Soapy" Smith recruited and dispatched a platoon of gunmen and dynamiters to man the City Hall tower.

Thousands of citizens jammed adjacent streets to watch the spectacle. A shot would have produced carnage. Fortunately no shot was fired, and the casualties consisted only of a few women who fainted in the press of the throng. Waite was persuaded to call in national troops to maintain order and status quo while the courts took up the question. The law upheld his right to remove his appointees, but by then the victory was a Pyrrhic one.

Waite's Populist regime gave the vote to Colorado women, and there were some crusty males, jaded on suffragette feathers and flutters, who firmly asserted *that* was as big a blunder as the City Hall War.

The Populist revolt in Colorado passed. It had not been the deep-rooted agrarian rebellion that seethed in the Midwestern states. The issue of silver alone had given the Colorado People's Party its brief hour of victory, and once Cleveland had done his worst, Centennial State politicians went back to orthodox alignments.

The injury to Colorado's economy remained, however. When the "Boy Orator of the Platte," William Jennings Bryan of Nebraska, began to flay the "gold bugs," Patterson and his *News* were happy to go back home to their Democratic party. Colorado roared its approval of Bryan's 1896 speech against the gold standard: "You shall not press down upon the brow of labor this crown of thorns, you shall not crucify mankind upon a cross of gold." Senator Henry Teller, six times elected by the people of Colorado and a Republican of national prominence and influence, bolted his party to the Bryan banner. His disaffection brought cannon firing on the lawn of the state Capitol in Denver, bonfires in the streets, and joyous parades.

In this soaring of hope and happiness the *News* gave everything it had to the campaign for Bryan. Patterson stumped the state personally, and the *News* thundered against the gold standard, Wall Street, and the bloated monopolistic corporations. Bryan carried Colorado in 1896, in 1900, and again in 1908 following his nomination for a third try by the Democratic National Convention which met in Denver's new City Auditorium.

The Republicans had returned to power within the state in 1894 by means of a vicious campaign based on religious and racial prejudices. The American Protective Association—predecessor to the Ku Klux Klan in Colorado politics—entered the picture and practically took over the party, which was so eager to win again that its candidates would not renounce the rabid anti-Catholicism of the APA. They straddled the issue, accepted APA support and dominance, and won.[5]

Chief rabble-rouser of the APA was one "Graveyard Johnny" Voight, pathological in his religious hatreds. Voight discovered that the city of Denver had deeded a portion of a congressional land grant to the diocese of Denver for use as Calvary Cemetery. This was illegal, he decided. So he attempted to "homestead" the cemetery, a plot of ground lying just east of present Cheesman Park. The courts beat him off, but "Graveyard Johnny" meantime was organizing APA "lodges" throughout the state. Working the scapegoat gambit in a time of unemployment and economic depression, the APA infiltrated the not unwilling Republican conventions and named its slate. During the regime of Governor Albert W. McIntire, 1895–97, no Catholic was permitted to hold any state office or job, however menial.

The Republicans came back in strength in the next few years, but between Bryanism, depression, and growing industrialization Colorado never again would be the Grand Old Party's exclusive preserve. In 1901, Tom Patterson rose up and defeated Senator Ed Wolcott, who had been keynoter of the Republican National Convention and prominently mentioned as McKinley's running mate instead of Teddy Roosevelt. Patterson brought Colorado's second Senate seat home from Massachusetts. He served in the Senate from 1901 to 1907.

In addition to slam-bang politics there were other diversions during this era to woo the minds of Coloradans away from Cleveland's "crime" and the sick mining industry. For one item, growth was continuing in spite of the panic of '93. By the turn of the century Denver had become a sizable little city of 133,859 persons, up from 106,713 in 1890. Enthusiasm ran high for the Spanish-American War. When the call came for sixteen hundred enlistments there were more volunteers than could be accepted. A camp was set up in then undeveloped City Park. The *News* now was large enough to have its own war correspondent—Arthur C. Johnson, Tom Patterson's nephew. Johnson sailed with the Colorado boys from San Francisco, and his dispatches told how the new 1st Colorado Regiment raised the flag over Manila on August 13, 1898.

[5]Thomas Fulton Dawson, *Life and Character of Edward Oliver Wolcott* (New York, 1911), Vol. I, pp. 219–20.

Their band played "There'll Be a Hot Time in the Old Town Tonight." That robustly raucous song, soon the darling of political rally bands everywhere, reputedly came from a Negro mammy in Cripple Creek via the girls of the ensemble at the Palace variety hall there.[6]

Denver's continued growth helped ease the depression, but it was gold that ended it. Cripple Creek gold. The mountains opened up again and smiled down on their Queen City.

The great days of Colorado silver mining ended abruptly in 1893. Most of the mines never recovered, and the ghost towns the tourists see, the sagging shaft houses, the sprawling mine dumps, weathered to ochers and purples, date from that year.

But in 1891, almost simultaneously with the first pangs of silver's death struggle, Cripple began to boom. Cripple Creek lies in a high basin, now denuded of its forest growth, immediately to the west of Pike's Peak. During the first quarter century of its life, 1891–1916, Cripple produced $340,000,000 in gold and an entirely new crop of mining millionaires. Since then, through 1952, the camp has pushed the total to beyond $700,000,000.[7] It is still one of the few places in Colorado where gold continues to be mined extensively.

The town of Cripple Creek spurted to 50,000 persons by 1900. One carload of ore brought an all-time record price of $219,040. A three-dollar-a-day carpenter, Winfield Scott Stratton, sold his Independence mine for $10,000,000 and became one of Colorado's leading philanthropists. When he died twelve women claimed to be his widow.[8] All in all the camp yielded twenty-seven men—average age, forty-two—who rated as millionaires. Among them were Spencer Penrose, Charles Tutt, Albert E. Carlton, Verner Z. Reed, Ed Giddings, all names famous in Colorado.

While Cripple Creek was booming Creede, discovered in the same year, was going broke. Creede was a silver camp farther southwest in the mountains, and it spewed forth nearly five million ounces of silver in 1892 just before the roof fell in. Among the characters attracted to Creede in its brief heyday were "Soapy" Smith, Bob Ford, and the dashing and elegant Richard Harding Davis. "Soapy" Smith found the pickings good. Ford, the "dirty little coward" who killed Jesse James, found death in his gambling hall.[9] Davis, epitome of the eternal sophomore, traveled west in 1892 for *Harper's Monthly* and reached Creede—which he pro-

[6]Hafen, *Colorado and Its People*, Vol. I, pp. 501–2; Fritz, *Colorado: The Centennial State* (New York, 1941), p. 445.

[7]The fabulous story in full detail is told by Marshall Sprague in *Money Mountain: The Story of Cripple Creek Gold* (Boston, 1953).

[8]Frank Waters is Stratton's biographer in *Midas of the Rockies* (New York, 1937; Denver, 1949).

[9]Nolie Mumey, *Creede: The History of a Colorado Silver Mining Town* (Denver, 1949), pp. 135ff.

nounced with the terminal *e*—in time to see $1,500,000 offered, and refused, for the Holy Moses mine. He was outraged by such economic insouciance: "Any man who will live in a log house at the foot of a mountain, and drink melted snow any longer than he has to do so, or refuse that much money for *anything*, when he could live in the Knickerbocker Flats, and drive forth in a private hansom with rubber tires, is no longer an object of public interest."[10] Davis was more impressed by the polo he saw being played at Colorado Springs on a field over which wild Indians had galloped scarcely three decades earlier.

Editor of the short-lived Creede *Chronicle* was Cy Warman, who subsequently joined the staff of the *Rocky Mountain News* and still later achieved a measure of turn-of-the-century fame as a versifier.[11] Warman summed up the habits of the silver camp:

> It's day all day in the day-time
> And there is no night in Creede.

When Creede went bust Warman came back to Denver and joined the *News* as railroad reporter. His poem, "Doing Railroads for the *Rocky Mountain News*," gives a good indication of the life of a reporter in the Denver of the 1890s:

It was sometime in the P.M. of the fall of '92
I had cashed in the Creede *Chronicle*—had nothing much to do—
I had seen the man of leisure who was loafing on the street
Who had every fad and fashion from his head down to his feet,
And this prince was a reporter; so I shined my Sunday shoes,
And went down to do the railroads for *The Rocky Mountain News*.

Now the city man was Martin, from McCullagh's *Democrat*,
And he glanced over his glasses as I doffed my derby hat—
I had owned a daily paper in the springtime of the year,
That had sunk ten thousand dollars; I had nothing then to fear—
I had planned that in the morning I would dally with the muse,
In the P.M. do the railroads for *The Rocky Mountain News*.

"Well, ahem, ahem!" said Martin, clearing cobwebs from his throat,
While the smoke from his Havana round my face began to float;
"I presume that you're in touch with the officials here in town,
Having worked for them; however, I shall have to send you down
To the police court." Then he coughed again and shed his overshoes,
"That's included with the railroads on *The Rocky Mountain News*.". . .

[10]Richard Harding Davis, *The West from a Car-Window* (New York, 1903), p. 68. (A collection of Davis' *Harper's* pieces.)

[11]Levette J. Davidson and Prudence Bostwick, *The Literature of the Rocky Mountain West* (Caldwell, Ida., 1939), pp. 67ff.

"We're a little bit short-handed—you will do the county courts;
And this evening, after dinner, drift around among the sports;
There's a prizefight down at Murphy's." Then he paused and rubbed his head.
"That's all I have to say now," this encyclopedia said.
I didn't say a word then, but I thought it beat the Jews
The way they did the railroads down on *The Rocky Mountain News*. . . .

I had buttoned up my overcoat, was headed for the stair,
When the quidnunc's restless fingers wandered thru his wealth of hair;
I had reached the elevator when he called me back and said:
"You will have to do the statehouse, for the statehouse man is dead."
My poor heart sank within me, but I couldn't well refuse,
Since it all went with the railroads on *The Rocky Mountain News*. . . .

"See the concerts at the churches in the early eve," he said;
"Try to do Dean Hart's cathedral where an heiress is to wed
An English dude from Dublin—Freeman won't be here today.
You may write about a column on What Old-Timers Say
About the San Juan Gold Excitement—but mind, we can't excuse
Any neglect of the railroads on *The Rocky Mountain News*."

I was off. For ten long hours thru the slush and snow and sleet,
Up the stone steps of the statehouse, out again and down the street,
Till I paused to feed at midnight—hit the bottle till my soup
Seemed a sea of strange assignments—every oyster was a scoop,
Mused on how the other papers would be burdened with the blues,
When they read about the railroads in *The Rocky Mountain News*.

After lunch I read my copy, which told how the Rio Grande
Had a good house, and the organ was wide open working sand.
'Twas a cold day for the criminals who proceed in wicked ways,
For they raided all the churches, and the dean got twenty days,
The soprano dropped her crown, the policeman warped his flues,
Throwing in too much cold water," said *The Rocky Mountain News*. . . .

. . . The next day I got a letter that would give a man the blues:
"This is good, but we can't read it," Signed: *"The Rocky Mountain
News."* . . .
Now I view the proud reporter as he swiftly sallies by,
A bob-tailed flush upon his cheek, a twinkle in his eye;
He has my sincere sympathy—I do not want his place,
I pine not for his twinkle, nor the flush upon his face;
No matter what inducements, I invariably refuse,
Since the day I did the railroads for *The Rocky Mountain News*.[12]

Creede's new silver, but more especially Cripple's new gold, helped
Denver weather through the mining crisis. Banks reopened and the
Mining Exchange, a sink of gloom for several years, began to do a lively

[12]Levette J. Davidson, ed., *Poems of the Old West* (Denver, 1951), pp. 173–75.

business again. Building continued. The opulent Brown Palace had its gala opening on August 12, 1892, just in time to greet the panic. But the hotel, since the stopping place of presidents and potentates, managed to stay open—probably because of its superior services. Among these was gratuitous cremation for any deceased guest who desired incineration without delay. (Up to the 1920s, when the basement crematory was discontinued, no guest had taken advantage of the service.) The Brown was paneled in onyx, and it offered a library, fresh cream from its own pampered cows, swimming pools, Turkish baths, billiard rooms, and bowling alleys. The management boasted that its bridal suites were so breath-taking that "hopeless old maids and bachelors would be legally justified in hanging themselves or each other, after a view of these lovely apartments." The laundry service was so rapid that "even the man fleeing from an unpaid board bill is overtaken by his clean linen."[13] The aging but well-preserved Brown Palace is still Denver's top-ranking hotel, and it stands high with travelers who know the world's finest inns. A sky-scraper annex, the Brown Palace West, is being completed, linked to the main building by a bridge over Tremont Place, but some of the 1890s décor of the *grande dame* of American hotels is being carefully preserved.

Creede's rude earthiness repelled Richard Harding Davis, but he found the Denver of the Brown Palace an oasis of civilization in a land of barbarians. He was fresh out of Lehigh and Johns Hopkins and much impressed by gentlemen's clubs. The posh Denver Club was an eye opener, and at the University Club he was amazed to find a membership that could "sing more different college songs in a given space of time than any other body of men I have met." Denver, he decided, was "a thoroughly Eastern city—a smaller New York in an encircling range of white-capped mountains."

> If you look up at its towering office buildings, you can easily imagine yourself, were it not for the breadth of the thoroughfare, in down-town New York; and though the glimpse of the mountains at the end of the street in place of the spars and mast-heads of the East and North rivers undeceives you, the mud at your feet serves to help out the delusion. Denver is a really beautiful city, but—and this, I am sure, few people in New York will believe—it has the worst streets in the country.
> . . . The citizen of Denver takes a modest pride in the public schools, the private houses, and the great mountains, which seem but an hour's walk distant and are twenty miles away; but he is proudest before all of two things—of his celery and his cablecars. . . .

Then New Yorker Davis concluded by anticipating what has become the standard cliché of visitors to *his* city. "The West is a very wonderful,

[13]*Rocky Mountain News*, Feb. 20, 1955, quoting a descriptive booklet issued by the Brown Palace in 1892.

large, unfinished, and out-of-doors portion of our country, and a most delightful place to *visit*."[14] The italics are his.

As the Denver tempo picked up again with towering buildings, Pascal celery, college songs, and cable cars, the *News* was getting ready for more expansion and another move. Circulation now was 23,918 daily, 31,924 Sunday, and in 1897 the deep, narrow quarters next to the entrance of the Patterson & Thomas Block were cramped. The paper was back to a spread-eagle format of nine columns splashed with bold cartoons. Publication was on a seven-day basis, and the subscription rate was down to twelve and a half cents a week or fifty-five cents a month. Headlines were appearing in red ink. The *News* had its own special bureau in Cripple Creek to report the life-giving boom. An early edition was being printed to catch the trains to Wyoming readers.

On March 27, 1897, Patterson moved his *News* two blocks down to a corner, ground-floor location in the Markham Hotel at the southeast intersection of Seventeenth and Lawrence streets. With the move came another new press. Into the new quarters went an 80,000-pound "triple-decker, straight-line" made by Walter Scott & Company of Plainfield, New Jersey. The press could "do everything but think," the *News* beamed proudly in its anniversary edition on April 23. Three rolls of paper fed simultaneously into the 12-foot-high Scott, permitting it to print, paste, cut, fold, and count papers ranging up to a gigantic 24 pages in size. The speed was dazzling: 24,000 impressions an hour, twice the rate of the two Gosses being replaced.

Typesetting machines were now in use. Ottmar Mergenthaler, Swabian clockmaker and immigrant American genius, had perfected his Linotype in July of 1884, but the machine didn't have much newspaper acceptance until the New York *Tribune* installed an improved version in 1886. When the Simplex model appeared in 1890 success was assured.[15] In Denver the *Times* stole a march on the *News* in adopting the complex new labor-saving machine. Records of the Mergenthaler Company show that six leased No. 1 models were shipped January 22, 1892, to the *Times*.[16] These were the first Linotypes to make their way west of the Mississippi. The following year the *News* raised the *Times*' ante and installed eight machines, adding another in 1894. By 1896 there were three thousand Linotypes in use throughout the world, and at least fifteen of them were chattering busily in the little upstart city of Denver.

The year 1893 also saw introduction of the first "type-writers" into the *News* editorial rooms. Some of the older reporters and editors were

[14]Richard Harding Davis, op. cit., pp. 215ff.

[15]Willi Mengel, *Ottmar Mergenthaler and the Printing Revolution*, (Brooklyn, 1954), pp. 52–56.

[16]Letter from Jackson Burke, director of typographic development, Mergenthaler Linotype Company, to the author, Mar. 5, 1958.

holdouts against the infernal new device that made so much noise and didn't give a man time to think. "Cap" Smith, for example, snorted at Calligraphs and Olivers and continued to write in his cryptographic script for the rest of his newspaper days. But gradually the machine took over from the quill, and the incidence of peptic ulcer in newspaper compositors must have nose-dived.

Except for "Cap" and a few other old-timers, the *News* editorial staff was shifting. Charles MacAllister Willcox, who had covered the City Hall War and invented "Dynamite Dolly," resigned as a reporter to go into business and become a leading merchant and social luminary. John C. Martin, his city editor, departed. The talented cartoonist Wilbur Steele was hired away, and E. B. Smith took over the easel as *News* staff artist in 1897. W. F. Stapleton had gone to the *Republican* out of political conscience. Fred Meredith resigned as managing editor in 1894 to return to farming, and Thomas E. McKenna held the post for twelve years. McKenna covered Creede for the *News* in 1892 and Cripple Creek in 1895. The last link with the founding editor was broken in 1904 when Byers' brother-in-law, W. R. Thomas, quit the paper to become history professor and authority on irrigation law at the State Agricultural College in Fort Collins. Thomas had been with the paper off and on for thirty-five years. He died in 1914.

One of the most famous turn-of-the-century *News* staffers was Edward Keating. He gave up an eighteen-dollar-a-month job as Western Union messenger in 1894 to become a copyholder and proofreader for the *Republican*. Soon thereafter he switched to the *News* proofroom and had worked his way up to telegraph editor when the paper moved down Seventeenth Street from Curtis to Lawrence. He was manning the wires the night the *Maine* blew up. Keating became city editor of the *Times*, 1902–5, and managing editor of the *News*, 1906–11. Among his other duties, in the pattern of Cy Warman and his railroads, Keating did much of the paper's political writing in the late nineties and became convinced that if others could get themselves elected he could too. Managing editor Tom McKenna gave him a thirty-day leave to campaign.

"When I told him what I wanted to do, Tom threw up his hands and read me off," Keating recalls. "Finally he gave me the leave but told me, 'Be sure to be back here the night after election'."

To everyone's surprise, Keating, then twenty-three, was elected city auditor in 1899 in a 6–1 walkaway. When his term expired in 1901 he reported back to McKenna and became political writer again. A deep-dyed Bryan liberal, the young Keating idolized his big boss, Tom Patterson, and still regards him as "the greatest man Colorado has seen up to date."

Keating left the *News* in 1911 to become an editor on his own with purchase of the Pueblo *Leader*, but almost immediately he was back in politics. He served as a member of the state Land Board, 1911–13, and in

1912 was elected to Congress, where he served two terms, 1913–19. Remaining in Washington, he took over the weekly newspaper, *Labor*, published by the railroad brotherhoods, and built it to a circulation of 1,000,000 copies. "I planned to stay with *Labor* six months," he says, "and I stayed thirty-three years." He retired as lifetime editor emeritus in 1953.

In the 1890s Denver was supporting six daily, thirty-seven weekly, and twenty-two monthly publications, in a town of just over 100,000 population. Along with the *News* the dailies were the *Republican*, *Times*, *Post*, *Sun*, and *Colorado Journal*, the latter two short-lived. One of the monthlies was John Brisben Walker's *Interocean*. Walker, who made and lost one fortune in Colorado, moved on to New York and founded *Cosmopolitan* magazine, which he sold to William Randolph Hearst for a million dollars. Walker died in Brooklyn in 1931, "stony broke again," the papers said. He had planned a castlelike summer White House for William Howard Taft on Mount Falcon west of Denver. Fire destroyed the huge building in 1910. Only its blackened stone walls remain.

The *News* moved into the bright new twentieth century with coverage of one of the most sickening mob crimes in the history of American violence, a lynching so coldly and deliberately calculated that the newspapers had time to string field telegraph wires to the scene.

On November 8, 1900, thirteen-year-old Louise Frost was found moaning, mortally wounded by fourteen dirk stabs, in a prairie slough near her farm home on the outskirts of Limon, eighty-six miles east of Denver. There were heel marks on her forehead and cheek. She died before a doctor could reach her home. It never was ascertained officially that she had been raped, although this was asserted for a fact by the Denver papers, which, with the sole exception of the *News*, made carnival of the story. The *Times* reported that Louise's pitiful little body lay in her two-room home, "appealing to the manhood of Lincoln county and of that state that her ruthless slayer be apprehended and the awful crime avenged." The *Republican* and the *Post* openly demanded lynching for the murderer. Mob mania seethed in the city.

Two days later a feeble-minded colored boy, Preston Porter, Jr., was arrested in Denver. He was sixteen, son of a railroad laborer who lived in a boxcar on a siding near Limon. He confessed that he had killed Louise on her way home from school. On November 16, Sheriff John W. Freeman of Lincoln County boarded a train with the shackled boy, "ostensibly" to take him to Hugo for trial, the *Times* said. The paper freely predicted that the boy was "on his way to a death as certain as was that of his victim . . . if possible it will be made more atrocious." The train would not be permitted to pass Limon, the *Times* said, and ranchers of the Limon area had threatened to come to Denver with Winchesters, "kill all resistance and batter the jails to dust."

The train did not pass Limon. It was flagged down, and Sheriff Freeman surrendered his prisoner without a struggle to a half-dozen armed men. With a rope around his neck, Preston was dragged out behind a wagon to the scene of his crime. The boy seemed to enjoy being the center of attention and tore leaves from the Bible in his hand to distribute to the crowd as souvenirs.

Everything was in readiness. Newspaper artists were on the ground, sketch pads in hand. Telegraph lines had been installed. The telegraphers used a stack of railroad ties as a desk. A crowd of hundreds was waiting. Many of the onlookers, a fair proportion of them women, had driven out from Denver by buggy to see the spectacle.

A railroad rail had been driven into the prairie at the precise spot where Louise had fallen. Around it a platform of scantlings was raised. Preston was chained feet and breast to the rail. Kindling wood was stacked about his feet and drenched with kerosene.

Louise's father, R. W. Frost, stepped forward and struck a match. "I can touch this match without a shake of my hand." He bent over and lighted the pyre. The crowd cheered. A dozen other men lighted the wood in other places. There was laughter at the boy's cries and writhing agony as he slowly died.

The *News* lashed out at the lynchers and spat editorial disgust on the morbid crowd. "More Ferocious Than Indians Callously Torturing Prey," the headline read. The *Times'* headline was an eight-column banner, "Death in Flames," to which an artist had added a blazing aura in red.

An inquest found the lynching to be the work of "parties unknown", although the ringleaders were well-identified and prominent Lincoln County ranchers. No one ever molested them.[17]

The burning became a national scandal, and Colorado smarted under the shocked attacks of the Eastern press. But in a few months the furore died away and the *News'* anger beat itself out on a wall of official refusal to act. The paper had a more pleasant business to which it could turn to wash away the bad taste.

It was moving day again. This time to the finest and most modern newspaper plant in town, and the paper's first home of its own since Byers' old News Block on Larimer Street. The new building was far uptown at 1720 Welton Street, so far up toward the retreating residential area, in fact, that the business office remained in the Markham Hotel until 1909 to be closer to the center of commerce.

Patterson's two-story house stood on the corner of Welton Street and Seventeenth across and down the street a short block from the brown sandstone Denver Club, for which he had little use. H. A. W. Tabor and his Baby Doe had lived diagonally across the intersection in the 1600

[17]The case was summarized in the *Rocky Mountain News*, June 2, 1929.

block of Welton Street. Patterson had been watching real estate trans-
actions, and he gambled that the downtown district was shifting up the
hill. He was right. The new building proved to be an ideal location for
the *News* for a half century, though the leg men of 1901 complained it
was a long hike to City Hall and Union Station. Denver never had a
"Park Row," but for a time just before the end of the century most of
the papers were concentrated in a six-block area bounded by Larimer
and Curtis streets, Seventeenth to Fifteenth. City Hall was nearby at
Fourteenth and Larimer, and the post office handy at Sixteenth and
Arapahoe.

Patterson put up his new plant just to the rear of his home, which
fronted on Seventeenth Street. In a few years he would move his
family on up to the de luxe residential district on Capitol Hill and the
old house would be built around with an "L" of one-story stores, some
of them later occupied by the *News'* business offices.

Circulation continued to rise, and Patterson built for the future. In
1900 the *News* was distributing 26,375 copies daily and 35,768 on
Sunday. The new building would provide for that sort of production plus
a healthy margin for growth. A 20-foot excavation was dug for the pressroom. A $75,000, two-story structure rose above ground, and a builder
could get a lot for $75,000 in 1901. Venetian wrought-iron ornamental
work, for example.

The architect was Frank E. Edbrooke, who had built the Tabor Grand
Opera House, the Brown Palace, and was completing the state Capitol.
Edbrooke was sent on a tour of the "offices of all the great newspapers
in the country to adapt to the use of this paper all that is latest and best
in time-saving and labor-saving devices." He turned out a design for a
four-floor structure specifically adapted to newspaper production. Then
he let his artistic soul soar for the Welton Street frontage:

> The façade design, it is believed, will prove the handsomest in Denver.
> The style is classic, as befits a home of wisdom and the art preservative.
> The first floor will have a combed copper-bronze front, and the second
> story will be bronze and granite colored brick with terra cotta trim-
> mings.[18]

Shoulder-high windows gave passers-by a view down on the two new
Goss presses, each "more than double the capacity of any other press in
Denver" and equipped with the "very latest color appliances." The presses
cost fifty-five thousand dollars and gave the *News* "greater printing
capacity than all of the presses of the other dailies combined." Bay
windows were set out from the second story, and above the Venetian
ironwork there was a battlemented cornice and a tall flagstaff. Until
the Patterson Building went up flush against the south wall of the *News*

[18]*Rocky Mountain News*, June 6, 1901.

there was a corner entrance with swinging doors on each side under archways of combed bronze. A veritable Temple of the Press.

All omens seemed auspicious and the sky was mile-high blue when the *News* moved uptown to its new home in the summer of 1901. But on the horizon had appeared that cloud which is always "no bigger than a man's hand." Shortly it would form itself into a fist, figuratively and literally.

CHAPTER SEVENTEEN

Yellow, Read and True Blue

THE *News* had no one but itself to blame for the Denver *Post*. When it went soaring off on glorious crusades with the Populists and Bryan, the hard-shelled Democrats were left with no place to go. Their leader, Tom Patterson, had turned his back on them. So they started their own newspaper. Neither they nor anyone else in Denver anticipated that the sickly cub would be "weaned on tiger milk."

The first *Post* appeared August 8, 1892. A group of leading die-hard Democrats got together $50,000 and rented dingy quarters at 1744 Curtis Street, just down in the next block from the *News*. W. P. Caruthers was general manager. The new sheet held the banner high for Grover Cleveland and also declared itself for purity—political, municipal, and female. It was promptly nicknamed "White Wings." But the events of 1892 made the name "Cleveland" a dirty word in Colorado, and if newspaper purity had as many cash subscribers as vocal advocates there would be more saints of the press. The first *Post*, blessed and sinless, died in its crib on August 29, 1893, shortly after its first birthday.

The second attempt was called the *Evening Post*, and the kitty was upped to $100,000. When the *Evening Post* began publication on June 22, 1894, the panic of '93 was still growling through Denver streets and scratching at the doors of closed banks. The office was in the red sandstone Chicago Block at 1734 Curtis Street, a couple of doors south from the crypt of its late-lamented predecessor. The change of address did not produce a change of fortunes. By autumn of the following year Democracy had regained none of its popularity, the *Evening Post* had won few subscribers, and the till was bare. The owners were more than happy to sell their $100,000 property for $12,500 to a thirty-four-year-old Kansas City lottery manipulator and a thirty-nine-year-old former Windsor Hotel bartender.[1]

Frederick Gilmer Bonfils supplied the money. Harry Heye Tammen contributed the idea of buying a dead horse and a shrewd appraisal of what Denver would stand for. Neither knew the first thing about newspapering. Some of his early signed editorials, in fact, indicate that Bonfils was barely literate, although he had been exposed to a West Point education. The cheerful, amoral Harry Tammen never pretended to

[1]Lawrence Martin, *So the People May Know* (Denver, 1951), pp. 5–7.

cultural accomplishments. On the contrary, he made it his pleasure to pose as a happy oaf. Happy, Harry Tammen undoubtedly was; an oaf, never. By an instinct as sure as Barnum's, he knew exactly what would make the suckers sit up and take notice. In the fall of 1895 he was in somewhat straitened circumstances, but until the panic hit he had been doing a highly lucrative business fleecing the tourists with a museum-curio store where one could view Moon-Eye the petrified Indian princess (acquired at auction from a bankrupt undertaker) and purchase one's choice of genuine redskin craftwork (made in Brooklyn) or authenticated scalps of Geronimo. Tammen was always the first to concede he was three quarters con man.

Harry Tammen's short figure was plump and soft; he detested exercise and had no use for the outdoors. He was relaxed, friendly, and generous, an honest, thoroughly engaging rogue. His partner was in nearly every way his opposite. About the only quality they shared was a consecrated determination to relieve unwary Denver of every dollar that wasn't nailed down.

Next after Buffalo Bill Cody, F. G. Bonfils was the handsomest man who ever walked the Denver streets. The eyes were blue and crackled with vitality. The hair was dark and curled in ringlets over a noble brow. Above a magnificently groomed and waxed mustache, the nose was patrician, ever so slightly aquiline. His chin and jaw were firm and prominent but subtly short of jutting. Although he stood only five feet ten, his erect, military bearing made him seem to tower over men much taller. "F.G." was impeccable in a noisy sort of way. His taste in suits ran to prominent checks. On him they looked good. Whereas Tammen looked as if he had slept in his clothes on a depot bench, Bonfils always seemed to have just stepped from a shower and been clothed by the brothers Brooks in a bold and giddy mood. The manner was reserved, lofty, and regal, and Bonfils strode the earth like a conqueror.

Corsica was in the family background, and Bonfils heard so much point made of the homeland and its most famous son that he came in time to believe himself a lineal descendant of Napoleon. The name originally had been Buonfiglio, but his father, a distinguished Missouri probate judge, had shortened it. The Kansas City *Star* said Bonfils had rung a few other and less derivative changes on the theme: E. Little, Silas Carr, M. Dauphin, and L. E. Winn. Various Missouri and Kansas officials were eager to establish contact with the elusive Mr. Winn to discuss the matter of the Little Louisiana Lottery. There were ugly charges that the lottery, promoted by Winn, had been won by Winn. Moreover, there were questions about certain lots Bonfils supposedly had sold in Oklahoma. The land turned out to be in Texas. By these and other means, the *Star* asserted, Bonfils had acquired a sizable fortune. It was at this point that Tammen, ever respectful of genius, learned about the Corsican and purposefully entered his life. Tammen always contended gaily that he had "landed a sucker" in Bonfils. As for Bonfils, he could afford to smile at his friend's crude brashness; whatever lotteries, real estate, and gambling had yielded, the *Post* would multiply many times over.

Gene Fowler has given a full accounting of Tammen and Bonfils in his incomparable *Timber Line*, surely the liveliest book ever written about an American newspaper and one which marches on and on through multiple printings. No one who did not live in Denver during the first three decades of the twentieth century can believe half what Fowler says. But if *Timber Line* reads like fantasy it is only because in this case, with only the most nominal literary license, fact is far more antic than fiction.

As time passed the town began to call them "Tam" and "Bon," not necessarily with affection. They maintained a stuffed baby elephant—named Tambon—in the city room, and they ran a circus as a logical ancillary to their style of newspapering. Bonfils had the doors removed from the cubicles in the gents' room lest his employees waste precious time. He professed a fatherly concern for each and every person on his payroll, from the street-corner newsie to the managing editor. He was particularly solicitous about their character development and was careful not to sap their morals or sow temptation in their pathways by paying inordinate salaries. Now and again Bon would appear on the balcony outside his office window and scatter bright new pennies to crowds of urchins below. This did not arise from softness of head or heart; Bonfils practiced a soulful reverence for coin of the land, whatever the denomination. It was promotion, a part of the partners' policy that there should always be something stirring and spectacular happening around the *Post*. On one occasion a local poetess timidly suggested remuneration for her verses which the *Post* had published. Bonfils was shaken by the crassness.

"You mean you want *money*?"

"I think my work should be paid for," the little lady said. "Don't you?"

"I am amazed," Bon said with a deep sadness. "My dear child, Jesus never asked for money."

Then there was the case of the svelte Miss Marguerite Frey. Miss Frey won a beauty contest sponsored by the *Post*. She went on to Chicago and won the national contest too. It was then disclosed by a disaffected member of the *Post* staff that the foresighted Bon had forced Miss Frey to sign a contract binding her to pay all her winnings to him in exchange for a place on the *Post* payroll at ten dollars a week.

Tam was inclined to be less devious. When he was brought into court on a contempt citation he shook his fist at the judge and declared: "You can put me in jail for twenty years, if you want, but I'll get you yet." The white-faced judge replied: "Case dismissed."

The partners painted their joint office a rich shade of plum and called it the Red Room. Denver soon learned to call it the Bucket of Blood. Tam and Bon dubbed their *Post* "The Paper with a Heart and Soul."

It was a fantastic partnership, but then the product was fantastic too. The *Post* was a lulu.

But most of the high jinks lay in the future on the sunny noonday of October 28, 1895, when Harry Tammen led his handsome and aristocratic "sucker" away from the check-signing which had made them newspaper publishers. If, as time went on, people would come to call Tammen a pirate, no one would use such a gross term to describe Bonfils. He was all corsair to the tips of his manicured fingernails, romantic, dashing, driven by dark furies.

Bonfils appears to have been somewhat disappointed at the run-down appearance of his new property.

"It's a piddling little paper now," Fowler quotes Tammen as saying in reassurance.[2] "But we'll wean it on tiger milk." It was a fair, reasonable, and accurate forecast.

The partners strolled arm in arm around the corner and found a vacant dry-goods store at 1019 Sixteenth Street, on the alley across the street from H. A. W. Tabor's opera house and the post office. They rented the two-story building and moved their paper in. Then they set about to stand Denver on its ear.

There were now four daily newspapers in Denver. The *Colorado Journal* had disappeared. The *Sun* went down in July 1894 in a merger with the *Times*, and the *Republican* had swallowed Eugene Field's *Tribune*. This left on the 1900 scene Tom Patterson's *News*, Senator Hill's *Republican*, the *Times*, now owned by David H. Moffat and his banker friends, and the twice-resurrected *Post*. With Bryan parboiling the "gold bugs" in scalding oratory, the *News* was happily back in the Democratic fold. The *Republican* and *Times* hewed to the GOP line, and the former so diligently carried water for the increasingly powerful "corporations" that it became known as the "Kept Lady of Sixteenth Street." The *Post* proudly proclaimed its independence, which, it soon became plain, arose less from firm convictions about journalistic impartiality than from canny estimates (or advance commitments) on which politicians would let Tam and Bon do their thinking.

Historian Jerome Smiley was a little dazed, in his gentleman-scholarly way, as he watched the fur fly. Writing in 1901, when the contestants were only warming up, he closed out his chronicles of Denver journalism as follows:

> The four daily newspapers of Denver are metropolitan in their methods, size and character, and every day lay before their readers the news of all the world. Each of the four issues weekly and Sunday morning editions. In every respect the Sunday issues take rank with those in

[2]Gene Fowler, *Timber Line* (New York, 1933), p. 88.

any city in the west. Indeed, it may fairly be said that there is no division of human activity in Denver in which more enterprise, greater energy, higher ability, are employed than in the production of our newspapers every day in the week. Political zeal in heated campaigns sometimes leads to perhaps undue manifestations of vigor but, after the Colorado custom that probably is an outgrowth of the altitude, of the climate, or the environment, our newspapers are fearfully and wonderfully in earnest in whatever they undertake to do.[3]

Battle lines were clearly drawn, and the earnestness at least fearful, if not deadly, as the *News* moved up to its new palace on Welton Street in the summer of 1901. For the first time since Gibson's *Herald* had beat it to the streets with a daily edition the *News* was encountering stiff competition. By 1902 the *Post* already had scored striking gains, and the *News* determined to narrow the opposition forces by one.

On October 8 of that year the *News* bought the *Times* from Moffat, who was in need of cash. (Moffat had committed his $9,000,000 personal fortune to the notion of drilling a six-mile hole through the Rockies for a railroad that would "put Denver on the main line." He lost his fortune and died in 1911 before the Moffat Tunnel was finally completed with public funds in 1928.) In the *Times* purchase Patterson and his son-in-law, R. C. Campbell, each put up half the price, which was not made public. The *Times*, an evening paper, moved to the *News* plant. Although it maintained its own identity and had a separate editorial staff, the *Times* was in effect an afternoon edition of the *News*. The operating corporation became the News-Times Publishing Company.

In the grab for new subscribers which soon developed, all the papers put on canvassing crews. The tintinnabulation of doorbells must have been deafening. Premiums were offered. One of the *News'* come-alongs in 1905 was a hand-powered vacuum cleaner. Frank Plumb, recently retired after nearly fifty years on the *News* staff, remembers the era:

I was a year out of a Chicago high school, and had come to Denver to make a living, preferably as a reporter. I had no training and few aptitudes for the job—merely an intense desire to get it with no clear idea how I would perform it. . . .

Thomas McGill, city editor of The News, was not a well man. He viewed me unenthusiastically. But he needed cubs who could do the work of copy boys. So he suggested that he would try me out, if I could work, say three months, without salary.

That seems on the niggard side. But if he had known exactly how ill-informed and inept I was, he probably would have suggested that I pay The News several dollars a week for the privilege of infesting the office.

[3]Smiley, *History of Denver*, pp. 672–74.

However, I had to have a wage that would return at least room rent and food. Mr. McGill suggested I see the circulation manager and get a job soliciting subscriptions. I could thus learn the city.

I did just that. The News and the Post then were engaged in a rugged battle for subscribers, advertising and prestige. We doorbell ringers were the expendable infantry in that war.

I "learned the city" and also learned to live on $5 or $6 a week. We were paid strictly on commission. The only time, after that, when I entered the editorial offices was when we were given hand-powered vacuum cleaners to offer as premiums to subscribers.

Our boss took us into Publisher Tom Patterson's sanctum. It had a blue Brussels carpet, the only carpet in the building. On this our boss sprinkled talcum powder, and demonstrated how the cleaner would suck it up.

The cleaner, frankly, was what now would be called a stinker. Persons to whom we offered it made suggestions that were neither polite nor practical, as to what we should do with it.

Finally I realized that we doorbell ringers were being routed so that we covered the same sections every 15 days. The housewives came to know our faces; dogs greeted us with bared fangs. . . .[4]

Vacuum cleaners were not enough. The *Post* was sweeping the city. The defunct but unburied sheet Bonfils and Tammen bought had claimed a questionable circulation of 6000 copies. Twenty-seven months later, at the end of 1897, the *Post* was distributed to 24,599 subscribers,[5] a figure which it had taken the *News* nearly fifty years to attain. By 1907 the *Post* circulation was 83,000, more than the combined total of its three competitors.

"Son," Tammen had told his city editor, "you've seen a vaudeville show, haven't you? It's got every sort of act—laughs, tears, wonder, thrills, melodrama, tragedy, comedy, love and hate. That's what I want you to give our readers."[6]

It was obvious that vaudeville was not dead in Denver. And it was a great show. One day an eight-column screamer in the biggest, boldest railroad Gothic type available: "DOES IT HURT TO BE BORN?" Next day a trout-fishing contest—won by F. G. Bonfils, outdoorsman, and no blushes. Denver was amazed, startled, fascinated, and left waiting, slack-jawed, to see what the *Post* would "pull" next. Scandals were exploited to the hilt, and there was a crucifixion of a public official or non-advertising businessman in each new edition. Everyone damned the *Post*—and nearly everyone subscribed. The *Post's* owners admitted with frankness that they cared not a whit for the community's respect so long as the community kept buying the paper.

[4]*Rocky Mountain News*, May 31, 1952.

[5]Martin, op. cit., p. 13.

[6]Ibid.

"Sure," Tammen conceded, "we're yellow, but we're read, and we're true blue."[7]

One of the *Post's* early victims was the distinguished local architect, F. E. Edbrooke, who had designed the *News* building. Attacks on the builder began appearing under the *Post's* "So the People May Know" standing head. (The *Post* had no editorial page; it would have been excess baggage since each article in and of itself was a full statement of the paper's passions and prejudices on the subject matter involved.) Edbrooke's office, however, was on an upper floor of the Tabor Opera House building across the street, and it looked right down into the Bucket of Blood. Whenever Bonfils or Tammen stepped to the window he could see Edbrooke above him cleaning a rifle. The attacks ceased.

Tammen's one journalistic rule, often expounded to his reporters as he lounged on their desks, was: "Hit 'em where they live." His partner, who did no desk-lounging, was more unctuous. It was Bonfils who was responsible for the slogans which appeared on the façade of the *Post* building: "'Tis a Privilege to Live in Colorado"; "You Are Now Standing Exactly One Mile above Sea Level." (You weren't, but it was close enough.) Bon's masterpiece was: "O, Justice, When Expelled from Other Habitations, Make This Thy Dwelling Place." The noble motto won the *Post* a highly talented artist.

Wilbur Steele, the city's first newspaper cartoonist, had left the *News* and was drawing for the *Republican* at the time the open invitation was extended to the fugitive Miss Justice. He drew a cartoon of that robed lady, her blindfold pushed aggressively up from one eye, her sword aloft, storming into the *Post* building with its slogan. Two figures tagged Tam and Bon were fleeing out the rear door. Bon was asking Tam: "Who is that *woman?*"

The town guffawed, and Tam along with it. Bon's amusement undoubtedly was more restrained. He never saw the slightest contradiction between what his slogan said and what his *Post* did. But he knew talent when he saw it. He offered more money and hired Steele away from the *Republican.*

Meanwhile the show went on. A lady aerialist in pink tights slid, hanging by her teeth, from an upper floor of the Gas & Electric Building to a platform in front of the new *Post* building at 1544 Champa Street, occupied in 1907. A large cash prize was offered for the first non-stop airplane flight around the world. Stipulation: the flight must begin and end in Champa Street. Welton Street might have an editorial page and good intentions, but it had no two-headed calves.

The old sober-sided *News* was concerning itself with other matters. Denver's rapid growth had pushed it definitely into the rank of cities, and like many another American city, Denver entered the twentieth

[7]Fowler, *Timber Line*, p. 99.

century stewing in a vat of malodorous municipal and corporate corruption. It was the era of the muckrakers. Lincoln Steffens surveyed the situation but passed over Denver's shame to expend his crusading energies on the scarcely less spectacular vices of Chicago, Minneapolis, and New York. John Reed, Upton Sinclair, and others lifted the lid on the Denver cesspool and commented in terms which obviously were radical, rabble-rousing, and troublemaking. The plain fact was that Denver was firmly in the grip of boodlers, bribe takers, petty politicians —and fat-cat corporations which knew how to manipulate the ilk.

Reflecting the personality, interests, and political ideals of its owner, the *News* was hip deep in the jungle, hacking away at the underbrush to clear the way for its vision of a better city. Patterson's eyes were failing now under the pressures of full-time law, full-time politics, and full-time publishing. He was wearing spectacles with thick, perfectly round lenses. But good eyesight was not essential to a knowledge of what was going on in Denver. A sense of smell was sufficient.

News policies in this fragrant milieu were extremely liberal, if not red-eyed radical by present-day yardsticks. The paper came out flatly and strongly for public ownership of railroads and utilities, and indicated it could easily be persuaded that banks should be "restored to the people." The *News* was in the van of the new "progressive" movement abroad in the land, stirred up by Populism, Bryan, Eugene V. Debs, and the muckrakers. It took the side of labor at every opportunity, and Patterson was often the defense counsel when union leaders or members were brought into court on charges which boiled down to non-conformity and fighting back. An armory of editorial lances was broken against the entrenched grafters in City Hall. The utilties, big corporations, "trusts," and mineowners got nothing but trouble from the *News*. The private water company, for example, was enterprisingly slicing itself chunks of Denver's progress at the rate of 242 per cent on its investment. The *News* uncovered the statistic and let out a howl that echoed up and down Seventeenth Street from the state Capitol to Union Station.

A campaign for public ownership was pressed intensively. It succeeded. The city took over operation of the water works. *News* crusades for municipal operation of the Denver Tramway Company transit lines and the light and power utilities did not fare so well. The traction company continued in private hands, though its present owners, caught between declining revenues and inadequate service in a city where nearly everyone drives to work, now might welcome having the city take over. The Public Service Company (gas and electricity) was fair game for the *News* and all the rest of the Denver press for decades. It managed to side-step municipal ownership, but sometimes it was a narrow squeak.

The Denver Gas & Electric Company, predecessor to Public Service, was deeply embroiled in the Cities Service scandal. On one of his many visits to Denver Henry L. Doherty ran afoul of bitter local enemies. The gas and electric company had sought a new long-term franchise in the 1906 election and won by only five hundred votes. The *News* then discovered that hundreds of ten-cent tax receipts had been issued to qualify electors in a balloting otherwise restricted to taxpayers. A cry went up, subpoenas were issued, and one of them caught the utilities king Doherty. In court he "crossed his arms and arrogantly refused to testify."[8] Judge Ben Lindsey threw him in jail for contempt. His lawyers managed to spring him after three days and two nights, and he fled to Lincoln, Nebraska, pausing on the steps of his Pullman to issue a dictum on the climate and the ancestry of the city which maltreated him: "Denver has more sunshine and sons of bitches than any place in the country."

Some months later Doherty's right-hand man, Frank W. Freuauff, a deacon of Central Presbyterian Church, lost his pocket diary or it was stolen from him. The little book made its way to the *News*, which published facsimiles of the pages. Each page carried a biblical quotation at its head: "Suffer little children" or "Blessed are the meek." But beneath the moral sentiments were listed the "Big Mitt" payments made during the election campaign. They totaled $67,690 to candidates and leaders of both parties. Mayor Speer was down for $4500, the president of the Board of Supervisors got $1600, a judge $400, several politically active preachers $550 each.

The bloodless City Hall War of "Bloody Bridles" Waite had pinpointed one of the weaknesses of Denver city government which left it prey to political harpies and palm-crossing trusts. Some of the municipal officers were appointed by the governor, some of them locally elected. When the two factions didn't choose to work together, which was often, city affairs bogged to a standstill. The result was an inefficient and ineffectual city government, racked with factional jealousies, sensitive to petty prerogatives, and thus divided in open invitation to those who might wish to advance private projects at the expense of public weal. There is nothing in the record to indicate that the invitation was ever spurned.

The *News* demanded for a long time a "home rule" amendment to the state constitution which would give Denver citizens full control over their city affairs. Finally, on November 4, 1902, the amendment was adopted. Denver freed herself from Arapahoe County, which dated back in name if not in boundaries to Kansas Territorial days, and became a co-extensive city and county. But when the first city charter was drawn and submitted for a vote in 1903 the "machine" went into action. The charter proposed to establish a system which would have severely restricted party spoils and made corporate domination more difficult. It was

[8]George Creel, *Rebel at Large* (New York, 1947), pp. 121–22.

defeated, and the *News* charged that more than ten thousand illegal ballots had been cast.[9]

A second charter was prepared and adopted. It multiplied elective and appointive offices, abolished the recall, made public ownership of utilities so difficult and costly it could not be resorted to, and, on a pose of taking city government out of politics, stipulated that elective offices were to be non-partisan. They immediately became, of course, bipartisan, with the full range of attendant evils and the obfuscation which made it difficult for the voter to know who or what he was voting for or to fix responsibility. Robert W. Speer, as a case in point, was nominally a Democrat. Yet he was maintained in the mayor's office for many years by a combination of Republican Seventeenth Street, neutral, but hardly disinterested corporations, the big-time gamblers like Ed Chase, small-time Democratic hacks, and the madams and proprietary pimps of the hookshops on Market Street. (Although Speer was a coreligionist in politics and a personal friend, Patterson fought him with the *News* at nearly every turn and in the face of the beatification of "Speer the Builder" by the garden-club crowd and other civic ostriches who saw only the lovely new parks and public works and dismissed city politics as a dirty business. Which it was. The *News*, for example, opposed Denver's pleasant mid-city Civic Center on the grounds, later proved, that it was primarily a real estate manipulation designed to line the pockets of Speer and his friends, and only incidentally an achievement in the march toward the City Beautiful.)

The myth of non-partisanship still haunts Denver voters. Although everyone in town knows or suspects a municipal candidate's party affiliation, both candidate and voter are legally bound to pretend they are politically unattached. As a result, mayors, city councilmen, and other elective officials establish their own individual machines, intermesh them *sub rosa* with one or both party organizations, and merrily roll along unburdened by the necessity of declaring themselves openly on party platforms or philosophies. Denver can rise up and throw the rascals out—an expedient seldom resorted to—but the bipartisan rigging makes party responsibility impossible.

Patterson and the *News*, bucking such a system from a frank and open partisan position, came into conflict with a notorious state Supreme Court. The corporations had entered into an agreement with Republican Governor James H. Peabody under which they were permitted to select the judges to be appointed to the supreme bench.[10] The *News* didn't like that situation a bit. Page-one editorials and cartoons appeared in June 1905, accusing the high court of being corrupt in personnel and

[9]Clyde Lyndon King, *The History of the Government of Denver with Special Reference to Its Relations with Public Service Corporations* (Denver, 1911), pp. 233–35.

[10]35 Colo. 325.

judicial decisions. The justices were baldly proclaimed to be tools of the utility and railroad corporations and the Republican bosses. The court, said the *News*, was the "Great Judicial Slaughter-house and Mausoleum," and a cartoon depicted the chief justice as the "Lord High Executioner" beheading virtuous Democrats. It was no sniping attack. Patterson stood on top of his battlements and waved his flag, daring reprisals. In a signed editorial in the *News* he declared:

> I am responsible for every one of them [the editorial attacks], and either wrote or approve of them. I believe they are fair and just criticism, and are fully warranted by what has transpired. . . . I consider the proceedings against me as a direct assault upon the freedom of the press, and I shall defend that ancient and important prerogative of free people with all my power.[11]

The Supreme Court had picked up the gage and cited Patterson for contempt. The case became an important one in the legal history of American press freedom. Patterson, with a battery of attorneys in support, replied, in effect: "In answer to the charge of contempt for saying these things, my only answer and defense is that they are true, and I hereby offer to prove them." The brief and the arguments were intricate, lengthy, and unavailing. Two of the justices sitting in judgment on him, Patterson declared, had obtained their seats as a part of the conspiracy. In his final verbal statement to the justices, robed, frothing, and *en banc*, the *News* publisher was even more strongly contemptuous in one of the most scathing arraignments ever addressed to an American bench:

> I can only say, if your honors please, that it is the most stupendous indictment that can be framed against this whole doctrine of constructive contempt; or, has it come to this in the United States, that the publisher of a newspaper, because men are judges, may not speak the truth of them as to their official actions, except at the peril of confinement in the common jail, the payment of heavy monetary penalties, or both?
>
> . . . if this is to be maintained, it simply means that we have in each of the states of this Union a chosen body of men who may commit any crime, who may falsify justice; who may defy constitutions and spit upon laws, and yet no man dare make known the fact.
>
> So far as I am concerned, if the court please, I am unwilling to be bound by such a system, and therefore, if no other result is to come from these proceedings beyond my own punishment, than the arousing of the public to the danger of such a power in the hands of any body of men, a great good will have been accomplished; more, perhaps, than is necessary to compensate for what I may suffer; and I only desire to say, further, before I sit down, that no matter what penalty the court may inflict, from this time forward I will devote myself—by the

[11]*Rocky Mountain News*, June 30, 1905.

consitutional amendment, if necessary, and by the decisions of the
court it has become necessary—to deprive every man and every body
of men of such tyrannical power, of such unjust and dangerous pre-
rogative, of the ability to say to publishers of newspapers: "While
about everything else you may speak the truth, no matter what our
offenses may be, you speak the truth with the open door of the jail
staring you in the face, or the depletion of what you may possess in
this world's goods, and probably of both."

If the court please, I am now ready to receive judgment of the court.[12]

The Colorado bar gasped. No one, ever, had called Supreme Court
justices tyrants to their faces. Perhaps it is reasonable to deduce that
Patterson really would have welcomed a jail sentence; it would have
made his case all the stronger. But the court didn't fall for the trap.
With Justice Robert W. Steele dissenting, it fined Patterson a thousand
dollars. To a man of his position and wealth, the penalty was a cowardly
slap on the wrist. The United States Supreme Court refused to accept
an appeal on an issue of jurisdiction.

Many years later, however, the federal high court handed down a
decision[13] which has been interpreted as sustaining Patterson's audacious
stand. The court overruled conviction of the publisher of the Toledo
News Bee for criticizing a federal court's decision. An attorney who now
is himself a member of the Colorado Supreme Court wrote that the
ruling ". . . wiped out the power of Federal courts to punish newspaper
publishers and editors in contempt proceedings. . . . It indicates that
the Supreme Court has sufficient stature to realize that Article 1 of the
Bill of Rights should prevail in a situation where it comes into conflict
with the judicial power to punish contempts. Thus a strong blow has
been struck for Freedom of Expression and Thomas Patterson's beliefs
have received recognition from the highest court in the land."[14]

The structure of fraud which permitted the buying of a Colorado
Supreme Court rested, basically, on prosaic ward heeling and ballot-box
stuffing. Votes were openly purchased. The ten-cent tax receipts have
been mentioned. Another gimmick brought to a high state of perfection
in Denver required adroit awkwardness. A voter suddenly would stumble
and slam into the ballot box, knocking it to the floor, breaking the glass
and scattering ballots. The graceless one then would apologize profusely
and insist that he be permitted to help pick up the spilled ballots. In
the course of the cleanup a quantity of fraudulent votes would be substituted.

In the silk-stocking precincts where such clumsy methods might have

[12]35 Colo. 395–99.

[13]Nye v. U.S., Apr. 14, 1941.

[14]William E. Doyle, "Patterson Vindicated," Dicta, Vol. 18, No. 7 (July 1941),
pp. 169–72.

been challenged, heelers canvassed the poll books carefully and made lists of the names of all voters who had recently died or moved. Professional voters then were employed to circulate between polling places and vote the names. Some of them were men of ready wit, equal to any emergency. Ed Keating recalls one who carried off an uncomfortable situation rather well. He was challenged and asked to repeat his name. He complied.

"My God!" said a woman waiting in line. "That's my husband's name."

"Madame," the con man replied instantly, "do not attempt to convince our friends that you are my wife."

He cast his phony ballot and stalked from the polls.[15]

One of the most devoted enemies of "Big Mitt" and his system was the undersized, argumentative gadfly Judge Benjamin Barr Lindsey. Close to fanatic in his crusading zeal for the underdog, Lindsey as a county judge became convinced something was wrong in the way the law handled juvenile offenders. He wanted a justice for children which would be "medicinal and restorative" rather than based on society's revenge against wrongdoing. He began hearing children's cases in that light and finally, in 1907, persuaded the legislature to establish for him the first juvenile court. National and world fame as a reformer and pioneer came to him. The irascible George Bernard Shaw once waited patiently for several hours in a London hotel lobby in order to shake Judge Lindsey's hand. But in Denver Lindsey was without honor.

His convictions that "there's no such thing as a bad boy", that environment counted more than heredity in shaping a young criminal, led him to inquire with terrier intensity into the backgrounds of the boys and girls who came before him. Economic and industrial abuses were the most common root cause, he announced, and these were being sustained by the corporate corruption of politics. Henceforth Ben Lindsey was the most active and shrill of Denver's unpopular reformers. He fought at the top of his voice and with every weapon he could reach, and he was both able politician and resourceful lawyer. He had the News as his ally through much of the battle. "The Beast"—as Lindsey called the machine—paid him back with personal vilification, slanders about his sex life, and threats of physical violence. The corporations boycotted the News. The paper lived through the disfavor of its major advertisers, but the machine got Lindsey. The vocal little man was often a bore and always a baiter of consciences, and so Denver ran him out of town as an undesirable citizen. The bar association, dominated by lawyers who had felt his lash, shut Lindsey off by disbarring him on a charge that had been previously aired and disproved. He left Denver and died in Los Angeles.[16]

15Rocky Mountain News, Aug. 10, 1955.

16Lindsey tells of his Denver years in The Beast (New York, 1911) and The Dangerous Life (New York, 1931).

During much of the wrestling with Lindsey's "Beast", the *Times* was on the other side of the fence from its onetime sister paper, the *News*. Patterson sold, or leased, the *Times* to Mayor Speer and William G. Evans, banker, president of the tramway company, and son of territorial Governor John Evans, and thereby spawned a foe. The *Times* joined the *Republican* in speaking for the corporations and attacking the do-goodism and wild-eyed Democratic socialism of the *News*. Later Evans turned the paper back to Patterson, who restored the *News-Times* morning and evening combination. The *Post* was the journalistic mercenary of the wars, shifting back and forth as fortunes changed and influential callers came visiting at the Bucket of Blood.

The *Post's* major contribution to trust busting was to set up a coalyard. Bonfils decided the "coal trust" was exacting toll from the people of his city, and he now had adopted the slogan of "Big Brother" for his paper. Big Brother would not permit this exploitation to continue. So the *Post* interrupted its parade of human flies and lady wrestlers and began selling coal. The advertisements said: "A Full Ton—and an Extra Lump." One ungrateful beneficiary of this public-spirited gesture suspiciously ran his load of coal across the city scales. He discovered the extra lump was missing, along with several others. Additional loads were weighed and found similarly short. The *News*, of course, chortled its glee all over the front page, and for a time Tam and Bon became "Nut" and "Lump" to *News* cartoonists and editorial writers.

One of the leading *News* editorialists of the day, a key broadswordsman in the thin but determined little phalanx, was George Creel, later to become a noted magazine writer, militant liberal, and Woodrow Wilson's public information chief in World War I. Creel hit Denver young, filled with outrage against life's injustices and red hot for anything whatsoever that looked like a holy war. He was swept up by the heady righteousness of Judge Lindsey's many causes and became one of the most aggressive lieutenants of the "Kids' Judge."

Creel started with the *Post*. He departed from Champa Street with wry comments on Bonfils' penuriousness and backward-hurled accusations of welshing and double cross. Years later in his autobiography Creel wrote that "Bonfils made me see avarice as a passion that gave more sheer pleasure than the love of women or the applause of men. Saving a nickel actually bathed him in happiness and content." This reminiscent outburst had its origins in a trip Creel made with Bonfils to Egypt.

Bonfils admired the phraseology very much when one of his writers described him as "friend of Presidents." He decided forthwith to carry a personal invitation to Teddy Roosevelt, urging him to visit Denver, "Climate Capital of the World." T.R. at this point was hunting on the upper reaches of the White Nile, but the whole tour could be charged off to editorial enterprise and promotion. Creel was assigned to go along and handle writing and reporting chores. The trip was nauseous for Creel. The millionaire publisher embarrasseed his sixty-dollar-a-week writer by giving the railroad porter a quarter for three days of service. The police in Naples had to rescue them from angry porters in a similar tipping set-to. Creel flatly refused his employer's proposal that they share a Pullman berth to reduce expenses, and he finally got a separate hotel room in Paris by jumping on Bon's stomach in the middle of the night "with a yell that rattled the windows."

"Nightmare," he explained. "Thought I was over them, but I reckon they're coming back."

Bonfils okayed less cozy quarters, but the cost preyed upon him for the rest of the trip and he became petulant and quarrelsome. When the safari returned to Denver, Creel was assessed half the expenses and the sum was deducted on the installment plan from his pay check. Still later, after Creel had joined the *News* staff and was lambasting the *Post's* attitude on civic reform, a "So the People May Know" memo appeared insinuating that five hundred dollars of the expense money had been stolen, though "The Post forgot all about it." Creel frothed in the *News* for February 3, 1913: "Mark the Post's royal disregard of money. . . . 'The money was never returned, and the Post forgot all about it.' What is one thousand dollars to the Post? A bagatelle! a trifle! Does it not offer million-dollar rewards for the first humming bird that flies over Pike's Peak? for the first trip to Mars? . . . There is an impudence so sublime that it is almost enchanting! Who does not know that money is the heart's blood of these men? Why, until every cent of the lost money was repaid them, they never knew rest, nor did I know peace."

Creel had left Denver for a semester on the staff of *Cosmopolitan* magazine before Patterson lured him back to Denver and the *News* in 1911 with the promise of a free hand in a slam-bang campaign to clean up the city. The young sin slayer, who lived in a cosmos of black and white, was in glory as he buckled on his armor and plunged in. He organized a task force headed by Judge Lindsey. Also in the group were Edward P. Costigan, later a United States senator, and Josephine Roche, a wealthy mineowner's daughter fresh out of Vassar with a heartful of dedication and a headful of liberal ideas. To assist in firing the rhetorical salvos Creel signed up a *News* writer, William MacLeod Raine, who, when his hour of crusading was done, would set down and write nearly fourscore shoot-'em-up novels about the Old West. Raine died in Denver in 1954 wearing the ten-gallon mortarboard of "dean of the Westerns."

The first objective was to get Mayor Speer. Creel describes the fray:

> The *News*, of course, was the spearhead of the movement; and in addition to heated editorials, I filled the front page with attacks and appeals. The corporations, fighting back, ordered an advertising boycott, but while it made a sizable dent in revenues, Senator Patterson stayed

put. The churches were also scared into opposition by rich parishoners, and only Father O'Ryan and Rabbi Kauvar, two dauntless souls, gave us pulpit support. Speer's board of education refused us the use of the schoolhouses, but we topped that hurdle by asking the people to open their homes, and neighborhood meetings proved most effective.[17]

At one point twenty-five thousand persons turned out to listen to firebrand speeches for three hours in a snowstorm. With this sort of support the reformers accomplished the unlikely. They whipped the Speer machine in 1912 and installed Henry J. Arnold as mayor—for one tempestuous term. The forces of right were jubilant, and the *News* crowed. But Tom Patterson, now in his seventies, was an old campaigner and wise to the ways of small men in large offices. He forecast that their man wouldn't remain hitched. Creel was detailed to take the post of police commissioner and keep his eye on the reform mayor.

Patterson was right. Both "Big Mitt" and Champa Street got to Arnold, and he went sour. Not, however, before Creel had a chance to get in some licks. He turned the police department inside out, and one of his first orders deprived patrolmen of their nightsticks. They would go unarmed "like the London Bobbies." The *Post* denounced the commissioner as a "tramp anarchist" and a "crackpot" and forecast that Denver's underworld would make mincemeat of the defenseless cops. Creel cited statistics to show that during the first ten months of the "clubless" period two policemen were beat up while twelve had been killed in melees before his order.

The *News* had forced Governor Henry A. Buchtel to shut down open gambling in 1907. There remained the street of sin, gaudy Market Street, the West's most wicked thoroughfare. Creel turned his attentions to the red lights. Denver had some seven hundred prostitutes plying their trade, and the police commissioner theorized that they were the victims of white slavers and male degradation. They could be reclaimed for virtue, he felt sure, by rounding them up and putting them in an atmosphere of Grade A milk and fresh air on a municipal farm. Abolishing vice also would cut down on the spread of venereal disease. This was the one time Patterson bucked. He approved of his headstrong moralist's efforts to close the parlor houses and cribs, but he didn't feel the words "syphilis" and "gonorrhea" belonged in the pages of his family newspaper. Creel argued. Finally Patterson gave in, but only on condition that he would not have to read a word of what Creel wrote about the menace of social disease.

Creel cracked down on the Tenderloin in 1913. He herded in the doves, gave them Wassermanns, and forced the tainted ones—about two thirds—to submit to treatment. The girls were entertaining nightly ten to twenty-five clients apiece, and it perhaps can be assumed that they

[17]Creel, op. cit., p. 97.

enjoyed the peace and quiet on Creel's health farm. But only temporarily. Creel was bounced out of office, and within a few months Market Street was humming as busily as ever with all the favorites back in business at the same old stands. Two years later, after prohibition had been voted in 1914, Sheriff Glen Duffield was more successful. He succeeded in closing down the district and scattering its courtesans to walk-up hotels and well-publicized telephone numbers. Scandalous Market Street was gone. Mattie Silks' palace of love at number 1942 eventually became, by substitution of a couple of letters, a warehouse. Denver never again could boast of a sin belt. There were still accommodations, of course, but they were scattered to dingy fleabags, and the oldest profession lost much of its glamor. For a time the "maid system" was instituted. Each rooming house was permitted not to exceed two maids on duty at any one time to change the hot sheets and otherwise minister to guests. John Polly, a *News* writer of a later era, scored a memorable scoop in the late 1930s when a minor fire broke out in one of the sleazy budgeted brothels. Polly started his story: "There hadn't been so much excitement at the Silver Dollar Rooms since a lost stranger came in and tried to rent a room. . . ." But it was the last fling of a ribald tradition. When Denver became a military town in the build-up for World War II, the army forced Mayor Benjamin F. Stapleton to banish even the "maids." No health farm was provided.

As scarlet pleasures fled before the lashes of Creel and Sheriff Duffield, man's indomitable inventiveness was providing Denver with other diversions. The automobile and the airplane were making their appearance.

A dashing young *News* photographer in a bowler hat was startling the town by driving up to assignments, clouded in dust and wreathed in explosions, at the wheel of a two-cylinder Maxwell runabout. The photographer was Harry Mellon Rhoads, and the car was one of the first in Denver. Harry got his start at seven dollars a week—a five-dollar gold piece and two silver cartwheels—on the *Republican* in 1900. He was eighteen then, and he covered his first photo assignments by bicycle and motorcycle. Four years later he joined the *News* and acquired his racy $750 Maxwell. Today, a portly and puckish little man who sometimes sports the latest in flat-topped hats, Harry is still handling daily picture assignments for the *News* and probably has a longer record of service than any other news photographer in America. He likes to drive young reporters past the corner of Forest Drive and Broadway to point out Denver's first service station, lately rebuilt but still doing business at the original location. Both of Harry's daughters and a son-in-law have also been *News* photographers. They are no longer on the darkroom staff, but Harry, ageless and elaborately courtly with the ladies, goes on forever. He angrily resents any effort of city editors to shield him from the more rigorous assignments.

Harry's camera remembers the first automobile on Denver streets, David W. Brunton's Columbia electric, which created a sensation when it appeared May 10, 1898.[18] On September 9, 1900, the *News* reported that John Brisben Walker had driven to an altitude of 11,000 feet on Pike's Peak. It was the highest an automobile had gone, although the summit of the peak was reached on August 12, 1901, by W. B. Felker and C. A. Yont. Present-day tourists drive to the top on a modern highway.

One of the first internal-combustion cars to reach Denver was purchased by Dr. F. L. Bartlett of Cañon City. It was shipped from Detroit to Denver by express and arrived in the summer of 1901. The *News* described it as the thirteenth Oldsmobile manufactured. The car was assembled, and Dr. Bartlett practiced driving in a sixty-acre field "back of the smelter." Then he set out cross country for Cañon City. The machine met a woman in a horse and buggy. The horse took fright and upset the buggy. Dr. Bartlett had to pay damages for terrorizing the countryside.

The *News* of January 15, 1902, recorded another milestone: "For the first time in the history of Denver an automobilist was fined in police court yesterday for driving his machine along the streets of the city at a speed which endangered the lives of pedestrians." E. S. Matheson was the goggled prisoner at the bar. Officer Asken testified that he arrested Matheson on Sixteenth Street. The culprit had been doing forty miles an hour. The automobilist demurred. Eight miles an hour. "Twenty-five dollars and costs," said the judge.

Harry Rhoads still preserves the glass-plate negatives he made on July 20, 1903, when the first automobile to cross the continent through Colorado visited Denver, six months out of San Francisco eastbound. It was a twelve-horsepower, one-cylinder Packard named "Old Pacific" and manned by E. T. Fetch and M. C. Karup. Somehow they had pushed their horseless carriage up the gorge from Grand Junction to Glenwood Springs and then over the Continental Divide to Denver.

The air age arrived in Denver close behind the automobile age. Harry Rhoads was at Overland Park race track with his camera on February 2, 1910, when Louis Paulhan, pioneering French aeronaut, undertook to demonstrate his flying machine to a skeptical West. The first American air show had been held in Los Angeles only two weeks before. Paulhan brought his Farman biplane to Denver in a boxcar, and there was much tinkering and French profanity through the day in the racetrack oval as the flimsy linen-covered plane was assembled and tested. Several trial runs were unsuccessful, and half the chilled crowd of thousands drifted away convinced the airplane was a hoax. Rhoads stayed on, and at dusk he got his picture for the *News*: Paulhan airborne ten feet above

[18]*Colorado Magazine*, Vol. VIII, No. 1 (Jan. 1931), pp. 4ff.

the racetrack on the first flight into Colorado's skies. Next day Paulhan cracked up trying to duplicate his feat, but he walked away unhurt and on April 27 won the London *Daily Mail's* $50,000 prize for covering 183 miles in twenty-four hours—London to Manchester.

Denver's first aircraft passenger, other than professional aviators, was a *Rocky Mountain News* reporter, Harvey V. Duell, future editor of *Liberty* magazine. To get a "birdman" feature story for the paper, Duell was flown for fifteen minutes—sixteen miles at an altitude of three hundred feet—on March 1, 1914, in a locally designed Wagner Biplane.

The first year of Denver aviation cost the life of one of America's earliest airmen. Ralph Johnstone, Walter Brookins, and Arch Hoxsey, who had learned their flying from the Wright brothers, brought three of the Wright planes to Denver in November. Johnstone was fresh from his October 31 triumph of setting a new altitude record of 9714 feet at Belmont Park, New York. In Denver, Johnstone's ship plunged nose down from 800 feet above Overland Park and he died in the tangle of struts and guy wires. It was America's second aviation death.

Strangely, Denver raised no monument to the courageous Johnstone, one of the handful of daring young men who blazed the sky trails. The oversight is strange because Denver, as much as any city, takes pride in historical markers and monuments to trail blazers. One of the most striking acts of civic commemoration is the Pioneer Monument, which stands in a plot of green at the busy intersection of Colfax Avenue and Broadway adjacent to Civic Center. It is a fountain and statuary group surmounted by a heroic-scale figure of a frontiersman on horseback beckoning the way west. The figure represents Kit Carson.

The bronze immortal might have been an Indian had it not been for a young *News* reporter named Al Runyon, later to become somewhat well known among guys and dolls of a distant city as Damon. An atavistic distaste for the savage redskin lingered in the Denver ethos well into the twentieth century, and prejudices against hair-lifters were still very much alive when Al Runyon was writing feature stories, sports, and Kiplingesque verse for the *News* in the first decade of the new epoch. Ed Keating was his managing editor. Al called him "Uncle Ed."

Keating tells the story of how Runyon changed the monument to Colorado pioneers. A drawing of the proposed statuary had been submitted to the *News*. At the top was an Indian in full regalia clutching the hackamore of his wild pinto. Around the base of the fountain "crouched men and women representing the sturdy pioneers who so gallantly fought their way across the plains," Keating remembers. The city room was outraged at this substitution of values. It was like honoring a Hun in Rome.

"I tell you what," Runyon suggested. "Give me this drawing and I'll take it up to the Brown Palace and show it to Captain Jack Howland. He'll have a fit and we'll have a great story.

Captain Jack was a self-taught painter whose considerable talents were greatly exalted in Denver's eyes by the fact that he was also a pioneer, a Union Army veteran, and an Indian fighter who had ranged from the plains of Oklahoma to the Canadian border. He hung around the lobby of the Brown and displayed his canvases of old-West scenes to upper-bracket tourists. (Those who bought made good investments; Howland paintings now command collector's prices.)

"When Captain Jack saw the drawing, he was so outraged he was tempted to reach for his 'shooting irons,'" Keating recalls. "But he restrained his wrath and gave Runyon an interview. It was as hot as we had hoped it would be. We plastered it on the front page."

The sculptor, Frederick MacMonnies, didn't stand a chance in the face of such opposition from the grand cham of local aesthetics. He hauled down the Indian and elevated Kit.

Alfred Damon Runyon came back to Colorado after Philippine service in the Spanish-American War with a determination to get ahead in the newspaper business and a deep conviction that he could do it. His father had been a printer for the papers in Pueblo, where the barefoot, motherless Al sometimes slept under the cases while his happy-go-lucky parent set type. He acquired an early exposure to the pleasures and pitfalls of newspapering. But along with a lifetime affection for the bugle call, "To the Colors," young Al brought back from the war another soldierly taste. He returned to Denver a two-fisted tosspot, and he had no talent for the sport. His bats were brutal and compulsive. They came into collision with his ambition. He had started on the *Post*, where the verdict was that he couldn't write even when sober. The notice of dismissal was unequivocal: he was tossed bodily into the street.

A witness to the ejection, however, was a pretty little thing named Ellen Egan, and she took pity on the bleary-eyed reporter. Ellen was society editor of the *News*. She persuaded her bosses to take on the then unpromising Al. It turned out to be an inspired decision, allowing for certain lapses, when other staffers were required to fill in. Runyon not only averted civic tragedy in the matter of the monument but he also delighted the city with his jingling verses and kept it laughing with an endless variety of stunts. Time would come when the *Post* would reconsider its harsh judgment and lure Runyon back with more money.

Martin Dunn, the veteran New York Hearst executive now retired to Hartsdale, was a contemporary of Runyon's Denver days, and they formed a lasting friendship. He remembers the young Runyon as a man of medium size and a "neat dresser."

"He was the silent sort," Dunn writes, "a good listener, friendly and courteous, but rationed himself on gabbing. In spite of that, he was well liked by other newspapermen. He was one of the most capable reporters on the *Rocky Mountain News* in the early 1900s. At first he did general assignments. Later he became interested in writing sports stories. He had a streak of humor in some of his stories. Not the slapdash type of humor, but touches that gave you a chuckle.

"At that time he had not muscled into a seat on the waterwagon. Sometimes in the middle of a running story he would get himself plastered. That happened on one occasion when he was doing a stunt for the *News*. He and 'Doc Bird' Finch, the cartoonist, were giving the town a laugh and arousing a great deal of interest with their exploit. And just like that, bango, Runyon hit the bottle too hard. Someone else pinch-hit on the yarn and didn't do so well."

Even then Runyon was serious about his writing, Dunn recalls. He "frequently would make a half-dozen false starts with the opening paragraph of his stories. When he got that to please him, the story went fast. He didn't use many fingers, but was a quick enough typist. From the beginning he had dreams of being a fictionist, and was writing short stories and trying them on the magazines. They were of a different type than those he wrote later about Broadway characters. No one could have foreseen the success that awaited him."

Damon Runyon, Jr., has in his recent memoir, *Father's Footsteps*, a letter from his father which also mentions the capers with Frank J. ("Doc Bird") Finch, who took his name from a gangling little spectacle-wearing bird with which he signed his cartoons. Runyon wrote his son:

> I don't want to brag, but I was the greatest newspaper stunt man of my time, not only in executing stunts but devising them. . . .
>
> I used to travel all over Colorado with a sketch artist named Finch doing a feature called "Me and Mr. Finch," covering fairs and festivals and church sociables and everything that brought as many as forty persons together anywhere. I did the writing and Finch the illustrating, but on the side Finch would give public chalk talks and I would lecture.
>
> It was a stunt in which Finch as "Doc Bird" (his cartoon character) met me as Santa Claus, at the Union Depot in Denver one Christmas week with a band and attended by a zillion children, that caused the *Post* to hire us away from the *News*. . . .
>
> I refereed prize fights, a practice that Gene Fowler, who was more or less my successor, continued. I went up in a balloon. I slept in flophouses as a hobo for color for a story. I did a hundred and one similar stunts and had a lot of fun doing them. . . .[19]

Damon, Jr., notes that he could always date the era of his father's friends by the name they used for him. If they called him "Damon", they were Broadway characters or New York newspapermen. Those who called him "Al" knew him in Denver.

Apparently one person in Denver caught a glimmer of Runyon's future glory. Ellen Egan's pity merged into affection, and then she fell in love with the difficult young man who pursued her with constant promises

[19]Damon Runyon, Jr., *Father's Footsteps* (New York, 1953), pp. 116–17.

of reform. Finally she agreed to marry him if he would quit drinking. Runyon decided it couldn't be done in Denver among hale companions of his salad years, but he wanted to move on and up anyway. Between Ellen and the drive to success the reform was accomplished. They were married and moved to New York in 1910, and Runyon forswore the bottled demon for the rest of his life. It was said that he could drink more coffee than anyone else who hung around Lindy's. "Loss of his patronage was felt by the distillers," Dunn comments.

Dunn also left Denver in 1910. Like Gene Fowler, he was born on the West Side along Mullen's Mill Ditch. He remembers the *News* of his boyhood as "the best newspaper in the Rocky Mountain region" and goes on:

It was a supplement to my education. Not only did it print the news of the day, but also features. At one time it ran a series of educational value, taking up scientific and other subjects. One of them was about the humorists of America. Mark Twain and others. It also gave a prize of several thousand dollars for the best novel by a new writer.

Along about 1890, the Rocky Mountain News was located at the southeast corner of Lawrence and 17th Street. Senator Patterson sometimes was on view to the passersby. Many times I saw him standing up, looking through that day's edition of his paper.

He was of good height, with a slight tendency to corpulence. An oddity was his hair. On the upper part of his head it was black; the lower part white. Looked as if he were wearing a black wig. But there was a lot of brain under his neatly combed hairs.

Senator Patterson was not what is known as a retiring man. He did not hesitate to run a column of his own. It was named "Between You and Me." He chatted away with the reader on any subjects that were on his mind, mostly things of immediate interest. Arthur Brisbane, years later, did a somewhat similar thing in the Hearst newspapers.

In a town where bright lawyers were stumbling over one another, Senator Patterson was in the forefront of the legal procession. His law firm usually defended any labor union officials who got into tangles with the law. Sometimes there were bits of violence that the law blamed on the unions. Patterson was always for the defense. . . .

Denver was quite a colorful town then. Many of the old pioneers were still alive. Big figures of the history-making years were active.

Walter S. Cheesman, a tall, big-chested fellow, owned the Denver water system. He was a great buyer of Denver real estate. Bought a chunk of land extending from Broadway to Lincoln avenue at Colfax avenue, now facing the Civic Center. As the years went by he put up a row of one-story taxpayers, but left several vacant lots at Lincoln. There was tethered Cheesman's cow, on one of the most valuable pieces of pasture land in the area. Every newly-arrived reporter would not be happy until he wrote a feature story about Cheesman's cow. . . .

Buffalo Bill Cody was followed in the streets by children, who liked the handsome old showman. His broad sombrero, white goatee and mustache, longish hair and high-heeled boots set him apart as something special. He used to put up at the old St. James Hotel, which I believe was on Curtis street between 15th and 16th. . . .

The red light district prospered. It was on Market street, extending north from 18th about five blocks. It boasted women of many nations, including Chinese and Japanese. Their cribs attracted sightseers, men and women, who wonderingly looked into the lighted brothels. At about that time there were three murders in the district, and residents of the cribs were in a state of terror. One after another, in a period of several months, three French women were strangled. No clue was left by the slayer or slayers, and the cases were unsolved.

Dunn broke into the newspaper business in 1900 and for ten years was a reporter, alternating between Patterson's evening *Times* and the *Post*, "depending on which paper offered me the most money." In New York he became city editor and Sunday editor of the *American* and *Journal-American*.

The shuttle between papers in Denver was standard procedure for the newsmen of the day. Salaries were low, and an offer of a couple of bucks more was always sufficient to overcome any institutional loyalties which inadvertently might have developed. Runyon went to New York at the princely stipend of sixty-five dollars a week. Frank Plumb once wrote about the difficulties reporters of the day had in maintaining their nourishment:

These foot soldiers of journalism found it easy to keep the poundage down. Salaries of $25 or $30 for the best, $5 to $20 for the less skilled, insured that they would not overeat. Covering assignments on Shank's mare gave sufficient exercise to burn up any adipose matter that might result from covering a banquet or a union picnic.

These lads spent only a minor fraction of their meager emolument on food, anyway. Their motto was: "Save your money to buy whisky." Damon Runyon epitomized their customs in a feature story about the wisest way to spend one's last two-bit piece.

If, he said, one found one's self with a lone quarter-dollar after a night in the Press Club poker game, it was advisable to spend 15 cents for a glass of whisky, a nickel for a sack of Bull Durham with cigaret papers, and five cents for coffee-and-rolls, or doughnuts.

Of course, reporters did eat in those days. But there was one paper whose employes were supposed to subsist on chameleon's airy fare. I won't name this one, because Scripps-Howard might not like it.

But there was a folk-story around 1910 to the effect that a reporter was sent to the hospital with a mysterious ailment. He was X-rayed, and the radiologist reported to the M.D.:

"This is clearly a case of prolonged starvation. There isn't a trace of food in the stomach or anywhere along the digestive tract."

"That doesn't mean a thing; the condition is normal for this patient," the M.D. soothed. "This lad is a reporter for the (deleted)."[20]

Plumb was referring to the Denver *Express*, which came into the picture in 1906 to give the city a fifth daily paper. The *Express* was founded by the Scripps-McRae League, which in the same year started the Pueblo *Sun* to give labor a voice in the growing southern Colorado industrial city. The Denver Scripps paper was a threadbare, pugnacious, and brave little six-day sheet that eked out a hand-to-mouth existence for twenty years on its courage and the give-'em-hell liberal tradition of E. W. Scripps, who boasted that he never bought or sold a newspaper. He founded papers from scratch, and knocked them on the head when they failed to make their way. The Pueblo *Sun* expired in that wise; the *Express* lives on through merger with the *News*. Such support as the *Express* had came from labor and the progressives. Like Patterson's *News*, the Scripps paper joined cause with the early labor movement in Colorado, and it was the only one of the four Denver papers with spunk enough to expose the Ku Klux Klan when it began running Colorado in the mid-twenties. It fought the tramway corporation, supported LaFollette in 1924, and if it was not highly popular on Capitol Hill, it could claim ninety-five per cent coverage of the houses in Globeville, a workingman's neighborhood. The ornaments of the *Express*' slender staff included Robert L. Chase, now associate editor of the *News*, Walden Sweet, George Burns, Jack Carberry, Georgia Hanfelder, Sam Nadler, Arch Northway, Charles H. Newell, who was editor from 1913 to 1916, and Edward T. Leech, who took over from Newell and later became editor of the Pittsburgh *Press*.

It was a time of notable newsmen and women in Denver. Al Runyon and Martin Dunn would go on to New York. Gene Fowler was coming up on the *Republican* under city editor James R. Noland, whose son, a Colorado district judge, firmly refuses election as governor. Ed Keating would go to Congress. Ellsworth Shawn, father of the dancer Ted Shawn, was a *Times* editorial writer. A gangling youngster down from the gold camp of Victor, Lowell Thomas, spent a year on the *News* staff, 1912–13, to help put himself through the University of Denver. William MacLeod Raine and George L. Knapp were preparing to write novels, and George Creel was working up the head of steam which would carry him into the front rank of latter-day muckrakers. A stage-struck Linotype operator at the *Post*, Burns Mantle, was getting a chance to write his first theatrical reviews. Arthur Chapman was trying his wings on the *Republican* before moving uptown to become the poetic spirit of the *Times*.

Some of the lights of a star-studded era won only local fame but are

[20]*Rocky Mountain News*, Nov. 29, 1954.

well remembered in Denver. Men like Wayne C. Williams, Frank Plumb, Luke J. Kavanaugh, and Herb Belford, son of the "Red Rooster," all News staff members. Art MacLennan and Thomas H. A. McGill, News city editors. John Moynihan, the quiet, ascetic News artist who was married briefly and unhappily to the noisy Texas Guinan. Abe Pollock, the News boxing "writer" whose daily column was evolved by sports department ghosts from a few pungent, ungrammatical pronouncements. The well-loved bachelor Abe, who founded a Press Club Christmas party for children, began predicting early that Jack Dempsey would be beaten, and he lived long enough to see his forecast confirmed. Joe McMeel was shuttling from the News to the Republican to the Post and back to the News as managing editor. Everyone in town knew the initials "F.W.W." At a time when leading writers were given a full page on Sunday in which to extend themselves, Frederick W. White wrote the highly popular "Page 13" feature for the Post. The News raided and captured F.W.W., a gentleman journalist of the old school, for a brief term on Welton Street. When White went back to the raucous Post his fellow clubmen couldn't understand the return to slumming. There was grousing at the country club until a member suggested an explanation: "There has to be one gentleman on the paper." Fowler says White was the only person in Denver of whom Bonfils stood in awe. The cultured F.W.W. discovered Burns Mantle and became an intimate of the theatrical greats of his day. He fathered four children, one of them the Colorado poetess, Lilian White Spencer. A son, Frank, later succeeded him as drama editor of the Post.

Distinguished newspaperwomen also came out of the lively ferment of Denver journalism in these times. Ellis Meredith (Mrs. Henry H. Clement), who had started as a proofreader for the News, became a noted Washington correspondent. Polly Pry (Mrs. Leonel Ross O'Bryan) once saved Bonfils' life and shielded Tammen with her voluminous skirts when a victim of the Post's highhandedness came calling on the Red Room and cut loose with a pistol. Both the partners were wounded, and Bonfils, who could not bear to be under obligation to anyone, never forgave Polly her good turn. She moved on to the Times. Helen Worden Erskine, later of the New York World, World-Telegram, and Collier's, also was on the Times staff a little later. Nell Brinkley had her easel at the Times and occasionally did work for the News. The "Brinkley girl" with her cascades of wavy hair later set a fashion in cartooning. Alice Rohe, sister of Mrs. Roy W. Howard, left the News staff in 1912 for the old New York World and subsequently became the first woman to manage a major overseas bureau for a wire service when she headed the United Press office in Rome. Her place as News book, music, and drama critic was taken by Hettie Cattell, who now rates as one of New York's hottest "rewrite men" on the Mirror. Kate Thomas Russell was society editor of the News for ten years prior to World War I, covering the high-level antics of the "Sacred 36" on a bicycle in white formal gown and elbow-length gloves.

Despite the parade of talents the battle was going against the *News* and *Times*. Sober political declamations—particularly when they were of a liberal order—could not compete with the *Post's* forty-one-mile roller-skating race to Greeley. The Bonfils-Tammen Eve, clad in a few square inches of leopard skin and planted in the wilds of Rocky Mountain National Park, attracted, for some reason, more attention and comment than the *News'* Sunday page of analytical book reviews.

There is a Gresham's law in journalism, too, and it was running against Tom Patterson and his papers. Although the *News* and *Times* had never ceased crusading in behalf of the people, the people didn't seem to be much interested. They were canceling their subscriptions and switching to the *Post* in order to keep themselves fully shocked, scandalized, and outraged by the terrible things Bon and Tam came up with for each edition. Patterson, like a lot of other newspaper editors before and since, must have shaken his head a little sadly. The "best people" waited upon him in a steady procession urging his support, granted liberally, for various causes in the interest of Higher Morality. But apparently neither the best people, their relatives, nor their friends read newspapers.

Patterson was getting along in years now. He had watched the *Post's* methods, at first, with openmouthed wonder, but he was Irish and it didn't take him long to learn how to fight back. In December of 1907 the *News* published an editorial charging, as libelously and as directly as possible, that the *Post* was blackmailing advertisers. Accompanying the attack was a cartoon depicting Bonfils as Captain Kidd.

Patterson, at sixty-seven, still walked daily from his home on Capitol Hill to his newspaper office on Welton Street. Punctually on schedule on the morning of December 26 he was cutting through a vacant lot when someone came up behind him and called out, "Good morning."

The nearsighted *News* publisher turned and caught a fist on the side of his head. The blow jolted off his thick glasses. Then he was belted again and fell to the ground. His upper plate was broken, and the jagged edges cut his mouth when more blows descended upon him as he lay prone.

Patterson groped among the weeds for his glasses, and when he had put them on he recognized the man standing over him. It was the forty-six-year-old Fred Bonfils, pale with rage and cussing with a mule skinner's vocabulary.

CHAPTER EIGHTEEN

The Education of John Shaffer

THE SRO sign was out in Judge Thomas Carlon's court on December 29, 1907, when the handsome, athletic Bonfils appeared to answer a warrant charging him with malicious assault and common brawling in the street.

Bonfils was fined fifty dollars, and Senator Patterson's testimony gave an indication of what the *News* was up against. The audience, gleefully partisan to Patterson's cause (and undoubtedly composed entirely of *Post* subscribers in good standing), broke into cheers and applause at several points. Judge Carlon found it necessary to hammer with his gavel and warn that he would clear the courtroom if such unjudicial deportment did not cease. The crowd which filled the room and spilled into the corridors waited in eager ill will for just deserts to be handed out to the man whose newspaper was universally deplored and uniformly read.

After an attempt to withhold the names of victims to shield them, he said, from reprisals, Patterson gave chapter and verse on the buccaneering which was bleeding his papers white. Bonfils' attorney, John T. Bottom, witlessly led the *News* publisher into the recital of *Post* blackmailing and strong-arm tactics in an effort to prove that Patterson was an enemy of the haughty Corsican and thus entitled to a clobbering in the street. The theory, pushed to its logical end, would have given Bonfils license to pound on much of the adult male population of Denver.

Patterson recalled, for example, the case of Edward Monash, who had been proprietor of a once busy little department store called The Fair. Monash decided to stop advertising in the *Post* and use space in the *News* and *Times*. The *Post* immediately began a series of articles exposing alleged violations of the child labor law at The Fair and unspeakable cruelties by Monash to his young employees. The attacks ended abruptly when Monash dropped the Patterson papers and returned to the *Post*.

Then there was A. J. Spengel, furniture dealer who gave his time *pro bono publico* as chairman of the city Board of Supervisors. Spengel also rashly switched advertising media. Suddenly he found himself accused in the *Post* columns of cheating the city, violating his oath as an official, and other pleasantries. "Mr. Spengel got tired, I suppose,"

Patterson testified wryly, "and resumed his advertising in the *Post*. Since then Mr. Spengel has been nothing but a good officer and a splendid citizen."

J. S. Appel, another merchant, was charged with maltreating women after he failed to comply with orders from Champa Street to send his advertising copy in. Mention also was made of an attempt by Bonfils to muscle in for a fifty-one per cent interest in a plan to race horses at Overland Park to benefit the Colorado Industrial Association, a non-profit outfit which hoped to arrange an annual exposition of agriculture, manufacturing, and livestock with funds raised by a race meeting. When Bonfils' generous proposal was rejected the *Post* put on its clerical collar and was scandalized that Colorado industry should stoop to *gambling* to finance its progress.

Why Bottom didn't shut Patterson off is a mystery perhaps best left to legal minds, but he kept right on baiting until the *News* publisher rifled the direct challenge from his witness chair: "We never said in the paper that Mr. Bonfils has no right to sue for civil damages. If the things printed about him in the *News* and the *Times* are untrue, he could impoverish me with fines in civil cases and sell out both newspapers. . . . I don't at all seek to waive responsibility. If Mr. Bonfils sees fit to bring a suit, I will justify. . . ." (Applause, chortles, and gavel pounding.) Then Patterson turned to Bonfils, sitting at his counsel's table: "If there is anything in that article that is libelous, you can have me prosecuted for criminal libel or can bring civil suit for damages; for, if they are untrue, you have been sadly libeled, and the man who would libel another in that way deserves punishment under the law."

Bonfils made no effort to prove any untruths. He paid his fifty dollars and costs and picked up operations where he had left off.

Colonel Lucius C. Paddock, editor of the Boulder *Camera*, spoke for the press of the state:

> Senator Patterson is over sixty-five years old and his assailant twenty years younger, though doubtless in a fair fight the editor of the *News* would give a good account of himself. The affair was disgraceful and calls for the severest reprobation of the press everywhere. . . . The truth is that the *Post* is daily a disgrace to journalism. Its policy is for the corruption of the morals of the state. It has raised the black flag of the buccaneer concealed beneath the folds of the American flag.

Patterson confessed publicly that he was perplexed about how to cope with *Post* methods, which combined the best techniques of trollop and highwayman. (He promptly was cartooned in the Paper with a Heart and Soul as "Old Perplexity.") His papers clearly were being driven to the wall. Circulation dwindled. Revenues fell. Advertisers couldn't, or wouldn't, run the risk of arousing displeasure in the Red Room by taking space in the *News* or *Times*. Moreover, ethical niceties aside, they got more for their money, reached more people, when they put their messages in the *Post*. It was not until many years later that Denver merchants began to realize they were being victimized by a near-monopoly situation. The *Post*, flexing its muscles as one of the greatest money-makers the American press has seen, was telling them when they could advertise, how much space they would take, and (adjustably) how much they had to pay for the privilege of intruding their dry goods and living-room suites into the circus of bathing-beauty contests, kids' brass bands, and pious pilgrimages to the Mount of the Holy Cross. Bonfils perfected a sliding scale of ad rates which penalized anyone reckless or foolish enough to patronize the other papers.

Patterson was aging, but the scrappy old Irishman never once pulled a punch. He fought back, to the best of his ability, straight through to the end. The town could see that he was being beaten, and badly, but he was admired and respected. Even those who turned up their noses at his long service to wild and radical political causes paid him honor as distinguished citizen. He was welcome in homes great and small. This rankled deep on Champa Street. Tammen didn't give a damn, and said so, but Bonfils, a strange and contradictory man, wanted to be liked by the city he plundered. He regarded himself as a civic benefactor deserving of love and gratitude. No one else did. Almost friendless, he sat alone nightly in his mansion on Capitol Hill with his power and his money around him.

Larry Martin, acid and keenly talented associate editor of the *Post*, now retired, makes the point in the official history of his paper that Bonfils was born with a caul.[1] This fortuity, according to legend, endowed Bon with good luck, insight, and protection against drowning. So far as is known drowning never threatened. Luck he had in boundless measure, and a clairvoyant sensitivity to profit and loss and what would make people talk about the *Post*. He parlayed the luck and insight into great wealth and a power probably greater than that of any other man in Denver's history. Yet many wondered if Fred Bonfils found his prizes satisfying. He seldom smiled. It was said—even charged in a legal brief—that he suffered from nightmares. As time went on he became pathetically eager for approval. His bright blue eyes sometimes were clouded with loneliness and puzzlement. No one, not even Harry Tammen, was close to him. There were no confidants. When a favorite dog died Bonfils was inconsolate, and Fowler says his bodyguard, Volney T. Hoggatt, sought to comfort the grieving millionaire: ". . . but, F. G., you still have *me*." It remained for Bonfils' devoted daughter to achieve, by graciousness and warmth, the values which he apparently found were passing him by. Generous, outgoing, sympathetic, Helen Bonfils makes friends of chance acquaintances, a skill foreign to her father's nature.

[1]Martin, op. cit., p. 9.

She has accomplished many philanthropies, endowing scholarships, building churches and hospitals, liberally supporting numerous charities.[2]

Bonfils was in many ways a baffling man: strong, disciplined, austere, yet subject to queer prejudices and saccharine sentimentalities, and capable of prodigious self-deceptions. Harry Tammen boasted that *he* was a rogue; the thought probably never crossed Bonfils' mind. To no one was this strange and powerful man more baffling than to his adversary on Welton Street. Senator Patterson knew how to handle the ordinary opponent; he had met and crossed foils with many of them, in politics, city government, the law, and newspaper publishing. The way to handle opponents was to fight them, vigorously, full-faced, and cleanly; there were rules. It required nearly twenty years for Patterson to learn that the proprietors of the *Post* had never heard of the Marquis of Queensberry, that this ruckus was catch as catch can, no holds barred and knee to the groin. How much he spent acquiring the education no one knows; Patterson did not lick his wounds publicly. Certainly he poured large sums of money into the *News* and *Times*, and though he died wealthy he would have been wealthier if Harry Tammen had not landed his sucker. Tom Patterson never found a formula for countering Bonfils and Tammen, but perhaps it was some consolation to him in the hereafter that neither of his successors did either.

Efforts of the *News* to match the *Post* style just didn't come off. Something was lacking in the way of abandon, and results were often as uncomfortable for everyone concerned as a professor of divinity at a stag party. Along about 1912, the year the weekly *News* dwindled away in its final illness, Patterson installed Henry D. Carbery as editor of the morning paper, probably with some misgivings about the modern age and a bit of the lonely feeling which must come to elderly men when they find themselves out of touch with contemporary mores. The violent-tempered Carbery was a man of lusty news appetites. His researches had led him to the conclusion that sex had proved itself and was not likely to pass out of fashion. Carbery was fond of stories with a spicing of risqué fluff to them. "Lace drawers yarns," he called them. These, he felt, would have a salutary effect on both the unambitious outlook and the diverted interest of *News* patrons, male and female. They would "stimulate our men readers and interest the women." Staff members of the period recall Carbery singing out hopefully across the newsroom to telegraph editor Jack LaHines: "Any lace drawers hanging on the telegraph lines today?"

Carbery's efforts to jazz up the staid old *News* led at one point to an ultimatum to police reporter Roy Giles, who was in a dry season and hadn't produced a sensation for more than a week. Giles was desperate. He knew Carbery meant the warning that he could look for another

[2]Mary Ellen and Mark Murphy, "Papa's Girl," *Saturday Evening Post* (Dec. 23, 1944), p. 14.

job if he failed to come up with a page-one exclusive. But there wasn't even a runaway horse on the blotter. He took his problem to a professional associate, "Bad News" Hawkins, who had been released that day as "cured" from the criminally insane ward at Denver General Hospital. Giles had supplied "Bad News" with used decks of cards from the Press Club during the treatment period, assigned by the courts after an unsuccessful effort to fix responsibility for a bag of stolen silverware. Hawkins listened sympathetically to his young friend's worries and comments on Carbery's origins. Then he made several low-voiced calls on the pressroom phone. An hour later he received a return call.

"Okay, Roy," he said, "your troubles are over. You've got your page-one scoop."

He instructed Giles to phone his rewrite desk that the mansion of a certain well-known millionaire had been burglarized. The thief had entered through a dining-room window, rifled the buffet of its sterling, and then opened the safe in the library, taking cash—Hawkins mentioned the sum to the decimal point—a diamond ring, a brooch, and two earrings. Giles was suspicious of a hoax but in his desperation took the plunge.

Next morning the tycoon picked up the *News* from his front porch and read about himself under a red-ink headline. He strode to the buffet. Silverware gone. He went in to his safe. Open and empty. Clamping his derby firmly over his ears, the plundered magnate marched down the hill to Senator Patterson's office on Welton Street. Two detectives were there before him. They had come to express their deep personal hurt that the *News* had not taken them into its confidence when it had knowledge of a major job. Giles was finally located in the Glenarm Turkish Baths and summoned to explain, if he could.

Giles declined to designate the wellsprings of his prescience, and Carbery backed him: "Man can't be fired for doing his duty. A newspaperman must never betray a confidence." The millionaire canceled his subscription in spite of Giles' offer to do what he could to have the swag returned. The reporter found "Bad News" in the City Hall pressroom dealing trial-run poker hands to himself. He broached the matter of restoring the valuables.

"Don't know what you're talking about, Roy," the cured burglar replied.[3]

Another subscription gone, and the millionaire had been an advertiser, too.

Roy Giles was the man to whom Gene Fowler took his first symptoms of newspaper illness for diagnosis. The young Gene was working as a twelve-dollar-a-week night watchman at the time but dreaming of the day when he would meet such interesting people. The preliminary

[3]Gene Fowler, *A Solo in Tom-Toms* (New York, 1946), pp. 271–77.

giddiness of the disease had set in, and Giles seemed to exude romance from every pore. Fowler recalls the following dialogue:

Fowler: "How did you happen to go into the newspaper business?"

Giles: "At a time when I was completely out of my head with a high fever and yellow jaundice."

F: "I'd like to get into it myself. I mean, as a reporter."

G: "God forbid! It's a harlot's life without the gaieties."

F: "Would you tell me the best person to see for a job? Maybe Mr. Carbery?"

G: "My boy, I wouldn't introduce my worst enemy to an editor. And if I had a son of my own, which is mathematically possible, I'd rather see him in Potter's Field than in a newspaper job."

F: "Then tell me why do *you* stay in it?"

G: "Good God of Hosts! This callow stranger asks why I stay among the pastepots and the stinking presses. Let me ask you something, my boy: Why does a galley slave stay at his oar? Why does a dope addict stay with his bottle of snow? Why does a tired husband stay with his wife? I'll tell you why: Because we're all chained to our hateful destiny."

Police reporters were a durable breed. Two of Giles' colleagues on the *News* staff were the crimson-haired John ("Red") Feeney and Paris B. Montgomery, a man who lived and died in the shadow of his own private cloud of gloom. Forbes Parkhill tells anecdotes about both of them in his robust almanac, *The Wildest of the West.*

The police pressroom was in the semibasement of old City Hall at Fourteenth and Larimer streets. It had once seen service as the city morgue, and it had a tile floor with drains. These grisly reminders of a macabre past had no effect on the hard-bitten scribes who inherited the room. In fact the facilities were more than a little utilitarian. The tile floor reduced the fire hazard among notoriously careless smokers, and an enterprising reporter of a slightly later era discovered the drain grills could be removed. Bottles of bootleg whiskey, expropriated on police raids, then could be suspended on strings down into the plumbing and kept safe from prying eyes. So much evidence disappeared in this fashion that it became routine for the Prohibition Squad to shake down the pressroom after each sally against the forces of spirituous evil. It is probably no compliment to the Denver police force of the time to record that the caches were never discovered.

The tile floor enters into Parkhill's yarn about Feeney. A suitcase full of seized marijuana leaves had been left temporarily by a trusting detective inside the pressroom door. This generated an argument about the soul-destroying and lethal qualities of the weed. A new reporter, just up from El Paso, claimed to have the word. One reefer, he asserted, merely hopped up a smoker, two turned him into a bloodthirsty savage without fear, and a few more would bring raving mania followed by

Western Collection, Denver Public Library

Goehner photo, courtesy Mrs. Lilllian Goldrick Johnson

Denver's "Professor. Owen J. Goldrick: first reporter, first schoolteacher, and author of the famous account of the "Great Deluge of '64." *Above:* As he appeared during his early years in Denver. *Below:* A later portrait.

A trio of sports. The man on the left is an early vintage Gene Fowler. Center: Abe Pollock, long-time *News* boxing writer. Right: Louie Newman, *News* sports staffer and later a Detroit boxing promoter.

THIS TABLET IS THE
PROPERTY OF THE STATE OF COLORADO

———

ON THIS SITE STOOD THE ORIGINAL HOME OF
THE ROCKY MOUNTAIN NEWS
FIRST NEWSPAPER ESTABLISHED IN
THE "PIKE'S PEAK GOLD REGION."
FOUNDED BY Wm.N.BYERS, APRIL 23,1859.
CHAMPION OF LAW AND ORDER IN
"JEFFERSON TERRITORY:" ADVOCATE OF
FAITH IN EMERGING COLORADO.
LOCATED ON NEUTRAL GROUND BETWEEN
PIONEER TOWNS, DENVER AND AURARIA.
BUILDING AND PRESS LOST IN GREAT
CHERRY CREEK FLOOD, MAY 19, 1864.

———

ERECTED BY
THE STATE HISTORICAL SOCIETY OF COLORADO
FROM
THE MRS. J. N. HALL FOUNDATION
COMMEMORATING THE 75TH ANNIVERSARY OF THE
FOUNDING OF COLORADO'S FIRST NEWSPAPER.
APRIL 23, 1934

Salute in bronze. This historical marker stands on the present Market Street bridge in Denver, close to the site of the *News* building swept away in the "Great Deluge" of 1864.

John L. Dailey as he appeared about the time he printed the first copy of the *News* in 1859.

John L. Dailey as a white-bearded civic leader about 1893.

William N. Byers

Mrs. Elizabeth Byers

Mollie Byers

Frank Byers

Family album. The Byers family in the 1860s.

Photo of Frank from Western Collection, Denver Public Library. Other portraits from the Sim T. Sopris album, courtesy Fred M. Mazzulla.

William N. Byers, founding editor, as he appeared in later life, full of honors and influence.

Thomas M. Patterson, Congressman, Senator, and owner of the *News*, 1892-1913.

Jay Gould and W. A. H. Loveland, right, pose for a Boston photographer during one of their railroad manipulations. Photo courtesy Hobart Loveland.

W. A. H. Loveland, owner of the *Rocky Mountain News*, 1878-1886.

Loveland as a young man in 1863. Photo courtesy Hobart Loveland.

John C. Shaffer, Chicago and Indianapolis financier, who owned the *News* from 1913 to 1926. A portrait made about 1937.

obert Talkin

The Jo Davidson bust of E. W. Scripps.

Roy W. Howard as he appeared about the time he purchased the *Rocky Mountain News*.

SCRIPPS AND HOWARD

Charles B. McCabe
(1935)

Charles E. Lounsbury
(1931-1935)

Herndon Davis

Edward T. Leech
(1927-1931)

Gysin

Harry M. Rhoads

(1937-1938)
Walter Morrow

Aubrey Graves
(1937)

Forrest Davis
(1936-1937)

A GALLERY OF EDITORS

JACK FOSTER

Editor of the *Rocky Mountain News* since 1941.

death. There were skeptics, and the man from El Paso offered to back his statements with the dollar remaining from his pay check.

"Red" Feeney was sleeping out the argument with his feet on his typewriter. His compatriots kindled a fire of old newspapers on the tiles beside his desk and poured the bushel of cured marijuana on the blaze. Then they closed doors and windows and went outside to observe progress of their scientific experiment through the semibasement windows, like medical students in a surgical amphitheater. It was agreed by the clinicians that if Feeney went mad and died the man from El Paso won the buck.

The smoke awakened Feeney. He stamped out the fire, opened the windows, and went back to his nap. The Texas reporter never forgave him.

The story about Paris B. Montgomery is in a similarly morbid mood but ends more finally. Monty was a meticulous craftsman but subject to a bottomless melancholia. His close friend was Bill Collier of the *Post*, later the biographer of "Soapy" Smith. Each spent considerable time and effort trying to reform the other's drinking habits. Monty was not the hilarious type of drinker. Alcohol plunged him deeper into his despair, and he had frequently threatened and several times attempted suicide. So Collier was shaken and entirely unsuspicious when he received a call from the undertaking parlors a block from City Hall.

"Prepare yourself for a shock, Bill. Poor Monty has been run down and killed by a runaway. Better come over right away."

Collier braced himself at Johnny Gahan's saloon, across Fourteenth Street, and hurried to the mortuary. A tiptoeing attendant led him past several sheet-draped figures to the slab at the end of the room. The sheet was drawn back to reveal the naked Montgomery, his body paled with talcum powder. Collier bent over his friend and wept.

"It's all my fault," he sobbed. "It couldn't have happened if he'd been sober, and I could have made him quit drinking. But I didn't. I feel like a murderer."

His tears splashed on the chest of the deceased.

The salty shower tickled, and the corpse was unable to restrain a giggle. Collier snatched up a wooden mallet and pursued the nude Monty around the room, out into the alley, and up Sixteenth Street to Curtis, where the theater crowds were just leaving the Tabor Grand Opera House. A cop disarmed Collier and loaned his overcoat to the exposed and shivering Montgomery.

The presence of a mallet in an embalming room puzzled Monty and preyed upon his already somber mind. When in his cups he would mutter his bewilderment or speak sadly of the "unimportance of owning a violin" and his "terrible sorrow" over never having possessed one. Not many months after his naked sprint up Sixteenth Street, Montgomery walked into the Press Club in the Kittredge Building. For a time he gloomily surveyed the game in which Colonel Gideon B. McFall was dealing and, as usual, acquiring the pay checks of several incorrigibly optimistic reporters, Gene Fowler among them. At last he announced that he was "tired on the inside," went over and sat down a few feet away under the polar-bear trophy on the wall, and swallowed cyanide. No one noticed until steward Jim Wong called out: "Monty got blue face!" At Colonel McFall's suggestion the chips on the table were swept up for a funeral fund.

With Fowler and the others in the game that night was a small, frail man soon to become and remain for forty years Denver's most beloved newspaper writer. Lee Casey once conceded that he was letter-perfect at pinochle, enjoyed poker except Kansas City Liz, but favored bridge as a better-mannered game. "Poker is a game of deception," he wrote; "bridge a game of information. There is no code of behavior for poker, whereas a bridge table is one of the few remaining examples of good manners." The ancient and cosmic attraction of the face-down card was a lasting problem, however. In time Casey, as one of several vice-presidents of the organization, established a Press Club house rule banning himself from the poker table. (He relaxed the rule briefly to instruct Ginger Rogers in the arts and sciences of table stakes during one of her visits to Denver.)

During his early days in the club game Casey was one of several young reporters who acquired an expensive education from the facile Colonel McFall. Lee and his crony Fowler became suspicious of the rapidity with which their slender wages were transferred from their pockets to those of McFall. They assigned Jim Wong to watch the dealer closely and notify them if he observed any indication of unfair advantage or extracurricular skills. Jim, a pillar of tradition in the Denver newspaper legend, was something more than inscrutable. "Colonel McFall plain good poker player," he reported back to the shorn lambs. "Casey and Fowler plain nuts."

Fowler has told in *A Solo in Tom-Toms* of the Big Snow of December 1913 and the Western fortitude with which its perils were borne. He, Casey, Jack Carberry, and Charles Carson became marooned by four feet of snow in the bungalow of Colonel McFall. For four days and five nights the game went on in relays while the storm carried down telephone lines and silenced the city's busy hum. At the end, when a rescue party with shovels and replacement bourbon arrived, Casey was out of pocket by two weeks' pay, but he drew himself up and squared his shoulders.

"I am exhausted but proud," he announced. "We have proved our ability to withstand the rigors of nature."

Lee Taylor Casey was born August 20, 1889, in Goshen, New York. Along with Vincent Astor and Ogden Nash, though for varied reasons and in different classes, he became an ornament on the alumni rolls of St. George's School in Newport, Rhode Island. He was a precocious scholar and entered the University of the South at the age of fifteen. There he received the classical education in Latin, Greek, theology, history, and philosophy which marked him henceforth in print, conversation, or friendly disputation in the mellow hours. Casey was one of the kindest and gentlest of men, and those who knew him—a company which embraces both bootblack and college president—would agree there is nothing florid in the assertion that he came close to realizing Sewanee's traditional ideal for her men: "That they shall not seek their own gain, but that they shall serve their people, and shall be ever as Christ's soldiers, gentle in all things, valiant in action, and steadfast in adversity."

In 1908, Casey joined the staff of the Kansas City *Star*, and he had just completed his apprenticeship in 1911 when he was struck down in a bout with tuberculosis which permanently withered his left arm. Like many other Coloradans of the day, he was brought to Denver "on a stretcher" under sentence of death. His mother nursed him through a two-year convalescence during which he virtually committed to memory the entire text of Gibbon's *Decline and Fall of the Roman Empire*. The Romans became a spiritual kin for Casey, and he often drew on the Latin greats for his writings. Health returned to him, though he was never robust physically. Slight, erect, soft-spoken, he moved unobtrusively through the crowd and acquired a following of devoted friends as large as one of his legions.

Lee became a reporter for the *Times* in 1913 and later moved to the morning-side *News*. Except for two one-year intervals he continued on the *News* staff for the rest of his life. In 1915 he went to the Chicago *Examiner*, but his health forced a return to Denver. For a nine-month academic year in 1919–20 he was on the faculty of the University of Colorado as professor of English and journalism. The latter word he scorned as pretentious. "A journalist is simply a broken-down newspaperman," he said. As a reporter Casey covered politics and state affairs, then he became associate editor and, for two brief and personally distasteful periods, acting editor. It was his column, originally titled "By Way of Observation," for which Casey is remembered. He began writing it in 1927, and it appeared daily to the morning of his death a quarter century later.[4]

The hiring of Lee Casey was one of the last major achievements of Senator Patterson for his *News*. A long, active, and productive life was running out for the man who had engineered Colorado statehood and sent his newspapers marching under the bright, bold banners of the Populists, Bryan, and the workingman. Only three years remained to him on October 23, 1913, when he sold the *News* and *Times* and retired to his home on Pennsylvania Street. He died there July 23, 1916, at the age of seventy-five, much respected and honored, even by proper

[4]Robert L. Perkin, "Lee Casey: A Memoir with Quotes," *Colorado Quarterly*, Vol. II, No. 3 (Winter, 1954), pp. 298ff.

citizens who had once denounced him as a dangerous crackpot and radical.

Purchaser of the Patterson papers was John C. Shaffer of Chicago and Indianapolis, financier, philanthropist, patron of the arts, and one of the founders of the Chicago Opera Company. As a practicing Methodist and worker for the YMCA, Shaffer arrived in Denver with a reputation for a lofty moral code. His middle name was Charles, but the *Post* promptly made it John Clean Shaffer. This pained the cultured Chicagoan, but more than that it puzzled him. Wasn't clean what every Christian gentleman should strive to be? Why should those queer, noisy ruffians on Champa Street use the word in a hooting tone?

Three days after buying the *News-Times*, Shaffer also acquired the *Republican* from Crawford Hill, son of Senator N. P. Hill. The *Republican* was merged with the *Times*, and Denver now was back to four daily newspapers.

Shaffer was a builder of financial empires. He was already a traction magnate several times over with streetcar companies operating in Indiana, Illinois, Tennessee, and Ohio. Then he branched out into grain brokerage and speculation and once shipped a world's record load of wheat. Newspapers appear to have been an afterthought. He was profoundly uninterested in the techniques, problems, or aspirations of newspapering and apparently saw in the press only a profitable business and a power tool. For a number of years he had owned the Chicago *Post*, which was being edited by his older son Carroll, and the *Star* papers of Indianapolis, Muncie, and Terre Haute, which he called the "Star League." Shortly before he moved innocently and unsuspectingly into the Denver scene he had bought the Louisville *Herald*. The Shaffer string thus stood at seven papers as he stepped up to challenge Bonfils and Tammen. It was a mismatch, for all of Shaffer's millions.

The *Post* picked up its gibing nickname from a speech Shaffer had made in Chicago defining his journalistic philosophies:

> I consider a daily newspaper a quasi-public institution for social, educational and moral betterment. A newspaper should give its readers all the news but should discriminate between clean and unclean news; likewise between clean and unclean advertising. The news and editorial pages should reflect a clean and healthy mentality. There is plenty of clean news to make any newspaper interesting.

Not only did this clash with nearly every one of the pragmatic rules under which the *Post* was zooming to success, but some question also developed in the years ahead about whether Shaffer himself really meant it. Teapot Dome clouded the issue, for example, as did the persistent rumor which buzzed about the *News* city room that he had ordered suppression of news about a corner on the Chicago grain market.

The day after he took control of the *News-Times* the new publisher was invited to appear before the Denver Chamber of Commerce and account for his hopes and dreams. Again he placed matters on an elevated plane:

> So far as my newspapers are concerned it will be our purpose to print all the news that is fit to print. We will appeal to citizenship rather than partisanship, and in all that we may do or try to do you can be assured there will be no muckraking. It is my ambition to publish newspapers that can be read in the home without offending the sanctity of the family circle or the moral sense of its readers. It will be my care to see that their columns are free from anything of an objectionable character, so that mother and daughter, sister and wife can peruse their contents with the assurance that they will not have to put it aside because of some feature or editorial that is not what it ought to be.

No lace drawers. No rocking of the boat where the utilities were concerned. Moreover Shaffer was substituting Republicanism for Patterson's Democracy in as abrupt a turnabout as Loveland's harsh abandonment of Byers' creed. This time it was the Democratic politicians who scurried about asking each other what the shift would mean.

Having paid his respect to fellow barons of commerce, Shaffer made a courtesy call on the Bucket of Blood. He found Tam in charge. Toward the end of a rather strained conversation Shaffer announced:

"Mr. Tammen, I am going to run my paper as Jesus Christ would run it."

"Why, you old son of a bitch!" boomed the irrepressible little Dutchman. "I'm going to run the Denver *Post* as George Washington would run it. Now what are you going to do about *that*?"[5]

Such uncouth language must have fallen as painful discord on the sensitive ear of the president of the Chicago Symphony Society, but it should have given him fair warning. Unfortunately, as the chief editorial writer of the *News* later observed, "neither Mr. Shaffer nor the founder of Christianity attended the editorial meetings" at which it was necessary to find ways of countering Big Brother.

Shaffer originally became interested in Denver through the frequent visits of his younger son Kent to Colorado for his health. It was generally understood that the *News-Times* property would become Kent's to operate. The health of the son never permitted him to take an active part in managing the papers, and he died in 1917. The father, however, fell under the spell of Colorado's climate and decided to make Denver his summer home. The family mansion, crammed with Shaffer's art collection, was in Evanston, Illinois. A part-time home in Denver would

[5]William L. Chenery, *So It Seemed* (New York, 1952), p. 51.

give him a chance to exercise another hobby, mountain climbing. So he bought a 12,000-acre ranch west of suburban Littleton and on it built a $100,000 colonial country seat which he named Ken-Caryl for his sons. There he raised blooded Herefords and entertained presidents. Teddy Roosevelt was his house guest, as was William Howard Taft. Shaffer spent five months of the year at Ken-Caryl, seldom coming into the city except for issues of great moment. One room of the big house was fitted out with news tickers and a direct wire to the Chicago grain pit.

Placed in charge of the business affairs of the *News-Times* was David Towne, subsequently general treasurer for Hearst. Henry D. Carbery temporarily continued as editor of the *News* and then gave way to William Forman and William L. Chenery. Forman, who had been sports editor of Shaffer's Chicago *Post*, became managing editor, and Chenery was installed as chief editorial writer. Shaffer retained for himself the title of editor and publisher, though he was seldom available for excoriation when irate subscribers came calling.

The ax fell without warning on the *Republican*. Gloom and resentment filled the old graystone building on the alley across Sixteenth Street from the Daniels & Fisher tower. Someone chalked a big "30" on the front door. William MacLeod Raine pecked out a final editorial. Up in the fourth-floor composing room printers passed a bottle and threw Linotype slugs to purge their ire. "Why should the spirit of mortal be proud?" assistant city editor Art MacLennan inquired of the unjust fates.

"I'll let you know sometime," Gene Fowler replied and departed for the Press Club.

Two days later, Fowler recalls, he awakened at a typewriter in the *News* city room to find himself trying to write a promotion piece for the "Swat That Fly!" campaign. MacLennan now was city editor of the *News*. Harry McCabe, the police reporter, Raine, the editorial writer, and other waifs of the storm had found harbor on either the *News* or the *Times*.

Another *Republican* orphan, Arthur Chapman, decided to set himself up as a free lance. He had achieved national fame with a poem, "Out Where the West Begins," which had appeared in his column, "Center Shots," two years earlier. The dust jacket of the 1917 Boston edition of Chapman's poetical works describes the poem as "the best-known bit of verse in America" and notes that it then was hanging framed in the office of the Secretary of the Interior in Washington. The verse has been a thing of beauty and a joy forever to Western chambers of commerce, though a candid Westerner might be hard put to demonstrate any truth in it. Embroidered among the forget-me-nots on sateen parlor pillows, however, or burned into leather keepsakes, "Out Where the West Begins" became the standard of poetical excellence in homes where the name "Milton" perhaps belonged only to the iceman. Today pulses are stirred somewhat less deeply, and possibly there are those who have never heard the lines. They run like this:

> Out where the handclasp's a little stronger,
> Out where the smile dwells a little longer,
>   That's where the West begins;
> Out where the sun is a little brighter,
> Where the snows that fall are a trifle whiter,
> Where the bonds of home are a wee bit tighter,
>   That's where the West begins.
>
> Out where the skies are a trifle bluer,
> Out where friendship's a little truer,
>   That's where the West begins;
> Out where a fresher breeze is blowing,
> Where there's laughter in every streamlet flowing,
> Where there's more of reaping and less of sowing,
>   That's where the West begins.
>
> Out where the world is in the making,
> Where fewer hearts in despair are aching,
>   That's where the West begins;
> Where there's more of singing and less of sighing,
> Where there's more of giving and less of buying,
> And a man makes friends without half trying—
>   That's where the West begins.

Not everyone west of the Missouri subscribed to the Chapman dogma, of course. Parodies were many and not long in coming. One anonymous poet, reprinted in *Trail* magazine for July 1927, took a catholic view of the brotherhood of man and found in his heart a tolerance even for Eastern dudes. He called his dissent "Pepper and Salt":

> Where does the West begin?
> Out where the boasting's a little stronger,
> Out where the hair grows a little longer,
> Where the talk is loud and runs to boast,
> And to press your pants is a crime, almost,
> Where the laugh is loud and the manners rude,
> And to shave your neck marks a man a dude—
> That's where the West begins.
>
> Where does the East begin?
> Where the streams are shallower and the hills are flat,
> And a man is judged by his coat and hat,
> Where the women boss and the men folk think
> That toast is food and tea is a drink.

Where the men use powder and the wrist-watch ticks
And everyone else but themselves are hicks—
That's where the East begins.

Now East is East and West is West,
They each have some bad and they each have some best.
For it isn't a matter of lines on a map
That makes a guy regular or makes him a sap.
The folks out West may run to brag,
And the knees of their pants may sort of sag
But there's many a guy in the boundless West
With a heart as staunch as his leather vest.
And there's many a guy in the East, by heck,
Who presses his pants and shaves his neck,
Who's got good nerve and a gilt-edged soul
If he does mess around with a finger bowl.

When the *Republican* folded Chapman established himself as the Great West Syndicate and began mailing out feature articles and pictures to Eastern newspapers. His famous by-line helped, and for a time he did well. His book of poems, meanwhile, was going through four editions. Then the approaching war in Europe began to fill the columns of newspapers everywhere. The market was shot for essays on Western scenery and ham-handed hospitality. Chapman closed down the Great West Syndicate in 1914 and moved up to Welton Street to join his former colleagues as managing editor of the *Times*.

His counterparts on the morning-side *News* were headed for trouble. The issue was the strike of thousands of coal miners in southern Colorado, a major conflict in the effort of the United Mine Workers to gain recognition from the Rockefeller-dominated Western fuel and steel industry. Forman and Chenery had been trying to play it straight, and with some success. The slumped circulation of the *News* had gained slightly when readers discovered they were getting, for the first time, unbiased news and independent editorial comment on the touchy situation. The Rockefeller interests were bigger than Colorado and knew it. So they ran things. In an atmosphere of venality the fractious independence of the *News* was rash and novel enough to attract considerable attention and some admirers.

The coal kings put the screws to Governor Elias M. Ammons and forced him to send the state militia into the mine towns. The future editor of *Collier's*, Chenery, assigned the future editor of *Liberty* magazine, Harvey Duell, to go along and observe the operation for the *News*. Gene Fowler went for the *Times*. Covering for the Scripps-McRae *Express* was the crusading Don McGregor. They soon discovered that strikebreakers of the notorious Baldwin-Felts organization, imported from West Virginia, were being placed in uniforms of Colorado National

Guardsmen. McGregor became so convinced of the justice of the miners' cause that he threw over his job and carried arms in one of their skirmishes with the militia. The *News* was trying to report the strike impartially and honestly. The *Express* went all the way in support of the UMW. Well into the twenties *Express* reporters were still barred from the state coal mine inspector's office.

The striking miners and their families, expelled from company-owned houses, gathered into tent colonies. One of the largest of these was at Ludlow. There, on April 21, 1914, the guardsmen and company detectives, using explosive bullets, machine-gunned and set fire to the grubby tent city. Thirteen women and children were burned to death, five men and a boy killed in the fighting. Three of the attackers, all guards for the Victor-American Fuel Company, also died.[6]

The "Ludlow Massacre" aroused immediate indignation across the country, but nowhere did it seethe more hotly than in the editorial rooms of the *Rocky Mountain News,* where twenty-nine-year-old William Chenery stood throughout the day of April 21 watching the dispatches come in. He wrote one mild editorial deploring the tragedy and suggesting that, since the Colorado National Guard was no longer a nonpartisan force engaged in maintaining public order, federal troops ought to be brought in. He showed the editorial to Forman and Dave Towne. Forman predicted that it would "raise hell" in spite of its reasonableness and temperate language. The business manager suggested, "If you're going to print that kind of an editorial, why not make it stronger?" Chenery tore up his first effort, sat down at his typewriter, and hammered out "The Massacre of the Innocents."

> The horror of the shambles at Ludlow is overwhelming. Not since the days when pitiless red men wreaked vengeance upon intruding frontiersmen and upon their women and children has this Western country been stained with so foul a deed.
>
> The details of the massacre are horrible. Mexico offers no barbarity so base as that of the murder of defenseless women and children by the mine guards in soldiers' clothing. Like whitened sepulchers we boast of American civilization with this infamous thing at our very doors. Huerta murdered Madero, but even Huerta did not shoot an innocent little boy seeking water for his mother who lay ill. Villa is a barbarian, but in his maddest excess Villa has not turned machine guns on imprisoned women and children. Where is the outlaw so far beyond the pale of humankind as to burn the tent over the heads of nursing mothers and helpless little babies?
>
> Out of this infamy one fact stands clear. Machine guns did the murder. The machine guns were in the hands of mine guards, most of whom were also members of the state militia. It was private war, with

[6]The full story of Ludlow and the Colorado coal wars is told from the miners' viewpoint in Barron B. Beshoar's biography of John R. Lawson, one of the UMW leaders, *Out of the Depths* (Denver, 1942 and 1957).

the wealth of the richest man in the world behind the mine guards.

Once and for all time the right to employ armed guards must be taken away from private individuals and corporations. To the state, and to the state alone, belongs the right to maintain peace. Anything else is anarchy. Private warfare is the only sort of anarchy the world has ever known, and armed forces employed by private interests have introduced the only private wars of modern times. This practice must be stopped. If the state laws are not strong enough, then the federal government must step in. At any cost, private warfare must be destroyed.

Who are these mine guards to whom is entrusted the sovereign right to massacre? Four of the fraternity were electrocuted recently in New York. They are the gunmen of the great cities, the off-scourings of humanity, whom a bitter heritage has made the wastrels of the world. Warped by the wrongs of their own upbringing, they know no justice and they care not for mercy. They are hardly human in intelligence, and not as high in the scale of kindness as domestic animals.

Yet they are not the guilty ones. The blood of the innocent women and children rests on the hands of those who for the greed of dollars employed such men and bought such machines of murder. The world has not been hard upon these; theirs has been a gentle upbringing. Yet they reck not of human life when pecuniary interests are involved.

The blood of women and children, burned and shot like rats, cries aloud from the ground. The great state of Colorado has failed them. It has betrayed them. Her militia, which should have been impartial protectors of the peace, have acted as murderous gunmen. The machine guns which played in the darkness upon the homes of humble men and women, whose only crime was an effort to earn an honest living, were bought and paid for by agents of the mine owners. Explosive bullets have been used on children. Does the bloodiest page in the French Revolution approach this in hideousness?

In the name of humanity, in the name of civilization, we have appealed to President Wilson. His ear heard the wail of the innocent, outraged and dying Mexico. Cannot the President give heed to the sufferings of his own people?

Think, Mr. President, of the captain of the strikers, Louis Tikas, whose truce with the gunmen was ended with his murder. Think of the fifty-one shots which were passed through the strike leader. Think of his body, which has lain exposed since his infamous killing. Then, with that vast power which has been committed to you as the executive of a great nation, attend to the misery wrought by an anarchistic lust for dollars. Without your speedy aid the poor and the needy, betrayed by the state, may be slaughtered to the last smiling babe.[7]

The editorial rattled windows in the White House. It was picked up and reprinted by many of the major newspapers and magazines of the nation. Wilson dispatched United States troops to Colorado, and peace finally came to the coal fields.

[7]Chenery, op. cit., p. 55.

Commenting on the editorial in his recent autobiography, Chenery wryly observes:

> Forman's forecast that it would raise journalistic hell in Colorado was a model of understatement. At the time the *Rocky Mountain News* had a circulation of about 16,000. The next morning the news circulation was trebled, and the paper was able to retain the same high circulation until I left and the policy was changed. No other newspaper had made so outspoken a protest against lawlessness in the coal mine war. Clearly the public welcomed a frank expression of editorial opinion. Literally thousands of letters were sent to the paper. We published full pages of letters for days after the event.[8]

Although there was a net gain, some of the letters were subscription cancellations rather than epistles of praise for bold journalism. The *News*, however, boasted of its enemies by publishing the cancellation notices along with the praise:

> Mr. Frank McDonough, Sr., a lawyer in the McPhee Bldg., informs us that he wishes to cancel his subscription to The Times, but will continue as a subscriber to The News "under compulsion" as he needs a morning newspaper. Mr. McDonough is mistaken. We have ourselves cancelled his subscription to The News, since we do not desire any compulsory subscribers.

> Mr. J. Foster Symes [later federal district judge] requests that we cancel The Times, but continue The News except on Sunday. We have cancelled all.

The Colorado Fuel & Iron Company filed a $500,000 libel suit against the *News* on April 27, though it never came to trial. A fuming committee from the Chamber of Commerce waited upon Chenery and Forman. The *News*, the committee said, was giving Colorado a bad name abroad. Such unfavorable publicity must stop. Chenery argued.

"We're getting nowhere with this pinhead," the committee chairman snorted. "Let's go."

Chenery continues the story:

> A day or two later I was informed that the Chamber of Commerce was planning an advertising boycott of the *Rocky Mountain News*. If the Chamber of Commerce could induce the department stores and other large advertisers to boycott the *News*, we would be hurt seriously. We found help from two powerful but quite unexpected sources. Former Senator Patterson . . . battled for us and against the boycott at the Chamber of Commerce meeting. Senator Patterson was an old man and a Democrat. His political life and his business life were all but

[8]Ibid., p. 57.

finished. Yet with nothing at stake for himself, he did battle against those who would intimidate his old paper by economic pressure. Our other ally was, of all people, Harry Tammen, co-owner of the Denver *Post*, the strongest paper financially in Denver. Tammen took the very practical view that if the *Rocky Mountain News* were subdued by an advertising boycott, the taste of victory might induce the boycotters to whip the *Post* into submission. Thus gradually the boycotters were defeated. That, incidentally, was an illuminating experience for me. I saw at first hand that it was not necessary to yield to advertising pressure and that if an editor were disposed to stand by his principles, he might find ways of defending himself against attack. Nothing that has happened to me in the subsequent thirty-five years has caused me to change this belief.[9]

Chenery stood fast, but Shaffer caved. A message came through from Chicago instructing the young editorial writer to "pursue a milder line." He resigned and went east to become editor of the New York *Globe* and then for twenty-five years editor and publisher of *Collier's*. Harvey Duell quit too. He became editor of *Liberty* and the New York *Daily News*. Shaffer transferred Forman back to the Chicago *Post*. City editor Arthur MacLennan and news editor Frank C. Farrar also went to Shaffer's Windy City paper, though the latter returned later as managing editor. Gene Fowler picked up and moved down the street to join Tammen and Bonfils for four robust years. Chenery recalls Fowler as one of the "very bright young men" on his staff and remembers that

> . . . Love and marriage hit Gene Fowler a resounding blow while I was still there to catch the echoes. In celebration of the event Fowler's father-in-law presented the young couple with a modest bungalow on the outskirts of Denver. Gene was a sports reporter and he also had a signed column of comment on sporting events and personages. This gave him a fairly free hand at choosing his texts. He was so much impressed with the wonder of his new home, and conceivably too with love and marriage, that every day for two months he wrote and published at the top of his column a poem in praise of his bungalow. The real estate business lost a lyrical advocate when Gene remained true to journalism and literature.[10]

With the departure of so many stalwarts and the about-face from progressive policies, morale of the *News* staff plunged almost as sharply as circulation figures. Within a few weeks after the paper began speaking in tones acceptable to the Chamber of Commerce and Seventeenth Street, the subscription lists were cut in half and the *News* once again was as vulnerable as ever to the *Post's* whoppings.

[9]Ibid., pp. 59–60.

[10]Ibid., p. 64.

It could have been a better fight. Shaffer had the resources and the *News-Times* staffs, in spite of the departures, still had talent. Lee Casey was beginning to make himself felt. Arthur Chapman remained at his post. Wilbur Daniel Steele, who would win fame as a novelist and modern master of the short story, did a hitch on the rim of the copy desk. Another famous writer, Courtney Ryley Cooper, was fired from the *News* by editors who decided he couldn't write. He went to the *Post* nursing his wounded pride and soon lengthy pieces in an elegantly purple prose began appearing under the by-line Ryley Cooper. But the slur still rankled, and more than a year later Cooper saw what he thought was an opportunity to put the Welton Street editors in their places. A lady named Stella Smith had become tired of matrimony and punctuated her disillusion with pistol shots into her husband. It made a famous trial in West Side Court. Cooper covered it for the *Post*. While waiting for the verdict to come in, however, he fell victim to good fellowship. Later that night he marched up the steep stairway to the *News* city room, sat down at a typewriter without a word to anyone, and worked with inspired diligence for more than an hour. This, obviously, would be a masterpiece which would impress those comma-smashers who had murdered his glowing style. Finally he slapped the copy on the city desk and stalked out with that regal dignity which comes only to headwaiters and offended drunks. The story was incoherent but the total effect was grand.

Subsequently Cooper became press agent for the Tammen-Bonfils circus and acquired the sawdust lore which he utilized effectively in a lean, hard-hitting, entirely unpurple style for many of his popular magazine stories. Between the two of them he and Gene Fowler managed to present a raucous front-curtain prologue to the Denver visit of Queen Marie of Rumania in November 1926. Fowler now was New York big time and was traveling with the royal entourage in the press Pullman immediately ahead of the queen's private car. Harvey Sethman, for many years lay executive of the Colorado Medical Society but then a *News* reporter, tells the story. Sethman's opposition on the assignment was Cooper. The special train pulled slowly into Union Station and a red carpet was run out. A delegation of social nabobs and civic dignitaries pressed forward to extend a formal welcome to the popular queen. After a short wait a stir about the private car indicated that the titled visitor was about to emerge. A hush fell over the crowd. In the short interval of silence Fowler came to the door of his car, spotted his dear, long-lost friend on the platform, and let out a Comanche war whoop:

"Coop! You old son of a bitch! How the hell are you?"

An instant later Queen Marie made her grand entrance into the Mile High City. There were some suggestions that Fowler, whose earlier Denver escapades had not been forgotten, should be turned over to the protocol division of the State Department for summary execution.

As World War I approached, other of Fowler's old cronies were still among the mainstays of Denver journalism. Jack Carberry, now with the *Express*, and "Red" Feeney, temporarily with the *Post*, knew more about the police department than most of the cops. What they didn't know the lean little cricket-active Ray Humphreys of the *Times* did. Harry McCabe of the *News*, senior factotum of the police beat, smiled indulgently on the scurryings of his young associates and phoned in his exclusives without stirring from his rickety chair in the pressroom. It was a formidable quartet, and detectives sometimes suspiciously accused one or more of the foursome of being on the scene before the crime occurred. They were often joined on crime stories of the day by Joseph E. Cook of the *Times*, today an august judge of the Denver District Court. Carberry currently is executive sports editor of the *Post* after years of service on the *News*. Humphreys, always a sleuth at heart, has been chief investigator for the Denver district attorney for decades. He still operates a typewriter with great speed, verve, and sustained violence, using a single finger of his right hand. If anything should happen to his right index finger half the true detective magazines in America would lose their most active correspondent.

When Humphreys and Joe Cook prepared to march off to war a farewell party was organized. They had originally tried to sign up with a proposed mounted regiment to be called "Teddy's Rough Riders." But a private regiment of horse, even with so luminous a heritage, was frowned upon by unromantic military authorities, and the prospective newsmen-warriors were forced to settle for less dashing roles. The party in their honor proceeded as farewell parties do until sometime after midnight, at which hour it was deemed appropriate to rent a horse, possibly as a final symbolic gesture. Jack O'Brien, a Shaffer penman and later a prominent San Antonio businessman, demonstrated his equestrian skills by riding the beast up the twenty-five narrow and squeaking steps to the *News* second-floor city room. It seemed hilarious at the time, Carberry remembers, and the pasty-faced troglodytes of the dog watch, nursing their coffee and ulcers, were properly startled when O'Brien rode hallooing through the swinging doors at the top of the stairs. His mount, however, took one look at the way he had come and refused to descend. The horse remained at pasture in the sports department, munching copy paper, until late next day when a heavy hauling company was engaged to lower him out a rear window with sling and winch. By that time the animal was burping sulphite wood pulp and the janitors were threatening to resign in a body. If they had wanted careers as white wings, they asserted, they would have joined the city sanitation department.

Old "Cap" Smith was still reviving the Colorado mining industry for each new edition and manicuring his nails menacingly with a fifteen-inch pair of shears. "Cap" wandered about the office with his pants sagging precariously and his suspenders drooped sorrowfully over his backside. In order to remain forever handsome and youthful the captain used a hair dye—shoe polish, the rest of the staff insisted—on his noble mustaches. But the doughty old veteran's eyes were not what they were in Loveland's day, and he could never seem to get the dye on evenly. The piebald effect was startling to strangers.

Another longtimer was James H. MacLennan, editorial writer whose enormous erudition was always spoken of with hushed respect. James H. was an emigrant Scot and no relation to Arthur MacLennan, the *News'* city editor. He encountered difficulty making the transition to the brash, unlearned twentieth century. For years he methodically turned out lengthy Sunday editorials, bristling with scholarship, about the more esoteric Hindu philosophies and the fiscal policies of the Phoenician Empire. No one was quite sure what the editorials meant, but they were tremendously impressive. Finally, midway in the twenties, Mac-Lennan was let go in the interest of gearing the editorial page to the fashionable urgencies of the new day. It was not a harsh discharge. True to his national instincts and in a gross flaunting of every newspaper tradition, James H. had saved his money. He continued to live in his bachelor's quarters at the plush Brown Palace. Consulting actuarial tables and his physician, MacLennan calculated that he would survive until he was eighty, and he began living on his principal at that precise rate. But he miscalculated. Shortly before mid-century the management of the Brown called the paper to say that the bookish old fellow, an admirable and desirable guest who but recently had been presented with a cake for his eightieth birthday, had quietly collapsed. He had not eaten for two days and was dead broke. Lee Casey and Joe McMeel arranged quarters for him at an old folks' home. He died at eighty-eight with the maximum budget of books from the public library at his elbow.

Day-side city editor for the *Times* during the World War I years was George Sanford Holmes, later the *News'* Washington correspondent for a quarter century or more. In addition to sound qualities as a practical newspaperman, Holmes had several more spectacular claims to local fame. For one, he wrote the lyrics to "Come to Cool Colorado", official hymn of the Kiwanis Club. For another, he authored a poem, "Only a Cop," which for many years was a part of the obsequies of any man behind a badge who died in line of duty. But many remembered Holmes for the first big story he had covered. "Weston the Walker," a notable heel-and-toe man of the times, was hiking about the country to spread the word on clean living. He decided to stroll from Omaha to Denver, and Holmes went out to meet him. Together they marched triumphantly into the city while the slightly winded Holmes made notes on the values of walking for health as opposed to the indolent evils of the cycling craze.

Jack Barrows, who fell into the primrose pathways of advertising, then was covering financial news, Seventeenth Street, and the hotels. Charles F. (Nick) Carter sat on the rim of the copy desk with Frank Plumb, fulminating about the illiteracy of reporters and in despair of the modern generation's spelling. Another copyreader, rewrite man, and Sunday feature writer was Frank A. McClelland, also known as "The Walrus" for his mustache. McClelland came to retirement age, was presented with the usual traveling bag, and departed for his small ranch in northern Colorado. In a few months he was back. "Damn quiet was getting on my nerves," he explained. Also on the copy desk was a deaf and dumb genius known then and remembered now as "The Dummy." His name was Will C. Ullrich, though no one used it. The nickname was rude but not disrespectful; for "The Dummy" generally was accepted as the most skillful copy editor Denver had seen.

Shifts were occurring on the feminine side of the office. Kate Russell left about the time war broke out. Hester (Hettie) Cattell already was gone. Soon after Shaffer purchased the News he conceived that the suffragette excitement might be exploitable through a newspaper for women edited entirely by women. He looked around over the staffs of his various newspapers and his eye fell on the capable, serious-minded Hettie with her enormous capacity for hard work. Hettie could do anything in the shop, was head over heels in love with the newspaper business and little concerned about such grubby matters as wages—all endearing qualities. For the News she was book reviewer, dramatic critic, covered all musical events, and filled in her spare time with feature writing. At one point she was given a two-page center fold to tell how it felt to spend twenty-four hours in the women's cell block of the state penitentiary. In January 1914, Shaffer called her to the editorship of his projected biddy-sheet in Evanston, Illinois. Original plans called for a daily, but the enlightened experiment wound up as a weekly. Masculine-minded Evanstonians destroyed the first issue of the North Shore Review, "the only newspaper in the world edited exclusively by women."

"The Review lasted about 18 months," Hettie recalls, "and during that time I was editor, managing editor, copy editor, makeup editor and copyboy—toting all the copy to the Chicago Evening Post to be printed there. The editor (me) was getting $25 a week and half the 'staff' (of about six) was kissing me good-morning every day. Honestly!"

Hettie escaped to the Chicago Examiner, then to the Tribune, and went on to New York to help found the Mirror in 1924. She has been a member of that paper's staff almost continuously since, covered the Lindbergh kidnap trial, the Hall-Mills case, and the Morro Castle disaster, trailed the Dionne quintuplets and chased Daddy Browning and Peaches all over Westchester County. Effusive bussing is not generally regarded as operational procedure at the Mirror.

Hettie's place on the distaff side of the News-Times city room was filled variously by Marie Keffer, Katherine Ann Porter, Mattie I. Durkee, and police reporter Harry McCabe's beauteous sister Ruth. Mattie, now Mrs. Cecil R. Connor of Denver, was the all-around girl reporter. Novelist Clyde Brion Davis, who later handled her articles as a *News* copyreader, remembers that she sought to elevate the dignity of prosaic hay by giving it a Hellenic spelling: "alphalpha." Katherine Ann Porter was society editor for the *News*, and Ruth McCabe tended similar chores for the afternoon *Times*. Impressionable males of the era speak nostalgically of Ruth's jet hair and Irish eyes. She was an unmerciful flirt, and all unattached hearts turned over when she walked to the drinking fountain. Among others, Art MacLennan wanted to marry her, but she ruled that his habits were too wild. Another of her admirers was the blond and boyish Pyke Johnson, who had climbed the rungs from copy boy to sports editor. Johnson today is past president and consultant to the Automotive Safety Foundation in Washington. His son Pyke, Jr., is editor in chief of Anchor Books, a division of the publishing house of Doubleday & Company. Pyke, Jr.'s birth was proudly announced among the box scores on the *News*' sports page, a distinction which has fallen to few book publishers. Pyke, Sr., was one of the first sports writers to suggest putting numbers on football players, for which he was denounced by coaches of the day. It would ruin their "hidden ball" plays.

When the nation changed its mind about being too proud to fight, the *News* sent seventy-five of its men and one of its women off to war. Mattie Durkee shipped out as a Red Cross worker. Along with Ray Humphreys, Jack O'Brien, and Joe Cook, *News* men who joined the colors included state editor Marty O'Toole, reporters Jack Barrows and Deane A. Dickason, and a young cub, Charles Lounsbury, who one day would become editor of the paper. Two of the men—Harvey Setchel and R. Hughes—didn't come back from France. Many of the others returned to take their old places on the staff, and three of them—Ray E. Olson, D. E. Jones, and H. F. Sciple—still are employees.

During the war Buffalo Bill Cody died in Denver. It was widely charged that his heart had been broken when Tammen and Bonfils took his world-touring Wild West Show away from him. Cody is buried atop Lookout Mountain overlooking Golden and Denver. The granite tomb is reinforced with concrete and railroad rails to discourage reciprocal body-snatching. Bill had specifically desired that he be buried on his ranch near Cody, Wyoming, but the *Post* took over promotion of the funeral, which was a splendid affair, and overruled the old showman's last wishes. The Cody grave, as the *Post* so accurately forecast, has become a signal tourist attraction.

So when the boys came home again the familiar sight of a queue of adoring children tagging the white-haired Cody about the streets was absent from the Denver scene. There were other changes. While the bravest and finest were away and unable to defend their rights, sneaky pecksniffs had pried open the U. S. Constitution and inserted national

prohibition. (Colorado actually had gone dry in 1914, but wet Wyoming
was so close to Denver that the drouth was scarcely noticeable.) The
nourishing free lunch, source of many a reporter's vitamins and proteins,
had disappeared. But it just wasn't true, as billed, that the doors of hell
had been slammed shut once and forever. Ministers were nonplused by
the turn of events, but police reporters were jubilant. Never had there
been such lurid crimes for them to cover. Political reporters reaped
benefits too. A case of petty corruption could be turned up any week in
almost any office at City Hall or the Statehouse. Lawyers and physicians
possessed of stomach pumps were busy as cranberry merchants. Some
broken homes were patched and a few barefoot children shod. All in all,
it was a happy time for nearly everyone. Drinking continued almost
unabated while the majesty of the law tumbled and things illegal acquired
the added attraction of titillating naughtiness. A noble if occasionally
abused beverage was demeaned into something called booze, a fluid of
dubious origins which caused blindness and other infirmities. Leadville
Moon—concocted, some said, of black powder and old miners' overalls
—flowed into Denver as if there were a pipeline down from the Cloud
City. Rumrunners' trucks disturbed the slumbers of good citizens living
near major highways. There was more fancy gunplay than there had
been since Charley Harrison left town.

Tastes and discriminations suffered sad diminishments. The police
reporters, caught short at one point with nothing in the old morgue
drains, conspired with orderlies at Denver General Hospital to siphon
off the alcohol from surgical specimens. The base crime came to olfactory
attention a few weeks later when the substituted tap water failed to
maintain an acceptable state of preservation in a priceless collection of
antique gall bladders, appendixes, and other viscera. By this time the
alcohol had been traded off to Turkey Joe, locally prominent for an
especially palatable bathtub gin, and the culprits never could be called
to account.

Some of the more enterprising News-Times newsboys on downtown
street corners saw in prohibition an opportunity to diversify. This led to
a rather peevish headline in the Post: "A Bottle of Booze with Every
News."

The News' puckish photographer, Harry Rhoads, was not then and is
not now a drinker. He attributes this to a haunting vision from his
childhood, though others say he has maintained such a high level of
exuberant good spirits for more than fifty years that artificial stimulation
would have been gilding the lily.

"When I was a boy," Harry explains, "I used to deliver the Republican.
Every morning about three o'clock I had to go down with my horse
and cart and pick up my papers. This was in the 1890s, and the private
wine rooms with side entrances for the ladies were doing a great business
in that neighborhood. When I'd come down the unpaved street with

my cart I'd see four or five women nearly every morning lying drunk in the cobblestone gutter. It got to bothering me so much that I decided I would never take up drinking."

In very recent years his physician has persuaded Harry—now in his late seventies—that a medicinal drop or two before meals might benefit his constitution and would not greatly damage his moral fiber. Harry now takes a careful one, though he probably still sees women in gutters in his mind's eye. This distresses him; for Harry is fond of ladies. There are social-set matrons of his acquaintance in Denver whom he has photographed as children, mothers, and grandmothers, each time with courtly flourishes. Harry has never forgotten the bow taught him at dancing school—one arm across his ample middle, the other across his back—and he employs it whenever presented to a lady. A cherubic and unspoiled soul, and everyone in Denver loves him.

Although Harry did not touch the stuff himself he was always broad-minded about others' thirsts. A special camera equipment case was provided him for use on raids. The bag would accommodate the cumbersome flash-powder equipment of the day with room left over for several bottles filched by light-fingered reporters or passed out by compassionate prohibition agents.

Harry assisted in providing refreshments for the grand opening of the present Denver Press Club in the early twenties. A large seizure of illicit liquor had been made. The booty was stored at the West Side Court building. Officers who had participated in the notable *coup* against Satan straightened their ties and awaited arrival of photographers to preserve their noble deed in the gazettes of the city. Harry computed how much flash powder would be required to blind his subjects temporarily without burning the building down. While the officers groped around in the smoke "Red" Feeney carried several cases of choice bonded out to Harry's Model T coupe.

Feeney then discovered that he had carelessly omitted from the photo some of the key figures of the occasion. These overlooked worthies had been standing coyly aside trying not to look hurt. The picture would have to be reposed. The officers brightened, smoothed their hair, and jostled each other into position. Harry fired again, and Feeney was able to make two more trips to the curb.

" 'Red' got so much liquor into that Ford I could hardly drive away," Harry says. "The back end was full and the seat propped up so high I couldn't reach the pedals. I took it all out to Eddie Day's house, handed it in through a side bedroom window and it was stashed under his bed. Everyone at the Press Club opening seemed to have a very nice time."

On another outing the flash-powder technique failed. Feeney and Rhoads were dispatched to accompany a raid on the Douglas County ranch of a prominent physician suspected of practicing illegal chemistry as a hobby. The doctor's milk house was found to contain neat rows of glistening, well-tended stills. Everything was spotless, hygienic and scientific, reflecting a high degree of professional pride. The doctor and his assistants were interrupted in the cellar as they fixed bonding labels to their product. Harry arranged the raiders and their captives so that each would receive full benefit, and cut loose with his Vesuvius. But Feeney stumbled at the top of the stairs and his samples of the "evidence" shattered into pitiful pools on the cellar floor. All was not lost, however. The thoughtful Harry earlier had taken the precaution of lugging several carboys of undecanted spirits down the road a piece and hiding them in the weeds. The enterprising journalists picked them up on their way back to the office.

"Red" Feeney at this point was back on the *News*. Like many of his associates, he made several circuits of the two papers before finally coming to rest. Eddie Day was another example of the mobility. At the *News* he held the positions of sports editor, city editor, and managing editor before moving down to Champa Street to snug harbor as managing editor of the *Post*. Eddie was a small and crusty Irishman who developed a devastating on-duty scowl to counterbalance an off-duty affability. He was a man of total prejudices and fixed ideas, and he liked any lead so long as it contained a well-tested cliché. He was particularly appreciative of stories which began "Mystery surrounds . . ." "Mystery surrounds the disappearance of John Doe. . . ." "Mystery surrounds the fate of Senate Bill 507. . . ." His reporters soon tumbled to the gimmick, and a miasma of mystery descended on the city and all its works. Having spent most of his life observing newspapermen at close range, Eddie sent his son to law school. Justice Edward C. Day, Jr., now sits on the Colorado Supreme Court.

Not all the *News* staff members were mere observers, beneficiaries, or victims of the Volstead experiment. Two had been active participants. One of them picked up his background for police reporting as a rum-runner in the Wyoming–Colorado trade. Sometimes his truck would have to crash through a road block of prohibition officers or hijackers, and bullets would be exchanged. Ben Cope had been a circus clown and then a dry agent before joining the *News* staff. One night Ben and the retired rumrunner got to comparing notes and discovered they had shot at each other in several dark encounters. The revelation did not disturb a beautiful friendship.

Clyde Brion Davis, novelist and historian of the arts of chance, came to the *News* in 1920 after making the "shocking discovery that the business office and the editorial department of the Denver *Post* were under the same roof." Davis has a tender memory of the ex-bootlegger, who enjoyed the rough reputation arising from his beyond-the-law past and did everything he could to enhance it, even to carrying a pistol with black bicycle tape around the grip. Davis recalls:

His remarkable facility in obtaining the facts quickly about such crimes as bank robberies led to rumors that he knew more than he should have known earlier than he should have known it. While he would have been the first to encourage that sort of rumor, I am convinced his edge came from an extraordinary talent for palship with cops. The police from the chief down to the rawest recruit adored him because, if his literary aptitude was meager, he still possessed a genius for spelling the names of policemen correctly.

I do believe his reputation for toughness was somewhat exaggerated because late one night he undertook to eliminate me and I am still here. This was in the hotel room of the late Guy Usher, a former railroad brakeman turned actor and at that time "heavy" in the Denham Theater stock company. Present besides our host were the former war correspondent, Louis Edgar Browne, and a clever little copy reader named Garry Garretson. My memory seems to be convenient enough so that I cannot recall the provocation and I cannot say what degree of justification our rumrunner friend had for his action. But, as some of Denver's crew of Western writers used to have it, "With a vile oath he drew his six gun, swearing he would have my life."

At that Guy Usher, Louis Browne and Garry Garretson departed, waiting down the hotel corridor, I suppose, for the boom that would signify the end of Davis. But I had been trained in the first war in what was called commando tactics in the second war and I knew his "six-gun" was a single-action .41-caliber that had to be cocked before it could be fired. So there was no boom and I returned the thing to him finally, after taking out the cartridges, because it had been a gift from the late revered Chief of Police Hamilton Armstrong. And the others came back and I suppose Guy Usher, who ended his days as a villain in Hollywood Westerns, poured a drink.

Some years later the rumrunner left the newspaper business and became, spare the mark! lingerie buyer for a Denver department store. Subsequently he operated his own ladies' ready-to-wear store in the East. Bootlegger, police reporter, lingerie, ready-to-wear. A full life.

John Chapman, the astringent drama critic for the New York *Daily News*, got his first by-line in the Denver *Times* a few years before Clyde Davis became a *News* stalwart. His revered father, Arthur, was still managing editor in 1917 when young Jack signed on at fifteen dollars a week to do a double, reporter and photographer. His first assignment was to cover a ladies' golf tournament at the Denver Country Club. He pleaded that he knew nothing about golf, but Eddie Day reassured him: "Aw, that's okay, kid. Just rewrite the story from tomorrow morning's *News*." His effort carried the credit line, "By Jack Chapman."

"I thought this was just buttering up the boss's son and completely undeserved besides, and said so," Chapman remembers. "I don't think I ever had another by-line in the *Times* during the two years I worked for the paper."

The son's memory recaptures a picture of his much-respected and
-admired father in action:

> I remember that Dad never took off his derby. In summer he'd
> take off his jacket, unbutton his vest and roll up his sleeves, but the
> hat was always on the back of his head. I think this was the trademark
> of a newspaperman then, the way a New York *World* "journalist"
> would later identify himself by carrying a stick.
>
> Dad hired a motley crew. Anybody who came West with TB was sure
> to get a hearing. Being a verse-writer himself, he was always sympathetic
> toward any young man who wanted to write poetry. Thus it was that
> he got Clifford Laube, who covered the Statehouse. Cliff later came
> to New York, where I got a job for him on the *News*, and later he
> switched to the New York *Times*, from which he finally retired with
> great honor.
>
> Dad was as quiet a man as a managing editor as he was as a father.
> Never yelled, never got upset. Once, though, he did show some irritation.
> The first edition was being made up and there was barely enough type
> for it. The racks of filler, or moonlight, were stripped bare. Dad com-
> plained to the city editor, George Sanford Holmes, about the lack of
> foresight in not having enough moonlight on hand. "Why don't you
> use your noodle?" he asked. From that time, filler was called "noodle
> stuff" by the staff.
>
> I recall my own work on the Denver *Times* as greatly exciting. Cover-
> ing police and having a police badge cleverly hidden on my vest, so that
> when I stood in the streetcar and held a strap the badge would show
> discreetly and people would know how important I was. One exciting
> time was Armistice Day, when the town went nuts and I had my
> Graphic. I still recall one picture of a small tailor shop whose pro-
> prietor had painted on the window, "We Made the Kaiser Running
> Pants."

Another of the incipient poets hired by Chapman senior for the *Times*
turned out to be Thomas Hornsby Ferril, intimate of Frost and Sandburg, essayist for *Harper's* and today the West's strongest poetic voice.
Ferril and his wife Helen now publish Professor Goldrick's old weekly
Herald as a legal journal and a vehicle for Tom's widely admired personal
essays. His lines to water, the West's god and goad, are illustrated by
murals in the rotunda of the Colorado State Capitol.

Ferril verses were not always so highly regarded. He began using
poems at the end of the column he was permitted to write after breaking
in on nearly every beat in town. Richard Le Gallienne noticed the
promising lines and praised them in the New York *Times*. Thereafter,
it was decided, the *News* would have to have a Ferril poem every week.
The weekly stint at five dollars a poem continued even after Ferril
left the paper a few years later, and many of the verses appeared in his
first book, *High Passage*. But one of the periodic retrenchments came.

"A janitor died," Tom recollects, "and it was discovered other adjustments could be made to effect a weekly payroll saving of a hundred and ninety-five dollars. Eddie Day suggested they drop Ferril and make it an even two hundred."

Tom also remembers another brush with the practical-minded Day, whose short temper and abrupt bursts of direct action made him a sort of stay-at-home Harold Ross (*The New Yorker's* Ross was born in the silver city of Aspen, Colorado). As a side line Day was in partnership with Pyke Johnson, Sr., in operation of a neighborhood motion picture house. Ferril at this date was doing a turn as drama and movie editor of the *Times* and naïvely attempting candid reviews. One night after Tom had gone home Eddie broke down the entertainment page and re-edited it along lines he felt were more likely to produce patrons at his box office and favors from the film exchanges. The name David O. Selznick appeared seventeen times.

It was during this era that the church editor broke his leg in a Peeping Tom episode. This gentleman, who shall remain anonymous, had been ordained by a splinter sect but found the earthly rewards of the clergy slender. He preached on Sundays and made up for the collection plate's deficiencies by editing a weekly church page for the *News*. This sometimes brought him to the office late at night. The six-story Orient Hotel had been built adjoining the *News* building on the north with only an areaway intervening. Its windows peered directly into the editorial rooms, and vice versa. Couples who patronized the Orient occasionally were distracted, or indifferent, and failed to draw the blinds. It was a constant temptation to pruriency, and, alas, a great many *News* staff members over a great many years succumbed. Including the reverend church editor. Thus it came about one night that the entire late force was in thrall when unexpected visitors mounted the stairs and entered through the swinging doors. In his haste to descend from a desk top the church editor fell and fractured his tibia.

The plight in which reporter Jack Steele found himself was only slightly less embarrassing. The brash Steele, caught short during an interview with John D. Rockefeller, Jr., touched the financier for a loan.

"I'm very sorry, my friend," Rockefeller said, "but I don't have any money with me. Could you take a check?"

Steele accepted a twenty-dollar check. But when he sought to cash it the suspicious bank tellers on Seventeenth Street flatly accused him of forgery and offered to call the cops.

The undauntable Harry Rhoads also had a brush with Rockefeller and his money on one of the steel king's several trips west during the labor troubles in the coal mines. Harry shot a picture of Rockefeller and his sons at Union Station, and Rockefeller, who didn't want his boys photographed, grabbed Harry by the collar.

"I want to buy that plate," Rockefeller said.

"You haven't got enough money to buy it," Rhoads told the richest man in the world. "It doesn't belong to me. It belongs to the *Rocky Mountain News*. See the city editor."

Rockefeller was disposed to argue the matter and kept a firm grip on Harry. The crowd which gathered around was partisan; ever since Ludlow the name "Rockefeller" hadn't been popular in Colorado.

"Hit him, Harry," one of the bystanders urged. "He can't do that to you. Hit him."

Harry concedes he never has had the figure for fisticuffs. "So I just talked to him," he says. "I asked him to be a gentleman about the matter and told him I was just doing my job. If he had objections he should see my city editor. That seemed to calm him down. We parted friends."

The picture appeared on page one next day, along with a full account of the Rhoads-Rockefeller dialogue. A photographer for the *Post* accepted five hundred dollars for *his* plate and got fired. Bonfils was sensitive about such prerogatives.

Then came Teapot Dome.

A reporter for the *Post* uncovered in 1922 information which linked Interior Secretary Albert B. Fall with the illegal leasing of the Teapot Dome naval oil reserve in Wyoming out of which oil tycoon Harry Sinclair testified he planned to make $100 millions. Bonfils, however, prudently withheld the story while printing editorial attacks on the leases. Meanwhile he became acquainted with a rival oilman who had been offended by being shut out of the deal. Teapot Dome now was becoming a national stench and the scandal was rocking the Harding administration, but the *Post's* attacks on Sinclair and E. L. Doheny abruptly ceased.

When the Senate investigating committee got to looking into the matter it discovered that Bonfils had shared in a million-dollar under-the-table settlement, a quarter in cash, three quarters more promised, from Sinclair.[11] Bonfils had decided Teapot Dome was not newsworthy after all. He was called to Washington to testify. He denied wrongdoing but in the midst of the uncomfortable questioning got a promotional plug into the record: "The Denver *Post* has the greatest circulation per capita of its publication city of any newspaper in the history of the world."

"I suppose Mr. Sinclair knew all that," Senator Lenroot commented dryly.

Malicious glee reigned on Welton Street. The corsair of Champa Street had finally been nabbed with his fist in the jam pot. What a story! The *News* gave it the full treatment—for one series of editions.

Next day, as the hearing in Washington proceeded, it was disclosed that John Clean Shaffer was involved too. Shaffer, who was always

[11]*Senate Report No. 794*, 68th Congress, 1st Session, June 6, 1924, p. 12.

pleased when biographers took note of his years as Sunday school superintendent, had written in to the plundering oilmen and suggested mildly that he be placed "on a parity" with Bonfils. The raiders decided that, viewed as a moral issue, there was merit to the suggestion. The sum of $92,500 was passed along.[12]

Joy subsided at the *News*. Staff members were crestfallen. Their own boss was a boodler too. And a cut-price boodler at that.

The little *Express* was in its glory. It was clean. Both the big papers had been trapped and tarred. Moreover the oil scandal dovetailed perfectly with its Scrippsian liberal policies. A young reporter, Bob Chase, was dispatched to Wyoming to give on-the-scene coverage from Teapot Dome, and the *Express* peeled off large strips of hide with rending noises as loud as could be provoked from its wheezing press.

A *News* reporter of the day, John P. Lewis, tells how it was on Welton Street:

> The *News* had an essential integrity that carried through as a heritage from Founder Byers. It wasn't shaken even by the revelation that Owner Shaffer was "in" on Teapot Dome.
>
> I have wondered since why those of us who worked on the *News* didn't throw up the sponge that time, and look elsewhere for work. Probably one of the reasons is that the logical "elsewhere" was the *Post*, and compared to Bonfils and Tammen, Shaffer was a pure, innocent orchid. More fundamental, perhaps, we had faith in the *News*— and it was the *News* we were working for, not John C. Shaffer and not his son, and the *News* had integrity, and we knew it.
>
> It was along about that time that the *Post* became strong enough for Bonfils to intimidate advertisers, to threaten those who planned to include the *News* in their schedules, and to punish those who did. One year, I recall, we learned that the *Post* had informed the officials of the annual Merchants' and Industrial Exposition held at the auditorium that if any advertising went to the *News*, the *Post* would carry none and would give no space to the event. The show management felt they had to give in, and sent word to the *News* to cancel a page or half-page or such that had been scheduled, but to send a bill for the space quietly and it would be paid. The *News* business management had the integrity to refuse to take pay for space that wasn't used, and the editorial side played it honest enough to cover the event regardless of advertising.
>
> That was the kind of a trap the *News* was in back in those days—and any move to yell bloody murder about it publicly was forestalled by the fact that publicity would merely put the informants in the line of fire to have their heads knocked off by the *Post*. No one would stand up and testify.

John Lewis went on from Denver to become editor of Marshall Field's ill-fated experiment in adless New York journalism, *PM*. Today he has

12Ibid.

achieved the goal dreamed of by half the working newspapermen in America, a weekly of his own, the *Journal-Transcript* of Franklin, New Hampshire. Lewis was a reporter for the *News* up to 1926, "everything from the Stockyards both ways," then city editor and assistant managing editor.

"It was a wonderful, fearful, rowdy time and place for newspapering," he writes, "especially for those of us who were just breaking in."

It was a time touched by the joyous insanities of prohibition, and those who survived it look back with nostalgia, I think, to the days of the speakeasy. It was a time touched by cancerous, fearful hatreds and intolerances. The Ku Kluxers all but controlled the state for a time. There were mobs and violence. Black Jack Jerome's strikebreakers were kicked into bloody insensibility in their overturned street cars at the very doors of the Cathedral before the federal troops restored order. It was a time of corruption. Nationally, the Harding regime came and went. Locally, police protection made Denver the home of America's finest confidence men until [District Attorney Philip S.] Van Cise brought in outside police and broke it up, meanwhile giving heart failure to all the owners of all the whorehouses in Denver by publicly measuring their properties for closing by way of conning the conmen into thinking he was after prostitutes, not thieves.[13]

There was a mystic side to the times. White-gowned Aimee Semple McPherson packed the auditorium with listeners and cluttered the wings with canes and crutches of the healed, some of whom went back to retrieve them next day. The House of David brought enlightenment to Arapahoe Street, and Jim Goodheart did his good works for the poor devils in the gutter until he stumbled and backslid in himself.

There was violence, crime, murder, suicide—whatever else was missed, we on the papers were intent about that and never let human tragedy slip by unheralded. There was thievery and incompetence in some of the banks, and long years before the national crash of '29, Denver had its own series of reverberating financial failures.

And there was vision. They were presumptuous, perhaps, but some people saw the growth that has since come about. The Moffat Tunnel was built, and water brought under the Divide and the Civic Center nurtured and developed at a time when most cities were building toward new slums and congestion. In the '20s, Denver had sort of an itch to be better than it was, and I wonder if that holds good today?

Lewis also remembers the night when the clown-dry agent-reporter Ben Cope took fifteen dollars—a week's pay—away from him at blackjack, and the Swedish pressroom foreman who complained to Eddie Day: "If today iss like yesterday, Yesus Christ, I hope it wasn't."

One of Lewis' predecessors as city editor was Ray Colvin, later of the Seattle *Post-Intelligencer*, who wore a porkpie hat, Arthur Chapman's

[13]For a full account of the cleanup of Denver's famed "Bunco Ring" see Philip S. Van Cise, *Fighting the Underworld* (Cambridge, 1936).

derby having passed from style. Frank Farrar came back from Chicago, did a term as managing editor, and went on to the San Francisco *Examiner*. Frank Farley became sports editor.

Sitting in as Colvin's assistant was William Mundhenk ("Judge") Beardshear, owlish behind horn-rimmed glasses and the dedicated enemy of ripe prose. Many a Denver newspaperman, including Clyde Davis, credits "Judge" Beardshear with teaching him how to write. Refusing many tendered promotions, Beardshear as assistant city editor of both the *News* and the *Post* continued to smash adjectives and correct spelling for several generations of Denver reporters. He was quiet and kindly, qualities seldom specified in the form sheet on city desk jockeys, and in his off-duty time immersed himself in books and classical music on his phonograph.

Shortly after Clyde Davis came to the *News* staff in 1920 he was joined by almost the entire staff of the student newspaper, *The Silver and Gold*, at the University of Colorado: Gene Lindberg, Deane A. Dickason, Harvey Sethman, "Doc" Joe Markey, Sam Jackson, and Norman G. ("Shorty") Fuller. One other, Hal Borland, went east to the Associated Press. Today he is a much-admired nature essayist and novelist, and editorial writer for the New York *Times*.

The junior journalists had slipped a rowdy and ribald "scandal edition" of the student paper past the not too watchful eye of journalism professor Lee Casey and had been bounced from school. It no doubt amused the *News* editor to hire virtually the whole disgraced phalanx; schools of journalism were in low repute in those days. University faculties, it was widely held in city rooms, didn't know what was going on in the *practical* world, and moreover had no sense of humor when it came to boyish capers.

At the end of the academic year Casey resigned his faculty post in Boulder and returned to the *News*. He always said that his parting shot was: "You can't fire me; I resign." Clyde Davis writes:

> The memory of Lee Casey needs no additional eulogy from me, but in my fairly wide experience I remember him as the most brilliant conversationalist I have ever known. He bullied me into reading hundreds of books I needed to read. I think he liked me because I was a good audience, and he kept me up all night many's the night talking history —early Roman, American, French—with or without a bottle.
>
> When Lee became a columnist and editorial writer he occasionally felt too tired to produce and would implore me to help him out. I managed to imitate his style by throwing in a reference to Marcus Aurelius or Pliny the Younger now and then. But he was making a lot more money than I and this thing got to be an old story. I finally demanded $2 for an editorial and $5 for a column and got it, although he deplored my mercenary nature. One March night he came into the office very late and very tired and asked me to write an editorial on St.

Patrick's Day. I agreed for two bucks in advance, which he paid, and after the home edition was put to bed I went back in the morgue, looked up St. Patrick and boiled out a chunk of Celtic whimsy. A couple of days later Lee came up behind me and gave me a couple of thumbs in the ribs. "Congratulate me, Sure Shot," he said, and handed me a couple of pieces of paper clipped together. One was a note in pencil which read approximately, "Great work, Mike, old boy. You'll find a $5 raise on your check next week—Jim." That was James A. Stuart, current Shaffer editor, who did not please Lee by calling him "Mike, old boy." The other paper was a letter to Mr. Stuart from the Royal Order of Hibernians, giving extravagant praise to the St. Patrick editorial.

What education I have came largely from Lee and from Judge Beardshear.

Shaffer's resident editorial director in Denver from February 1921 to March 1923 was James Arthur Stuart, who had served the Muncie *Star* and gone on to the Indianapolis *Star* as city and news editor between 1905 and 1921. Stuart came west with a reputation as a high-class operator, and he earned both the affection and respect of his staff. He, in turn, remembers it as "the best staff any newspaper ever had." One of his notable achievements was to help his fellow Indiana University alumnus, Jesse Newlon, build up the Denver public schools from their post-World War I slump. The *Post* was hurrahing the taxpayers in a personal vendetta with schools Superintendent Newlon, who was labeled a tax-eater for wanting to build classrooms. Stuart threw the support of the *News-Times* to Newlon, and an eight-million-dollar bond issue was voted. Newlon later headed Columbia University's Teachers College.

When Stuart went back to Indianapolis in 1923 his admiring employees gave him a send-off with an acrostic:

> S is for Sympathy, winning you friends,
> T is our Trust that you'll gain all your ends,
> U, Understanding has brought you success,
> A is the Aims that your papers express,
> R is for Right which you prize more than gold,
> T is the Truth that you strive to uphold:
>
> So here is a wish from the News-Times to you,
> Happiness, health and prosperity too.

Stuart became managing editor of the Indianapolis *Star* and has been its editor since 1946.

Stuart's managing editor for the *News* was William C. Shanklin, and the frivolous Stanley K. Cochems had succeeded Frank Farrar in the opposite-number job for the day-side *Times*. Mary Coyle, Margaret Harvey, Helen Black, Mattie Durkee, and Helen C. Hine were among his newshens, and Eileen O'Connor was on the switchboard.

Clyde Davis was slot man—head of the copy desk; "slotterino," he calls the job—from 1923 to 1929. Two of his rim men had connections of note. Lionel Moise moved to the *News* from the Kansas City *Star*, where, it was asserted by all *Star* men, he had taught Ernest Hemingway the writing trade. Then there was John Edward Francis Scott Key Fitzgerald—cousin of F. Scott Fitzgerald—who, critics said, had remained untaught.

Frederic Babcock, now literary editor of the Chicago *Tribune*, viewed the parade of such talent from the *Post* side of the fence and looks back on the Denver of that era as "one of the best training grounds for newspaper work—if you could stand the headlong pace there you could get a job anywhere in the country." Babcock joined the *Post* staff in 1924 and soon became drama editor, with Betty Craig as his assistant. In the field of entertainment, he recalls that Denver was proud of her native sons Douglas Fairbanks and Paul Whiteman and gave its patronage liberally to the Denham Theater, where Gladys George played stock, and to the old wooden summer theater at Elitch's Gardens, where Edward G. Robinson, Harold Lloyd, Fredric March, and other famous actors got their start or labored to perfect their art.

Denver to Babcock was "the most hospitable of cities" and the hospitality was not reserved for actors and musicians. "Every celebrity, political or otherwise, who came to town had to show up at our Denver Press Club before filling his other engagements. And woe unto him who failed to answer the summons. The staff members of the *News*, *Times*, *Post* and *Express* fraternized freely, and we didn't look with favor on anybody who didn't recognize our importance in the scheme of things."

Some of Babcock's contemporaries and Press Club companions—Casey, Davis, Lewis, and others—rode out the insane period when the Ku Klux Klan reigned in Colorado. The organization came to Colorado in 1920 and within a few years claimed to have signed up thirty thousand night-shirted loons under the leadership of Grand Dragon John Galen Locke, a physician and big-game hunter who looked like a fat Mephistopheles. The Klansmen, puffing big CYANA (Catholics, You Are Not Americans) cigars, exerted influence beyond their numbers. In the election of 1924 they took over city and state, installed nominally Republican Governor Clarence J. Morley in the Statehouse, and nominally non-partisan Mayor Benjamin F. Stapleton in City Hall. They controlled the legislature, dictated appointments in the Denver police department. Ida Libert Uchill, historian of the Jews in Colorado, says that at one point the Klan controlled a majority of the judges of the Denver District Court. "One Jewish and one Catholic lawyer worked for the Klan . . . either of these two lawyers had to be hired by the Jews or Catholics in order to receive any form of just treatment by the judges."[14]

The Klan's rise in Colorado never has been satisfactorily explained.

[14]Uchill, op. cit., pp. 160–63.

Perhaps it is too soon for a dispassionate, non-libelous analysis. Some of the ex-kleagles still walk Denver streets in positions of influence, and one of the Klan's major political hatchet men, long a top official of the state GOP, died only recently. At any rate the "Kolorado Klavern" didn't have too much in common, so far as overt actions were concerned, with the Southern branch of the order. Its persecutions of minorities— Jews, Catholics, Negroes and, to a lesser extent, Spanish-Americans— were economic and social rather than physical. No lynchings ever were proved against the Klan—though it would have been difficult to do so, with police force, courts, and state officials enrolled or under domination. Fiery crosses were burned on top of Table Mountain and Ruby Hill, and one plan was laid to kidnap and castrate the independent and aggressive district attorney, Philip S. Van Cise. The operation was to be performed by a Klan surgeon under aseptic conditions but no anesthesia. Van Cise escaped by ramming his automobile into two pursuing machines.

Principally, however, the pleasant fellows bonded together in the Klan—many of them from the "better element"—seem to have been allied to line their own pockets, wield political control, and purge their mean little frustrations in orgies of "white supremacy." Then, of course, there was the social and cultural attraction of the women's fife and drum corps. Klansmen patronized a list of "approved" merchants and other businessmen on a reciprocal back-scratching basis, and boycotted the stores of Jews and Catholics.

The *News* shamefully climbed into bed with the Klan, though it did not endorse the hallucinations of its dogma. The *Post* took pot shots at targets of opportunity but was careful not to offend advertisers, many of whom were Klansmen or unwilling to buck the economically powerful group.

Only the small, budget-ridden Scripps-McRae *Express*—contemptuously referred to by the *Post* as "That Rooster on Mint Alley"—stood its ground. The *Express* fought the hooded nonsense with every bit of its not very robust strength, scolding, exposing, shaming, and satirizing. Its current editor was Sidney Whipple, a banty rooster fighter like his paper and later drama critic for the New York *World-Telegram*. His reporters dug out a roster of the Klan, heavy with important names, and the list of members was published in the *Express* for all the world to see. The exposed politicians and civic leaders could read their names from across the street. The *Express* recently had received a magazine of 18-point matrices for one of its Linotypes, and Whipple ordered the names set in the big type, eight columns wide. For its pains the *Express*, of course, was boycotted by advertisers, threatened, shot at from speeding automobiles, and boiled in oratory at "konklaves."

At the *News* the managing editor was an ardent white supremacist and a red-blooded Klansman, and the advertising department tried to walk on eggs. Many of the staff members laughed at the antics or were indifferent. A few were in bitter opposition. City editor Eddie Day, a Catholic, planted one of his reporters into the Klan in order to receive private intelligences and to keep track of what his boss was up to. When the head national goon of the KKK paid a state visit to Denver he and his henchmen cornered Harry Rhoads in a suite at the Brown Palace and in relays tried to sweat him into membership. Day had to call on friendly Irish cops to spring his photographer loose from the trap.

By 1926, however, the Klan madness had run its course, although the lunatic die-hards attempted to keep the idea alive with Locke's Minute Men of America and something called the Order of Equals. The *News* was able to shake off its unsavory associations and concentrate its attentions on holding off the *Post*.

Shaffer and his methods were no match for the red-meat eaters of Champa Street. At a distance it appears that the Chicago grain man was totally dazzled and bemused by the fancy footwork of Tammen and Bonfils. When they weren't clouting him behind the ear from an unexpected quarter they had bribed the referee to hit him with the water bucket or a ring post. And when direct action seemed superfluous they just bluffed the former Sunday school teacher out of his britches. It had started at the very beginning.

When Shaffer bought the *Republican* he found himself with two valuable morning Associated Press franchises. The *Post* owned an afternoon franchise but had no AP service for its Sunday morning edition. Tammen tried to get Shaffer to release his excess morning privileges, but even Clean John saw what that would mean and refused to sell. The *Post* thereupon began printing coupons with which an aroused citizenry could petition Champa Street to provide a "live and worthwhile morning paper." After a few weeks of this Tammen paid a call on Shaffer. Gene Fowler supplies the dialogue in *Timber Line*:

Tammen: "How about selling us the Sunday AP franchise?"

Shaffer: "Oh, no. Be sensible."

Tammen: "That's all I wanted to know. Well, then, we're going to start a morning paper next Monday."

Shaffer: "You are joking."

Tammen: "Come here, kid, and look out your window. I want you to see something I brought over."

In the street below was a *Post* truck filled with small bundles of paper.

Tammen: "John, that truck is full of coupons we have received from Denver people, each one duly signed, imploring us to start a morning *Post*. Joking, eh?"

Shaffer (thoughtfully): "If you *really* intend to start a morning paper, I, of course, can't afford to have you enter a field which I myself narrowed by scrapping the *Republican*."

Tammen: "We can't afford it either, kid, but we'll do it."

Shaffer: "Here's what I'll do. I'll *give* you the Sunday AP rights, if you'll call off your plan for a morning *Post.*"

Tammen: "Shake, kid. Now you're showing some sense."

Thus the *Post* acquired a franchise worth perhaps a hundred thousand dollars without laying out a cent, and Tammen went back to Champa Street chuckling. He and Bonfils had no intention of starting a morning paper at this time, and all but a few hundred of the coupons in the truck were blank sheets of newsprint cut up to proper size by *Post* clerks.

If it wasn't bluffs it was monkeys. To promote one of its stunts the *Post* turned loose a barrel of monkeys in the Statehouse. The simians climbed up inside the dome, unscrewed light bulbs, and peppered onlookers five floors below. It was a mess, but it made people talk about, and by some irrational mechanism subscribe to, the *Post.* A talented vaudevillian stood in front of the *Post* building with a fork in his mouth and caught a turnip thrown from the twelfth floor of the Foster Building across the street. This, too, enhanced circulation. The Big Brother, champion of all his siblings everywhere, arranged for the deportation of an Italian peanut vendor in City Park who gave short weight to children and thereby touched Bon's tender heart.

And so it went, from bad to worse for the *News* and from big to bolder for the *Post.* There seemed to be no answer to the riddle, and the *News* took a licking.

Jake ("Humpy") Sobule and John Levand, a pair of geniuses, were in charge of street circulation for the *Post.* They conceived the notion that their newsies were frail, undernourished, and in need of healthful recreation. A heavily publicized health program was set up for the boys to build their bodies and redeem them from juvenile delinquency. The humanitarians of the city applauded enthusiastically, and then it developed that the sole activity of the *Post* "health farm" was instruction in the manly art. As the boys completed their course and acquired the rudiments it was casually suggested to them that there seemed to be no logical reason why newsies for the *News* and *Times,* particularly if smaller in stature, should have the unfair advantage of good locations on downtown corners. The toned-up *Post* boys got the idea, and *News* vendors got bloody noses.

The *Post* didn't miss a bet.

At last the awed Shaffer threw up his hands and fell back on Chicago, tottering, bruised in purse and sensibilities. He sold the *News* and *Times,* and the aggressively expanding Scripps-Howard organization came to town to try its luck as challenger.

Shaffer went home to his mansion in Evanston, where he died at ninety on October 5, 1943. Denver, he must have reflected in his declining years, had not been ready for clean, educational, uplifting journalism.

CHAPTER NINETEEN

Born to Survive

ACTION, NOT PROMISES, IS POLICY
OF NEWS, SAYS ROY W. HOWARD

SO READ the headline on Saturday, November 27, 1926.
The best show in town the previous day had been a matinee performance at the Denver Chamber of Commerce. It commanded more interest, packed more drama than any hairbreadth, cliff-hanger serial then playing in the city's movie "palaces." Richard Dix was appearing in *The Quarterback*, and the Hall-Mills case was getting the banner lines. But the star Denver wanted to see and hear more about was Roy Wilson Howard. The mystery of the preacher and his choir leader diminished before the question of what was to become of the *Rocky Mountain News*. The town had been buzzing since Tuesday.

At noon on Friday three hundred of the city's leading businessmen crowded into the Chamber of Commerce luncheon room to hear what the aggressive, high-powered, and dapper man from New York would say.

The copyreader who later handled the story wrote a sour head. He could have done much better. Possibly he was working under wraps; there hadn't been opportunity yet to gauge the likes and dislikes of the new boss in the matter of headlines. So he played it with caution.

Actually Howard delivered a headline writer's dream of a speech. It was short, to the point, and left 'em laughing. The talk, Gene Fowler says, "was as sweet an uppercut as anyone had cheered since the days of Bob Fitzsimmons." Howard stood up, paid his respects to Chamber President Richard M. Crane, and let fly in staccato, rapid-fire bursts:

We're coming in here neither with a tin cup nor a lead pipe.

We will live with and in this community and not on or off it.

We are nobody's big brother, wayward sister, or poor relation.

You are probably not concerned with where we come from, but we can assure you that whenever we go back we will be welcome. [A chop at Bonfils' lack of popularity in Kansas City and various points in Oklahoma.]

The Rocky Mountain News, conceived in high ideals and public spiritedness, was born to be a survivor.

Our obligation to you is to give you newspapers that in news coverage, entertaining features and sound editorial policies are equal to any in the United States. . . .

We come here simply as news merchants. We're here to sell advertising and sell it at a rate profitable to business houses.

But first we must produce a newspaper with news appeal that will result in a circulation to make that advertising effective.

We will run no lottery. [Another dig, and fully appreciated.]

We seek no downfall of competition. We feel the field in Denver is favorable for clean competition of the sort that makes for news service of the highest type. . . .

We have sense of humor enough to know that a challenger never looks as good as a champion—before the fight.

Then he sat down. The room rocked with laughter and quivered in anticipation of the bloodletting. Howard couldn't have issued a bolder invitation to battle if he had stridden a couple of blocks down Champa Street and tossed a brick through the window of the Bucket of Blood. He knew exactly what he was doing, and the reaction was not long in coming.

The fresh turning point in the career of the *News* came on November 22, 1926. Preliminary negotiations had been a well-kept secret, but on that day Roy Howard, as chairman of the board of the Scripps-Howard Newspapers, and John C. Shaffer sat down in Denver and completed the deal. The purchase was announced next morning in the *News*, which said the price was "approximately $1,000,000," for which Scripps-Howard acquired both the *News* and the *Times*. The organization, its name changed from Scripps-McRae in 1923, already was publishing the Denver *Express*.

The consideration, in more precise figures, was $750,000—$300,000 in cash, $450,000 in assumed bonds. Correspondence between Roy Howard and W. W. Hawkins at the time indicates that the initial plan was to buy only the afternoon *Times*. Most Scripps-Howard papers, then and since, have been P.M. journals. But Shaffer wanted to get out of Denver, absolutely and forever, and he pressed for a package deal. He had tried to bargain with another purchaser at $1,200,000, but it was no sale.

Advertising linage indicates that Shaffer's two papers were grossing close to two million dollars a year in revenues, plus approximately half a million in annual circulation receipts, but he was taking no profit. The costs of scrapping with the *Post* were not small ones, and the moral exercise he was getting as conductor of a non-profit operation in clean journalism didn't balance off well against the personal vilification he was taking. He was anxious to sell. Howard met first with Shaffer in Chicago early in October, indicated a lukewarm interest, and made a tentative offer of $750,000 of which $250,000 would be cash and $500,000 in assumed obligations. Shaffer wrote October 14 proposing $300,000

cash plus the assumption of $600,000 of the $708,000 bonds outstanding. He pleaded that even this would leave him with a $250,000 loss
in the deal. Howard stuck to his $750,000 offer in a letter on October
20 but was willing to go to $300,000 cash. He argued that this was "a
rather high price to pay for the privilege of getting into a fight that is so
certain to be very expensive, very long drawn out and probably never
very profitable from a monetary standpoint." Shaffer gave his preliminary
agreement in a letter on November 6 and arrangements were made for
the November 22 meeting in Denver. He was squeaking through with
a net of $42,000 in his wallet. Perhaps he felt that, all things considered,
he was lucky to be getting out of Denver with a whole shirt.

In the preliminary planning for Scripps-Howard expansion in Denver
the *Rocky Mountain News* once again narrowly side-stepped extinction.

Robert Paine Scripps, third son of the founder, at this point was
editorial director of the organization and president of the E. W. Scripps
Company. He surveyed the Denver situation and made an acute report
to Howard in a letter dated September 28, 1926. It was he who suggested that the *Times* only be bought from Shaffer, or, as an alternative,
$300,000 be spent on the *Express* to promote it. The *Express* either
should be closed down or resuscitated. He wrote:

> The Express is the only newspaper outfit in town that has not been
> definitely and publicly connected with one or more scandalous financial
> and political deals. In other words we have a monopoly on whatever
> virtue may exist in the journalistic profession in Denver. But this is a
> foundation to build on and not a house anybody can live in.

Scripps recalled that sometime earlier there had been discussion of
the possibility of putting Carl Magee, the scrappy editor of the Albuquerque *Tribune* who had uncovered much of the Teapot Dome mess, or
"some other spectacular editor" in command of the *Express* to tear into
Bonfils with a personal fight. As an afterthought Scripps wrote Howard,
"I am of the opinion that there is nothing we could say, or prove, about
the Post or Bonfils that would especially interest the people of Denver.
There is nothing that would not be an old story to them. The only
way I think we can win in Denver is by putting out a really good and
adequate newspaper."

The total advertising and circulation gross of the *Express* then was
about $200,000 annually, but Bob Scripps had a loyalty to the paper
his father had started. He proposed a plan under which the *News* would
be reduced to a six-day paper and then, after about a year, be sold or
permitted to die. The two "lame ducks"—the *Express* and the *Times*—
would be put together, and their Sunday edition would replace that of
the *News*. Scripps examined Denver circulation records carefully and
shrewdly observed that the *Post*'s sales in the far corners of the West,

much heralded by the "League of Rocky Mountain States" (a *Post*-conceived *entente* which existed only in Bon's mind), actually was a liability to local retail advertisers. Subscribers in the Black Hills of South Dakota didn't do much for the merchant on Sixteenth Street except raise his advertising rates. The *Times* had 17,374 city and suburban subscribers and the *Express* 13,046 (out of total circulations of 24,521 and 14,533 respectively). Combining the two would give the *Express-Times* a local readership of 30,410, a figure which might be built up to challenge the *Post's* 82,672 local subscribers (out of 161,154 total). In any event the much higher percentage of locally concentrated circulation could be made a talking point for ad salesmen on their lonely rounds. Scripps thought it was worth a college try. Events failed to follow his blueprint, however, and of the four newspapers involved only the sinewy *News* and the blustering *Post* showed staying power.

When Shaffer and Howard got down to dollars in their bargaining Scripps gave his approval to the purchases, indicating that the top price he was willing to pay was $750,000, though he thought $500,000 a lot more reasonable.

The men who met in Denver November 22, 1926, to put their signa-tures to the deal had known each other slightly for a long time. Roy Howard grew up in Indianapolis, and from 1903 to 1905 he had been sports editor for the Indianapolis *Star*.[1] This, however, was before Shaffer owned the *Star*.

There cannot have been much community of interest at the bargaining table that November day. Shaffer, at seventy-three, was retiring from the battle, beaten. He hadn't been really interested in newspapers any-way; he was a financier, a highly successful speculator, and the press was merely an auxiliary cog in his power complex. To the young man on the other side of the table news and newspapers were everything. Howard, at forty-three, was filled with the expansive self-confidence of a man who is on his way to the top and knows it. The first impression he left on his new Denver employees was that of a man so loaded with energy and optimism that he couldn't sit still; he seemed to fidget, to skitter when he walked.

Howard's previous ten days had been busy ones. In addition to the *News* and *Times*, he bought in that period the Memphis *News-Scimitar* and the Knoxville *Sentinel*. The Memphis paper had been merged with the Scripps-Howard *Press* there, and the *Sentinel* with the Knoxville *News*, also a prior member of the Scripps group. With the purchase of the *News-Times* the organization now stood at twenty-five daily news-papers, the largest string in the country, and it was purposefully and self-consciously at spring tide. Before the next year was out Howard would invade New York City by acquiring the *Telegram*.

[1] John H. Sorrells, *A Handbook of Scripps Howard* (Memphis, 1948), pp. 72–80.

In Denver, the *News* announced on November 23, the *Times* and the *Express*, both afternoon papers, would be merged to form the Denver *Evening News*, appearing nightly six days a week. The venerable *News* would continue as a morning paper, daily and Sunday.

John Shaffer's final statement, published on page one beneath the announcement of the purchase and merger, hints the pathos of a wealthy father's vanished hopes for a dead son. "When I purchased the News and Times," he wrote, "my son, Mr. Kent Shaffer, lived here and was in reasonably good health, and it was my intention to give the papers to him so that he would eventually come into possession of the property and management." But Kent Shaffer died, and "hence there is no one in my family that desires to own and operate the papers." Then Shaffer bestowed his blessing on Roy Howard and quit the field.

On the editorial page the new management declared itself further under the heading, "Denver's Newspaper Merger—The Meaning":

> In a newspaper sense, Denver is unique.
> For years this great city has been marked journalistically by one large and three comparatively small daily publications. The trend has been more and more toward a monopoly by the largest, the Denver Post, published by F. G. Bonfils. . . .
> That trend has threatened Denver for some time with a newspaper dictatorship. Such a situation is attributable to a number of causes.
> First, the very agile and very adroit publishing ability of F. G. Bonfils, who, by one means or another, has been able to force his newspaper ahead in a divided field.
> Second, an over-crowded competitive condition that has made possible the growth of one newspaper at the expense of the others. That condition could be corrected by only one process—a merger such as that which has now been brought about.
> We believe that a dictatorship of Denver's newspaper field by the Denver Post would be nothing less than a blight, and we believe, furthermore, that because of recent developments the time is ripe for challenging that dictatorship. Hence the merger and the pledge that the resources of the Scripps-Howard organization are behind this move to correct what we consider a sinister journalistic situation. . . .
> The Scripps-Howard organization is prepared to spend whatever is required. It knows the price and is ready to pay it.
> IT IS HERE TO STAY. . . .

The editorial went on to promise the city a day-by-day betterment in the quality of the twins soon to become known as "the NEWSpapers."

In a signed editorial on November 24 the erudite Scot, James H. MacLennan, recently honored with a doctorship of letters by the University of Colorado, gave a generous and graceful farewell to the former owner. Shaffer, he wrote, had been a net gain for the city and state with his "high ideals" and the "religious atmosphere" that "pervaded his editorial policies." But the new owners, MacLennan asserted, would lead the citizenry

OUT OF BONDAGE

The people of Denver today may be likened to the children of Israel escaping from the bondage of the Egyptian, and the people of this city have before them now "the pillar of a cloud by day and a pillar of fire by night" to guide them and protect them; and they know not that they are safe in their goings and comings and there is nothing for them to be afraid of so long as they walk uprightly before God and man. . . .

Editor & Publisher, the trade journal, was of approximately the same opinion though somewhat less biblical in overtone. "War is on at Denver," *E&P* said December 4.

. . . Denver long has been represented as living under the cloud of contemptible journalism. . . . These stories [about Bonfils and his *Post*] have been used to justify practically every assault that has been made upon the honor of the American press. The shame and humiliation of them has become a part of the consciousness of every sincere journalist. . . .

It was a holy crusade out there in the West to cleanse the souls of conscientious journalists everywhere, and the trade journal was betting its money on Scripps and Howard. It predicted a "short and sanguinary" war and a "new deal for the community."

The *News,* modesty aside, republished the *Editor & Publisher* comments on December 10, and throughout the week following the purchase it, too, had hammered at the theme of a new era for Denver. On November 25 there was a page-one cartoon by James Lynch showing "Father Denver" serving up a roast turkey labeled "Clean Constructive Journalism." Shaffer had promised much the same thing thirteen years earlier, but this time there was a difference: the new owners had come to town expecting and ready for a knock-down, drag-out brawl.

Next day there was a full-page house ad heralding "A New Deal in Denver" and reprinting an *Evening News* editorial which had reviewed the paper's proud history and pointed with pride to "An Unbroken Tradition." Nearby was a coupon which subscribers could clip and send in to get the evening paper at forty cents a month, evening with Sunday for sixty cents, or the morning and Sunday for seventy cents. "WATCH US GROW!" was the tag line on the ad.

The editions of Sunday, November 28, reprinted the original editorial statement, and there was another cartoon by Lynch. This time it was a robed woman tagged "Independent Press." The lady was armed vigilantly with a naked sword, "Facts," but in the background appeared a handsome rainbow across which streamed "The Rocky Mountain News . . . The Denver Evening News . . . Scripps-Howard Merger" in promise of a better world to be. Page eight was given over to a biography and large picture of E. W. Scripps surrounded by columns of "What Other Colorado Newspapers Think of Merger." A typically bellicose comment came from the crusty Boulder *Daily Camera*, which never wasted any affection on Bonfils:

> . . . Remains to be seen if the Scripps-Howard syndicate can revive The News. . . . We hope the new owners will win. God knows Colorado needs a newspaper at the capital.

On the facing page an eight-column line, "Scripps-Howard a Romance of American Journalism," appeared over an article which sought to explain what kind of an outfit this was that moved with such reckless self-confidence into the dragon's lair. Photos of Roy Howard and other Scripps-Howard and *News* officials illustrated the article. Shown were G. B. ("Deac") Parker, Scripps-Howard editorial director; William G. Chandler, then head of the Ohio group of Scripps papers; Thomas L. Sidlo, Scripps' Cleveland attorney, who had helped close the deal; L. E. Judd, editor of the Akron, Ohio, *Times-Express*; Tom Dowling, circulation director for the organization; R. E. ("Josh") Wilson, who had edited the Denver *Express* in its last days; James H. MacLennan, editorial writer for the *News*; E. C. Day, assistant managing editor of the *News-Times*; George Sanford Holmes, *News-Times* managing editor; Walden E. Sweet, the crack reporter who had been managing editor of the *Express*; and a young Lee Taylor Casey, listed as *Times* editorial writer.

This was a part of the task force being assembled to engage the *Post*. Even more fire power would be added as the days and weeks advanced.

Several factors combined to make a fight in Denver seem like a good idea at the time. In the first place Scripps-Howard was in a period of major expansion. New papers were being founded or purchased, and soon the organization would be functioning from the Atlantic to the Pacific, Ohio to Alabama, a strong force in American journalism. A buoyant spirit of vital growth and high destiny hummed in the ranks. New worlds were in flux, and worlds were made for conquest. "Raise your sights!" was the going phrase. Moreover Denver appeared to be a likely spot for one of the expansion moves because of the experience with the local situation well earned over the years in keeping the *Express* afloat against devastating odds. This would be no sally by strangers into the dark alleys of a far city; nobody was green, and no one had the slightest expectation that Bonfils would roll over and play dead.

Another factor lay in the United Press. The wire service also was growing, and Howard wanted to establish its dominance. Aside from Albuquerque, Denver was the only active spot in the West linked to the UP network. A strong newspaper was needed in Denver to back up UP's efforts to cover a large, remote, but often newsworthy region where nearly all the local newspapers were members of the rival Associated Press. The UP was Howard's baby. He had sired it in 1907 when he was a twenty-four-year-old stripling and his only material interest a single ten-dollar share of common stock.[2] And he had built it, Louis M. Lyons has written, in his own image: "fast, enterprising, ingenious, dramatic, innovating."[3] The United Press had a world to win in Denver too.

"The UP was not established to be a second-class AP," Howard says. "I hoped to produce what I had wanted when I was a telegraph editor: a service which would be as human, vital and pulsating as a good local newspaper. We wanted to cover, not the routine and the cut-and-dried, but to get at the individual involved in an event and his motivations, often more interesting than the event itself. Our aim was to concentrate on personality and motivations. The more the AP clucked, the more we scratched. I also wanted a great international press association to tell the U.S. story throughout the world. It then was being told very poorly abroad by means of rewrites in the more or less official services such as Reuters and Havas."

The very practical matter of improving UP coverage was part of it, but an element of high-minded, crusading zeal also went into the decision to buy the *News-Times*. E. W. Scripps had died only a few months earlier, in March, on his yacht off the Liberian coast, and he bequeathed to his newspapers a bold and vigorous liberal tradition of iconoclasm, equality of opportunity, and political independence. His heretical notions about the dignity of the workingman and the rights of union labor were very much in the minds of leaders of the organization in the autumn of 1926. The same heritage, a decade later, would put Scripps-Howard in the forefront of the fight for Franklin D. Roosevelt and the early New Deal. Reminiscing with friends recently, Howard recalled that he and his top-level associates were disturbed and worried by the "bitter reaction" which seized American political and economic thinking during the lush regime of Calvin Coolidge. The country, it seemed to them, needed more papers of courage and integrity that could raise hell constructively in the Scrippsian fashion. Howard ran his finger down a directory of newspapers and stopped at Denver. *There* was a vital and growing city, capital of the burgeoning West, in which a

[2]The fifty-year history of the United Press is told by Joe Alex Morris in *Deadline Every Minute* (New York, 1957).

[3]*New York Times Book Review*, Nov. 10, 1957.

Scripps burr under the saddle seemed calculated to produce beneficial results for all concerned.

Howard puts it this way:

"Why Denver? Well, in the first place the Coolidge administration was on. Scripps-Howard was proud of its liberalism. The economy was on the upgrade, and we couldn't get anyone interested in liberal politics. Bob Scripps and I got the idea that the firm had expanded and was a success and that everyone seemed to be interested only in making money. We felt we owed it to ourselves and the memory of the old man and our position in journalism to make a fight for what we believed in.

"The Shaffer papers were in no sense progressive. They were old-line Black Republican with a Mark Hanna philosophy—and Shaffer had as much business tackling Bon and Tam as I Jim Jeffries.

"In a moment of weakness or aberration, I went through the list for the toughest city spot where there would be an opportunity for Scripps-Howard journalism, a place to justify our existence. My success in finding the toughest spot was phenomenal. At any rate, we decided Denver was an ideal place to demonstrate our tradition by making an expenditure in the public service. We had intended a reasonably generous contribution. We got much more than we bargained for."

Like the News itself, Scripps-Howard carried with it an inheritance of toughness and durability, a disposition to challenge the status quo, and a well-earned good name. In neither case was the character casually acquired. The News had earned its reputation by long and faithful service and by enduring multiple disasters, including Bonfils and Tammen. That of Scripps-Howard rested on the foundation of a powerful and compelling personality.

Edward Wyllis Scripps was born June 18, 1854, at Rushville, Illinois, the thirteenth child of an emigrant English bookbinder. He grew up on his father's farm there, a strange and special sort of boy whose acute rationalizations foreshadowed the man. Ritually, farm boys have many chores, but young Scripps would sit in a fence corner reading books and bossing other youths he employed to do his work. The neighbors called him lazy. He regarded himself, then and always, as a realist. Why should he spend his time and energies on labor when he could employ others to do the work, take a profit on the management, and free his hours for the matters of intellect and spirit which were his main concern? To him this was not a Tom Sawyer brand of canniness or trickery but only a sensible, intelligent ordering of human existence. His family was not well to do, and it had required planning and thrift to accumulate the capital which permitted him to employ labor rather than expend it. The executive urge sprouted early and went on to full flower. Yet Scripps never was the idle and patrician overseer. He drove himself mercilessly, and twice during his lifetime worked himself into physical breakdowns by long hours, close attention to multitudinous detail, and a consuming ambition which he never was able fully to justify in his own philosophically inclined mind.

E.W., as he was always called, broke into the newspaper business at eighteen as a six-dollar-a-week collector for the Detroit *News*, founded by his older brother, James E. The family sank every penny it had into the paper, and gradually it began to prosper. E.W. worked his way up to city editor but he wasn't happy. He wanted independence, and he was constitutionally, emotionally, and in every other way unsuited for the role of employee. So with $10,000 capital he set up in business for himself in Cleveland. On November 2, 1878, the first number of his *Penny Press* appeared.[4] (The "Penny" was dropped from the name November 10, 1884.)

There were several things distinctive about the *Penny Press*. In the first place it sold for half the price of its competitors, and there were only two other one-cent papers in the country, the New York *Daily News* and the Chicago *Daily News*. Secondly, it was for the laboring man, full-faced and stridently, at a time when most employers took better care of their draft horses than their workers. Then, to top it all, the *Press* was independent politically. Nearly every other paper in the nation was a party organ, wholly committed one way or the other, hewing to the line through bad candidates or sour issues. Scripps declared in his first issue:

> We have no politics, that is, in the sense of the word as commonly used. We are not Republican, not Democrat, not Greenback, and not Prohibitionist. We simply intend to support good men and condemn bad ones, support good measures and condemn bad ones, no matter what party they belong to. We shall tell no lies about persons or policies for love, malice, or money. It is no part of a *news*paper's business to array itself on the side of this or that party, or fight, lie, or wrangle for it. The newspaper should simply present all the facts the editor is capable of obtaining concerning men and measures before the bar of the public and then, after having discharged its duty as a witness, be satisfied to leave the jury in the case—the public—to find the verdict. . . .

Against all contrary predictions, the *Press* made its way. Once it did, Scripps lost interest. He spent a lifetime, and amassed a fortune, managing successful newspaper properties by remote control and devoting most of his energy to attempts at squeezing shoestring operations into success by forcing them to turn a profit. Scripps played the percentages, and he had a couple favorite ones. His papers were always edited for the ninety-five per cent of the population that lived on wages and sweat. The rich five per cent could expect nothing from him. The second percentile maxim was equally hard-nosed: each dollar of invest-

[4]Dick McLaughlin, *From Humble Beginnings* . . . (Cleveland, 1953), pp. 4ff.

ment was to yield fifteen cents annually in net profit. A new newspaper was given a modest capitalization, a minimum of equipment, frequently secondhand, and pushed off the dock to sink or swim. By the time its first anniversary rolled around the journal was expected to be in the black, or to shave operating expenses until it was. It was Scripps' theory that a newspaper enterprise should be starved into making money, and that, once the fifteen per cent return was made, anything extra could be plowed back into the business for expansion.

Scripps enjoyed picturing himself as a skinflint. But he constantly exhorted employees to organize themselves into unions and bargain with him, or any other employer, for higher pay and better working conditions. At one point the business manager of a Scripps paper discovered that a young circulation employee had tapped the till for four thousand dollars. The manager proudly wired E.W. that the sum had been made good by taking a mortgage on the home of the boy's mother. Scripps fired a telegram back: "You will not prosecute. You will at once cancel mortgage. You will put $4000 loss in your profit and loss statement, due to damned poor management."

From Cleveland, Scripps branched out to the St. Louis *Chronicle*, the Cincinnati *Post*, and thence to a total of forty-four daily newspapers scattered over the map of America. It is said this was more newspapers than any other man before or since has founded, purchased, or controlled. Milton A. McRae became his partner, and the chain of papers took the name of the Scripps-McRae League in 1889. The League founded the two Colorado Scripps papers, the Denver *Express* and the Pueblo *Sun*. The latter was one of the unfortunates that never learned to swim. In 1920, Roy W. Howard was made chairman of the board of the Scripps-McRae organization at the direct order of E.W. Soon thereafter the name was switched to Scripps-Howard. E.W. by now had retired from active management, and his son Robert P. took over as editorial director.

E.W. set down three paramount rules for his newspapers: that they must make a profit, that they must champion the workingman, and—though he was not notably or formally a religious man—that they should obey the Ten Commandments. There were elaborations, of course, and personal "disquisitions" on policy to the editors, but these were the fundamental precepts.

Despite his insistence on profit making, Scripps was interested primarily in the editorial policies, rather than the business affairs, of his papers. He felt, indeed, that an editorial position favorable to and supported by his ninety-five per cent was the *only* route to financial success. Thus he established a policy, still in effect in the Scripps-Howard organization, which makes the editor of any paper the superior of the business manager and final authority on any disputed issue. It was, he said, the "etiquette" of Scripps papers that an approach to the editorial department should never be made through the advertising office. Scripps editors also were assigned the responsibility of censoring their advertising columns. All of these accomplishments, individually and in bulk, served to strengthen and advance the position of a free and independent press.

In another way, too, Scripps' cranky individualism and distant control freed the hand of his own and competing editors in cities across the land. Scripps spent most of his time on his Miramar estate outside San Diego, where he was inaccessible to pressures and impervious to callers who might slip through the gates with subornation on their busy minds. On his own papers he conferred freedom from the designs of local politicians, editing advertisers, and "the interests." Where one paper was free it became more difficult to whipsaw the others.

In addition to newspapers Scripps also established supply lines to sustain them. He laid the groundwork for the United Press, which provided a source of national and international news for papers shut out by the then cozy and exclusive policies of the Associated Press. The first great daily newspaper feature service, the Newspaper Enterprise Association, was a Scripps creation in 1902. His own lifetime interest in science led in 1920 to the establishment and endowment of Science Service, the initial sustained effort at expert reporting of scientific news.

Outside the field of journalism Scripps' scientific bent led him to establish and finance, with his older sister Ellen, the Scripps Institution of Oceanography of the University of California, and the Scripps Foundation for Population Research at Miami University in Ohio.

Probably Scripps was a genius. Certainly he was a glorious old Tartar, one of the giants of his era. In nearly every respect he was an extraordinary man, and it must have been difficult, at least, to work or live with him as associate or employee. His ferocious individualism and unorthodox methods brought him great wealth. This permitted him to cultivate his will, which was strong, and his eccentricities, which were numerous. Like many another vital and highly energized man, E.W. regarded all those who were not geared up to his ratio as lazy, stupid, or perverse. He was egotistical—with gnawing self-doubts, frankly confessed to. His specialty was the achieving of goals—only to question, in the end, whether they were what he really wanted.

A voracious reader, Scripps sampled the full range of literature from theology to demography, and his restless mind was stocked with an eclectic knowledge which made it possible for him to converse freely and to the point with lawyers and scientists, sculptors and muckrakers. Emotionally, he was sympathetic; intellectually, a logician and cynic. He shunned the limelight and was so little known that he gleefully recalled many occasions on which his partner McRae was publicly recognized as Mr. Scripps. He had no taste for the social pleasures, the attitudes, or the company of other rich men. He wore rough clothes, boots, and a little black skullcap much like a rabbi's. Cigar ashes dribbled on his vest, and his language often was vehemently inelegant. He enjoyed horses and yachts, and owned a number of each. For the last four years of his life his 180-foot motor yacht *Ohio* was his home. He died aboard the *Ohio* off Monrovia on the night of March 12, 1926, after a dinner and good conversation over cigars in the shipboard library. He was just short of his seventy-second birthday. The last order he left was that he be buried at sea.[5]

Despite parental pressures Bob Scripps never really wanted to become a newspaper executive. As a young man in his late teens he pictured himself as a writer and essayist on literary, intellectual, and aesthetic levels, and a poet. He even published one small volume of his poems. He was a friend of Jack London and other California writers of his time, and his father encouraged him in the literary life. At the same time E.W. was a frank critic: the verses were pretty puny, he wrote, and the output was too small. Bob wasn't sticking with it intensely enough. Get to work, the father advised; find yourself. Stop playing the dilettante. The son was sensitive, generous, sympathetic, and for a time called himself a socialist. One of his poems is entitled "Song of a Soil Slave." He tried the newspaper business from both within and without the Scripps concern, and he sampled other occupations, including rough-necking in the California oil fields, where all of his pay for one season went to help out a fellow worker who had broken his leg in an accident. Bob was still in his teens, and his father was constantly prodding him, demanding that he hurry up and mature, settle down and come into the business. In his very early twenties the son began to take hold, under-studying his father at Miramar. When World War I brought E.W. out of retirement Bob went with him to Washington and at twenty-one was made editor in chief of the Scripps papers. E.W. retired again in 1922 and turned over the controlling interest in his newspaper empire to Bob.

Those who knew Bob Scripps always speak first of him as a thorough-going gentleman, altruistic, soft-spoken, kindly. He was "generous to a fault," Roy Howard says, and "couldn't tell a lie if he wanted to." Bill Chandler speaks of him as "a big man in personality" with "marvelous patience and restraint." He reposed great confidence in his associates and employees, Chandler says, and "never butted in." He "carried to the limit the putting of responsibility on local managers, and he had a great ability to size up men and properties." Bob Scripps was the planner and student, gave few orders, and made little show of his authority. His principal exercise of power was in the appointment of editors. He visited the *News* plant in Denver many times, but always without throwing his weight around. He was a family man, lived simply, and remembered first names. Bob was a big man, over six feet and burly, and he walked with a slightly hunched, rolling ease. Like his father, he died at sea, sailing a ketch in Matamoros Bay in March of 1938. He is buried at

[5]For a full-scale biography see Negley D. Cochran, *E. W. Scripps* (New York, 1933).

Miramar among the eucalyptus trees he helped plant as a boy.

On the foundation E.W. laid down, and with the quiet support of Bob Scripps in the background, Roy Howard built monuments to the founder's vision and his own unflagging industry and dedication. But the metaphor is not really an apt one. Nothing about Roy Howard's dazzling career has been stolid or heavy with immobility, and he erects no showy pillars to his own or anyone else's vanity. The key words are energy, action, and dash. The equilibrium is not that of mass at heavy rest but of force in sustained motion.

Roy Howard was born January 1, 1883, in Gano, Ohio, and grew up in Indianapolis. He went to work early to support his widowed mother. He ran dancing classes in high school to help out, and as high school correspondent for the Indianapolis *News* he earned as much as thirty-five dollars a week at space rates. His bosses counted the days until his graduation so they could promote him to full-time reporter at eight dollars. He augmented his income by secretly carrying three paper routes. The young Roy, who had wanted to be a surgeon, was loaded with drive, brass, and impatience with oldsters who already were getting in his way. Within a few months he was sports editor of the Indianapolis *Star*, and before he was twenty-three he was holding down the assistant telegraph editor's slot on the St. Louis *Post-Dispatch*. He quit when he was passed over for promotion in favor of a man of thirty.

"They've just appointed an old crock with a beard to the job I should have had," he wrote a friend, Ray Long, managing editor of Scripps' Cincinnati *Post*. "Do you have a job for me?"[6]

Roy had taken a vacation in 1904 and gone to New York, where he tried to get on the staff of the *World* but was blocked at the reception desk. "If I had got by that receptionist," he mused recently, "I might today be reading copy on the *World* instead of being its editor." He went to the *Post-Dispatch* on January 1, 1905, and remembers O. K. Bovard as "probably the greatest city editor ever, but a cold son of a bitch." His telegram to Ray Long produced results, and he joined the Cincinnati *Post* as assistant managing editor, a position seldom granted to a youngster. But he was eager for the big time in New York. He persuaded the Scripps-McRae League that it needed a metropolitan correspondent and that he was the man for the job. He got it. When Publishers' Press was purchased by Scripps in 1906, Roy, who now had been eligible to vote for two full years, was made its manager. *He* made of *it* his first major achievement; for the hastily organized, makeshift Publishers' Press soon evolved into the world-wide United Press.

The Publishers' Press was flung together because Scripps and a few other newspaper titans in the afternoon field feared a news monopoly by the recently organized Associated Press, a membership organization

[6]Morris, op. cit., p. 24.

whose rules for admittance had many of the characteristics of an exclusive men's club. All the Scripps-McRae papers were afternoon sheets, and E.W. charged that the AP was discriminating against the P.M.s in favor of the big morning journals which had been instrumental in organizing the non-profit, co-operative news service. To break the monopoly Scripps merged the Publishers' Press with his own Scripps-McRae Press Association and an even smaller service linking his Pacific coast papers called the Scripps News Association. The new organization, named the United Press Associations, sent out its first telegraphic report on July 15, 1907, and the man in operating charge—at thirty-three dollars a week— was news manager Roy Howard. In the Scripps pattern, UP was a profit-making outfit. It would sell its news to all comers who had the price, and there were 369 of them on the first day.

As his life moved toward its close E.W. totted up scores and decided that his major contribution to American journalism had been the organization of United Press. He had forestalled monopoly control over the free flow of information. Any publisher—or anyone who wanted to start a new journal—had available to him a source of national and international news. He could not be silenced by the franchise system of the AP, which allotted one morning and one afternoon membership to each city.

Scripps' money and vision created United Press, but the man who built it to the point where it would realize aspirations—and yield revenues—was the terrier-busy Roy Howard. The physical size of the young news manager was no gauge of his ambition, capacities, or drive. Or his self-confidence. The story is told of Howard's first meeting with Scripps at the Miramar ranch. E.W. had several other visitors that day, by coincidence all of them small men, and Howard was kept waiting. Finally he was ushered into the presence.

"My God!" commented Scripps. "Another *little* one?"

Howard was undismayed and unawed. "Well, Mr. Scripps," he said, "perhaps another little one, but this time a *good* one."

Scripps eyed his visitor with new interest. "Hmm," he chuckled. "Well, for one thing, you'll never lick anybody's boots."[7]

Howard whipped the new organization into life, pushing, crowding, cutting corners, lashing himself equally with his skeleton crew of over-worked and underpaid reporters. Sometimes he personally would dictate bulletin stories directly to the telegraph operators. Typewriters were too slow for the pace at which he wanted UP to operate. By 1912, Howard was elected chairman of the board of directors. The following year he was made president.

From Miramar and his yacht Scripps was watching the rapid rise and the canny feats of the young man to whom he gave free rein and with

[7]Morris, op. cit., pp. 26–27.

whom he was almost never in direct communication. What he saw was convincing. In 1920, when the Scripps string of papers was reorganized, E.W. persuaded Howard to leave the presidency of United Press and become general manager of the Scripps-McRae League and assistant chairman of the board of the E. W. Scripps Company. The switch was not an easy one for Howard, even though the shape of the future was by now more or less apparent. The breakneck pace, the constant demands, and the instantaneous decisions of the United Press were the very zest of living to Howard, who throughout his long career has insisted upon regarding himself as a reporter rather than an executive. He wanted to be a writing reporter but somehow always wound up bossing the operation. He was promoted to board chairman only a few months after he joined the League.

Three years after Howard transferred primary allegiance from the Scripps news service to the Scripps papers themselves, his name was added to the masthead, E.W. retired, and Howard began a new life at forty as president and board chairman of the Scripps-Howard Newspapers. He turned over the chairmanship to William W. Hawkins in 1936 but continued as president until 1953, when his son Jack succeeded him. In the thirty years he built the organization into an operation which grossed $140,000,000 in 1952 from a press association and news picture service (United Press), three radio and three television stations, two newspaper syndicates (NEA and United Features), and nineteen newspapers with a total circulation of more than 4,000,000 copies daily. During 1925, the last full year of Scripps' life, receipts totaled $28,000,000. Howard not only discharged faithfully the trust E.W. placed in him but went on to build higher, farther, and more solidly than the founder had dreamed.

The public personality of Roy Howard has been a controversial one. His brash energies often tire and occasionally annoy both acquaintances and associates. His much-discussed reverence for budgets has served sometimes to wring dry and sap the morale of competent and loyal employees, but criticism of the Scripps-taught close-fistedness comes most freely, of course, from persons unburdened by the responsibility of maintaining financial health in a huge and high-cost economic complex. His policies, methods, and politics have been questioned and disputed, and giants are seldom without their detractors, but Howard's personal integrity is unchallenged, and there's no wishy-washiness. Once he has taken a stand no one is left with any doubts about what it is.

Strangely enough Howard's decisions are not overriding in the Scripps-Howard organization, although it would be odd indeed if they were not highly respected on their flat record of success. A large measure of autonomy exists for local editors. They ballot, for example, on which presidential candidate the organization will support, and they have a free hand in local endorsements. In the top echelon of the general management internal policies take shape out of free, and on occasion heated, discussion. Candor is a commodity freely dispensed but seldom received by high officialdom in any industry, yet Howard demands and gets it.

In fact some of the frankest evaluations of the man have come, not in a *New Yorker* profile or the columns of the *Guild Reporter*, but from a close friend and lieutenant of many years, John Sorrells, in the official *Handbook of Scripps-Howard:*

> . . . He is a complex personality, full of contradictions. He is considerate by nature, but will call important conferences for the end of the day when his associates are fagged; he forms quick and positive opinions, but will often put off making a decision. Roy is realistic, yet has an infinite capacity for rationalization; he is persuasive in argument, but is a soft touch for a salesman. He is skeptical and wary, but can be taken in by sheer charm; he forms instant likes and prejudices, but has little capacity for nursing a grudge.

> The keynote in Roy's temperament is action. In the vernacular of sports, his instinct is to get rid of the ball. Yet in Roy, action is harnessed to imagination: he can plan the course of his action and vision the end result . . . he likes to manage, and his administrative interests cover a wide range. He once took an associate to task for permitting his wife to endure the birth of a ten-pound baby; Roy thought his associate should have managed things to have a child of lesser weight.

> Roy will arrange your itinerary, secure you rooms, diagnose your ailment, show you how to bone a fish or pronounce the name of French cuisine, just as readily and as competently as he will analyze the fit of your jacket, edit your story or tell you what's wrong with your front page. . . .

> Roy is subject to a good deal of criticism by his close associates in the General Management. (This criticism is open and aboveboard with no holds barred—a characteristic of Scripps-Howard management and operation.) Some of them think he pays too close attention to detail, that he is overly impulsive. Roy usually pleads guilty to both indictments and by so doing saves a lot of argument. . . .

> Roy has an assertive and waspish manner that is frequently a trial to his associates, especially when he feels that his judgment is based upon personal experience or upon the record. . . .

> Roy is positive in his opinions, but generally accepts the majority view of his associates even when it conflicts with his own best judgment. But he always takes full responsibility for the result of any course of action, irrespective of whether he defers or prevails in council. He has no fondness for "I told you so." . . .

Howard has no fondness for personal publicity either. His infrequent public appearances have come in discharge of the obligations of his position or to achieve some serious purpose, usually involving the editorial ideals of journalism. But he does like to be where things are going on: that's where the news is. He likes to be known as a man who is in the center of the main stream. He makes no show of his means and has built no San Simeon, not even a Miramar. He once owned a yacht but gave it up. It was a purposeless waste of time and energy, and it kept him out of touch. Isolation is no boon to Howard; he has absolutely none of the recluse instincts Scripps had. His lifetime has been spent bucking the heaviest, most agitated currents he could find—and a deep reportorial instinct has led him straight to storm centers. He once was offered an ambassadorship, he is admitted to the privy councils of political kingmakers and, acting on a legitimate news break any reporter would have seized, he was the man responsible for the famous premature armistice of World War I on November 7, 1918.[8] Today Howard lives quietly and unostentatiously in Manhattan with his wife, the former Margaret Rohe, herself a newspaper and magazine writer before her marriage. He has passed on much of his control of the Scripps-Howard enterprises to younger men. Still the largest minority stockholder, he remains chairman of the executive committee and editor of the chain's New York link, the *World-Telegram and Sun*. He enjoys the prize fights occasionally but has no box at the opera.

Howard's sketch biographers[9] have passed over several items of personality which tend to humanize a figure usually presented as formidable and caught, a little breathless, between planes. One of these is the candor which Howard not only exercises liberally as his own birthright of free speech, a matter well documented by his detractors, but also insists upon from his professional intimates, a fact little known outside the top circles of the organization. He is not addressed in hushed tones of awe, and he has little respect for the man who does not speak his mind. A wholly inaccurate portrait of Howard sometimes has been offered, picturing a canny financier who tempers editorial policy to the ring of the cash register. Actually he is an extremely jealous guardian of the Scripps policy of editorial supremacy. Editors are in command. By official definition advertising is a by-product in the marketing of Scripps-Howard's wares; the major product is news and the newspaper itself.

The dress—polychromatic checked and striped shirts, flashy ties, and a dapper cut to suits and waistcoats—originally was a calculated experiment and since probably has become habit, certainly a trade mark. Roy once explained to a friend that he adopted the dress because he realized that his stature, slightly under average, would not attract much attention. "By God, I want people to know I'm around—you don't get in on things

[8]Howard has told the inside story of the mix-up in Webb Miller's *I Found No Peace* (New York, 1936), pp. 90–108.

[9]There is no full-length biography. Profiles are provided by Sorrells, pp. 72–80, Cochran, pp. 222–26, Morris, pp. 23–31, all previously cited; and by Forrest Davis in John E. Drewry, ed., *Post Biographies of Famous Journalists* (Univeristy of Georgia, 1942), pp. 167–86.

otherwise." Both he and his friend Ray Long, also a small man, bloomed out by design and almost simultaneously. Early pictures of them together show a dashing pair, leaning on sticks, wearing spats, boutonnieres, and their glasses on wide black ribbons. Later Howard was credited with being the man who inaugurated the vogue of the midnight-blue dinner jacket.

Howard is perfectly amiable about the snide comments his dress sometimes evokes. When he came to Denver in 1926 he was not well known by sight to the *News-Times* staff. George McIntyre, an *Evening News* reporter, took one critical look at the sartorial splendor of the stranger around the office and asked: "Who's the crapshooter?" Howard was near enough to overhear. A few days later he and McIntyre passed each other on the narrow stairway.

"Got time for a little craps?" Howard inquired.

Crapshooting—or something equivalent to it in terms of the newspaper business—must have been very much on Howard's mind when he moved into Denver in November of 1926. He knew the venture was going to cost him money. What he didn't realize at the time was how much and for how awfully long. Years later, when the red ink still was flowing, he confessed that "every time I hear the word Denver it gives me dyspepsia."

"Battle of the Century"

THE impress of two of the strongest personalities in American journalism now was brought to bear on the shaping character of the *Rocky Mountain News*. To the pioneering courage of Byers were added the underdog social philosophy and waste-not, want-not economics of Scripps. To the heritage of Loveland's new-era vision and Patterson's tenacious integrity came the propulsive force of the alert and purposeful Howard, reporter incarnate.

A pedigree of titans, surely. Yet somehow, somewhere along the way, the alignment of the genes went temporarily awry.

Possibly the mile-high altitude of Denver turned otherwise level heads light. Perhaps the Colorado air, universally asserted to be winelike in nature, was responsible. Or it could have been that vast magnetic storms on the surface of the sun disrupted from its implacable course the "isothermal zodiac and axis of intensity" which good old Governor Gilpin identified. According to the calculations of its discoverer, this all-powerful, destiny-molding axis passes exactly through the city of Denver, and it may be assumed, therefore, that any cosmic short circuit would yield profound derangements. Who can say the causes? Except that it was not midsummer and the moon was not full.

Whatever the reasons—and some of them, obviously, were not caprices —the *News* dived headlong and hooting into the wackiest slugging match since Punch and Judy. Denver was treated to two years of such fantastic newspaper competition as taxes the credulity of anyone who was not an eyewitness. Those who survived it called the contest the "Battle of the Century," and although a relative peace now has reigned for some thirty years the commotion on the Western frontier evoked an amazed interest so general that it is still talked about with chuckles and headshakes wherever newsmen gather in press clubs or corner bars to relive lustier days.

The din was earsplitting. Signal bombs rocked the downtown district. Brass bands paraded. An airplane swooped over the city at perilously low altitudes so that none should miss the benefits of periodic shrieks from an outsized siren mounted beneath the wing and capable of drowning the noise of the engine.

There was skulduggery in the night. Newspapers were systematically filched from the doorsteps of subscribers by agents, presumably dark-cloaked, who followed delivery boys on their nocturnal rounds. Advance information on what the other paper would attempt next was valued highly, and networks of espionage were woven. The *News* had a pipe line into the *Post* composing room along which flowed advance tips on forthcoming feature stories and promotions. The game of I Spy reached its climax when the hotel room used for strategic planning by *News* generals was bugged with a concealed microphone.

Generosity and premiums rained on the populace as manna from the heavens. If one became impatient with the calculated procrastinations of a serialized novel in the pages of the *Post,* the whole book could be obtained free with a subscription to the *News.* Once a week the "Peach" edition of the *News* was given away to everyone on the streets. For a time Denver automobilists could run their machines on largess. Free gasoline went with every want ad.

There were beauty queens, limerick contests, touring clubs, and flag-pole sitters. The *News* put one of the latter atop a post in front of the new business and advertising office opened in the Johnson Building at Seventeenth Street and Glenarm Place, around the corner from the Welton Street plant, although today it is not clear what kind of business the paper hoped to attract with such aerial shenanigans. Both papers staged elaborate World Series parties in the streets in front of their offices, loudspeakers blaring and huge electric boards visualizing the plays. Anything to keep the town stirred up. The goal, one of the survivors of the era has said, was to win a "gee whiz reaction" to each new edition.

Quite aside from the mad scramble of promotions and contests, the pace was a dizzying one for the news departments too. Cheap crime stories which today would not be published in either paper then were wrung dry through several days of new leads, new angles, spread dragnets, and underworld tips before finally dwindling away: "Police Baffled by Peanut Stand Holdup." Every hapless streetwalker became a "key figure" in "white slave ring" and mystery surrounded any slum suicide. On penalty of having their hearts cut out by meat-eating city editors, beat men were required to produce something on every story that would top what the opposition had printed. The hopped-up reporters played grimly at breakneck speed their sport of scoops, that family-circle recreation which newsmen pursue so earnestly to the total indifference or amused tolerance of everyone else. Ten minutes or less represented the margin between news and ancient history, although it may be questioned whether Denver's awed newspaper readers were aware that time had been telescoped or properly grateful for the enterprise which made it so. It was Chicago-style journalism straight out of *The Front Page,* but by the time Ben Hecht and Charles MacArthur got around to writing the play in 1928 Denver, if not Chicago, had quieted down somewhat.

In retrospect two features of the "battle of the century" stand out as prominently as a typographical error in an eight-column headline. First, it was an exceedingly costly contest for the two men who had to pay the bills. Secondly, it was entirely out of character for one of the adversaries.

The *Rocky Mountain News* had a tradition of proper newspapering behind it. Perhaps it had even been ponderous and deadly on occasion. Moreover the Scripps-Howard organization had built its expanding success on hardhitting, levelheaded reporting conservatively presented with a minimum of screaming heads and no giveaway gimmicks. That sort of journalism was being practiced in every other city where there were Scripps papers. Yet in Denver, of a sudden, all bets were off. Restraint was cast to the mountain breezes. Stunts on Champa Street were matched by bigger and better antics on Welton Street—Gresham's law of journalism in operation again—and the high jinks luxuriated. Top-ranking Scripps-Howard officials wise in experience and tested in capabilities converged on Denver from New York and Ohio, alighted from their trains in full possession of their wits, and then immediately began bolting down safety valves and stoking on the coal. Nothing was too expensive, or too fantastic, to be tried once.

The casual regard for money in large quantities was aberrant for *both* opponents. Down in the Red Room, Bonfils suffered acute spasms of grief when he consulted his balance sheets, and the Scripps-Howard organization was noted far and wide for close husbandry. By that true and tested route old E.W.'s original ten thousand dollars had been built into a vast newspaper empire, and the founder's lessons in thrift were not lost on his successor. Most of the papers in the chain were carefully managed, modestly profitable operations, and now they were called upon to support in profligacy a pair of scarlet sisters out in Denver. Other Scripps editors must have felt that mountain madness indeed had seized the organization.

Howard and Bonfils had had a chance, a few years earlier, to test each other's metal. In one respect the two men were alike: both were tough dealers, steady of nerve, and unflinching when the chips were down. Bonfils had tried to run a bluff and had been caught holding a bobtailed flush.

The *Post*, which boasted on page one above the masthead that it utilized every news service known to mortal man, was a subscriber to Roy Howard's growing United Press. Suddenly, in 1920, Bonfils ignored his contract, dropped the UP, and refused to pay his tithe. Monthly bills for the unused news went into the wastebasket. UP sued for violation of contract, and the court found for Bonfils. Two appeals were made to the Colorado Supreme Court, but each time the high court remanded the case back on technicalities. Howard decided to make a trip to Denver to see if personal bargaining could succeed where lawyers failed. He called on Bonfils in his office at 10 A.M. on July 4, 1920. A rehearing of the breach-of-contract suit was scheduled for the following Monday.

Howard remembers that he was admitted to the Red Room promptly but then was kept waiting for several minutes. Bon was reading a well-thumbed Bible. He ignored his caller with some deliberation while he finished reading the verse then engaging his meditations. Finally he looked up soulfully and brightened into a cordial greeting.

There was small talk, and Bon agreeably suggested that the two of them take a week off and go fishing in the hills. Be my guest. Howard said no, thanks, that his time was pre-empted, and now if they could just get down to brass tacks on the matter of the UP's due bills. The two publishers sparred for nearly an hour and made no progress. At length Roy ran out of patience.

"Okay, okay," he told Bonfils. "We'll just let the lawyers have another bout at it."

Thereupon Bon drew a folded piece of paper from his desk drawer and apologized:

"Awfully sorry to have to do this, but here's a summons for your appearance in court next Monday. I have been deputized to serve it on you."

"Great," Howard countered and reached for the paper. "I'd *really* like to see if the Colorado trout are biting, and this summons will justify my staying over. We'll go fishing over the weekend."

Bon rested his steel-blue eyes on his visitor, put the "summons" away, and reached for his checkbook.

"Bon always was Chesterfieldian, and never more so than that day," Howard says. "We came to an agreement in fifteen minutes."

The United Press also was involved in one of Howard's first maneuvers after he threw the challenge direct in his speech to the Denver Chamber of Commerce. He was proud of his news service, wanted to make it dominant and to prove that top-notch newspapers could be published using UP news exclusively. The NEWSpapers dropped their membership in the Associated Press with a flourish, and Howard reduced the value of the AP franchise on the books from two hundred thousand dollars to zero. Full-page ads appeared pointing to the triumphs scored by the nimble UP and denouncing the attempted "news monopoly" of the rival service. The UP could break the monopoly wide open and would prove it in the columns of the NEWSpapers.

Shaffer had made Tammen a present of a Sunday AP franchise. Now Bonfils, running his circus alone after Tam's death in 1924, had the gift of a morning franchise too. He used it promptly to carry through on the gulling Tammen had given the trusting John Shaffer. The *Morning Post* appeared January 3, 1927, with Bill Shanklin, late of the *News* staff, as managing editor. The battle was joined—around the clock.

The *Morning Post* said of itself: ". . . gladiator invincible, fearless, determined, with a giant's strength, a philosopher's mentality. . . . It will be the champion of every good, and pure, and noble, and holy, and righteous cause, and the faithful and unceasing defender of righteousness, justice, decency, law and order; it will be the opponent of every wrong and evil thing, of every form of crime, oppression, greed, selfishness and lawlessness. . . ."

The brash new magazine, *Time*, used a different set of descriptives in its issue of January 17: "Last week a loud noise was heard in the Rocky Mountains. . . . It was the new newspaper in Denver, the *Morning Post*. It had been started to drown out the *Rocky Mountain News* at the Rocky Mountain breakfast table. . . ." *Time* went on to record that during the fall gubernatorial campaign the *News* had called the *Post* "a blackmailing, blackguarding, nauseous sheet which stinks to high heaven and is the shame of newspapermen the world over." The *News* also had linked Bonfils' name with various pleasantries of word and phrase. *Time* catalogued them: "shame, disgrace, bandit, brigand, lawless, prostitution of the press, rapacity, bunco game, scaly monstrosity, mountebank, hybrid ogre."

The *Morning Post* urged Denver to consider its civic pride grievously affronted by the offhand way the NEWSpapers had quit the AP. It trumpeted: "This greatest city between the Missouri River and the Pacific Ocean, east and west, and from the north pole to the City of Mexico north and south in this longitude, has been belittled, humiliated and wantonly and willfully disgraced by the selfishly bringing about of the abandonment of the morning Associated Press service in Denver." But the new matutinal philosopher now would remedy *that*.

"What a time!" Clyde Brion Davis comments thirty years later. "Oh, my *God*, what a time!"

The first issue of the *Morning Post* contained a whopping fifty-two pages. But the grapevine had brought word uptown of the *Post's* intentions; the *News* saw the bet and raised. Welton Street got out sixty-eight pages the same morning. Veritable Leviathans for time and place. The newsprint mills of Canada signed on emergency crews and went into extra shifts.

The *News* characterized the *Morning Post* as a clumsy, snorting "Baby Elephant," pointed to its own even greater size, and added the tag line "The Newspaper Situation in Denver Has Changed Considerably in the Last 24 Hours." The slogan appeared regularly thereafter whenever the NEWSpapers landed a blow and could point to drawn blood. Jim Lynch cartooned the new arrival on page one as a lumbering, frightened pachyderm emerging from a circus tent. A ringmaster labeled "Bon" was cracking a whip. Blindfolded Justice was standing on the elephant's back juggling four cubes tagged "B-U-N-K."

The *Post* snapped back that the *News* was the "Wildcat of Welton Street." This suited the *News* forces just fine. If the contest was to take a zoological turn, what better symbol than a wildcat? The *News* staff members rather fancied themselves as lithe, sure-footed, and ferocious.

A defunct bobcat was obtained, mounted in a fierce and snarling pose, and placed on display for all the town to see. The lifelike artistry was the work of Jonas Brothers, Denver taxidermists to whom half America's big-game hunters ship their Kodiak bears and Bengal tigers for mounting as trophies, and their wildcat was a major triumph of symbolic aggressiveness.

The day the Baby Elephant appeared the *News* scored a pell-mell exclusive of high derring-do. No newspaper east of California had been able to offer its sports fans action pictures of the Rose Bowl game until many days after interest had died away. Max B. Cook, now aviation editor for the Scripps-Howard newspapers, determined to turn the trick for the *News* and thus dim the debut of the *Morning Post*. Cook then was promotion editor of the Cleveland *Press*, and he was one of the experts dispatched to Denver to help the NEWSpapers get started on their holy war. Cook made arrangements with the Los Angeles office of the Newspaper Enterprise Association. When Stanford and Alabama played to their memorable 7–7 tie on January 1 a fast car picked up negatives in Pasadena and sped them to Los Angeles for processing. The pictures were placed aboard the eastbound night flight of the fledgling United States air-mail service. All that night and most of the next day, Sunday, the little plane droned eastward. Denver had no direct air-mail service in those days; the high mountains immediately to the west were an impassable barrier. The slender coast-to-coast airway was routed by way of southern Wyoming over the same low saddle in the Continental Divide which served the Oregon pioneers, the California argonauts, and the Union Pacific Railroad. Nearest lighted airport to Denver was at Cheyenne, a hundred and ten miles north, and the plane was due there Sunday night. It landed an hour and a half early. A *News* squad was waiting to snatch the pictures.

At the wheel of a rakish Chrysler was Floyd Clymer, Denver motor enthusiast, former race driver, and today a noted historian of the horseless buggy era. With him were his adventurous wife, mechanic Louis Holt, Max Cook, and a bubbling young reporter, Jack Foster, Jr. Clymer raced for Denver at top speed in the dusk of a prairie winter day. Half the distance was rough with chuckholes, the other half sheeted with ice. Yet Clymer hit speeds up to eighty-five miles an hour and took the corners in wide skids. He set a new Cheyenne–Denver record: 109 minutes for 110 miles. The Rose Bowl photos made even the bulldog edition. The Baby Elephant had to make its bow with sports pages innocent of Rose Bowl pictures. Bitter blow!

Roy Howard remained in personal command in Denver for many weeks. Top officials, experts, and trouble shooters were brought in, and new blood from other Scripps papers to build up the staffs. An entire floor of the Cosmopolitan Hotel, one of Denver's finest, was taken over to house the high brass and provide conference rooms for their tactical sessions.

Harold Hall, later for many years business manager of the New York *Times* and at this time president of the Scripps-Howard Newspaper Supply Company, was placed in charge of the purse strings. He untied them and stretched the mouth of the bag wide. Each day for the next two years he would have to dig a little deeper. Along with Howard, Hall, and Cook, the top echelon included George B. Parker, Scripps-Howard editorial director from New York; Bill Chandler, later president of the Scripps-Howard Supply Company; and Jack Foster, Sr., managing editor of the Cleveland *Press* and the organization's top trouble shooter. A few weeks after the battle started Jack Foster, Jr., "Young Jack," surprised his father, "Old Jack," by turning up in Denver. A keen shaveling, eager for adventurous scoops, Young Jack had wangled a transfer from the Cleveland *Press*. A newspaper war in Denver promised action and glory and was not to be missed.

Chosen to edit the NEWSpapers was Edward T. Leech, a former Denver boy whose father had been superintendent of the United States Mint. As a youth Ed Leech carried papers for the *Times*, and he had been a cub on the old *Republican*. He moved over to the reportorial staff of the *Express* in 1912 at the age of twenty and was appointed its editor in 1916. After a season or two with the Scripps papers in Memphis he was sent to Birmingham, where he founded the *Post* for the organization in 1921. Later he became editor of the Pittsburgh *Press*. Mild-mannered, tenacious, and a true working editor, Leech's penchant for hard-hitting political campaigns and exposés got him thrown in jail both in Memphis, where he locked horns with the Crump machine, and in Birmingham. Denver police treated him somewhat more gently, though Bonfils roughed him up a bit—with the help of the police department. The *Morning Post* baldly demanded that the police and firemen get out and solicit subscriptions under threat of withdrawing its support of a pay raise then pending. The boys in blue dutifully punched doorbells for several weeks.

A. J. Gillis, who had been business manager of the *Express*, was appointed to the same position for the two NEWSpapers. Joseph L. Cauthorn, now president of the San Francisco *News*, was brought in to help out, and Harold Hall was in town for nearly six months overseeing the entire business and financial end of the hostilities. Fred Anderson, circulation manager of the San Francisco *News*, assisted in the frenetic drive for subscribers and street sales. Wilfrid C. Bussing, later business manager of the Evansville *Press*, was made advertising manager. Bussing also was an *Express* alumnus. He was later succeeded as *News* ad manager by M. F. Riblett.

As one who was on the scene and watched the build-up of forces, slot man Clyde Davis remembers it this way:

First came the staff of the little Denver *Express*, headed by Managing Editor Walden Sweet, who assumed he was to take over. But poor Walden failed to reckon with those master politicians Eddie Day and Lee Casey. Before he could find a place to hang his hat Walden was out on the street on general assignments. [Later Sweet went to the *Post*.]

Roy Howard himself was on hand at first and Deac Parker and Jack Foster. . . . Then there were the "Kokomo Boys." That's what we called them, although I doubt that any were actually from Kokomo. They were from places like Akron, Columbus and maybe French Lick and they had come to show us how to put out a newspaper.

Practically the first thing Scripps-Howard did on Welton Street was to throw the Associated Press franchise out the window. F. G. Bonfils caught it on the first bounce. . . .

It wasn't so bad for the *Evening News*. They had the United Press, even then a capable news-gathering agency. But the sole wire service left for the *Rocky Mountain News* was the United News, then the United Press night feature service with one puny Morse wire leading into Denver—eight hours of Morse wire for feature stories by Sam Love and others, market gossip, sports, bulletins, corrections, late news, everything.

It had been announced fairly definitely that our purpose now was to run the Denver *Post* out of town, and we began to put out a big, wide-open paper. When I say wide-open, I mean wide-open. We were a full-size, eight-column sheet then, and we started putting out 30 and 40 and even 50-page editions with nearly 200 columns of yawning news space.

The nightly wire report was completely ridiculous in those circumstances, filling no more than six or eight columns, and the big blond Kokomo Boy who was in charge until we got an official editor apparently hadn't the faintest idea of our problem or of what was going on. Happily, I have forgotten this Kokomo Boy's name. He'd come in late at night, ask to see carbons of the United News report, go through the tiny little stack and say blandly to me, "Nice report tonight, wasn't it?"

How were we filling that gigantic paper? Well, the local staffs, augmented by the boys and girls from the old *Express*, really pounded out copy, and for once in their lives their stories were allowed to run full length. Then, I was coming to work at noon or before, stopping at a newsstand to buy the bulldog editions of the St. Louis *Post-Dispatch*, Detroit *Free Press*, San Francisco *Chronicle* and other papers that had large staffs of correspondents, and I went through these sheets with scissors, avoiding copyrighted pieces and AP feature stories, but clipping them up and sending them to the composing room head to come. And by the time the night-side copyreaders began to drift in, there'd be proofs about the startling monster seen in the Irish Hills of Michigan and the interesting fact that the three-toed owl of New Zealand has three toes on each foot.

News of the Denver newspaper war attracted alleged newspaper people from everywhere, and we hired anyone who said he was a copy-reader. Most of them weren't, but some of them learned.

Unlike most of the Kokomo Boys, who just stood around mostly thinking up stupid questions to ask, Jack Foster *père* spotted the copy desk as the hottest corner of the shop and sat on the rim night after night, working a full shift. He, of course, was a real newspaperman, although he did post one notice on the bulletin board declaring that no reporter should write a sentence long enough to require a comma.

In the old days we had used the New York *Times* style book, and no doubt we were a bit stodgy in some respects. So, when I'd throw a head back to Mr. Foster and say, "Sorry, we have a rule that you can't end the first line with a preposition," he'd squint at me over his stogy and say, "That rule has just been repealed."

Young Jack Foster then was a sensitive adolescent who wrote a daily verse called "Drifting in Denver" and four or five columns of local copy. He wanted to take over the Sunday book page which I had been handling for several years, and I gladly let him have it. I did not tell him, however, that under the Shaffer management I was being paid five dollars a week extra for that chore. I continued to draw the weekly fin, and Jack had the fun.

Working conditions improved after a few weeks when Ed Leech was brought up from Birmingham and the Kokomo Boys went back to Kokomo. Leech was a real newspaperman even though he never had worked on a paper large enough to have a copy desk. At first he had a few curious ideas about the function of that institution. It took some argument over several weeks to convince him that copyreaders didn't need typewriters for head-writing.

Clyde Davis' attitude toward the "Kokomo Boys" reflects a haughty tradition of Denver journalism which dates back at least to Eugene Field's man who worked with Dana on the *Sun*. Denver newspapermen will fight bitterly among themselves and slit each other's throats gaily for a news beat, but they close ranks against imports, particularly outsiders who conceive their mission in Indian country to be educational. Having produced a rather impressive roster of big-timers, the Denver fourth estate doesn't take kindly to carpetbaggers. The fierce competitive situation which has existed for seventy-five years or more has made the city a prime training ground for young reporters and desk men, perhaps second only to Chicago, and while many Denver men have "gone east" to positions of prominence, very few adventurous souls moving in the opposite direction have made much of a splash in the Denver puddle. By and large Denver trains her own. Possessors of high-powered reputations are likely to find the mountain air chilly and the apprenticeship rough.

Forbes Parkhill tells in *The Wildest of the West* of the sad fate of a New Yorker, somewhat given to airs, who sought to make the grade as a Denver police reporter. The visiting expert dropped disparaging remarks about hick methods and proposed remedial measures. Irritation mounted. The semibasement pressroom at old City Hall had branch telephones connected directly to each paper but also a glassed-in public phone booth occasionally used for confidential conversations with bootleggers and girl friends. The New Yorker always used the booth, implying that every story he phoned in was a "beat." The coziness revolted his colleagues, and they ganged up on him.

"What happens when you big-shot New Yorkers get scooped?" one of them inquired innocently.

"Well," the visitor explained loftily, "competition in New York is mighty tough. You come back from an assignment with an exclusive or you don't come back."

"That so?" a local veteran replied. "Out here it's different. You've got to settle with the boys you've scooped. We're right touchy about such things. What kind of a gun do you pack?"

"Why, I've never found it necessary to carry firearms."

The Denver reporters drew pistols (borrowed from friendly cops) and put them beside their typewriters. "What was the name of that guy from the East who put one over on us last January?"

"Slips my mind," was the reply, "but you can find it on his headstone out at Riverside Cemetery."

The New Yorker paled a little but force of habit took him to the phone booth to give his next story to a rewrite man. His competitors rushed the booth and overturned it with him inside. As he crawled out of the broken glass the locals pulled their pistols and began shooting into the ceiling. (A bulwark of solid nineteenth-century masonry protected the mayor in his office directly overhead.) Parkhill, who was one of the locals, says the visiting journalist streaked for Union Station without stopping to collect his pay.

At the *News* the boys from Kokomo were followed a few years later by a delegation which promptly became known as the "Ohio Gang." None of the gang had much staying power. One of the more recent victims of the provincial hauteur was a blond young man named John Keats whose books, *The Crack in the Picture Window, Schools without Scholars,* and *The Insolent Chariots,* have given good accounts of themselves on best-seller lists. Keats came to the *News* from Washington shortly after World War II with an advance billing which did nothing to soften his reception. Worst suspicions were confirmed within a few weeks when the competent but undiplomatic Keats began proposing certain changes in methodology and dropping suggestions for improvement of policy. They may have been good suggestions, too, but unfortunately the air congealed around them. The isolation Keats suffered was brutal. He fell back on Washington with Rocky Mountain hoarfrost an inch deep on his shoulder blades. The tradition which frosted him is not defended; it is merely recorded.

Local journalistic heroes are less likely to be men who burned up the *Herald Trib* or the Philly *Record* than home-grown boys who have borne the heat of the day. Men like the *News'* associate editor, Robert L. Chase, who proved an indestructible city editor through several rounds of Kokomo visitations and Ohio Gangs. Lanky and dour, Chase's natural forte is the crepe-hung jeremiad combined with the question "Why?" and the demand "Prove it." He is much mellowed of late, but cubs who broke in under him can summon up a cold sweat on the hottest day by remembering the devastating, entirely unprofane monosyllables with which he greeted stupidity and blunders. Chase is, spare the phrase, a newspaperman's newspaperman, and he came by the palm honestly by way of a thorough knowledge of his city, an ability to pound into his subordinates what he had learned, and a faculty for keeping his head when everyone else is pacing the ceiling. "A solid character," Clyde Davis says of him.

Chase is one of two former members of the *Express* staff who have stood by the *News* through thin and thick to the present day. The other is Georgia Hanfelder, once the *Express'* bookkeeper and now cashier for the *News*. A third *Express* alumnus is Denver County Judge David Brofman, whose court sometimes appears in lists of legal superlatives as the largest single-judge county court in the country. Brofman was a police reporter for the *Express* until a circulation contest was held. He got subscriptions from so many cops that it was decided literature's loss should be commerce's gain and he was put in the circulation department. When the merger came Brofman went to the *Post* briefly as a police reporter but then returned to the *News* circulation department, studying law at night, until he was admitted to the bar in 1929. Arch Northway, who retired in 1958 as a circulation bookkeeper, also came from the *Express* to the *News* in the merger.

As 1926 ended, staffs for the NEWSpapers took shape in readiness for the heavy work ahead. The *Morning Post* now was out of the rumor stage, and a high degree of just-before-the-battle exhilaration tingled on Welton Street. Ed Leech arrived from Birmingham to take over the editorship. George Sanford Holmes became managing editor of the *Rocky Mountain News*, and Eddie Day took the same spot for the *Evening News*. Lee Casey was editorial writer for the evening paper. R. E. ("Josh") Wilson, who had been editor of the *Express* in its last days, became associate editor and editorial writer. James H. MacLennan continued to turn out editorials and a full page of esoteric dicta for the Sunday paper. Presiding over the night-side copy desk was Clyde Davis. Copyreaders of the time included George Burns, Lucius E. ("Hump") Humphrey, Frank Plumb, and Grey J. Tipton.

Charles E. Lounsbury, onetime *News* police reporter, was brought back from the *Post* and a side job as publicity manager for Universal Films to assist Max Cook as promotion editor. Within two years Lounsbury was managing editor and another three saw him in the editor's chair. Between them Cook and Lounsbury conjured up most of the stunts, hairbreadth adventures, and shrill war cries of the "gee whiz" years. If, at a distance, some of their antics now appear to have been touched with madness, they seemed the work of sheer genius at the time.

John P. Lewis was city editor for the morning paper. His counterpart on the afternoon side was Frank Farley. Mrs. Joseph Emerson Smith and Dorothy Knox shared the society editorships. Richard M. Scott handled the A.M. financial page, and Thomas H. Walker the state desk. Harry G. Baker laid out the paper as make-up editor. Among others riding desk jobs were Joe McMeel and the quiet, much-respected "Judge" Beardshear. The reportorial staff at various points in the hectic biennium included Bob Chase, Kaspar Monahan, Wallis M. Reef, Jack Carberry, Harvey Sethman, Gene Lindberg, Deane Dickason, Max Greedy, John Polly, Allen ("Big Fat Duck") Bartlett, Milus Gay, Loudon Kelly, Maurice ("Spider") Leckenby, Scott Hershey, George McIntyre, Gordon Porter, Gene Cervi, Alberta Pike, who won from grudging males the admission that she was one of the town's top newspapermen, and the future editor, "Young Jack" Foster.

Foster would have cast a long shadow ahead of himself—except that he was a skinny kid and moved too fast to cast a shadow of any kind. Indefatigable, then as now, one full shift was not enough to drain off his superabundant energies. He served on the staffs of *both* papers, turning up morning, noon, and midnight with reams of copy. He never was exactly sure which paper he was working for. Jack had grown up underfoot in the Cleveland *Press* city room, and he had been doing rewrite there when the prospects of a Donnybrook in Denver brought him west. He covered general assignments for the NEWSpapers, sat in on the rewrite desk, and wrote not one but two daily columns, both involving original poetry. His "The Water Hole" column appeared in the *Rocky Mountain News*, and "Drifting in Denver," an illustrated poem signed "J.F.," was a feature of the *Evening News*. He also handled the Sunday book page with Bill Beardshear as his most faithful reviewer. In his spare time Foster climbed mountains and cultivated friendships in Denver's Chinese colony. H. Allen Smith, then a cub on the *Post*, recalls that Foster was his opposition two years hand running in coverage of Cheyenne's famous Frontier Days rodeo. "We had a lot of fun together in Cheyenne, and now and then I even got out to the fairgrounds. Jack never missed a performance."

Smith left Denver in 1929 to win undying fame as "the screwball's Boswell" and the man who called J. P. Morgan "Toots" to his face, but he has bequeathed journalism some memoirs of his Denver days in *Low Man on a Totem Pole*. Bonfils, he remembers, "took a personal interest in me for a time and let me write many of the stories which appeared in his paper about Frederick G. Bonfils."

I came on duty at the paper at eight o'clock in the morning. Bonfils arrived ten minutes later. There ensued each day a little drama that I shall never forget. The men's toilet was across the big room from Bonfils' private office. It contained six booths, three on either side of the room. Bonfils decided one day to have the doors taken off these booths—then a man could sit down and talk with the man or men across the way.

Precisely at eight-thirty each morning it was his custom to emerge briskly from his private office and cross the floor to the men's room. It was always fun to watch the minor executives as soon as the clock reached eight twenty-five. One by one they would leave their desks and head for the can. Then at eight-thirty Bonfils would cross the room. There was always a scramble for five of the booths, but one of the center positions was left open for the boss.

He would enter and cry out, "Good morning!"

"Good morning, boss!"—from five booths. Then he would take his place, and production of the day's newspaper would be officially under way.

Smith knew "Josh" Wilson as a valiant who "drank straight alcohol out of a gallon glass jug and compelled me to read Plutarch. . . . I always considered it a fine compliment that he referred to me as 'the youngest old reprobate on earth.'" Smith records that when Wilson died later in Wichita he "evoked from Westbrook Pegler a eulogy that had not a single insult in it."

Most of the other giants of the day have also departed the scenes of their ponderous frolics and heroic smitings. Bob Chase remains, and Max Greedy, now news editor. The kindly, soft-spoken (but arousable) Greedy came to the *News* in January 1927, after seasoning on the *Post*, Pueblo *Chieftain*, Little Rock *Gazette*, and Los Angeles *Times*, and he has been there since except for a brief hiatus during which he was an official of the *Register* system of national Catholic newspapers published from Denver. He ran the gantlet from reporter and copyreader through city editor, slot man, and telegraph editor to his present position.

The evergreen Harry Rhoads, of course, is still on hand. During 1926–28 he and J. Winton Lemen formed the photographic staff for both papers. They worked shifts which circled the clock, were on call twenty-four hours a day seven days a week, but had the privilege of taking alternate Sundays off.

Kaspar Monahan left Denver to become drama editor of the Pittsburgh *Press*. For a quarter century or more Harvey Sethman has been lay executive of the Colorado Medical Society. John Polly has held executive positions on papers in Knoxville, Salt Lake City, and Long Beach, California. Loudon Kelly is with the Denver bureau of the AP. Like John Lewis, "Spider" Leckenby has won nirvana as editor of his own weekly newspaper, the Steamboat Springs, Colorado, *Pilot*, founded by his pioneering father. Gene Cervi edits a sprightly and popular business weekly in Denver, the *Rocky Mountain Journal*, which bases its success among a highly conservative following on the unlikely formula of shirt-tearing, Vesuvius-like eruptions of moralistic breast beating and the deliberate baiting of all Republicans and nearly all financiers. Cervi regards himself as "the conscience of the Denver press," calls the proprietors of the *Post* megalomaniacs and the *News* the "19th button on Roy Howard's green pistachio shirt."

Allen Bartlett, later editor of the Scripps-Howard Houston *Press*, gave himself the nickname "Big Fat Duck." Bart was a college wrestler and weighted in at something close to two hundred and twenty pounds. During the era of high journalistic enterprise he got himself stuck in a ventilator shaft while eavesdropping on a closed union meeting. "There I was, like a big fat duck."

Gene Lindberg now writes poetry and science, a combination he finds logical, for the *Post*, but one of his greatest literary triumphs failed to see print. Lindberg was covering the police beat for the *Evening News*. An itinerant passion play came to town and two of the leading actors, portraying Jesus and Judas, got drunk after the first performance. They wobbled down Sixteenth Street and became embroiled in an unbiblical argument in front of Joslin's dry-goods store. It ended when one punched the other through the plate-glass window and the paddy wagon arrived. Lindberg wrote the story and submitted his own headline:

JESUS SETTLES 2000-YEAR-OLD GRUDGE;
KNOCKS JUDAS THROUGH PLATE GLASS WINDOW

Gene's story was published, but the headline was deleted in deference to public sensibilities. Denver boasts a phenomenal per capita ratio of churches.

Wally Reef now is information director for the Colorado Highway Department, and Jack Carberry has gone over to the *Post*, where he is executive sports editor and indulges in snide remarks about "the morning fishwrapper." In 1926 they formed an unbeatable crime reporting team. They cleaned up a notorious Colorado Springs murder case, and Reef won a personal commendation from Roy Howard as "the greatest detective in America." H. Allen Smith remembers that "Wally Reef was always getting me in trouble at West Side Court."

> I took things easy over there. About once a week he'd saunter in and loaf around for a while, acting as if he'd just happened by, and then the next morning the *News* would burst forth with a big exclusive from the DA or some judge, and Johnny Day [*Post* city editor and brother of Eddie Day of the *News*] would eat my butt out, saying, "For Christ's sake can't you learn to keep your eye on that goddam Wally Reef?" I never learned to do it.

The *News* sports staff included Vernon ("Curly") Grieve as morning editor, Lowell L. Leake in afternoon command, Abe Pollock, Volney Wash, Ham Beresford, N. C. ("Tub") Morris, and a redheaded kid who hung out with a racy crowd at Totman's Drugstore. Chet Nelson was breaking in covering high school athletics. He joined the full-time staff in 1932, became sports editor in June 1934, and is rated as a civic benefactor for keeping bookmakers off relief.

Drama editor was the patrician and beauteous Helen Marie Black, whose brother, now District Judge William A. Black, had worked in the *News* business office. Today Helen is manager of the Denver Symphony. In 1926, Clyde Davis asserts, she was "a bright girl who couldn't spell but who had a genius for innocent double entendres."

At one point eight artists labored at *News* easels to maintain aesthetics on a high plane. They were headed by the cartoonist Jim Lynch and Charlie Wunder. Reporter Chet Letts could fill in if needed; his experience as an artist stretched back to the day of scratchboard plates. It was a time of much vignetting and prettying up of newspaper photos with doodads and curlicues; the unadorned "art" of the present-day newspaper would have been beneath contempt as lacking flair and style. *News* artists of the mad twenties were kept busy adding frosting and Spencerian scrollwork to the mug shots of dignitaries and parachutists. It was also a time of diagrammatic reporting: a Maltese cross to mark where the body had lain, a bold dotted line to show how the bank robbers fled to the high-powered getaway car purring at the curb.

Another *News* staff member of the day requires special billing. Denver has produced a long run of superior woman journalists: Ellis Meredith, Patience Stapleton, Polly Pry, Alice Rohe, Hettie Cattell, Frances Wayne, Alberta Pike—a goodly sorority which asked no quarter of male competitors, gave none, and scorned the traditionally feminine fields of social news, fashions, and entertainments. But none of the lady newspapermen carved her initials so deeply into the trunk of Denver journalism as an Irish girl who scored beats with aplomb, undertook adventures with dash, and succeeded often in the dangerous game of playing practical jokes on Eddie Day, a curmudgeon type and frequently humorless. H. Allen Smith, Clyde Davis, and John Lewis all have reminiscences of Mary Coyle.

Lewis remembers a day when an Indian chief, visiting the office for an interview about the old West, became distracted and sought to strike a bargain in blankets for the "blue dress squaw" working at a typewriter across the room. "It would have made a hell of a buy no matter how many blankets," Lewis comments. "The squaw was Mary Coyle." She is now Mary Coyle Chase, wife of the *News* associated editor and Pulitzer-prize playwright for her *Harvey*. The persistent legend is that Bob and Mary were married on their lunch hour, while waiting for a jury to come in or some such brief and unromantic interlude. In due course Mary retired from newspapering. *Harvey* and her other plays were written amid the tumults of rearing three robust boys and the cross-bearing which goes with being the wife of a morning newspaperman, a pitiful situation of cold dinners, loneliness, social hibernation, and inattention, as the wife of any morning newspaperman will certify.

"All of us, including Mary, got a big kick out of the Indian incident," John Lewis continues, "but I got none out of the week I was damned fool enough to assign Mary to take a shot of scopolamine, then being used experimentally as a truth serum, before a convention of peace officers. It was all good fun when Chief Reed interrogated her, under the influence, about the theft of a picture taken in the routine course of duty in the kind of journalism that used to prevail in Denver. But it wasn't fun that Mary developed an infection from the shot. She didn't recover for days, and my grayer hairs never did turn dark again."

H. Allen Smith writes:

> During my period in Denver the emphasis was more on getting pictures than on getting prose. All of us were accomplished picture-stealers because the rule in most cases was, first get the picture, then worry about the story. I seem to remember being in a semi-darkened room in the home of a woman who had committed suicide, and Mary Coyle was there for the *News*. She was sitting on top of a low bureau and suddenly I noticed, in the dimness, that she had opened the top drawer a bit and her hand was creeping into it—seeking a picture, of course. I sidled over and suddenly gave the drawer a slam. It damn near cut her fingers off and she yelled like an asthmatic bobcat.

Then there was the day Mary's house caught fire. She had been covering a murder trial and was dictating her story to a rewrite man, Clyde Davis recalls, when he interrupted to inform her that fire had broken out in her closet at home. "All right," Mary replied, "but let me finish my story first." Meanwhile her wardrobe was destroyed. "It wouldn't have been so bad except that I had bought a brand-new dress only the day before and it burned up before I ever had a chance to wear it." Roy Howard and Bob Scripps sent word to get a new dress and send the bill.

When the pioneer bore of the Moffat Tunnel was completed on February 27, 1927, Mary was on hand in defiance of the firmly held superstition of tunnel men that a woman underground is the acme of bad-luck omens. Togged out in men's clothes, her hair bunned up under a cap, she passed for a hard-rock miner and so was present for the holing-through, the first woman to traverse the tunnel. The first man to go through was young Jack Foster. Mary entered from the east portal, Jack from the west. It was a tense and historic moment. The six-mile tunnel under the Continental Divide northwest of Denver would place the city on a direct transcontinental railroad route for the first time. David

Moffat had sunk his entire nine-million-dollar fortune into the dream, and the people of northern Colorado ponied up another fifteen million in a bond issue which is still being paid off. When the last few feet of the viscera of James Peak were blasted aside, Foster scrambled over the debris, grabbed Mary and kissed her, then streaked for the tunnel entrance and a telephone. He got his scoop; the *News* was first on the streets.

Foster scored again a year and a day later, when the main railroad tunnel was completed paralleling the pioneer bore, which had been drilled as an exploratory measure and to provide multiple headings for the drillers. Today the original tunnel carries water through the mountains to keep Denver lawns green. Realization of the long-cherished goal of a railroad under the peaks was, of course, major news in Colorado, and both the *News* and the *Post* made elaborate plans for covering the ceremonial completion and signaling it to the populace. The *Post* announced it would set off bombs the moment word came through. The *News* quietly fixed up its own bombs on the roof of the Welton Street building. Bruce Gustin covered the event for the *Post*, and Foster, now an experienced tunnel specialist, drew the assignment for the *News*. By tying up the only telephone near the entrance, Foster got his flash through first and the *News'* bombs cut loose—thirty-six of them in thunderous succession. "The roar shook the downtown district," he wrote later. "The explosion tore a hole through our roof, broke several panes of glass and shook couples out of each other's arms in the Orient Hotel." The Battle of the Century was at full cry.

Signal bombs, flagpole sitters, and other custard pies were not the only weapons. Scripps-Howard introduced its own brand of reporting and news writing: snappy, brief, simply written, vigorous. The *News* up to this point had never cast off entirely the modes and manners of turn-of-the-century journalism, which impressed itself with long-winded erudition, stentorian tones, and polysyllables. During the Shaffer regime, moreover, the *News* had drowsed off in the coverage of local news. Bob Chase remembers that when he was on the *Express* daily tabulations were made of the number of local stories appearing in the four papers. The *Post*, where Bonfils held to the extreme position that "a dog fight in Champa Street is more important than war in Europe," would have sixty or more stories and items each day. The *Express* crowded out of its skeleton staff and into its poverty-restricted space up to thirty home-town articles daily. But the *News* and *Times* frequently appeared with as few as six or eight local articles, and these were usually lengthy and pontifical. The *Post* still had no editorial page, and any major news story was a witches' brew of policy, warped facts, shibboleth, and sacred cow. The news was regarded on Champa Street merely as a convenient hook on which to display the strong opinions of Bonfils and his lieutenants. The new policy of snap and clarity for the *News* sought to rescue the paper from its recent habits of deadly dullness and would prove, it was hoped, a sparkling contrast to the heavily underscored opinions of the *Post*. The new era on Welton Street was spelled out in a style book which was printed and distributed to all staff members of the NEWS-papers. Some excerpts:

. . . The general style of these papers aims at simplicity—short words, short sentences, short paragraphs, without excessive punctuation.

We want good writing, but not fancy writing—clear, terse English, which says the thing to be said in the least number of words. We want plenty of life and vitality and color—things which come from simple, vigorous relation of facts, rather than from an over-liberal use of adjectives.

We want brevity, thru the elimination of needless words and details. This is a busy age, and people haven't the time nor inclination to wade thru long-winded stories to pick out a few essential facts.

We want punch. Say your most interesting thing right off the bat, without introduction. Hook the reader's attention, and he will then finish the story.

We want headlines with snap. Tell the essential part of your story in the head, directly and vigorously. Figure that the average reader wants to dodge reading as many stories as possible, in order to do something else, and that it's up to you to grab his attention and hold it.

But in seeking to secure brevity, punch and vigor, never sacrifice accuracy. Above all, these papers must try to be accurate and fair. We need color—but only such color as comes from the relation of facts —not the kind that is supplied by imagination. While we want to take advantage to the fullest of every possibility of a story, this should be done without exaggeration and false emphasis. We mustn't over-praise our friends and belittle our enemies. We are on the sidelines watching the game, in which the players are good and bad, friendly and hostile— and our part is to report it correctly and interestingly.

In starting your story, pick the big fact and say it without pause or introduction, with the same vigor you would display in sending a telegram where every word counted. Get the feature and lead with it.

In choosing between two words, pick the shorter and more common and better understood.

Avoid long qualifying phrases and involved sentences.

We have no blacklists. We have no long rules and taboos; no sacred cows and forbidden subjects; no outside businesses and ambitions. We simply want to print accurate, complete, intelligent and interesting newspapers.

Suggestions and criticisms are welcome. Ideas are always in demand. Originality is forever at a premium. Every reporter and desk man and other employee is invited to contribute suggestions and criticisms and ideas. This isn't a one-man band, nor a twelve-man band. . . .

Do not editorialize in the news columns or headlines. Adjectives and names which carry with them an editorial opinion are to be avoided outside the editorial columns. The news columns are for straight, unbiased facts, without opinion or editorial emphasis. . . .

Scripps-Howard also "sprazzed up" the office physically, in the phrase of John Lewis. It had been a place of creaking, battered desks, "over which you could drape one leg while pecking at the typewriter." The writing machines were "the oldest and best Underwoods ever made." Along the wall, Lewis remembers, were three stand-up telephones in open booths for use of the reporters. "The city editor for the morning side had a grand, swinging, flexible arm for his telephone so he could push it around to an assistant over the cluttered desks, and a fine, big, insanitary rubber ear guard to aid in hearing. There was running water, of course—we were strictly modern—but that was in the toilets, and the drinking stuff was in a cooler over by the state editor's desk. The ice was always melted by the time the News men came in, and the cups were gone, too, so the morning staff took quick gulps from dissolving cups devised of newsprint copy paper. The stomach thus acclimated to sulphite and pulp had little to fear from any but the stronger liquors of those prohibition days."

New desks were added, more telephones, and typewriters recent enough to have standard keyboards. An ingenious hanging microphone and earpiece contraption was rigged up for rewrite men. Staff members were added so rapidly that often there weren't enough typewriters and desks to go around, and reporters beat out their stories in shifts. One day the staff came to work and discovered that the dingy walls, covered with scribblings near every desk, had been painted, thereby destroying forever a fascinating directory of valuable telephone numbers of bootleggers, friendly females, and news sources.

The composing and pressrooms were not neglected. Thirteen new Linotype machines were installed, and Ludlow head-setting equipment. Three new Hoe Decuple presses were put in, one on February 1, 1927, the others a month later. Each had an 80-page capacity and could rev up at 36,000 forty-page papers an hour.

The bustle, the staff-building, and the refurbishing of the News, physically and spiritually, did not escape the watchful eye of the Big Brother, of course, not even at the beginning. The Post learned as soon as anyone that Jack Foster, Sr., and Max Cook were headed west from the Cleveland Press. A letter was dispatched to the opposition paper, the Cleveland News, inquiring about what tricks these gentlemen would have up their sleeves. Word came back that they might try localizing serial fiction. Cook had developed the technique for the Press. It involved editing of local street names and familiar landmarks into a routine piece of newspaper serial fiction, thereby, it was hoped, increasing local interest. Sometimes the stories were illustrated with photos of a home-grown beauty who posed as the heroine against a background of recognizable scenes. Recently Cook had applied the local Cleveland touches to Eleanor Meherin's novel, *Chickie*, a bit of titillating fluff which promised more than it delivered in the way of Jazz Age raciness.

The *Post* was not a newspaper to let moss grow on the gears. It bought the rights to *Chickie*, added the home-town embellishments, and persuaded an overdeveloped teenager to pose for the pictures in rolled hose and cloche hat. The camera-struck girl undertook the assignment on speculation. She would get no pay, of course, but she was assured that Hollywood scouts undoubtedly would be watching.

A couple of hitches arose, however. The *Post* made the mistake of shooting only a few advance shots of their cut-price queen, and it developed that Charles Lounsbury of the *News* knew her family. When he explained to mother and father that the heroine of *Chickie* became conspicuously pregnant out of wedlock in the mid-chapters, the *Post* lost its model. There was a confusing switch of heroines abruptly at Chapter Four. It is not recorded whether the *Post's Chickie* ever made it to Hollywood; Lounsbury may have deprived the films of a notable bosom.

Then Jack Foster, Sr., issued an order and Tom Dowling brought in a freight-car load, ten thousand copies, of *Chickie* books from Chicago. Anyone could have a copy free by subscribing to the *News* or placing a want ad in the Sunday paper. Moreover Max Cook snapped up the Denver serial rights to Eleanor Meherin's *newest* sizzler, *Denny*, and it was announced that it would be published in *two* installments on successive Sundays. The *News* would permit no dawdling while the villain leered and the heroine played coy.

The *Post's Chickie* promotion collapsed.

The papers were slugging it out, toe to toe. Soon the sun, no less, became a pawn in the contest. Bonfils took over and supervised a solar eclipse. The *Post* staff astronomer filled the paper for weeks with columns of heavenly statistics, and everyone was invited down to Champa Street —bring your own dark glasses—to see the phenomenon which, it was suggested, had been arranged by Big Brother as a celestial diversion for his many small dependents. A crowd of obedient thousands turned out. But as the sunlight dimmed briefly, an electric sign flickered into life on the roof of a building across the way:

THE SUN IS OUR ONLY RIVAL—AND HE IS OFF THE JOB
Read the NEWSpapers

The coup was humiliating, but Bonfils could shrug it off. After all, the whole affair had cost nothing. What *really* hurt was when the *Evening News* began giving away copies of its early "Peach" edition one afternoon each week just before the *Post* appeared. Hordes of schoolboys and girls were employed to see that each person on the downtown streets got his "Peach." (So called from the color of the paper; the *Post* used red.) The day of the gratuitous distribution was shifted each week and was a closely held secret. As a result the *Post* was unable to prepare for the inevitable slump in its sales that day, and the circulation department had to "eat" thousands of papers. The horrible cost, it was asserted, drove Bonfils closer to drink than at any time in a wholly abstemious career. A countermeasure was not delayed. For a time the *Morning Post* was deposited free of charge on the doorstep of *every* non-subscriber on a delivery route—*every* morning. *That* ended *that*.

It was a time frantic with "extras." Any transoceanic flight, sashweight murder, or prize fight was occasion to start up the presses off hours and send leather-lunged newsboys whooping through the dark streets to edify readers roused in their nightshirts. Bennie Bee, now a Denver municipal employee but then a *Post* hustler and "world's champion newsboy" by personal fiat of Bonfils, recalls selling six thousand papers on the Sacco-Vanzetti execution. Another of Bennie's feats was to get himself arrested in New York in 1923—he was on a busman's tour "to see how the other half lives," he says—hollering a *Journal* extra so loudly that it disturbed Times Square. Sam Nadler, street circulation manager for the *News*, offered the talented Bennie seventy-five dollars a week plus commissions to switch loyalties. It was more than anyone in the editorial department short of executive rank was getting.

The night of the Dempsey–Tunney fight in September 1927 the *News* parked a large truck at Sixteenth and Champa streets, just around the corner from the *Post* building. Concealed under the tarpaulin were a dozen newsboys. The minute the fight was over they spilled from the truck shouting a fight extra to the crowd gathered in front of the *Post* to hear the "free broadcast" via loudspeakers. The papers were sold out in a few minutes, and it was a mystery how they could have been published so rapidly—until someone took a look at one of them. The fight news in it consisted of a headline announcing the victor, a lead which did the same, and a long story confected out of all the advance information the sports department could lay its hands on. Subsequently it came out that the *News* during the afternoon had printed twenty-five hundred copies heralding a Dempsey victory, a like number for a Tunney win, and all five thousand papers were loaded aboard the truck to await developments. The twenty-five hundred persons who bought the fight extra that night probably account, in part, for the dogged subscriber resistance the *News* later encountered.

Today in Denver, as elsewhere, the newspaper extra is a relic of the past. Changes in newspaper reading habits are partially responsible, along with the fact that more frequent and larger editions keep most newspaper pressrooms humming through much of the publication day. On a fast-breaking story today a newspaper will replate, improving the edition then running on the presses with a minimum loss of valuable press time. Radio, too, with its unlimited time for "flashes," blunted the effectiveness and salability of the noisy extra.

Radio came to Denver in 1921 when Dr. W. D. Reynolds, a fascinated spare-time follower of Marconi's marvel, moved his pioneer station, KLZ, up from Colorado Springs to broadcast from a residential-area bungalow which sprouted strange antennae. Streams of motorists drove by the Reynolds house to gape at the new wonder of the age. In 1924, KLZ was joined by KOA, one of the earliest 50,000-watt stations.[1] Denver was proud of her big voice of the "ether." It "put this burg on the map" for the avid fans who sat up half the night over cat-whisker crystal sets and one-tube superheterodynes to "get Cincinnati," an accomplishment by which one acquired caste. Today the air waves above Denver are crowded by the signals of five television channels and nineteen radio stations, including one which furthers the mission of the Pillar of Fire religious sect and another which speaks in Spanish.

During the late thirties the *News* co-operated with KVOD in a long series of nightly broadcasts which "re-created" the news of the day. In addition to her other duties of interviews, general assignments, and rewrite, the competent Alberta Pike turned out the script from carbon copies of local stories and the day's wire report. Each person who figured in the news that day was given a speaking part. Staff members who were handy at air time had a script thrust into their hands and became actors. The broadcast originated from among the bound volumes of back issues in the morgue, with the chatter of teleprinters as authenticating background sound. Frank Plumb handled the "character" parts and all dialects, from Chinese to Swahili. Barron B. Beshoar, now Denver bureau manager for *Time-Life* and then the *News'* ace Statehouse man, took any role which called for a political windbag type. The program was one of many local efforts to exploit the "romance" of the newsroom on the air. More recently KLZ-TV brought its television cameras into the *News* city room to focus their big eyes on the controlled madness which is election night coverage.

In 1927 and 1928, however, infant radio had raised no hindrance to the game of extras. When Chamberlin and Levine flew east across the Atlantic in June 1927, on the first non-stop flight to Germany, the *Post* shot off a signal bomb to mark every hundred miles of progress, simultaneously shucking a new extra from its hot presses. Early Sunday morning the marathon stint became wearying. The fliers were close to their goal, and so the *Post* took a chance and closed out the feat with a 1 A.M. extra which announced a safe landing at Berlin. Later in the day, when it became known that the plane had been forced down a few miles short of Berlin, the *News* brought out a hairsplitting extra

[1]Hafen, *Colorado and Its People*, Vol. I, pp. 584–85.

which gave the "true facts." Welton Street rubbed it in by giving much of the front page to a photostatic reproduction of the *Post's* final extra. Another sample, the *News* scolded, of how Big Brother was misleading the people of Denver with shoddy and inaccurate journalism. About a month earlier, both papers had plastered the city with extras about the historic crossing of Charles A. Lindbergh. Denver apparently wanted the extras. It bought them like mad, and they contributed their decibels to the general din.

Contests were epidemic. The *Evening News* ran a limerick competition with cash prizes for the "lost lines" and Max Cook behind the scenes as "Limerick Larry." The two NEWSpapers combined to offer a trip around the world to the town's "most popular school teacher." A coupon was printed daily in each paper for the casting of votes. The contest was a spirited and highly popular one, and it gave the *Post*, an experienced ante-raiser, ideas. Champa Street countered with contests for best girl, best stenographer, best fireman. Voting coupons became currency, and Bennie Bee says there was a time when newsboys could get up to twenty-five cents each for papers just before a new voting deadline. Mike Mongone, a local Runyonesque character, reportedly spent nearly $10,000 trying to win the "best waitress" contest for the pert and popular Ada Cummings of the Edelweiss Restaurant, long the hangout of Denver's dawn patrol (Leonard Cahn of the *News* sports staff, commanding). It is some measure of the frenzy of the contests that Ada didn't win. Perry Clemens, a traffic cop at Fifteenth and Larimer streets, sank $2000 into coupons to win a $150 tailor-made uniform which was the prize in the "best policeman" contest.

The *News* was publishing half a full-length novel each Sunday, and serial fiction was sprinkled through the week in an effort to maintain the inflated circulation gains. When the serial *Joy* began running, "The Biggest Night in South Denver's History" was staged on South Broadway, Max Cook recalls. The heroine herself led a parade of allegedly pretty girls down the avenue amid flares, bombs, and the blaring of bands. A crowd of thousands lined the streets, extra streetcars were pressed into service, and the district underwent one of its worst traffic tie-ups.

An elaborate Travel and Service Bureau was opened by the NEWSpapers on Sixteenth Street, Denver's main commercial artery, in the Neusteter Building. Fay Lamphier, national beauty-contest winner, was hostess in charge, and the furnishings set the paper back $40,000, a tidy sum even in the Coolidge boom times. There was a big globe of the world for a chandelier and a $1500 mural by Allen True, a leading Denver artist, of the Scripps-Howard lighthouse. The chandelier set the *News* back $32,000 in itself—and, Roy Howard adds, a dollar was worth one hundred cents in those days. Monthly operating costs exceeded $1000, and for this the bureau was expected merely to "be nice" to the public. It was to pass out information and promotional literature to tourists and townspeople, distribute educational pamphlets, receive club and church notices and other handouts and, incidentally, accept want ads. There was a Western Union branch desk, restrooms, a domestic science department, and a conference room which could be booked without charge.

Another activity of the bureau was to operate the News Tour Club, an organization capitalizing on the motorcar craze and giving away free road atlases of the nation at a time when these were not available at every corner filling station. The map of Colorado contained in the atlas shows that the only paved highways in the state linked Denver with Greeley, Boulder, Castle Rock, Golden, and Morrison. There were brief stretches of hardtop on the fringes of a few other major towns.

The sponsoring papers described themselves modestly on the back of the atlas:

> Today in Denver, the Rocky Mountain News and Denver Evening News—the NEWSpapers of Denver—are the papers that are read and liked by the substantial, constructive and worthwhile citizens—and the reasons for this are very simple.
>
> The character and ability of the personnel comprising of [sic] their editorial and news-gathering staffs, is unapproached in the Rocky Mountain Region.
>
> Their reporting and interpreting of the news each day is known to be fair, just, liberal and sparkling with lively interest.
>
> Their columns abound in Features of the highest rank—O. O. McIntyre's "New York Day by Day"—daily Editorials by Glenn Frank; daily essays by Dr. Frank Crane; "Just Folks" by Edgar A. Guest; daily humor by Abe Martin.
>
> Financial and Market pages capably edited. The only Book Review page in the Rocky Mountain Region. Church and Religious Activities of Denver given comprehensive, interesting treatment. Sunday articles by the most famous writers of the nation.
>
> Mark Sullivan, Frank T. Simonds, the Reverend Thomas B. Gregory, Lady Mary, J. J. Geller, Bruce Barton, Fannie Hurst, Albert Payson Terhune, Roe Fulkerson, Alexander Woollcott, as well as weekly articles by Roger Babson on "Business Analysis." The Sunday NEWS also is the only newspaper published between the Missouri River and the Pacific Coast having a Rotogravure supplement [not for long; the Post soon added one].
>
> These are just a few of the reasons why the NEWSpapers of Denver—The Rocky Mountain News and Denver Evening News—are read and appreciated by all the better class of citizens TODAY in Denver.

In salute to the "better class" element of Denver, Eddie Guest even supplied a personal and touching tribute via the columns of the *News:*

Here is a city where manhood counts.
Here is a city where courage mounts
As high as the peaks of the mountains tall,
Here's where the Flag comes first of all. . . .

Under such blandishments, how could a substantial, constructive, and worth-while citizen resist becoming a subscriber to the NEWSpapers? Especially when one's name might be the cause of the sounding of sirens? (The *News* had a siren on its roof, the *Post* a big bell. The bell tolled and the siren's tail was twisted whenever circulation gains were scored.)

The *News'* shrieking siren was also employed to promote a new serial story, *The Daughter of Midas*. It was fixed to the underside of an airplane, and young Jack Foster was given the privilege of going aloft to operate it in the night skies over the city. Foster held a control button, and each time he pressed it the siren would howl and an electric sign under the wing would light up.

The airplane was still new enough to Denver to make such stunts modest pinnacles of promotional genius. The city's first airways service was inaugurated in May 1926, when a branch line began operating from Pueblo via Denver to Cheyenne to join the main transcontinental route. Colorado Airways Inc. was the operator, and the planes utilized the Don Hogan "airdrome" at East Twenty-sixth Avenue and Oneida Street, an area now planted row on row with residences.[2] The *News* soon was using Colorado Airways and its successor, Colorado–Wyoming Airways, to carry its papers to Casper and other Wyoming cities "with the speed of the wind."

Arrival of the first airmail plane back in Denver on its northbound flight from Pueblo was made the occasion for an air show.

> . . . Unique air stunts in which Diavolo Steiner defied the power of gravity with feats of wing-walking and trapeze stunts followed; later he dropped from the plane in a parachute. . . . Members of four Indian tribes, the Denver & Rio Grande Western band and the G.A.R. fife and drum corps added further entertainment. . . .[3]

At about the same time Denver's first Lowry Field was established just east of the Park Hill Country Club, then the farm of Clayton College. The field was the home of the Colorado National Guard's 120th Observation Squadron, which droned over the city in surplus DeHavilland biplanes. This area, too, has now grown to homes, but the name of the field is retained for the huge installation of the U. S. Air Force Technical Training Command at which the Air Force Academy

[2] Ibid., Vol. I, pp. 574.

[3] *Rocky Mountain News*, June 1, 1926.

got its start. Both fields salute the memory of Francis Brown Lowry, a Denver boy killed in France in 1918.

The young air age soon embroiled the *News* and the *Post* in another battle. The *News*, which takes pride in an unbroken record of support for air progress in Colorado, was boosting the selection of a new site for a municipal airport, now Stapleton Field, farther east from the settled part of Park Hill. The *Post* called the proposal "Brown Cannon's steal" because a local financier, currently in disfavor in the Red Room, owned the land the city planned to buy. An alternate site was suggested —where Bonfils owned land. The *News* frothed at the audacity while the *Post* shouted that the new airport, finally purchased in 1928, was too far out from the city in a "wilderness of sand dunes and Russian thistles." Today the city has grown entirely around Stapleton Field and extension of runways to meet jet transport requirements is a serious problem.

Ammunition in this and other battles was not confined entirely to newsprint, sirens, bells, and low-altitude stunting. Persons unknown tossed a handful of bolts into the *News*' presses, causing extensive damage. For a period guards had to be maintained day and night in the pressroom. Then someone began systematically stealing copies of the morning *News* from the doorsteps of subscribers, and a flood of "I didn't get my paper" complaints swamped the circulation department. The filching ceased when a large cash reward was offered for the arrest and conviction of paper snitchers. Meanwhile the editorial writers made the life of the chief of police a bed of nails for the negligence of his gumshoes in not running down the thieves.

Espionage and counterespionage flourished. The Scripps-Howard executives made a practice of meeting daily in one of their Cosmopolitan Hotel suites to hatch plans and blueprint fresh sorties. At one of these sessions, Max Cook calls to mind, a conferee suddenly pulled a bed away from the wall. There on the floor was a small microphone with wires leading through the wall. Instead of yanking the snooper out by its roots, the staff parley switched to loud discussion of a plan to raise the salaries of all editorial department employees next day. There had been much raiding of staffs back and forth. By coincidence, Bonfils immediately announced salary boosts for all his editorial staff.

The kiddies, of course, were not neglected despite all the distractions of combat. Presumably at great cost, the *News* brought in Peter Pan to operate the Rocky Mountain Sunshine Club, a page of high-level goodies which no self-respecting kid today would touch with tongs. It was assumed, possibly, that all the good, clean, positively motivated little boys and girls in Denver would badger their parents into subscribing to the *News* in order to keep up with the good, clean, syrupy fun.

One of the shrillest crescendos was reached in the great gasoline war. The *News*, with a liberal policy of premiums, took the lead in classified advertising away from the *Post* for the first time in twenty years. On

February 4, 1927, the *News* appeared with 26 pages of classified advertising in a 112-page paper. The 96-page *Post* had only 14 pages of want ads. Bonfils was stung into action. He found a dealer who was willing to pony up in return for the publicity, and the *Post* announced with a fanfare of trumpets that it would give two gallons of gasoline free to every person who took a want ad in the forthcoming Sunday paper. Gasoline then was selling at twenty-one cents a gallon. The *News* immediately countered with an offer of three gallons from any one of twenty service stations around town. The *Post* went to four—after calming its restive petrol merchant with a promise to *pay* him for half the gas, a drastic step which clearly indicates the gravity of the situation. But the *News* would not be bested: five gallons! Bonfils passed, and the *News* had to move desks out onto the sidewalk on Seventeenth Street in front of the Glenarm Place business office to accommodate the crowds of persons who were willing to take a twenty-five cent want ad in exchange for a week's free operation of their cars. The line of ad buyers stretched uptown to the Brown Palace. Police were called out to keep order. Sandwiches and coffee were served. The clerks scribbled fourteen hours straight on Friday and twelve hours on Saturday. The *News* printed fifteen thousand ads—and the victory cost forty thousand dollars. The gasoline-throwing contest was not resumed the following week, although the *News* made sure everyone in Denver knew the *Post* had been licked. A brass band was hired and marched down to Champa Street to serenade the *Post* with "The Old Grey Mare Ain't What She Used to Be" and "Bye, Bye, Blackbird."

In the midst of the hurrah competing newsmen of both papers put aside the bladder and bells to bid farewell to one of the finest of good companions. When Wong Gum Chung went home to China there were tears in the eyes of cynics who could and did betray their best friends for the momentary glory of a scoop. Jim Wong was steward of the Denver Press Club from 1905 to 1927. From the era of Damon Runyon down to the gasoline war he was the warm friend and impassive confidant of every newspaperman in town. He nursed them through hangovers and broken love affairs, gave them wise advice, loaned them cash in financial crises. He worried over his hard-drinking "cyanide kids" and set for them an example of thrift, industry, moderation, and patience which few of them followed. His black hair turned silver in their service, and he taught many of them all they ever learned about being gentlemen.

At one point Jim Wong had been private cook to "Black Jack" Pershing on the Mexican border. At another he operated a restaurant in the mining boom town of Silverton. Then he came to the Press Club. He left briefly three times for trips home to his native village inland from Canton. On the first trip he married and fathered a son. The following two trips yielded daughters. But each time his family remained behind when Jim returned to his post in Denver. On a salary of fifteen dollars a week—augmented, it was suspected, by manipulations in the Hop Alley lottery—Jim accumulated twenty thousand dollars in gold. The hoard was buried in a vase under the concrete floor of his home in China.

"It will keep all of you for life, in case I don't come back," he told his wife. "Take one gold piece at a time. Each coin will care for you and the children two months."

Lee Casey wrote of Jim:

> Every good waiter is courteous and considerate by the very nature of his calling because he devotes his life to the service of others.
>
> Jim Wong was that, and more. He was the wise and kindly guide of a generation of Denver newspapermen, all of whom learned from him something of the graces of irony and urbanity combined with deep understanding and sympathy.
>
> I never knew a better man. I never had a better friend.

Early in 1927, Jim decided to go home to China for good. Denver newspapermen turned out in a body to see him off on the train. A hired instrumental trio played inappropriately cheerful music. Jim wept as the train pulled out, and so did his "cyanide kids." Today his portrait, signed in Chinese, hangs in a place of honor in the Press Club. Autographed pictures of every President since McKinley are relegated to a secondary position. Word came back in 1937 that Jim had died.[4]

The truce declared when Jim went back to China lasted a brief hour or so. When the train departed both sides brushed away sentiment and returned to the tooth-and-claw business at hand. By and large the Battle of the Century was played out on a level of low farce or comic opera, and frivols burr themselves into the memory more deeply than serious grapplings with the contemporary problems, which lose much of their weightiness as time passes. But sober, intelligent journalism was being practiced in Denver along with the capers.

At a time when, according to George Seldes, the impeccable New York *Times* was flirting irresponsibly with a rising young Fascist regime in Italy,[5] the *Rocky Mountain News* was much less self-consciously hammering away in its own back yard for better schools, an end to prohibition-era lawlessness, unionization of coal miners, planning for the air age, and a dozen other progressive causes. Completion of the vital Moffat Tunnel was one of the *News* campaigns, and the paper lent vigorous support to the rebuilding of Denver's public school system, badly run down during and after World War I. Editorial weight was thrown behind a major bond issue, which eventually carried. The *Post*

[4]Dowell Livesay, "We Remember Jim Wong," *Rocky Mountain Life*, Vol. II, No. 10 (Dec. 1947), p. 17.

[5]George Seldes, *Freedom of the Press* (New York, 1935), pp. 194–214.

was negative. It was trying to run the current school board president out of town for refusal to be dominated, and it viewed with alarm the horrible cost of building schools.

The support given to plans for a municipal airport was only part of a long-term drive by the *News* for improved air facilities. It demanded the beacon-lighting of airways, and urged the painting of town names on barn roofs to guide pilots in a day before the development of radio navigational aids.

Almost alone in the state, and at a heavy cost of popularity among the "right-minded," the *News* pounded away for repeal of the prohibition amendment. It pointed to the unparalleled lawlessness spawned by prohibition, the governmental corruption, the deaths and cases of blindness which resulted from bad liquor. Morality and temperance had been sapped, instead of strengthened, by the attempt to enact self-control, the *News* insisted, and in the process the dignity of the law had suffered. The vast industry of bootlegging was documented in news stories and attacked editorially. Organized crime, with roots in Chicago's gangland and Sicily's Mafia, had come to Colorado. These were unpopular arguments, even with some persons who had a regular bootlegger, but the *News* persisted. The *Post*, again, was on the other side. Bonfils was a strong-minded prohibitionist, and his paper, if not its staff, was as dry as the prairie in August.

There were I.W.W. labor troubles in the Colorado coal fields, and in 1927 state police were used to break a strike. The *News* denounced the strikebreakers and the officials who permitted them to function, and urged the miners to organize themselves in the United Mine Workers as a step toward labor peace.

A long undercover investigation in which Harvey Sethman used his camera to document the alteration of court records with ink eradicators and erasures led to exposure of a crooked receivership ring in Denver and the surrounding suburban area. Sethman wrote a series of articles which opened up a noisome mess in which a number of persons had lost their life savings. The Sethman series resulted in legislative action to revise Colorado's receivership laws. The man who had been mysteriously appointed receiver for a large number of suburban businesses, George W. Beck, was shot and killed in the Kittredge Building barbershop by one of the victims, and a prominent Denver attorney was disbarred. Many *News* readers probably didn't understand the legal technicalities, though they saw the results, and the paper went on the blacklist of a circle of Denver businessmen and attorneys who were profiting from the secret milking operation.

Loan sharks and usurers came under attacks which later built up into a full-blown campaign that again won legislative revision of statutes. News stories and columns by Lee Casey exposed shocking conditions of brutality and neglect in the Colorado State Penitentiary at Cañon

City, and there were editorial demands for reform long before the series of bloody, fiery riots which shook the prison.

As the automobile age advanced small towns set up speed traps for motorists as a means of augmenting local revenues. The courts of rustic justices of the peace became centers of legalized brigandage. The *News*, always a champion of the horseless carriage and its devotees, set up a clamor against the parasite towns, losing subscribers in each.

Many of these campaigns took the unpopular side, and they cost the paper as much in public acceptance, advertising support, and circulation as was won by the frantic promotions, the giveaways, and the gimmicks. Yet they were clung to with the same courage and constancy that Byers had displayed in his fights with the Bummers. The era was not entirely one of froth and feathers.

There were some gains, of course. Advertisers began coming back to the *News* in spite of the penalties this cost them in higher rates at the *Post*. During 1926, *News* circulation was 29,933 mornings, 24,521 evenings, and 55,589 Sundays. This went to 40,033 morning, 51,722 evening, and 93,701 Sunday in 1928. The high point was 110,000 briefly for the Sunday *News*. And the cost in dollars and nervous energy was disproportionate.

It had been a wonderful, mad, exciting battle for the journalistic troops which fought it. They became so enthralled and exhilarated by their stunts and scoops that they forgot to notice that the town was growing weary of the turmoil. The public was sick of nerve-shattering bombs and the bragging, promotional prose which filled both papers. A diet of flagpole sitters for breakfast and lady wrestlers for supper began to pall. Merchants were becoming annoyed at their role of shuttlecock between the battledores of the papers' advertising departments.

The two men who had to pay the bills became *very* weary of ladling red ink. Scripps-Howard, it was disclosed later, lost nearly three million dollars in two years scoring a few inconclusive victories. Bonfils, in turn, had sunk an estimated two million into his *Morning Post*. The Baby Elephant had turned out to be a white one. Its drains on the money-making afternoon *Post* were disclosed a few years later, in 1930, when Bon almost sold out. An audit then disclosed that the *Post* in 1920 had gone into the charmed and exclusive circle of American newspapers earning more than a million dollars a year. During the subsequent decade the only years when earnings dropped below the million mark were 1927 and 1928, when the *Morning Post* was contesting with the *News*.[6]

Both Roy Howard and Bonfils were ready to call off the shooting match.

The *News* had spent heavily, won a few gains, taken fair measure of the *Morning Post*, but had done little to disturb the dominance of the

[6]Fowler, *Timber Line*, p. 468.

evening *Post*. Looking back in the inexpensive freedom of hindsight, a couple of errors in policy and tactics seem evident. Scripps-Howard abandoned in Denver the prudent operating methods which were serving it well in a score of other cities. The thrill of a battle for mile-high stakes put the whole affair on a plane of highly charged emotional stimulation. Vital energies, and much gold, were drained off in larking on the battlements. Moreover the enemy was permitted to choose both weapons and battleground. The *Post*, quite naturally, chose ballyhoo: Houdini hanging by his heels, crazy-quilt contests, bathing beauties in sham snowball fights, a pack of mongrels turned loose in City Hall, Indian war dances in Champa Street, and picnics at the Old Ladies' Home—with someone else providing the lemonade. The battlefield was a circus arena, and Bonfils was the man who *owned* a circus. The *News* was an awkward amateur.

Thus the time came for Roy Howard to make another speech to the Denver Chamber of Commerce.

The date was November 9, 1928. Bob Chase covered the luncheon meeting and wrote the story. Attendance records again were shattered. Some three hundred and fifty businessmen crowded in with an anticipatory tenseness as great as they had displayed two years earlier. There weren't enough seats to go around, and some of the commercial leaders had to stand in the doorway.

Bon was to have spoken, too, but he was ill and sent his nephew, Major F. W. Bonfils, the *Post's* business manager, to represent him. The younger Bonfils made public the five-million-dollar loss figure and the weariness of the gladiators.

Tyson Dines, president of the chamber, commented hopefully on the "beginning of a golden age in Denver" and disclosed that "the lion and the lamb have lain down together" without designating which was which.

Then it was Howard's turn to speak. He ended the fight in the same crisp good humor with which he had started it.

"In closing some brief and expensive remarks before this club two years ago," he began, "I referred to the fact that the challenger never looks as good as the champion before the fight.

"Having tested that, I want to say that the challenger does not of necessity look as good as the champion *after* the fight.

"Two years ago, when I spoke before you, I had no notes. As a consequence I have been signing notes since that time. Today I speak from notes."

He pointed out that he was wearing the same suit he had worn to the earlier luncheon. "I have heard it said here in Denver that we have lost our shirt. I want to demonstrate that, even so, we have saved the coat and pants."

Negotiations had been concluded Sunday night. Bonfils had purchased the *Evening News*, Scripps-Howard the *Morning Post*. Both papers suspended, hastily, with their editions of Monday, November 5. At the same time the remaining papers, the morning *News* and the evening *Post*, raised their prices to three cents daily and ten cents Sunday from two cents and five cents. Howard, as chairman of the board of Scripps-Howard Newspapers, had written a by-line piece for page one of the Monday *News*:

> In the interest of progress and welfare of the community and in response to the economic demands of the situation, the Denver newspaper publishers today announce the reduction of the local field to one morning, one evening and two Sunday morning papers. . . .
>
> The move is designed to correct a situation which has proved itself unsound, wasteful and prejudicial to both the publishers and the business interests of Denver. It is a move in harmony with the spirit and the tendency of the times—with the national movement to eliminate waste and duplication of effort in the interest of better service to the public. . . .
>
> During the two years . . . Denver has witnessed a journalistic duel that has had few equals in recent years, either from the standpoint of spectacularity or on the basis of expenditures involved. Fortune has flirted with both sides and advantages have been won and lost.
>
> The Evening News has been one of the best newspapers in the nationwide chain. It has been more conservative in both dress and character, more condensed and less colorful than its competitor, the Denver Post. . . .
>
> The plain truth of the matter, plus a sportsmanlike desire to give credit where credit is due, compels the frank admission that after having been offered two years' opportunity to judge of a result which had involved the employment of much ingenuity and the expenditure of several million dollars, an overwhelming majority of the people of Denver and the adjacent newspaper field continued their preference for the type of evening paper produced by F. G. Bonfils in The Evening Post, rather than for the type offered by Scripps-Howard in The Evening News.
>
> After two years of editorial enterprise and expensive effort on the part of The Evening News there has been a material increase in both circulation and advertising patronage. This support has not been sufficient, however, to indicate a change in the evening newspaper reading habit great enough to constitute an actual demand for a second evening paper.
>
> On the other hand, The Rocky Mountain News under Scripps-Howard management has enjoyed a re-birth. Its circulation has more than doubled. It is obviously filling a niche that is all its own and is meeting a well-defined demand. Coincidentally, the Denver Morning Post has been facing all the resistance and the heavy expenditures that are the inevitable fate of a pioneering experiment in the field of journalism. . . .

Without a grouch or a grudge, The Denver Evening News salutes its surviving competitor in the evening field, The Denver Post, and wishes it success. It has been a good fight. Neither alibis nor excuses are in order. None will be offered.

On the other hand, The Rocky Mountain News, proud of its achievements and of the cordial support it has received, welcomes the new order of things and steps forward to the task of supplying Denver's morning newspaper needs with a full sense of its new opportunity and its new responsibility, and with a determination to give to this community the best that money and effort will produce in the way of a well-balanced, highly informative, ultra-modern morning newspaper. . . .

Howard wrote that the Associated Press service also would return to the columns of the *News*. The AP had been dropped, he explained, because its rules would have prevented the *Evening News* from passing on its news to the other twenty-four Scripps-Howard papers, all of which were using United Press exclusively. The *Rocky Mountain News* would be the only morning paper in the organization, and thus there would be no conflict with AP bylaws.

To the Chamber of Commerce luncheon Howard offered more intimate details on the transaction. The unlamented newspaper war, he said, had been something like a duel of two snapping turtles, which, according to superstition, "never let go until it thunders." He had gone to Bonfils and "talked like thunder. . . . I thought it was time for both of us to get in out of the wet." The war also was putting both papers "in contempt of their public."[7]

He expressed regret that his honorable opponent had been kept away from the luncheon. A cold was responsible, "not any deafness as a result of our conferences.

"By his absence, I have the advantage of Mr. Bonfils," Howard said. "I might add, parenthetically, that this is one of the few occasions on which I could claim that distinction." He referred to the presidential election earlier that week. Al Smith had got the applause but Hoover the votes. "Two years ago you gave me your applause and you very largely gave Mr. Bonfils your subscriptions and your advertising. Today I feel particularly big hearted—and I'll be entirely forgiving if you reverse the process."

Chairman Dines had held up an orange as symbol of the new golden age dawning. Howard commented wryly that he had been "under the impression we were growing lemons in Denver," and he mused that running a newspaper is like playing shortstop: "One must accept a lot of chances and handle them rapidly. The runner will not wait while you decide whether to throw to first or second."

[7] *Editor & Publisher*, Vol. 61, No. 25 (Nov. 10, 1928), p. 25.

But now, he said, beanball pitching, venom, unfair practices, and discriminatory rates were at an end.

There would be no ending of lusty competition, of course, but "arguments will be conducted with facts, rather than gasoline."

And so an armistice came to the Battle of the Century.

Dark Days in the Far West

NEXT came the lean and hungry years, the tempering. Adversity, boon companion of a youthful frontier newspaper, returned to live with the *Rocky Mountain News* as it had in those young seasons when marauding Indians cut off supplies of paper for printing or plunged Denver into isolation by tearing down the telegraph lines. The belt was drawn tight again to the farther notches.

Such had been the progress of life and journalism toward economic complexity, however, that poverty itself was expensive. It would be nearly two decades before black ink returned to the ledgers of the *News* with any consistency, and in that bleak interval another half million dollars were lost in the sorry business of just hanging on. But the talent for survival reasserted itself, and the *News* did hang on. Roy Howard stood fast. Fortunately his purse by now was a deep one, though it is small wonder he felt impelled to reach for the antacid pills whenever the thought of Denver crossed his mind.

The armistice was a quiet one. No one was in a mood for crowing. Flags remained furled and bunting in storage. No medals were passed out to ink-stained warriors. When the fight had been hot the fine, brave noise of lusty smitings had carried into the city rooms of the most remote newspapers in America. Adventurous mercenaries had hurried to the colors—and fattened pay checks—from all quarters. Now the exodus was as rapid as the influx had been. The cheerless task of marching patrol on the chill battleground was left to the winter soldiers, the old pros, the hard-bitten mustangs.

Demobilization on Champa Street was abrupt. Virtually the entire staff of the *Morning Post* was summarily discharged, with neither thanks nor dismissal pay. H. Allen Smith, who had cannily acquired a skill in the highly specialized field of reporting Bonfils doings for Bonfils papers, was retained. Others departed, among them Joe Alex Morris. Morris is remembered in Denver as a fired-up cub, fresh out of the University of Missouri journalism school, who bounced onto the *Morning Post* staff in 1927 just in time to have his head chopped off a few months later. He moved on to the United Press in Washington and a distinguished career as correspondent and foreign editor. Recently, after terms as foreign editor of the New York *Herald Tribune* and managing editor of *Collier's*, Morris has been biographer of the United Press in *Deadline Every Minute*.

On Welton Street the firings were fewer. Some staff members put in for transfers to other and more hopefully situated Scripps-Howard papers. Some wandered away on their own volition to try their luck in foreign print shops. The dispirited or grimly tenacious remnants of the staffs of the NEWSpapers were merged into one force for the *Rocky Mountain News*. Morale was low. The high crusade—run the *Post* out of town—had failed in its mission of journalistic sanitation.

Gloom sat on the typewriters in the second-floor city room on Welton Street. It didn't help at all that the whole town believed the *News* had taken a horrible licking. Certainly it appeared that way, and the *Post* emerged as cock of the walk for years to come. Actually, however, the two-year war ended in a much more even draw than anyone suspected at the time, and the last blow in the hostilities was scored by Roy Howard. Considering the shrewd ways and parsimonious nature of his opponent, it was a crowning stroke.

Howard was hurt. There was no doubt about that. The balance sheets on his Denver foray ran red with a $2,300,000 deficit. And it was he who initiated the peace talks. But Bonfils was hurt too. He admitted publicly to a loss of two million plus. How deeply this cut—or how much unadmitted red ink was flowing—can now be indicated for the first time.

Bonfils was so anxious to kill his till-tapping *Morning Post* and get in out of the wet that he laid a quarter of a million dollars in *cold cash* on the line!

In major newspaper negotiations today a quarter million, give or take, would scarcely justify exclamatory punctuation. But this was 1928, when any major fraction of a million dollars still had shock power, and the man who paid out the dollars was Fred Bonfils. The same man who once lectured George Creel on the evils of overtipping waiters and who required that his own relatives dig down at the ticket wagon for admittance to his Sells-Floto circus.

Suspension of the directly competing papers was accomplished by cross purchase. No money changed hands in this phase of the bargaining. Scripps-Howard bought the *Morning Post*, Bonfils the *Evening News*, and the nominal values of the papers were assumed to be exactly equal. Then Howard submitted the proposition that his getting out of the evening field represented a greater sacrifice than Bon's retiring from morning journalism. A cumshaw of $250,000 ought to about square things. Bonfils, pained by the expensive appetites of his two-year-old Baby Elephant, sighed and agreed. Possibly he was not at his best at this point. His sensitivities were sorely troubled, and the distractions of unaccustomed deficits perhaps threw him off balance as a bargainer. At any rate the man from New York again bested at his own game a dealer generally conceded to have been one of the keenest, toughest operators in American journalism.

As it turned out the deal, so far as Howard was concerned, was incidental to a Wyoming elk hunt.

"A bunch of us were up in the Bridger Lakes region after elk," Howard remembers. "T. Joe Cahill arranged the hunt for us, out of Cody. T. Joe then was Wyoming's fish and game chief. I got myself an old bull. Old and tough. It took four shots to put him down. That was on October 28.

"Well, once I had my elk I broke off the hunt, hopped a train and went down to Denver. On Tuesday, that would be October 30, I paid a call on Bon at his office. Bon was all courtesy and grace that day. I laid it on the line to him.

" 'Fred,' I told him, 'we're beating each other's brains out and getting nowhere. We both have enough money to keep this thing going as long as the other guy. Unless you get some sadistic thrill out of this, I propose we call it off.'

"Bon leaned over and tapped me on the knee in that fatherly way of his. 'Why, Roy,' he said, 'how can you say such a thing? There has never been anything sadistic in my relationship with you or your newspaper.' He pretended to be shocked that I had used the word."

Howard outlined his proposal for a truce. "Sounds very interesting," Bonfils said. For the next five days the two publishers met daily in Howard's suite at the Cosmopolitan Hotel. Two sessions a day, ten to twelve, two to five, and Bon always was punctual.

"After the second day, Bonfils started going over and over the same ground," Howard says. "It puzzled me until I finally tumbled to what he was up to. The old fox was trying to trap me in a lie. I wasn't trying to be foxy at all. Bon was too slick and too smart for that, and I knew it. He was devious and he was smooth.

"Finally, when he decided he wasn't going to catch me in a changed story, he turned on the charm and we closed out the deal in forty-five minutes. I've been in thirty-five different newspaper purchases and deals in my time, and never one easier than this one once Bon was satisfied I was dealing off the top of the deck, and that I was giving him a true picture of our intentions and abilities. Bonfils knew every phase of his business intimately. Prodigious memory."

The bargain was wrapped up on Sunday night, November 4. Along with the cross-purchase arrangement and the cash settlement, a three-year agreement was reached—and signed next day—for a laundering of Denver journalism. Bon agreed to put away the lead pipe. He promised he would not "solicit, make or accept" advertising contracts with "rates, rebates, position, etc." that would penalize the *News*. Despite his able memory, this clause of the agreement apparently slipped his mind after a short while. Advertising managers of the two papers were to meet and agree on classification of local and national advertising for rate-making purposes. There would be no more circulation contests, premiums, bonuses to street sellers. It was agreed that the *Post's* hours of publication would be 9 A.M. to 9 P.M., those of the *News* from 9 P.M. to 9 A.M. Neither Sunday paper would appear before six Saturday evening. Cass Herrington, who had been Bonfils' attorney through the negotiations, was to referee any dispute which might arise. By telegraph, Kent Cooper, chief of the Associated Press, gave his blessing to a transfer of the *Morning Post's* AP franchise back to the *News*. After details were smoothed out the publishers sat down and drafted statements for their respective Monday papers, and Howard fired a wire to Bob Scripps: CLOSED DEAL TONIGHT STOP WE RECEIVE QUARTER MILLION.

When Bonfils unexpectedly fell for the cash-settlement proposal Howard generously proposed that the matter be held in confidence to permit the proud Corsican to save face. Bon's sense of personal dignity was as stiff as that pride of body which gave him a carriage like a formal sentry's. His secret has been kept for thirty years and is revealed now for the first time. No word of it appeared in the truce announcements printed by the *News* and *Post*, although *Editor & Publisher* in its report of the transaction indicated there had been a sweetening of the deal.[1] The *Editor & Publisher* report never received confirmation from Scripps-Howard or the Red Room, and Howard sent Bonfils a note from New York on November 16 expressing hope that his cold was better and reassuring him that *E&P's* speculations were not based on anything Scripps-Howard had disclosed.

The quarter million was nearly enough to keep the *News* afloat through the years of dolor ahead. From December 1928 through 1942, Scripps-Howard records show, the *News* lost about $400,000. Bon's $250,000 went a long way toward paying the bill for the holding operation while the *News* struggled to re-establish a success formula.

Reflections on this wry quirk of fortune probably deepened Bonfils' distaste for "foreigners," and the *Post* always had made a fetish of blatant provincialism. Sulphuric comments on the "invasion of Denver" by the "foreign-owned press" had been, in fact, the *Post's* first salvo when Scripps-Howard came to town, though why Roy Howard was an invader and Shaffer had not been was never explained to Champa Street's many little brothers. In his first speech to the Chamber of Commerce, Howard had quipped that the *Post's* fuss about foreigners may have led his listeners to expect they would be addressed by "a Chinese mandarin, a Persian shah or a Bulgarian peasant." Scripps-Howard, he pointed out, was no more an alien to Rocky Mountain shores than the Union Pacific Railroad, the Swift Packing Company, or any one of a number of big

[1] *Editor & Publisher*, Vol. 61, No. 25 (Nov. 10, 1928).

organizations which contributed sizably to the Denver economy. Howard also might have reminded Bonfils that he and Tammen had been foreigners themselves when they operated the noisy Kansas City *Post* from 1909 to 1922. *They* had departed Kansas City taking $1,290,000 *out*. Scripps-Howard poured $3,300,000 into Denver before a cent flowed in the opposite direction.

William G. Chandler, then president of the Ohio group of Scripps-Howard newspapers and later general business manager and president of the Scripps-Howard Supply Company, was on the scene in Denver when the battle started and took special interest in its fiscal logistics. He notes that it would have been extremely unlikely that an individual publisher, be he ever so native to the banks of the Platte, would have had the resources to make the fight Scripps-Howard did. Silas Bent called it "Denver's Holy Newspaper War" in the *Independent*,[2] and if virtue did not triumph in this instance other worthy crusades also have been known to fall short of laudable objectives.

Certainly in terms of mere survival it was fortunate that Colorado's oldest newspaper at this point was a member of a family of broad and well-developed resources. Family connections saw the *News* through its hour of gloom and then through nearly a quarter century of financial drouth such as would have impoverished an individual or local owner. The family, moreover, could weigh certain intangibles against the harsh facts of perennial operating losses and achieve a balance forbidden to a purely local ownership.

"Under Jim Scripps our papers had been hog-tied to their budgets," Bill Chandler says. "Roy was and is a fighter. When he went into that Denver situation with his eyes wide open, he wanted to let people know that individual Scripps-Howard papers would and could fight. That they would and could fight *back* and were not sitting ducks dependent entirely on their own local resources. Specifically, he wanted to show that the *Rocky Mountain News* would fight, if necessary, and would spend, if necessary.

"It was news to everyone in the country that anyone would dare to spit in Bon's eye. We feel the losses in Denver were more than paid off in other cities by the prestige won in making that fight."

The *News* in its time of need thus had the advantages of the unorthodox system of operating policy which Roy Howard built and extended along the patterns E. W. Scripps had cut out. It is a system not often employed among corporations of large geographical span and is wholly unique among national newspaper organizations. It is not generally understood and on occasion has been willfully misunderstood by critics who raise monolithic specters of absentee control over the information and comment available to 3,026,724 readers of nineteen papers

[2]*Independent*, May 21, 1927.

in eighteen major cities.[3] In practice the Scripps-Howard system combines the efficiency and economy of nationwide services—editorial, financial, housekeeping, supply, legal—with a maximum of local policy-making freedom and responsibility. No regional vice-president of a national corporation enjoys a fraction of the independence exercised daily by the editor of a Scripps-Howard paper. The editor does not take policy problems to the general management for solution, and there are no "musts" among the editorials, news dispatches, and feature articles available to him through the various Scripps-Howard services. An editorial on national affairs written in Washington may be published in San Francisco and Pittsburgh, and hit the wastebasket in Houston and New York. It is no more a "canned" editorial than would be a similar essay drafted for the New York *Times* in Washington under the guidance of James Reston. Scripps-Howard papers are not edited with a cookie cutter. They are, in fact, highly individualistic journals, and in some cities—notably Cleveland, Memphis, and Denver—they have built reputations through many years of community service and civic participation as intensely "local" institutions.

The pooling of resources provides the individual papers, in times of disasters comparable to Bonfils, the sort of comforting cushion which caught the *News* and sustained it through the thirties and forties. It also makes possible national and international coverage of Pulitzer prize stature such as is denied to all but a handful of the largest and wealthiest of wholly local newspapers. Few isolated papers can afford a Washington bureau of the quality which offers to Scripps-Howard papers the skills of men like Andrew Tully, Charles T. Lucey, and a dozen other talented capital correspondents. Foreign correspondence of the caliber of Jim Lucas and the late Ernie Pyle also is beyond the means of most papers. Yet services of this nature are available as much to the modest Evansville *Press* and Albuquerque *Tribune* as to the metropolitan *World-Telegram and Sun.*

This familial relationship is unclear to many persons. Perhaps a run-down on the structure of Scripps-Howard is needed to clarify the position the *Rocky Mountain News* has occupied since November 1926.

Scripps-Howard is not in itself a corporation. Each newspaper is published by a separate corporation. In the case of the *News* the corporate entity is the Denver Publishing Company, incorporated under the laws of the state of Colorado.

A majority of the stock in each Scripps-Howard newspaper is held by

[3]In addition to the *Rocky Mountain News*, member papers of the organization today are: Albuquerque *Tribune*, Birmingham *Post-Herald*, Cincinnati *Post and Times-Star*, Cleveland *Press*, Columbus *Citizen*, El Paso *Herald-Post*, Evansville *Press*, Fort Worth *Press*, Houston *Press*, Indianapolis *Times*, *Kentucky Post* (Covington), Knoxville *News-Sentinel*, Memphis *Commercial Appeal*, Memphis *Press-Scimitar*, New York *World-Telegram and Sun*, Pittsburgh *Press*, San Francisco *News*, and Washington *News*.

the E. W. Scripps Company, with headquarters in Cincinnati. Jack R. Howard, Roy's forty-eight-year-old son and a seasoned newsman who deliberately beat his way up the ranks, succeeded his father as president of the Scripps Company on January 1, 1953.[4] At the same time Charles E. Scripps, second eldest (then thirty-three) grandson of old E.W., took over from W. W. Hawkins as chairman of the board. Although, like Jack Howard, he was an heir apparent, six-foot Charles Scripps shared young Howard's distaste for learning the business from the top down. He also has worked as a reporter for his own and other newspapers, and a year of this self-imposed apprenticeship was spent on the staff of the *Rocky Mountain News*.

Fortune has described the E. W. Scripps Company as "dynastic in matters of control, informal in methods of organization, and all but imperial in dimensions." It has grown from a $28,000 operation in 1879 to $28,000,000 in 1925—the last full year of E. W. Scripps' life—to $50,000,000 in 1940 and on to $140,000,000 in the 1950s when Roy Howard and Hawkins, Charles Scripps' stepfather, moved aside to make way for the younger men. Roy's voice continues to be heard in the top echelons as chairman of the executive committee, and he also retains the position of editor of the *World-Telegram and Sun*.

The Scripps Company holds the controlling interest in the *Rocky Mountain News*. There are 10,000 shares of capital stock in the Denver Publishing Company. Of these, 2500 shares are common voting stock and 7500 are non-voting. The Scripps Company owns all 2500 voting and 6500 of the non-voting shares. The remaining 1000 shares are locally held.

Approximately seventy-five per cent of the Scripps Company, in turn, is owned by the E. W. Scripps Trust, the family trust set up by E.W. to establish succession of his heirs to the newspaper empire he created. Under terms of E.W.'s will his third son, Robert Paine Scripps, was sole trustee until his death in 1938, when Roy Howard became an interim trustee until Bob Scripps' sons attained their majorities. Today Charles Scripps is chairman of the family board of trustees. His elder brother, Robert P. Scripps, Jr., is vice-chairman, but he inherited a love of the soil from his grandfather and prefers ranching at Pecos, Texas, to active newspapering. The third trustee is Edward W. (Ted) Scripps II, youngest of Bob Scripps' sons. In the pattern of his brother Charles, Ted is learning the business as a non-titled employee of his own papers. During the past two years he has been a working member of the *Rocky Mountain News* staff, covering general assignments and the Statehouse as a reporter and writing a Sunday column. An affable and unassuming young man, he occupies a rank-and-file reporter's desk in the *News* city room and moves quietly through the day-to-day clatter. (Ted has been initiated into the

[4]*Newsweek*, Sept. 29, 1952; *Fortune*, Oct. 1953.

raffish traditions of Denver journalism at the irreverent annual banquet which memorializes a deceased *Post* political reporter who was cordially disliked, built a reputation on other men's work, and welshed on his gin-rummy debts. A leading lobbyist and notable victim of the welshing is host to the Statehouse press corps for the dinner, held during the session of the state legislature. Veteran newsmen who knew the deceased are asked to comment on his career, and a formal effort is made each year to speak well of the dead. The effort never comes off. It quickly progresses into a scandalous anthology of excoriating anecdotes punctuated by toasts to the departed brother, wherever he may be.)

The E. W. Scripps Trust, through the Scripps Company, also holds a controlling interest in the affiliated enterprises: United Press International, UPI Newspictures, the Newspaper Enterprise Association, United Feature Syndicate, and Scripps-Howard Radio Inc., of which Jack Howard also is president. Scripps-Howard Radio operates WEWS-TV in Cleveland, WCPO and WCPO-TV in Cincinnati, and WNOX in Knoxville. Roy Howard shares ownership with the Scripps heirs as holder of the largest minority interest in the Scripps Company. The family trust maintains headquarters with those of the Scripps Company in Cincinnati.

The Scripps-Howard Supply Company, headed by William G. Chandler as president, has its main office in New York and its operating base in Cleveland. Legal department for the complex also is in Cleveland, along with the main editorial and business offices of NEA.

Employees of the nineteen newspapers have the opportunity of sharing in ownership through the Scripps-Howard Investment Company, a non-operating company with an unsalaried board of directors. The investment company holds stock in most of the newspapers. Its own shares carry a nominal par value and have a record of well above average earnings for the thousands of employees who have put savings into them.

The general management of the Scripps-Howard newspapers functions from the twenty-second floor of the Grand Central Building at 230 Park Avenue in New York City. The outfit never has been much for show. Its general offices are Spartan-plain and somber in décor, almost shabby when compared with the lavish showcases in which many a smaller organization installs its top executives. The office of Roy Howard, who picked up an affection for the Orient on his world travels, is furnished to his taste in Chinese lacquers. Jack Howard occupies a smaller, unglorified office nearby.

He serves as general editorial manager of the concern, with Jack H. Lockhart as his assistant. Also in the top management group are Roy Howard, Bill Chandler, and Mark Ferree, general business manager. For major policy-making sessions, Charles Scripps flies in from Cincinnati (sometimes piloting the company airplane himself) and editor in chief Walker Stone comes up from Washington.

Washington is editorial headquarters for the chain, as to both foreign and national news. The editorial services are accomplished through the Scripps-Howard Newspaper Alliance, home base for the string of capital and foreign correspondents, editorial writers, and columnists whose work is available to member papers. Frank R. Ford is SHNA editor. Working with him are the bearers of such familiar by-lines as Ludwell Denny, Jim Lucas, Charles T. Lucey, Daniel M. Kidney, Fred W. Perkins, Dickson Preston, Andrew Tully, John Troan, R. H. Shackford, Jack Steele, Marshall McNeil, Oland D. Russell, Gene Wortsman, Ruth Finney, Mrs. Walter Ferguson (from Tulsa), and Albert M. Colegrove (from San Francisco). H. M. Talburt, whose editorial cartoons are a regular feature of most Scripps-Howard papers, also works in Washington.

How does this all work out in the daily whirl of news gathering and publishing?

The late John H. Sorrells, then executive editor for the chain, explained it this way:

> The General Management has administrative authority with respect to all of the newspapers: it selects editors and business managers, formulates certain over-all policies—editorial and business—and gives counsel and direction to editors and business managers as circumstances require.
>
> The local managers have wide discretion in the formulation of local policy and the direction of local activities. While business practices do not vary greatly between papers and cities, editorial and news policies derive primarily from local and regional conditions and interests. Scripps-Howard editors have broad powers of decision in such matters.
>
> Scripps-Howard editors also have a defined responsibility and authority with respect to certain matters of internal policy on the newspapers. A major concept in Scripps-Howard is the idea that its canons of good taste must apply to all departments equally, hence the final authority, and responsibility, for determining the acceptability of advertising rests on the editor. As a corollary to this, and to give force to the editor's hand, the composing room is under his control and direction.[5]

Fortune magazine took a look at the operation at the time Jack Howard and Charles Scripps moved into command and reported:

> The precise status and authority of the young men are no more subject to exact definition than those of the men who preceded them. Nothing is more perishable than daily journalism's commodity, the solid but fleeting facts that can only be sold fresh. To sell them profitably, important decisions on publishing and editorial policy must be made regularly to give passing news continuing acceptability. But Scripps-Howard's top decisions have never emerged from an organizational chart. The complexities of this business made group deliberation

[5]Sorrells, op. cit., pp. 15–16.

necessary long before the appearance of committees in other large enterprises and led to delegation of authority long before the word decentralization was used by such companies as General Motors. . . .

Since it is unlikely that newspapers are going to cost less to produce, the long-run profitability of Scripps-Howard depends on marketing decisions. And the marketing of Scripps-Howard's highly perishable commodity is no small undertaking in a world deafened with noises and alarms, and sated with something as sensational as the possibility of being blown to bits.

In the news business generally, decisions do not emerge by standard corporation practices. Part of the policy at Scripps-Howard, for instance, consists of having no policies about the United Press, an asset to the company only so long as it is independent. Editorial policy on local and state issues is settled by local editors. Policy on important national affairs is set by all the editors and the top executives at a formal once-a-year conclave and by frequent informal discussions, queries, and suggestions over leased wires. Among top executives it is impossible to state the exact sphere of any man's activities, except for special functions like soliciting advertising and buying newsprint. It can be said that management in Scripps-Howard dictates very little.[6]

In his recent autobiography Louis B. Seltzer, sometimes known as "Mr. Cleveland," writes of his appointment to the editorship of E. W. Scripps' first paper, the Cleveland *Press:*

> In a measure greater than any other newspaper organization in America, the Scripps-Howard concern has traditionally accorded independent judgment to its individual editors. I was to make use of this latitude in the future, not infrequently to the acute distress of Roy Howard and others in the ownership and management of the papers. Their unswerving support, even when I am sure they believed me to be wrong, is one of the most gratifying aspects of my approximately forty years with Scripps-Howard.[7]

This, then, is the structure and gearing of the outfit which backed up the *Rocky Mountain News* as it emerged, bloody but unvanquished, from the bout with Fred Bonfils. Changes came to the *News.* Mostly they were of the scrimping sort that accompany poverty. At one point reporters and copyreaders were required to turn in the stub of a copy pencil before they could requisition a new one. And sometimes the advertising in a single issue was scarcely sufficient to cover the cost of the copy pencils worn down in preparing it.

Changes came to the *News,* and also to Bonfils. The settlement seemed to sadden him. Perhaps he came to realize that over the long haul he couldn't win. Certainly he had not parted blithely with the

[6]*Fortune,* Oct. 1953, pp. 167, 176.

[7]Louis B. Seltzer, *The Years Were Good* (New York, 1956), p. 176.

quarter million dollars he paid for the privilege of getting out of a fight. He had, indeed, lost face, even if no one in Denver knew it. Bon was a brooder, and a brooder, with his private stocks of secret woes, can suffer internally though all the world proclaim him a tranquil conqueror. Bonfils' essay at morning journalism had proved a costly experiment, and yet it must have pained the parent to kill off his baby before the toddler was two years old. And the expectations for its future had been so high. But now the infant paragon was gone, without once having a chance to prove how it worshiped the right and the good and the beautiful.

Whatever the sources of his discontent, Bonfils became in the next few years a subdued and even lonelier man. A worrisome little frown creased his noble brow. His moods were brittle, sad, and philosophic. He seemed to become less assured. For the first time he began to be sensitive to criticism. He was cut by man's ingratitude, and hurt that Denver didn't accept him as the benefactor of humankind and Big Brother he wanted to appear and perhaps in his odd logic actually believed himself to be.

He spoke often, in conversation and in print, about the need for devotion to the common weal. Gene Fowler has recalled how Bon conceived the notion that Colorado's No. 1 auto license plate, held for years by a pioneer motorist, should be conferred instead upon the state's "worthiest citizen"—as selected by the Denver *Post*. The idea caught on. During the first year the distinctive license plate went to Emily Griffith, founder and principal of Denver's Opportunity School, a pioneer center in the American adult-education movement. The town applauded. Denver has always been proud of Emily Griffith and her school, where thousands of immigrants have been taught English and the Constitution and hordes of workingmen and women have learned trades or qualified for high school diplomas by off-hours study. Yes, spunky little Emily Griffith surely was Denver's "worthiest citizen."

The following year the No. 1 license was fixed to the automobile of Fred G. Bonfils—and remained there for years to come.

Strangely enough, this instance of almost pathetic hunger for public acclaim was passed off in Denver with only a few hoots from the *News* and smiling headshakes on street corners. The city had become fairly well inured to such seizures, although there were times when indignation boiled over.

One of these occasions came at a meeting of the Jane Jefferson Club in the Brown Palace at which sentiments were being whipped up for a primary election campaign in August 1932. The retiring state chairman of the Democratic party, editor Walter Walker of the Grand Junction *Sentinel*, took the opportunity to purge himself of certain strong feelings about Bonfils.

A reporter for the *News*, Maurice Leckenby, asked for a text of the remarks and he was given one, though doubt was expressed that the paper would dare publish them. But a full accounting of Walker's speech appeared in print next morning. Bonfils immediately sued the *News* for libel, alleging injuries which would require two hundred thousand dollars to heal.

Preliminary sparring was by deposition, and Philip Van Cise, attorney for the *News*, finally won the legal right to question Bonfils before a notary public. Bonfils answered a few questions and then clamped his jaw shut. The line of Van Cise's inquiry indicated that the entire Bonfils biography, from Oklahoma land manipulations to lotteries to Teapot Dome, was to become a matter of public record. Bon clapped his derby on his head and departed in a tower of rage.

Van Cise countered with a motion to district court that Bonfils be cited for contempt for failing to answer the questions. The *News'* motion said that counsel Van Cise was prepared to prove, by Bonfils himself, the truth of forty-one points of justification for Walter Walker's remarks.

The judge ruled that Bonfils would have to appear in January 1933 to answer such questions as the keen Van Cise cared to propound.

Bonfils was spared this further invasion of his private history, and the libel suit never came to trial. One afternoon late in January he went home early from the Red Room with a cold. The infection spread and a middle-ear operation was performed, but a week later, early on the morning of February 2, Bonfils died of encephalitis at the age of seventy-two. It was the end of an era for the American press. The last of the giants of personal journalism was gone.

As dawn spread over the Mile-High City he had considered his fief by Divine Providence, Bonfils did not have to witness a final indignity. The *News* beat his paper to the streets with word of his death. By twenty minutes, in a contest of extras. A tip that Bon was dying had come to Joe McMeel, then managing editor for the *News*. Reporters Gene Cervi and Harry Walker were dispatched to the Bonfils mansion on East Tenth Avenue abutting Cheesman Park to mount a nightlong vigil. They watched oxygen tanks from Children's Hospital being carried in, and saw the Rev. Hugh L. McMenamin, rector of the Cathedral of the Immaculate Conception, come and go. In his last hours Bonfils had called for a priest and been baptized in the Catholic Church.

The eastern sky began to pale, and lights went on in the mansion. A cab drew up, and Volney Hoggatt, Bon's long-time bodyguard and companion, got out. Cervi and Walker cornered the cabby, who said Hoggatt had told him, "Bonfils is dead." The word was phoned to the *News*, where the story had been in preparation all night, Wally Reef writing. Confirmation was needed. *Post* staff members, routed from their beds, denied the report. So *News* reporters got on the telephones, calling every mortuary in town, posing as members of the Bonfils household and demanding to know when a car would be sent. Finally one mortuary protested that its car already was on the way. It was enough. Max Greedy wrote the headlines and the presses rolled. The *News* had its scoop.

It was big news, of course, that death was prouder and stronger than the seemingly invincible Bonfils, and considering the day and the circumstances, extras were fully justified, though, again, it is extremely doubtful that very many startled citizens bothered to notice who scooped whom by twenty minutes. The solemn and sweaty rites of the news beat had been observed with formal diligence that morning on Welton and Champa streets, but Bonfils would have understood. His paper, he often asserted, was "first in everything," and he had caused that it should be emblazoned in the masthead that the *Post* was "The Best Newspaper in the U.S.A."

Later in the day of February 2 the *Post's* regular editions came out with every column rule on page one turned, creating so many black borders and margins that a casual visitor might have wondered if the press had broken down. The entire front page, save only for the weather forecast and Arthur Brisbane's column, was required to do justice to the passing. Inside, the obituary, photos, and messages of grief and appraisal spread over five pages.

Herbert Hoover sent condolences. Jack Dempsey attended the funeral along with merchants and politicians, many of whom at one time or another had felt the lash of Bonfils' power.

Bonfils left twenty million dollars, a gold-headed cane which subsequently was found to conceal a gun, and a wealth of legend which Denver cherishes and keeps alive with retellings and embroideries. Perhaps there's something of a subconscious community masochism in this. As Lee Casey commented in reviewing Fowler's *Timber Line*, if the reign of F. G. Bonfils was a scandal and harmful, the fault lay primarily with the town that submitted to it.[8] And certainly the *News* had done everything it could to foment rebellion.

As time rolled on from 1928, however, the *News* spoke with less and less vigor and to fewer and fewer listeners. Circulation dropped, and advertising revenues followed the dismal curve downward. The tally of subscribers dwindled to a corporal's guard of deep-rooted old-timers who respected the paper's ancient lineage, of irreconcilables who hated the *Post*, and of "best people," principally resident on Capitol and Park hills, who could afford two daily newspapers even during a depression. Much of Denver's wealth always has been concentrated east and south of midtown. In the eighties and nineties some of the mining kings and merchant princes chose the bluff west of the Platte for their ornate Victorian mansions, a few of which still stand, centered around the old town of Highland that William Byers had helped lay out. The Platte bottoms, however, filled up with railroad yards and an industrial and slum section. Viaducts were built to carry streetcars and auto traffic over

[8] *Rocky Mountain News*, Oct. 31, 1933.

the district, but analysts of Denver real estate say the eyesore area forced building of the more affluent neighborhoods to the south and east. The sharp growth of recent years has scrambled this economic geography somewhat, but in the thirties the people who worried about stock market values rather than the price of bread lived up the hill to the east or south along and beyond Cherry Creek, and it was in these areas that *News* carriers delivered most of their papers. The "quality" circulation was one of the few talking points available to Grosse Smith, E. A. Murphy, Parkhill Harvey, Con Hecker, and the other *News* advertising salesmen. They managed to get the message through to just enough merchants to keep the paper from looking like a Sunday school leaflet. Even so there were days when it wasted to as few as twelve yawning pages almost innocent of commercial pleadings. This, of course, compounded misery in geometrical progression, since research has shown that many patrons, particularly women, buy a newspaper as much for its advertising as for its red-hot exclusive news beats.

Circulation dropped from the high-water mark of 110,000 to a low of 33,400. During the three months ended June 30, 1928, the *Rocky Mountain News* and the *Evening News* circulated to a total of 92,587 patrons, and the Sunday paper to 105,675. By September 30, 1934, when bottom was touched, the daily average was down to 33,421, and the Sunday circulation hit its low point of 41,920 a year earlier. Meanwhile advertising linage was skidding from 8,151,851 lines in 1928 to 3,785,309 in 1940. Ribs were showing on a gaunt, much-subdued Wildcat of Welton Street.

Still the *News* clung on, backpedaling like a groggy prize fighter with more courage than punch power. Bob Boyd, who had majored at half-back on the University of Denver football team, took over from Dave Stein in April 1931 as circulation manager and fought a dogged retreat for every withdrawing subscriber. Upstairs in the city room a minimal editorial staff which adversity taught to be quick on its feet was turning out a quietly competent product without frills. Flamboyance was out the window. Conservatism in methods and make-up approached Kansas City *Star* levels. The loyal little staff gave a good account of itself against mounting odds, but its victories went largely unnoticed and an air of hand-to-mouth existence dampened any inclination of morale to soar. Down in the gloomy basement the presses, prematurely aged by the pounding they took during the Battle of the Century, were held together with baling wire, mucilage, and the improvising genius of a soft-spoken machinist named Charlie Larsen.

All in all the configuration of dark omens was such as to sour milk in the pasture. The stars were out of orbit, and buzzards circled overhead for fifteen long years. Somebody wasn't holding his mouth right. Everything that possibly could go awry did. Anything that under even improbable and hostile conditions would have been a roaring success wasn't. The *News* had scarcely regrouped its dwindling forces to with-stand siege when the roof caved in on American prosperity.

Repercussions of the October 1929 stock market crash did not reach Denver immediately. In fact *News* ad linage took a half-million hop upward in 1929, reaching the highest point it would achieve in the next nineteen years. Neither 1930 nor 1931 was badly off, but in 1932 the long decline began. National economic reversals are usually slow in coming to Denver. It is not primarily a manufacturing town, and it is far from being a one-industry city like some steel, auto, and textile centers. The widely diversified economy is based principally on distribu-tion, processing, and service industries. Fluctuations, both up and down, are less likely to be sharp ones. The 1958 recession, for example, did not have much over-all effect on Denver. *News* advertising revenues showed steady gains to new record-breaking levels. A similar stability was dis-played, at first, as the nation plunged into the Dirty Thirties.

By 1932 and 1933, however, Denver had joined the rest of the country in the slough. There were soup kitchens on Larimer Street, and doleful men in ragged GI overcoats from World War I dragged dispiritedly up Seventeenth Street to haunt the entrances to the Brown Palace in hope of handouts. The railroad yards filled up with hungry wanderers, shuffling about the country in chase of rumors of work. Emily Griffith's Opportunity School began to teach classes in gold panning, an art which had all but disappeared. Hundreds of the unemployed daily climbed down into the concrete-walled bed of Cherry Creek to wash sands which had been almost undisturbed since the Pike's Peak gold rush. Some of them took out two and three dollars a day in dust and trudged up West Colfax Avenue to deposit it at the mint.

Bishop Frank Rice of the Liberal Church Inc., the skid-row divine who laid the ghost of cannibal Packer, set up a center for relief services at his bare little meetinghouse in a vacant store on the alley off Larimer Street. The bishop concerned himself primarily with the "undeserving poor." There were, he argued, numerous high-minded moral and Chris-tian philanthropists affiliated with the uptown churches who were willing to contribute to the welfare of the deserving poor. He would take care of the other kind. Besides, he didn't insist on gratitude. At the Liberal Church hungry men were fed first and then had hymns sung to them. Other missions operated on a sterner system of ethics. Their soup was poured *after* prayers, frequently long-winded.

Bishop Rice's tactics in gathering alms to support his work occasionally approached strong-arm methods. He not only did not hesitate to put the bite on the town's leading clubmen and business princes, but he made a practice of calling on them regularly and frequently to remind them of their brotherhood with his congregation of bums, down-and-outers, winos, and ne'er-do-wells. Thus it came to pass that Rice paid a call at the carpeted offices of Gerald Hughes, first-magnitude banker and lawyer, in the International Trust Building. It was the second time in two days that Hughes had been subjected to ecclesiastical audience. He had come through the day before, and now he demurred to an additional tithe. The mendicant was escorted firmly to the door.

In the corridor Bishop Rice went down on his knees and began to pray, in a voice that carried through every partition in the building, for the redemption of the banker's immortal soul. The intercession ran something in this vein:

> Oh, Lord, in Thy infinite compassion, look down with mercy and forgiveness on Thy sinner Gerald Hughes! He is a good man, but he sometimes forgets. He will go home tonight to dine on roast squab under glass. Let not this luxury harden his heart to the plight of his brothers, starving tonight in the streets of Denver. We ask Thee to guide the footsteps of Thy sinner Gerald Hughes through the many perils of wealth and high living. He means well, but the temptations are many. . . .

Hughes stepped out and thrust a ten-dollar bill into the clasped hands of the kneeling supplicant. Rice opened one eye to take note of the denomination, then turned his enraptured face upward.

"Amen!" he shouted. "Thank you, Lord, for so promptly coming to the rescue of Thy sinner."

Rice shared in full the poverty of his parishioners. He ate the same food he served to them, and when there was nothing on hand to boil into soup he, too, went hungry. His clothes were ragged, his reversed collar soiled. He slept on a pallet in one corner of his mission. There was never any question that the gifts he wheedled or extorted went where they were supposed to go.

The specialty of the Liberal Church was the succoring of unfortunates everyone else had abandoned. When a Colorado boy was convicted of a particularly revolting and violent murder in California, Bishop Rice sought to go to the wretched youth's comfort. He put on a robe of sackcloth and appeared at Union Station clutching a brown paper bag filled with wood ashes. Then he climbed aboard a Colorado & Southern train, strewed the ashes over the white sheets of his Pullman berth, bedded himself, and tuned up in a wail of lamentations. The conductor threw him off the train at Pueblo. Rice sued for, and recovered, damages to his episcopal dignity—and spent the money on a round of turkey dinners at his mission.

Rice was a frequent visitor to the editorial rooms of the *News*, partly because Lee Casey was such a soft touch and partly because he had an acute appreciation of the values of publicity. He returned thanks for donations and editorial mention by distributing red hats and other church honors, along with more mundane gratuities. John Polly in his column, "The Reporter Who Gets Around," gave out with a particularly fine notice, and Rice told him: "The Lord will repay you for what you've done, and I hope to buy you a drink." One day Rice appeared in the office and formally invested Lee Casey as a "Major Prophet" of the Liberal Church. Later Bob Chase was created a cardinal, and Mary Coyle was officially decreed to be an "angel." Several bishoprics were established, although in one case there was a conflict in diocesan boundaries. When "Young Jack" Foster left Denver for New York and a promotion on the staff of the *Telegram*, Rice designated him Bishop of Broadway, obviously an evangelical assignment. Possibly he forgot that earlier he had installed Jack Howard as a cardinal and Bishop of All Journalism.

The desperation and want against which Bishop Rice, among others, struggled were by no means exclusively urban specters. The happy farmer had ceased to whistle behind his plow. While President-elect Franklin Roosevelt laid plans for Muscle Shoals and the Tennessee Valley experiment at remaking the good but recalcitrant earth, sons of the soil in Colorado were in open revolt against the moneylenders. Rebellion flared in the northeastern corner of the state at Julesburg, whence the early *News* had sent its pony express to pick up word of Lincoln's election. Five hundred bitter farmers gathered at the farm of George A. Jones, a mile north of town, and heard how he had lost his two hundred and forty acres to the bankers. He had deeded his farm to his creditors in order to be allowed to remain on it with a lease. Then his three thousand dollars worth of machinery had been repossessed. Wiped out. Farm gone, and now even the tools of a humble tenant. The assembled farmers listened to the story, marched to town in a growling mob, seized the entire lot of machinery, and returned it to the Jones place.[9] Elsewhere symbolic nooses dangled from barn doors to discourage outside bidders at foreclosure auctions. Neighbors rallied to the sales, bid in the foreclosed property at Woolworth prices—two cents for a horse, five cents for a binder—returned it all to the original owner, and stomped off home again.

In this sort of a topsy-turvy world the *News* was struggling to regain its poise. The odds ran long against success.

A series of editors and business managers bucked the hoodoo. Several of these men later became, in other cities, top-ranking newspaper executives with reputations for the golden touch. In Denver each failed to find a success formula. The touch was uniformly and dismally leaden. Highly competent men with enviable records for sober judgment, diligence, and profit making were placed in command of the *News*. A few held their own, some rocked the boat. Minor successes were scored, only to be wiped out by new reversals. Gray-haired experience was tried, and aggressive youth. Neither jelled. Most of the editors played it close and sought to balance the books by bare living and rigid economies. A couple

[9]*Rocky Mountain News*, Feb. 3, 1933.

spent expansively. Others tried the middle course. All three routes led only to dead ends.

The *News*, improbably, lived through both its friends and its foes.

Whatever it is that gives a newspaper endurance, the *News* had it. Probably part of the explanation lies in the quiet continuity provided by a few hard-bitten craftsmen, practical, competent realists like Bob Chase, Max Greedy, and a handful of others, who stayed at their desks and got out a paper while the town tittered over executive shenanigans and sharp operators tried to walk off with the roof over their heads. Lee Casey surely was a factor of survival. His column quickly established itself, and for many years it was the most popular single feature in either Denver newspaper. There were readers who bought the *News* only for Casey's wise, tolerant, kindly, but always provocative comments. Casey seldom thundered, and he was bookish at a time when books were widely regarded as the quaint toys of professors and hardly a diet for red-blooded, money-making go-getters. Some of the causes Casey gently advocated never seemed to catch fire, but the effect was cumulative. For the most part the men who were Casey's bosses have been almost forgotten in Denver. Casey, who flaunted every rule of "popularity" by nosing around publicly in Gibbon and Virgil, is remembered, and it is he, not they, who supplies the illustrative quotes for a number of principles outlined in a standard textbook on editorial writing.

Why rehash history? Casey once asked himself in print, writing about War I while War II was hot. For a very good reason, he answered. It sometimes shows that we can learn from experience.

> Colorado generally and Denver especially threw reason overboard. Public officials engaged in what seemed to be a contest of hysteria. . . . The Denver school system was the first in the country to outlaw the instruction in German language or literature, and the University of Colorado was a close second. (Today, as an essential part of the war effort, Japanese language courses have been established at Boulder and classes in German continue.) . . . Denver, not by official pronouncement but by common impulse, changed sauerkraut to liberty cabbage and hamburger to liberty steak. . . . Two full years after the armistice, stay-at-home super-patriots demanded and got the cancellation of a concert by Fritz Kreisler solely because Mr. Kreisler had served in the Austrian army. . . .[10]

Casey certainly, but perhaps also the sense of historical perspective which he voiced and the paper itself represented, gave the *News* substance and staying power through the days when dissolution and collapse seemed more in the cards. The *News* did not slight its long memory when the War Relocation Authority began to move Japanese-American

[10]*Rocky Mountain News*, Mar. 29, 1944; quoted by A. Gayle Waldrop, *Editor and Editorial Writer* (New York, 1948 and 1955), pp. 187–88.

families from the west coast to concentration camps at Granada, Colorado, and Heart Mountain, Wyoming. The *Post* wrapped itself in the flag and climbed on a jingo charger. "A Jap Is a Jap," it snarled, and Governor Ralph L. Carr was blistered for permitting a WRA camp to be located on patriotic Colorado soil. The *News* sent its editor and reporters to Granada and Heart Mountain for a calm appraisal of the threat. They found the camps neat, clean, and orderly, the Nisei loyal and well behaved. The whole relocation project was a shameful broadcast slur on a defenseless minority, the *News* asserted, and talk of threats to Rocky Mountain security was utter hogwash. The articles and editorials strengthened Governor Carr's position, and the subsequent spotless record of the two camps vindicated the paper's judgment. But it was not a popular stand for the *News* to take; Denver's Post No. 1 of the American Legion, one of the country's largest, was loving the sounds that issued from Champa Street. It would have been much more politic for the *News* to remain silent and remember Pearl Harbor.

The *News*' attitude on WRA was no way to win a popularity contest. But possibly it reflected the character which both was shaped by and sustained the paper through its long winter.

The stripping down to lean, flat-bellied essentials began soon after the firing ceased in 1928. It was not, of course, a voluntary matter. Fat men and plump institutions, it is observable, seldom slough off their chubbinesses with any great degree of ease or enthusiasm. For the *News*, the cost in humbled pride was dear. There was the matter of the sepia-colored Sunday rotogravure section, for example. It had been a proud day when the section was added, the first of its kind in all the West. It had proved so popular in those days of the infancy of photo journalism that the *Post* was forced to copy the feature. Now, in 1930, the section was too expensive a luxury, and it was dropped. The fact that the *Post* continued *its* section for many years didn't help a bit.

There were shiftings and shufflings as the staff shook down to subsistence levels. Eddie Day left the managing editorship and went to the *Post* to fill the same slot. Joe McMeel, one of his successors, also moved down to Champa Street. "Young Jack" Foster, ambition aflame, invaded New York. John P. Lewis was another pilgrim who turned his face eastward to become, in 1936, editor of *PM* in New York. As the depression deepened and retrenchment followed retrenchment, Clyde Brion Davis departed to join Ray Colvin on the Seattle *Post-Intelligencer*, later hopped across the country to the Buffalo *Times*, then a member of the Scripps-Howard family, and finally left the newspaper business to become a full-time novelist in Connecticut. Bill Beardshear, Walden Sweet, and Gene Cervi switched to the *Post*, Mary Coyle Chase abandoned journalism for motherhood. Radio "newscasting" beckoned to Wally Reef. Harvey Sethman became the executive secretary of the Colorado State Medical Society. When "Curly" Grieve went to the San Francisco *Examiner*

gravel-voiced Jack Carberry took over as sports editor, but he, too, succumbed to the lures of the *Post* and left Ham Beresford and N. C.
("Tub") Morris to fill the gap while Chet Nelson was working up to
become chief sport in June 1934. Loudon Kelly went to the Denver
bureau of the Associated Press and stayed. The *Post* hired state editor
Tom Walker as financial editor. His son Harry remained with the *News*
and eventually also took over coverage of business and market news.
For a time the Denver financial pages were a father-son duel.

Some went, some came, and a few held fast. Among the newcomers
were Tommy Hinman, Ben Blumberg, and Warren B. Lowe, now business editor after a term as city editor. The depression made the writing
of magazine fiction a perilous pastime, and Forbes Parkhill came back
to ride the rim of the copy desk for a spell at thirty-five dollars a week.
Dick Henry covered City Hall (1935–1941) and became so attached to
the place that he married the City Council secretary. Up on Capitol
Hill, pint-sized Barron B. Beshoar was covering the Statehouse run in
the footsteps of Lee Casey and Bob Chase. Later Beshoar held executive
posts with *Time-Life* in Denver, New York, Los Angeles, and now back
in Denver again. The stalwarts of the era also included John Polly,
Alberta Pike, George Burns, and "Spider" Leckenby. Bob Chase and
Max Greedy each did turns on the city desk, Chase for several go-rounds
before moving up to managing editor and associate editor. "Duke" Led-
ford and Ken Bundy joined Harry Rhoads in the darkroom, as did both
of Harry's daughters, Mitzi and Harriet. Anne New was society editor.
Eve Bennett, now a writer of popular children's books, handled sob-
sister assignments and club news. Leonard Cahn moved against the
stream and switched from the *Post* to the *News* sports staff. Toward
the latter stages of the bleak season Clair Jordan, Ed Oschmann, and
Pasquale Marranzino broke in as cubs. Jordan hatched out as a sports
writer, Oschmann took over from Dick Henry at City Hall, and Marranzino today is Denver's most avidly read local columnist.

The succession of editors began with Edward T. Leech, who was
called back home to Denver from Birmingham as field marshal in the
war with the *Post*, Leech became editor of both the morning and
evening *News* in January 1927. He was born in Denver June 17, 1892,
and as a boy was a carrier for the *Times*. After two years at the University
of Colorado he joined the staff of the *Republican* at a wage of eight
dollars weekly. He switched to the Scripps-McRae *Express* in 1913 and
three years later, at the age of twenty-three, he was its editor. He went
to the Memphis *Press* in March 1917 as managing editor. A year later,
and not yet twenty-seven, he was appointed editor of the *Press*. Within a
few months he was in a rough-and-tumble fight with the Crump machine
and for ten days wrote his editorials from behind the bars of Shelby
County jail while serving a sentence for contempt of court. He was escorted to jail by a brass band and a parade of anti-Crump dignitaries.

The band serenaded the prisoners with "The Memphis Blues." When Leech got out there was a mass indignation meeting in Court Square, and the fiery young editor was toasted at a victory dinner in the Tennessee Club. In 1924, Bob Scripps and Roy Howard founded the Birmingham *Post* and tapped Leech for the editorship. He made jail in Birmingham too; a judge decided his editorial comments on the Ku Klux Klan offended the flower of Southern manhood. Leech always said he liked the Memphis jail better.

Back in Denver he took lumps of another kind through two wild years of newspaper war and three years of the armed truce and retrenchment that followed. He was transferred in 1931 to the editorship of the Pittsburgh *Press*, purchased by Scripps-Howard in 1923. He remained in charge of the *Press* until his death and built a notable career and a national reputation on a record of outstanding community service. When he died, December 11, 1949, Leech was the senior editor of the Scripps-Howard organization.[11]

Early in his incumbency at the *News*, Leech hired a young reporter named Charles E. Lounsbury to serve as promotion editor under the tutelage of Max Cook. Lounsbury had been a *News-Times* police reporter from 1919 to 1921, then had gone to the *Post*. His father, George F. Lounsbury, also had been a Denver newspaperman and later became chief editorial writer for the Milwaukee *Sentinel*. When Cook suggested to him that he come back to the *News* the ambitious young Lounsbury wanted to know if Scripps-Howard philosophy permitted a promotion editor to become managing editor and top editor. "I told him it sure did," Cook recalls. "Inside of five years, Chuck made both jobs."

Lounsbury was appointed editor in 1931 when Leech left for Pittsburgh. As promotion editor he had stormed up many of the capers and giveaways during the hostilities. Then he became city editor and, when Eddie Day departed, succeeded him as managing editor. Lounsbury, too, was a Denver native. He was born April 5, 1898, and, like Leech, was an alumnus of West Denver High School. He attended Colorado College. His early career as a police reporter was not hampered by the fact that he was a nephew of Deputy Police Chief H. Rugg Williams. But neither his journalistic parentage nor his connections with the police force equipped him with solutions to the woes of the *News*, now sunk deep in the depression. He was given a leave of absence in 1935 and the following year left Denver to become managing editor of the Des Moines *Register-Tribune* Syndicate, a position he held at his death on November 2, 1952.[12]

[11]Sorrells, op. cit., pp. 289–92; *Scripps-Howard News*, Vol. 1, No. 2 (Jan. 1927); *Rocky Mountain News*, Dec. 12, 1949; *What Next?* (undated, unsigned pamphlet, Memphis, 1918?).

[12]*Rocky Mountain News*, Nov. 3, 1952; Denver *Post*, Nov. 3, 1952.

Before Lounsbury left for the greener fields of the corn belt Charles B. McCabe arrived in town by the 1935 equivalent of jet propulsion. McCabe was a ball of fire, and for a brief regency gave the city an old-style hotfoot. He had been burning up the Middle West as a salesman for the United Press service, and great things were expected of him when he was sent to Denver in March and given the title of publisher of the *News*, the only time that title was bestowed. McCabe remembers that shortly after his arrival some of his new friends enticed him into a poker game with William C. Shepherd, who took over as editor of the *Post* following Bonfils' death, without revealing to him the identity of the monosyllabic, cigar-chewing Shep. "I lost substantially," McCabe writes, "and Bill won about what I lost. The next day it was all over Denver that the new publisher of the *Rocky Mountain News* 'came, saw and was conquered' by Shep."

Nonetheless McCabe built fires. He also chased them. The new publisher left a standing order with Sam Nadler to hurry around with a circulation truck whenever a fire alarm sounded. Sometimes he was on the scene before his own police reporters, who enjoyed no such taxi service. McCabe's editorial methods were in that hairbreadth vein, and they were also lavish in a style which quickly won him the local nickname of "Champagne Charlie." One of his stunts was to sponsor the appearance of an evangelist in City Auditorium. McCabe himself wrote the headline: "5000 Hear Word of God." He lost twenty pounds in his first three months on Welton Street but added substantially to circulation figures with whoop-te-do promotions reminiscent of the previous decade. In the midst of it all he found time to go fishing before coming to the office in the mornings. He recalls:

> When I told Lee Casey that I was catching trout up Bear Creek Cañon, he had his doubts. It appears that Bear Creek had been fished out fifty years before!
>
> In any event, I was invited to take part in a fishing contest which included some of the fellows at the office. We were dropped off at various points on the stream and were to fish our allocated number of pools and then check to see who had done the best. When I completed my stretch of water the other contestants, who hadn't bothered to fish at all and were laughing up their sleeves at me, were waiting. I had actually caught a half-dozen trout. What Lee and the boys did not realize was that a cloudburst had permitted fish to escape from a hatchery or other storage area into Bear Creek.

As one of his efforts McCabe even changed the name of the paper—briefly. He made it the *Denver News*. The protests came flooding in immediately. The aging "Sage of the Rockies," Chauncey Thomas, spoke for those who complained of sacrilege:

So you have changed the name of The Rocky Mountain News that my family founded—the oldest and most illustrious business name in the state. Is "Pikes Peak" next under the guillotine you have erected for our Western nomenclature? I was spanked in The Rocky Mountain News editor's office 60 years ago for piing type. My first writing was in The Rocky Mountain News—1886. That is just 49 years ago. And now it is the "Denver News." What will the Rockies do for a newspaper? I also preferred the Larimer st. skyline, seen on page one every morning for a half-century. Denver is not Colorado, much less the Rocky Mountains. Your move reminds me of the attempt to change the name of the Tabor Grand Opera House a few years back.

"So fleet the works of man back to the earth again
"Ancient and holy things fade like a dream!"
"Tabor" and "Rocky Mountain News" alike.[13]

McCabe retreated hastily and restored the full name. The familiar masthead Thomas respected—a drawing of the city's sky line beneath an arch of the words "Rocky Mountain"—came back a little later, only to be dropped again. In 1941 a new sky line was placed behind the name, and the style has been continued since.

The McCabe conflagration lasted ten months, until December 1935. The eye of Hearst had been attracted to the billows of smoke and flame on the Western horizon, and he summoned McCabe to New York as publisher of the *Mirror*. The salary lure reportedly ran to six digits, and McCabe justified it by pushing *Mirror* circulation to seven. Both he and the Hearst organization apparently were satisfied with the arrangement; McCabe today is still publisher of the Manhattan paper. He took with him to New York his Denver city editor, Glenn Neville, who had joined the *News* staff as a reporter in 1927. Neville has been executive editor of the *Mirror* since 1943.

One slant on McCabe and his regime at the *News* has come from Gene Cervi, who viewed them from Champa Street. Cervi describes McCabe as "a fascinating rocket in American journalistic skies."

. . . Swaggering, adventurous, friendly and thoroly delightful in a shocking sort of way, the Denver-trained McCabe achieved his own idea of heaven on earth this month when his nasty-minded New York *Mirror*, one of the worst daily newspapers in the world, succeeded in gathering the largest crowd in history (two and a half million people, he said) on the beach at Coney Island to see Charlie shoot off—not ideas—but fireworks on July 3.

McCabe, tall and handsome in his tanned hawk face, was one of the most sparkling and unpredictable newspapermen ever turned out in the local Scripps-Howard mill. After running Roy Howard around $100,000 in the red to mock up an artificial 23 per cent gain in Rocky Mountain News circulation, he whirl-winded out of here and into New

[13]*Rocky Mountain News*, Mar. 25, 1935.

York to take over Hearst's dirty, run-down sheet 10 years ago. He took the wheezing and limp rag from 250,000 anemic circulation daily and shot it up past the million mark, making a terrific name for himself and lots of profit for Hearst. He also pushed the *Mirror* to more than 2,200,000 circulation on Sunday, which is an otherwise holy day. . . .[14]

And so Charlie McCabe, too, had caught an eastbound flyer from Denver. Next!

Next came Forrest Davis, who sported a Charlie Chan mustache and beard and was preceded to Denver by a high-powered reputation. He had edited the Evansville, Indiana, *Journal*, written several books, been a Washington and foreign correspondent for the Detroit *Free Press*, covered the Scopes monkey trial for the New York *Herald Tribune*. Then he had gone to the *World-Telegram* and of late had been a general correspondent for the Scripps-Howard newspapers. Davis took over the editorship of the *News* in July 1936 and appointed Larry L. Sisk as his managing editor. Thereafter he was seldom in the office. He was by every instinct a leg man, a reporter, a writer. McCabe rated reporters a dime a dozen; in his book desk men made the newspaper. Davis held diametrically opposing views. Reporters were everything, and who were these people who sat around the city room all day and never seemed to do anything productive? Copyreaders of the Davis era say he never seemed to grasp the process by which a story became a portion of a printed newspaper. Reporters and columnists have more charitable memories of him.

With his beard and his egghead reputation, Davis lent the *News* a certain flair, and he was in lively demand as a luncheon speaker. One of his major contributions to practical newspaper management in Denver was to re-establish the gimmick of giving the paper away once each week as a come-on sampling of the populace and in order to guarantee advertisers a minimum circulation. Advertisers were scarce, and things were tough all over. Davis also lasted less than a year. Early in the spring of 1937 he packed his bags. Subsequently he became associate and Washington editor of the *Saturday Evening Post*, co-editor of the extreme right-wing fortnightly, *The Freeman* (in 1932 he had found the profit motive "unnecessary" and somewhat scandalous in his book, *What Price Wall Street?*), and today he is Washington correspondent for the Cincinnati *Enquirer*.[15]

Managing editor Larry Sisk hung around for an even shorter period than his boss. To succeed him, Davis brought in from New York an up-and-coming young man who had been confidential secretary to W. W. Hawkins, board chairman of the E. W. Scripps Company, and later had edited the *Scripps-Howard News*, house organ for the chain.

[14]*Cervi News Service*, July 24, 1947.

[15]New York *World-Telegram*, May 27, 1932; Drewry, op. cit., pp. 2–4.

When Davis left, Aubrey Graves took over as editor in April 1937. A dapper man with a thin mustache, Graves was energetic, determined, and eager to lift the *News* from its pit. But he could find no handles for lifting, and his tenure was brief. He was out by September. Graves also went east and today is Sunday editor of the Washington *Post*, owns a ninety-acre farm across the river in Virginia, and strengthens himself against any memories of Rocky Mountain journalism by rearing Tennessee walking horses. During his short occupancy of the front office Graves installed Eugene Fisher as managing editor. Fisher, a onetime tackle for the University of Missouri, was big and handsome, and also tough and competent. Nothing in the city or the city room escaped his eye. He is remembered for his bull-like voice and a nervous habit of slapping his desk with an eighteen-inch steel printer's ruler while deep in thought. The pounding startled everyone else, but Gene found it conducive to thinking. Fisher departed with a characteristic brusqueness. One morning about one-thirty he put on his coat and hat, strode to the swinging doors, roared out, "Don't forget to check the jumps," and left. There had been an epidemic of error in getting "jumps"—the portions of stories continued from page one to inside pages—in the spot where the page-one continued lines said they would be found. Fisher issued his final order and was gone; the *News* was becoming a graveyard of newspaper reputations.

During the Graves regime the Denver branch of Heywood Broun's heretical union for newspapermen signed its first contract in Colorado with the *News*. The agreement was reached June 24, 1937, and signed by Graves and George V. Burns, union president, then on the *News* copy desk. It became effective July 12 and provided for a five-day, forty-hour work week and a pay scale which began at fifteen dollars for copy boys and went to twenty for beginning reporters, who got forty dollars after three years of experience.

The Denver Newspaper Guild was organized more than a year earlier. George Burns had laid out a dollar for a room in the Adams Hotel at Eighteenth and Welton streets, and interested newsmen on both the *News* and *Post* were invited to drop around for a meeting. Those who attended from the Welton Street shop were: Burns, Richard Henry, Don Montgomery, Chester Nelson, Pat Burgess, Glenn T. Neville, John Polly, Robert Chase, Alberta Pike, Warren B. Lowe, Francis M. Plumb, Eddie Grant, Maxwell G. Greedy, and Barron B. Beshoar. The only *Post* staff member who showed up was Vincent M. Dwyer, today managing editor of the *News* but then a police reporter on Champa Street. A few weeks later Burns was elected president, Chase and Plumb vice-presidents, Beshoar secretary, and Greedy treasurer. A letter was written to the editor, Charlie Lounsbury, informing him of the organization, and then everyone concerned pulled in his neck and waited for lightning to strike.

"We were all proud of ourselves and positive that we had to organize," Chase recalls, "but we were scared. We didn't know if we would have jobs after that letter was received."

No one was fired, however, and as time passed the guild won a wider and wider membership. Contracts have been signed annually or biennially between the guild and the *News* since 1937, and there has never been a guild strike in Denver.[16]

Early in September 1937, about the time the radical forty-hour week went into effect, Walter Morrow was appointed not only editor of the *News* but also editor in chief of the Southwest group of Scripps-Howard newspapers, thereby reviving briefly an earlier practice of regional supervision in the organization.[17] In addition to the *News*, the Southwest group included the *Oklahoma News* in Oklahoma City, the Fort Worth *Press*, Houston *Press*, El Paso *Herald-Post*, and Albuquerque *Tribune*. Morrow was to make his headquarters in Denver, bail out the *News*, and also keep his eye on the less troublesome colts in his string.

At forty-three, Walt Morrow had earned a high regard for smooth, effective newspaper management. He came to Denver from six successful years as editor of the Akron *Times-Press*, and he had also served in executive capacities on papers in Memphis, Pittsburgh, Buffalo, East Lansing, Cleveland, and New York. He was born March 25, 1894, in Crawfordsville, Indiana, attended the University of Oklahoma, and got his start on journals in the former Indian Territory. He broke in on the staff of the *Daily Oklahoman* in Oklahoma City. Later he was editor of the McAlester *News*, Okmulgee *Times*, and Ponca City *News*.

Surely with this wealth of experience he would be able to lead the *Rocky Mountain News* out of the darkness. Alas. Skills which were equal to all crises in a dozen other cities met their match in Denver.

Morrow was a working editor: shirt open at the collar, tie askew, suit rumpled and liberally sprinkled with ashes. A portly man, he puffed and gasped around an ever present cigarette as he grappled personally with every phase of the *News* operation. He was an expansive operator, and he tried spending and sprucing up as answers to the paper's chronic debility. A local Sunday magazine section was started, sparkling with literary pages which offered cash prizes for the encouragement of home-grown poets. Morrow brought in Adolph ("Bud") Sypher from Ohio as his city editor. Sypher was the sardonic type, like in the movies. He shunted men who knew the town into sidetrack spots where they could do the least good, and his notion of local news coverage was to dispatch

[16]*Rocky Mountain News*, June 25 and Sept. 9, 1937; *Brief History of the Denver Newspaper Guild* (Denver, 1955); Bill Miller, "The Denver Guild and How it Started," *Byline*, Vol. 1, No. 4 (Nov. 1957), pp. 12ff.

[17]*Rocky Mountain News*, Sept. 7, 1937.

a reporter to interview a woman who had given birth in the streets on "how it felt."

Neither Morrow's experience nor the dollars he spent accomplished any noticeable upturn. He moved on late in 1938, became editor of the Columbus *Citizen* in 1942, and president of the American Retail Federation in 1945. He died July 14, 1949, in Phoenix, Arizona.

Lee Casey, then for some years associate editor, took over from Morrow as acting editor and hated every minute of it. The many practical, routine details bored him, the budget making, the dull reports to be written, the endless stream of callers, each with his hand out for some special service or favor. Lee complained bitterly of having to cope with recurrent mechanical problems in the composing room, and his soft heart made it torture to fire an employee. He cheerfully admitted that he was not cut from executive cloth. He'd much rather be reading Gibbon or Anatole France and writing about historical parallels between the Peloponnesian War and modern times.

Seven editors in eleven years, and not one of them a physician with a cure for the *News'* multiple ailments.

The dreary years were not entirely without their light moments of course. Editor Lounsbury was driven to sputtering apoplexy one afternoon during the pre-Christmas season when he received a telephone call from a lady who identified herself as the mother superior of Queen of Heaven Orphanage. Readers of the *News* had contributed several baskets of dolls as a gesture toward brightening the season for the orphan girls, and the gifts had been delivered earlier in the day. The good sister wanted to thank the paper for its part in the kind act, but, she went on, how did it happen that the dolls were uniformly without panties? Shameful. What was the *News* trying to do, destroy the morals of her young charges?

"But, Sister . . ." Lounsbury pleaded.

"I think you're a lecherous old man," the voice said, and there was a click on the wire.

Lounsbury emerged from his private office, ruefully contemplating the many and varied hazards of an editor and abusing the fates which made him a newspaperman instead of a ribbon clerk. Then he saw one of his female reporters come laughing from the city-room phone booth with the "outside" line. He canned the joker on the spot.

The same girl earlier had given Eddie Day a bad time over Goodfellow apples. The *News* Goodfellows Club was a Yuletide organization which annually during the depression collected baskets of food for distribution to the poor. Day's caller informed him, heatedly and in dialect, that the apples in her basket were filled with worms. He should come immediately and sort out and remove the offending fruit from her home.

Ken Bundy, later a dignified regent of the University of Colorado and owner-publisher of several Colorado weekly newspapers, realized a photographer's dream of retaliation. Press photographers are among the most put-upon of mortals. Persons who will themselves crowd into the front row of group shots, waving goofily at the camera, become self-appointed defenders of the privacy of any other person on whom a lens is trained. Usually the hides of photographers are thick enough to take almost anything the obstructionist public wants to hand out, but sometimes a man can be pushed too far and on this occasion Bundy was. He had been assigned the Labor Day parade and brought along a stepladder so that he could shoot over the heads of the crowd. One man in the crowd took exception to the presence of a news camera and jostled the ladder each time Ken was set for a picture. Finally Bundy climbed down, snatched the man's straw boater from his head, and stomped on it. He was still jumping up and down on the shattered hat when police arrived. The city editor had to go to the police building and give personal assurances that Bundy henceforth would not tamper with the headgear of citizens and voters.

The *News*, of course, was outnumbered by the opposition on every assignment. Where the *Post* would send four men, a sob sister, and two photographers to cover a story, the *News* could spare one hurried reporter and a photographer who had a half dozen other appointments within the hour. *News* men said this was just about as it should be, that one *News* reporter was the equivalent of at least five small-bore *Post* staffers, but they were whistling in the dark and knew it.

The *News* composing room, however, possessed one asset not to be topped in the *Post's* composing room, or any other. This jewel took the form of John Garrison, Linotype operator. In one person Garrison combined the rarely associated distinctions of president of the University of Chicago Alumni Association and chief of the Rocky Mountain Sunshine Club, a friendly circle of nudists. This sachem of the bare-bottom set is still a *News* printer. Like all dutiful Chicago alumni, he reads Disraeli and the other Great Books for light recreation. He also runs a stockbrokerage firm on the side and eats pecks of health-giving apples while rattling out prodigious amounts of almost errorless type from the console of his mighty Mergenthaler.

But John Garrison is not the sort of asset a newspaper can put into the bank, and the *News* was banking few assets of any kind between 1928 and the early forties.

Why did Scripps-Howard hang on in Denver? Surely the pleasures of publishing at consistent losses must have palled on even the stoutest and most dedicated of hearts. Why didn't someone just tap the *News* on the head and end the misery? The questions have been put to the men in the New York office who had to answer them at the time.

"Scripps-Howard doesn't quit very often," William Chandler replied. "We felt all along that there was room for a Scripps-Howard morning paper in Denver. We tried to look at the encouraging signs, rather than the losses.

"We also hung on because the *News* gave Scripps-Howard better national coverage. The *News* fills a big gap on the map. The operation is a two-way street, you know. The *News* helped UP and NEA with coverage of a big Western area.

"And then I suppose we were emotionally involved, too, and we recognized that the *News* was an old paper with a fine history, a long record of service to Denver. Papers have personalities, just as human beings do. The *Rocky Mountain News* is one that does. Circulation, sales, profits are not the whole answer. In some towns no paper has it— character and quality. Some have it, some don't. The *News* does."

Roy Howard, the man who had to pick up the tab, had much the same explanation.

"We didn't quit in Denver because Denver is a key spot in Scripps-Howard," he said. "We made mistakes, and there were unfortunate editors, but the Denver experience was one of the greatest lessons I ever learned in the newspaper business. We wanted a paper in Denver, and we were willing to fight and pay for it.

"There are certain cities where you feel you need a paper, and the considerations are not just economic. The Washington *News* is the same sort of situation. We wanted a show window for Scripps-Howard in the nation's capital so we could let congressmen see what we were saying in their own communities. In the same way we wanted a Western paper in Denver as part of a balanced national program.

"We all felt that way, not just me. *I* didn't do anything, and I hate that damn perpendicular pronoun. *All* of us realized, I think, that when you get the right combination of editor, business manager, and program you eventually win. It took some time before we finally hit on the right combination, but we did. It frequently happens in American journalism that when you're trying for an editorial result and to render service that the chances for success become greater than if you were just trying to make money. But you still need a sound economic situation."

The situation in Denver was far from sound, and the balance sheets showed it. The lawyers and businessmen in the Scripps-Howard general management group began reminding their idealistic editorial colleagues, with some insistence, of the unpretty facts of life. Determinations wavered. Finally the whole matter was threshed out at a financial meeting in New York on April 16, 1940, and the *News* came close to dying that day. Some of those in authority argued that the losses should be written off as money down the drain and Scripps-Howard should pull out of Denver. They made a convincing case. But there was one strong dissenting voice.

"It virtually had been decided to turn the key in Denver," Jack Howard remembers. "Being brash and inexperienced, I protested vigorously. It seemed to me inconceivable that the only morning paper in a city the size of Denver couldn't survive, particularly since it had only one other competitor.

"It was Deac Parker who said that if I felt so strongly about it, why didn't I do something about it. I said I would. In a matter of days, I went to Denver, met Al Houser, who had been business manager in San Diego and then was trouble-shooting around, and together we looked over the problem.

"We concluded there was hope for the *Rocky Mountain News*. My conclusion was undoubtedly based on inexperience, and if it doesn't sound uncharitable, Al's conclusion was probably due to the fact that he didn't have any other job at the time. Anyway, we returned to New York and secured a reprieve which led to a new life for the *News*. I don't take credit for the new life, but I sure can accept, in all modesty, credit for the reprieve."

The general management took up the matter of the *News* again on May 8, listened to Jack Howard's report, and decided that it would require time and more money but there seemed to be a way out. The *News* and its troubles were wrapped into a package and handed to young Howard as a personal special project.

Although he had been president of Scripps-Howard Radio, this was his first major assignment on the newspaper side of the organization. A dozen years later he would be in command of the entire operation. In 1940 he was still fighting his big battle: to make his own way, live his own life, in the shadow of a famous father.

Jack Rohe Howard was born August 31, 1910, in New York City. He went to Exeter, in which he still takes a personal interest as one of the school's most active alumni, and in 1932 was graduated from Yale. During the summers of his college years he worked for the United Press in London, Rotterdam, Paris, and New York. In order to get to his job in London he signed on as a steward and waited tables aboard the SS *Leviathan*. Howard is no stranger to the ranks of newspapering. He has worked as reporter, copyreader, telegraph editor, and news editor, beginning in 1932 in Tokyo on the *Japan Advertiser* and then on the Shanghai *Evening Post and Mercury*. Before leaving the Orient he was briefly UP correspondent in Harbin, Manchukuo. Back in the United States he got a job as courthouse reporter for the Indianapolis *Times*, by chance the same beat his father had covered thirty years earlier. He also worked in Indianapolis as police reporter, rewrite man, and copyreader, then went to the Washington *Daily News* as telegraph editor and news editor under Ernie Pyle and John O'Rourke.

In 1936, Jack switched briefly to radio at Knoxville and a year later moved to New York as president of Scripps-Howard Radio. He has been in the New York office since, except for navy service during World War

II. He became assistant to John H. Sorrells, executive editor of the chain, in 1939 and succeeded his father as president in 1953. Sorrells has left this close-up sketch of his onetime assistant:

> . . . Jack served a pretty rigorous apprenticeship before he finally got himself equipped with a small, one-window office, a secretary and a phone of his own. As a matter of fact, Jack's apprenticeship began when he was a small fry.
>
> Like most men with sons, Roy had a sense of dynasty, and it was natural that he should want his son to carry on with his chosen career. Besides the shop talk that inevitably went on around the house of a newspaperman, Jack took what amounted to a reading course in some of Roy's correspondence; he met, in his home and elsewhere, a great many of his father's acquaintances who were either figures in journalism, or who made news in their time. His training was deliberately pointed for a newspaper career. . . .
>
> The old saying, "as the twig is bent, the tree will grow," has validity when it's certain the twig has been bent. Many fathers make sincere and, they believe, faithful efforts to refrain from trying to shape the twig to their own desires, but few of them can resist the temptation. Further, it requires a supple twig, sound at the core, to resist efforts to bend it this way or that. The hardest thing Jack has faced, and perhaps his greatest accomplishment, has been his successful determination to grow according to his own ideas and designs.
>
> The easiest thing he could have done was to go into some other line of business, or into some other newspaper concern. A man takes chances with his own growth and future stature, when he comes up in the shadow of his father's reputation and accomplishments. It is no easy thing to stand for the measurement of comparisons.
>
> Jack decided to take it the hard way—to hazard the shadow, to stand for the measurements. He believed that he would be able to walk in his own shoes, on his own path, at his own gait. He has done that, to an extraordinary degree. . . .
>
> Jack has quick perceptions; he learns fast and retains what he learns. He has a knack for figures, and statistical data do not frighten him. He is inclined to keep his own counsel.
>
> Jack has the capacity to put himself in the other fellow's shoes; he is tolerant and generous in his estimate of people, and he rarely speaks unkindly to anyone. In a controversy, his convictions might be no less strong than Roy's, but Jack has greater capacity for understanding the other fellow's side of it. It is Roy's nature to stir things up—Jack's instinct is to harmonize dissensions. Every now and then he undertakes to pick up some of the chips Roy scatters about.
>
> Jack likes people; he is intensely loyal to his friends. He likes parties that generate fun of a slightly rowdy sort. . . . He travels mostly by plane, likes to fish and hunt, and enjoys driving a car, an art at which he is expert despite one bad spill.[18]

[18]Sorrells, op. cit., pp. 126–31.

Late in the fall of 1940, Jack Howard asked a young man about his own age to drop up to 230 Park Avenue from the *World-Telegram* plant far downtown on Barclay Street. There was an editorship vacancy. Would the young man like it? The response could have been bottled and sold as a tonic. Jack Foster was headed back to Denver.

Up from Slavery

A PROPER history usually ends at some convenient date, often arbitrary, well into the past. There are hazards involved in attempting otherwise—even when the purpose is wholly informal. For history, be it ever so unceremonious, is above all else perspective; and there's no place to stand for a good, true look in depth at contemporary times. What seems to be important or notable or interesting in the current scene may lose by tomorrow all claim to significance, leaving behind only a sort of semihumorous quaintness. This is a truism which becomes, eventually, a sobering reality for every professional newspaperman: nothing is so new as the next edition. And nothing is quite so old, everyone knows, as yesterday's paper. Lee Casey once wrote that, in the largest sense, neither the biography of a man nor the history of a city can be written while either is alive. Possibly the position is extreme, since it would rule out Lee's own good friend Gibbon and would confine to such municipalities as Thebes and Trebizond the privilege of "our fair city" record-keeping; but the general rule is sound and surely it applies also to a newspaper. Time makes the only valid judgments in these matters, and there has been no time.

Yet to leave Denver and the *Rocky Mountain News* on the eve of the still unresolved World War II would be to omit what seems to be, at this moment, the brightest chapter in their continuing joint story. What has happened since then cannot be ignored here. The judgments can be only tentative, in the long view, but they cannot be dodged on the easy pleading that no one knows yet whether it all means anything, historically or philosophically. That is a decision for poets, anyway.

Two apparent facts stand out: change and growth, the one to be expected in the natural order of organic things like newspapers and cities, the other not necessarily so. Denver has changed and grown tremendously during the 1940s and '50s, and the *News* with it. Few cities in America have grown so rapidly, and few newspapers. The parallel still is precise. And it is not a universal or national pattern. There are American cities whose growth became essentially stabilized, for good or bad, in spite of an undiminished shift of population from farm to town during these mid-century decades. Even in still growing cities many daily newspapers have died.

The *News* came close to being one of the deceased.

When young Jack Howard was handed the *News* and its problems as a prize package in 1940 the outlook, he concedes, did not justify his optimism that something could be done. He spent much of the year commuting between New York and Denver. His initial visits caused staff apprehensions that the ax, finally, was about to fall. Long and critical conferences were held with Lee Casey, who was acting editor, and George Burns, then business manager. Howard and Al Houser met with T. M. Pepperday, Western business manager for Scripps-Howard, with circulation manager Bob Boyd, the pressroom crew, the ad soliciters.

"We tried to emphasize that we were not in with axes but had vitamins to distribute," Howard recalls. "But we were not too encouraged. Sins of omission, rather than of commission, seemed to be responsible for the plight. The editorial product was not the major problem. It stood up well measured against itself. I spent a lot of time trying to relax the paper. It seemed tense and inflexible."

Typography was spruced up. The comics were worked over, and the Sunday magazine and features improved. Effort was made to work "bright spots" of pleasant, humorous, or relaxed articles and features into the increasingly war-dominated and gloomy news budget. Daily program listings of all Denver radio stations were inaugurated. The *Post*, following its long-time custom, had enemies among the radio stations and imperially refused to recognize the existence of several. A comprehensive listing by the *News* proved popular.

Howard paid calls on the corporal's guard of advertisers, and patiently made the rounds of a much longer list of merchants whose advertising was needed. A. B. Trott of Daniels & Fisher's, always a friend of the *News*, assured him that the "horse is not dead," Jack remembers.

The old masthead picturing the Denver sky line was restored. Herndon Davis, talented local artist, was employed to do a series of paintings of historic Denver mansions and buildings, text by Joseph Emerson Smith. The series rang bells with old-timers, and James Quigg Newton, financier and intimate of Casey's, bought the paintings for presentation to the Denver Public Library's Western Collection. Howard observed on June 6 that circulation looked good and on July 24 that it had hit a new daily high. Home delivery in the city went above 23,000 copies for the first time. Ed Leech came to town during the summer and said he felt the paper never looked better. Staff morale was climbing out of the ruts.

Howard was back in September. He worked over the Sunday edition. Deliberate efforts were made to evoke letters to the editor. Praise, argument, or what not—anything but that awful silence out there on the other side of the presses. Local news coverage was stepped up, and it was noticed that as the war situation deteriorated in Europe public reaction was better to any small scraps of good news, local or national, than to all the elaborate war reports being poured into print. American isolation was dying hard.

A universal copy desk was installed to handle news from all departments except sports. Walter Morrow had tried a fragmented system in which each department did its own editing and headline writing. In October a saleslady jumped to her death from an upper floor of the Denver Dry Goods Company. The store asked that its name not be associated with the tragic incident. The temptation to comply must have been strong; the Denver Dry ad account was one of a very few that amounted to more than nickels and dimes. The *Post* withheld the store's identity in its late editions that afternoon, but Howard decided the name would have to be used lest injury be done to other downtown stores, many of which were non-advertisers.

Jack attended the stereotypers' picnic and confessed afterward that he drank more beer than he really wanted. He relaxed amiably about the city room and business offices, drawing slowly on his pipe, listening and watching. Gradually he became accepted as an ally rather than a hatchet man from the New York office. The pruning knife was sharpened to lop off the free distribution of 70,000 copies of the paper to Denver doorsteps every Friday morning. The blanket giveaway produced an artificial circulation bulge and some revenues, but Howard was seeking a sounder operation.

Meanwhile Roy Howard had suggested Jack Foster for the vacant editorship. Foster was young, energetic in Roy's own coattail-scorching pattern, and he had been doing a good job on the *World-Telegram*. H. W. (Bill) Hailey begged for the job of business manager in Denver. Many of his associates calculated he had come loose at the hinges. But Hailey had been a Westerner much of his life, had learned to roll his own from Bull Durham, and he was sick of shuttling between Connecticut and the Grand Central Building as director of promotion and research for the Scripps-Howard national advertising department ever since 1936. There wasn't a friendly horse to be seen on the whole New York, New Haven & Hartford line.

Hailey came to Denver in October of 1940, and Foster the following month. A new team was on the field, and they started play, in Roy Howard's phrase, "with the ball behind their own goal line."

Jack C. Foster was born June 29, 1906, in St. Joseph, Missouri, where his father was city editor of the *Gazette*. He spent his boyhood in Oklahoma City and Cleveland, and by the time he was seven was a part-time office boy at the Cleveland *Press*. He was covering sports at fifteen, and at nineteen had served a turn at nearly every job in the newsroom from running the switchboard to police reporting and make-up. He literally grew up in the *Press* plant, took a sabbatical two years at Western Reserve University, and became a full-time cub

under Max Cook, then city editor. In 1926 he was doing general assignments and rewrite for the *Press* when the stirring sounds of newspaper
war in the West reached his ears. He applied for a transfer to Denver
and for more than two years gave and took his lumps in the wild fray.
Jack switched to New York to write a daily radio column for the
Telegram in February 1929—the president of the National Broadcasting
Company once said there were only two honest radio columnists in
America, and Foster was one of them—and he was assistant city editor
in 1931 when the *World* was purchased. But his health broke, and he
was a long two years recovering it, followed by another two years on
a world tour which was part convalescence and part a writing assignment
for the Scripps-Howard organization. He was back at the *World-
Telegram* in 1937 as departmental editor and then as assistant executive
editor to Lee Wood. He hadn't been back long when he found a bride, a
pixy Georgia belle, on the staff. He and Frances Mangum were married
August 30, 1938.

Like the founding editor of the *News*, Foster is a mountain climber.
His holidays are spent in the hills, hiking, skiing, and jeeping. He and
his wife remodeled an old house in Idaho Springs as an operating base
for their tours. They collect ghost towns and abandoned mines, and
there's scarcely a back road or a mountain trail in the state they do
not know. Jack often walks to work for his health, which now is robust,
and sometimes writes a column about what he sees on his walks. The
pieces frequently are nature essays, love letters to the Colorado sky,
birds, trees, parks, peaks, and stray dogs. He is a man very much in love
with the place where he lives. He is also fond of travel in Italy—the
Italian government returned the admiration by making him a *Cavaliere
Ufficiale*—of Anatole France, airedales, Chinese cookery, and St. Francis
of Assisi. He is normally gregarious, enjoys a party, and is no hermit,
but he likes to be alone, reading or pottering about in the mountains with
his dog. "It does something for me that is hard to explain," he once said.

As an editor Foster is a working newspaperman first and an executive
only secondarily. He is a writing editor who declares his shots: "I'll have
a piece this afternoon"—and then consistently squeaks through scant
minutes under the final deadline. It's difficult to keep him out of the
center of a fast-breaking story. He wants to handle the rewrite, read
copy, write the headline; meanwhile wishing out loud that he could
be the leg man and really get in on the action. He once interrupted
a ski outing at Winter Park to help capture an escaped gunman-killer
on a train in Middle Park. He phoned his story, sped back over snowy
Berthoud Pass, and reached Denver in time to read proof, do the head,
and supervise make-up. A photo layout in the making is to Jack as
strong drink is to an alcoholic: he can't leave it alone. Any subeditor
with a handful of fresh prints and a vision of an eye-stopping layout
must hide the pictures from Foster or the job will be whisked away

from him. All of this comes under the heading of "having the boss in your hair while you've got a job to do" and it might slow the operation, except that Foster is swifter, surer, and more proficient at any of the tasks than almost any member of his staff. He didn't forget the routines of the trade when he became a policy maker.

Foster is not a second guesser as a boss—probably because he participates in or makes nearly every major decision in advance. The *News* is a highly personalized operation, centering on Jack's uncanny and fully proved sixth sense about the public's mood and interests. His subordinates reach hour-to-hour decisions by guessing or knowing what Jack would want. This is neither as poisonous nor as much a shot-in-the-dark technique as it might seem.

In the first place Jack and his staff know each other very well, and they work together in a wholly relaxed atmosphere. Foster is not the sort of editor who cushions himself behind several ranks of assistants, and his operation escapes the tensions and uncertainties such insulation ordinarily creates. He is on a first-name, give-and-take basis with each staff member. The door of his office stands wide open. Any reporter is welcome to walk in—if he can find a gap in the steady stream of callers. Jack is a good judge of capabilities, and he never neglects to note, and encourage, individual special interests. His staff members, in their turn, soon come to know the boss. There's never much doubt in anyone's mind about what he likes and wants. And the first of his wants is a simple, unpretentious telling of the news. He does not admire "heavy" news heavily reported "for the record" or to evoke illusions of false dignity, omniscience, or infallibility.

In the second place Foster is persuadable. He has his fair human portion of prejudices and blind spots, but in the councils at which major decisions are reached or policies formed his mind is no clamshell. He makes the final determinations and accepts responsibility for them; he does not bulldoze the discussions in which they are shaped, and the men closest to him are not yes-men. Associate editor Bob Chase, acrid and even at times downright negativistic, always can be counted upon to submit a growling, outspoken dissent if he feels one is called for, and he keeps a sharp needle handy to puncture projects inflated with spur-of-the-moment exuberance. He relishes the role of devil's advocate. Managing editor Vincent M. Dwyer is a direct, much-respected former city editor and police reporter with a tough competence built on experience. He is also Irish, and on occasion he gets it up in support of what he considers right, proper, and efficacious. Ordinarily soft-spoken, Dwyer can become jut-jawed with conviction and drive his points home, quite literally, with finger jabs to the other fellow's chest. Sometimes the other fellow is Foster. But neither Chase nor Dwyer, nor anyone else, is in doubt about who's running the *Rocky Mountain News*.

The firmness is seldom overt and never imperious. Foster does not summon his managing editor; he asks, "Have you got a minute, Vince?" A cub reporter will be called into the front office with the same phrase. It's one clue to the personality.

Foster is warm, responsive, and approachable. He is an excellent listener. There's a strong streak of the poet in his nature, and it asserts itself in a quick sensitivity. Jack Howard says of him: "His antennae are out all the time. The slightest disturbance registers." His enthusiasms are spontaneous and boundless and his vitality exhausting to others. The pace he sets for himself is headlong. He slowed down long enough in 1948 to go into a hospital and have his appendix removed, and the city-room wit offered to make book that "when they cut open the boss's belly, they'll find nothing but one great big adrenal gland."

The abundant energy and enthusiasm go a long way toward explaining Foster's dominance of his newspaper and the dramatic progress it has made under his direction. The recent success of the *News* is intimately involved with the Foster personality and almost entirely dependent upon his capacities. He assumes not only the line responsibilities of command but also the staff functions of feeding up ideas, supervising their execution, and nursing through the final product. In a single day Jack's restless mind can spark off enough ideas to keep his relatively small staff occupied for a week. Subordinates sometimes complain they're so busy following through on Foster's hunches that they seldom have a chance to try out one of their own. All of this runs counter to much accepted executive and management theory, since it supposedly tends to thwart initiative in young men on their way up, but the ultimate measure of management is its pragmatic success or failure, and the core fact of Foster's editorship is dazzling success. He took a journal which was starving to death, surviving on largess and sufferance, and turned it into one of the top-ranking morning newspapers of America, a force in its community such as it had not been since both were new and starting out together.

Foster's partner in the spectacular conversion was a fortuitous combination of complementary qualities. Howard William Hailey is deliberate, slow-moving, and slow-spoken in a deep, gravelly bass. He is as imperturbable as Foster is effervescent. Short, compact, and muscular, with a sun-lined and weathered face, Bill Hailey looks like a Western rancher, which he was, part time, and is now again in retirement. He loves horses and does his own chores. The gruffness and hardheaded practicality conceal an intense loyalty which Bill would just as soon nobody ever noticed.

Hailey was born July 8, 1892, in Calhoun County, Illinois. He ran a weekly newspaper in Barry, Illinois, as his first job out of high school. From it he accumulated a stake which permitted him to enroll in the University of Missouri journalism school, but he left college in 1917 to serve with the American Ambulance Field Service in France. He switched to the newborn Army Air Corps and rounded out his World War I service as a Red Cross relief worker in the Balkans. Following the war, he kicked around the West in advertising and magazine work, with stops in Denver, Colorado Springs, El Paso, and Phoenix before joining Scripps-Howard in 1931 as promotion manager of the El Paso *Herald-Post*. He held the same job with the San Francisco *News* and then went to New York in 1936 as director of promotion and research for the entire chain. Formal appointment as business manager of the *Rocky Mountain News* came January 15, 1941. Ill health forced Bill's retirement in 1957 to a small ranch near Sebastopol, California. His successor is B. W. (Wally) Lewis, who joined the *News* advertising staff in November 1941.

The first years were not auspicious for the new team of Hailey and Foster. As they took over circulation was 41,799 daily and 44,645 Sunday. Advertising linage was at its lowest ebb in more than a decade; only 3,785,309 lines were published during 1940. Neither set of figures would drop as low again, but for the first couple of years it was a grim struggle against long odds and dead-weight inertia. Foster spruced up the old paper, lit fires among all but extinguished embers, and gradually began to draw out the freer, briefer, livelier brand of journalism which has become his trade mark; but the gains were discouragingly small and slow in coming. The *News* was getting to be a better, more readable newspaper, but no one seemed to notice, and the advertisers, Hailey recalls, "continued to give us a good ignoring."

Then war came again. The *News* got out its big type, as it had for Robert E. Lee and the hopeful Sibley, for Roman Nose and Sitting Bull, Aguinaldo, Kaiser Bill. On Sunday, December 7, 1941, the presses rolled steadily through the day with a series of five "War Extras" dated Monday morning, December 8. The dust was cleaned from old, battered wooden types three inches deep to spell out: "JAPAN DECLARES WAR ON UNITED STATES! Bombers, 'Chute Troops Attack Honolulu. Heavy Damage Reported." A front-page editorial, "The Drumming Guns," leaned on Kipling:

> "Till, dazed by many doubts, he wakes
> The drumming guns that—have no doubts"

Kipling wrote that, back in 1894, of "An American" and "The American Spirit."

America has been attacked. The drumming guns are sounding, and many problems have been solved on yesterday's Sabbath day. Chief of these is the problem of national unity. We will have that unity—from here in.

America now turns, as Kipling said, "A keen, untroubled face home, to the instant need of things."

World War II wrenched and changed Denver, as it wrenched and changed America. The young men went away, to write home from or die in far-off places never before on local maps. Denver learned where Guadalcanal was—one of her boys was a hero there—and Anzio, where many died. The pace of the city quickened, and other young men in khaki came to replace, momentarily, those who went away. Lowry Field was activated in 1937 in buildings which had been constructed in 1903–4 as Agnes Phipps Memorial Sanatorium for tuberculars, far out on the southeastern fringe of the city with much open prairie intervening. The build-up was rapid. By 1942 forty million dollars had been spent on construction and sixteen million for equipping a key Army Air Corps technical training command center. Soon Lowry was training 15,500 students annually in armament, photo, and clerical courses. Following the war, Lowry Field became Lowry Air Force Base, and it is still a major training installation with personnel totaling ten thousand upward. It became the "Summer White House" for President Eisenhower and the temporary home of the Air Force Academy when it was established in 1954. The Academy moved, during the summer of 1958, to its new campus in the foothills fifty miles south of Denver and just north of Colorado Springs. Meanwhile Denver grew up to and virtually surrounded Lowry and its huge hangars and runways.

Lowry was not the only military post. Southwest of the city is Fort Logan, dating back to 1887. Dwight D. Eisenhower had been a second lieutenant there when he met the Denver girl who became his bride. Fort Logan was reactivated and the old post became in succession an Air Corps clerical school, induction center, convalescent shelter for wounded fliers, a discharge center, Veterans Administration hospital, and finally a national cemetery.

Construction began in April 1942 for twenty-million-dollar Buckley Field, east from Lowry, named for Lieutenant John Harold Buckley of Longmont, killed in France during World War I. Buckley was an armament school for the Air Corps. Today it is a naval air station and home field for the Colorado Air National Guard. At Colorado Springs, Peterson Air Field was created, also in April 1942, as a tactical air photo school. Subsequently it became headquarters for Second Air Force and was used for training of heavy bombardment groups. It was named in honor of Lieutenant Edward L. Peterson of Englewood, first pilot who lost his life there. Peterson Field was followed by Ent Air Force Base within the city of Colorado Springs, now headquarters of the North American Air Defense Command and charged with the mission of defending the entire continent.

Other air bases were built at La Junta and Pueblo. South of Colorado Springs, Camp Carson, named for Kit Carson, was built in 1942 and became Colorado's largest ground troops installation. High in the Holy Cross National Forest, twenty-five miles northwest of Leadville at Pando, ski troopers were trained at Camp Hale, beginning in the winter of 1942–43. Camp Hale honored the memory of General Irving Hale, leader of Colorado troops in the Spanish-American War, whose name is also perpetuated by Hale Parkway in Denver.

At Aurora, Denver's immediate eastern suburb, Fitzsimons Army Hospital was greatly expanded. The hospital was built in 1918 and named for Lieutenant William T. Fitzsimons, first United States officer killed in the First World War. Construction started in 1938 on a new 1800-bed hospital building which was completed just before war came.

War-born industry hummed in the Denver area. West of town, the $122,000,000 Denver Ordnance Plant was constructed in 1941–42 for production of small-arms ammunition and artillery shells. The sprawling plant now is the Denver Federal Center, headquarters of various governmental agencies including the main research and planning branch of the U. S. Bureau of Reclamation. Northeast of the city the Rocky Mountain Arsenal began production in 1942 of incendiary bombs, gases, and other chemical warfare weapons. The army opened the Denver Medical Depot in 1942. At Stapleton Airfield a center for the modification of heavy bombers operated for three years beginning in July 1942. A thousand miles from tidewater, Denver became, by quirk of the fortunes of war, a shipbuilding town. A combine of relatively small metal-working manufacturers turned out prefabricated escort vessels for the navy and landing barges and floating piers for the army. The first Denver-built warship, named the USS *Mountain Maid*, was sent off to Mare Island in 1942 with "Pike's Peak to Tokyo—or Bust!" chalked on her hull.[1]

War created special problems for a newspaper desperately trying for a comeback. Paper, gasoline, and tire rationing all hit at the *News* with disproportionate vengeance. Horse lover Bill Hailey sought to solve a part of his delivery riddle by buying two nags and a pair of antique milk wagons to make the rounds of downtown street corners. The horses were christened Blue Streak and Sunrise after two of the *News'* editions. Street circulators Sam Nadler and Morris Cohen, city boys born and bred, had never driven horses before. The beasts sensed, as horses will, that their apprehensive drivers could be intimidated. Nadler and Cohen were victims repeatedly of what beyond doubt were the last and final runaways on downtown Denver streets. The *News* cavalry was quartered at the old Elephant Corral on Blake Street, goal and stopping place of covered-wagon trains in the early 1860s.

The newspaper business, by and large, is a young man's game, and the war cut deeply into the staff. There are fifty-six names on the honor-roll plaque in the lobby of the *News* building. Four of the *News* men

[1]Hafen, *Colorado and Its People*, Vol. I, pp. 587ff.

were killed in action: Ben ("Dago") Hoffman, Robert P. Deering, Myerl D. Saucerman, and William J. Rose. Many of the others returned to their old places on the staff, and a dozen or more are still on the job.

In 1941 and 1942 the young men began to leave, and the shortages began to arrive. Shoes, rubber, gasoline, nylons, steel, meat, and sugar. By September of 1941 an additional 2600 subscribers had been coaxed onto *News* circulation lists. But even so modest a gain—and everyone hoped to do better—was a mixed blessing with prospects excellent that, sooner or later, newsprint would be rationed to American newspapers. Bill Hailey saw the rationing coming. A couple of weeks after Pearl Harbor he called a meeting of Foster, Lee Casey, George Burns, Bob Boyd, and Wally Lewis to attempt a forecast of what paper rationing and other war problems would mean to the *News*. In course of the discussion Hailey tossed out a suggestion that scorched the varnish on the conference table.

He explained that when he had been riding the commuter's merry-go-round between New York and Connecticut he had started out buying two morning newspapers, the *Times* and the *Daily News*, to read on the train. As time went on he discovered he was arriving at the office with the *Times* unopened. He stopped buying the big paper and read only the smaller, more convenient one. He had acquired the tabloid habit. No one, he insisted, really enjoyed reading a tarpaulin-sized newspaper which demanded a spreadeagle posture of the arms and unlimited elbow room. How about converting the staid old *Rocky Mountain News* into a tabloid? "Now just wait a minute before you pass snap judgment."

Hailey ticked off some advantages. In the first place, ease of reading. A tab could be read on streetcars and busses, sure to grow increasingly crowded with auto production cut off and tires and gas on allotment. A tab could be read more easily at the breakfast table. It could be spread out more conveniently on a housewife's kitchen counter or a businessman's desk. A boon to bifocal wearers. The pace of wartime life was quickening; busy but events-conscious readers would appreciate a simpler, more direct, briefer and livelier presentation of the news. Then, take a look at it from the viewpoint of the advertiser. The smaller page size would permit more effective selling at lower cost. A full-page ad would become an even greater bargain. The small advertiser, particularly, would benefit. His modest ad would get more eye attention, would be less likely to be lost somewhere below the fold of a large-sized page. An advertiser could dominate a page at a fraction of current cost, and there would be more pages available for domination. Moreover, newsprint rationing was ahead, Hailey predicted flatly, and here was the crux of the situation. Circulation was inching upward, but the *News* would have less and less paper to print on. In a newspaper, bulk is salable, he insisted; no one wants to buy a skinny paper, and the already slender *News* was headed toward emaciation as the war days passed. A sixteen-page tabloid would look and feel a lot more like a newspaper than a six- or eight-page dodger in full size. Available space would also be increased. By turning the chases sideways two five-column pages could be set into each eight-column form, thereby gaining a full column of valuable space for each two tabloid pages printed. Hailey also took a look at mass psychology. Something drastic, spectacular, with shock value was needed if the *News* intended to score the major gains for which everyone was working. Conversion to a tabloid would make Denver sit up and take notice that the *News* was a new and better paper. The advantages were obvious. Besides, Bill argued, big papers were merely a tradition that had become a rut. They weren't modern.

Burns and Lewis bought the pitch. Foster, Casey, and Boyd were hesitant. Maybe tabs were all right for New York and Chicago, but would the West go for one? "Tabloid" was a soiled word; it had been to bed too often with sensation and sloppy, hairbreadth reporting at the top of the lungs. To many persons the word meant a style of journalism, not just a page size. And it was a style, Foster and Casey felt, that Denver and Colorado might not cotton to. Foster was trying to get out a paper that was warmer, friendlier, closer to the readers, that paid attention to the decent everyday emotions of generosity, sympathy, and neighborliness. The strident tabloid reputation didn't seem to fit. Hailey countered: they were scaring themselves with a word. There was no reason why form should dictate content. Get out exactly that kind of a paper but offer it more conveniently. "Tabloid" was not another word for sin; it was only one way of printing a newspaper.

Finally, early in January, agreement was reached that the switch might work. The *News* was slowly dying anyway. Something bold and decisive had to be done. Hailey went to New York to submit his idea to the Scripps-Howard general management. He was sent on down to Washington to outline the plan to editor in chief Parker. Then, back in New York on a Monday morning, a full-dress session of the top brass met to go over the proposal in detail. Hailey sold his package to all the group except one. Paul Patterson, controller and general counsel, was pessimistic. It wouldn't work. "Better to close the door and throw the key away," he said. "Might as well save the few thousand dollars that are left."

Jack Howard and Hailey flew from New York to Tucson, where Roy Howard was vacationing, and word was sent to Jack Foster in Denver to meet them there. In a three-hour meeting Roy was low on prospects that the *News* could be saved. He didn't like the tabloid idea. He had seen it tried before and it was the "beginning of the death rattle." Denver, he felt, wouldn't go for such revolutionary tinkering with her oldest institution. At the end, however, he agreed. Go ahead and try it, he said; it would be better for the paper to "die of heart failure than creeping cancer."

Foster and Hailey went to work with B. W. (Wally) Lewis, then advertising director, now business manager. Elaborate experimental dummies of news layout and advertising arrangement were prepared, torn apart, and remade. A secret room at the Albany Hotel was rented in which plans were developed and presentations made to key advertisers. No word of the change-over was permitted to leak out; it would be a startling move, and full impact was to be exploited. At last, after three months of experimentation and development, the *News* appeared on Monday morning, April 13, 1942, in five-column format. There was a bold black headline on the front page: "Reds Shatter 12 German Tank Attacks." Beneath the headline appeared a four-column photo of a landslide in California, and a page-one box said, "Here We Are! . . . the new Rocky Mountain News geared to the swift pace of modern times." On the editorial page, a one-column inset of page one of Vol. I, No. 1, accompanied an explanation of the conversion.

THE NEWS: A RE-BIRTH

The Rocky Mountain News appears today in a new form—a form in keeping with the demands of the times.

The page size is smaller. It is easier to handle, easier to read.

More emphasis is put on pictures. This is in keeping with the faster tempo of American life. Sometimes a photographer with a flick of a finger can tell a story far more vividly than any of us can spin in words.

Headline type is bolder, more vigorous, more legible. News stories are terser, more compact.

Pace of living has quickened. Pulse of production has been speeded up. With the revolutionary change of Colorado life has come the need for a crisper, more direct, more dynamically human type of daily newspaper.

The new Rocky Mountain News is designed to supply that need.

* * *

Exactly 83 years ago this month the first issue of The Rocky Mountain News rolled from William N. Byers' hand press on the bank of Cherry Creek. That was before either Denver or Colorado existed even in name.

We are proud of the tradition of this newspaper. Its history and growth have been part of the history and growth of the community and state.

Since that first issue appeared, Denver has been transformed from a mining camp to a great city.

Unlike other great American cities, Denver is not a seaport, it does not lie on a navigable stream, it lacks the natural resources that made Pittsburgh and Cleveland inevitably great.

Its development has come mainly from the courage and loyalty and vision of its people and the ability of its people to find new solutions for new problems. Had it not been for these human qualities and strength, Denver today would not be a great city but a whistling post on some spur line.

* * *

A big job has been done. There are jobs as big just ahead.

This is a transition period. People are shouldering greater responsibilities and meeting new demands. Their requirements are different. News has become more vital than ever—but it must be made compact, simple, easy to get at. The worker on the way to the first shift at the Ordnance Plant cannot stop and twist himself out of shape to find an item deep within an inside page. Stories must be easy to read. Pictures must stand out.

The same requirements hold for advertising. Advertising—the right sort of advertising—is, of course, important news. It too should stand out, be easy to read.

The new Rocky Mountain News is designed to meet these needs. All the services and departments will continue—the United Press and Associated Press, Scripps-Howard Newspaper Alliance, the Chicago Daily News Foreign Service, the Acme Telephoto and Picture Service, Denver's only editorial page, the national and local columnists, the comics and, every Sunday, the great new magazine, Parade.

We change form eagerly because we know this change is an improvement, in keeping with the faster pace.

Colorado's first newspaper today becomes its youngest. Like Denver, it keeps step with the times.

April 13, 1942, also was the day Molly Mayfield was born.

Mrs. Molly Mayfield resists classification. She is no twittering Dorothy Dix. She is not merely Mrs. Fixit. John Gunther, who in 1947 found Denver "fascinatingly strange . . . immobile . . . the most self-sufficient, isolated, self-contained and complacent city in the world," described Molly's work as "the most original Advice to the Lovelorn column in the United States."[2] But advice to the lovelorn doesn't adequately describe Molly's art. There's more to it than that. She manages to be both saucy and levelheaded in her advice to the hundreds of correspondents whose letters reach her desk each day. She also is a bit of a minx and something of a tease, vivacious, mature, and always interesting. Gene Cervi once described her as "a combination big sister, mother-confessor, and female Scattergood Bains . . . an object of abiding respect wherever circulation figures are discussed."

Her column, "Dear Mrs. Mayfield," started off pretty much in pattern. She advised the wife of an Air Corps lieutenant to stick with him even though she didn't like military life. Buck up, there's a war on. A boy-crazy thirteen-year-old girl was taken on Molly's knee for a chastening:

[2]John Gunther, Inside U.S.A. (New York, 1947), pp. 223–24.

"Now, honestly don't you think 13 is a little young for beaux? Thirteen is such a nice age, if you'll just act 13. Not so long now and you'll be a young lady. Do enjoy this short time that goes before! Your mother is quite right—mothers so often are!—and I'm sure in your heart you know she is! M.M." Proper enough, and conventional. Correspondence grew more lively very soon.

A Denver wife wrote in to confess a unique revenge. Her husband was making a business trip to Kansas City and had packed his bag. The laundry delivered some clean shirts. The wife opened the suitcase to put the shirts in and found a frilly, gift-wrapped package inside. She opened it, of course, and found a sexy, sheer nightgown. "I mixed itching powder with sachet and sprinkled it all over the nightgown," the female Machiavelli told Molly. "Then I re-wrapped it and put it back in the bag. What should I do now, Dear Mrs. Mayfield?" A dirty trick, Molly chuckled, "but I loved it." The wife was advised to sit tight and play it innocent. Errant husbands were "usually big babies." Smite 'em hip and thigh, but dead-pan, sister, and cool.

"I never did hear further from my correspondent," Molly said later. "Always hoped I would. I'd give a pretty penny to know how things worked out in Kansas City."

But Molly is more than just a formidable adversary in the battle of sexes, and no mere entertainer. She's a power to be reckoned with in Denver. (And elsewhere. She now is syndicated to forty-five papers in the United States and Canada.)

She launched a campaign for a Better Business Bureau, and got one. When the city became lax in garbage collection she raised Ned and almost singlehandedly reorganized the sanitation services. She obtained pianos for churches, wheel chairs for invalids, and pool tables for USOs. In two days she collected fifteen hundred dollars to buy an automobile with special controls for a legless veteran. Glass eyes, then almost exclusively the product of a German art, became virtually unobtainable. Bushnell Veterans Hospital in Salt Lake City appealed to Molly. She asked for contributions and soon had several gross in assorted colors, including bloodshot. Orphans are entertained, and Molly throws an annual Christmas party for crippled children. The taxi companies fight with each other to provide the free transportation for Molly's guests. When a crisis developed out of the shortage of diaper pins, her readers came forth with tubfuls, and Molly rationed them out to service wives.

A Canadian Air Force unit at Calgary asked Molly if she could help obtain a Rocky Mountain canary as a mascot. A Rocky Mountain canary is a burro, and Colorado is fond of them. One of the most famous was Prunes, a gentle and musical mine jack, who aged gracefully and died happy as a pampered pet about the streets of Fairplay in South Park. Fairplay erected a monument to the memory of Prunes and speaks the name with reverence. The Fairplay Chamber of Commerce helped Molly get a burro for the Canadians. The lop-eared little beast was christened Prunes II by the governor in ceremonies in front of the *News* building while a band played and thousands wept. Before the war was over Molly had sent off Prunes III, IV, and V as military mascots.

Thousands of dollars have been contributed to the Molly Mayfield Foundation. They are expended by a volunteer board of directors to provide medical services—in several cases rare and highly technical surgery—to restore hope to the hopeless.

At the request of a soldier in the South Pacific, Molly bought and delivered a cocker spaniel to a North Denver girl as a reminder that she should wait until Johnny came marching home. Another soldier in England asked if Molly would deliver two dozen roses to his wife on their first anniversary. Molly would.

Some of her correspondents were screwballs. One elderly lady wrote daily—and delivered the letters personally. She would stride into the *News* office, fold the letter into a toy airplane, and sail it majestically down the aisle of the business office. Another woman confided periodically over a period of four years that she was about to be kidnaped or slain by hate-filled relatives. One day she sent Molly a box of gumdrops given her by one of the relatives. She wanted Molly to taste them and see if they were poisoned.

Denver quickly earned a GI rating as a good "soldiers' town." There were USOs, community parties, and dances. Veterans' groups arranged mountain outings for skiing and trout fishing. There were long waiting lists of families who wanted a soldier to come to Sunday dinner. And the native girls were friendly. Denver girls were living it up; never had the competitive bidding for dates been so brisk. Mrs. Mayfield fussed happily over her boys, complimented them on their appearance and deportment, arranged dates, smoothed over lovers' quarrels, and publicly spanked the B-girls in the clip joints.

Mrs. Mayfield scored a hit early. Husbands read her to see what new deviltry she was cooking up. Housewives and mothers found that she gave sensible, down-to-earth advice interestingly. They liked her exchange service, by means of which one could swap a parakeet for green trading stamps, a crib for a tricycle. But the GIs at Lowry and Buckley fields adored her. As they shipped out they spread her fame to all the salty seas. Grimy clippings of her column passed from hand to hand on shipboard and at far-off bases. The crew of a bomber in the Pacific named their plane "Dear Mrs. Mayfield" and sent her a photo. On a steaming day in January 1945 at Hollandia, New Guinea, a sailor leaned over the rail of his ship and made conversation with a soldier patrolling the wharf below.

"Where ya from, Mac?"

"Denver."

"Oh, Molly Mayfield's home town."

"Yeah. Quite a gal, eh?"

"You said it. Quite a gal."

The person behind "Molly Mayfield" is Mrs. Jack Foster. Her name never appears in connection with the column or its good works, and she takes no public bows, but the identity has become an open secret. Frankie Foster is a charmer, and the staff of the *News* enjoys telling the story of how their boss won her. Both were working for the New York *World-Telegram*. Jack had made up *his* mind and done everything in his power to convince Frankie that life as Mrs. Foster would be unrelieved bliss. Frankie was wavering, but she had plenty of suitors and, besides, being a New York career girl seemed pretty nice—temporarily, at least. Her by-lines were getting bigger all the time. But then an ugly little office rumor got started that the higher-ups were regarding her work as something short of indispensable. She graciously succumbed to Jack's entreaties. Some few safe years later Jack confessed he had planted the rumor himself.

With the help of his bride and others, Foster was putting out a better paper in 1942. The new *News* was a different kind of tabloid. It did not tear its shirt, bleed gore on its readers, or give keyhole reports on divorce suits. It seldom "scooped" unaware couples on prominent pregnancies. The page-one headlines were not much different, except bigger and blacker, from those of the Kansas City *Star*, the maiden aunt of American newspapers. The emphasis was on local news, when war developments permitted, and the approach was on a friendly, neighbor-to-neighbor basis. Sometimes it slopped over into a poisonous folksiness, and there were other errors, but gradually Foster's own personal warmth began to pervade his paper. He taught his reporters to write in freer, less wooden styles. He asked for originality and imagination—and some of the high flights were wowsers—in an effort to cast off the shackles of conventional dullness and journalese. Reporters were urged to talk with the people they were writing for, instead of trying to impress them.

To advance its program of more and better pictures, the *News* began receiving photographs by wire on June 9, 1941, via Acme Telephoto, predecessor to United Press International Newspictures. The telephoto machine became the "magic lantern" in city-room slang.

A "Service Edition" was inaugurated May 10, 1942. This was a quarter page of "News of the Home Front" set to narrow column measure and arranged so that it could be clipped out and mailed to men overseas or in training camps. Some of the items in the first issue included: "The crabapples are blooming on S. Marion Street Parkway. . . . The lilacs are gorgeous this year. So are apples; cherry and plum blossoms almost gone. . . . This has been an odd spring, with bright, warm days sandwiched in between cold storms that bent the trees with snow, filled reservoirs, caused floods, soaked the ground. The mountains shine high-piled with snow, off west. Crops and range will be good this year. . . .

The Auditorium was thronged all one day with the Grandpas' Registration—45 to 64. Said one, 'I know what this is for. They're going to extract the silver from our hair, the gold from our teeth, the lead from our pants—and junk us!' . . . Mrs. Rob Roy Buirgy, wife of a U. S. Bureau of Reclamation engineer, becomes Colorado's Heroine of the Week for sponsoring the 'adopt a soldier' idea. They entertain soldiers, write 'em, send 'em cookies. Want to be adopted?"

The innovations and redoubled efforts yielded some progress but not enough. The September 1, 1942, report of the Audit Bureau of Circulations showed the News had added more than 5000 subscribers daily and Sunday. Totals stood at 48,179 daily, and 53,415 Sunday. But the war was draining away his young staff faster than Foster could train replacements, and the newsprint squeeze was on. On some days the News appeared as a slim, adless paper of sixteen pages. Then papers without advertising became routine on Saturdays and Mondays. Advertisers were being won back to the News, but the paper now was forced to ration space to them because of the newsprint shortage.

The low point came as 1943 began. Again a decision had to be reached on whether the News could keep its doors open. The war news was bad, and prospects looked entirely bleak. Fold it up, some said. But it was discovered that cash assets totaled only thirty thousand dollars—not enough to pay off the help and shut down the plant. The News would have to keep publishing, at least until the bank balance could be brought up to the point where the old paper might die gracefully, untainted by bankruptcy or repudiation.

"Along about February, something happened," Foster says. "It still isn't clear to me what it was. I suppose a great many factors entered into it." The war news had taken a turn for the better. Molly Mayfield was going strong. Lowry Field was booming, and the town was thick with new uniforms and with new faces of strangers who had come to the city to man the war industries. Most of Denver's military and industrial build-up had come during 1942, and the accumulating forces reached a critical point so far as the News was concerned in February 1943. The tabloid format began to be popular, and Foster's lively innovations were catching on. Linage turned upward. Circulation began gaining in figures Bob Boyd rated statistically and geographically solid.

From this point onward the contemporary history of the Rocky Mountain News becomes a dramatic success story. There was a slight slump in circulation in 1944, when rising production costs and loss of ad revenues by space rationing forced a price increase from three to five cents a copy on May 1. Aside from this, the years from 1943 to the present have been a period of constant and phenomenal growth. Circulation more than trebled. Advertising linage grew seven times, and for more than a decade has established a new record in each successive year. Seldom has a newspaper come so far so fast.

When the war ended the staff began to re-expand and mesh itself into the unit, which was able to sustain and even increase the momentum. Pasquale ("Pocky") Marranzino, Ed Oschmann, James H. Briggs, Dan Cronin, Ed Williams, Jack Castel, and Clair Jordan, among others, came home and shucked off their uniforms to resume their old places. Jack McQuaid, Jim Pierson, and Nick Cunningham moved back to their posts in the advertising department. During the war years the *News* had relied heavily on women to plug the gaps in a business which is essentially masculine. At one point Harry Rhoads and his daughters made up the photographic force. Frances Melrose, now entertainment editor and drama critic, became a mainstay of the city staff. Dorothy Collins was society editor, passing the job along to her assistant, Darlene Wycoff. Darlene, a statuesque, barefooted broth of a girl, evolved into the currently sedate fashions editor who is among the leaders of the semi-annual New York sessions of American dress designers and their critics. Her high level of romping good spirits around the office once led to a grousing dictum from Frank Plumb at the rim of the copy desk: "All big society editors should be cut in half to make two assistants."

The war had also brought some old-timers back into the harness. Men like Bob Seymour, a veteran whose service to Denver journalism dated back nearly half a century. Seymour sharpened up a batch of soft black pencils and sat in for several years on the copy desk.

On July 23, 1945, it was announced that managing editor Edwin D. Minteer was leaving the staff to become executive editor of the Albuquerque *Journal*. Bob Chase, city editor off and on for nine of his eighteen years with the *News*, moved up to managing editor. His assistant, Gene J. Lowall, took over the city desk.

As peace returned, a new crop of reporters, soon to make their by-lines familiar in Denver, moved in from military service or clutching ink-fresh diplomas: Leo Zuckerman, Tom Gavin, Sam Lusky, Jack Gaskie, Bob Collins, Wesley French, Henry Still, Duncan Clark, Betty Caldwell, Bill Miller, Al Nakkula, Pat King, and Carol Untiedt and Elizabeth Wyner, both of whom became society editors. Jack Shannon succeeded Angelo O'Dorisio as chief editorial artist. Frank Willis and Robert Stapp switched from the *Post*, Willis to become librarian and Stapp the town's cleverest feature writer. Morton Margolin moved over from the Associated Press. Bill Peery, another fugitive from the *Post*, relieved Harry Rhoads as chief photographer, and Richard Davis and Robert Talkin joined the darkroom force. Leonard Tangney and Paul Lilly signed on, becoming respectively features editor and head of the copy desk. City editors of the era, in approximate chronology, were Warren Lowe (now business and financial editor), Vincent Dwyer, Dan Cronin, Bill Brenneman, Sam Lusky, and Henry Still, the incumbent.

A couple of the by-lines were pen names. Johnny Timberline, a sort of domestic Lucius Beebe with overtones of Cholly Knickerbocker, from time to time has commented on food, drink, and social giddiness in a preciously elegant style contrived to represent everything the rest of the paper tries to avoid. Willy Columbine began roaming the Colorado highways to report on doings in Skull Creek, Two Buttes, and Wild Horse. Willy attends the rodeos and inquires into the aspirations of local chambers of commerce.

The *News* gave Denver for a spell its first male society editor, a Western anachronism as startling as striped morning pants in a line camp. Jack Mohler was appointed to the job in December 1952, at his own request, and there were no wisecracks. Jack was an ex-police reporter, smoked cigars, and was a veteran of the army's campaign in Leyte. He left the *News* to become editor and publisher of the Colorado Springs *Free Press* for several years and now is a columnist for the Houston *Press*.

There were other occupational hazards. Photographer Bob Talkin spent several months mending in a hospital after he was trampled by a rodeo bucking horse which took offense at Bob's plans for a close-up action shot. Jack Gaskie, now a highly respected specialist in education news, acquired part of his own education because his desk stood close to the railing beyond which visitors entered the city room. Late one night a stranger leaned over the rail to ask Jack if he could arrange three witnesses to a holograph will. The caller wanted to leave his (unworking) gold mines, valued (he estimated) at two and a half million, to endow in perpetuity a free house of ill fame for Denver. The will made bequests of fifty cents to a first wife and a dollar to a second. Marranzino and Mohler, who teamed dangerously as practical jokers, shocked city editor Danny Cronin out of his usual laconic calm when they hired a midget to hide in his locker. Diminutive Al Nakkula, who has contributed more than his fair share to the newspaper lore of Denver, sought for some time to uphold singlehandedly the bibulous traditions of the press. Came a drear New Year's Day, but Nakkula bustled clear-eyed at his typewriter. A suffering colleague inquired pleasantly about how Al had made out the night before. "Ha," the little Finn snorted contemptuously, "*amateur* night! I was in bed by ten o'clock."

Between gambols, Cronin and Marranzino, Nakkula, Gaskie, and the rest were helping cover and report a five-alarm explosion.

CHAPTER TWENTY-THREE

The Years That Shook Denver

DENVER has experienced several periods of sharp growth during her first hundred years. In the beginning the gold rush brought a massive population suddenly. But only a small fraction of those who came stayed. Solid growth began with the railroad era in the early 1870s. The eighties, heyday of the silver kings, contributed another spurt, and a third came in the first decade of the twentieth century when tourists, health seekers, and home hunters began to discover the climate. From about 1910 until the shape-up for the Second World War, Denver slumbered and lazed along, a quiet, pleasant, and handsome small city, but a little backward, too, parochially content, a retreat out of the main stream. Population gained slowly. Young men who were going places went elsewhere to find the places. Denver was called the "reluctant capital" of the West, the "city of dead pioneers." It was "prematurely gray," someone said.

And then, almost overnight, Denver was a boom town again.

With the same abruptness in which the Pike's Peakers had created Auraria from prairie-dog flats and willow bottom, Denver changed into a large city. It became, in the years immediately after World War II, one of the dozen or so "exploding metropolises" about which the editors of *Fortune* and *Harper's* have become concerned, along with Lewis Mumford, nearly all city planners and urban sociologists, and every man who drives his car to work. The Denver explosion was both more violent and more precipitate than most of the rest. In a little over a decade population of the Denver metropolitan area more than doubled. The equivalent of a city the size of Oakland or Atlanta was piled in rapid heapings on all that the previous nine decades had accomplished. Postwar growth was in many places dramatic; in Denver it was melodramatic.

Why? The question has not been answered satisfactorily. Basic resources, of course, and the jobs and opportunities that grow out of them. Oil, minerals, cattle, wool, the high-value products of irrigated agriculture, the bumper grain crops (sometimes) of dry-land plains exploited increasingly (and often brutally) with mass-production tools and methods. Then the cumulative effect of an expanding population on itself, the rolling snowball, especially when the economy was largely a service one to begin with. More than half the wage earners keep busy by taking in each other's washing and repairing each other's shoes. Denver has found that in its economy one basic job supports 1.536 service jobs and 6.6 persons in the total population.[1]

War industry put the expansion in motion about 1942: the Denver Ordnance Plant, bomber modification at Stapleton Airfield, shipbuilding and other metals fabrication, the Rocky Mountain Arsenal, rubber products, stepped-up food processing. "Defense" industry helped sustain the momentum with new factories for aircraft parts, electronic instruments, atom bombs, and guided missiles. The supersecret Rocky Flats atomic energy plant, tucked away in a foothills arroyo northwest of the city, was completed at a cost of $45,000,000 in 1952 and has been expanded several times since. Denver never has found out precisely what goes on there, but several thousand men are employed in jobs that rate as "basic." The $125,000,000 Rocky Mountain Arsenal, manufactory and storehouse of deadly nerve gas and other chemical warfare agents, also underwent several expansions. More recently, in 1956, the Martin Company built its $35,000,000 Buck Rogers installation to the southwest and began work on $380,000,000 in contracts for the Titan, largest of America's intercontinental missiles. A sizable electronics industry has grown up satellite to the Martin development. Soon, Denver is told, there'll be a vast laboratory north of Stapleton Airfield on Rocky Mountain Arsenal land to push forward research toward an atom-powered airplane. On the prairie southeast of the city, once the bombing range for Lowry Field, dirt is beginning to move for huge underground launching stations for the Titan missile. Under construction near Cheyenne, well within Denver's sphere of influence, are launching pads for the Atlas missile.

Accompanying the military and defense industry growth was a steady increase in other federal activities—and Denver always has enjoyed a favorable balance of trade where federal tax dollars are concerned. Boosters sometimes have called the city the "Little Capital of the U.S.A." because of the many offices and branches of nearly every federal department and agency. In 1954 the federal civilian payroll in the Denver area was estimated at $76,000,000 annually.[2] Four years later, in a preliminary estimate, the U. S. Census Bureau made it $96,000,000 to approximately 18,800 civil service employees.

Available brains and professional skills helped. The National Bureau of Standards moved its radio propagation and low-temperature physics laboratories from Washington to a foothills site south of Boulder (seventeen miles away by the new postwar turnpike) to take advantage

[1]E. T. Halaas and others, *Working Denver: An Economic Analysis* (Denver Planning Office, 1953), pp. 27–28, 155–56.

[2]Denver Chamber of Commerce, *Industrial Survey of Denver* (1954), p. P-1.

of scientific man power clustered around the University of Colorado. Fresh strides were taken as a regional and national medical center of rank. New hospitals and research labs were added to the complex which already included Fitzsimons Army Hospital, world's largest military hospital. Biggest of the additions was the 500-bed Veterans Adminstration Hospital, integrated with the University of Colorado Medical Center. During the postwar years Denver medical scientists made basic and widely heralded contributions in the fields of cellular growth, hypothermia, heart surgery, virology, embryology, and the chemotherapy of tuberculosis.

The long, and continuing, campaign of the *Rocky Mountain News* for air progress paid off among the Russian thistles and sand dunes east of town. Seven major air lines now serve the city, and for four of them Denver is a principal operating base. Their big air liners drone constantly over the city, coming and going or "stacked up" and flying in circles to await landing instructions. Any glance overhead also takes in the contrails of jets. The long, thin man-made clouds go well with the blue Western sky. Often they catch and preserve the sunset long after the town and the peaks are in darkness. A city which ranks not higher than twenty-second in population (twenty-fourth in the 1950 census) now has the nation's eighth busiest airport, according to the Civil Aeronautics Authority's 1957 tabulation of arrivals and departures.

And tourists, of course. Vacationists, dudes, convention delegates, and other visitors long have formed a renewable natural resource in Denver, as elsewhere in the West.[3] Its exact dimensions are difficult to gauge, but no one in Denver underestimates the importance of the resource or fails to be aware of the harvest. Tourism, also, grew in the postwar period. In 1950, it is estimated, Denver played host to 1,469,000 visitors who— bless them!—left behind something on the order of $61,000,000 for food, lodging, and souvenirs of the Golden West.[4] Travel now has climbed to the point where it is computed that Denver each year entertains three visitors for every one resident. Latest estimate is that 2,907,000 visitors came to Denver in 1958 and spent more than $68,000,000.[5]

With the Juilliard Quartet taking up summer residence at Aspen and uranium prospectors with Geiger counters poking about in every cañon, nuclear physicists thinking long thoughts, with new dams being built and new tunnels being drilled, airplanes flying, missiles roaring, and Air Force cadets marching, with Texans and New Yorkers building sky-scrapers and chemists wringing oil from dry and solid rocks—all in all, it was an era of expansive change. Colorado hadn't been in such a

[3]For an engaging history of Western tourism, see Earl Pomeroy, *In Search of the Golden West: The Tourist in Western America* (New York, 1957).

[4]Halaas, op. cit., pp. 82–87.

[5]Denver Convention and Visitors Bureau.

ferment since John Gregory discovered his gulch. Perhaps the mountain West was becoming, as Morris Garnsey forecast early in the after-war decade, the new economic frontier for America.[6]

But Professor Garnsey appended some reservations and warnings to his provocative forecast, and most if not quite all of the growth factors which have been mentioned here were in operation in many other metropolitan areas which did not grow, as Denver grew, faster than America itself. People are, after all, the basic resource, and the West, for all its recent and rapid flowering, still doesn't have people. Colorado is by far the most populous of the Mountain States, yet its population density is 15.5 persons per square mile compared with 56.2 for the nation, 243 for Pennsylvania, and 719 for New Jersey. And nearly half Colorado's people are concentrated in the Denver area.

Population growth in Denver, and for Colorado as a whole, has outstripped resource development. So large a segment of the economy is based on "big government" and international tensions that a declaration of peace, unlikely as that may seem, could prove an economic disaster to Denver. Tourists, for all their delightful dollars, do not make for stability; if the budget pinches a vacation trip is likely to be among the first of family cutbacks. Moreover there is a point at which a service and distributive economy can no longer feed upon itself, at which a further accretion of population, lacking admixture of new wealth in proper ratio, becomes not an asset but a liability.

The clear and dominating fact in Denver, however, is spectacular growth, and neither federal subsidies nor basic resource development adequately explain it.

One has to fall back, at least in part, on a large intangible, almost in the realm of mysticism, which has operated upon mankind ever since Jason went after the Golden Fleece. The West, time out of mind, has been a mystery and a goal. The major shiftings of the earth's restless peoples have always been toward the west. In America, particularly, the "westward movement" has been a continental surge which has beguiled historians and poets. If it is a wholly rational migration the precise mechanics have not yet been established.

Economic opportunity doesn't do, entirely, as an explanation. Notwithstanding easy materialist theories, the pioneer did not always better himself when he came west; usually he found that he worked harder and earned less, but somehow things balanced off. Since his day there have always been Westerners—in the Ohio valley, on the Illinois and Iowa prairies, in the Colorado mountains, on the California strand—who have turned their backs on the larger rewards offered by the older, more

[6]A comprehensive and thoughtful summary of the potential of the Mountain States is offered in Morris E. Garnsey, *America's New Frontier: The Mountain West* (New York, 1950).

affluent societies to the eastward. "I wouldn't move back there for twice my salary." And some of those who say it mean it.

Perhaps the westering impulse is mechanistic, or maybe the answer lies rooted somewhere in the homely phrase "elbow room." Perhaps there is deep spiritual need for a room with a view, for uncrowding and uncluttering. Whatever the explanation—economic, spiritual, mystic, physical, or plain dumb perversity—America's westward movement continues, and at an increasing pace even though the continent presumably was settled and the frontier gone in 1890.

More than two centuries passed before the center of United States population vaulted over the Alleghenies. Since then, in half the time, the theoretical balancing point of the American people has marched westward nearly halfway across the continent. In 1940 the center was in Indiana. Ten years later it had moved on west to Illinois, and the 1960 census undoubtedly will disclose a further western shift.

For the past twenty years the trans-Mississippi West, except for a few rural-agricultural states, has grown economically and population-wise at rates well exceeding those of the nation as a whole. Much of the drift of the national center of balance to the west is explained by the spectacular growth of the three Pacific coastal states, but the Mountain States also underwent development at rates exceeding national averages, and Denver was in the forefront of the boom-time parade. During the decade 1930–40 the eight mountain states gained 12.1 per cent in population while the nation was increasing at a rate of 7.2 per cent. Between 1940 and 1950 the Mountain State increase was 22.3 per cent, ranged against 14.3 for the nation. Every indication is that since 1950 the comparison has been equally disproportionate, and probably greater. Denver, Colorado, and the Mountain States contain only a small fraction of the total United States inhabitants, but the portion is increasing sharply. (See Table I, p. 576.)

Net monthly migration to metropolitan Denver currently is calculated at 1600 persons, and the area has become one of the half dozen fastest-growing areas in its population class (500,000 to 850,000). The 38 per cent expansion between 1940 and 1950 put Denver at seventh rank in this group of sixteen areas. An estimate of a further 20 per cent increase between 1950 and 1955 advanced the area to fourth rank.[7] The most recent study of these civic mushrooms puts Denver ahead another notch to third place.[8] This latter report estimates Denver's growth between 1950 and 1957 at 37.5 per cent, exceeded only by San Diego's 55 per cent and Houston's 41 per cent. And the Denver Chamber of Commerce

[7] E. T. Halaas, *Population and Economic Trends in the Denver Metropolitan Area and the Rocky Mountain Region.* Interstate Commerce Commission Docket No. MC–263 Sub. 74 (Salt Lake City, 1955), pp. 5–10.

[8] City of Houston Planning Office, Jan. 1, 1957.

computes that the 1950–57 growth was 44.5 per cent rather than 37.5, going on to assert, moreover, that the 1950–58 increase was at a rate of 47.9 per cent.

TABLE I

POPULATION GROWTH RATES IN PERCENTILES

	Denver Metropolitan Area	Colorado Minus Denver Area	Colorado	Eight Mountain States	United States
1900–1910	59.4		48.0	57.3	21.0
1910–1920	21.2	16.0	17.6	26.7	14.9
1920–1930	17.9	6.7	10.2	11.0	16.1
1930–1940	15.7	4.7	8.4	12.1	7.2
1940–1950	38.0	5.5	18.0	22.3	14.5

SOURCES: U. S. Census Bureau data as interpreted by Econometric Institute, *Industry in Denver and the Denver Industrial Area,* a report for the United States National Bank of Denver (Denver, 1950); and Halaas, op. cit., pp. 7–13. The Denver area is a standard Census Bureau metropolitan area comprising Denver, Adams, Arapahoe, and Jefferson counties.

Such estimates are notoriously subject to optimistic coloration, since chambers of commerce and planning offices are themselves peopled almost exclusively by more-the-merrier patriots. But if the Denver forecasts to date have been enthusiastic, they have been hard put to keep up with themselves, and none of the estimators yet has been tagged with an inflated statistic. On the eve of the 1950 census, for example, one prediction was for 413,000 for the city proper and 561,000 for the metropolitan area.[9] The federal tabulators found 415,000 and 564,000. E. T. Halaas and his associates forecast in *Working Denver* (1953) that the area would have a minimum of 819,000 residents by 1970 and a

[9]Econometric Institute, *Industry in Denver and the Denver Industrial Area,* a report for the United States National Bank of Denver (Denver, 1950).

maximum of possibly 931,000. But by 1958 claim already was being made to 833,700 persons, and a new projection was looking for 1,100,000 by 1970.[10] The arithmetical growth rate is likely to take a sharp hop upward in 1960, when it is anticipated the Census Bureau will enlarge the metropolitan area by inclusion of Boulder County with its 65,000 persons (up 34.6 per cent from 1950).

America's face was turned west in the postwar decade as it never had been before, not even in the dramatic days of the gold rushes.[11] The migrations, early and late, converted a "diggings" into a city. (See Table II, p. 578.)

Nor is population the only index. The West also is growing faster than the rest of the nation in rates of increase in employment, personal income, bank assets, capital spending, and manufacturing (value added). *U. S. News & World Report*, viewing the phenomenon with Eastern eyes, recently made a rough measure of comparative regional growth patterns by taking unweighted averages of these five economic indicators plus population.[12] It found that since 1940 the seventeen Western states have grown 66 per cent faster than the nation as a whole. Nineteen Northeastern states were 18 per cent under the national rate, and the twelve Southeastern states showed a 24 per cent gain.[13]

Another disinterested observer, Donald I. Rogers, business and financial editor of the New York *Herald Tribune* took a firsthand look in 1956 and found Colorado a "state of numerous economies" which was "expanding and diversifying in so many directions that even the most optimistic residents have been amazed." Equally amazed, he went on, "are the legions of new investors, many of whom are seasoned veterans from other growth areas."[14] And Yale's city planning authority, Christo-

[10]John G. Welles, "Colorado in 1970: A Forecast," *Western Business Review*, Vol. II, No. 2 (May 1958), pp. 78–87.

[11]For other comments and statistics on the westward movement as it has affected Denver and Colorado see Garnsey, op. cit., pp. 8–9, 19–22; *Newsweek*, Oct. 27, 1958.

[12]Oct. 24, 1958.

[13]The report's findings with respect to the West and the Northeast can be summarized thus:

	West	Northeast
Capital outlay for plant and equipment	up 930 per cent	up 531 per cent
Population	up 55 per cent	up 25 per cent
Employment	up 108 per cent	up 44 per cent
Personal income	up 455 per cent	up 285 per cent
Bank assets	up 379 per cent	up 160 per cent
Industrial product (value added by manufacturing)	up 770 per cent	up 411 per cent

[14]New York *Herald Tribune*, Apr. 8, 1956.

pher Tunnard, predicted in *Harper's* for August 1958 that by 1975 most
Americans will be living in only fifteen great, sprawling, multinamed
urban areas. One of the supercities, he indicated, will develop along the
already highly urbanized axis which extends from Cheyenne to Pueblo
through Denver. Time was, and not far distant, when on an auto trip

TABLE II
HOW DENVER GREW

	Area within City (Square Miles)	City	Population Metropolitan Area
1864	3.52	No official record	
1870	6.08	4,759	
1880	6.08	36,629	
1890	17.02	106,713	
1900	47.92	133,859	
1910	58.75	213,381	246,800
1920	58.75	256,491	299,100
1930	58.75	287,861	352,500
1940	58.75	322,412	407,800
1950	67.18	415,786	563,832
1958	73.70	530,000	833,700

NOTE: Figures for 1958 are the Oct. 1 estimates of the Denver Chamber of Commerce.

from Cheyenne to Pueblo a visitor could have a liberal sample of the
"wide-open spaces" which have been the West's stock in trade. Today
cities, towns, and suburbs coalesce along much of the route. There are
traffic lights at highway intersections where the hunting for ring-necked
pheasants was good five years ago.

Both the soaring statistics of Denver's population explosion and the
cheerful forecasts that it will continue apace are supported by most of
the other indices.[15]

[15]A few of them, as supplied by the Denver Chamber of Commerce: Assessed valuation—$710,426,550 in 1950, $1,468,338,200 in 1957 (up 107 per cent); bank clearings (twelve major banks)—$5,972,010,341 in 1950, $10,344,769,300 in 1957 (up 72 per cent); construction valuation—$105,796,000 in 1950, $172,729,660 in 1957 (up 66 per cent); Colorado oil production—23,000,000 barrels in 1950, 55,000,000 in 1957 (up 139 per cent); peak month employment—221,700 in 1950, 322,000 in 1957 (up 45 per cent); retail sales—$687,039,000 in 1950, $1,123,700,000 in 1957 (up 63 per cent); passenger automobile registrations—188,353 in 1950, 312,708 in 1957 (up 66 per cent); per family expendable income after taxes—$4457 in 1950, $6044 in 1957 (up 35.6 per cent); value added by Colorado manufacturing—$340,795,000 in 1950, $641,074,000 in 1956 (up 85 per cent). Except as indicated, the figures are for the Denver metropolitan area, a phrase which thus far has served very nicely for descriptive purposes. The city has shown a rather admirable restraint in talking about itself; "Greater Denver" occurs only rarely.

It hasn't all been peaches and cream of course. Denver's municipal coffers have been scraped bare for the increased services to meet the growing needs, and the patience of citizens has been taxed by the new one-way streets and the lack of parking space (despite a lavish experiment in city-owned parking garages and lots). The city has experienced nearly every one of the problems and challenges outlined by the editors of *Fortune*,[16] and even in trying to cope with a few of them. The *Fortune* writers noticed that in Denver, in spite of the urban sprawl, demand continues lively for apartment space close to the downtown district. New and lofty apartment houses have been springing up consistently on Capitol Hill, many of them on ground once occupied by the big brownstone mansions of the mining kings. But most of Denver's new problems orient themselves in the opposite direction. The suburbs now are growing at a more rapid clip than the heart city itself, and they have become the "bedroom towns" for tens of thousands of workers who add to municipal expenses and contribute little in the way of taxes. Yet a city payroll tax was rejected by the city dwellers who must themselves assume the unshared burden.

Some efforts have been made toward beautifying the cityscape, both downtown and through the development of additional parks, one of which was named for Mamie Eisenhower. Civic Center has been further expanded as a mid-city focal point by construction of a new public library, quarters for the Denver Art Museum, a downtown building for the University of Denver, a third annex to the state Capitol, and conversion of the old library into a headquarters for the all-important Water Department. Denver residents don't quite genuflect when they pass the Water Department, but the impulse is strong. The new Civic Center development has been accomplished without encroaching on the pleasant area of grass, trees, and well-tended flower beds.

Anyone who cuts down a tree in Denver these days, for whatever reason, usually has to reckon with the *Rocky Mountain News* columnists and editorial writers. The city mourns the passing of trees, individually, one by one: the elms at Courthouse Square, the old hackberry which had shaded carriages in the 1400 block of Court Place. Some resistance is developing to the uglier aspects of megapolis, but the city has not yet come to grips—though it has made two halfhearted passes at it—with the first-magnitude challenge of a severely blighting lower downtown district. The area from Larimer Street to the river has become an eyesore comparable to Con Edison's heap of grime next door to the United Nations in Manhattan.

The center of gravity of the downtown district shifted steadily up the hill during the postwar boom years, and it was in the uptown area that new and handsome towers went poking up into the squat sky line.

16*The Exploding Metropolis* (New York, 1958).

William Zeckendorf, the New York real estate wonder boy who got together the UN site, started the remaking of the Denver profile with his $13,000,000 Mile High Center. He also built the new May-D&F department store on Courthouse Square, once the site of the Arapahoe County courthouse, and across from it now is building the Denver Hilton Hotel. More than any of the other builders, Zeckendorf has taken into account the need of city dwellers for urban vistas: pools of water with fountains, a bit of something green and growing, a quiet nook with a stone bench, a sunken ice-skating rink.

Zeckendorf's lead as a sky-line maker was followed by the Murchison brothers of Dallas, John D. and Clint, Jr., looking for new places to put oil millions to work. They put up the $7,000,000 Denver Club Building and then, in 1958, completed the $10,000,000, 365-foot First National Bank tower, currently Denver's tallest. Oil exploration, development, marketing, and refining luxuriated in the Rockies during the forties and fifties, and Denver became the hub of much of the activity. The oil interests banded together to erect the Petroleum Club Building on United Nations Square at the head of Sixteenth Street, and several of the companies individually constructed office buildings. The National Farmers Union contributed to the sky-line changes with its new headquarters topped by a lighted pylon which forecasts the weather. The slender, sand-colored spire of the Brown Palace West is scheduled for completion early in 1959, and the happy Irish boniface Charlie O'Toole will have more guests to welcome to the old hotel which boasts it is "where the world registers." O'Toole would like to change the name of Tremont Place—which runs past his door and under the second-story bridge to his annex—back to the original Clency Street.

The era saw political eruptions also. Pipe-smoking Dan Thornton, wealthy Gunnison cattle raiser who started out as a Texas cotton sharecropper and a Hollywood movie cowboy, recaptured the Statehouse for the Republicans briefly from 1951 to 1955 with *News* support. Another *News* candidate, a Democrat, took over at City Hall and raised a cloud of dust. Quigg Newton, a thirty-five-year-old silk-stocking and navy veteran, unseated Benjamin Franklin Stapleton, seventy-seven, mayor five times over for twenty-four years, nearly a quarter of his city's history. Robert Stapp wrote:

> . . . After 24 years of Stapleton rule, the conclusion seemed inescapable that Denver had the kind of government it wanted—honest, imperious, resistant to change, slow moving, stodgy and safe.
> But that wasn't the kind of government young Quigg Newton wanted. . . . Like many other returning veterans, he felt that his native city was missing the boat. . . .
> Returning veterans were clamoring for houses, but an antiquated building code stymied large-scale, low-cost construction. Downtown

streets were choked with automobiles, driving endlessly around the blocks looking for parking places. Garbage overflowed in alleys. Visitors and new residents complained they couldn't find their way around because of illegible street signs. Residential streets were pocked with chuckholes.

Some of the outlanders who were pouring into the city had the temerity to complain about these things. They were rebuffed with the withering reminder that if they didn't like it they could damned well go back where they came from. . . .[17]

Newton was elected in 1947 and soon became one of the forces shaking the new Denver. He appointed a young cabinet and began cleaning a run-down house, catching up on improvements which had been put off for decades. He gave Denver a regime of conspicuously good, honest, and impartial government and an administration which attracted national attention for its vigor and enterprise. The American Municipal Association tapped Newton for a term as its president. The new-era mayor left office in 1953, became for several years executive vice-president of the Ford Foundation in New York, and now has returned home as president of the University of Colorado.

The *News* teamed with Yale-man Newton and with the late Dr. Florence Sabin, famous Denver woman scientist, for a broad-scale re-fashioning of health conditions in both city and state. Surveys had disclosed that Denver and Colorado were not, as advertised for seventy years, so healthful that the undertakers were starving. Newton turned municipal health services inside out and placed them under professional direction for the first time in a quarter century. The *News* made a major campaign in support of the "Sabin Health Laws," a code which reorganized the State Health Department from its basic regulations to its top personnel. Even the microbes got a good stirring up in the new and changing Denver.

Denver is still a city in which people deliberately choose to live, more of them every year, but there are dissenters who fight a philosophical rear-guard action against the changes. Poet-essayist Tom Ferril spoke for them in 1954. Too many tourists, he felt, had been given a taste of Colorado and now wanted to come back and stay.

I was born in Denver. I love every square inch of Colorado's 66,718,080 acres, but when somebody writes to me, asking how to spend a pleasant vacation in our beautiful Rocky Mountains, my innards tie up into knots. I loathe tourists, I hate myself when I get crowded into being one; my dearest friend, in the role of tourist, becomes leprous in my sight. . . . About a third [of the visitors to the Rockies] want to return, according to studies by the University

[17]Robert Stapp, "Denver: A City Wakes Up," *Frontier*, Dec. 15, 1949, pp. 5-7.

of Colorado, while two out of five insist that they are coming back to become permanent residents.

My antipathy to the whole business arises in part from this last point, but I don't blame the tourists half as much as I blame us Westerners ourselves. Our whole idea is to lure as many people as possible and get them to live here for keeps. The plain truth is that we are overloading a most tenuous water supply with people and industries—in an area that depends fundamentally, and must continue to depend on agriculture. . . .

Denver amazes me, I cannot understand it; the Denver area now has more than half a million people with large suburban business centers and supermarkets sprawling out over the once remote prairies where I used to hunt rabbits. From my window, as I write, I see two huge new skyscrapers and more are on the way. They too must have water.

Every drop of water out in this country is already appropriated. Speculative cloud seeding is very popular; the water table is sinking as competition for underground water increases; and at the moment, Coloradans on both sides of the mountains are fighting like wildcats over transmountain diversion of water. But if Colorado's water war seems insoluble, there is unanimous agreement between the warriors, civic boosters all: we simply *must* have more people and more industries; we must lure more tourists and corral as many as we can to stay forever. . . .[18]

The water wars Ferril mentions have been resolved in part, and Denver has obtained for herself a visible future supply which it is estimated will be sufficient for a city of 1,900,000 residents. A $75,000,000 bond issue was voted in 1955 to provide for expansions of the water system, including more dams and a new tunnel under the mountains to bring Pacific-slope moisture to Atlantic-slope users.

Water is the limiting factor, but now that there seems to be enough of it, at least for immediate purposes, the heady ardors of aggrandizement can be resumed and Tom Ferril's dark apprehensions tucked away deep and unnagging in the Denver subconscious. Denver probably has been no more blatant about it all than any other American city on the prod, and most citizens recognize the growth ceiling which water imposes. At the same time it is for the most part pleasant and invigorating to be involved with a growing thing. Residents of some years' standing are modestly pleased to have several hundred thousand new arrivals confirm their prior judgment that Denver is the best place to live. And the newcomers themselves are enjoying the excitements and advantages of metropolitan life with sun, green, and Mount Evans thrown into the bargain.

Ray Perkins, whose name and tinkling piano are well known to any radio fan of the twenties and thirties, is one of the newcomers. He

[18]Thomas Hornsby Ferril, "Tourists, Stay Away from My Door," *Harper's*, May 1954, pp. 77–78.

sketched an outline of the new Denver's special brand of civic pride in a bit of patter set to music for the Newspaper Guild's 1950 Gridiron Show:

> Oh there's no place like Denver,
> It sure is a wonderful town.
>> The women are pretty, the men are so witty,
>> In fact, we admit it's the world's greatest city.
> Our mayor is no cheap politician,
> He takes no political trail,
>> Quigg Newtral, we're sure, will remain sweet and pure
>> For the honor of Denver and Yale.
> Oh there's no place like Denver,
> Where a smile takes the place of a frown.
>> Our traffic's a problem—the worst in the West—
>> Mister Barnes keeps on trying, and gives us no rest;
>> He's driving us nuts, but it's all for the best,
> And it sure is a wonderful town—
> A most remarkable town.

So the remarkable town grew and flourished. And so did the *Rocky Mountain News*—but at an even more rapid rate.

Men who came back to the *News* staff after the war were bemused and delighted by what had happened and was continuing to happen to the threadbare sheet they had left. The figures Mary Barron and Margaret Kelly sent up from the circulation department were scarcely believable. A new golden age was arriving.

By 1950 a newspaper which had been at death's doorway only seven years earlier was making a name for itself in national ratings. On August 26 a full-page house ad appeared to suggest that ". . . Maybe We Shouldn't Hide Our Light under a Bushel."

In a decade of accelerating growth, The Rocky Mountain News has become one of the big, important morning newspapers of America.

Among all morning tabloid newspapers, the daily circulation of The News is exceeded only by two in New York, one in Boston, and one in Chicago. . . .

The News ranks third among all tabloid morning newspapers in advertising linage. Our total is surpassed only by the New York Daily News and the Chicago Sun-Times. The News ranks fourth among all tabloids—morning or evening—just behind these two and the Los Angeles Daily News. . . .

The News' penetration, or coverage, of Denver and the retail trading zone is much greater than that of any New York, Chicago, Philadelphia or Los Angeles daily newspaper, and is much more complete than that of many first-circulation newspapers, such as the notable Detroit News, St. Louis Post-Dispatch or San Francisco Examiner. . . .

In certain classifications The News leads such powerful newspapers as: Atlanta Constitution, Detroit Free Press, San Francisco Chronicle, Los Angeles Examiner, Dallas News, Indianapolis Star, New York Herald Tribune.

In July, The News reached the highest circulation, daily and Sunday, in 91 years [129,585 daily, 139,994 Sunday]. It is a gain of more than 100 percent in five years and the figure was reached without premiums, insurance offers or similar stimulants.

Should we hide our light under a bushel? This advertising and circulation growth has made newspaper history in America. These have been exciting years.

Three factors have been equally important in this dramatic success story. They are: (1) the alert, intelligent, receptive public of Denver and the West, which has appreciated the *new* News and rewarded it with increasing patronage and readership; (2) the sound judgment of Denver advertisers, who have increasingly depended on The News as a partner and a strong constructive force in the development of their own businesses; and finally (3) the quality and vivid newsworthiness of the News *as a newspaper*.

One hundred per cent growth in five years. It was more than the city itself or any other of its institutions had experienced. Circulation of the daily *News* broke over the 100,000 mark in 1948, and the Sunday *News* had made it a year earlier. Advertising linage followed the steep curve upward. Far behind were the slim, sixteen-page leaflets of the war years. The *News* now was publishing sixty or more pages daily, a hundred or more on Sundays.

Morale and self-assurance rose with the indicators of material success. News handling became more confident and sure. Editorials began to speak once again in a language which assumed people were listening. Political victories were won. The occasional campaigns—such as that which backed the Sabin health code—were forceful and effective. Professional awards and honors came to staff members, and Bill Peery's camera was winning for him a steady procession of national prizes. The staff grew in size to meet the demands of wider and deeper coverage. Specialists were developed in such fields as education, medicine, science, and water resources. The luxuries which make superior journalism possible, and which are all but denied to impoverished newspapers however courageous, were returning to the *News*. For the first time in forty years the paper was back in the stature it had enjoyed in the days when its readers called it "Old Reliable" and it was the prime mentor and first champion of a frontier town.

The narrow, cramped plant at 1720 Welton Street which had seemed a veritable temple of the "art preservative" when it was built in 1901 became, by 1949, confining and inefficient for the rapidly expanding operation. The *News* began to look around for a new home. Scripps-

Howard officials and real estate experts came to town in April to survey the situation, and Roy Howard and G. B. Parker arrived in July for further talks. Howard made a return visit to Champa Street for a detailed appraisal of the old plant of the Denver *Post*, which also was planning expansion. A rumor made the rounds that the *News* might buy and convert the Sears, Roebuck retail store on Broadway, later remodeled into the United States National Bank Building of the Mile High Center. Finally business manager Bill Hailey announced on December 9 the purchase of eleven lots at 400 West Colfax Avenue, west across Delaware Street from the Denver Mint. The site then was occupied by a string of one-story stores, some run-down flats, and a few old residences doing service as rooming and apartment houses. It offered a half block (125 feet) of frontage on busy West Colfax, which carries transcontinental Highway 40 through Denver, and 275 feet of depth south along still tree-lined Delaware Street.

Buildings on the site were wrecked and removed during 1950 and excavation started in November. Construction of the new printing office began April 19, 1951, under supervision of the Austin Company of Cleveland, specialists in the design and erection of publishing plants.

Meanwhile, as the red brick and reinforced concrete plant took shape, the *News* was making do with the creaking old office on Welton Street—and crowding another 5000 gain in circulation out of the two timeworn presses.

The ancient double-deckers were threshing away at the home edition early on the morning of January 29, 1951, when the *News* lost its noblest Roman. A heart attack claimed Lee Casey, friend of all the ancients and nearly everyone of importance in Denver, as the presses rolled out Chapter VIII (the Peloponnesian War) of "Uncle Lee's History of the World." The Peloponnesian War, he had written, could be called the "Irreconcilable Conflict."

For, after close to 24 centuries, the supreme issue had not been settled. Yet it may be settled during our lifetimes. Technically, the war was between Athens and Sparta. Actually, it was a war between two ways of life—just as the war in which Americans are dying today. There are no exact parallels in history. But there are some similarities. And the similarity of this war in the Fifth Century B.C. and the war in Korea is quite close. . . .

The Attica of that day, including Athens, had rather less than Denver's present population; Sparta, with its subject towns and villages, perhaps slightly more. Yet there could be no actual compromise. For the Athenians . . . believed that the state should be the servant of the people. The Spartans believed, with equal intensity, that the people should be the slaves of the state. That was the ageless contest between the free spirit and the closed mind. . . .

As we know, the Athenians lost the war. Probably they deserved to lose it. For they forsook their own principles. Freedom of speech and freedom of thought were preserved for Athenians, slaves excepted, but for Athenians alone. . . .

Next day George V. Kelly, later administrative assistant to Mayor Will Nicholson, Quigg Newton's successor, wrote the obituary. Memorial services were conducted in the Episcopal Cathedral of St. John's-in-the-Wilderness on February 1. Dr. Robert L. Stearns, then president of the University of Colorado, delivered the principal eulogy to an assembly which included most of the city's top civic and business leaders, waitresses, bartenders, panhandlers, cops, clergymen and professors, gamblers, bellhops, and at least one bootblack. The 38th General Assembly paused in its legislative labors to adopt a memorial.

For about five years before his death Casey had been ribbing the local undertakers by "shopping around" publicly for his funeral and reporting his findings in his column. He wanted, he said, something "neat but not gaudy. . . ."

> . . . What I'm trying to arrange is a nice, pleasant, rather quiet sort of affair, without jukeboxes or quartets—you know, as modest and dignified and enjoyable as the situation might warrant. . . .
>
> Being a thoughtful sort, I got the idea it would be nice for the folks if I got my funeral arrangements out of the way and especially if I got them paid for in advance. Having lived on credit all my life, I imagined it would be pleasant to die with a receipted bill all ready for the mourners, if any. That would make the parting less of a sweet sorrow, if you know what I mean. . . .
>
> I wished no more than the low limit as to hacks, especially in view of the fact that I did not expect a large turnout—no civic celebration, in other words—and there was no need for him [the undertaker] to prepare a large bouquet carrying the message "From Al"—or "From Charley," for that matter. Although I would not haggle about the matter, I thought cremation preferable. Actually, I thought I was being very nice about the whole deal, making it as cheap as possible for my-self and as easy as possible for the spectators to endure. . . .

The rock-bottom price, Lee reported, was $127.50, which he ruled was too costly. "So, although I feel the smack of age in me, some relish of the saltness of time, I think I'll keep right on living for a while." Casey died, in the fine old Western expression, with his boots on. He was a winter soldier, and a craftsman; he would have preferred to go out with the presses pounding.

Lee had requested cremation. In September 1953 his ashes were placed within the brick wall of the lobby of the new building on West Colfax and the opening sealed with a small bronze plaque: "Here Rest the Ashes of Lee Taylor Casey Beloved by His Fellow Workers and the Readers of the Rocky Mountain News for Forty Years. 1889–1951."

The death of Casey left a large gap and many memories.

As the staff adjusted to his absence Bob Chase moved up to fill the vacant post of associate editor, city editor Vince Dwyer became managing editor, and Dan Cronin took the city desk. Cronin had been succeeded by Bill Brenneman by the time the new building was ready for occupancy in May of 1952.

The plant had cost $1,000,000 to build and another $1,500,000 to equip. There were 75,000 square feet of space on two floors and a cavernous basement for the reel rooms of the presses and storage of 1500 tons of newsprint and 4000 gallons of ink. The structure occupied full width of the site and 200 feet of its depth. The rear 75 feet were reserved for loading docks and the maneuvering and maintenance of circulation and paper-handling trucks. Installed in the pressroom were ten units of Hoe color-convertible presses which raised capacity from 80 to 128 pages at a speed of 45,000 copies an hour. (By 1956 it was necessary to add another four units.) The first floor contained advertising, business, and circulation offices in the front and the mailing room at the rear. Editorial offices were fitted out across the breadth of the second floor, with composing room, stereotyping and engraving departments to the rear. Into the composing room went twenty-five typesetting machines. (Today there are twenty-nine.)

Moving days, as they always are, were proud ones. The *News* flooded its readers with statistics, historical summaries, and an item-by-item account of the transfer. Police reporter Ken Wayman, the paper said, had refused to be shut out of the excitement of the moving. He had turned his desk around in the pressroom at the Police Building. Sam Lusky, who was covering a trial at West Side Court, would symbolically switch chairs at the press table. Open-house receptions were held for a full week after the first editions rolled from the new presses dated June 1, 1952. Then the *News* got back to business of growing spectacularly. There were now 350 employees compared with 125 in 1940.

The old building Tom Patterson had built in his back yard on Welton Street was converted into lavish temporary quarters for the Denver Club, then homeless while its new skyscraper was being built. Columnist Marranzino reported on April 9, 1953, that "old newspaper plants never die; they go out in bursts of technicolor." The entryway at the foot of the steep stairs had been redone in pink and black with sketches copied from drawings by Michelangelo. Ed Hamlyn's engraving department now was the private barbershop, with personal shaving mugs bearing leading Denver names. A chichi ladies' dining room with imitation french doors leading out to gardens of wallpaper flowers occupied the approximate former locations of the desks of George Dyer and Delmas Corey, Bob Boyd's veteran assistant circulation managers. The composing room had bloomed out in yellow and green. Darlene Wycoff discovered on a visit a few days after Marranzino's that the pressroom had become a wine cellar and the city room held billiard tables. She also noted that simulated windows of leaded glass had been installed to block any untoward views into the Orient Hotel. The Denver Club occupied its glorified newspaper office for about two years. Then, in February and March of 1955, the building was scrapped. The site now is a parking lot.

At the new building Bob Chase completed the revision Lee Casey had started of the *News'* style book for its staff writers. Chase's admonitions in the 1953 edition were brief and to the point:

The Style Book . . . does not take the place of the dictionary or the grammar books. A writer consults these whenever necessary. This applies to sports writers as well as writers in other departments. . . .

In general, we aim at brevity, clarity and accuracy.

Use short words, short sentences, short paragraphs. . . .

Write as simply as possible to make reading easy for your reader.

Write dialect only with special permission. Animals may speak only with special permission of the city editor.

Be sure quotations are accurate, in meaning as well as letter, and that they sound that way. Try to keep the language pure in quotations, but don't go high hat.

The written word is usually slightly more formal than the spoken. But most of us do not speak, even for quotation, as a professor of philosophy would write. . . .

By 1954 circulation had topped 150,000 daily, up 214 per cent since 1942 in the metropolitan area and 252 per cent over all. Advertising in the same period had gained 39 per cent to 18,656,360 lines, a total greater for the year than that published by such prominent papers as the St. Louis *Globe-Democrat*, Chicago *Sun-Times*, San Francisco *Chronicle*, New York *Mirror*, Hartford *Courant*, and Providence *Journal*.[19] (Table III, p. 589, details the *News'* rise from its dark days of the thirties.)

All of this against competition which was never gentle. The *Post* was still publishing in Denver, though much less flamboyantly than in the garish days of Bonfils and Tammen. It became a much-chastened newspaper with the arrival in 1946 of Palmer Hoyt of the Portland *Oregonian* as editor and publisher. The "Paper with the Heart and Soul" still has the larger circulation and publishes more advertising, but the *News* now has far outstripped its onetime dominating rival in rates of gain. In 1954, for example, the *News'* city-zone circulation increase over 1942 was 214 per cent while the *Post's* was 54 per cent. In 1957 the *News* gained 211,037 lines of advertising over 1956. The *Post* lost 676,299 lines. But the *Post*

[19]*Media Records*, 1954.

is a young newspaper; great things may be expected of it once it sloughs off its adolescent chubbiness.

The *News,* once the weakest sister in the Scripps-Howard family, now publishes more advertising than all but three papers in the chain—the Pittsburgh *Press,* Memphis *Commercial-Appeal,* and the Cleveland *Press.* And a study by the New Orleans *Times-Picayune* for March 1958 shows that the *News* ranked third—after the Kansas City *Times* and the Washington *Post-Times-Herald*—among all the morning newspapers of the nation in the intensity with which it covers its town with city-zone subscribers and retail sales. The Chicago *Tribune* stood in eleventh place, the New York *Daily News* twelfth, the New York *Times* thirty-second, and the New York *Herald Tribune* thirty-third.

TABLE III
ROCKY MOUNTAIN NEWS GROWTH, 1932–1958

	Circulation (12-month average)		Advertising Linage (12-month total)
	DAILY	SUNDAY	
1932	36,464	45,797	5,228,716
1933	34,941	41,920	5,696,133
1934	33,421	42,257	5,400,027
1935	35,796	44,106	5,274,608
1936	37,417	44,755	5,133,601
1937	38,749	44,620	4,932,410
1938	38,189	43,466	4,214,461
1939	39,044	42,501	3,843,788
1940	40,209	43,820	3,785,309
1941	43,487	46,589	4,150,620
1942	45,752	50,589	3,875,944
1943	51,319	53,434	4,271,819
1944	56,526	57,015	3,841,637
1945	59,057	59,653	4,047,670
1946	72,356	76,627	6,162,179
1947	91,913	103,826	7,164,056
1948	108,100	119,048	10,452,888
1949	119,954	130,689	12,100,642
1950	129,585	139,994	13,663,743
1951	141,524	150,281	14,672,662
1952	144,646	154,571	16,782,931
1953	145,866	154,791	18,046,229
1954	149,079	155,031	18,656,360
1955	154,877	159,293	22,011,113
1956	159,936	163,550	22,544,071
1957	157,358	165,846	22,755,108
1958	160,155	165,039	23,291,809

SOURCES: Auditor's reports, Audit Bureau of Circulations; *Media Records.* The circulation totals for 1958 are for six months ended Sept. 30.

It was an improbable and dramatic comeback for a newspaper which so often had been snatched from the brink of the grave. Several persons have attempted to explain it.

Ken Bundy, a *News* alumnus, said in his Gunnison, Colorado, *Courier*: " . . . we are thankful for the resurgence of the News. We are not sure Denver would do nearly so well with only one newspaper; and few people realize today how narrow the margin was between giving up the paper and continuing publication. Jack Foster is quick to give credit to all his staff, but perhaps to him belongs the greatest personal credit. He probably worked longer hours, without ever a moment's loss of enthusiasm from a thousand setbacks (and we can remember scores of them) than anybody who ever held the editorship of a metropolitan daily newspaper. . . ."[20]

From retirement, Bill Hailey comments: "No one feature makes a newspaper, but Molly Mayfield has certainly made an outstanding contribution. Good sports coverage is important, women's interest news a must and a spread of advertising is also essential. . . . If there is a general statement that spells our success, it's giving the public something it liked and were willing to pay for, and to do that we had to build teamwork inside. Jack and I really were the quarterbacks who called signals for the best newspaper team in the whole country."

Jack Foster also ticks off several factors: "War—the big news commanded much interest and got us started on the way. Paper rationing, it developed, was a blessing in disguise. It helped us train our staff in writing and editing more tightly. Molly Mayfield, of course. Then there were the intangibles involved in the loosening up of the staff, getting more freedom in writing, giving each man a feeling he was important. We got a liveliness and a humanizing of the news which was dramatically different from what the *Post* was doing. We were after circulation rather than revenue, and it showed in the kind of paper we got out."

Jack Howard feels that "no one thing was wholly responsible. There was a series of fortunate situations. The change in format to a tabloid was dramatic, a shock treatment. The expansion and transformation of Denver was a big factor. Between 1926 and 1939, there was little or no change in Denver, as I observed the town. But between 1941 and 1946 there was a huge change. The war helped the paper in that it benefited from the great increased interest in news. The personalities of Jack and Bill were important. Jack's a kind of romantic guy. He fell in love with Denver and Colorado, and he's in tune with the country. He's a poet and has warmth in depth. Sensitive to people. And he's a reporter, too— that's basic."

Roy Howard puts it bluntly: "The secret of the success in Denver? There are many factors, but with a newspaper, as with a ball team, success

[20]Quoted in *Colorado Editor*, July 1952, p. 18.

usually centers on two men—the battery. On a ball team it is the pitcher and the catcher who form the battery. On a newspaper it is the editor and the business manager.

"The *Rocky Mountain News* flashed to success with a journalistic battery consisting of Jack Foster as the editor, and Bill Hailey as the business manager. Being myself a product of the editorial department, not only my judgment, but my prejudice, necessitates my rating Jack Foster as the number one factor in the paper's successful re-birth. However, as I am quite sure Jack Foster does, I rate Bill Hailey's business management as an outstanding contribution to the paper's spectacular come-back. With a business manager less efficient and less co-operative, the editor's best efforts would have been under a great handicap."

In remaking his newspaper editor Foster had to capture the attention and good wishes of a city much distracted by its own dynamics. The years were busy ones, and reporters were kept on the hop getting it all down on paper, the great and the small.

Horse and dog racing came to tracks in the suburban fringe after pari-mutuel betting was legalized. The Denver Bears baseball team was revived in 1946 and became, for a time, the leading farm for the training of rising young New York Yankees. Voting machines replaced the hand-marked ballot. Television arrived in 1952 after being delayed several years by the national "freeze" on new stations. The old gilt and plush Broadway Theater, where Anna Held and Edwin Booth once emoted, was wrecked in the remodeling of the Cosmopolitan Hotel.

The Denver Club, lair of political and financial king-makers, gave way to a skyscraper at Seventeenth Street and Glenarm Place. Old City Hall came down, and a crowd of 300,000 persons, largest ever, turned out to watch dynamiters blast to earth a tall smokestack, landmark relic of the mining days and all that remained of the Omaha & Grant Smelter.

California and Stout became Denver's first one-way streets in 1949. Henry A. Barnes, who now wrestles with Baltimore motorists, was appointed city traffic engineer in 1947 and a year later inaugurated the "Barnes Dance," an experiment in organized confusion by which pedestrians are permitted to cut diagonally across downtown intersections while automobiles wait. The system gave rise to the new traffic lights, now in use in many cities, which command pedestrians to "Walk."

Shopping centers with malls, flower gardens, and acres of parking space began to appear in residential districts. The taxpayers built a $2,000,000 annex to City Auditorium and then remodeled the old portion into a municipal theater and concert hall. The Denver Symphony made strides under Saul Caston, once associate conductor to Ormandy in Philadelphia. Tax money put up the $2,600,000 Denver Coliseum in the Stockyards district, principally for the annual National Western Stock Show but also used for circuses, conventions, and ice skating. Municipal parking garages were erected at a cost of $4,000,000—and made only a slight dent in the need for auto room. The last streetcar rolled through town on June 3, 1950, giving way first to trolley coaches and finally to motor busses. The people of Denver voted $21,000,000 in bonds for their school system in 1948, another $30,000,000 in 1952.

General Eisenhower came to vacation before taking over command of NATO forces, and President Eisenhower returned to rest, golf, fish for trout, paint mountains, and then to suffer a heart attack. The Air Force Academy got its start at Lowry Field before moving south to its new campus against the foothills north of Colorado Springs. Four million dollars worth of improvements went into Stapleton Airfield. Helicopters began hovering over the city with their throbbing blades. The City Park Zoo added an elephant and a hippopotamus.

One awkward moment incident to the booming was hushed up. The vast oil development—Colorado produced 3,000,000 barrels in 1944, 32,000,000 in 1954—was being watched from afar. It was made the occasion of a state visit and inspection tour by the chief of an oil-rich Middle East principality who will be designated as the Emir of Onam lest an international incident be provoked. The Emir settled himself in the Presidential Suite at the Brown Palace and summoned his hosts. Delightful city, everything just fine. And now would they be so kind as to supply him with a female companion for the duration of his stay. Blonde, he specified. If the part-time odalisque proved pleasing, the Emir promised, she would have a diamond for her navel. Denver's official greeters coughed, shuffled their feet, and consulted the State Department protocol officer attached to the royal party. The diplomat submitted that, naturally, he could say nothing officially . . . but . . . well . . . Middle East oil *was* rather important. There are in town gentlemen of low habits who claim to have seen the diamond, a large one.

One thing and another, the forties and fifties were lively days for Denver. The city was a little astonished at itself, amazed but mostly delighted at the fantasy of growth. Residents who had lived in the town through only a few of the sleepy prewar years shook their heads and talked like oldest settlers: "Why, I can remember when . . ." One could almost halfway believe in the prediction of Governor Gilpin that Denver would become the veritable pivot of all Creation.

Yet through it all Denver has clung to many of the folkways of the city it used to be. The manner is relaxed and easy. It's a first-name town, and a resident for any length of time at all grouses about the new hubbub when he fails to meet at least one person he knows in every block of a stroll down Seventeenth Street. Citizens begrudge the loss of each tree to the widening of boulevards. The proliferation of traffic lights and one-way streets is resented as a creeping invasion of traditional Western freedoms, even while it is admitted that it would be impossible to get through the city without them. The times are dynamic, for sure, and all the new activity and diversity is vitalizing and profitable—and yet the noise level is rising, the old-timers say, and people seem to be more in a hurry, less neighborly than they once were.

Jack Foster, who *is* neighborly, still is on the job, and his newspaper, down to the moment of the closing of this chronicle, still was advancing.

And Denver still was thriving.

The mid-century years remade the city and its oldest institution, but the two of them seemed likely to take their joint renaissance in stride. They can remember when they both lost their heads over gold dust, and there was the grand day they turned out with the crowds to welcome the railroad. Denver and the *Rocky Mountain News* have seen a lot of commotion these first one hundred years, together all the way.

Epilogue

Sunrise Edition

ANNIVERSARIES are real nice parties—for those who are having them. The guests of honor are swept up and mildly exhilarated by a decent pride and certain passing illusions of immortality. Those who drop around to pay their respects warm themselves, briefly, in the glow. But only briefly. Proper words of congratulation are murmured about the achievement of the tenth, fiftieth, or hundredth milepost, and then everyone gets back to the more immediate business of living his own biography. The human capacity to sing "Happy birthday to you . . ." with conviction falls somewhere short, it must be conceded, of perfect empathy.

People are not attracted to Denver because it is a place of honorable antiquity. They live there because it is vital, alive, and youthful, a pleasant place of sun, elbow room, and expanding opportunity. The sum of a city's birthdays is less important than its personality, schools for the children, and the possibilities it offers for the good life, by whatever definition.

And people do not subscribe to a newspaper merely because it is a hundred years old. The patrons of the *Rocky Mountain News* grow steadily in number for other reasons less antiquarian in flavor. But continuity is involved, and character.

The past is indeed prologue, and neither the personality of a city nor the character of a newspaper is acquired offhand. Both are earned over the years. Some of the years of a city, and of a newspaper, have to be lived down. Others can be lived up to. Denver and the *News* have shared a few of each kind, and no experience is ever truly lost on a man, a city, or a journal.

Right now all portents are bright, and this joint story should end on a modestly rising inflection. Perhaps a symbol or two would be in mood.

A newspaper in whose columns is preserved the whole of the history of a city and a state might well borrow, in all humility, the words cast in bronze at the entrance to the Government Printing Office in Washington and printed (both more appropriately and more perdurably) on aged, stained paper in an Edinburgh print shop:

THIS IS A
PRINTING-OFFICE
CROSS-ROADS OF CIVILIZATION
REFUGE OF ALL THE ARTS AGAINST THE RAVAGES OF TIME
ARMORY OF FEARLESS TRUTH AGAINST WHISPERING RUMOR
INCESSANT TRUMPET OF TRADE
FROM THIS PLACE WORDS MAY FLY ABROAD
NOT TO PERISH AS WAVES OF SOUND BUT FIXED IN TIME
NOT CORRUPTED BY THE HURRYING HAND BUT VERIFIED IN
PROOF
FRIEND, YOU STAND ON SACRED GROUND:
THIS IS A PRINTING-OFFICE

But for the *News* there are symbols closer at hand. A visitor who enters through the glass doors of the printing office on West Colfax Avenue in Denver, Colorado, can see them any day and make his own selection.

Facing the entrance is a reproduction of the Scripps-Howard lighthouse and its familiar slogan, "Give Light and the People Will Find Their Own Way." The motto generally is ascribed to Dante, but the lineage is obscure. Carl McGee, crusading Western editor, adopted the words and the illustrative lighthouse for his Albuquerque *Tribune* early in the 1920s, and Roy Howard passed them along to the rest of the papers. Scholars have tried to trace down the origins in Dante. The closest they have come are Lines 67–69 in Purgatory XXII of *The Divine Comedy*: "*Facesti come quei che va di notte che porta il lume dietro e a se non giova ma dopo se fa le persone dotte.*" Literally: "Thou didst as one who passing through the night bears a light behind, that profits not himself but makes those who follow wise." Somewhere along the way this was edited and condensed into the motto McGee admired, a slogan singularly appropriate for a newspaper. Newspapers often proclaim themselves to be the "voice" of something or other, usually large and far-flung, or they promise to print everything that can decently be printed, or they are, simply, the greatest of a given segment of geography up to and including the globe. The *News* promises only to turn on the light.

In the lobby of the *News* building there is on permanent exhibit an old hand press similar to the one which gave Colorado its first newspaper on the stormy night of April 22, 1859. Looking down from one wall is an oil portrait of the founding editor, William N. Byers. It is a primitive painting, and rudely done. The perspective is shallow, the lighting flat and harsh. Brush strokes are crude but bold, the colors earthy, and the approximation of a man which the anonymous artist offers is roughhewn. So, also, were Byers and his times.

On the opposite wall are large photo murals of two breath-takingly beautiful scenes in the Rockies, the towering Tetons of Wyoming and

Berthoud Pass in Colorado. They represent the area the *News* aspires
to serve.

Within the wall itself are the ashes of Lee Casey, an enduring part
of the structure he helped to build over nearly half of its existence.

And then there is the rugged bronze portrait bust Jo Davidson did
of crusty old Edward Wyllis Scripps, who said:

A newspaper is a thing of growth and properly conducted is ever-
lasting.

Perhaps that is the proper punctuation for the story of a newspaper
that reported to a new city both atom-powered aircraft and the election
of Abraham Lincoln.

ACKNOWLEDGMENTS

ANY ESSAY in history, however free-wheeling, stands on many shoulders. My debts to persons and books are enormous in the present instance, and they extend over a period of some twenty years. It would be ungracious not to acknowledge the many courtesies, kindnesses, and acts of assistance and guidance which I have received, and yet a full listing of them would be unmanageable. I hope all those who have loaned me their time, memories, books, documents, and other good offices will understand my plight and accept their individual full shares of my large gratitude. Much as I have leaned on others, I still claim for myself, of course, all responsibility for inadvertent error and any outraging opinions expressed. My deep and special thanks are offered to:

First of all, Jack Foster, editor of the *Rocky Mountain News*, who released me from other duties, granted me complete freedom of expression, and in every other way, including moral support, created ideal conditions for a labor of this kind.

Gene Fowler for generously interrupting his own work to write the foreword, and for his succinct and salty words of encouragement.

Roy Howard, Jack Howard, and William Chandler, who made available to me their recollections, correspondence, and other papers.

E. W. (Ted) Scripps II for lending me his copy of *The Random File* of unpublished letters and other writings by his incomparable grandfather.

Alys Freeze and Ina Aulls of the Western Collection, Denver Public Library, and their unfailingly obliging assistants Opal Harber, Katherine Hawkins, Margaret Howie, Mary Hanley, and Margaret Campbell.

Executive Director Maurice Frink, historian Agnes Wright Spring, archivist Dolores C. Renze, and librarians Glenn Johnson, Jr., and Frances Shea of the Colorado State Historical Society.

W. D. Aeschbacher, director, and John B. White and Elizabeth Radtke of the Nebraska State Historical Society for researches far more generous than I had any right to expect; and to the State Historical Society of Iowa, William J. Petersen, superintendent.

"Alumni" of Denver journalism who assisted me greatly by remembering. Particularly to Clyde Brion Davis and John P. Lewis for their lavish assistance; and also to H. Allen Smith, Lowell Thomas, John Chapman, William L. Chenery, Frederic Babcock, Martin Dunn, James A. Stuart, Hettie Cattell, Charles B. McCabe, Aubrey Graves, Max B. Cook, Edward Keating, Forrest Davis, and Frank White.

To others who also searched their memories or records: Robert L. Chase, H. W. Hailey, Max Greedy, the late Sam Nadler, Harry Rhoads, Francis M. Plumb, Harold E. Neave, Thomas Hornsby Ferril, Damon Runyon, Jr., Fred Graham, Ray Humphreys, Bennie Bee, C. Parkhill Harvey, Jack Carberry, Gene Lindberg, Harvey Sethman, M. A. Ransom of San Carlos, California; and Walter Pickart of Gary, Indiana.

To the gentle Miss Grace Dailey for the pleasant chats which brought her father to life for me, and for the use of her voluminous scrapbooks and family albums.

Lillian Goldrick Johnson of Hickory, North Carolina, for making available to me a wealth of previously undiscovered material concerning her esteemed great-uncle, "Professor" Goldrick.

To that fine bookman Fred A. Rosenstock, who gave me use of the unpublished Rankin diary and other manuscript material from his private collection.

Fred M. Mazzulla for loans from his fabulous collection of old photographs; and to other of my fellow members of the Denver Westerners upon whose writings, professional, scholarly, and avocational, I have drawn freely: Dr. Philip W. Whiteley, Arthur H. Carhart, Forbes Parkhill, Dr. LeRoy R. Hafen, the late Levette J. Davidson, Alonzo E. Ellsworth, Kenneth E. Englert, Dr. Nolie Mumey, Don Griswold, Clarence Jackson, Edwin A. Bemis, Barron B. Beshoar, the late Colin Goodykoontz, Alan Swallow, Daniel A. Stone, Charles R. Ryland, Charles B. Roth, Francis B. Rizzari, Numa L. James, Dabney Otis Collins, and Erl H. Ellis.

Also to Denver County Judge David Brofman for photostats of Byers material from the files of his court; to Charles S. Reed, president of the Bank of Bellevue, Nebraska; Gene Lines, director of information services, Denver Public Schools; Lawrence C. A. Arany, librarian, the Indianapolis *Star*; Charles Eberstadt of Edward Eberstadt & Sons, New York City; Senator John A. Carroll, for assistance in obtaining government documents; and to Lloyd Jacquet of the McBride Company, New York, for a useful bibliography.

Peter J. Peaquin and Russell T. Wolfe of R. Hoe and Company, and Jackson Burke of the Megenthaler Linotype Company assisted me with specialized problems, as did Cranston Williams and R. V. Lang of the American Newspaper Publishers Association.

Material on W. A. H. Loveland was generously supplied by Abner Hobart Loveland of Nanuet, New York, Francis P. Loveland of Colorado Springs, and Harold M. Dunning of Loveland, Colorado.

Grateful acknowledgment is made to the Bancroft Library, University of California, Berkeley, for permission to utilize manuscript material in its Colorado collection. Benjamin P. Draper's laboriously prepared index to Colorado manuscripts in the Bancroft was invaluable in leading me to those I needed. Helpful searches were made for me by the Library of

Congress, Huntington, Newberry, Yale, University of California at Los Angeles, Omaha Public, and New York State libraries and the Sutro Branch of the California State Library. Thanks also are due for the freedoms given me in the Western Room, Norlin Library, University of Colorado.

Appreciative admiration goes to Melva Potter, cryptographer and typist, who typed an exceedingly scrawled-upon manuscript.

I shall stand long in debt to my editors, Timothy Seldes and Walter Bradbury of Doubleday & Company for their skills, suggestions, infinite patience, and (I hope I have not exhausted it) their friendship.

Finally, and with all the love of a traveler returned, my devotion and gratitude to Ethel, Linda, and Mike, husbandless and fatherless these many months.

Denver
December 1958

ROBERT L. PERKIN

Bibliography

THE primary source has been the files of the *Rocky Mountain News* itself. Nearly every sentence of this book could carry a footnote reference to some issue of the *News*, but I have sought to spare the casual reader at least some of the citations. Manuscript, periodical, and other sources of a documentary nature are indicated in the footnoting. The following list of books seeks to serve three aims. It is, first, a list of works consulted. It also may be useful as a guide to further reading. Thirdly, no comprehensive bibliography on Denver now exists, and perhaps this can be considered a first essay in that direction, although a few books have been included which deal with general history or journalism and do not touch directly on Denver. No effort has been made to distinguish between primary and secondary sources; the distinction will be apparent to those to whom it is a matter of importance. Where there are several editions, I have cited the edition consulted, which is not always the first and often is merely the most available.

R.L.P.

Adams, James Truslow. *The Epic of America*. Boston, 1931.

Alter, J. Cecil. *James Bridger: A Historical Narrative*. Reprint ed., Columbus, 1951.

Andreas, A. T., pub. *History of the State of Nebraska*. Chicago, 1882.

Athearn, Robert G. *Westward the Briton*. New York, 1953.

————. *William Tecumseh Sherman and the Settlement of the West*. Norman, 1956.

Atwood, Wallace W. *The Rocky Mountains*. New York, 1945.

Babcock, Louis M., ed. *The Denver Annual*. Denver, 1890.

Baggs, Mae Lacy. *Colorado: The Queen Jewel of the Rockies*. Boston, 1918.

Baker, James H., and Hafen, LeRoy R. *History of Colorado*. Denver, 1927.

Bancroft, Caroline. *Gulch of Gold: A History of Central City, Colorado*. Denver, 1958.

————. *The Melodrama of Wolhurst*. Lakewood, Colorado, 1952.

————. *Mile High Denver*. Lakewood, 1952.

————. *Silver Queen: The Fabulous Story of Baby Doe Tabor*. Denver, 1950.

Bancroft, Hubert Howe. *History of Nevada, Colorado, and Wyoming; Volume XXV of The Works of Hubert Howe Bancroft*. San Francisco, 1890.

Barker, William J., ed. *Boldly They Rode*. Lakewood, Colorado, 1949.

Barns, George C. *Denver, the Man*. Wilmington, Ohio, 1949.

Beadle, J. H. *Western Wilds and the Men Who Redeemed Them.* Cincinnati, 1878.

Beebe, Lucius, and Clegg, Charles. *Narrow Gauge in the Rockies.* Berkeley, 1958.

Berge, Wendell. *Economic Freedom for the West.* Lincoln, 1946.

Berger, Meyer. *The Story of the New York Times.* New York, 1951.

Beshoar, Barron B. *Out of the Depths.* Denver, 1942 and 1957.

Billington, Ray Allen. *The Far Western Frontier: 1830–1860.* New York, 1956.

————. *Westward Expansion.* New York, 1949.

Bird, Isabella L. *A Lady's Life in the Rocky Mountains.* New York, 1879.

Blake, Forrester. *Denver, Rocky Mountain Capital.* Denver, 1945.

Bloch, Don, ed. *Denver Westerners' Brand Book: 1949.* Denver, 1950.

Bluemel, Elinor. *Emily Griffith and the Opportunity School of Denver.* Denver, 1954.

Bollinger, Edward T. *Rails That Climb: The Story of the Moffat Road.* Santa Fe, 1950.

Bonner, T. D. *The Life and Adventures of James P. Beckwourth.* New York, 1931.

Bowles, Samuel. *The Switzerland of America.* Springfield, Massachusetts, 1869.

Brandon, William. *The Men and the Mountain: Frémont's Fourth Expedition.* New York, 1955.

Brayer, Herbert O., ed. *Denver Westerners' Brand Book: 1945.* Denver, 1946.

————, ed. *Denver Westerners' Brand Book: 1947.* Denver, 1949.

————. *Pike's Peak . . . or Busted!: Frontier Reminiscences of William Hawkins Hedges.* Evanston, Illinois, 1954.

Byers, William N. "History of Colorado" in *Encyclopedia of Biography of Colorado.* Chicago, 1901.

————and Kellom, John H. *Hand Book to the Gold Fields of Nebraska and Kansas.* Denver, 1949 facsimile.

Carhart, Arthur H. *Colorado.* New York, 1932.

————. *Water—Or Your Life.* Philadelphia, 1951.

Carson, Andrew C. *Colorado: Top of the World.* Denver, 1912.

Casey, Lee, ed. *Denver Murders.* New York, 1946.

Century Publishing and Engraving Company, pub. *Encyclopedia of Biography of Colorado.* Chicago, 1901.

Chapman, Arthur. *Out Where the West Begins.* Boston, 1917.

————. *The Story of Colorado.* Chicago, 1924.

Chapman Publishing Company, pub. *Portrait and Biographical Record of Denver and Vicinity.* Chicago, 1898.

Chenery, William L. *So It Seemed.* New York, 1952.

Churchill, Allen. *Park Row.* New York, 1958.

Clark, Ira G. *Then Came the Railroads.* Norman, 1958.

Cochran, Negley D. *E. W. Scripps.* New York, 1933.

Collier, William Ross, and Westrate, Edwin Victor. *Dave Cook of the Rockies.* New York, 1936.

————. *The Reign of Soapy Smith.* New York, 1935.

Collins, Dabney Otis, ed. *Denver Westerners' Brand Book: 1948*. Denver, 1949.

Colorado State Planning Commission. *Colorado: 1956–1958: Year Book of the State of Colorado*. Denver, 1958.

Commager, Henry Steele. *The Blue and the Gray*. Indianapolis, 1950.

Commissioner of Indian Affairs. *Report*. Washington, 1863.

Conard, Howard Louis. *"Uncle Dick" Wootton: The Pioneer Frontiersman of the Rocky Mountain Region*. Columbus, 1950 reprint.

Cook, David J. *Hands Up!* Denver, 1882.

Crampon, L. J., and Lemon, R. D. *Recreation Resources and Facilities of Colorado*. Denver, 1957.

Creel, George. *Rebel at Large*. New York, 1947.

Crozier, Emmet. *Yankee Reporters: 1861–65*. New York, 1956.

Darrah, William Culp. *Powell of the Colorado*. Princeton, 1951.

Davidson, Levette J., ed. *Poems of the Old West*. Denver, 1951.

————and Bostwick, Prudence. *The Literature of the Rocky Mountain West*. Caldwell, Idaho, 1939.

Davis, Carlyle Channing. *Olden Times in Colorado*. Los Angeles, 1916.

Davis, Clyde Brion. *The Arkansas*. New York, 1940.

————. *"The Great American Novel——"*. New York, 1938.

————. *Something for Nothing*. New York, 1956.

Davis, E. O. *The First Five Years of the Railroad Era in Colorado*. Denver, 1948.

Davis, Richard Harding. *The West from a Car-Window*. New York, 1903.

Dawson, J. Frank. *Place Names in Colorado*. Denver, 1954.

Dawson, Thomas Fulton. *Life and Character of Edward Oliver Wolcott*. New York, 1911.

De Boer, S. R. *Around the Seasons in Denver Parks and Gardens*. Denver, 1948.

Denver Planning Office. *A Demonstration Plan for Central Denver*. Denver, 1957.

Devine, Edward T., and others. *The Denver Tramway Strike of 1920*. Denver, 1921.

De Voto, Bernard. *Across the Wide Missouri*. Boston, 1947.

Dier, Caroline Lawrence. *The Lady of the Gardens: Mary Elitch Long*. Hollywood, 1932.

Dill, R. G. *The Political Campaigns of Colorado*. Denver, 1895.

Dixon, William Hepworth. *New America*. Philadelphia, 1867.

Donnelly, Thomas C., ed. *Rocky Mountain Politics*. Albuquerque, 1940.

Drewry, John E., ed. *Post Biographies of Famous Journalists*. New York, 1942.

Driggs, Howard R. *Westward America*. New York, 1942.

Dunham, Harold H., ed. *Denver Westerners' Brand Book: 1950*. Denver, 1951.

Dunning, Harold Marion. *Over Hill and Vale*. Boulder, 1956.

Dyer, John L. *The Snow-Shoe Itinerant*. Cincinnati, 1890.

Ellis, Erl H., ed. *Denver Westerners' Brand Book: 1954*. Denver, 1955.

Emmitt, Robert. *The Last War Trail: The Utes and the Settlement of Colorado*. Norman, 1954.

Fallis, Edwina H. *When Denver and I Were Young*. Denver, 1956.

Farwell, Byron. *The Man Who Presumed*. New York, 1957.

Federal Writers' Project. *Colorado: A Guide to the Highest State*. New York, 1941.

Fenwick, Robert W. *Red Fenwick's West: Yesterday and Today*. Denver, 1956.

Ferril, Thomas Hornsby. *I Hate Thursday*. New York, 1946.

Ferril, Will C. *Sketches of Colorado*. Denver, 1911.

Field, Eugene. *The Complete Tribune Primer*. Boston, 1901.

————. *A Little Book of Western Verse*. New York, 1895.

Fisher, John S. *A Builder of the West: The Life of General William Jackson Palmer*. Caldwell, 1939.

Flannery, L. G., ed. *John Hunton's Diary: 1873-'75*. Lingle, Wyoming, 1956.

Fleming, Roscoe. "Denver: Civic Schizophrenic" in Allen, Robert S., *Our Fair City*. New York, 1947.

Foote, Shelby. *The Civil War*. New York, 1958.

Fortune, editors of. *The Exploding Metropolis*. New York, 1958.

Fossett, Frank. *Colorado: Its Gold and Silver Mines, etc.* New York, 1879.

Fowler, Gene. *Salute to Yesterday*. New York, 1937.

————. *A Solo in Tom-Toms*. New York, 1946.

————. *Timber Line*. New York, 1933.

Frémont, J. C. *Report of the Exploring Expedition to the Rocky Mountains in the Year 1842*. Washington, 1845.

Frink, Maurice, ed. *Denver Westerners' Brand Book: 1953*. Denver, 1954.

————with Jackson, W. Turrentine, and Spring, Agnes Wright. *When Grass Was King*. Boulder, 1956.

Fritz, Percy Stanley. *Colorado: The Centennial State*. New York, 1941.

Fuller, Harlin M., and Hafen, LeRoy R., eds. *The Journal of Captain John R. Bell*. Glendale, 1957.

Gandy, Lewis Cass. *The Tabors*. New York, 1934.

Gantt, Paul H. *The Case of Alfred Packer the Man-Eater*. Denver, 1952.

Gard, Wayne. *Frontier Justice*. Norman, 1949.

Garnsey, Morris E. *America's New Frontier: The Mountain West*. New York, 1950.

————and McNickle, Roma K. *Colorado's Natural Resources—Opportunity and Challenge*. Denver, 1957.

Garrard, Lewis H. *Wah-to-yah and the Taos Trail*. Norman, 1955 reprint.

Garth, Thomas Russell. *The Life of Henry Augustus Buchtel*. Denver, 1937.

Ghent, W. J. *The Early Far West: A Narrative Outline 1540–1850*. New York, 1936.

Gilpin, William. *Mission of the North American People*. Philadelphia, 1874.

Goodykoontz, Colin, ed. *Papers of Edward P. Costigan Relating to the Progressive Movement in Colorado: 1902–1917*. Boulder, 1941.

Goss, C. Chaucer. *Bellevue, Larimer & Saint Mary: Their History, Location, Description and Advantages*. Bellevue, Nebraska, 1859.

Grable, F. C. *Colorado: The Bright Romance of American History*. Denver, 1911.

Graham, Charles A., and Perkin, Robert L. "Denver: Reluctant Capital" in West, Ray B., Jr., ed. *Rocky Mountain Cities*. New York, 1949.

Greeley, Horace. *An Overland Journey from New York to San Francisco.* New York, 1860.

Grinnell, George Bird. *The Fighting Cheyennes.* Norman, 1956.

Griswold, Don L. and Jean Harvey. *The Carbonate Camp Called Leadville.* Denver, 1951.

————. *Colorado's Century of "Cities."* Denver, 1958.

Gunther, John. *Inside U. S. A.* New York, 1947.

Hafen, LeRoy R. *Colorado and Its People.* New York, 1948.

————. *Colorado Gold Rush: Contemporary Letters and Reports, 1858 –1859.* Glendale, 1941.

————. *Colorado: The Story of a Western Commonwealth.* Denver, 1933.

————. *Pike's Peak Gold Rush Guidebooks of 1859.* Glendale, 1941.

————. *Overland Routes to the Gold Fields, 1859.* Glendale, 1942.

———— and Hafen, Ann W. *Rufus B. Sage: His Letters and Papers.* Glendale, 1956.

————and Rister, Carl Coke. *Western America.* New York, 1950.

Halaas, E. T., and others. *Working Denver: An Economic Analysis.* Denver, 1953.

Hale, William Harlan. *Horace Greeley: Voice of the People.* New York, 1950.

Hall, Frank. *History of the State of Colorado.* Chicago, 1889.

Hart, H. Martyn. *Recollections and Reflections.* Denver, 1917.

Hart, John L. Jerome. *Fourteen Thousand Feet: A History of the Naming and Early Ascents of the High Colorado Peaks.* Denver, 1931.

Hayes, Augustus Allen. *New Colorado and the Santa Fe Trail.* New York, 1880.

Henderson, Junius, and others. *Colorado: Short Studies of Its Past and Present.* Boulder, 1927.

Hensley, Andrew A., ed. *Denver: Pencil Sketches and Graver Strokes.* Denver, 1886.

Hill, Alice Polk. *Colorado Pioneers in Picture and Story.* Denver, 1915.

Holbrook, Stewart H. *Dreamers of the American Dream.* New York, 1957.

————. *The Rocky Mountain Revolution.* New York, 1956.

Hollister, Ovando J. *History of the First Regiment of Colorado Volunteers.* Denver, 1863.

————. *The Mines of Colorado.* Springfield, 1867.

Horner, John Willard. *Silver Town.* Caldwell, 1950.

Howe, Elvon L., ed. *Denver Westerners' Brand Book: 1952.* Denver, 1953.

Ingersoll, Ernest. *The Crest of the Continent.* Chicago, 1885.

Jackson, Clarence S. *Pageant of the Pioneers: The Veritable Art of William Henry Jackson.* Minden, Nebraska, 1958.

————. *Picture Maker of the Old West: William H. Jackson.* New York, 1947.

Jackson, W. Turrentine. *Wagon Roads West.* Berkeley, 1952.

James, Numa L., ed. *Denver Westerners' Brand Book: 1957.* Denver, 1958.

Karsner, David. *Silver Dollar: The Story of the Tabors.* New York, 1932.

Kemp, Donald C. *Colorado's Little Kingdom.* Denver, 1949.

Kerby, Robert Lee. *The Confederate Invasion of New Mexico and Arizona: 1861–1862.* Los Angeles, 1958.

King, Clyde Lyndon. *The History of the Government of Denver with Special Reference to Its Relation with Public Service Corporations.* Denver, 1911.

Kohl, Edith Eudora. *Denver's Historic Mansions.* Denver, 1957.

Kraenzel, Carl Frederick. *The Great Plains in Transition.* Norman, 1955.

Krakel, Dean. *South Platte Country.* Laramie, 1954.

Larimer, William Henry Harrison. *Reminiscences.* Lancaster, Pennsylvania, 1918.

Lavender, David. *Bent's Fort.* New York, 1954.

———. *The Big Divide.* New York, 1948.

———. *One Man's West.* New York, 1943.

Lee, Mabel Barbee. *Cripple Creek Days.* New York, 1958.

Lewis, Lloyd, and Smith, Henry Justin. *Oscar Wilde Discovers America 1882.* New York, 1936.

Lindsey, Benjamin B., and O'Higgins, Harvey J. *The Beast.* New York, 1911.

———and Borough, Rube. *The Dangerous Life.* New York, 1931.

Livesay, Dowell. *Denver—and the Middle Trail.* Denver, 1927.

Llewellyn, Karl N., and Hoebel, E. Adamson. *The Cheyenne Way.* Norman, 1941.

Long, Margaret. *The Smoky Hill Trail.* Denver, 1943.

Looms, George. "Denver: Washed Whiter'n Snow" in Aikman, Duncan, ed. *The Taming of the Frontier.* New York, 1925.

Lowie, Robert H. *Indians of the Plains.* New York, 1954.

McCabe, Charles R., ed. *Damned Old Crank: A Self-Portrait of E. W. Scripps.* New York, 1951.

McClure, A. K. *Three Thousand Miles through the Rocky Mountains.* Philadelphia, 1869.

McCoy, Joseph G. *Historic Sketches of the Cattle Trade of the West and Southwest.* Columbus, 1951 reprint.

McCracken, Harold. *Portrait of the Old West.* New York, 1952.

MacKellar, Thomas. *The American Printer.* Philadelphia, 1889.

McLaughlin, Dick. *From Humble Beginnings . . .* Cleveland, 1953.

McMechen, Edgar Carlisle. *The Life of Governor Evans.* Denver, 1924.

———. *The Moffat Tunnel of Colorado.* Denver, 1927.

———. *Robert W. Speer: A City Builder.* Denver, 1919.

McMenamin, Hugh L. *The Pinnacled Glory of the West.* Denver, 1912.

McMurtrie, Douglas C., and Allen, Albert H. *Early Printing in Colorado.* Denver, 1935.

Majors, Alexander. *Seventy Years on the Frontier.* Chicago, 1893.

Malone, Thomas H. *Colorado and Its Queenly Capital.* Denver, 1900.

Martin, Lawrence. *So the People May Know.* Denver, 1951.

Mathews, Mitford M. *A Dictionary of Americanisms on Historical Principles.* Chicago, 1951.

Mazzulla, Fred M. and Jo. *Cripple Creek and the Pike's Peak Region: The First 100 Years.* Denver, 1956.

Mengel, Willi. *Ottmar Mergenthaler and the Printing Revolution.* Brooklyn, 1954.

Miller, Webb. *I Found No Peace*. New York, 1936.

Monaghan, Jay. *The Overland Trail*. Indianapolis, 1947.

Moody, Ralph. *The Home Ranch*. New York, 1956.

————. *Little Britches*. New York, 1950.

————. *Man of the Family*. New York, 1951.

Morris, Joe Alex. *Deadline Every Minute*. New York, 1957.

Morton, J. Sterling, and others. *Illustrated History of Nebraska*. Lincoln, 1906.

Mumey, Nolie. *Bloody Trails along the Rio Grande: The Diary of Alonzo Ferdinand Ickis*. Denver, 1958.

————. *Clark, Gruber and Company (1860–1865): A Pioneer Denver Mint*. Denver, 1950.

————. *Creede: The History of a Colorado Silver Mining Town*. Denver, 1949.

————. ed. *Denver Westerners' Brand Book 1951*. Denver, 1952.

————. *History of the Early Settlements of Denver*. Glendale, 1942.

————. *James Pierson Beckwourth: An Enigmatic Figure of the West*. Denver, 1957.

————. *March of the First Dragoons to the Rocky Mountains in 1835: The Diaries and Maps of Lemuel Ford*. Denver, 1957.

————. *Pioneer Denver*. Denver, 1948.

Murray, Charles A., and others. *Newspaper Career of E. D. Cowen*. Seattle, 1930.

Nankivell, John N. *History of the Military Organizations of the State of Colorado*. Denver, 1935.

Nebraska State Historical Society. *Proceedings and Collections*. Lincoln, 1902.

Nevins, Allan. *Frémont: The West's Greatest Adventurer*. New York, 1928.

Norfleet, J. Frank, as told to Hines, Gordon. *Norfleet*. Sugar Land, Texas, 1927.

Oakes, D. C. *Traveler's Guide to the New Gold Mines in Kansas and Nebraska*. New York, 1859; Denver, 1947 facsimile.

O'Connor, Richard. *Bat Masterson*. New York, 1957.

Olson, James C. *History of Nebraska*. Lincoln, 1955.

Ormes, Robert M., ed. *Guide to the Colorado Mountains*. Denver, 1952 and 1955.

Overton, Richard C. *Gulf to Rockies: The Heritage of the Fort Worth and Denver-Colorado and Southern Railways, 1861–1898*. Austin, 1953.

Parker, Thomas D., ed. *Denver, the Beautiful*. Denver, 1902.

Parkhill, Forbes. *The Law Goes West*. Denver, 1956.

————. *The Wildest of the West*. New York, 1951; Denver, 1957.

Parkman, Francis. *The Oregon Trail*. New York, 1943.

Parsons, Eugene. *A Guidebook to Colorado*. Boston, 1911.

Peake, Ora Brooks. *The Colorado Range Cattle Industry*. Glendale, 1937.

Petersen, William. *A Critical Survey of Several Forecasts of the Population of Colorado*. Denver, 1957.

Peterson, Virgil V., ed. *Denver Westerners' Brand Book: 1946*. Denver, 1947.

Phillips, Paul C., ed. *Life in the Rocky Mountains: A Diary . . . by W. A. Ferris*. Denver, 1940.

Pike, Zebulon Montgomery. *Exploratory Travels through the Western Territories, etc.* Denver, 1889.

Pitzer, Robert Claiborne. *Three Frontiers: Memories, and a Portrait of Henry Littleton Pitzer.* Muscatine, Iowa, 1938.

Pomeroy, Earl. *In Search of the Golden West: The Tourist in Western America.* New York, 1957.

Poor, M. C. *Denver, South Park & Pacific.* Denver, 1949.

Porter, Henry M. *Pencilings of an Early Western Pioneer.* Denver, 1929.

Preuss, Charles. *Exploring with Frémont.* Norman, 1958.

Quiett, Glenn Chesney. *They Built the West: An Epic of Rails and Cities.* New York, 1934.

Ralph, Julian. *Our Great West.* New York, 1893.

Rex, Wallace Hayden. *Colorado Newspaper Bibliography, 1859–1933.* Denver, 1939.

Richardson, Albert D. *Beyond the Mississippi.* Hartford, 1867.

Robock, Stefan H. *Water Resources of Colorado.* Denver, 1957.

Rockwell, Wilson. *Sunset Slope.* Denver, 1956.

————. *The Utes: A Forgotten People.* Denver, 1956.

Runyon, Damon, Jr. *Father's Footsteps.* New York, 1953.

Ryland, Charles S., ed. *Denver Westerners' Brand Book: 1956.* Denver, 1957.

Sabin, Edwin L. *Kit Carson Days.* New York, 1935.

Sage, Rufus B. *Scenes in the Rocky Mountains.* Philadelphia, 1846.

Sandoz, Mari. *The Buffalo Hunters.* New York, 1954.

————. *Cheyenne Autumn.* New York, 1953.

Saunderson, Mont H. *Western Land and Water Use.* Norman, 1950.

Schoberlin, Melvin. *From Candles to Footlights: A Biography of the Pike's Peak Theater, 1859–1876.* Denver, 1941.

Seldes, George. *Freedom of the Press.* New York, 1935.

Seltzer, Louis B. *The Years Were Good.* New York, 1956.

Shaw, Luella. *True History of Some of the Pioneers of Colorado.* Hotchkiss, Colorado, 1909.

Shoemaker, Len. *Saga of a Forest Ranger.* Boulder, 1958.

Smedley, William. *Across the Plains in '62.* Denver, 1916.

Smiley, Jerome C. *History of Denver.* Denver, 1901.

————. *Semi-Centennial History of the State of Colorado.* Chicago, 1913.

Smith, H. Allen. *Low Man on a Totem Pole.* Garden City, 1941.

Smith, Henry Nash. *Virgin Land: The American West as Symbol and Myth.* Cambridge, 1950.

Smith, Thomas L. *Denver Illustrated.* Denver, 1893.

Sorensen, Alfred. *The Early History of Omaha.* Omaha, 1876.

————. *The Story of Omaha.* Omaha, 1923.

Sorrells, John H. *A Handbook of Scripps-Howard.* Memphis, 1948.

Spencer, Elma Dill Russell. *Gold Country: 1828–1858.* San Antonio, 1958.

Sprague, Marshall. *Massacre: The Tragedy at White River.* Boston, 1957.

————. *Money Mountain: The Story of Cripple Creek Gold.* Boston, 1953.

Spring, Agnes Wright. *A Bloomer Girl on Pike's Peak.* Denver, 1949.

Stegner, Wallace. *Beyond the Hundredth Meridian.* Boston, 1954.

Steinel, Alvin T. *History of Agriculture in Colorado.* Fort Collins, 1926.

Stone, Irving. *Men to Match My Mountains: The Opening of the Far West,*
     1840–1900. New York, 1956.
Stone, Wilbur Fisk. *History of Colorado.* Chicago, 1918.
Stone, William G. *The Colorado Hand-Book: Denver and Its Outings.* Den-
     ver, 1892.
Swallow, Alan, ed. *Denver Westerners' Brand Book: 1955.* Denver, 1956.
Taylor, Bayard. *Colorado: A Summer Trip.* New York, 1867.
Thayer, William M. *Marvels of the New West.* Norwich, Connecticut, 1888.
Thompson, Slason. *Eugene Field: A Study in Heredity and Contradictions.*
     New York, 1901.
Tierney, Luke. *History of the Gold Discoveries on the South Platte River.*
     Pacific City, Iowa, 1859; Denver, 1949 facsimile.
Toll, Roger W. *The Mountain Peaks of Colorado.* Denver, 1923.
Tonge, Thomas. *Denver by Pen and Picture.* Denver, 1898.
Turner, Frederick Jackson. *The Frontier in American History.* New York,
     1920.
Turner, T. G., and C. E., pub. *Turner's Guide from the Lakes to the Rocky
     Mountains.* Chicago, 1868.
Uchill, Ida Libert. *Pioneers, Peddlers and Tsadikim.* Denver, 1957.
Van Cise, Philip S. *Fighting the Underworld.* Cambridge, 1936.
Vanderblue, Homer B. *Denver the Industrial City.* Denver, 1921.
Van Tuyl, F. M., and Crabtree, E. H. *Colorado's Mineral Resources.* Den-
     ver, 1957.
Vestal, Stanley. *Jim Bridger: Mountain Man.* New York, 1946.
————. *Kit Carson: The Happy Warrior of the Old West.* Boston, 1928.
————. *Warpath and Council Fire.* New York, 1948.
Vickers, William B. *History of Denver.* Chicago, 1880.
Villard, Henry. *The Past and Present of the Pike's Peak Gold Regions.*
     St. Louis, 1860; Princeton, 1932 reprint.
Wade, Mason, ed. *The Journals of Francis Parkman.* New York, 1947.
Wakeley, Arthur C. *Omaha: The Gate City, and Douglas County.* Chicago,
     1917.
Waldrop, A. Gayle. *Editor and Editorial Writer.* New York, 1948 and 1955.
Wallace, Edward S. *The Great Reconnaissance: Soldiers, Artists and Scien-
     tists on the Frontier 1848–1861.* Boston, 1955.
Waters, Frank. *Midas of the Rockies.* New York, 1937; Denver, 1949.
Watson, Elmo Scott. *The Professor Goes West: Reports of Major John
     Wesley Powell's Explorations: 1867–1874.* Bloomington, Illinois, 1954.
Webb, Walter Prescott. *The Great Frontier.* Boston, 1952.
————. *The Great Plains.* Boston, 1936.
Wellman, Paul I. *Death on Horseback: Seventy Years of War for the Ameri-
     can West.* Philadelphia, 1947.
————. *Glory, God and Gold.* New York, 1954.
Wharton, J. E. *History of the City of Denver.* Denver, 1866, reprint 1909.
Whitford, William Clarke. *Colorado Volunteers in the Civil War.* Denver,
     1906.
Whiting, Lilian. *The Land of Enchantment.* Boston, 1906.
Whitman, Walt. *Complete Prose Works of Walt Whitman.* New York, 1914.
Wilde, Oscar. *Impressions of America.* Sunderland, 1906.

Wilder, Walter Lawson. *Robert Wilbur Steele: Defender of Liberty*. Denver, 1913.

Willard, James, and Goodykoontz, Colin B. *The Trans-Mississippi West*. Boulder, 1930.

Williams, Albert N. *Rocky Mountain Country*. New York, 1950.

—————. *The Water and the Power*. New York, 1951.

Willison, George F. *Here They Dug the Gold*. New York, 1946.

Wolle, Muriel Sibell. *Stampede to Timberline: The Ghost Towns and Mining Camps of Colorado*. Boulder, 1949.

Wood, Stanley. *Over the Range to the Golden Gate*. Chicago, 1912.

Woodbury, Frank S. *Tourists' Guide Book to Denver, 1882*. Denver, 1882.

Wyer, Malcolm Glenn, ed. *Art in Denver*. Denver, 1928.

Index

Denver *Tribune*, on Byers' departure, 325–26

Denver Typographical Union No. 49, 33

Denver Water Supply Company, 327

Depression, in Denver, 533–34

Devor, J. R., 197

DeVoto, Bernard, 151; on Gilpin, 233

Dickerson, J. S., 352

Dickson, T. C., 73–74

Dixon, William Hepworth, on Denver, 153

Dodd, Capt. Theodore H., 245

Dodge, Gen. Grenville M., chooses Union Pacific route, 305

Dodge, Col. Henry, 63

Dogs, free ads for lost, 41

Doherty, Henry L., on Denver, 409

Dominguez, Francisco A., 59

Downing, Maj. Jacob, 264

Dragoon, U. S., tour of, 63–64

Dry Creek, gold at, 29

Duell, Harvey, 438, 440, 444

Dunn, Martin, on *Rocky Mountain News*, 422; on Runyan, 420–21

Dunn, William, 225

Dwyer, Vincent M., 555, 587

Early History of Omaha, The (Sorenson), 58–59

Easter, John, 71

Edbrooke, F. E., 407

Egan, Ellen, and Runyan, 420–22

Elbert, Samuel H., 133

Elkins, Stephen B., and Patterson, 382

Ellsworth, L. C. 333

Emigrants, Pike's Peak, and Indians, 89–92; slogans of, 87

Emigration, the returning, Byers on, 97–98, 99; Franklin, Indiana, *Democrat* on, 103; Hannibal *Messenger* on, 100; New York *Ledger* on, 101, 102, 103

Emu, filler on, 42

Encyclopedia of Biography of Colorado, 30n.

Englert, Kenneth, on "Reynolds Raid," 250

Escalante, Silvestre Vélez de, 59

Evans, John, 40, 133; banking activities of, 161; and Byers, 257–58; character of, 256–57; and Denver Pacific, 305; and Denver schools, 152; and Indian

wars, 262–69; rescues Byers' family, 221

Evans, William G., 333

Evening Post, 401–07; in coal business, 414; battle of with *News*, 485ff.

Faithful, Emily, on Denver, 348

Fall Leaf, and gold, 70

Farming, importance of in West, 43–44

Farrar, Frank C., 444

Feeney, John ("Red"), 446; Parkhill on, 432–33; and Rhoads, 451–52

Ferril, Hellie, 151

Ferril, Thomas Hornsby, 151; 454–55; on Denver, 581–82

Ferril, Will C., 361

Field, Eugene, 9; on *News*, 355, 363–64

Field, Marshall, fortune of, 356

Fire, Denver's, 209–10

"First Two Years, The," (Pierce), 30n.

Fisher, Eugene, 543

Fisher, Rev. George, 150

Fitzpatrick, Tom "Broken Hand," 61

Fitzsimmons Army Hospital, 20

Flood, Denver's, 211; Goldrick on, 212–19; Indian's warning of, 211; toll of, 219–24

Florence *Courier*, the, 39

Floyd, John B., 244, 245

Ford, Capt. James H., 245

Ford, Capt. Lemuel, journal of, 64

Forest, Eliza "Mountain Charley," career of, 112

Forsyth, Maj. George A., 288

Fort Jackson, 63

Fort Kearney, 32

Fort Laramie, post office at, 48

Fort St. Vrain, 32, 36

Fortune, on Scripps-Howard, 525, 527

Foster, Jack C. ("Young Jack"), 40, 496, 499–501, 550, 553–56, 560–62, 566–67; on growth of *News* 590

Fouts, William, 109

Fowler, Gene, 438, 440, 444; on Bonfils and Tammen, 403, 404; on "Cap" Smith, 339; Chenery on, 444; and Cooper, 445

Fraeb, Henry, 63

France, Lewis B., 323; and Beckwourth, 170

Frank Leslie's Illustrated Newspaper, on Wootton building, 30

Franklin, Indiana, *Democrat*, on returning emigration, 103

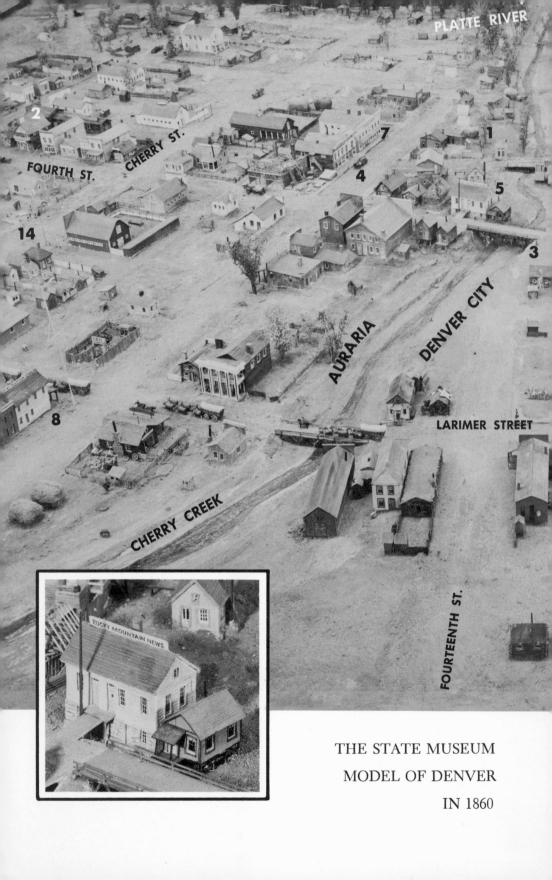

PLATTE RIVER

2

FOURTH ST.   CHERRY ST.

7   1

4   5

14   3

AURARIA   DENVER CITY

8   LARIMER STREET

CHERRY CREEK

ROCKY MOUNTAIN NEWS

FOURTEENTH ST.

THE STATE MUSEUM
MODEL OF DENVER
IN 1860

MICRONUTRIENTS IN AGRICULTURE

Second Edition

Soil Science Society of America Book Series

Books in the series are available from the Soil Science Society of America, 677 South Segoe Road, Madison, WI 53711 USA.

1. MINERALS IN SOIL ENVIRONMENTS. Second Edition. 1989.
   J. B. Dixon and S. B. Weed, *editors*　　R. C. Dinauer, *managing editor*

2. PESTICIDES IN THE SOIL ENVIRONMENT: PROCESSES, IMPACTS, AND MODELING. 1990.
   H. H. Cheng, *editor*　　S. H. Mickelson, *managing editor*

3. SOIL TESTING AND PLANT ANALYSIS. Third Edition. 1990.
   R. L. Westerman, *editor*　　S. H. Mickelson, *managing editor*

4. MICRONUTRIENTS IN AGRICULTURE. Second Edition. 1991.
   J. J. Mortvedt et al., *editors*　　S. H. Mickelson, *managing editor*

Micronutrients in Agriculture

Second Edition

Editorial Committee: J. J. Mortvedt, chair
F. R. Cox
L. M. Shuman
R. M. Welch

Managing Editor: S. H. Mickelson

Editor-in-Chief SSSA: R. J. Luxmoore

Number 4 in the Soil Science Society of America Book Series

**Published by: Soil Science Society of America, Inc.
Madison, Wisconsin, USA**

1991

Soil Science Society of America, Inc.
677 South Segoe Road, Madison, Wisconsin 53711 USA

Library of Congress Cataloging-in-Publication Data

Micronutrients in agriculture / editor, J.J. Mortvedt. — 2nd ed.
     p.   cm. — (The Soil Science Society of America book series :
no. 4)
   Includes index.
   ISBN 0-89118-797-9
   1. Trace elements in agriculture. 2. Trace elements in nutrition.
3. Micronutrient fertilizers. I. Mortvedt, J.J. (John J.). II. Series.
S587.5.T7M5 1991
631.8'1—dc20
                                             91-17987
                                               CIP

Printed in MEXICO

CONTENTS

FOREWORD

The sustenance and well being of humankind are inexorably linked to the stocks of essential nutrients in the bio-geosphere and their capacity for cycling and manipulation. Nutrient management is fundamental to agriculture and its ability to minimize environmental impacts.

The capacity to produce usable plant biomass depends upon the adequacy and balance of mineral nutrients. Well-managed agricultural ecosystems require knowledge about native nutrient stocks, the chemical form(s) in which nutrients occur, protocols for determining nutrient levels in soils and plants, the functions and interactions of nutrients in plants and animals, the mechanisms of nutrient uptake, sorption-desorption and equilibria reactions in soils, diagnosis of nutrient deficiencies in plants and animals, plant responses to nutrient deficiencies and management, and manipulation of nutrients through formulations and application technologies.

This publication is an updated and revised version of the first edition of *Micronutrients in Agriculture* published in 1972. It includes current thinking and knowledge on the concepts of mineral essentiality in plants with reference to the beneficial role or significance of such elements as sodium, nickel, aluminum, lanthanum, and cerium. Future research agendas are also identified.

Fred P. Miller, *president*
Soil Science Society of America

PREFACE

In 1971, the Soil Science Society of America and the Tennessee Valley Authority cosponsored a symposium to review micronutrient problems in soils and in plant and animal nutrition. The papers were published as the first edition of *Micronutrients in Agriculture* by SSSA in 1972. The book has been used throughout the world as a reference and textbook since that time. It is primarily intended for graduate students and researchers in agricultural, biological, environmental, and nutritional sciences interested in the subject matter comprising each chapter who already have a thorough understanding of biochemistry, physiology, and soil science. However, it will serve as an excellent up-to-date reference book for everyone interested in the micronutrients—boron, chlorine, copper, iron, manganese, molybdenum, and zinc.

This book, the second edition, contains information primarily obtained since the first edition was published, although some material from the first edition was repeated where no new information was available. While the general subject matter is similar to that in the first edition, emphasis was changed to address newly emerging areas in micronutrient research. The 18 chapters in this book were written by outstanding scientists who are authorities on micronutrient problems in soils and in plant, animal, and human nutrition. Eleven chapters of the first edition were deleted or combined and three new subject areas were included in this revision. The previously published subject areas covered in this edition are: (1) Chemistry of micronutrients in soils, (2) Micronutrient uptake, translocation, functions and interactions in plants, (3) Diagnosis and correction of micronutrient deficiencies, (4) Micronutrient fertilizer technology, and (5) Trace elements in animal nutrition. The new subject areas are: (1) Micronutrients and disease resistance or tolerance in plants, (2) Trace elements in human nutrition, and (3) Beneficial elements, functional elements, and possible new essential elements.

The editorial committee gratefully acknowledges the authors of this volume and their organizations for their cooperation and support. The editors also wish to extend their special thanks to Sherri Mickelson and Theresa Shinners-Gray and to other members of the Headquarters offices of the SSSA for their work in editing and preparing the manuscripts for publication. Assistance by anonymous reviewers of each chapter also is appreciated.

John J. Mortvedt, *chair*
Tennessee Valley Authority
Muscle Shoals, Alabama

Fred R. Cox
North Carolina State University
Raleigh, North Carolina

Larry M. Shuman
University of Georgia
Griffin, Georgia

Ross M. Welch
U.S. Plant, Soil, & Nutrition Laboratory
Ithaca, New York

CONTRIBUTORS

William H. Allaway	Soil Scientist (retired), U.S. Plant Soil and Nutrition Laboratory, 14 Ogden Road, Ithaca, NY 14850
Colin J. Asher	Professor of Agriculture, Department of Agriculture, The University of Queensland, Queensland 4072, Australia
Ward Chesworth	University of Guelph, Guelph, Ontario, Canada N1G 2W1
Robin D. Graham	Associate Professor of Agronomy, Waite Agricultural Research Institute, Department of Agronomy, University of Adelaide, Glen Osmond 5064, Australia
Robert D. Harter	Professor of Soil Chemistry, Department of Forest Resources, University of New Hampshire, Durham, NH 03824
William A. House	Research Physiologist, USDA-ARS, U.S. Plant, Soil, and Nutrition Laboratory, Cornell University, Ithaca, NY 14853
G. V. Johnson	Professor of Soil Science, Department of Agronomy, Oklahoma State University, Stillwater, OK 74078
J. Benton Jones, Jr.	Professor Emeritus of Horticulture, Vice President, Micro-Macro International, Inc., 183 Paradise Blvd., Suite 108, Athens, GA 30607
Leon V. Kochian	Plant Physiologist, USDA-ARS, U.S. Plant, Soil and Nutrition Laboratory, Cornell University, Ithaca, NY 14853
Joe Kubota	Soil Scientist (retired), Soil Conservation Service, USDA, Ithaca, NY 14850
Xingen Lei	Graduate Research Assistant, Animal Science Department, Michigan State University, East Lansing, MI 48824
W. L. Lindsay	Professor of Soils, Department of Agronomy, Colorado State University, Fort Collins, CO 80523
Horst Marschner	Professor, Institut für Pflanzenernährung, Universität Hohenheim, Postfach 70 05 62, 7000 Stuttgart 70, Germany
D. C. Martens	Professor of Soil Science, Crop and Soil Environmental Sciences, Virginia Polytechnic Institute and State University, Blacksburg, VA 24061-0404
H. J. Mascagni, Jr.	Assistant Professor of Agronomy, Northeast Research and Extension Center, University of Arkansas, Keiser, AR 72351
Elwyn R. Miller	Professor of Animal Science, Animal Science Department, Michigan State University, East Lansing, MI 48824
John T. Moraghan	Professor of Soil Science, Department of Soil Science, North Dakota State University, Fargo, ND 58105
John J. Mortvedt	Senior Scientist, Agricultural Research Department, National Fertilizer and Environmental Research Center, Tennessee Valley Authority, Muscle Shoals, AL 35660
W. A. Norvell	Research Soil Scientist, U.S. Plant, Soil, and Nutrition Laboratory, Cornell University, Ithaca, NY 14853

Volker Römheld Professor, Institut für Pflanzenernährung, Universität Hohenheim, Postfach 70 05 62, 7000 Stuttgart 70, Germany

Larry M. Shuman Associate Professor of Soil Chemistry, Department of Agronomy, Georgia Experiment Station, University of Georgia, Griffin, GA 30223-1797

J. T. Sims Associate Professor of Soil Science, Department of Plant and Soil Sciences, University of Delaware, Newark, DE 19717-1303

F. J. Stevenson Professor of Soil Chemistry, Department of Agronomy, University of Illinois, Urbana, IL 61801

Duane E. Ullrey Professor of Animal Science, Department of Animal Science, Michigan State University, East Lansing, MI 48824

Darrell R. Van Campen Laboratory Director, USDA-ARS, Plant, Soil and Nutrition Laboratory, Cornell University, Ithaca, NY 14853

Michael J. Webb Research Fellow, Waite Agricultural Institute, Department of Agronomy, University of Adelaide, Glen Osmond 5064, Australia

Ross M. Welch Plant Physiologist and Professor of Plant Nutrition, USDA-ARS, U.S. Plant, Soil, and Nutrition Laboratory, Cornell University, Ithaca, NY 14853

D. T. Westermann Soil Scientist, USDA-ARS, Rt. 1, 3793N, 3600E, Kimberly, ID 83341

Conversion Factors for SI and non-SI Units

Conversion Factors for SI and non-SI Units

To convert Column 1 into Column 2, multiply by	Column 1 SI Unit	Column 2 non-SI Unit	To convert Column 2 into Column 1, multiply by
Length			
0.621	kilometer, km (10^3 m)	mile, mi	1.609
1.094	meter, m	yard, yd	0.914
3.28	meter, m	foot, ft	0.304
1.0	micrometer, μm (10^{-6} m)	micron, μ	1.0
3.94×10^{-2}	millimeter, mm (10^{-3} m)	inch, in	25.4
10	nanometer, nm (10^{-9} m)	Angstrom, Å	0.1
Area			
2.47	hectare, ha	acre	0.405
247	square kilometer, km^2 (10^3 m)^2	acre	4.05×10^{-3}
0.386	square kilometer, km^2 (10^3 m)^2	square mile, mi^2	2.590
2.47×10^{-4}	square meter, m^2	acre	4.05×10^3
10.76	square meter, m^2	square foot, ft^2	9.29×10^{-2}
1.55×10^{-3}	square millimeter, mm^2 (10^{-3} m)^2	square inch, in^2	645
Volume			
9.73×10^{-3}	cubic meter, m^3	acre-inch	102.8
35.3	cubic meter, m^3	cubic foot, ft^3	2.83×10^{-2}
6.10×10^4	cubic meter, m^3	cubic inch, in^3	1.64×10^{-5}
2.84×10^{-2}	liter, L (10^{-3} m^3)	bushel, bu	35.24
1.057	liter, L (10^{-3} m^3)	quart (liquid), qt	0.946
3.53×10^{-2}	liter, L (10^{-3} m^3)	cubic foot, ft^3	28.3
0.265	liter, L (10^{-3} m^3)	gallon	3.78
33.78	liter, L (10^{-3} m^3)	ounce (fluid), oz	2.96×10^{-2}
2.11	liter, L (10^{-3} m^3)	pint (fluid), pt	0.473

Mass

Column 1 → Column 2	Column 1 SI Unit	Column 2 non-SI Unit	Column 2 → Column 1
2.20×10^{-3}	gram, g (10^{-3} kg)	pound, lb	454
3.52×10^{-2}	gram, g (10^{-3} kg)	ounce (avdp), oz	28.4
2.205	kilogram, kg	pound, lb	0.454
0.01	kilogram, kg	quintal (metric), q	100
1.10×10^{-3}	kilogram, kg	ton (2000 lb), ton	907
1.102	megagram, Mg (tonne)	ton (U.S.), ton	0.907
1.102	tonne, t	ton (U.S.), ton	0.907

Yield and Rate

Column 1 → Column 2	Column 1 SI Unit	Column 2 non-SI Unit	Column 2 → Column 1
0.893	kilogram per hectare, kg ha^{-1}	pound per acre, lb acre^{-1}	1.12
7.77×10^{-2}	kilogram per cubic meter, kg m^{-3}	pound per bushel, bu^{-1}	12.87
1.49×10^{-2}	kilogram per hectare, kg ha^{-1}	bushel per acre, 60 lb	67.19
1.59×10^{-2}	kilogram per hectare, kg ha^{-1}	bushel per acre, 56 lb	62.71
1.86×10^{-2}	kilogram per hectare, kg ha^{-1}	bushel per acre, 48 lb	53.75
0.107	liter per hectare, L ha^{-1}	gallon per acre	9.35
893	tonnes per hectare, t ha^{-1}	pound per acre, lb acre^{-1}	1.12×10^{-3}
893	megagram per hectare, Mg ha^{-1}	pound per acre, lb acre^{-1}	1.12×10^{-3}
0.446	megagram per hectare, Mg ha^{-1}	ton (2000 lb) per acre, ton acre^{-1}	2.24
2.24	meter per second, m s^{-1}	mile per hour	0.447

Specific Surface

Column 1 → Column 2	Column 1 SI Unit	Column 2 non-SI Unit	Column 2 → Column 1
10	square meter per kilogram, m^2 kg^{-1}	square centimeter per gram, cm^2 g^{-1}	0.1
1000	square meter per kilogram, m^2 kg^{-1}	square millimeter per gram, mm^2 g^{-1}	0.001

Pressure

Column 1 → Column 2	Column 1 SI Unit	Column 2 non-SI Unit	Column 2 → Column 1
9.90	megapascal, MPa (10^6 Pa)	atmosphere	0.101
10	megapascal, MPa (10^6 Pa)	bar	0.1
1.00	megagram per cubic meter, Mg m^{-3}	gram per cubic centimeter, g cm^{-3}	1.00
2.09×10^{-2}	pascal, Pa	pound per square foot, lb ft^{-2}	47.9
1.45×10^{-4}	pascal, Pa	pound per square inch, lb in^{-2}	6.90×10^3

(continued on next page)

Conversion Factors for SI and non-SI Units

To convert Column 1 into Column 2, multiply by	Column 1 SI Unit	Column 2 non-SI Unit	To convert Column 2 into Column 1, multiply by
Temperature			
$1.00 (K - 273)$	Kelvin, K	Celsius, °C	$1.00 (°C + 273)$
$(9/5 °C) + 32$	Celsius, °C	Fahrenheit, °F	$5/9 (°F - 32)$
Energy, Work, Quantity of Heat			
9.52×10^{-4}	joule, J	British thermal unit, Btu	1.05×10^3
0.239	joule, J	calorie, cal	4.19
10^7	joule, J	erg	10^{-7}
0.735	joule, J	foot-pound	1.36
2.387×10^{-5}	joule per square meter, J m^{-2}	calorie per square centimeter (langley)	4.19×10^4
10^5	newton, N	dyne	10^{-5}
1.43×10^{-3}	watt per square meter, W m^{-2}	calorie per square centimeter minute (irradiance), cal cm^{-2} min^{-1}	698
Transpiration and Photosynthesis			
3.60×10^{-2}	milligram per square meter second, mg m^{-2} s^{-1}	gram per square decimeter hour, g dm^{-2} h^{-1}	27.8
5.56×10^{-3}	milligram (H$_2$O) per square meter second, mg m^{-2} s^{-1}	micromole (H$_2$O) per square centimeter second, μmol cm^{-2} s^{-1}	180
10^{-4}	milligram per square meter second, mg m^{-2} s^{-1}	milligram per square centimeter second, mg cm^{-2} s^{-1}	10^4
35.97	milligram per square meter second, mg m^{-2} s^{-1}	milligram per square decimeter hour, mg dm^{-2} h^{-1}	2.78×10^{-2}
Plane Angle			
57.3	radian, rad	degrees (angle), °	1.75×10^{-2}

Electrical Conductivity, Electricity, and Magnetism

To convert Col. 2 → Col. 1, multiply by	Column 1	Column 2	To convert Col. 1 → Col. 2, multiply by
10	siemen per meter, S m⁻¹	millimho per centimeter, mmho cm⁻¹	0.1
10⁴	tesla, T	gauss, G	10⁻⁴

Water Measurement

To convert Col. 2 → Col. 1, multiply by	Column 1	Column 2	To convert Col. 1 → Col. 2, multiply by
9.73×10^{-3}	cubic meter, m³	acre-inches, acre-in	102.8
9.81×10^{-3}	cubic meter per hour, m³ h⁻¹	cubic feet per second, ft³ s⁻¹	101.9
4.40	cubic meter per hour, m³ h⁻¹	U.S. gallons per minute, gal min⁻¹	0.227
8.11	hectare-meters, ha-m	acre-feet, acre-ft	0.123
97.28	hectare-meters, ha-m	acre-inches, acre-in	1.03×10^{-2}
8.1×10^{-2}	hectare-centimeters, ha-cm	acre-feet, acre-ft	12.33

Concentrations

To convert Col. 2 → Col. 1, multiply by	Column 1	Column 2	To convert Col. 1 → Col. 2, multiply by
1	centimole per kilogram, cmol kg⁻¹ (ion exchange capacity)	milliequivalents per 100 grams, meq 100 g⁻¹	1
0.1	gram per kilogram, g kg⁻¹	percent, %	10
1	milligram per kilogram, mg kg⁻¹	parts per million, ppm	1

Radioactivity

To convert Col. 2 → Col. 1, multiply by	Column 1	Column 2	To convert Col. 1 → Col. 2, multiply by
2.7×10^{-11}	becquerel, Bq	curie, Ci	3.7×10^{10}
2.7×10^{-2}	becquerel per kilogram, Bq kg⁻¹	picocurie per gram, pCi g⁻¹	37
100	gray, Gy (absorbed dose)	rad, rd	0.01
100	sievert, Sv (equivalent dose)	rem (roentgen equivalent man)	0.01

Plant Nutrient Conversion

multiply by	Elemental	Oxide	multiply by
2.29	P	P_2O_5	0.437
1.20	K	K_2O	0.830
1.39	Ca	CaO	0.715
1.66	Mg	MgO	0.602

Chapter 1

Geochemistry of Micronutrients

WARD CHESWORTH, *University of Guelph, Guelph, Ontario, Canada*

The geochemistry of the six micronutrients, B, Mn, Fe, Cu, Zn, and Mo, is clearly treated in the first edition of this book. This chapter compliments Krauskopf's (1972) in that any undue repetition of his approach has been avoided. Thus, in discussing the general geochemistry of the micronutrients, the role of plate tectonics has been stressed (an emphasis that was scarcely possible at the time of the first edition and in describing the behavior of these elements at the earth's surface, a pedological slant is provided, in keeping with the intended readership. However, before the geochemistry is presented, it will be useful to summarize the basic chemistry involved. This review will be kept brief, to avoid repeating details to be found in later chapters.

The principal source of geochemical information here is the Handbook of Geochemistry edited by K.H. Wedepohl (1969–1978).

I. GENERAL PROPERTIES OF THE ELEMENTS

Chemically, the fundamental property of all elements is their electronic configuration; it is this that determines chemical periodicity (Fig. 1-1). Figure 1-2 shows a number of basic properties of the micronutrient elements within the framework of general trends in the periodic system.

The elemental properties that depend on electronic structure include atomic and ionic radii (and volumes), ionization energy, electron affinity, electronegativity, standard redox potential, valence (and oxidation state), enthalpies of fusion, vaporization and sublimation, bond energy, enthalpy of ion solvation, ion mobility, enthalpies of compound formation, and lattice energies. Several of these properties are among those that have been used by various authors to interpret the geochemical behavior of elements. Values of the more commonly used properties for micronutrient elements are given in Table 1-1. A more complete listing will be found in Rosler and Lange (1972), in which the properties are defined and their significance made clear. Examples of their use will be found later in this chapter in Table 1-4, and Fig. 1-7.

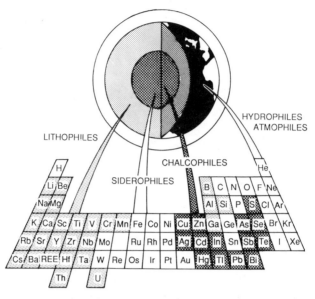

Fig. 1-1. The periodic table incorporating a geochemical classification of the elements. Hydrophile and atmophile elements have an affinity for water and the atmosphere, respectively. The lithophiles, chalcophiles, and siderophiles prefer silicate, sulphide, and iron, respectively (after Allègre, 1982).

II. SPECIFIC PROPERTIES OF THE ELEMENTS

A. Group IIIA Elements: Boron

The group IIIA elements are B, Al, Ga, In, and Tl. Atomic size increases in this sequence, as with similar groups in the periodic table. Although, as a result of the lanthanide contraction, Tl is smaller than might have been expected. The last three elements, which have d, and in the case of Tl, f electrons, are more complex in their chemical behavior than B and Al.

Boron, in particular, shows little similarity to the other members of the group, apart from the fundamental similarity of the outer electronic configuration (s^2p^1). It is the only element whose outer-shell vacancies outnumber the valence electrons without imparting metallic properties. Yet, it is also not typically nonmetallic, because its electrons are not localized in covalent bonds in the elemental state. Therefore, B is commonly considered to be a metalloid, a classification borne out by its electronegativity, which, at 2.0, is close to the borderline between metallic and nonmetallic elements. The quoted ionic radius for B has little meaning since B is always covalent in compounds. The energy needed to remove its three outer electrons is too high to be compensated by lattice or hydration energies. In spite of this, Lebedev (1960) refers to the existence of B^{3+} bonds.

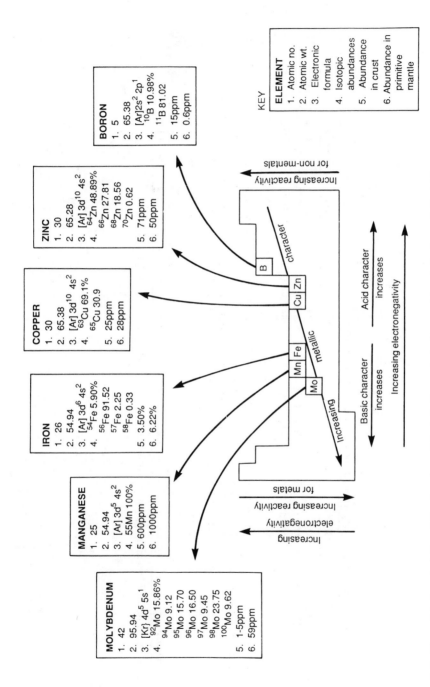

Fig. 1–2. Elemental characteristics of the six micronutrients in the context of general trends in the periodic table.

Table 1-1. Some basic chemical properties of the micronutrient elements.†

	Boron	Manganese	Iron	Copper	Zinc	Molybdenum
Radii: Atomic (Å)	0.98	1.27	1.26	1.28	1.34	1.39
Ionic (C.N.)	0.01 (3) 0.11 (4)	Me(II) 0.83 Mn(III) 0.65 Mn(IV) 0.53	Fe(II) 0.78 Fe(II) 0.65	Cu(I) 0.77 Cu(II) 0.73	0.60 (4) 0.74 (6)	Mo(III) 0.69 Mo(IV) 0.65 Mo(V) 0.61 Mo(VI) 0.59
Covalent (Å)	0.84–0.92	1.02–1.6	1.23–1.39	1.29–1.38	1.34–1.46	1.23–1.31
Ionization potentials (ev)	(I) 8.298 (II) 25.154 (III) 37.930	(I) 7.435 (II) 15.640 (III) 33.667 (IV) 55.2	(I) 7.870 (II) 16.168 (III) 30.651	(I) 7.726 (II) 20.292	(I) 9.394 (II) 17.964	(I) 7.099 (II) 16.15 (III) 27.16 (IV) 46.4 (V) 61.2 (VI) 68
Electronegativity	2.0	1.5	1.8	1.9	1.6	1.8

† For examples of their use in interpreting geochemical behavior, see Table 1–4 and Fig. 1–7.

By contrast, the other elements of the group can form trivalent ions, with Tl also capable of losing the single p electron to form a unipositive ion. The three valence electrons of B can be delocalised between 3 or 4 orbitals to form triangular sp^2 or tetrahedral sp^3 hybrids, structural units that occur in all the common borate minerals. Since B has the ability to accept an electron pair, it is a weak Lewis acid. The rest of the group is either amphoteric (e.g, Al) or basic (e.g., Tl).

Because the size of atoms or ions in the periodic table increases downwards, and from left to right, atoms or ions that lie diagonally, one beneath the other, tend to be approximately the same size, and to show similar geochemical behavior in instances in which that behavior depends on size. For this reason, the crystal chemistry of borates is generally similar to that of silicates, and can substitute for Si in silicates and aluminosilicates. It does so especially in sheet silicates. However, because of its ability to assume a three-fold as well as a four-fold coordination, its chemistry is more complex than that of Si.

B. d Block Elements

Manganese, Fe, Cu, Zn, and Mo all have electronic configurations involving 3d and, in the case of Mo, 4d orbitals. All except Zn have incomplete d orbitals and are correctly transition elements. As such, they show the typical transition element characteristic of multiple oxidation states. Zinc with its complete $3d^{10}4s^2$ outer electron configuration is not a transition element and, invariabily shows an oxidation state of II in its compounds.

Elements or ions with incompletely filled d orbitals (except where the d orbitals are half filled) may depart notably from the spherical symmetry inherent in the concepts of atomic or ionic radius. The directed nature of d orbitals also means that when a transition element is incorporated into a crystal structure or a coordination complex the neighboring atoms or ligands may adjust, so that the classic coordination geometries (tetrahedral, octahedral, etc.) become distorted. The Jahn-Teller Effect, in which ligands are repelled by d orbitals directed at them, is an example of this. The crystal (or ligand) field exerted by its nearest neighbors on a transition element may also force single d electrons to pair up into low- spin configurations, in which the minimum number of d orbitals is occupied, as opposed to high spin, in which the maximum number is occupied.

The common coordination geometries found among transition elements in nature are square planar, tetrahedral, or octahedral. For a given element, each geometry generates its own cationic radius. The latter also varies with oxidation state, and with the high- and low-spin characteristics of the ion, so that transition elements may have several ionic radii. The most recent tabulation illustrates this fact (Shannon, 1976). Natural ligands, such as O_2, OH^-, Cl^-, F^-, and H_2O, all exert weak fields so that, in nature, only high-spin complexes are common. Consequently the ionic radii shown in Table 1–1 are for the high-spin condition in those cases in which there was a choice.

1. First Transition Series—Mn, Fe, and Cu

The highest valency exhibited by an element of the first transition series is equal to the sum of all 3d and 4s electrons. This state does not exist for Fe and Cu, and for Mn the VII oxidation state is not found in nature. High oxidation states decrease in stability from left to right in the series. Increasing oxidation number makes the oxides of an element increasingly acidic, while the halides become more covalent and susceptible to hydrolysis. For oxy-anions, the higher valence states (i.e., greater than III) are characterized by tetrahedral coordination, with oxides formed in lower valence states having octahedrally coordinated atoms. Complexes in aqueous solution or in crystal structures, with 4, 5, or 6 coordinated cations, are found for state (II) and (III). Oxidation state (I) is only found in nature for Cu. All three elements form aquo-ions of the type $[M(H_2O)_6]^{2+}$.

2. Group IIB Elements—Zn

Elements of this group, Zn, Cd and Hg, have a $d^{10}s^2$ outer electronic configuration. By mobilization of the two s electrons, all can achieve the oxidation state (II). In addition, Hg(I) exists. Because of the stability of the filled d shell, these elements show few of the characteristics of transition elements. Zinc has a much greater similarity with the main group element, Mg, because the two have isomorphous compounds. However, Zn is more covalent than Mg (cf. electronegativities: Zn = 1.8, Mg = 1.2). Within the group, Zn and Cd show many similarities, with Hg differing markedly from both. In complex formation, the d^{10} configuration imparts no crystal field stabilization so that coordination number is simply a function of size and polarizing power of the cation. Thus, Zn(II) forms mainly tetrahedral complexes {e.g., $[Zn(H_2O)_4]^{2+}$}.

3. Second Transition Series—Mo

Many of the general aspects of the chemistry of second-row transition elements are similar to those of the first row, but there are significant differences in the stabilities of the various oxidation states. In the second series, the lower oxidation states are generally less stable, and higher oxidation states are more stable, than the equivalent element in the first series. For example, Mo (III) is relatively unimportant in the chemistry of that element, whereas the trivalent state plays a great role in the chemistry of Cr. By contrast, Mo (VI) is very stable, particularly as the MoO_4^{2-} ion, which, unlike the first row ions CrO_4^{2-} and MnO_4^-, is not a powerful oxidizer and so has quite a diverse chemistry. The second-row elements, followed in the periodic table by the lanthanides (with the consequent lanthanide contraction), show a much greater similarity to their related elements in the third row. Specifically, the chemistries of Mo and W are much alike.

III. GEOCHEMICAL NATURE OF TERRESTRIAL SYSTEMS

Besides water and the atmospheric gases, most of the nutrients needed by plants and animals, and certainly the six micronutrients, are geological in provenance; i.e., they come from the lithosphere. This means that the internal geological cycle, by which the lithosphere is formed, is of crucial importance in any fundamental consideration of soil fertility. Consequently, the internal cycle is discussed first to show how the interior of the earth, particularly the mantle, has served throughout geological time as a source of new materials for maintaining the fertility of the earth's surface, and hence the viability of the biosphere.

A. Importance of the Internal Cycle in Soil Fertility

The internal geological cycle, which is driven by radiogenic heat, involves the convective stirring of the mantle and the melting that produces the materials of the crust. The crust and part of the mantle welded to it make up the lithosphere, the outer zone of the solid earth. This is fragmented into plates. Convection in the mantle moves the plates around relative to each other, giving rise to such phenomena as earthquakes, igneous activity, metamorphism, mountain building, and, of course, continental drift. The boundaries, or cracks, between plates offer routes by which mantle-derived material can reach the surface. This modern, plate tectonic picture of the earth is illustrated in Figure 1–3.

In effect, the mantle is a reservoir of potential plant nutrients. Over the 4.5 billion yr of earth history, melting in the mantle, latterly beneath plate boundaries, but more generally in the earliest Precambrian, has continued to add solids, gases, and water to the lithosphere, atmosphere, and hydrosphere. This has created, and with much feedback, maintained the surface of the earth as an abode for life. Without this contribution by the internal geological cycle, the planet earth would be as dead as the moon (Chesworth, 1982).

The mantle, therefore, is of fundamental importance to life on earth. The upper section is predominantly made up of magnesian silicates with significant amounts of Ca and Fe. By comparison with the crust, it is enriched in heavier elements. This is because the melting that produced the crust has preferentially removed the relatively light elements, which then migrate upward in magma.

At its most uncomplicated, the process can now be seen in the basaltic extrusions along oceanic ridges. By contrast, the magmatic processes along plate boundaries where mountian building is going on are more complex. For example, subduction, in which oceanic lithosphere sinks below continental lithosphere (a characteristic feature of such boundaries), allows crustal materials to be incorporated into melts there, including some that were once at the earth's surface. This results in a kind of hybridization between crust and mantle. Because of this, an intermediate volcanic rock called andesite tends to predominate over basalt. Throughout the course of earth's history, con-

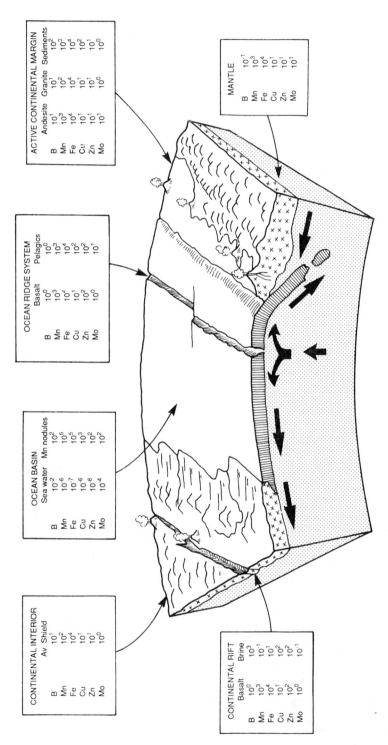

Fig. 1–3. The plate tectonic model of the interaction of the earth's crust and mantle. Order of magnitude elemental concentrations in μg/kg.

Table 1-2. Composition of the surface of the continental crust; an approximation of the average soil parent material.†

			Oxide (weight percent)					
SiO$_2$	TiO$_2$	Al$_2$O$_3$	FeO	MgO	CaO	Na$_2$O	K$_2$O	Total
66.0	0.5	15.2	4.5	2.2	4.2	3.9	3.4	99.0
			Micronutrient element					
	B	Mn	Fe	Cu	Zn	Mo		
			mg kg^{-1}					
	15	600	35 000	25	71	1.5		

† Taylor and McClennan (1985).

tinents have continually grown by the addition of essentially andesitic material to their active margins. It is not surprising, therefore, that the average composition of the continental crustal surface is close to andesite in composition (Table 1-2). This can serve as a kind of average parent material of the land surface of the earth (the latter being predominantly continental, of course). In terms of volume, oxygen constitutes well over 90% of the surface of the crust (i.e., soil parent material), and for this reason the crust has been called an oxysphere.

B. The Crust as an Oxysphere

Obviously because the crust is an oxysphere the crust and its component materials at the atomic level have an architecture that is largely determined by the way that oxygen atoms and ions stack together. In fact, the simplest model for the crust is that of a close packed, three-dimensional array of oxygen anions (Fig. 1-4). The net negative charge is balanced by cations occupying holes in the structure in three-, four-, six- and 12-fold coordination with oxygen, all of which are coordination numbers permitted in close packed structures. The fact that some elements also assume eight-fold coordination in nature, a coordination number not permitted by close packing, is an indication that the close packed model is only an approximation, although on the whole, it is a good one.

The fundamental, organized unit of the crust is the mineral phase. The most common minerals of the outer part of the earth are shown in Table 1-3. Again, most of the minerals named have structures that approximate close packing, with oxygen as the main structure-determining element. For example, olivine is almost perfectly close packed, though plagioclase with eight-fold oxygen in its structure is only approximately close packed. However, the main point is that oxygen is so abundant an element in the crust, by volume, that it is bound to play a decisive role in the structure of the most common minerals. In addition, the ways in which the other elements, including the micronutrients, fit into the structures of the common minerals will largely depend on how these elements coordinate with oxygen. This, in turn, depends on the general chemical nature of the element to be considered.

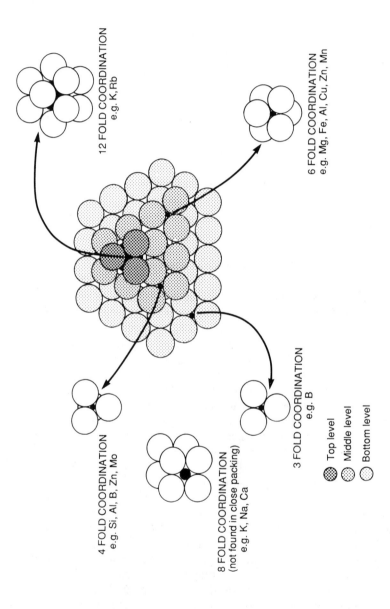

12 FOLD COORDINATION
e.g. K, Rb

6 FOLD COORDINATION
e.g. Mg, Fe, Al, Cu, Zn, Mn

4 FOLD COORDINATION
e.g. Si, Al, B, Zn, Mo

8 FOLD COORDINATION
(not found in close packing)
e.g. K, Na, Ca

3 FOLD COORDINATION
e.g. B

⬤ Top level
⬤ Middle level
◯ Bottom level

Fig. 1–4. Close packing of oxygen anions as a model for the crust of the earth, showing typical coordination structures for the micronutrients and other representative elements.

Table 1-3. The most common minerals of the crust and their abundances.†

Mineral	Abundance, %
Quartz	12
K-feldspar	12
Plagioclase	39
Mica	5
Pyroxene	11
Olivine	3
Clay minerals (and chlorite)	4.6
Calcite (and aragonite)	1.5
Dolomite	0.5
Magnetite (and titanomagnetite)	1.5
Others	4.9

† Ronov and Yaroshevsky (1969).

IV. NATURAL OCCURRENCES OF THE ELEMENTS

Iron is a major element geologically and occurs in relatively high concentrations in many rocks. The remaining elements are minor (Mn) or trace elements, so that their general level of concentration is low. However, some environments and processes considerably enrich each of the six individually. This section addresses the environments and processes in the context of the modern theory of plate tectonics under three headings: (i) the ocean ridge system; (ii) active continental margins; and (iii) continental interiors. The Appendix at the end of this chapter lists the common minerals that contain the micronutrients.

A. Ocean Ridge System

The ocean ridge systems are constructive plate boundaries where basalt, produced by relatively shallow melting, rises from the mantle and is added to the sea floor. The mantle itself, dominantly an ultrabasic combination of magnesian olivine and pyroxene with a minor amount of a Ca aluminosilicate, partially melts below the ridge. All six elements are preferentially enriched in the melt. In this form, they move upward as the basalt is emplaced in the rift of the oceanic ridge. Over billions of years, processes such as this have depleted the upper mantle in lithophile elements.

When the basalt crystallizes, new ferromagnesian phases (predominantly pyroxene) more Fe rich than mantle ferromagnesians, precipitate together with oxide phases (magnetite and ilmenite). Manganese, Cu, Zn, and Mo can all substitute for Fe in these minerals. Neither pyroxene nor the other essential mineral of basalt, plagioclase, provide suitable crystallographic sites for the incorporation of B, so that it tends to remain in the melt until the end stages of crystallization, when an aqueous fluid may separate from the magma. This takes up the B and, as an acid hydrothermal fluid augmented by hot seawater circulating through the volcanic pile, scours the already solid basalt and picks up notable quantities of d-block elements in solution, principally as Cl^- complexes. When the circulating seawater convects back to the sea bed, and is diluted and chilled by fresh seawater, a characteristic suite of heavy metals is added to the pelagic muds alongside the ridge system. These include the five d-block elements of interest here, together with other metals. The Mn nodules found in many areas of pelagic sedimentation derive much of their Mn from the same source, with an additional increment from atmospheric sources. The nodules and the metal-rich muds are a significant future source of economically important metals. Meanwhile, B remains in solution to be added to the borate stock of seawater.

B. Active Continental Margins

The oceanic lithosphere, with its veneer of sediments, is moved away from the ridge by plate tectonic forces. When it encounters an active continental margin it generally moves back into the mantle, below the continental edge, by a process called subduction. Some of its sedimentary load, with additions from the eroding continent, is scraped away, but some, with connate water, is subducted as well. The downward slab is gradually subjected to increased pressures and temperatures, and responds by first metamorphosing and then by partially melting at a deeper level. The metamorphism drives off part of the volatile content, which is principally H_2O, with CO_2 as the next most important constituent.

Boron may be taken up by this aqueous phase and can then migrate upward into the continental crust. Melting may actually occur not only in the downward slab, but also in the mantle wedge trapped between the slab and the continental lithosphere, as well as in the continental lithosphere itself. The melts that form depend on temperature, total pressure, activities of H_2O, CO_2, and other volatiles, and degree of melting, but the characteristic magma produced below the continental lithosphere or at its base is andesitic in composition. This, with its dissolved charge of volatile components, rises up into the continental block to facilitate a second melting. This time, acid magma is produced which later crystallizes to produce the vast granite batholiths of the world's orogenic belts.

Crystallization of the granitic magmas can have important consequences for three of the micronutrient elements. First, B tends to accumulate to the last stages of crystallization, when one or both of two reactions may occur. The B may concentrate to a high enough degree that tourmaline crystallizes from the melt. Also, the melt may become H_2O saturated so that a separate volatile phase is produced. If this occurs, tourmaline-bearing pegmatites can form and the aqueous phase can carry B (and other components with an affinity for H_2O) into the surrounding rock, which thereby undergoes B metasomatism.

A second set of consequences affects metallic elements, particularly Cu and Mo. Volatile-bearing granitoid magmas are sometimes catastrophically depressurized, for example, by a fracturing of the rocks that envelop the magma chamber. The drop in pressure allows volatiles (chiefly H_2O) to escape into surrounding fissures and the magma rapidly solidifies. The aqueous phase, rich in complexing anions, can carry large amounts of Cu and Mo, which are deposited as it cools. In essence, this is how the great Cu and Mo porphyries of the Pacific rim have formed.

The continental block, of course, is where most of the subaerial weathering on the planet occurs. This complex of processes is discussed in section V.

C. Continental Interiors

The interior of a continent possesses four geological features of interest in the present context: old-fold mountain belts, ancient shelf seas, continental rift systems, and Precambrian shields. The features of old-fold mountain belts are similar to active continental margins, of which they are fossil examples.

Ancient shelf seas cover continental platforms with shallow water sediments; chiefly sandstones, shales, limestones, and, occasionally, evaporites. In many parts of the world the limestones act as host to large Pb-Zn deposits of the Mississippi Valley type. The metals have precipitated from hot aqueous solution, which may have travelled long distances and may ultimately be connected with igneous activity. The evaporites form in periodically closed lagoons where evaporation brings down Ca, Mg, Na, and K salts (characteristically as carbonates, sulfates, and chlorides) in the order of increasing solubility product. Boron, for which the sea is the major sink, also joins the solid phases at this stage, although it is not usually in its own minerals in this type of evaporite. Usually, it is incorporated into the clay-phase illite.

A number of well recognized rift systems exist within the continental crust. In fact, the mid-Atlantic oceanic rift began as a rift within the super continent of Pangea sometime in the Mesozoic. As such, it was initially similar to the present East African rift and, similarly, it served as a conduit for volcanic rocks and for a significant efflux of hydrothermal solutions. These, charged with anionic ligands, including borate, were capable of carrying large concentrations of d-block elements as complexes. In the present context, the most notable metallic mineral deposits formed from this type of solution are the Cu deposits of the Mesozoic red beds from both sides of the Atlantic.

A second important type of mineral deposit is associated with this tectonic environment. Usually, continental rifts are regions of internal drainage, closed to the sea. Consequently, salt lakes are common and, where such features coincide with the drier climatic zones of the planet, salt beds form by evaporation. Major $B_2O_7^{2-}$ deposits (e.g., Searles Lake, California) have formed in this way; the B originates in part from the weathering of pre-existing rocks, but most significantly from $B_2O_7^{2-}$-rich thermal waters.

The Precambrian shield regime contains a prominent time break. The younger, Proterozoic rocks appear to have formed by plate tectonic mechanisms and contain environments similar to those already described. There is one seemingly unique occurrence at Sudbury in Ontario, however, which merits attention because of its size. Although this is the world's largest Ni deposit, it was first discovered and developed as a Cu deposit. The metals are found close to the bottom of a layered, basic igneous structure, which appears to be part of a deformed meteorite impact site.

Below the Proterozoic, the earlier Archaean rocks show evidence that they were formed under radically different conditions and that they lack the linear tectonic features associated with plate motions in the later geological record. The Archaean rocks are notable repositories of heavy metal deposits, among which Cu, Zn and the noble metals are common. Some of these are associated with the granitoid rocks that make up about two-thirds of all exposed rock. However, the largest deposits are found in the metavolcanic greenstone belts as so-called volcanic exhalative deposits formed by a mechanism similar to that described for the origin of the metal-rich muds that lie alongside some oceanic ridge systems.

V. SOIL WEATHERING SYSTEM

The geochemistry of the earth's surface is dominated by the external geological cycle, which involves the interaction of four great chemical reservoirs; the lithosphere, hydrosphere, atmosphere, and biosphere. The interaction is driven by solar energy, and the lithosphere forms a point of contact between the external cycle and the internal one that formed it. The interplay of the two cycles is shown in Fig. 1–5.

On the earth's land areas, the four reservoirs come together to form a fifth reservoir which has been called the pedosphere, but which is shown simply in Fig. 1–6 as the soil. In effect, this is a diagrammatic representation of the relationship between soil and the soil-forming factors, emphasizing the interaction of the factors, rather than their independence from each other.

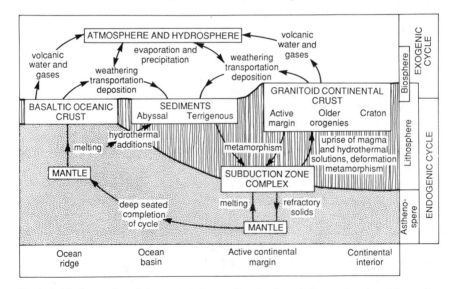

Fig. 1–5. The interaction of the exogenic (external) and endogenic (internal) cycles of the earth.

A. Weathering

Weathering in soils and weathering below the zone of soil formation are considered by some to be qualitatively different (Jackson & Sherman, 1953). The major chemical difference between the two is the heightened role of organic matter in soils. This qualitative division is accepted here as a convenient basis for the following discussion, although it is more realistic to view the two weathering compartments as being gradational one into the other. Although organic components in the soil illustrates an obvious difference between the two zones, a fundamental similarity also exists, since it is the solid/water interface that controls the chemistry of weathering, including the rate processes (Stumm, 1986) in both weathering compartments.

1. Weathering in the Sedimentary Regime

The overall process of weathering in the sedimentary regime has been succinctly described in the following terms, ''Weathering on the continents takes place in a flow system. Dilute rain and ground waters of quite constant composition at a given location are renewed continuously at the exposed mineral surfaces. This reaction medium is relatively acidic and poor

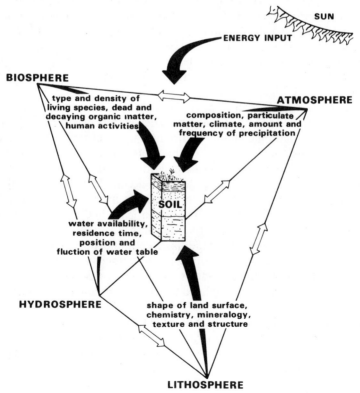

Fig. 1–6. The interactions of the four great chemical reservoirs at the earth's surface which, powered by solar energy, produce soil.

Table 1-4. Relative bond strengths between cations and oxygen anions.

Bond	Approximate relative strength
Si—O	2.4
B—O (tourmaline)	2.2
Ti—O	1.8
Zr—O	1.8
Al—O	1.65
Fe(III)—O	1.4
Mg—O	0.9
Fe(II)—O	0.85
Mn—O	0.8
Ca—O	0.7
K—O	0.27
Na—O	0.25

† Modified from Nicolls (1963).

in cations, the average ratio of cation equivalents to protons being of order 10^3. The net result for silicate weathering, is a replacement of the cations in the aluminosilicate lattices by protons. Resulting structural accommodations lead to release of silica along with the cations and the production of stripped or degraded phases, clays. If primary weathering is regarded as the titration of quenched, high temperature disequilibrium igneous rocks by acidic volcanic volatiles then the continents are inevitably overtitrated, acting as a sink for protons,'' (Edmond et al., 1979).

As the above quotation makes clear, hydrolysis is the principal type of chemical reaction encountered, although redox and solution-precipitation reactions also take place.

An initial control on an element's release into the weathering zone is the strength of the bond that holds it to a particular mineral structure. Nicholls (1963) suggested that ionic charge and radius are measures of this, according to the formula $2z/(r + 1.40)^2$ (Table 1-4). The parameter appears to be a reasonable guide in that it would lead one to expect that minerals such as quartz, rutile, zircon and tourmaline might accumulate in the detrital fraction of a sediment, whereas the ferromagnesian minerals would be less likely to accumulate. In other words, B could be enriched in the residual materials of the weathering system, while the elements, including d-block micronutrients, hosted by ferromagnesian phases could be mobilized in the aqueous phase. To what degree this mobilization materializes would depend on elemental solubilities in natural waters. According to Goldschmidt (Mason & Moore, 1982) this can also be related to ionic radius and ionic charge (Fig. 1-7).

Taylor and McClennan (1985), provided a different way of looking at elemental mobilities in the weathering zone, by using the ratio $Ky(sw) = Xy(sw)/Xy(uc)$, where $Xy(sw)$ is the concentration of element y in seawater, and $Xy(uc)$ is the concentration of y in the continental upper crust. Since seawater is the ultimate sink of the dissolved matter produced in the weathering system, comparing its composition with that of the earth's surface, the source of that matter, yields a measure of the order of mobility of the vari-

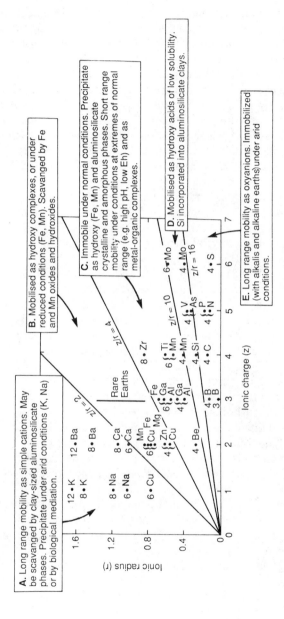

Fig. 1–7. A geochemical division of the elements and their behavior in the weathering zone, based on ionic radius vs. ionic charge. The numerals beside each point specify the coordination number for that particular element.

ous ions. Values for the elements are: B, -0.52, -2.1; Mo, -2.1; Cu, -4.9; Zn, -5.2; Mn, -6.3; and Fe, -8.9. A second parameter, residence time in the ocean, is also important. Values for the elements are: B, 7.2; Mn, 1.5; Fe, -0.16; Cu, 3.0; Zn, 3.1; and Mo, 5.5.

Combining the two parameters divides the chemical elements into three categories: Category 1 elements have very high Ky(sw) ≥ -3; and long residence time ≥ 5, yielding strong partitioning in natural waters and high mobility in the aqueous phase. Boron and Mo are included in Category 1, together with Na, Mg, K, and Ca. Category 2 elements have very low $K \leq -6$; short residence time ≤ 3, and are quantitatively transferred to clastic sediments. Category 2 elements include Fe and Mn, as well as Al, Ti, and Zr. Between these categories is Category 3, which includes Cu and Zn, as well as Si, W, V, Ge, and (close to the boundaries between Category 2 and 3) Ga. It is possible to make a case that Category 3 elements tend to be adsorbed on the surface of clastic particles. Aluminum, Fe, and Mn phases would be the principal scavengers. This is in agreement with the ideas of Li (1981) who said that the "adsorption of elements on the hydrous oxide surface of Fe oxide, Mn oxide and clay minerals is the most common ultimate removal mechanism of most of the elements from the ocean." This will not be true for those elements in the crystal structures of detrital particles or incorporated into their own authigenic phases.

According to Li (1981), K, Rb, Cs, Be, Sc, and Ga are mainly correlated with the aluminosilicate detritus phase in pelagic clays and in Mn nodules. Correlated with the Fe oxide phases are anions or oxyanions (e.g., P, S, Se, Te, As, B, Sn, I, Br, F, U, Pb, Hg, etc.), and hydroxide complexes of tri and tetra-valent cations (e.g., Ti, Ge, Zr, Hf, Th, Y, rare earths, In, Pd, Cr, etc.). Incorporated onto Mn-oxide phases are monovalent and divalent cations (e.g., Mg, Ca, Ba, Ti, Co, Ni, Cu, Zn, Bi, Ag, Cd, etc.) and oxyanions with a high affinity for Mn, such as Mo, W, and Sb in seawater. Magnesium, Ca, and Ba in pelagic clays are also related to other phases, such as aluminosilicates, carbonates, and barite.

Special environments exist in the sedimentary regime in which elements that are normally mobile are immobilized and elements that are normally immobile can be mobilized. This is most obvious in the case of redox variations. For example, in Drever's (1974) model for the Precambrian banded Fe formations, Fe is mobilized as Fe^{2+} under a low pO_2 and, if S^{2-} is low, it will not precipitate. Highly acid and oxidizing environments provide further examples (e.g., White Island, New Zealand), of oxidizing S^{2-} deposits (including acid sulfate soils) where Al and Fe (as Fe^{3+}) can be mobilized. In arid regions, where evaporation greatly exceeds atmospheric precipitation, even the most mobile elements (including B) are precipitated. In spite of these exceptions, the general behavior of the elements in the sedimentary regime, can be expected as that described above.

2. Weathering in the Pedosphere

As with weathering in the sedimentary regime generally, the principal reactions that occur in soils are acid base, oxidation reduction, and solution

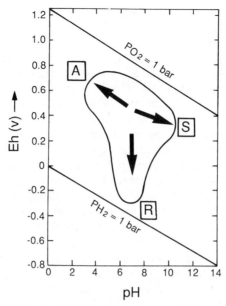

Fig. 1–8. The Eh-pH framework of the weathering zone. The outlined area with the arrows represents the limit of the most common environments at the earth's surface (based on Jenkins and Jones, 1980). The arrows indicate geochemical trends in typical weathering environments.

precipitation. Consequently, the most important chemical operators in weathering systems can be considered to be the proton, the electron, and H_2O. In fact, the stability field of water in terms of redox potential (Eh or pE) and pH as master variables has served as a convenient framework for reactions in the weathering zone since the pioneering work of Baas-Becking et al. (1960) and Krumbein and Garrels (1952).

The pe-pH field of interest for most soils is relatively restricted (Fig. 1–8) if a number of rather rare environments of the earth's surface (acid sulfate soils and weathering V deposits, to name two) are ignored. Figure 1–8 shows three salients, each corresponding to one of three major tendencies of soil evolution. These three main lines of geochemical evolution for the vast majority of soils are, again, most conveniently shown in terms of pe and pH as master variables.

3. Details of the Three Salients and Weathering Trends

Two of the weathering trends are in oxidized systems and evolve toward acid or alkaline end points, respectively. The third evolves toward a reduced, or hydromorphic, end point (Lelong et al., 1976). Each is dominated by different physico-chemical processes:

   a. The acid trend is common in weathering and is found in humid regions on materials with generally unimpeded drainage. It is qualitatively similar to the weathering trend already described above for the sedimentary regime. The quote by Edmond et al. (1979) in section

V is equally applicable. Thus, the water moves predominantly downward, hydrolysis is the principal reaction, and leaching produces a change in the products of weathering toward compositions made up chiefly of resistate and hydrolysate elements in the Goldschmidt-Mason scheme (Mason and Moore, 1982). These products can be expressed rather well in the simple four-component system SiO_2-Al_2O_3-Fe_2O_3-H_2O (Chesworth, 1975), which can be looked upon as a residua system toward which this trend evolves.

b. The alkaline trend occurs in relatively arid zones, with net annual water movement upward in the weathering zone. However seasonal distribution of rainfall determines that, for part of the year, there is enough water to effect a solution and downward leaching of soil components. However, capillary uprise and evaporation of soil water are the distinctive features of this pedogenesis, and evaporation and precipitation result. What this means geochemically, is that the four-component system toward which the acid trend evolves is joined by an accumulation of components from the two soluble zones of Goldschmidt's diagram (Mason and Moore, 1982), principally Na^+, K^+, Ca^{2+}, and Mg^{2+} among the cations, and Cl^-, CO_3^{2-} and SO_4^{2-} among the anions.

c. The reduced trend is found in waterlogged soils where the partial pressure of O_2 is several orders of magnitude lower than the atmospheric value. Redox reactions are of obvious importance, particularly those involving Fe and Mn. If CO_3^{2-} and S^{2-} values are low, these elements are removed in the groundwater. If they are high, carbonates, sulfides, or both may precipitate. Characteristically, this trend is found on low landscapes in materials of a heavy texture.

In all three trends, the soil water behavior is critical. Most soil waters are saturated or oversaturated with respect to Al and Fe hydroxides and quartz (Drever, 1988). Others are saturated with respect to various alumino-silicate clay phases, many are saturated with respect to calcite, and few are saturated with respect to more soluble phases, such as gypsum or halite.

B. Boron in the Weathering Regime

Boron shows two principal patterns of behavior in the weathering regime. The most uncomplicated is its behavior as a residual element. For example, tourmaline from high-temperature rocks is very resistant to chemical breakdown in the weathering zone. Consequently, it accumulates in the clastic fraction of sediments and sedimentary rocks.

Boron's second type of behavior is more complicated. From primary silicates, in which it occurs as a trace element, it goes into solution, with H_3BO_3 as the dominant species in the zone of soil formation (Fig. 1–9A). In this form it is very mobile and easily lost, so weathering lowers the value compared with that of the parent rock. In soils, it can be taken up by the biomass and held by decayed organic matter, or adsorbed on the fine mineral fraction. Boron's adsorption by one or other of the soil fractions is very temporary in geological terms. Eventually, via river water (0.01 mg kg^{-1}), it will reach the sea where it accumulates in solution. There, it is augmented by volcanic additions, which is why the mean B content of sedimentary rocks (about 100 mg kg^{-1}) is ten times greater than for magmatic rocks. For shales specifically, the enrichment factor is 100. In the sea, the level of B is controlled principally by adsorption on Fe and Al hydoxides (mainly Fe, according to Li, 1981), and incorporation in illite as the permanent sink. The amount that is taken up has been used as a measure of salinity, but other factors (e.g., B concentration, temperature, crystallinity, surface area, and duration of contact) make such interpretations difficult to accept. Also, organic matter will compete for B in estuaries (as in soils). Its affinity for organic matter is the reason that coal ash tends to be rich in B.

Because of these two modes of behavior, the distribution of B in sediments tends to be bimodal; i.e., it can be found in the coarse (detrital) and fine (illite, sericite, and Fe hydroxide) fractions.

A third type of behavior is less common, although it leads to the development of deposits that are economically important. In this behavior, B, largely from hydrothermal solutions, is concentrated by evaporation in closed basins under arid conditions (e.g., Searles Lakes, California; Felmy & Weare, 1986).

During diagenesis at temperatures $> 60\,°C$, B-enrichment takes place. Spivack and Edmond (1987) present evidence to show that several cycles of weathering, burial, and diagenesis are necessary before B enrichment in shales, compared with igneous rocks, can be explained. The isotopic evidence (Swihart & Moore, 1989) also supports the view that much sedimentary B has experienced several episodes of mobilization and redistribution.

C. Manganese in the Weathering Regime

The general behavior of Mn in the earth surface environment is determined by the following factors: (i) Valence of Mn in the weathering solid. Manganese is divalent in the low pO_2 of most magmatic and metamorphic systems, and therefore, is found as such in primary phases. States (III) and (IV) are only found at high pO_2. The Mn (II) compounds are the most soluble. (ii) pH and Eh. As with Fe, Mn is soluble at the surface of the earth under relatively acid and reducing conditions (Fig. 1-9B). However, the field of significant solubility for Mn is much broader than that for Fe, which accounts for the separation of one element from the other in weathering environments (Krauskopf, 1976). Under oxidizing and near-neutral conditions, Mn is immobilized as oxide phases (principally MnO_2). As with any metal capable of assuming more than one ionic state, the behavior of Mn is coupled to the chemical behavior of O, S, and C in the general weathering zone, joined by N in soils. (iii) Nature of the solid Mn phases present in primary rocks. Manganese is generally present, substituting for Fe (II) in ferromagnesian and oxide minerals. Under earth surface conditions it forms Mn oxides of various degrees of hydration and crystallinity. These are important in con-

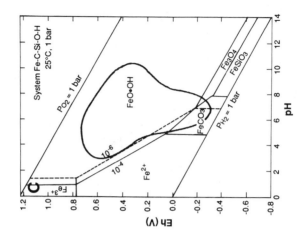

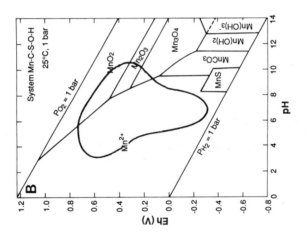

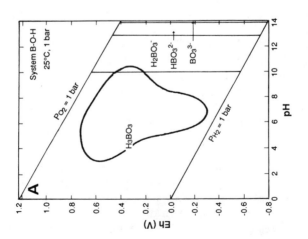

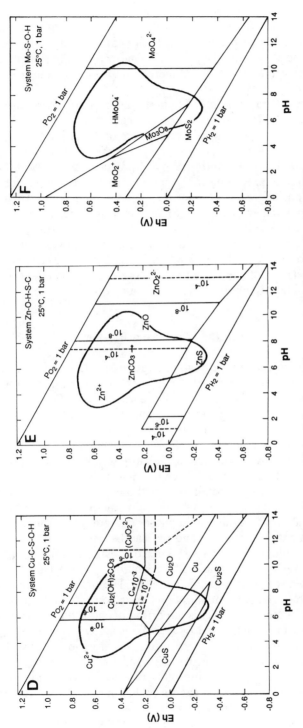

Fig. 1-9. Eh-pH diagrams for the six micronutrients. Additional details and diagrams can be found in Brookins (1988).

trolling the behavior of other elements in that the latter may be adsorbed onto Mn oxide surfaces. (iv) Complex formation. The field of solubility of Mn can be increased by complex formation with both inorganic and organic ligands. (v) Microbial activity. This is becoming increasingly recognized as important in the formation of Mn minerals in surface and near-surface environments (Ferris et al., 1987).

The important characteristics of Mn in the sedimentary environment are as follows. Manganese (IV) is overwhelmingly the most important oxidation state. Adsorption seems to catalyze the slow rate of oxidation between (II) and (IV). The low concentration of Mn in most surface waters and, hence, its generally low mobility, is controlled by Mn oxide and $MnCO_3$ solubilities, depending on the prevailing redox conditions. Redox control also accounts for the much greater fractionation between Fe and Mn in the sedimentary, compared with igneous or metamorphic environments. The surfaces of secondary oxides of Mn control the behavior of certain trace elements by adsorption. Manganese coatings on clastic particles attract Cu and Zn, among others (Buckley, 1989). Finally, Mn is one of the elements that accumulates in pelagic sediments about active oceanic ridges and, also more generally, as nodules distributed over the ocean floor.

D. Iron in the Weathering Regime

The factors used above (i through v) in discussing the solubility of Mn in the sedimentary environment were, with slight differences, first used by Berner (Wedepohl, 1969–1978) to clarify the geochemistry of Fe at the earth's surface. They need not be enumerated again, but the following specific features of the geochemistry of Fe are noteworthy. In primary minerals (ferromagnesian and oxide phases), Fe (II) is more common than Fe(III) and, as with Mn, the lower oxidation state is the more soluble. Under most normal conditions in soils, Fe is immobilized as a hydroxide or hydrated oxide phase, and only under gleyed conditions or those of high redox under extreme acidity (e.g., acid sulfate soils or in acid mine drainage) is it notably mobile. An indication of possible solid phases that control the solubility of Fe under various conditions of Eh and pH can be seen in Fig. 1–9C. The secondary hydroxy phases of Fe, as with Mn, control the solubilities of many trace elements by surface adsorption. Complexation by inorganic and by organic ligands extends the field of Fe solubility. The organic component is particularly important in the Fe mobilization during podzolization (Chesworth & Macias, 1985). Microbial activity is important in controlling the behavior of Fe, particularly in reducing and in acid oxidizing environments.

Two specific environments have received much attention from sedimentary geochemists: the so-called red beds environment and that of the sedimentary Fe formations. The former indicates continental conditions in the geological past, while the latter indicates a period in the Precambrian when Fe appears to have been mobilized on an immense scale, possibly indicating a time in the history of the earth when a reducing atmosphere prevailed.

The general behavior of Fe in the weathering zone can be summarized under four headings. (i) In an oxidizing environment, with atmospheric O_2 dominant, Fe forms goethite as the stable mineral (or other hydroxy phases metastably) as the normal trend. For high S^{2-}, low CO_3 (the acid sulfate environment), jarosite may form. In organic-rich conditions, Fe is transported as chelates in solution. (ii) In a reducing environment, with bacteria using C to reduce Fe(III) to Fe(II), and SO_4 to S, high S^{2-} yields pyrite, low S^{2-} and high CO_3 yields siderite, and Fe(III) remains in solution if both S^{2-} and CO_3 are low. (iii) Glauconite is the only authigenic Fe silicate forming in modern sediments, although Fe smectites occur in the weathering zone, transiently, as alteration products of ferromagnesian phyllosilicates. (iv) Iron is transported principally as fine, particulate hydroxides, or as coatings on detrital grains. Sorting is accomplished by different settling rates.

E. Copper in the Weathering Regime

Copper is released into the weathering environment, chiefly when the ferromagnesian minerals that constitute its principal host break down. The only other source that may be important, particularly in granitoid rocks, is the sulfide, chalcopyrite. The Eh-pH diagram (Fig. 1-9D) shows that conditions under which Cu can be mobilized in solution are severely restricted by malachite, by $Cu(OH)_2$, or CuS. They may be restricted even more by the adsorption of Cu on clay-sized particles (Li, 1981), with divalent Cu showing a preference for fine-grained Mn, rather than Fe or aluminosilicate phases (but compare Johnson, 1986). The resulting low solubility results in Cu's low mobility in the weathering zone. Complexation, particularly with Cl (in the connate waters of marine sediments) and with organic ligands in pedological environments may increase the mobility of Cu in favored circumstances.

Because of its generally low mobility during weathering, Cu accumulates (supergene enrichment) in the zone of alteration above Cu deposits. The stable secondary phase in such oxidizing environments appears to be malachite rather than the similar hydroxy-carbonate, azurite, (Chesworth, 1972). Malachite has also been suggested as the solution-limiting phase for Cu in the sea (Wedepohl, 1969–1978), although the latest work makes this seem unlikely (Symes & Kester, 1984).

F. Zinc in the Weathering Regime

The primary source of Zn is the ferromagnesian minerals, or the sulphide, sphalerite (ZnS). As sphalerite, it may accumulte as a detrital phase, but normally the primary phase can be expected to break down to release Zn(II) into the environment. Since Zn has only one valence state, its solution chemistry is not as complicated as other d-block elements. Whether or not there is significant leaching of Zn in a weathering material depends mainly on pH (see Fig. 1-9E). The more basic conditions lead to the immobilization of Zn as a CO_3 or OH phase, (Zachara et al., 1989) and reduced conditions lead to the precipitation of ZnS where S is available.

Zinc may also precipitate in phosphatic environments, so that up to 0.1% Zn is found in P fertilizers. As with Cu (and many other d-block elements) the mobility of Zn may be further restricted by its adsorption on the surface of clay-sized particles. According to Li (1981), Mn hydroxides are the preferred adsorbent. In soils and estuarine sediments, organic residues provide another possible site of adsorption. Adsorption, in fact, is definitely implicated in the low mobility of Zn, in that its concentration in natural waters (the average for groundwater in the USA is about 40 $\mu g\ kg^{-1}$) is always less than would be predicted from the solubility products of the CO_3 or OH phase of the metal.

The fact that plants accumulate Zn by a factor of about 10, in addition to the generally low mobility of Zn, means that soils may be slightly higher in Zn than their parent material.

Cadmium has similar crystallochemical properties to Zn and tends to be present in high concentrations in ZnS. Potentially, this could cause toxicity problems in the vicinity of weathering Zn deposits.

G. Molybdenum in the Weathering Regime

The primary source of Mo in the weathering zone is again the ferromagnesian minerals, with the sulfide molybdenite (MoS_2) common in certain granitoids. When released into the earth-surface environment, there is a slow oxidation to Mo(VI) and it enters solution as one of a number of anions. Figure 1–9F shows some of the possibilities, although higher molybdates and thiomolybdates (which may form in waters of neutral or basic pH) have been ignored in constructing the diagram.

Because of the wide range of conditions under which Mo is soluble, it is probably the most mobile of all metallic elements, except the alkalies and the alkaline earths (and possibly Re), but coprecipitation and adsorption can cut down expected mobility. As with other minor metals, Fe and Mn exert a major control, and virtually all the excess of Mo in terrestrial rocks is associated with Fe and Mn hydroxides, and hydrated oxides, with the Mn mineral preferred over the Fe mineral. Coprecipitation on S^{2-} phases (e.g., FeS) also occurs.

Molybdenum is enriched in pelagic, anoxic, C-rich sediments. This suggests that organic matter acts as an agent for Mo concentration in the sedimentary environment, although little work has been done on this aspect of the geochemistry of the element. Pelagic sediments tend to be enriched in a characteristic suite of metals, which in addition to Mo and the other micronutrients, Mn, Fe, Cu, and Zn also include other d-block elements. These arise from hydrothermal additions at mid-oceanic ridges. They rarely are found in the stratigraphic record and, therefore, rarely occur as the parent materials for soils.

VI. SUMMARY

In general, weathering of the primary materials of the lithosphere proceeds through three stages (Fig. 1–10). The soil progresses from an early stage, in which the inherent nutrient content is potential rather than realized, to an intermediate stage, characterized by the presence of 2:1 sheet silicates. These silicates can hold nutrient elements in a form available to plants. Finally, a late stage is reached in which 1:1 sheet silicates, oxides, and hydroxides dominate, and where much of the nutrient content has leached away. This stage is the least fertile, although the tropical rain forest demonstrates that an efficient nutrient recycling system in the biomass can result in a flourishing, though fragile, ecosystem even on these materials.

Given enough time, all soils would reach the late stage of Fig. 1–10, but fortunately, a number of geological processes intervene to renew the fertility of the land and prevent the planet from becoming completely barren (Chesworth, 1980). The most fundamental of these is the addition of volcanic materials to the surface, which results in the mantle fertilizing the crust. All six of the micronutrient elements are added to the land in this way. However, once they are part of the crust, other processes such as igneous differentiation, metamorphism, mountain building, and erosion may intervene before the micronutrients become a part of the soil via weathering processes.

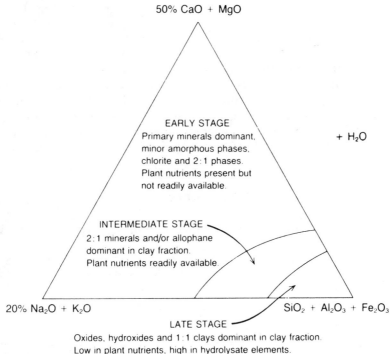

Fig. 1–10. Suggested three stages of weathering from primary igneous materials (Chesworth, 1975).

The primary source of B in most soils is tourmaline and the volatile emanations of volcanoes. Evaporation in closed basins has resulted in $B_2O_7^{2-}$ concentrations large enough to provide a B source for fertilizers. The primary source of the five d-block elements are the ferromagnesian silicates, the oxides, and sulfides. All five form notable ore deposits. In the weathering zone, all six micronutrients become available to plants in solution. The amount that remains in solution is controlled by precipitation (e.g., Fe and Mn), chelation, and adsorption onto aluminosilicate phases, Fe and Mn hydroxides and hydrated oxides (Jenne, 1968), and organic matter. Adsorption, which takes place at the solid-water interface, is a kind of two-dimensional condensation in which reactive ions accumulate on solid surfaces via surface coordination and exchange (Stumm, 1986). It is one of the key processes needed to understand the behavior of the micronutrients at the earth's surface. New instrumental techniques (e.g., secondary ion mass spectrometry [SIMS]) and the development of new physical models of the surface state, make this aspect of low-temperature geochemistry one of the currently most promising areas of research.

The chemistry of the weathering zone, especially in soils, is complex and daunting, and we may be forced to retreat to the use of empirical methods (McBride, 1989) to describe and predict elemental behavior. As McBride (1989) adds, future advances depend on maintaining and developing a theoretical framework. Furthermore, the straightforward application of even simple chemical concepts (Evans, 1989) yields many insights. If the planet is to be managed in the best interests of life on earth such applications must continue to be developed. In particular, an important direction for future studies concerns the problem of speciation. It is no longer sufficient for the geochemist to determine the overall content of a particular element in natural waters. The form that element takes is crucial to its chemical behavior and, particularly, to its biochemistry (Duffield & Williams, 1989). Since many of the relevant species are present at levels much too low to determine directly, speciation depends on the elaboration of sophisticated models for machine computation (e.g., GEOCHEM). Continued refinement of such models is necessary.

APPENDIX

Natural occurrences of the micronutrient elements

Copper   All the important ore minerals are sulfides: chalcopyrite ($CuFeS_2$), digenite (Cu_9S_5), chalcocite (Cu_2S), bornite (Cu_5FeS_4), enargite ($Cu_3A_5S_4$), and tetrahedrite ($Cu_{12}Sb_4S_{13}$).

Zinc   The important ore mineral is the sulfide, sphalerite (ZnS). Less important: smithsonite ($ZnCO_3$).

Iron   The important ore minerals are oxides, hematite (Fe_2O_3) and magnetite (Fe_3O_4). Other minerals: goethite (FeOOH), ferrihydrite [$Fe(OH)_3$], siderite ($FeCO_3$), jarosite [$KFe_3(OH)_6(SO_4)_4$], ferromagnesian silicates.

Manganese   Generally important ore minerals are the oxides, pyrolusite (MnO_2) and psilomelane ($BaMn_9O_{18} \cdot 2H_2O$). Locally important are rhodochrosite ($MnCO_3$) and braunite ($MnSiO_3$). The ferromanganese nodules of the ocean floor are mixtures of iron and manganese oxides and hydroxides.

Molybdenum The only important ore is the sulfide, molybdenite (MoS_2).

Boron   The economic sources are borates, e.g. borax $Na_2B_4O_5(OH)_4 \cdot 8H_2O$. Tourmaline [$Na(Mg, Fe, Mn, Li, Al)_3Al_6(Si_6O_{18})(BO_3)_3(OH, F)_4$ is a common accessory mineral.

REFERENCES

Allègre, C.J. 1982. Isotope geodynamics. Earth Planet. Sci. Lett. 86:175–203.

Baas-Becking, L.G.M., I.R. Kaplan, and D. Moore. 1960. Limits of the natural environment in terms of pH and oxidation reduction potential. J. Geol. 68:243–284.

Brookings, D.G. 1988. Eh-pH diagrams for geochemistry. Springer-Verlag New York, New York.

Buckley, A. 1989. An electron microprobe investigation of the chemistry of ferromanganese coatings on fresh water sediments. Geochim. Cosmochim. Acta 53:115–124.

Chesworth, W. 1972. Thermodynamic study of the relative stability of malachite and azurite in soils. Soil Sci. 113:303–307.

Chesworth, W. 1975. Soil minerals in the system Al_2O_3-SiO_2-H_2O: Phase equilibrium model. Clays Clay Miner. 23:55–60.

Chesworth, W. 1980. The haplosoil system. Am. J. Sci. 280:969–985.

Chesworth, W. 1982. Late Cenozoic geology and the second oldest profession. Geosci. Can. 9:54–61.

Chesworth, W., and F. Macias. 1985. pe, pH and podzolization. Am. J. Sci. 285:128–146.

Drever, J.I. 1974. Geochemical model for the origin of Precambrian banded iron formations. Geol. Soc. Am. Bull. 85:1099–1106.

Drever, J.I. 1988. The geochemistry of natural waters. Prentice Hall, New Jersey.

Duffield, J.R., and D.R. Williams. 1989. Chemical speciation. Chem. Br. 25:375–378.

Edmond, J., J.B. Corliss, and L.I. Gordan. 1979. Ridge crest hydrothermal metamorphism in the Galapagos spreading center and reverse weathering. p. 383–390. *In* Maurice Ewing Ser. 2, Am. Geophys. Union, Washington, DC.

Evans, L.J. 1989. Chemistry of metal retention by soils. Environ. Sci. Technol. 23:1046–1056.

Felmy, A.R., and J.H. Weare. 1986. The prediction of borate mineral equilibria in natural waters—Application to Searles Lake, California. Geochim. Cosmochim. Acta 50:2771–2783.

Ferris, F.G., W.S. Fyfe, and T.J. Beveridge. 1987. Manganese oxide deposition in a hot spring microbial mat. Geomicrobiol. J. 5:33–42.

Jackson, M.L., and G.D. Sherman. 1953. Chemical weathering of minerals in soils. Adv. Agron. 5:219–318.

Jenkins, D.A., and R.G.W. Jones. 1980. Trace elements in rocks, soils, plants and animals. p. 1–20. *In* B.E. Davies (ed.) Applied soil trace elements. John Wiley and Sons, New York.

Jenne, E.A. 1968. Controls of Mn, Fe, Co, Ni, Cu and Zn concentrations in soils and water: The significant role of hydrous Mn and Fe oxides. p. 337–387. *In* Trace inorganics in water. Adv. in Chem. Ser. 73, Am. Chem. Soc., Washington, DC.

Johnson, C.A. 1986. The regulation of trace element concentrations in river and estuarine waters contaminated with acid mine drainage: The adsorption of Cu and Zn on amorphous Fe oxyhydroxides. Geochim. Cosmochim. Acta 50:2433–2438.

Krauskopf, K.B. 1967. Introduction to geochemistry. McGraw-Hill, New York.

Krauskopf, K.B. 1972. Geochemistry of micronutrients. p. 7–40. *In* J.J. Mortvedt et al. (ed.) Micronutrients in agriculture. SSSA, Madison, WI.

Krumbein, W.C., and R.M. Garrels. 1952. Origin and classification of chemical sediments in terms of pH and oxidation reduction potentials. J. Geol. 60:1–33.

Lebedev, W.I. 1968. The influence of the character of chemical links on the phenomena of the isomorphism of boron in silicates. Series Geol. Geog., Leningrad Univ., 15:28–38.

Lelong, F., Y. Tardy, G. Gradin, J.J. Trescases, and B. Boulange. 1976. Pedogenesis, chemical weathering and processes of formation of some supergen ore deposits. p. 93–173. *In* K.L. Wolf (ed.) Handbook of strata-bound and stratiform ore deposits. Vol. 3. Elsevier, New York.

Li, Yuan-Hui. 1981. Ultimate removal mechanisms of elements from the ocean. Geochim. Cosmochim. Acta 45:1659–1664.

Mason, B., and C.B. Moore. 1982. Principles of geochemistry. John Wiley and Sons, New York.

McBride, M.B. 1989. Reactions controlling heavy metal solubility in soils. p. 1–56. *In* B.A. Stewart (ed.) Advances in soil science. Vol. 10. Springer-Verlag New York, New York.

Nicholls, G.D. 1963. Environmental studies in sedimentary geochemistry. Sci. Prog. (New Haven) 51:12–31.

Ronov, A.B., and A.A. Yaroshersky. 1969. Chemical composition of the earth's crust. p. 37–57. *In* P.H. Hart (ed.) The Earth's crust and upper mantle. Monograph 10. Am. Geophys. Union, Washington, DC.

Rosler, H.J., and H. Lange. 1972. Geochemical tables. Elsevier, New York.

Shannon, R.D. 1976. Revised effective ionic radii in oxides and fluorides. Acta Crystallogr. 25:925–946.

Spivak, A.J., and J.M. Edmond. 1987. Boron isotope exchange between seawater and the oceanic crust. Geochim. Cosmochim. Acta 51:1033–1044.

Stumm, W. 1986. Coordinative interactions between soil solids and water—An aquatic chemist's point of view. Geoderma 38:19–30.

Swihart, G.H., and P.B. Moore. 1989. A reconnaissance of the boron isotope composition of tourmaline. Geochim. Acta 53:911–916.

Symes, J.L. and D.R. Kester. 1984. Thermodynamic stability studies of the basic copper carbonate mineral, malachite. Geochim. Cosmochim acta 48:2219–2229.

Taylor, S.R., and S.M. McClennan. 1985. The continental crust. Its composition and evolution. Blackwell, Oxford, England.

Wedepohl, K.H. 1969–1978. Handbook of geochemistry. Section 5, Boron by C.L. Christ and H. Harder. Section 25, Manganese by D.R. Peacor and K.H. Wedephol. Section 26, Iron by R. Berner, S. Ghose, and R.F. Mueller. Section 29, Copper by J. Zemann and K.H. Wedephol. Section 30, Zinc by B. Brehker and K.H. Wedephol. Section 42 by H.T. Evans, F.T. Manheim, and S. Landergren. Springer-Verlag New York, New York.

Zachara, J.M., J.A. Kittrick, L.S. Dake, and J.B. Harsh. 1989. Solubility and surface spectroscopy of zinc precipitates on calcite. Geochim. Cosmochim. Acta 53:9–19.

Chapter 2

Geographic Distribution of Trace Element Problems

ROSS M. WELCH, *USDA-ARS, Ithaca, New York*

WILLIAM H. ALLAWAY, *Ithaca, New York*

WILLIAM A. HOUSE, *USDA-ARS, Ithaca, New York*

JOE KUBOTA, *Austin, Texas*

I. PERSPECTIVES

Much of the information presented here is based on the original chapter written by Kubota and Allaway (1972) for the first edition of this book. Additional patterns of trace element distributions published since 1972, especially in countries other than the USA, are included. As in the earlier chapter, the term trace elements is used instead of micronutrients because some trace elements are toxic to either plants or animals, whereas others are required by animals, but not by plants.

Geographic patterns of trace element problem areas may involve broad regions where the problem is almost universal on all the agricultural lands. Other geographic patterns may be localized and involve only certain parts of fields or pastures, with the remaining area being free of the problem. In a few cases, trace element deficiency or toxicity may be the result of a simple deficiency or excess of the trace element in the soil parent material. Trace element problems occurring in other areas may be more complex because of interactions among available levels of two or more elements in the soil. Moreover, some trace element problems may occur only in certain plant species or even plant genotypes of the same species.

Over the past 20 yr, there has been increasing interest in the effects of human activities on localized patterns of trace element toxicities in plants, animals, and humans. Some examples include Cd toxicity resulting from the disposal of sewage sludge on agricultural lands, aerial deposition of Pb on foliage growing near sites of heavy vehicular traffic, and Se toxicity in animals resulting from either disposal in catchments of Se-containing drainage waters from irrigated lands or improper disposal of scrubber solutions from electrostatic precipitators in coal-burning plants.

Investigations into the cause of regionalized or localized problems of trace element deficiency or toxicity have, at times, led to very important advances in the knowledge of elements essential or toxic to plants or animals. Studies of the anomalous geographic distribution of goiter among the world population led to the discovery that iodine (I) plays a role in the prevention of very serious human health problems. Additionally, attempts to find the cause of a mysterious livestock ailment in parts of Australia led to the discovery of the essential role of Co in ruminant nutrition.

II. GEOGRAPHIC PATTERNS OF TRACE ELEMENT PROBLEMS

A. Soils

Soil is the primary source of trace elements for plants and, through feed and food crops, for animals and humans, respectively. Therefore, soil factors are nearly always involved in regional or local trace element problems (i.e., deficiencies or toxicities). Patterns of trace element problems may be evident only when certain crops are grown, when specific agricultural practices are followed, or when certain diets are fed to specific kinds of animals or to humans.

Both soil parent material and soil profile development influence the amounts of trace elements available to plants. But these two factors operate very differently for different trace elements. Plants with high concentrations of Mo are found only on poorly drained (i.e., poorly aerated) soils developed on parent materials high in Mo; well drained soils in the same area produce forages with much lower Mo levels. In contrast, poorly aerated soils tend to produce plants with much lower Se concentrations than do well-aerated soils developed from the same type of parent material. More detailed effects of soil factors on trace element availability to plants, with resultant geographic patterns of trace element problems, are presented by Allaway (1986) and Kubota (1980), and in Section V of this chapter.

B. Plants

Many trace element problems in animals and humans occur because the mineral nutrient requirements and tolerances of higher plants may differ both qualitatively and quantitatively from those of animals and humans (Allaway, 1986). For example, most higher plants can grow normally and produce optimum growth without having sufficient quantities of Se or I that are necessary to satisfy animal or human requirements. In addition, in high-Se areas, some plants can accumulate very high concentrations of Se without any effect on their growth, but grazing animals that eat these plants may develop Se toxicity or selenosis. Furthermore, B toxicity in plants is common in some arid regions of the world, whereas B toxicity is rare in animals or humans, usually occurring only under experimental conditions.

Many of the trace elements considered essential for animals and humans are not known to be essential for all higher plants. Among these trace elements are I, F, Se, Co, As, Li, Cr, Si, Sn, and V (Nielsen, 1984, 1986). Even if a trace element is required by plants, the concentration of the element considered to be optimal for a particular plant may not meet the required dietary level for animals or humans. Additionally, some plants can contain excessive concentrations of trace elements (e.g., Cu and Mo) that are harmful to grazing animals, but not to the plants. When certain high-Si grass species are fed to ruminants, grass digestibility is reduced (Van Soest, 1982).

The ability of plants to accumulate trace elements in their edible parts varies between plant species and among genotypes within species (Peterson, 1972; Welch, 1986). Thus, there are genetic controls over the trace element concentrations found in edible portions of higher plants. These genetic differences can affect the nutritional status of animals and the geographic distribution of the trace element problem areas (Allaway, 1986). For example, the accumulation of Se by Se-accumulator plants {e.g., Twogrooved loco (*Astragalus bisulcatus* Hook.) and Alkali Princesplume (*Stanleya bipinnata* [Pursh.] Britt)} and their consumption by grazing livestock in western regions of the USA is primarily responsible for selenosis in the animals.

Genetically controlled differences in trace element concentrations among common forages, feed, and food crops can be important factors in the geographic distribution of nutritional problems. For example, forage legumes usually contain adequate levels of Co to meet the requirements of grazing livestock, but forage grasses generally lack sufficient amounts of Co to meet the needs of livestock (Kubota & Allaway, 1972). Many grains, including corn (*Zea mays* L.), sorghum grain (*Sorghum bicolor* L.), and barley (*Hordeum vulgare* L.) usually contain inadequate levels of Mn to meet the nutritional needs of poultry, whereas other grains, including wheat (*Triticum aestivum* L.) and oat (*Avena sativa* L.) grain (Allaway, 1986), can contain adequate Mn levels for poultry.

Different varieties (i.e., cultivars) of ryegrass (*Lolium multiflorum* Lam.) grown on the same soil have been reported to contain very large differences in I concentration in their leaves (see references cited in Allaway, 1986). Differences in the accumulation of Zn by inbred lines of corn are also known. A ten-fold difference in Se concentration among various varieties of soybean has also been reported. Genetic variations in the ability of plants to accumulate trace elements have been reviewed (Brown et al., 1972; Gerloff & Gabelman, 1983; Graham, 1984). No new varieties of food crops have been developed for the sole purpose of improving their nutritional quality with respect to trace elements.

C. Water and Air as Sources of Localized Trace Element Toxicities

Most of the trace elements that are eaten by humans and animals are derived from the soil through the plant. However, there are a few cases in which toxic concentrations of trace elements can be traced directly to water from certain wells, or indirectly to land application of drainage waters.

Boron toxicity in plants has resulted from the use of certain wells or waste waters for irrigation in some areas of California (Kelley & Brown, 1928). One of the earliest reports of Cd toxicity in people was traced to the flooding of rice (*Oryza sativum* L.) with waters that drained from a mine (Kobayashi, 1971). There has also been concern over the possibility of Cd toxicity resulting from the application of sewage sludge to agricultural lands (Chaney, 1977).

Water is the primary source of F ingested by humans in some regions of the world. Levels of F (as fluoride) in certain well waters are sufficiently high to cause fluorosis in animals and mottled enamel in human teeth (Underwood, 1977). This is a special problem in areas of the western USA, where water used for drinking and irrigation is obtained from thermal wells or springs rich in fluoride.

In Mexico, the use of high-Se drainage water from a mine spoil resulted in Se toxicity in animals (Williams et al., 1940). In this case, a stream draining a silver-mine spoil dump was used to irrigate feed and food crops near the village of Irapuato in Chihuahua. Maladies of unconfirmed cause had been observed in animals and humans in the area for some time. Alfalfa on land irrigated with river water downstream from the mine dump was found to be high in Se and animals in the area showed definite signs of selenosis. Humans in the area suffered from a number of health problems suggestive of selenosis, but the exact cause of the problems could not be definitely established.

A resurgence of concern over Se toxicity from drainage water occurred when fish and waterfowl in the Kesterson reservoir in the San Joaquin valley of California were found to be suffering from Se toxicity (Ohlendorf et al., 1986; Tanji et al., 1986). Irrigation water applied to land on the west side of the San Joaquin valley drained through soil where Se occurred. The Se was leached out of the soil and was transported through the San Luis Drain to a series of shallow ponds in a wildlife refuge. The water evaporated or seeped away annually, and new additions of drainage water were added during the next irrigation season. Although the irrigated soils were not highly seleniferous, Se toxicosis in the wildlife refuge was observed after 3 to 5 yr of drainage water additions. As a result, other irrigation projects in the western USA were studied. Apparently, Se toxicity is most likely to be found where seleniferous drainage waters are confined in a closed sink that is subject to repeated annual additions of the drainage water.

The deposition of aerosols of F onto vegetation near industrial plant sites where F-bearing raw materials are processed has been implicated in chronic fluorosis of humans and animals (Underwood, 1977). Plants growing near highways, certain ore processing plants, or areas where Pb-based paints have flaked off are frequently high in Pb (Lagerwerff, 1972). Whenever a trace element problem occurs because of airborne deposition, the relative importance of food and forage crop ingestion or of direct inhalation upon the magnitude of the problem is difficult to assess.

III. TECHNIQUES FOR MAPPING TRACE
ELEMENT PROBLEM AREAS

Some of the first maps of trace element problems in the USA were prepared by Beeson (1945). Beeson intended to show areas where either plant or animal production was adversely affected by deficiencies or toxicities of both major and trace elements. The maps were prepared primarily by literature surveys and by personal communications with soil scientists, agronomists, horticulturists, and animal nutritionists at the state agricultural experiment stations. Some later versions of Beeson's maps were partially based on plant analyses. These maps were fairly widely cited, and were used by feed and fertilizer producers to plan market strategies. As time went on, it became evident that problem areas for certain elements could not be adequately shown on USA maps at practical scales. The usefulness of these maps for planning the regional distribution of fertilizers and animal feeds has diminished because of changes in farming practices and animal rations.

Berger (1962) published maps showing recommended use of micronutrient fertilizers in the USA, on a state-by-state basis. These maps were compiled using communications with state experiment station workers and fertilizer control officials.

Beginning in the 1950s, scientists at the U.S. Plant, Soil, and Nutrition Laboratory in Ithaca, NY, embarked on a program of mapping areas of Co, Mo, and Se deficiencies and/or toxicities from data based on analyses of plants from specific sites. The elements studied were selected because of reports of nutritional problems in animals in specified areas or regions. Using geological and soil association maps, selected sampling sites were typical of major, fairly widespread agricultural soils. Specific plants, usually forage crops, were sampled. Those plant parts that would normally be consumed by foraging livestock were collected. Accumulator plants were sampled whenever possible. For example, samples of black gum (*Nyassa sylvatica*), a Co accumulator, were collected in studies concerning the distribution of Co deficiency in the USA. Areas where animal production problems, resulting from deficiencies or imbalances in trace elements, had not been observed were sampled in the same way as problem areas. Results from this program have been summarized (Kubota et al., 1987). Maps of low-Se forage areas (in relation to animal requirements) have been very widely cited and used by animal nutritionists and by investigators of human health problems.

The analysis of stream sediments for trace elements has been widely used in England, Wales, Scotland, and Ireland. With this technique, samples of screened (<0.2 mm, –80 mesh) sediments are analyzed for a number of trace elements and unusually high concentrations are tracked up the stream system to their source. Thornton (1977) used this technique to locate areas where Mo concentrations in forages are marginally high for ruminant animals.

The U.S. Geological Survey has used total analysis of the soil, usually surface soils, to identify areas of high or low trace element concentrations (Shacklette & Boerngen, 1984). Normally, sampling sites are randomly selected on grid maps without regard to the kind of soil found at the specific site.

These surveys are not directed primarily toward problems of plant or animal nutrition, and have been of limited value in locating areas of trace-element deficiency or toxicity in plants, animals, or humans.

IV. GEOGRAPHIC DISTRIBUTION OF PROBLEM AREAS

A. Boron

Boron is essential to plants and there is increasing evidence that B may also be required for normal mineral metabolism in mammals (Nielsen, 1986). Factors affecting the B content of plants include soil type, soil B content, soil pH, amount of precipitation, and plant species. Boron deficiency in crop plants occurs throughout the USA (Berger, 1962). Various crops differ markedly in their susceptibility to B deficiency. Monocotyledons generally have less B than do dicotyledons. Symptoms of B deficiency may occur when plant B content is < 15 mg kg^{-1} dry matter (National Research Council, 1980a). In China, the geographical distribution of B deficiency in crops coincided with the distribution of B-deficient soils (Zheng et al., 1982). In the USA, B deficiency has been observed in crop plants grown on light-textured sandy soils, acid soils, calcareous soils, and soils with relatively low amounts of organic matter (Bradford, 1966). There is no apparent geographic pattern of B deficiency in plants in the USA that can clearly be related to soils; the pattern of occurrence of B deficiency probably reflects geographic areas where plants with a high-B requirement are grown. Plants with high-B requirements include alfalfa (*Medicago sativa* L.), apples (*Malus domestica* Borkh.), and certain root (red beets [*Beta vulgaris* L.]; sugar beets; turnip [*Brassica rapa* L.]) and cruciferous crops (cabbage [*Brassica oleracea* var. capitata L.]; cauliflower [*Brassica oleracea* var. botrytis L.]) (National Research Council, 1980a). Boron is frequently added to fertilizers for plants that require high amounts of B.

Boron toxicity usually occurs when plant-B levels exceed 200 mg kg^{-1} dry wt. (National Research Council, 1980a). In newly developed fields in the San Joaquin Valley in California, B toxicity has been observed in crops grown on soils with high-B availability (Kubota, 1980). Additionally, plants with high concentrations of B have been observed in other regions of the western USA. Boron toxicity in plants may be common in semiarid regions with alkaline soils (Bradford,1966; Cartwright et al., 1984).

Boron intake by animals varies with the B content of drinking water, feed, and forages. Naturally occurring B deficiency in livestock has not been demonstrated. Boron toxicosis in animals is primarily an experimental phenomenon, but Underwood (1977) reported that, in Russia, B toxicity occurred in lambs grazing high-B plants growing on solonetz and solonchak soils. Similar calcareous and saline soils are found in Nevada, but B toxicity in livestock has not been reported in these areas.

B. Cobalt

Cobalt is required by animals because it is an integral part of the essential metabolite vitamin B_{12}. Furthermore, Co is required by the N_2-fixing bacteria in legume-root nodules. Microflora in the reticulo-rumen of ruminants can use inorganic Co or the Co compounds found in plants to synthesize vitamin B_{12}, which is then absorbed in the lower digestive tract to meet the nutritional requirements of the ruminant. In some nonruminant herbivores, vitamin B_{12} may be synthesized by microflora in the lower digestive tract and then excreted in the feces. These animals may then obtain their required vitamin B_{12} by coprophagy. However, most nonruminant animals, including humans, must obtain their required vitamin B_{12} by consumption of animal products or dietary supplements.

Problems of poor growth in ruminant animals, now known to be due to Co deficiency, were recognized in certain areas of the USA and Australia by early settlers. The nature and extent of these problems, the discovery that they were the result of low levels of Co in local forages, and their correction by Co supplementation is described by Underwood (1977). Following the confirmation of Co deficiency in parts of New Hampshire and Florida, soil scientists at the U.S. Plant, Soil, and Nutrition Laboratory initiated an extensive program to delineate Co-deficient areas in the USA. The results of this program, along with appropriate maps, have been published (Kubota & Allaway, 1972; Kubota et al., 1987). Legumes containing less than 0.07 mg Co kg^{-1} dry weight were found growing on soils derived from the White Mountain Granite, and on glacial till and outwash from this granite in the northeastern USA. Similar concentrations of Co in legumes were found on sandy Spodosols along the southeastern seaboard in the USA, especially in Florida. Legumes growing in other parts of the USA generally contained more than 0.07 mg Co kg^{-1} dry weight, the level considered to be adequate to meet the nutritional needs of ruminant animals. Grasses usually contain less than this amount of Co, regardless of where they are grown.

Plant requirements for Co, or more accurately the Co requirements of N_2-fixing rhizobia in legume-root nodules, are very low in terms of available soil Co. Field cases of legume responses to Co fertilization are very rare.

Excess Co is not highly toxic to animals, and Co-fortified salt blocks and mineral supplements have been used to correct Co deficiency in cattle and sheep in the USA. In Australia, Co-bearing rumen pellets have been used, especially for sheep. There has also been extensive use of Co-fortified superphosphate in Australia and New Zealand. Therefore, Co deficiency is rarely a major cause of poor livestock production in developed countries.

C. Copper

Copper is essential for both plants and animals. Plant Cu concentration is influenced by plant species, stage of growth, plant part, and various soil properties and amendments. The Cu status of soils in the USA has been summarized (Kubota, 1983). Soil Cu concentration is markedly affected by

the parent material from which the soil formed. Soils formed from weathered
bedrock have the highest Cu content. Soils formed in the unconsolidated lower
Atlantic Coastal Plain deposits have the least amount of Cu. In the USA
(Kubota, 1983) and in The Netherlands (Hartmans, 1970), the Cu content
of forages is not affected markedly by the amount of Cu in soils; however,
in New Zealand the concentration of Cu in alfalfa is highly related to soil
Cu content (Forbes, 1978).

Based on samples of various legume forages grown on a wide range of
USA soils, Kubota (1983) prepared a map showing the geographical distribution pattern of Cu in legumes (Fig. 2-1). The medium and range in concentration of Cu in legumes from the broad region of acid soils in the East
was nearly the same as that in legumes from the mainly alkaline and calcareous soils in the West. Legume Cu concentrations were relatively low (≤ 6
mg kg^{-1} in 35% of samples) in several areas, including the central wheat
belt, the low-Co areas of New England (Kubota & Allaway, 1972), and the
lower Atlantic Coastal Plain.

Copper deficiency has been observed in various crops and fruit trees
(Reuther & Labanauskas, 1966). In the USA, Cu deficiency is usually associated with specialized crops grown on peat and muck soils (Histosols)

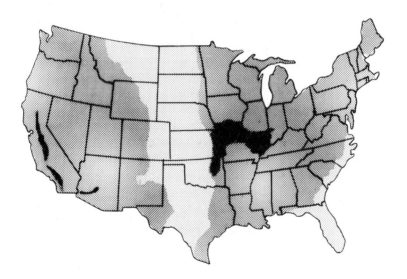

Areas where 50% or more of legumes have 10–12+ mg kg^{-1} of copper

Areas where 40–70% of legumes have 6–10 mg kg^{-1} of copper

Areas where 35% or more of legumes have 6 mg kg^{-1} or less of copper

Fig. 2-1. Generalized distribution of Cu concentrations in legumes of the USA (Kubota, 1983).

(Kubota, 1980). However, Cu deficiency has been observed in plants grown in other soils, particularly in the sandy soils in Florida (Kubota & Allaway, 1972). In China, Cu deficiency in plants appears to be associated with organic or sandy soils (Zheng et al., 1982). Throughout the world, Cu deficiency has occurred in plants grown on acid Histosols. The term reclamation disease has been used to describe Cu deficiency in plants grown on Histosols when these soils were brought into agricultural production.

Forages are the primary sources of Cu for grazing livestock, and Cu deficiency in grazing animals occurs naturally in many parts of the world. Copper deficiency caused by inadequate Cu content in forage is rare (Reid & Horvath, 1980), but it has been observed in western Australia (Davis & Mertz, 1987). In the USA, Cu and Co deficiencies have occurred concomitantly in cattle grazing forages growing in Florida (Underwood, 1981). However, rather than being a simple dietary deficiency, most Cu deficiencies that occur naturally in grazing animals are conditioned by dietary factors that interfere with the absorption or use of the dietary Cu (Underwood, 1981). Sulfur and Mo are two dietary factors that greatly influence Cu metabolism. Areas of Mo-induced Cu deficiency have been identified in the USA (Kubota, 1975, 1976) and in other regions of the world (Thornton, 1977; Underwood, 1981; Davis & Mertz, 1987).

The use of Cu-containing chemicals, such as fungicides and antihelmintics, in agriculture and veterinary medicine has resulted in Cu toxicity in plants and animals (National Research Council, 1980b). Naturally occurring Cu toxicity generally is not seen in plants (Kubota & Allaway, 1972), but it does occur in livestock. Sheep are more sensitive to Cu toxicity than are other species of livestock. Copper poisoning has occurred in sheep grazing forages that contain either excessively high levels of Cu or normal Cu levels, but with very low levels of Mo (Underwood, 1981). Moreover, Cu toxicoses with hemolytic crises may occur when sheep consume plants that contain certain hepatotoxic alkaloids (Underwood, 1981). Sheep consuming forage treated with swine or poultry manures, from animals fed diets supplemented with high levels of Cu, can also result in Cu toxicity (Owen, 1981).

D. Iodine

Iodine, required by animals, but not by higher plants, is an essential constituent of thyroid hormones. An adequate intake of I is necessary for normal differentiation, development, and growth of humans and animals. Iodine deficiency is the primary cause of endemic goiter, a disease of humans and animals that has been recognized for many years (Langer, 1960). In addition to goiter, I deficiency may cause other disorders, including retarded brain development and impaired mental function (Hetzel, 1986; Hetzel & Maberly, 1986). Hetzel (1983) proposed that the term "goiter" be replaced by the phrase "iodine-deficiency disorders" (IDD), since goiter does not adequately represent current knowledge on the wide spectrum of adverse conditions resulting from I deficiency.

Areas throughout the world in which there is a high incidence of IDD are described or illustrated in map form in several reviews and books (Kelly & Snedden, 1960; Stanbury & Hetzel, 1980; Underwood, 1981; Dunn et al., 1986). Lack of dietary I is the major cause of IDD. Additionally, goitrogens and antithyroid agents occurring naturally in some foods and waters may be etiologic factors in IDD (Gaitan et al., 1986).

Humans and animals obtain I primarily from food and, secondarily, from drinking water, but the recommended amount of dietary I varies with age and physiological status. Since the amount of I in food and water depends markedly on the I content in the soil, the incidence of IDD has been linked to factors that affect the I content of soils. The broad geographic distribution of I deficiency over a variety of landscapes suggests that I deficiency results from complex interactions among several environmental factors that vary in importance from area to area. The biogeochemical I cycle and the geological history of an area are important factors affecting I distribution and availability for human and animal consumption (Beckers & Delange, 1980; Fuge & Johnson, 1986; Koutras et al., 1980; Koutras, 1986).

The ocean is the primary source of I in nature. Through various mechanisms (Fuge & Johnson, 1986), a substantial amount of I regularly enters the atmosphere from the ocean. The combustion of fossil fuels also adds I to the atmosphere. Atmospheric I is carried by winds and deposits on land with rain or snow so that the superficial soil layers are enriched with I. Most of the I is deposited with the first rains, probably because of condensation and adsorption of atmospheric I on dust particles. In some areas, human and animal wastes applied to soils contribute some I. The I content of soils varies markedly, but soils have more I than do the rocks from which they were formed. Soil I content is influenced by I deposition from precipitation and other sources, distance from the sea, organic matter content, clay content, pH, history of glaciation, geological age, and extent of erosion and weathering (Fuge & Johnson, 1986; Goldschmidt, 1954; Koutras et al., 1980).

Many of the I-deficient areas in the world were glaciated during relatively recent geological time. The glaciation removed the I-rich surface soil and it was replaced by geologically young, low-I soil. In other regions, I-deficient areas are found in mountains or at high altitudes, regions where I may be readily leached from the superficial soil layers. Some I-deficient regions are in areas removed from oceanic influences or in areas where there is low annual precipitation.

Recognition that I deficiency caused goiter ultimately resulted in preventative programs. In North America, I supplementation is accomplished mainly by providing iodized salt, but injections of iodized oil are used in some areas of the world. Moreover, the intake of I from adventitious sources, particularly I adventitiously added to dairy foods, has increased in industrial nations. However, IDD have persisted in many regions of the world despite the availability of corrective measures.

Kubota and Allaway (1972) presented a map showing regions of the USA where goiter was prevalent in people before the extensive use of iodized salt. Relatively recent nutritional surveys indicated that goiter still existed in the

USA, but few people were I deficient and a natural goiter belt was no longer evident (Trowbridge et al., 1975; Matovinovic & Trowbridge, 1980). Areas in the USA formerly noted for goiter include the Great Lakes states, the Dakotas, Montana, Idaho, Washington, Oregon, Nevada, Utah, Colorado, Wyoming, western Nebraska, and the southeastern states of the Appalachian Range (Matovinovic & Trowbridge, 1980). Much of this broad area has been glaciated, but there are notable exceptions. The loess plains in Washington, parts of Washington and Oregon covered by geologically young deposits of volcanic ash, and the broad lacustrine plains and sand plains in the Great Lakes states merge with glaciated regions and are included in the I-deficient belt. A feature common to this broad area is the presence of relatively recent geological deposits. Glaciated areas lying within the influence of atmospheric I sources have a low incidence of goiter (McClendon, 1939).

Recognition of the role of I in the etiology of IDD, clarification of the biochemistry of I in the thyroid gland, identification of I-deficient regions, and initiation of I supplementation programs are classical contributions to trace element research. Without proper I supplementation, IDD will continue to occur in areas where foods and forages produced on I-deficient soils are the main source of nutrients for livestock and people.

E. Iron

Iron deficiency is a worldwide problem occurring in numerous crops (Korcak, 1987; Marschner, 1986; Vose, 1982), various human population groups (e.g., pregnant women; Morris, 1987), and certain types of farm animals (e.g., baby pigs; Morris, 1987). Usually, Fe deficiency occurs not because of its scarcity in the environment, but because of various factors that either inhibit its absorption or impairs its use in metabolic processes of an organism (National Research Council, 1979).

For crop plants, Fe-deficiency chlorosis is a general problem occurring throughout the world in various regions, on various soil types, and in many Fe-inefficient crop species (Mortvedt, 1975; Sillanpää, 1982; Vose, 1982; Wallihan, 1966). The wide range of plant species susceptible to Fe deficiency generally obscures geographic patterns that might exist worldwide. Usually, Fe deficiency is associated with fruit trees and crop plants grown in arid regions and on alkaline soils developed from calcareous materials. However, it can also occur on acid soils. Usually, Fe deficiency problems in crops are very localized because of the frequently erratic occurrence of problem soils within a given area.

In the USA, the intermountain region contains the largest area of soils that are potentially deficient in available Fe for certain sensitive crops. Mortvedt (1975) estimated that there were more than 4.8 million ha, or about 5% of the cultivated area in 22 states west of the Mississippi River, that were prone to producing Fe deficiency in Fe-inefficient crops. These areas included widespread parts of Utah, an area of alkaline, irrigated soils across southern Idaho, and a wide belt of soils extending from Nebraska in the north to Kansas, Colorado, western Oklahoma, eastern New Mexico, northwest Texas, and beyond in the south (Vose, 1982).

The erratic nature of Fe deficiency can be seen in Iowa where about one-third of the soybean is grown on soils of low-Fe availability. These areas are very localized because of the intermixing of bands of calcareous and non-calcareous soils within the state. Similar conditions are found in California where small areas of soil with Fe-availability problems can result in Fe chlorosis in responsive crops. In Florida, Fe deficiency in citrus trees is found in both alkaline calcareous soils and acidic sandy soils. The Fe-deficient, acidic Florida sands actually contain very low total Fe levels, a relatively rare occurrence in nature.

In certain regions of Europe, Fe deficiency is also a problem in sensitive crops. Furthermore, certain crops grown on arid, alkaline, and alkaline saline soils in countries of the eastern Mediterranean, the Near East, India (e.g., in Madhya Pradesh and Andhra Pradesh; Katyal & Vlek, 1985), and Bangladesh are also susceptible to Fe deficiency. In eastern and western Africa (e.g., The Congo, Ghana, Nigeria, Kenya, Senegal, and Zaire), Fe deficiencies can occur locally (Kang & Osiname, 1985; Vose, 1982). In the global study of the micronutrient status of soils reported by Sillanpää (1982), the lowest Fe levels were reported for certain areas of Malta, Mexico, Turkey, and Zambia. Iron deficiencies have also been reported for crops in West Bengal and for several crops grown on high pH, calcareous upland soils in Indonesia (Katyal & Vlek, 1985). Iron deficiencies have also been reported for certain crops in several countries in Central and South America (León et al., 1985). Iron deficiency in plants also occurs in various states in Australia including South Australia, Victoria, and Western Australia (Donald & Prescott, 1975).

Iron toxicity is a problem for a limited number of plant species cultivated under unique conditions (Vose, 1982), such as rice grown under flooded conditions in acid soils. In the East, these areas include parts of Korea, Japan, China, Vietnam, Thailand, Burma, Bangladesh, Malaysia, Philippines, Indonesia, and Sri Lanka. In Africa, there is an acid soil belt where Fe toxicity can occur that extends across equatorial Africa and includes Senegal, Gambia, Liberia, and Sierra Leone (Kang & Osiname, 1985). In South America, Colombia has also reported Fe toxicity problems. High levels of available Fe in soils can also lead to excessive Fe-induced micronutrient deficiencies in some crops cultivated on soils that are poor in certain micronutrient metals. For example, high levels of Fe have been reported to induce Mn deficiencies in bean plants (Vose, 1982).

Iron deficiency in livestock is not a widespread problem. Iron deficiency anemia can occur in piglets raised in confinement and in older pigs when provided with high-Cu feed to elevate growth rates (Morris, 1987). Iron deficiency is not a problem in other farm animals maintained under natural conditions. Iron deficiency anemia in humans is a major, worldwide health problem (Morris, 1987), and it is one of the most prominent mineral deficiencies in humans, occurring most often in children and pregnant women (National Research Council, 1979). However, this form of anemia is not associated with Fe deficiencies in soils or plants, but rather with low Fe availability in the diet and/or low Fe intake in general (Reinhold, 1988).

F. Manganese

Soil, plant, climatic, and human factors interact to determine the geographic distribution patterns of Mn problem areas throughout the world (Reuter et al., 1988). These areas include Mn toxicity in crops, and Mn deficiency in plants and in certain farm animals, and possibly in some groups of humans. Soils deficient in Mn can cover broad areas in various regions of the world that encompass many soil types. They can also be localized and confined to isolated areas within a single field. Because plant roots absorb Mn as the divalent cation, environmental factors that change its concentration in the soil solution that bathes plant roots can potentially affect the accumulation of Mn in plant tops. These factors include soil physical, chemical, and/or biotic properties (Graham et al., 1988) that limit root growth or Mn availability to roots. These include such properties as adverse weather conditions (e.g., excessive or inadequate rainfall), high concentrations of other elements that interact with Mn absorption, translocation, or use by plants (e.g. Si, Fe, Ca), soil organic matter content, soil aeration, soil acidity, and root pathogens (i.e. nematode infections that limit root growth).

Soils associated with less than adequate levels of available Mn include: (i) shallow, peaty soils developed over calcareous subsoils; (ii) marsh and alluvial soils developed from calcareous parent materials; (iii) calcareous soils with poor drainage and high organic matter content; (iv) calcareous black sands; (v) over-limed, reclaimed acid heath soils; (vi) calcareous grassland soils recently cultivated; (viii) black garden soils high in organic matter and lime; and (viii) sandy, acidic soils low in total native-Mn content (Labanauskas, 1966; Reuter et al., 1988).

Manganese deficiency in crops is widespread in Canada and the USA, especially on reclaimed calcareous soils, peats, and mucks found in the Great Lakes region, and coarse-textured and poorly drained soils in the Atlantic Coastal Plain states (Reuter et al., 1988). In Mexico, and in Central and South America, Mn deficiencies have been reported for certain crops in a number of countries including Costa Rica, El Salvador, Honduras, Nicaragua, Guatemala, Ecuador, Peru, Venezuela, Colombia, Bolivia, and Brazil (León et al., 1985). Usually, Mn-deficient problem soils are calcareous.

In England, Mn deficiency is seen in crops grown in peaty soils and mineral soils that contain high levels of organic matter. In some European countries, Mn deficiency is more strongly correlated to soil texture then to organic matter content. For example, Mn deficiency in Sweden is associated with coarse-textured soils, whereas in the Netherlands, inadequate levels of available Mn are found in both coarse- and fine-textured soils (even some marine clay polders). In Denmark, some excessively limed, coarse-textured soils, and some calcareous soils high in organic matter are prone to producing Mn-deficient crops. Manganese problems are commonly associated with podzol and brown forest soils in Scotland, especially those with low bulk density, impeded drainage, and resultant poor aeration.

In northern China (Zheng et al., 1982) and in some semiarid regions of India (Katyal & Vlek, 1985), certain calcareous soils (e.g., Vertisols) have been identified as being Mn-deficient. There is a broad range of Mn-deficient soils in Australia including areas in the states of Western Australia, South Australia, and Victoria. Some of these soils may have an absolute deficiency of Mn, whereas others are problem soils because of low-Mn availability (Donald & Prescott, 1975).

Manganese deficiency is only a minor problem in western Africa. However, it does occur in certain crops, such as oil palm (*Elaeis guineensis* Jacq.) in the Congo, the Ivory Coast, and in east-central and southern Nigeria (Kang & Osiname, 1985).

In his worldwide study, Sillanpää (1982) reported that the low availability of Mn is usually associated with alkaline soils (i.e., countries with large areas of calcareous soils are more likely to have Mn-deficiency problems). Malta had the highest incidence of alkaline soils, followed by India, Pakistan, Syria, Italy, Egypt, and Lebanon. Thus, these countries are more likely to have Mn-deficient soils than other countries that do not have as high a proportion of calcareous soils.

In many parts of the world, Mn toxicity is more important than Mn deficiency in crop plants. Manganese toxicity in plants is associated with poorly drained, acid soils. However, plants and plant tissues can differ in their tolerance to excessive Mn conditions. Tolerance to Mn toxicity is affected by several factors including (i) plant genotype; (ii) growth media Si concentration; (iii) temperature; (iv) light intensity; and (v) physiological leaf age (Horst, 1988). Soil management factors, such as type of fertilizer applied and liming practices, can also affect the occurrence of Mn toxicity conditions (Labanauskas, 1966). Thus, geographic patterns of Mn toxicity in crops may be indistinct and difficult to detect because of the interactions of these numerous environmental and genetic factors.

Manganese deficiency in animals and humans is not widely recognized. In animals, it occurs most often in poultry and is associated with high-grain diets or diets with excessive Ca and P, which interferes with the absorption of Mn (Matrone, 1977; Hurley & Keen, 1987). While Mn deficiency is not recognized as a problem for humans, some groups of people may be at risk of developing a less than optimal Mn status because of poor dietary habits (Kies, 1987).

G. Molybdenum

Molybdenum is required by plants, but the requirement in terms of critical concentrations in plant tissue is very low. Nevertheless, use of Mo fertilizers has resulted in striking increases in plant production in a number of areas of the world. High levels of available Mo have not depressed plant growth, but high levels of Mo in forages may seriously interfere with Cu metabolism in animals. This situation is most often found in ruminants and is not common in monogastric animals. Molybdenum deficiency in plants and Mo-induced Cu deficiency (molybdenosis) in animals occur in definite geographic patterns. Plants with Mo deficiency usually are found in broad areas of acid, well-drained soils. Plants with excessive concentrations of Mo often occur in localized areas with poorly drained soils that are frequently alkaline. Relationships between Mo levels in soils, and plant or animal production have been reviewed by (Allaway, 1976; Kubota, 1975, 1976; Kubota et al., 1987).

Molybdenum deficiency in plants in the USA is found on some soils that are formed from parent materials that are very low in Mo. These soils are usually acid, but liming of the soil to increase the availability of native soil Mo does not result in yields as high as those obtained from areas receiving both lime and Mo. On some acid soils, liming alone will increase the solubility of native soil Mo to optimum levels. Areas fitting these two types of situations are substantially confined to the eastern USA (Fig. 2-2).

Plants with Mo concentrations sufficiently high to cause molybdenosis in cattle and sheep are generally confined to poorly drained sites where the soils are formed from high-Mo parent materials, usually alluvium from igneous rocks or shales. In the USA, these sites are confined to intermountain valleys in the West (Fig. 2-2). High-Mo plants also occur on poorly drained

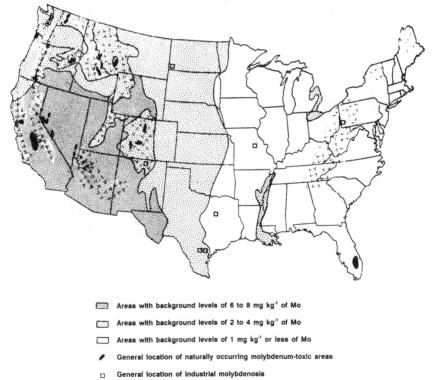

▨ Areas with background levels of 6 to 8 mg kg^{-1} of Mo

▨ Areas with background levels of 2 to 4 mg kg^{-1} of Mo

☐ Areas with background levels of 1 mg kg^{-1} or less of Mo

✔ General location of naturally occurring molybdenum-toxic areas

☐ General location of industrial molybdenosis

Fig. 2-2. Generalized regional pattern of Mo concentration in legumes of the USA (Kubota, 1976).

organic soils (Histosols) in South Central Florida; well drained soils in the same area produce plants with much lower Mo concentrations. The association of high-Mo plants with poorly drained soils is also found in other parts of the world. There are very few reported cases of molybdenosis in livestock grazed on well-drained soils.

Geographic patterns of soils that are deficient in available Mo or provide excessive amounts of Mo that cause molybdenosis in animals are partly dependent on variations in the Mo content of the parent material. High-Mo parent material usually forms soil that contains adequate levels of Mo for plants. Poorly drained soils formed from low-Mo parent materials are rarely associated with molybdenosis. The effect of soil drainage (i.e., aeration) on the chemistry of the soil Fe is probably the dominant reason for the geographic distribution of plants high or low in Mo. The ferric (Fe III) compounds of Mo are much less soluble than are the ferrous (Fe II) compounds. In well-drained soils where the active Fe is predominately in the ferric (Fe III) oxidation state, probably as hydrous oxides, insoluble ferric molybdates or ferric oxide molybdate complexes are formed, and the level of plant-available Mo is very low. In poorly drained soils, Fe is present in the ferrous (Fe II) oxidation state and the more soluble ferrous molybdates or molybdites are formed, resulting in high levels of Mo in the plants.

Molybdenum deficiency in plants is usually corrected by uses of Mo-fortified fertilizers, sprays, or seed treatments. Low amounts of Mo are required per unit area of land and overuse has not resulted in damage to plant growth. Although there is potential for causing molybdenosis in animals from excessive Mo fertilization of soils used for forage production, the hazard is low since well-drained soils readily fix Mo in insoluble forms. Molybdenosis in ruminant animals is usually treated by adding Cu to the diet. Since Cu toxicity is a potential problem in ruminant animals, elevated levels of Cu supplementation should be carefully confined to areas where molybdenosis is known to occur.

H. Selenium

In the early 1930s, high Se concentrations in plants were found to be responsible for a number of documented animal production problems in parts of the western USA. Following this discovery, an extensive effort to delineate the areas where plants with high Se concentration occurred was initiated by the USDA, the South Dakota and Wyoming State Agricultural Experiment Stations, and botanists at Columbia University. An account of these studies is provided by Anderson et al. (1961).

Researchers found that a group of plants, called Se accumulators, contained markedly higher concentrations of Se than did other plants growing in the same immediate area. Some species of *Astragalus, Stanleya, Xyeorrhza, Oonopsis*, and other Se-accumulating plants contained > 50 mg Se kg^{-1}, whereas range grasses and crop plants such as wheat or rye (*Secale cereale* L.) growing very close to Se accumulators contained < 10 mg Se kg^{-1}. The location of high-Se areas was facilitated by collection and analysis of the

Se accumulator plants. The sites that produced plants with toxic concentrations of Se were generally small areas where shales of Cretaceous or Permian geologic age were exposed on or near the surface, or where material such as loess, alluvium, or glacial till, derived primarily from these shales, was the soil parent material. In these areas the soil was nearly always well drained and neutral to alkaline in reaction. Spot maps, showing locations where Se-accumulator plants occur, are provided by Rosenfeld and Beath (1964). These maps can show countries or similarly sized regions where high-Se plants occur, but cannot show the extremely localized areas where the hazardous sites are dispersed among those producing nontoxic vegetation. Crop plants and range grasses that contain >4 to 5 mg Se kg^{-1}, the amount considered to be potentially detrimental to animals, were generally confined to parts of fields or farms.

Following the studies of Se toxicity in the USA, areas producing vegetation with potentially toxic concentrations of Se were identified in a number of other countries. Farmers and ranchers minimized livestock losses by avoiding the most dangerous areas in their grazing practices and by diluting crops harvested from these areas with crops harvested from nontoxic areas. The practice of blending wheat from a number of different sources by the milling industry was found to eliminate danger of human Se toxicity in the USA.

After the discovery that irrigation drainage water impounded in the Kesterson Wildlife Refuge in California caused Se toxicity in fish and wildfowl, concern was raised over a potential widespread hazard to wildlife and people from similar sources throughout western USA. Investigations by the U.S. Department of Interior have indicated that the hazard is not as widespread as feared, but it is evident that disposal of Se-containing irrigation drainage water, and leachate from fly ash and mine spoils in closed sinks or evaporation ponds, should be closely monitored for potential Se toxicity to fish and wildlife. The public health hazard from disposal of irrigation drainage water appears to be very low.

Mapping of areas where the Se concentration in crops is too low to meet farm animal requirements for dietary Se was started at the U.S. Plant, Soil, and Nutrition Laboratory in 1963, following the discovery that White Muscle Disease, and some similar livestock and poultry problems, were responsive to Se therapy. The mapping program was designed on the basis of earlier research on the geology of Se toxicity in the western USA, in addition to generalized knowledge on the regional occurrence of Se-responsive diseases in livestock. A version of the map produced is shown in Fig. 2–3 (Kubota & Allaway, 1972). The original data for this map and discussions of the geologic and soil genetic factors, with the incidence of White Muscle Disease in the delineated areas, are provided with the original publication of the map (Kubota et al., 1967) and in the first edition of this book (Kubota & Allaway, 1972).

This map proved to be very useful to livestock producers, veterinarians, and animal nutritionists, and to the U.S. Food and Drug Administration in its decision to permit Se supplementation of livestock feeds. Maps

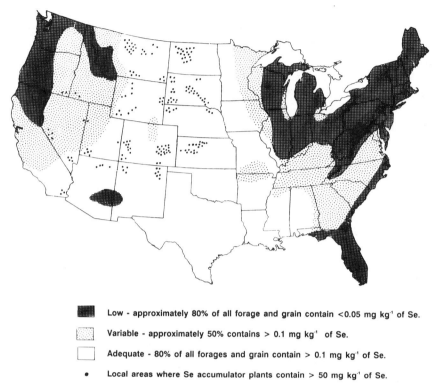

Low - approximately 80% of all forage and grain contain <0.05 mg kg⁻¹ of Se.

Variable - approximately 50% contains > 0.1 mg kg⁻¹ of Se.

Adequate - 80% of all forages and grain contain > 0.1 mg kg⁻¹ of Se.

• Local areas where Se accumulator plants contain > 50 mg kg⁻¹ of Se.

Fig. 2–3. Geographical distribution of low-, variable-, and adequate-Se areas in the USA (Kubota & Allaway, 1972).

of the Se status of crops have been compiled for a number of other countries including Canada, New Zealand, Venezuela, and most of Northern Europe. A discussion of mapping of Se areas in other countries is given by Gissel-Nielsen et al. (1984). Scientists in China thoroughly mapped Se concentrations in crops in that country (Keshan Disease Research Group of the Chinese Academy of Medical Sciences, 1979). The impetus for this mapping was the observation that people in some areas of China were seriously affected by Se toxicity and, in other areas, by Se deficiency. A description of this program and a nationwide map is provided by Liu et al. (1984). The areas where human Se-deficiency diseases are prevalent in China are characterized by very low concentrations of Se (<0.02 mg kg^{-1}) in local food crops. These very low concentrations in food crops are reflected by very low concentrations of Se in human blood and some other tissues. Table 2–1 indicates the relationship between Se in crops and the concentrations in human blood as found in various countries. In some countries, such as the USA, interregional distribution of foods tends to mask differences in blood Se levels between high- and low-Se areas.

A number of methods are used in different countries for amelioration of Se deficiency in people and animals. In the Se-deficient areas of China,

Table 2-1. Selenium content of cereal grain, estimated human dietary intake of Se, and Se concentration in whole blood of people in China, New Zealand, and the USA.[†]

	Se in cereal grain	Se intake	Blood Se
	mg kg^{-1}	mg d^{-1}	mg L^{-1}
Peoples Republic of China[†]			
Low Se area (Keshan Disease)	0.005–0.007	0.011	0.021
Se adequate area	0.020–0.040	0.116	0.095
High Se area (selenosis)	0.5–28.5	4.99	3.2
New Zealand[‡]	0.018–0.073	0.028	0.068
United States of America[§]	0.026–0.665	0.132	0.22

† Modified from Yang et al. (1983).
‡ Modified from Thomson and Robison (1980).
§ Modified from Sander et al. (1987).

people are provided with supplements directly, either by use of Se pills or selenized table salt. In New Zealand and Finland, selenate-Se fertilizers or sprays providing about 10 g Se ha^{-1} are applied annually to provide protective, but nontoxic levels of Se in crops and pastures. In Australia, a slow release Se-containing rumen bolus has been extensively used for sheep and cattle. In other developed countries, including the USA, Se-fortified animal feed supplements and Se injections are used in Se-deficient areas. Guiding the use of Se supplements for people and animals to areas where it is needed has been the most important use of maps of Se concentration. A recent review is available that examines the scientific literature concerning Se in agriculture and the environment (Jacobs, 1989).

I. Zinc

Zinc deficiency in plants is widespread throughout the world (Bould et al., 1984; Viets, 1966). Zinc deficiencies have also been reported in livestock (e.g., pigs, poultry, and cattle) and in certain human population groups, such as pregnant women and young children (Donald & Prescott, 1975; Hambidge et al., 1986; Reinhold, 1988; Underwood, 1981). Usually, Zn deficiency in plants is associated with high-pH soils because of their low Zn availability status or with coarse-textured, highly leached, acid soils because of their low total Zn content. Negative interactions between Zn and several other essential elements (e.g., P) can also lead to Zn deficiencies in plants (Robson & Pitman, 1983). Usually, Zn-deficient sites are found where specialized crops are grown and there are no broad uniform regions of soils or soil parent materials (Kubota, 1980). In humans, Zn deficiency often is associated with either dietary antinutritive factors that depress Zn bioavailability (i.e., interfere with Zn absorption and/or use), or with diets low in red meats and other animal proteins. Also, a rare autosomal, recessively inherited disorder, acrodermatitis enteropathica, leads to severe Zn deficiency in humans (Hambidge et al., 1986).

There is a poorly defined geographic pattern of Zn deficiency in plants reported for the 48 contiguous states of the USA (Hodgson et al., 1971; Kubota & Allaway, 1972). This is largely the result of the variations in the frequency of small local Zn-deficient areas in various regions of the USA. These geographic patterns can be influenced by various environmental factors that reduce or enhance Zn availability to plants, or by differences in the efficiency of Zn absorption and use between plant species, and even between different varieties within a species (Lindsay, 1972; Viets, 1966).

In the western USA, regions of irrigated lands used to produce crops that are sensitive to Zn deficiency are usually affected, but even here, severe Zn deficiency may be confined to spots within a field (Kubota & Allaway, 1972). Thus, relatively little of the soil in the West is affected by Zn deficiency. The eastern boundaries of this Zn deficiency pattern roughly correspond to the eastern edge of the calcareous soil region (approximately the 100th meridian).

Zinc deficiencies in plants are reported in the southeastern quarter of the USA (i.e., the region lying east of the 100th meridian, and south of the Ohio and Potomac rivers), but these reports are less frequent from this section than from the western section. In the Southeast, Zn deficiency is associated with sandy, well-drained, acid soils or with soils developed from phosphatic rock parent materials (e.g., in Kentucky and Tennessee). The southeastern USA contains the largest contiguous areas of Zn deficiency; the Florida citrus-producing Lakeland (thermic, coated Typic Quartzipsamments) and associated soil-series zone contains some of the largest single areas of Zn deficiency in the USA.

The lowest incidence of Zn deficiency in the USA is found in the Northeast (Kubota & Allaway, 1972). This is especially true for the areas covered by slightly to moderately acid Mollisol soils in the central part of the Corn Belt (i.e., in Iowa, Missouri, Illinois, and Indiana). Zinc deficiency in the Lakes States, Pennsylvania, New Jersey, New York, and New England is not as common as in other parts of the nation, but it does occur in susceptible crops in some local areas in these regions.

Sillanpää (1982), in his global study of the micronutrient status of soils, reported that Zn deficiency in plants is probably present in almost every country studied, excluding Belgium and Malta. Iraq, Turkey, India, and Pakistan had the lowest soil Zn levels, but Syria, Lebanon, Mexico, Italy, Nepal, Tanzania, and Thailand also registered shortages of soil Zn. Sillanpää and Vlek (1985) and León et al. (1985) reported that the most prominent documented areas for Zn deficiency in the tropics occur in Brazil, Chad, Nigeria, India, and the Philippines. Unfortunately, the Zn status of some of the largest areas in the tropics have not been studied in any detail (e.g., the Amazon basin and the Llanos in Latin America, the Congo basin in Africa, and the Indo-Chinese Peninsula in Asia). In Africa, Zn deficiencies have been reported in Nigeria, Guinea, the Ivory Coast, Sierra Leone, Sudan, and Zimbabwe (Kang & Osiname, 1985). In many of these places, Zn deficiency has been induced by using lime to increase soil pH from about 4.5 to about 7.0.

In Asia (Katyal & Vlek, 1985), Zn deficiency is found more frequently in the arid and semiarid regions than in the humid and subhumid regions of India. The northeastern, semiarid region of Thailand was considered to have a higher incidence of Zn deficiency than other areas in that country.

The north-central plains of West Java, the tropical soils of Taiwan, and the poorly drained, calcareous paddy soils of China have been reported to be Zn-deficient (Zheng et al., 1982). The Philippines have also reported spectacular responses to Zn fertilization in some soils used to produce rice. Severe Zn deficiency has also been reported in Sri Lanka near Matale (Katyal & Vlek, 1985).

In Australia, Zn deficiency is widespread in certain regions, including parts of Western Australia, Queensland, South Australia, Victoria, and New South Wales (Donald & Prescott, 1975). Zinc deficiency is associated with Cu and Mo deficiencies in some areas of mainly acid sandy or gravelly lateritic soils formed over granitic gneiss. Western coastal soils formed from aeolian calcareous or leached siliceous sands over limestone are also Zn-deficient, as are some of the grey and brown loams and sands in the western wheat belt. In fact, the state of Western Australia has the distinction of having the largest single contiguous area of Zn deficiency in the world (i.e., >8 million ha). In the southern coastal soils, Zn deficiency is associated with sand on clay over Jurassic sediments.

Soils can contain phytotoxic levels of Zn, but this is vary rare under natural conditions. In one area of northern New York in the USA, Zn toxicity was observed in vegetable crops grown on fields reclaimed from drained peat soils; Zn accumulated as ZnS during formation of the soils (Staker, 1943). Usually, Zn toxicity in plants is the result of human activity, such as mining or metal smelting.

J. Other Trace Elements

Since 1970, 11 additional trace elements have been proposed to be required by animals and, possibly, humans. These elements are As, B, Br, Cd, F, Pb, Li, Ni, Si, Sn, and V (Nielsen, 1984). Except for Ni and B, none of these elements are considered to be essential for all higher plant life. Although it has recently been established that Ni is essential to higher plants (Eskew et al., 1983; Brown et al., 1987), there are currently no known regions of Ni deficiency in the world. However, in the past, the discovery of an essential micronutrient for plants has led to reports of field responses to the newly discovered micronutrient, even though some of the researchers initially suggested that their findings might only be a laboratory curiosity. For example, the discovery that Mo was an essential micronutrient for higher plants was initially thought to be of academic interest only (Arnon & Stout, 1939). Molybdenum was required at such low concentrations by higher plants that the researchers believed that no soils in the world would be deficient in this trace element. Currently, however, there are millions of hectares throughout the world that are known to be deficient in available Mo concentrations for higher plant growth. Indeed, millions of hectares of agricultural lands in Australia alone would not be productive today if it had not been for this discovery.

In addition to establishing the essentiality of trace elements, increased interest in others has been generated by the application of new technologies to the multielemental analyses of biological tissues for a wide range of trace elements. These methods include nuetron activation analysis; inductively coupled, Ar plasma, emission spectrometry; and inductively coupled, Ar plasma, mass spectrometry. For example, Sr, Sc, Cs, Ba, Ge, Rb, Ag, Ti, Zr, Be, Bi, Ga,Au, In, Nb, Sc,Te, Tl, and W have been detected in various types of organisms (Nielsen, 1986). The geographic distribution of these trace elements has not been studied in detail.

Excessive concentrations of Cd, accumulated in leafy vegetables grown in certain spots of a few fields in the Salinas Valley of California (Burau et al., 1981), stimulated interest in the geographic distribution of Cd and other trace elements in major food crops in the USA. Results of a national survey indicated that crop genetic factors were more important than fertility, soil, and environmental factors in determining the concentration of various trace elements (i.e., Cu, Fe, Mn, Mo, Se, Zn, Ni, Pb, and Cd) in selected food crops grown across major production regions of the USA (Wolnik et al., 1983, 1985).

Papers have been published in the USA on the geographic distribution of various trace elements in rocks, soils, and plants (Cannon, 1971; Cannon & Davidson, 1967; Connor & Shacklette, 1975; Shacklette, 1980; Shacklette & Boerngen, 1984). Most of these studies were associated with ground water surveys, geologic mapping, and mineral prospecting. Few authors of papers concerning these trace elements have interpreted their findings in relation to the trace element nutrition of plants, animals, and humans, because almost nothing is known about these relationships.

V. RESEARCH NEEDS AND APPLICATIONS

Various metals have been used for utilitarian or ornamental purposes for centuries, and it was recognized during the last century that some of these metallic elements occurred in biological systems. However, their essentially to plants and animals was not established until the present century. Also, it was established that either an excess or a lack of specific trace elements caused specific metabolic disorders.

Trace element research has been stimulated by the development of sensitive analytical techniques. For example, the application of atomic absorption to studies of trace elements in soils, plants, and animals provided large amounts of information on the function and distribution of trace elements in the environment. Many of these studies focused on one element at a time because of limited analytical technology. Instruments capable of multielement analyses have been developed, and even greater amounts of information will be obtained as they are used to determine, simultaneously, the concentrations of several elements in geological or biological samples. Efficient management of the collected data will require increased use of computers and specialized software.

There has been increased awareness of and research on interactions, both among trace elements, and between trace elements and other dietary constituents. Increased use of multielement analytical methods may reveal additional interrelationships among elements. Also, multielement analyses are needed to clarify some of the interactions that are known.

In developed countries, identification of geographical areas where trace element problems occur in people may be obscured by various factors, including the widespread distribution of food and increased consumption of prepared foods that have been purposely or adventitiously supplemented with trace elements. In developing countries, trace element problems in people may be obscured by other dietary deficiencies, microbial diseases, or parasites. Consequently, trace element anomalies in the soil-plant-animal system are likely to be identified initially in livestock, because they obtain most of their food from relatively small geographical areas. Since animal production may be affected by less-than-optimum levels of trace elements, techniques are needed to easily identify marginal trace element deficiencies in animals. Moreover, additional research is needed to determine the influence of trace element status on immunological responses in animals.

Geographical variations in concentrations of some elements (e.g., Co, Cu, Mo, and Se) in plants have been identified and mapped for some countries. Some of these maps need to be refined (e.g., distribution of Cu in the central wheat-producing region of the USA). Research on the soil and plant aspects of the environmental cycling of these elements should be continued and extended to other essential (Zn, Mn) or toxic (Cd, Pb) trace elements. Relative to animals, areas where vegetative concentrations of these elements are naturally deficient, marginal, or excessively high need to be identified and mapped. Concurrently, amounts of available trace elements in soils and waters should be determined. Moreover, the forms in which various elements occur in the environment need to be determined. Data concerning the geographical distribution of trace elements in the environment will be necessary for interdisciplinary, epidemiological studies conducted to confirm or refute any association between human diseases and the geochemical environment.

Research is needed to assess the influence of agricultural and industrial activities on the environmental distribution of trace elements. Amounts and availabilities to plants of trace elements in soils may be affected by various crop production and soil management techniques. Modern agricultural practices may contribute to the development of trace element problems in animals. Disposal of certain types of municipal or industrial waste products (e.g., heavy-metal polluted sewage sludge or fly ash) on agricultural lands may complicate trace element problems.

REFERENCES

Allaway, W.H. 1976. Perspectives on molybdenum in soils and plants. p. 317–339. *In* W.R. Chappell and K.K. Peterson (ed.) Molybdenum in the environment. Vol. 2. Marcel Dekker, New York.

Allaway, WH. 1986. Soil, plant, animal and human interrelationships in trace element nutrition. p. 465–488. *In* W. Mertz (ed.) Trace elements in human and animal nutrition. Vol. 2. 5th ed. Academic Press, New York.

Anderson, M.S., H.W. Lakin, K.C. Beeson, F.F. Smith, and E. Tucker. 1961. Selenium in agriculture. USDA-ARS Agric. Handb. 200. U.S. Gov. Print. Off., Washington, DC.

Arnon, M.B., and P.R. Stout. 1939. Molybdenum as an essential element for higher plants. Plant Physiol. 14:599–602.

Beckers, C., and F. Delange. 1980. Iodine deficiency. p. 199–217. *In* J.B. Stanbury and B.S. Hetzel (ed.) Endemic goiter and endemic cretinism. John Wiley and Sons, New York.

Beeson, K.C. 1945. The occurrence of mineral nutritional diseases of plants and animals in the United States. Soil Sci. 60:9–13.

Berger, K.C. 1962. Micronutrient deficiencies in the United States. J. Agric. Food Chem. 10:178–181.

Bould, C., E.J. Hewitt, and P. Needham (ed.). 1984. Diagnosis of mineral disorders in plants. Vol. 1. Principles. Chemical Publ., New York.

Bradford, G.R. 1966. Boron. p. 33–61. *In* H.D. Chapman (ed.) Diagnostic criteria for plants and soils. Univ. of California, Berkeley, CA.

Brown, J.C., J.E. Ambler, R.L. Chaney, and C.D. Foy.1972. Differential responses of plant genotypes to micronutrients. p. 389–418. *In* J.J. Mortvedt et al. (ed.) Micronutrients in agriculture. SSSA, Madison, WI.

Brown, P.H., R.M. Welch, and E.E. Cary. 1987. Nickel: A micronutrient essential for higher plants. Plant Physiol. 85:801–803.

Burau, R.G., W.F. Jopling, C.V. Martin, and G.F. Snow. 1981. Monterey basin pilot monitoring project. Vol. 1 and 2. Dep. Land, Water and Air, Univ. of California, Davis.

Cannon, H.L. 1971. The use of plant indicators in ground water surveys, geologic mapping, and mineral prospecting. Taxon. 20:227–256.

Cannon, H.L., and D.F. Davidson. 1967. Relation of geology and trace elements to nutrition. Spec. GSA Paper 90, U.S. Geol. Surv., Denver.

Connor, J.J., and H.T. Shacklette. 1975. Background geochemistry of some rocks, soils, plants, and vegetables in the conterminous United States. Geol. Surv. Professional Paper 574-F. U.S. Gov. Print. Office, Washington, DC.

Cartwright, B., B.A. Zarcinas, and A.H. Mayfield. 1984. Toxic concentrations of B in a red-brown earth at Gladstone, South Australia. Aust. J. Soil Res. 22:261–272.

Chaney, R.L. 1977. Microelements as related to plant deficiencies and toxicities. p. 235–279. *In* L.F. Elliot and F.J. Stevenson (ed.) Soils for the management of organic wastes and waste waters. SSSA, CSSA, and ASA, Madison, WI.

Davis, G.K., and W. Mertz. 1987. Copper. p. 301–364. *In* W. Mertz (ed.) Trace elements in human and animal nutrition. Vol. 1. 5th ed. Academic Press, New York.

Donald, C.M., and J.A. Prescott. 1975. Trace elements in Australian crop and pasture production, 1924–1974. p. 7–37. *In* D.J.D. Nicholas and A.R. Egan (ed.) Trace elements in soil-plant-animal systems. Academic Press, New York.

Dunn, J.T., E.A. Pretell, C.H. Daza, and F.E. Viteri (ed.). 1986. Towards the eradication of endemic goiter, cretinism, and iodine deficiency. World Health Org. Sci. Publ. 502. WHO, Washington, DC.

Eskew, D.L., R.M. Welch, and E.E. Cary. 1983. Nickel: an essential micronutrient for legumes and possibly all higher plants. Science 222:621–623.

Forbes, E.A. 1978. Investigations into the availability to lucerne (*Medicago sativa*) of Cu applied to yellow-brown pumice soils. I. Farm survey of Cu in lucerne and soil. N.Z. J. Agric. Res. 21:629–636.

Fuge, R., and C.C. Johnson. 1986. The geochemistry of iodine—a review. Environ. Geochem. Health 8:31–54.

Gaitan, E.,R.C. Cooksey, and R.H. Lindsay. 1986. Factors other than iodine deficiency in endemic goiter: Goitrogens and protein-calorie malnutrition (PCM). p. 28–44. *In* J.T. Dunn et al. (ed.) Towards the eradication of endemic goiter, cretinism, and iodine deficiency. World Health Org. Sci. Publ. 502. WHO, Washington, DC.

Gerloff, G.C., and W.H. Gabelman. 1983. Genetic basis of inorganic plant nutrition. p. 453–480. *In* A. Läuchli and R.L. Bieleski (ed.) Inorganic plant nutrition. Springer-Verlag New York, New York.

Gissel-Nielsen, G., U.C. Gupta, M. Lamand, and T. Westermarck. 1984. Selenium in soils and plants and its importance in livestock and human nutrition. Adv. Agron. 37:397–460.

Goldschmidt, V.M. 1954. Geochemistry. The Clarendon Press, Oxford, England.

Graham, R.D. 1984. Breeding for nutritional characteristics in cereals. Adv. Plant Nutr. 1:57–102.

Graham, R.D., R.J. Hannam, and N.C. Uren (ed.). 1988. Manganese in soils and plants. Kluwer Academic Publ., Boston.

Hambidge, K.M., C.E. Casey, and N.F. Krebs. 1986. Zinc. p. 1-137. *In* W. Mertz (ed.) Trace elements in human and animal nutrition. Vol. 1. 5th ed. Academic Press, New York.

Hartmans, J. 1970. The detection of Cu deficiency and other trace element deficiencies under field conditions. p. 441-448. *In* C.F. Mills (ed.) Trace element metabolism in animals. E. & S. Livingstone, London.

Hetzel, B.S. 1983. Iodine deficiency disorders (IDD) and their eradication. Lancet 2:1126-1129.

Hetzel, B.S. 1986. The concept of iodine-deficiency disorders (IDD) and their eradication. p. 109-114. *In* J.T. Dunn et al. (ed.) Towards the eradication of endemic goiter, cretinism, and iodine deficiency. World Health Org. Sci. Publ. 502. WHO, Washington, DC.

Hetzel, B.S., and G.F. Maberly. 1986. Iodine. p. 139-208. *In* W. Mertz (ed.) Trace elements in human and animal nutrition. Vol. 2. 5th ed. Academic Press, New York.

Hodgson, J.F., W.H. Allaway, and R.B. Lockman. 1971. Regional plant chemistry as a reflection of environment. p. 57-72. *In* H.L. Cannon and H.C. Hopps (ed.) Environmental geochemistry in health and disease. Geological Soc. Am. Memoir 123. Geol. Soc. Am., New York.

Horst, W.J. 1988. The physiology of manganese toxicity. p. 175-188. *In* R.D. Graham et al. (ed.) Manganese in soils and plants. Kluwer Academic Publ., Boston.

Hurley, L.S., and C.L. Keen. 1987. Manganese. p. 185-223. *In* W. Mertz (ed.) Trace elements in human and animal nutrition. Vol. 1. 5th ed. Academic Press, New York.

Jacobs, L.W. (ed.). 1989. Selenium in agriculture and the environment. SSSA Spec. Publ. 23. ASA, CSSA, and SSSA, Madison, WI.

Kang, B.T., and O.A. Osiname. 1985. Micronutrient problems in tropical Africa. Fert. Res. 7:131-150.

Katyal, J.C., and P.L.G. Vlek. 1985. Micronutrient problems in tropical Asia. Fert. Res. 7:69-94.

Keeshan Disease Research Group of the Chinese Academy of Medical Sciences. 1979. Epidemiologic studies on the etiologic relationship of selenium and keeshan disease. Chin. Med. J. (Peking) 94:477-482.

Kelley, W.P., and S.M. Brown. 1928. Boron in soils and irrigation waters of southern California and its relation to citrus and walnut culture. Hilgardia 3:445-458.

Kelly, F.C., and W.M. Snedden. 1960. Prevalence and geographical distribution of endemic goiter. p. 27-233. *In* Endemic goiter. World Health Org. Monogr. Ser. 44. WHO, Geneva, Switzerland.

Kies, C. 1987. Nutritional bioavailability of manganese. Am. Chem. Soc., Washington, DC.

Kobayashi, J. 1971. Relation between "itai-itai" disease and the pollution of river water by cadmium from a mine. p. 1-7. *In* Proc. 5th Int. Water Pollution Res. Conf., San Francisco, CA. (1-7) July-August 1970.

Korcak, R.F. 1987. Iron deficiency chlorosis. Hortic. Rev. 9:133-185.

Koutras, D.A. 1986. Iodine: Distribution, availability, and effects of deficiency on the thyroid. p. 15-26. *In* J.T. Dunn et al. (ed.) Towards the eradication of endemic goiter, cretinism, and iodine deficiency. World Health Org. Sci. Publ. 502. WHO, Washington, DC.

Koutras, D.A., J. Matovinovic, and R. Vought. 1980. The ecology of iodine. p. 185-195. *In* J.B. Stanbury and B.S. Hetzel (ed.) Endemic goiter and endemic cretinism. John Wiley and Sons, New York.

Kubota, J. 1975. Areas of molybdenum toxicity to grazing ruminants in the western United States. J. Range Manage. 28:252-256.

Kubota, J. 1976. Molybdenum status of United States soils and plants. p. 555-581. *In* W.R. Chappell and K.K. Petersen (ed.) Molybdenum in the environment. Vol. 2. The geochemistry, cycling and industrial uses of molybdenum. Marcel Dekker, New York.

Kubota, J. 1980. Regional distribution of trace element problems in North America. p. 443-466. *In* B. Davies (ed.) Applied soil trace elements. John Wiley and Sons, London.

Kubota, J. 1983. Copper status of United States soils and forage plants. Agron. J. 75:913-918.

Kubota, J., and W.H. Allaway. 1972. Geographic distribution of trace element problems. p. 525-554. *In* J.J. Mortvedt et al. (ed.) Micronutrients in agriculture. SSSA, Madison, WI.

Kubota, J., W.H. Allaway, D.F. Carter, E.E. Cary, and V.A. Lazer. 1967. Selenium in crops in United States in relation to selenium responsive diseases in animals. J. Agric. Food Chem. 15:448-453.

Kubota, J., R.M. Welch, and D.R. Van Campen. 1987. Soil-related nutritional problem areas for grazing animals. Adv. Soil Sci. 6:189-215.

Labanauskas, C.K. 1966. Manganese. p. 264-285. *In* Diagnostic criteria for plants and soils. Univ. California Div. Agric. Sci., Riverside, CA.

Lagerwerff, J.V. 1972. Lead, mercury and cadmium as environmental contaminants. p. 593–636. *In* J.J. Mortvedt et al. (ed.) Micronutrients in agriculture. SSSA, Madison, WI.

Langer, P. 1960. History of goiter. p. 9–25. *In* Endemic goiter. World Health Org. Monogr. Series 44. WHO, Geneva, Switzerland.

León, L.A., A.S. López, and P.L.G. Vlek. 1985. Micronutrient problems in tropical Latin America. Fert. Res. 7:95–129.

Lindsay, W.L. 1972. Zinc in soils and plant nutrition. Adv. Agron. 24:147–186.

Liu, C.H., Z.H. Lu, Q. Su, Y.Q. Duan, and Y.Y. Jin. 1984. Regional deficiency of feedstuffs in China. p. 47–52. *In* G.F. Combs Jr. et al. (ed.) Selenium in biology and medicine. Part A. Van Nostrand Reinhold Publ. Co., New York.

Marschner, H. 1986. Mineral nutrition of plants. Academic Press, New York.

Matovinovic, J., and F.L. Trowbridge. 1980. North America. p. 31–67. *In* J.B. Stanbury and B.S. Hetzel (ed.) Endemic goiter and endemic cretinism. John Wiley and Sons, New York.

Matrone, G. 1977. Manganese. p. 29–39. *In* Geochemistry and the environment. Vol. II. The relationship to other selected trace elements to health and disease. Natl. Acad. Sci., Washington, DC.

McClendon, J.F. 1939. Iodine and the incidence of goiter. Univ. Minnesota Press, Minneapolis.

Morris, E.R. 1987. Iron. p. 79–142. *In* W. Mertz (ed.) Trace elements in human and animal nutrition. Vol. 1. 5th ed. Academic Press, New York.

Mortvedt, J.J. 1975. Iron chlorosis. Crops and Soils Magazine 27:10–12.

National Research Council. 1979. Iron. Univ. Park Press, Baltimore.

National Research Council. 1980a. Boron. p. 71–83. *In* Mineral tolerance of domestic animals. Natl. Acad. Sci., Washington, DC.

National Research Council. 1980b. Copper. p. 162–183. *In* Mineral tolerance of domestic animals. Natl. Acad. Sci., Washington, DC.

Nielsen, F.H. 1984. Ultratrace elements in nutrition. Annu. Rev. Nutr. 4:21–41.

Nielsen, F.H. 1986. Other elements: Sb, Ba, B, Br, Cs, Ge, Rb, Ag, Sr, Sn, Ti, Zr, Be, Bi, Ga, Au, In, Nb, Sc, Te, Tl, W. p. 415–463. *In* W. Mertz (ed.) Trace elements in human and animal nutrition. Vol. 2. 5th ed. Academic Press, New York.

Ohlendorf, H.M., D.J. Hoffman, M.K. Saiki, and T.W. Aldrich. 1986. Embryonic mortality and abnormalities of aquatic birds: Apparent impacts of selenium from irrigation drainwater. Sci. Total Environ. 52:49–63.

Owen, C.A. 1981. Copper deficiency and toxicity acquired and inherited, in plants, animals, and man. Noyes Publ., Park Ridge, NJ.

Peterson, P.J. 1972. Unusual accumulations of elements by plants and animals. Sci. Prog. (Oxford) 59:505–526.

Reid, R.L., and D.J. Horvath. 1980. Soil chemistry and mineral problems in farm livestock. A review. Anim. Feed Sci. Technol. 5:95–167.

Reinhold, J.G. 1988. Problems in mineral nutrition: a global perspective. p. 1–55. *In* K.T. Smith (ed.) Trace minerals in foods. Marcel Dekker, New York.

Reuter, DJ., A.M. Alston, and J.D. McFarlane. 1988. Occurrence and correction of manganese deficiency in plants. p. 205–224. *In* R.D. Graham et al. (ed.) Manganese in soils and plants. Kluwer Academic Publ., Boston.

Reuther, W., and C.K. Labanauskas. 1966. Copper. p. 157–179. *In* H.D. Chapman (ed.) Diagnostic criteria for plants and soils. Univ. California Div. Agric. Sci., Riverside.

Robson, A.D., and M. Pitman. 1983. Interactions between nutrients in higher plants. p. 47–180. *In* A. Läuchli and R.L. Bieleski (ed.) Inorganic plant nutrition. Springer-Verlag New York, New York.

Rosenfeld, I., and O.A. Beath. 1964. Selenium. Academic Press, New York.

Sander, D.H., W.H. Allaway, and R.A. Olson. 1987. Modification of nutritional quality by environment and production practices. p. 45–82. *In* R.A. Olson and K.J. Frey (ed.) Nutritional quality of cereal grains. Agron. Monog. 28. ASA, CSSA, and SSSA, Madison, WI.

Shacklette, H.T. 1980. Elements in fruits and vegetables from areas of commercial production in the conterminous United States. U.S. Geological Survey Professional Paper 1178. U.S. Gov. Print. Office, Washington, DC.

Shacklette, H.T., and J.C. Boerngen. 1984. Element concentrations in soils and other surficial materials of the conterminous United States. U.S. Geol. Surv. Professional Paper 1270. U.S. Gov. Print. Office, Washington, DC.

Sillanpää, M. 1982. Micronutrients and the nutrient status of soils: A global study. FAO Soils Bull. 48. FAO, United Nations, Rome.

Sillanpää, M., and P.L.G. Vlek. 1985. Micronutrients and the agroecology of tropical and Mediterranean regions. Fert. Res. 7:151–167.

Staker, E.V. 1943. Progress report on the control of zinc toxicity in peat soils. Soil Sci. Soc. Am. Proc. 7:387–392.

Stanbury, J.B., and B.S. Hetzel. 1980. Endemic goiter and endemic cretinism. John Wiley and Sons, New York.

Tanji, K.K., A. Läuchli, and J. Meyer. 1986. Selenium in the San Joaquin Valley. Environ. 28:6–11, 34–39.

Thomson, C.D., and M.F. Robinson. 1980. Selenium in human health and disease with emphasis on those aspects peculiar to New Zealand. Am. J. Clin. Nutr. 33:303–323.

Thornton, I. 1977. Biogeochemical studies on molybdenum in the United Kingdom. p. 341–369. In W.R. Chappell and K.K. Petersen (ed.) Molybdenum in the environment. Vol. 2. The geochemistry, cycling and industrial uses of molybdenum. Marcel Dekker, New York.

Trowbridge, F.L., K.A. Hand, and M.Z. Nichaman. 1975. Findings relating goiter and iodine in the ten states nutrition survey. Am. J. Clin. Nutr. 28:712–716.

Underwood, E.J. 1977. Trace elements in human and animal nutrition. 4th ed. Academic Press, New York.

Underwood, E.J. 1981. The mineral nutrition of livestock. Commonwealth Agricultural Bureaux, London.

Van Soest, P.J. 1982. Nutritional ecology of the ruminant. O&B Books, Inc., Corvallis, OR.

Viets, F. 1966. Zinc deficiency in the soil-plant system. p. 90–127. In A. Prasad (ed.) Zinc metabolism. Charles C. Thomas Publ., Springfield, IL.

Vose, P.B. 1982. Iron nutrition in plants: A world overview. J. Plant Nutr. 5:233–249.

Welch, R.M. 1986. Effects of nutrient deficiencies on seed production and quality. Adv. Plant Nutr. 2:205–247.

Wallihan, E.F. 1966. Iron. p. 203–212. In H.D. Chapman (ed.) Diagnostic criteria for plants and soils. Univ. of California, Berkeley.

Williams, K.T., H.W. Lakin, and H.G. Byers. 1940. Selenium occurrence in certain soils in the United States, with a discussion of related topics. Fourth Report. USDA Tech. Bull. 702. U.S. Gov. Print. Office, Washington, DC.

Wolnik, K.A., F.L. Fricke, S.G. Capar, G.L. Braude, M.W. Meyer, R.D. Satzger, and R.W. Kuennen. 1983. Elements in major raw agricultural crops in the United States. 2. Other elements in lettuce, peanuts, potatoes, soybeans, sweet corn, and wheat. J. Agric. Food Chem. 31:1244–1249.

Wolnik, K.A., F.L. Fricke, S.G. Capar, M.W. Meyer, R.D. Satzger, E. Bonnin, and C.M. Gaston. 1985. Elements in major raw agricultural crops in the United States. 3. Cadmium, lead, and eleven other elements in carrots, field corn, onion, rice, spinach, and tomatoes. J. Agric. Food Chem. 33:807–811.

Yang, G., S. Wang, R. Zhou, and S. Sun. 1983. Endemic selenium intoxication of humans in China. Am. J. Clin. Nutr. 37:872–881.

Zheng, Liu, Zhu Qi-qing, Tang Li-hua, Xu Jung-xiang, and Yen Chu-liang. 1982. Geographical distribution of trace elements—deficient soils in China. (In Chinese.) Acta Pedol. Sin. 19:209–223.

Chapter 3

Micronutrient Adsorption-Desorption Reactions in Soils[1]

ROBERT D. HARTER, *University of New Hampshire, Durham, New Hampshire*

Any commentary on the chemistry of ions in soil must include consideration of mineral solubility, precipitation of secondary compounds, and reactions at the solid-solution interface. These reactions are particularly important in the discussion of micronutrient availability to plants. A schematic of the source, distribution, and fate of soil micronutrients is presented in Fig. 3–1. Ideally, micronutrient concentration in solution is maintained at a level sufficient to supply plant needs, while minimizing leaching losses. If too little is available, plant deficiencies can occur. If too much is available, not only is the nutrient susceptible to leaching, but plants may suffer toxicity responses. For some micronutrients, such as Cu, the difference between deficiency and toxicity can be narrow. Since adsorption-desorption reactions tend to be faster than precipitation-dissolution processes, adsorption at solid-solution interfaces can be a dominant factor in regulating micronutrient concentration in solution.

A variety of methods have been used to characterize surface reactions, ranging from thermodynamic strategies based on double layer theory to empirical adsorption isotherm studies. This chapter will concentrate on the more empirical aspects of understanding micronutrient adsorption/desorption reactions. The approaches to studying ion interactions with surfaces will be examined, followed by a discussion of adsorption mechanisms, and, finally, by a review of current knowledge about individual micronutrients.

I. EXPERIMENTAL METHODS

Two basic systems have been used to measure sorbate retention in soils: (i) a static system in which reactions are allowed to approach or reach equilibrium; and (ii) a flow-through system in which solute removal from

---

[1] Scientific contribution no. 1638 from the New Hampshire Agricultural Experiment Station.

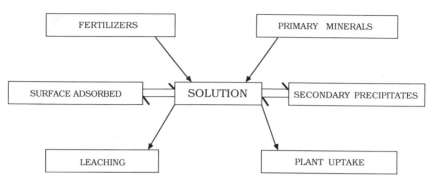

Fig. 3–1. Partition and fate of micronutrients in soil.

solution is evaluated. The chosen approach depends on research objectives and the types of soil reactions being modeled.

Movement of solutes in soil generally is divided into that in macropores and micropores. Solution in the macropores is subject to gravitational forces, and is directly impacted by soil wetting and drying processes. Micropore solution is held against gravity, and is not so directly affected by wetting and drying processes. Chemical processes within the micropores, therefore, may approach or reach equilibrium. The equilibrium may be periodically perturbed by ion diffusion to or from the macropores, or by evapotranspiration processes.

The static system is assumed to represent reactions in soil micropores, whereas the flow-through system represents changes in solution concentration resulting from both macropore surface reactions and diffusion into the micropores. Each has advantages and disadvantages, and complete understanding of soil adsorption/desorption processes can only be achieved through use of both approaches.

The difficulty of controlling experimental variables, such as solution ionic strength and composition, pH, or temperature, in the field dictates that either technique must be applied in the laboratory. Equilibration time for static systems is normally ≤ 1 wk; 1 h is commonly used. Thin-layer flow-through experiments use similar time periods. This means that long-term reactions, which may alter forms and provide new sorption sites, are not operative. Flow-through experiments often use soil columns to simulate the soil profile. These are typically run for longer periods, but they seldom include the rest periods that occur in nature. Therefore, both systems can underestimate ion retention that occurs in the soil. Most of our knowledge regarding soil sorption processes has, however, been obtained by these two techniques.

A. Adsorption/Desorption Isotherms

Information collected in static system experiments usually is presented graphically in adsorption or desorption isotherms. These isotherms provide a convenient visual demonstration of ion retention or release, and a means of assessing surface retention capacity. Experimentally, a given amount of

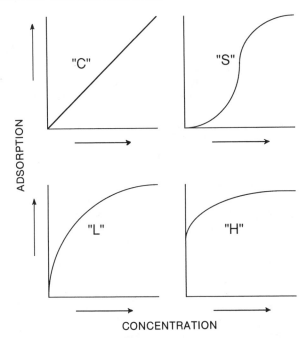

Fig. 3-2. Schematic diagram of the four basic adsorption isotherm shapes suggested by Giles et al. (1974).

adsorbate is mixed with a given amount of solution. All variables, except adsorbate concentration in solution, are held constant. The amount of adsorbate retained by the surfaces is determined after an appropriate reaction time and is plotted against the equilibrium solution concentration. The nature and shape of the resulting plot can provide useful information on the type and strength of bonding, and the retention capacity of the soil.

Giles et al. (1974) evaluated a variety of adsorption isotherms and developed a useful system for isotherm classification based on isotherm shape, a summary of which is presented in Fig. 3-2. They also provided a theoretical explanation for the formation of the four isotherm shapes. The C (constant partition) isotherm indicates that surface retention is controlled by sorbate concentration in solution (i.e., the reaction is first order). The S isotherm indicates that sorption involves a sorbate-sorbate interaction at the surface. The L (Langmuir) isotherm results when sorption energy declines as surface coverage increases. This isotherm frequently includes a C portion at low surface coverage. The H (high affinity) isotherm is a special case of the L, which indicates that specific sorption sites are present on the surface and all sorbate is removed from solution until the sites are saturated. Finally, the slope of the isotherm is indicative of sorption energy. For any given system, low energy sites will allow more sorbate to remain in solution (or to be desorbed) than will high energy sites.

Soil scientists have made extensive use of both adsorption and desorption isotherms to characterize the nature of soil retention phenomena. The most obvious use of the isotherms is to compare the relative amounts of adsorbate that soils can retain under given circumstances. As noted, the isotherm shapes also provide information on the strength by which the sorbate is held to the soil and an indication of the bonding mechanisms. It must be recognized, however, that the technique has some deficiencies. Most notably, isotherm development sometimes requires solute concentrations in excess of that observed in nature. Also, the soil/solution ratios used in the laboratory are usually not representative of whole soils.

B. Breakthrough Curves

The primary method of presenting and evaluating flow-through experiments is the so-called breakthrough technique. Breakthrough curves are produced from column studies. The column contains a soil that has been either carefully removed from the field in as undisturbed a state as possible, or has been sieved and appropriately packed into a column. A desired solution is effused onto the soil surface, and the effluent solution is monitored for adsorbate concentration. The results are usually presented as a plot of either effluent adsorbate concentration, or fraction of input in the effluent vs. pore volumes displaced (Fig. 3–3). Data acquisition is straightforward and results are easily understood.

Evaluation of the results in terms of processes occurring in the soil, however, can be difficult and tenuous. As percolating solution moves through the soil column, solute is removed by diffusion into micropores, as well as by surface adsorption. Therefore, flow paths, diffusion processes, and retention mechanisms all affect observed changes in percolate chemistry. As indicated by Bolt (1982), difficulty in evaluating all parameters dictates that some guesswork will be incorporated into the final interpretations. Despite the limitations, breakthrough curves provide useful soil sorption information and are often used to predict solute infiltration.

II. MODELS

While experimental data are an essential foundation ingredient for scientific knowledge, precise understanding of scientific phenomena and precise

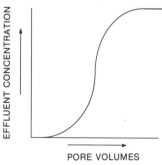

Fig. 3–3. An illustration of breakthrough curves.

communication among scientists usually requires the establishment of models. These models are valuable for understanding systems and predicting response. An exhaustive discussion of models would require more space than can be justified here, so commentary will be limited to those models that have an empirical basis.

A. Adsorption Equations

Although adsorption isotherms can be useful in interpreting adsorption phenomena, presenting large amounts of data in this manner can be confusing. Mathematical models are helpful for summarizing and comparing such data. The Freundlich and Langmuir Equations have been popular among soil scientists, but others have been used as well.

1. Freundlich Equation

Early efforts to express empirical soil adsorption data in mathematical form led Van Bemmelen (1878) to formulate the expression

$$x/m = KC^{1/n} \qquad [1]$$

where x/m is the amount of solute adsorbed per unit mass, C is concentration of solute in solution at equilibrium, and K and n are equation constants. The expression later became known as the Freundlich equation after he demonstrated its general applicability to adsorption phenomena (Freundlich, 1909). With the emergence of a general theory of surface adsorption in the early 1900s, attempts were made to use conformance to the equation as proof of ion retention by adsorption. Although similar attempts may still be found in the literature, Fisher (1922) effectively quelled this trend by pointing out the equation's empirical nature, and that conformance to theory could not be proved by conformance to an empirical equation. However, it remains an effective means of summarizing adsorption data that happens to define a hyperbolic relationship of the type illustrated in Fig. 3–4a.

2. Langmuir Equation

A second equation has proved to be more problematic in application. On the basis of kinetic theory, Langmuir (1918) developed the expression

$$x/m = MbP/(1 + bP) \qquad [2]$$

for the sorption of gasses on planar surfaces. In this case, x/m is the amount of gas sorbed per unit area, P is the equilibrium gas pressure, and M and b are equation constants where M is an expression of the sorption capacity and b is related to isotherm slope. Those using this equation to characterize solid-solution reactions have replaced pressure (P) with equilibrium solution concentration (C). The equation defines a parabolic relationship (Fig. 3–4b) and the adsorption maximum term makes it attractive for fitting an equa-

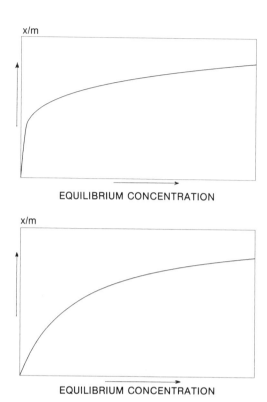

Fig. 3-4. General plot shapes for the Freundlich (a) and Langmuir (b) Equations.

tion to empirical data. It has been extensively used to evaluate ion retention by soils. The fit of empirical data to the equation has been used as proof of an adsorption mechanism.

Equations can be used to model empirical data, but as Veith and Sposito (1977) point out, equations cannot be used to determine retention mechanisms. Adsorption reactions never occur in the absence of concomitant solution and/or surface changes. Although these changes may be difficult to measure, Veith and Sposito (1977) have demonstrated that, without such corroborative evidence, surface reaction interpretations cannot be associated with the equation constants.

Harter and Smith (1981) identified eight assumptions made by Langmuir (1918) in the development of his equation. These include considerations of site uniformity, monolayer coverage, reversibility, sorbate movement on the surface, sorbate-sorbate interactions, and independence of reactions at each site. Three additional assumptions relating to specific sorption of the solvent, solvent-solute interactions, and unoccupied site energy are necessary in adapting the equation to solid-solution reactions. Harter and Smith (1981) concluded that the majority of these assumptions were not valid for gaseous adsorption to planar surfaces, and were even less likely to be valid for solid/solution sorption reactions. Subsequently, Harter (1984) found that calculated sorption maxima could be in error by 50% or more, even when the data apparently fit the Langmuir Equation.

The lack of empirical data fit to the Langmuir Equation has led to development of the multisurface Langmuir Equation. While any number of surfaces can be assumed, the two-surface equation

$$x/m = [M_1 b_1 C/(1 + b_1 C)] + [M_2 b_2 C/(1 + b_2 C)] \qquad [3]$$

is the one normally used. The subscripts indicate constants for the two different surfaces. However, Sposito (1982) noted that any smooth, convex/concave line that approaches a maximum asymptote can be modeled by any universal equation that has four independently adjustable parameters (of which Eq. [3] is an example). Sposito (1982) therefore concluded that the two-surface Langmuir Equation cannot be used as proof that adsorption had occurred on two distinctly different types of surfaces. Other modifications of the equation can also be found, but applications are usually limited and modifications share the limitations of the basic Langmuir Equation.

Despite limitations, the Langmuir Equation does have utility in soil sorption work. Certain data sets fit the Langmuir Equation (or modifications thereof) better than the Freundlich Equation, which makes it useful for curve fitting. However, both equations should be considered empirical. The equation constants can be used to compare data sets, but should not be used for surface reaction interpretations without independent evidence corroborating the interpretations.

3. Temkin Equation

The Temkin Equation provides a relatively minor contribution to the soil scientist's data evaluation strategy, but it is used with sufficient frequency to be noted here. The model for this equation is a linear decrease in adsorption energy as the amount of adsorption increases. As noted by Barrow (1978), the basic Temkin Equation is complex, but if very high and very low adsorption values are ignored, it can be reduced to

$$x/m = a \ln(bC) \qquad [4]$$

where a and b are constants. Plots of adsorption as a function of log concentration are linear if data fit the model for this equation. The equation has had limited applicability in soil science, since the Freundlich or Langmuir Equations will usually provide a better fit to data.

4. Constant Capacitance

Surface complexation models are a different approach to modeling adsorption reactions. The constant capacitance model is the simplest and most commonly used of several recently developed surface complexation models. It was essentially defined in its present form by Stumm et al. (1980). As noted by Sposito (1984), it is a molecular description of inner-sphere[2] surface-complexation reactions. While it was developed to describe the ligand exchange of anions with surface hydroxyls, it is possible to use the model for cation retention if the cation forms inner-sphere complexes with the surface hydroxyl groups.

The model requires, first, the development of a series of equations that define all pertinent reactions. These equations take the form

$$SOH_{s\;(s)}^{+} \leftrightarrow SOH_{(s)} + H_{(aq)}^{+} \tag{5}$$

$$SOH_{(s)} \leftrightarrow SO_{(s)}^{-} + H_{(aq)}^{+} \tag{6}$$

where SOH^n represents surface hydroxyls of charge $\pm n$, and the subscripts (s) and (aq) indicate surface and aqueous phase, respectively. Similar equations must be written for all possible reactions involving OH ligand exchange or proton exchange. For example, in addition to Eq. [5] and [6], modeling a molybdate reaction might require inclusion of (Motta & Miranda, 1989):

$$SOH_{(s)} + H_2MoO_{4(aq)} \leftrightarrow SHMoO_{4(s)} + H_2O \tag{7}$$

and

$$SOH_{(s)} + H_2MoO_{4(aq)} \leftrightarrow SMoO_{4\;(s)}^{-} + H_{(aq)}^{+} + H_2O \tag{8}$$

Next, conditional equilibrium constant (K') equations are written for each of the reactions. In developing the equations for K', it is appropriate to use ion activity ([]) for aqueous phases and mole fraction (X) for the surface phases. Thus, for the generic equation

$$A_{(s)} + B_{(aq)} \rightarrow C_{(s)} + D_{(aq)} \tag{9}$$

the conditional equilibrium constant equation would be written as

$$K' = X_C[D]/X_A[B] \tag{10}$$

Finally, a series of intrinsic, equilibrium constant [$K_{(int)}$] equations, one for each reaction, can be written in the form

$$K_{(int)} = K'\exp(-F\psi/RT) \tag{11}$$

where F is Faraday's constant, ψ is the surface potential, R is the gas constant, and T is the absolute temperature. The set of equations established

---

[2]Complexation is commonly divided into inner-sphere and outer-sphere reactions. Inner-sphere reactions involve direct bonding to the surface, while outer-sphere reactions include attachment of larger (e.g., hydrated) ions at a finite distance from the surface. Inner-sphere complexation usually involves ionic or covalent bonding and outer-sphere complexation would frequently be via electrostatic bonding. For example, specific sorption of Zn^{2+} at surface hydroxyl sites (Eq. [28]) and exchange of borate for surface hydroxyls (Eq. [31]) would both be inner-sphere reactions, whereas nonspecific exchange of an anion or cation for another anion or cation on the surface would be an outer-sphere reaction.

(Eq. [4]–[10]) can then be used in a computer program such as GEOCHEM (Sposito & Mattigod, 1980) or MINTEQ (Felmy et al., 1984) to establish speciation and ion distribution in the system. Westall (1980) has provided the necessary algorithms for the solution.

The purpose of the constant capacitance model is different from that of the Freundlich and Langmuir models, but it will usually model sorption isotherm data with reasonable accuracy. In addition, by using the parameters calculated, it is possible to evaluate changes in surface electrochemical properties as a result of the sorption reaction.

B. Kinetics

Extensive use of reaction rates for characterizing sorption reactions at the solid-solution interface is a relatively recent development. As pointed out by Thomas (1977), the work of Gedroiz and Hissink early in the 20th century was sufficiently definitive to discourage further evaluation. Certainly, Hissink's (1924) report that exchange reactions were completed within 3 min would tend to discourage others from considering kinetics as a profitable line of investigation. Increasing concern for micronutrient and heavy metal reactions in the soil, and accumulating evidence that isotherm studies have limited applicability to these reactions have led to a renewed interest in soil adsorption/desorption reaction rates.

1. Classical

In examining any reaction

$$\text{Reactants} \leftrightarrow \text{Products} \tag{12}$$

the rate of reaction depends on the number and concentrations of both reactants and products. The way in which the reaction rate depends on concentrations can sometimes be indicated by the order of reaction (Laidler, 1950). If reaction rate depends on the first power of one reactant concentration, it is considered to be first order; if it is dependent on the product of two reactants' concentrations, it is second order, and so forth. In reality, soil sorption reactions are probably not first order, and are dependent on both sorbate concentration and availability of sorption sites on the solid surface.

$$\text{Sorbate} + \text{Sorption sites} \leftrightarrow \text{Products} \tag{13}$$

However, sorption sites tend to be a fixed quantity, so sorbate concentration can be kept low enough that the reaction rate is dependent only on the sorbate in solution. Under this experimental condition, the reaction can be treated as first order, and is often referred to as being pseudo-first order. Since micronutrient concentrations in solution are usually very low, this condition is reasonable.

Using classical first-order kinetics, the above reaction (Eq. [12]) can be expressed as

$$dC/dt = -k_f C + k_r A \qquad [14]$$

The change in solution adsorbate concentration (C) with time (t) is dependent on a forward rate coefficient (k_f) multiplied by the solution concentration and a reverse rate coefficient (k_r) multiplied by the amount of adsorbate on the surface (A). There are three ways in which this equation can be evaluated and fit to empirical data. If the reverse reaction can be neglected, either by blocking or by measuring only the instantaneous reaction at the initiation of the reaction, the equation becomes

$$dC/dt = -k_f C \qquad [15]$$

which integrates to

$$-\ln C = k_f t \qquad [16]$$

Thus, if the reaction is first order or pseudo-first order, a plot of log concentration as a function of time will yield a linear relationship with slope of k_f.

If neither forward nor reverse reaction can be controlled, the reaction can still be evaluated on the basis of Swearington and Dickinson's (1932) distance from equilibrium (Laidler, 1950; Eyring et al., 1980). At equilibrium, the rate of reaction (dC/dt) becomes zero, so Eq. [14] can be written

$$0 = -k_f C_{eq} + k_r A_{eq} \qquad [17]$$

where C_{eq} and A_{eq} indicate the solution concentration and the amount of solute on the surface at equilibrium, respectively. The problem of comparing solution concentration with an amount of solute retained by the surface can be solved by using the ratio C/C_o, where C_o is the concentration at $t = 0$. The ratio C/C_o will be independent of the units in which the sorbate is expressed (Harter, 1989). If $A = 0$ at $t = 0$, the amount of surface retention can be conveniently expressed as $(1 - C/C_o)$, and Eq. [17] becomes

$$0 = -k_f C_{eq}/C_o + k_r(1 - C_{eq}/C_o) \qquad [18]$$

Substituting this expression into Eq. [14] and integrating, yields

$$\ln(C/C_o - C_{eq}/C_o) = \ln(1 - C_{eq}/C_o) - k_r t/(C_{eq}/C_o) \qquad [19]$$

A plot of log distance from equilibrium ($C/C_o - C_{eq}/C_o$) as a function of time will be linear with a slope of k_r. The forward rate coefficient is obtained from evaluation of Eq. [18]. This solution assumes that the rate coefficients are constant for all times $t_o \leq t \leq t_{eq}$. The ratio of the forward-to-reverse rate coefficients (thermodynamic equilibrium constant) is usually taken as being constant, or nearly so, but the individual rate coefficients can vary over the reaction period. Thus, Eq. [19] is best used as the reaction approaches equilibrium.

Finally, if neither of the preceding is feasible, for example, if the instantaneous forward or reverse reaction cannot be evaluated or if the reaction comes to a steady state rather than equilibrium, Eq. [14] can be integrated with no assumptions (Harter, 1989). Continuing to express the concentration as a ratio, multiplying by -1 and integrating, yields the expression.

$$\ln[k_f C/C_o - k_r(1 - C/C_o)] - \ln(k_f) = -(k_f + k_r)t \qquad [20]$$

which is valid if no sorbate is present on the surfaces at $t = 0$ (The equation can be appropriately adjusted if sorbate is pre-existent on the surfaces). It is impossible to plot this expression, but the availability of modern microcomputers makes evaluation possible, in which case it is more convenient to express the concentration ratio as a function of time:

$$C/C_o = [1/(k_f + k_r)] \{k_f \exp[-(k_f + k_r)t] + k_r\} \qquad [21]$$

With sufficient observations, it is possible to obtain both rate coefficients by iterative curve-fitting techniques.

2. Empirical

According to Aharoni (1984), three equations have been used to empirically describe the kinetics of chemisorption. While the three following equations are applied empirically, they do have a theoretical background that validates their use.

In the power equation:

$$dq/dt = kt^n \qquad [22]$$

the amount adsorbed is indicated by q, t is time, and k and n are constants.

In the Langmuir-type equation:

$$dq/dt = a(q_{eq} - q) \qquad [23]$$

a is a constant related to the rate constant, and q_{eq} is the amount of sorbate on the surface at equilibrium. The equation is a modification of one of Langmuir's (1918) equations, developed on the basis of first-order kinetics (Pajares et al., 1978).

In the Elovich Equation:

$$dq/dt = a \exp(-bq) \qquad [24]$$

a and b are constants. Low (1960) notes the applicability of the Elovich Equation to chemisorption reactions, particularly slow adsorption. It is the most purely empirical of the three, although similar equations have been developed on the basis of various theories.

The Elovich equation has been useful in describing sorption to heterogeneous surfaces (Aharoni & Ungarish, 1976). However, application of the equation to empirical data nearly always requires that a pre-Elovichian sorption process be assumed to occur instantaneously at $t = 0$. The common goal of kinetics research is to provide a basis for postulating reaction mechanisms. This is awkward at best if one must start by assuming an unknown pre-reaction reaction.

The Elovich Equation has been considered generally valid and has been applied to the entire time range of experiments, but Ungarish and Aharoni (1981) have pointed out that the requirement to include an arbitrary term to account for the pre-Elovichian sorption made this equation little more than a curve-fitting device. The power equation and the Langmuir-type equation are also useful for data fitting purposes, but of limited value for mechanism postulation. Low (1960) indicated that the Elovich Equation was developed because other expressions were often unable to adequately model observed sorption reactions.

The increasing availability of computers over the past quarter century has led to curve fitting by computer optimization. Using a Langmuir approach, Lindstrom et al. (1970) developed the equation

$$dQ/dt = k_f[(1 - Q)(1 - Q/2) \exp(-bQ)]$$

$$+ k_r \{[1 - Q/2] \exp[b(2 - Q)] - [Q^2/2] \exp[bQ]\} \qquad [25]$$

where Q is the fraction sorbed at time t (i.e., $Q = q_t/q_{eq}$) and b is a constant. The forward and reverse rate coefficients and the constant were estimated, and Q values at any time, t, were obtained by numerical evaluation. Harter (1989) has used a slightly different approach, developing Eq. [21] on the basis of classical kinetics. He also estimates the rate coefficients and calculates adsorption by numerical evaluation. In both cases, the parameters are adjusted until calculated adsorption matches empirical observations.

3. Flow Models

Parallel to the previous discussion of experimental techniques (Sect. II), two approaches are used to conduct and evaluate adsorption rate studies. The foregoing discussion is primarily applicable to evaluating batch systems in which reactants are combined and the reaction is followed to equilibrium. Therefore, it is comparable to adsorption isotherm studies. An alternative flow-through system (commonly termed the *miscible displacement* technique), comparable to breakthrough studies, is also being used by soil scientists. Sorbate concentration is kept constant and reaction products are continually removed, so a different model must be used for evaluation.

By continual removal of reaction products, the reverse reaction need not be considered, but because ion mass balances are not constant, results cannot be simply evaluated according to Eq. [16]. Even though the reacting solution is maintained at a constant concentration, the soil surfaces are a fixed quantity and the sorption sites will be filled or depleted as the reaction progresses. This problem can be overcome by evaluating only the instantaneous reaction at $t = 0 + \delta$. Logistically, this is difficult unless the reaction rate is relatively slow.

Most researchers have adopted a modification of the transport model used by soil physicists (Selim et al., 1977) to quantify miscible displacement data. When used for this purpose, Skopp and McCallister (1986) have indicated that it should be of the form

$$a(dC/dt) = b(C_{in} - C_{out}) - c(dS/dt) \qquad [26]$$

where a and c are constants related to volume of the soil, b is a constant related to cross-sectional area and flux rate, S is the amount sorbed, and $(C_{in} - C_{out})$ is the drop in concentration across a soil disc (i.e., a very short soil column). Jardine and Sparks (1984) have attempted to use the miscible displacement technique to obtain apparent rate coefficients, but validity of this approach is still to be ascertained.

III. ADSORPTION MECHANISMS

Although a variety of forces can bind ions together, only a few forces bind ions to colloids in an adsorbed phase. Since most ions tend to hydrate in aqueous systems, short-range inter-ion forces are of minimal importance, and bonding is primarily achieved by long-range forces. Of these, electrostatic attraction, or coulombic forces, is the most important. When coulombic interaction is operative, it usually involves ion exchange processes in which similarly charged ions are exchanged on an oppositely charged surface. This leads to nonspecific outer-sphere adsorption of ions, which is the dominant sorption mechanism for retention of alkali and alkali earth elements. Measurement of cation (or anion) exchange is a quantitative expression of this process. The reaction is rapid ($<$2–3 min) and reversible.

Similar processes are operative in soil retention of micronutrients, but exchange is not the only mechanism by which these ions are bonded to the soil particles. All micronutrients except B and Cl are transition elements, which means the outer electrons are in high energy d orbitals. If a transition element does not expend its energy by forming oxyacid anions in aqueous systems, as does Mo, it can induce a charge on an otherwise uncharged colloid. Essentially, this is a colloidal extension of the chemical ligand field theory, comparable to the ion exchange colloidal extension of the crystal field theory.

Each ion requires a particular ion configuration at the colloid surface (either organic or inorganic) that matches the needs of the d orbital electrons. Thus, the sorption site is only available if the ion that matches the site is present, and the ion is retained by inner-sphere complexation on specific

Table 3-1. Some representative pK_a values for soil constituents.

Colloid edge sites (Jackson, 1960)	
Reaction	pK_a
$-Al_2O-H \leftrightarrow -Al_2O^- + H^+$	12^+
$-Si-O-H \leftrightarrow -Si-O^- + H^+$	9.5
$-Al,Si-O-H^{+1/2} \leftrightarrow -Al,Si-O^{-1/2} + H^+$	7.0
$-Al-O-H_2^{+1/2} \leftrightarrow -Al-O-H^{-1/2} + H^+$	5.0

Organic compounds	
Functional groups	
Aliphatic acids (Sposito, 1989)	≈ 1 to 5
Amines, protonation (Morrison & Boyd, 1971)	≈ 4 to 10
Phenolic hydroxides (Morrison & Boyd, 1971)	≈ 10
Acid phenols (Lewis & Broadbent, 1961)	< 4

Sorbate ions (Smith & Martell, 1989)	
Reaction	
$Cu^{2+} + H_2O \leftrightarrow CuOH^+ + H^+$	7.5
$Zn^{2+} + H_2O \leftrightarrow ZnOH^+ + H^+$	9.0
$H_2MoO_4 \leftrightarrow H^+ + HMoO_4^-$	4.0
$HMoO_4^- \leftrightarrow H^+ + MoO_4^{2-}$	4.24
$B(OH)_3 + H_2O \leftrightarrow B(OH)_4^- + H^+$	9.2

adsorption sites. By this means, small amounts of one ion may be retained by a soil even in the presence of large amounts of a more strongly bonded ion.

The presence of specific adsorption sites can present problems in the quantitative evaluation of a reaction process, because a calculated charge balance for the soil solution is often disrupted. Whether the process involves counterbalancing hydrolysis or other poorly understood reactions, specific adsorption is often characterized by an inability to measure an increase of similarly charged ions in or a loss of counterions from the equilibrium solution. In addition, specifically adsorbed ions are not easily removed, so subsequent desorption may not confirm sorption of the ion.

Ellis and Knezek (1972) have indicated that hydrolysis plays a role in micronutrient retention by soils. In most cases, hydrolysis is not a direct sorption mechanism, but affects the valence state of the hydroxylated ion. The presence or absence of a OH^- ion attached to a cation can affect the reactivity to specific sorption sites. Ions can also react with OH^- groups at the edges of either inorganic colloids, or alcoholic and phenolic hydroxyls on organic matter. Conditions leading to retention by this mechanism involve complex interactions among ion properties, colloid properties, and solution conditions.

Interactions between the ion and the surface can depend on both the pK_a of the surface functional group and the pK for hydrolysis (or protonation) of the sorbed ion, examples of which are provided in Table 3-1. Charged surfaces tend to have a higher H^+ activity than does the solution as a whole (Michaels & Morelos, 1955; Benesi, 1956; Harter & Ahlrichs, 1967; Mortland, 1968; Raman & Mortland, 1969; Bailey & Karickhoff, 1973). Thus, if the solution pH is near or slightly above the pK_a for protonation of an uncharged molecule, the higher H^+ activity near the surface may be enough to protonate the molecule, with subsequent bonding to the negatively charged surface. The reaction

$$\text{Surface}^- \ldots H^+ + \text{Oxyion}^0 \rightarrow \text{Surface}^- \ldots H\text{-Oxyion}^+ \quad [27]$$

would appear similar to hydrogen bonding, but in fact the bond has the nature and strength of an electrochemical bond.

The oxyanions of Mo and B, in particular, will be unprotonated in the solution phase if the pH of the solution is above the pK_a for protonation. However, they could become protonated in the more acid environment of the charged surface, with the H^+ ion serving as a bridge between the ion and the surface. This is a semispecific sorption mechanism in that sorption tends to vary according to the ion pK_a for protonation, rather than the electron configuration of the ion.

In certain cases, such as micronutrient retention by oxide or carbonate surfaces, distinctions between adsorption and precipitation are not clear. This is particularly true when the transition elements are sorbed to Mn oxides. As noted by McKenzie (1977), Mn oxides carry high negative charges in all but extremely acid conditions and have high sorption capacities. Cobalt is particularly attracted to the surfaces of Mn oxides, but Cu and Zn are also strongly sorbed by certain Mn-oxide minerals. McKenzie (1972) has found that sorption is consistent with crystal field theory, which predicts that elements with higher crystal-field stabilization energies will form inner-sphere complexes, displacing Mn from the surface layers of Mn-oxides.[3] Once such transitional element ions are attached to the surface, conditions again become favorable for the attachment of additional Mn ions. This process can result in Mn nodules with high Cu and Zn contamination (McKenzie, 1977).

A similar type of sorption by other surfaces has been noted; for example, Zn by carbonates (Jurinak & Bauer, 1956) and Fe/Al oxides (Kalbasi et al., 1978; Okazaki et al., 1986; Ghanem & Mikkelsen, 1988). Brümmer et al. (1983) have presented an excellent discussion of the evidences for precipitation vs. adsorption of Zn by soils. Pulford (1986) has argued that reactions with soils involve both surface adsorption and a precipitation mechanism. As one examines the evidence relating to micronutrient (especially Cu and Zn) retention by oxide and carbonate surfaces, and perhaps by alumino-silicate surfaces as well, it becomes apparent that both sorption and precipitation mechanisms are involved and that distinction between the two will not be easily defined.

IV. SORPTION REACTIONS OF INDIVIDUAL MICRONUTRIENTS

The seven micronutrient elements can be divided into four groups: Fe-Mn, Cu-Zn, Mo-B, and Cl. Adsorption plays a minimal role in the avail-

---

[3] Crystal field stabilization energies are related to *d* orbital energy splitting as the atoms come together to form crystal bonds (Cotton & Wilkinson, 1980).

ability of Fe and Mn to plants. Most soils contain relatively large quantities of these two elements, and precipitation and oxidation reactions control their availability. Oxides and hydrous oxides of these elements are important substrates for soil retention of other micronutrients. The individual reactions of Fe and Mn will not be discussed here. Copper and Zn are similar in their reactions, therefore they will be discussed as a unit. Molybdenum and B normally occur as oxyacid anions and will also be discussed as a unit. Chlorine, the seventh micronutient, occurs as a monovalent anion. Since it is weakly retained on surfaces and sorption is of limited importance to its availability, it will not be discussed here.

A. Copper and Zinc

Copper and Zn are both similar and different in their reactions. Both are divalent in soil systems. The univalent state is accessible to Cu, but requirements for this state are unlikely to occur in soils. While there have been reports of a univalent Zn, its existence has not been confirmed (Cotton & Wilkinson, 1980) and necessary conditions are unlikely to be found in soils. Zinc, while being listed as a transitional element, has no unpaired electrons; both the 3d and 4s orbitals are filled. Therefore, the ion is formed by loss of the 4s electrons and reactions tend to be somewhat similar to those of Ca. At the same time, the presence of 10 3d electrons does affect the way Zn interacts with surfaces.

Both Cu and Zn will hydrolyze in aqueous systems, with ion pK_a at 7.5 and 9.0 (Table 3–1), respectively (Smith & Martell, 1989). As illustrated in Table 3–2, hydrated forms of these ions are unlikely to exist in aqueous systems with pH below about 6.0. As the pH approaches neutrality, however, Cu is rapidly hydrolyzed to $Cu(OH)_2^0$. Zinc tends, instead to hydrolyze to $ZnOH^+$, and the uncharged $Zn(OH)_2^0$ begins to appear only at pH levels near 8.0. The results of this disparity are expressed in retention mechanism differences.

Harter (1983) has indicated that Zn is probably retained on nonspecific, exchange complex sites throughout the pH range of soils, whereas Cu may be precipitated at the higher pH ranges. However, Pickering (1980) noted that the pH required for precipitation of hydroxy-Cu and Zn could be decreased if colloids were present. In addition, Bolland et al. (1977) have postulated that surface affinity for the monocharged and uncharged hydroxy

Table 3-2. Effect of pH on solution composition of Cu and Zn, expressed as percent in solution (after Harter, 1983).

pH	4	5	6	7	8
Cu^{2+}	100	100	96	33	1
$CuOH^+$			2	7	1
$Cu(OH)_2^0$			2	56	92
Zn^{2+}	100	100	98	83	31
$ZnOH^+$			2	17	64
$Zn(OH)_2^0$					5

complex ions could be high enough to unbalance solution equilibria. Whatever the mechanism(s) involved, Anderson and Christensen (1988) show that pH is more important than any other single property in controlling Zn mobility.

1. Sorption by Clays

Zinc sorption by pure and soil clays has been commonly reported (Reddy & Perkins, 1974; Shuman, 1975, 1976; Kabata-Pendias,1980; Tiller et al., 1984a, b; Pal & Sastry, 1985; Krishnasamy et al., 1985; Rahmatullah & Sandhu, 1985; Puls & Bohn, 1988). While Cu sorption by clays has received less attention, clays have been shown to be a retention site for this ion as well (Steger, 1973; Kabata-Pendias, 1980; Sposito et al., 1981; Traina & Doner, 1985a).

Ellis and Knezek (1972) and Shuman (1980) have pointed out that clays are capable of sorbing both Cu and Zn in excess of CEC. At near-neutral or alkaline pH levels, they attributed the excess retention either to surface precipitation or sorption of the univalent $M(OH)^+$ form. Wakatsuki and Kawaguchi (1975) found that Cu was sorbed by kaolinite and kaolinitic soil clays at solution Cu activities lower than that required for oxide/hydroxide precipitation. Zinc was not sorbed at such low activities unless the suspension pH was at or above neutrality. They interpreted this to indicate that Cu is retained by specific sorption sites on clays, while Zn was retained on nonspecific sites in acid soils, and on specific sites in neutral and alkaline soils.

It appears that the mechanisms are more complex than such simple explanations would indicate, but there is certainly a strong relationship between retention and matrix pH (Bingham et al., 1964; DuPlessis & Burger, 1971; Reddy & Perkins, 1974; Payne & Pickering, 1975), as well as a relationship between retention and cation exchange capacity (Reddy & Perkins, 1974; Farrah et al., 1980; Abd-Elfattah & Wada, 1981).

While Kabata-Pendias and Pendias (1984) maintain that the ability of soil minerals to remove Cu from solution is dependent on the mineral surface charge, the relationship between CEC and Cu or Zn retention is not always straightforward. For example, while Farrah et al. (1980) found retention to be in the expected order of montmorillonite > illite > kaolinite, Kabata-Pendias (1980) reported the order of retention as montmorillonite > kaolinite > illite.

Rao et al. (1974) observed that soil clays dominated by kaolinite and illite had higher Zn sorption capacities than did those dominated by montmorillonite. On the other hand, Krishnasamy et al. (1985) ascertained that Zn retention by the clay fraction was greatest in montmorillonite-dominated soils, and Rahmatullah and Sandhu (1985) detected little relationship between Zn retention and mineralogy of the soil clays. These divergent results may arise from variations in mineralogy and differences in surface conditions. Both can exert a larger impact on sorption than does the exchange capacity. Okazaki et al. (1989) reported a direct relationship between the SiO_2/Al_2O_3 ratio of synthetic aluminosilicates, and Cu or Zn adsorption. They attribute their results to differences in Al coordination within the mineral structure.

Jenne (1968) argued that retention is more a function of hydrous Mn and Fe oxides on clay surfaces than on the properties of the surfaces themselves.

Looking at six whole soils, Shuman (1988) reported that removal of either organic matter or Mn oxides decreased Zn sorption, but that Fe-oxide removal increased sorption. In other investigations, Cu sorption by kaolinite has been shown to be related to the ion of saturation (Gupta & Harrison, 1981) and to surface coverage of humic acid (Gupta & Harrison, 1982). In the latter case, the reported effect was to decrease retention, even though Cu is known to be complexed by organic materials (Kabata-Pendias & Pendias, 1984). Since Gupta and Harrison (1981, 1982) were studying aquatic systems, the surfaces could be sufficiently different to explain these apparently contradictory observations.

2. Sorption by Hydrous Oxides

According to Jenne (1968) hydrous oxides play a significant role in the control of Cu and Zn concentrations in soil solution, and numerous researchers have found these nutrients to be retained by hydrous oxide surfaces. Reports are readily available of Cu and Zn retention by hydrous iron oxides (Forbes et al., 1976; Bolland et al., 1977; Barrow et al., 1981; Okazaki et al., 1986; Ghanem & Mikkelsen, 1988), hydrous manganese oxides (McKenzie, 1972; Loganathan & Burau, 1973; Gadde & Laitinen, 1974; Loganathan et al., 1977; Kabata-Pendias, 1980), and hydrous aluminum oxides (Shuman, 1977; Kalbasi & Racz, 1978; McBridge, 1978; Peralta et al., 1981; Barrow, 1986).

Retention of metal ions by oxide surfaces is inversely dependent on the degree of crystalinity (Okazaki et al., 1986) and, since the oxides have variable charge, the extent to which retention occurs is dependent on the pH of the solution (Barrow, 1987a). Kalbasi et al. (1978) reported that both specific and nonspecific adsorption occur in Zn retention by Fe and Al oxides. Their data supported the specific adsorption mechanism proposed by Quirk and Posner (1975); that is, the sorbed Zn forms a ring structure as follows:

$$
\begin{array}{c}
\text{H} \\
\text{O} \\
\diagdown \quad / \text{ H} \\
\text{Fe} - \text{OH} \\
/ \\
\text{O} \\
\diagdown \\
\text{Fe} - \text{OH} \\
/ \diagdown \text{ H} \\
\text{O} \\
\text{H}
\end{array}
\quad + \text{ Zn}^{2+} \rightarrow \quad
\begin{array}{c}
\text{H} \\
\text{O} \\
\diagdown \quad / \text{ H} \\
\text{Fe} - \text{O} \\
/ \qquad \diagdown \\
\text{O} \qquad\qquad \text{Zn} \; + \; 2\text{H}^+ \\
\diagdown \qquad / \\
\text{Fe} - \text{O} \\
/ \diagdown \text{ H} \\
\text{O} \\
\text{H}
\end{array}
\qquad [28]
$$

This mechanism would result in irreversible Zn incorporation into the surface of Fe (or Al) oxide. Kalbasi et al. (1978) also reported that Zn could be nonspecifically retained at only one oxygen, resulting in the replacement of one mole of H^+ per mole of Zn^{2+}. In this case, they felt a Cl^- ion would accompany the Zn, either as a complex or as an associated counter-ion. The ratio of specific to nonspecific adsorption increased with increasing pH, as would be expected for the proposed mechanisms.

Predictably, surface conditions strongly influence Cu or Zn sorption by hydrous oxides. Numerous authors have noted a direct relationship between soil pH and metal ion retention. Cavallaro and McBride (1984) observed that removal of oxides from soil clays significantly reduced Cu and Zn retention, whereas removal of organic matter from the surfaces did not. Removal of the oxides also caused a dramatic increase in the pH at which increased retention occurred. The effect was more noticeable for Zn than for Cu. Traina and Doner (1985b) reported a Cu-induced release of Mn(II) during sorption to Mn-oxide surfaces, but only if Mn(II) was present on the surface prior to sorption. The presence of Co(II) in the solution increased the magnitude of the reaction, presumably because of concomitant oxidation of Co and the reduction of Mn at the surface.

The presence of PO_4 on the surface has also been shown to affect retention. Barrow (1987b) reported PO_4 could either increase or decrease Zn retention by soil, depending on the pH. Ghanem and Mikkelsen (1988) indicated that sorbed P lowers the zero point of charge on oxide surfaces, with a resultant increase of negative charge with which metal ions may react. On the other hand, Bolland et al. (1977) felt that sorption of PO_4 onto oxide surfaces simply provided either additional negative charges or complexation sites with which Zn reacted. Barrow (1986) does note that PO_4-retaining and Zn-retaining materials in soil differ in their behavior from that of pure oxides of Fe and Al.

In studying the effect of phosphate on the sorption of Cu by Al hydroxide, McBride (1985) observed decreased sorption of Cu when PO_4 was present. Using electron spin resonance, he demonstrated that the sorbed PO_4 blocked the coordination of Cu^{2+} to the surface AlOH groups.

3. Sorption by Organic Matter

Organic matter plays a major role in the soil retention of both Cu and Zn (Shuman, 1980; Petruzzelli et al., 1981; Stevenson & Fitch, 1981; Kabata-Pendias & Pendias, 1984). It appears to be particularly important in the retention of Cu by certain soils. Shuman (1979), for example, found that about one-third of the Cu in 10 southern soils was found in the organic matter, whereas only about 1/10 of the Zn was in this fraction.

The organic fraction, in particular, seems to be a source of specific Cu-sorption sites in the soil (McLaren & Crawford, 1973; Kadlec & Keoleian, 1986), perhaps because the ion is unique in its ability to form inner-sphere complexes at a wide range of pH levels (McBride, 1981). Conversely, organic complexation could lead to increased mobility in the soil, since Cu and Zn are known to form stable complexes with fulvic acid (Schnitzer & Skinner, 1966; Kabata-Pendias & Pendias, 1984).

Complexation of the metals by organics can also affect retention by mineral surfaces. For example, Goh et al. (1986) demonstrated increased retention of both Cu and Zn by Al precipitation products when tannic acid was present during precipitation. They attributed the increased sorption capacity to exposed edges as well as to the presence of carboxylate and phenolic groups on the surface. Zabowski and Zasoski (1987) indicate that the presence of sewage sludge leachate decreased soil retention of Cu, but increased Zn retention by the mineral horizons. The observed differences could not be explained by differences in solution metal activities, and a competitive sorption mechanism was proposed.

In contrast to sorption by clear Na-montmorillonite surfaces, Inskeep and Baham (1983) reported a dramatic decrease in Cu sorption with increase in pH when water-soluble extracts of forest litter layer, sewage sludge, or peat were present. These observations were related to a high Cu-ligand stability constant and the charge characteristics of the organic molecules, which promoted sorption of the organic molecule by the clay surface at low pH.

Bar-Tal et al. (1988) demonstrated decreased Zn sorption by smectite in the presence of fulvic acid. Elrashidi and O'Connor (1982b) similarly recounted that the presence of EDTA significantly decreased Zn sorption by soil, indicating that competition exists between the ligand and soil sorption sites. Small amounts of organics in solution have been shown to increase solution-Cu concentrations above that expected for ionic Cu in equilibrium with inorganic sorption sites or precipitated forms (McLaren et al., 1981).

Complexation of metals by carboxylate groups is commonly proposed as a mechanism of retention. Boyd et al. (1981b) found electron-spin resonance evidence that Cu(II) is sorbed to humic acid by forming two inner-sphere bonds with oxygen atoms. Subsequent infrared evaluation of Cu-humic acid complexes (Boyd et al., 1981a; Piccolo & Stevenson, 1982) indicated that the two bonds were unlikely to result from a complex with a single carboxylate group. They proposed the formation of a chelate ring of either two adjacent carboxylate groups or a carboxylate and an adjacent phenolic OH group, with an oxygen atom from each group forming a single bond with Cu^{2+}.

$$[29]$$

Boyd et al. (1979, 1981b) also provided evidence for Cu^{2+} interaction with amide groups and pyridine rings by inducing a charge on the N lone-pair electrons. The latter would be consistent with Chase's (1989, unpublished data) inability to balance Cu loss from and cation gain to solution upon Cu sorption by soil. Evidence of bonding mechanisms and the nature of these bonds can be a source of controversy, but the bulk of the evidence seems to indicate that carboxylate groups, phenolic OH groups, and N lone-pair electrons are dominant retention sites (Stevenson & Fitch, 1981).

B. Boron and Molybdenum

Boron has a high affinity for oxygen and in nature always occurs as the oxygenated ion, mainly as hydrated borates (Cotton & Wilkinson, 1980). Bonding will normally occur with three OH groups to form $B(OH)_3$. Boron can readily coordinate with three or four oxygen ions, and the borate ion ($B[OH]_4^-$) forms by the addition of a hydroxyl rather than by the loss of a proton from $B(OH)_3$ (pK = 9.2). Thus, $B(OH)_3$ acts as a Lewis acid (Keren & Bingham, 1985). Hydrolysis constants of other ionic species are so high that B species other than $B(OH)_3$ and $B(OH)_4^-$ are unlikely to be of practical importance at the pH levels of soils.

The tendency of B to form polymers consisting of B–O–B bonds may, however, be important under certain circumstances. The reaction

$$3B(OH)_3 \leftrightarrow B_3O_3(OH)_4^- + H^+ + 2H_2O \qquad [30]$$

has a pK of 6.8 (Keren & Bingham, 1985), which indicates that the complex makes a significant contribution to B in solution at pH levels near or above neutrality when $B(OH)_3$ activities approach 0.1. While this combination, in itself, is likely to occur only in arid-region soils, the tendency for polymerization to occur may result in specific bonding with other soil components.

Except in unweathered sediments, where it may occur as the sulfide (Norrish, 1975), Mo will normally occur in aqueous systems as the oxyanion, MoO_4^{2-}. Molybdic acid differs from $B(OH)_3$ in that the acid dissociation constants are low enough ($pK_1 = 4.0$, $pK_2 = 4.24$) that deprotonated forms will dominate throughout the pH range of most soils (Lindsay, 1979). Like borates, the MoO_4^{2-} ion tends to polymerize in solution. This tendency seems to be particularly enhanced by acidification (Cotton & Wilkinson, 1980), which could, in part, explain the low availability of Mo in acid soils (Kabata-Pendias & Pendias, 1984).

In recent reviews, Evans and Sparks (1983), Gupta et al. (1985), and Keren and Bingham (1985) have pointed out that the partition of B between soil solution and soil surfaces is affected by clay mineral types, content, and specific surface area, mineralogy of the sand and silt fractions, sesquioxides, organic matter content, soil pH, ion on the exchange complex, and soil salinity. Elrashidi and O'Connor (1982a) found that percent Fe-oxides and percent organic C were major factors in explaining the variation in sorption by 10 arid-region soils.

Boric acid is known to complex with diol functional groups.[4] This has been suggested as a sorption mechanism on soil organic matter (Gupta et

---

[4] Diols are dihydric alcohols or phenols.

al., 1985; Evans, 1987). Despite their support for this sorption mechanism, Gupta et al. (1985) have questioned the concept that soil B associated with organic matter is complexed. They believe that organic-associated B could come from the microbial biomass.

The bulk of opinion seems to be that $B(OH)_3$ and the borate ion undergo inner-sphere ligand exchange with hydrous Fe and Al oxides, forming two metal–O–B bonds. This mechanism has been previously discussed by Ellis and Knezek (1972), who suggest that the reaction occurs as

$$
\begin{array}{cccccccc}
\text{H} & \text{H} & & & & \text{H} & & \\
\text{O} & \text{O} & & \text{HO} \quad \text{O} & & \text{O} & \text{O} \quad \text{O} & \\
\diagdown\diagup \cdots \diagup & & \diagdown\diagup & & \diagdown\diagup \cdots \diagup\diagdown\diagup & & \\
\text{M} \quad \text{M} & + & \text{B} & \rightarrow & \text{M} \quad \text{M} \quad \text{B} & + 2H_2O & [31] \\
\diagdown\diagup\diagdown & & \diagup\diagdown & & \diagdown\diagup\diagdown\diagup\diagdown & & \\
\text{O} \quad \text{O} & & \text{HO} \quad \text{OH} & & \text{O} \quad \text{O} \quad \text{OH} & & \\
\text{H} & & & & & & \\
\end{array}
$$

They also note that borate may be bonded through exchange of a single OH$^-$ ion. Even when B has been sorbed by clays, there is evidence that the reaction is either to sesquioxide surface coatings (Evans & Sparks, 1983) or to comparable sites at mineral edges (Keren & Talpaz, 1984; Keren & Bingham, 1985; Goldberg & Glaubig, 1986).

Regardless of the sorbate, acidity seems to be critical in controlling B sorption by soil constituents. As expected from the pK for hydrolysis of the $B(OH)_3$ molecule, maximum sorption of B tends to occur in the alkaline region. In all cases, sorption is reported to be proportional to pH in the acid regions, with peak sorption occurring at about pH 8.0 for Fe and Al oxides (Bloesch et al., 1987; Goldberg & Glaubig, 1985, 1988), possibly slightly lower for some Al oxides (Ellis & Knezek, 1972; Keren & Gast, 1983), and somewhat higher for clay minerals (Keren & Mezuman, 1981; Goldberg & Glaubig, 1986).

As with the cations, surface conditions are very important in the retention of anions. For example, Keren and Talpaz (1984) have shown that not only is B retention higher at high pH, but Ca-saturated clays retain more B than do Na-saturated clays. In addition, they report dramatically increased retention when the particle size of the clay is reduced, indicating that sorption occurs at positively charged edge sites. Beyrouty et al. (1984) suggest that B either replaces or bonds to surface hydroxy ligands of Al hydroxide gels. Bloesch et al. (1987) reported a reduction of B sorption in the presence of PO_4, indicating that the two ions compete for the same types of sites. Competition would be expected, since PO_4 is known to bond to Al-hydroxide surfaces in a similar manner to that indicated.

The age of hydroxide surfaces is particularly important in controlling the amount of B that will be sorbed. Fresh Al hydroxide gels tend to adsorb large amounts of B, which decreases rapidly with age of the gels (Beyrouty et al., 1984). This is consistent with the increased crystallinity that occurs as the gel is aged, resulting in decreased surface area and sites for reaction.

Both B and Mo are strongly sorbed by volcanic ash soils (Bingham et al., 1971; Gonzalez et al., 1974; Hue et al., 1988), which suggests that both have a particular attraction to Al-hydroxide surfaces. However, it would appear that Mo is retained by organic matter and Fe-oxide surfaces to a greater extent than is B (Karimian & Cox, 1978). Jarrell and Dawson (1978) attributed the major role in Mo retention to amorphous Fe oxides. In any case, the retention of Mo is pH dependent, with the maximum sorption occurring between pH 3.0 and 5.0 (Misra et al., 1977).

The occurrence of maximum sorption at about the pK_a of H_2MoO_4 is typical of specifically sorbed species. Barrow (1977) indicated that such an observation was difficult to explain on the basis of simple competition between hydroxide and the MoO_4^{2-} ion. He suggested a two-step process in which the negatively charged MoO_4^{2-} ion initially replaces anions such as Cl^- or NO_3 at mineral edges and oxide surfaces, and subsequently forms an inner-sphere complex with the surface. However, it may be noted that the similarity of the first and second dissociation constants (Table 1-1) result in transitory appearance of the mono-acid at about pK_1 (Fig. 3-5). Therefore, if the mono-acid is specifically adsorbed, maximum sorption would occur near the pK_a. One can more simply arrive at the same inner-sphere complex by assuming a reaction of the $HMoO_4^-$ ion with the surface according to the reaction.

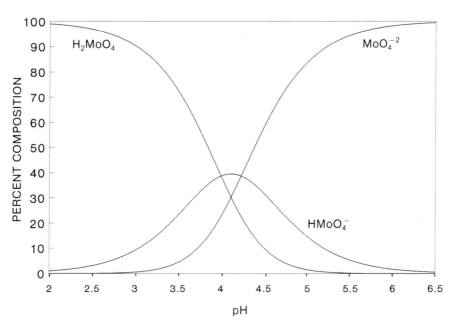

Fig. 3-5. Relationship of molybdate ion species to pH.

$$\begin{array}{c}\diagdown \\ \text{Al} \\ \diagup \diagdown \\ \diagdown \quad \text{O} \cdots \text{H}^+ + \text{HMoO}_4^- \rightarrow \\ \diagdown \diagup \\ \text{Al} \\ \diagup\end{array} \qquad \begin{array}{c}\diagdown \\ \text{Al} \quad\quad \text{O} \\ \diagup \diagdown \quad | \\ \diagdown \quad \text{O} - \text{Mo} - \text{O} + \text{H}_2\text{O} \qquad [32] \\ \diagdown \diagup \quad | \\ \text{Al} \quad\quad \text{O} \\ \diagup\end{array}$$

As the pH increases above the pK_a for the H_2MoO_4 molecule, Mo adsorption decreases, both because the availability of mono-acid in solution decreases and because the positive charge on the surface is decreasing. Since the proposed inner-sphere ligand-exchange sorption mechanism is similar to that which is normally assumed for soil retention of PO_4, competition between these two ions is predicted. Indeed, Roy et al. (1986) provided experimental support for this mechanism, reporting significant reduction of Mo sorption in the presence of PO_4.

V. SUMMARY AND FUTURE RESEARCH NEEDS

Adsorption isotherms have provided the majority of information about micronutrient adsorption by soils. This work has been supplemented by flow-through studies and, more recently, by kinetics. A variety of models compatible with the empirical data have been developed and used. These models are useful for summarizing data, but too often the fit of data to a curve is taken as proof that adsorption has occurred. Efforts are being integrated as more sophisticated models are developed. Through such holistic approaches a better understanding of adsorption processes can be achieved.

Adsorption reactions are likely to be a major factor in the availability of B, Cu, Mo, and Zn to plants. We have acquired a basic cognizance of the types of surfaces that will adsorb these micronutrients and the relative amounts of each retained under given conditions. In particular, concerns about heavy metals in the environment have catalyzed research efforts on Cu and Zn adsorption by soils and soil materials. Understanding of B and Mo adsorption reactions is less well developed and additional studies are needed. Surface adsorption mechanisms, particularly those involving organics, are not completely understood and research directed toward this end continues.

Adsorption/desorption kinetics is increasingly becoming an area of investigation for soil chemists. While the primary impetus for this research has been concern about movement of ions to ground water, it does have implications for movement to plant roots. As plant nutrition research moves more toward consideration of energetics, there will also be an increasing need for information on the thermodynamics of adsorption/desorption processes. Development of appropriate techniques for obtaining this information will be a primary challenge in the decades ahead.

REFERENCES

Abd-Elfattah, A., and K. Wada. 1981. Adsorption of lead, copper, zinc, cobalt, and cadmium by soils that differ in cation-exchange materials. J. Soil Sci. 32:271-283.

Aharoni, C. 1984. Kinetics of adsorption: the S-shaped z-t plot. Adsorpt. Sci. Technol. 1:1-29.

Aharoni, C., and M. Ungarish. 1976. Kinetics of activated chemisorption. Part 1. The non-elovichian part of the isotherm. J. Chem. Soc. Faraday Trans. 72:400-408.

Anderson, P.R., and T.H. Christensen. 1988. Distribution coefficients of Cd, Co, Ni, and Zn in soils. J. Soil Sci. 39:15-22.

Bailey, G.W., and S.W. Karickhoff. 1973. An ultraviolet spectroscopic method for monitoring surface acidity of clay minerals under varying water content. Clays Clay Miner. 21:471-477.

Barrow, N.J. 1977. Factors affecting the molybdenum status of soils. p. 583-595. In W.G. Chappell and K.K. Petersen (ed.) Molybdenum in the environment. Vol. 2. Marcel Dekker, New York.

Barrow, N.J. 1978. The description of phosphate adsorption curves. J. Soil Sci. 29:447-462.

Barrow, N.J. 1986. Testing a mechanistic model. VI. Molecular modelling of the effects of pH on phosphate and on zinc retention by soils. J. Soil Sci. 37:311-318.

Barrow, N.J. 1987a. Reactions with variable-charge soils. Martinus Nijhoff Publ., Dordrecht, Netherlands.

Barrow, N.J. 1987b. The effects of phosphate on zinc sorption by a soil. J. Soil Sci. 38:453-459.

Barrow, N.J., J.W. Bowden, A.M. Posner, and J.P. Quirk. 1981. Describing the adsorption of copper, zinc and lead on a variable charge mineral surface. Aust. J. Soil Res. 19:309-321.

Bar-Tal, A., B. Bar-Yosef, and Y. Chen. 1988. Effects of fulvic acid and pH on zinc sorption on montmorillonite. Soil Sci. 146:367-373.

Benesi, H.A. 1956. Acidity of catalyst surfaces. I. Acid strength from colors of adsorbed indicators. J. Am. Chem. Soc. 78:5490-5494.

Beyrouty, C.A., G.E. Van Scoyoc, and J.R. Feldkamp. 1984. Evidence supporting specific adsorption of boron on synthetic aluminum hydroxides. Soil Sci. Soc. Am. J. 48:284-287.

Bingham, F.T., A.L. Page, N.T. Coleman, and K. Flach. 1971. Boron adsorption characteristics of selected amorphous soils from Mexico and Hawaii. Soil Sci. Soc. Am. Proc. 35:546-550.

Bingham, F.T., A.L. Page, and J.R. Sims. 1964. Retention of Cu and Zn by H-montmorillonite. Soil Sci. Soc. Am. Proc. 28:351-354.

Bloesch, P.M., L.C. Bell, and J.D. Hughes. 1987. Adsorption and desorption of boron by goethite. Aust. J. Soil Res. 25:377-390.

Bolland, M.D.A., A.M. Posner, and J.P. Quirk. 1977. Zinc adsorption by goethite in the absence and presence of phosphate. Aust. J. Soil Res. 15:279-286.

Bolt, G.H. 1982. Movement of solutes in soil: principles of adsorption/exchange chromatography. p. 285-348. In G.H. Bolt (ed.) Soil chemistry. B. Physico-chemical models. Elsevier Scientific Publ. Co., Amsterdam, Netherlands.

Boyd, S.A., L.E. Sommers, and D.W. Nelson. 1979. Infrared spectra of sewage sludge fractions: evidence for an amide metal binding site. Soil Sci. Soc. Am. J. 43:893-899.

Boyd, S.A., L.E. Sommers, and D.W. Nelson. 1981a. Copper(II) and iron(III) complexation by the carboxylate group of humic acid. Soil Sci. Soc. Am. J. 45:1241-1242.

Boyd, S.A., L.E. Sommers, D.W. Nelson, and D.X. West. 1981b. The mechanism of copper(II) binding by humic acid: an electron spin resonance study of a copper(II)-humic acid complex and some adducts with nitrogen donors. Soil Sci. Soc. Am. J. 45:747-749.

Brümmer, G., K.G. Tiller, U. Herms, and P.M. Clayton. 1983. Adsorption-desorption and/or precipitation-dissolution process of Zn in soils. Geoderma 31:337-354.

Cavallaro, N., and M.B. McBride. 1984. Zinc and copper sorption and fixation by an acid soil clay: effect of selective dissolutions. Soil Sci. Soc. Am. J. 48:1050-1054.

Cotton, F.A., and G. Wilkinson. 1980. Advanced inorganic chemistry. 4th ed. Wiley Interscience Publ., New York.

DuPlessis, S.F., and R.D.T. Burger. 1971. The specific adsorption of copper by clay minerals and soil fractions. Agrochemophysica 3:1-10.

Ellis, B.G., and B.D. Knezek. 1972. Adsorption reactions of micronutrients in soils. p. 59-78. In J.J. Mortvedt et al. (ed.) Micronutrients in agriculture. SSSA, Madison, WI.

Elrashidi, M.A., and G.A. O'Connor. 1982a. Boron sorption and desorption in soils. Soil Sci. Soc. Am. J. 46:27-31.

Elrashidi, M.A., and G.A. O'Connor. 1982b. Influence of solution composition on sorption of zinc by soils. Soil Sci. Soc. Am. J. 46:1153–1158.

Evans, C.M., and D.L. Sparks. 1983. On the chemistry and mineralogy of boron in pure and mixed systems: a review. Commun. Soil Sci. Plant Anal. 14:827–846.

Evans, L.J. 1987. Retention of boron by agricultural soils from Ontario. Can. J. Soil Sci. 67:33–42.

Eyring, H., S.H. Lin, and S.M. Lin. 1980. Basic chemical kinetics. John Wiley and Sons, New York.

Farrah, H., D. Hatton, and W.F. Pickering. 1980. The affinity of metal ions for clay surfaces. Chem. Geol. 28:55–68.

Felmy, A.R., D.C. Girvin, and E.A. Jenne. 1984. MINTEQ—A computer program for calculating aqueous geochemical equilibria. EPA-600/3-84-032. USEPA, Athens, GA.

Fisher, E.A. 1922. The phenomena of absorption in soils: a critical discussion of the hypotheses put forward. Faraday Soc. Trans. 17:305–316.

Forbes, E.A., A.M. Posner, and J.P. Quirk. 1976. The specific adsorption of divalent Cd, Co, Cu, Pb, and Zn on goethite. J. Soil Sci. 27:154–166.

Freundlich, H. 1909. Kapillarchemie. Akademische Verlagsgesellschaft, Leipzig, Germany.

Gadde, R.R., and H.A. Laitinen. 1974. Studies of heavy metal adsorption by hydrous iron and manganese oxides. Anal. Chem. 46:2022–2026.

Ghanem, S.A., and D.S. Mikkelsen. 1988. Sorption of zinc on iron hydrous oxide. Soil Sci. 146:15–21.

Giles, C.H., D. Smith, and A. Huitson. 1974. A general treatment and classification of the solute adsorption isotherm. I. Theoretical. J. Colloid Interface Sci. 47:755–765.

Goh, T.B., A. Violante, and P.M. Huang. 1986. Influence of tannic acid on retention of copper and zinc by aluminum precipitation products. Soil Sci. Soc. Am. J. 50:820–825.

Goldberg, S., and R.A. Glaubig. 1985. Boron adsorption on aluminum and iron oxide minerals. Soil Sci. Soc. Am. J. 49:1374–1379.

Goldberg, S., and R.A. Glaubig. 1986. Boron adsorption and silicon release by the minerals kaolinite, montmorillonite, and illite. Soil Sci. Soc. Am. J. 50:1442–1448.

Goldberg, S., and R.A. Glaubig. 1988. Boron and silicon adsorption on an aluminum oxide. Soil Sci. Soc. Am. J. 52:87–91.

Gonzalez, R., B.H. Appelt, E.B. Schalscha, and F.T. Bingham. 1974. Molybdate adsorption characteristics of volcanic-ash-derived soils in Chile. Soil Sci. Soc. Am. Proc. 38:903–906.

Gupta, G.C., and F.I. Harrison. 1981. Effect of cations on copper adsorption by kaolin. Water Air Soil Pollut. 15:323–327.

Gupta, G.C., and F.I. Harrison. 1982. Effect of humic acid on copper adsorption by kaolin. Water Air Soil Pollut. 17:357–360.

Gupta, U.C., Y.W. Jame, C.A. Campbell, A.J. Leyshon, and W. Nicholaichuk. 1985. Boron toxicity and deficiency: a review. Can. J. Soil Sci. 65:381–409.

Harter, R.D. 1983. Effect of soil pH on adsorption of lead, copper, zinc, and nickel. Soil Sci. Soc. Am. J. 47:47–51.

Harter, R.D. 1984. Curve-fit errors in Langmuir adsorption maxima. Soil Sci. Soc. Am. J. 48:749–752.

Harter, R.D. 1989. A new modeling compatible solution to the first order kinetics equation. Soil Sci. 147:97–102.

Harter, R.D., and J.L. Ahlrichs. 1967. Determination of clay surface acidity by infrared spectroscopy. Soil Sci. Soc. Am. Proc. 31:30–33.

Harter, R.D., and G. Smith. 1981. Langmuir equation and alternate methods of studying "adsorption" reactions is soils. p. 167–182. In R.H. Dowdy et al. (ed.) Chemistry in the soil environment. ASA Spec. Publ. 40. ASA, Madison, WI.

Hissink, D.J. 1924. Base exchange in soils. Faraday Soc. Trans. 20:551–566.

Hue, N.V., N. Hirunburana, and R.L. Fox. 1988. Boron status of Hawaiian soils as measured by B sorption and plant uptake. Commun. Soil Sci. Plant Anal. 19:517–528.

Inskeep, W.P., and J. Baham. 1983. Competitive complexation of Cd(II) and Cu(II) by water-soluble organic ligands and Na-montmorillonite. Soil Sci. Soc. Am. J. 47:1109–1115.

Jardine, P.M., and D.L. Sparks. 1984. Potassium-calcium exchange in a multireactive soil system: I. Kinetics. Soil Sci. Soc. Am. J. 48:39–45.

Jarrell, W.M., and M.D. Dawson. 1978. Sorption and availability of molybdenum in soils of western Oregon. Soil Sci. Soc. Am. J. 42:412–415.

Jenne, E.A. 1968. Controls on Mn, Fe, Co, Ni, Cu, and Zn concentrations in soils and water: the significant role of hydrous Mn and Fe oxides. Adv. Chem. 73:337–387.

Jurinak, J.J., and N. Bauer. 1956. Thermodynamics of zinc adsorption on calcite, dolomite, and magnesite-type minerals. Soil Sci. Soc. Am. J. 20:466–471.

Kabata-Pendias, A. 1980. Heavy metals sorption by clay minerals and oxides of iron and manganese. Miner. Polonica 11(2):3–13.

Kabata-Pendias, A., and H. Pendias. 1984. Trace elements in soils and plants. CRC Press, Inc., Boca Raton, FL.

Kadlec, R.H., and G.A. Keoleian. 1986. Metal ion exchange on peat. p. 61–93. In C.H. Fuchman (ed.) Peat and water. Elsevier Applied Science Publ. Ltd., Oxford, England.

Kalbasi, M., and G.J. Racz. 1978. Association of zinc with oxides of iron and aluminum in some Manitoba soils. Can. J. Soil Sci. 58:61–68.

Kalbasi, M., G.J. Racz, and L.A. Loewen-Rudgers. 1978. Mechanism of zinc adsorption by iron and aluminum oxides. Soil Sci. 125:146–150.

Karimian, N., and F.R. Cox. 1978. Adsorption and extractability of molybdenum in relation to some chemical properties of soil. Soil Sci. Soc. Am. J. 42:757–761.

Keren, R., and F.T. Bingham. 1985. Boron in water, soils and plants. Adv. Soil Sci. 1:229–276.

Keren, R., and R.G. Gast. 1983. pH-dependent boron adsorption by montmorillonite hydroxy-aluminum complexes. Soil Sci. Soc. Am. J. 47:1116–1121.

Keren, R., and U. Mezuman. 1981. Boron adsorption by clay minerals using a phenomenological equation. Clays Clay Miner. 29:198–204.

Keren, R., and H. Talpaz. 1984. Boron adsorption by montmorillonite as affected by particle size. Soil Sci. Soc. Am. J. 48:555–559.

Krishnasamy, R., K.K. Krishanmoorthy, and T.S. Manickam. 1985. Zinc adsorption isotherms for soil clays. Clay Res. 4:92–95.

Laidler, K.J. 1950. Chemical kinetics. McGraw Hill Book Co., New York.

Langmuir, I. 1918. The absorption of gasses on plane surfaces of glass, mica, and platinum. Am. Chem. Soc. J. 40:1361–1382.

Lewis, T.E., and F.E. Broadbent. 1961. Soil organic matter-metal complexes: 3. Exchange reactions of model compounds. Soil Sci. 91:341–348.

Lindsay, W.L. 1979. Chemical equilibria in soils. Wiley-Interscience Publ., New York.

Lindstrom, F.T., R. Haque, and W.R. Coshow. 1970. Adsorption from solution. III. A new model for the kinetics of adsorption-desorption processes. J. Chem. Phys. 74:495–502.

Loganathan, P., and R.G. Burau. 1973. Sorption of heavy metal ions by a hydrous manganese oxide. Geochim. Cosmochim. Acta 3:1277–1293.

Loganathan, P., R.G. Burau, and D.W. Fuerstenau. 1977. Influence of pH on the sorption of Co^{2+}, Zn^{2+}, and Ca^{2+} by a hydrous manganese oxide. Soil Sci. Soc. Am. J. 41:57–62.

Low, M.J.D. 1960. Kinetics of chemisorption of gases on solids. Chem. Rev. 60:267–312.

McBride, M.B. 1978. Retention of Cu^{2+}, Ca^{2+}, Mg^{2+}, and Mn^{2+} by amorphous alumina. Soil Sci. Soc. Am. J. 42:27–31.

McBride, M.B. 1981. Forms and distribution of copper in solid and solution phases of soil. p. 25–45. In Loneragan et al. (ed.) Copper in soils and plants. Academic Press, Sydney, Australia.

McBride, M.B. 1985. Sorption of copper(II) on aluminum hydroxide as affected by phosphate. Soil Sci. Soc. Am. J. 49:843–846.

McKenzie, R.M. 1972. The sorption of some heavy metals by the lower oxides of manganese. Geoderma 8:29–35.

McKenzie, R.M. 1977. Manganese oxides and hydroxides. p. 181–193. In J.B. Dixon and S.B. Weed (ed.) Minerals in the soil environment. SSSA, Madison, WI.

McLaren, R.G., and D.V. Crawford. 1973. Studies on soil copper(II): The specific adsorption of copper by soils. J. Soil Sci. 24:443–452.

McLaren, R.G., R.S. Swift, and J.G. Williams. 1981. The adsorption of copper by soil materials at low equilibrium solution concentrations. J. Soil Sci. 32:247–256.

Michaels, A.S., and O. Morelos. 1955. Polyelectrolyte adsorption by kaolinite. Ind. Eng. Chem. 47:1801–1809.

Misra, S.G., K.C. Mishra, and P.C. Mishra. 1977. Retention and release of molybdenum by soils. p. 597–618. In W.G. Chappell and K.K. Petersen (ed.) Molybdenum in the environment. Vol. 2. Marcel Dekker, New York.

Morrison, R.T., and R.N. Boyd. 1971. Organic chemistry. 2nd Ed. Allyn and Bacon, Boston.

Mortland, M.M. 1968. Protonation of compounds at clay mineral surfaces. Trans. Int. Congr. Soil Sci., 9th 1:691–699.

Motta, M.M., and C.F. Miranda. 1989. Molybdate adsorption on kaolinite, montmorillonite and illite: constant capacitance modeling. Soil Sci. Soc. Am. J. 53:380–385.

Norrish, K. 1975. Geochemistry and mineralogy of trace elements. p. 55–81. In D.J.D. Nicholas and A.R. Egan (ed.) Trace elements in soil-plant-animal systems. Academic Press, New York.

Okazaki, M., K. Kimiwada, and H. Katsumata. 1989. Adsorption of ions on synthetic amorphous aluminosilicates with different SiO_2/Al_2O_3 molar ratios and coordination numbers of aluminum. Soil Sci. Plant Nutr. (Tokyo) 35:109–118.

Okazaki, M., K. Takamidoh, and I. Yamane. 1986. Adsorption of heavy metal cations on hydrated oxides and oxides of iron and aluminum with different crystallinities. Soil Sci. Plant Nutr. (Tokyo) 32:523–533.

Pajares, J.A., J.L. Garcia, and S.W. Weller. 1978. Kinetics of chemisorption of CO_2 on scandia: A new rate equation. J. Catal. 52:521–530.

Pal, D., and T.G. Sastry. 1985. Sorption of zinc on kaolinitic soil clays. Clay Res. 4:55–60.

Payne, K., and W.F. Pickering. 1975. Influence of clay-solute interactions on aqueous copper ion levels. Water Air Soil Pollut. 5:63–69.

Peralta, F., E. Bornemisza, and A. Alvarado. 1981. Zinc adsorption by andepts from the central plateau of Costa Rica. Commun. Soil Sci. Plant Anal. 12:669–682.

Petruzzelli, G., G. Guidi, and L. Lubrano. 1981. Interactions among heavy metals and organic matter in soil. p. 686–689. In Proc. Int. Conf. Heavy metals in the environment, Amsterdam. September 1981. Commission of the European Communities and World Health Organization, Edinburgh, Scotland.

Piccolo, A., and F.J. Stevenson. 1982. Infrared spectra of Cu^{2+}, Pb^{2+}, and Ca^{2+} complexes of soil humic substances. Geoderma 27:195–208.

Pickering, W.F. 1980. Zinc interaction with soil and sediment components. p. 71–112. In J.O. Nriagu (ed.) Zinc in the environment, Part I: Ecological cycling. John Wiley and Sons, New York.

Pulford, I.D. 1986. Mechanisms controlling zinc solubility in soils. J. Soil Sci. 37:427–438.

Puls, R.W., and H.L. Bohn. 1988. Sorption of cadmium, nickel, and zinc by kaolinite and montmorillonite suspensions. Soil Sci. Soc. Am. J. 52:1289–1292.

Quirk, J.P., and A.M. Posner. 1975. Trace element adsorption by soil minerals. p. 95–107. In D.J.D. Nicholas and A.R. Egan (ed.) Trace elements in soil-plant-animal systems. Academic Press, New York.

Rahmatullah, I.B., and G.R. Sandhu. 1985. Fixation of zinc by some rice soil clays under upland conditions. Commun. Soil Sci. Plant Anal. 16:615–620.

Raman, K.V., and M.M. Mortland. 1969. Proton transfer reactions at clay mineral surfaces. Soil Sci. Soc. Am. Proc. 33:313–317.

Rao, K.B., C.C. Biddappa, M.S. Mithyantha, and N.G. Perur. 1974. Zinc sorption on clay soils. Proc. Indian Nat. Sci. Acad., Part B 40:299–302.

Reddy, M.R., and H.F. Perkins. 1974. Fixation of zinc by clay minerals. Soil Sci. Soc. Am. Proc. 38:229–231.

Roy, W.R., J.J. Hassett, and R.A. Griffin. 1986. Competitive coefficients for the adsorption of arsenate, molybdate, and phosphate mixtures by soils. Soil Sci. Soc. Am. J. 50:1176–1182.

Schnitzer, M., and S.I.M. Skinner. 1966. Organo-metalic interactions in soils: 5. Stability constants of Cu^{++}-, Fe^{++}-, and Zn^{++}-fulvic acid complexes. Soil Sci. 102:361–365.

Selim, H.M., J.M. Davidson, and P.S.C. Rao. 1977. Transport of reactive solutes through multilayered soils. Soil Sci. Soc. Am. J. 41:3–10.

Shuman, L.M. 1975. The effect of soil properties on zinc adsorption by soils. Soil Sci. Soc. Am. Proc. 39:454–458.

Shuman, L.M. 1976. Zinc adsorption isotherms for soil clays with and without iron oxides removed. Soil Sci. Soc. Am. J. 40:349–352.

Shuman, L.M. 1977. Adsorption of Zn by Fe and Al hydrous oxides as influenced by aging and pH. Soil Sci. Soc. Am. J. 40:703–706.

Shuman, L.M. 1979. Zinc, manganese, and copper in soil fractions. Soil Sci. 127:10–17.

Shuman, L.M. 1980. Zinc in soils. p. 39–69. In Nriagu (ed.) Zinc in the environment, part I: Ecological cycling. John Wiley and Sons, New York.

Shuman, L.M. 1988. Effect of removal of organic matter and iron- or manganese-oxides on zinc adsorption by soil. Soil Sci. 146:248–254.

Skopp, J., and D. McCallister. 1986. Chemical kinetics from a thin disc flow system: theory. Soil Sci. Soc. Am. J. 50:617–623.

Smith, R.M., and A.E. Martell. 1989. Critical stability constants. Vol. 6. 2nd supplement. Plenum Press, New York.

Sposito, G. 1982. On the use of the Langmuir equation in the interpretation of "adsorption" phenomena: II. the "two-surface" Langmuir equation. Soil Sci. Soc. Am. J. 46:1147–1152.

Sposito, G. 1984. The surface chemistry of soils. Oxford Univ. Press, New York.

Sposito, G. 1989. The chemistry of soils. Oxford Univ. Press, New York.

Sposito, G., K.M. Holtzclaw, C.T. Johnston, and C.S. Levesque-Madore. 1981. Thermodynamics of sodium-copper exchange on Wyoming bentonite at 298 °K. Soil Sci. Soc. Am. J. 45:1079–1084.

Sposito, G., and S.V. Mattigod. 1980. GEOCHEM: A computer program for the calculation of chemical equilibria in soil solution and other natural water systems. Kearney Foundation of Soil Science, Univ. of California, Riverside, CA.

Steger, H.F. 1973. On the mechanism of the adsorption of trace copper by bentonite. Clays Clay Miner. 21:429–436.

Stevenson, F.J., and A. Fitch. 1981. Reactions with organic matter. p. 69–95. In J.F. Loneragan et al. (ed.) Copper in soils and plants. Academic Press, Sydney, Australia.

Stumm, W., R. Kummert, and L. Sigg. 1980. A ligand exchange model for the adsorption of inorganic and organic ligands at hydrous oxide interfaces. Croat. Chem. Acta 53:291–312.

Swearington, L.E., and B.N. Dickinson. 1932. The rate of adsorption from solution. J. Phys. Chem. 36:534–545.

Thomas, G.W. 1977. Historical developments in soil chemistry: ion exchange. Soil Sci. Soc. Am. J. 41:230–238.

Tiller, K.G., J. Gerth, and G. Brümmer. 1984a. The sorption of Cd, Zn and Ni by soil clay fractions: procedures for partition of bound forms and their interpretation. Geoderma 34:1–16.

Tiller, K.G., J. Gerth, and G. Brümmer. 1984b. The relative affinities of Cd, Ni and Zn for different soil clay fractions and goethite. Geoderma 34:17–35.

Traina, S.J., and H.E. Doner. 1985a. Co, Cu, Ni, and Ca sorption by a mixed suspension of smectite and hydrous manganese dioxide. Clays Clay Miner. 33:118–122.

Traina, S.J., and H.E. Doner. 1985b. Heavy metal induced releases of manganese (II) from a hydrous manganese dioxide. Soil Sci. Soc. Am. J. 49:317–321.

Ungarish, M., and C. Aharoni. 1981. Kinetics of chemisorption. Deducing kinetic laws from experimental data. J. Chem. Soc. Faraday Trans. 1 77:975–985.

Van Bemmelen, J.M. 1878. Das absorptionsvermogen der ackererde. Landwirtsch. Vers. Stn. 21:135–191.

Veith, J.A., and G. Sposito. 1977. On the use of the Langmuir Equation in the interpretation of "adsorption" phenomena. Soil Sci. Soc. Am. J. 41:697–702.

Wakatsuki, T.H. Furukawa, and K. Kawaguchi. 1975. Specific and non-specific adsorption of inorganic ions. II. Specific adsorption of cations on kaolinite and kaolinitic soil clays. Soil Sci. Plant Nutr. (Tokyo) 21:351–360.

Westall, J. 1980. Chemical equilibrium including adsorption on charged surfaces. p. 33–44. In M.C. Kavanough and J.O. Leckie (ed.) Particulates in water. Am. Chem. Soc., Washington, DC.

Zabowski, D., and R.J. Zasoski. 1987. Cadmium, copper, and zinc adsorption by a forest soil in the presence of sludge leachate. Water Air Soil Pollut. 36:103–113.

Chapter 4

Inorganic Equilibria Affecting Micronutrients in Soils

W. L. LINDSAY, *Colorado State University, Fort Collins, Colorado*

Solid phases play an important role in determining the solubility relationships of nutrients in soils. Whenever a nutrient element in the soil solution exceeds the equilibrium concentration of a mineral, that mineral can precipitate. Conversely, whenever the concentration of a nutrient in the soil solution drops below the equilibrium solubility of a solid phase, that solid can dissolve. Thus, solid phases buffer the solubility of nutrients in soils and, in this way, directly affect the availability of plant nutrients.

The rates at which minerals attain equilibrium in soils differ widely. Some reach equilibrium within a few hours, others take years, and still others may never attain equilibrium. Furthermore, many solid phases in soils are amorphous or they contain significant amounts of extraneous ions. Jenne (1968) proposed that hydrous oxides of Mn and Fe furnish the principal matrix into which less abundant elements are often adsorbed, coprecipitated, or occluded.

The manner in which inorganic solid phases tend to interact with other components in the soil is depicted graphically in Fig. 4–1. As plants absorb nutrients from solution (Reaction 1), the concentration of nutrients next to the absorbing root decreases. Nutrients held on the soil exchange sites come into solution (Reaction 4) to replenish those being depleted. Removal of nutrients from solution causes solid phases to dissolve (Reaction 6), which restores depleted ions from solution and replenishes them on soil exchange sites (Reaction 3). Microorganisms also remove nutrients from solution in the course of their life cycles (Reaction 7). During the decomposition of organic matter, nutrients are released to the soil soluton (Reaction 8). In Fig. 4–1, Reactions 7 and 8 are drawn with dashed lines to indicate that microorganisms are often involved in these reactions, and that normal equilibrium and kinetic relationships may be modified by enzymatic and metabolic activities.

Soils consist of dynamic systems in which numerous chemical reactions occur. Nevertheless, solid phases provide ultimate control of the concentrations of their constituent ions in solution. By knowing which micronutrient minerals are present in soils, and their thermodynamic properties and reac-

Dynamic Equilbria in Soils

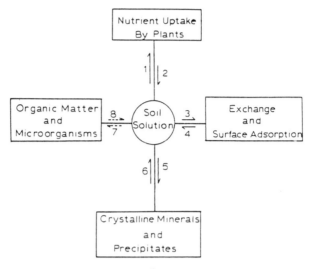

Fig. 4–1. Dynamic equilibria occurring in soils.

tion rates, the solubility of micronutrients in soils can be better predicted. Equilibrium, in its true sense, is probably never attained in soils. Soils change constantly due to fluctuating temperatures, moisture relationships, and biological activity. In one soil a mineral may precipitate and be stable; in another it may be unstable and dissolve. Rapidly changing conditions often favor the formation of amorphous or poorly crystallized solids, with partial substitution of secondary ions. The thermodynamic properties of such solids are difficult to define. Too often scientists abandon theoretical considerations when they find that simplified models cannot always be validated.

The purpose of this chapter is to examine the inorganic solubility relationships of micronutrients in soils. Prime consideration is given to solid phases and associated solution species, with theoretical predictions augmented, in some cases, by experimental measurements of micronutrient solubilities in soils.

I. IRON

A. Iron Oxides

Iron in most primary minerals occurs in the Fe(II) oxidation state. During weathering in an oxygenated environment, these minerals dissolve, release Fe^{2+}, which oxidizes to Fe^{3+} and precipitates as insoluble Fe(III) oxides. The solubility relationships of Fe in well-aerated soils are largely controlled by these Fe(III) oxides. There are several different kinds of Fe oxides, each with a different solubility (Schwertmann, 1988). Figure 4–2, taken from Lind-

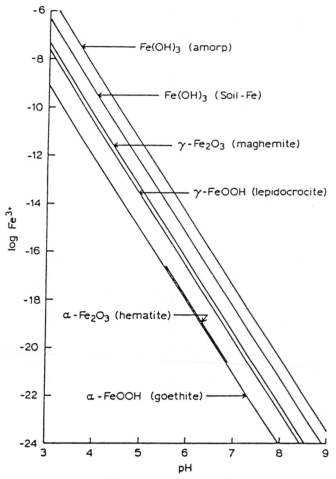

Fig. 4–2. The activity of Fe^{3+} in equilibrium with various Fe(III) oxides (Lindsay, 1979, reproduced with permission from John Wiley and Sons Inc.).

say (1979), compares the solubility of several of the commonly reported Fe(III) oxides.

Freshly precipitated amorphous $Fe(OH)_3$ (amorp) is the most soluble Fe(III) oxide. It precipitates rapidly following the addition of soluble Fe(III) salts or following increases in soil pH and/or redox levels. The other Fe(III) oxides depicted here are listed in order of decreasing solubilities: $Fe(OH)_3$ (soil-Fe), Fe_2O_3 (maghemite), FeOOH (lepidocrocite), Fe_2O_3 (hematite), and FeOOH (goethite). Soil-Fe will be discussed in greater detail below. The solubility of $Fe(OH)_3$ (amorp) is 3630 times more soluble than that of goethite (Lindsay, 1979). Except under special conditions, the transformation of one Fe(III) oxide to another in soils occurs only slowly. The extremely low solubilities of these minerals account in part for their slow rates of transformation to other minerals. Thus, several Fe(III) oxide minerals may persist together in soils for long periods of time without simply being transformed in their entirety to the most insoluble mineral form. Small diffusion gradients associated with these insoluble minerals, due to the tendency to form porous weathering rinds on the surface of weathering minerals, account in part for the sluggish reaction rates.

In recent years, ferrihydrite also has been identified as an Fe(III) oxide mineral in soils and other natural environments. Schwertmann (1988) describes ferrihydrite as a highly disordered Fe(III) oxide mineral of very fine particle size (on the order of a few nanometers). He designated the stoichiometry of ferrihydrite as $5Fe_2O_3 \cdot 9H_2O$, but its structure has not been fully elucidated. Its solubility, expressed as the log of the ion activity product of $(Fe^{3+})(OH^-)^3$, is reported to be in the range 37.0 to 39.4 (Schwertmann & Taylor, 1989). This solubility range exceeds that of the crystalline Fe(III) oxides shown in Fig. 4–2.

One might ask which of all the possible Fe minerals really control Fe solubility in soils. Norvell and Lindsay (1982a) set about to answer this question. They added soluble $FeCl_3$ to a near-neutral soil and then used a chelation method (Norvell & Lindsay, 1982b) to follow the relationship of log $(Fe^{3+})(OH^-)^3$ with time. Their results, reported in Fig. 4–3, show that the apparent dissociation product of ferric hydroxide decreased gradually over a 30-d period and eventually stabilized near a log value of -39.3. Measurement of the $Fe(OH)_3$ ion-activity product in several soils that did not receive soluble Fe additions also yielded values near -39.3. This value is the best estimate of the solubility of Fe in soils and has been designated soil-Fe. The exact solubility of ferrihydrite and the effect of particle size on its solubility are not sufficiently known to conclude for certain that ferrihydrite is responsible for the Fe solubility measurements such as those depicted in Fig. 4–3, but such a conclusion is strongly suggested.

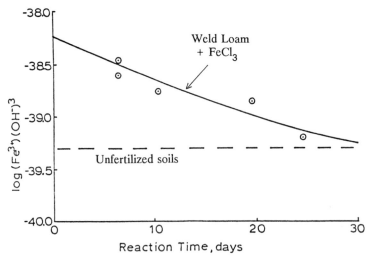

Fig. 4–3. Changes in the ferric hydroxide ion product of a Weld loam (fine, montmorillonitic, mesic Aridic Paleustoll) following the addition of $FeCl_3$. The dashed line represents unfertilized soil, showing a log $K° = -39.3$, which is designated as soil-Fe (Norvell & Lindsay, 1982b).

B. Solution Species of Iron

Free Fe^{3+} in aqueous solutions hydrolyzes to yield a number of hydrolysis species, and also combines with inorganic anions to form soluble Fe(III) complexes. These solution species are shown in Fig. 4-4 under the condition that soil-Fe controls Fe^{3+} activity. Iron(III) hydrolysis species appear near the top of this diagram, indicating that they are more abundant than most other Fe^{3+} complexes. The region of minimum Fe solubility ($10^{-10.4}$ M) occurs between pH 7.5 and 8.5 which is, coincidentally, the pH range of most calcareous soils. Iron deficiency in plants frequently occurs in calcareous soils. Addition of inorganic salts offers little help in correcting Fe deficiencies, because the Fe^{3+} complexes are insignificant at realistic inorganic-ligand levels compared with the hydrolysis species. Addition of soluble Fe(III) salts may temporarily precipitate $Fe(OH)_3$ (amorp), which would shift all of the lines in Fig. 4-4 upward by 0.84 log units. However, within a few days or

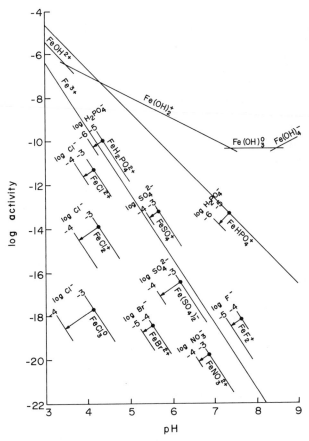

Fig. 4-4. Inorganic complexes of Fe(III) in equilibrium with soil-Fe compared with the Fe(III) hydrolysis species.

weeks, $Fe(OH)_3$ (amorp) would transform to soil-Fe once more, and the solubility levels for Fe would return to those depicted in Fig. 4–4.

Research findings suggest that plants need in excess of 10^{-8} M of soluble Fe to supply their nutritional needs (Schwab & Lindsay, 1989). Inorganic Fe(III) oxides cannot maintain this level of soluble Fe in soils above pH 5.5 to 6. Either chelation by natural or synthetic chelates, or reduction of Fe(III) to Fe(II) is necessary to raise the solubility of Fe in soils above this critical level (Lindsay & Schwab, 1982). Reduction is discussed in the following section, while chelation is discussed in Chapter 7.

C. Redox Level Effect

Variations in soil redox levels provide another means of increasing the solubility of Fe in soils. Normally soils are considered well aerated with Fe(III) oxides controlling the solubility of Fe. However, reduction occurs in soils near respiring roots, in microsites where organic matter is actively being degraded, and generally throughout submerged soils. Figure 4–5 depicts how changes in redox level affect the activity of Fe^{2+} in equilibrium with various Fe minerals. The redox parameter (pe + pH) used here has been de-

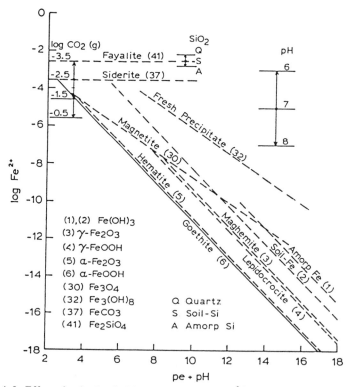

Fig. 4–5. Effect of redox level, CO_2 (g), and silica on Fe^{2+} maintained by various Fe minerals at pH 7, showing shifts for other pH values (Lindsay, 1979, reproduced with permission from John Wiley and Sons Inc.).

scribed elsewhere (Lindsay, 1979; Lindsay & Sadiq, 1983). A value of zero corresponds to the redox level imposed by one atmosphere of H_2 (g) in an aqueous system, and a value of 20.8 corresponds to equilibrium of aqueous systems with one atmosphere of O_2 (g).

Redox measurements in most well-aerated soils generally range from pe + pH 12 to 16. The upper value for this range results, in part, from instability of the Pt electrode used for redox measurements in oxygenated systems. Hence, the true upper limit in well-aerated soils may be somewhat higher. Equilibrium with atmospheric O_2 (g) is generally not attained in natural environments; however, the high activation energy associated with this reaction, along with the continual release of electrons through biological respiration by plant roots and microorganisms, tends to keep soils more reduced. The diagram in Fig. 4–5 was drawn for pH 7.0, but can easily be interpreted for other pH values as well through use of the pH-arrow sketch in the upper right-hand corner of the diagram. A unit increase in pH shifts all lines in the diagram upward by two log units, and a corresponding decrease in pH shifts the lines downward by two log units.

Figure 4–5 shows that if soil-Fe controls Fe solubility pe + pH would have to be < 10.0 (at pH 7) or 8.0 (at pH 8) in order for Fe^{2+} activity to exceed the 10^{-8} M level required by plants (Schwab & Lindsay, 1989). Consequently, well-aerated soils that lie in the pe + pH range above 12 cannot be expected to supply sufficient soluble Fe for plants. Submerged soils used for growing rice, however, usually have pe + pH values near 4.0. Under these conditions, Fe is sufficiently soluble to meet the needs of plants (Sajwan & Lindsay, 1986; Hanif et al., 1986).

Schwab and Lindsay (1989) show that Fe-deficient soybean [*Glycine max* (L.) Merr.] have the ability to lower the redox level of a nutrient solution below pe + pH 7. Based on this observation, they concluded that the release of electrons near actively absorbing roots is a major mechanism by which Fe-stressed plants are able to increase the solubility and availability of Fe to meet their nutritional needs. Plant cultivars often differ in their abilities to produce reducing environments next to their root surfaces. Hence, plants differ in their ability to obtain available Fe from soils.

Elevated levels of soluble Fe have been observed in some soils and natural environments. Often these levels correspond to the solubility of freshly precipitated $Fe_3(OH)_8$ (ferrosic hydroxide) (Ponnamperuma et al., 1967; Schwab & Lindsay, 1983; Sajwan & Lindsay, 1986). The solubility of this mixed-valence solid (designated as fresh precipitate) is represented in Fig. 4–5; it is more soluble than most of the other minerals shown. It apparently persists for extended periods of time (Schwab & Lindsay, 1983) after a formerly reduced soil has been drained. Its presence maintains Fe at high levels, and extends the redox range for adequate Fe up to pe + pH 14. The formation and persistence of this mixed-valence Fe oxide in nonflooded soils is believed to be associated with alternating redox conditions, where Fe is solubilized within reduced microsites and then precipitated nearby at more oxidized sites (Lindsay & Schwab, 1982).

II. MANGANESE

A. Manganese Solid Phases

Manganese solubility in soils can be limited by various Mn minerals, including oxides and the carbonate. Changes in redox level and pH have a profound effect on the solubility of Mn maintained by such minerals (Fig. 4-6). The oxidation state of Mn in these minerals varies from Mn(II) in $MnCO_3$ to Mn(IV) in MnO_2 (pyrolusite). In redox environments below pe + pH 14 (or slightly higher, depending on partial pressure of CO_2), $MnCO_3$ is the most stable Mn mineral. Schwab and Lindsay (1983) demonstrated that Mn^{2+} activity in the calcareous soils they examined reflected equilibrium with $MnCO_3$. In the pe + pH range 14 to 16.6, trivalent MnOOH is most stable and limits the solubility of Mn; whereas above pe + pH 16.6, MnO_2 (pyrolusite) is most stable. Other predominantly Mn(IV) minerals, such as $MnO_{1.9}$ (nsutite) and $MnO_{1.8}$ (birnessite), hold a small part of their Mn in

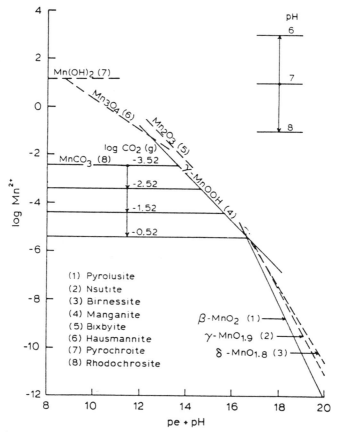

Fig. 4-6. Effect of redox level and CO_2 (g) on the solubility of Mn minerals at pH 7, showing shifts of two log units for each unit change in pH (Lindsay, 1979, reproduced with permission from John Wiley and Sons, Inc.)

a lower oxidation state, and are slightly more soluble than pyrolusite. The minerals $Mn(OH)_2$, Mn_3O_4, and Mn_2O_3 are much too soluble to persist in soils.

Figure 4–6 is drawn for pH 7, but can be interpreted for other pH values by using the pH-arrow sketch in the upper right hand corner of the diagram. As noted, all lines move upward two log units for each unit decrease in pH and down two log units for each unit increase in pH. Lowering redox level and pH increases Mn solubility, whereas increasing them decreases Mn solubility. In acid soils, Mn minerals can become so soluble that Mn toxicities frequently occur. Liming these soils raises pH and eliminates Mn toxicities.

The solubility of Mn in soils is often lower than that suggested by equilibrium with the Mn minerals of Fig. 4–6. This suggests that other, more insoluble Mn forms may be present. Boyle and Lindsay (1986) identified several Mn phosphate minerals, including trivalent $MnPO_4 \cdot 1.5H_2O$. The solubility diagram in Fig. 4–7 shows how different P minerals could interact with this mineral to further lower the activity of Mn^{2+}. The activity of Mn^{2+} is shown in equilibrium with $MnPO_4 \cdot 1.5 H_2O$, which is in turn in equilibri-

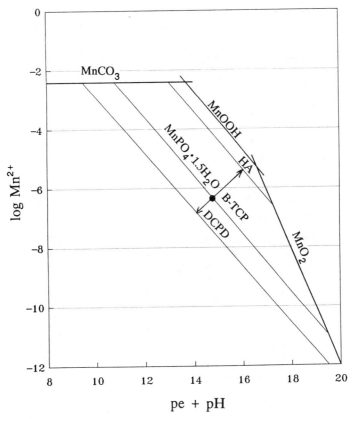

Fig. 4–7. Comparison of trivalent Mn phosphate solubilities with values for various Mn oxides and carbonate at pH 7.

um with various P minerals, including $CaHPO_4 \cdot 2H_2O$ (DCPD), $Ca_3(PO_4)_2$ (β-TCP), and $Ca_5(PO_4)_3OH$ (hydroxyapatite). The more soluble P minerals, predictably, depress Mn^{2+} activity the most.

Recently Lindsay and Brennan (1987) measured the ionic activities of Mn^{2+} and $H_2PO_4^-$ in several neutral and calcareous soils to which P had been added. The measured $H_2PO_4^-$ and Mn^{2+} activities correspond to equilibrium with $MnPO_4 \cdot 1.5H_2O$ and β-TCP, represented by the intermediate solubility line in Fig. 4–7. Such results strongly suggest that Mn phosphates may be responsible for decreasing the solubility of Mn^{2+} in soils for which the quantity of labile P exceeds that of labile Mn. In soils where labile Mn exceeds labile P, however, the solubility controls of Mn would likely remain with the oxides and the carbonate.

B. Solution Species of Mn

Solution species of Mn are numerous, and most are affected by changes in redox and pH (Lindsay, 1979). The most abundant solution species of Mn at pe + pH 16.6 are plotted in Fig. 4–8. Manganite and pyrolusite can coexist at equilibrium at this redox level. In addition, the activities of Cl^- and SO_4^{2-} have been fixed at 10^{-3} M, and CO_2 (g) has been fixed at $10^{-4.52}$ MPa ($10^{-3.52}$ atm), the average for the atmosphere. The solution chemistry of Mn under these conditions is relatively simple, with Mn^{2+} as the major solution species. The $MnSO_4^0$ ion pair would become even more significant at higher SO_4^{2-} activities. Ten-fold increases in Cl^- and SO_4^{2-} ac-

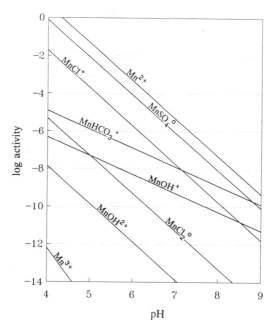

Fig. 4–8. Solution species of Mn in equilibrium with manganite and pyrolusite at pe + pH 16.6, when Cl^- and SO_4^{2-} are at 10^{-3} M and CO_2 is at $10^{-4.52}$ MPa ($10^{-3.52}$ atm).

tivities would increase $MnCl^+$ and $MnSO_4^0$ activities, respectively, by one log unit. The $MnOH^+$ and $MnHCO_3^+$ species would become significant only at uncommonly high pH or at high CO_2 levels. Ten-fold increases in CO_2 (g) would raise the latter species by one log unit. The ionic species $MnCl_2^0$, $MnOH^{2+}$, and Mn^{3+} are very low, while others (e.g., Mn^{4+}, MnO_4^-, and MnO_4^{2+}) are even lower and fall below the diagram. The solution chemistry of Mn is dominated by Mn^{2+}, with neither solution complexes, hydrolysis species, nor redox changes altering this fact significantly.

III. ZINC

A. Zinc Solid Phases

Figure 4-9 shows the solubility relationships imposed by various Zn minerals in soils. It is apparent that ZnO, Zn hydroxides, and $ZnCO_3$ are much too soluble to persist. In fact, they are often used as Zn fertilizers. Even in calcareous soils of pH 8, they would maintain approximately 10^{-4} $M Zn^{2+}$ or higher. The mineral Zn_2SiO_4 (willemite) is of intermediate solu-

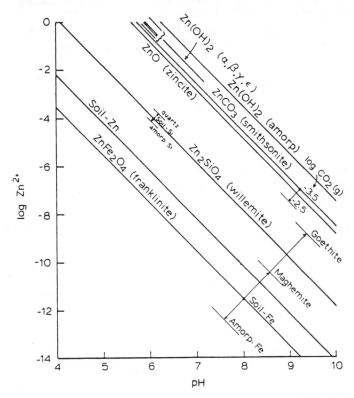

Fig. 4-9. The solubility of various Zn minerals in soils compared with soil-Zn (Lindsay, 1979, reproduced with permission from John Wiley and Sons).

bility and could possibly have a more significant effect on Zn solubility in soils. The most stable Zn mineral in Fig. 4–9 is $ZnFe_2O_4$ (franklinite). This mineral contains both Zn(II) and Fe(III), so the solubility of Zn^{2+} maintained by this mineral is affected by the concurrent solubility of Fe^{3+}. Changes in solid-phase controls on Fe solubility, from $Fe(OH)_3$ (amorp) to FeOOH (goethite), shift the activity of Zn^{2+} across most of the lower part of this diagram.

Researchers have sought to determine which Zn minerals are most likely to actually control Zn^{2+} activity in soils. Norvell and Lindsay (1969) and Lindsay and Norvell (1969) used a chelation method to measure and calculate Zn^{2+} activities in soils. They considered the reaction:

$$Zn^{2+} + soil \rightleftharpoons Zn\text{-}soil + 2H^+ \qquad [1]$$

for which their measurements gave a log $K° = -5.8$. In other words,

$$Zn^{2+} = 10^{5.8} (H^+)^2 \qquad [2]$$

The soil-Zn line in Fig. 4–9 corresponds to this measured solubility relationship. It seems likely that franklinite could be the mineral responsible for ultimately controlling Zn^{2+} activity in soils.

Figure 4–10, taken from Ma and Lindsay (1990), summarizes some recent measurements of Zn^{2+} activities in soils. Included are results from their

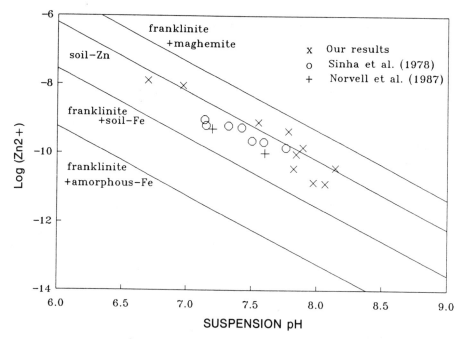

Fig. 4-10. Measured Zn^{2+} activity in soils compared with franklinite and soil-Zn (Ma & Lindsay, 1990).

own work along with those of Norvell et al. (1987) and Sinha et al. (1978). These solubility relationships are almost identical to the original soil-Zn solubility measurements of Norvell and Lindsay (1969) and Lindsay and Norvell (1969). Such results reinforce the hypothesis that franklinite may indeed be the Zn mineral that ultimately controls Zn solubility in soils.

Applications of P fertilizer are known to induce Zn deficiency in plants growing on many soils. Is there a Zn-phosphate mineral that is sufficiently insoluble to account for this problem? Figure 4–11 depicts the solubility relationship of one possible Zn phosphate, $Zn_3(PO_4)_2 \cdot 4H_2O$, under the condition that total P in solution is controlled at 10^{-4} M. If the concentration of P were $< 10^{-4}$ M, the equilibrium level of Zn^{2+} supported by the Zn-phosphate mineral would be even higher. Since $Zn_3(PO_4)_2 \cdot 4H_2O$ is considerably more soluble than soil-Zn, it cannot be expected to fix Zn into more unavailable forms. In fact, its high solubility suggests that it would be both a good Zn fertilizer and even a good P fertilizer when properly applied. Boawn et al. (1957) and Allen and Terman (1966) show that Zn phosphate is a good Zn fertilizer when it is finely ground and mixed with soil.

B. Solution Species of Zinc

Zinc complexes can increase the solubility of Zn over that of free Zn^{2+}. The extent to which various complexes might contribute to soluble Zn is depicted in Fig. 4–12. The assumptions used in developing this diagram are that (i) all species are in equilibrium with soil-Zn; (ii) the activities of NO_3^-, Cl^-, and SO_4^{2-} are fixed at 10^{-3} M; and (ii) the activity of $H_2PO_4^-$ is fixed at 10^{-5} M. Ten-fold increases in the anionic activities would shift the respec-

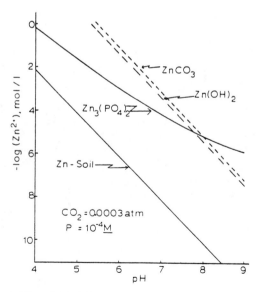

Fig. 4–11. The solubility of $Zn_3(PO_4)_2$ compared with values for other Zn minerals and for soil-Zn.

tive complexes upward one log unit. Thus, the graphs can be interpreted for other anionic activities as well.

Below pH 7.7, Zn^{2+} is the predominant Zn species in solution. Above this pH, $ZnOH^+$, and eventually $Zn(OH)_2^0$, dominate. The $ZnSO_4^0$ ion pair is the most abundant Zn complex, while complexes of NO_3^-, $H_2PO_4^-$, and Cl^- would be significant only at much higher levels of these anions. Solution complexes definitely need to be taken into consideration when total inorganic Zn in the soil solution is speciated while calculating Zn^{2+} activities.

If the Zn^{2+} activity were to rise above that supported by soil-Zn, all complexes in Fig. 4–12 would also increase by the same factor. The relative abundance of the various complexes would remain the same as long as the anionic activities remained unchanged. Availability of Zn to plants can be expected to follow the total solubility of Zn in solution.

Points a and b in Fig. 4–12 indicate that at pH 5 the concentration of Zn^{2+} in solution is approximately 10^{-4} M (6.5 mg kg^{-1}) and at pH 8 it is 10^{-10} M (0.007 mg kg^{-1}). The solubility of Zn is highly pH dependent and decreases 100-fold with each unit increase in pH. Zinc deficiencies can be induced by over-liming acid soils. At low pH values, some Zn^{2+} may be

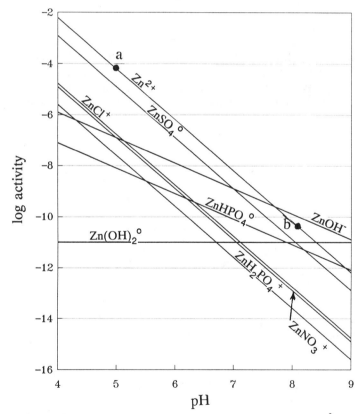

Fig. 4–12. Solution species of Zn in equilibrium with soil-Zn when Cl^-, SO_4^{2-}, and NO_3^- are at 10^{-3} M, and $H_2PO_4^-$ is at 10^{-5} M.

present on the exchange complex of soils, but at high pH values, the level of Zn^{2+} in solution is so low that very little Zn^{2+} is held on the exchange complex.

Carroll and Loneragan (1969) reported that 10^{-7} to 10^{-8} M Zn levels are critical for plant growth in continuous-flow nutrient cultures. Halvorson and Lindsay (1977) demonstrated that the critical level of Zn^{2+} for corn (*Zea mays* L.) is near $10^{-10.6}$ M when Zn is supplied by a chelate, which eliminates most diffusional gradients even within the free space roots. Thus, Zn deficiencies in plants can be expected in slightly acid and, particularly, in alkaline soils, where inorganic Zn in equilibrium with soil-Zn decreases to between 10^{-8} and 10^{-10} M. Next to absorbing roots, the concentration of Zn would be even lower due to root absorption of Zn and the establishment of diffusional gradients.

IV. COPPER

A. Copper Solid Phases in Oxidized Soils

The solubilities of various Cu minerals that might be expected in soils are depicted in Fig. 4–13. The $CuCO_3$(c), $Cu_3(OH)_2$ (azurite), $Cu(OH)_2$(c), $Cu_2(OH)_2CO_3$ (malachite), and CaO (tenorite) are all too soluble to persist, particularly in acid soils. The least soluble of these minerals is CuO (tenorite), which would maintain approximately 10^{-2} M Cu^{2+} at pH 5 and 10^{-8} M Cu^{2+} at pH 8. Inorganic Cu in soil is usually much less soluble.

The mineral $CuFe_2O_4$ (cupric ferrite) is approximately three orders of magnitude less soluble than tenorite. Since this ferrite mineral contains both Cu(II) and Fe(III), the solubility of Cu^{2+} in equilibrium with the mineral changes as the activity of Fe^{3+} changes. As Fe^{3+} shifts from equilibrium with $Fe(OH)_3$ (amorp) to soil-Fe and then to maghemite, the corresponding Cu^{2+} in equilibrium with cupric ferrite would also change, as seen in the lower portion of Fig. 4–13.

The soil-Cu line shown at the bottom of the Fig. 4–13 corresponds to the reaction:

$$\text{soil-Cu} + 2H^+ \rightleftharpoons Cu^{2+} \qquad [3]$$

for which Norvell and Lindsay (1969; 1972) determined a log $K° = 2.8$. In their study, CuEDTA an CuDTPA were reacted with five soils with various pH levels. The chelated Cu remaining in solution after 30 d, along with the associated pH, were used to estimate the log $K°$ value for the above reaction. The soils used in this study were aerated with laboratory air to represent well-oxidized conditions. The activity of Cu^{2+} represented by soil-Cu is approximately 10^{-3} that of Zn^{2+} in equilibrium with soil-Zn. All minerals in Fig. 4–13 are more soluble than soil-Cu, except for $CuFe_2O_4$ (cupric ferrite) in equilibrium with $Fe(OH)_3$ (amorp). Formation of $Fe(OH)_3$ requires either an alternating redox condition or the presence of anaerobic

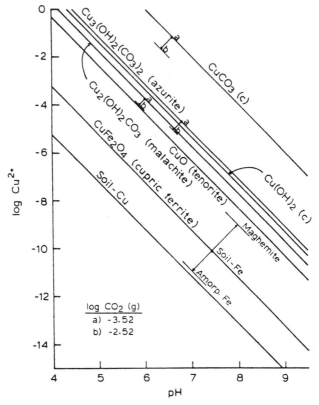

Fig. 4–13. Solubility of various Cu minerals in well-oxidized soils compared with soil-Cu (Lindsay, 1979, reproduced with permission from John Wiley and Sons Inc.).

microsites, even in the well-areated soil. Further studies are needed to exa-mine the implications of such solubility relationships.

B. Copper Solid Phases in Reduced Soils

When soils are reduced, the ratio of Cu^+ to Cu^{2+} increases according to the reaction:

$$Cu^{2+} + e^- \rightleftharpoons Cu^+ \qquad [4]$$

for which the log $K° = 2.62$ (Lindsay, 1979). This means that, for a redox level of pe = 2.62, Cu^{2+} and Cu^+ activities are equal and will change ten-fold for each unit change in pe. As shown in Fig. 4–14, $Cu_2Fe_2O_4$ (cuprous ferrite) becomes more insoluble than soil-Cu as the redox level decreases. The solubilities of Cu^{2+} and Cu^+ in equilibrium with the various solid phases displayed at the top of this diagram are given as a function of pe + pH (Lindsay & Sadiq, 1983). When soils go from oxidized to reduced conditions, the solid-phase controls of Cu would change from soil-Cu to

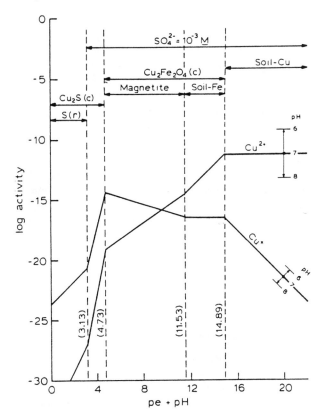

Fig. 4-14. Effect of redox on the stability of Cu minerals and on the activities of Cu^+ and Cu^{2+}, which they maintain. Drawn at pH 7, with shifts shown for pH 6 and 8 (Lindsay, 1979, reproduced with permission from John Wiley and Sons Inc.).

$Cu_2Fe_2O_4$ (cuprous ferrite), and finally to Cu_2S (cuprous sulfide). The most abundant Cu species in solution is Cu^{2+}, which is controlled at approximately 10^{-11} M under well-oxidized conditions at pH 7. Copper activities controlled by the solid phases shown in Fig. 4-14 are very low, and emphasize the complexity of Cu redox reactions interacting with Fe oxides and sulfides.

C. Solution Species of Copper

So far, Cu^{2+} and Cu^+ species in solution have been discussed. The hydrolysis and complex species of Cu(II) are provided in Fig. 4-15 under the conditions that all species are in equilibrium with soil-Cu and that all anions are fixed at 10^{-3} M, except for $H_2PO_4^-$, which is fixed at 10^{-5} M. The CO_2(g) level is assumed to be atmospheric $10^{-4.52}$ MPa ($10^{-3.52}$ atm). Below pH 6.9, Cu^{2+} is the dominant solution species, along with the $CuSO_4^0$ ion pair at slightly elevated SO_4^{2-} levels. Above pH 6.9, $Cu(OH)_2^0$ is the dominant solution species and, in equilibrium with soil-Cu, maintains dissolved Cu at approximately 10^{-11} M. At log CO_2 (g), values ten-fold greater than atmospheric $CuCO_3^0$ species would equal or exceed $Cu(OH)_2^0$.

Significant Cu(I) species in solution include $CuCl^0$ and $CuCl_2^-$. At 10^{-3} M Cl^- activity, however, neither of these species exceed Cu^+. It is evident from Fig. 4-14 that Cu^+ activity is very low, approaching 10^{-15} M or less at pH 7. The Cu^+ activity increases by only one log unit for each unit decrease in pH. Thus, Cu(I) complexes in soils are of only minor significance.

In examining the depressed solubility relationships of Cu shown in Fig. 4-14, it is surprising that Cu deficiencies in plants are not more prevalent. Copper is able to form strong complexes with soluble organic matter and, for this reason, its total solubility in soils is often greatly enhanced (Hodgson et al., 1966). This enhanced solubility, along with stronger affinity of Cu^{2+} for uptake carriers that transport ions across cell membranes, may account for the greater uptake of Cu by plants than would be expected from inorganic Cu levels alone.

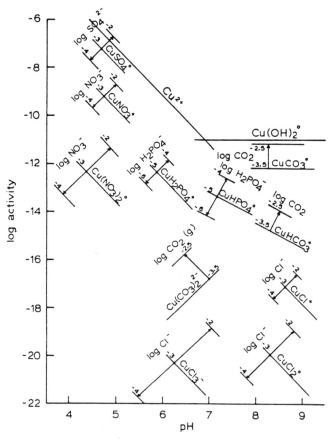

Fig. 4-15. Solution complexes of Cu^{2+} in equilibrium with soil-Cu (Lindsay, 1979, reproduced with permission from John Wiley and Sons Inc.).

V. BORON

Few studies have been conducted that attempt to identify solid-phase controls on B solubility in soils. Most of the common B minerals are much too soluble for such purposes. Gupta (1979) reviewed various factors that affect B concentrations in soil solutions. Most workers have focused on adsorption rather than on solid-phase controls of B solubility (Sims & Bingham, 1968).

Tourmaline, of chemical formula [$Na(Fe, Mg)_3Al_6(OH)_4(BO_3)_3Si_6O_8$], is a stable B mineral that might control B solubility in soils. However, no reliable solubility data have been reported for this mineral. For this reason, the question of B-solubility controls by tourmaline has not been resolved.

Figure 4-16 has been constructed to represent the general understanding of B solubilities in soils. The dissociation constants of H_3BO_3 (boric acid) were used to develop the pH-activity relationships that coexist among these solution species. The B solubility data reported by Phillipson (1953) were used to represent measured B levels for a large number of soils. The horizontal $H_3BO_3^0$ line was allowed to pass through these solubility points

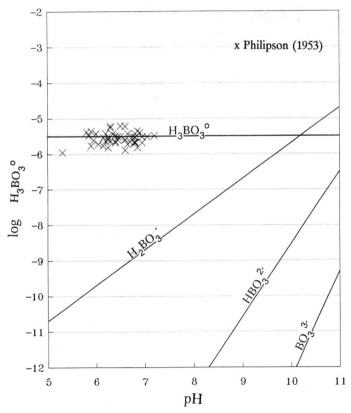

Fig. 4-16. Boron species in solution, drawn to reflect equilibrium with the average soluble B levels in 49 soils in Sweden.

to provide a tie to possible solid-phase controls. Since $H_3BO_3^o$ is the dominant solution species below pH 10.25, it seemed appropriate to use this approach. This line is designated the soil-B line, and represents a mean level of approximately $10^{-5.5}$ M B for this group of soils. Two other sets of data, from Bingham et al. (1972) and from Gestring and Soltanpour (1984), show scattered distribution nearer to 10^{-5} M $H_3BO_3^o$, with some B levels as high as $10^{-4.5}$, or 10 times the soluble levels reported by Phillipson (1953). Boron addition to soils usually raises the levels of soluble B, as was shown in Fig. 4–3 for Fe, which then decrease again over time.

Solid-phase controls of B solubility in soils, and especially the possible role of tourmaline, need further investigation.

VI. MOLYBDENUM

A. Molybdenum Solid Phases

The solubilities of several common Mo minerals are shown in Fig. 4–17. The data points included in this diagram are from Vlek and Lindsay (1977), and represent solubility measurements for several soils in the pH range from 6 to 8. Soluble Mo ranged from 10^{-8} to 10^{-6} M, which compares reasonably well with Mo solubilities of approximately $10^{-7.5}$ for several Indiana soils of pH 6.5, as reported by Lavy and Barber (1964).

The minerals in the upper part of the diagram are too soluble to persist in soils. In soils of high pH, it is possible that $CaMoO_4$ may provide some limit on the solubility of Mo. Usually Mo solubility increases rapidly with increase in pH, as Ca^{2+} activity is depressed by $CaCO_3$. Another mineral that could control the solubility of Mo in soils is $PbMoO_4$ (wulfenite). The reported level of Pb in an average soil (16 mg kg^{-1}) is greater than that of Mo (2 mg kg^{-1}), so it is possible that Pb could control Mo solubility. Even with Pb^{2+} activity limited to 10^{-8} M, as suggested by Vlek and Lindsay (1977), wulfenite could depress MoO_4^{2-} levels to approximately 10^{-8} M. Below pe + pH 4.6, MoS_2 (molybdenite) is extremely insoluble (Lindsay, 1979), and can depress Mo solubility to very low levels. Plants capable of surviving in such reduced environments usually transport oxygen from the stems to the roots, so that the slightly oxidized environment of the roots provides adequate available Mo, even in the presence of extremely insoluble molybdenite.

B. Solution Species of Molybdenum

A solubility value of MoO_4^{2-} = $10^{-7.5}$ M at pH 6.5, which corresponds closely to measurements by Lavy and Barber (1964) and Vlek and Lindsay (1977), was used to establish Fig. 4–18. This figure shows that MoO_4^{2-} is the major species in solution above pH 4.0, whereas $HMoO_4^-$ and $H_2MoO_4^o$ are of progressively lesser importance as the pH increases. Lower Mo oxidation states are of little significance in soils. Liming of acid soils is known

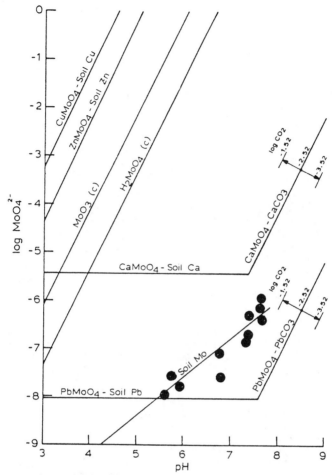

Fig. 4-17. Solubilities of several Mo minerals compared with Mo solubility measurements for soils by Vlek and Lindsay (1977).

to increase both the solubility and availability of Mo. One anomaly that needs further investigation is the pH dependence of Mo solubility in soils. In Fig. 4-18, MoO_4^{2-} is drawn with a slope of 2, which corresponds to theoretical expectations. The experimental points of Vlek and Lindsay (1977) in Fig. 4-17, however, reflected a slope closer to unity.

VII. SUMMARY AND RESEARCH NEEDS

Inorganic solid phases of micronutrients in soils establish long-term limits on the solubility of these elements. Thus, precipitation and dissolution reactions are important mechanisms that govern micronutrient availability to plants. Because of the very low total contents of most micronutrients in soils, it is often difficult to pinpoint specific minerals that control solubility.

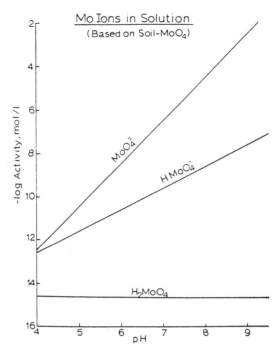

Fig. 4–18. Solution species of Mo shown in equilibrium with soil-Mo, which has a value of $10^{-7.5}$ M at pH 6.5.

Unfortunately, many of the solid phases that contain micronutrients in soils are poorly characterized. Instead of discrete crystalline minerals, these phases often consist of amorphous solids with mixed matrices into which various micronutrients are incorporated. Usually, it is difficult to apply thermodynamic solubility relationships to such solids, and yet considerable progress has been made. Measured concentrations of Fe^{3+}, Zn^{2+}, Cu^{2+}, $H_3BO_3^0$, and MoO_4^{2-} have been used to define the solubility levels at which these micronutrients are generally held in soils, as a function of pH. Terms such as soil-Fe, soil-Zn, soil-Cu, soil-B, and soil-Mo have been used to define these measured solubility relationships.

Iron oxides play a dominant role in governing Fe solubility in soils. A chelation method for measuring metal ion activities has helped to pinpoint activity relationships of Fe^{3+}, which heretofore have been impossible to measure, except in extremely acid soils. Redox level has been shown to have a marked effect on Fe solubility, likely via the formation of a mixed valency ferrosic hydroxide, which is capable of temporarily keeping Fe in more soluble form than are the Fe(III) oxides.

A trivalent Mn phosphate, $MnPO_4 \cdot 1.5H_2O$, has been shown to form in many soils and to exert a depressing effect on Mn^{2+} solubility. The relative amounts of labile Mn and P determine whether Mn solubility can be controlled by phosphates or, instead, by Mn oxides and carbonates.

Use of the chelation method to measure soil-Zn levels strongly suggests that $ZnFe_2O_4$ (franklinite) may be an important mineral phase that controls Zn solubility in soils. This observed solubility relationship helps to explain the behavior of Zn in soils and its subsequent availability to plants.

Solid phases that control Cu solubility in soils are less well known, but Cu^{2+} activity measurements made by the chelation method strongly suggest that $CuFe_2O_4$ (cupric ferrite) may govern Cu solubility in well-oxidized soils. Similar measurements need to be performed in reduced soils. Theoretical considerations show that $Cu_2Fe_2O_4$ (cuprous ferrite) is more stable in reduced soils than cupric ferrite and, thus, may provide an important solubility control. This possibility needs further testing.

Tourmaline is a highly complex aluminosilicate that is often suggested as a mineral that controls B solubility in soils. When finely divided tourmaline is used as a B fertilizer, it does not correct B deficiency, which suggests that tourmaline may indeed depress B concentrations below the critical level needed by plants. However, since the solubility of tourmaline as a function of pH is not known, this hypothesis has not been tested. Boron solubility in many soils seems to be buffered near $10^{-5.5}$ M, but the specific solid phases responsible for this control are unknown.

Molybdenum is present in soils at very low levels. The exact minerals that control its solubility are unknown, but $PbMoO_4$ (wulfenite) has been suggested as a possibility. Solubility measurements for Mo in soils generally range from 10^{-6} to 10^{-8} M. Further work is needed to identify the solid phases responsible for this control.

REFERENCES

Allen, S.E., and G.L. Terman. 1966. Response of maize and sudangrass to zinc in granular micronutrients. p. 255–256. In G.V. Jacks (ed.) Soil chemistry and fertility. Trans. Meet. Comm. 2 and 4. Int. Soc. Soil Sci. Aberdeen Univ. Scotland. September 1966. Univ. Press, Aberdeen, Scotland.

Bingham, F.T., A.W. Marsh, and R. Branson, R. Mahler, and G. Ferry. 1972. Reclamation of salt-affected soils in Western Kern County. Hilgardia 41:195–211.

Boawn, L.C., F.G. Viets, Jr., and C.L. Crawford. 1957. Plant utilization of zinc from various types of zinc compounds and fertilizer materials. Soil Sci. 83:219–229.

Boyle, F.W., Jr., and W.L. Lindsay. 1986. Manganese phosphate equilibrium relationships in soils. Soil Sci. Soc. Am. J. 50:588–593.

Carroll, M.D., and J.R. Loneragan. 1969. Responses of plant species to concentrations of Zn in solution: II. Rates of Zn absorption and their relation to growth. Aust. J. Agric. Res. 20:457–463.

Gestring, W.D., and P.N. Soltanpour. 1984. Evaluation of the ammonium bicarbonate-DTPA soil test for assessing boron availability to alfalfa. Soil Sci. Soc. Am. J. 48:96–100.

Gupta, V.C. 1979. Boron nutrition of crops. Adv. Agron. 31:273–307.

Halvorson, A.D., and W.L. Lindsay. 1977. The critical Zn^{2+} concentration for corn and the nonabsorption of chelated zinc. Soil Sci. Soc. Am. J. 41:532–534.

Hanif, M., C.J. deMooy, and W.L. Lindsay. 1986. Effect of alternate flooding and drying on the pH and redox of submerged soil. J. Agron. Crop Sci. 156:253–259.

Hodgson, J.F., W.L. Lindsay, and J.F. Trierweiler. 1966. Micronutrient cation complexing in soil solution: II. Complexing of zinc and copper in displaced solution from calcareous soils. Soil Sci. Soc. Am. Proc. 30:723–726.

Jenne, E.A. 1968. Controls on Mn, Fe, Co, Ni, Cu, and Zn concentrations in soils and water: The significant role of hydrous Mn and Fe oxides. p. 337–387. *In* Trace inorganics in water. Adv. Chem. Ser. 73. Am. Chem. Soc., Washington, DC.

Lavy, T.L., and S.A. Barber. 1964. Movement of molybdenum in the soil and its effect on availability to the plant. Soil Sci. Soc. Am. Proc. 28:93–97.

Lindsay, W.L. 1979. Chemical equilibria in soils. Copyright © 1979 by John Wiley & Sons, Inc. Wiley-Interscience, New York.

Lindsay, W.L., and E.W. Brennan. 1987. Speciation and solid phase control of Mn in soils. p. 171. *In* Agronomy Abstracts. ASA, Madison, WI.

Lindsay, W.L., and W.A. Norvell. 1969. Equilibrium relationships of Zn^{2+}, Fe^{3+}, Ca^{2+}, and H^+ with EDTA and DTPA in soils. Soil Sci. Soc. Am. Proc. 33:62–68.

Lindsay, W.L., and M. Sadiq. 1983. Use of pe + pH to predict and interpret metal solubility relationships in soils. Sci. Total Environ. 28:169–178.

Lindsay, W.L., and A.P. Schwab. 1982. The chemistry of iron in soil and its availability to plants. J. Plant Nutr. 4:821–840.

Ma, Qiying, and W.L. Lindsay. 1990. Divalent zinc activity in arid-zone soils obtained by chelation. Soil Sci. Soc. Am. J. 54:719–722.

Norvell, W.A., H. Dabkowska-Haskret, and E.E. Cary. 1987. Effect of phosphorus and zinc fertilization on the solubility of Zn^{2+} in two alkaline soils. Soil Sci. Soc. Am. J. 51:584–588.

Norvell, W.A., and W.L. Lindsay. 1969. Reactions of EDTA complexes of Fe, Zn, Mn, and Cu with soils. Soil Sci. Soc. Am. Proc. 33:86–91.

Norvell, W.A., and W.L. Lindsay. 1972. Reactions of DTPA chelates of iron, zinc, copper, and manganese with soil. Soil Sci. Soc. Am. Proc. 36:773–788.

Norvell, W.A., and W.L. Lindsay. 1982a. Estimation of the concentration of Fe^{3+} and $(Fe^{3+})(OH^-)^3$ ion product from equilibria of EDTA in soil. Soil Sci. Soc. Am. J. 46:710–715.

Norvell, W.A., and W.L. Lindsay. 1982b. Effect of ferric chloride additions on the solubility of ferric iron in a near-neutral soil. J. Plant Nutr. 5:1285–1295.

Phillipson, T. 1953. Boron in plants and soils with special regard to Swedish agriculture. Acta Agr. Scand. 3:121–242.

Ponnamperuma, F.N., E.M. Tianco, and T.A. Loy. 1967. Redox equilibria in flooded soils. I. The iron hydroxide systems. Soil Sci. 103:374–382.

Sajwan, K.S., and W.L. Lindsay. 1986. Effects of redox on zinc deficiency in paddy rice. Soil Sci. Soc. Am. J. 50:1264–1269.

Schwab, A.P., and W.L. Lindsay. 1983. The effect of redox on the solubility and availability of manganese in a calcareous soil. Soil Sci. Soc. Am. J. 47:217–220.

Schwab, A.P., and W.L. Lindsay. 1989. A computer simulation of Fe(III) and Fe(II) complexation in nutrient solution. II. Experimental. Soil Sci. Soc. Am. J. 53:34–38.

Schwertmann, U. 1988. Occurrence and formation of iron oxides in various pedoenvironments. p. 267–308. *In* J.W. Stucki et al. (ed.) Iron in soils and clay minerals. NATO ASI Series C 127. D. Reidel Publ. Co., Boston.

Schwertmann, U., and R.M. Taylor. 1989. Iron oxides. p. 379–438. *In* J.B. Dixon and S.W. Weed (ed.) Minerals in soil environments. 2nd ed. SSSA, Madison, WI.

Sims, J.R., and F.T. Bingham. 1968. Retention of boron by layer silicates, sesquioxides, and soil materials: II. Sesquioxides. Soil Sci. Soc. Am. Proc. 32:364–369.

Sinha, M.K., S.K. Dhillon, K.S. Dhillon, and S. Dyanand. 1978. Solubility relationships of iron, manganese, copper, and zinc in alkaline and calcareous soils. Aust. J. Soil Res. 16:19–26.

Vlek, P.L.G., and W.L. Lindsay. 1977. Thermodynamic stability and solubility of molybdenum minerals in soils. Soil Sci. Soc. Am. J. 41:42–46.

Chapter 5

Chemical Forms of Micronutrients in Soils

L. M. SHUMAN, *University of Georgia, Georgia Station, Griffin, Georgia*

Soils are complex media with solid, liquid, and gaseous phases. The solid phase is composed of inorganic and organic matter, and living organisms. Soils are both chemically and physically diverse, not only in composition, but in the dynamic changes that take place due to biological, environmental, and gravitational influences. Thus, micronutrients are just as diverse in their chemical and physical forms, which are expected to change due to perturbations of the system. The purpose, then, for investigating the forms of micronutrients in soils is to determine their distribution among the solid and liquid phases of the soil, and to relate these forms to bioavailability.

Much of the micronutrients associated with the solid phase is not available for plant uptake. In fact, <10% generally are in soluble and exchangeable forms (Lake et al., 1984). However, redistribution among forms, due to changes in soil properties brought about by natural or anthropogenic causes, makes the so-called capacity factor important for micronutrients. Studies that determine how changes in properties bring micronutrients into available forms are important, especially to determine from which form they become available and what changes are necessary to cause redistribution. Research on forms of metals is gaining momentum because of the environmental consequences of adding metals to soils in waste materials. Thus, not only are the forms themselves important, but possibly of even greater significance are the potential changes among forms due to outside influences.

This chapter will emphasize applications of selective sequential extraction techniques to agronomic problems. Much of the literature on selective sequential extraction has been in the areas of geochemistry (Chao, 1984) and environmental science (Lake et al., 1984). Therefore, many references will cite fractionation research outside of agronomy, but the results and conclusions will have implications relative to the general bioavailability of micronutrients. Single soil-extraction techniques designed to predict deficiencies and toxicities are covered elsewhere and will not be a part of this review. Soil processes will be mentioned only as they relate to metal redistribution among forms. Finally, the micronutrients considered are those that are needed by plants in small amounts (Zn, Cu, Mn, Fe, B, and Mo), and are not trace elements or microelements, which would exclude Fe, a major soil constituent.

This review will emphasize the current literature on selective sequential extraction and the application of these techniques to study changes in the forms of micronutrients. The first section will consider the various pools of micronutrients in soils, which constitute the forms that are to be determined by the sequential extraction techniques. The second section concerns the techniques themselves and how certain procedures were chosen. The third section deals with applications of the techniques to study redistribution of micronutrients among fractions, and the relationships of the changes in distribution to plant bioavailability.

I. POOLS OF MICRONUTRIENTS IN SOILS

The content of soils and rocks indicate that in terms of amount, Zn, Cu, Mn, Mo, and B are trace elements and Fe is a macro element (Krauskopf, 1972). These elements can be divided among pools in soils, according to conceptual forms. The terms usually applied to these micronutrients are ion exchangeable, adsorbed, organic-bound, hydrous oxide segment, and lattice component micronutrients (Pickering, 1981). Micronutrients in the soil solution could also be included in this list.

A. Micronutrients in the Soil Solution

Without a doubt the soil solution is the central focus of soil chemistry, since it is from this medium that plants absorb nutrients and it is the center of all important soil chemical processes (Lindsay, 1979). The element concentrations in soil solution are in constant flux, influenced by a host of factors including moisture, pH, temperature, oxidation/reduction status, fertilizer additions, and plant uptake. Soil water content is most important, in that, under wet conditions, elements dissolve or move by diffusion and with the water under gravitational influence. As the soil dries, the ions in solution become more concentrated, and can precipitate or be adsorbed. Even though this dynamic equilibrium is recognized, in selective fractionation schemes this form can only be extracted with water or dilute salt solutions in greater solution-to-solid ratios than are found in natural soils.

Most of the metallic micronutrients in soil solution are not in a free ionic form, but are complexed with both inorganic and organic ligands. Therefore, the total content in solution is not as important as the chemical species (Sposito, 1983), which, to a great extent, determine plant availability. Organic ligands act as carriers to the plant root (Lindsay, 1979). Metal chelation by organics is discussed in detail elsewhere in this book.

B. Surface Adsorbed and Exchangeable Micronutrients

The micronutrients exist in solution as charged ions and, as such, are attracted to the charged surfaces of colloids. The more prevalent colloids are the layer alumino-silicates, hydrous oxides of Al, Fe, and Mn, and solid organic matter. Extensive literature relates the adsorption of metals on these colloidal surfaces to their concentration in solution, and to other variables such as pH, concentration of other metals, and presence of various organic and inorganic ligands. Jenne (1968) described these variables and asserted that sorption and desorption mainly from oxide surfaces controlled the amounts of metals in solution. Besides sorption models, surface complexation models have also been presented to describe these phenomena (Sposito, 1983). This monograph devotes a section in Chapter 3 to these reactions and they will not be discussed here. Exchangeable and adsorbed ions usually are grouped as one pool and are extracted together, although some schemes make distinctions between weakly adsorbed (nonspecific sites) and strongly held ions (specific sites).

C. Micronutrients Associated with Organic Matter

Soil organic matter occurs in various forms, including water-soluble and solids in various degrees of decomposition. Micronutrients are associated with these materials by being incorporated in the structure of the less decomposed material, by chelation, which causes resistance to exchange, and by exchange and adsorption sites, both specific and nonspecific. Organic matter is closely associated with other fractions, such as the Fe oxides and sulfides, which makes specific extractions difficult (Warren, 1981).

D. Micronutrients Associated with Oxides and Carbonates

Oxides of Fe and Mn have a significant effect on micronutrient reactions in soils because they commonly occur as coatings or concretions and as discrete particles of colloidal dimensions, and by their strong affinity for metal ions (Chao & Theobald, 1976). In fact, Jenne (1968) named them as the principal factor in the fixation of Zn, Cu, and other metals in soils and sediments. In calcareous soils, metals can also be associated with carbonates. Manganese oxides are less abundant than Fe oxides, but they exhibit a greater chemical reactivity and are present in many more mineral forms (Chao & Theobald, 1976). Thus, trace element concentrations are often high in the Mn oxides (Taylor & McKenzie, 1966). Metals are associated with the oxides by adsorption, surface complex formation, ion exchange, penetration of the crystal lattice, and coprecipitation. Zinc, Mn, and Mo are coprecipitated with Fe oxides; Zn and Fe with Mn oxides; and Mn and Fe with carbonates (Sposito, 1983).

E. Micronutrients in Primary Minerals and Secondary Alumino-Silicate Minerals

A majority of the micronutrient metals are found in the crystal structures of the highly resistant primary and secondary minerals, which comprise the residual fraction after all other extractants have been employed

(Shuman, 1985). Krauskopf (1972) and Sposito (1983) provide tables that show how micronutrients occur in primary minerals. Two of these types are sulfides for Zn, Cu, and Fe, and carbonates for Zn, Cu, Mn, and Fe. These forms usually are less resistant to extraction and are taken as a separate fraction or dissolved with one of the other fractions, such as the organic fraction. However, the majority of the metals in this class are associated with silicate minerals in isomorphous substitution sites within primary or secondary minerals.

II. SELECTIVE CHEMICAL EXTRACTION OF MICRONUTRIENTS FROM SOILS

After defining the pools of micronutrients in soils, the next step is to examine the chemical extraction procedures that are used to selectively determine the micronutrients in these pools. It is well recognized that these methods are not specific, but are only selective, and are employed to study the distribution among principal components (Campbell et al., 1988). The most appropriate sequence to employ is a subject of current research efforts (Miller et al., 1986), but is generally from the least to the most aggressive reagents and from the least to the greatest extremes in temperature and stirring or shaking. The fractions are, by necessity, operationally defined, but have advanced from early empirical approaches to those based on sound principles (Chao, 1984). This section will describe the most frequently used procedures for selective fractionation, some arguments over the reason that they are considered selective, and some of the problems encountered.

A. Extraction Procedures for Specific Soil Fractions

1. Water Soluble Fraction

If separated, the water-soluble fraction is the first fraction to be dissolved. The extractant is purified water, and the only variables among procedures is the soil-to-solution ratio, and the shaking method and time. In Fig. 5-1, only five methods specifically mention this fraction. The soil-to-solution ratio was 1:5 in all cases but shaking varied from 20 min with a 1 h presoak (Gatehouse et al., 1977) to 2 h (Mathur & Levesque, 1983). Jin et al. (1987) also includes a water-soluble fraction in his procedure for B. As early as 1949, it was reported that water extraction did not remove Mn and Cu combined with the organic matter (Heintze & Mann, 1949), indicating water extraction's specificity.

Amounts of metals brought into solution by water usually are very low and often cannot be detected by analytical methods. Metals may be significant in this fraction where micronutrient fertilizers or sewage sludge have recently been applied. Thus, the water-soluble fraction usually is not separated, unless there is a reason to expect it to be significant because of the treatments imposed.

2. Exchangeable Fraction

The exchangeable metals are held by electrostatic forces on colloid surfaces and, unlike the major cations Ca^{2+}, Mg^{2+}, K^+, H^+, and Al^{3+}, a majority are held in specific sites with high affinity for the metal. Thus, large excesses of cations are necessary to replace them. Common cations used are Ca^{2+}, Mg^{2+}, and NH_4^+, usually at a concentration of one molar (Fig. 5-1). Divalent ions should have greater replacing power than monovalent, but monovalent ions such as K^+ can replace some ions held between the layers of clay minerals.

Anions used for the exchangeable salts are Cl^-, NO_3^-, and CH_3COO^- (OAc^-). Chloride is often preferred because it will not cause appreciable pH change or affect other fractions. However, it is a stronger complexing anion than NO_3^- and, for that reason, NO_3^- salts have been used (Stover et al., 1976, Sposito et al., 1982, Shuman, 1985; Singh et al., 1988). Pickering (1986) noted that NO_3^- salts have received little attention and are at least as effective as Cl^- salts, without the uncertainties introduced by the complexing of Cl^-. Acetate is very commonly used (Fig. 5-1) with a solution pH of 7, but Lakanen (1962) preferred to use pH 4.65 to estimate exchangeable and readily soluble metals. Lowering the pH will undoubtedly release more metals; however, these may come from other than exchange sites as the clays are hydrolyzed. Acetate has been criticized as nonspecific for exchangeable ions, also dissolving carbonates (Robbins et al., 1984), and dissolving or complexing oxide coatings (Gibbs, 1973).

3. Sorbed Fraction

As mentioned above, much of the metal adsorbed on soil colloids occurs on specific exchange sites, which are not exchangeable with salt extractants. Therefore, several schemes devised for soil or sewage sludge samples include a sorbed or specifically sorbed fraction. Those for geochemical or sediment samples usually do not. Three of the example procedures in Fig. 5-1 employ 2.5% acetic acid for this fraction, all based on McLaren and Crawford's (1973) procedure for Cu in soils. They considered this Cu to originate from specific sites on oxides and clay minerals, thus mainly from inorganic sites. Stover et al. (1976) removed these adsorbed metals from wastewater sludge by forming soluble metal-fluoride complexes with KF at a pH of 6.5. For sludge-amended soils, Sposito et al. (1982) altered Stover's procedure to use three water extractions to solubilize the specifically sorbed fraction. Jin et al. (1987) used mannitol for specifically sorbed B. Amounts of metals in this fraction generally are very small.

4. Organic Fraction

Organic fraction procedures are difficult to choose because they often dissolve other fractions as well. The usual approach oxidizes the material to release the metals. These methods also oxidize sulfides, and so combine the fractions. Another approach disperses the organic colloids. Some proce-

Reference	Water sol.	Exch.	Sorbed	Organic	MnO	AFeO	CFeO	Carbonate	Sulfide	Residual
Grimme, 1967b		$MgCl_2$[a]		NaOH/EDTA		Acid NH_4Ox[§]	NH_4Ox + Zn			$HClO_4$
Gibbs, 1973				$NaOCl$[c]		CBD[b]				$LiBO_2$, HNO_3[d]
Zyrin, 1974	H_2O[a]	NH_4OAc[b§] pH 4.8		H_2O_2[d]	Acid NH_4Ox, UV light[e]			1M HCl to pH 3.5[c]		20% HCl[f]
Gupta and Chen, 1975	H_2O[a]	NH_4OAc[b]		H_2O_2[e]	Acid HA[d§]		HA + 25% HOAc[f]	1M HOAc[c]		HNO_3, HF $HClO_4$[g]
McLaren & Crawford, 1973		$CaCl_2$	HOAc	$K_4P_2O_7$	Acid NH_4Ox, UV light					HF
Stover, et al., 1976		KNO_3	KF, pH 6.5	$Na_4P_2O_7$				EDTA	HNO_3	
Gatehouse et al., 1977	H_2O[a]	NH_4OAc[b]		H_2O_2[d]	HA + NH_4OAc[c]		Hydrazine HCl[e]			$HClO_4$[f]
Hoffman & Fletcher, 1978				$NaOCl$[a]	Acid HA[c]	Acid NH_4Ox[d]	CBD, H_2O_2[e]	HCl, pH 3[b]		HNO_3, $HClO_4$[f]
Tessier, et al., 1979		$MgCl_2$[a]		H_2O_2, NH_4OAc[d]	HA + 25% HOAc[c]			NaOAc/HOAc pH 5[b]		HF, $HClO_4$[e]

Reference	Extractants (left to right)
Sposito, et al., 1982	H_2O[a], KNO_3, H_2O, 3X, NaOH, EDTA, HNO_3
Mathur & Levesque, 1983	$CaCl_2$[b], HOAC[d], DTPA[e], $CaCl_2$ + HQ[c], HCl[f], KCN[g], HF, $HClO_4$[e]
Meguellati et al., 1982	$BaCl_2$[a], H_2O_2 NH_4OAc[b], HA + 25% HOAC, NH_4OAc[d], HOAC + $NaOAc$[c], HF, $HClO_4$
Goldberg & Smith, 1984	$CaCl_2$, EDTA, HQ + NH_4OAc, Acid NH_4Ox, UV light
Robbins et al., 1984	Na dodecyl SO_4 + $NaHCO_3$[b], HA + Na citrate, pH 5[c], HOAc + $NaOAc$[a], HF, HNO_3[d]
Shuman, 1985	$Mg(NO_3)_2$, NaOCl, Acid HA, Acid NH_4Ox, Acid NH_4Ox Ascorb. Acid, HF, HCl, HNO_3
Miller, et al., 1986	H_2O[a], $Ca(NO_3)_2$[b], $Pb(NO_3)_2$[c] $Ca(NO_3)_2$, $K_4P_2O_7$[e], Acid HA[d], Acid NH_4Ox[f], Acid NH_4Ox[g], Acid NH_4Ox UV light, Aqua Reg.[h] HF
Mandal and Mandal, 1987	NH_4OAc, $Cu(OAc)_2$, Acid NH_4Ox, CBD

Superscript letters indicate sequence of extractants when they are not in order from left to right.
AFeO is amorphous iron oxide; CFeO is crystalline iron oxide.
Ox is oxalate; OAc is acetate; HA is hydroxylamine.

Fig. 5-1. Sequential extraction methods used for micronutrient fractions.

dures use chelating agents to extract the metals chelated by the soil humic material, such as those of Mathur and Levesque (1983) and Goldberg and Smith (1984).

Bascomb (1968) was one of the first to suggest pyrophosphate ($K_4P_2O_7$) to extract organic fraction (McLaren & Crawford, 1973; Stover et al., 1976; Iyengar et al., 1981; Miller et al., 1986). Pyrophosphate complexes the cations, which stabilize the organic matter, causing it to disperse. Pyrophosphate evidently does not dissolve sulfides (Chao, 1984), which would be useful if sulfides were to be separated from the organic fraction. The major criticism of the extractant is that is also solubilizes part or all of the amorphous Fe oxides (Shuman, 1982). A recent study using Moessbauer spectroscopy verified that pyrophosphate dissolves no particular form of Fe (Parfitt & Childs, 1988). However, others feel that pyrophosphate does not dissolve significant amounts of Fe oxides (McKeague, 1967; McKeague & Schuppi, 1982; Chao, 1984). Miller et al. (1986) recognized that pyrophosphate solubilized oxides and that hydroxlyamine hydrochloride ($NH_2OH \cdot HCl$) did not. They recommended putting hydroxylamine ahead of pyrophosphate in the sequence, thus removing the oxides before the organic fraction.

Acid peroxide has been used to destroy organic matter from clays prior to mineralogical analysis (Kittrick & Hope, 1963). It appears in several sequential procedures in Fig. 5-1 and was used in the earlier procedure by Shuman (1979). It has several drawbacks: (i) it extracts the Mn oxide fraction; (ii) it dissolves any sulfides present (Gupta & Chen, 1975; Gatehouse et al., 1977); and (iii) it can form oxalates, which attack Fe oxides (Lavkulich & Weins, 1970). Some of these problems can be avoided by placing the acid peroxide after the Mn oxide and amorphous Fe oxide fractions (Tessier et al., 1979). However, oxalate, which is often used for these fractions, will extract metals from organic matter (Kuo et al., 1983). The addition of pyrophosphate to H_2O_2 greatly increases the amount of organic matter extracted (Sequi & Aringhieri, 1977), but this adds one problematic extractant to another in terms of organic metal extraction.

Another oxidizing agent, NaOCl at pH 8 to 9.5, has found wisespread use in sequential procedures. It has been found to be more effective than H_2O_2 for extracting organic matter with less destruction of carbonates and oxides (Anderson, 1963; Lavkulich & Wiens, 1970; Omueti, 1980, 1981). The same was true for NaOBr (Bourget & Tanner, 1953). This reagent, like H_2O_2, dissolves sulfides, and the high pH may precipitate metals (Hoffman & Fletcher, 1981). Hoffman and Fletcher (1981) used a pH 3 water wash following NaOCl to redissolve any precipitated metals, but the amounts were extremely low. Hypochlorite oxidizes Mn to permanganate to produce a pink color in soil extracts (Anderson & O'Connor, 1972), which may indicate that NaOCl solubilized Mn oxides. However, Uren et al. (1988) presented data to indicate that NaOCl dissolves $\leq 0.1\%$ of the Mn in lithiophorite and birnessite, the common forms of Mn oxides in soils (Taylor & McKenzie, 1966). Thus, NaOCl seems to be a good compromise for an organic extractant, dissolving the most metals from the fraction and the least from others (Shuman, 1983).

Besides H_2O_2, $K_2P_4O_7$, and NaOCl, there are several other approaches that have been proposed. Sodium hydroxide was used by Grimme (1967b) and Sposito et al. (1982). Adding EDTA to NaOH increased the extracted organic Fe without attacking inorganic Fe (Grimme & Wiechman, 1969). Shuman (1983) added DTPA to NaOCl to chelate the released metals, but found that the DTPA dissolved portions of the Fe oxide fraction. Copper acetate has been used to displace metals strongly held by organic sites (Mandal & Mandal, 1987a, b; Murthy & Schoen, 1987). Iron organic complexes were observed using NH_4OAc-dipyridyl indicator (Childs, 1981). Robbins et al. (1984), who recognized problems with oxidizers and found that strong bases degrade clays, used a dispersing sufactant sodium dodecyl sulfate in dilute $NaHCO_3$ at pH 8.8.

5. Oxide Fraction

a. Manganese Oxide Fraction. To solubilize the Mn oxides, a reducing agent that will reduce Mn, but not Fe, is required. Dion et al. (1947) suggested hydroxylamine for extracting Mn, since it solubilized more Mn than hydroquinone and was preferred because of the lack of a hydroquinone residue. Hydroxylamine has become standard for selective extraction of Mn oxides. Most procedures that include it use the method of Chao (1972), who employed $0.1\ M$ hydroxylamine in $0.01\ M$ HNO_3 at pH 2, which he reported to dissolve 85% of the Mn oxide and only 5% of the Fe in various sediments. Several studies have corroborated that hydroxyl-amine is specific for Mn oxides (Frampton & Reisenauer, 1978; Shuman, 1982). Jin et al. (1978) used this procedure for the Mn oxide fraction for B. Tokashiki et al. (1986) found that hydroxylamine dissolved birnessite, but not lithiophorite, both of which are common in soils. The citrate-bicarbonate-dithionite (CBD) method (Mehra & Jackson, 1960), used for crystalline Fe oxides, dissolved lithiophorite.

Most of the methods that dissolve Fe oxides will also remove Mn oxides. They are indicated in Fig. 5–1, where one reagent is used for both the Mn and Fe oxides. They will be discussed later. Daniels et al. (1962) used sodium dithionite ($Na_2S_2O_4$) for Mn, and indicated that pH and reducing conditions controlled the amount extracted. Of course, this reagent will also dissolve Fe oxides. As mentioned above, acid H_2O_2 will dissolve Mn oxides and was used by Taylor and McKenzie (1966) as a Mn specific reagent. This method is useful if the organic fraction has been removed beforehand.

b. Amorphous Iron Oxide Fraction. One of the earliest and most popular methods for extracting the amorphous or microcrystalline Fe oxides is that of McKeague and Day (1966). The extractant is $0.2\ M$ ammonium oxalate at pH 3. The samples are shaken in the dark for 4 h to prevent photolytic reduction. It has been verified that this procedure dissolves the amorphous Fe fraction and does not dissolve the more crystalline Fe fraction (McKeague, 1967; Dudas & Harward, 1971). On a soil sample that has not been pre-extracted, the difference between pyrophosphate Fe and the McKeague-procedure Fe was considered to be the amorphous Fe oxide fraction

(McKeague et al., 1971). Pawluk (1972) indicated that a double extraction with acid oxalate solubilized amorphous Fe oxides, but that there is a continuum between the amorphous and crystalline phase, which made exact separation difficult. Parfitt and Childs (1988) found, using Mossbauer spectrometry, that the oxalate extraction dissolves ferrihydrite.

Another selective extractant developed more recently consists of 0.25 M hydroxylamine in 0.25 M HCl at 50 °C for 30 min in a shaker bath (Chao & Zhou, 1983). The results agree with those using the McKeague and Day (1966) Method; < 1% of the crystalline Fe is dissolved. The method was better than oxalate for anomaly enhancement in geochemical exploration (Filipek et al., 1982). Ross et al. (1985) modified the procedure to use a wide soil:solution ratio (1:250) and to shake overnight at room temperature. The procedure should be useful for selective dissolution schemes, but is too recent to have had much application.

Several other techniques have been tested for amorphous Fe oxides. Tiron (4,5-dihydroxy-m-benzene disulfonic acid, disodium salt) solution at 0.1 M, pH 10.5, and 80 °C for 1 h has been examined using model compounds (Biermans & Baert, 1977). The procedure has not appeared in fractionation procedures. Borggaard (1979) suggested EDTA solutions at various pH levels, concentrations, and shaking times. However, since the shaking times were 3 to 9 mo, the method is not routinely applicable. He was able to show that EDTA did dissolve amounts of Fe similar to oxalate and that crystalline Fe oxides were not attacked (Borggaard, 1981a, 1982). His attempt to shorten the shaking time using high temperatures resulted in dissolving cyrstalline Fe oxides (Borggaard, 1981b).

c. **Crystalline Iron Oxide Fraction.** Figure 5–1 shows a great variation in the methods used for the crystalline Fe oxide fraction. Probably the best known method is that of Mehra and Jackson (1960) using dithionite in a citrate/bicarbonate buffer (CBD), developed to remove all the Fe and Al oxides from soil clays prior to mineralogical examination (e.g., Kittrick & Hope, 1963). Dithionite is often contaminated with Zn, requiring a purified reagent. Also, the method can precipitate metal sulfides. It has been used as a general oxide extractant dissolving the Mn oxide, amorphous Fe oxide, and crystalline Fe oxide fractions, or it has been used more selectively after the removal of the first two. This is true of all the crystalline Fe oxide extractants. The CBD method was applied to Fe fractionation for soil characterization and found to be satisfactory after using pyrophosphate and oxalate (McKeague & Day, 1966; McKeague, 1967; McKeague et al., 1971; Pawluk, 1972). Arshad et al. (1972) found that CBD dissolved little of the silicate clays. Recent studies using X-ray diffractions and Moessbauer spectrometry show that CBD is specific for goethite and hematite as well as ferrihydrite (Borggard, 1988; Parfitt & Childs, 1988).

Another popular method uses oxalate solutions with UV light (DeEndredy, 1963; Schwertmann, 1964). It is used in several fractionation schemes shown in Fig. 5–1. A fluorescent lamp was used by Kawai (1977) with 0.1

M oxalic acid to remove Fe oxides. Grimme (1967b) used Zn as a reductant with oxalate for the crystalline oxide fraction, a method suggested by Haldane (1956) that produces no precipitation and does not attack layer aluminosilicates. Shuman (1982, 1985) employed ascorbic acid as a reductant with oxalate, bypassing the problems of standardizing UV methods and the problems associated with CBD.

To dissolve all soil oxides, 1 M hydroxylamine with 25% acetic acid was developed (Chester & Hughes, 1967). Frampton and Reisenauer (1978) distinguished between Mn oxides and crystalline Fe oxides by varying the hydroxylamine concentration and the acid (HNO_3 vs. acetic). Robbins et al. (1984) buffered the hydroxylamine with Na citrate at pH 5 to prevent an attack on silicates, which can occur with the low pH acetic acid.

Several other extractants for the crystalline Fe fraction have been presented. Hydrazine HCl was employed by Gatehouse et al. (1977) in their fractionation procedure (Fig. 5-1). Wang et al. (1981) concluded that Tiron was better for removing amorphous materials than dithionite in a citrate-bicarbonate buffer or 0.5 M NaOH. The CBD did not remove all the amorphous Al and the NaOH dissolved the phyllosilicates.

6. Carbonate and Sulfide Fraction

Two groups of carbonates important to metal chemistry and present in alkaline soils are the Ca/Mg carbonates, which adsorb and occlude metals, and the metal carbonates themselves. Acids are useful to dissolve the carbonates, but the acid must not be so strong as to attack the silicates. Using 1 M NaOAc made to pH 5 with HOAc completely dissolves calcite without attacking silicates (Robbins et al., 1984) and dissolves dolomite (Tessier et al., 1979). Stover et al. (1976) suggested EDTA, which solubilized 91% of model metal carbonates while solubilizing < 10% of the sulfides. This method was adapted by Sposito et al. (1982) for their fractionation procedure. Finally, acids alone have been employed, even though they may attack layer silicates. Gupta and Chen (1975) used 1 M HOAc, Mathur and Levesque (1983) used 0.1 M HCl, and Zyrin et al. (1974) reacted soils with 1 M HCl until pH reached 3.5.

Few fractionation procedures include sulfides as a separate fraction. Since oxidizing agents dissolve sulfides, if H_2O_2 or NaOCl are used for the organic fraction, the sulfide metals will be combined with that fraction, as acknowledged by Gupta and Chen (1975) and Gatehouse et al. (1977). Based on pH stability, HNO_3 was used by Stover et al. (1976) to dissolve metal sulfides not extracted by prior reagents in their scheme. Sposito et al. (1982), who patterned their procedure after that of Stover, also used HNO_3. Mathur and Levesque (1983) employed 0.1 M KCN for sulfides, but gave no information about its specificity. Potassium chlorate-HCl was more selective for sulfides in bedrock geochemistry than H_2O_2, aqua regia, or HNO_3-$HClO_4$ (Olade & Fletcher, 1974).

7. Residual Fraction

The remaining silicates and other resistant minerals are brought into solution by digesting with HF, HNO_3, HCl, or $HClO_4$ in heat-resistant plastic containers, either open or in bombs under pressure. An older method, nearly abandoned today, uses fusion with alkali salts and dissolution in HNO_3 (Gibbs, 1973). An alternate approach leaches the residual solids with strong mineral acids without completely destroying the matrix and assumes the majority of the metals will be extracted. A 90% HNO_3/10% HCl digestion was found adequate for total metals in a U.S. Bureau of Standards new industrial river sediment, but for selected estuarine sediments, the recovery was low (Sinex et al. 1980). Aitang and Hani (1983) reported that 2 M HNO_3 solubilized 59 and 68% of total Cu and Zn, respectively, and 3 M HCl solubilized 59 and 85% of the total Cu and Zn, respectively. Thus, total element concentrations are not well approximated by methods that do not destroy the sample completely.

B. Problems with Extracting Specific Micronutrient Forms

Selective sequential extraction to measure discrete forms of metals is an attractive method that yields data that can help solve problems, gain new insights, and aid in proving research hypotheses. However, the technique is not without certain problems, which are well recognized, but have only recently been addressed by research. The most obvious is selectivity of the reagents. Other problems include readsorption and precipitation of the micronutrient of interest.

1. Selectivity for Specific Forms

Selectivity is relative and the procedure is chosen that dissolves the greatest amount of one fraction and the least of the others. For example Guy et al. (1978) found that H_2O_2 did not release all the Cu from the organic fraction and 1 M NH_4Cl did not release all the exchangeable Cu^{2+} from model sediments. Tipping et al. (1985) used Shuman's (1982) procedure to separate Mn oxides and Fe oxides. They found good selectivity for Zn and Mn, but did not find Ca and Pb in the correct fractions according to electron microprobe analysis.

A recent report by Borggaard (1988) showed that pyrophosphate and oxalate were not entirely selective. The nature of the dissolved phase for ETDA is also obscure. Rudd et al. (1988) concluded that the selectivity and efficiency of reagents differ when used in sequence with other reagents, and that sample preparation influenced fractionation in model compounds for sewage sludge. Using model sediments, Kheboian and Bauer (1987) concluded that metals were not recovered in the appropriate fractions using Tessier's (Tessier et al., 1979) procedure. Tessier and Campbell (1988) rebutted that the methods Kheboian and Bauer used were not correct, in that the added metals were not necessarily in the same forms that they would be found in nature. Tessier and Campbell (1988) acknowledged the operational nature of the method, but despite its drawbacks, asserted that it serves very well to solve research problems.

2. Readsorption of Micronutrients on Less Labile Forms

The amount of metal that is released from a certain fraction and subsequently readsorbed is difficult to define experimentally. Rendell et al. (1980) found that metals in uncontaminated sediments were adsorbed after extraction with many reagents, including HCl, hydroxylamine, NH_4OAc, CBD, and HOAc. Roger (1986) warned that readsorption is always a problem, that minimizes the metals in the first steps of a fractionation procedure and overestimates them in the last. One method employed to overcome readsorption uses repeated extractions with the same reagent. Robbins et al. (1984) extracted up to five times. However, Belzile et al. (1989) found that readsorption was not a problem with spiking samples for Zn and Cu if they were not spiked outside the range of experimental error. Thus, in some cases readsorption is not considered a severe problem, and where it is suspected, repeated extraction should serve to solubilize readsorbed metals.

3. Other Problems of Selective Extraction

Precipitation of metals during extraction is often acknowledged as a potential problem. Sequi and Aringhieri (1977) stated that metals may precipitate as hydroxides in organic matter extraction with either H_2O_2 or pyrophosphate. Hoffman and Fletcher (1981) used an acid wash following the high pH NaOCl extraction to redissolve precipitated hydroxides. They also used H_2O_2 to redissolve metal sulfides precipitated during dithionite extraction. Washes between fractions to eliminate excess reagent could lead to problems due to metal loss in the wash itself (Dong et al., 1985). Even sample handling prior to extraction can be critical to the results as well as the presence or absence of O_2 during extraction, especially when dealing with submerged sediments or soils (Rapin et al., 1986). Finally, differences in individual laboratory techniques could be a source of error when comparing results because of the multitude of steps involved. Robbe (1987) compared the results with Tessier's (Tessier et al., 1979) Method between 17 laboratories and found good accuracy. However, as with the references cited above, he found that the metals in each solution were not necessarily representative of the metal quantity in that phase, indicating problems in selectivity.

III. REDISTRIBUTION AMONG MICRONUTRIENT FORMS

Besides providing information about the forms of micronutrients in soil in general, selective extraction methods can be employed to study dynamics of changes in forms. It is in this application that the method becomes most useful by determining whether a particular perturbation of the system will cause metals to redistribute among forms. The ultimate redistribution into more or less bioavailable forms is the most important practical application of the method. This section will discuss each micronutrient in turn, considering the redistribution among forms caused by various inputs, including micronutrient additions and changes in pH, organic matter, and oxidation/reduction status. Also, the changes over time and those due to differences in location or soil depth, tillage, and other factors will be discussed.

A. Zinc Redistribution

Most of the total Zn in soils exists in unavailable forms. Thus, the percentage of Zn in the more plant-available forms, such as the water-soluble, exchangeable, and organic, are low compared with less plant-available forms in the oxide and residual fractions (Berthet et al., 1984; Emmerich et al., 1982; Hickey & Kittrick, 1984). The water-soluble and exchangeable pools of Zn are considered very bioavailable, the carbonate are potentially available, and the residual are nonlabile or nonavailable, according to LeClaire et al. (1984). They found that organic Zn was correlated with DTPA-extractable Zn. Thus is may also be considered plant available. Likewise, Singhania et al. (1983) reported that since Zn in an organic slurry is largely in the exchangeable and organic forms, it was more available than that from $ZnSO_4$.

Both Harrison et al. (1981) and Hickey and Kittrick (1984) found that Zn was higher both in mobility and bioavailability than was Cu in soils where these metals had been added as contaminants or in sewage sludge. Levesque and Mathur (1988) related the water-soluble and exchangeable fractions to the intensity factor and concluded that the sum of the two fractions may form the basis of a good soil test for available Zn. Zinc that is DTPA extractable, as well as other extractable forms, are often correlated with the more available fractions, such as exchangeable and organic fractions, and thus, are considered plant available (Rappaport et al., 1986; Shuman, 1986, 1988b). However, Rappaport et al. (1986) found that organic-fraction Zn was negatively correlated with DTPA Zn, indicating that a portion of this fraction is not plant available. Iyengar et al. (1981) used a multivariable equation with six Zn fractions and soil pH, which accounted for 94% of the Zn uptake by corn (*Zea mays* L.). Thus, the more easily soluble fractions are related to plant availability and have even been used to predict plant response to added micronutrients.

1. Zinc Additions to Soils

Fractionation techniques are often employed to study Zn forms after it has been applied as a component of sewage sludge. The Zn found in soil amended with sewage sludge is usually low in the more bioavailable water-soluble, exchangeable and organic forms compared with the other forms (Adams & Sanders, 1984; Sposito et al., 1982). However, increases in these forms compared with unamended soil are considered to be important environmentally (Knudtsen & O'Connor, 1987; Schalscha et al., 1980). Zinc in soils contaminated by other means, such as from smelters, is often found in the exchangeable and organic forms (Miller & McFee, 1983; Miller et al., 1983). However, Hickey and Kittrick (1984) reported that Zn-contaminated soil had high amounts of Zn in the Fe and Mn-oxide fractions (39%). Added Zn in a field experiment was found in both plant-available and nonavailable forms (Mullins et al., 1982a). Zinc in street dusts and roadside soils was in the carbonate, and Fe and Mn oxide forms (Harrison et al., 1981). Zinc distribution in these studies may have been influenced more by soil property changes caused by the addition of organic matter in sewage sludge, than by the added Zn itself.

2. Soil pH Changes

A large body of literature indicates that micronutrient metals become less plant available as soil pH increases. Zinc distribution in fractions also is affected by pH changes, usually increasing in more plant-available fractions as pH decreases (Sims, 1986; Neilsen et al., 1986). Increasing pH decreased Zn in the water-soluble fraction (El-Kherbawy & Sanders, 1984) and in the exchangeable fraction (Elsokkary & Lag, 1978; Iyengar et al., 1981; Sanders et al., 1986; Sims, 1988). An example of Zn redistribution from the exchangeable to the oxide fraction as pH is increased is provided in Fig. 5-2. Increasing soil pH also increased Zn in the organic fraction (Estepp & Keefer, 1969; Shuman, 1986). On the other hand, Neilsen et al. (1986) found that,

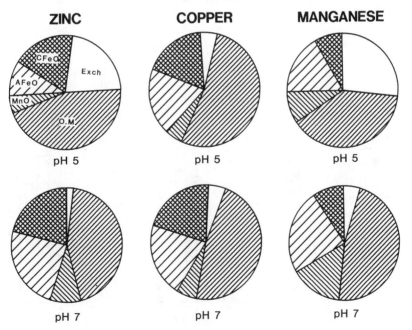

Fig. 5-2. Effect of pH on Zn, Cu, and Mn in soil fractions as an average of four soils. (From Sims, 1986.)

with acidification, Zn was redistributed from the residual to the exchangeable and organic fractions, which would increase Zn plant availability.

3. Organic Matter Amendments

The amount of Zn found in the organic fraction generally is higher than that in the exchangeable fraction (Sanders et al., 1986). The organic fraction Zn is quite naturally related to the amounts of organic material in the soil (Elsokkary & Lag, 1978; Iyengar et al., 1981; Mandal et al., 1986; McGrath et al., 1988). Organic matter additions to soils, whether as sewage sludge, manures, or plant material, usually cause redistributions of the soil Zn. Added organic matter caused applied Zn to increase in all fractions, except the crystalline Fe oxides and the residual, indicating an increase in bioavailability (Mandal et al., 1988). The same reasearch group found that increasing organic matter increased organic and exchangeable fraction Zn, and decreased the oxide fractions due to reducing conditions that make Zn more bioavailable (Mandal & Mandal, 1987a, b).

Manure amendment increased the water-soluble fraction Zn, which is the form highest in bioavailability (Singhania et al., 1983). Organic matter additions resulted in Zn redistribution from the oxide to the organic fraction (Fig. 5–3). In another study, the Zn shifted to the Mn and Fe oxide fractions from the other fractions indicating a decrease in availability (Shuman, 1988b). Thus, other factors besides organic matter additions can influence Zn redistributon. Adding organic matter can alter other soil properties, such as pH and redox status, and cause varying redistributions depending on the specific conditions involved.

3. Alteration of Oxidation and Reduction Status

Submerging soils causes the Eh to decrease and the pH to increase (Lindsay, 1979). This causes the oxides to become more soluble and release adsorbed and occluded metals. Thus, oxidation/reduction changes are very likely to bring about redistributions of Zn and other metals among fractions.

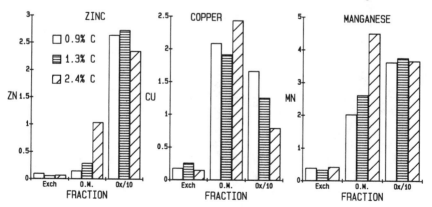

Fig. 5–3. Effect of organic carbon on Zn, Cu, and Mn in soil fractions. Ox/10 is the oxalate fraction value divided by 10. (From McGrath et al., 1988).

Keeping soils constantly wet increased Zn in the inorganic (oxide) fractions, but alternate wetting and drying caused increases in the organic fraction (Estepp & Keefer, 1969). Mandal and Mandal (1987a) reported that waterlogging or alternate wet and dry conditions caused decreases in the exchangeable, organic, and amorphous Fe oxide fraction Zn. However, earlier, they found that submergence increased organic and amorphous Fe oxide Zn (Mandal & Mandal, 1986).

Hazra et al. (1987) reported that reducing conditions decreased exchangeable and organic Zn, while increasing amorphous and crystalline Fe oxide Zn. These results are in contrast with those of Sims and Patrick (1978) who found that reducing conditions caused Zn to increase in the exchangeable and organic fractions and decrease in the oxide fractions, as did the data of Ghanem and Mikkelsen (1987) (Fig. 5-4). Thus, even though contradictions are evident, we know that the exchangeable, organic, and oxide fractions are affected, and that the usual pattern is for reducing conditions to increase Zn availability.

5. Effect of Time on Redistribution

Selective sequential extraction has been useful in tracking the forms of metals added to soils as they change with time. Initially, added metals exist in soluble fractions, which are highly bioavailable, and, with time, revert to the less soluble oxide and residual fractions, which are less plant available (Sarkar & Deb, 1985; Silviera & Sommers, 1977; Emmerich et al., 1982). However, exceptions abound where metals may become more available to biota with time.

In untreated soil, Zn was highest in the residual-sulfide fraction, but where sewage sludge had been applied for 7 yr, Zn was in the carbonate and

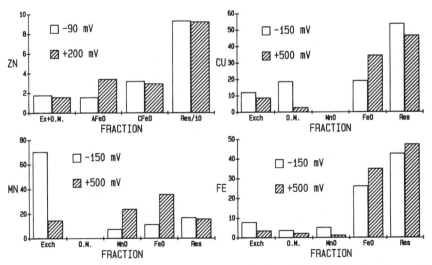

Fig. 5-4. Effect of Eh on Zn, Cu, Mn, and Fe in soil fractions. Ex + O.M. is the exchangeable plus the organic fraction. Res/10 is the residual value divided by 10. (Zinc data from Ghanem & Mikkelsen, 1987; Cu, Mn, and Fe data from Sims & Patrick, 1978).

organic fractions, indicating that the sewage sludge incresed Zn availability (Chang et al., 1984). However, there was no redistribution found in analyzing at 4-wk intervals between planting and harvest. Over a 13-yr period, Zn decreased in all fractions, but most depletion resulted from the acid-soluble and weakly adsorbed fractions, which are highly plant available. Thus, in this instance, Zn became much less plant available with time (Brar et al., 1986).

In a pot experiment, added Zn initially existed in the acid-soluble or clay fraction, which is very unavailable. With time, the acid-soluble Zn decreased and the organic Zn increased, indicating a shift to more available forms (Keefer & Estepp, 1971). This result contradicts that found above in which Zn usually reverted to less-available forms. Sposito et al. (1983) found that Zn from sewage sludge increased in the carbonte fraction with time (Fig. 5-5), which is somewhat similar to that found by Steinhilber and Boswell (1983), in which exchangeable- and carbonate-fraction Zn from sewage sludge increased with time. Thus, the Zn in these studies became less plant available with time.

6. Other Factors Affecting Redistribution

Selective extraction has been used for a variety of soil chemical studies that do not fit in the above categories. Zinc in contaminated soil was immobile, since Zn in all fractions decreased sharply with depth and existed largely in the crystalline Fe oxides, with only small amounts in the amorphous Fe oxides (Kuo et al., 1983). Likewise, Chandi and Takkar (1982) found that added Zn was confined to the 0 to 30-cm depth. They examined the influence of cropping systems on Zn in fractions, which, in turn, influence soil pH, organic matter, and $CaCO_3$. A cereal-cereal system caused low

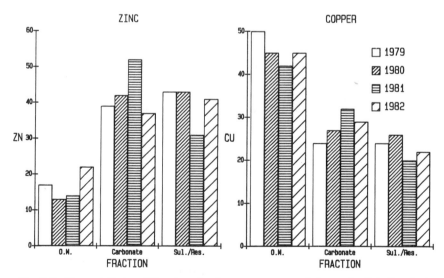

Fig. 5-5. Zinc and Cu in soil fractions for 4 yr as an average of three soils. Sul./Res. is the residual sulfide fraction. (From Sposito et al., 1983.)

exchangeable Zn^{2+}, a legume-millet system caused low adsorbed Zn, and a cereal-legume system caused low organic fraction Zn.

Lindau and Hossner (1982) found no differences in Zn fractions between marshes at different locations. Tillage treatments had little effects on Zn in fractions (Shuman & Hargrove, 1985). However, added P redistributed Zn from the Mn-oxide and crystalline Fe-oxide fractions to the exchangeable fraction for eight soils, presumably making it more plant available (Shuman, 1988a). In another study, however, the P level did not influence the Zn distribution in fractions (El-Kherbawy & Sanders, 1984). Added Cu altered Zn forms, increasing the more mobile and available forms by displacing them from tightly bound sites (Mathur & Levesque, 1983). Zinc adsorption was decreased after removal of Fe oxides (Cavallro & McBride, 1984) and Mn oxides (Shuman, 1988d). Zinc adsorption was also decreased by organic matter removal, but Mn oxides seem to play the most important role in Zn adsorption, according to these adsorption experiments following selective extraction.

B. Copper Redistribution

Like Zn, Cu is found largely in unavailable forms, according to fractionation techniques. Copper in the water-soluble and exchangeable forms are considered to be plant available, whereas that associated with organic matter may be so tightly bound as to be relatively unavailable (Mathur & Levesque, 1983). Shuman (1985) reported that Cu was found mainly in the silt and clay fractions of 16 acid topsoils and next, in the Fe and Mn oxide fractions, none of which are, immediately plant available. Levesque and Mathur (1988) considered the water-soluble and exchangeable Cu to be the intensity factor, which, when added together, could make a good soil test for plant-available Cu. They, along with Hickey and Kittrick (1984), indicated that Cu had less mobility and bioavailability than Zn and that Cu resided mostly in nonavailable forms.

3. Copper Additions to Soils

Copper behaves somewhat differently from the other metals studied because of its strong ability to bind with organic matter. The organic-fraction Cu is high compared with that for other metals, even though the absolute amounts are low (Grimme, 1967a; Harrison et al., 1981; Hickey & Kittrick, 1984; Hoffman & Fletcher, 1978; Kuo et al., 1983; Miller & McFee, 1983). Copper is usually high in the carbonate fraction for alkaline soils and in the Fe-oxide fractions for acid soils, probably due to occlusion and strong adsorption (Hickey & Kittrick, 1984; Kuo et al., 1983; Miller et al.,1983; Sims, 1986; Sposito et al., 1982; Elsokkary & Meshref, 1984). As with other metals, adsorbed and exchangeable Cu are the smallest fractions (Adams & Sanders, 1984; Sanders et al., 1986; McGrath et al., 1988; Miller & McFee, 1983; Sposito et al., 1982).

In untreated soil, Cu was highest in the sulfide-residual fraction, but with sewage sludge addition, the Cu level in the carbonate and organic fractions increased more than for the other fractions (Chang et al., 1984). Mathur and Levesque (1983) found that Cu added to organic soils reverted to tightly bound forms, but for mineral soils these forms were lower. Copper, then, is found in highest quantities in the less bioavailable fractions, but it is higher in the organic fraction than for the other micronutrients.

2. Soil pH Changes

Although there have been some exceptions, soil pH changes exert little influence on Cu distribution among fractions (Levesque & Mathur, 1986; Shuman, 1986; Sims, 1986) (Fig. 5–2). El-Kherbawy and Sanders (1984) found that pH did not influence Cu in soil solution, but increasing the pH decreased Cu in the exchangeable fraction, making it less bioavailable (Sanders et al., 1986; Elsokkary & Lag, 1978). Increasing soil pH redistributed Cu from the exchangeable and organic fractions to water-soluble, Mn-oxide and Fe-oxide fractions (Sims & Patrick, 1978). Thus, Cu lost from the exchangeable fractions changed into less soluble, less bioavailable fractions as the pH was increased. This finding was corroborated by Sims (1986), who reported that lime additions reduced exchangeable and sorbed Cu, and increased Cu in the more tightly bound fractions.

3. Organic Matter Amendments

Since Cu is associated with organic matter, it would be expected that organic matter additions would cause a redistribution of Cu among fractions, especially to increase the organic-fraction Cu. However, this result has not always been found (Fassbender & Seekamp, 1976; Shuman, 1988b). Elsokkary and Lag (1978) reported that the organic fraction and all the oxide-fraction Cu values were related to soil organic-matter content. Figure 5–3 shows an increase in the organic Cu and a decrease in the oxide fraction with organic-matter additions, indicating a possible increase in bioavailability. The organic-fraction Cu was highest in organic soils compared with mineral soils. The importance of organic matter in influencing metals was in the order of Cu > Zn > Mn (McGrath et al., 1988). Since Cu is associated with the organic fraction, its complexing by organic ligands and subsequent release by microbes should be emphasized in studies of chemical forms (Sims, 1988).

4. Effect of Time on Redistribution

Copper added to organic soils, or added in sewage sludge or manures will revert to the more insoluble and plant-unavailable fractions with time (Mullins et al.,1982b). The Cu added to peat soils changed to more and more nonreactive forms, causing less replacement of weakly held metals (Mathur and Levesque, 1988; Mathur et al., 1985). Copper in Cu-enriched manure added to soils initially existed in specifically adsorbed forms, but after 12 d, some was found in the Mn and amorphous Fe oxides, indicating a shift away from plant availability (Miller et al., 1987). Sposito et al. (1983) found that Cu added in sewage sludge to arid-zone soils increased the carbonate-fraction Cu, accompanied by a decrease in the sulfide-residual Cu with time (Fig. 5–5). They explained that this reversion was due to $CuCO_3$ formation accompanying a mineralization of the organic matter in the sludge. Other studies have found little change in Cu forms with time (Emmerich et al., 1982) or an increase in more easily extracted forms (Silviera & Sommers, 1977).

5. Other Factors Affecting Redistribution

Copper in all fractions decrease with soil depth (Kuo et al., 1983). Organic and amorphous Fe-oxide Cu decrease with depth in a podzolic soil under cultivation (Grimme, 1967a). Lindau and Hossner (1982) found few differences among Cu in fractions for marshes in different locations. Even though tillage treatments can alter organic matter content, pH, and P concentrations at the soil surface, tillage had only minor effects on the Cu distribution in soil fractions (Shuman & Hargrove, 1985). Increases in Eh (oxidation) redistributed Cu from exchangeable and organic fractions into the Fe-oxide fraction, reducing plant availability (Fig. 5–4). Copper mobilized due to the reduction of oxides after submergence is associated with the water-soluble and organic fractions. Although El-Kherbawy and Sanders (1984) found no redistribution of Cu due to soil P level, Shuman (1988a) reported that added P shifted Cu from the residual to the exchangeable fractions for four fine-textured soils, presumably making it more plant available. Studies on Cu adsorption after selective extraction show that amorphous Fe oxides are more important than organic matter in adsorption (Cavallaro & McBride, 1984), and that oxide forms in general and organic coatings have a high affinity for metals (Lion et al., 1982).

C. Manganese Redistribution

Manganese as well as Fe is somewhat different from the other metals considered because of large component often resides in the Mn-oxide and Fe-oxide fraction, which is susceptible to being released and becoming plant available, with changes in pH and Eh status. Most of the total Mn in 16 topsoils was found in the Mn-oxide and organic fractions (Shuman, 1985), which are more soluble and, therefore, easier to redistribute to plant available forms than the Fe-oxide and residual forms. The capacity factor for Mn is the carbonate, easily reducible, and weakly complexed forms, which can become plant available with changes in pH or redox (Mathur & Levesque, 1988). Qute a few studies have related water-soluble, exchangeable- and organic-fraction Mn to plant available forms, as measured by commonly used soil testing extractants (Levesque & Mathur, 1988; Shuman, 1986, 1988b; Sims et al., 1979).

Using ^{54}Mn, Goldberg and Smith (1984) found that Mn existed mostly in the water-soluble/exchangeable, organic, and easily reducible (Mn oxide) fractions, which are the most bioavailable. Likewise, Mathur and Levesque

(1988) found Mn to be high in the water-soluble plus exchangeable fraction for 55 organic soils. Sims et al. (1979) using ^{54}Mn, found that the Mn-oxide fraction was higher in Mn (45% of the total) than any other factions. In 16 acid southeastern topsoils, Mn was highest in the organic fraction, followed by the Mn-oxide fraction (Shuman, 1988c). Manganese added to acid soils was found primarily in the exchangeable and organic fractions (Shuman, 1988b). In organic soils, 50% of the Mn was found in the organic plus sulfide fraction, but in mineral soils, more was found in the Mn-oxide fraction (Hoffman & Fletcher, 1978). Hoffman and Fletcher (1978) found little Mn in the Fe oxide fractions, whereas Kuo et al. (1983) reported that Mn was high in the amorphous Fe-oxide fraction and low in the crystalline Fe-oxide fraction. Thus, Mn is usually found in forms that are associated with the organic matter and Mn oxides, but, as shown below, Mn is sensitive to pH and Eh changes, and can easily be redistributed among chemical forms.

1. Soil pH Changes

A decrease in soil pH will mobilize Mn from various fractions and increase its concentration in the soil solution, often in other more soluble and bioavailable fractions, such as the exchangeable and organic (El-Kherbawy & Sanders, 1984; Sims et al., 1979; Sims & Patrick, 1978). Sims (1986) reported that the exchangeable Mn, a plant-available form, was high at low soil pH levels (< 5.2), and the organic and Fe-oxide fraction Mn, which is lower in availability, was high at higher soil pH levels (Fig. 5-2). For a sandy soil with very low total Mn, increasing pH increased the organic-fraction Mn (Shuman, 1986). Jarvis (1984) found that low pH soils contained low levels of exchangeable Mn and high, easily reducible Mn (Mn-oxide fraction). Here again, the low pH did not seem to increase the soluble-Mn fractions. Manganese, then, is quite labile in its movement between forms, and it is difficult to predict its form based on soil properties, such as pH.

2. Organic Matter Amendments

Adding organic matter in the form of ground wheat (*Triticum aestivum* L.) straw caused a shift of Mn from less soluble and less plant-available forms to the exchangeable and organic forms, presumably because of reduction effects (Shuman, 1988b). However, McGrath et al. (1988) indicated that organic matter did not affect Mn as much as it did Cu or Zn, even though organic Mn increased with an increase in organic C (Fig. 5-3).

3. Other Factors Affecting Redistribution

Drying soils has an influence on Mn solubility. Goldberg and Smith (1984) found that by air-drying soils, water-soluble plus exchangeable and the organic-fraction Mn increase. The short-term effects of air-drying soils, which imposes oxidizing conditions, may result in a similar effect as from long-term reducing conditions. Exchangeable Mn is high under long-term low Eh (reducing conditions) from the oxide fractions that are reduced, thus mobilizing Mn to move into more easily soluble and more plant-available fractions, (Fig. 5–4). This effect is also seen under field conditions as Mn is distributed differently among fractions depending on drainage (McLaren, 1988). In poorly drained soils, the organic fraction Mn and the Mn-oxide fraction Mn are high compared with well-drained soils. However, both the amorphous and crystalline Fe-oxide fractions as well as the residual Mn are low in poorly drained soils, showing a redistribution from the more insoluble form to more soluble forms as drainage becomes increasingly poor. Lindau and Hossner (1982) found differences in Mn in fractions between marsh locations, presumably because of drainage resulting in different oxidation/reduction conditions.

Tillage influences soil pH, organic matter, and the concentration of fertilizer ions on or near the soil surface. No-tillage management lowered exchangeable and amorphous Fe-oxide Mn and raised organic-fraction Mn compared with conventional and minimum tillage (Shuman & Hargrove, 1985). Phosphate additions shifted Mn from the residual and crystalline Fe oxide to the Mn-oxide and amorphous Fe-oxide fractions, but had little effect on the more bioavailable exchangeable and organic-fraction Mn (Shuman, 1988a). However, El-Kherbawy and Sanders (1984) found little influence of P on Mn in fractions. Added Cu apparently displaced Mn from tightly bound sites, changing it to more mobile and available forms (Mathur & Levesque, 1983).

D. Iron Redistribution

As with the other metals, the intensity factor or the most plant-available forms of Fe are the water-soluble and exchangeable (Levesque & Mathur, 1988; Mathur & Levesque, 1988). Changes in soil properties, such as pH or redox status, can bring more insoluble Fe into these fractions, increasing Fe availability, or shift Fe from these fractions, making it less plant available. In organic soils, 50% of the Fe was found in the organic plus sulfide fraction (NaOCl), but little was found in this form in mineral soil horizons (Hoffman & Fletcher, 1978). Most of the Fe resides in the amorphous and crystalline Fe-oxide and residual fractions (Shuman, 1979, 1985; Hoffman & Fletcher, 1978).

Mathur and Levesque (1988) found most Fe in what they referred to as capacity-factor Fe (strongly complexed Fe) compared with intensity-factor Fe, which was the water-soluble plus exchangeable Fe. Water-soluble Fe is low, but is an important fraction to plant availability (Knudtsen & O'Connor, 1987). They found that the organic and carbonate forms of Fe were lower than with Zn. Iron, then, is very high in the oxide forms since it actually makes up two of the pools of metals that are separated by selective sequential extraction, the amorphous and crystalline Fe oxides.

Imposing reducing conditions on soils mobilizes the Fe-oxide fraction, which becomes associated with the exchangeable, organic, and Mn-oxide fractions, making it more plant available. Increases in soil pH or Eh (oxidizing conditions) shift Fe from the exchangeable and organic forms to the water-soluble and Fe-oxide fractions (Fig. 5-4). Shuman (1988b), in adding organic matter to soil, caused reducing conditions with alternate wetting and drying. Iron changed from the less soluble forms to the exchangeable and organic forms in response to the increased organic matter. Iron in fractions differed among marsh locations, probably due to different oxidation/reduction states (Lindau & Hossner, 1982). Tillage can affect pH and other soil properties.

No-tillage systems decreased amorphous Fe oxide and residual Fe, and increased exchangeable and organic Fe compared with conventional and minimum tillage (Shuman & Hargrove, 1985). In a sandy soil, increasing pH decreased exchangeable- and organic-fraction Fe, presumably reducing plant availability (Shumn, 1986). Adding P to eight soils caused decreases in crystalline Fe oxide and residual Fe, and increases in amorphous Fe-oxide Fe (Shuman, 1988a). The P most likely decreased soil pH initially, causing solubilization of the crystalline Fe oxides, which reprecipitated in amorphous forms as the pH increased.

E. Boron and Molybdenum Redistribution

These elements have not been examined to any great extent by fractionation procedures. Boron fractionation was studied recently in relation to its availability to corn using 14 soils (Jin et al., 1987). Up to 0.34% of the total B existed in the water-soluble form, 0 to 0.23% was nonspecifically adsorbed (exchangeable), 0.05 to 0.30% was specifically adsorbed, 0.23 to 1.52% was in the Mn oxide form, 2.8 to 34.4% was in the amorphous Fe-oxide form, 17.5 to 73.9% was in the crystalline Fe oxide form, and 2.4 to 79.2% was in the residual form. Jin et al. (1987) found that the B available to corn was in the water-soluble, nonspecifically adsorbed (exchangeable), specifically adsorbed, and Mn-oxide fractions, whereas unavailable B was found in the amorphous and crystalline Fe oxide forms.

Molybdenum was extracted to obtain the water-soluble, amorphous Fe oxide, and total Mo contents from nine alluvial and five calcareous desert Egyptian soils (Elsokkary & Baghdady, 1973). The amounts of Mo in these fractions were 0.42, 1.61, and 13.41 mg kg^{-1}, respectively, in the alluvial soils, and 0.38, 0.55, and 8.76 mg kg^{-1}, respectively, in the desert soils. From 88 to 94% of the Mo was considered to be unavailable. In organic samples, about half of the Mo was in the organic plus sulfide fraction, but in mineral soil horizons (B and C horizons), very little of the total Mo was in the organic fraction. The carbonate and Mn oxide fractions also contained low amounts of Mo. However, most (20–50%) of the Mo was in the amorphous Fe-oxide and the crystalline Fe-oxide fractions. Unlike the other micronutrients, Mo was very low in the residual fraction (Hoffman & Fletcher, 1978, 1981). It is not surprising to fine Mo predominately in the amorphous Fe-oxide fraction, since an extraction with oxalate has long been used as a measure of plant-available Mo (Grigg, 1953).

IV. SUMMARY

The general approach to study chemical forms of micronutrients in soils has been to define the solid phase pools of micronutrients, to find chemical procedures for measuring the micronutrients in these forms, and, finally, to apply these methods to investigate the redistribution of micronutrients among these forms and subsequent changes in plant availability. Often, research has used an empirical approach to define reagents and procedures for selective extraction. However, more recently, authors have been critical of these approaches, and have attempted to better define each fraction and to develop more specific procedures.

No particular selective sequential extraction technique for soils is necessarily the best for all cases. The procedure must be related to the research objectives and the nature of the samples. Procedures may vary when attempting to characterize soils, study potential toxicity of metals in waste materials, determine micronutrient mobility in soils, etc. The types of forms that are sought may vary with the type of soil. For example, Shuman (1985) did not seek a water-soluble fraction in acid soils because the micronutrients in that fraction are so low as to be nondetectable. Neither carbonate nor sulfide fractions were determined because these fractions are generally not present in the well-drained, acid soils of the southeastern USA.

The differences in technique are especially evident outside soil and environmental science in geochemical exploration or studies on river, lake, or marine sediments. However, within soil science it may be useful to standardize techniques for selective sequential extraction so that comparisons can be made of research results from various laboratories. At present, such comparisons are made, as evidenced in this review, but the comparisons are not precisely valid because of variations in methods for the same fraction or differences in sequence.

Selective fractionation methods have several limitations; they are nonspecific to some degree and have problems with readsorption and precipitation. These errors increase as the number of steps increase, since they are often additive. However, these limitations are not so serious as to negate the conclusions in most research applications and usually do not result in any more variability than the variations in sampling (Pickering, 1986). The reliability of a given procedure must be acknowledged and taken into account when drawing conclusions from any set of selective extraction data. New approaches as well as ways of improving old methods should be sought. Some of the new methods that are being proposed use buffered solutions to help prevent an attack on fractions further downstream in the sequence; for example, the hydroxylamine-citrate, pH 5, method for oxides by Robbins et al. (1984). Lastly, more research with model soils needs to be undertaken to help define the fractions that a reagent will dissolve, such as the one by Kheboin and Bauer (1987) on model sediments.

Perhaps the most important application of these techniques to soil science has been to study micronutrient redistribution among fractions caused by changes in soil properties. Micronutrients appear to shift from less to more soluble fractions in response to decreasing soil pH or Eh, and to increases in organic matter and P levels. When added as salts or in sewage sludge, micronutrients enter soluble fractions initially, but revert to less soluble fractions with time. Other changes in soils, such as drying, tillage, or additions of other metals than the one being studied, have also caused redistributions. Micronutrients in the water-soluble, exchangeable, and sometimes in the organic fractions usually are the plant-available forms, according to studies with plants and to correlations of fraction values to those from commonly used soil testing extractants. Thus, redistributions into or away from these fractions are associated with increases or decreases in plant availability, respectively.

Selective sequential extraction techniques for determining micronutrient forms in soils have not been used as extensively as in other earth sciences, such as geochemistry. The potential for developing and applying these techniques for soil science is high at this time. This review points to an almost complete lack of selective sequential extraction data for B and Mo, probably because they are not considered environmental threats. As selective sequential extraction methods are further refined, they should find many applications to soil science research, especially in studying redistribution among fractions due to perturbations of the soil chemical environment.

REFERENCES

Adams, T., and J.R. Sanders. 1984. The forms of zinc, copper and nickel in sludge-treated soils and their relation to the composition of the soil solution. p. 400–405. *In* R. Perry (ed.) Environmental contamination. CEP Consultants, Edinburgh, Scotland.

Aitang, H., and H. Hani. 1983. Dissolving heavy metals from soils with acids in order to approximate total element content. Z. Pflanzenernaehr. Bodenkd. 146:481–493.

Anderson, J.U. 1963. An improved pretreatment for mineralogical analysis of samples containing organic matter. Clays Clay Miner. 10:380–388.

Anderson, J.U., and G.A. O'Conner. 1972. Production of permanganate ion by sodium hypochlorite treatment to remove soil organic matter. Soil Sci. Soc. Am. Proc. 36:973–975.

Arshad, M.A., R.J. St. Arnaud, and P.M. Huang. 1972. Dissolution of trioctahedral layer silicates by ammonium oxalate, sodium dithionite-citrate-bicarbonate, and potassium pyrophosphate. Can. J. Soil Sci. 52:19–26.

Bascomb, C.L. 1968. Distribution of pyrophosphate extractable iron and organic carbon in soils of various groups. J. Soil Sci. 19:251–268.

Belzile, N., P. Lecomte, and A. Tessier. 1989. Testing readsorption of trace elements during partial chemical extractions of bottom sediments. Environ. Sci. Technol. 23:1015–1020.

Berthet, B., J.C. Amiard, C. Amiard-Triquet, and C. Metayer. 1984. Experimental study of the relationship between the physicochemical forms of zinc and its bioavailability. Application to the agricultural utilization of sewage sludges. Plant Soil. 82:231–246.

Biermans, V., and L. Baert. 1977. Selective extraction of the amorphous Al, Fe, and Si oxides using an alkaline tiron solution. Clay Miner. 12:127–135.

Borggaard, O.K. 1979. Selective extraction of amorphous iron oxides by EDTA from a Danish sandy loam. J. Soil Sci. 30:727–734.

Borggaard, O.K. 1981a. The effect of temperature on the selectivity of EDTA as an extractant for amorphous iron oxides. Geoderma 26:121–124.

Borggaard, O.K. 1981b. Selective extraction of amorphous iron oxides by EDTA from selected soils of Denmark and Tanzania. J. of Soil Sci. 32:427–432.

Borrggaard, O.K. 1982. Selective extraction of amorphous iron oxides by EDTA from selected silicates and mixtures of amorphous and crystalline iron oxides. Clay Miner. 17:365–368.

Borggaard, O.K. 1988. Phase identification by selective dissolution techniques. p. 83–98. *In* J.W. Stucki et al. (ed.) Iron in soils and clay minerals. D. Reidel Publ. Co., Norwell, MA.

Bourget, S.J., and C.B. Tanner. 1953. Removal of organic matter with sodium hypobromite for particle-size analysis of soils. Can. J. Agric. Sci. 33:579–585.

Brar, S.P.S., D. Singh, and Y.S. Deol. 1986. Zinc pools and their availability to maize-wheat rotation. J. Agric. Sci. 106:405–410.

Campbell, P.G.C., A.G. Lewis, P.M. Chapman, A.A. Crowder, W.K. Fletcher, B. Imber, S.N. Luoma, P.M. Stokes, and M. Winfrey. 1988. Biologically available metals in sediments. Nat. Res. Council of Canada, Div. Chem. Ottawa, Ontario.

Cavallaro, N., and M.B. McBride. 1984. Zinc and copper sorption and fixation on acid soil clay: Effect of selective dissolutions. Soil Sci. Soc. Am. J. 48:1050–1054.

Chandi, K.S., and P.N. Takkar. 1982. Effects of agricultural cropping systems on micronutrients transformation. I. Zinc. Plant Soil 69:423–436.

Chang, A.C., A.L. Page, J.E. Warneke, and E. Grgureiv. 1984. Sequential extraction of soil heavy metals following a sludge application. J. Environ. Qual. 13:33–38.

Chao, T.T. 1972. Selective dissolution of manganese oxides from soils and sediments with acidified hydroxylamine hydrochloride. Soil Sci. Soc. Am. Proc. 36:764–768.

Chao, T.T. 1984. Use of partial dissolution techniques in geochemical exploration. J. Geochem. Explor. 20:101–135.

Chao, T.T., and P.K. Theobald, Jr. 1976. The significance of secondary iron and manganese oxides in geochemical exploration. Econ. Geol. 71:1560–1569.

Chao, T.T., and L. Zhou. 1983. Extraction techniques for selective dissolution of morphous iron oxides from soils and sediments. Soil Sci. Soc. Am. J. 47:225–232.

Chester, R., and M.J. Hughes. 1967. A chemical technique for the separation of ferro-manganese minerals, carbonate minerals, and adsorbed trace elements for pelagic sediments. Chem. Geol. 2:249–262.

Childs, C.W. 1981. Field tests for ferrous iron and ferric-organic complexes (on exchange sites or in water-soluble forms) in soils. Aust. J. Soil Res. 19:175–180.

Daniels, R.B., J.F. Brasfield, and F.F. Riecken. 1962. Distribution of sodium hydrosulfite extractable manganese in some Iowa soil profiles. Soil Sci. Soc. Am. Proc. 26:75–78.

DeEndredy, A.S. 1963. Estimation of free ferric oxides in soils and clays by a photolytic method. Clay Miner. Bull. 5:209–217.

Dion, H.G., P.J.G. Mann, and S.G. Heintz. 1947. The "esily reducible" manganese of soils. J. Agric. Sci. 37:17–32.

Dong, A., G.V. Sunsiman, and G. Chesters. 1985. Release of phosphorus and metals from soils and sediments during dispersion. Soil Sci. 139:97–99.

Dudas, M.J., and M.E. Harward. 1971. Effect of dissolution treatment on standard and soil clays. Soil Sci. Soc. Am. Proc. 35:134–140.

El-Kherbawy, M.I., and J.R. Sanders. 1984. Effects of pH and phosphate status of a silty clay loam on manganese, zinc, and copper concentrations in soil fractions and in clover. J. Sci. Food Agric. 35:733–739.

Elsokkary, I.H., and N.H. Baghdady. 1973. Studies on molybdenum in some soils of Egypt. Alexandria J. Agric. Res. 21:451–460.

Elsokkary, I.H., and J. Lg. 1978. Distribution of different fractions of Cd, Pb, Zn, and Cu in industrially polluted and nonpolluted soils of Odda region, Norway. Acta Agric. Scand. 28:262–268.

Elsokkary, I.H., and H.. Meshref. 1984. The chemical fractionation of soil copper in Egyptian alluvial soils. Mitt. Dtsch. Bodenkundl. Ges. 39:13–18.

Emmerich, W.E., L.J. Lund, A.L. Page, and A.C. Change. 1982. Solid phase forms of heavy metals in sewage sludge-treated soils. J. Environ. Qual. 11:178–181.

Estepp, R., and R.F. Keefer. 1969. Fractionation of soil zinc after application of zinc-65 to two soil series kept continuously moist or alternatively wetted and dried. W. Va. Acad. Sci. 41:85–92.

Fassbender, H.W., and G. Seekamp. 1976. Fractions and solubility of heavy metals Cd, Co, Cr, Cu, Ni and Pb in soils. Geoderma 16:55–69.

Filipek, L.H., T.T. Chao, and P.K. Theobald. Jr. 1982. Comparison of hot hydroxylamine hydrochloride and oxalic acid leaching of stream sediment and coated rock samples as anomaly enhancing techniqeus. J. Geochem. Explor. 17:35–47.

Framptom, J.A., and H.M. Reisenauer. 1978. The association of Co, Ni, Cu, and Zn with Fe and Mn oxides in soils and soil concretions. p. 24. *In* Agronomy abstracts. ASA, Madison, WI.

Gatehouse, S., D.W. Russell, and J.C. Van Moort. 1977. Sequential soil analysis in exploration geochemistry. J. Geochem. Explor. 8:483–494.

Ghanem, S.A., and D.S. Mikkelsen. 1987. Effect of organic matter on changes in soil zinc fractions found in wetland soils. Commun. Soil Sci. Plant Anal. 18:1217–1234.

Gibb, R.J. 1973. Mechanisms of trace metal transport in rivers. Science 180:71–73.

Goldberg, S.P., and K.A. Smith. 1984. Soil manganese: E values, distribution of manganese-54 mong soil fractions, and effects of drying. Soil Sci. Soc. Am. J. 48:559–564.

Grigg, J.L. 1953. A rapid method for the determination of molybdenum in soils. Analyst 78:470–473.

Grimme, H. 1967a. Distribution of copper fractions in gray brown podzolic soils developed from loess. Z. Pflanzenernaehr. Dueng. Bodenkd. 116:125–136.

Grimme, H. 1967b. The fractional extraction of soil copper Z. Pflanzenernaehr. Dueng. Bodenkd. 116:207–222.

Grimme, H., and H. Wiechmann. 1969. Extraction of organically bound iron Z. Pflanzenernaehr. Dueng. Bodenk. 122:268–279.

Gupta, S.K., and K.Y Chen. 1975. Partitioning of trace metals in selective chemical fractions of near shore sediments. Environ. Lett. 10:129–158.

Guy, R.D., C.L. Chkrabarti, and D.C. McBain. 1978. An evaluation of extraction techniques for the fractiontion of copper and lead in model sediment systems. Water Res. 12:21–24.

Haldane, A.D. 1956. Determination of free oxide in soils. Soil Sci. 82:483–489.

Harrison, R.M., D.P.H. Laxen, and S.J. Wilson. 1981. Chemical associations of lead, cadmium, copper, and zinc in street dusts and roadside soils. Environ. Sci. Technol. 15:1378–1383.

Hazra. G.C., B. Mandal, and L.N. Mandal. 1987. Distribution of zinc fractions and their transformation in submerged rice soils. Plant Soil 104:175–181.

Heintze, S.G., and P.J.G. Mann. 1949. Studies on soil manganese. J. Agric. Sci. 39:80–95.

Hickey, M.G., and J.A. Kittrick. 1984. Chemical partitioning of cadmium, copper, nickel, and zinc in soils and sediments containing high levels of heavy metals. J. Environ. Qual. 13:372–376.

Hoffman, S.J., and W.K. Fletcher. 1978. Selective sequential extraction of Cu, Zn, Fe, Mn, and Mo from soils and sediments. p. 289–299. In J.R. Watterson and P.K. Theoblad. (ed.) Geochemical exploration 1978, IMM Publ.

Hoffman, S.J., and W.K. Fletcher. 1981. Organic matter scavenging of copper, zinc, molybdenum, iron and manganese, estimated by sodium hypochlorite extraction (pH 9.5). J. Geochem. Explor. 15:549–562.

Iyengar, S.S., D.C. Martens, and W.P. Miller. 1981. Distribution and plant availability of soil zinc fractions. Soil Sci. Soc. Am. J. 45:735–739.

Jarvis, S.C. 1984. The forms of occurrence of manganese in some acidic soils. J. Soil Sci. 35:421–430.

Jenne, E.. 1968. Controls on Mn, Fe, Co, Ni, Cu and Zn concentrations in soils and waters: The significant role of hydrous Mn and Fe oxides. p. 337–387. In Trace inorganics in water. Adv. Chem. Ser. 73.

Jin, J., D.C. Martens, and L.W. Zelazny. 1987. Distribution and plant availability of soil boron fractions. Soil Sci. Soc. Am. J. 51:1228–1231.

Kawai, K. 1977. Estimation of the amount of amorphous material for characterizing andosols. Soil Sci. Soc. Am. J. 41:1171–1175.

Kittrick, J.A., and E.W. Hope. 1963. A procedure for the particle-size separation of soils for X-ray diffraction analysis. Soil Sci. 96:319–325.

Keefer, R.F., and R. Estepp. 1971. The fate of [65]zinc applied to two soils as zinc sulphate and zinc EDTA. Soil Sci. 112:325–329.

Kheboian, C., and C.F. Bauer. 1987. Accuracy of selective extraction procedures for metal separation in model aquatic sediments. Anal. Chem. 59:1417–1423.

Knudtsen, K., and G.A. O'Connor. 1987. Characterization of iron and zinc on Albuquerque sewage sludge. J. Environ. Qual. 16:85–90.

Krauskopf, K.B. 1972. Geochemistry of micronutrients. p. 7–40. In J.J. Mortvedt et al. (ed.) Micronutrients in agriculture. SSSA, Madison, WI.

Kuo, S., P.E. Heilman, and A.S. Baker. 1983. Distribution and forms of copper, zinc, cadmium, iron, and manganese in soils near a copper smelter. Soil Sci. 135:101–109.

Lakanen, E. 1962. On the analysis of soluble trace elements. Ann. Agric. Fenn. 2:109–117.

Lake, D.L., P.W.W. Kirk, and J.N. Lester. 1984. Fractionation, characterization, and speciation of heavy metals in sewage sludge and sludge-amended soils. A review. J. Environ. Qual. 13:175–183.

Lavkulich, L.M., and J.H. Wiens. 1970. Comparison of organic matter destruction by hydrogen peroxide and sodium hypochlorite and its effects on selected mineral constituents. Soil Sci. Soc. Am. Proc. 34:755–758.

LeClaire, J.P., A.C. Chang, C.S. Levesque, and G. Sposito. 1984. Trace metal chemistry and arid-zone field soils amended with sewage sludge: IV. Correlations between zinc uptake and extracted soil zinc fractions. Soil Sci. Soc. Am. J. 48:509–513.

Levesque, M.P., and S.P. Mathur. 1986. Soil tests for copper, iron, manganese, and zinc in histosols: 1. The influence of soil properties, iron, manganese, and zinc on the level and distribution of copper. Soil Sci. 142:153–163.

Levesque, M.P., and S.P. Mathur. 1988. Soil tests for copper, iron, manganese and zinc in histosols: 3. A comparison of eight extractants for measurement of active and reserve forms of the elements. Soil Sci. 145:215–221.

Lindau, C.W., and L.R. Hossner. 1982. Sediment fractionation of Cu, Ni, Zn, Cr, Mn, and Fe in one experimental and three natural marshes. J. Environ. Qual. 11:540–545.

Lindsay, W.L. 1979. Chemical equilibria in soils. John Wiley and Sons, New York.

Lion, L.W., R.S. Altmann, and J.O. Leckie. 1982. Trace-metal adsorption characteristics of estuarine particulate matter: Evaluation of contributions of Fe/Mn oxide and organic surface coatings. Environ. Sci. Technol. 16:660–666.

Mandal, B., B.R. Halder, and L.N. Mandal. 1986. Distribution of different forms of zinc in some rice growing soils. J. Indian Soc. Soil Sci. 34:488–492.

Mandal, B., G.C. Hazra, and A.K. Pal. 1988. Transformation of zinc in soils under submerged conditions and its relation with zinc nutrition of rice. Plant Soil 106:121–126.

Mandal, L.N., and B. Mandal. 1986. Zinc fractions in soils in relation to zinc nutrition of lowland rice. Soil Sci. 142:141–148.

Mandal, L.N., and B. Mandal. 1987a. Transformation of zinc fractions in rice soils. Soil Sci. 143:205–212.

Mandal, L.N., and B. Mandal. 1987b. Fractionation of applied zinc in rice soils at two moisture regimes and levels of organic matter. Soil Sci. 144:266–273.

Mathur, S.P., and M.P. Levesque. 1983. The effects of using copper for mitigating histosol subsidence on: 2. the distribution of copper, manganese, zinc, and iron in an organic soil, mineral sublayers, and their mixtures in the context of setting a threshold of phytotoxic soil-copper. Soil Sci. 135:166–176.

Mathur, S.P., and M. Levesque. 1988. Soil tests for copper, iron, manganese, and zinc in histosols: 2. the distribution of soil iron and manganese in sequentially extractable forms. Soil Sci. 145:102–110.

Mathur, S.P., M.P. Levesque, and S.S. Singh. 1985. The effects of using copper for mitigating histosol subsidence on: 4. the yield and nutrition of flooded rice grown on histosols, mineral sublayers, and their mixtures. Soil Sci. 140:133–142.

McGrath, S.P., J.R. Sanders, and M.H. Shalaby. 1988. The effect of soil organic matter levels on soil solution concentrations and extractabilities of manganese, zinc, and copper. Geoderma 42:177–188.

McKeague, J.A. 1967. An evaluation of 0.1 M pyrophosphate and pyrophosphate-dithronite in comparison with oxalate as extractants of the accumulation products inpodzols and some other soils. Can. J. Soil Sci. 47:95–99.

McKeague, J.A., J.E. Brydon, and N.M. Miles. 1971. Differentiation of forms of extractable iron and aluminum in soils. Soil Sci. Soc. Am. Proc. 35:33–38.

McKeague, J.A., and J.H. Day 1966. Dithionite and oxalate-extractable Fe and Al as aids in differentiating various classes of soils. Can. J. Soil Sci. 46:13–22.

McKeague, J.A., and P.A. Schuppli. 1982. Changes in concentration of iron and aluminum in pyrophosphate extracts of soil and composition of sediment resulting from ultracentrifugation in relation to spodic horizon criteria. Soil Sci. 134:265–270.

McLaren, R.G. 1988. Forms of mnganese in some soils of different drainage status developed in greywacke alluvium. p. 9–10. In M.J. Webb et al. (ed.) Int. Symp. on Manganese in Soils and Plants: Contributed papers, Glen Osmond, South Australia, Australia. 22–26 Aug. Manganese Symposium 1988, Inc., Adelaide, South Australia, Australia.

McLaren, R.G., and D.V. Crawford. 1973. Studies on soil copper. I. The fractionation of copper in soils. J. Soil Sci. 24:172–181.

Meguellati, N., D. Robbe, P. Marchandise, and M. Astruc. 1982. The value of selective mineralization for the follow-up of metallic pollutants associated with sediments. French J. Hydrol.
3:275–287.

Mehra, O.P., and M.L. Jackson. 1960. Iron oxide removal from soils and clays by a dithionite-
citrate system buffered with sodium bicarbonate. Clays Clay Miner. 7:317–327.

Miller, W.P., D.C. Martens, and L.W. Zelazny. 1986. Effect of sequence in extraction of trace
metals from soils. Soil Sci. Soc. Am. J. 50:598–601.

Miller, W.P., D.C. Martens, and L.W. Zelazny. 1987. Short-term transformations of copper
in copper-amended soils. J. Environ. Qual. 16:176–181.

Miller, W.P., and W.W. McFee. 1983. Distribution of cadmium, zinc, copper, and lead in soils
of industrial northwestern Indiana. J. Environ. Qual. 12:29–33.

Miller, W.P., W.W. McFee, and J.M. McFee. 1983. Distribution of cadmium, zinc, copper,
and lead in soils of industrial northwestern Indiana. J. Environ. Qual. 12:29–33.

Mullins, G.L., D.C. Martens, S.W. Gettier, and W.P. Miller. 1982a. Form and availability
of copper and zinc in a Rhodic Paleudult following long-term $CuSO_4$ and $ZuSO_4$ applications. J. Environ. Qual. 11:573–577.

Mullins, G.L., D.C. Martens, W.P. Miller, E.T. Kornegay, and D.L. Hallock. 1982b. Copper
availability, form, and mobility in soils from three annual copper-enriched hog manure
applications. J. Environ. Qual. 11:316–320.

Murthy, A.S.P., and H.G. Schoen. 1987. A comparative study of the soil zinc fractions determined by chemical methods and electrol-trafiltration (EUF) and their relations to zinc
nutrition in rice. Plant Soil 102:207–210.

Neilsen, D., P.B. Hoyt, and A.F. MacKenzie. 1986. Distribution of soil Zn fractions in British
Columbia interior orchard soils. Can. J. Soil Sci. 66:445–454.

Olade, M., and K. Fletcher. 1974. Potassium chloritehydrochloric acid: A sulphide selective
leach for bedrock geochemistry. J. Geochem. Explor. 3:337–344.

Omueti, J.A.I. 1980. Sodium hypochlorite treatment for organic matter destruction in tropical
soils of Nigeria. Soil Sci. Soc. Am. J. 44:878–880.

Omueti, J.A.I. 1981. The effect of H_2O_2 and NaOCl pretreatment for organic matter removal
on selected mineral constituents in some Nigerian soils. Commun. Soil Sci. Plant Anal.
12:139–146.

Parfitt, R.L., and C.W. Childs. 1988. Estimation of forms of Fe and Al: A review and analysis
of contrasting soils by dissolution and Moessbauer methods. Aust. J. Soil Res. 26:121–144.

Pawluk, S. 1972. Measurement of crystalline and amorphous iron removal in soils. Can. J.
Soil Sci. 52:119–123.

Pickering, W.F. 1981. Selective chemical extraction of soil components and bound metal species. CRC Crit. Rev. Anal. Chem. 12:233–266.

Pickering, W.F. 1986. Metal ion speciation-soils and sediments (a review). Ore Geol. Rev.
1:83–146.

Rapin, F., A. Tessier, P.G.C. Campbell, and R. Carignan. 1986. Potential artifacts in the
determination of metal partitioning in sediments by sequential extraction procedure. Environ. Sci. Technol. 20:836–840.

Rappaport, B.D., D.C. Martens, T.W. Simpson, and R.B. Rencan, Jr. 1986. Prediction of
available zinc in sewage sludge-amended soils. J. Environ. Qual. 15:133–136.

Rendell, P.S., G.E. Battey, and A.J. Cameron. 1980. Adsorption as a control of metal concentrations in sediment extracts. Environ. Sci. Technol. 14:314–138.

Robbe, D., 1987. Interlaboratory comparison of sequential extraction procedures. p. 360–362.
In S.E. Lindberg and T.C. Hutchinson (ed.) Heavy Metals in the Environment. Proc. Int.
Conf., Vol. I., New Oreleans, LA. September. Oak Ridge Natl. Lab., Oak Ridge, TN.

Robbins, J.M., M. Lyle, and G.R. Heath. 1984. A sequential extraction procedure for partitioning elements among co-existing phases in marine sediments. College of Oceanography,
Oregon State Univ., Corvallis.

Roger, B. 1986. Comparison study of two selective extraction procedures: Readsorption phenomenon during mineralization. Environ. Technol. Lett. 7:539–546.

Ross, G.J., C. Wang, and P.A. Schuppli. 1985. Hydroxylamine and ammonium oxalate solutions as extractants for iron and aluminum from soils. Soil Sci. Soc. Am. J. 49:783–785.

Rudd, T., J.A. Campbell, and J.N. Lester. 1988. The use of model compounds to elucidate
metal forms in sewage sludge. Environ. Pollut. Ser. A:50:225–242.

Sanders, J.R., T.M. Adams, and B.T. Christensen. 1986. Extractability and bioavailability of
zinc, nickel, cadmium and copper in three Danish soils sampled 5 years after application
of sewage sludge. J. Sci. Food Agric. 37:1155–1164.

Sarkar, A.K., and D.L. Deb. 1985. Fate of fertilizer zinc in a black soil (vertisol). J. Agric. Sci. (Cambridge) 104:249–251.

Schalscha, E.B., M. Morales, I. Ahumada, T. Schirado, and P.F. Pratt. 1980. Fractionation of Zn, Cu, Cr, and Ni in wastewaters, solids and in soil. Agrochimica 24:361–367.

Schwertmann, U. 1964. The differentiation of iron oxide in soils by a photochemical extraction with acid ammonium oxalate. Z. Pflanzenernaehr. Dueng. Bodenkd. 165:194–202.

Sequi, P., and R. Aringhieri. 1977. Destruction of organic matter by hydrogen peroxide in the presence of pyrophosphate and its effect on soil specific surface area. Soil Sci. Soc. Am. Proc. 41:340–342.

Shuman, L.M. 1979. Zinc, manganese, and copper in soil fractions. Soil Sci. 127:10–17.

Shuman, L.M. 1982. Separating soil iron and manganese-oxide fractions for microelement analysis. Soil Sci. Soc. Am. J. 46:1099–1102.

Shuman, L.M. 1983. Sodium hypochlorite methods for extracting microelements associated with soil organic matter. Soil Sci. Soc. Am. J. 47:656–660.

Shuman, L.M. 1985. Fractionation method for soil microelements. Soil Sci. 140:11–22.

Shuman, L.M. 1986. Effect of liming on the distribution of manganese, copper, iron, and zinc among soil fractions. Soil Sci. Soc. Am. J. 50:1236–1240.

Shuman, L.M. 1988a. Effect of phosphorus level on extractable micronutrients and their distribution among fractions. Soil Sci. Soc. Am. J. 52:136–141.

Shuman, L.M. 1988b. Effect of organic matter on the distribution of manganese, copper, iron, and zinc in soil fractions. Soil Sci. 146:192–198.

Shuman, L.M. 1988c. Forms of manganese in soil. p. 29–30. In M.J. Webb et al. (ed.) Int. Symp. on Manganese in Soils and Plants: Contributed papers, Glen Osmond, South Australia, Australia. 22–26 Aug. 1988. Manganese Symposium 1988 Inc., Adelaide, South Australia, Australia.

Shuman, L.M. 1988d. Effect of removal of organic matter and iron- or manganese-oxides on zinc adsorption by soil. Soil Sci. 146:248–254.

Shuman, L.M., and W.L. Hargrove. 1985. Effect of tillage on the distribution of manganese, copper, iron and zinc in soil fractions. Soil Sci. Soc. Am. J. 49:1117–1121.

Silviera, D.J., and L.E. Sommers. 1977. Extractability of copper, zinc, cadmium, and lead on soils incubated with sewage sludge. J. Environ. Qual. 6:47–52.

Sims, J.T. 1986. Soil pH effects on the distribution and plant availability of manganese, copper, and zinc. Soil Sci. Soc. Am. J. 50:367–373.

Sims, J.T. 1988. Fate of heavy metals in organic wastes produced by the Delaware Solid Waste Authority. Newark Proj. Rep., Univ. of Delaware, Newark, DE.

Sims, J.L., P. Duangpatra, J.H. Ellis, and R.E. Phillips. 1979. Distribution of available manganese in Kentucky soils. Soil Sci. 127:270–274.

Sims, J.L., and W.H. Patrick, Jr. 1978. The distribution of micronutrient cations in soil under conditions of varying redox potential and pH. Soil Sci. Soc. Am. J. 42:258–262.

Sinex, S.A., A.Y. Cantillo, and G.R. Helz. 1980. Accuracy of acid extraction methods for trace metals in sediments. Anal. Chem. 52:2342–2346.

Singh, J.P., S.P.S. Karwasra, and M. Singh. 1988. Distribution and forms of copper, iron, and manganese, and zinc in calcareous soils of India. Soil Sci. 146:359–366.

Singhania, R.A., E. Reitz, H. Söchtig, and D.R. Sauerbeck. 1983. Chemical transformation and plant availability of zinc salts added to organic manure. Plnt Soil 73:337–344.

Sposito, G. 1983. The chemical forms of trace metals in soils. p. 123–170. In I. Thornton. (ed.) Applied environmental geochemistry. Academic Press, San Diego, CA.

Sposito, G., C.S. LeVesque, J.P. LeClaire, and A.C. Chang. 1983. Trace metal chemistry in arid-zone field soils amended with sewage sludge: III. Effect of time on the extraction of trace metals. Soil Sci. Soc. Am. J. 47:898–902.

Sposito, G., L.J. Lund, and A.C. Chang. 1982. Trace metal chemistry in arid-zone field soils amended with sewage sludges: I. Fractionation of Ni, Cu, Zn, Cd, and Pb in solid phases. Soil Sci. Soc. Am. J. 46:260–264.

Steinhilber, P., and F.C. Boswell. 1983. Fractionation and characterization of two aerobic sewage sludges. J. Environ. Qual. 12:529–534.

Stover, R.C., L.E. Sommers, and D.J. Silviera. 1976. Evaluation of metals in wastewater slu J. Water Pollut. Control Fed. 48:2165–2175.

Taylor, R.M., and R.M. McKenzie. 1966. The association of trace elements with man minerals in Australian soils. Aust. J. Soil Res. 4:29–39.

Tessier, A., and P.G.C. Cambell. 1988. Comments on the testing of the accuracy of an extraction procedure for determining the partitioning of trace metals in sediments. Anal. Chem. 60:1475–1476.

Tessier, A., P.G.C. Campbell, and M. Bisson. 1979. Sequential extraction procedure for the speciation of particulate trace metals. Anal. Chem. 51:844–851.

Tipping, E., M.B. Hethering, J. Hilton, D.W. Thompson, E. Bowles, and J. Hamilton-Taylor. 1985. Artifacts in the use of selective chemical extraction to determine distribution of metals between oxides of manganese and iron. Anal. Chem. 57:1944–1946.

Tokashiki, Y., J.B. Dixon, and D.C. Golden. 1986. Manganese oxide analysis in soils by combined X-ray diffraction and selective dissolution methods. Soil Sci. Soc. Am. J. 50:1079–1084.

Uren, N.C., C.J. Asher, and N.E. Longnecker. 1988. Techniques for research on manganese in soil-plant systems. p. 309–328. *In* R.D. Graham et al. (ed.) Manganese in soils and plants. Kluwer Academic Publ., London.

Wang, C., H. Kodama, and N.M. Miles. 1981. Effect of various pretreatments on X-ray diffraction patterns of clay fractions of podzolic B horizons. Can. J. Soil Sci. 61:311–316.

Warren, L.J. 1981. Contamination of sediments by lead, zinc, and cadmium: A review. Environ. Pollut. Ser. B:2:401–436.

Zyrin, W.G., A.I. Obukhov, and G.V. Motuzova. 1974. Forms of micronutrients in the soils of the USSR and methods of their investigation. Trans. Int. Congr. Soil Sci. 10th II:350–357.

Chapter 6

Organic Matter-Micronutrient Reactions in Soil

F. J. STEVENSON, *University of Illinois, Urbana, Illinois*

Organic substances play a key role in the soil micronutrient cycle. A wide array of organic compounds are involved, including biochemicals of the type known to occur in living organisms, and a series of yellow to black substances referred to as humic acid (HA) and fulvic acid (FA).

Knowledge of the nature of the organic ligands that form complexes with metal ions, and of the properties of the complexes thus formed, will lead to a better understanding of factors that affect trace elements availability to plants. This chapter will emphasize organic matter influence on micronutrient cycling, the distribution of naturally occurring organic ligands, trace elements speciation in the soil solution, and the nature and stability of the complexes with HA and FA. Unless otherwise specified, the findings and observations will apply to those micronutrients that occur in cationic form (i.e., Cu, Fe, Mn, and Zn). Due to their strong tendencies to form covalent bonds with oxygen, B and Mo normally exist in anionic form (i.e., as $H_2BO_3^-$ and MoO_4^-). However, some B may exist as borate complexes with organic matter.

I. SIGNIFICANCE OF COMPLEXATION REACTIONS

The formation of metal-organic complexes has the following effects on the soil micronutrient cycle:

1. Micronutrient cations that would ordinarily precipitate at the pH values found in most soils are maintained in solution through complexation with soluble organics. Many biochemicals synthesized by microorganisms form water-soluble complexes with trace elements. Complexes of trace elements with FA are also water soluble.
2. Under certain conditions, metal ion concentrations may be reduced to a nontoxic level through complexation with soil organics. This is particularly true when the metal-organic complex has low solubility,

such as in the case of complexes with HA and other high-molecular-weight components of organic matter.

3. Various complexing agents mediate transport of trace elements to plant roots, and, in some cases, to other ecosystems, such as lakes and streams.

4. Organic substances can enhance the availabilities of insoluble phosphates through complexation of Fe and Al in acid soils, and Ca in calcareous soils.

5. Chelation plays a major role in the weathering of rocks and minerals. Lichens, for example, enhance the disintegration of rock surfaces to which they are attached through the production of chelating agents.

II. THE MICRONUTRIENT CYCLE

An outline of the micronutrient cycle in soil is depicted in Fig. 6–1. Trace element availability to plants is affected by reactions that involve the formation of soluble and insoluble complexes with organic substances. Transformations carried out by microorganisms are also important.

A unique feature of the micronutrient cycle involves trace-element enrichment of the upper portion of the solum (and the organic matter contained therein) due to long-term upward translocation by plant roots and subsequent incorporation into the surface layer of the soil through plant-litter decay. Overall aspects of the micronutrient cycle in soil have been discussed by Sposito and Page (1984) and Stevenson (1986).

A. Micronutrient Cycle in Agricultural Soils

Essentially, every aspect of the chemistry of micronutrients in soils is related to reactions that involve organic substances (see Fig. 6–1). Individu-

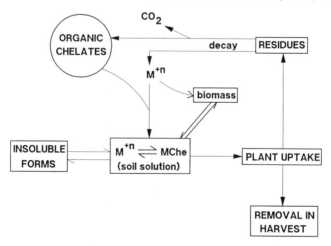

Fig. 6–1. Micronutrient cycle in soil. (Adapted from Stevenson, 1986).

al effects of organic matter-mineral interactions are difficult to quantify and vary from soil to soil, depending on pH, type and amount of clay minerals, organic matter content, and management practice. An important factor is micronutrient recycling through the return of plant residues. The quantity recycled depends on the nature of the plant and its intended use, micronutrient distribution within the plant (roots, stems, leaves, and grain), and whether the nonharvested residues are left in the field. In some plants, the micronutrient is concentrated in the roots, thus it is returned to the soil even though the top growth is removed.

It is well known that organic matter is lost when soils are first cultivated, and that a new steady-state level is attained that is characteristic of the current cropping system (Stevenson, 1982, 1986). Concomitant changes are expected to occur in the cycling of micronutrients, due to lowering of organic matter content and changes in the quantity of plant residues returned to the soil. In a recent study, McGrath et al. (1988) found that organic matter content influenced soil solution concentrations and extractabilities of applied Cu, Mn, and Zn.

Considerable quantities of micronutrients are often added to the soil through animal manures, particularly in grazed pastures. The micronutrient content of farmyard manure is significantly higher than in plants, which is attributed to organic C losses during decay (for comparative data, see Stevenson & Ardakani, 1972, Table 2). The application of 5000 kg ha^{-1} of farmyard manure to the soil results in the addition of the following approximate quantities of micronutrients: B, 0.1 kg; Cu, 0.08 kg, Co, 0.005 kg, Mn, 1.0 kg; Zn, 0.48 kg; and Mo, 0.01 kg. The rate at which these micronutrients are released depends on conditions affecting microbial activity, and is greatest in warm, moist, well-aerated soils of approximately neutral reaction.

1. Organically Bound Forms of Micronutrient Cations

The micronutrient cation pools in soils can be divided into: (i) water soluble (free plus complexed); (ii) exchangeable; (iii) specifically adsorbed; (iv) organically complexed, but water insoluble; (v) insoluble inorganic precipitates, and (vi) held in primary minerals (see Ch. 5). The importance of the organically complexed pool arises from findings indicating that organically bound forms of the micronutrient cations are more available to plants than the inorganic forms of pools insoluble inorganic precipitates and those held in primary minerals (McLaren & Crawford, 1973; Murthy, 1982; Mandal & Mandal, 1986).

Organically bound micronutrient cations are commonly determined by soil extraction with a complexing agent (e.g., pyrophosphate at 0.1 M concentration) or by release to exchangeable forms by organic matter oxidation (Shuman, 1983, 1985).

In the study conducted by McLaren and Crawford (1973), from 20 to 50% of the Cu in 24 soils of diverse types occurred in organically bound forms. They concluded that the amount of Cu available to plants (exchangeable and soluble Cu) was controlled by equilibria involving specifically adsorbed forms (Cu extracted with 2.5% CH_3COOH) and the organically bound fraction. The suggested relationship between the three forms was as follows:

$$\text{Exchangeable and soluble Cu} \rightleftharpoons \text{Specifically adsorbed Cu} \rightleftharpoons \text{Organically bound Cu}$$

Shuman (1979) obtained the following percentages of three micronutrients that occurred in organically bound forms in 10 representative soils of the southeastern USA: Cu, 1.0 to 68.6%; Mn, 9.5 to 82%; and Zn, 0.2 to 14.3%. A somewhat similar range for Zn (0.1–7.4%) was obtained by Iyengar, et al. (1981) for 19 soils from the Appalachian, Coastal Plain, and Piedmont regions of Virginia. In other work, Sedberry and Reddy (1976) found that an average of 2.6% of the Zn in 10 Louisiana soils was organically combined. As one might expect, considerable variation exists in the distribution of organically bound forms of micronutrient among the various size fractions of soil (Shuman, 1979).

Boron and Mo are unique among the micronutrient elements in that they normally occur in anionic forms ($H_2BO_3^-$) and MoO_4^{2-}) and thus, are subject to losses through leaching. However, the main form of B (the only non-metal in the group) may be combined with organic matter, primarily as borate complexes (I) with compounds that contain the cis-hydroxyl group, such as saccharides.

I

As organic matter is mineralized by microorganisms, B is released to readily available forms. Temporary B deficiency in plants during periods of drought has been attributed to reduced mineralization of B in organically bound forms. Yermiyako et al. (1988) found that the sorption capacity of composted organic matter for B (on a weight basis) was at least four times greater than for clay and soils. This was attributed to chemical association between B and organic molecules, such as carbohydrates.

Conversion of soluble forms of the micronutrient cations to insoluble organic forms can occur through solid-phase complexation by humates present as coatings on clay surfaces, as well as by the formation of soluble complexes that subsequently become associated with mineral surfaces through adsorption. Some polyvalent cations link humic complexes to clay surfaces; others occupy peripheral sites and are available for exchange with ligands of the soil solution.

2. Speciation of Micronutrient Cations in the Soil Solution

Increasing attention is being given to soluble organic substances as carriers of micronutrient cations in the soil solution. However, quantitative data are limited. This is attributed to the following (Stevenson & Fitch, 1986):

1. Micronutrient cation concentrations in the soil solution are normally very low, often of the order of 10^{-8} to 10^{-9} M, thereby creating severe analytical problems in determination.
2. Micronutrients may exist in many different chemical forms.
3. Extracts typical of the soil solution are not easily obtained.
4. The amounts and chemical forms of any given micronutrient in the soil solution varies with time and may be affected by the method of sample preparation, including soil drying and storage.

Although most metal complexes with biochemical compounds (and FA) are mobile, evidence indicates that leaching losses are negligible from most fine-textured agricultural soils. As noted later, downward movement of Fe and other cations is common in forest soils.

Methods for determining organically bound micronutrient cations in the soil solution include: (i) addition of a known complexing agent, which forms a complex that can be removed with an immiscible solvent; (ii) separation of charged inorganic species on a cation-exchange resin; (iii) recovery of the metal-organic complex through dialysis; and (iv) analysis of the free cation with an ion-selective electrode (ISE) or by anodic stripping voltammetry (ASV). In the second method, neutral- and anionic-inorganic forms of the cations are not adsorbed, but can be calculated from known thermodynamic data, thereby providing a measure of organically bound cations from the difference between total soluble cations and nonadsorbed inorganic species.

Hodgson et al. (1965), using the immiscible displacement approach, obtained the following percentages of three micronutrient cations that occurred in organically bound forms in the displaced soil solutions of some New York surface soils: Cu, 76 to 99%; Co, 0 to 69%; and Zn, 5 to 90%. In a subsequent study, higher percentages for Cu (98–99%) and Zn (28–99%) were obtained for some Colorado calcareous soils (Hodgson et al., 1966). In both studies, organic bound forms were taken as the difference between the total concentration of trace element in solution and the amounts recovered as the free cation (i.e., any inorganic complexes that might have been present were not taken into account).

Sanders (1983) used the ion-exchange equilibrium technique to determine complexed forms of Co, Mn, and Zn in aqueous extracts of five soils in England. His estimates were considerably lower than those noted above. Olomu et al. (1973) found that practically all of the soluble Fe in some flooded soils was complexed with organic matter, whereas Mn was either not complexed or weakly complexed.

Camerynck and Kiekens (1982) used a combination of cation- and anion-exchange resins to determine the speciation of select metals in the water-soluble fraction of a sandy soil. Copper and Fe were largely present as stable complexes, Mn was largely present in the free ionic form, and Zn was evenly distributed between these two forms. In other work, a chelating resin in the Ca form, and containing a sufficient amount of the trace element to maintain a constant activity in solution, was used to determine free and complexed forms of Zn, Ca, and Cd in sludge-amended soils (Hendrickson & Corey, 1983). Affinity of the soil solution ligands was approximately $10^{5.5}$ times greater for Zn and Cd than for Ca.

A major limitation of using ISE for determining free-metal ions involves the rather low sensitivity of the technique. Furthermore, only a few divalent cations can be measured (Cu^{2+}, Pb^{2+}, Cd^{2+}, and Ca^{2+}). For both ISE and ASV, electrode response is affected by pH, ionic strength, and sorption of organics on the electrode surface (Bresnahan et al., 1978; Greter et al., 1979; Bhat et al., 1981). A scheme that involves ASV measurements, in conjunction with separations obtained with a chelating resin, was used by Jeffery and Uren (1983) to determine the lability of Cu and Zn in displaced soil solutions.

Ion-selective electrodes appear to have greatest potential for estimating Cu, Pb, or Cd where rather high concentrations would be expected in the soil solution, such as in sludge-amended soils. Sanders (1982), however, used a procedure suitable for determining very low concentrations of Cu^{2+} ($< 10^{-6}$ M) in displaced soil solutions. Essentially, the approach involved calibration of the electrode with a known chelating agent (malonic acid). In contrast to results obtained for Mn and Zn, using the ion-exchange equilibrium method (Sanders, 1983), essentially all of the soluble Cu in the soils Sanders examined was found to occur in organically bound forms.

Metal ion speciation in the soil solution has been predicted on the basis of analytical data for cations, anions, and soluble organic matter, for which computer models (e.g., GEOCHEM, MINEQ, etc.) have been applied (Lighthart et al., 1983; Bourg & Vedy, 1986). The approach is only applicable to systems that have been well characterized with regard to cationic (e.g., K^+, Na^+, NH_4^+, H^+, Ca^{2+}, Mg^{2+}, Cu^{2+}, Mn^{2+}, etc.) and anionic (Cl^-, HCO_3^-, NO_3^-, SO_4^{2-}, etc.) species, and, ideally, for the types and amounts of organic ligands. In general, these studies have shown that metals that form strong chelate complexes (e.g., Cu^{2+}) occur mostly in organically complexed forms, whereas those that form weak complexes (e.g., Zn^{2+}) are found mostly in free ionic forms.

As suggested above, the condition of electrochemical neutrality must be maintained in the soil solution. Accordingly, the total quantity of cations in ionic forms must equal total anionic content (inorganic plus dissociated acidic functional groups). Cronan et al. (1978) estimated organically bound forms of trace elements in the leachates of some New Hampshire subalpine forests using the deficit between total cations and inorganic anions.

3. Role of Microorganisms

Microorganisms affect the availability and cycling of micronutrients by releasing them during decay of plant and animal residues, through synthesis of biochemical chelating agents, by oxidation/reduction of a micronutrient (e.g., Fe and Mn), and through indirect transformations resulting from pH or oxidation/reduction potential changes (Alexander, 1977).

Microorganisms require the same micronutrients as higher plants and compete with plants for available micronutrients when levels are suboptimum for growth. Accordingly, some of the micronutrients returned to the soil in crop residues, or solubilized from the soil, are immobilized and incorporated into the biomass, ultimately to be released to inorganic forms by cell lysis. The relationship is analogous to N immobilization when crop residues with wide C/N ratios are applied to soil.

Several studies have shown that additions of carbonaceous crop residues to micronutrient-deficient soils can reduce the availability and relative efficiency with which an applied micronutrient is used by the plant. This effect can be explained by micronutrient immobilization during microorganism decay of the residues.

Unlike Cu, Co, and Zn, both Fe and Mn can be oxidized to higher valence states, from which highly insoluble oxides and phosphates can be formed. Thus, a significant effect of microorganisms on the micronutrient cycle is the oxidation/reduction of Fe and Mn. As drainage becomes impeded, and as the oxidation potential (Eh) approaches 0.2 V, Fe^{3+} and Mn^{4+} can be reduced to Fe^{2+} and Mn^{2+}, respectively. The oxidized form of Mn (Mn^{4+}) is essentially unavailable to plants.

A sludge-like deposit, consisting of a mixture of Fe oxides and insoluble organic matter (bacterial cell bodies and waste products), is often formed in tile drainage systems, such as are used in Florida citrus groves. The deposit prevents the tile from functioning properly by blocking the passageway.

4. Chelation Reactions in the Rhizosphere

Numerous studies have shown that soil from the rhizosphere contains higher quantities of organic acids and other biochemical chelating agents than nonrhizosphere soil (Stevenson, 1967; Stevenson & Ardakani, 1972). By inference, it is usually assumed that this enhanced availability of micronutrients to the plant is beneficial.

The rhizosphere is a favorable habitat for the proliferation of organic acid-producing microorganisms. Also, as will be shown later, plant roots exude a wide variety of organic substances that have micronutrient complexing properties. Differences in plant species' susceptibility to micronutrient deficiencies have often been attributed to variations in the plant's ability to synthesize and excrete metal complexing organics (Hodgson, 1963).

5. Organic Complexing Agents' Role in Enhancing the Availability of Insoluble Phosphates

Organic matter can affect the availability of native and fertilizer P in several ways, including: (i) complexation of Fe, Al, and Ca by naturally occurring organic ligands; (ii) competition between humates and phosphate ions for absorbing surfaces; (iii) formation of protective coatings over colloidal sesquioxides; and (iv) formation of phospho-humic complexes through bridging with Fe and/or Al (Stevenson & Ardakani, 1972).

The action of organic acids and related compounds in solubilizing mineral phosphates has been attributed to stable complex formation with Fe^{3+} and Al^{3+} in acid soils and Ca^{2+} in calcareous soils, with release of phosphate to soluble forms. Similar reactions may be involved in preventing fixation of P added as fertilizer, or formed *in situ* by weathering of minerals or decay of organic matter. The compounds most effective in releasing P from insoluble Fe and Al phosphates, or in reducing precipitation, are those that form highly stable chelate complexes with metal ions.

Little work has been done on the role of phospho-humic complexes in increasing P availability.

6. Micronutrient-Enriched Organic Products as Soil Amendments

Considerable interest has been shown in the fertilizer value of micronutrient-enriched organic products (Chen & Stevenson, 1986). Most work has focused on Fe-organo complexes as sources of Fe for sensitive crops growing on deficient soils; with few studies investigating Mn and Zn. Among the Fe-enriched products found to be effective in increasing Fe uptake are composts of plant refuse, forest by-products (lignosulfonates and polyflavonoids), peat, lignites, and animal manures. Their effectiveness in improving the Fe nutrition of the test crop is usually attributed to their similarity to soil organic matter and, in particular, the humic substances they contain.

The extensive research that has been done on natural organic products as carriers of Fe and other micronutrient cations for plants has been reviewed by Chen and Stevenson (1986). In general, it would appear that enriched products can improve the uptake of micronutrients by plants growing on deficient soils, although less efficiently than for synthetic chelates (i.e., EDTA, EDDHA, etc.). On a cost/unit basis, natural products have often compared favorably with synthetic chelates because larger quantities can be applied for the same cost. In experiments conducted by Chen et al. (1982a, b), application rates of Fe as Fe-enriched peat were considerably higher than those of Fe as FeEDDHA, with the basic concept that higher rates could be justified by the lower price (and possible longer duration of effect). Except for solubility, the Fe-enriched peat was superior to the commercial preparation.

B. Forest Ecosystems

It is well known that the cycling of micronutrient cations in forest soils (i.e., Alfisols and Spodosols) is profoundly influenced by complexation reactions with organic substances. A conceptual model of micronutrient fluxes in the forest floor and adjacent compartments is shown in Fig. 6-2.

In many forest ecosystems, metal ions can accumulate in the organic topsoil due to strong binding by humified organic matter (Heinrichs & Mayer, 1980; Friedland et al., 1984). On the other hand, water percolating through the thick mat of decomposing litter (O_1 and O_2 horizons) contains a wide array of organics that can enhance the dissolution of minerals, with mobilization of associated micronutrients (Blaschke, 1979; Blaser et al., 1980a, b;

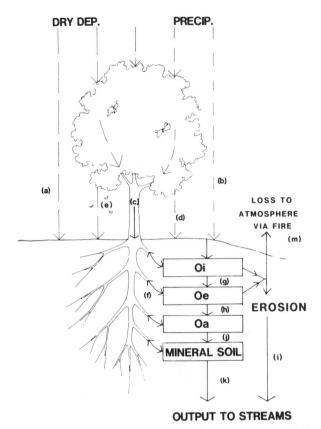

Fig. 6–2. Conceptual model of trace element fluxes in a forest ecosystem (Friedland et al., 1984). Additions to the soil occur through direct impact on the forest floor (a, b), stemflow (c), throughfall (d), and litter fall (e).

Cronan & Aiken, 1985; Pohlman & McColl, 1988). Other sources of organic ligands include canopy leachates, stem flow, root exudates, and root decomposition products. As will be noted later, mycorrhizal fungi have been implicated in the mobilization of Fe in Fe-deficient soils.

1. Weathering of Rocks and Minerals

Although it is a general phenomena, the subject of rock weathering is covered herein because metal ion solubilization and transport is particularly pronounced in humid soils under forest vegetation.

It has long been appreciated that organic compounds produced in the biosphere, together with components of stable humus, enhance the weathering of rocks and minerals, and that they are involved in the transport of micronutrients during soil formation. The initial stage of organic weathering is characterized by colonization of rock surfaces by lichens and other organisms that produce chelating agents effective in solubilizing divalent and trivalent cations from silicate minerals. With time, organic chelates of plant

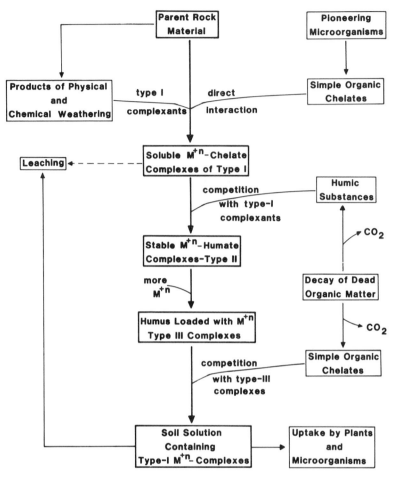

Fig. 6-3. Role of organic matter on the translocation and biological availability of trace elements (Stevenson [1986], as adapted from Zunino & Martin [1977a]). (Reproduced by permission of John Wiley & Sons, New York.)

origin, or synthesized by soil microorganisms, further contribute to the weathering process and serve as agents for the transport of Fe, Al, and other cations.

Zunino and Martin (1977a, b) developed a unified concept for the role of organic substances on the translocation and biological availability of micronutrient cations in soil (Fig. 6-3). In advanced stages of soil formation, simple organics (e.g., aliphatic organic acids) produced by microorganisms were believed to be involved in the binding of metal ions; termed type-I complexes. With time, complexes of type II were formed with newly formed humic substances, which were regarded as being more stable and less biologically available than type I. As binding sites become saturated, complexes less stable than type II are formed, termed type-III complexes. Biochemical chelating agents were believed to compete successfully for metal ions of type-III to form type-I complexes, thereby facilitating uptake by the plant.

Mineral weathering by organic acids and other chelating biochemicals occurs in two ways: lowering of pH due to ionization of COOH groups ($COOH \rightleftharpoons COO^- + H^+$), and, equally important, through formation of chelate complexes. For any given pH, weathering is usually enhanced in the presence of a chelating agent. The elements released may be taken up by plants, converted to insoluble forms, or bound to clay and insoluble humic matter.

Numerous studies (reviewed by Stevenson & Ardakani, 1972), have shown that an unusually high proportion of the microorganisms associated with the raw soil of rock crevices and the interior of porous, weathered stones produce organic acids, with silicate mineral decomposition under laboratory conditions. Lichens also initiate the disintegration of the rock surfaces to which they are attached through synthesis of complex polymeric phenols, referred to as lichen acids.

Extensive literature has developed on the dissolution of rocks and minerals through the action of organic substances (Huang & Schnitzer, 1986, for additional information). The nature and distribution of biochemicals produced in the pedosphere are discussed in Section III.

2. Eluviation and Transport of Iron and Other Polyvalent Cations

In addition to affecting the solubilization and disintegration of soil-forming rocks and minerals, organic substances serve as agents for the downward translocation of metal ions. Complexation results in differential leaching of metal ions according to their ability to form coordination complexes with organic ligands. Thus, Fe, Al, and such strongly complexed elements as Cu^{2+} are eluted to a greater extent than weakly complexed ones. At the pH levels found in most soils, hydrolysis reactions lead to the formation of insoluble oxides of the metal ions. When complexed by organic ligands, metal ions are maintained in solution and can be transported into the lower soil horizons, and, hence, to lakes and streams in percolating waters.

Eluviation of Fe^{3+}, Al^{3+}, and other metal cations as soluble organic complexes occurs to some extent in most leached soils, but the process is particularly pronounced in the Spodosols (formerly Podzol). These soils have developed under climatic and biologic conditions that have resulted in the downward movement of sesquioxides and organic matter into the B horizon. The organic surface layer of the soil, consisting largely of forest litter in various stages of decomposition, is underlain by a lightly colored eluvial horizon, A_2, which has lost substantially more sesquioxides than silica. This horizon is, in turn, underlain by a darkly colored illuvial horizon, B, in which the major accumulation products are organic matter and sesquioxides.

Stobbe and Wright (1959) reviewed the major processes involved in the formation of Spodosols. They reported that the prevailing concept was that polyphenols, organic acids, and other complexing substances in percolating waters from the surface litter bring about the solution of sesquioxides, with formation of soluble metal-organic complexes. A second theory is that polymeric phenols (e.g., FA) are the primary agents (De Coninck, 1980). According to this concept, mobile organic colloids percolating downward through the soil profile form complexes with Fe and Al until a critical saturation level is attained, with subsequent precipitation. Partial decay of organic matter in the B horizon would further saturate the complex. Once started, accumulation would be self-perpetuating, since the free oxides thus formed would cause further precipitation of the sesquioxide-humus complex. On periodic drying, the organic matter complex may harden, thereby restricting movement below the accumulation zone. De Coninck (1980) concluded that, in the mobile state, metal-humate complexes are highly hydrated (i.e., they are hydrophylic). However, during transition to the solid state, hydration water is lost and the complexes become hydrophobic.

The concept that organic substances are solely responsible for the translocation of Fe and Al in Spodosols has not been universally accepted. A recent theory postulates that, in some Spodosols, Fe and Al are transported as hydroxy-silicate sols (i.e., Al as imogolite and allophane). Soluble organic colloids migrating downward are then precipitated on the previously deposited imogolite and allophane (Anderson et al., 1982). Farmer et al. (1983) attributed the fomation of the B horizon in "Hydromorphic Humus Podzols" to coprecipitation arising from organic-rich surface waters mixing with Al from groundwater.

In all likelihood, several processes are involved in Spodosol formation, the relative importance of each being dependent on environmental conditions.

III. BIOCHEMICAL COMPOUNDS AS CHELATING AGENTS

Two types of organic constituents in soil form stable complexes with micronutrient cations: (i) defined biochemicals, such as simple aliphatic acids, hydroxamate siderophores, phenols and phenolic acids, complex polymeric phenols, and sugar acids; and (ii) components of stable humus, such as HA and FA. The importance of biochemical compounds as chelating agents arises from the fact that most complexes are water-soluble; complexes with humic substances are generally insoluble (for reactions of micronutrient cations with humic substances see Sections IV and V).

Biochemical compounds are ubiquitous in soils and would be expected to play a particularly prominent role in those environments in which conditions are favorable for microorganism proliferation, such as the rhizosphere (Rovira, 1969) and near decomposing plant residues (Bruckert, 1970). In most cultivated soils, the amounts found in the soil solution at any one time are low and variable, and represent a balance between synthesis and destruction by microorganisms. Although data are lacking, one would expect to find relatively high amounts in early spring as decomposition of plant residues commences, less during the hot summer months due to reduced microbial activity, and more once again in early fall when plant growth ceases and crop residues start to decay. Factors affecting the production of biochemical compounds

Table 6-1. Key biochemical compounds that form complexes with micronutrient cations.

Compound	Occurrence
Citric, tartaric, lactic, and malic acids	Produced by bacteria in the rhizosphere and during decay of plant remains. Identified in root exudates, aqueous extracts of forest litter, and canopy drippings
Oxalic acid	Produced by fungi in forest soils, including mycorrhizal fungi. Particularly abundant in acid soils.
Hydroxamate siderophores	Produced in the rhizosphere and by ectomycorrhizal fungi. Greater amounts may be produced when organisms are under Fe stress.
Phenolic acids	Formed through decay of plant residues (lignin). Abundant in canopy drippings and leachates of forest litter. Involved in the mobilization and transport of Fe in acid soils.
Polymeric phenols	Present in high amounts in leachates of forest litter. Produced by lichens growing on rock surfaces.
2-Ketogluconic acid	Synthesized by bacteria living on rock surfaces and in the rhizosphere. Particularly abundant in habitats rich in decaying organic matter.
Mugineic acid	Identified in root washings of Fe-deficient graminaceous plants.

include the moisture status of the soil, plant type and stage of growth, cultural practice, and climate (temperature and rainfall). Soils amended with manures and other organic wastes would be expected to be relatively rich in metal-binding biochemicals.

A major source of soluble organics in forest soils are residues that reach the soil in the form of leaves, branches, and other organic debris. Following deposition, a wide array of organic substances are produced during the various stages of decomposition and washed into the mineral layer (A horizon) in percolating waters (Section II). Organic chelating substances are also found in canopy drippings and stem flow.

Although the concentration of any given biochemical or class of compounds in the soil solution may be slight, the accumulative effect of all complexing species may be appreciable. In many soils, particularly those that are well supplied with organic matter, the combined total of potential chelate formers in the aqueous phase appears to be sufficient to account for the minute quantities of micronutrients in the soil solution, often in the milligram per liter range.

An incomplete list of biochemical chelating agents, along with a description of the environments under which they occur, is presented in Table 6-1. Concentrations of individual biochemical species in the soil solution are approximately as follows (Stevenson & Fitch, 1986):

Simple organic acids	1×10^{-3} to 4×10^{-3} M
Amino acids	8×10^{-5} to 6×10^{-4} M
Phenolic acids	5×10^{-5} to 3×10^{-4} M
Hydroxamate siderophores	1×10^{-8} to 1×10^{-7} M

The importance of any given biochemical compound or ligand type in the binding of micronutrient cations varies with environmental conditions in the soil, including the nature of the organic ligand being synthesized, and the type and amount of competing cations. As suggested earlier, binding is normally carried out by a relatively large number of biochemicals present in small amounts rather than by a few dominate species at high concentrations. Iron, a trivalent cation, is preferentially complexed over divalent species (Cu^{2+}, Mn^{2+}, Zn^{2+}, etc.); of the divalent cations, the general order is: Cu > Co > Zn > Fe > Mn. Cobalt is included in the list because it is required by animals.

Specificity for binding is also influenced by the nature of the organic ligand. Organic compounds with the greatest potential for binding Fe^{3+} are those that contain oxygen (i.e., COOH and phenolic-, enolic-, and aliphatic-OH groups). Nitrogenous substances (amino acids and porphyrins) have a high affinity for Cu^{2+} and Ni^{2+} (Arland et al., 1958).

Typical Fe^{3+} complexes with biochemical compounds are shown below.

Citrate

II

Hydroxamate

III

Catecholate

IV

A. Low-Molecular-Weight Organic Acids

Low-molecular-weight organic acids are of particular interest due to their ubiquitous nature and their ability to form chelate complexes with micronutrient cations. Various aspects of the dynamics of organic acids in soil have been discussed by Wang et al. (1967).

A wide array of low-molecular-weight aliphatic acids have been reported in soil, of which the following play a key role in the formation of complexes with divalent and trivalent cations: citric, oxalic, succinic, lactic, fumaric, and tartaric, among others. Citric and oxalic acids are of special importance by virtue of their wide distribution in the pedosphere, and since they form highly stable complexes with trace elements.

The concentration of organic acids in the soil solution is of the order $1 + 10^{-3}$ to 4×10^{-3} M (Stevenson, 1967). Substantially higher concentrations can be found in the rhizosphere, in aqueous extracts of forest litter, and possibly in soils amended with organic wastes. Leachates from the forest canopy also contain aliphatic organic acids. Anaerobic conditions are particularly suitable for organic acid production.

Excretion products of roots include a variety of organic acids, many of which (e.g., citric, oxalic, and tartaric) are capable of forming stable complexes with metal ions (Rovira, 1969). Smith (1976) reported that organic acids were the most abundant compounds in tree root exudates. Mench et al. (1988) found that organic acids were major components of the low-molecular-weight exudates of corn (*Zea mays* L.).

Considerable emphasis has recently been given to the importance of oxalic acid as a chelator of Fe^{3+} (as well as Al^{3+} and Ca^{2+}) in forest soils (Graustein et al., 1977). Many fungi are prolific producers of $H_2C_2O_4$, including the vesicular-arbuscular mycorrhizal fungi, where CaC_2O_4 crystals can form at the soil-hyphae interface (Cromack et al., 1979; Malajczuk & Cromack, 1982; Jurinak et al., 1986).

B. Hydroxamate Siderophores

Although relatively abundant in soil (to 6%), Fe is often unavailable to plants because of its low solubility under near neutral and alkaline conditions. Thus, Fe availability in calcareous soils is thought to be highly dependent on organic chelating agents, notably those in root excretions or produced by rhizosphere microorganisms.

There is abundant evidence to indicate that hydroxamate siderophores play an important role in the Fe nutrition of plants growing on calcareous soils. These substances, which contain the reactive group –CO-NOH– represent a class of microbially synthesized, Fe^{3+}-transport moieties with exceptionally high stability constants ($\sim 10^{32}$). Greater amounts appear to be produced when the organism is under severe Fe stress. A chelate structure of Fe^{3+} with hydroxamate was shown earlier in Structure III.

Biologically significant amounts of hydroxamate siderophores have been observed in soil (10^{-8} to 10^{-7} M at 10% moisture) (Powell et al., 1980; Cline et al., 1983). The amounts in rhizosphere soil are particularly high (Powell et al., 1980, 1982). Hydroxamate siderophores have been shown to be produced by soil bacteria and fungi, including ectomycorrhizal fungi (Szaniszlo et al., 1981). Jurkevitch et al. (1988) found that a *Pseudomonas putida* strain isolated from the roots of peanut (*Archis hypogaea* L.) excreted yellow-green fluorescent siderophores (unidentified) when grown under Fe-deficient conditions.

C. Polyphenols and Phenolic Acids

Interest in phenolic substances in soil arises largely from their potential alleopathic properties. However, they also form stable complexes with metal ions and thus, are believed to be important in the transport of Fe^{3+} and other metal ions in forest soils (Section III). The concentration of phenolic acids in the solution phase of agricultural soils has been estimated at 5×10^{-5} to 3×10^{-4} M (Stevenson, 1967).

Phenolic compounds are intermediates in the decay of lignin by microorganisms. They have also been shown to be synthesized by such microscopic fungi as *Stachybotrys atra, S. chartarum*, and *Epicoccum nigrum* when grown on nonlignin C sources (Martin & Focht, 1977). Particularly high concentrations have been observed in aqueous extracts of decomposing organic matter on the forest floor (O_1 and O_2 horizons), as well as canopy leachates.

Phenolic constituents released during lignin decay include 4-hydroxybenzoic, protocatechuic (3,4-dihydroxybenzoic), vanillic (4-hydroxy-3-methoxybenzoic), syringic (3,5-dimethoxy-4-hydroxybenzoic), 4-hydroxycinnamic, gallic (3,4,5-trihydroxybenzoic), and ferulic (4-hydroxy-3-methoxycinnamic) acids and their aldehydes (Stevenson, 1986). Whitehead et al. (1982) found that 4-hydroxybenzoic, vanillic, 4-hydroxycinnamic, and ferulic acids were widely distributed in agricultural soils. Those compounds that occur as aldehydes and methoxy derivatives are relatively ineffective in binding micronutrient cations. However, they can be readily transformed to more active types through the activities of microorganisms (i.e., vanillin may be transformed to protocatechuic acid through demethylation and oxidation).

Of the phenolic acids, those containing two or more OH groups are particularly effective in forming complexes with metal ions, such as protocatechuic (V), gallic (VI), and caffeic (VII) acids.

COOH   COOH   CH=CH-COOH

                        OH   HO   OH   OH

        OH   OH   OH

Protocatechuic   Gallic   Caffeic
V   VI   VII

Particularly high concentrations of phenolics have been observed in aqueous extracts of decomposing organic matter on the forest floor (Section II), as well as canopy leachates. Kuiters and Sarink (1986) identified 18 phenolics in litter leachates, many of which can form complexes with metal ions. The phenolic composition of forest soils depends partly on tree species (Kuiters & Denneman, 1987). Vance et al. (1986) concluded that protocatechuic acid was of some importance in the transport of Fe and Al in Spodosols.

The biological stability of phenolic acids is enhanced by polymerization and condensation into complex products, thereby extending the time in which they may interact with polyvalent cations. Enzymatic- and autoxidation-polymerization reactions are common occurrences. Phenolic constituents in soil can be visualized as first converting to their quinone forms, and then to HA and FA. Complexation of micronutrient cations by humic substances is discussed in Sections IV and V.

D. Polymeric Phenols

Polymeric phenols are those substances that contain more than one aromatic ring and the phenolic OH group. They include the flavonoids, which comprise one of the largest and most widespread group of secondary plant products. Typical structures are as follows:

Catechin
VIII

Gallocatechin
IX

The ability of lichens to dissolve mineral substances from rocks and minerals, and absorb micronutrients within their tissues is well known. They produce a variety of complex polymeric phenols, often referred to as lichen acids, which form highly stable complexes with metal ions. Typical examples are shown by Structures X and XI. Friedmann (1982) found that lichens of unusual organization live between the crystals of porous rocks in the frigid deserts of Antarctic dry valleys, where their activity leads to rock weathering and Fe mobilization.

X

XI

Another group of potential chelate formers are the hydrolyzable tannins. These constituents consist of gallic and/or hexahydroxydiphenic acids (digallic acid) bound to a sugar moiety through a glycosidic linkage. Tannin has numerous, free phenolic-hydroxyl sites to which Fe^{3+} and other polyvalent cations can be bound.

To some extent, the metal-binding properties of the soluble organic matter in forest litter can be attributed to polyfunctional organic moieties that have analytical characteristics and acidic functional groups similar to that of FA (Blaser et al., 1980a, b).

E. Miscellaneous Compounds

Other potential chelating compounds in soil include sugar acids, organic phosphates, phytic acid, sugars (formation of borate complexes), chlorophyll and chlorophyl-degradation products, and porphyrins. The significance of these constituents in complexing metals in soil is unknown.

Gluconic, glucuronic, and galacturonic acids are common metabolites of microorganisms. Early work (reviewed by Stevenson, 1967) indicated that habitats rich in organic matter contained large numbers of microorganisms capable of synthesizing 2-ketogluconic acid (2-oxo-glucose). This compound was shown by Moghimi et al. (1978) to be the predominate organic acid in the rhizosphere of wheat seedlings (*Triticum aestivum* L.).

Proteinaceous substances and polysaccharides are also capable of forming complexes with trace elements. As much as 30% of the soil organic matter occurs as saccharides, only a small portion of which can be accounted for as polysaccharides. Mucilaginous coatings of microbial origin adhering to mineral particles have been found to contain Fe, as well as Al, Si, and other cations. Evidence for complexing of Fe and Al by soil polysaccharides has been obtained by Saini (1966). Tan and Loutit (1976, 1977) and Stojkovski et al. (1986) found that the extracellular material (slime) of a variety of rhizosphere bacteria can bind Mo, and thereby reduce its availability to plants.

A wide array of free amino acids have been reported in soils (Stevenson, 1986). Under optimum conditions for microbial activity, their concentration in the soil solution is of the order of $8 \times 10^{-5}\,M$ to $6 \times 10^{-4}\,M$. *A priori*, it would appear that amino acids play a secondary role to organic acids as chelating agents in soil.

In other work, Takagi (1976) and Takati et al. (1984) identified mugineic acid, a metal-complexing amino acid, in root washes of Fe-deficient oats (*Avena sativa* L.) and rice (*Oryza sativa* L.). Washings from the roots of Fe-sufficient plants contained smaller amounts of mugineic acid than those of deficient plants, indicating that production was enhanced under conditions of Fe stress.

IV. TRACE METAL INTERACTIONS WITH HUMIC SUBSTANCES

A. Chemical Nature of Humic and Fulvic Acids

In most soils, the bulk of the organic matter consists of complex substances (i.e., HA and FA) whose basic structures are largely unknown despite extensive study. They are best described as a series of acidic, yellow to black polyelectrolytes with highly variable molecular weights (Stevenson, 1982). As normally defined, HA is the material extracted from soil with alkaline solutions and precipitated upon acidification; FA is the fraction that remains in solution. The organic matter that is not solubilized by alkali is referred to as the humin fraction and usually makes up about 20% of the soil organic matter. The nature of this material is unknown, but may consist of: (i) HA-like substances so intimately bound to clay minerals that the two cannot be separated; (ii) highly condensed (humified) material with a high C content (>60%), and thereby insoluble in alkali; (iii) fungal melanins, and (iv) paraffinic substances (Aiken et al., 1985). Fulvic acids are somewhat lower in molecular weight than HA's.

Table 6-2. Oxygen-containing functional groups in humic and fulvic acids.[†]

Material	Total acidity	COOH	Acidic OH[‡]	Weakly acidic alcoholic OH	C=O
		recorded range, cmol kg^{-1}			
Humic acids	560–890	150–570	210–570	20–496	10–560
Fulvic acids	640–1420	520–1120	30–570	260–950	120–420

† For documentation, see Stevenson (1982).
‡ Usually reported as phenolic OH.

The FA fraction normally contains appreciable amounts of low-molecular-weight biochemical compounds and polysaccharides. Separation of generic FA can be accomplished by sorption-desorption on a macroreticular resin, such as XAD-8 (Aiken et al., 1985). Due to their low molecular weights, FA's are more mobile than HA's, and they constitute the predominant form of humic matter in natural waters.

1. Nature of Binding Sites

The abilities of humic substances to form complexes with micronutrient cations can be accounted for by their unusually high contents of oxygen-containing functional groups, which include COOH, phenolic-, enolic-, and alcoholic-OH, and C=O. The distribution of functional groups in HA and FA, as recorded in the recent literature, is summarized in Table 6-2. Total acidities for FA are substantially higher than for HA. Both COOH and acidic OH groups (presumed to be phenolic OH) contribute to the acidic nature of these substances, with COOH as the most important especially in FA.

Humic substances, from whatever source, are highly variable in composition. Emphasis will be given herein to HA, the predominant form of humic substances in most agricultural soils.

The basic structure of soil HA is believed to be an aromatic ring of the di- or trihydroxy-phenyl type (i.e., molecule contains phenolic-OH groups) bridged together by –O–, –CH$_2$–, –NH–, and other groups (including aliphatics), and containing COOH groups, both attached directly to the ring and on aliphatic side chains. Some oxygen may exist as quinone C=O. In the natural state, HA contains attached proteinaceous and carbohydrate residues, which are also capable of forming complexes with micronutrient cations. Humic acids from wet sediments (i.e., lakes and streams) are more aliphatic in nature than those of terrestrial soils (Aiken et al., 1985).

Typical structural elements that have been reported for soil HA's and that have the potential for forming complexes with micronutrient cations are as follows:

XII   XIII   XIV

XV   XVI   XVII

In practice, binding of micronutrient cations occurs at a continuum of reactive sites, ranging from weak forces of attraction to the formation of strong coordinate links. Binding of Cu^{2+}, for example, could occur through: (i) a water bridge (Structure XVIII); (ii) electrostatic (coulombic) attraction to a COOH group (Structure XIX); (iii) formation of a coordinate link with a single donor group (Structure XX); and (iv) formation of a chelate (ring) structure, such as with a COOH-phenolic OH site combination (Structure XXI).

XVIII

XIX

XX   XXI

Binding would be expected to first occur at those sites that form coordinate ring structures. Thus, structures of type XXI represent the predominant forms of complexed trace elements when humic substances are abundant. Binding at the weaker sites (Structures XVIII and XIX) become increasingly important as the stronger sites are saturated. Micronutrient cations that form highly stable complexes (i.e., Fe^{3+} and Cu^{2+}) are complexed to a greater extent (and at the stronger binding sites) than those that form weak complexes (i.e., Mn^{2+} and Zn^{2+}). Many investigators have emphasized the formation of chelate rings (Structure XXI), but it is unlikely that they are the sole, or even most prominent, structural unit of complexation.

Results of infrared (IR) spectroscopy studies have confirmed that COOH groups (or, more precisely, carboxylate ions, COO-) play a prominent role in the complexing of divalent and trivalent cations by HA and FA. Some IR evidence indicates that OH, C=O, and NH groups may also be involved (Vinkler et al., 1976; Boyd et al., 1979; Piccolo & Stevenson, 1981).

Considerable controversy exists about the extent to which COO- linkages are covalent or ionic. The asymmetric stretching vibration of COO- in ionic bonds occurs in the 1630 to 1575 cm^{-1} region; when coordinate links are formed, the frequency shifts to between 1650 to 1620 cm^{-1}. Frequency shifts with metal-humate complexes are variable and slight, a result that may be due to the formation of mixed complexes. Interpretations in the 1620 cm^{-1} region are further complicated because of interference from covalent bonding with other groups (Piccolo & Stevenson, 1981).

Results of electron spin resonance spectroscopy (ESR) studies have also been inconclusive (Bloom, 1981). Lakatos et al. (1977) reported that HA binding of Cu^{2+} occurred through a N donor atom and two carboxylates (COO$^-$). On the other hand, McBride (1978) concluded that only oxygen donors (i.e., COO$^-$) were involved; furthermore, a single bond was observed. In contrast, spectral data obtained by Boyd et al. (1981a, b, 1983) were consistent with the formation of Cu-chelate complexes with two oxygen donor groups (Structure XXI). McBride (1982) concluded that only a small proportion of the acidic groups of FA were involved in the formation of inner-sphere complexes with Mn^{2+}.

Electron spin resonance spectra of improved resolution were obtained by Senesi et al. (1985) using a procedure that involved removal of excess Cu^{2+} by a cation-exchange resin. At a Cu/FA molar ratio of 0.02, the spectra provided evidence for three different coordination environments for bound Cu. Goodman and Cheshire (1976) and Cheshire et al. (1977) obtained evidence indicating that Cu retained by a peat HA after acid washing was coordinated to porphyrin-type groups. Indirect evidence for the formation of highly stable complexes has come from experimental difficulties in obtaining metal-free HA preparations from soil (Nissenbaum & Swaine, 1976; Cheshire et al., 1977; Povoledo & Pitze, 1979).

2. Solubility Characteristics of Metal-Humate Complexes

Humic substances form both soluble and insoluble complexes with micronutrient cations, depending on pH, presence of salt (ionic strength effect), and degree of binding site saturation. In native soil, the complexes are largely insoluble, due in part to interactions with clay minerals. Because of their lower molecular weights and higher contents of acidic functional groups, FA metal complexes are less susceptible to precipitation than HA.

Mechanisms that affect the solubility of humic substances in the presence of polyvalent cations include:

1. Precipitation due to protonation, with reduction of charge on the humic polymer (i.e., the molecule becomes more hydrophobic).
2. Formation of hydroxy complexes of the metal ion at high pH values.
3. Formation of chain-like structures through metal-ion bridges, as shown by Structure XXII.

XXII

4. Attachment to clay particles and oxide surfaces, such as through metal-ion links. The bulk of the organic matter in most soils is bound to clay minerals, probably through links with Fe, Al, and other polyvalent cations, as illustrated below:

XXIII

Net charge reduction on the humate molecule occurs through COO^- group reaction with polyvalent cations. This, in turn, causes the stretched configuration of the humic molecule to collapse, thereby reducing solubility. As chain-like structures are formed, and as oxygen containing functional groups become neutralized, precipitation increases.

B. Binding Capacities

Approaches used to determine the binding capacities of humic substances for metal ions include: proton release (van Dijk, 1971; Stevenson, 1976, 1977), metal ion retention as determined by competition with a cation-exchange resin (Crosser & Allen, 1977), anodic stripping voltammetry (Guy & Chakrabarti, 1976; O'Shea & Mancy, 1976), ion-selective electrode measurements (Buffle et al., 1977; Bresnahan et al., 1978; Fitch & Stevenson, 1984), and dialysis (Zunino & Martin, 1977a, b).

Still another approach involves the determination of binding sites that are occupied, for which ultraviolet (UV) and fluorescence spectroscopic techniques have been used (Ryan & Weber, 1982; Ryan et al., 1983; Gamble et al., 1985). Because of greater sensitivity, fluorescence spectroscopy provides data for binding under conditions more typical of natural environments (i.e., low concentrations of organic matter). Fluorescence of organic ligands is quenched when complexation occurs; thus, differentiation of free sites from bound sites can be made. An additional advantage of the fluorescence method is that solution-phase complexation can be separated from solid-phase adsorption (Gamble et al., 1985).

The maximum binding capacity for any given metal ion is approximately equal to the content of acidic functional groups, primarily COOH. An exchange acidity of 500 $cmol_c$ kg^{-1} HA corresponds to a retention of about 160 mg of Cu^{2+} g^{-1}. Assuming a C content of 56% for HA, one Cu^{2+} atom is bound per 60 C atoms in the saturated complex.

Factors influencing the quantity of metal ions bound by humic substances include pH, type and amount of acidic functional groups, ionic strength, and molecular weight. For any given pH and ionic strength, trivalent cations are bound in greater amounts than divalent ones; for the latter, those forming the strongest coordination complexes (e.g., Cu^{2+}) are bound to a greater extent than weakly coordinated ones (e.g., Mn^{2+} and Zn^{2+}).

1. pH Effects on Metal Ion Complexation

The effect of pH on metal ion complexation results from: (i) hydrolysis reactions involving the formation of monomeric species and polymers of the metal ions, and (ii) changes in extent of ionization of COOH groups. The effect of pH on the formation of monomeric and polymeric species of micronutrient cations is discussed in Ch. 4. In brief, an increase in pH above about 4.5 leads to hydrolysis of the metals with formation of oxide hydrates.

Humic and fulvic acids act as weak-acid polyelectrolytes in which ionization of COOH groups is controlled by pH, thereby affecting their ability to bind metal ions. Binding can be influenced in other ways, such as through conformational changes in the macromolecule.

2. Influence of Salts and Competing Cations

The binding of metal ions by humic substances is influenced by electrolytes in two ways. First, activity coefficients of charged inorganic species are dependent on ionic composition of the solution. At the same ionic strength, the activities of trivalent cations are reduced more than those of divalent cations, which, in turn, are reduced to a greater extent than monovalent cations. For solutions with ionic strengths between 0.001 and 0.1, the physical size of the ion must also be taken into consideration.

A second effect is due to cation competition for binding sites on the ligand. For macromolecules, there exists the potential for a variety of configurational arrangements based on the type and nature of the interacting cation. Ghosh and Schnitzer (1980) suggest that humic substances behave like rigid spherocolloids at high humic concentrations, at low pH, or at high concentrations of electrolyte. On the other hand, they behave like flexible, linear colloids at low humic concentrations, neutral pH, or at low ionic strength.

C. Role of Organic Matter and Clay in Retention of Applied Micronutrients

Clay and organic colloids are major soil components involved in retention of applied micronutrients. However, individual effects are not as easily ascertained as might be supposed, for the reason that, in most mineral soils, organic matter is intimately bound to the clay, probably as a clay-metal-organic matter complex (Structure XXIII). Accordingly, clay and organic matter function more as a unit than as separate entities, and the relative contribution of organic and inorganic surfaces to adsorption depends on the extent to which the clay is coated with organic substances. The amount of organic matter required to coat the clay varies from one soil to another and depends on both type and amount of clay. For soils with similar clay and organic matter contents, organic matter contribution to micronutrient binding is highest when the predominant clay mineral is kaolinite and lowest when it is montmorillonite.

Another important factor in the binding of divalent cations is the extent to which binding sites on organic surfaces are occupied by trivalent cations, notably Fe and Al.

D. Reduction Properties

Humic substances may catalyze the reduction of Fe^{3+} to Fe^{2+} and of anionic MoO_4^{2-} to Mo^{5+} (Goodman & Cheshire, 1982; Lakatos et al., 1977; Skogerboe & Wilson, 1981). Reduction of ionic species is considerably important in soil and water systems because the solubility characteristics of the metal ions, and, hence, mobilities are modified. The technique of electron spin resonance (ESR) spectroscopy has been used in conjunction with Mössbauer spectroscopy to obtain information on oxidation states and site symmetries of Fe bound by HA and FA (Kodama et al., 1988).

V. STABILITY CONSTANTS OF METAL COMPLEXES WITH HUMIC SUBSTANCES

An important characteristic of a metal-organic complex is its stability constant, the value of which provides an index of the cation's affinity for the ligand. Computer models is one area that has used stability constant data (e.g., GEOCHEM, MINEQ, etc.). These models are designed to predict the speciation of metal ions in the soil solution. Additional information provided by stability constant measurements include: (i) binding capacities of humic substances for micronutrients as a function of pH and ionic strength; (ii) dissociation rate or lability of the complexes; and (iii) kinetics of complex formation.

The utility of stability constant data can be illustrated by the following hypothetical example. Assume that the weight of an acre-foot of soil is 0.9 $\times$ 10^6 kg (2 $\times$ 10^6 lbs) and that 2.73 kg of a micronutrient (e.g., Zn^{2+}) is introduced and mixed uniformly to plow depth. The total quantity of Zn^{2+} in the top soil is increased by 3 mg kg^{-1} and its concentration in the soil solution at field capacity (assuming a moisture content of 20%) becomes 15 mg L^{-1}, provided all of the added Zn^{2+} is water soluble. On the assumption that most of the Zn^{2+} is complexed by insoluble organic matter, and that only 1 $\times$ 10^{-6} is dissociated, the concentration of Zn^{2+} in the solution phase is only about 15 $\times$ 10^{-6} mg L^{-1}.

Several difficulties are encountered in determining stability constants of metal-soil organic matter complexes. Humic substances from different sources are heterogeneous with respect to molecular weight and content of reactive functional groups. Also, pH profoundly affects the ionization of acidic groups and, thereby, the number of sites available for binding. Several types of binding sites are undoubtedly present (Structures XII to XVII) and the site(s) forming the most stable complex(es) will react first. The possibility also exists that HA's and FA's contain binding sites that are chemically identical, but which interact with metal ions in such a way that binding at one site affects binding at subsequent sites, Another complication involves conformational changes in the macromolecule, which may accompany changes in pH or neutral salt concentration.

A. Limitations in Stability Constant Measurements

Stability constants are classified according to the type of reaction they describe. The overall reaction is:

$$jM + iL \rightleftharpoons M_jL_i \qquad [1]$$

where j and i are the number of moles of metal ion and ligand molecules in the complex, respectively, and the terms M, L, and M_jL_i represent molar concentrations of free M, free L, and the complex, respectively. The overall formation (equilibrium) constant (K) is given by:

$$K = \frac{(M_jL_i)}{(M)^j(L)^i} \qquad [2]$$

The reciprocal of the formation constant is called a dissociation constant. In this discussion, the terms formation and stability constants are used interchangeable.

Table 6–3. Methods used to measure metal-soil organic matter reaction parameters.

	Method	Value measured	Reference
Two-step process: Separation and analysis	1. Ion-exchange/AA, colorimetry	M or M_b	Schnitzer & Hansen, 1970
	2. Ion-exchange, radiology	M	Ardakani & Stevenson, 1972 Rosell et al., 1977
	3. Gel filtration, UV	M	Mantura & Riley, 1975 Mantura et al., 1978
One-step process: Analysis in situ	1. Fluorescence quenching	L_b or L	Saar & Weber, 1980a Ryan & Weber, 1982 Ryan et al., 1983 Gamble et al., 1985
	2. Spectrophotometry	L	Blaser et al., 1980a Langford & Khan, 1975
	3. Ion-selective electrode (ISE)	M	Bresnahan et al., 1978 Buffle et al., 1977 Cheam & Gamble, 1974 Saar & Weber, 1980a, b Sposito & Holtzclaw, 1979 Sposito et al., 1979
	4. Anodic stripping voltammetry (ASV)	M	Greter et al., 1979 O'Shea & Mancy, 1976 Bhat et al., 1981

Calculating stability constants has not always allowed for side reactions involving the metal ion, the ligand, or both. Side reactions involving the ligand include protonation of reactive sites ($L^- + H^+ \rightleftharpoons HL$). To avoid problems with the formation of chloro complexes (MCl^+, MCl_2), NO_3^- has often been used as the supporting electrolyte. Sposito and Holtzclaw (1979) concluded that perchlorate is the preferred media.

Irrespective of the approach used for calculating stability constants, some determination must be made for free and bound forms of the ligand or metal ion. As noted in Table 6–3, both direct and indirect methods have been used to determine the desired parameter (i.e., M, M_b, L, or L_b). In most cases, M is the measured quantity. Early work to determine stability constants was done by competition between the ligand and a cation-exchange resin for the metal ion. Ion-selective electrodes (ISE) and anodic stripping voltammetry (ASV) are frequently used; other techniques include potentiometric base titrations, bioassay, spectrophotometric titration, spectrofluorometry, gel filtration, and dialysis (Table 6–3). Advantages and limitations of ISE and ASV have been discussed by Bresnahan et al. (1978) and Bhat et al. (1981).

Choice of method for determining the extent of binding is critical in two ways. First, humic substances may contain two or more specific reactive sites, and the lower limit of detection will place a restriction on the highest stability constant that can be measured. A second aspect is in regard to the measured parameter. For example, with a divalent cation as the central group, the amount of ligand bound to the complex based on proton release data is ($ML + 2ML_2$). In the case of ISE, the quantity ($ML + ML_2$) is determined. The two only agree when 1:1 complexes are formed.

The concentrations of reactants and products ideally should be expressed in molar units. Due to lack of molecular-weight data, this has seldom been possible with humic substances (Bresnahan et al., 1978; Sposito et al.,1979; Saar & Weber, 1980a, b). Most often, this parameter has been expressed in terms of reactive site concentration (nL_t) where n is the number of binding sites and L_t is the molar concentration of the ligand. Methods for estimating nL_t include potentiometric titration (Stevenson, 1976, 1977; Takamatsu & Yoshida, 1978), spectrophotometric titration and bioassay (Blaser et al., 1980a, b), fluorescence quenching (Saar & Weber, 1980a; Ryan et al., 1983; Gamble et al., 1985), equilibrium dialysis (Zunino & Martin, 1977a, b), and cation exchange with synthetic resins (Crosser & Allen, 1977). Humic substances are extremely heterogeneous, and most values are reported as conditional stability constants that are a function of pH, ionic strength, and concentration of reactants.

B. Modeling Approaches

Several types of reactions can be visualized. The simplest case is 1:1 binding ($i = j = 1$). More complex, but mathematically solvable, is the formation of mononuclear complexes with two or more binding substrates. The central group may be the metal ion (formation of ML_i complexes) or the macromolecule (formation of M_jL complexes). Both approaches have been used in metal binding studies of humic substances. A more difficult system to solve is one in which polynuclear complexes are formed (M_jL_i). Greater attention needs to be given to these complexes in the future.

A survey of mathematical models for the determination of stability constants of metal complexes with humic substances has been provided by Fitch and Stevenson (1984) and Stevenson and Fitch (1986).

1. Formation of 1:1 Complexes

Early measurements for conditional stability constants were performed using a method based on the competition between the ligand and a cation-exchange resin for the metal ion (i.e., Schubert's ion-exchange equilibrium method) and the continuous variation method of Job. In most cases, the experimental data were interpreted in terms of the formation of 1:1 complexes.

Limitations of the ion-exchange equilibrium method as applied to humic substances have been outlined elsewhere (Stevenson & Ardakani, 1972; Smith et al., 1986). One requirement is that the ligand must be present in excess amounts relative to the metal ion. This has not been the case in some studies with humic substances. A modified version of the ion-exchange equilibrium method has been described by Ardakani and Stevenson (1972).

The method of continuous variation, or Job's Method, is based on changes in the absorption characteristics of the metal ion or ligand when a complex is formed. Optical density measurements are made for a series of solutions that contain variable ratios of ligand and metal ion, while maintaining a constant reactant concentration. The point at which absorbance

Table 6-4. Conditional and overall stability constants (log K) for the Co^{2+}, Cu^{2+}, Mn^{2+}, and Zn^{2+} complexes of FA. The formation of 1:1 complexes is assumed.

Metal ion and source	Supporting electrolyte	pH				Reference
		5	6	7	8	
Co						
soil	0.1 M KCl	4.10				Schnitzer & Hansen, 1970
peat	0.02 M Tris				4.51	Mantoura et al., 1978
Cu†						
soil	0.1 M KCl	4.00				Schnitzer & Hansen, 1970
	0.1 M NaClO₄	4.35				Cheam & Gamble, 1974
	0.1 M NaNO₃	4.00				Buffle et al., 1977
	0.1 M KNO₃	4.68	5.03	5.45		Ryan & Weber, 1982
	0.1 M KNO₃		5.04			Ryan et al., 1983
peat	0.02 M Tris				7.85	Mantoura et al., 1978
Mn						
soil	0.1 M KCl	3.70				Schnitzer & Hansen, 1970
peat	0.02 M Tris				4.17	Mantoura et al., 1978
Zn‡						
soil	0.1 M KCl	3.70				Schnitzer & Hansen, 1970
soil	0.1 M KNO₃		3.60			Ryan et al., 1983
peat	0.02 M Tris				4.83	Mantoura et al., 1978

† A range in log K of 8.1 to 9.1 (pH 5) was obtained by Rosell et al. (1977) for the HA's from four soils from Argentina.
‡ Results for Zn-HA complexes are included in Fig. 6-4.

reaches a maximum corresponds to the maximum number of ligands bound in the complex. A Job plot is subsequently prepared by plotting changes in optical density against the molar ratio of ligand to metal ion, from which the necessary information is obtained for calculating log K. As Crosser and Allen (1977) and MacCarthy and Mark (1976) pointed out, results obtained with humic substances can be affected by light scattering due to precipitation of the complexes, thereby leading to erroneous log K values. In some studies, supplemental light scattering measurements have been made to detect the onset of aggregation (Ryan et al., 1983; Gamble et al., 1985).

Table 6-4 provides an indication of the range of log K values that have been recorded for assumed 1:1 complexes of Co, Cu, Mn, and Zn with FA. A wide range of values is evident, even at the same pH. The extent to which the findings reflect differences in the nature of the humic material is unknown. Stabilities of the complexes at pH 8 follow the approximate order of the well-known Irving Williams stability series (Mantoura et al., 1978), that is, Cu > Zn > Co > Mn.

Figure 6-4 shows log K values for Zn^{2+} complexes with HA as influenced by pH. Although log K values for any given pH are highly variable, a definite trend is evident. Matsuda and Ito (1970) observed a range in log K from 4.2 to 10.8 for 29 Zn-HA complexes (pH 7.0) and from 3.9 to 9.3 for 32 Zn-FA complexes. Adsorption strength of HA for Zn was believed to increase with an increase in degree of humification.

Stability constants of metal-soil organic matter complexes appear to be generally lower than those for complexes of the same metal ions with com-

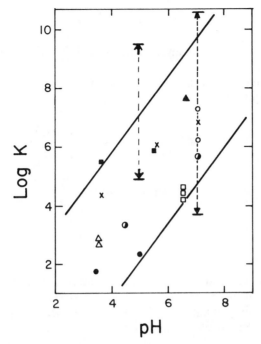

Fig. 6-4. Effect of pH on stability constants (log K) of Zn organic matter complexes. Adapted from Stevenson and Ardakani (1972), modified to include data obtained by Rosell et al. (1977) for 4 HA's at pH 5 (range shown by vertical dashed line at pH 5). The vertical dashed line at pH 7 indicates the range of values reported by Matsuda and Ito (1970) for 29 HA's and 32 FA's.

mercial chelating agents, such as EDTA. They are also lower than those of complexes with many, but not all, naturally occurring biochemical compounds, including certain amino acids and aliphatic hydroxy acids. These observations, which require confirmation, have significant practical implications regarding the transport and availability of micronutrients to plants.

2. Metal Ion as the Central Group

When the metal ion is the central group, which is usually the case with small molecules, a series of species of the type ML_i are obtained. For humic substances, the metal ion may: (i) combine with reactive sites on two separate molecules and, thereby, link the two together; and/or (ii) combine with two reactive sites on the same molecule, as suggested by Bloom (1981) for Mn^{2+} binding by soil organic matter.

As applied to HA and FA, complexation is regarded as a competitive reaction between the metal ion and H^+ for the reactive site. For a divalent cation (e.g., Cu^{2+}), the reactions are:

$$M^{2+} + HL \overset{b_1}{\rightleftharpoons} ML^+ + H^+ \qquad [3]$$

$$ML^+ + HL \overset{b_2}{\rightleftharpoons} ML_2 + H^+ \qquad [4]$$

where HL represents the associated form of the binding site (e.g., COOH or phenolic OH).

Two successive formation constants (b_1 and b_2) are required, one for each ligand group that adds to the complex.

$$b_1 = \frac{(ML^+)(H^+)}{(HL)(M^{2+})}; \qquad b_2 = \frac{(ML_2)(H^+)}{(HL)(ML^+)} \qquad [5]$$

The overall formation constant, B_2, is given by:

$$B_2 = b_1 b_2 = \frac{(ML_2)(H^+)^2}{(HL)^2(M^{2+})} \qquad [6]$$

A functional relationship exists between constants obtained in this manner and those obtained for the reaction of the metal ion with the dissociated form of the reactive site [i.e., $M^{2+} + L^- \rightleftharpoons ML^+$; $k_1 = (ML^+)/[(M^2)(L^-)]$. The relationship is given by:

$$b_i = K_a k_i \qquad [7]$$

where K_a is the ionization constant for the acidic group.

The potentiometric method requires calculations for the free ligand or binding site (L^-) and $\bar{n}$, the average number of ligand molecules (binding sites) bound per metal ion. The latter, referred to as Bjerrum's Formation Function, is calculated as:

$$\bar{n} = \frac{(L_t) - (HL) - (L^-)}{(M_t)} = \frac{(ML^+) + 2(ML_2)}{(M^{2+}) + (ML^+) + (ML_2)} \qquad [8]$$

where L_t and M_t are the total concentrations of ligand and metal ion, respectively.

In general terms, $\bar{n}$ is related to the stability constant through the relationship:

$$\sum_{n=0}^{n=N} (\bar{n} - n)B_n(HL/H^+)^n = 0 \qquad [9]$$

For 2:1 complexes, the desired constants can be obtained from the following equation, using the method of least squares:

$$\frac{\bar{n}}{(\bar{n} - 1)(HL/H^+)} = \frac{(2 - \bar{n})(HL/H^+)}{(\bar{n} - 1)} B_2 - b_1 \qquad [10]$$

Alternately, a graphical approach can be used, in which case a formation curve is prepared by plotting $\bar{n}$ vs. $p(HL/H^+)$ and selecting individual b_i values as half integer values of $\bar{n}$.

In this method, titration curves are obtained for the ligand in the presence and absence of variable amount of metal ion. Values for (HL), the concentration of undissociated acidic functional groups, are obtained at several pH readings along the titration curve, using the relationship:

$$(HL) = (L_t) - (KOH) - (H^+) + (OH^-) \qquad [11]$$

where L_t is the amount of base consumed to the end point and (KOH) is the concentration of added base after allowance for dilution.

The concentration of dissociated functional groups (L^-) is then calculated from ionization constants (K_a) for each pH reading, as determined by analysis of titration curves of the humic material in the absence of metal ions. For any given pH, (L^-) is obtained from the relationship

$$(L^-) = HL(K_a/H^+) \qquad [12]$$

Several values for $\bar{n}$ are next obtained by substituting into Eq. [8] known values for L_t and M_t, and the experimentally determined values of HL and L^-. From this information, values for the overall constant (B_2) can be obtained using Eq. [10], and hence K_2 from Eq. [7].

A complication of using titration data to calculate stability constants is that the curves are horizontally displaced in the near-neutral and alkaline pH ranges. This is apparently due to the release of an otherwise nontitratable H^+ from the humic acid and/or protons from hydration water of the metal bound in 1:1 complexes (van Dijk, 1971; Stevenson, 1976, 1977). To solve this problem, a procedure has been used involving sequential additions of the metal ion at constant pH (pH returned to initial starting point after each addition). The assumption is made that the metal ion reacts with the dissociated form (L^-) of the reactive group and that protons are subsequently released as ionization equilibrium is reestablished ($HL \rightleftharpoons L^- + H^+$). At pH values below ~5.5, release of protons from hydration water of the metal ion is suppressed, thereby facilitating the calculations. From measurements for the accumulated amount of base required to return the pH to the desired value for each incremental addition of Cu^{2+}, the various parameters are obtained for calculating $\log K_2$.

Results obtained for the Cu^{2+} and Zn^{2+} complexes of a soil HA, as influenced by ionic strength, are given in Fig. 6-5. A pronounced increase in $\log K_2$ is shown with a decrease in ionic strength, which is to be expected. Log K_2 values obtained at low salt concentrations are more likely to represent conditions existing in the soil solution than those at high salt concentrations.

Overall stability constants, as obtained above, are not directly comparable with those reported in the previous section for 1:1 complexes. However, estimated $\log k_1$ values (i.e., [$\log K_2$]/2) for Cu^{2+} and Zn^{2+} complexes were

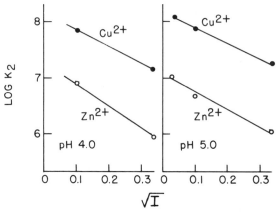

Fig. 6–5. Overall stability constants (log K_2) for Cu^{2+} and Zn^{2+} complexes of a soil HA at two pH values as affected by ionic strength (I). (Adapted from Stevenson, 1977).

of the same order of magnitude as those reported in Table 6-4 for 1:1 complexes.

Takamatsu and Yoshida (1978) used a closely related approach to determine stability constants of Cu^{2+}-HA complexes. In this case, free Cu^{2+} was estimated by ISE measurements and the number of reactive sites was proposed to be equivalent to the content of acidic functional groups as estimated by base titration. Successive stability constants were obtained from the relationship:

$$\frac{M_t - (M^{2+})}{(M^{2+})(L^-)^2} = \frac{k_1}{(L^-)} + k_1 k_2 \qquad [13]$$

where k_1 and k_2 are related to b_1 and b_2 by Eq. [7].

The left side of Eq. [13] was plotted vs. $1/(L^-)$, from which k_1 and $k_1 k_2$ were obtained from the slope and intercept, respectively. The total concentration of metal ions, M_t, was known and M^{2+} was obtained from the ISE measurements. Values for L^- were determined by differences between L_t (known) and HL plus sites bound in the complex. Equation [13] is limited because an inherent correlation exists between $1/(L^-)^2$ of the Y variable and $1/(L^-)$ of the X variable.

The equation relating log $k_1 k_2$ (i.e., log K_2) to pH for the Cu^{2+} complexes was: log $k_1 k_2 = 8.65 + 0.65$ (pH − 5).

Explanations given by Takamatsu and Yoshida (1978) for the variation in log $k_1 k_2$ with pH were: (i) complexing at one site affects binding of the metal cation to an adjacent site; (ii) in the higher pH region, metal ions are bound selectively to functional groups that form the strongest complexes, but which are protonated in the lower pH region; and (iii) steric stabilization occurs through chelate ring formation.

In other work, Young et al. (1982) used potentiometric base titration to study Cu^{2+} binding to the soluble polycarboxylates from a peat and a mineral soil. Constants were calculated for the equilibria:

$$Cu^{2+} + 2L^- \rightleftharpoons CuL_2: \qquad \beta_{Cu} = (CuL_2)/(Cu^{2+})(L^-)^2, \qquad [14]$$

$$Cu^{2+} + 2LH \rightleftharpoons CuL_2 + 2H^+: \quad \beta_{Cu}^H = (CuL_2)(H^+)^2/(Cu^{2+})(LH)^2. \quad [15]$$

Log β_{Cu}^H values varied from -1.26 to -1.80, and were unaffected by pH or the degree of dissociation of acidic functional groups. In contrast, log β_{Cu} values drastically increased with increasing dissociation of acidic groups, with values of 0.5 to 2.8 for the completely protonated sample (low pH) and 7.6 to 9.3 for the fully dissociated sample (high pH).

3. Macromolecule as the Central Group

In this approach, the formation of a series of $M_1L, M_2L \ldots M_jL$ complexes is assumed. The reaction can be described by j stability constants, as follows:

$$M + L = ML \qquad (k_1) \qquad\qquad [16]$$

$$ML + M = M_2L \qquad (k_2) \qquad\qquad [17]$$

$$M_{j-1}L + M = M_jL \qquad (k_j) \qquad\qquad [18]$$

As was noted earlier, binding is characterized by a formation function, ν, defined as:

$$\nu = \frac{\text{molar concentration of bound metal ion}}{\text{molar concentration of polymer}} \qquad [19]$$

The quantity ν can be regarded as the average number of metal ions associated with each macromolecule L:

$$\nu = \frac{\text{sites bound}}{\text{polymer concentration}}$$

$$= \frac{(M_b)}{(L_t)} = \frac{(LM) + 2(M_2L) + \ldots j(M_jL)}{(L) + (LM) + \ldots (M_jL)} \qquad [20]$$

where M_b is the concentration of bound metal ion, L_t the polymer concentration, and j is the number of metal ions bound to the polymer. By substitution of the association constants $k_1, k_2, \ldots k_n$ into Eq. [20] the following is obtained.

$$\nu = \frac{k_1(M) + 2k_1k_2(M) \ldots + jk_1k_2 \ldots k_j(M)}{1 + k_1(M) + k_1k_2(M) \ldots + k_1k_2 \ldots k_j(M)} \qquad [21]$$

When all combining sites are identical, ν is related to the overall binding constant, K_o, by the equation:

Table 6-5. Plotting approaches for analysis of experimental binding data.

Plot	Form of the equation	Plot	
		Y	X
Scatchard	$\nu/M = nK_o - \nu K_o$ or $\theta/M = K_o - \theta K_o$	ν/M θ/M	ν θ
Reciprocal (Langmuir)	$M/\nu = M/n + 1/nK_o$ or $M/M_b = M/nL_t + 1/nL_t K_o$	M/ν M/M_b	M M
Double reciprocal	$1/\nu = 1/n + 1/nK_oM$ or $1/M_b = 1/nL_t + 1/nL_t K_oM$	$1/\nu$ $1/M_b$	$1/M$ $1/M$
Hill	$\log [\theta/(1 - \theta)] = \log K^* + n\log M$	$\log [\theta/(1 - \theta)]$	$\log M$

$$\nu = \frac{jK_o(M^{2+})}{1 + K_o(M^{2+})} \qquad [22]$$

In the absence of a known molecular weight, the formation constant can be expressed in terms of binding-site concentration, nL_t.

$$\theta = \frac{\text{molar concentration of bound metal ion}}{\text{total number of reactive sites}} = \frac{M_b}{nL_t} = \frac{\nu}{j} \qquad [23]$$

which, by substitution into Eq. [22], yields:

$$\theta = \frac{K_o(M^{2+})}{1 + K_o(M^{2+})} \qquad [24]$$

Eq. [22] and [24] can be arranged in a number of ways to yield information about the number of classes of sites and the stability constant for each class (K_1, K_2, etc.). Plotting can be performed as a Scatchard Plot (ν/M vs. ν; θ/M vs. θ), a reciprocal plot (M/ν vs. M), a double reciprocal plot ($1/\nu$ vs. $1/M$), and a Hill Plot {log $[\theta/(1 - \theta)]$ vs. log M}. The various approaches and plotting variables are listed in Table 6-5.

Values for the number of reactive sites (nL_t) can be obtained in several ways, such as by potentiometric titration for total acidity or from metal-ion retention data for maximum binding ability.

An approach used by Buffle et al. (1977) to study the binding of Cu^{2+} to FA can be shown to have the same form as the double reciprocal plot; the approach of Zunino and Martin (1977a, b) is equivalent to a Hill Plot. Fitch and Stevenson (1984) pointed out that stability constants obtained by the Hill Plot are unreliable when binding at one site decreases binding affinity at subsequent sites, which appears to be the case for metal complexes with humic substances, as noted below.

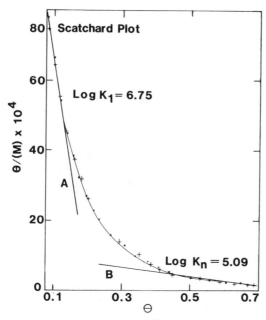

Fig. 6-6. Scatchard Plot for the binding of Cu^{2+} by a soil HA (Fitch & Stevenson, 1984).

The Scatchard Plot approach (see Table 6-5) has been the method of choice of most investigators (Bresnahan et al., 1978; Saar & Weber, 1980a, b; Sposito et al., 1979; Fitch & Stevenson, 1984). Nonlinear curves have been obtained, from which stability constants for binding at two classes of sites (logs K_1 and K_2) have been calculated. Thus, Eq. [24] becomes:

$$\nu = \frac{K_1(M^{2+})}{1 + K_1(M^{2+})} + \frac{K_2(M^{2+})}{1 + K_2(M^{2+})} \qquad [25]$$

A typical Scatchard Plot is shown in Fig. 6-6. The dissection of Scatchard Plots into two segments is somewhat arbitrary. Additional sites can be observed by assigning linear segments to the plots (Fitch & Stevenson, 1983). A five-site model was proposed by Cabaniss and Shuman (1988) for binding Cu^{2+} to a Suwannee river FA.

The curvilinearity of Scatchard Plots may be due to: (i) a continuum of bindings sites, each with a slightly different affinity for the metal ion; (ii) electrostatic effects, such that complexation at one site decreases the tendency of a neighboring functional group to complex another metal ion; and (iii) formation of ML_2 complexes (i.e., metal ion is the central group). Irrespective, constants obtained by the Scatchard Plot method are to be regarded as average stability constants, which vary with solution composition, such as concentration of humic material (Perdue & Lytle, 1983a, b).

Table 6-6. Stability constants for Cu binding by FA's from several sources using the Scatchard Plot approach.[†]

Source of FA	Supporting electrolyte	pH	Log K_1	Log K_n	Reference
Soil	0.1 M KNO_3	4.0	5.60	3.95	Bresnahan et al., 1978
Water	0.1 M KNO_3	4.0	5.48	4.00	Bresnahan et al., 1978
Water	0.1 M KNO_3	4.7	6.00	3.85	Bresnahan et al., 1978
Soil	0.1 M KNO_3	5.0	6.00	4.08	Bresnahan et al., 1978
Water	0.1 M KNO_3	5.0	5.95	3.70	Bresnahan et al., 1978
Soil	0.1 M KNO_3	6.0	6.30	3.77	Bresnahan et al., 1978
Water	0.1 M KNO_3	6.0	6.11	3.85	Bresnahan et al., 1978
Water	0.01 M NaCl	8.0	8.80	8.05	Mantoura & Riley, 1975
Peat	0.01 M NaCl	8.0	8.51	7.16	Mantoura & Riley, 1975

[†] Log K_1 = binding at strongest (measurable site). Log K_n = binding at weakest site.

Stability constants for the complexes of Cu^{2+} with FA from various sources are provided in Table 6-6. The values are recorded in terms of binding at the strongest measurable site (log K_1) and the weakest site (log K_n); most constants are recorded for a two-site system. As expected, log K values increase with increasing pH.

Fitch et al. (1986) pointed out that, with ISE, the magnitude of log K_1 depends on the availability (and reliability) of data at low values of ν (i.e., low saturation of binding sites). With a technique that permits measurements for Cu^{2+} at concentrations $< 10^{-8}$ M, a log K_1 of 8.2 was obtained for a Cu-HA complex at pH 4 and an ionic strength of 0.005. This value is two orders of magnitude higher than those recorded in Table 6-6 for measurements made at higher Cu^{2+} concentrations. On this basis, it would appear that many estimates for log K_1 are low because of failure of ISE to measure the free form of the metal ion at low saturation levels. Marinsky et al. (1982) included a term for electrostatic interactions in their calculations for the stability constant of a Cu^{2+}-HA complex and concluded that Cu was bound as $RCOOCu^+$ with a log K of about 1.3.

Gamble et al. (1970) and Cheam and Gamble (1974) proposed using a differential equilibrium function to describe binding of metal ions to humic substances. MacCarthy (1977) and MacCarthy and Smith (1978) have treated humic substances as mixtures of nonidentical molecules. In the model proposed by Perdue and Lytle (1983a, b), humic substances are treated as a complex mixture of ligands that form complexes with a continuous distribution of log K values (a normal Gaussian distribution was suggested). The approach has been referred to as a continuous multiligand model. Advantages and disadvantages of the Gaussian Distribution Model has been discussed by Perdue and Lytle (1983b).

VI. SUMMARY

Extensive research has been carried out on organic matter-micronutrient reactions in soil since the 1972 publication of *Micronutrients in Agriculture*.

Major attention has been given to chemical speciation of trace elements in the soil solution, influence of organic matter in ameliorating Al^{3+} toxicities in acid soils, chelation reactions in the rhizosphere, mechanisms of metalion binding by humic substances, and stability constant measurements and their interpretations. Whereas numerous studies have confirmed the importance of organic matter to the soil micronutrient cycle, details are lacking in several key areas; notably, genetic and environmental factors influencing production of chelating biochemicals in the rhizosphere, the role of organic matter in micronutrient cation transport to plant roots, and competition of ligand type (i.e., biochemicals and humic substances) for metal ions. There is an urgent need to upgrade methodologies for determining organically bound forms of micronutrient cations in the soil solution. In the future, genetic alteration of soil microorganisms shows promise for enhancing micronutrient availability to plants growing on deficient soils.

Serious problems are encountered in the determination of stability constants of metal complexes with humic substances. A variety of methods have been applied, and considerable progress has been made, but agreement has not yet been reached as to how the data can best be analyzed and interpreted. The need for future research in this area is evident.

REFERENCES

Aiken, G.R., D.M. McKnight, R.L. Wershaw, and P. MacCarthy (ed.). 1985. Humic substances in soil, sediment, and water. John Wiley and Sons, New York.

Alexander, M. 1977. Introduction to soil microbiology. 2nd ed. John Wiley and Sons, New York.

Anderson, A.H., M.L. Berrow, V.C. Farmer, A. Hepburn, J.D. Russell, and A.D. Walker. 1982. A reassessment of podzol formation processes. J. Soil Sci. 33:125–136.

Ardakani, M.S., and F.J. Stevenson. 1972. A modified ion-exchange technique for determination of stability constants of metal-soil organic matter complexes. Soil Sci. Soc. Am. J. 36:884–890.

Arland, S., J. Chatt, and N.R. Davies. 1958. The relative affinities of ligand atoms for acceptor molecules. Chem. Soc. London. Quart. Rev. 12:265–273.

Bhat, G.A., R.A. Saar, R.B. Smart, and J.H. Weber. 1981. Titration of soil-derived fulvic acid by copper(II) and measurement of free copper(II) by anodic stripping voltammetry and copper(II) selective electrode. Anal. Chem. 53:2275–2280.

Blaschke, H. 1979. Leaching of water-soluble organic substances from coniferous needle litter. Soil Biol. Biochem. 11:581–584.

Blaser, P., H. Flühler, and J. Polomski. 1980a. Metal binding properties of leaf litter extracts: I. Soil Sci. Soc. Am. J. 44:709–716.

Blaser, P., W. Landolt, and W. Flühler. 1980b. Metal binding properties of leaf litter extracts: II. Soil Sci. Soc. Am. J. 44:717–720.

Bloom, P.R. 1981. Metal-organic matter interactions in soil. p. 129–150. In Chemistry of the soil environment. ASA Spec. Publ. 40. ASA, CSSA, and SSSA, Madison, WI.

Bourg, A.C.M., and J.C. Vedy. 1986. Expected speciation of dissolved trace metals in gravitational water of acid soil profiles. Geoderma 38:279–292.

Boyd, S.A., L.E. Sommers, and D.W. Nelson. 1979. Infrared spectra of sewage sludge fractions: Evidence for an amide metal binding site. Soil Sci. Soc. Am. J. 43:893–899.

Boyd, S.A., L.E. Sommers, and D.W. Nelson. 1981a. Copper (II) and iron (III) complexation by the carboxylate group of humic acid. Soil Sci. Soc. Am. J. 45:1241–1242.

Boyd, S.A., L.E. Sommers, D.W. Nelson, and D.X. West. 1981b. The mechanism of copper(II) binding by humic acid: An electron spin resonance study of Cu(II)-humic acid complex and some adducts with nitrogen donors. Soil Sci. Soc. Am. J. 45:745–749.

Boyd, S.A., L.E. Sommers, D.W. Nelson, and D.X. West. 1983. Copper(II) binding by humic acid extracted from sewage sludge: An electron spin resonance study. Soil Sci. Soc. Am. J. 47:43–46.

Bresnahan, W.T., C.L. Grant, and J.H. Weber. 1978. Stability constants for the complexation of copper(II) ions with water and soil fulvic acids measured by an ion selective electrode. Anal. Chem. 50:1675–1679.

Bruckert, S. 1970. Influence des composes organiques solubles sur la pedogenese en melieu acide. Ann. Agron. 21:421–452.

Buffle, J., F.-L. Greter, and W. Haerdi. 1977. Measurement of complexation properties of humic and fulvic acids in natural waters with lead and copper ion-selective electrodes. Anal. Chem. 49:216–222.

Cabaniss, S.E., and M.S. Shuman. 1988. Copper binding by dissolved organic matter: I. Suwannee river fulvic acid equilibria. Geochim. Cosmochim. Acta. 52:185–193.

Camerynck, R., and L. Kiekens. 1982. Speciation of heavy metals in soils based on charge separation. Plant Soil 68:331–339.

Cheam, V., and D.S. Gamble. 1974. Metal-fulvic acid chelation equilibrium in aqueous $NaNO_3$ solution. Hg(II), Cd(II), and Cu(II) fulvate complexes. Can. J. Soil Sci. 54:413–417.

Chen, Y., J. Navrot, and P. Barak. 1982a. Remedy of lime-induced chlorosis with iron-enriched muck. J. Plant Nutr. 5:927–940.

Chen, Y., B. Steinitz, A. Cohen, and Y. Elber. 1982b. The effect of various iron-containing fertilizers on growth and propagation of Gladiolius grandiflorus. Sci. Hortic. (Amsterdam) 18:169–175.

Chen, Y., and F.J. Stevenson. 1986. Soil organic matter interactions with trace elements. p. 73–116. In Y. Chen and Y. Avnimelech (ed.) The role of organic matter in modern agriculture. Martinus Nijhoff, Dordrecht, Netherlands.

Cheshire, M.V., M.I. Berrow, B.A. Goodman, and C.M. Mundie. 1977. Metal distribution and nature of some Cu, Mn, and V complexes in humic and fulvic acid fractions of soil organic matter. Geochim. Cosmochim. Acta 41:1131–1138.

Cline, G.R., P.E. Powell, P.J. Szaniszlo, and C.P.P. Reid. 1983. Comparison of the abilities of hydroxamic and other natural organic acids to chelate iron and other ions in soil. Soil Sci. 136:145–157.

Cromack, K., P. Sollins, W.C. Graustein, K. Speidel, A.W. Todd, G. Spycher, C.Y. Li, and R.L. Todd. 1979. Calcium oxalate accumulation and soil weathering in mats of hypogenous fungi Hysteranqium crassum. Soil Biol. Biochem. 11:463–468.

Cronan, C.S., and G.R. Aiken. 1985. Chemistry and transport of soluble humic substances in forested watersheds of the Adirondack Park, New York. Geochim. Cosmochim. Acta 49:1697–1705.

Cronan, C.S., W.A. Reiners, R.C. Reynolds Jr., and G.E. Lang. 1978. Forest floor leaching: Contribution from mineral, organic, and carbonic acids in New Hampshire subalpine forests. Science 200:309–311.

Crosser, M.L., and H.E. Allen. 1977. Determination of complexation capacity of soluble ligands by ion exchange equilibrium. Soil Sci. 123:176–181.

De Coninck, F. 1980. Major mechanisms in formation of spodic horizons. Geoderma 24:101–128.

Farmer, V.C., J.O. Skjemstad, and C.H. Thompson. 1983. Genesis of humus B horizons in hydromorphic humus podzols. Nature (London) 304:342–344.

Fitch, A., and F.J. Stevenson. 1983. Stability constants of metal-organic matter complexes: Theoretical aspects and mathematical models. p. 645–669. In S.S. Augustithis (ed.) The significance of trace elements in solving petrogenetic problems and controversies. Theoprastus Publ. S.A., Athens, Greece.

Fitch, A., and F.J. Stevenson. 1984. Comparison of models for determining stability constants of metal complexes with humic substances. Soil Sci. Soc. Am. J. 48:1044–1050.

Fitch, A., F.J. Stevenson, and Y. Chen. 1986. Complexation of Cu(II) with a soil humic acid: Response characteristics of the Cu(II) ion-selective electrode and ligand concentration effects. Org. Geochem. 9:109–116.

Friedland, A.J., A.H. Johnson, T.G. Siccama, and D.L. Mader. 1984. Trace metal profiles in the forest floor of New England. Soil Sci. Soc. Am. J. 48:422–425.

Friedmann, E.I. 1982. Endolithic microorganisms in the Antarctic cold desert. Science 215:1045–1052.

Gamble, D.S., C.H. Langford, and A.W. Underdown. 1985. Light scattering measurements of Cu(II)-fulvic acid complexing: The interdependence of apparent complexing capacity and aggregation. Org. Geochem. 8:35–39.

Gamble, D.S., M. Schnitzer, and I. Hoffman. 1970. Cu^{2+}-fulvic acid chelation equilibrium in 0.1 M KCl at 25°C. Can. J. Chem. 48:3197–3204.

Ghosh, K., and M. Schnitzer. 1980. Macromolecular structures of humic substances. Soil Sci. 129:266–276.

Goodman, B.A., and M.V. Cheshire. 1976. The occurrence of copper-porphyrin complexes in soil humic acids. J. Soil Sci. 27:337–347.

Goodman, B.A., and M.V. Cheshire. 1982. Reduction of molybdate by soil organic matter: EPR evidence for formation of both Mo(V) and Mo(III). Nature (London) 299:618–620.

Graustein, W.C., K. Cromack Jr., and P. Sollins. 1977. Calcium oxalate: Occurrence in soils and effect on nutrient and geochemical cycles. Science 198:1252–1254.

Greter, F.-L., J. Buffle, and W. Haerdi. 1979. Voltammetry study of humic and fulvic substances. J. Electroanal. Chem. 101:211–279.

Guy, R.D., and C.L. Chakrabarti. 1976. Analytical techniques for speciation of heavy metal ions in the aquatic environment. Chem. Can. 28:26–29.

Heinrichs, H., and R. Mayer. 1980. The role of forest vegetation in the biogeochemical cycle of heavy metals. J. Environ. Qual. 9:111–118.

Hendrickson, L.L., and R.B. Corey. 1983. A chelating-resin method for characterizing soluble metal complexes. Soil Sci. Soc. Am. J. 47:467–474.

Hodgson, J.F. 1963. Chemistry of the micronutrient elements in soils. Adv. Agron. 15:119–159.

Hodgson, J.F., H.R. Geering, and W.A. Norvell. 1965. Micronutrient cation complexing in soil solution: I. Soil Sci. Soc. Am. Proc. 29:665–669.

Hodgson, J.F., W.L. Lindsay, and J.F. Trierweiler. 1966. Nutrient cation complexing in soil solution: II. Soil Sci. Soc. Am. Proc. 30:723–726.

Huang, P.M., and M. Schnitzer (ed.). 1986. Interactions of soil minerals with natural organics and microbes. ASA Spec. Publ. 17. ASA, CSSA, and SSSA, Madison, WI.

Iyengar, S.S., D.C. Martens, and W.P. Miller. 1981. Distribution and plant availability of soil zinc fractions. Soil Sci. Soc. Am. J. 45:735–739.

Jeffery, J.J., and N.C. Uren. 1983. Copper and zinc species in the soil solution and the effects of soil pH. Aust. J. Soil Res. 21:479–488.

Jurinak, J.J., L.M. Dudley, M.F. Allen, and W.G. Knight. 1986. The role of calcium oxalate in the availability of phosphorus in soils of semiarid regions: A thermodynamic study. Soil Sci. 142:255–261.

Jurkevitch, E., Y. Hadar, and Y. Chen. 1988. Involvement of bacterial siderophores in the remedy of lime-induced chlorosis in peanut. Soil Sci. Soc. Am. J. 52:1032–1037.

Kodama, H., M. Schnitzer, and E. Murad. 1988. An investigation of Fe(III)-fulvic acid complexes by Mössbauer spectroscopy and chemical methods. Soil Sci. Soc. Am. J. 52:994–998.

Kuiters, A.T., and C.A.J. Denneman. 1987. Water-soluble phenolic substances in soils under several coniferous and deciduous tree species. Soil Biol. Biochem. 19:765–769.

Kuiters, A.T., and H.M. Sarink. 1986. Leaching of phenolic compounds from leaf and needle litter of several deciduous and coniferous trees. Soil Biol. Biochem. 18:475–480.

Lakatos, B., T. Tibai, and J. Meisel. 1977. ESR spectra of humic acids and their metal complexes. Geoderma 19:319–338.

Langford, C.H., and T.R. Khan. 1975. Kinetics and equilibrium of binding of Fe^{3+} by a fulvic acid. Can. J. Chem. 53:2979–2984.

Lighthart, B., J. Baham, and V.V. Volk. 1983. Microbial respiration and chemical speciation in metal-amended soils. J. Environ. Qual. 12:543–548.

MacCarthy, P. 1977. An interpretation of stability constants for soil organic matter-metal ion complexes under Schubert conditions. J. Environ. Sci. Health Part A 12:43–59.

MacCarthy, P., and H.B. Mark Jr. 1976. An evaluation of Job's method of continuous variation as applied to soil organic matter-metal ion interaction. Soil Sci. Soc. Am. J. 40:267–276.

MacCarthy, P., and G.C. Smith. 1978. Metal binding by ligand mixtures: a quantitative model. p. 472–480. In D.D. Hemphill (ed.) Trace substances in environmental health. Univ. of Missouri, Columbia.

Malajczuk, N., and M. Cromack, Jr. 1982. Accumulation of calcium oxalate in the mantle of ectomycorrhizal root of Pinus radiata and Eucalyptus marginata. New Phytol. 92:527–531.

Mandal, L.N., and B. Mandal. 1986. Zinc fractions in soil in relation to zinc nutrition of lowland rice. Soil Sci. 132:141–148.

Mantoura, R.F.C., A. Dickson, and J.P. Riley. 1978. The complexation of metals with humic materials in natural waters. Est. Coast. Mar. Sci. 6:387–408.

Mantoura, F.F.C., and J.P. Riley. 1975. The use of gel filtration in the study of metal binding by humic acids and related compounds. Anal. Chim. Acta. 78:193–200.

Marinsky, J.A., S. Gupta, and P. Schindler. 1982. The interaction of the Cu(II) ion with humic acid. J. Colloid Interface Sci. 89:401–411.

Martin, J.P., and D.D. Focht. 1977. Biological properties of soils. p. 115–169. In L.F. Elliott and F.J. Stevenson (ed.) Soils for management of organic wastes and waste waters. ASA, CSSA, and SSSA, Madison, WI.

Matsuda, K., and S. Ito. 1970. Adsorption strength of zinc for soil humus: III. Soil Sci. Plant Nutr. (Tokyo) 16:1–10.

McBride, M.B. 1978. Transition metal bonding in humic acid: An ESR study. Soil Sci. 126:200–209.

McBride, M.B. 1982. Electron spin resonance investigation of Mn^{2+} complexation in natural and synthetic organics. Soil Sci. Soc. Am. J. 46:1137–1143.

McGrath, S.P., J.R. Sanders, and M.H. Shalaby. 1988. The effects of soil organic matter levels on soil solution concentrations and extractabilities of manganese, zinc and copper. Geoderma 42:177–188.

McLaren, R.G., and D.V. Crawford. 1973. Studies on soil copper: I. J. Soil Sci. 24:172–181.

Mench, M., J.L. Morel, A. Guckert, and B. Guillet. 1988. Metal binding with root exudates of low molecular weights. J. Soil Sci. 39:521–527.

Moghimi, A., M.E. Tate, and J.M. Oades. 1978. Characterization of rhizosphere products including 2-ketogluconic acid. Soil Biol. Biochem. 10:283–287.

Murthy, A.S.P. 1982. Zinc fractions in wetland rice soils and their availability to rice. Soil Sci. 133:150–154.

Nissenbaum, A., and D.J. Swaine. 1976. Organic matter-metal interactions in recent sediments: the role of humic substances. Geochim. Cosmochim. Acta. 40:809–816.

Olomu, M.O., G.J. Racz, and C.M. Cho. 1973. Effect of flooding on the Eh, pH, and concentrations of Fe and Mn in several Manitoba soils. Soil Sci. Soc. Am. Proc. 37:220–224.

O'Shea, T.A., and K.H. Mancy. 1976. Characterization of trace metal-organic interactions by anodic-stripping voltammetry. Anal. Chem. 48:1603–1607.

Perdue, E.M., and C.R. Lytle. 1983a. A critical examination of metal-ligand complexation models: Application of defined multiligand mixtures. p. 295–313. In R.F. Christman and E.T. Gjessing (ed.) Aquatic and terrestrial humic materials. Ann Arbor Science Publ., Ann Arbor, MI.

Perdue, E.M., and C.R. Lytle. 1983b. Distribution model for binding of protons and metal ions by humic substances. Environ. Sci. Technol. 17:654–660.

Piccolo, A., and F.J. Stevenson. 1981. Infrared spectra of Cu^{2+}, Pb^{2+}, and Ca^{2+} complexes of soil humic substances. Geoderma 27:195–208.

Pohlman, A.A., and J.G. McColl. 1988. Soluble organics from forest litter and their role in metal dissolution. Soil Sci. Soc. Am. J. 52:265–271.

Povoledo, D., and M. Pitze. 1979. Preparation of low-ash humic acids, and the accompanying losses of organic materials, from Canadian lake sediments and a gleysol. 1979. Soil Sci. 128:1–8.

Powell, P.E., G.R. Cline, C.P.P. Reid, and P.J. Szaniszlo. 1980. Occurrence of hydroxamate siderophore iron chelators in soils. Nature (London) 287:833–834.

Powell, P.E., P.J. Szaniszlo, G.R. Cline, and C.P.P. Reid. 1982. Hydroxamate siderophores in the iron nutrition of plants. J. Plant Nutr. 5:653–673.

Rosell, R.A., A.M. Miglierina, and L.Q. De Novilla. 1977. Stability constants of some complexes of Argentine humic acids and micronutrients. p. 15–21. In Soil organic matter studies. Vol. 2. Int. Atomic Energy Agency, FAO, Vienna, Austria.

Rovira, A.D. 1969. Plant root exudates. Bot. Rev. 35:35–57.

Ryan, D.K., C.P. Thompson, and J.H. Weber. 1983. Comparison of Mn^{2+}, Co^{2+}, and Cu^{2+} binding to fulvic acid as measured by fluorescence quenching. Can. J.Chem. 61:1505–1509.

Ryan, D.K.,and J.H. Weber.1982. Fluorescence quenching titration for determination of complexing capacities and stability constants of fulvic acid. Anal. Chem. 54:986–990.

Saar, R.A., and J.H. Weber. 1980a. Comparison of spectrofluorometry and ion-selective electrode potentiometry for determination of complexes between fulvic acid and heavy-metal ions. Anal. Chem. 52:2095–2100.

Saar, R.A., and J.H. Weber. 1980b. Lead(II) complexation by fulvic acid: how it differs from fulvic acid complexation of copper(II) and cadmium(II). Geochim. Cosmoschim. Acta 44:1381–1384.

Saini, G.R. 1966. Sequestering of iron and aluminum by soil polysacchardies. Curr. Sci. 10:259-261.

Sanders, J.R. 1982. The effect of pH upon the copper and cupric ion concentrations in soil solutions. J. Soil Sci. 33:679-689.

Sanders, J.R. 1983. The effect of pH on the total and free ionic concentrations of manganese, zinc, and cobalt in soil solutions. J. Soil Sci. 34:315-323.

Schnitzer, M., and E.H. Hansen. 1970. Organo-metallic interactions in soils: 8. An evaluation of methods for the determination of stability constants of metal-fulvic acid complexes. Soil Sci. 109:333-340.

Sedberry, J.E., and C.N. Reddy. 1976. The distribution of Zn in selected soils in Louisiana. Commun. Soil Sci. Plant Anal. 7:10-17.

Senesi, N., D.F. Bocian, and G. Sposito. 1985. Electron spin resonance investigation of copper(II) complexation by soil fulvic acid. Soil Sci. Soc. Am. J. 49:114-119.

Shuman, L.M. 1979. Zinc, manganese, and copper in soil fractions. Soil Sci. 127:10-17.

Shuman, L.M. 1983. Sodium hypochlorite methods for extracting microelements associated with soil organic matter. Soil Sci. Soc. Am. J. 47:656-660.

Shuman, L.M. 1985. Fractionation method for soil microelements. Soil Sci. 140:11-22.

Skogerboe, R.K., and S.A. Wilson. 1981. Reduction of ionic species by fulvic acid. Anal. Chem. 53:228-232.

Smith, W.H. 1976. Character and significance of forest tree root exudates. Ecology 57:324-331.

Smith, G.C., T.F. Rees, P. MacCarthy, and S.R. Daniel. 1986. On the interpretation of Schubert plot slopes for metal-humate systems. Soil Sci. 141:7-9.

Sposito, G., and K.M. Holtzclaw. 1979. Copper(II) complexation by fulvic acid extracted from sewage sludge as influenced by nitrate versus perchlorate background ionic media. Soil Sci. Soc. Am. J. 43:47-51.

Sposito, G., K.M. Holtzclaw, and C.S. LeVesque-Madore. 1979. Cupric ion complexation by fulvic acid extracted from sewage sludge-soil mixtures. Soil Sci. Soc. Am. J. 43:1148-1155.

Sposito, G., and A.L. Page. 1984. Cycling of metal ions in the soil environment. p. 287-322. In H. Sigel (ed.) Metal ions in biological systems: Vol. 8. Circulation of metals in the environment. Marcel Dekker, New York.

Stevenson, F.J. 1967. Organic acids in soil. p. 119-146. In A.D. McLaren and G.H. Peterson (ed.) Soil biochemistry. Marcel Dekker, New York.

Stevenson, F.J. 1976. Stability constants of Cu^{2+}, Pb^{2+}, and Cd^{2+} complexes with humic acids. Soil Sci. Soc. Am. J. 40:665-672.

Stevenson, F.J. 1977. Nature of divalent transition metal complexes of humic acids as revealed by a modified potentiometric titration method. Soil Sci. 123:10-17.

Stevenson, F.J. 1982. Humus chemistry: Genesis, composition, reactions. John Wiley and Sons, New York.

Stevenson, F.J. 1986. Cycles of soil: Carbon, nitrogen, phosphorus, sulfur, micronutrients. John Wiley and Sons, New York.

Stevenson, F.J., and M.S. Ardakani. 1972. Organic matter reactions involving micronutrients in soils. p. 79-114. In J.J. Mortvedt et al. (ed.) Micronutrients in agriculture. SSSA, Madison, WI.

Stevenson, F.J., and A. Fitch. 1986. Chemistry of complexation of metal ions with soil solution organics. p. 29-58. In P.M. Huang and M. Schnitzer (ed.) Interactions of soil minerals with natural organics and microbes. ASA Spec. Pub. 17. ASA, CSSA, and SSSA, Madison, WI.

Stobbe, P.C., and J.R. Wright. 1959. Modern concepts of the genesis of podzols. Soil Sci. Soc. Am. Proc. 23:161-164.

Stojkovski, S., R. Payne, R.J. Magee, and V.A. Stanisich. 1986. Binding of molybdenum to slime produced by Pseudomonas aeruqinosa PA01. Soil Biol. Biochem. 18:117-118.

Szaniszlo, P.J., P.E. Powell, C.P.P. Reid, and G.R. Cline. 1981. Production of hydroxamate siderophore iron chelators by ectomycorrhizal fungi. Mycologia 73:1158-1174.

Takagi, S. 1976. Naturally occurring iron-chelating compounds in oat- and rice-root washings: 1. Soil Sci. Plant Nutr. 22:423-433.

Takamatsu, T., and T. Yoshida. 1978. Determination of stability constants of metal-humic complexes by potentiometric titration and ion-selective electrodes. Soil Sci. 125:377-386.

Takati, S-I., K. Komoto, and T. Takemoto. 1984. Physiological aspects of mugeneic acid: a possible phytosiderophore of graminaceous plants. J. Plant Nutr. 7:469-477.

Tan, E.L., and M.W. Loutit. 1976. Concentration of molybdenum by extracellular material produced by rhizosphere bacteria. Soil Biol. Biochem. 8:461–464.

Tan, E.L., and M.W. Loutit. 1977. Effect of extracellular polysaccharides of rhizosphere bacteria on the concentration of molybdenum in plants. Soil Biol. Biochem. 9:411–415.

Vance, G.F., D.L. Mokma, and S.A. Boyd. 1986. Phenolic compounds in soils of hydrosequences and developmental sequences of Spodosols. Soil Sci. Soc. Am. J. 50:992–996.

van Dijk, H. 1971. Cation binding of humic acids. Geoderma 5:53–67.

Vinkler, P., B. Lakatos, and J. Meisel. 1976. Infrared spectroscopic investigations of humic substances and their metal complexes. Geoderma 15:231–242.

Wang, T.S.C., S-Y. Cheng, and H. Tung. 1967. Dynamics of soil organic acids. Soil Sci. 104:138–144.

Whitehead, D.C., H. Dibb, and R.D. Hartley. 1982. Phenolic compounds in soil as influenced by the growth of different plant species. J. Appl. Ecol. 19:579–588.

Yermiyaho, U., R. Keren, and Y. Chen. 1988. Boron sorption on composted organic matter. Soil Sci. Soc. Am. J. 52:1309–1313.

Young, S.D., B.W. Bache, and D.J. Linehan. 1982. The potentiometric measurement of stability constants of soil polycarboxylate-Cu^{2+} chelates. J. Soil Sci. 33:467–475.

Zunino, H., and J.P. Martin. 1977a. Metal-binding organic macromolecules in soil: 1. Hypothesis interpreting the role of soil organic matter in the translocation of metal ions from rocks to biological systems. Soil Sci. 123:65–76.

Zunino, H., and J.P. Martin. 1977b. Metal-binding organic macromolecules in soil: 2. Characterization of the maximum binding ability of the macromolecules. Soil Sci. 123:188–202.

Chapter 7

Reactions of Metal Chelates in Soils and Nutrient Solutions

W. A. NORVELL, *U.S. Plant, Soil, and Nutrition Laboratory, Ithaca, New York*

Chelating agents are added to soils and nutrient solutions because they increase the solubility of metal cations. Increases in metal solubility and mobility frequently improve micronutrient metal availability to plants. The extent of metal chelation depends on the simultaneous equilibria of chelating agents with many cations, and on the stability of the chelates formed. The importance of chelation is reduced by the adsorption of chelate species on solid phases, and by the decomposition of chelating ligands by microorganisms or light. These reactions also influence the uptake of potentially toxic metals by plants, and the transport of these metals in surface waters and ground waters. The equilibria, adsorption, and degradation of metal chelates and chelating agents are considered below. This chapter is primarily concerned with the common aminopolyacetate chelating agents that are added to soils or nutrient solutions. These chelating agents and several others mentioned below are listed in Table 7–1.

I. METAL CHELATE EQUILIBRIA

Simultaneous equilibria among cations and chelating ligands influence the forms and concentrations of many metals in soil and water. Individually, each equilibrium reaction may be described by an equilibrium constant. For example, the reaction between metal, M^{a+}, and ligand, L^{b-}, to form the metal chelate ML^{a-b} is represented by

$$M^{a+} + L^{b-} \rightarrow ML^{a-b} \qquad [1]$$

with the equilibrium constant $K = (ML)/(M)(L)$, in which ionic charges are omitted for simplicity. Collectively, such expressions can describe the equilibrium distribution of metal and ligand species in solutions that contain many components. The assumption of equilibrium in reactions of metal

Table 7-1. Common chemical names and abbreviations for several chelating agents.

Name	Abbreviation(s)
Bathophenanthrolinedisulfonic acid	BPDS
Citric acid	CIT
trans-1,2-Cyclohexylenedinitrilotetraacetic acid	CDTA (DCTA)
Diethylenetrinitrilopentaacetic acid	DTPA
Ethylenediiminobis(2-hydroxyphenyl)acetic acid	EDDHA (EHPG, APCA)
Ethylenediaminemonoacetic acid	EDMA
Ethylenediamine-N,N'-diacetic acid	EDDA
Ethylenedinitrilotetraacetic acid	EDTA
Ethylenedinitrilotriacetic acid	ED3A
Ethylenebis(oxyethylenetrinitrilo)tetraacetic acid	EGTA
N,N'-Bis(2-hydroxybenzyl)ethylenedinitrilo-N,N'- diacetic acid	HBED
N-(2-Hydroxyethyl)ethylenedinitrilotriacetic acid	HEDTA (HEEDTA)
N-(2-Hydroxyethyl)iminodiacetic acid	HIDA (HEIDA)
Iminodiacetic acid	IDA
Nitrilotriacetic acid	NTA

ions and chelating agents is reasonable because these reactions are generally reversible and comparatively rapid.

The use of equilibrium models to describe chelation and complexation reactions in solution has been greatly facilitated by the development of readily accessible computer programs, such as GEOCHEM, MINEQL, MINTEQ, PHREEQE, REDEQL, and WATEQ (Sposito & Mattigod, 1980; Nordstrom et al., 1979; Brown & Allison, 1987; Parkhurst et al., 1982). Quantitative predictions of chelate equilibria can now be carried out on increasingly powerful personal computers as well as on mainframe computers. Extensive and growing compilations of equilibrium constants are widely available, and their accuracy is continually improving. Even so, it is still helpful to be able to quickly and visually assess the likely behavior of chelating agents in soils without studying tables of thermodynamic data or actually carrying out the speciation calculations. In this sense, the main objective of this author's chapter in the first edition of this book (Norvell, 1972) remains valid: to merge knowledge about soil chemistry and chelate stability to predict the chelation reactions of micronutrient and heavy metals in soil solution.

The equilibrium calculations discussed below were carried out on a personal computer using the program GEOCHEM (Sposito & Mattigod, 1980), as modified by Parker et al. (1987). Comparisons of metal chelation are provided for ten chelating agents that have been or may be added to soils or nutrient solutions: CDTA, CIT, DTPA, EDTA, EDDHA, EGTA, HBED, HEDTA, HIDA, and NTA. HIDA was included, along with NTA and CIT, as ligands that are used or have been considered as sequestering agents or builders in cleaning products, and which may reach soils in wastewaters. HBED, used by Chaney (1988b) in plant culture solution, was included because of its high selectivity for Fe(III).

Reasonably complete sets of stability constants are available for the chelates of these ligands with the metals Al, Ca, Cd, Co, Cu, Fe(II), Fe(III), Hg, Mg, Mn, Ni, Pb, and Zn. Values for the stability constants were taken from the compilation of critical values selected by Martell and Smith (1974, 1982). These values are summarized in Table 7-2. As always, it should be recognized that any collection of equilibrium constants is imperfect. In the future, some values will be revised, some will be rejected, and others will be added as knowledge of these reactions grows.

A. Metal Chelate Equilibria in Aerobic Soils

Chelating agents have the opportunity to form chelates with many cations in soil solution. The extent to which chelates are formed with any particular metal depends on simultaneous equilibria of the ligand with all competing cations. Because of their ubiquitous presence in most soils, the divalent and trivalent cations Ca^{2+}, Mg^{2+}, Fe^{3+}, and Al^{3+} always compete for chelating ligands and must be considered. The solubility relationships described below are generally similar to those previously chosen in models of chelate equilibria in soils (Norvell, 1972; Lindsay, 1979). These relationships provide a reasonable representation of the concentrations of Ca^{2+}, Mg^{2+}, Fe^{3+}, and Al^{3+} in soil solution.

The chemical activity of Fe^{3+} was represented by the solubility of hydrous Fe(III) oxides with a pIAP (negative log of the ion activity product) of 39.3 (Norvell & Lindsay, 1982b). The activity of Al^{3+} was set by Al oxide with a pIAP of 34.0, equivalent to the solubility of gibbsite (Lindsay, 1979). This solubility relationship is about four fold lower than that previously chosen (Norvell, 1972) and should provide a more realistic representation of Al^{3+} concentrations in soil solution. The activity of Ca^{2+} was assumed to be 0.003 mol L^{-1}, unless controlled at lower levels by the solubility of $CaCO_3$ with a pIAP of 8.4. The activity of Mg^{2+} was assumed to be 0.001 mol L^{-1}, unless restricted by the solubility of $MgCO_3$ with a pIAP of 7.5. The partial pressure of CO_2 was set at 0.0003 MPa, approximately 10 times greater than atmospheric levels, to better represent the conditions in soils. The pH of the soil solution was varied from 4 to 9; and a constant ionic strength of 0.015 mol L^{-1} was chosen for simplicity. The concentration of each chelating agent was set at 0.1 mmol L^{-1}, which is a reasonable approximation of the amount that might be added to soils. This assumed concentration has little effect on the comparisons presented, because essentially all of the important chelate species have a 1:1 ratio of metal to ligand, and results are expressed as mole fractions.

Stability calculations were carried out, as described above, for each of the 10 chelating agents in equilibrium with Fe^{3+}, Al^{3+}, Ca^{2+}, and Mg^{2+} in soil solution. In general, these calculations show that Fe^{3+} and Al^{3+} compete most effectively for chelating ligands at low pH, where the solubility of these metals is greatest; whereas Ca^{2+} and Mg^{2+} are more effectively chelated at high pH. The resulting stability-pH diagrams are similar to those presented earlier (Norvell, 1972), so they are not presented again here. However, new summary diagrams for Fe and Al are included here to incorporate the results from HIDA and HBED, and to show the changes in pre-

Table 7-2. Selected formation constants for ten chelating agents.†

Reaction stoichiometry	Log of formation constant‡									
	$CDTA^{4-}$	$DTPA^{5-}$	$EDTA^{4-}$	$EDDHA^{4-}$§	$EGTA^{4-}$	$HBED^{4-}$	$HEDTA^{3-}$	$HIDA^{2-}$	NTA^{3-}	CIT^{3-}¶
H + L = HL	12.9	11.2	10.7	12.2	10.0	13.0	10.3	8.9	10.1	6.1
2H + L = H_2L	19.4	20.3	17.3	22.9	19.2	24.5	15.9	11.1	12.8	10.7
3H + L = H_3L	23.2	25.0	20.2	31.8	22.1	33.0	18.7	--	14.9	13.8
4H + L = H_4L	25.8	27.9	22.4	38.3	24.3	37.9	--	--	--	--
5H + L = H_5L	27.5	30.1	23.9	--	--	--	--	--	--	--
Ca + L = CaL	14.2	12.0	11.6	8.2	11.9	10.3	9.0	5.1	7.2	4.3
Ca + L + H = CaHL	--	18.6	15.0	17.7	15.9	19.2	--	--	--	8.7
Ca + L + 2H = CaH_2L	--	--	--	25.1	--	27.0	--	--	--	12.1
Ca + 2L = CaL_2	--	--	--	--	--	--	--	--	9.1	--
2Ca + L = Ca_2L	--	14.4	--	--	--	--	--	--	--	--
Mg + L = MgL	12.1	10.6	9.8	9.0	6.3	11.5	7.8	3.8	6.3	4.2
Mg + L + H = MgHL	--	17.9	13.9	18.2	14.1	19.9	--	--	--	8.5
Mg + L + 2H = MgH_2L	--	--	--	26.3	--	27.2	--	--	--	11.9
Al + L = AlL	21.1	20.6	18.0	--	15.9	--	15.6	8.2	12.9	9.1
Al + L + H = AlHL	23.6	25.2	20.7	--	20.1	--	17.7	--	14.8	12.1
Al + L = AlOHL + H	13.0	13.0	11.9	--	10.3	--	10.4	--	7.5	5.6
Al + L = $Al(OH)_2L$ + 2H	--	--	1.0	--	1.4	--	0.9	--	-1.0	--
Fe(III) + L = Fe(III)L	31.5	29.9	26.5	35.4	22.0	41.2	21.0	12.1	17.0	12.3
Fe(III) + H + L = Fe(III)HL	--	33.7	28.0	--	--	--	--	--	--	--
Fe(III) + L = Fe(III)OHL + H	21.6	19.8	18.8	--	--	--	16.8	9.6	12.7	9.4
Fe(III) + L = $Fe(III)(OH)_2L$ + 2H	--	--	--	--	--	--	--	--	--	--
Fe(III) + 2L = $Fe(III)L_2$	--	--	8.9	--	--	--	7.6	3.9	4.7	--
2Fe(III) + 2L = $[Fe(III)OHL]_2$ + 2H	--	--	--	--	--	--	--	--	25.4	23.0
Fe(II) + L = Fe(II)L	19.9	17.6	15.3	15.3	12.8	--	13.0	7.1	9.1	5.6
Fe(II) + H + L = Fe(II)HL	22.9	23.4	18.2	--	17.3	--	15.8	--	11.2	9.5
Fe(II) + L = Fe(II)OHL + H	--	8.3	5.8	--	--	--	3.9	--	-1.8	--
Fe(II) + L = $Fe(II)(OH)_2L$ + 2H	--	-1.8	-4.6	--	--	--	-6.4	--	--	--

Reaction										
Fe(II) + 2L = Fe(II)L₂	--	--	--	--	--	--	--	10.6	13.3	--
2Fe(II) + L = Fe(II)₂L	--	21.4	--	--	--	--	--	--	--	--
Cd + L = CdL	20.9	20.2	17.4	14.2	17.5	18.5	13.9	7.6	10.6	4.5
Cd + H + L = CdHL	24.1	24.9	20.5	23.1	21.2	26.9	16.3	--	--	8.8
Cd + L + 2H = CdH₂L	--	28.4	--	31.2	--	33.8	--	--	--	12.0
Cd + 2L = CdL₂	--	--	--	--	--	--	--	12.9	14.7	--
2Cd + L = Cd₂L	20.6	23.3	--	--	--	--	--	--	--	--
Co + L = CoL	23.7	20.4	17.3	--	13.4	20.9	15.3	8.4	11.2	5.8
Co + L + H = CoHL	--	25.8	20.5	--	18.7	28.9	--	--	--	9.6
Co + L + 2H = CoH₂L	--	29.2	--	--	--	34.7	--	--	--	12.3
Co + 2L = CoL₂	--	--	--	--	--	--	--	12.8	14.8	--
2Co + L = Co₂L	22.9	24.9	--	--	--	--	--	--	--	--
Cu + L = CuL	26.3	22.6	19.7	25.0	17.1	22.4	18.3	12.1	13.9	6.7
Cu + L + H = CuHL	--	27.9	22.9	33.2	18.6	31.3	20.8	--	15.6	10.3
Cu + L + 2H = CuH₂L	--	31.1	--	38.4	23.1	36.7	--	--	--	13.3
Cu + L + 3H = CuH₃L	--	33.9	--	--	--	--	--	--	--	--
Cu + L = CuOHL + H	--	--	--	--	--	--	--	3.4	4.4	2.1
Cu + 2L = CuL₂	--	--	--	--	--	--	--	16.2	17.8	--
Cu + 2L = CuL₂OH + H	--	--	--	--	--	--	--	6.9	--	--
2Cu + L = Cu₂L	25.8	30.2	--	--	23.4	--	--	--	--	--
Hg(II) + L + H = Hg(II)L	29.1	27.6	22.5	--	23.9	--	20.8	--	15.1	8.7
Hg(II) + L + H = Hg(II)HL	--	32.3	25.8	--	27.2	--	--	--	--	11.7
Hg(II) + L = Hg(II)OHL + H	14.9	--	13.0	--	--	--	12.1	--	--	--
Mn + L = MnL	18.5	16.8	14.8	--	13.2	15.8	11.6	5.9	8.3	4.5
Mn + L + H = MnHL	21.5	21.6	18.2	--	17.5	23.7	--	--	--	8.6
Mn + L + 2H = MnH₂L	--	--	--	--	--	30.5	--	--	--	--
Mn + 2L = MnL₂	--	--	--	--	--	--	--	9.9	11.3	--
2Mn + L = Mn₂L	--	19.6	--	--	--	--	--	--	--	--
Ni + L = NiL	21.2	21.4	19.5	20.7	14.5	20.3	17.9	9.7	12.3	6.1
Ni + L + H = NiHL	24.1	27.5	23.0	28.5	19.9	29.1	20.5	--	--	9.8
Ni + L + 2H = NiH₂L	--	30.8	--	34.8	--	35.8	--	--	--	12.7
Ni + L = NiOHL + H	--	--	--	--	--	--	--	-1.2	1.1	--
Ni + 2L = NiL₂	--	--	--	--	--	--	--	14.8	16.7	--

(continued on next page)

Table 7–2. Continued.†

Reaction stoichiometry	Log of formation constant‡									
	$CDTA^{4-}$	$DTPA^{5-}$	$EDTA^{4-}$	$EDDHA^{4-}$§	$EGTA^{4-}$	$HBED^{4-}$	$HEDTA^{3-}$	$HIDA^{2-}$	NTA^{3-}	CIT^{3-}¶
Pb + L = PbL	21.3	19.9	19.0	16.1	15.6	19.3	16.3	9.8	12.1	5.2
Pb + L + H = PbHL	24.3	24.8	22.1	26.0	20.9	28.5	18.5	--	--	9.5
Pb + L + 2H = PbH_2L	--	--	--	33.5	--	35.3	--	--	--	12.7
Pb + L = PbOHL + H	--	--	--	--	--	--	--	1.4	--	--
Pb + 2L = PbL_2	--	--	--	--	--	--	--	14.2	--	--
Zn + L = ZnL	20.4	19.5	17.5	17.8	13.6	19.4	15.4	8.8	11.5	5.6
Zn + L + H = ZnHL	23.5	25.6	10.7	25.8	18.8	27.9	--	--	--	10.4
Zn + L + 2H = ZnH_2L	--	28.9	--	32.7	--	34.1	--	--	--	12.3
Zn + L = ZnOHL + H	--	--	--	--	--	--	--	-0.7	1.1	--
Zn + 2L = ZnL_2	--	--	--	--	--	--	--	12.6	14.6	--
2Zn + L = Zn_2L	--	24.8	--	--	17.4	--	--	--	--	--

† From Martell and Smith (1974, 1982). In general, formation constants are included for chelate species expected to represent >0.1% of the total ligand present or >1% of the particular metal associated with that ligand within the pH range considered. Ionic charges in formation reactions are omitted for simplicity, and L is used to represent the chelating ligand in each reaction.

‡ Formation constants are given at an ionic strength of 0.01, which is a reasonable approximation of the ionic strength of many soil and nutrient culture solutions. Formation constants for reactions involving H^+ are expressed as mixed constants, wherein H^+ is expressed as its activity to simplify calculations involving pH. The Davies Equation was used to adjust constants for differences in ionic strength.

§ The chelating agent EDDHA is supplied as a mixture of its racemic and meso-isomers. After this chapter was prepared, formation constants for these isomers were reported which show substantial differences in the stability of their chelates with several important metals (see R.M. Smith and A.E. Martell. 1989. Critical stability constants, Vol. 6, Plenum Press, New York). Predictions for EDDHA based on older values, including those in this chapter, must be reassessed. Equilibria of the two isomers of EDDHA must be evaluated independently.

¶ The CIT constants listed for M(OH)L may represent chelates of the form $M(H_{-1})L$, which have the same reaction stoichiometry with respect to CIT, H, and metal ion. Stability constants for Al-CIT chelates were not included by Smith and Martell (1974, 1982). The values presented here were taken from Motekaitis and Martell (1984).

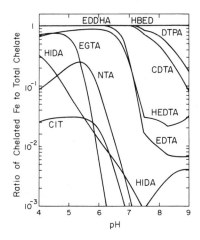

Fig. 7-1. Comparison of ten chelating agents as chelates for Fe^{3+} in soil solution from pH 4 to 9. Equilibrium was assumed between 0.1 mmol L^{-1} chelating agent and Fe^{3+}, Al^{3+}, Ca^{2+}, and Mg^{2+} in a model soil solution under aerobic conditions.

dicted chelation of Fe and Al that arise from several revised stability constants and the different solubility relationship chosen for Al^{3+}.

1. Iron and Aluminum

Figure 7-1 shows the predicted chelation of Fe in soil solution. EDDHA[1] and HBED form exceedingly stable Fe chelates and remain fully associated with Fe from pH 4 to 9, despite competition from Al, Ca, and Mg. DTPA and CDTA are expected to provide reasonably effective chelation of Fe in acidic or moderately alkaline soils, whereas EDTA and HEDTA should lose their effectiveness above pH 7. The Fe chelates of HIDA, NTA, EGTA, and, especially, CIT are less stable, but even these ligands may chelate low to moderate amounts of Fe under acidic conditions. A comparison of Fig. 7-1 with stability diagrams for Fe presented earlier (Norvell, 1972), shows that the expected importance of several Fe chelates is now greater. These changes arise because competition from Al^{3+} is reduced by the lower solubility assumed for Al oxide in the present soil solution model. In contrast, the expected chelation of Fe by NTA is lower than before, because upward revision of the stability constants for Al-NTA more than compensates for the lower solubility of Al^{3+}.

Norvell (1972) noted a reasonable agreement between stability predictions for Fe chelates and several experimental studies of the reactions of chelates in soil. Recent research also supports these predictions and the relative rankings shown in Fig. 7-1 (Norvell & Lindsay, 1972; Aboulroos et al., 1983; Norvell, 1984; Boxma, 1981; Erich et al., 1987; Singh & Sinha, 1977; Nabhan et al., 1977). These studies and others (Lucena et al., 1988; Lahav & Zipori, 1978; Vlek et al., 1974; Norvell & Lindsay, 1982b) confirm the major importance of competition between Fe^{3+} and Ca^{2+} for most chelating ligands in soil solution.

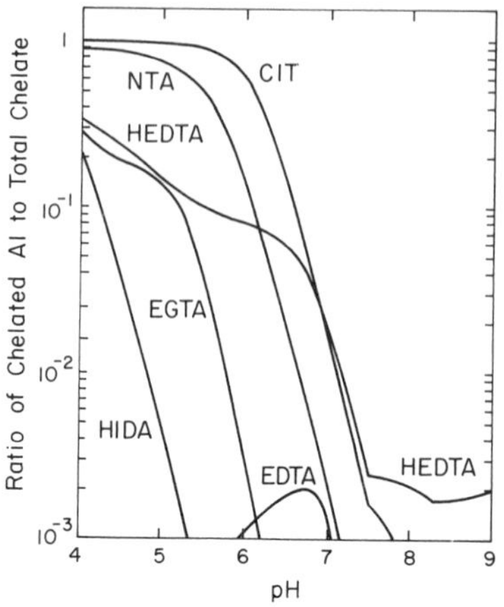

Fig. 7-2. Comparison of eight chelating agents as chelates for Al^{3+} in soil solution from pH 4 to 9. Equilibrium was assumed between 0.1 mmol L^{-1} chelating agent and Fe^{3+}, Al^{3+}, Ca^{2+}, and Mg^{2+} in a model soil solution under aerobic conditions. No stability constants for EDDHA and HBED chelates of Al were available. The Al chelates of DTPA and CDTA were too unstable to appear within this figure.

Chelation of Al is restricted largely to acidic conditions in soils (Fig. 7-2), where Al^{3+} concentrations are relatively high. Even so, competition from Fe severely limits chelation of Al by most ligands. Chelating agents with low selectivity for Fe, such as CIT and NTA, are best able to associate with Al. HEDTA, EGTA, and HIDA also appear to be moderately effective. None of the chelating agents should chelate Al effectively at alkaline pH values. In comparison with earlier predictions (Norvell, 1972), chelation of Al is reduced because of the lower solubility assumed for Al^{3+}, and a slight downward revision in the stability constants for several of the Al chelates. Conversely, an increase in the stability constant for Al-NTA has had the opposite effect. Predictions of Al chelation have two important limitations. First, there is a large uncertainty in the stability constants for most chelates (Motekaitis & Martell, 1984). Second, even the solubility of gibbsite overestimates Al^{3+} concentrations in some soils, and thus, the predictions of Fig. 7-2 may represent the upper range for Al chelation by these ligands.

The reactions of Al chelates in soils have not been investigated specifically. Indirect support for the low predicted stability of Al chelates is provided by the absence of significant amounts of soluble Al when EDTA or Fe-EDTA is reacted with soil (Norvell & Lindsay, 1982b). As extractants for Al at pH 5.3, five chelating agents were ranked in the order NTA $\geq$ HEDTA $\approx$ DTPA > EDTA $\gg$ EGTA in a solution in which Ca was the only important competing cation (Norvell, 1984). This order is reasonable for competition between Al and Ca, but EGTA was less effective than would be expected from stability considerations alone. Hern et al. (1988) found that the addition of EDTA to an acid soil solubilized some Al, but this would be expected because effective competition from Fe^{3+} and other cations was eliminated by the high rates of EDTA added. In a study of Al uptake by ryegrass (*Lolium perenne* L.), Muchovej et al. (1986) found NTA much more effective than CIT in increasing the extractable Al in a slightly acid soil after 10 wk of incubation. However, the failure of CIT to maintain Al in a soluble or exchangeable form was probably due to its rapid biodegradation rather than to inherent instability of its Al chelates.

2. Micronutrient Metals and Heavy Metals

The reactions that control the solubility of most micronutrient and heavy metals in soils are not known. As a result, specific concentrations of their metal chelates cannot be predicted with confidence. Even so, the relative effectiveness of the chelation of micronutrient and heavy metals in soil solution can still be measured. One measure of this effectiveness is the distribution of a chelated metal among the component ligands of a mixture in which each chelating ligand is present in equal concentration. This distribution has the advantage of being independent of the concentration of metal, as long as its concentration is small relative to that of the chelating agents. This condition is usually met in aerobic soils, because the concentrations of micronutrient and heavy metals in solution are generally low. The generality of these comparisons is enhanced further because the distribution of the chelated trace metal is largely independent of the concentration of chelating agents when the chelates that are formed contain metal and ligands in predominantly a 1:1 ratio, as is the case for the ligands considered here.

Figures 7–3a to 7–3i compare the effectiveness of trace metal chelation in the model soil solution described above, in which Fe^{3+}, Al^{3+}, Ca^{2+}, and Mg^{2+} are the dominant competing cations. The mole fraction of chelated trace metal associated with each component ligand is shown as a function of pH. Note that this mole fraction provides information on the distribution of chelated metal among competing ligands and not on the proportion of a chelating agent associated with the metal. Comparisons are included for chelates of the divalent trace metals Zn, Cu, Mn, Ni, Fe, Co, Cd, Pb, and Hg with each of the chelating agents for which reasonable stability constants were available. The ratio of free trace-metal ion to chelated trace metal is also included in these figures to provide a measure of the importance of chelation to the metal being considered (this ratio is inversely related to ligand concentrations and is shown for 0.1 mmol L^{-1} concentration of each chelating agent). The results for each metal are combined in a single figure to permit direct comparisons among as many ligands as possible.

Figure 7–3a suggests that DTPA should be the most effective chelating agent for Zn in calcareous soils, followed by HEDTA, CDTA, and EDTA. NTA and HIDA are about three log units or 1000-fold less effective than DTPA; and chelation of Zn by EGTA, EDDHA, CIT, and HBED should be negligible. In the acid to neutral pH range, HEDTA should be the dominant chelator of Zn, but EDTA, NTA, and HIDA also are relatively effective. None of the ligands is likely to chelate Zn effectively in strongly acid soils, as shown by the relatively large fraction of free Zn^{2+}, even in the presence of 0.1 mmol L^{-1} concentrations of each chelating ligand. Comparison of data in Fig. 7–1, 7–2, and 7–3a suggests correctly that Zn chelation by DTPA, HEDTA, CDTA, and EDTA is limited predominately by competition from Fe in acidic soils and from Ca in alkaline soils. With

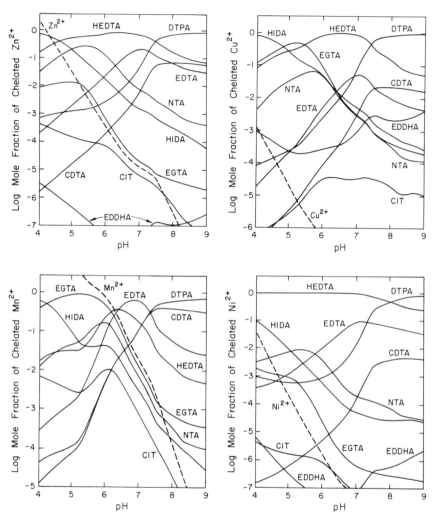

Fig. 7-3. Distribution of trace metal ions among several chelating agents in soil solution from pH 4 to 9. Equilibrium was assumed among the divalent trace metal ion, chelating agents at 0.1 mmol L^{-1}, and Fe^{3+}, Al^{3+}, Ca^{2+}, and Mg^{2+} in a model soil solution under aerobic conditions:

      a) Zn^{2+} b) Cu^{2+} c) Mn^{2+}
      d) Ni^{2+} e) Fe^{2+} f) Co^{2+}
      g) Cd^{2+} h) Pb^{2+} i) Hg^{2+}.

    In each figure, the mole fraction of the chelated trace metal is largely independent of its concentration and those of the chelating agents. The mole ratio of free cation to total chelated metal, shown as the dashed line, is included as a measure of the extent of chelation. This ratio is inversely related to the concentration of chelating ligands, e.g., if these concentrations were reduced 10-fold, then the relative proportion of free trace metal ion would increase 10-fold and the dashed curve would shift upward by one log unit.

    No curves are shown for the HBED chelates of Zn, Cu, Mn, Ni, Co, Cd, and Pb, or the EDDHA chelates of Fe(II) and Cd because these species were too unstable to appear within the range of mole fractions plotted. No predictions are given for the EDDHA chelates of Mn, Co, and Hg, the HBED chelates of Fe(II) and Hg, or the HIDA chelate of Hg, because stability constants were unavailable.

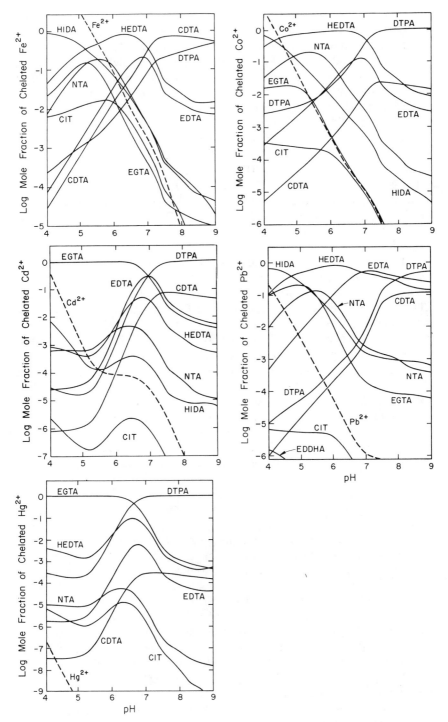

Fig. 7-3. Continued.

EDDHA and HBED, competition from Fe prevents effective Zn chelation at any soil pH. For NTA, HIDA, CIT, and EGTA, competition from Ca is the major limitation to Zn chelation at most pH values.

Experimental studies of Zn transport (Gupta & Deb, 1984; Sinha & Prasad, 1977), Zn dissolution (Aboulroos et al., 1983; Singh & Sinha, 1977; Lucena et al., 1987), and Zn chelate additions (Aboulroos, 1981; Singh et al., 1981; Elsokkary, 1980; Norvell & Lindsay, 1969; Norvell & Lindsay, 1972) support the predicted effectiveness of DTPA, EDTA and HEDTA in slightly acidic and alkaline soils, and the very poor chelation by CIT and EDDHA at all pH values. NTA has been moderately effective in chelating Zn in sediments and sludge-soil mixtures (Banat et al., 1974; Chau & Shiomi, 1972; Allen & Boonlayangoor, 1978; Garnett et al., 1985). Reports of poor mobility of Zn-CDTA and high mobility of Zn-EDDHA (Essington & Nishita, 1966), and of effective dissolution of Zn by EDDHA (Wallace & Wallace, 1983) appear anomalous in relation to other research and to the expected stabilities of these chelates.

The relative stabilities of Cu chelates are shown in Fig. 7–3b. Copper is a strongly chelated metal, as indicated by the low importance of free Cu^{2+} compared with chelated forms. DTPA, especially, and HEDTA, EDTA, and CDTA are relatively effective chelators for Cu in alkaline soils in which Ca is the main competing cation. Experimental studies of DTPA and EDTA in soils provide support for these predictions (Singh & Sinha, 1977; Aboulroos, 1981; Norvell & Lindsay, 1969; Norvell & Lindsay, 1972; Sinha et al., 1977). Competition from Fe restricts the chelation of Cu at low pH, but HEDTA has the potential to chelate Cu effectively under moderately acidic conditions. EDDHA appears to have some limited potential as a chelator for Cu under alkaline conditions. However, experimental results indicate that Cu^{2+} solubility in soils is generally too low to allow effective chelation even when Cu-EDDHA itself is added (Nabhan et al., 1977; Aboulroos, 1981). EGTA, HIDA, and NTA have the greatest ability to chelate Cu under moderately acidic conditions. At low pH, none of the ligands is particularly effective, and soluble organic materials in soil solution may provide similar levels of complexation as noted earlier (Norvell, 1972).

Comparison of Mn chelates in Fig. 7–3c suggests that only DTPA, CDTA, EDTA, and HEDTA have any potential for chelating Mn, and this potential exists only in slightly acidic or alkaline soils. The other ligands do not form Mn chelates that exceed the importance of free Mn^{2+}, except at high pH, where Mn solubility is so low that even the most effective chelating agents are unlikely to retain Mn in solution. The difficulty of keeping chelated Mn in soil solution is well documented (Aboulroos, 1981; Norvell, 1972; Ryan & Hariq, 1983; Lindsay et al., 1966). Mn solubility in aerobic soils is generally too low for Mn chelation to occur on more than a temporary basis.

As shown in Fig. 7–3d, DTPA should form the most stable chelates of Ni at high pH, followed by HEDTA, EDTA and CDTA. At other pH values, HEDTA is clearly most effective, followed by EDTA, DTPA, NTA and HIDA. At low pH, only HEDTA seems likely to raise soluble Ni much above the concentrations of Ni^{2+}. Little is known about the reactions of Ni chelates in soils. Fujii et al. (1983) reported that small amounts of Ni were solubilized by additions of Cd-EDTA in soil. Wallace et al. (1977) observed that EDTA and DTPA increased the uptake of Ni by soybean [*Glycine max* (L.) Merr.] and bush bean (*Phaseolus vulgaris* L.). Several studies have demonstrated that NTA can dissolve small amounts of Ni from metal-rich river sediments or sewage-treated soil (Allen & Boonlayangoor, 1978; Banat et al., 1974; Garnett et al., 1985; Stoveland et al., 1979).

Although Fe(III) is the dominant form of Fe in aerobic soils, ferrous Fe(II) is also present, at least transiently, and is the main form of Fe available to many plants (see Ch. 9; Chaney et al., 1972). An understanding of Fe^{2+} chelation has proven useful in studies of Fe uptake by soybean, and interest in Fe^{2+} chelation in soil and in the rhizosphere is growing rapidly (Chaney et al., 1972; Schwab & Lindsay, 1989a, b). The potential for Fe^{2+} chelation in soil solution can be evaluated, without assumptions regarding solid phases or redox reactions, by considering Fe^{2+} as a trace constituent. This comparison is shown in Fig. 7–3e for the chelating ligands considered in this chapter. Among these ligands, CDTA, DTPA, HEDTA, and EDTA have the greatest potential to chelate Fe^{2+}. However, none of these ligands is particularly effective under acidic conditions, as shown by the relative abundance of ionic Fe^{2+} in comparison with chelated Fe(II). Ligands containing di–imine N donor groups, such as BPDS, are generally much more effective as Fe^{2+} chelators than are ligands with aminopolyacetate or carboxylate donor groups.

DTPA stands alone as the most effective chelating ligand for Co^{2+} in soil solution at high pH, as shown in Fig. 7–3f. HEDTA becomes the predominant chelator as pH decreases to acidic values, followed by DTPA, EDTA, and NTA. Concentrations of free Co^{2+} are relatively large in comparison with those of several of its chelates. EGTA, CIT, HBED, and even HIDA and NTA, are unlikely to have a major effect on Co in soil solution.

DTPA at high pH and EGTA at low pH are the dominant chelators of Cd in equilibrium with the major cations in soil solution (Fig. 7–3g). These ligands and EDTA should be similar in importance in slightly acidic conditions, and HEDTA and CDTA are also relatively effective. Unless their concentrations are quite large, HIDA and NTA are unlikely to be important. EDDHA, HBED, and CIT show virtually no potential as chelators for Cd in soil solution.

The most stable chelates of Pb^{2+} in alkaline soils are EDTA, DTPA, and HEDTA as indicated by Fig. 7–3h. CDTA should be somewhat less effective, while NTA, HIDA, and EGTA should be relatively ineffective. HEDTA forms the most stable chelate in moderately acidic soil solution; and none of the ligands chelates Pb^{2+} effectively at low pH. Chelates of CIT, EDDHA, and HBED should be unimportant in soil solutions of any pH. Little is known about the reactions of Pb chelates in soil. DTPA has been shown to significantly increase Pb solubility in Pb-contaminated calcareous soil (Sadiq, 1983), and to increase Pb uptake by plants (Patel et al., 1977). NTA is reported to increase Pb solubility in metal-rich sediment and soil (Allen & Boonlayangoor, 1978; Banat et al., 1974; Garnett et al., 1985).

Figure 7–3i suggests that DTPA is by far the most stable chelator of Hg^{2+} in alkaline soil solutions. DTPA, EGTA, and HEDTA are comparable at slightly acidic pH values, whereas EGTA is most effective at lower pH. Even though several aminopolyacetate ligands are capable of chelating Hg^{2+}, it should be remembered that Hg^{2+} forms extraordinarily stable complexes with halide anions (Lindsay, 1979). For example, Cl^- at concentrations in the millimolar range would complex Hg^{2+} in acidic soil solutions as effectively as any of the chelating agents considered here, except EGTA. Even lower concentrations of Br^- and I^- would be more effective than Cl^-. Thus, significant chelation of Hg^{2+} by aminopolyacetate ligands is probably restricted to alkaline conditions, in which DTPA would be the most effective chelator.

B. Metal Chelate Equilibria in Anaerobic Soils

Many soils are subject to prolonged or transient anaerobiosis. Even in aerobic soils, reducing conditions can exist in localized zones where oxygen diffusion is restricted, microbial respiration is rapid, or active reduction of specific substrates by roots occurs. Changes in redox alter the form and solubility of several metals, and can have a major effect on metal chelate equilibria.

Knowledge of the reactions that control the composition of anaerobic soil solutions is not yet adequate to warrant predictions of specific concentrations of metal chelates, but many useful comparisons can still be made. A soil solution model that reflects the major increases in concentrations of Mn^{2+} and Fe^{2+} as soils become more reduced is adequate for this purpose. The solubility controls for major ions chosen by Lindsay (1979) and Sommers and Lindsay (1979) are suitable: $Fe(OH)_3$-Fe_3O_4-$FeCO_3$-CO_2 for Fe^{2+} and Fe^{3+}, MnO_2-$MnOOH$-$MnCO_3$-CO_2 for Mn^{2+}, and $CaCO_3$-CO_2 for Ca^{2+}. These relationships provide a qualitatively reasonable and thermodynamically plausible description of the concentrations of the major cations competing for ligands as a function of changing redox.

Lindsay (1979) and Sommers and Lindsay (1979) presented equilibrium calculations using the above model to show that the importance of Mn chelates should increase rapidly as soils become reduced, and Mn^{2+} is released by Mn(III,IV) oxides. For many chelating agents, such as EDTA, chelates of Mn should become dominant under even mildly reducing conditions. As reduction continues, Fe^{2+} concentrations increase to significant levels as Fe(III) oxides become reduced. Chelates of Fe(II) would become dominant for most ligands under strongly reducing conditions in which Fe^{2+} concentrations would be limited by the solubility of $FeCO_3$. These general trends in metal chelation are supported by limited experimental studies of EDTA and DTPA, which show that competition from Fe^{2+} and Mn^{2+} can limit the stabiity of chelated Cu and Zn in soils under reducing conditions (Reddy & Patrick, 1977).

The model described above was adopted to compare the chelating agents that are considered in this chapter as chelates for micronutrient and heavy metals under varying redox conditions. The comparisons were made at pH 7 and a CO_2 partial pressure of 0.005 MPa, which approximate conditions found in many reduced soils. Concentrations of Mn, Fe, and Ca were assumed to be controlled by their respective solid phases. Divalent Cd, Co, Cu, Hg, Ni, Pb, and Zn were included at trace levels, as was done for aerobic soil conditions.

Comparisons among the chelating ligands may be grouped conveniently into three redox ranges: (i) relatively well-aerated soils in which competition from Fe^{3+}, Al^{3+}, and Ca^{2+} dominates chelate equilibria; (ii) moderately reduced soils in which Mn^{2+} concentrations are high and many Mn chelates are important; and (iii) highly reduced conditions in which both Fe^{2+} and Mn^{2+} concentrations are high and Fe(II) chelates often dominate. Table 7–3 ranks the chelating ligands as chelators of nine divalent metals in the three redox ranges. The rankings are based on the distribution of chelated trace metal among the various ligands competing under identical conditions. The relative rankings of the free trace-metal cations are shown for an assumed concentration of 0.1 mmol L^{-1} for each chelating agent. For Fe^{2+} and Mn^{2+}, the comparisons are based on the metal concentrations established by the solid phases in the model.

The relative effectiveness of many ligands is not altered by changing redox. For example, HEDTA is the dominant chelator for several metals at all redox levels. Similarly, EGTA appears to be the best chelating ligand for Cd^{2+} at all redox levels, and its superiority actually increases under highly reducing conditions. The relative effectiveness of other ligands changes with changing redox. The most prominent among these is EDDHA, which becomes a much better chelating ligand for other metals as Fe^{3+} concentrations decline with increased reduction. This effect is most obvious for Cu^{2+} because Cu-EDDHA chelates are also reasonably stable. EDDHA is likely to be one of the most effective chelators for Cu^{2+} under reducing conditions, whereas it is one of the least effective chelators under well-oxidized conditions. Redox-sensitive chelate equilibria involving EDDHA may be important near root surfaces where Fe(III) reduction would cause sharp decreases in the activity of Cu^{2+} and, to a lesser extent, other metals. Similar reactions involving other highly stable Fe(III) chelates also have the potential to influence the availability of micronutrient and heavy metals near reduction sites. As better models of anaerobic soils and the rhizosphere become available, more specific predictions of metal-chelate equilibria will become possible.

C. Metal Chelate Equilibria as Indicators of Metal-Ion Activities

The concentrations of micronutrient metals and heavy metals present as free-metal ions in soil solution usually are too small for direct measurement. Chelate equilibria can provide an indirect measure of metal-ion activities in much the same way as pH indicators provide a measure of H^+ ion activity. The relationship among metal chelates (*ML*), ligands (*L*), and cations (*M*) shown in Eq. [1], is identical in form to relationships among

Table 7–3. Ranking of chelating agents for divalent metals under slightly, moderately, and highly reduced conditions in soil solution near pH 7.†

Degree of reduction	Ranking of chelating agents
	Cd^{2+}
High	EGTA > DTPA > EDTA > NTA > CDTA ≈ HEDTA > HIDA > Cd^{2+} > CIT > EDDHA > HBED
Moderate	EGTA > DTPA > EDTA > CDTA ≈ HEDTA > NTA > HIDA > Cd^{2+} > CIT > EDDHA > HBED
Slight	EGTA ≈ EDTA > DTPA > HEDTA ≈ CDTA > NTA > HIDA > Cd^{2+} > CIT > EDDHA > HBED
	Co^{2+}
High	DTPA > HEDTA > EDTA ≈ NTA > HIDA > CDTA > EGTA ≈ CIT ≈ Co^{2+} > HBED
Moderate	HEDTA > DTPA > EDTA > NTA ≈ CDTA > HIDA > EGTA > Co^{2+} ≈ CIT > HBED
Slight	HEDTA > DTPA > EDTA > CDTA > NTA > HIDA > EGTA > CIT ≈ Co^{2+} > HBED
	Cu^{2+}
High	EDDHA > HEDTA > DTPA ≈ HIDA ≈ EGTA > NTA ≈ EDTA > CDTA ≈ CIT > Cu^{2+} ≈ HBED
Moderate	HEDTA > DTPA > HIDA > EDTA ≈ NTA ≈ EGTA > EDDHA ≈ CDTA > CIT > Cu^{2+} > HBED
Slight	HEDTA > DTPA ≈ EDTA > HIDA ≈ EGTA ≈ NTA ≈ CDTA > EDDHA > CIT > Cu^{2+} > HBED
	Fe^{2+}
High	HEDTA ≈ CDTA > DTPA > HIDA > EDTA > NTA > Fe^{2+} > CIT > EGTA > EDDHA
Moderate	HEDTA ≈ CDTA > DTPA > EDTA > HIDA ≈ NTA > Fe^{2+} > CIT > EGTA > EDDHA
Slight	HEDTA > CDTA ≈ EDTA > DTPA > HIDA ≈ NTA > Fe^{2+} > CIT > EGTA > EDDHA
	Hg^{2+}
High	EGTA ≈ DTPA > HEDTA > EDTA > CDTA ≈ NTA > CIT > Hg^{2+}
Moderate	DTPA > EGTA > HEDTA > EDTA > CDTA > NTA > CIT > Hg^{2+}
Slight	DTPA > EGTA > HEDTA > EDTA > CDTA > NTA > CIT > Hg^{2+}

Mn^{2+}

High	EDTA ≈ EGTA ≈ Mn^{2+} > DTPA > NTA > CDTA ≈ HEDTA ≈ HIDA > CIT > HBED
Moderate	EDTA > HEDTA > DTPA > CDTA > Mn^{2+} > EGTA > NTA > HIDA > CIT > HBED
Slight	EDTA > HEDTA > DTPA ≈ CDTA > Mn^{2+} > EGTA > NTA > HIDA > CIT > HBED

Ni^{2+}

High	HEDTA > EDTA > DTPA > NTA > HIDA > EDDHA > CDTA > EGTA > CIT > Ni^{2+} > HBED
Moderate	HEDTA > EDTA > DTPA > NTA > HIDA ≈ CDTA > EGTA > CIT > NI^{2+} ≈ EDDHA > HBED
Slight	HEDTA > EDTA > DTPA > NTA ≈ CDTA > HIDA > EGTA > CIT > NI^{2+} ≈ EDDHA > HBED

Pb^{2+}

High	HEDTA > NTA > HIDA > DTPA > EDTA ≈ EGTA > CDTA > EDDHA > Pb^{2+} > CIT > HBED
Moderate	HEDTA > NTA ≈ DTPA ≈ HIDA ≈ CDTA > EDTA > EGTA > Pb^{2+} > CIT > EDDHA > HBED
Slight	HEDTA > EDTA ≈ DTPA > CDTA ≈ NTA > HIDA > EGTA > Pb^{2+} > CIT > EDDHA > HBED

Zn^{2+}

High	HEDTA > NTA ≈ EDTA > DTPA > HIDA > CDTA ≈ EDDHA > EGTA ≈ Zn^{2+} ≈ CIT > HBED
Moderate	HEDTA > EDTA ≈ DTPA ≈ NTA > CDTA > EGTA > Zn^{2+} ≈ CIT > EDDHA > HBED
Slight	HEDTA > EDTA ≈ DTPA > NTA ≈ CDTA > HIDA > EGTA > Zn^{2+} ≈ CIT > EDDHA > HBED

† The dominant competing cations at the three redox levels are: Fe^{2+}, Mn^{2+}, and (for EDDHA and HBED) Fe^{3+} under highly reduced conditions; Mn^{2+}, Ca^{2+} and Fe^{3+} under moderately reduced conditions; and Fe^{3+} and Ca^{2+} under slightly reduced conditions. Stability constants were not available for EDDHA chelates of Co^{2+}, Hg^{2+}, and Mn^{2+}, or for HBED chelates of Fe^{2+} and Hg^{2+}. Rankings for Fe^{2+} under highly reduced conditions and for Mn^{2+} under slightly and moderately reduced conditions are included, but represent comparisons in which these cations are major competitors for ligands, not minor constituents.

weak acids, conjugate bases, and H^+ ions. This equivalence is emphasized by comparing the familiar expression describing pH in a solution of a weak acid with the corresponding expression describing pM for a metal chelate:

$$pH = \log K_H - \log(HA/A) \qquad pM = \log K_M - \log(ML/L) \qquad [2]$$

where pM represents $-\log(M)$, K_H and K_M are formation constants, HA/A is the concentration ratio of weak acid to conjugate base, and ML/L is the concentration ratio of metal chelate to ligand. If the free-ligand concentration is too small or otherwise difficult to measure, it can often be described by an equally simple auxiliary reaction for another metal, so that the expression for pM becomes:

$$pM = \log K_M - \log K_N - \log[(ML)(N/NL)] \qquad [3]$$

where N and NL are a second cation and chelate that have concentrations that can be measured. As with pH indicators, the useful concentration range for metal-ion indicators is dictated by the stability constants for the component equilibria. The calculations required to find pM are usually straightforward, and can be carried out easily with one of the available chemical speciation programs.

The conceptual simplicity of this approach does not necessarily extend to its application in soils. At least three additional factors must be considered before reasonably accurate estimates of metal-ion activities in equilibrium with soils can be determined. First, the concentrations of metals and metal chelates, which are needed to calculate metal-ion activities, must themselves represent equilibrium with the soil. This equilibrium is not easily achieved, because the exchange of metal ions between chelates and soils is often very slow. The approach to equilibrium is slowed further if large amounts of metal must be exchanged, or if soil supplies of the metal become depleted. Second, adsorptive losses of some chelating agents can be severe, causing metal losses unrelated to metal activities in solution. Adsorption may create a need for accurate ligand analyses if any of the required chelate concentrations must be determined by difference. And third, biodegradation of chelating agents may reduce their concentrations and create unknown amounts of product ligands with altered chelating abilities. These three factors create conflicting needs with regard to the length of reaction. The first two factors favor prolonged studies to allow close approach to equilibrium, but the third compels us to minimize reaction times.

Norvell (1970) and Norvell and Lindsay (1982b) proposed to accommodate these conflicting objectives by: (i) using short reaction times; (ii) using simple distribution coefficients to correct for rapid adsorption reactions; and (iii) estimating equilibrium concentration ratios by interpolation. EDTA chelates, ranging from 0 to 100% associated with Fe, were reacted for about 1 wk with soils of slightly acidic pH. After correcting for adsorption reactions, the initial and final mole fraction of Fe chelates were compared (Fig. 7-4). The equilibrium mole fraction was found at the intersection of the ex-

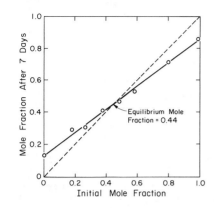

Fig. 7–4. Estimation of the equilibrium mole fraction of Fe-EDTA in a soil at pH 6.8 by comparing the mole fraction measured after 7 d with the mole fraction present initially after adding EDTA chelates. Redrawn from Norvell and Lindsay (1982b).

perimental curve and the diagonal line which represented no exchange of Fe^{3+} between chelate and the soil. Thus, equilibrium was approached from above and below. At the point of equilibrium, no Fe^{3+} exchange with soil phases was required. The composition of this equilibrium solution provided the information needed to calculate the concentration of free Fe^{3+} ions. This concentration was equivalent to a $p(Fe^{3+})(OH^-)^3$ of 39.3 in the three soils studied.

The general approach described above for metal ion activity measurements was used subsequently by others, although analyses for the chelating agent were not always included to confirm the absence of adsorption or degradation. Vlek et al. (1974) studied the solubility of several Fe oxides and jarosite, using Ca or Zn as auxiliary cations in reactions with EDTA. The solubility values they obtained for these solid phases were in reasonable agreement with thermodynamic data. Norvell and Lindsay (1982a) used EDTA equilibria to show that fertilization of a near-neutral soil with Fe salts would increase the solubility of Fe^{3+} into the range of amorphous $Fe(OH)_3$. However, after several weeks, it returned to a lower level characteristic of the soil. Using DTPA, Dayanand and Sinha (1984) found that the solubility of Fe in some high pH soils was in the range of amorphous Fe(III) oxides.

Activities of Zn^{2+} and Cu^{2+} in alkaline soils have been measured several times with EDTA or DTPA equilibria (Sinha et al., 1977, 1978; Singh, 1982; Norvell & Lindsay, 1969, 1972; Lindsay & Norvell, 1969; Norvell et al.,1987). The results attest to the very low solubility of these micronutrient metals in soil solution even when equilibrium is approached from above. A few of these studies calculated Mn^{2+} activities as well, but the values were based on very low levels of soluble Mn and may be unreliable. Norvell et al. (1987) used EDTA equilibria to measure the effects of P and Zn fertilization on Zn^{2+} activities, and found a small suppression of Zn solubility from P applied to a calcareous soil. Fujii et al. (1983) used Cd^{2+} as the auxiliary cation and Cl^- as an auxiliary ligand in measurements of Zn, Cu, Ni, and Fe activities with EDTA in sludge-amended soils. Their work and that of Vlek et al. (1974) point out that a variety of auxiliary metals and ligands may prove useful in measurements of metal-ion activities in soils.

D. Metal Chelate Equilibria in Plant Nutrient Solutions

Stewart and Leonard (1954) and Hewitt (1966) have reviewed the early efforts to supply available Fe to plants growing in nutrient culture solutions. Supplying Fe was a formidable task because of the ready precipitation of Fe as insoluble oxides and phosphates. However, in 1951, Jacobson reported that Fe-EDTA could supply soluble Fe in hydroponic culture of tomato (*Lycopersicon esculentum* Mill.), sunflower (*Helianthus annuus* L.), corn (*Zea mays* L.), and barley (*Hordeum vulgare* L.) (Jacobson, 1951). His success with EDTA led to widespread use of synthetic chelating agents as carriers of Fe in experimental hydroponic systems. Today, most studies involving plants grown in nutrient solution include Fe as the chelate of one of several chelating agents, including EDTA, DTPA, EDDHA, and HEDTA.

The successful use of Fe chelates to supply available Fe has not been matched by an equally successful understanding of the effects that chelating agents have on the chemistry of nutrient solutions. Unexpected deficiencies, toxicities, and confusing interactions among micronutrient metals are commonly encountered in hydroponically grown plants, and the use of chelated metals is often viewed more as art than science. Despite these frustrations, nutrient solutions are relatively simple in composition. Common principles of chemical equilibria can provide valuable help in understanding the behavior of the metal cations and chelating agents. The availability of computer programs for chemical speciation greatly simplifies nutrient solution modeling.

Many of the problems encountered in the use of chelated Fe in nutrient solutions are illustrated in Fig. 7–5a and 7–5b. These figures show the expected distribution of chelated metals and metal ions in a quarter-strength Johnson Solution with full-strength micronutrients, except that Fe was included as 25 μmol L^{-1} Fe-EDTA. The composition of this solution was (in

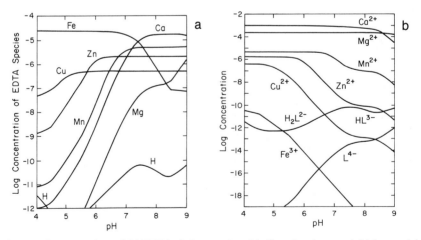

Fig. 7–5. Concentrations of (a) EDTA chelate species of indicated cations, and (b) free-metal ions and free-ligand species as a function of pH in a hydroponic nutrient solution (quarter-strength Johnson Solution) with Fe added as 25 μmol L^{-1} Fe-EDTA.

μmol L^{-1}): 1000, Ca; 250, Mg; 1500, K; 500, NH$_4$; 25, Fe; 5, Mn; 2, Zn; 0.5, Cu; 3500, NO$_3$; 300, SO$_4$; 500, PO$_4$; 50, Cl; 25, B; 0.1, Mo; and 25, EDTA.

Figure 7–5a shows that EDTA is predominately associated with Fe at low pH, but that low concentrations of Cu and Zn also are chelated. The competition from Cu^{2+} and Zn^{2+} displaces some Fe^{3+}, which tends to form highly insoluble hydrous oxides or hydroxy-phosphates even at low pH. As Fe^{3+} concentrations decrease with increasing pH, the activity of the free-EDTA ligand rises, and the activities of free Cu^{2+}, Zn^{2+}, and Mn^{2+} decline (Fig. 7–5b). Predictions of metal speciation in Hoagland Solution show similar decreases in concentrations of Zn^{2+}, Cu^{2+}, and Cd^{2+}, with increasing pH in the presence of several chelating agents (Chaney, 1988a; Halvorson & Lindsay, 1977). Obviously, a major result of adding chelated Fe is to introduce high pH sensitivity into the concentrations of all micronutrient metal ions, because the free ligand is regulated by the pH-sensitive solubility of Fe oxides. Recognizing that nutrient solutions may change in pH by one or more pH units during short periods of plant growth, it is clear that concentrations of free-metal ions may change by several 100- or 1000-fold in poorly buffered nutrient solutions. Buffering of pH reduces these uncertainties, but other reactions that disturb the activity of Fe^{3+} in solution, such as the reduction of Fe^{3+} to Fe^{2+} by roots or light, can also cause large fluctuations in the activities of other metal ions.

The failure of chelating agents to buffer micronutrient metal ions is largely due to the fact that the chelate buffer is usually added entirely in one form, i.e., as the Fe-chelate. The marked effects of the concentration of added ligand on metal chelation are shown in Fig. 7–6a and 7–6b, where it is assumed that the EDTA concentration is varied in a quarter-strength Johnson Solution, which contains Fe^{3+} at 25 μmol L^{-1}. In the absence of EDTA, virtually all of the added Fe^{3+} should precipitate as hydrous Fe(III) oxides,

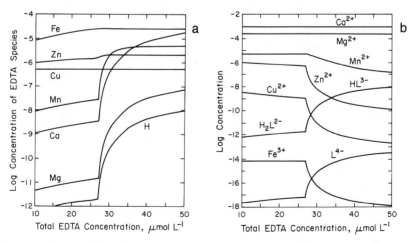

Fig. 7–6. Effect of adding EDTA to a hydroponic nutrient solution (quarter-strength Johnson Solution) containing 25 μmol L^{-1} of Fe at pH 6. Concentrations of (a) EDTA chelate species and (b) free-metal ions and free-ligand species.

which have highly pH-dependent solubilities as discussed above. As EDTA
is added, chelation of all metals increases and Fe(III) oxides dissolve as Fe-
EDTA forms. However, these oxides continue to control concentrations of
Fe^{3+} and the EDTA free ligand until sufficient EDTA is added to chelate
virtually all of the added Fe, Cu, and Zn, i.e., about 27.5 μmol L^{-1}, in this
example. Above this concentration, the EDTA is in excess of strongly chelated
metals and the free ligand rises rapidly. Activities of Fe^{3+}, Cu^{2+}, and Zn^{2+}
fall sharply and Mn^{2+} declines as further EDTA is added. With a modest
excess of EDTA, the free ligand becomes buffered by equilibria between
Ca^{2+} and Ca-EDTA. Activities of Fe^{3+}, Cu^{2+}, Zn^{2+}, and, to a lesser extent, Mn^{2+} are now buffered by EDTA, and freed from disturbance by the
pH-dependent solubility of Fe oxides.

The improved stability in concentrations of chelated metals and metal
ions, resulting from adding extra EDTA to quarter-strength Johnson Solution, is shown in Fig. 7–7a and 7–7b. Inclusion of 25 μmol L^{-1} EDTA, in
addition to 25 μmol L^{-1} Fe-EDTA, produces nearly constant concentrations
of metal EDTA chelates and constant activities of all metal ions from about
pH 4.5 to almost 7.5, where Fe(III) oxides start to precipitate despite the
additional EDTA. The range of effective buffering can be extended by increasing the excess of EDTA, but this benefit must be weighed against the
possibility of depressing metal activities to the point of inducing deficiencies. Comparison of Fig. 7–5b and 7–7b emphasizes the marked contrast between successful versus unsuccessful buffering of metals in nutrient solutions
of almost identical composition. These calculations suggest that equilibria
of metal chelates should be considered carefully in selecting the composition
of nutrient culture solutions, as well as in the interpretation of results.

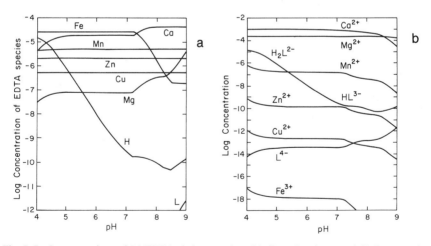

Fig. 7–7. Concentrations of (a) EDTA chelate species of indicated cations, and (b) free-metal
ions and free-ligand species as a function of pH in a hydroponic nutrient solution (quarter-
strength Johnson Solution) containing an excess of EDTA above the concentrations of
micronutrient metals. The total EDTA concentration was 50 μmol L^{-1}, of which 25 μmol
L^{-1} was added as Fe-EDTA.

Chelation has been recognized for many years as a factor that reduces the availability or toxicity of metals to roots (Brown et al., 1960; DeKock & Mitchell, 1957). Halvorson and Lindsay (1972) improved the understanding of this competition with models of metal speciation in nutrient solutions. Stability-pH diagrams similar to Fig. 7–5 were prepared for EDTA, EDDHA, DTPA, EGTA, and CDTA in modified Hoagland Solution. These diagrams and those of Cline et al. (1982) emphasized the importance of the pH-dependent solubility of Fe oxides and Fe phosphates as factors that regulate competition among metals for added ligands in nutrient solutions. Halvorson and Lindsay (1977) used equilibrium speciation calculations to evaluate the relation between the concentration of free Zn^{2+} in solution and the availability of Zn to corn. Comparisons of Zn^{2+} concentrations and yields suggested that a pZn^{2+} of about 10.6 was required for corn grown in nutrient solution that contained DTPA.

Several research groups have added chelating agents at concentrations above those of micronutrient metals in an effort to regulate specific metal ions. Dragun et al. (1976) depressed Cu^{2+} concentrations with a large excess of DTPA in a study of Cu availability and toxicity to corn. Their results suggested that a $pCu^{2+} > 13$ could induce Cu deficiency, although their method of growing the upper portion of roots in soil and the lower portion in nutrient solution makes interpretation of this work more difficult. Eskew et al. (1984) used a small excess of EDTA to suppress and buffer Ni^{2+} concentrations in a study of the functions of Ni in soybean. They found that leaf-tip necrosis was 20 times more common in plants grown in nutrient solution with Ni^{2+} buffered at $pNi^{2+} > 15$ than in plants grown at $pNi^{2+} \sim 9$. This study shows the effectiveness of chelating agents as scavengers of contaminant metals, a function that is very useful in investigations of trace-metal uptake by plants.

Schwab (1981) and Schwab and Lindsay (1989a, b), using excesses of BPDS, DTPA, and CDTA in equilibrium models and experimental studies, indicated that a pFe^{2+} concentration of about 9 was a threshold value for Fe^{2+} uptake by Fe-stressed soybean. Uptake was proportional to the log concentration of Fe^{2+} in the range of $pFe^{2+} = 6.5$ to 9. Their results and an evaluation of data in the literature suggested that roots of Fe-stressed soybean could effectively reduce chelated Fe(III) to Fe^{2+} by imposing reducing conditions equivalent to pe + pH ≤ 7.

Chaney et al. (1989) has discussed the advantages of metal buffering in nutrient solutions, and prepared equilibrium diagrams showing that metal ion concentrations can be held relatively constant despite pH changes. These concepts were applied by Chaney et al. (1988) in studies of Fe, Cu, Zn, and Mn availability to soybean and tomato. In DTPA-buffered solutions, deficiencies of Zn, Cu, and Mn occurred at concentrations below $pZn^{2+} = 10.8$, $pCu^{2+} = 15.8$, and $pMn^{2+} = 8.6$. In related work, Bell et al. (1988) found that barley required Fe^{3+} concentrations greater than $pFe^{3+} = 18.5$ for normal growth in nutrient solutions containing EDTA. However, uptake by tomato was not prevented by even much lower concentrations because reduction of Fe(III) released Fe^{2+} at adequate levels.

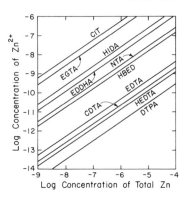

Fig. 7–8. Effect of total Zn concentration on concentrations of Zn^{2+} maintained by 10 chelating agents in hydroponic nutrient solutions (quarter-strength Johnson Solutions) containing 50 μmol L^{-1} of chelating agent, 25 μmol L^{-1} Fe, 5 μmol L^{-1} Mn, and 0.5 μmol L^{-1} Cu.

Norvell et al. (1989) used buffering by HEDTA to regulate micronutrient metals in a study of the effects of Zn^{2+} concentrations on barley root permeability. Figure 7–8 shows some of the equilibrium calculations that contributed to the selection of HEDTA as the chelating ligand. Based on the studies by Chaney et al. (1988) and Halvorson and Lindsay (1977), buffering of Zn^{2+} concentrations in the range of $pZn^{2+} = 9$ to 11 was considered essential. Among the chelating agents considered, CIT, EGTA, HIDA, EDDHA, NTA, and HBED were rejected as buffers because they could not maintain Zn^{2+} in the desired range unless total Zn could be held at concentrations below $pZn = 8$ (Fig. 7–8). Such low concentrations are difficult to achieve because contamination often provides more Zn than treatments, and the buffer capacity for Zn^{2+} is poor. In contrast, EDTA, CDTA, HEDTA, or DTPA appeared able to provide adequate buffering in a convenient concentration range for total soluble Zn. HEDTA was chosen from among this group because, in addition to buffering Zn^{2+}, HEDTA could simultaneously provide adequate levels of Fe^{3+} and Cu^{2+} for the growth of barley. Preliminary results from this study suggested that reductions in growth and disturbances in P and K uptake occurred for Zn^{2+} concentrations below $pZn^{2+} = 10.3$.

The equilibrium calculations and experimental studies described above demonstrate some of the benefits from successfully regulating metal-ion concentrations in nutrient culture solution. Buffering with chelating agents permits the study of ion uptake and other plant processes at metal ion concentrations that are stable, yet low enough to realistically represent conditions in agricultural soils.

II. ADSORPTION OF CHELATING AGENTS

Adsorption or "fixation" of chelating agents in soils was recognized in early investigations of the agricultural uses of synthetic chelating agents (Stewart & Leonard, 1954; Wallace et al., 1955). Many characteristics of adsorption were identified by studies conducted in the mid-1950s, even though there were difficulties in distinguishing among the losses of metals and ligands caused by adsorption, degradation, and competitive equilibria with soil cations (Wallace et al., 1955; Hemwall, 1958; Stewart & Leonard, 1955; Wallace & Lunt, 1956; Lunt et al., 1956; Hill-Cottingham & Lloyd-Jones, 1957, 1958). The factors affecting adsorption included the type of chelating agent, the associated metal ion, time, pH, salt concentrations, and soil texture.

Much of the emphasis in this early work was placed on Fe chelates because of the importance of supplying adequate Fe to many crops. Wallace et al. (1955) added the Fe chelates of EDTA, DTPA, HEDTA, CDTA, and EDDHA to soils, and found that varying amounts of Fe and chelating agent were lost. In 4 d, chelating agent losses in a calcareous loam ranged from 7 to 30% and were ranked EDDHA $\ll$ CDTA $<$ EDTA, DTPA $<$ HEDTA. Losses in a moderately acid clay soil ranged from 0 to 51% and were ranked EDDHA $\ll$ EDTA $<$ DTPA, CDTA $<$ HEDTA. Adsorption, rather than degradation, was identified as the cause of these losses, because the ligands could be recovered by extracting with a strong base.

Relatively rapid losses of EDTA from Fe-EDTA were reported by Lunt et al. (1956), who found average losses of 26 and 20% respectively in calcareous and noncalcareous soils. In the noncalcareous soils, the ratio of Fe to EDTA loss was 1:1, suggesting that the chelate might be adsorbed intact. Hill-Cottingham and Lloyd-Jones (1957, 1958) studied the reaction of six Fe chelates in a calcareous soil for periods extending to 30 d. Adsorption of chelating agent occurred mainly in the first day and ranged from about 10 to 75% of the total. Losses were ranked EDDHA $<$ CDTA $<$ EDTA $<$ DTPA $<$ HEDTA $<$ HEDDA, which was similar to the ranking found by Wallace et al. (1955) and later by others in a variety of soils (Assaad & Awad, 1981; Aboulroos et al., 1983; Norvell & Lindsay, 1969, 1972). Adsorption of chelating agents by peat may differ from that by soils, in that losses of EDDHA from Fe-EDDHA can be relatively large at low pH (Boxma, 1981).

Wallace and Lunt (1956) observed that losses of a chelating ligand varied when added with different metals. Losses of EDDHA from its Zn and Mn chelates were large, but no measurable losses from Fe-EDDHA were found. Aboulroos (1981) and Aboulroos et al. (1983) found severe adsorption of EDDHA when associated with Zn, Cu, Na, and, especially Mn in alkaline soils. Losses from Fe-EDDHA were negligible under similar conditions. Lindsay et al. (1966) also observed serious losses of EDDHA that was added to soil as the unstable Zn-EDDHA chelate. These results suggest that adsorption of chelating ligands is influenced not only by the form added, but also by continuing changes in speciation that occur during reactions with soil.

Adsorption of EDTA and DTPA is influenced by the associated metal, but not as strongly as found for EDDHA. Wallace and Lunt (1956) reported that the Mn and Fe chelates of EDTA lost $<20\%$ of the EDTA in an acidic clay soil, whereas losses from Zn-EDTA were $<5\%$. Moderate losses of about 20% of EDTA were found in calcareous soil by Aboulroos (1981), irrespective of the form added. Norvell and Lindsay (1969) reacted EDTA chelates of Fe, Zn, Cu, Mn, and Na with suspensions of soils ranging from pH 5.7 to 7.9. Adsorption of ligand varied from 5 to 25%, with the greatest losses occurring from Fe-EDTA in acid soils, and the least for Zn-EDTA and Cu-

EDTA in alkaline soils. Lahav and Hochberg (1975a) also found negligible adsorption of Zn-EDTA in a sandy soil that would adsorb more than 50% of EDTA from Fe-EDTA. Moderate losses of total ligand from several DTPA chelates were reported by Norvell and Lindsay (1972). Losses in suspensions of three acid soils ranged from 5 to 60%, and were greater for Na-DTPA and Mn-DTPA than for the chelates of Fe, Zn, or Cu. In two alkaline soils, the losses ranged from 0 to 23%, and were greater for DTPA added with Fe, Mn and Na than that added with Zn or Cu. Aboulroos et al. (1983) and Aboulroos (1981) obtained generally similar results. Elliott and Denneny (1982) found that sorption of EDTA from Cd-EDTA was small. The above studies suggest that adsorption of the EDTA and DTPA chelates of divalent metals is relatively small in moderately acid and alkaline soils when the chelates themselves are stable.

Hill-Cottingham and Lloyd-Jones (1957, 1958) observed that the amount of chelating ligand adsorbed by soil was approximately proportional to the concentration of Fe-chelate present in solution. This relationship was observed with EDTA, DTPA, HEDTA, CDTA, HEDDA, and EDDHA over a ten-fold range in concentration. Proportionality between adsorbed EDTA and concentration of Fe-EDTA was found also by Lahav and Hochberg (1975a, 1976). They used this relation to model the losses of Fe chelates that occurred during flow through soil columns. Norvell and Lindsay (1982b) verified the proportionality of adsorption to concentration for Fe-EDTA and Ca-EDTA, and used the relationships to interpret changes in the speciation of EDTA in studies of Fe solubility in slightly acidic soils. Even though simple proportionality is unlikely to hold true over wide concentration ranges or for all soils, it often provides a reasonably accurate and mathematically simple description of chelate adsorption.

The adsorption of NTA in soils has received attention primarily from environmental scientists concerned with the removal of NTA from wastewaters. Adsorption is of interest as a mechanism to remove NTA during any time lag before biodegradation of NTA becomes effective. Dunlap et al. (1972) and Baek and Clesceri (1986) measured losses of NTA added as Na-NTA to several soils and described the sorption with Freundlich isotherms, although the relationship between sorption and concentration in most of the soils could also be approximated as linear. Their results suggest that adsorption of NTA could vary from as little as 25% to >90% in soils ranging in texture from a loamy fine sand to a clay loam. However, continuous loading of NTA-enriched wastewaters on even the most adsorptive soils would quickly saturate the adsorption sites and permit NTA to pass through unimpeded until biodegradation began. Allen and Boonlayangoor (1978) obtained very similar results from the reaction of NTA-enriched river waters with river sediments. They observed also that adsorption took <2 h and was reversible within 2 d. Little appears to be known about the influence of associated metal on the adsorption of NTA, but the ready biodegradability of this ligand makes detailed knowledge of its adsorption reactions less important.

Despite the involvement of adsorption in virtually all studies of metal chelate reactions in soils, neither the mechanisms nor the sites of adsorption are known. This is not surprising considering the diversity of chelate species and soil surfaces that may be involved. Soil clays were implicated as major adsorbents of chelating agents by Wallace and Lunt (1956) and Lunt et al. (1956). This suggestion is undoubtedly correct because the clay-size fraction of soils contains the majority of the surface area, but it does not identify which mineral or organic surfaces are important. As would be expected, the negatively charged surfaces of clay minerals were not effective at adsorbing the predominately anionic chelate species (Hemwall, 1958; Stewart & Leonard, 1955), and positively charged sites on Fe oxides, Al oxides, and other colloids were suggested to be more important.

Adsorption by surfaces with pH-dependent charge, such as oxides, is suggested also by the tendency for losses of EDTA and DTPA chelates to decline with rising pH (Norvell & Lindsay, 1969, 1972). This trend is similar to the effects of pH on the adsorption of several anions on oxide surfaces (Hingston et al., 1968). Benjamin and Leckie (1981) have called this behavior ligand-like adsorption, in contrast with metal-like adsorption which increases with pH. Several studies have noted that adsorption of chelates by soils is enhanced by elevated concentrations of salts, particularly Ca salts (Wallace & Lunt, 1956; Lahav & Hochberg, 1975b; Hochberg & Lahav, 1978; Norvell, 1970). This effect is compatible with the expected suppression of the electrical double layer around predominately negatively charged surfaces, which would permit freer access of anionic species to adsorption sites (Bolt & Warkentin, 1958).

Adsorption of chelating agents by specific Fe and Al oxides may be similar to that that occurs with soil oxides. The net surface charge of Fe and Al oxides is pH dependent, changing from predominately positive at low pH to negative at high pH. The point of zero charge is usually > pH 7 and often as high as pH 9. Adsorption of the anionic ligands of EDTA, DTPA, HEDTA, CDTA, and NTA by the Fe oxide, hematite, was found to decline slowly as pH rose from about 3 to 10 (Chang et al., 1983). Adsorption occurred at pH levels above, as well as below, the point of zero charge of about pH 7, showing a degree of specific chemisorption in the binding of these anionic ligands in opposition to the net negative surface charge. Another indication of specific surface reactions was that the adsorption of EDTA added negative charge to the surface, thereby reducing the isoelectric point (pH of zero electrophoretic mobility) from a pH of about 7 to 4. NTA, EDTA, and HEDTA were adsorbed somewhat more extensively than DTPA and CDTA, but the differences among them were small.

Bowers and Huang (1985) conducted similar experiments with bayerite, an Al oxide with a point of zero charge > pH 9. In contrast to the results with hematite, the adsorption of anionic metal-free chelating ligands on bayerite was not similar (Fig. 7-9). Whereas the adsorption of EDTA, DTPA, and EGTA declined with pH, especially at pH > 5 or 6, adsorption of CDTA and HEDTA was relatively insensitive to pH. Bowers and Huang (1985) suggested that the cyclohexane ring of CDTA and the hydroxyethyl group of

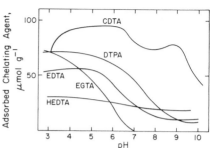

Fig. 7-9. Adsorption of CDTA, DTPA, EDTA, EGTA, and HEDTA on the aluminum oxide bayerite. The initial chelating agent concentration was 0.1 mmol L^{-1}, equivalent to 100 μmol chelating agent per gram of oxide. Redrawn from Bowers and Huang (1985).

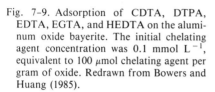

HEDTA may have allowed additional bonding of a hydrophobic nature, although is not clear why this should be significant on Al oxide and not on the Fe oxide discussed above. The adsorption of CDTA was much greater than the adsorption of HEDTA, which contrasts with their behavior on hematite, and also with the extent of adsorption of their Fe chelates in soils.

In other experiments, Bowers and Huang (1986) reacted several metal chelates of EDTA with bayerite. The adsorption of EDTA from solutions of Ni-EDTA was very similar to that shown for metal-free EDTA in Fig. 7-9. The EDTA and Ni from Ni-EDTA were adsorbed in a 1:1 ratio from pH 3 to 10, suggesting that the entire metal chelate was adsorbed. The adsorption of Cu, Cd, Pb, and Zn from solutions of their EDTA chelates was similar to the adsorption of Ni from Ni-EDTA, suggesting that the relatively strong chelates of all these metals were bound intact.

The ligand-like behavior of EDTA chelates, in conjunction with the insensitivity of their adsorption to the characteristics of the chelated metal, suggests that adsorption occurred through association of ligand groups with the surface. The alternative of linking the ligand to the surface through a chelated metal would have been likely to cause metal-dependent behavior, which was not observed. Adsorption of Ni-EDTA or metal-free EDTA reduced the surface charge slightly, presumably due to a small degree of specific bonding between these anionic species and the oxide. The similarities are remarkable among the various EDTA chelates and the metal-free EDTA ligand in their adsorption on bayerite. At present, it is not clear if this generality extends to the adsorption of EDTA species on other oxides or to the adsorption of other chelating agents on this Al oxide.

The adsorption of metal chelates and chelating ligands by soils remains poorly understood. Full understanding of these reactions will always be impeded by the complexity of soil surfaces, continuing changes in chelate speciation, and concurrent degradation of the chelating ligand. Further studies of chelating agent adsorption by well-characterized solid phases are needed to better elucidate the nature of adsorption in soil.

III. BIODEGRADATION OF CHELATING AGENTS

The chelating agents commonly added to soils and nutrient solutions are organic compounds. As such, they are subject to biodegradation into simpler compounds, ultimately into CO_2, water, and inorganic salts. Many factors influence the rate and extent of degradation. These factors include the resistance of the chelating agent itself, its concentration, the metals with which it is associated, the presence of a competent and acclimated microbial population, and factors such as temperature, aeration, other substrates, etc. that influence the activity of organisms. The biodegradation of chelating agents clearly reduces their effectiveness as metal carriers in soil and water. Biodegradation is detrimental to most of the agronomic uses of chelating agents, but it can be an advantage from the standpoint of waste disposal because chelation may promote the dispersal of toxic metals into the environment. Among the commonly used chelating agents, the biodegradation of NTA has been studied most extensively because of its use as a metal sequestering agent in industrial processes, detergents, and cleansers. These and other uses of NTA result in its incorporation in liquid and solid wastes, many of which are discharged to soils, surface waters, and ground waters.

A. Extent and Rate of NTA Biodegradation

The extent of degradation of NTA in soil can be quite variable, ranging from very little to virtually complete. Tiedje and Mason (1974) measured biodegradation of NTA in aerobic soils at field moisture capacity. After 24 d, the release of $^{14}CO_2$ from ^{14}C-labeled NTA ranged from 35 to 80% in 11 surface soils, and from <5 to 80% in 11 subsoils. Recovery of approximately three-quarters of the ^{14}C as CO_2 was considered to represent essentially complete degradation, because about one-quarter of the C from NTA is incorporated into microbial biomass (Tiedje & Mason, 1974; Ward, 1986). Degradation of NTA in surface soils always equaled, and usually exceeded, that in the underlying subsoil. Degradation was not obviously correlated with soil characteristics such as texture, pH, cover crop, or drainage. In organic soil or sewage-treated soil, there was a lag of several days before degradation rates accelerated, but this was not observed in surface or subsurface mineral soils.

Consistently rapid degradation of NTA from large additions (600 mg NTA kg^{-1} soil) was reported by Tabatabai and Bremner (1975) in five Iowa soils with a moderate range in soil characteristics. More than 90% of extractable NTA was lost in just 10 d under aerobic conditions. Complete metabolism of NTA was indicated by the recovery as NO_3-N of much of the N added as NTA. Ward (1986) added ^{14}C-labeled NTA at low rates (1 or 2 mg kg^{-1}) to subsoils collected from septic tank fields that were exposed to NTA in leachates. Sixty-five percent of the ^{14}C was recovered as CO_2 in 20 to 30 d under aerobic conditions, although most losses occurred in the first 10 d.

Degradation of NTA has also been studied in columns of soil or sediment, frequently in conjunction with the application of water enriched in sewage effluent. For example, Baek and Clesceri (1986) found more than 99% removal of NTA from septic tank effluent passing through a sandy soil following about 25 d of acclimation. Effective biodegradation of NTA has been reported also in sand beds (Hrubec & Delft, 1981), soil columns (Dunlap et al., 1972; Kuhn et al., 1987), river sediments (Kuhn et al., 1987), natural waters (Larson et al., 1981; Larson & Davidson, 1982), and sewage treatment processes (Perry et al., 1984).

Complete degradation of NTA in aerobic soils and sediments can occur in less than a day, but it may require several weeks or months. The apparent half-times for degradation range from a few hours to many days (Kuhn et al., 1987; Baek & Clesceri, 1986; Ward, 1986; Tiedje & Mason, 1974). The most rapid degradation rates have been reported in columns of soil or sediment to which NTA was continuously applied. In river waters already exposed to NTA, biodegradation was also very rapid, with rates of decomposition approaching those for citrate and glucose (Thompson & Duthie, 1968; Larson & Davidson, 1982). In river waters not acclimated to NTA, a week or two was required before degradation rates increased to comparable levels (Chau & Shiomi, 1972; Larson & Davidson, 1982). Degradation rates generally are reported to increase with the concentration of NTA, but an additional period of adaptation may be required after a major increase in concentration before efficient degradation resumes (Kuhn et al., 1987; Larson & Davidson, 1982).

Anaerobiosis frequently inhibits or eliminates biodegradation of NTA. Tiedje and Mason (1974) reported that the degradation of NTA in soils ceased when anaerobic conditions were imposed, resumed only partially under an atmosphere of 0.1% O_2 in N_2, but resumed fully with 1% O_2 or more. Dunlap et al. (1972) found little degradation of ^{14}C-NTA during effluent passage through saturated and largely anaerobic columns of soil. Larson et al. (1981) found a five-fold reduction in NTA degradation in river water samples as dissolved O_2 decreased from 13.2 to 0.3 mg L^{-1}. It appears that NTA degrades poorly under anaerobic conditions in sewage digesters that receive primary sludge (Kirk et al., 1982; Moore & Barth, 1976).

In contrast to the detrimental effects of anaerobiosis noted above, Tabatabai and Bremner (1975) found rapid degradation of NTA in soil under anaerobic as well as aerobic conditions. Degradation was apparently complete in < 10 d, and NH_4^+ increased in amounts equivalent to most of the NTA lost. Essentially complete degradation was also observed by Ward (1986) in soils under strict anaerobic conditions. Kuhn et al. (1987) observed a initial reduction, but rapid recovery, of the degradation of NTA in river water passing through columns of river sediment under anaerobic conditions.

A possible explanation for the wide differences in NTA degradation found under anaerobic conditions is suggested by the research of Ward (1986) and Kuhn et al. (1987). Their results established a clear link between NTA decomposition under anaerobic conditions and the presence of NO_3^-. Ward (1986) found that denitrification of NO_3^- to N_2O and the degradation of ^{14}C-NTA to $^{14}CO_2$ both increased with increasing NO_3^- concentrations. Although denitrification occurred somewhat before the release of $^{14}CO_2$, the results suggested that NO_3^- served as an alternate electron acceptor, permitting NTA degradation to proceed in the absence of oxygen. Degradation of NTA did not occur in the absence of NO_3^- in either study

(Ward, 1986; Kuhn et al., 1987). Thus, differences in available NO_3^- and in the activity of denitrifying organisms may explain many of the discordant effects of anaerobiosis on NTA degradation.

Decreases in temperature reduce the rate of NTA degradation under aerobic or anaerobic conditions, but under aerobic conditions the rates sometimes recover as the degrading organisms adapt. In soil acclimated to NTA at 24 °C, Tiedje and Mason(1974) found that degradation was lower at 12.5 °C and virtually eliminated at 2 °C. However, soil acclimated to NTA at 12.5 °C degraded NTA rapidly at that temperature, and also was able to degrade NTA slowly at 2 °C. These results suggest that different populations of organisms had developed to carry out degradation at the different temperatures. In water filtering through columns of sediment, a drop in temperature from 20 to 10 °C, or from 10 to 5 °C, slowed degradation of NTA by about a factor of two (Kuhn et al., 1987). Under aerobic conditions the rates recovered after several days. However, under anaerobic conditions, recovery was incomplete. This work and that of Enfors and Molin (1973) suggest that NTA degradation may be more temperature sensitive when oxygen is absent. Larson et al. (1981) measured the temperature dependence for NTA degradation in river water and found a four-fold increase from 2 to 23 °C, with a Q_{10} of 2, typical for biological reactions. In sewage treatment processes too, the biodegradation of NTA is often reduced at low temperature, especially below 10 °C (Perry et al., 1984).

B. Mechanism of NTA Biodegradation

Decomposition of NTA is accompanied by the oxidation of most of the C to CO_2 and the release of most of the N as inorganic N, under both aerobic and anaerobic conditions (Ward, 1986; Tabatabai & Bremner, 1975; Thompson & Duthie, 1968; Tiedje & Mason, 1974; Kuhn et al., 1987). Under aerobic conditions, the N released from NTA is nitrified to NO_3^-, whereas the N is released mainly as NH_4^+ during anaerobic degradation. Both C atoms in the acetate groups of NTA are metabolized at equal rates by microorganisms from soils and wastewaters (Tiedje & Mason, 1974; Thompson & Duthie, 1968; Firestone & Tiedje, 1978). Some organisms can use NTA as a source of energy, C, and N (Enfors & Molin, 1973; Focht & Joseph, 1971).

The pathway for aerobic degradation of NTA has been studied in cultures of *Pseudomonas* bacteria (Firestone & Tiedje, 1978; Focht & Joseph, 1971). The methylene C of an acetate appears to be oxidized, causing cleavage of the C-N bond, and releasing IDA and glyoxylate as products. No intermediates that precede IDA have been found. A repetition of this oxidation splits IDA into a second glyoxylate and the amino acid glycine. Glycine and glyoxylate are then metabolized through normal biochemical pathways, releasing the N as NH_4^+ and the C as CO_2. Firestone and Tiedje (1978) showed that the initial oxidation of the methylene C in NTA was carried out in a *Pseudomonas* bacterium by an enzyme they called NTA-monooxidase, in the presence of NADH, oxygen, and Mn^{2+}. Similar pathways have been proposed by others and may be followed generally in organisms capable of

NTA degradation (Warren, 1974). Degradation in soil is undoubtedly similar, as suggested by the absence of a lag phase for IDA degradation in soils acclimated to NTA (Tiedje & Mason, 1974).

The pathway for degradation of NTA under anaerobic conditions is less well understood, but NO_3^- appears to be necessary. This requirement was clearly shown by Ward (1986) and Kuhn et al. (1987) for degradation in soil and sediment. The NO_3 probably serves as an alternate electron acceptor in the absence of oxygen, as suggested by Enfors and Molin (1973) for the degradation of NTA by several facultative anaerobes isolated from mud in sewage-polluted waters.

C. Effects of Metals on NTA Degradation

Warren (1974) summarized studies in soils, waters, and wastewaters showing that NTA degradation was inhibited occasionally by Cu and Zn, and frequently by Hg, Cd, and Ni. Degradation was not usually affected by the presence of common metals, such as Na, Ca, Mg, Mn, and Fe. Metal concentrations as well as metal characteristics influence the extent of degradation. For example, in *Pseudomonas* cultures, Firestone and Tiedje (1975) noted roughly equal rates of degradation of NTA chelates of Ca, Mg, Na, Mn, Cu, Zn, Fe, and Cd, but no degradation of Ni-NTA, at the relatively low concentration of 0.02 mmol L^{-1}. However, the Cd, Zn, and Cu chelates of NTA also inhibited degradation when the concentrations were 50-fold higher.

Most studies of the effect of metals on degradation are difficult to interpret because of inadequate information concerning the forms of metal and metal chelate actually present following addition. Madsen and Alexander (1985) recognized the importance of metal chelate speciation, and used equilibrium calculations to design solutions for testing NTA biodegradation. Media were prepared with ^{14}C-labeled NTA, predominately in the form of H, Ca, Mg, Al, or Fe chelates, and subjected to degradation by a mixture of organisms from sewage. Only the Ca chelate was degraded to CO_2 in these cultures; no mineralization of other forms of NTA was detected. Further experiments with one bacterium, *Listeria* sp., eliminated the possibility of an overall Ca deficiency and suggested strongly that Ca-NTA was the only form that could be degraded. Separate experiments with lake water also showed that NTA degradation was retarded by low concentrations of Ca. A special role for Ca in the degradation of NTA was suggested earlier by the studies of Vashon et al. (1982) and others (Warren, 1974).

Further work is warranted on the Ca requirement of organisms in NTA biodegradation. Limitations to NTA degradation appear possible in some natural waters and perhaps even in a few soils of very low basic cation content. However, in most soils, the concentrations of Ca should be adequate to keep much of the NTA in the form of Ca-NTA (Norvell, 1972). As pointed out by Warren (1974), the breakdown of resistant NTA chelates probably occurs after their conversion into biodegradable forms. The relatively low stability of the NTA chelates of micronutrient and heavy metals encourages their conversion into Ca-NTA in soil and water, which should certainly facilitate decomposition.

D. Biodegradation of EDTA and Other Chelating Agents

Among the other aminopolyacetate chelating agents, only the degradation of EDTA has received much study. Tiedje (1975, 1977) found that ^{14}C-tagged EDTA was slowly degraded to CO_2 in soils, sediments, and microbial cultures. In 15 wk, 10 to 46% of EDTA was degraded in 11 surface soils, but only 3 to 4% was degraded in 3 subsoils. Addition of organic matter to one soil increased degradation. Samples collected in winter degraded EDTA more rapidly than summer samples, perhaps because of the stimulation of microorganisms by the organic compounds released by freezing and thawing. EDTA did not degrade in anaerobic soil or sediment, but did so when aeration improved. Soil characteristics other than aeration did not appear to be related to the rate of decomposition. Samples of EDTA, labelled with ^{14}C at each of the three positions for C, released [14]CO_2 at roughly similar rates, suggesting that biodegradation was completed without any major accumulation of intermediates. Also, intermediates could not be identified in soil extracts. Except at very high rates of addition, the degradation of EDTA did not require a period of acclimation, suggesting that EDTA was being co-metabolized by existing populations of microorganisms. The EDTA chelates of Cu, Cd, Zn, Mn, Ca, and Fe were degraded at equal rates, but Ni-EDTA was degraded only half as rapidly. As with NTA, the effects of added metals are likely to be influenced by exchange reactions with other cations.

Several groups have reported that organisms isolated from raw sewage, sewage effluents, and sediments were unable to degrade EDTA (Madsen & Alexander, 1985; Bunch & Ettinger, 1967; Enfors & Molin, 1973). However, Belly et al. (1975) reported that EDTA added as Fe-EDTA was degraded rather effectively by a highly concentrated population of mixed organisms from an aerated lagoon that received EDTA in wastewaters. About 30% of ^{14}C-tagged EDTA was released as [14]CO_2 in 5 d. Intermediate products were detected even more rapidly. Analyses by gas chromatography showed that as EDTA was lost, IDA and ED2A accumulated during the first 2 d. Smaller amounts of NTA, EDDA, EDMA, and glycine appeared between 2 and 4 d. Several pathways for metabolism are possible with these intermediates, one of which would be oxidative cleavage of acetate groups to produce glyoxylate and, in sequence, ED3A, EDDA, and EDMA in reactions similar to NTA degradation. While the concentrations of organisms used in this study were unusually high, the results do suggest that adapted organisms have the potential to degrade EDTA quite rapidly, even though this does not represent the usual experience in soils.

Information on the biodegradation of other chelating ligands is extremely limited. Bunch and Ettinger (1967) suggested that DTPA, HEDTA, and CDTA, as well as EDTA, were relatively resistant to biodegradation because they all retained their chelating capacity after 1 wk in cultures that were able to degrade NTA and HIDA. In soils, the persistence of soluble chelates in solution over several weeks provides some assurance that the degradation of EDTA, DTPA, CDTA, HEDTA, and EDDHA is not particularly rapid (Hill-Cottingham & Lloyd-Jones, 1957, 1958; Norvell & Lindsay, 1969). Reports that Fe-EDDHA fails on occasion to keep Fe in solution (Wallace & Wallace, 1983; Ryan & Hariq, 1983) may indicate degradation, but this effect could also be caused by sorption or other factors. With DTPA, Norvell and Lindsay (1972) found that the loss of $^{14}CO_2$ from ^{14}C-tagged acetate groups was more rapid than the loss of chelating capacity in several soils. They suggested that partial degradation of DTPA had occurred, yielding product ligands with some chelating ability but fewer than the five acetate groups initially present on the ligand.

IV. PHOTODEGRADATION OF CHELATING AGENTS

Organic compounds, such as simple organic acids and aminopolyacetate chelating agents, which contain carboxylic acid functional groups, are subject to photodegradation when bonded to Fe^{3+} and certain other metal ions (Adamson et al., 1968). Photodegradation of chelating agents is obviously unlikely to be significant in soils, but it can be very important in hydroponic solutions, as well as in surface waters that receive chelating agents in drainage from agricultural soils or waste treatment systems.

Photoreduction of metal chelates is highly dependent on the nature of the associated metal. The Fe(III)-chelates appear to be the most photoreactive among the chelates of common metals. The photosensitivity of Fe(III)-EDTA has been recognized for many years (Jones & Long, 1952; Hill-Cottingham, 1955). When exposed to light, the yellow-brown color of Fe(III)-EDTA solutions diminishes as Fe(II)-EDTA and other colorless products form. Later, these solutions become cloudy and orange-brown as Fe^{2+} is reoxidized by oxygen to form insoluble Fe(III) oxides. Extensive degradation of Fe(III)-EDTA can occur after a few hours in strong light, but the chelate is quite stable when stored in the dark. With Fe(III)-EDTA, photodegradation is caused by light with wavelengths ranging from the UV into the visible (Natarajan & Endicott, 1973). The Fe(III)-chelates of NTA, HEDTA, and DTPA also are readily photodegraded (Trott et al., 1972; Hill-Cottingham, 1955). In addition, the EDTA and NTA chelates of Co(III) and Cu(II) are photoreactive (Natarajan & Endicott, 1973; Langford & Quance, 1977), and there is some evidence that the EDTA chelates of Mn(II) and Co(II) may degrade, although the reaction mechanisms are not clear (Lockhart & Blakeley, 1975a).

Photodegradation reactions of aminopolyacetic acid chelates appear to involve photoreduction of the metal via a ligand to metal charge transfer followed by irreversible oxidation of the associated carboxyl group (Langford & Carey, 1987; Adamson et al., 1968). Photoreduction of Fe(III) is a single electron process, whereas organic oxidations are generally two electron processes. As a result, the initial oxidized products of the single electron transfer to the carboxyl group are thought to be CO_2 and an unstable free radical.

For the species Fe(III)EDTA$^-$, the reaction is thought to proceed through photoexcitation of a Fe(III) carboxyl bond, reduction of Fe(III) with loss of CO_2 and formation of a ligand free radical, reaction of the free radical with a second Fe(III)EDTA$^-$ to produce Fe(II)EDTA^{2-} and an unstable ligand intermediate, and finally, loss of CH_2O (formaldehyde) and a proton from the ligand intermediate to yield Fe(II)ED3A$^-$ (Carey & Langford, 1973; Lockhart & Blakeley, 1975b). These reactions, shown below, are compatible with the usual product ratio of Fe(II):CH$_2$O:CO$_2$ at 2:1:1 found for photodegradation of Fe(III)EDTA$^-$ (Natarajan & Endicott, 1973; Carey & Langford, 1973).

$$\text{Fe(III)EDTA}^- \xrightarrow{\text{light}} [\text{Fe(III)*EDTA}]^- \qquad [4]$$

$$[\text{Fe(III)*EDTA}]^- \rightarrow [\text{Fe(II)ED3A--CH}_2 \cdot]^- + CO_2 \qquad [5]$$

$$[\text{Fe(II)ED3A--CH}_2 \cdot]^- + \text{Fe(III)EDTA}^- \rightarrow [\text{Fe(II)ED3A} = CH_2] + \text{Fe(II)EDTA}^{2-} \qquad [6]$$

$$[\text{Fe(II)ED3A} = CH_2] + H_2O \rightarrow \text{Fe(II)ED3A}^- + CH_2O + H^+ \qquad [7]$$

In the presence of air, the Fe(II)-chelates of ED3A and EDTA are oxidized by oxygen to the corresponding Fe(III)-chelates, so that the net result of the above reactions is the loss of an acetate group from EDTA with release of ED3A, CO_2, and formaldehyde. Photodegradation continues with further decarboxylation, yielding the products EDDA, IDA, EDMA and glycine (Carey & Langford, 1973; Lockhart & Blakeley, 1975b). NTA is a conceivable intermediate in the photodegradation of EDTA, but it has never been detected. The degradation of Fe(III)-EDTA occurs more rapidly at slightly acid rather than alkaline pH values, and the reaction path may be pH sensitive (Lockhart & Blakeley, 1975b).

EDTA chelates of Co(III) photodegrade at appreciable rates too, but the ratio of simple products is different than for Fe(III)EDTA$^-$; i.e., Co(II):CH$_2$O:CO$_2$ = 2:1:2 (Langford & Quance, 1977; Natarajan & Endicott, 1973). The reaction mechanism for Co(III) is thought to be different than for Fe(III) because of the kinetic resistance of Co(III) to reduction. Because of this resistance, the second Co(III)EDTA$^-$ involved in the reaction is not reduced simply to Co(II)EDTA^{2-}. Instead, the EDTA in the second Co(III)EDTA$^-$ is degraded and loses an additional CO_2 (Langford & Quance, 1977).

The photodegradation of Fe(III)-NTA appears to occur by the same general mechanism as described above for Fe(III)-EDTA, with the immediate production of IDA, formaldehyde, and CO_2 (Trott et al., 1972). It is very likely that other Fe(III)-polyaminopolyacetate chelates degrade by similar decarboxylation mechanisms. The EDTA and NTA chelates of Cu(II) photodegrade more slowly than those of Fe(III), but the mechanism is thought to be similar, except that Cu(II) is reduced to Cu(I) (Moffett & Zika, 1987; Langford et al., 1973).

Plant nutrient solutions that contain chelating agents should always be shielded from light to prevent photodegradation. Photodegradation reduces the concentrations of the added chelating agent, creates product ligands of differing characteristics, and releases hydrous Fe oxides, which bind other nutrients and have highly pH-dependent solubility. These effects create additional confusion in interpreting the responses of plants to chelated metals in nutrient solutions.

V. SUMMARY

Existing knowledge of soil chemistry and chelate stability can be integrated in simple equilibrium models that provide useful predictions of metal chelation in soils. Competition from Fe^{3+}, Al^{3+}, and Ca^{2+} in aerobic soils limits the ability of chelating ligands to chelate other metals. Under anaerobic conditions, Fe^{2+} and Mn^{2+} compete very strongly for chelating agents and limit the chelation of other metals. In addition to serving as metal carriers in soils, metal chelates can serve as valuable indicators of free-metal-ion activities, which are otherwise too low for direct measurement. Knowledge of chelate equilibria and metal-ion activities is valuable for understanding metal-ion reactions in soil and metal uptake by plants. Simple modifications in the composition of plant nutrient solutions can stabilize the concentrations of micronutrient and heavy metal ions at desired levels, prevent the precipitation of unwanted solid phases, and eliminate extreme fluctuations in metal-ion activities with changing pH. Widely available and increasingly user-friendly computer programs for chemical speciation help to promote better understanding of metal chelate equilibria in soils, nutrient solutions, and natural waters.

The effectiveness of chelating agents as metal carriers in soils and solutions can be severely limited by adsorption and decomposition. The adsorption of metal chelates and chelating ligands by soils remains poorly understood, largely because of the complexity of the surfaces and mechanisms involved. Chelate species differ markedly in the extent of their adsorption. Unstable metal chelates, such as Zn-EDDHA and many Mn chelates, appear particularly prone to adsorption. Studies of the adsorption of chelates by specific minerals in chemically simple systems should improve our understanding of the mechanisms of adsorption in soils. Biodegradation severely limits the persistance of simple chelating ligands such as NTA, HIDA, and CIT in soils and waters. There is evidence that the Ca chelate of NTA may be degraded preferentially. Degradation of NTA occurs under anaerobic as well as aerobic conditions, but then appears to require NO_3^- as an alternate electron acceptor. The polyaminopolyacetate chelating agents, such as EDTA, are much more resistant to biodegradation. EDTA, NTA, HEDTA, DTPA, and, presumably, all the aminopolyacetate chelating agents photodegrade when chelated with Fe(III) or, to a lesser extent, with metals such as Co(III), Cu(II), and Mn(II). The biodegradation and photodegradation of NTA and EDTA appear to involve sequential losses of acetate groups. Degradation of chelating agents confuses the interpretation of chelate equilibria in soils and nutrient solutions by destroying the ligands or by altering their characteristics.

REFERENCES

Aboulroos, S.A. 1981. Reaction of EDTA, DTPA, and EDDHA complexes of zinc, copper, and manganese with a calcareous soil. Z. Pflanzenernaehr. Bodenkd. 144:164–173.

Aboulroos, S.A., E.A. El Beissary, and A.A. El Falaky. 1983. Reactions of the iron chelates and the sodium salts of EDTA, DTPA and EDDHA with two alkaline soils, and their effectiveness during growth of barley. Agron. Ecosystems 8:203–214.

Adamson, A.W., W.L. Waltz, E. Zinato, D.W. Watts, P.D. Fleischauer, and R.D. Lindholm. 1968. Photochemistry of transition-metal coordination compounds. Chem. Rev. 68:541–585.

Allen, H.E., and C. Boonlayangoor. 1978. Mobilization of metals from sediment by NTA. Verh. Int. Ver. Theor. Angew. Limnol. 20:1956–1962.

Assaad, F.F., and F. Awad. 1981. The stability of iron chelates in calcareous soils. Z. Pflanzenernaehr. Bodenkd. 144:77–86.

Baek, N.H., and N.L. Clesceri. 1986. NTA biodegradation and removal in subsurface sandy soil. Water Res. 20:345–349.

Banat, K., U. Forstner, and G. Muller. 1974. Experimental mobilization of metals from aquatic sediments by nitrilotriacetic acid. Chem. Geol. 14:199–207.

Bell, P.F., R.L. Chaney, and J.S. Angle. 1988. Ferric activity in chelator-buffered nutrient solutions necessary to provide adequate Fe for barley. p. 229. In Agronomy abstracts. ASA, Madison, WI.

Belly, R.T., J.J. Lauff, and C.T. Goodhue. 1975. Degradation of ethylenediaminetetraacetic acid by microbial populations from an aerated lagoon. Appl. Microbiol. 29:787–794.

Benjamin, M.M., and J.O. Leckie. 1981. Conceptual model for metal-ligand-surface interactions during adsorption. Environ. Sci. Technol. 15:1050–1057.

Bolt, G.H., and B.P. Warkentin. 1958. The negative adsorption of anions by clay suspensions. Kolloid Z. 156:41–46.

Bowers, A.R., and C.P. Huang. 1985. Adsorption characteristics of polyacetic amino acids onto hydrous γ-Al_2O_3. J. Colloid Interface Sci. 105:197–215.

Bowers, A.R., and C.P. Huang. 1986. Adsorption characteristics of metal-EDTA complexes onto hydrous oxides. J. Colloid Interface Sci. 110:575–590.

Boxma, R. 1981. Effect of pH on the behaviour of various iron chelates in sphagnum (moss) peat. Commun. Soil Sci. Plant Anal. 12:755–763.

Brown, D.S., and J.D. Allison. 1987. MINTEQA1, an equilibrium metal speciation model: Users Manual. EPA/600/3-87/012. U.S. Environ. Protect. Agency, Athens, GA.

Brown, J.C., L.O. Tiffin, and R.S. Holmes. 1960. Competition between chelating agents and roots as factors affecting absorption of iron and other ions. Plant Physiol. 35:878–886.

Bunch, R.L., and M.B. Ettinger. 1967. Biodegradability of potential organic substitutes for phosphates. p. 393–396. In Proc. 22nd Ind. Waste Conf. Purdue Univ. Engr. Bull. Ext. Ser. 129.

Carey, J.H., and C.H. Langford. 1973. Photodecomposition of Fe(III) aminopolycarboxylates. Can. J. Chem. 51:3665–3670.

Chaney, R.L. 1988a. Metal speciation and interactions among elements affect trace element transfer in agricultural and environmental food-chains. p. 219–260. In J.R. Kramer and H.E. Allen (ed.) Metal speciation: Theory, analysis, and application. Lewis Publ., Inc., Chelsea, MI.

Chaney, R.L. 1988b. Plants can utilize iron from Fe-N,N ′-di-(2-hydroxybenzoyl)-ethylenediamine-N,N ′-diacetic acid, a ferric chelate with 10^6 greater formation constant than Fe-EDDHA. J. Plant Nutr. 11:1033–1050.

Chaney, R.L., P.F. Bell, and B.A. Coulombe. 1989. Screening strategies for improved nutrient uptake and utilization by plants. HortScience 24:565–572.

Chaney, R.L., P.F. Bell, and I.F.S. Melo. 1988. Activity of microelement cations required by plants in DTPA-buffered nutrient solutions. p. 231. *In* Agronomy abstracts. ASA, Madison, WI.

Chaney, R.L., J.C. Brown, and L.O. Tiffin. 1972. Obligatory reduction of ferric chelates in iron uptake by soybeans. Plant Physiol. 50:208–213.

Chang, H.C., T.W. Healy, and E. Matijevic. 1983. Interactions of metal hydrous oxides with chelating agents, III. Adsorption on spherical colloidal hematite particles. J. Colloid Interface Sci. 92:469–478.

Chau, Y.K., and M.T. Shiomi. 1972. Complexing properties of nitrilotriacetic acid in the lake environment. Water Air Soil Pollut. 1:149–164.

Cline, G.R., P.E. Powell, P.J. Szaniszlo, and C.P.P. Reid. 1982. Comparison of the abilities of hydroxamic, synthetic, and other natural organic acids to chelate iron and other ions in nutrient solution. Soil Sci. Soc. Am. J. 46:1158–1164.

Dayanand, D., and M.K. Sinha. 1984. Solubility of native forms of iron, manganese, copper and zinc in calcareous soils. Indian Soc. Soil Sci. 32:427–436.

DeKock, P.C., and R.L. Mitchell. 1957. Uptake of chelated metals by plants. Soil Sci. 84:55–62.

Dragun, J., D.E. Baker, and M.L. Risius. 1976. Growth and element accumulation by two single-cross corn hybrids as affected by copper in solution. Agron. J. 68:466–470.

Dunlap, W.J., R.L. Cosby, J.F. McNabb, B.E. Bledsoe, and M.R. Scalf. 1972. Probable impact of NTA on ground water. Ground Water 10:107–117.

Elliott, H.A., and C.M. Denneny. 1982. Soil adsorption of cadmium from solutions containing organic ligands. J. Environ. Qual. 11:658–662.

Elsokkary, I.H. 1980. Reaction of labelled $^{65}ZnCl_2$, $^{65}ZnEDTA$ and $^{65}ZnDTPA$ with different clay-systems and some alluvial Egyptian soils. Plant Soil 54:383–393.

Enfors, S.O., and N. Molin. 1973. Biodegradation of nitrilotriacetate (NTA) by bacteria. I. Isolation of bacteria able to grow anaerobically with NTA as a sole carbon source. Water Res. 7:881–888.

Erich, M.S., J.M. Duxbury, D.R. Bouldin, and E. Cary. 1987. The influence of organic complexing agents on iron mobility in a simulated rhizosphere. Soil Sci. Soc. Am. J. 51:1207–1214.

Eskew, D.L., R.M. Welch, and W.A. Norvell. 1984. Ni in higher plants: Further evidence for an essential role. Plant Physiol. 76:691–693.

Essington, E.H., and H. Nishita. 1966. Effect of chelates on the movement of fission products through soil columns. Plant Soil 24:1–23.

Firestone, M.K., and J.M. Tiedje. 1975. Biodegradation of metal-nitrilotriacetate complexes by a *Pseudomonas* species: mechanism of reaction. Appl. Microbiol. 29:758–764.

Firestone, M.K., and J.M. Tiedje. 1978. Pathway of degradation of nitrilotriacetate by a *Pseudomonas* species. Appl. Environ. Microbiol. 35:955–961.

Focht, D.D., and H.A. Joseph. 1971. Bacterial degradation of nitrilotriacetic acid (NTA). Can. J. Microbiol. 17:1553–1556.

Fujii, R., L.L. Hendrickson, and R.B. Corey. 1983. Ionic activities of trace metals in sludge-amended soils. Sci. Total Environ. 28:179–190.

Garnett, K., P.W.W. Kirk, J.N. Lester, and R. Perry. 1985. The effect of nitrilotriacetic acid on the solubilities of metals in soil-sludge mixtures. J. Environ. Qual. 14:549–553.

Gupta, G.N., and D.L. Deb. 1984. Effect of chelating agents on zinc diffusion in two soils. Z. Pflanzenernaehr. Bodenkd. 147:533–539.

Halvorson, A.D., and W.L. Lindsay. 1972. Equilibrium relationships of metal chelates in hydroponic solutions. Soil Sci. Soc. Am. Proc. 36:755–761.

Halvorson, A.D., and W.L. Lindsay. 1977. The critical Zn^{2+} concentration for corn and the nonabsorption of chelated zinc. Soil Sci. Soc. Am. J. 41:531–534.

Hemwall, J.B. 1958. Reaction of ferric ethylenediamine tetraacetate with soil clay minerals. Soil Sci. 86:126–132.

Hern, J.L., H.A. Menser, R.C. Sidle, and T.E. Staley. 1988. Effects of surface-applied lime and EDTA on subsoil acidity and aluminum. Soil Sci. 145:52–57.

Hewitt, E.J. 1966. Sand and water culture methods used in the study of plant nutrition. Tech. Commun. 22 (revised 2nd ed.). Commonwealth Agricultural Bureaux, Farnham Royal, Bucks, England.

Hill-Cottingham, D.G. 1955. Photosensitivity of iron cnelates. Nature 175:347–348.

Hill-Cottingham, D.G., and C.P. Lloyd-Jones. 1957. Behaviour of iron chelates in calcareous soils. I. Laboratory experiments with Fe-EDTA and Fe-HEEDTA. Plant Soil 8:263–274.

Hill-Cottingham, D.G., and C.P. Lloyd-Jones. 1958. Behaviour of iron chelates in calcareous soils. II. Laboratory experiments with some further chelating agents. Plant Soil 9:189–201.

Hingston, F.J., R.J. Atkinson, A.M. Posner, and J.P. Quirk. 1968. Specific adsorption of anions on goethite. Trans. Int. Congr. Soil Sci. 9th 1:669–678.

Hochberg, M., and N. Lahav. 1978. Movement of iron and zinc applied as EDTA complexes in soil columns. Plant Soil 50:221–225.

Hrubec, J. and W. van Delft. 1981. Behaviour of nitrilotriacetic acid during groundwater recharge. Water Res. 15:121–128.

Jacobson, L. 1951. Maintenance of iron supply in nutrient solutions by a single addition of ferric potassium ethylenediamine tetra-acetate. Plant Physiol. 26:411–413.

Jones, S.S., and F.A. Long. 1952. Complex ions from iron and ethylenediaminetetraacetate: General properties and radioactive exchange. J. Phys. Chem. 56:25–33.

Kirk, P.W.W., J.N. Lester, and R. Perry. 1982. The behaviour of nitrilotriacetic acid during the anaerobic digestion of sewage sludge. Water Res. 16:973–980.

Kuhn, E., M. van Loosdrecht, W. Giger, and R.P. Schwarzenbach. 1987. Microbial degradation of nitrilotriacetate (NTA) during river water/groundwater infiltration: Laboratory column studies. Water Res. 21:1237–1248.

Lahav, N., and M. Hochberg. 1975a. Kinetics of fixation of iron and zinc applied as FeEDTA, FeEDDHA, and ZnEDTA in the soil. Soil Sci. Soc. Am. Proc. 39:55–58.

Lahav, N., and M. Hochberg. 1975b. Fixation of iron and zinc applied as chelates into a soil column during leaching. Soil Sci. Soc. Am. Proc. 39:1213–1215.

Lahav, N., and M. Hochberg. 1976. A simple technique for characterizing the stability of metal chelates in the soil. Soil Sci. 121:58–59.

Lahav, N., and I. Zipori. 1978. Fixation of iron applied as FeEDTA: effect of calcium concentration and soil solid phase. Soil Sci. Soc. Am. J. 42:255–257.

Langford, C.H., and J.H. Carey. 1987. Photocatalysis by inorganic components of natural water systems. p. 225–239. In R.G. Zika and W.J. Cooper (ed.) Photochemistry of environmental aquatic systems. Am. Chem. Soc., Washington, DC.

Langford, C.H., and G.W. Quance. 1977. Photochemical decomposition of EDTA coordinated to cobalt(III): products, thermal reactions, and evidence for outer sphere alcohol oxidation by the excited state. Can. J. Chem. 55:3132–3135.

Langford, C.H., M. Wingham, and V.S. Sastri. 1973. Ligand photooxidation in copper(II) complexes of nitrilotriacetic acid. Environ. Sci. Technol. 7:820–822.

Larson, R.J., G.G. Clinckmaille, and L. Van Belle. 1981. Effect of temperature and dissolved oxygen on biodegradation of nitrilotriacetate. Water Res. 15:615–620.

Larson, R.J., and D.H. Davidson. 1982. Acclimation to and biodegradation of nitrilotriacetate (NTA) at trace concentrations in natural waters. Water Res. 16:1597–1604.

Lindsay, W.L. 1979. Chemical equilibria in soils. John Wiley & Sons, Inc., New York.

Lindsay, W.L., J.F. Hodgson, and W.A. Norvell. 1966. The physico-chemical equilibrium of metal chelates in soils and their influence on the availability of micronutrient cations. Int. Soc. Soil Sci., Trans. Comm. II & IV:305–316.

Lindsay, W.L., and W.A. Norvell. 1969. Equilibrium relationships of Zn^{2+}, Fe^{3+}, Ca^{2+}, and H^+ with EDTA and DTPA in soils. Soil Sci. Soc. Am. Proc. 33:62–68.

Lockhart, H.B., Jr., and R.V. Blakeley. 1975a. Aerobic photodegradation of X(N) chelates of (ethylenedinitrilo)tetraacetic acid [EDTA]: Implications for natural waters. Environ. Lett. 9:19–31.

Lockhart, H.B., Jr., and R.V. Blakeley. 1975b. Aerobic photodegradation of Fe(III)-(ethylene dinitrilo)tetraacetate (ferric EDTA), Implications for natural waters. Environ. Sci. Technol. 9:1035–1038.

Lucena, J.J., A. Garate, and O. Carpena. 1987. Iron-chelates evaluation in a calcareous soil. Plant Soil 103:134–138.

Lucena, J.J., A. Garate, and O. Carpena. 1988. Theoretical and practical studies on chelate-Ca-pH system in solution. J. Plant Nutr. 11:1051–1061.

Lunt, O.R., N. Hemaidan, and A. Wallace. 1956. Reactions of some polyamine polyacetate iron chelates in various soils. Soil Sci. Soc. Am. Proc. 20:172–175.

Madsen, E.L., and M. Alexander. 1985. Effects of chemical speciation on the mineralization of organic compounds by microorganisms. Appl. Environ. Microbiol. 50:342–349.

Martell, A.E., and R.M. Smith. 1974. Critical stability constants. Vol. 1: Amino acids. Plenum Press, New York.

Martell, A.E., and R.M. Smith. 1982. Critical stability constants. Vol. 5: First supplement. Plenum Press, New York.

Moffett, J.W., and R.G. Zika. 1987. Photochemistry of copper complexes in sea water. p. 116–130. *In* R.G. Zika and W.J. Cooper (ed.) Photochemistry of environmental aquatic systems. Am. Chem. Soc., Washington, DC.

Moore, L., and E.F. Barth. 1976. Degradation of NTA acid during anaerobic digestion. J. Water Pollut. Control Fed. 48:2406–2409.

Motekaitis, R.J., and A.E. Martell. 1984. Complexes of aluminium(III) with hydroxy carboxylic acids. Inorg. Chem. 23:18–23.

Muchovej, R.M.C., V.G. Allen, D.C. Martens, L.W. Zelazny, and D.R. Notter. 1986. Aluminum, citric acid, nitrilotriacetic acid, and soil moisture effects on aluminum and iron concentrations in ryegrass. Agron. J. 78:138–145.

Nabhan, H.M., J. Vanderdeelen, and A. Cottenie. 1977. Chelate behaviour in saline-alkaline soil conditions. Plant Soil 46:603–618.

Natarajan, P., and J.F. Endicott. 1973. Photoredox behavior of transition metal-ethylenediaminetetraacetate complexes. A comparison of some group VIII metals. J. Phys. Chem. 77:2049–2054.

Nordstrom, D.K., L.N. Plummer, T.M.L. Wigley, et al. 1979. A comparison of computerized chemical models for equilibrium calculations in aqueous systems. p. 857–892. *In* E.A. Jenne (ed.) Chemical modeling in aqueous systems. Am. Chem. Soc., Washington, DC.

Norvell, W.A. 1970. Solubility of Fe^{3+} in soils. Ph.D. diss. Colorado State Univ., Fort Collins. (Diss. Abstr. 71-05353).

Norvell, W.A. 1972. Equilibria of metal chelates in soil solution. p. 115–138. *In* J.J. Mortvedt et al. (ed.) Micronutrients in agriculture. SSSA, Madison, WI.

Norvell, W.A. 1984. Comparison of chelating agents as extractants for metals in diverse soil materials. Soil Sci. Soc. Am. J. 48:1285–1292.

Norvell, W.A., H. Dabkowska-Naskret, and E.E. Cary. 1987. Effect of phosphorus and zinc fertilization on the solubility of Zn^{2+} in two alkaline soils. Soil Sci. Soc. Am. J. 51:584–588.

Norvell, W.A., and W.L. Lindsay. 1969. Reactions of EDTA complexes of Fe, Zn, Mn, and Cu with soils. Soil Sci. Soc. Am. Proc. 33:86–91.

Norvell, W.A., and W.L. Lindsay. 1972. Reactions of DTPA chelates of iron, zinc, copper, and manganese with soils. Soil Sci. Soc. Am. Proc. 36:778–783.

Norvell, W.A., and W.L. Lindsay. 1982a. Effect of ferric chloride additions on the solubility of ferric ion in a near-neutral soil. J. Plant Nutr. 5:1285–1295.

Norvell, W.A., and W.L. Lindsay. 1982b. Estimation of the concentration of Fe^{3+} and the $(Fe^{3+})(OH^-)^3$ ion produce from equilibria of EDTA in soil. Soil Sci. Soc. Am. J. 46:710–715.

Norvell, W.A., R.M. Welch, and L.V. Kochian. 1989. Effects of apoplasmic Zn^{2+} activity in barley roots on uptake of Zn, root-cell membrane potential, and fluxes of H^+ and K^+. p. 248. *In* Agronomy abstracts. ASA, Madison, WI.

Parker, D.R., L.W. Zelazny, and T.B. Kinraide. 1987. Improvements to the program GEOCHEM. Soil Sci. Soc. Am. J. 51:488–491.

Parkhurst, D.L., D.C. Thorstenson, and L.N. Plummer. 1982. PHREEQE-A computer program for geochemical calculations. Rep. WRI-80-96, U.S. Geol. Surv., Reston, VA.

Patel, P.M., A. Wallace, and E.M. Romney. 1977. Effect of chelating agents on phytotoxicity of lead and lead transport. Commun. Soil Sci. Plant Anal. 8:733–740.

Perry, R., P.W.W. Kirk, T. Stephenson, and L.N. Lester. 1984. Environmental aspects of the use of NTA as a detergent builder. Water Res. 18:255–276.

Reddy, C.N., and W.H. Patrick, Jr. 1977. Effect of redox potential on the stability of zinc and copper chelates in flooded soils. Soil Sci. Soc. Am. J. 41:729–732.

Ryan, J., and S.N. Hariq. 1983. Transformation of incubated micronutrient chelates in calcareous soils. Soil Sci. Soc. Am. J. 47:806–810.

Sadiq, M. 1983. Complexing of lead by DTPA in calcareous soils. Water Air Soil Pollut. 20:247–255.

Schwab, A.P. 1981. Stability of Fe chelates and the availability of Fe and Mn to plants as affected by redox. Ph.D. diss. Colorado State Univ., Fort Collins. (Diss. Abstr. 81-26453).

Schwab, A.P., and W.L. Lindsay. 1989a. A computer simulation of Fe(III) and Fe(II) complexation in nutrient solutions: II. Applications to growing plants. Soil Sci. Soc. Am. J. 53:34–38.

Schwab, A.P., and W.L. Lindsay. 1989b. A computer simulation of Fe(III) and Fe(II) complexation in limited nutrient solution: I. Program development and testing. Soil Sci. Soc. Am. J. 53:29–34.

Singh, R., and M.K. Sinha. 1977. Reactions of iron chelates in calcareous soil and their relative efficiency in iron nutrition of corn. Plant Soil 46:17–29.

Singh, S.P. 1982. Control of Zn, Cu and Mn activities in alkaline and calcareous soils equilibrated with EDTA. J. Agric. Sci. 98:203–207.

Singh, S.P., M.K. Sinha, and N.S. Randhawa. 1981. Effectiveness of Zn-EDTA, EDTA, zinc fulvate and fulvic acid in maintaining Zn and other cations in alkaline soil solution. Indian J. Agric. Sci. 51:427–431.

Sinha, M.K., S.K. Dhillon, and K.S. Dhillon. 1977. Zinc chelate reactions in alkaline soils. Aust. J. Soil Res. 15:103–113.

Sinha, M.K., S.K. Dhillon, K.S. Dhillon, and S. Dyanand. 1978. Solubility relationships of iron, manganese, copper and zinc in alkaline and calcareous soils. Aust. J. Soil Res. 16:19–26.

Sinha, M.K., and B. Prasad. 1977. Effect of chelating agents on the kinetics of diffusion of zinc to a simulated root system and its uptake by wheat. Plant Soil 48:599–612.

Sommers, L.E., and W.L. Lindsay. 1979. Effect of pH and redox on predicted heavy metal-chelate equilibria in soils. Soil Sci. Soc. Am. J. 43:39–47.

Sposito, G., and S.V. Mattigod. 1980. GEOCHEM: A computer program for the calculation of chemical equilibria in soil solutions and other natural water systems. Kearney Found. Soil Sci., Riverside, CA.

Stewart, I., and C.D. Leonard. 1954. Chelated metals for growing plants. p. 775–809. In N.F. Childers (ed.) Mineral nutrition of fruit crops. Horticultural Publ., New Brunswick, NJ.

Stewart, I., and C.D. Leonard. 1955. Use of isotopes for determining the availability of chelated metals to growing plants. Proc. Int. Conf. Peaceful Uses At. Energy, 1st 12:159–164.

Stoveland, S., R. Perry, and J.N. Lester. 1979. Influence of detergent builders on metal solubility in activated sludge. Effl. Wat. Treat. J. 19:513–519.

Tabatabai, M.A., and J.M. Bremner. 1975. Decomposition of nitrilotriacetate (NTA) in soils. Soil Biol. Biochem. 7:103–106.

Thompson, J.E., and J.R. Duthie. 1968. The biodegradability and treatability of NTA. J. Water Pollut. Control Fed. 40:306–319.

Tiedje, J.M. 1975. Microbial degradation of ethylenediaminetetraacetate in soils and sediments. Appl. Microbiol. 30:327–329.

Tiedje, J.M. 1977. Influence of environmental parameters on EDTA biodegradation in soils and sediments. J. Environ. Qual. 6:21–26.

Tiedje, J.M., and B.B. Mason. 1974. Biodegradation of nitrilotriacetate (NTA) in soils. Soil Sci. Soc. Am. Proc. 38:278–283.

Trott, T., R.W. Henwood, and C.H. Langford. 1972. Sunlight photochemistry of ferric nitrilotriacetate complexes. Environ. Sci. Technol. 6:367–368.

Vashon, R.D., W.J. Jones, and A.G. Payne. 1982. The effect of water hardness on nitrilotriacetate removal and microbial acclimation in activated sludge. Water Res. 16:1429–1432.

Vlek, P.L.G., T.J.M. Blom, J. Beek, and W.L. Lindsay. 1974. Determination of the solubility product of various iron hydroxides and jarosite by the chelation method. Soil Sci. Soc. Am. Proc. 38:429–432.

Wallace, A., and O.R. Lunt. 1956. Reactions of some iron, zinc, and manganese chelates in various soils. Soil Sci. Soc. Am. Proc. 20:479–482.

Wallace, A., R.T. Mueller, O.R. Lunt, R.T. Ashcroft, and L.M. Shannon. 1955. Comparisons of five chelating agents in soils, in nutrient solutions, and in plant responses. Soil Sci. 80:101–108.

Wallace, A., E.M. Romney, J.W. Cha, S.M. Soufi, and F.M. Chaudhry. 1977. Nickel phytotoxicity in relationship to soil pH manipulation and chelating agents. Commun. Soil Sci. Plant Anal. 8:757–764.

Wallace, G.A., and A. Wallace. 1983. Clay fixation of metal chelates as a factor in their usability by soil application to correct micronutrient deficiencies. J. Plant Nutr. 6:439–446.

Ward, T.E. 1986. Aerobic and anaerobic biodegradation of nitrilotriacetate in subsurface soils. Ecotoxicol. Environ. Saf. 11:112–125.

Warren, C.B. 1974. Biodegradation of nitrilotriacetic acid and NTA-metal ion complexes. p. 473–496. In M.A.Q. Khan and J.P. Beberka, Jr. (ed.) Survival in toxic environments. Academic Press, New York.

Chapter 8

Mechanisms of Micronutrient Uptake and Translocation in Plants

LEON V. KOCHIAN, *USDA-ARS, Cornell University, Ithaca, New York*

Since the publication of the first edition of *Micronutrients in Agriculture* in 1972, significant progress has been made in certain areas of plant ion absorption and translocation, particularly in relation to the transport of macronutrients and related ions. Advances in technologies and methods associated with diverse areas, such as membrane isolation and the subsequent solubilization of membrane transport proteins from these membranes and their reconstitution into artificial liposomes, various microelectrode techniques, including ion-selective microelectrodes, extracellular vibrating microelectrodes, and patch clamp methodology, and most recently, molecular biology investigations of transport proteins, have advanced our understanding of molecular and cellular aspects of some ion transport systems. However, research in the areas of plant micronutrient uptake and long-distance transport has not progressed as rapidly for two reasons. First, there has simply been less research conducted in the area of micronutrient transport, which is the result, primarily, of a lack of proper research funding for this important area of plant nutrition. Since 1972, the bulk of the work in this area has focused on Fe absorption into plant cells, which indeed, has resulted in a significant increase in our understanding of Fe transport and nutrition. Considerably fewer investigations have been conducted into the transport of the other micronutrients and, in some cases, Mn and Mo transport in particular, little new research has been carried out over the past 15 yr.

Second, research into micronutrient cation (Fe^{3+}, Cu^{2+}, Zn^{2+}, Mn^{2+}, and Ni^{2+}) transport has been complicated by the chemical nature of these reactive species; that is, the tendency of these cations to form metal-organic complexes of varying stability, size, and charge (Tiffin, 1972). Therefore, it is not sufficient (or safe) to assume that the mechanisms of macronutrient and micronutrient transport differ only in the lower requirements of the micronutrient transport systems for substrate, and that all that can be learned from studying macronutrient transport systems can be extrapolated directly to the micronutrients. Certainly, many of the general aspects of ion absorption related to thermodynamic driving forces and the structure/function of membranes and membrane transport proteins apply to the transport of all ions. However, the interrelationship of metal-chelate chemistry with micronutrient cation transport at the membrane, organ, and whole-plant level requires that plant and soil scientists working in this area focus on some complex topics, including forms of the metal chelates in the rhizosphere, whether chelate splitting is occurring at the root-cell plasma membrane, forms of the micronutrient cations transported into plant cells, and the nature of the metal-chelate complexes, both within cells and involved in long-distance transport (i.e., in the xylem and phloem). These extremely complicated problems have significantly hampered progress in this area.

This chapter will focus on advancements in our understanding of micronutrient absorption and translocation that have occurred since the publication of the first edition of *Micronutrients in Agriculture*; for earlier work the reader is referred to the chapters on micronutrient uptake (Moore, 1972) and translocation (Tiffin, 1972) in the first edition. Additionally, for background on plant mineral nutrition in general, the reader is referred to the texts of Epstein (1972), Glass (1989), and Marschner (1986), and the review by Clarkson and Hanson (1980). The essential micronutrients with the exclusion of Cl and Mo will be considered; Mo was excluded because almost no research on Mo uptake in plants has been conducted over the last 15 yr. Readers should note that Ni was added to this list based on the demonstration of its essentiality in legumes (Eskew et al., 1983) and, ultimately, in other higher plants (Brown et al., 1987). As mentioned above, research into plant Fe absorption has accounted for the bulk of the work in this area over the past 17 yr. Hence, considerably more space will be devoted to mechanisms of Fe absorption and transport than to the other micronutrients. In terms of chapter organization, general aspects of ion transport at the membrane, root, and whole-plant level will first be discussed. Subsequently, mechanisms of absorption of Fe, Mn, Cu, Zn, B, and Ni into the plant cell will be considered, and then translocation of the specific micronutrients in the xylem and phloem will be analyzed.

I. GENERAL ASPECTS OF ION ABSORPTION AND TRANSLOCATION

A. Ion Absorption into Plant Cells

The concept that plant tissues consist of two separate pathways for ions and water movement, the apoplasm and symplasm, has been widely accepted by plant scientists for a number of years. The apoplasm, or continuum of interconnected cell walls, is considered to be readily permeable to water and ions (Läuchli, 1976). The symplasm can be viewed, quite simply, as the cytoplasm of all living cells, connected via plasmodesmata, and bounded by the plasma membrane of each cell. Hence, in the root, the first and primary "barrier" to selective and regulated uptake of nutrient ions into the plant is the plasma membrane of epidermal and cortical cells. Accordingly, much of the research on ion absorption at the cellular level has focused on plasma membrane (and tonoplast or vacuolar membrane) transport systems.

1. Membrane Structure: The Carrier Hypothesis

It is now widely accepted that the plasma membrane and tonoplast are structurally quite similar to other biological membranes, consisting of a continuous lipid bilayer into which globular proteins are inserted (for a review, see Robinson, 1985). The lipid composition of both membranes is complex, consisting of phospholipids, glycolipids, sterols, and sterol glycosides (Poole, 1988). The lipid bilayer is relatively impermeable to ions; therefore, the transport of macronutrient and micronutrient ions into the cell is facilitated by specific transport proteins inserted into the lipid bilayer.

The carrier hypothesis, which is based on the concept that ion transport across biological membranes is mediated by membrane transport proteins, has evolved from research spanning some 50 yr. In the early part of this century, although the lipid bilayer structure of cellular membranes had not yet been fully developed, many researchers were beginning to realize that plant (and animal) cells were bounded by a nonaqueous layer that was impermeable to electrolytes (Osterhout & Stanley, 1932). The first discussion of the carrier concept in relation to plant transport processes arose from the work of van den Honert (1937) on phosphate uptake in sugar cane. In this study, he hypothesized that the cellular mechanism of phosphate uptake was analogous to a rotating conveyor. During this era, the classical work of Hoagland and Broyer (1936), introducing excised low-salt roots as an experimental material for ion absorption studies, had tremendous impact on the field. Subsequently, resesarch with excised root systems that focused primarily on the rapid absorption of K^+ by plant cells led a number of researchers to hypothesize that special structures must exist that would facilitate ion uptake across this outer boundary (Jacobsen & Overstreet, 1947; Osterhout, 1950, 1952).

The carrier hypothesis was further developed by Epstein and coworkers who were the first to apply the concepts of classical enzyme kinetics to plant ion absorption (Epstein & Hagen, 1952). They postulated that specific alkali cation transport systems operated in a fashion analogous to substrate-specific enzymes, and demonstrated that, at low substrate concentrations, alkali cation uptake followed Michaelis-Menten kinetics, whereas at higher substrate levels, transport could be mediated by a second system that deviated from classical Michaelis-Menten form (Epstein et al., 1963; Leggett & Epstein, 1956). This pioneering work had a significant influence on the field of plant membrane transport, and triggered much research and controversy. Conflicting hypotheses were presented concerning the cellular and subcellular location of the various transport systems (Laties, 1969), and whether the complex uptake kinetics observed for most substrates in plant tissues and organs was the result of multiple transport systems, as hypothesized by Epstein and colleagues, or due to the operation of a single complex transport system (Nissen, 1974). Although there are obvious dangers in treating ion transport into a complex organ, such as a root, in such simplified terms, this type of research was extremely important in establishing the concept that the absorption (and extrusion) of mineral nutrients and related ions is mediated by specific membrane-transport proteins. For more detailed reviews of this topic, the reader is referred to Epstein (1976), Kochian and Lucas (1988), and Nissen (1974).

More recently, evidence for the involvement of membrane proteins in ion transport has been shown from work involving the use of isolated membrane vesicles for ion transport research. Most of the work in this area has centered on the H^+-translocating ATPases (or H^+ pumps) of the plasma membrane and tonoplast in plant cells (Poole, 1988; Spanswick, 1981, 1989). Demonstrations of ATP-dependent H^+ transport in plasma membrane and tonoplast vesicles have been made by a number of laboratories (Bennett et al., 1984; Churchill & Sze, 1983; De Michelis et al., 1983; DuPont et al., 1982; Hager & Helmle, 1981; Stout & Cleland, 1982), whereas ATP-dependent Ca^{2+} transport has been shown in microsomal membrane (mixture of membrane vesicles from different cellular membranes) fractions (Buckhout, 1983; Gross & Marme, 1978). More direct evidence for protein-mediated ion transport has come from transport studies involving reconstitution of isolated transport enzymes into artificial lipid vesicles. Vara and Serrano (1982) were the first to demonstrate ATP-dependent H^+ transport with a reconstituted, plasma membrane ATPase from oat (*Avena sativa* L.) roots. Subsequently, ATP-dependent H^+ transport has been demonstrated with reconstituted, microsomal membrane ATPases from corn (*Zea mays* L.) roots (O'Neill & Spanswick, 1984). Finally, a Ca^{2+} transport protein has been solubilized from the tonoplast of oat roots, reconstituted into liposomes, and has been shown to catalyze Ca^{2+}/H^+ exchange (Schumaker & Sze, 1989).

It is now widely recognized from biochemical studies, such as those just detailed, along with electrophysiological studies using the patch clamp technique (Hille, 1984; Sakmann & Neher, 1983), that different classes of transport proteins reside in the cellular membranes of all living organisms. These include ATPases that function as primary active transport systems (transport against an electrochemical potential gradient), cotransport and antiport systems that use the energy stored in the transmembrane H^+ gradients generated by the plasma membrane and tonoplast H^+-ATPases to drive active transport of another ion (secondary active transport), and ion channels that mediate passive ion transport. The various transport systems will be discussed in more detail in the section on plasma membrane and tonoplast ion transport.

2. Active vs. Passive Transport

The thermodynamics of ion transport across membranes will briefly be considered, particularly in light of the lack of a consistent definition for active ion transport in much of the agronomically oriented literature on micronutrient transport. In this review, the definition of active transport first proposed by Ussing(1949), transport against an electrochemical potential gradient, will be used in order to be consistent with the current literature concerning biophysical aspects of plant ion transport. It must be stressed that the less rigorous definition for active ion transport, uptake that exhibits a dependency on metabolism, should not be used, since it has been frequently demonstrated that passive cation uptake (K^+ in particular) via ion channels is primarily driven by the voltage gradient across the plasma membrane of plant cells (membrane potential), which is generated in part by metabolic processes. Therefore, many cation uptake systems may be dependent on cellular metabolism and still be passive transport systems.

The electrochemical potential of an ion thermodynamically indicates the free energy for that ion that is available for performing work (Nobel, 1983). For an ion species, j, the electrochemical potential is given as:

$$\mu_j = \mu_j^* + RT \ln a_j + z_j FE \qquad [1]$$

where μ_j^* is the chemical potential of ion j in its standard state, R is the gas constant, T is the temperature in degrees Kelvin, a_j is the chemical activity of j, z_j is the valency (with sign), F is the Faraday constant, and E is the electrical potential. The driving force for the movement of ion j across a membrane in the x dimension is the gradient of the electrochemical potential, $d\mu_j/dx$, obtained by differentiating Eq. [1]:

$$\frac{d\mu_j}{dx} = \frac{-RT}{a_j} \times \frac{da_j}{dx} - z_j F \frac{dE}{dx} \qquad [2]$$

The negative sign in Eq. [2] indicates that the gradient is directed from higher to lower electrochemical potential.

Equation [2] indicates that the driving force consists of two components, one depending on the activity gradient for j and the other on the gradient in electric potential. When an ion is in passive equilibrium across a membrane, its electrochemical potential is the same on each side of the membrane. When this occurs, $d\mu_j/dx$ equals zero, and Eq. [2] becomes:

$$z_j F \frac{dE}{dx} = \frac{-RT}{a_j} \times \frac{da_j}{dx} \qquad [3]$$

If Eq. [3] is now integrated across the membrane from outside (o) to inside (i), Eq. [4] is obtained after some simple algebraic rearrangement:

$$E_j^i - E_j^o = E_j^N = \frac{RT}{z_j F} \ln \frac{a_j^o}{a_j^i} \qquad [4]$$

Equation [4], known as the Nernst equation, describes the passive distribution of j across a membrane; the electrical potential difference in equilibrium with the activity gradient is the Nernst potential (E_j^N) for ion j. If the numerical values for R and F are inserted into Eq. [4], and the natural logarithm is converted to the common logarithm to the base 10, Eq. [4] becomes:

$$E_j^N = \frac{59.2}{z_j} \log \frac{a_j^o}{a_j^i} \quad \text{mV at } 25\,^\circ\text{C}. \quad [5]$$

Thus, for a monovalent cation, a 10-fold accumulation gradient (accumulated inside) can be exactly balanced by a membrane potential of -59 mV; whereas for a divalent cation, the same 10-fold accumulation gradient can be balanced by a membrane potential of -29 mV. Because root cells often maintain membrane potentials across the plasma membrane in the range of -120 to -180 mV, there is a large electrical driving force for passive divalent cation uptake. If a divalent cation is passively distributed across the plasma membrane, a membrane potential of -120 mV could balance an accumulation ratio of 10 000:1. Therefore, when one considers the uptake of the micronutrient cations (Fe^{3+}/Fe^{2+}, Cu^{2+}, Zn^{2+}, Mn^{2+}, and Ni^{2+}), if they are transported into root cells in an unchelated form, it is not necessary to invoke active transport processes. Instead, it is quite reasonable to hypothesize that micronutrient cation uptake is facilitated by passive ion flux through divalent cation channels, with the major component of the driving force arising from the negative membrane potential maintained across the plasma membrane of plant cells.

3. Plasma Membrane and Tonoplast Ion Transport Systems

The plasma membrane and tonoplast are the limiting membranes of the two major compartments of the cell, the cytoplasm and vacuole. They regulate the flow of nutrients into and within the cell through the action of specific ion transport systems at both membranes. In order to maintain a relatively constant ionic environment in the cytoplasm, which is the site of intense biochemical activity for the cell, it is obvious that some transport systems at both membranes must work in concert, notably those for protons and Ca^{2+} (Poole, 1988). Furthermore, each membrane performs specific roles. The plasma membrane is the major boundary between the external environment and the cell for solutes, as well as the site of reception for various exogenous signals and the site of secretion of cell wall materials. The vacuole, on the other hand, is the major site for the storage of osmotically active ions (K^+, Cl^-, malate), as well as a lysosomal compartment for various potentially toxic materials and a storage compartment for proteins. Because of these specific roles, each membrane has its complement of unique transport systems, as well as transport systems operating in coordination for the storage, retrieval, and translocation of nutrient ions. A number of reviews have been written dealing with plasma membrane and tonoplast ion transport processes. For a more detailed examination of this topic, the reader is referred to the reviews of Poole (1978, 1988), Serrano (1988), Spanswick (1981, 1989), and Sze (1985).

a. **Plasma Membrane Transport Systems.** Although the mechanisms of nutrient transport are still poorly characterized, we have progressed over the last 17 yr from a situation in which the transport of every ion or neutral solute was considered separately, to a situation in which the chemiosmotic theory, as introduced by Mitchell (1970), has been a somewhat unifying concept for ion transport systems (Spanswick, 1989). The plasma membrane H^+-ATPase, which transports H^+ out of the cytoplasm, is the central component in this chemiosmotic scheme (Poole, 1978, 1988; Spanswick, 1981). The operation of the H^+-ATPase generates an electrochemical potential gradient for protons across the plasma membrane. This gradient, or proton motive force, provides the energy to drive secondarily active transport systems, or proton cotransport systems (Fig. 8-1). In terms of nomenclature associated with proton-substrate-coupled cotransport systems, a symport refers to the transport of protons and the accompanying solute in the same direction, whereas antiport or exchange refers to the transport of protons in one direction and the transport of the accompanying solute in the opposite direction. In both cases, coupled transport is facilitated by the same membrane protein. Additionally, the H^+-ATPase is an electrogenic ion pump, which means that it transports net charge across the membrane and can make a significant contribution to the negative membrane potential. The membrane potential of higher plant cells can be considered as the sum of a diffusion potential resulting from the total, passive, ionic fluxes across the plasma membrane, and a hyperpolarization (tendency towards more negative voltages) component caused by the electrogenic proton pump (Spanswick, 1981). Therefore, not only is the proton pump an energy source for secondary active transports, it also contributes much of the electrical driving force for passive cation transport through ion channels (Fig. 8-1).

The plant plasma membrane H^+-ATPase can be identified by its stimulation by K^+, the formation of a phosphoenzyme intermediate during its reaction cycle, and its sensitivity to inhibition by vanadate. It is similar in structure and reaction mechanism to plasma-membrane-type ATPases from other organisms, including the Na^+, K^+-ATPase of animal cells, the yeast (*Saccharomyces cerevisiae*) and fungal (*Neurospora crassa*) plasma membrane H^+-ATPase, the sarcoplasmic reticulum Ca^{2+}-ATPase, the gastric mucosa H^+, K^+-ATPase, and the K^+-ATPase of *Escherichia coli* (Poole, 1988). These transport proteins consist of one major 100 kDa polypeptide that spans the membrane and carries out both ATP hydrolysis and ion transport. The gene for the plant plasma-membrane H^+-ATPase has recently been cloned (from *Arabidopsis thaliana*) and exhibits structural similarities and sequence homology with the other cation-translocating ATPases discussed previously (Harper et al., 1989).

As mentioned above, it has been hypothesized that the plasma membrane transport of a number of mineral ions and organic solutes is coupled with the movement of protons back into the cell down the H^+ electrochemical potential gradient. Proton-coupled transport should exhibit several distinctive characteristics, including a stoichiometric relationship between substrate transport and the associated proton flux, a dependency of substrate transport on the H^+ electrochemical gradient, transient effects on the H^+ activity at the outer surface of the plasma membrane immediately following substrate addition, and effects on the membrane potential and membrane current, if the net charge of substrate plus protons transported across the membrane is not zero (Poole, 1988; Reinhold & Kaplan, 1984). In practice, characterization of proton-coupled transport can be difficult because of the lack of techniques for measuring unidirectional H^+ fluxes, and because of the tendency for the H^+-ATPase to change its H^+-transport activity in response to changes in membrane potential and/or H^+ activity on either side of the membrane. Thus, changes in transport parameters measured in

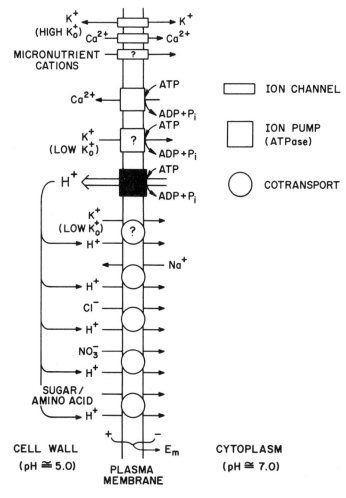

Fig. 8-1. Model representing current knowledge (and beliefs) concerning solute transport at the plasma membrane of plant cells. Primary ion-translocating ATPases are represented by squares, secondary cotransport systems by circles, and ion channels by rectangles. Central to this transport scheme is the H^+-translocating ATPase (solid square). More speculative transport systems are marked with question marks.

relation to proton-coupled substrate transport (membrane potential, membrane current, external pH) may be due to changes in H^+-pump activity and not the H^+-substrate cotransport.

In terms of specific proton-coupled transport systems operating at the plant-cell plasma membrane, a considerable amount of information has been presented in the literature in support of the proton symport of both sugars and amino acids (Reinhold & Kaplan, 1984). For a number of anion transport systems, anion-proton symport has been hypothesized based primarily on electrophysiological studies (Fig. 8-1). These include a $2H^+$-Cl^- symport in *Chara* cells (Beilby & Walker, 1981; Sanders, 1980), Cl^--H^+ symport in barley (*Hordeum vulgare* L.) roots (Jacoby & Rudich, 1980), NO_3^--H^+ cotransport in *Lemna gibba* cells and corn roots (McClure et al., 1990; Ullrich & Novacky, 1981), and $2H^+$-$H_2PO_4^-$ symport in *Lemna* (Ullrich-Eberius et al., 1981). Finally, active Na^+ extrusion has been hypothesized to occur via a Na^+-H^+ antiport, based on observations of stimulation of Na^+ efflux by low external pH values and application of the fungal toxin, fusicoccin, which has been shown to stimulate activity of the H^+-ATPase, and hence, increase the proton motive force driving Na^+ efflux (Colombo et al., 1979; Jeschke, 1980; Ratner & Jacoby, 1976). It should be noted that, in all of the papers mentioned here, evidence has been presented that is consistent with proton-coupled transport, but rigorous proof is still lacking.

Before leaving the subject of plasma membrane H^+ pumps, the rather controversial topic of plasma-membrane redox-driven proton pumps will briefly be discussed. In recent years, there has been a proliferation of publications reporting results in support of one or more electron transport systems operating at the plasma membrane to transfer *both* reducing equivalents and H^+ out of the cell (Craig & Crane, 1980; Lin, 1982, 1984; Misra et al., 1983). Most of the evidence in support of this hypothesis has been derived from studies in which relatively impermeant electron donors and acceptors (e.g., NADH and ferricyanide) have been added to plant cells, tissues, and protoplasts, and observations of stimulated H^+ efflux and solute uptake were observed. Based on these types of findings, some researchers have argued that a plasma-membrane redox-driven H^+ pump could operate parallel to the H^+-ATPase as an alternative energy source for H^+-coupled transport (for a review, see Møller & Lin, 1986). However, a number of more recent publications contradict these earlier findings, and include NADH and ferricyanide-inhibited H^+ efflux and solute uptake in sugarcane (*Saccharum officinarum* L.) suspension-cell protoplasts and corn roots (Kochian & Lucas, 1985; Rubinstein & Stern, 1986; Thom & Maretzki, 1985). Recently, there has been considerable interest in the role of plasma-membrane redox systems in plant ion transport, and reasonable evidence exists for plasma-membrane-associated redox activity (Bienfait, 1985; Kochian & Lucas, 1988; Lüttge & Clarkson, 1985; Moller & Lin, 1986). However, other than mediating Fe^{3+} reduction as a requirement for subsequent Fe^{2+} absorption in roots of nongraminaceous plants (Bienfait, 1988a; Chaney et al., 1972; Römheld & Marschner, 1986a), the role(s) of plasma-membrane redox systems in H^+ efflux and other transport processes is still poorly understood.

Other cation-translocating ATPases also operate in the plasma membrane. Calcium-transporting ATPases appear to be associated with the plasma membrane (Dieter & Marme, 1980) and the endoplasmic reticulum (Buckhout, 1984; Bush & Sze, 1986). These transport systems function to pump Ca^{2+} out of the cytoplasm and help to maintain extremely low (<1.0 mmol m^{-3}) free Ca^{2+} levels in the cytosol. The absorption of K^+ at low substrate levels (<0.2 mol m^{-3}) appears to be a thermodynamically active process (Cheeseman & Hanson, 1980; Pitman, 1976) and, until recently, has been hypothesized to be a K^+, H^+ exchange ATPase. However, evidence in support of a K^+-H^+ cotransport has been presented for *Neurospora* (Rodriguez-Navarro et al., 1986). In maize roots, based on a lack of stoichiometric coupling between K^+ and H^+ fluxes as measured with ion-selective microelectrodes, either a K^+-H^+ cotransport or a K^+-ATPase have been hypothesized (Kochian et al., 1989; Newman et al., 1987). For a more detailed review of this topic, the reader is referred to Kochian and Lucas (1988).

In recent years, there has been considerable interest focused on passive cation transport across plant cell membranes mediated by ion channels. Because of the relatively impermeable nature of the hydrophobic lipid bilayer to hydrated ions, the passive ionic permeabilities of membranes are just as dependent on transport proteins as are active ion transport systems. Until recently, ion channels could only be studied by electrophysiological investigations of the giant algal cells. But with the application of the patch clamp technique to plant cells, a number of different ion channels in plant membranes are being characterized (see Hedrich & Schroeder, 1989; MacRobbie, 1988; Takeda et al., 1985). Much more work on ion channels has been conducted on animal tissues, particularly in relation to excitable membranes, and a number of different classes of channels specific for K^+, Na^+, and Ca^{2+} have been identified and characterized (Hille, 1984). The patch clamp technique, which is reviewed in detail by Sakmann and Neher (1983), is based on sealing a patch of membrane across the tip of a microelectrode. With the appropriate electronic circuitry, ionic currents across the membrane patch can be quantified and, if patch pipette microelectrodes of a sufficiently small diameter are used, ion currents through single channels can be studied.

The ion channel can be thought of as a macromolecular pore in a cell membrane (Hille, 1984), and channels can be distinguished from carrier-mediated, enzyme-type active transport systems by the rate of ion flux through them. Ion channels can transport quite rapidly and can turn over at a rate as high as 10^6 ions/second (Hille, 1984). In contrast, cation-translocating ATPases are much more sluggish; the H^+-ATPase in *Neurospora* has a turnover value of only several hundred H^+/second. In a simplistic sense, it is useful to think of ion channels as water-filled pores, whereas active transport proteins can be considered enzyme-type carriers with discrete binding sites. Despite this distinction, ion channels exhibit reasonable specificity, probably due to the radius of the pore and electrostatic properties at the mouth of the pore. Additionally, ion channels can exhibit substrate-dependent saturation (Hille, 1984). Therefore, in some ways ion channels can exhibit enzyme-type properties. The best characterized ion channels in higher plants are K^+

channels, which have been demonstrated in the plasma membrane of guard cells (Schroeder et al., 1984), *Samanea* pulvinar cells (Moran et al., 1987), and corn suspension cells (Ketchum et al., 1989). Although Ca^{2+} channels have not been described in the plasma membrane of plant cells, it is quite likely that they exist in analogy to Ca^{2+} channels identified in animal cell membranes. Figure 8–1 depicts a simple model summarizing the identified and hypothesized transport systems in the plasma membrane of plant cells.

Cation uptake via ion channels may be an important mechanism for the absorption of the micronutrient cations (Fe, Mn, Zn, Cu, and Ni). If these micronutrients are transported across the plasma membrane as free ions, then the large electrical gradient (membrane potential, negative inside) across the plant plasma membrane would provide the driving force for passive micronutrient cation flux through ion channels. One interesting sidelight (and potential problem) of channel-mediated micronutrient-cation uptake is the potential for binding of the micronutrient cations to various protein ligand groups (amino-N, sulfhydryls, O). If Cu^{2+} is used as an example, it is known that Cu^{2+} may bind fairly tightly to proteins, especially to sulfhydryl groups in S-containing amino acids. Given the fairly low rates for absorption of micronutrients into plant cells, along with the potential for binding to membrane proteins, it may be reasonable to speculate that, in addition to enzyme-type ion "pumps" and ion channels involved in passive transport, a third class of transport protein exists that is similar to an enzyme with discrete binding sites for the ion in question, but is involved in the passive uptake of micronutrient cations. Thus, as proposed by Graham (1981) for Cu^{2+}, it is possible that Cu^{2+} binds to a plasma-membrane transport protein at the external face of the membrane, is transferred (via an unknown mechanism) to the inner face of the membrane down the electrochemical potential gradient for Cu^{2+}, and is released in the cytoplasm due to the lower electrochemical potential for Cu^{2+} in this compartment (which provides a greater probability for release). The fact that many of the micronutrient cations exist as metal chelates further complicates this scenario, and forces us to consider the possibility that the transport protein contains metal-chelate recognition sites at the outer face of the plant plasma membrane, as has been shown for Fe-siderophore absorption in bacteria (Lewin, 1984). Additionally, because changes in pH and redox potential influence the binding and release of transition metals with organic ligands, the pH and E_H of microdomains on each side of the plasma membrane could play an important role in micronutrient cation uptake.

b. Tonoplast Transport Systems. The primary energy-transducing transport protein in the tonoplast membrane is the H^+-translocating ATPase, which, like the plasma membrane H^+ pump, serves to convert ATP energy to proton gradient energy. The tonoplast H^+-ATPase transports protons from the cytoplasm, where the pH is near neutrality, to the acidic vacuole (pH $\approx$ 5.0). Thus, it maintains an electrochemical potential gradient for protons directed from the vacuole to the cytoplasm. It is markedly different from the plasma membrane H^+-ATPase, in that it is stimulated by Cl^-, inhibited by NO_3^-, and is insensitive to vanadate inhibition. The tonoplast ATPase has a multimeric structure that includes two polypeptides of about 70 to 60 kDa, which have nucleotide binding sites, and a smaller polypeptide of 16 kDa that binds DCCD and may include the H^+ channel (Manolson et al., 1985; Randall & Sze, 1986). Recently, a tonoplast H^+-translocating pyrophosphatase (PPase) has been identified that uses high energy pyrophosphate as a substrate and acidifies the vacuole in a similar manner to that of the tonoplast H^+-ATPase (Rea & Poole, 1985; Rea & Sanders, 1987). The pyrophosphatase is stimulated by K^+, inhibited by Na^+, and is insensitive to anions. The significance of having two potential tonoplast H^+ pumps operating in parallel is not clear at this time. However, Rea and Sanders (1987) analyzed the equilibrium thermodynamics for both the tonoplast ATPase and PPase, and found that, under physiological conditions (ΔpH across the tonoplast of 2 to 3 pH units), the ATPase operates as a H^+ pump. However, the thermodynamically favorable reaction for the PPase was the reverse reaction [i.e. the synthesis of pyrophosphate, using the trans-tonoplast proton gradient established by the ATPase to drive the synthetic reaction (Rea & Sanders, 1987)]. The authors suggest that the tonoplast PPase may be one of a subset of energy-conserving enzymes that are dependent on pyrophosphate for activity.

Evidence in support of proton-coupled transport systems at the tonoplast comes primarily from work with isolated tonoplast vesicles (Blumwald, 1987). A tonoplast Ca^{2+}/H^+ antiport system has been described (Bush & Sze, 1986; Schumaker & Sze, 1985) that appears to operate in concert with the plasma membrane Ca^{2+}-ATPase to remove Ca^{2+} from the cytoplasm, thus maintaining low levels of cytosolic Ca^{2+}. Also, a Na^+/H^+ antiport has been characterized in red beet tonoplast vesicles, which facilitates the accumulation of Na^+ in the vacuole (Blumwald & Poole, 1985a). Finally, Blumwald and Poole (1985b) have presented evidence consistent with the operation of a NO_3^--H^+ symport at the tonoplast, which would enable the plant cell to retrieve NO_3^- from the vacuole. It has been suggested that a similar mechanism may operate for the transport of organic acids (malate) out of the vacuole during stomatal function or during Crassulacean acid metabolism (Poole, 1988).

The operation of the tonoplast H^+-ATPase generates a small electrical potential across the tonoplast (interior positive) that has been hypothesized to be the driving force for Cl^- and NO_3^- uptake via ion channels (Blumwald & Poole, 1985b). Also, the patch clamp technique has been used to study ion transport in vacuoles isolated from barley leaves (Hedrich et al., 1986). These researchers found evidence for a nonselective ion channel that can carry both malate and K^+ into or out of the vacuole, driven by the concentration gradients for either ion, as well as by the electrical gradient established by the H^+-ATPase. A summarizing model for the various tonoplast transport systems described here is presented in Fig. 8-2.

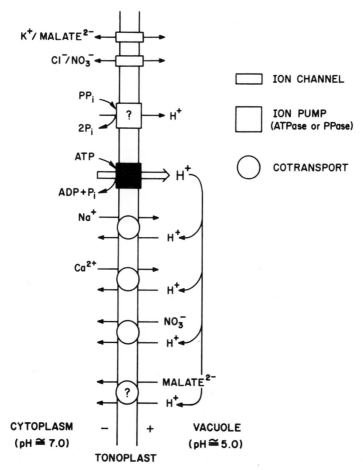

Fig. 8-2. Model representing the various solute transport systems operating at the tonoplast membrane. Primary ATPases are represented by squares, cotransport systems by circles, and ion channels by rectangles. The H^+-translocating ATPase, which transports protons from the cytoplasm into the vacuole, is highlighted as the solid square. More speculative transport systems are marked with question marks.

B. Radial Ion Transport Across the Root

Ion and water movement from the soil solution into and across the root to the xylem, is generally thought of in terms of two parallel pathways, the apoplasm and the symplasm. In terms of apoplasmic transport, ions can diffuse through the water-filled pores of the cell walls of the epidermal and cortical cells, but are restricted from further radial apoplasmic movement by the Casparian strip in the radial and transverse walls of the endodermis. Hence, it is generally accepted that ions enter the symplasm via absorption across the plasma membrane of root epidermal and/or cortical cells, move symplasmically through plasmodesmata connecting adjacent cells until they

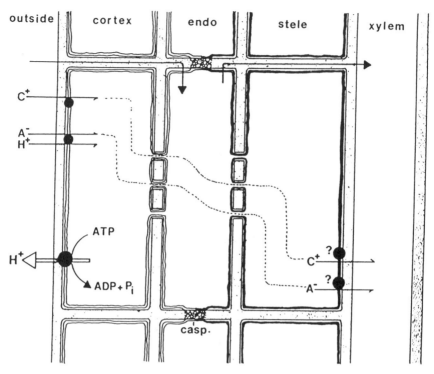

Fig. 8–3. Simplified model depicting the apoplasmic and symplasmic pathways for ions from the external solution to the lumen of the xylem vessels within the root. From Clarkson (1988).

reach the stele, and subsequently, are unloaded into the xylem vessels and moved to the shoot in the transpiration stream. This model is depicted in Fig. 8–3. It is beyond the scope of this review to consider this pathway in detail; for this, the reader is referred to the reviews of Clarkson (1988), Läuchli (1976), Pitman (1982), and Spanswick (1976). This section will focus on certain aspects of radial ion flux across the root that may have a bearing on micronutrient transport.

1. Apoplasmic Transport

The concept of the apoplasm, first introduced by Münch (1930), treats the interconnected walls of the plant cells and the water-filled xylem vessels as a single unit. It is often considered that ions can freely diffuse through the apoplasm, at least up to the Casparian strip, and that the cell walls allow relatively unhindered access to the epidermal and cortical plasma membrane. However, in reality, plant cell walls are extremely complex heterogeneous structures, which can greatly influence and restrict the movement of ions via diffusion and mass flow.

At the root surface, the epidermis is often covered with a polysaccharide gel material, called the mucigel, which can influence the water and ionic relations in the rhizosphere. The mucigel is both plant and microbial in origin, and arises from secretions of slime-producing cells at the root cap, sloughed off cells from the root cap, and soil microbes (Foster, 1981; Lucas, 1987). It has often been speculated that the carboxyl groups on the polysaccharides within the mucigel influence ion absorption into the root (Chaboud & Rougier, 1984). This may be particularly important for the micronutrient cations, because the mucigel has a high binding affinity for polyvalent cations (Clarkson & Sanderson, 1969) and could influence movement of the micronutrient cations to the epidermis.

The cell wall is quite complex, and consists of cellulose microfibrils that are from 5 to 9 mm across and are embedded in a matrix of noncellulosic polysaccharides (pectins and lignins) and glycoproteins (Nobel, 1983). The pores in the walls are created by the interstices of the cellulose microfibril bundles, and produce a tortuous pathway for ions and water. There have been few attempts to determine the porosity of cell walls; the work of Carpita et al. (1979) with radish (*Raphanus sativus* L.) roots and cocklebur (*Xanthium strumarium* L.) palisade cells indicated that cell walls may have a size exclusion of between 3 to 5 nm. The pores are lined with materials of considerable cation exchange capacity, due to fixed carboxyl groups of the galacturonic and glucuronic acid components of pectins and hemicelluloses. These fixed negative sites can restrain the movement of cations and greatly complicate calculations of diffusion in the apoplasm (Clarkson, 1988). It has been estimated that the diffusive resistance of the cell walls is 100 to 1000 times greater for monovalent cations, and 10 times greater for monovalent anions, than an equivalent thickness of solution (Walker & Pitman, 1976). However, because of the relatively high levels of Ca^{2+} that normally are found at the root surface (> 1 mol m^{-3}), it is likely that the cation exchange capacity of the cell wall is saturated by Ca^{2+}, particularly when the low concentrations of micronutrient ions in soil solution are considered.

Nonetheless, due to the complex makeup of cell walls, there are a number of potential organic ligand groups that could bind micronutrient cations quite tightly within the cell walls. This is particularly true for a reactive species such as Cu^{2+}, which is bound strongly by the walls and is not desorbed by Ca^{2+} (Graham, 1981). Therefore, the data from many of the earlier studies on absorption of Cu^{2+} into the root may be confounded by the binding of significant amounts of Cu^{2+} to the root cell walls. Because very little information is available concerning the relationship of the apoplasm to micronutrient transport, at this time we can only speculate that, due to the reactive nature of most of the micronutrients, the root epidermal and cortical apoplasm may play a more important role in micronutrient cation transport than macronutrient cation transport.

2. Site of Ion Entry into the Root Symplasm

Most plant biologists accept the notion that ion absorption from the root apoplasm can occur into the cells of both the epidermis and cortex. However, there is still some controversy in the literature concerning the relative importance of the root surface vs. the cortex to ion absorption, particularly at low ion concentrations (Anderson, 1976; Kochian & Lucas, 1983; Läuchli, 1976; van Iren & Boers-van der Sluijs, 1980). Using a theoretical model for Rb^+ uptake into barley roots, Bange (1973) found that the model generated only reasonable profiles when transport was restricted to the epidermis. The studies of van Iren and Boers-van der Sluijs (1980) offered experimental support for this hypothesis. These researchers investigated K^+ uptake by assuming that plasmolysis would sever plasmodesmata, thereby symplasmically isolating each cortical and epidermal cell of a barley root. Autoradiographic localization of $^{86}Rb^+$, accumulated by the root following plasmolysis, was generally limited to the root periphery. From these results, the authors have hypothesized that ion absorption into the symplasm occurs at the epidermis (i.e., the apoplasmic pathway and subsequent uptake by the cortical cells is of little significance).

The criticism that must be leveled at this work is that it may be erroneous to base a hypothesis that concerns "normal" transport function on data obtained from a system in which transport physiology may have been dramatically changed by plasmolytic treatment. Furthermore, the work of Anderson and Reilly (1968) concerning fluid exudation from the xylem of corn roots indicated that the cortical cells do have the capacity to absorb ions. They found that surgical removal of the epidermis and outer cortex of excised corn roots did not prevent significant fluxes of ions and H_2O to the xylem.

Kochian and Lucas (1983) examined this issue by using radioactively labelled sulfhydryl reagents, [^3H] N-ethyl maleimide (NEM) and [^{203}Hg] p-chloromercuribenzene sulfonic acid (PCMBS). A brief (30–60 s) exposure of corn roots to either NEM or PCMBS dramatically reduced K^+ influx into the root without affecting root respiration. Autoradiographic localization studies revealed that sulfhydryl binding occurred almost exclusively in the cells of the root periphery. However, protoplasts isolated from corn root cortical tissue exhibited significant $^{86}Rb^+$ influx, the kinetics of which were identical in shape to those obtained with excised corn roots (cf. Kochian & Lucas, 1982, 1983). These results suggest that, although cortical cells possess the capacity to absorb ions, at the low concentrations likely to be present in normal soils, K^+ influx into the root symplasm most probably occurs at the root periphery.

The results discussed above indicate that the primary site of entry for ions into the root symplasm is stil not clearly elucidated. For conditions applicable to micronutrient ion absorption at the root surface (i.e., low micronutrient concentrations), epidermal uptake may be the critical site for entry into the symplasm. Whether this is due merely to depletion of an already low concentration of a nutrient ion to levels that prevent significant diffusion into the root apoplasm, physical barriers impeding radial penetration into the apoplasm, or actual physiological differences between epidermal and cortical cells remains to be resolved.

3. Ion Transport into the Xylem

A symplasmic pathway for ion movement, from the epidermis to the xylem parenchyma, was first proposed by Crafts and Broyer (1938). In their hypothesis, the cortex was the site where nutrients, like K^+, were taken up into the symplasm by active, O_2-dependent processes. Movement to the stele occurred via plasmodesmata, and release into the xylem vessels occurred by diffusion, or leakage, since the compact tissue of the stele was thought to be low in O_2. The technical expertise was not available to test this hypothesis until many years later, when Bowling (1973) inserted O_2-sensitive microelectrodes into primary lateral roots of sunflower (*Helianthus annuus* L.). He found that for these fairly narrow roots (diam. = 0.5 mm), O_2 diffusion into the stele was quite rapid and little O_2 depletion was detected. It is now accepted that all the cells of the plant root have access to sufficient O_2 to maintain normal aerobic respiration.

The concept that the innermost limiting boundary of the symplasm is the plasma membrane of the xylem parenchyma cells is central to models of ion unloading into the xylem; therefore, ions are unloaded from the xylem parenchyma into mature (dead) xylem vessels. Although there is a general consensus that ions are unloaded into mature xylem vessels, it has been proposed by Hylmö (1953) that ion accumulation in the root involves uptake into vacuoles of living xylem vessels, which upon maturation release their contents into the translocation stream. Although this model received some degree of support in the mid-1970s (see Davis & Higinbotham, 1976), Läuchli et al. (1978) provided irrefutable evidence that ion transport occurs across the stele into mature xylem vessels. It is perhaps indicative of the complexity of the root that hypotheses like the Crafts and Broyer (1938) and Hylmö (1953) models have been so difficult to disprove. It is interesting to note that the Hylmö model was recently resurrected by McCully et al. (1987), in which X-ray microprobe was used on bulk, frozen-hydrated tissue to examine the K^+ concentrations within the late-maturing xylem vessels of field-grown corn plants. Surprisingly, K^+ values in the range of 150–400 mol m^{-3} were detected. Clearly, these levels of K^+ could only be established by transport across the tonoplast of these maturing vessels. In view of these findings, McCully et al. (1987) suggest that, since the living, late-maturing xylem elements contain the highest K^+ concentrations of any cells in the root, at least a portion of the nutrient ion flux into the xylem is initially unloaded into living xylem elements. In view of all the available data, it seems that a combination of the two routes may not be completely unrealistic.

Until quite recently, the general model for ion unloading into the xylem vessels required only one active step, involving absorption from the soil solution into the root symplasm. Electrophysiological measurements of the transroot potential (electrical potential difference between xylem sap and external solution), along with measurements of the ionic composition of the xylem sap and estimates of the ionic concentrations in the xylem parenchyma, suggested that ion unloading from the xylem parenchyma into the xy-

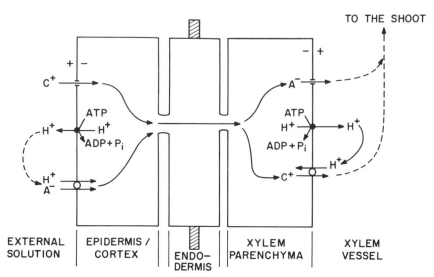

Fig. 8-4. Transport model representing the transport processes thought to be involved in the acquisition of nutrient ions from the soil solution and their subsequent transport from the symplasmic compartment of the root into the xylem vessels. Redrawn from Hanson (1978).

lem vessels was a passive process (Ansari & Bowling, 1972; Davis & Higinbotham, 1969). However, more recently, Hanson (1978) was the first to apply Mitchell's chemiosmotic hypothesis to solute transport at the plasma membrane of the xylem parenchyma. A "speculative" model was developed in which he placed two "opposing" H^+-translocating ATPases in the plasma membranes of the outer cortex and the stelar parenchyma (Fig. 8-4). The impermeable nature of the Casparian strip of the endodermis separated the apoplasmic solutions of the cortex and stele, with the symplasm operating as a bridging osmotic unit. Transport of cations and anions was suggested to have occurred by various uniport and antiport systems.

An important prediction of the Hanson (1978) hypothesis involved the transroot potential, measured between the apoplasm of the xylem and the bathing medium, which should have two opposing electrogenic components. Okamoto et al. (1978), working with an excised hypocotyl-root system from *Vigna sesquipedalis*, were able to demonstrate, via electrophysiological measurements, the existence of opposing electrogenic pumps between the surface of the hypocotyl and the xylem vessels. De Boer et al. (1983) constructed a similar experimental system to investigate the trans-root potential of two Plantago species. By lowering the O_2 partial pressure surrounding the roots, they obtained electrophysiological evidence consistent with a sequential inhibition of, first, the epidermal plasma membrane proton pump and, subsequently, the plasma membrane pump of xylem parenchyma cells within the root.

Because of the obvious difficulties of studying membrane transport systems buried within the root, it has been necessary to depend on indirect measurements of xylem transport such as the electrophysiological studies detailed above. There is reasonable evidence that a plasma membrane proton pump is involved in the energization of nutrient ion release into the xylem. However, it is not apparent how the H^+ fluxes across the xylem-symplast boundary are coupled to other ion fluxes. As depicted in Fig. 8-4, the cation and anion transport systems that operate to release ions into the xylem may be considerably different from those that function at the root surface. Additionally, because so little is known about the transport of micronutrients at the membrane level, the nature of micronutient ion release into the xylem is not understood at this time.

C. Long Distance Ion Transport

1. Xylem Transport

Once ions are unloaded into the xylem vessels, they are transported to the tops by the physical processes governing bulk water flow in the xylem; that is, they are swept along in the transpiration stream. The driving force for transpiration arises from the gradient in water potential that exists between the air and the water-filled pores in the mesophyll cell walls lining the stomatal cavities in the leaf. This water-potential gradient, along with the cohesive properties of water and the attraction of water molecules for the cellulose microfibrils in the walls (adhesion), operates to generate a tensional component at the top of the continuous column of water that exists from the leaf cell walls through the column of xylem vessels in the shoot to the root. Hence, transpiration arises when water is pulled from the root to the top, and mineral ions and organic solutes are transported to the tops along with the water.

Obviously, the rate of transpiration influences ion transport to the top. However, the effect of transpiration on ion absorption into the root, and the subsequent unloading of ions into the xylem, is less clear (Clarkson, 1988). Even at high transpiration rates, depletion of certain ions at the root surface occurs, which indicates that the mass flow of water through the soil to the root surface often does not significantly influence the availability of ions at the root surface. Also, it has often been observed that ions tend to move across the root faster than does the mass flow of water. This point is supported by the observation that the ion concentrations of the xylem sap collected from exuding excised roots are often more than 10-fold greater than the external solution (Table 8-1), which can also be taken as evidence for membrane transport-mediated ion unloading into the xylem. In general, the influence of transpiration on ion transport is most significant when ion concentrations at the root surface are high (Clarkson, 1988). Therefore, transpiration probably does not play a significant role in micronutrient absorption into and across roots. However, transpiration may play a significant role in translocating certain micronutrients to the tops (particularly B), which will be discussed later.

Because the mechanism of ion translocation to the top is primarily one of mass flow in nonliving xylem vessels, interactions can occur between cat-

Table 8-1. Ion concentrations in the external solution bathing the root and in the xylem exudate of marrow (*Cucurbita maxima*) seedlings.†

Ion	Concentration, mol m^{-3}	
	External solution	Xylem exudate
K^+	0.5	12.8
Na^+	0.2	0.3
Ca^{2+}	0.15	5.1
NO_3^-	1.0	7.1
$H_2PO_4^-$	0.01	0.2

† Data from Clarkson (1974).

ions in the sap and the negatively charged carboxyl groups of the xylem vessel walls. These interactions are strongest for polyvalent cations. It has been proposed that the cation-binding sites in the xylem vessel walls may retard the movement of polyvalent cations (particularly Ca) in the transpiration stream (Bell & Biddulph, 1963). However, the concentration of Ca^{2+} in the xylem sap is usually high enough (~ 5 mol m^{-3}; see Table 8-1) that the cell wall cation-binding sites should be saturated with Ca^{2+}, and thus, should not significantly influence the movement of micronutrient cations in the xylem.

The ionic and organic composition of the xylem sap is quite complex, consisting of a wide range of mineral ions (both macronutrients and micronutrients), along with organic acids, amino acids, and other organic ligands that can complex micronutrients and facilitate their movement to the shoot. This complexity is demonstrated in Table 8-2, in which the composition of the xylem and phloem sap from *Nicotiana glauca* is shown (data from Hocking, 1980). The pH of the xylem sap appears to be regulated in the range of pH 5.5 to 6.0, based on xylem perfusion studies (Clarkson et al., 1984; Clarkson & Hanson, 1986). This pH regulation may be due in part to the buffering capacity of organic acids (malate, citrate, etc.) in the xylem sap,

Table 8-2. Concentrations of organic and inorganic solutes in the xylem and phloem exudates of *Nicotiana glauca*.

Solute	Xylem exudate (tracheal) pH = 5.6–5.9	Phloem exudate (stem incision) pH = 7.8–8.0
	mol m^{-3}	
Sucrose	ND‡	450–490
Ammonium	0.5	.25
K	5.2	94.1
P	2.1	14.0
Cl	1.8	13.7
Ca	4.7	2.1
Mg	1.4	4.3
Fe	0.01	0.17
Zn	0.02	0.24
Mn	0.004	0.016
Cu	0.002	0.02

† Data from Hocking (1980).   ‡ ND represents not detectable.

and also due to the activity of a stelar H^+ pump and associated proton-coupled cotransports. Furthermore, from a study of the xylem sap in silver maple (*Acer saccharinum*), Morris and Swanson (1980) found that the xylem sap reduction potential was also fairly constant. The point to be made here is that, although the xylem sap is a complex solution, the plant exerts some degree of control over its composition. The chemical-organic environment in the xylem will have a significant influence on metal-complex chemistry as it relates to translocation of micronutrients in the xylem.

2. Phloem Transport

In contrast to xylem transport, which uses nonliving tissue for the conducting pathway, long-distance transport in the phloem takes place in living cells. The phloem consists of sieve cells, closely associated companion cells, and phloem parenchyma. The translocation pathway consists of sieve cells connected end-to-end to form sieve tubes. At maturity, sieve tubes have lost their nuclei and tonoplast, while their plasma membrane remains intact. The end walls between two adjoining sieve tube elements form the sieve plate, which contains many pores that are lined, but not covered, by the plasma membranes of the two cells. Therefore, solution moving in the phloem does not have to cross any membranes as it flows within the sieve tubes.

Although the mechanism of solute movement in the phloem still has not been clearly established, the pressure flow hypothesis, first proposed by Münch (1930), still seems to be the best model for phloem translocation. The Münch Hypothesis proposes that fluid movement in the phloem is driven by a gradient in hydrostatic pressure. The pressure gradient results from sucrose loading at the source end of the phloem (mature leaves) and sucrose unloading at the sink end (roots, young leaves, shoot apices, fruits, and seeds). The loading and unloading of solutes at each end of the long-distance pathway results in localized changes in water potential in the sieve tubes, such that water moves into the sieve tube at the source end. This increases the hydrostatic pressure and leaves the sieve tube at the sink, which results in a localized drop in pressure. This pressure gradient leads to mass flow analogous to that in the xylem; the only difference is that, in the xylem, fluid flow is driven by a negative gradient in pressure.

Mineral nutrient ions, including the micronutrients, move via mass flow in the phloem. As seen in Table 8-2, the phloem sap has a high concentration of organic solutes (mostly sucrose), considerably higher concentrations of most mineral macronutrients and micronutrients than what is found in the xylem, and a much higher pH (≈ 8.0 vs. ≈ 5.5 for xylem). Although not shown in Table 8-2, the phloem also contains fairly high concentrations of organic acids, amino acids, and amides (Marschner, 1986), all of which are potential ligands for the micronutrient cations. Almost nothing is known concerning the loading and unloading of mineral ions in the phloem. Potassium is particularly notable because of its high concentration in the phloem (~ 100 mol m^{-3}). It has been suggested that K^+ fluxes across the plasma membrane of the sieve-tube/companion cell complex may help to facilitate H^+

Table 8-3. Mobility of mineral elements in the phloem.†

	Elements	
Mobile	Intermediate	Conditionally mobile‡
P	Fe	Ca
Na	Zn	Sr
Mg	Cu	Ba
P	Mn	B
S	Mo	
Cl		

† Modified from Bukovac and Wittwer (1957).
‡ Conditional mobility indicates that the mineral elements generally thought to be phloem immobile may have some mobility in certain situations (different developmental stages of the plant, etc.).

pumping (via the H^+-ATPase) by charge balancing electrogenic H^+ efflux out of the sieve cell (Giaquinta, 1983). This would assist in maintaining the transmembrane H^+ gradient that has been hypothesized to drive sucrose uptake into the sieve tube via sucrose-H^+ cotransport (for a review, see Lucas & Madore, 1988).

Except for B and Mo, all of the essential micronutrients have been found in reasonable quantities in the phloem. It is unclear however, whether a high concentration in the phloem is indicative of high phloem mobility of that nutrient. Studies of phloem mobility of mineral nutrients have been conducted based on movement of radiotracers for individual nutrient ions from their application point (source leaf) to a sink organ. From such studies, Bukovac and Wittwer (1957) devised the classification scheme for phloem mobility shown in Table 8-3. The lack of work on this important topic is illustrated by the observation that, although the scheme in Table 8-3 was presented in 1957, it is still widely cited today as a definitive work in this area.

Several points should be made concerning considerations of mineral nutrient phloem mobility. First, although the total phloem concentration of a particular mineral element may be high, the mobility of that ion may be quite low. This is the case for Ca, which is found in the phloem in concentrations around 2 mol m^{-3}, but apparently has a low phloem mobility. Although the total Ca concentration in the phloem is high, the chemical conditions in the phloem sap (high pH, high phosphate concentration) are such that most of this Ca may be relatively immobile, and the concentration of mobile Ca (either free Ca^{2+} or Ca bound in low molecular weight complexes) is probably quite low (Raven, 1977). Furthermore, the use of radioactive Ca as a tracer for Ca could yield artifactual results, if the mobile Ca resides in a pool that is a small fraction of the total plant Ca and is not easily accessed by applying radiolabeled Ca to the surface of a source leaf. Second, even if the radiotracer studies used to develop the scheme in Table 8-3 can be used to determine the phloem mobility of a particular mineral element, the possibility exists that the value for phloem mobility of that mineral nutrient may only be applicable for that specific point in time for that particular plant species. It may be true, particularly for the micronutrients, that phloem mobility varies during plant development. During different developmental stages of the plant, it is possible that a particular micronutrient may exist in different forms that vary in mobility. For example, Loneragan (1981) has suggested that Cu^{2+} be considered "variably mobile" following observations of high Cu^{2+} mobility during some stages of plant development and low mobility during other stages.

II. MICRONUTRIENT ABSORPTION INTO ROOTS

A. Iron

As was stated in the introduction, over the past 15 yr, far more interest and research has been directed toward the elucidation of the mechanisms and regulation of Fe absorption than all the other micronutrients combined. Accordingly, reasonable progress has been made in our understanding of the complexities of Fe acquisition and utilization by plants. Therefore, a significant portion of this review will be spent considering the cellular aspects of Fe absorption into the plant. Unfortunately, space constraints will not allow many of the aspects of Fe absorption to be considered in detail. Therefore, the reader is directed toward the reviews of Bienfait (1985, 1988a). Römheld and Marschner (1986a), and Chaney and Bell (1987) for a more in-depth analysis of this problem.

Although Fe is quite abundant in the earth's crust, comprising approximately 5% of the lithosphere (Norrish, 1975), its availability in well-aerated soils is quite low, due to the specifics of Fe chemistry in aerobic environments. In aerobic systems, the solubility of inorganic Fe depends on ferric oxides in the soil according to the reaction:

$$\text{soil } Fe(OH)_3 + 3H^+ \rightleftharpoons Fe^{3+} + 3H_2O \qquad [6]$$

Hence, as solution pH is reduced from 8 to 4, the concentration of Fe^{3+} in solution will increase from about 10^{-17} to 10^{-5} mol m^{-3} (Römheld & Marschner, 1986). Additionally, Fe^{3+} will readily hydrolyze; therefore, total soluble Fe in solution is the sum of Fe^{3+} and its soluble hydrolysis products [e.g., $Fe(OH)_2^+$ and $Fe(OH)_4^-$]. Certainly, soil redox potential can influence Fe solubility, as Fe^{2+} is considerably more soluble than Fe^{3+}. However, in the range of pH values associated with many soils (and physiological conditions; pH $\approx$ 6.0–8.0), the Fe^{3+} species dominates, as Fe^{2+} is readily oxidized. Therefore, in most well-aerated soils, the minimum solubility of total inorganic Fe is fixed in the range of 10^{-8} to 10^{-6} mol m^{-3}. The concentrations of soluble Fe that have been measured in soil solutions are usually higher than those calculated from equilibrium reactions, in the range of 10^{-5} to 10^{-3} mol m^{-3}, because of the complexation of soil-Fe with soluble organic ligands (Olomu et al., 1973). These organic ligands can be the result of degradation of organic matter (e.g., fulvic acid) or can be siderophores (Fe chelating compounds released by soil bacteria and fungi, or plant roots; Powell et al., 1982).

Complexed ferric ion (Fe^{3+}) appears to be the dominant form of Fe available for absorption by the plant (in well-aerated soils). The concentration of complexed Fe required for optimal plant growth is around 10^{-4} to 10^{-2} mol m^{-3}, which is an order of magnitude higher than the levels of complexed Fe in the soil solution (Lindsay & Schwab, 1982; Römheld & Marschner, 1986a). Thus, it is necessary for plants to increase the availability of soil-Fe for absorption. That plants are successful in efficiently "mining" Fe from the soil is indicated by their ability to maintain tissue-Fe levels between 50 and 100 mg kg^{-1} dry weight (DW) in the face of low levels of available soil Fe (Römheld & Marschner, 1986a). The processes that plants use to accomplish this aim have been the focus of much of the research in Fe nutrition over the past 15 yr.

It appears that plants can use two distinct strategies to solubilize and absorb Fe from the soil. Either plants can reduce Fe(III)-complexes at the root surface and absorb the Fe^{2+} ions produced via this root-associated reduction, or they can excrete specific Fe(III)-binding, low molecular weight, organic polydentate ligands, known as phytosiderophores, which solubilize Fe^{3+} ions and make them available for absorption. These two strategies appear to be employed by distinctly separate taxonomic groupings of plants, with the phytosiderophore-based mechanism restricted to the grass family (Poaceae), and the Fe(III) reduction mechanism employed by the dicots and the monocots not included in the Poaceae (Römheld & Marschner, 1986a). The processes involved in and associated with the Fe(III) reduction strategy have been studied in much more detail than the mechanisms used by the grasses, and will be considered first.

1. Iron Uptake Via Iron Reduction

Results from research over the past decade have answered the question concerning why grasses, such as corn, cannot effectively obtain Fe from nutrient solutions that contain Fe complexed to strong synthetic chelators like EDDHA [ethylenediaminedi-(O-hydroxyphenylacetate)], while dicots can grow quite effectively when Fe(III)-EDDHA is the sole Fe source. Brown et al. (1961) were the first to note that when strong Fe(III) chelators such as EDTA (ethylene diaminetetraacetate) and EDDHA were applied in molar excess of Fe, the absorption of Fe was inhibited in grasses, but not dicots. Also, Tiffin et al. (1960) demonstrated that Fe-deficient dicots could split Fe from Fe(III)-EDDHA, absorbing the Fe, while leaving the EDDHA in solution. The definitive work concerning this problem came from Chaney et al. (1972), who were the first to demonstrate that the mechanism of Fe absorption involves an obligatory reduction of chelated Fe(III) [supplied as Fe(III)-EDDHA] in Fe-deficient soybean roots. This resulted in the release of the Fe^{2+} ion from the chelate and subsequent Fe^{2+} absorption into the root. The main evidence in support of this hypothesis involved the observation that the application of the Fe(II)-chelator, BPDS (Bathophenanthrolinedisulfonate), to the nutrient solution in excess of Fe(III)-EDDHA, resulted in a 99% inhibition of Fe uptake, measured as translocation of ^{59}Fe to the tops. They explained these results by hypothesizing that, following the reduction of Fe(III) at the root surface, BPDS was acting as a Fe^{2+} ion trap by binding the ion at the root surface, thus preventing its absorption.

Subsequent research on the role of Fe(III) reduction in Fe absorption has indicated that, in response to Fe deficiency, dicots and nongraminaceous monocots can exhibit a number of interrelated physiological and anatomical changes in their roots. These alterations appear to be an integrated response aimed at increasing the plant's ability to solubilize and absorb Fe from the environment. These responses to Fe deficiency include the following.

1. An enhancement of root-associated Fe(III) reduction, which appears to be due to the induction of a plasma membrane Fe(III) reductase in root cells (Ambler et al., 1971; Bienfait et al., 1983; Chaney et al., 1972; Römheld & Marschner, 1979).
2. An enhancement of H^+ efflux by root cells (Brown & Jones, 1974; Landsberg, 1981; Römheld & Marschner, 1981a, 1984; Römheld et al., 1984; Venkat Raju & Marschner, 1972).
3. Accumulation of citrate and malate in the roots (Brown & Chaney, 1971; Landsberg, 1986; Tiffin, 1970).
4. The induction of transfer cells and increased formation of root hairs in the epidermal and hypodermal cell layers of the root (Kramer et al., 1980; Landsberg, 1982, 1986; Romheld & Marschner, 1981a).
5. An enhancement of phenolic accumulation and release by the root (Brown & Ambler, 1974; Römheld & Marschner, 1981a, 1983).
6. A distinct localization of the above responses to Fe deficiency (particularly, enhanced reduction, H^+ efflux, and transfer cell formation) to a small zone behind the root apex of the young roots (Kramer et al., 1980; Landsberg, 1982, 1986; Römheld & Marschner, 1981a).
7. Increased absorption of Fe (Brown & Ambler, 1974; Chaney et al., 1972; Römheld & Marschner, 1979, 1981; Tiffin & Brown, 1961).

There appears to be a general acceptance in the literature that most nongraminaceous plants respond to Fe deficiency by exhibiting most or all of the responses listed above. The reality of the situation is much more complex, in that some plants exhibit most of the above responses, whereas other plant species lack certain important responses (such as increased H^+ efflux or transfer cell formation). In some cases, certain plant species exhibit responses that differ significantly from some of those listed above. The one constant that appears to be exhibited by all of the plants that employ this strategy is an obligatory reduction of Fe(III) at the root surface. Therefore, this aspect of the Fe deficiency response will be discussed first, and then some other important responses listed above will be considered. In the appropriate places in this section, cases that deviate from the "normal" Fe deficiency response will be discussed.

a. Reduction of Ferric Chelates. In demonstrating that Fe(III) chelates must be reduced prior to uptake, Chaney et al. (1972) also speculated that the reduction was mediated by a membrane-bound reducing system that transferred electrons from the cytosol to the external face of the plasma membrane. The mechanism of Fe(III) reduction has been the subject of much discussion, particularly in relation to the question of the role of soluble, excreted Fe(III) reductants vs. reduction at the plasma membrane. Several researchers have shown that Fe-deficient roots can excrete compounds capable of reducing Fe(III) in the external solution (Brown & Ambler, 1973; Brown & Jones, 1973; Olsen et al., 1981; Römheld & Marschner, 1981). Some of these excreted compounds have been identified as phenolics, primarily caffeic acid (Hether et al., 1984), and it has been suggested that these excreted compounds could make a significant contribution to Fe(III) reduction by the root (Olsen & Brown, 1980a, b; Olsen et al., 1981). However, there is a rather convincing body of evidence that argues against soluble Fe(III) reduction in the root apoplasm and/or in the rhizosphere. Also, there is very strong evidence in support of a plasma membrane-bound Fe(III) reductase. Evidence against Fe(III) reduction occurring in the rhizosphere follows.

A number of groups have reported that the organic compounds excreted by roots of Fe-deficient plants could not account for the rapid rates of Fe(III) reduction that were measured (Barrett-Lennard et al., 1983; Bienfait et al., 1983; Chaney et al., 1973; Römheld & Marschner, 1983). For example, in work characterizing Fe(III) reduction by either peanut (*Arachis hypogaea* L.) roots or by phenolics released to the external solution by the roots (of Fe-deficient plants). Römheld and Marschner (1983) found that the kinetics and pH optimum for Fe(III) reduction by excreted reductants were dramatically different from the same parameters for root-mediated Fe(III) reduction. Furthermore, the released phenolics could not effectively reduce Fe supplied as stable Fe(III) chelates, such as Fe(III)-EDTA (which the roots could), and they calculated that the rate of phenolic release would have to be 200 times higher than measured, in order to support the rates of Fe(III) reduction measured with the peanut roots. It has been observed that the excretion of soluble "reductants" occurs mainly during periods of H^+ excretion (Brown & Jones, 1974; Marschner et al., 1974; Olsen & Brown, 1980a), and a number of researchers have suggested that the release of phenolics may be a response to acid stress-induced membrane injury (Bienfait, 1988a; Chaney & Bell, 1987). It should be noted here that the speculation has been raised that released phenolics might act not as reductants, but as Fe(III) chelators in the rhizosphere (Julian et al., 1983; Römheld & Marschner, 1983), solubilizing Fe(III) ions from insoluble ferric hydroxides in the soils and increasing the availability of Fe(III) for reduction at the plasma membrane. However, Chaney and Bell (1987) have questioned the ability of caffeic acid to chelate Fe(III), at least in calcareous soils, based on the observation that caffeic acid forms weaker chelates with Fe(III) than do citrate and malate. These organic acids are often found in significant quantities in the roots and rhizosphere of Fe-deficient plants.

There is a large body of evidence that strongly supports the existence of a plasma-membrane-bound Fe(III) reductase system that facilitates Fe(III) reduction in response to Fe deficiency. Bienfait's group demonstrated that Fe(III) reduction by roots of Fe-deficient bean (*Phaseolus vulgaris* L.) plants exhibited kinetics consistent with that of matrix-bound enzymes (Bienfait et al., 1983). Subsequently, they showed that exposure of Fe-deficient roots to Fe(III)-EDTA elicited a rapid depolarization of the root-cell membrane potential (Sijmons et al., 1984b). More recently, a more detailed characterization of the electrophysiology of roots of the single-gene mutant of pea (*Pisum sativum* L.), named E107, that accumulates toxic levels of Fe in its leaves has been conducted. It was demonstrated that, in the regions of the root that were involved in Fe(III) reduction, exposure to Fe(III)-EDTA elicited a depolarization of the membrane potential that was not due to secondary alterations of other electrogenic (H^+ and K^+) transport processes (Grusak et al., 1989; L.V. Kochian, unpublished data, 1989). Using the Fe(II) chelate, BPDS, it was possible to separate the depolarization into a reduction component (transfer of electrons from the cytosol to the outer face of the plasma membrane) and a depolarizing Fe(II) ion uptake component. These results are strong evidence for a membrane-mediated reduction. Wergin et al. (1988) conducted an electron microscope examination of Prussian blue staining [a specific stain for Fe(III) reduction] of root hairs from Fe-deficient tomato plants. They showed that the Prussian blue accumulated between the plasma membrane and cell wall. The strongest evidence for an Fe reductase localized in the plasma membrane of root cells is from the recent work of Buckhout et al. (1989), using plasma membrane vesicles isolated from Fe-deficient and Fe-replete tomato (*Lycopersicum esculentum* L.) roots via aqueous two-phase partitioning techniques. It was demonstrated that plasma membranes isolated from the roots of Fe-deficient plants exhibited a two-fold increase in NADH-dependent Fe(III)-citrate reduction over plasma membranes from roots grown under Fe-sufficient conditions. This is a conclusive demonstration of a plasma-membrane-bound reductase in plant cells. Based on the above evidence, the model illustrating Fe uptake via Fe(III) reduction presented in Fig. 8–5 has an inducible Fe(III) reductase (R_i) as an integral component.

Bienfait (1985, 1988a) has suggested that roots contain two reductase activities in dicots and nongraminaceous monocots; one that can reduce Fe(III) chelates and ferricyanide, and another capable of reducing only ferricyanide (called the standard system — R_s in Fig. 8–5). The system that could reduce both Fe(III) chelates and ferricyanide would be the inducible reductase (R_i in Fig. 8–5) described above. Bienfait's group has presented evidence implicating NADPH as the cytosolic electron donor for this reductase (Sijmons et al., 1984a). However, the more recent work of Buckhout et al. (1989) demonstrated that NADH is the direct electron donor, not NADPH. Bienfait has hypothesized that the ferricyanide-reducing system is a separate reductase. There is also evidence for a reductase that is not involved in Fe uptake that appears to be expressed in all root cells, including those of grasses, and may be involved in other physiological functions (Rubinstein et al., 1984). Buckhout et al. (1989) have challenged this hypothesis, based on their observation that both ferricyanide reduction and Fe(III) chelate reduction increased two-fold in plasma membranes isolated from Fe-deficient plants over those isolated from Fe-sufficient plants. However, in our recent work on Fe absorption and Fe-dependent electrical properties in pea roots,

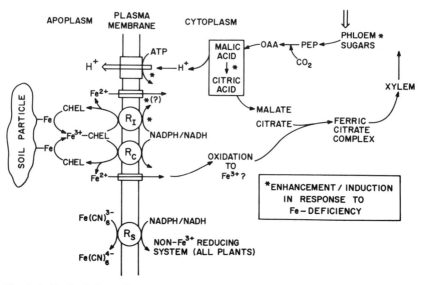

Fig. 8-5. Ferric-chelate reduction-based model depicting the various physiological processes thought to be involved in the reduction of Fe(III) at the root-cell plasma membrane, and the subsequent absorption of Fe(II) ions into the root cells of dicot and nongraminaceous monocot plants. Central to this model is the inducible Fe(III) reductase (R_i) in the plasma membrane that is induced in response to Fe deficiency. A constitutive Fe(III) reductase (R_c) is hypothesized to function under Fe-sufficient conditions.

it was found that, in regions of the root that are involved in ferric reduction, both Fe(III)EDTA and ferricyanide elicited a depolarization, whereas in root regions not involved with reducing Fe, only ferricyanide caused a depolarization of the membrane potential (L.V. Kochian, unpublished data, 1989). This is strong evidence in support of two distinct reductase systems.

 b. **Stimulation of H^+ Efflux.** It has long been known that in response to Fe deficiency, many dicots and some nongraminaceous monocots will increase their rate of acidification of the rhizosphere (Brown, 1978; Brown & Ambler, 1974; Oertli & Jacobsen, 1960). This response has not been seen in grasses (Landsberg, 1984; Römheld & Kramer, 1983). Certainly, such a response would be advantageous in terms of acquiring Fe from the soil, since lowering the rhizosphere pH will increase the solubility of Fe(III) ion. It has been suggested that this acidification under Fe deficiency is due to a stimulation of the plasma membrane H^+-ATPase (but see discussion below), as the ATPase inhibitors DES and DCCD inhibit the Fe deficiency-induced acidification (Landsberg, 1982; Römheld et al., 1984). There is considerable variability in this response. In nutrient solution containing all NO_3^--N, some species demonstrate a considerable stimulation of rhizosphere acidification during Fe deficiency (for example, tomato, sunflower, and peanut), whereas others, notably soybean [*Glycine max* (L.) Merr], are much less successful at acidifying the rhizosphere in nutrient solution containing NO_3^--N (Chaney & Bell, 1987).

The nature of the mechanistic coupling between Fe deficiency and stimulated H^+ efflux is not known at this time, but evidence has been presented that implicates organic acids, primarily citrate and malate. Organic acids are known to accumulate in Fe-deficient plants (Iljin, 1951). Subsequently, Rhoads and Wallace (1960) showed that CO_2 fixation was stimulated under Fe deficiency, and most recently, Bienfait et al. (1989) demonstrated a close coupling between CO_2 fixation and rhizosphere acidification during Fe deficiency-induced acidification in bean roots. If one considers these results, along with reports of increased levels of PEP carboxylase in Fe-deficient roots (Landsberg, 1986), and stimulation of sugar transport via the phloem from the shoot to the root of Fe-deficient bean plants (De Vos et al., 1986), it is possible to develop a speculative model linking these various processes during Fe deficiency. As hypothesized by Bienfait (1988a) (and included in the Fe reductase-based Fe transport model in Fig. 8–5), in response to Fe deficiency, there is a stimulation of phloem transport to the roots. The physiological basis of this stimulation is not known. This would provide an increased C pool in the roots, which, along with the elevated root PEP carboxylase activity, could result in increased malate synthesis and, ultimately (via the Krebs Cycle), increased levels of citrate. At physiological pH values, both organic acids would dissociate, yielding cytoplasmic protons. Hence, the increased H^+ efflux could be a kinetic effect on the H^+-pump of higher cytoplasmic H^+ concentrations. Finally, the increased citrate levels could subsequently facilitate transport of Fe in the xylem, as the primary form of xylem Fe has been reported to be a Fe(III)-citrate complex (Tiffin, 1972).

However, other explanations for the stimulation of net H^+ efflux during Fe deficiency can be suggested. Because it is not possible to measure unidirectional H^+ fluxes, it is difficult to ascertain the actual molecular mechanism responsible for this particular Fe deficiency response. As shown in the plasma-membrane transport model (Fig. 8–1), the H^+-ATPase is responsible for acidifying the rhizosphere, but a number of other putative proton cotransport systems are functioning that can consume or produce extracellular protons. Nitrate uptake is particularly important, as it is the most rapidly absorbed anion and appears to be mediated by a $NO_3^- $-$H^+$ cotransport (Ullrich, 1987). Therefore, increased rhizosphere acidification in response to Fe deficiency could be a secondary effect resulting from an inhibition of NO_3^- absorption in Fe-deficient plants. Indeed, Fe-deficiency-stressed roots from species that exhibit significant acidification often absorb less NO_3^- and other anions, and absorb more cations in response to Fe deficiency, such that the bulk nutrient solution pH can drop below 4.0 (Brown & Jones, 1974; Römheld & Marschner, 1984; Venkat Raju et al., 1972). This could explain, in part, the lack of an acidification response in grasses, which appear to absorb and reduce more nitrate than dicots (Pate, 1973). Therefore, an Fe-deficiency-induced acidification could exist in grasses, but may be masked by a greater NO_3^- uptake, particularly if NO_3^- uptake is insensitive to Fe deficiency in grasses. This point is supported by the observation that, when nitrate reductase activity was suppressed in maize roots, a stimulation of H^+ efflux was observed in response to Fe deficiency (Landsberg, 1979).

c. Localization of Iron Deficiency Stress Responses Along the Root.
Some of the Fe deficiency responses [Fe(III) reduction and increased H^+
efflux] have been shown to be localized in a fairly small zone behind the root
apex in a number of plant species. For example, Fe(III) reduction was shown
to be localized to a region from approximately 1 to 2 cm back from the root
apex in soybean (Ambler et al., 1971) and tomato (Brown & Ambler, 1974).
Subsequently, Römheld and Marschner (1981b) showed that Fe(III) reduction, Fe uptake, and H^+ extrusion were localized in the terminal 1.5 cm of
roots from Fe-deficient sunflower plants. Associated with these responses
are observations of transfer cell (specialized cells with plasma membrane
elaborations that are postulated to be associated with high rates of nutrient
transport [Pate and Gunning, 1972]) and increased root hair formation, and
regions of root swelling. It has been suggested that these morphological
changes are associated with the spatial localization of Fe(III) reduction and
uptake, and H^+ excretion (Kramer et al., 1980; Landsberg, 1980; Römheld
& Kramer, 1983). Based on these findings, Landsberg (1982) has hypothesized that transfer cells are a prerequisite for Fe-deficiency-induced acidification and increased Fe(III) reduction. A caveat to the reader regarding this
hypothesis concerns changes in root anatomy and/or morphology in response
to alterations in plant mineral nutrition (deficiency or toxicity) that could
be the result of impaired root growth and development, and not part of a
plant's strategy to acquire mineral nutrients, such as Fe. For example, if Fe
deficiency inhibits the elongation of root cells near the apex (in the zone of
elongation), while cell division and membrane synthesis continue at a normal rate, it is possible that root epidermal and cortical cells similar in appearance to transfer cells could result (with plasma membrane elaborations),
but without the absorptive capacity usually ascribed to transfer cells. Furthermore, it should be noted that certain toxicity responses, such as Al toxicity, cause alterations in root morphology and anatomy similar to those
reported for Fe deficiency (swelling of root apex, disorganization of the
plasma membrane; see Taylor, 1988).

Not all dicots exhibit a localization of the Fe-deficiency responses to
the region behind the root apex. For example, Fe-efficient Hawkeye soybean exhibits an increased Fe(III) reductase capacity (Brown & Ambler, 1973),
but it does not develop transfer cells or show an increased acidification of
the rhizosphere (Brown & Jones, 1976; Landsberg, 1982). Also, Sijmons and
Bienfait (1983) have visualized Fe(III) reduction along roots of Fe-deficient
bean plants, based on the reduction of Nitro-Blue Tetrazolium salt (Nitro-
BT) by the Fe(III) reductase system, which resulted in the formation of a
blue precipitate on the roots. They showed that, in response to Fe deficiency, the young laterals reduced the Nitro-BT all along their root surface, with
the exception of the root apex. Grusak et al. (1990) visualized reduction of
Fe^{3+} along roots of Fe-deficient pea plants by using the techniques of
Marschner et al. (1982), which involve placing the roots in agar containing
the Fe(III) chelate [0.1 mol m^{-3} Fe(III)-EDTA]. The agar also contained
the Fe(II) chelate, BPDS, in excess of the Fe(III)-EDTA (0.3 mol m^{-3}). As
the roots reduce Fe(III)-EDTA, ferrous ions are released from the chelate
and are "captured" by BPDS before they can be absorbed by the roots, form-

ing a red Fe(II)-BPDS$_3$ complex. Grusak and coworkers found that, in response to Fe deficiency, Fe(III) reduction at the root surface was induced at all regions of the primary and lateral roots except the terminal 1–2 cm. It is not surprising that variability in the localization of the Fe-stress response exists from species to species. Actually, what is surprising (at least to this author), is that so many dicot species appear to restrict Fe uptake in response to Fe deficiency to a small localized zone near the root apex. In this region, the xylem is not usually fully mature, and this region is not usually considered the primary site for the absorption of mineral nutrients destined for translocation to the shoot.

d. Model for Iron Absorption via Plasma Membrane Ferric Reduction. Information concerning the various aspects of Fe absorption in response to Fe deficiency in dicots and nongraminaceous monocots is integrated in the transport model presented in Fig. 8–5. It should be noted that almost nothing is known concerning the actual mechanism for the absorption of Fe^{2+} across the plasma membrane. In this model, it is speculatively proposed that the transport protein is an ion channel, based on what is now known concerning passive ion fluxes. Also, the induction of this putative transport protein in response to Fe deficiency is not well understood. That is, it is not known whether there is an inducible Fe(II) ion channel that is synthesized along with the Fe(III) reductase system in response to Fe deficiency. It is also uncertain whether increased Fe absorption is merely a kinetic response to increased concentrations of Fe(II) ion at the outer surface of the plasma membrane, and therefore, solely the result of increased Fe(III) reduction.

A related problem that should be considered is the nature of the Fe absorption system in Fe-sufficient dicots. Most of the research on Fe absorption has focused on the physiological processes that are induced in response to Fe deficiency. Although Fe absorption may be mediated totally by the system induced by Fe deficiency, the possibility exists that a different Fe uptake system operates under Fe-replete conditions. It has not been conclusively shown that plasma membrane reduction of Fe is necessary for Fe absorption in Fe-sufficient plants (Longnecker & Welch, 1986). Furthermore, there is evidence in the literature that, under certain conditions, dicot roots can absorb Fe in its complexed form (Hill-Cottingham & Lloyd-Jones, 1965; Jeffries & Wallace, 1968; Römheld & Marschner, 1981b, 1983). There are experimental/technical problems with some of this research that tends to confound data interpretation (use of extremely high chelate levels, lack of identification of ^{14}C in plants as ^{14}C-labeled chelate). However, there is enough evidence to support this contention that some groups, including Römheld and Marschner (1983), have suggested that there exists a basal level of Fe-chelate uptake in dicots that operates along with the mechanism of Fe uptake involving Fe(III) reduction and absorption of Fe^{2+} ions. Some very recent work supports the hypothesis that differences exist between the Fe uptake systems employed by Fe-sufficient and Fe-deficient plants based on the observation that Fe absorption (measured both by ^{59}Fe uptake and by electrophysiological methods) in roots of Fe-sufficient pea plants was relatively insensitive to inhibition by the Fe(II) chelate, BPDS, while the same BPDS treatment dramatically inhibited Fe absorption in roots from Fe-deficient plants (Grusak et al., 1989a; L.V. Kochian, unpublished data, 1989). These results suggest that two separate systems operate in the plasma membrane of dicot roots, one under Fe-sufficient conditions (labeled R_c for constitutive reductase in Fig. 8-5) and the other in response to Fe deficiency (labeled R_i for inducible reductase in Fig. 8-5). It should be noted in Fig. 8-5 that, although the constitutive system is depicted as a Fe(III) reductase, the possibility exists that this system is not involved in Fe(III) reduction.

2. Iron Uptake Via Release of Phytosiderophores

As stated previously, it is widely recognized that grasses differ from other plants based on their inability to use Fe when supplied as stable Fe(III) chelates such as EDDHA. Because of this inability, along with the absence of Fe-deficiency-induced responses normally observed in dicots (an increase in H^+ excretion and reductase activity), grasses have been characterized as "Fe-inefficient" (Brown, 1978). However, when grasses and dicots are grown in calcareous soils, which have low levels of available Fe, the grasses often are more effective than the dicot plants in resisting Fe-deficiency chlorosis (Chaney, 1984; Römheld et al., 1982). Marschner et al. (1974) were probably the first to hypothesize that grasses acquire Fe from the soil by a different mechanism than that employed by dicots.

Takagi (1976) was the first to show that washings from rice (*Oryza sativa* L.) roots contained a compound that could solubilize ferric iron, and in response to Fe deficiency, both oat and rice roots exhibited a stimulated release of Fe(III) chelating compounds. In a later paper, Takagi et al. (1984) showed that this response was specific for grasses (i.e., the roots of dicots do not release Fe chelating compounds under Fe deficiency). Subsequent work, primarily by Japanese scientists, has been aimed at characterizing these compounds. They have been identified as nonprotein amino acids; mugineic and avenic acid are two of the chelating compounds that have been characterized. The pathways for biosynthesis are still not known, but these amino acids are structurally related to nicotianamine, a compound found primarily in the shoots of green plants that has been shown to induce regreening of a chlorotic mutant of tomato, possibly through mobilizing Fe for intercellular and intracellular transport (Scholz & Böhme, 1980). However, mugenic acid and, presumably, avenic acid form fairly stable chelates with Fe(III) and less stable chelates with Fe^{2+}, while nicotianamine appears to be a Fe(II) chelate. Therefore, while the mugenic acid class of compounds appear to be Fe(III) chelates excreted into the rhizosphere for Fe absorption, it has been hypothesized that nicotianamine functions as a Fe(II) carrier within plant cells, and possibly from cell to cell (Scholz et al., 1985). Recent work from Takagi's group has shown that only a few different (but related) Fe chelating compounds are released from the roots of a wide range of graminaceous species. These compounds include mugeneic acid, 2″-deoxy mugeneic acid, 3-hydroxy- and 3-epi-hydroxy-mugeneic acid, and avenic acid (Kawai et al., 1988).

These Fe(III) chelating compounds have been named phytosiderophores after the well-characterized Fe uptake system in microorganisms, which utilizes the release of very specific Fe-chelating compounds called siderophores (Neilands, 1981) (derived from the Greek for "iron bearers"). In the bacterium, *E. coli*, this system is a beautifully orchestrated Fe operon of three genes encoding for the siderophore, one gene encoding for the membrane receptor, and a nearby reglatory sequence made of a repressor, promoter, and operator regions (Lewin, 1984). In response to Fe deficiency, the siderophore and membrane receptor are synthesized. The released siderophore, which is quite specific for Fe(III), binds Fe(III) ion outside of the cell. The Fe(III)-siderophore complex binds to the specific receptor at the outer membrane, and then either Fe(III) ion is reduced to Fe(II) as it crosses the membrane or the Fe-siderophore complex is transported intact into the cell. When the Fe requirement for the bacterium has been met, the excess Fe binds to a repressor protein, and the Fe-protein complex binds to the operator region of the operon and turns off the system.

Much less is known concerning the mechanism of Fe-phytosiderophore uptake in grasses. Römheld and Marschner (1986b) have observed in barley roots that Fe uptake from Fe(III)-phytosiderophores was from 100 to 1000 times more rapid than from synthetic chelates such as EDTA. They also showed that Fe(III) reduction was not involved in the uptake mechanism, and have postulated a specific membrane transport protein at the plasma membrane that facilitates the uptake of the intact Fe(III)-phytosiderophore complex. However, at this time, there is no direct evidence for this uptake system. In the model for Fe-phytosiderophore uptake in Fig. 8–6, two possibilities for Fe uptake via phytosiderophores are presented; either the intact

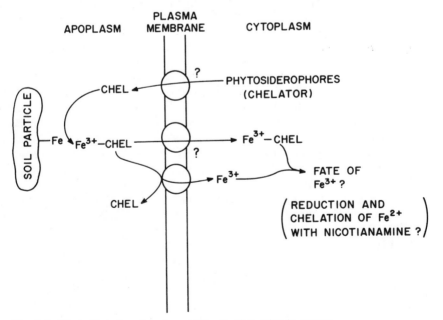

Fig. 8–6. Phytosiderophore-based model for Fe absorption in grasses.

complex is transported or the complex is split at the outer face of the plasma membrane, and Fe is absorbed and phytosiderophores are released to the external solution. More recently, Marschner et al. (1987) demonstrated that the enhanced release of phytosiderophores was localized to the apical zones of the seminal and lateral roots of barley, which in analogy to the localization of Fe mobilization in dicots, prompted them to propose that root growth plays a key role in the acquisition of Fe from the soil.

3. Future Work in Iron Absorption

Although much has been learned concerning the mechanisms and regulation of Fe uptake in plants, there are still many more questions than answers. Through the application of recent advances in a number of fields, including microelectrode technology, membrane biochemistry, and molecular biology, we should be able to begin to unravel the mysteries surrounding Fe uptake at the molecular level. The use of mutants that are defective at specific sites of Fe absorption and utilization, such as those used to elucidate the molecular mechanism of Fe absorption in bacteria, should be quite effective. For example, Bienfait (1988b) has recently isolated plasma membranes from the roots of the single-gene *fer* mutant of tomato, which cannot develop the Fe-deficiency stress response, and from the wild-type *FER* genotype, both grown under Fe-deficient and Fe-replete conditions. Bienfait has identified two plasma membrane proteins that are always present in the membranes of low-Fe grown wild-type plants, but absent in the Fe-replete wild type, and both low and high Fe-grown *fer* mutants. He has developed a model in which the *FER* gene encodes for a regulatory protein that binds to the DNA sequence involved in the Fe-deficiency stress reactions (stimulated H^+ efflux, reductase activity, etc.) and activates the genes responsible for these reactions. When the protein binds Fe^{2+} ion, the protein changes its conformation and no longer can activate the same gene sequence. Although this model is quite speculative, it is the starting point for some potentially exciting future research.

We have recently been characterizing another single-gene mutant involved in Fe absorption, designated E107, which has been shown to accumulate Fe in its leaves to extremely high levels (as high as 12 000 mg kg DW^{-1}; Kneen et al., 1989; Welch & LaRue, 1989). A physiological characterization of the mutant indicates that Fe(III) reduction and uptake are turned on constantly, regardless of the Fe status of the plant (Grusak et al., 1989, 1990). That is, the pea mutant behaves as though it is Fe deficient, even as it is accumulating Fe to toxic levels in the shoot. Subsequent work on this mutant will involve a molecular approach, which first will focus on the identification of differences in proteins associated with the mutant and wild-type peas. The ultimate goal will be the identification of the gene and gene product(s) that are responsible for the excess Fe accumulation in E170. This type of approach, although difficult, may prove to be quite productive in learning more about the molecular regulation of Fe absorption in plants.

B. Manganese

Manganese is absorbed into the plant mainly as the free Mn^{2+} ion. In the soil, Mn^{2+} concentrations can vary greatly, from <0.1 mmol m^{-3} in well-aerated alkaline soils to >400 mmol m^{-3} in submerged soils (Gilmour, 1977). The Mn^{2+} concentration needed to support adequate plant growth also spans a wide range, with concentrations between 0.25 and 3.6 mmol m^{-3} considered adequate for most species based on studies in flowing nutrient solution (Asher & Edwards, 1983). More recently, a wider range of concentrations supporting adequate plant growth was reported, from 0.01 to 50.0 mmol m^{-3}, which apparently reflected differences between plant species (Asher, 1987).

Unlike Fe, there has been little recent work (over the last 15 yr) on Mn transport in plants, a fact that was commented upon in the recent review of Mn upake by Clarkson (1988). As Clarkson laments, "Serious research on Mn transport has not advanced much in a period in which nearly all of our contemporary thinking about the way in which ion transport is organized and energized has grown up." Most of the work on Mn transport that will be reviewed here has focused on kinetic and metabolic considerations.

As stated above, Mn^{2+} is the form of Mn absorbed from the soil. Manganese can form complexes in the rhizosphere with organic ligands of plant and microbial origin, which may increase the mobility of Mn in the rhizosphere (facilitating diffusion up to the root-cell plasma membrane). There is contradictory evidence concerning uptake of Mn from metal-chelate complexes. Barber and Lee (1974) found that Mn supplied as the EDTA chelate was absorbed much more slowly than the free cation, and evidence in support of a splitting of the Mn(II)-EDTA complex prior to Mn^{2+} uptake was presented. On the other hand, the same paper presents seemingly contradictory evidence for stimulation of Mn uptake in barley plants by microbially released organic compounds. Thus, the relative significance of chelated Mn to plant-Mn absorption is still not clearly understood.

1. Kinetic and Metabolic Aspects of Manganese Absorption

The time-dependent kinetics of Mn^{2+} uptake in roots is characterized by an initial rapid phase of uptake (30–60 min). The Mn^{2+} absorbed during this time is freely exchangeable with Ca^{2+} or Mn^{2+}, and appears to be uptake into the root apoplasm based on the employment of compartmental analysis methods (Page & Dainty, 1964). This initial phase is followed by a slower linear phase that is constant for at least 5 h and results in the accumulation of Mn that is much less readily exchanged (Maas et al., 1968). This second phase is, quite likely, Mn transport into the symplasm.

Concentration-dependent kinetics have been conducted from solutions ranging in concentration from 1 to 1000 mmol m^{-3} (Bowen, 1969, 1981; Landi & Fagoli, 1983; Maas et al., 1968; Page, 1961). In general, saturation kinetics were observed, with kinetic parameters (as summarized by Clarkson, 1988) ranging from 4 to 16 mmol m^{-3} for K_m values and V_{max} values ranging from 0.3 to 1.0 μmol g fresh weight $(FW)^{-1}$ h^{-1} (gFW = gram fresh weight of root tissue).

If Mn is absorbed as the free Mn^{2+} ion, then a large inwardly directed electrochemical gradient for uptake would exist, and one could speculate that passive Mn^{2+} uptake occurs via a divalent cation channel, with the driving force primarily due to the negative membrane potential. Inhibition of metabolism could have a secondary effect on Mn^{2+} uptake, eliciting an inhibition through a decrease in the membrane potential. However, there is no consensus in the literature concerning the dependence of Mn^{2+} uptake on metabolism. Page and Dainty (1964) showed that 1 mol m^{-3} potassium cyanide (KCN) had no effect on Mn^{2+} uptake (from a 0.1 mol m^{-3} $MnCl_2$ solution) in oat roots. However, dinitrophenol (DNP) and azide strongly inhibited Mn^{2+} uptake in excised maize roots (Maas et al., 1969), and DNP inhibited uptake by 80% in excised sugarcane leaves (Bowen, 1969).

2. Interactions with Other Ions

The primary nutrient interaction for Mn is with Fe; there have been a large number of reports linking Fe and Mn nutrition. Many of these probably are due to chemical interactions at the root-soil interface. For example, for plants that respond to Fe deficiency by a stimulation of reductase activity, Mn mobilization and uptake may be increased, primarily due to a stimulated acidification of the rhizosphere (increasing the solubility of Mn^{2+}) and increase reduction of Mn(IV) to Mn(II) (Marschner, 1988). In calcareous soils with low available Fe and Mn, these Fe-deficiency response mechanisms can prevent Mn deficiency (Moraghan, 1985), whereas in calcareous soils with only low Fe levels, this response may cause excess Mn^{2+} uptake and Mn toxicity (Moraghan, 1979). The absorption of Mn^{2+} has been reported to be inhibited by other divalent cations such as Ca^{2+}, Mg^{2+}, and Zn^{2+} (Maas et al., 1969; Robson & Loneragan, 1970), although the mechanism of the inhibition is not clear.

As suggested by Clarkson (1988), there appears to be a disparity between the kinetic constants for Mn^{2+} uptake and the levels of free Mn^{2+} in soil solutions. The uptake of Mn^{2+} appears to be facilitated by a transport system that, although it does not transport Mn rapidly, has a capacity for uptake that far exceeds the needs of the plant. Based on the estimates of Clarkson (1988), the rate of absorption determined from the kinetic experiments outlined above may be from 100 to 1000 times greater than necessary to meet the needs of the average plant. This point suggests that the information obtained concerning Mn^{2+} uptake as it has been studied in the laboratory to date, may not reflect the operation of the transport system as it functions in the intact plant in the field. Obviously, much remains to be learned concerning the regulation and mechanism of Mn^{2+} uptake in plants. It seems that the lack of understanding concerning the transport of this micronutrient does not arise from technical limitations in studying Mn^{2+} transport, but mainly from a lack of sufficient research directed at the problem.

C. Zinc

Like Mn, most of the work on Zn uptake has focused on kinetic characterizations of uptake, and the role of metabolism in its absorption. Zinc is absorbed primarily as the divalent cation and Zn^{2+} concentrations that support adequate plant growth range from 0.05 to 0.25 mmol m^{-3}, with Zn toxicities observed above concentrations of 3 to 6 mmol m^{-3} (Carroll & Loneragan, 1968). The concentration of Zn^{2+} in soil solutions is often quite low, ranging from 0.01 to 1.0 mmol m^{-3} in calcareous soils.

Several investigations into the kinetics of Zn^{2+} uptake have been conducted. Schmid et al. (1965), studying $^{65}Zn^{2+}$ uptake from either a 1 or 5 mmol m^{-3} $ZnCl_2$ solution in excised barley roots, reported that uptake was linear over the first 2 h, with a large component (60%) of this uptake being diffusion into and binding in the apoplasm, and the rest due to a plasma-membrane transport-mediated process. In terms of the concentration-dependent kinetics of Zn^{2+} uptake in plants, a situation similar to that for Mn is seen. Saturation kinetics are often observed, with K_m values that appear to be quite high, ~50 mmol m^{-3} (Bowen, 1981, 1986; Ramani & Kannan, 1978), in light of the fact that the concentration of Zn^{2+} considered adequate is well below 1 mmol m^{-3}. More recently, kinetic parameters of Zn^{2+} uptake in intact maize roots were determined by the solution depletion method of Claassen and Barber (1974), using a more realistic concentration range (0 to 1.5 mmol m^{-3}) than that employed in some earlier studies (Mullins & Sommers, 1986). This approach yielded a K_m value for uptake of between 1.5 and 2.2 mmol m^{-3}, which appears to be more realistic for field-grown plants.

Compartmental analysis techniques were employed by Santa Maria and Cogliatti (1988) in order to determine the unidirectional Zn^{2+} fluxes and half-times for exchange of Zn^{2+} in subcellular compartments. Under steady-state conditions, a significant efflux of Zn^{2+} across the plasma membrane was found that was 65 to 85% of the Zn^{2+} influx. The compartmental analysis yielded results consistent with three compartments in series. The compartment assigned to the apoplasm had a $t_{1/2}$ of 0.08 h and occupied from 8 to 14% of the root volume. Based on this assessment, a Zn concentration in the apoplasm of around 0.5 mol m^{-3} was estimated. This high concentration suggests that significant Zn adsorption is occurring in the Donnan free space. The next fastest exchanging compartment had a $t_{1/2}$ of 0.55 h, accounted for about 8% of the total root content, and is suggested to be the cytoplasm. The slowest exchanging compartment had a $t_{1/2}$ of 134 h and contained 76% of the total root Zn. Some anomalous kinetic aspects of this slowest component suggest that it could be more complex than simply vacuolar Zn and may be partially due to the binding of Zn in organic complexes in the vacuole or cytoplasm.

Because Zn is apparently transported across the plasma membrane as free Zn^{2+}, the thermodynamic considerations discussed earlier for Mn^{2+} also apply for Zn^{2+}. There appear to be some contradictory findings in the literature concerning the coupling of Zn^{2+} uptake to metabolism. There have been a number of reports in algae, barley roots, and bean plants, suggesting that Zn^{2+} uptake is not metabolically dependent, based on a lack of response to metabolic inhibitors (Broda et al., 1964; Gutknecht, 1961, 1963; Rathore et al.,1970). Others, however, have presented strong evidence in support of a metabolically controlled transport of Zn^{2+}. Bowen (1969) demonstrated that Zn uptake in sugarcane leaf tissue was dependent on metabolic energy, based on observations of significant inhibitions by low temperature and a variety of metabolic inhibitors. Giordano et al. (1974) also found that DNP severely depressed Zn uptake from solutions containing either 0.005 or 5 mmol m^{-3} Zn^{2+} in intact rice seedlings. They suggested that the contradictory results concerning the role of metabolism in Zn^{2+} uptake may be due to differences in experimental conditions (Zn concentration, inhibitor concentration, influence of other ions) and, particularly, the use of unreasonably high Zn^{2+} concentrations in some of the earlier studies.

In terms of nutrient interactions, the main interacting ion for Zn^{2+} is Cu^{2+}. Schmid et al. (1965) showed that Cu strongly inhibited Zn^{2+} uptake, whereas Mn had no effect. Bowen (1969) showed that Cu competitively inhibited Zn^{2+} uptake, and suggested that they competed for the same transport site. Although transport physiologists like to think that there are separate transport proteins for each important nutrient, it is possible that for some of the divalent micronutrient cations, such as Zn^{2+} and Cu^{2+}, a single cation channel could mediate the transport of both ions into the cell. Obviously, this speculation awaits the test of future research efforts.

D. Copper

Copper in biological systems is predominantly in the Cu^{2+} oxidation state, which has great significance in terms of Cu absorption into plants from soil solutions, because most organic chelates bind Cu^{2+} strongly (Graham, 1981). In soil solutions, up to 98% of the Cu^{2+} is complexed to low molecular-weight organic compounds (Hodgson et al., 1966). Total Cu concentration in the earth's crust is usually below 1 mol m^{-3} (Hodgson et al., 1966) and, because most of this is insoluble or complexed, the concentration of available Cu^{2+} is considerably lower. In plants grown in nutrient solution, the concentration of Cu^{2+} considered adequate for growth is quite low, around 0.02 mmol m^{-3} (Graves & Sutcliffe, 1974).

The Cu^{2+} ion has a high affinity for peptide N and S, and binds quite strongly to proteins, especially proteins high in cysteine residues. Also, due to its affinity for carbonyl, carboxyl, sulfhydryl, and phenolic groups, all of which are found in cell walls, there is a strong and specific adsorption of Cu^{2+} to cell walls that is not easily desorbed (Harrison et al., 1979). It should also be noted that because Cu(II) can be reduced to Cu(I) in the range of physiological redox potentials, the significance of the absorption of Cu(I) by roots should not be ignored (Graham, 1981).

1. Kinetic and Metabolic Aspects of Copper Absorption

As has been described previously for the other divalent micronutrient cations, if free Cu^{2+} ion is the predominant species absorbed by the root, there exists a large electrochemical potential gradient for passive Cu^{2+} uptake into plant cells, possibly via ion channels (for a more detailed consideration of the thermodynamics of Cu^{2+} uptake, see Graham, 1981). However, because a majority of the Cu in soil solutions exists as Cu complexes, the Cu species that is transported across the plasma membrane has a direct bearing on thermodynamic aspects of uptake. There is considerable evidence that free Cu^{2+} ion is the absorbed species. A number of researchers have demonstrated that Cu is absorbed more rapidly from Cu^{2+} solutions than from solutions of Cu complexed to synthetic chelators such as DTPA (diethylenetriaminepentaacetic acid) or EDTA (Dragun et al., 1976; Harrison et al., 1979, 1984; Wallace, 1980). Also, Goodman and Linehan (1979), using electron paramagnetic resonance spectrometry to study root Cu absorption, presented evidence consistent with the dissociation of Cu from EDTA during absorption from a Cu(II)-EDTA solution.

A number of studies using the Cu radioisotope, ^{64}Cu, and excised roots to investigate Cu^{2+} absorption kinetics have been conducted (Cathala & Salsac, 1975; Goren & Wanner, 1971; Harrison et al., 1978, 1979; Hiatt et al., 1963; Landi & Fagoli, 1983; Veltrup, 1976, 1977) and have yielded results consistent with Michaelis-Menten saturation kinetics. However, as pointed out by Graham (1981), the results of some of these studies are difficult to interpret, because Cu^{2+} was not adequately desorbed from the cell walls. More than half of the Cu in the root may be bound to cell wall sites (Cathala & Salsac, 1975; Hiatt et al., 1963). Some of this Cu is ionically bound along with other cations on the negatively charged cation-binding sites of the cell wall; however, much of the Cu^{2+} is strongly bound to cell-wall organic ligands involving N, O, and S atoms. This coordinately complexed Cu cannot be desorbed in the traditional manner, using solutions that contain excess Ca^{2+}, but can be desorbed with nonradioactive $^{63}Cu^{2+}$ (Harrison et al., 1979). For studies in which the cell wall Cu was properly accounted for, rates of Cu^{2+} absorption have been shown to be among the lowest of any micronutrient (Graham, 1981). In the concentration range approximating soil solutions (0.001 to 1.0 mmol m^{-3}), rates of from 0.1 to ~3.0 nmol gFW^{-1} h^{-1} have been observed. At much higher concentrations (5.0 to 10.0 mmol m^{-3}), a wider range of absorption values has been reported, from 6 to 500 nmol gFW^{-1} h^{-1} (see Graham, 1981, for summary).

The metabolic requirements for Cu^{2+} absorption have not been fully resolved. Some of the earlier studies suggested that Cu^{2+} uptake was not metabolically regulated, based on insensitivity to anaerobiosis and metabolic inhibitors (Cathala & Salsac, 1975; Goren & Wanner, 1971). However, because of improper desorption of cell wall Cu^{2+}, many of these studies were actually investigating Cu^{2+} binding in the apoplasm. Bowen (1979) has reported that metabolism is required for Cu uptake based on observations of inhibition of Cu^{2+} absorption into excised barley and sugar cane roots by metabolic inhibitors. Unfortunately, the method employed to desorb Cu from the cell walls was not detailed in this study. As Graham (1981) points out, because of a lack of properly conducted studies on the metabolic requirements for Cu^{2+} uptake (use of intact plants, meaningful concentration ranges, proper desorption techniques), this important aspect of Cu^{2+} uptake is still not properly understood.

As mentioned above, based on thermodynamic considerations, membrane transport of divalent cations can be mediated by proteinaceous ion channels. However, because of the tendency for Cu^{2+} to bind rather strongly to proteins, Graham (1981) has suggested that Cu^{2+} uptake could be facilitated by a carrier-type protein that can bind Cu^{2+} on either side of the plasma membrane, but would have a greater probability of release of Cu^{2+} inside the cell due to the lower electrochemical potential for Cu^{2+} in this compartment. Thus, Cu^{2+} uptake could occur by a passively driven, carrier-type membrane protein.

2. Interactions with Other Ions

There have been several reports of effects of other ions Cu^{2+} absorption. As was mentioned above for Zn^{2+}, a number of researchers have observed mutually competitive interactions between Cu^{2+} and Zn^{2+} (Bowen, 1979; Chaudry & Loneragan, 1972; Giordano et al., 1974). Bowen (1979) found that Cu and Zn competitively inhibited the uptake of the other ion and proposed that both ions were absorbed by the same transport system. In terms of other interactions, K^+ was shown to decrease Cu^{2+} uptake in sunflower (Graham, 1979). In this study, it was proposed that the inhibition was due to the depolarizing effect of K^+ on the membrane potential, thus decreasing the electrochemical gradient for Cu^{2+} absorption. Interestingly, although Cu and N interact quite strongly in terms of nutritional effects (Loneragan, 1981), there appears to be no significant effect of NO_3^- or NH_4^+ ions on Cu^{2+} uptake.

E. Nickel

Since the publication of the first edition of *Micronutrients in Agriculture*, there has been a significant increase in interest in Ni as a plant micronutrient. The discovery in 1975 that Ni is a component of the enzyme, urease (Dixon et al., 1975), which is present in many plant species (Welch, 1981), has been integral in sparking this interest. Subsequently, work in Welch's laboratory established the essentiality of Ni in legumes (Eskew et al., 1983) and, subsequently, all higher plants (Brown et al., 1987). Nickel levels in Ni-adequate plant tissues are extremely low, ranging between 0.2 and 5 mmol m^{-3}, and adequate growth for most plants can be maintained in solutions containing Ni at concentrations below 1 mmol m^{-3} (Brown et al., 1987; Welch, 1981).

There have been a handful of reports concerning Ni uptake in plants. Because most of the Ni absorption studies have arisen from concerns about heavy-metal pollutants, the investigations have been conducted in relation to Ni toxicity. Hence, unnaturally high concentrations have often been used, which may tend to yield results that are not representative of the Ni^{2+} transport system that functions to provide Ni at the very low levels needed to sustain growth. Cataldo et al. (1978) studied Ni absorption into intact soybean plants from $NiCl_2$ solutions radiolabeled with $^{63}Ni^{2+}$; uptake was studied over a wide range of Ni concentrations, from 0.02 mmol m^{-3} to an extremely high concentration of 100 mmol m^{-3}. They found that free-space Ni^{2+} could be desorbed with either Ca^{2+} or nonradioactive Ni^{2+} solutions, and that most of the apoplasmic Ni^{2+} was bound ionically to fixed negative charges in the cell wall. The uptake kinetics over this very broad concentration range was interpreted as consisting of three separate phases. The first phase represented Ni^{2+} uptake over the concentration range from 0.075 to 0.25 mmol m^{-3}, which would be considered a reasonable level for the plant in the field. The K_m value for uptake over this concentration range was 0.5 mmol m^{-3}. Kinetic analysis indicated that both Cu^{2+} and Zn^{2+} competitively inhibited Ni^{2+} uptake, which suggests, quite speculatively, that all three ions could be transported by the same (or similar) transport systems.

Körner et al. (1986) studied Ni^{2+} uptake in excised barley roots, again using a rather high Ni^{2+} concentration (10 mmol m^{-3}) in the uptake solution. They found that, at this Ni^{2+} concentration, a large proportion of the Ni^{2+} absorbed after 30 min resided in the free space. Most of the free-space Ni^{2+} was ionically bound, but there was a small proportion of tightly bound apoplasmic Ni^{2+}, which presumably was complexed to organic ligands in the walls. There was a small proportion of the uptake that represented transport into the root symplasm, and this Ni^{2+} uptake component was highly sensitive to metabolic inhibition with DNP. In a subsequent paper, the effects of Ca^{2+} and other divalent cations on Ni^{2+} uptake were studied by Körner et al. (1987). They found that both Ca^{2+} and Mg^{2+} inhibited Ni^{2+} uptake noncompetitively by an unknown mechanism, whereas Cu^{2+}, Zn^{2+}, and Co^{2+} all competitively inhibited Ni^{2+} absorption. They suggested that all four divalent cations were transported via the same mechanism, based on their similar ionic radii.

Finally, Aschmann and Zaososki (1987) examined the kinetics and metabolic dependency of Ni^{2+} uptake in intact oat seedlings and also in excised roots from oat seedlings. Again, an unreasonably high Ni^{2+} concentration (10 mmol m^{-3}) was used for many of the uptake experiments. Nonetheless, Ni^{2+} uptake was very sensitive to metabolism, based on observations of dramatic reductions in absorption following low temperature treatment (2°C), anaerobiosis, or DNP application. Concentration-dependent kinetic studies were conducted from uptake solutions ranging in Ni^{2+} concentration from 0.5 to 28 mmol m^{-3}. Michaelis-Menten kinetics were observed and kinetic analysis yielded a K_m value of 12 mmol m^{-3}, which seems unreasonably high and probably reflects the high concentrations used for the study.

It should be obvious, that, as in the case of Cu^{2+}, there is a real need for detailed characterization of the physiology of Ni^{2+} uptake using intact plants and conducting experiments at realistic (< 1.0 mmol m^{-3}) Ni^{2+} concentrations.

F. Boron

In biological and soil solutions, B occurs mainly as boric acid, $B(OH)_3$, which is a very weak acid that accepts OH^- rather than donate H^+:

$$B(OH)_3 + 2H_2O \rightleftharpoons B(OH)_4^- + H_3O^+ \quad pK_a = 9.25 \qquad [7]$$

Therefore, at physiological pH values, the primary B species in soil or nutrient solution is the undissociated boric acid. Because of this, it is unclear from the literature as to whether B uptake is primarily diffusion of boric acid through the lipid bilayer, or if it occurs by a membrane protein-mediated process (for a detailed review of this topic and plant B transport in general, see Raven, 1980). Bingham et al. (1970) investigated B absorption in excised barley roots and found that boric acid absorption was unaffected by solution pH, which ranged from 3.0 to 7.0. They also showed that boric acid was not accumulated in the tissue, and the addition of metabolic inhibitors (KCN, DNP) or exposure to low temperatures had no influence on B absorption. Hence, they hypothesized that B absorption was a physical process, which resulted from the diffusion of undissociated boric acid across the lipid bilayer of the root-cell plasma membrane. Subsequently, Oertli and Grgurevic (1975) came to the same conclusion following an investigation into the relative importance of the two forms of boric acid, $B(OH)_3$ and $B(OH)_4^-$, for B absorption. They found that relative B uptake (uptake at pH 6 = 100%) decreased with increasing pH value of the uptake solution in a manner consistent with the decrease of the fraction of undissociated boric acid at more alkaline pH values. Therefore, they proposed that B in the plant tissue rapidly approached diffusive equilibrium with the B in the external solution, and this equilibrium was governed by the concentration of undissociated boric acid in the external solution. In his detailed review on transport of boric acid in plants, Raven (1980) estimated the permeability of plant cell membranes to boric acid. The calculated permeability coefficient was in the range of at least 10^{-6} cm s^{-1}, which was high enough to account for the fluxes usually observed across plant-cell membranes. Raven went on to suggest that, in light of the rather high passive permeability of plant membranes to boric acid, the operation of active or at least metabolically driven membrane transport of boric acid would most likely be, energetically, quite expensive.

Despite these studies, there have been many reports of active, or at least carrier-mediated, boric acid transport in plants. However, some of this research is complicated by a particular chemical property of boric acid, which involves the formation of mono- or di-esters of boric acid with cis-diol groups by the reactions depicted in Fig. 8–7. A number of plant compounds contain poly-OH groups in the cis-diol configuration and can react with boric acid. These compounds include a number of sugars and sugar derivatives, including sugar alcohols and uronic acids.

Therefore, boric acid can bind both to the cell walls and in the symplasm of plant cells (Bowen & Nissen, 1976; Tanaka, 1967; Thellier et al., 1979). Binding of boric acid in intracellular compartments could have a significant effect on how results from research into boric acid transport are interpreted. For example, a demonstration of net B influx into plant cells, where tissue B concentration exceeds the external boric acid concentration, may not necessarily mean that active transport is occurring. An alternative explanation would be that boric acid is diffusing into the symplasm and forming stable esters with cis-diol groups, which would then allow for the diffusion of more free boric acid into the cell.

This complicating factor should be considered in light of a number of reports of active boric acid transport in plants, which includes the earlier work of Thellier and colleagues (Thellier & Ayadi, 1967; Thellier & Le Guiel, 1967; Thellier & Tromeur, 1968), and the work of Bowen (1968, 1969, 1972) and Bowen and Nissen (1976). Therefore, reports of B accumulation in plant tissues to concentrations exceeding the external solution may be due to boric acid ester formation, which was not determined in many of these studies. Other evidence presented in support of active or carrier protein-mediated B transport are uptake kinetic curves that appear to be one or several Michaelis-Menten curves, suggestive of carrier-mediated transport, and inhibition of uptake by metabolic inhibitors.

A number of investigators have suggested that boric acid is transported by a combination of active and passive transports. Wildes and Neales (1971) presented evidence from work with carrot (*Daucus carota*) that is consistent with the operation of both active transport [probably of $B(OH)_4^-$] and passive transport of $B(OH)_3$. On the other hand, Nissen (1974) has suggested that active transport of undissociated boric acid occurs at low external concentrations, whereas at higher concentrations, passive diffusion dominates.

The most detailed analysis of B fluxes in plant tissues has been the work of Thellier et al. (1979) conducted on duckweed (*Lemna minor* L.). Compartmental analysis of boric acid fluxes were carried out, using enriched sources of the stable isotope of boron, ^{10}B (natural abundance of 19.8%), as a tracer for the more abundant ^{11}B isotope (natural abundance of

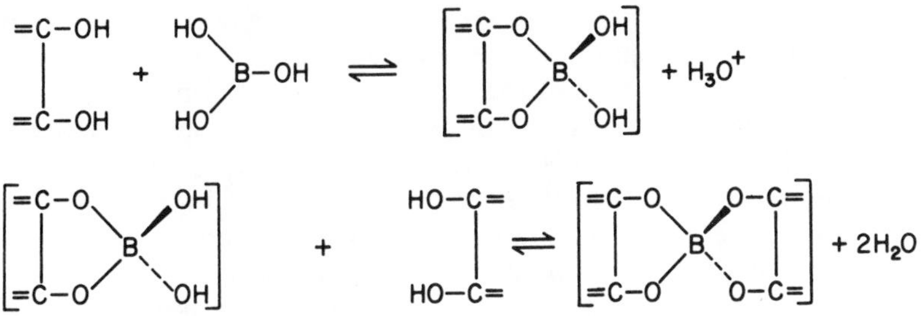

Fig. 8-7. Reactions yielding the formation of mono-esters and di-esters of boric acid with cis-diol groups.

80.2%). They found evidence for four compartments; the first two appear to be in the cell walls, and consist of B in the water-free space and very stable boric acid di-esters. The other two compartments were found to be in series with the free-space compartment and were hypothesized to be the cytoplasm and vacuole. They suggested that the greater concentration of boric acid in the symplasm was due to ester formation with *cis*-diols, and not to active transport. Therefore, in this work, Thellier's group altered their view of the thermodynamics of boric acid from active transport to passive diffusion and subsequent ester formation within the cell.

In summary, it is unclear as to the exact nature of boric acid transport across plant cell membranes. If it is due simply to passive diffusion across the lipid bilayer, then B would probably be the only essential nutrient that is absorbed via a nontransport protein-mediated process. It is difficult to envisage how the plant would regulate B uptake by this transport mechanism. Alternatively, B absorption may be a combination of active transport and passive diffusion. Certainly this interesting problem awaits further research. The availability of new technologies and methods for monitoring B transport in plants, such as the inductively coupled, plasma mass spectrometer, should provide for more rapid progress in the future.

III. MICRONUTRIENT TRANSPORT WITHIN AND BETWEEN CELLS

One aspect of micronutrient transport that has been emphasized in this review is the effect that the reactive nature of the micronutrient cations has on the transport of these species into and within plants. The micronutrient cations (Fe^{3+}/Fe^{2+}, Mn^{2+}, Zn^{2+}, Cu^{2+}, and Ni^{2+}) are potentially toxic species in biological systems, because of their tendency to react with organic ligands, and because some of the micronutrient cations (i.e., Fe^{3+}/Fe^{2+}, Mn^{2+}, and Cu^{2+}) can be involved in oxidation-reduction reactions that can produce harmful free radicals (Hendry & Brocklebank, 1985). Therefore, once these ions enter the plant symplasm, it is to the plant's benefit to maintain free ion activities at very low levels by forming low-molecular-weight organic complexes with the micronutrient cations. Although little research has been conducted on this topic, there is some experimental evidence that suggests that the plant forms specific low-molecular-weight organic compounds for the complexation of micronutrient cations, and this complexation facilitates the transport of the nutrients within and between cells.

The best characterized system (although still quite speculative), in terms of intracellular and intercellular micronutrient transport, is the role of the nonprotein amino acid, nicotianamine, as a soluble endogenous Fe transporter in plant cells. Scholz and coworkers have conducted an extensive characterization of the tomato mutant, *chloronerva*, which has a defect in chlorophyl synthesis (causing interveinal chlorosis) that appears to be due to impaired Fe mobility. They have shown that nicotianamine is missing from this plant, and that application of nicotianamine to the leaves results in movement of Fe throughout the leaf blade and leaf regreening (see, for example, Budesinsky et al., 1980, 1981; Scholz et al., 1985). This regreening of chlorotic tissue following nicotinamine application was shown to be widespread among higher plants (Rudolph & Scholz, 1972), and nicotianamine has been widely found in higher plants (Rudolph & Scholz, 1972). Therefore, Scholz and his colleagues have speculated that nicotianamine is responsible for Fe transport within and between cells.

It has been demonstrated that, unlike the related nonprotein amino acids (mugeneic and avenic acid), which are Fe(III) chelators, nicotianamine forms more stable chelates with Fe(II) ion (Benes et al., 1983). Therefore, if nicotinamine is responsible for cellular Fe transport in both grasses and other plants, then different processes may be involved in different groups of plants. As shown in the model for Fe uptake based on plasma-membrane Fe reduction in Fig. 8–5 (for dicots and nongraminaceous monocots), the fate of the Fe^{2+} ion is unclear once it enters the cell. Based on the above model, Fe(II) ion would be complexed with nicotianamine, and would then be "shuttled" within and between cells as the Fe(II)-nicotianamine complex. However, as will be discussed later, the predominant form of Fe in the xylem sap may be Fe(III)-citrate (Tiffin, 1972). Therefore, before entering the xylem sap, cellular Fe(II) iron may be oxidized to Fe^{3+}; this possibly occurs as the Fe is transported across the plasma membrane of the xylem parenchyma cells into the xylem vessels. For grasses, the situation may be different. It has been suggested that Fe enters the root cells in grasses either as the intact Fe(III)-siderophore complex or as Fe^{3+} ion, after a membrane-mediated splitting of the Fe-siderophore complex (Fig. 8–6). Therefore, once the ferric ion enters the symplasm, it must be reduced to Fe^{2+}, presumably by a cytoplasmic reductase, before binding to nicotianamine. Because of a lack of information concerning the form of Fe in the symplasm of plant cells, it should be stressed that these models are highly speculative.

There is almost no information concerning models for complexation and the subsequent intercellular and intracellular transport of the other micronutrient cations. Scholz et al. (1985) found that the *chloronerva* tomato mutant exhibited excess Fe absorption into the roots, which was reduced to normal levels by application of nicotianamine to either the nutrient solution or the shoots. They speculated that nicotianamine was part of a regulatory system for Fe uptake that was based on formation of Fe(II)-nicotianamine complex in the cytoplasm following membrane-mediated Fe(III) reduction and the subsequent Fe^{2+} absorption. They stressed that this was quite speculative, and the actual workings of the model are unclear. In a subsequent paper, Scholz et al. (1987) found that the tomato mutant also exhibited greater rates of Mn^{2+}, Zn^{2+}, and Cu^{2+} uptake compared with the wild-type plant, and that this increased uptake was reduced to the level of the wild-type plant by the application of nicotianamine. Therefore, they suggested that nicotianamine may not be a specific symplasmic carrier for Fe^{2+}, but may be a general carrier for all of the divalent heavy-metal cations.

The only other work relating to the symplasmic transport of the other micronutrient cations concerns the recent discovery of a class of heavy-metal-binding peptides in plants that have been called phytochelatins (Grill et al., 1985, 1987). The peptides consist of a chain of repeating glutamine-cysteine residues (from two to eight repeats) with a glycine residue at the carboxy-terminus. These compounds have been shown to increase in some plants in response to the application of heavy metals, and the primary role of these compounds has been hypothesized to be a detoxification mechanism in response to heavy-metal stress (Grill et al., 1986, 1987; Robinson & Jackson, 1986). However, because these compounds chelate certain essential micronutrient cations and are induced upon exposure to Zn^{2+}, Cu^{2+}, and Ni^{2+}, it has been suggested that they may play a role in the intercellular and intracellular movement of these micronutrients (Robinson & Jackson, 1986; Walker & Welch, 1987). Again, as has been stated for many other aspects of micronutrient transport, this important and very poorly understood area of micronutrient nutrition certainly would benefit from more intensive future research.

IV. LONG-DISTANCE MICRONUTRIENT TRANSLOCATION

There has been very little progress in our understanding of micronutrient translocation in the xylem and phloem over the past 15 yr. Again, this is due, in part, to little research interest directed toward this topic. Also, there are obvious technical limitations in accessing the xylem and phloem sap without significantly altering the processes and chemistry involved in long-distance micronutrient transport in the intact plant. Most of the work in this area has dealt with two subjects: the forms that the micronutrients take in the xylem, usually as complexes with organic and inorganic ligands, and also the effect of transpiration on the movement of micronutrients from the root to the top. Most of the work on the chemistry of the xylem sap has been conducted with plants whose tops have been severed, through the collection of xylem sap that exudes from the excised root due to root pressure. Certainly there are difficulties in modeling nutrient flow via transpiration in the xylem in intact plants with this type of excised system. Also, the analytical procedures used to analyze xylem (and phloem) sap often are conducted under conditions considerably different than those in situ. Therefore, the complex metal-chelate chemistry that is so important to micronutrient translocation could quite possibly be altered in vitro studies (different ionic strengths, pH buffers, redox potentials, etc.), such that data interpretation becomes equivocal. Because of the greater difficulties in accessing phloem sap, even fewer studies have been conducted on micronutrient transport in the phloem. The delicate nature of the phloem and the tendency for the sieve plates to be blocked with callose upon cutting into the sieve tubes are the primary problems in obtaining phloem sap. In order to obtain enough phloem sap to detect the low levels of micronutrients in the sap, plants such as castor-bean (*Ricinus communis*), that bleed freely from shallow cuts in the stem are often used (Milburn, 1971). The obvious limitations of this technique are the availability of only a few plant species for phloem studies, and the problems of micronutrient contamination of the phloem sap by other tissues. Indicative of the lack of recent progress (and interest) in this topic is that there are no recent reviews in this area. Therefore, the reader is referred to Tiffin (1972, 1976) for a more detailed consideration of the subject.

The chemical composition of the xylem and phloem sap are complex and quite different from each other (see Table 8–2). The xylem sap is buffered at a pH value of around 5.5, and is considerably more dilute than the phloem. In addition to the inorganic constituents shown in Table 8–2, the xylem sap contains organic acids (mostly malate, citrate, and maleic acid) and amino acids in the mol m^{-3} range (< 10.0 mol m^{-3}; Butz & Long, 1979; White et al., 1981a). The phloem on the other hand usually has a pH value around 8.0, has a considerably higher solute concentration (mostly sucrose and K$^+$), and also contains a similar complement of organic acids and amino acids as found in the xylem, but at higher concentrations. Therefore, because metal complexation is quite sensitive to solution pH, ionic strength, and solute concentration (White et al., 1981b), the very different compositions of the xylem and phloem suggest that quite different micronutrient complexes exist in each long-distance pathway. In order to elucidate the nature of these complexes, much more detailed knowledge of xylem and phloem composition from various plant species must be obtained.

One area in which some progress has been made is the use of computer-based models such as CHELATE (White et al., 1981b) and GEOCHEM (Sposito & Mattigod, 1980), which can be used to calculate all the equilibrium species (free-metal ions, metal complexes, free ligands, etc.) in a system such as xylem or phloem sap. White et al. (1981a, b, c) have analyzed the metal-chelate chemistry of the xylem sap obtained from the stem exudate of soybean and tomato with the CHELATE program. They first performed a detailed analysis of the xylem sap inorganic and organic composition, and then used the data in conjunction with the CHELATE program to calculate the distribution of metals in various complexes. This type of work is an important starting point in developing an understanding of the complex interactions that occur in the plant in terms of metal-chelate interactions. However, the lack of knowledge in this area is underscored by the necessity, in the work by White and colleagues, to make many assumptions concerning xylem sap composition that could easily result in erroneous conclusions based on the computer program calculations.

Another point to consider involves the mechanism of the unloading of micronutrient cations from the xylem parenchyma to the xylem sap. For most of the micronutrient cations, the concentration of total micronutrient in the xylem sap is probably greater than the cytoplasmic concentration of the xylem parenchyma (see, for example, calculations and measurements for Cu^{2+} in sunflower xylem exudate; Graham, 1979). If xylem parenchyma cells, like other plant cells, maintain a significant membrane potential (interior negative), then there also exists an electrical gradient opposing micronutrient cation transport into the xylem. Therefore, the possibility exists that active transport systems must exist for the unloading of micronutrient cations into the xylem. Of course, it must be remembered that this situation is complicated by the fact that as the micronutrient cations enter the xylem, they are complexed by organic and amino acids. Hence, the concentration of free micronutient cations may be extremely low in the xylem sap. Similar conceptual problems arise when one considers the loading and unloading of micronutrient cations into and out of the phloem. However, the problems are even greater with the phloem because even less is known about the concentration and forms of micronutrients in the phloem sap.

A. Iron

1. Iron Transport in the Xylem

In terms of long-distance transport of trace metals, including the micronutrient cations, the metals usually are found in solutions in which the organic ligands are considerably more concentrated than the metals. Usually, the transported metal-ligand complexes are in the form of anionic complexes (Tiffin, 1976). There is evidence that Fe is transported in the xylem as a Fe(III)-citrate complex. Tiffin (1966, 1970) electrophoretically analyzed the xylem exudate from soybean and sunflower following the absorption of ^{59}Fe by the roots. The Fe was shown to be in an anionic complex, and it was shown that a citrate peak co-migrated with the Fe peak, as determined by electrophoresis. There was also a much larger peak of free citrate that migrated more slowly than the complex. So it appears that citrate, which has a strong affinity for Fe(III) ion, is present well in excess of the concentration needed to complex all of the Fe^{3+} in the xylem, even in the presence of the other organic ligands that have a lesser affinity for Fe(III) ion. From the mobility of the Fe(III) citrate peak, Tiffin (1976) speculated that the form of the complex is the Fe(III) citrate dimer, $Fe_2Cit_2^-$, which should be quite stable under the conditions in the xylem, according to the calculations of Timberlake (1964). It should be noted that because citrate contains three COOH groups, all of which should be deprotonated in a complex with Fe(III), the only way for this Fe-citrate complex to be anionic is for the OH group on the citric acid to lose a proton. In the work of White et al. (1981b) with the CHELATE program, their model predicted that essentially all of the Fe in the xylem was complexed to citrate. However, it was unclear as to the molecular nature of the Fe-citrate complex in their model.

Because the experimental conditions by which xylem sap is collected, and Fe and Fe-complexes are isolated, can vary significantly from the conditions in the intact plant (in terms of E_H, pH, ionic strength, possible organic ligands), the possibiity exists that, during the isolation procedure, the naturally occurring forms of Fe could undergo changes in redox state and ligand binding. For example, both Fe(II) and Fe(III) complexes could occur in the xylem, but during the extraction and isolation procedures, the Fe(II) ion could be oxidized to Fe(III), yielding the erroneous result that all of the xylem Fe exists as Fe(III) complexes [such as Fe(III) citrate].

2. Iron Transport in the Phloem

As seen in Table 8-2, Fe is found in the phloem in concentrations that exceed those in the xylem (Ziegler, 1975). Iron is considered to be "intermediately mobile" in plants (see Table 8-3; Ziegler, 1975) and has been shown to be exported from the leaves (Brown et al., 1965; Bukovac & Wittwer, 1957). However, other than the recent work by Maas et al. (1988), very little work has been conducted on the form of Fe in the phloem. The alkaline pH of the phloem will have a significant influence on the form of the Fe complex. Because Fe(III) ion is extremely insoluble at alkaline pH values, the possibility exists that both Fe(II) and Fe(III) ion exists in the phloem (see below).

Recently, some interesting work on the involvement of phloem Fe in the regulation of the Fe-deficiency stress response in dicots was conducted by Bienfait and colleagues. This work addressed the role of the shoot and the root in regulating Fe absorption under Fe deficiency stress. Bienfait et al. (1987), working with potato (*Solanum tuberosum* L.), clearly showed that the characteristic Fe deficiency response [increased Fe(III) reductase activity, stimulated H^+ extrusion, and root hair development] was exhibited in potato roots from which the shoots had been removed. Thus, they concluded that the roots control the Fe deficiency response. However, because foliar Fe levels are closely regulated, it is hard to conceive of a regulatory system that does not include feedback signals from the shoot to the root. In the work of Bienfait et al. (1987), they suggested that the shoot could exert a modulating influence on the expression of the root-regulating responses through either sugars or Fe transported in the phloem from the shoot to the root.

They investigated this hypothesis in more detail recently, in a study that examined the role of phloem Fe in the regulation of the Fe deficiency response expressed in roots (Maas et al., 1988). In this study, the phloem exudate was collected from the stem of both Fe-deficient and Fe-sufficient castorbean plants. Analysis of the phloem Fe indicated that it exists as an anionic complex of a molecular weight of ~2400. It appears that most of the complexed Fe is in the Fe(III) form, but there is a continuous reduction-oxidation of Fe occurring in the phloem, such that there is a low, but significant, level of Fe(II) ion in the phloem. It is unclear if the Fe(II) ion is complexed or exists as the free ion.

The Fe content of the phloem was lower in Fe-sufficient plants than in Fe-deficient plants (7 and 20 mmol m^{-3}, respectively). Also, it was observed that if Fe-EDTA was applied to the leaves of Fe-deficient bean (*Phaseolus vulgaris*) plants, the Fe content of the roots was increased in 2 d, and a concomitant decrease in the Fe deficiency response in the roots was found. Therefore, they concluded that the leaf Fe content is reflected in the Fe levels in the phloem, and enough Fe can be carried in the phloem to the roots to influence the development of the Fe deficiency stress response in the roots.

B. Manganese

1. Manganese Transport in the Xylem

Manganese can move quite easily in the xylem sap, and a very wide range of concentrations have been reported in the xylem, from 1 to 3500 mmol m^{-3} (see Loneragan, 1988, for a detailed review of Mn translocation). Apparently, Mn levels in the xylem are not closely regulated, and reflect the environmental variables influencing Mn and water availability to the roots. Several studies have indicated that Mn is transported predominantly as Mn^{2+} ion in the xylem (Graham, 1979; Tiffin, 1972). In the studies of White et al. (1981b) using the CHELATE program, they calculated that less than one-half of the Mn in the xylem exudate of soybean and tomato was weakly complexed to citric and malic acids, and the rest existed as the free ion. They also pointed out that the weak bonding of Mn to organic ligands could result in alterations in the Mn complex during sample collection and analysis. Generally, Mn is thought to exist in the xylem sap as the free ion in equilibrium with unstable complexes with organic acids.

2. Manganese Transport in the Phloem

Most of the work on phloem translocation of Mn has come from analysis of phloem sap and from studies on the transport of radioactive ^{54}Mn^{2+} applied to the leaves. Analysis of phloem sap has yielded a wide range in Mn concentrations, from 2 to 1000 mmol m^{-3} (Loneragan, 1988). In general, the concentration of phloem Mn is much higher than that found in the xylem. Because the phloem contains higher concentrations of amino acids and organic acids, one would expect a high degree of Mn complexation. However, Van Goor and Wiersma (1976) analyzed the forms of Mn in the phloem sap of castorbean and found that most of the Mn existed as free Mn^{2+}, whereas some was complexed to organic compounds with molecular weights of 1000 to 5000.

Based on the transport of ^{54}Mn^{2+} applied to leaves, Mn is usually characterized as "intermediately mobile" (Marschner, 1986). However, Loneragan (1988) has quite properly pointed out the shortcomings of this technique. This method establishes that some radioactive Mn can be translocated from the leaves when it is painted on the leaves. However, it provides no evidence for translocation of endogenous Mn from the leaf cells into the phloem. Also, because the leaves are painted with ^{54}Mn^{2+} of a high specific radioactivity, movement of radiolabel out of the leaves may not reflect significant transport of total Mn to sink regions.

3. Redistribution of Manganese

The picture concerning redistribution of Mn throughout the plant is complex. In Mn-adequate plants, Mn concentrations are generally higher in the roots than in the leaves (Loneragan, 1988). As the plants experience Mn deficiency, Mn concentrations decrease rapidly in the roots and stems, but remain high in the older leaves (Loneragan, 1988). It appears that Mn can be mobilized easily from the root to the shoot in the xylem, but is poorly mobilized from the older leaves via the phloem. In some species, the remobilization of Mn in the phloem is even more complex. In lupines (*Lupinus angustifolius* L.) grown with adequate Mn (containing high concentrations of Mn in their roots), that are subsequently placed in Mn-deficient conditions, the young leaves, which are supplied by the phloem, quickly become Mn deficient. However, the developing seeds, which are also fed by the phloem, continue to receive adequate Mn for quite some time (Hannam et al., 1985).

Therefore, as reviewed by Loneragan (1988), this complex behavior by Mn does not fit into the traditional classification scheme for phloem mobility (Table 8–3). That is, Mn is phloem mobile when moving into developing seeds, and is simultaneously phloem immobile for mobilization out of older leaves and roots to the young leaves. These problems certainly warrant further work, particularly in relation to problems concerning Mn deficiency that limit crop productivity in certain soils throughout the world.

C. Copper

The translocation and distribution of Cu within plants is complicated because, among the micronutrient cations, Cu^{2+} binds most strongly to organic N-ligands such as proteins and amino acids. Thus, the metal-complex chemistry, as it relates to Cu, plays an extremely important role in the movement of Cu. For a more detailed review of this topic, the reader is referred to Loneragan (1981).

1. Copper Transport in the Xylem

Copper has been found in the xylem exudate in a fairly wide range of concentrations, from trace amounts to concentrations as high as 14 mmol m^{-3} (Loneragan, 1981). Also, xylem Cu levels can vary as a result of changes in environmental conditions. For example, Cu levels in the xylem exudate of lupine varied from 4 mmol m^{-3} at dawn to 0.4 mmol m^{-3} at dusk (Hocking et al., 1978). Because of the lack of a radioisotope for Cu with a reasonably long half-life, it has been difficult to study the forms of Cu in the xylem. Because the xylem sap has moderate levels of nitrogenous compounds (amino acids, amides, and ureides; Pate, 1980), all of which can complex Cu^{2+} quite strongly, it is generally accepted that Cu is complexed in the xylem with organic-N ligands. In an electrophoretic study of the xylem exudate from four different dicot plants, all of the Cu was found in one or more anionic complexes, possibly with amino acids (Tiffin, 1972). Because Cu^{2+} has been shown to be adsorbed quite readily by root cell walls, the Cu in the xylem must be complexed in order to move freely to the tops. As Loneragan (1981) speculates, the absorption of Cu by cells of the leaves from the xylem sap probably involves a transport mechanism similar to that employed by the root cells, in order to obtain Cu from the fairly strong complexes.

2. Copper Transport in the Phloem

Phloem transport of Cu has been studied primarily by analysis of the phloem exudate, translocation studies of radioactive $^{64}Cu^{2+}$ applied to the leaves, and observations of the changes in leaf-Cu content over time. There have been some problems with research into phloem Cu for two reasons. First, because of the lack of a reasonably long-lived radioisotope translocation studies are difficult to conduct. Second, analysis of phloem exudates has been complicated by contamination from other nonphloem tissues.

Copper is found in the phloem in concentrations ranging from 3 to 140 mmol m^{-3} (Loneragan, 1981). Because of the alkaline pH value of the phloem and the high concentrations of nitrogenous compounds, the probability that phloem-Cu is complexed to soluble organic N compounds is even higher than in the xylem. The previously mentioned studies of Bukovac and Wittwer (1957), in which radioactive Cu^{2+} was painted on the leaves of bean seedlings and translocation of radioactive Cu was visualized with autoradiography, caused the authors to classify Cu as "partially mobile." However, as noted by Loneragan (1981), the autoradiographs do not support this conclusion because very little Cu movement was observed. This work was complicated by the fact that most of the foliarly applied Cu^{2+} was probably bound to the leaf cell walls and the results were probably not representative of in vivo phloem translocation. However, strong evidence in favor of significant phloem mobility of Cu has been presented from field studies demonstrating that, when Cu was sprayed on certain limbs of Cu-deficient almond [*Prunus dulcis* (Miller)] trees, the leaves and kernels on unsprayed limbs recovered from Cu deficiency and their Cu levels increased significantly (Kester et al., 1961).

However, the concept of phloem mobility for Cu is complex because the young leaves of many plants are often the first to show Cu deficiency (Bussler, 1981), which is often interpreted to mean that the nutrient is phloem immobile. It appears that the answer to this apparent contradiction lies in the observation that, under certain conditions, leaf Cu is highly immobile in the phloem and, at other times, it is highly mobile (the reasons for this will be discussed below). Hence, Loneragan has suggested that the term "variably mobile" be used to describe the behavior of Cu in the phloem (Loneragan, 1981).

3. Redistribution of Copper

The concentration of Cu in roots is generally higher than that in the shoots. As the concentration of Cu in the uptake solution is increased, the root-Cu concentration increases much more rapidly than in the shoot (Graves, 1978; Jarvis, 1978). Much of this Cu in the roots is associated with cell walls. When plants are transferred from Cu-sufficient to deficient conditions, the roots appear to retain much of their Cu, even in the face of severe deficiencies (Jarvis & Robson, 1982). The reasons for this Cu immobilization in the roots are not understood.

In the shoots, Cu distribution appears to be correlated with the distribution of N. Hill et al. (1979) has shown a very close correlation between Cu and N levels in the oldest leaves of wheat in relation to Cu nutrition and shading. Loneragan (1981) has analyzed much of the available data concerning the redistribution of both Cu and N under various conditions, and has presented a hypothesis that quite reasonably explains the available data. He has hypothesized that the variable phloem mobility of Cu is directly linked to N metabolism and transport. That is, as Cu enters the leaf it is bound to proteins and is not available for retranslocation, even under Cu-deficient conditions, until the leaves senesce and the proteins are hydrolyzed. Then, Cu is exported out of the leaves as complexes with the nitrogenous compounds that are produced by the hydrolysis of the proteins. This hypothesis explains the confusing results concerning phloem mobility presented earlier, and is a good foundation for further studies into the physiology of Cu translocation as it relates to Cu deficiency.

D. Zinc and Nickel

Very little research has been conducted on the translocation of Zn and Ni in plants; therefore, these micronutrients will be considered only briefly. There have been several studies of Zn in the xylem exudate of various plants, which have reported Zn concentrations ranging from ~ 4 to 22 mmol m^{-3} (Clark et al., 1986; Hocking, 1980; Hocking et al., 1978; White et al., 1981a). In terms of the forms of Zn in the xylem, it is unclear from the earlier work of Tiffin (1972) whether Zn exists as the free Zn^{2+} ion or if it is complexed with organic acids. The more recent theoretical work of White et al. (1981b) with the CHELATE computer program suggests that, in soybean and tomato, there is significant complexation with citric and malic acids. In terms of phloem Zn, Hocking (1980) found fairly high concentrations of Zn in the phloem of *Nicotiana* (~ 240 mmol m^{-3}), which was about 10 times higher than the Zn concentration in the xylem for the same plant. There is evidence for complexation of Zn in the phloem. Van Goor and Wiersma (1976) found that all of the Zn in the phloem exudate of castorbean was complexed in an anionic organic complex of molecular weight between 1000 and 1500. More recently, Taylor et al. (1988) analyzed the phloem sap of orange trees [*Citrus sinensis* (L.)] and grapefruit (*Citrus × paradisi* Macfad.) for Zn, in relation to a study of citrus blight. They found a highly anionic organic complex of zinc with a molecular weight of around 4000. Using diethylaminoethyl (DEAE)-Sephadex chromatography of the Zn-binding fraction, the existence of at least four different anionic species was revealed, of which two occurred in healthy plants and two in diseased plants. The Zn-binding compounds appear to be part of the class of compounds called phytochelatins described earlier.

Tiffin (1972) has analyzed the concentration and forms of Ni in the xylem exudate of a number of different plants. The xylem concentration for Ni, when plants were grown on a reasonable Ni^{2+} concentration (0.5 mmol m^{-3}), ranged from 0.5 to 2.4 mmol m^{-3}. From electrophoretic analysis of the xylem sap, it appears that a portion of the Ni is complexed in an anionic, low-molecular-weight complex, whereas the rest of the Ni exists as free Ni^{2+} ion. More recently. Cataldo et al. (1988) analyzed the xylem exudate of soybean for Ni. They found that Ni was found associated with both organic acids and amino acid ligands. They noted that the number and distribution of specific Ni-complexes varied with plant age, and appears to be related to the changes in the amino and organic acid composition in the xylem as the plant matures. In terms of Ni in the phloem, Wiersma and Van Goor (1979) have analyzed the form of Ni in the phloem sap of castorbean and found it existed as an anionic complex with a molecular weight between 1000 and 5000. Finally, a recent study of the phloem mobility of Ni^{2+} in pea and geranium [*Pelargonium zonale* (L.)] plants was conducted, based on the translocation of radioactive $^{63}Ni^{2+}$ applied to source leaves. They found that Ni^{2+} was translocated quite readily out of the source leaf in both species. Keeping in mind the experimental limitations of this technique discussed previously, it appears that Ni is quite phloem mobile.

E. Boron

The small amount of work that has been conducted on B translocation indicates that long-distance transport of this essential micronutrient, as is also the case for the transport of B across membranes, is not clearly understood. The general idea presented in plant texts is that B moves from the root to the top in the xylem, closely following the transpirational movement of water. There appears to be very limited movement of B in the phloem, which is significant in terms of the requirements of shoot apices and reproductive structures for B. For a more detailed treatment of B transport in higher plants, the reader is referred to the review of Raven (1980).

1. Boron Transport in the Xylem

In terms of the transport of B (as boric acid) into the xylem, and the subsequent translocation of B to the shoot, the mass flow of water appears to significantly influence these processes (Raven, 1980). The interrelationship between B and water fluxes can be complex, for it could involve the movement of B to the root surface via mass flow, accumulation of B in the root, and the subsequent translocation to the shoot. Bowen (1972) investigated the effects of varying the transpiration rate on B uptake into sugar cane and found that, at different transpiration rates, various ratios of B uptake to water uptake were observed. However, this ratio was always significantly greater than the ratio of B to water in the external solution, which implies that roots exert some control over B uptake into the plant. Boron translocation to the shoot was also studied and Bowen found that the shoot-B content could be predicted by the root-B content and the water flux in the xylem. That is, once B is absorbed into the root, it appears to be freely available for passive transport into and through the xylem. This would indicate that the B concentration in the xylem stream and the root would be approximately equal. As Raven (1980) has pointed out, this was probably true in the work of Bowen because very low transpiration rates were used and the roots were probably not at steady state with the relatively high external B concentration used during the experiment.

Evidence in support of some amount of root regulation of B transport into the xylem can be derived from discrepancies between calculations of B concentrations in the xylem sap (1 to 65 mmol m^{-3}) and much higher root-B levels (100 to 1000 mmol m^{-3}; Brown & Jones, 1971; Gauch, 1972; Mengel & Kirkby, 1982). Experimental evidence supporting this point can be found in the work of Brown and Jones (1971) with B-efficient and B-inefficient cultivars of tomato. When both cultivars were grown under B-deficient conditions, the root-B concentrations were similar, yet the B concentration in the xylem sap and shoots of the B-inefficient cultivar were much lower than in the efficient cultivar. These results indicate that B transport in the xylem is not merely by passive diffusion. More recently, Halbrooks et al. (1986) looked at the effects of varying the transpiration rate in red beet (by imposing various relative humidity [RH] regimes) on B uptake and translocation. They found that growth rates were much faster under high RH conditions and significantly affected data interpretation. When all of the measured parameters were expressed per unit dry weight, it was found that increasing the transpiration rate increased B uptake into the roots, but not translocation to the shoot. They found that shoot growth rate and B accumulation in shoots were closely correlated, and proposed that B translocation to the shoot is controlled by rates of dry matter accumulation in the shoot during periods of rapid growth.

2. Boron Transport in the Phloem

Generally, it is believed that B is not translocated in the phloem, that is, B is "phloem immobile." However, this area is marked by some confusion and controversy. There have not been many studies analyzing phloem levels of B. The most detailed was that Tammes and van Die (1966) with *Yucca*, in which the B concentration in the phloem exudate obtained from the severed peduncle supporting the inflorescence was found to be ~ 1.0 mol m^{-3}. Although this is considerably lower than the B levels in the source leaves (34 mol m^{-3}) or the sink inflorescence (2 mol m^{-3}), it is still reasonably high. It could be argued that this phloem B is probably bound via esters with *cis*-diols (sugar alcohols), but this is purely speculation. Therefore, based on this one study, it appears that B does enter the phloem. Oertli and his colleagues have put forth an interesting hypothesis to explain the apparent phloem immobility of B (Oertli & Ahmed, 1971; Oertli & Richardson, 1970). They demonstrated that B enters the bark (presumably the phloem) of cotton (*Gossypium hirsutum* L.), remains water soluble, and can be translocated if the bark is separated from the xylem with wax paper. They have hypothesized that because boric acid can easily cross plant membranes, it readily enters (and leaves) the phloem sieve tubes. Based on available data, they made the reasonable assumption that the xylem sap entering the leaves has a low B concentration, and that evapotranspiration leads to high B concentrations in the leaves. Subsequently, the B enters the phloem and is translocated out of the leaf. Due to the close proximity of the xylem and phloem in the petiole, along with the concentration gradient for B from the phloem to the xylem, the ability for B to cross membranes, and the rapid transpirational water flux in the xylem back into the leaf, boric acid in the phloem would move into the xylem and be swept back into the leaf. Raven (1980) has attempted to make the model more quantitative by using known or calculated values for xylem and phloem B levels, phloem and xylem transport rates, and an approximate permeability coefficient for B, and has found that the qualitative model of Oertli and Richardson (1970) is substantiated by these calculations.

There have been several studies that have used the stable B isotope, ^{10}B, as a stable tracer for the ^{11}B isotope. The ^{10}B isotope was applied to source leaves in white clover (*Trifolium repens* L.) and radish, in order to monitor the translocation of B out of the leaves (Chamel et al., 1981; Martini & Thellier, 1980). Keeping in mind the potential problems with this technique as discussed earlier for radioisotopes (Loneragan, 1981), evidence for some phloem mobility of B has been found. Martini and Thellier (1980) found that about 98% of the applied B was bound at the site of application, presumably through ester bond formation with *cis*-diols in the cell walls. However, the other 2% of the B was highly mobile, and this translocated B correlated with an alleviation of B deficiency in the untreated tissue. Chamel et al. (1981) found similar results with radish. All of these seemingly contradictory results indicate that, again, very little is known about the translocation of another essential micronutrient and much more research into this important and interesting problem is needed.

V. CONCLUSION: FUTURE PROSPECTS

As has been pointed out regularly in this review, since the publication of the first edition of this book, there has been significant progress concerning our understanding of the mechanisms and regulation of micronutrient transport and translocation in a few specific areas (mostly concerning Fe). In contrast, over the same period, our understanding of membrane physiology and ion transport in general has increased significantly. One of the reasons for a lack of progress in many areas of micronutrient transport is simply a lack of research directed toward these topics. Certainly, in light of our lack of understanding concerning the acquisition and utilization of these essential nutrients, along with demonstrations of significant micronutrient deficiencies and toxicities limiting crop productivity and quality in many soils throughout the world, much more research effort should be directed toward these areas. Furthermore, with the recent technological and conceptual advances in a number of areas that are related to micronutrient nutrition, which include advancements in the areas of molecular biology, microanalytical techniques, computer applications, and membrane biology, biologists have a new array of powerful tools and techniques at their disposal that should allow them to start to unravel these complex problems at the molecular, cellular, and whole plant level.

ACKNOWLEDGMENTS

I would like to thank Drs. Ross Welch and Michael Grusak of the U.S. Plant, Soil, and Nutrition Laboratory, USDA-ARS, for their helpful discussions during the preparation of this manuscript, and to Mr. Jon Shaff and Dr. Grusak for their invaluable assistance in preparing this manuscript.

REFERENCES

Ambler, J.E., J.C. Brown, and H.G. Gauch. 1971. Sites of iron reduction in soybean plants. Agron. J. 63:95–97.

Anderson, W.P. 1976. Transport through roots. p. 129–156. *In* U. Lüttge and M.G. Pitman (ed.) Encyclopedia of plant physiology, new series. Vol. 2B. Springer-Verlag, Berlin.

Anderson, W.P., and E.J. Reilly. 1968. A study of the exudation of excised maize roots after removal of the epidermis and outer cortex. J. Exp. Bot. 19:19–30.

Ansari, A.Q., and D.J.F. Bowling. 1972. The effect of water and salt fluxes on the transroot electrical potential in *Helianthus annuus*. J. Exp. Bot. 23:641–650.

Aschmann, S.G., and R.J. Zaososki. 1987. Nickel and rubidium uptake by whole oat plants in solution culture. Physiol. Plant. 71:191–196.

Asher, C.J. 1987. Effects of nutrient concentration in the rhizosphere on plant growth. Proc. Congr. Int. Soc. Sci., 13th 5:209–215.

Asher, C.J., and D.G. Edwards. 1983. Modern solution culture techniques. p. 94–119. *In* A. Läuchli and R.L. Bieleski (ed.) Encyclopedia of plant physiology, new series. Vol. 15A. Springer-Verlag, Berlin.

Bange, G.G.F. 1973. Diffusion and absorption of ions in plant tissue. III. The role of the root cortex cells in ion absorption. Acta Bot. Neerl. 22:529–542.

Barber, D.A., and R.B. Lee. 1974. The effect of microorganisms on the absorption of manganese by plants. New Phytol. 73:97–106.

Barrett-Lennard, E.G., H. Marschner, and V. Römheld. 1983. Mechanism of short-term FeIII reduction by roots. Evidence against the role of secreted reductants. Plant Physiol. 73:893–898.

Beilby, M.J., and N.A. Walker. 1981. Chloride transport in *Chara*. I. Kinetics and current-voltage curves for a probable proton symport. J. Exp. Bot. 32:43–54.

Bell, C.W., and O. Biddulph. 1963. Translocation of calcium. Exchange *versus* mass flow. Plant Physiol. 38:610–614.

Benes, I., K. Schreiber, H. Ripperberger, and A. Kircheiss. 1983. Metal complex formation by nicotianamine, a possible phytosiderophore. Experientia 39:261–262.

Bennett, A.B., S.D. O'Neill, and R.M. Spanswick. 1984. H^+-ATPase activity from storage tissue of *Beta vulgaris*. I. Identification and characterization of an anion-sensitive H^+-ATPase. Plant Physiol. 74:538–544.

Bennett, A.B., and R.M. Spanswick. 1983. Solubilization and reconstitution of an anion-sensitive H^+-ATPase from corn roots. J. Membr. Biol. 75:21–31.

Bienfait, H.F. 1985. Regulated redox processes at the plasmalemma of plant root cells and their function in iron uptake. J. Bioenerg. Biomembr. 17:73–83.

Bienfait, H.F. 1988a. Mechanisms in Fe-efficiency reactions of higher plants. J. Plant Nutr. 11:605–629.

Bienfait, H.F. 1988b. Proteins under the control of the gene for Fe efficiency in tomato. Plant Physiol. 88:785–787.

Bienfait, H.F., R.J. Bino, A.M. VanDer Bliek, J.F. Duivenvoorden, and J.M. Fontaine. 1983. Characterization of ferric reduced activity in roots of Fe-deficient *Phaseolus vulgaris*. Physiol. Plant. 59:196–202.

Bienfait, H.F., L.A. DeWeger, and D. Kramer. 1987. Control of development of iron-efficiency reactions in potato as a response to iron deficiency is located in the roots. Plant Physiol. 83:244–247.

Bienfait, H.F., H.J. Lubberding, P. Heutink, L. Linder, J. Visser, R. Kaptain, and K. Dijkstra. 1989. Rhizosphere acidification by iron deficient bean plants: the role of trace amounts of divalent metal ions. A study on roots of intact plants with the use of ^{11}C- and ^{31}P-NMR. Plant Physiol. 90:359–364.

Bingham, F.T., A. Elseewi, and J.J. Oertli. 1970. Characteristics of boron absorption by barley roots. Soil Sci. Soc. Am. J. 34:613–618.

Blumwald, E., and R.J. Poole. 1985a. Na^+/H^+ antiport in isolated tonoplast vesicles from storage tissue of *Beta vulgaris*. Plant Physiol. 78:163–167.

Blumwald, E., and R.J. Poole. 1985b. Nitrate storage and retrieval in *Beta vulgaris*: effects of nitrate and chloride on proton gradients in tonoplast vesicles. Proc. Natl. Acad. Sci. USA 82:3683–3687.

Bowen, J.E. 1968. Borate absorption in excised sugar cane leaves. Plant Cell Physiol. 9:467–472.

Bowen, J.E. 1969. Absorption of copper, zinc, and manganese by sugar cane tissue. Plant Physiol. 44:255–261.

Bowen, J.E. 1972. Effect of environmental factors on water utilization and boron accumulation and translocation in sugar cane. Plant Cell Physiol. 13:703–711.

Bowen, J.E. 1979. Kinetics of boron, zinc, and copper uptake by barley and sugar cane. p. 24. *In* W.L. Berry and A. Wallace (ed.) Trace element stress in plants. Proc. Int. Symp. Trace Element Stress, Los Angeles, CA. 6–9 Nov. 1979. Lab. Nuclear Med. Radiation Biol., Univ. of California, Los Angeles.

Bowen, J.E. 1981. Kinetics of active uptake of boron, zinc, copper, and manganese in barley and sugar cane. J. Plant Nutr. 3:215–223.

Bowen, J.E. 1986. Kinetics of zinc uptake by two rice (*Oryza sativa*) cultivars. Plant Soil 94:99–106.

Bowen, J.E., and P. Nissen. 1976. Boron uptake by excised barley roots. I. Uptake into the free space. Plant Physiol. 57:353–357.

Bowling, D.J.F. 1973. Measurement of a gradient of oxygen partial pressure across the intact root. Planta 111:323–328.

Broda, E., H. Dresser, and G. Findenegg. 1964. Wirkung von dinitrophenol, azid, und anaerobiose auf die zinkaufnahme durch algen. Naturwissenschaften 51:361–362.

Brown, J.C. 1978. Physiology of plant tolerance to alkaline soils. p. 257–276. *In* G.A. Jung (ed.) Crop tolerance to suboptimal land conditions. ASA Spec. Publ. 32. ASA, CSSA, and SSSA, Madison, WI.

Brown, J.C., and J.E. Ambler. 1973. "Reductants" released by roots of Fe-deficient soybeans. Agron. J. 65:311–314.

Brown, J.C., and J.E. Ambler. 1974. Iron stress response in tomato (*Lycopersicon esculentum*). 1. Sites of Fe reduction, absorption, and transport. Physiol. Plant. 31:221–224.

Brown, J.C., and R.L. Chaney. 1971. Effect of iron on the transport of citrate into the xylem of soybeans and tomatoes. Plant Physiol. 47:836–840.

Brown, J.C., and W.E. Jones. 1971. Differential transport of B in tomato (*Lycopersicon esculentum* Mill.). Physiol. Plant. 25:279–287.

Brown, J.C., and W.E. Jones. 1974. pH changes associated with iron-stress response. Physiol. Plant. 30:148–152.

Brown, J.C., and W.E. Jones. 1976. A technique to determine iron efficiency in plants. Soil Sci. Soc. Am. Proc. 40:398–405.

Brown, J.C., L.O. Tiffin, A.W. Specht, and J.W. Resnicky. 1961. Stability and concentration of metal chelates, factors, in iron chlorosis of plants. Agron. J. 53:85–90.

Brown, J.C., S. Yamaguchi, and J. Leal-Diaz. 1965. Evidence for translocation of iron in plants. Plant Physiol. 40:35–38.

Brown, P.H., R.M. Welch, and E.E. Cary. 1987. Nickel: a micronutrient essential for all higher plants. Plant Physiol. 85:801–803.

Buckhout, T.J. 1983. ATP-dependent Ca^{2+} transport in endoplasmic reticulum isolated from roots of *Lepidium sativum*. Planta 159:84–90.

Buckhout, T.J. 1984. Characterization of Ca^{2+} transport in purified endoplasmic reticulum membrane vesicles from *Lepidium sativum* L. roots. Plant Physiol. 76:962–967.

Buckhout, T.J., P.F. Bell, D.G. Luster, and R.L. Chaney. 1989. Iron-stress reduced redox activity in tomato (*Lycopersicum esculentum* Mill.) is localized on the plasma membrane. Plant Physiol. 90:151–156.

Budesinsky, M., H. Budzikiewicz, Z. Prochazka, H. Ripperger, A. Romer, G. Scholz, and K. Schreiber. 1980. Nicotianamine, a possible phytosiderophore of general occurrence.. Phytochemistry 19:2295–2297.

Budesinsky, M., Z. Prochazka, H. Budzikiewicz, A. Römer, H. Ripperger, K. Schreiber, and G. Scholz. 1981. On the normalizing factor for the tomato mutant *chloronerva*. XI. Mass and nmr spectroscopic investigations of the phytosiderophore nicotianamine and some of its derivatives. Tetrahedron 37:191–196.

Bukovac, M.J., and S.H. Wittwer. 1957. Absorption and mobility of foliar applied nutrients. Plant Physiol. 32:428–435.

Bush, D.R., and H. Sze. 1986. Calcium transport in tonoplast and endoplasmic reticulum vesicles from cultured carrot cells. Plant Physiol. 80:549–555.

Bussler, W. 1981. Physiological functions and utilization of copper. p. 213–234. *In* J.F. Loneragan et al. (ed.) Copper in soils and plants. Academic Press, New York.

Butz, R.G., and R.C. Long. 1979. L-Malate as an essential component of the xylem fluid of corn seedling roots. Plant Physiol. 64:684–689.

Carpita, N., O. Sabulase, D. Montezinos, and D.P. Delmer. 1979. Determination of pore size of cell walls of living plants. Science 105:1144–1147.

Carroll, M.D., and J.F. Loneragan. 1968. Response of plant species to concentrations of zinc in solution. I. Growth and zinc content of plants. Aust. J. Agric. Res. 19:859–868.

Cataldo, D.A., T.R. Garland, and R.E. Wildung. 1978. Nickel in plants. I. Uptake kinetics using intact soybean seedlings. Plant Physiol. 62:563–565.

Cataldo, D.C., K.M. McFadden, T.R. Garland, and R.E. Wildung. 1988. Organic constituents and complexation of nickel(II), iron(III), cadmium(II), and plutonium(IV) in soybean xylem exudates. Plant Physiol. 86:734–739.

Cathala, N., and L. Salsac. 1975. Absorption of copper by the roots of corn (*Zea mays*) and sunflower (*Helianthus annuus*). Plant Soil 42:65–83.

Chaboud, A., and M. Rougier. 1984. Identification and localization of sugar components of rice (*Oryza sativa* L.) root cap mucilage. J. Plant Physiol. 116:323–330.

Chamel, A.R., A.M. Andreani, and J.F. Eloy. 1981. Distribution of foliar-applied boron measured by spark-source mass spectrometry and laser-probe mass spectrography. Plant Physiol. 67:457–459.

Chaney, R.L. 1984. Diagnostic practices to identify iron deficiency in higher plants. J. Plant Nutr. 7:47–67.

Chaney, R.L., and P.F. Bell. 1987. Complexity of iron nutrition: lessons for plant-soil interaction research. J. Plant Nutr. 10:963–994.

Chaney, R.L., J.C. Brown, and L.O. Tiffin. 1972. Obligatory reduction of ferric chelates in iron uptake by soybeans. Plant Physiol. 50:208–213.

Chaudry, F.M., and J.F. Loneragan. 1972. Zinc absorption by wheat seedlings and the nature of its inhibition by alkaline earth cations. J. Exp. Bot. 23:552–560.

Cheeseman, J.M., and J.B. Hanson. 1980. Does active K^+ ion influx to roots occur? Plant Sci. Lett. 18:81–84.

Churchill, K.A., and H. Sze. 1983. Anion-sensitive, H^+-pumping ATPase in membrane vesicles from oat roots. Plant Physiol. 71:610–617.

Claassen, N., and S.A. Barber. 1974. A method for characterizing the relation between nutrient concentration and flux into roots of intact plants. Plant Physiol. 54:564–568.

Clark, C.J., P.T. Holland, and G.S. Smith. 1986. Chemical composition of bleeding xylem sap from kiwifruit vines. Ann. Bot. 58:353–362.

Clarkson, D.T. 1974. Ion transport and cell structure in plants. McGraw-Hill, London.

Clarkson, D.T. 1988. Movements of ions across roots. p. 251–304. *In* D.A. Baker and J.L. Hall (ed.) Solute transport in plant cells and tissues. Longman Scientific and Technical, Essex, England.

Clarkson, D.T., and J.B. Hanson. 1980. The mineral nutrition of higher plants. Annu. Res. Plant Physiol. 31:239–298.

Clarkson, D.T., and J.B. Hanson. 1986. Proton fluxes and the activity of a stelar proton pump in onion roots. J. Exp. Bot. 37:1136–1150.

Clarkson, D.T., and J. Sanderson. 1969. The uptake of a polyvalent cation and its distribution in the root apices of *Allium cepa*: tracer and autoradiographic studies. Planta 89:136–154.

Clarkson, D.T., L. Williams, and J.B. Hanson. 1984. Perfusion of onion root xylem vessels: a method and some evidence of control of the pH of the xylem sap. Planta 16:361–369.

Colombo, R.A., A. Bonetti, and P. Lado. 1979. Promoting effects of fusicoccin on Na$^+$ efflux in barley roots. Plant. Cell Environ. 2:281–285.

Crafts, A.S., and T.C. Broyer. 1938. Migration of salts and water into xylem of roots of higher plants. Am. J. Bot. 24:415–431.

Craig, T.A., and F.L. Crane. 1980. Evidence for a trans-plasma membrane electron transport system in plant cells. Proc. Indian Acad. Sci. 90:150–155.

Davis, R.F., and N. Niginbotham. 1969. Effects of external cations and respiratory inhibitors on electrical potential of the xylem exudate of excised corn roots. Plant Physiol. 44:1383–1392.

Davis, R.F., and N. Higinbotham. 1976. Electrochemical gradients and K$^+$ and Cl$^-$ fluxes in corn roots. Plant Physiol. 57:129–136.

De Boer, A.H., H.B.A. Prins, and P.E. Zanstra. 1983. Biphasic composition of trans-root potential in roots of *Plantago* species: involvement of spatially separated electrogenic pumps. Planta 157:259–266.

De Michelis, M.I., M.C. Pugliarello, F. Rasi-Caldogno. 1983. Two distinct proton translocating ATPases are present in the membrane vesicles from radish seedlings. FEBS Lett. 162:85–90.

De Vos, C.R., H.J. Lubberding, and H.F. Bienfait. 1986. Rhizosphere acidification as a response to iron deficiency in bean plants. Plant Physiol. 81:842–846.

Dieter, P., and D. Marme. 1980. Calmodulin activation of plant microsomal Ca^{2+} uptake. Proc. Natl. Acad. Sci. USA 77:7311–7314.

Dixon, N.E., C. Gazzola, R.L. Blakely, and B. Zerner. 1975. Jack-bean urease. A metalloenzyme. A simple biological role for nickel. J. Am. Chem. Soc. 97:4131–4133.

Dragun, J., D.E. Baker, and M.L. Ricius. 1976. Growth and elemental accumulation by two single-cross corn hybrids as affected by copper in solution. Agron. J. 68:466–470.

DuPont, F.M., A.B. Bennett, and R.M. Spanswick. 1982. Localization of a proton-translocating ATPase on sucrose gradients. Plant Physiol. 70:1115–1119.

Epstein, E. 1972. Mineral nutrition of plants: Principles and perspectives. John Wiley and Sons, New York.

Epstein, E. 1976. Kinetics of ion transport and the carrier concept. p. 70–94. *In* U. Lüttge and M.G. Pitman (ed.) Encyclopedia of plant physiology. Vol. 2B. Springer-Verlag, Berlin.

Epstein, E., and C.E. Hagen. 1952. A kinetic study of the absorption of alkali cations by barley roots. Plant Physiol. 27:457–474.

Epstein, E., D.W. Rains, and O.E. Elzam. 1963. Resolution of dual mechanisms of potassium absorption by barley roots. Proc. Natl. Acad. Sci. USA 49:684–692.

Eskew, D.L., R.M. Welch, and E.E. Cary. 1983. Nickel: an essential micronutrient for legumes and possibly all higher plants. Science 222:621–623.

Foster, R.C. 1981. The ultrastructure and histochemistry of the rhizosphere. New Phytol. 89:263–273.

Gauch, H.G. 1972. Inorganic plant nutrition. Dowden, Hutchinson, and Ross, Stroudsburg, PA.

Giaquinta, R.T. 1983. Phloem loading of sucrose. Annu. Rev. Plant Physiol. 34:347–387.

Gilmour, J.T. 1977. Micronutrient status of the rice plant. I. Plant soil solution concentrations as a function of time. Plant Soil 46:549–557.

Giordano, P.M., J.C. Noggle, and J.J. Mortvedt. 1974. Zinc uptake by rice as affected by metabolic inhibitors and competing cations. Plant Soil 41:637–646.

Glass, A.D.M. 1989. Plant nutrition. An introduction to current concepts. Jones and Bartlett Publ., Boston.

Goodman, B.A., and D.J. Linehan. 1979. An electron paramagnetic resonance study of the uptake of Mn(II) and Cu(II) by wheat roots. p. 67–82. *In* J.L. Harley and R.S. Russell (ed.) The soil-root interface. Academic Press, London.

Goren, A., and H. Wanner. 1971. The absorption of lead and copper by roots of *Hordeum vulgare*. Schweiz. Bot. Ges. Berichte 80:334–340.

Graham, R.D. 1979. Transport of copper and manganese to the xylem exudate of sunflower. Plant Cell Environ. 2:139–143.

Graham, R.D. 1981. Absorption of copper by plant roots. p. 141–163. *In* J.F. Loneragan et al. (ed.) Copper in soils and plants. Academic Press, New York.

Graves, C.J. 1978. Uptake and distribution of copper in *Chrysanthemum morifolium*. Ann. Bot. 42:117–125.

Graves, C.J., and J.F. Sutcliffe. 1974. An effect of copper deficiency on the initiation and development of flower buds of *Chrysanthmum mortifolium* grown in solution culture. Ann. Bot. 38:729–738.

Grill, E., E.L. Winnacker, and M.H. Zenk. 1985. Phytochelatins: the principal heavy-metal complexing peptides of higher plants. Science 230:674–676.

Grill, E., E.L. Winnacker, and M.H. Zenk. 1987. Phytochelatins, a class of heavy-metal-bonding peptides from plants, are functionally analogous to metallothioneins. Proc. Natl. Acad. Sci. USA. 84:439–443.

Gross, J., and D. Marme. 1978. ATP-dependent Ca^{2+} uptake into plant membrane vesicles. Proc. Natl. Acad. Sci. USA 75:1232–1236.

Grusak, M.A., R.M. Welch, and L.V. Kochian. 1989. A transport mutant for the study of plant root iron absorption. p. 61–66. *In* J. Dainty et al. (ed.) Plant membrane transport: The current position. Elsevier Press, Amsterdam, Netherlands.

Grusak, M.A., R.M. Welch, and L.V. Kochian. 1990. Physiological characterization of a single-gene mutant of *Pisum sativum* exhibiting excess ion accumulation. I. Root ferric iron reduction and iron uptake. Plant Physiol. 94:1353–1357.

Gutknecht, J. 1961. Mechanism of radioactive zinc uptake by *Ulva lactuca*. Limnol. Oceanogr. 6:426–431.

Gutknecht, J. 1963. ^{65}Zn uptake by benthic marine algae. Limnol. Oceanogr. 8:31–38.

Hager, A., and M. Helmle. 1981. Properties of an ATP-fueled, Cl⁻-dependent proton pump localized in membranes of microsomal vesicles from maize coleoptiles. Z. Naturforsch. 36:997–1008.

Halbrooks, M.C., L.A. Peterson, and T.T. Kozlowski. 1986. Effects of transpiration rate on boron uptake by roots and translocation to shoots of table beets (*Beta vulgaris* L.). J. Plant Nutr. 9:1157–1170.

Hannam, R.J., R.D. Graham, and J.L. Riggs. 1985. Redistribution of manganese in maturing *Lupinus angustifolius* cv. Illyarrie in relation to levels of previous accumulation. Ann. Bot. 56:821–834.

Hanson, J.B. 1978. Application of the chemiosmotic hypothesis to ion transport across the root. Plant Physiol. 62:402–504.

Harper, J.F., T.K. Surowy, and M.R. Sussman. 1989. Molecular cloning and sequence of cDNA encoding the plasma membrane proton pump (H⁺-ATPase) of *Arabidopsis thaliana*. Proc. Natl. Acad. Sci. USA 86:1234–1238.

Harrison, S.J., N.W. Lepp, and D.A. Phipps. 1978. Uptake of copper by excised roots. I. A modified experimental technique for measuring ion uptake by excised roots; and its application in determining uptake characteristics of free copper ions in excised *Hordeum* roots. Z. Pflanzenphysiol. 90:443–450.

Harrison, S.J., N.W. Lepp, and D.A. Phipps. 1979. Uptake of copper by excised roots. II. Copper desorption from the free space. Z. Pflanzenphysiol. 94:27–34.

Harrison, S.J., N.W. Lepp, and D.A. Phipps. 1984. Uptake of copper by excised roots. IV. Copper uptake from complexed sources. Z. Pflanzenphysiol. 113:445–450.

Hedrich, R., U. Flugge, and J.M. Fernandez. 1986. Patch-clamp studies of ion transport in isolated plant vacuoles. FEBS Lett. 204:228–232.

Hedrich, R., and J.I. Schroeder. 1989. The physiology of ion channels and electrogenic pumps in higher plants. Annu. Rev. Plant Physiol. 40:539–569.

Hendry, G.A.F., and K.J. Brocklebank. 1985. Iron-induced oxygen radical metabolism in water-logged plants. New Phytol. 101:199–206.

Hether, N.H., R.A. Olsen, and L.L. Jackson. 1984. Chemical identification of iron reductants exuded by plant roots. J. Plant. Nutr. 7:667–676.

Hiatt, A.J., D.F. Amos, and H.F. Massey. 1963. Effect of aluminum on copper sorption by wheat. Agron. J. 55:284–287.

Hill, J., A.D. Robson, and J.F. Loneragan. 1979. The effects of copper supply and shading on retranslocation of copper from mature wheat leaves. Ann. Bot. 43:449–457.

Hill-Cottingham, D.G., and C.P. Lloyd-Jones. 1965. The behavior of iron chelating agents with plants. J. Exp. Bot. 16:233–242.

Hille, B. 1984. Ionic channels of excitable membranes. Sinauer Associates, Sunderland, MA.

Hoagland, D.R., and T.C. Broyer. 1936. General nature of the process of salt accumulation by roots with description of the experimental methods. Plant Physiol. 11:471–507.

Hocking, P.J. 1980. The composition of phloem exudate and xylem sap from tree tobacco (*Nicotiana glauca* Grah.). Ann.Bot. 45:633–643.

Hocking, P.J., C.A. Atkins, and P.J. Sharkey. 1978. Diurnal patterns of transport and accumulation of minerals in fruiting plants of *Lupinus angustifolius* L. Ann. Bot. 42:1277–1290.

Hodgson, J.F., W.F. Lindsay, and J.F. Trierweiler. 1966. Micronutrient cation complexation in soil solution: II. Complexing of zinc and copper in displaced solution from calcareous soils. Soil Sci. Soc. Am. Proc. 30P:723–726.

Hylmö, B. 1953. Transpiration and ion absorption. Physiol. Plant 6:333–405.

Iljin, W.S. 1951. Metabolism of plants affected with lime-induced chlorosis (Calciose): II. Organic acids and carbohydrates. Plant Soil 3:339–351.

Jacobsen, L., and R. Overstreet. 1947. A study of the mechanism of ion absorption by plant roots using radioactive elements. Am. J. Bot. 34:415–420.

Jacoby, B., and B. Rudich. 1980. Proton-chloride symport in barley roots. Ann. Bot. 46:493–498.

Jarvis, S.C. 1978. Copper uptake and accumulation by perennial ryegrass grown in soil and solution culture. J. Sci. Food Agric. 29:12–18.

Jarvis, S.C., and A.D. Robson. 1982. Absorption and distribution of copper plants with sufficient and deficient supplies. Ann. Bot. 50:151–160.

Jeffries, R.A., and A. Wallace. 1968. Detection of iron ethylenediamine di(o-hydroxyphenyl-acetate) in plant tissue. Agron. J. 60:613–616.

Jeschke, W.D. 1980. Involvement of proton fluxes in the K^+-Na^+ selectivity at the plasmalemma; K^+-dependent net extrusion of sodium in barley roots and the effect of anions and pH on the sodium fluxes. Z. Pflanzenphysiol. 98:155–175.

Julian, G., H.J. Cameron, and R.A. Olsen. 1983. Role of chelation by orthodihyroxy phenols in iron absorption by plant roots. J. Plant Nutr. 6:163–175.

Kawai, S., S.I. Takagi, and Y. Asato. 1988. Mugeneic acid-family phytosiderophores in root-secretes of barley, corn, and sorghum varieties: TLC and HPLC examination. J. Plant Nutr. 11:633–642.

Kester, D.E., K. Uriu, and T. Aldrich. 1961. Copper deficiency in almonds and its response to treatment. Proc. Am. Soc. Hortic. Sci. 77:286–292.

Ketchum, K.A., A. Shrier, and R.J. Poole. 1989. Characterization of potassium-dependent currents in protoplasts of corn suspension cells. Plant Physiol. 89:1184–1192.

Kneen, B.E., T.A. LaRue, R.M. Welch, and N.F. Weeden. 1989. *brz-* a gene conditioning decreased nodulation, increased iron uptake and leaf necrosis in *Pisum sativum* (L.) cv. 'Sparkle'. Plant Physiol. 93:717–722.

Kochian, L.V., and W.J. Lucas. 1982. Potassium transport in corn roots. I. Resolution of kinetics into a saturable and linear component. Plant Physiol. 70:1723–1731.

Kochian, L.V., and W.J. Lucas. 1983. Potassium transport in corn roots. II. The significance of the root periphery. Plant Physiol. 73:208–215.

Kochian, L.V., and W.J. Lucas. 1985. Potassium transport in corn roots. III. Perturbation by exogenous NADH and ferricyanide. Plant Physiol. 77:429–436.

Kochian, L.V., and W.J. Lucas. 1988. Potassium transport in roots. p. 94–178. *In* J.A. Callow (ed.) Advances in botanical research. Vol. 15. Academic Press, New York.

Kochian, L.V., J.E. Shaff, and W.J. Lucas. 1989. High-affinity K^+ uptake in maize roots: A lack of coupling with H^+ efflux. Plant Physiol. 91:1202–1211.

Körner, L.E., I.M. Moller, and P. Jensen. 1986. Free space uptake and influx of Ni^{2+} in excised barley roots. Physiol. Plant. 68:583–588.

Körner, L.E., I.M. Moller, and P. Jensen. 1987. Effects of Ca^{2+} and other divalent cations on uptake of Ni^{2+} by excised barley roots. Physiol. Plant. 71:49–54.

Kramer, D., V. Römheld, E. Landsberg, and H. Marschner. 1980. Induction of transfer-cell formation by iron-deficiency in the root epidermis of *Helianthus annuus* L. Planta 147:335–339.

Landi, S., and F. Fagoli. 1983. Efficiency of manganese and copper uptake by excised roots of maize genotype. J. Plant Nutr. 6:957–970.

Landsberg, E.C. 1979. Einfluss des Saürestoffwechsels und der Nitratreduktion auf Eisenmangelbedingte Veränderungen des Substrat-pH-wertes bei Mono-und Dikotyle Pflanzenarten. Ph.D. diss. Technical Univ., Berlin.

Landsberg, E.C. 1980. Fe-deficiency stress induced development of transfer cells in the epidermis of red pepper roots. Plant Physiol. 65:S-83.

Landsberg, E.C. 1981. Organic acid synthesis and release of hydrogen ions in response to Fe deficiency stress of mono- and dicotyledonous plant species. J. Plant Nutr. 3:579–591.

Landsberg, E.C. 1982. Transfer cell formation in the root epidermis: a prerequisite for Fe-efficiency. J. Plant Nutr. 5:415–433.

Landsberg, E.C. 1984. Regulation of iron-stress-response by whole-plant activity. J. Plant Nutr. 7:609–621.

Landsberg,E.C. 1986. Function of rhizodermal transfer cells in the Fe stress mechanism of *Capsicum annuum* L. Plant Physiol. 82:511–517.

Laties, G.G. 1969. Dual mechanisms of salt uptake in relation to compartmentation and long distance transport. Annu. Rev. Plant Physiol. 20:89–116.

Läuchli, A. 1976. Apoplasmic transport in tissues. p. 3–34. *In* U. Lüttge and M.G. Pitman (ed.) Encyclopedia of plant physiology. Vol. 2B. Springer-Verlag, Berlin.

Läuchli, A., M.G. Pitman, U. Lüttge, D. Kramer, and E. Ball. 1978. Are developing xylem vessels the site of ion exudation from root to shoot? Plant Cell Environ. 1:217–223.

Leggett, J.E., and E. Epstein. 1956. Kinetics of sulfate absorption by barley roots. Plant Physiol. 31:222–226.

Lewin, R. 1984. How microorganisms transport iron. Science. 225:401–402.

Lin, W. 1982. Responses of corn root protoplasts to exogenous reduced nicotinamide adenine dinucleotide: oxygen consumption, ion uptake, and membrane potential. Proc. Natl. Acad. Sci. USA 79:3773–3776.

Lin, W. 1984. Further characterization on the transport property of plasmalemma NADH oxidation system in isolated corn root protoplasts. Plant Physiol. 74:219–222.

Lindsay, W.L., and A.P. Schwab. 1982. The chemistry of iron in soils and its availability to plants. J. Plant Nutr. 5:821–840.

Loneragan, J.F. 1981. Distribution and movement of copper in plants. p. 165–188. *In* J.F. Loneragan et al. (ed.) Copper in soil and plants. Academic Press, New York.

Loneragan, J.F. 1988. Distribution and movement of manganese in plants. p. 113–124. *In* R.D. Graham et al. (ed.) Manganese in soils and plants. Kluwer Academic Publ., Dordrecht, The Netherlands.

Longnecker, N., and R.M. Welch. 1986. The relationships among iron-stress response, iron-efficiency and iron-uptake of plants. J. Plant Nutr. 9:715–727.

Lucas, W.J. 1987. Functional aspects of cells in root apices. p. 27–52. *In* P.J. Gregory et al. (ed.) Root development and function. Cambridge Univ. Press, Cambridge, England.

Lucas, W.J., and M.A. Madore. 1988. Recent advances in sugar transport. p. 35–84. *In* J. Preiss (ed.) The biochemistry of plants: A comprehensive treatise. Vol. 14. Academic Press, New York.

Lüttge, U., and D.T. Clarkson. 1985. Mineral nutrition: Plasmalemma and tonoplast redox activities. p. 73–86. *In* H.D. Behnke et al. (ed.) Progress in botany. Vol. 47. Springer-Verlag, Berlin.

Maas, E.V., D.P. Moore, and B.J. Mason. 1968. Manganese absorption by excised barley roots. Plant Physiol. 43:527–530.

Maas, E.V., D.P. Moore, and B.J. Mason. 1969. Influence of calcium and manganese on manganese absorption. Plant Physiol. 44:796–800.

Maas, E.V., D.A.M. van de Wetering, M.L. van Beusichem, and H.F. Bienfait. 1988. Characterization of phloem iron and its possible role in the regulation of Fe-efficiency reactions. Plant Physiol. 87:167–171.

MacRobbie, E.A.C. 1988. Stomatal guard cells. p. 453–497. *In* D.A. Baker and J.L. Hall (ed.) Solute transport in plant cells and tissues. Longman Scientific, Essex, England.

Manolson, M.F., P.A. Rea, and R.J. Poole. 1985. Identification of 3-O-(4-benzoyl) benzoyl adenosine 5′-triphosphate- and N,N′-dicyclohexylcarbodiimide-binding subunits of a higher plant H$^+$-translocating tonoplast ATP-ase. J. Biol. Chem. 260:12273–12279.

Marschner, H. 1986. Mineral nutrition of higher plants. Academic Press, New York.

Marschner, H. 1988. Mechanisms of manganese acquisition by roots from soils. p. 191–204. *In* R.D. Graham et al. (ed.) Manganese in soils and plants. Kluwer Academic, Dordrecht, The Netherlands.

Marschner, H., A. Kalisch, and V. Römheld. 1974. Mechanism of iron uptake in different plant species. p. 273–281. 7th Int. Colloq. Plant Analysis and Fertilizer Problems. Vol. 2, Hanover, PA.

Marschner, H., V. Römheld and M. Kissel. 1987. Localization of phytosiderophore release and iron uptake along intact barley roots. Physiol. Plant. 71:157–162.

Marschner, H., V. Römheld, and H. Ossenberg-Neuhaus. 1982. Rapid method for measuring changes in pH and reducing processes along roots of intact plants. Z. Pflanzenphysiol. 105:407–416.

Martini, F., and M. Thellier. 1980. Use of an (*n*, α) nuclear reaction to study the long-distance transport of boron in *Trifolium repens* after foliar application. Planta 150:197–205.

McClure, P.R., L.V. Kochian, R.M. Spanswick, and J.E. Shaff. 1990. Evidence for cotransport of nitrate and protons in maize roots. I. Effects of nitrate on the membrane potential. Plant Physiol. 93:281-289.

McCully, M.E., M.J. Canny, and R.F.M. Van Steveninck. 1987. Accumulation of potassium by differentiating metaxylem elements of maize roots. Physiol. Plant. 69:73-80.

Mengel, K., and E.A. Kirkby. 1982. Principles of plant nutrition. 3rd ed. Int. Potash Inst., Bern, Switzerland.

Milburn, J.A. 1971. An analysis of the response in phloem exudation on application of massage to *Ricinus*. Planta 100:143-154.

Misra, P.C., T.A. Craig, and F.L. Crane. 1983. A link between transport and plasma membrane redox system(s) in carrot cells. J. Bioenerg. Biomembr. 16:143-152.

Mitchell, P. 1970. Membranes of cells and organelles: morphology, transport, and metabolism. Symp. Soc. Exp. Biol. 20:121-166.

Møller, I.M., and W. Lin. 1986. Membrane-bound NAD(P)H dehydrogenases in higher plant cells. Annu. Rev. Plant Physiol. 37:309-334.

Moore, D.P. 1972. Mechanisms of micronutrient uptake by plants. p. 171-198. *In* J.J. Mortvedt et al. (ed.) Micronutrients in agriculture. SSSA, Madison, WI.

Moraghan, J.T. 1979. Manganese toxicity in flax growing on certain calcareous soils low in available iron. Soil Sci. Soc. Am. J. 49:668-671.

Moraghan, J.T. 1985. Manganese deficiency in soybeans as affected by FeEDDHA and low soil temperature. Soil Sci. Soc. Am. J. 49:1584-1586.

Moran, N., K. Iwasa, G. Ehrenstein, C. Mishke, C. Bare, and R. Satter. 1987. Effects of external K^+ on K^+ channels in *Samanea* protoplast. Plant Physiol. 83:S-112.

Morris, R.L., and B.T. Swanson. 1980. Xylary pH and reduction potential levels of iron-stressed silver maple (*Acer saccharinum* L.). Plant Physiol. 65:387-388.

Mullins, G.L., and L.E. Sommers. 1986. Cadmium and zinc influx characteristics by intact corn (*Zea mays* L.) seedlings. Plant Soil 96:153-164.

Münch, E. 1930. Die Stoffbewegungen in der Pflanze. Gustav Fischer, Jena, GDR.

Neilands, J.B. 1981. Iron absorption and transport in microorganisms. Annu. Rev. Nutr. 1:27-46.

Newman, I.A., L.V. Kochian, M.A. Grusak, and W.J. Lucas. 1987. Fluxes of H^+ and K^+ in corn roots. Characterization and stoichiometries using ion-selective microelectrodes. Plant Physiol. 84:1177-1184.

Nissen, P. 1974. Uptake mechanisms: Inorganic and organic. Annu. Rev. Plant Physiol. 25:53-79.

Nobel, P.S. 1983. Biophysical plant physiology and ecology. W.H. Freeman and Co., New York.

Norrish, K. 1975. The geochemistry and mineralogy of trace elements. p. 55-81. *In* D.J.D. Nicholas and A.R. Egan (ed.) Trace elements in soil-plant-animal systems. Academic Press, New York.

Oertli, J.J., and N.Y. Ahmed. 1971. Artificially induced mobility of boron. Z. Pflanzenernaehr. Bodenkd. 128:97-104.

Oertli, J.J., and E. Grgurevic. 1975. Effect of pH on the absorption of boron by excised barley roots. Agron. J. 67:278-280.

Oertli, J.J., and L. Jacobsen. 1960. Some quantitative considerations in iron nutrition in higher plants. Plant Physiol. 35:683-688.

Oertli, J.J., and W.F. Richardson. 1970. The mechanism of boron immobility in plants. Physiol. Plant. 23:108-116.

Okamoto, H., K. Ichino, and K. Katou. 1978. Radial electrogenic activity in the stem of *Vigna sesquipedalis*: involvement of spatially separate pumps. Plant Cell Environ. 1:279-284.

Olomu, M.O., G.J. Racz, and C.M. Cho. 1973. Effect of flooding on the E_H, pH and concentrations of Fe and Mn in several Manitoba soils. Soil Sci. Soc. Am. Proc. 37:220-224.

Olsen, R.A., J.H. Bennett, D. Blume, and J.C. Brown. 1981. Chemical aspects of the Fe stress response mechanism in tomatoes. J. Plant Nutr. 3:905-921.

Olsen, R.A., and J.C. Brown. 1980a. Factors related to iron uptake by dicotyledonous and monocotyledonous plants. I. pH and reductant. J. Plant Nutr. 2:629-645.

Olsen, R.A., and J.C. Brown. 1980b. Factors related to iron uptake by dicotyledonous and monocotyledonous plants. II. The reduction of Fe(III) as influenced by roots and inhibitors. J. Plant Nutr. 2:647-660.

O'Neill, S.D., and R.M. Spanswick. 1984. Solubilization and reconstitution of a vanadate-sensitive H^+-ATPase from the plasma membrane of *Beta vulgaris*. J. Membr. Biol. 79:245-256.

Osterhout, W.J.V. 1950. The mechanism of accumulation. Biol. Bull. 90:308-309.

Osterhout, W.J.V. 1952. The mechanism of accumulation in living cells. J. Gen. Physiol. 35:579–594.

Osterhout, W.J.V., and W.M. Stanley. 1932. The accumulation of electrolytes. V. Models showing accumulation and a steady state. J. Gen. Physiol. 15:667–682.

Page, E.R. 1961. Location of manganese taken up in short term absorption by oat roots. Nature (London) 189:597.

Page, E.R., and J. Dainty. 1964. Manganese uptake by excised oat roots. J. Exp. Bot. 15:428–443.

Pate, J.S. 1973. Uptake, assimilation and transport of nitrogen compounds by plants. Soil Biol. Biochem. 5:109–119.

Pate, J.S. 1980. Transport and partitioning of nitrogenous solutes. Annu. Rev. Plant Physiol. 31:313–340.

Pate, J.S., and B.E.S. Gunning. 1972. Transfer cells. Annu. Rev. Plant Physiol. 23:173–196.

Pitman, M.G. 1976. Ion uptake by plant roots. p. 95–128. In U. Lüttge and M.G. Pitman (ed.) Encyclopedia of plant physiology. Vol. 2, Part B. Springer-Verlag, Berlin.

Pitman, M.G. 1982. Transport across plant roots. Q. Rev. Biophys. 15:481–554.

Poole, R.J. 1978. Energy coupling for membrane transport. Annu. Rev. Plant Physiol. 29:437–460.

Poole, R.J. 1978. Plasma membrane and tonoplast. p. 83–105. In D.A. Baker and J.L. Hall (ed.) Solute transport in plant cells and tissues. Longman Scientific and Technical, Essex, England.

Powell, P.E., P.J. Staniszlo, G.R. Cline, and C.P.P. Reid. 1982. Hydroxamate siderophores in the iron nutrition of plants. J. Plant Nutr. 5:653–673.

Ramani, S., and S. Kannan. 1978. Zinc absorption and transport in young peanut seedlings. Commun. Soil Sci. Plant Anal. 9:311–316.

Randall, S.K., and H. Sze. 1986. Properties of the partially purified tonoplast H^+-pumping ATPase from oat roots. J. Biol. Bhem. 261:1364–1371.

Rathore, V.S., S.H. Wittwer, W.H. Jyung, Y.P.S. Bajaj, and M.W. Adams. 1970. Mechanisms of zinc uptake in bean (Phaseolus vulgaris) tissues. Physiol. Plant. 23:908–919.

Ratner, A., and B. Jacoby. 1976. Effect of K^+, its counter anion, and pH on sodium efflux from barley root tips. J. Exp. Bot. 27:843–852.

Raven, J.A. 1977. H^+ and Ca^+ in phloem and symplast: Relation of relative immobility of the ions to the cytoplasmic nature of the transport path. New Phytol. 79:465–480.

Raven, J.A. 1980. Short- and long-distance transport of boric acid inplants. New Phytol. 84:231–249.

Rea, P.A., and R.J. Poole. 1985. Proton-translocating inorganic pyrophosphatase in red beet (Beta vulgaris L.) tonoplast vesicles. Plant Physiol. 77:46–52.

Rea, P.A., and S. Sanders. 1987. Tonoplast energization: Two H^+ pumps, one membrane. Physiol. Plant. 71:131–141.

Reinhold, L., and A. Kaplan. 1984. Membrane transport of sugars and amino acids. Annu. Rev. Plant Physiol. 35:45–83.

Rhoads, W.A., and A. Wallace. 1960. Possible involvement of dark fixation of CO_2 in lime-induced chlorosis. Soil Sci. 89:248–256.

Robinson, D.G. 1985. Plant membranes: Endo- and plasma membranes of plant cells. John Wiley and Sons, New York.

Robinson, N.J., and P.J. Jackson. 1986. "Metallothionein-like" metal complexes in angiosperms; their structure and function. Physiol. Plant. 67:499–506.

Robson, A.D., and J.F. Loneragan. 1970. Sensitivity of annual (Medicago) species of manganese toxicity as affected by calcium and pH. Aust. J. Agric. Res. 21:223–232.

Rodriguez-Navarro, A., M.R. Blatt, and C.L. Slayman. 1986. A potassium-proton symport in Neurospora crassa. J. Gen. Physiol. 87:649–674.

Römheld, V., and D. Kramer. 1983. Relationship between proton efflux and rhizodermal transfer cells induced by iron deficiency. Z. Pflanzenphysiol. 113:73–83.

Römheld, V., and H. Marschner. 1979. Fine regulation of iron uptake by the Fe-efficient plant Helianthus annuus. p. 405–417. In J.L. Harley and R.S. Russell (ed.) The soil-root interface. Academic Press, London.

Römheld, V., and H. Marschner. 1981a. Iron deficiency stress induced morphological and physiological changes in root tips of sunflower. Physiol. Plant. 53:354–360.

Römheld, V., and H. Marschner. 1981b. Effect of Fe stress on utilization of Fe chelates by efficient and inefficient plant species. J. Plant Nutr. 3:551–560.

Römheld,V., and H. Marschner. 1983. Mechanism of iron uptake by peanut plants. I. Fe^{+3} reduction, chelate splitting, and release of phenolics. Plant Physiol. 71:949–954.

Römheld, V., and M. Marschner. 1984. Plant-induced pH changes in the rhizosphere of "Fe-efficient" and "Fe-inefficient" soybean and corn cultivars. J. Plant Nutr. 7:623–630.

Römheld, V., and H. Marschner. 1986a. Mobilization of iron in the rhizosphere of different plant species. p. 155–204. In B. Tinker and A. Läuchli (ed.) Advances in plant nutrition. Vol. 2. Praeger Scientific, New York.

Römheld, V., and H. Marschner. 1986b. Evidence for a specific uptake system for iron phytosiderophores in roots of grasses. Plant Physiol. 80:175–180.

Römheld, V., H. Marschner, and D. Kramer. 1982. Responses to Fe deficiency in roots of "Fe-efficient" plant species. J. Plant Nutr. 5:489–498.

Römheld, V., C. Muller, and H. Marschner. 1984. Localization and capacity of proton pumps in roots of intact sunflower plants. Plant Physiol. 76:603–606.

Rubinstein, B., and A.I. Stern. 1986. Relationship of transplasmalemma redox activity to proton and solute transport by roots of Zea mays. Plant Physiol. 80:805–811.

Rubinstein, B., A.I. Stern, and R.G. Stout. 1984. Redox activity at the surface of oat root cells. Plant Physiol. 76:386–391.

Rudolph, A., and G. Scholz. 1972. Physiologische Untersuchungen an der Mutante chloronerva von Lycopersicon esculentum Mill. IV. Über eine Methode zur quantitativen Bestimmung des "Normalisierungsfaktors" sowie über dessen Vorkommen im Pflanzenreich. Biochem. Physiol. Pflanz. 163:156–168.

Sakmann, B., and E. Neher. 1983. Single-channel recording. Plenum Press, New York.

Sanders, D. 1980. The mechanism of Cl^- transport at the plasma membrane of Chara corallina. I. Cotransport with H^+. J. Membr. Biol. 53:129–141.

Santa Maria, G.E., and D.H. Cogliatti. 1988. Bidirectional Zn-fluxes and compartmentation in wheat seedling roots. J. Plant Physiol. 132:312–315.

Schmid, W.E., H.P. Haag, and E. Epstein. 1965. Absorption of zinc by excised barley roots. Physiol. Plant. 18:860–869.

Scholz, G., and H. Böhme. 1980. Biochemical mutants in higher plants as tools for chemical and physiological investigations—a survey. Die Kulturpflanze 28:11–32.

Scholz, G., G. Schlesier, and K. Seifert. 1985. Effect of nicotianamine on iron uptake by the tomato mutant 'chloronerva'. Physiol. Plant. 63:99–104.

Scholz, G., K. Seifert, and M. Grün. 1987. The effect of nicotianamine on the uptake of Mn^{2+}, Zn^{2+}, Cu^{2+}, Rb^+ and PO_4^{3-} by the tomato mutant chloronerva. Biochem. Physiol. Pflanz. 182:189–194.

Schroeder, J.I., R. Hedrick, and J.M. Fernandez. 1984. Potassium selective single channels in guard cell protoplasts of Vicia faba. Nature (London) 312:361–362.

Schumaker, K.S., and H. Sze. 1985. A Ca^{2+}/H^+ antiport system driven by the proton electrochemical gradient of a tonoplast H^+-ATPase from oat roots. Plant Physiol. 79:1111–1117.

Schumaker, K.S., and H. Sze. 1989. Solubilization and reconstitution of the oat root vacuolar H^+/Ca^{2+} exchanger. p. 243–248. In J. Dainty et al. (ed.) Plant membrane transport: The current position. Elsevier Press, Amsterdam, Netherlands.

Serrano, R. 1988. Structure and function of proton translocating ATPase in plasma membranes of plants and fungi. Biochim. Biophys. Acta 947:1–28.

Sijmons, P.C., and H.F. Bienfait. 1983. Source of electrons for extracellular Fe(III) reduction in iron deficient bean roots. Physiol. Plant. 59:409–415.

Sijmons, P.C., F.C. Lanfermeijer, A.H. DeBoer, H.B.A. Prins, and H.F. Bienfait. 1984a. Depolarization of cell membrane potential druing trans-plasma membrane electron transfer to extracellular electron acceptors in iron-deficient roots of Phaseolus vulgaris L. Plant Physiol. 76:943–946.

Sijmons, P.C., W. Van Den Briel, and H.F. Bienfait. 1984b. Cytosolic NADPH is the electron donor for extracellular FeIII reduction in iron-deficient bean roots. Plant Physiol. 75:219–221.

Spanswick, R.M. 1976. Symplasmic transport in tissues. p. 35–53. In U. Lüttge and M.G. Pitman (ed.) Encyclopedia of plant physiology. Vol. 2B. Springer-Verlag, Berlin.

Spanswick, R.M. 1981. Electrogenic ion pumps. Annu. Rev. Plant Physiol. 32:267–289.

Spanswick, R.M. 1989. The role of H^+-ATPases in plant nutrient transport. p. 243–256. In J.B. St. John et al. (ed.) Frontiers of membrane research in agriculture. Rowman and Allanheld, Totowa, NJ.

Sposito, G., and S.V. Mattigod. 1980. GEOCHEM: A computer program for the calculation of chemical equilibria in soil solutions and other natural water systems. Kearney Foundation of Soil Sci., Univ. of California, Riverside, CA.

Stout, R.G., and R.E. Cleland. 1982. Evidence for a Cl $^-$-stimulated Mg ATPase proton pump in oat root membranes. Plant Physiol. 69:798–803.

Sze, H. 1985. H $^+$-translocating ATPases: advances using membrane vesicles. Annu. Rev. Plant Physiol. 36:175–208.

Takagi, S. 1976. Naturally occurring iron-chelating compounds in oat and rice root washings. I. Activity measurement and preliminary characterization. Soil Sci. Plant Nutr. 22:423–433.

Takagi, S., K. Nomoto, and T. Takemoto. 1984. A physiological aspect of mugeneic acid, a possible phytosiderophore of graminaceous plants. J. Plant Nutr. 7:469–477.

Takeda, K., A.C. Kurkdjian, and R.T. Kato. 1985. Ionic channels, ion transport and plant cell membranes: potential applications of the patch-clamp technique. Protoplasma 127:147–162.

Tammes, P.M.L., and J. van Die. 1966. Studies on phloem exudation from *Yucca flaccida* Haw. IV. Translocation of macro and micro nutrients by the phloem sap stream. Kon. Ned. Akad. Weten. C69:655–660.

Tanaka, H. 1967. Boron absorption by plant roots. Plant Soil 27:300–308.

Taylor, G.J. 1988. The physiology of aluminum phytotoxicity. p. 123–164. *In* H. Sigel and A. Sigel (ed.) Metal ions in the biological system. Aluminum and its role in biology. Vol. 24. Marcel Dekker, New York.

Taylor, K.C., L.G. Albrigo, and C.D. Chase. 1988. Zinc complexation in the phloem of blight-affected citrus. J. Am. Soc. Hortic. Sci. 113:407–411.

Thellier, M., and A. Ayadi. 1967. Contribution a l'étude d'interactions ioniques sulfate-borates lors del'absorption par la *Lemna minor* L. C.R. l'Acad. Sci., Paris, Ser. D. 266:99–104.

Thom, M., and A. Maretzki. 1985. Evidence for a plasmalemma redox system in sugarcane. Plant Physiol. 77:873–876.

Tiffin, L.O. 1966. Iron translocation. II. Citrate/iron ratios in plant stem exudates. Plant Physiol. 41:515–518.

Tiffin, L.O. 1970. Translocation of iron citrate and phosphorus in xylem exudate of soybean. Plant Physiol. 45:280–283.

Tiffin, L.O. 1972. Translocation of micronutrients in plants. p. 199–229. *In* J.J. Mortvedt et al. (ed.) Micronutrients in agriculture. SSSAJ, Madison, WI.

Tiffin, L.O. 1976. The form and distribution of metals in plants: an overview. p. 315–333. *In* H. Drucker and R.E. Wildung (ed.) Biological implications of metals in the environment. Vol. 42. Energy research and development administration symposium ser., Richland, WA. 29 Sept.–1 Oct. 1975. Nat. Tech. Info. Service Conf.-750929, U.S. Dep. of Commerce, Springfield, VA.

Tiffin, L.O., and J.C. Brown. 1961. Selective absorption of iron from iron chelates by soybean plants. Plant Physiol. 36:710–714.

Tiffin, L.O., J.C. Brown, and R.W. Krauss. 1960. Differential absorption of metal chelate components by plant roots. Plant Physiol. 35:362–366.

Timberlake, C.F. 1964. Iron-malate and iron-citrate complexes. J. Am. Chem. Soc. 164:5078–5085.

Ullrich, W.R. 1987. Nitrate and ammonium uptake in green algae and higher plants. Mechanism and relationship with nitrate metabolism. p. 32–38. *In* W.R. Ullrich et al. (ed.) Inorganic nitrogen metabolism. Springer-Verlag, Berlin.

Ullrich, W.R., and A. Novacky. 1981. Nitrate-dependent membrane potential changes and their induction in *Lemna gibba*. Plant Sci. Lett. 22:211–217.

Ullrich-Eberius, C.I. Novacky, A. Fischer, and U. Lüttge. 1981. Relationship between energy-dependent phosphate uptake and the electrical membrane potential in *Lemna gibba* G1. Plant Physiol. 67:797–801.

Ussing, H.H. 1949. Transport of ions across cellular membranes. Physiol. Rev. 29:127–155.

van den Honert, T.H. 1937. Over eigenschappen van plantenwortels, welke een rol spelen bij de opname van voedingszouten. Natuurkd. Tijdschr. Ned. Indie. 97:150–162.

Van Goor, B.J., and D. Wiersma. 1976. Chemical forms of manganese and zinc in phloem exudates. Physiol. Plant. 36:213–216.

Van Iren, F., and P. Boers-van der Sluijs. 1980. Symplasmic and apoplasmic radial ion transport in plant roots. Cortical plasmalemmas lose absorption capacity during differentiation. Planta 14:103–107.

Vara, F., and R. Serrano. 1982. Partial purification and properties of the proton-translocating ATPase of plant plasma membranes. J. Biol. Chem. 257:12826–12830.

Veltrup, W. 1976. Concentration dependent uptake of copper by barley roots. Physiol. Plant. 36:217–220.

Veltrup, W. 1977. The uptake of copper by barley roots in the presence of zinc. Z. Pflanzenphysiol. 83:201–205.

Venkat Raju, K., and H. Marschner. 1972. Regulation of iron uptake from relatively insoluble iron compounds by sunflower platns. Z. Pflanzenernaehr. Bodenkd. 133:227–241.

Venkat Raju, K., H. Marschner, and V. Römheld. 1972. Studies on the effect of iron supply on ion uptake, substrate pH and production and release of organic acids and riboflavin by sunflower plants. Z. Pflanzenernaehr. Bodenkd. 132:177–190.

Walker, C.D., and R.M. Welch. 1987. Low molecular weight complexes of zinc and other trace metals in lettuce leaf. J. Agric. Food Chem. 35:721–727.

Walker, N.A., and M.G. Pitman. 1976. Measurement of fluxes across membranes. p. 93–126. In U. Lüttge and M.G. Pitman (ed.) Encyclopedia of plant physiology. Vol. 2A. Springer-Verlag, New York.

Wallace, A. 1980. Effect of chelating agents on uptake of trace elements when chelating agents are applied to soil in contrast to when they are applied to nutrient cultures. J. Plant Nutr. 2:171–175.

Welch, R.M. 1981. The biological significance of nickel. J. Plant Nutr. 3:345–356.

Welch, R.M., and T.A. LaRue. 1989. Physiological characteristics of Fe accumulation in the 'Bronze' mutant of Pisum sativum L., cv 'Sparkle' E107 (brz brz). Plant Physiol. 93:723–729.

Wergin, W.P., P.F. Bell, and R.L. Chaney. 1988. Use of SEM, X-ray analysis and TEM to localize Fe^{3+} reduction in roots. p. 392–393. In G.W. Bailey (ed.) Proc. 46th Microscopy Soc. Am., 1988. San Francisco, CA. San Francisco Press, San Francisco, CA.

White, M.C., F.D. Baker, R.L. Chaney, and A.M. Decker. 1981b. Metal complexation in xylem fluid. II. Theoretical equilibrium model and computational computer program. Plant Physiol. 67:301–310.

White, M.C., R.L. Chaney, and A.M. Decker. 1981c. Metal complexation in xylem fluid. III. Electrophoretic evidence. Plant Physiol. 67:311–315.

White, M.C., A.M. Decker, and R.L. Chaney. 1981a. Metal complexation in xylem fluid. I. Chemical composition of tomato and soybean stem exudate. Plant Physiol. 67:292–300.

Wiersma, D., and B.J. Van Goor. 1979. Chemical forms of nickel and cobalt in phloem of Ricinus communis. Physiol. Plant. 45:440–442.

Wildes, R.A., and T.G. Neals. 1971. The absorption of boron by discs of plant storage tissues. Aust. J. Biol. Sci. 24:873–882.

Ziegler, H. 1975. Nature of transported substances in plants. p. 59–100. In M.H. Zimmermann and J.A. Milburn (ed.) Transport in plants, encyclopedia of plant physiology. New Ser., Vol. 1. Springer-Verlag, Heidelberg, W. Germany.

Chapter 9

Function of Micronutrients in Plants

V. RÖMHELD AND H. MARSCHNER, *Institut für Pflanzenernährung,*
Stuttgart, Germany

Micronutrients and macronutrients are elements with specific and essential physiological functions in plant metabolism (Epstein, 1965; Marschner, 1986). Compared with macronutrients, micronutrients are required for growth in lower amounts, and serve mainly as constituents of prosthetic groups in metalloproteins and as activators of enzyme reactions. As constituents of prosthetic groups, micronutrients catalyze redox processes by electron transfer (mainly the transition elements Fe, Mn, Cu, and Mo), they form enzyme-substrate complexes by coupling enzyme and substrate (e.g., Fe and Zn), or they enhance enzyme reactions by influencing the molecular configuration of an enzyme or substrate (e.g., Zn). For the nonmetals, B and Cl, there are no well-defined element-containing enzymes or other essential organic compounds known in which these micronutrients are present.

In the following sections dealing with the functions of the individual micronutrients, metals that function in plants by valency change (Fe, Mn, Cu, and Mo) are considered first, followed by metals in which valency changes do not occur (Zn), and then the nonmetals (B, Cl). The functions of Ni as a micronutrient are discussed together with the beneficial elements in Ch. 18. A review, including many references, on the functions of micronutrients has been published elsewhere (Marschner, 1986).

I. IRON

A. Physico-chemical Properties and Physiological Functions

Iron as a transition element is characterized by easy change of the oxidation state ($Fe^{III} \rightleftharpoons Fe^{II}$) and by its ability to form octrahedral complexes with various ligands. Depending on the ligand, the redox potential of Fe (II/III) varies widely. This variability gives Fe its special importance in biological redox systems. As shown by Mössbauer spectrometry, the main oxidation state of Fe in plants is the ferric form [Fe(III)]. The ferrous form

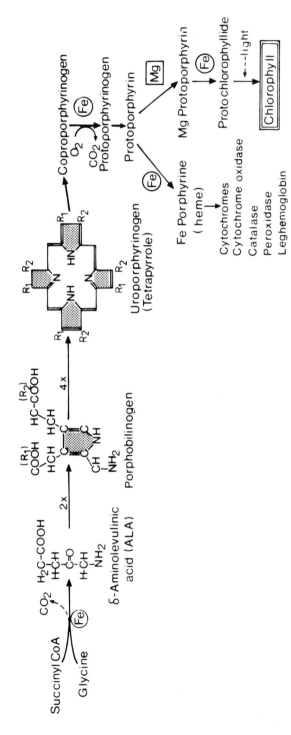

Fig. 9-1. Role of Fe in biosynthesis of heme coenzymes and chlorophyll.

[Fe(II)] and the highly toxic free Fe^{2+} are normally below the detection level in plants, but can reach values up to 20% of the total Fe under certain circumstances (Machold et al., 1968; Goodman & DeKock, 1982).

There are two major groups of Fe-containing proteins: heme proteins and Fe-S proteins. Heme proteins include the various cytochromes, which are characterized by a heme Fe-porphyrin complex as a prosthetic group (Fig. 9–1). Other heme proteins are cytochrome oxidase, catalase, peroxidase, and leghemoglobin, which occurs in root nodules of legumes. In Fe-S proteins, Fe is coordinated to the thiol group of cysteine or to inorganic S as clusters, or to both:

$$-Cys-S \diagup \underset{Fe}{\diagup} \overset{S}{\underset{S}{\diagdown}} \underset{Fe}{\diagup} \overset{S-Cys-}{\diagdown} \qquad [1]$$

$$-Cys-S \diagdown \qquad \qquad \diagdown S-Cys-$$

The most well-known Fe-S protein is ferredoxin. Other Fe-S proteins have functions in metabolic processes, such as photosynthesis (Fig. 9–2), SO_4 and SO_3 reduction, respiration, the tricarboxylic acid cycle, and N_2 fixation. In addition to its functions in heme and Fe-S proteins, Fe activates a number of enzymes including aminolevulinic acid synthetase, coproporphyrinogen oxidase (Fig. 9–1), and plays a role in the synthesis of ribonucleic acid.

The photosynthetic electron transport chain in the thylakoid membranes of chloroplasts consists of various Fe-containing heme groups and Fe-S clusters (Fig. 9–2). With Fe deficiency, therefore, there is a decrease in the concentrations of chlorophyll and other light-harvesting pigments (carotene and xanthophyll), as well as in the activities of electron carriers of both photosystems. Thus, a sharp decline in photosynthetic activity takes place, whereas respiration remains unaffected (Table 9–1). This indicates that Fe deficiency primarily affects chloroplast development and function rather than mitochon-

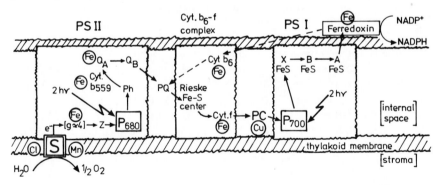

Fig. 9–2. Role of Fe and other micronutrients in the photosynthetic electron transport chain. PS = photosystem (PS I, PS II); S = water-splitting enzyme; g ≃ 4 = non-heme Fe-S group; Z = tyrosine residue-containing electron donor to P 680; P 680 = primary electron donor of PS I; Ph = primary electron acceptor pheophytin; Q_A = quinone-Fe complex; PQ = plastoquinone; Cyt = cytochrome; PC = plastocyanin; and X, B, and A = Fe_4S_4 proteins. Schematically drawn as Z scheme. (Based on Terry & Abadia, 1986; Rutherford, 1989.)

Table 9-1. Concentrations of Fe, chlorophyll and components of photosystem I (P 700, cytochromes, proteins), photosynthetic electron transport capability, and respiratory activity in tobacco (*Nicotiana tabacum* L.) leaves with varying Fe nutritional status.[†]

Fe treatment	Fe	Chlorophyll a + b	PS I components			Photosynthetic e⁻ transport capability		Respiratory activity
			P 700	Cyto-chromes	Pro-tein	PS II	PS I	
		μg cm^{-2} leaves	—pmol cm^{-2}—		μg cm^{-2}	μequiv. cm^{-2} h^{-1}		μmol CO$_2$ cm^{-2} h^{-1}
+Fe, control	1.44	89	545	599	108	56	840	3.46
−Fe	0.25	26	220	201	38	30	390	3.53
−Fe + foliar Fe[‡]	1.16	64	430	474	79	36	764	3.50

[†] Data compiled from Pushnik & Miller (1989).
[‡] 10 days after foliar Fe application.

dria function (in which cytochrome oxidase is the terminal step of the respiratory chain; Pushnik & Miller, 1989).

Although Fe deficiency does not seem to affect general parameters of leaf growth, such as cell numbers per unit leaf area or number of chloroplasts per cell, it decreases the chloroplast volume and protein content per chloroplast (Terry & Abadia, 1986). The various functions of Fe in the development and function of chloroplasts suggests that the causes for chlorosis in Fe-deficient plants are complex, and not simply the expression of an Fe requirement for chlorophyll biosynthesis (Fig. 9–1).

Lower concentrations of carbohydrates in Fe-deficient plants are not likely an expression of limited enzymatic capacity for fixation and reduction of CO_2, but rather an impairment of photosynthetic electron transport (Terry & Abadia, 1986). Mitochondrial structure and function in respiration are not affected by Fe deficiency (Table 9–1). Although the enzyme, aconitase, in the tricarboxylic acid cycle is a Fe_3-S_3 cluster protein (Brouquisse et al., 1986) and its activity is lower with Fe deficiency, the accumulation of organic acids in roots of Fe-deficient plants probably is not caused by impaired aconitase activity (De Vos et al., 1986).

Ferredoxin (non-heme Fe_2-S_2 protein) decreases in leaves of Fe-deficient plants similarly to chlorophyll. Because of various functions of ferredoxin (e.g., reduction of NADP$^+$, NO_2 and SO_4, and assimilation of NH_3), several metabolic disturbances are, therefore, to be expected as a result of Fe deficiency. Although NO_3-reductase contains heme Fe, the accumulation of NO_3 in Fe-deficient leaves is presumably an expression of a decrease in ferredoxin and, thus, NO_2 reduction (Alcaraz et al., 1986), and in protein synthesis, particularly of thylakoid proteins of PS I (Table 9–1; Terry & Abadia, 1986). The inhibition of synthesis of distinct thylakoid proteins, even with mild Fe deficiency, probably is the result of a decrease in chloroplast ribosomal RNA or messenger RNA (Terry & Abadia, 1986). This reduction in synthesis and impairment in assembly of ribosomes in leaf cells becomes more evident with severe Fe deficiency (Lin & Stocking, 1978).

In legumes suffering from Fe deficiency, nodulation by *Bradyrhizobium* is inhibited, probably as a result of impaired proliferation of the bacteria during early nodule development, rather than by decreased synthesis of leghemoglobin (O'Hara et al., 1988).

Iron deficiency preferentially affects the content and composition of thylakoid lipids in general and of galactolipids in particular (Nishio et al., 1985). Changes of the lipid matrix in thylakoids could be one of the initial alterations associated with Fe deficiency (Abadia et al., 1988).

Iron also is involved in lipid metabolism due to the enzyme lipoxygenase (Boyer & Van der Ploeg, 1986), which contains one non-heme Fe per molecule. This enzyme preferentially catalyzes oxidation of linoleic and linolenic acid to a variety of compounds, including traumatin and jasmonic acid. Due to this function of lipoxygenase, Fe also could play a role in growth and development, senescence, and disease resistance (Hildebrand, 1989).

Catalase and peroxidase are heme enzymes whose activities are decreased with Fe deficiency. Catalase activity of leaves is a suitable indicator for Fe nutritional status (Marschner, 1986). Catalase facilitates the dismutation of H_2O_2 to H_2O and O_2 and takes part in the detoxification system of toxic oxygen-free radicals (see Fig. 9–8, Section V). As with other Fe-containing enzymes, peroxidases are abundant in plants and catalyze oxidative processes using H_2O_2 associated with a transient change of Fe(III) to Fe(IV) in the porphyrin ring.

Cell-wall-bound peroxidases are abundant in the rhizodermis and endodermis of roots, and catalyze the polymerization of phenolics to lignin. Accordingly, phenolics accumulate in roots with Fe deficiency. Iron deficiency also inhibits suberization in roots by depressing the activity of a suberin-specific peroxidase (Römheld, 1987).

Inhibition of xanthine oxidase with Fe deficiency impairs purine metabolism (Schlee et al., 1968), and may lead to accumulation of riboflavin in roots of various dicotyledoneous plant species.

B. Critical Tissue Concentrations and Deficiency Symptoms

About 80% of the Fe in leaves is localized in the chloroplasts (Terry & Abadia, 1986). In the chloroplasts of Fe-deficient plants, the lamellar Fe increases at the expense of stromal Fe, whereas the relative amount of extrachloroplastic Fe ($\sim 20\%$) remains unchanged. According to Hewitt (1983), about 9 and 19% of the leaf Fe is bound as heme Fe and Fe-S proteins, respectively. In the stroma of plastids, Fe can be stored as phytoferritin, which consists of a protein shell with up to 5000 atoms of ferric oxide phosphate in crystalline form (Seckbach, 1982). The concentration of phytoferritin is high in dark-grown leaves (up to 50% of the total Fe), but decreases rapidly during regreening.

The critical deficiency concentrations (CDC) of Fe in leaves range from 30 to 50 mg kg^{-1} dry weight basis (Bergmann, 1988). The CDC are presumably considerably higher in fast-growing meristematic and expanding tissues, presumably in the range of 200 mg kg^{-1} for total Fe and 60 to

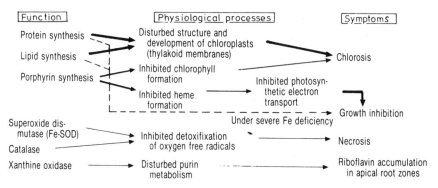

Fig. 9–3. Possible relationship between physiological functions of Fe and visual symptoms of Fe deficiency.

80 mg kg^{-1} for HCl-extractable Fe (Häussling et al., 1985). Extractable Fe, often defined as "active Fe," is usually a better parameter than total Fe for Fe nutritional status, especially for field-grown plants. The critical toxicity concentrations (CTC) for total Fe are quite high, measuring 400 to 1000 mg kg^{-1} (Bergmann, 1988). However, precise definition of both CTC and CDC for Fe are difficult, as the proportions of Fe(III) precipitations preferentially in the apoplast, and of the highly toxic free Fe^{2+} in the cytoplasm and its organelles, are not known.

In shoots, the first visible symptom of Fe deficiency is chlorosis of young leaves. In spite of a decrease in chlorophyll concentration, the leaves expand normally (Terry & Abadia, 1986). Iron-deficiency chlorosis in young leaves is reversible unless necrotic spots occur with severe deficiency. When Fe deficiency becomes severe, cell division is also inhibited (Abbott, 1967); thus, leaf growth is impaired. When limited, Fe is preferentially translocated from the roots to the shoot apex. Therefore, inhibition of shoot meristem activity and leaf growth are the exception rather than the rule. Possible relationships between visual symptoms and physiological functions of Fe are summarized in Fig. 9–3.

Roots respond to Fe deficiency with a range of morphological and physiological changes, which can be classified into two strategies and which play an important role in enhanced acquisition of Fe (Römheld, 1987; also see L.V. Kochian, Ch. 8).

II. MANGANESE

A. Physico-chemical Properties and Physiological Functions

In plants, Mn is present mainly as Mn^{II}. It forms only relatively weak bonds with organic ligands, in which it can be readily oxidized to Mn(III), Mn(IV), and Mn(VI). Because of its relative ease in undergoing change in oxidation state, Mn plays an important role in redox processes, such as elec-

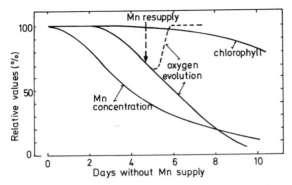

Fig. 9-4. Effect of withdrawal of Mn supply and resupply (leaf incubation) on Mn and chlorophyll concentration and photosynthetic O_2 evolution of youngest, open, leaf blades of subterranean clover grown in nutrient solution. (Based on Nable et al., 1984.)

tron transport in photosynthesis and detoxification of oxygen-free radicals. However, with the exceptions of the water-splitting enzyme associated with PS II and the Mn-containing superoxide dismutase (SOD), Mn does not play a role as an integral component of enzymes (metalloproteins), but acts at least in vitro as activator of many enzymes. As an enzyme activator, Mn can be replaced in many instances, especially by Mg. In view of the wide Mg/Mn concentration ratio occurring in plants, however, the physiological role of Mn as an activator in vivo is questionable in some cases.

The most well-known function of Mn is its involvement in photosynthetic O_2 evolution (Hill Reaction) in chloroplasts (Fig. 9-2). Electrons are liberated by the water-splitting enzyme S, which contains four Mn atoms, and are transferred to photosystem II. With the release of one molecule of O_2, the Mn atoms in the water-splitting enzyme S are reduced in one or two steps, whereas the reoxidation of the Mn atoms occurs sequentially in four steps (Rutherford, 1989). Due to this key function in the water-splitting reaction, Mn deficiency primarily affects photosynthesis and O_2 evolution. Inhibition of photosynthesis occurs even with mild Mn deficiency without affecting chloroplast ultrastructure and chlorophyll concentration (Fig. 9-4). A decrease in chlorophyll concentration as a consequence of a breakdown of the chloroplast structure occurs only with severe Mn deficiency. In agreement with this observation, structurally bound Mn in thylakoid membranes is held much more strongly than Mn in the water-splitting enzyme. Resupplying Mn to deficient plants reactivates photosynthetic O_2 evolution within 24 h (Fig. 9-4), whereas ultrastructure and chlorophyll formation are more difficult to restore (Kriedemann et al., 1985).

As with other superoxide dismutases (Cu-Zn-SOD and Fe-SOD), Mn-SOD also plays an important role in protecting cells against the deleterious effects of superoxide-free radicals, which are formed in the various biochemical reactions in which molecular O_2 is involved. The Mn-SOD is present in mitochondria, peroxisomes, and glyoxysomes.

The level of soluble carbohydrates is greatly reduced in Mn-deficient plants, particularly in the roots (Table 9-2). This is mainly caused by the

Table 9-2. Effect of Mn deficiency on growth and composition of bean.†

Parameter	Leaves		Roots	
	+Mn	−Mn	+Mn	−Mn
Dry weight, g/plant	0.64	0.46	0.21	0.14
Soluble carbohydrates, g kg^{-1}	17.5	4.0	7.6	0.9
Protein N, g kg^{-1}	52.7	51.2	27.0	25.6
Soluble N, g kg^{-1}	6.8	11.9	17.2	21.7

† Based on Vielemeyer et al. (1969).

inhibition of photosynthesis (Fig. 9-4). Manganese-requiring enzymes for carbohydrate synthesis have not been clearly identified in C_3 plants, whereas in C_4 plants, at least the two enzymes, nicotinamide adenine dinucleotide (NAD) malic enzyme and phosphoenolpyruvate carboxykinase, have an absolute Mn requirement that cannot be replaced by Mg. On the other hand, the NADP malic enzyme and phosphoenolpyruvate carboxylase are activated by either Mg or Mn. Despite these differences between C_3 and C_4 species in Mn requirements for photosynthesis, sensitivity to Mn deficiency is similar in C_3 and C_4 species. Although Mn may also act as structural constituent of ribosomes, the protein content is not specifically decreased with Mn deficiency (Table 9-2). Increased levels of soluble N, amino acids, and mainly, NO_3, in Mn-deficient plants are not a consequence of lower NO_3 reductase activity (Leidi & Gomes, 1985), but rather a shortage of carbohydrates (C-skeletons) and a lower demand for reduced N in the new growth.

The ureides allantoin and allantoic acid are the main transport forms of fixed N_2 in tropical legumes. These ureides have to be converted to amino acids for utilization in developing seeds by the Mn-dependent allantoate-amido hydrolase (Winkler et al., 1988).

Despite ample carbohydrate supply, growth of isolated roots is severely inhibited by Mn deficiency, but can be reactivated by resupplying Mn within a few hours (Abbott, 1967). This growth inhibition results mainly from reduction in cell elongation and not cell division (Neumann & Stewart, 1968), indicating that factors other than carbohydrate shortage are also involved in growth inhibition with Mn deficiency. Factors may include inhibited synthesis of lipids or secondary metabolites such as gibberellic acid and isoprenoids.

Concentrations of the chloroplast membrane constituents, glycolipids and polyunsaturated fatty acids, are reduced by up to 50% in Mn-deficient leaves. In seeds, the oil content may decrease and the composition change with Mn deficiency. It is not clear to what extent these effects of Mn on lipid metabolism are related to the function of Mn in the coupling of C_2 units of long-chain fatty acids.

Manganese acts as an important cofactor for a number of key enzyme reactions involved in the biosynthesis of plant secondary metabolites (Graham, 1983; Burnell, 1988). Manganese activates the deoxy-D-arabinoheptulosonate-7-phosphate-synthetase of the shikimic acid pathway and the final step of lignin synthesis. Thus, with Mn deficiency, concentrations of metabo-

Table 9-3. Effect of tissue Mn concentrations on the content of total phenolics and lignin in wheat plants grown in nutrient solution with high NO_3 supply.†

Components	Tissue Mn concentration, mg kg^{-1}			
	4.2	7.8	12.1	18.9
	Shoots			
Phenolics, g kg^{-1} fresh wt.	1.2	1.5	1.7	1.8
Lignin, % dry wt.	4.0	5.8	6.0	6.1
	Roots			
Phenolics, g kg^{-1} fresh wt.	0.5	0.5	0.5	0.5
Lignin, % dry wt.	3.2	12.8	15.0	15.2

† Based on Brown et al. (1984).

lites associated with the shikimic acid pathway, such as aromatic amino acids, phenolics, coumarins, lignins, flavonoids, and indole acetic acid, are lower (Burnell, 1988). Lower concentrations of phenolics, lignin (Table 9-3) and flavonoids in Mn-deficient tissue might be partly responsible for a decrease in disease resistance of Mn-deficient plants (Graham, 1983). The key role of Mn in plant defense mechanisms is further indicated by the increase in Mn concentrations of tissues at the infection sites of parasites (Leusch & Buchenauer, 1988).

Manganese is required as a constituent of phytoene synthetase and as an activator for kaurene synthetase in the isoprenoid pathway. Therefore, growth retardation with Mn deficiency can also be causally related to inhibited synthesis of various products of this isoprenoid pathway (e.g., carotenoids, chlorophyll, gibberellic acid, sterols, and quinones; Wilkinson & Ohki, 1988).

B. Critical Tissue Concentrations and Deficiency Symptoms

The CDC of Mn for shoot dry matter production range from 10 to 15 mg kg^{-1} in mature leaves for various plant species such as barley (*Hordeum vulgare* L.), wheat (*Triticum aestivum* L.), cotton (*Gossypium hirsutum* L.), and soybean [*Glycine max* (L.) Merr.] (Hannam & Ohki, 1988). The CDC in mature wheat leaves are 7.7, 12.6, and 16.5 mg kg^{-1} for chlorophyll formation, dry matter production and photosynthesis, respectively. These differences in the CDC for chlorophyll formation and for photosynthesis are in agreement with results shown in Fig. 9-4. In contrast to most other plant species, in *Lupinus angustifolius* CDC for vegetative growth, and in particular for seed production and quality are much higher (30 mg kg^{-1}) than for photosynthesis (17 mg kg^{-1}) (Hannam & Ohki, 1988).

In contrast to the narrow CDC in most plant species, the CTC vary over a wide range for various plant species, from 100 in bean (*Phaseolus vulgaris* L.), to 650 in clover (*Trifolium subterraneum* L.), and 5000 mg kg^{-1} in lowland rice (*Oryza sativa* L.) (Hannam & Ohki, 1988). These CTC not only vary between plant genotypes, but also within a given genotype depending on culture method (nutrient solution/soil culture), Si supply, temperature, and light intensity (Horst, 1988).

Well-known symptoms of Mn deficiency in cereals include greenish grey spots, flecks, and stripes on the more basal leaves (grey speck), whereas in dicotyledons, interveinal chlorosis of the younger and middle-aged leaves dominate. In contrast to Fe-deficiency chlorosis, the chlorosis induced by Mn deficiency is not uniformly distributed over the whole leaf blade, and tissues may rapidly become necrotic. Preferential transport of Mn from roots to the shoot apex may explain why the deficiency symptoms are often more severe on middle leaves than on the youngest leaves. Various seed disorders in Mn-deficient legumes are common, such as dark discoloration on cotyledons of pea (*Pisum sativa* L.) and some other legumes ("marsh spots"), and cracks of the testa in seeds of lupins ("split seeds").

III. COPPER

A. Physico-chemical Properties and Physiological Functions

Copper as a transition element with an electron-filled 3d shell, shares similarities with Fe, such as highly stable formation of chelates and easy electron transfer ($Cu^{II} \rightleftharpoons Cu^{I}$). Thus, it is of comparable importance in physiological redox processes. In contrast to Fe, Cu-containing enzymes can react directly with molecular O_2 and, thus, catalyze preferentially terminal oxidation processes.

The various Cu proteins are important in processes such as photosynthesis, respiration, detoxification of superoxide radicals, and lignification. The content or the activities of the Cu-containing proteins are drastically reduced with Cu deficiency (Table 9-4).

Photosynthetic electron transport (Fig. 9-2) is influenced by Cu at various sites. The most obvious effect of Cu deficiency is lower contents of plastocyanin, which results in a decreased photosynthetic electron transport (Table 9-4). Copper deficiency also changes the lipid composition of thylakoid membranes, in particular polypeptides, which affect the efficiency of plastoquinone in electron transfer between both photosystems. Photosystem II also

Table 9-4. Plastocyanin and chlorophyll concentration, photosynthetic electron transport and activities of Cu-containing enzymes in pea leaves with varying Cu nutritional status.[†]

Cu concentration	Plasto-cyanin	Chloro-phyll	Photosynthetic electron transport of PS I	Enzyme activity		
				Amine oxidase	Ascorbate oxidase	Cu-Zn-SOD
mg kg^{-1}	mmol mol^{-1} chlorophyll	mmol kg^{-1}	relative values of +Cu control	mol kg^{-1} protein h^{-1}		EU[‡] mg^{-1} protein
6.9	2.4	4.9	100	0.86	730	22.9
3.8	1.1	3.9	54	0.43	470	13.5
2.2	0.3	4.4	19	0.24	220	3.6

† Based on Ayala and Sandmann (1988).
‡ Enzyme units.

is inhibited with severe Cu deficiency, and pronounced changes in the ultrastructure of the chloroplasts occur (Herriques, 1989).

In the mitochondrial electron transport chain the terminal oxidase, cytochrome-c-oxidase, contains two atoms of both Cu and Fe in heme configuration. Despite a drastic decrease in cytochrome oxidase activity, the respiration rate is not affected even with severe Cu deficiency. This indicates that the oxidase is either very stable or is present in large excess in mitochondria, and therefore, not causally involved in the growth reduction with Cu deficiency (Bussler, 1981). The "alternative oxidase" in the respiratory pathway is a Cu-containing enzyme, which is also important for desaturation of long-chain fatty acids such as oleic and linoleic acids in microsomes.

Of the various superoxide dismutase isoenzymes (SOD, see section V), the Cu-Zn-SOD is mainly localized in the stroma of chloroplasts, where the Cu atom is directly involved in the detoxification of superoxide radicals (O_2^-) generated during photosynthesis. The activity of the Cu-Zn-SOD is much lower with Cu deficiency (Table 9–4).

The decrease in photosynthetic electron transport with Cu deficiency (Table 9–4) decreases the rate of CO_2 fixation, and the concentration of starch and soluble carbohydrates (especially sucrose) in plants during vegetative growth, and is a main factor responsible for low dry matter production with severe Cu deficiency (Botrill et al., 1970; Mizuno et al., 1982). However, reduction of fruit or seed yield already occurs with mild Cu deficiency, mainly as a result of male sterility, rather than decreased photosynthetic CO_2 fixation (Table 9–5; Bussler, 1981).

Although Cu can affect the synthesis of certain apoenzymes (e.g., diamine oxidase), possibly by modulating the level of translatable mRNA (Delhaize et al., 1986), the effect of Cu on N metabolism seems mainly to be indirect. Accumulation of soluble N compounds (NO_3, amino acids) with Cu deficiency is neither typical nor the result of a general inhibition of protein synthesis (Botrill et al., 1970).

Copper deficiency in legumes depresses nodulation and the N_2-fixation rate, leading to N deficiency symptoms, which can be overcome by application of mineral N. Nevertheless, in contrast to Mo and Co, there seems to be no specific higher Cu requirement for N_2 fixation in nodules than for the host plant growth. This indicates that depressed N_2 fixation in Cu-deficient legumes is presumably an indirect effect, possibly due to a shortage in carbohydrates.

Table 9–5. Effect of Cu supply on straw and grain yield of wheat grown in sand culture.†

Cu supply, mg pot^{-1}	Yield, g pot^{-1}	
	Straw	Grain
0	6.7	0
0.1	10.5	0
0.4	12.9	1.0
2.0	12.7	10.5

† Based on Nambiar (1976).

Table 9-6. Effect of Cu nutritional status on cell-wall composition of young leaves of wheat.†

Treatment	Cu concentration	Cell wall content	Cellulose	Hemi-cellulose	Lignin	Phenolics Total	Ferulic acid
	mg kg^{-1}	% dry matter		% of cell wall		% dry matter	
+Cu	7.1	46.2	46.8	46.7	6.5	0.73	0.50
−Cu	1.0	42.9	55.3	41.4	3.3	0.82	0.69

† Based on Robson et al. (1981).

High N supply in nonlegumes can accentuate Cu deficiency and the requirement of Cu application for obtaining maximum yield on certain soils (Thiel & Finck, 1973; Robson & Reuter, 1981). This higher Cu requirement probably is related to a lower availability of Cu in plants of high N nutritional status (see L.V. Kochian, Ch. 8, for further discussion).

Phenolase and laccase are Cu-containing enzymes acting as oxidases of phenols or tyrosine in the biosynthetic pathway of quinones, melanotic substances, alkaloids, or lignin. With mild Cu deficiency, the activity of both enzymes (Marziah & Lam, 1987) already is lower, leading to the accumulation of phenols and a decrease in lignification (Table 9-6) as well as in melanotic substances. Thus, Cu may play an important role in disease resistance due to its role in the production of a mechanical barrier (lignin), and by suppressing fungal growth by favoring the formation of melanotic substances that act as phytoalexins.

The delay on flowering and senescence, which is often observed in Cu-deficient plants (Reuter et al., 1982), might be caused by elevated indole-acetic acid (IAA) concentrations resulting from the accumulation of certain phenolics, which inhibit IAA oxidase.

In general, Cu deficiency depresses reproductive growth (formation of seeds and fruits) more than vegetative growth (Table 9-5). In addition to nonviability of pollen, other causes of male sterility include, presumably, a lack of starch in the pollen and inhibited pollen release from the stamens as a result of impaired lignification of the anther cell walls. In addition, an abnormal development of both tapetum and microspores has been proposed as a cause of male sterility (Jewell et al., 1988).

The Cu-containing amine oxidases catalyze the oxidative deamination of monoamines and diamines, also of polyamines, such as putrescine and spermidine. Amine oxidases are abundant in legumes (Delhaize et al., 1986) and their activities are decreased with Cu deficiency (Table 9-4). Because polyamines are considered secondary messengers, the effects of Cu deficiency on development processes also may be related to polyamine metabolism.

Ascorbate oxidase oxidizes ascorbic acid to L-dehydroascorbic acid, and may act as a terminal respiratory oxidase or as a redox shuttle, together with gluthathione in chloroplasts. The ascorbate oxidase activity is markedly reduced with Cu deficiency (Table 9-4) and, thus, may be used as an enzymatic indicator for the Cu nutritional status of plants (Delhaize et al., 1986).

B. Critical Tissue Concentrations and Deficiency Symptoms

The CDC of Cu in vegetative organs range from 1 to 3.5 mg kg^{-1}, varying among plant species, plant part, plant age, and various environmental factors such as N supply and drought stress (Thiel & Finck, 1973; Robson & Reuter, 1981). In general, the CDC in the youngest emerged leaf are less affected by environmental factors, and thus, are more sensitive and reliable indicators of the Cu nutritional status (Robson & Reuter, 1981).

For most crop species, the CTC of Cu in the leaves are >15 to 30 mg kg^{-1} (Robson & Reuter, 1981). The CTC in certain Cu-tolerant species and ecotypes (metallophytes) can be as high as 1000 mg kg^{-1} (Woolhouse, 1983).

Typical symptoms of Cu deficiency are chlorosis (white tip, reclamation disease), necrosis, leaf distortion, and dieback. These symptoms occur preferentially in young shoot tissues and are expressions of poor redistribution of Cu in Cu-deficient plants (Loneragan, 1981). Enhanced formation of tillers (cereals) and auxillary shoots (dicots) are secondary symptoms caused by necrosis of apical meristems. The reduced lignification with Cu deficiency leads to other common deficiency symptoms, such as wilting (impaired water transport); shoot bending; lodging, mainly of cereals; and reduced disease resistance (Bussler, 1981; Graham, 1983). The most spectacular symptoms of Cu deficiency are reduced seed or fruit yield caused mainly by male sterility (Table 9-5).

IV. MOLYBDENUM

A. Physico-chemical Properties and Physiological Functions

In contrast to Fe, Mn, and Cu, the transition element Mo exists in plants as an anion, primarily in its highest oxidized form, Mo(VI), but also as Mo(IV) and Mo(V). Due to its electron configuration, Mo(VI) shares many chemical similarities with vanadium and, particularly, tungsten. The functions of Mo in plants are related to electron transfer reactions.

In higher plants, only a few Mo-containing enzymes are known: NO_3 reductase and SO_3 oxidase, and in nodulated legumes, nitrogenase and xanthine dehydrogenase. These molybdo-enzymes are multicenter electron-transfer proteins with many similarities, including the amino acid sequence of the apoenzyme.

Nitrate is reduced in the cytoplasm by NO_3 reductase, a dimeric enzyme with three electron-transferring prosthetic groups per subunit: flavin (FAD), heme, and Mo (Fig. 9-5). During NO_3 reduction, electrons are transferred directly from Mo to NO_3. A close relationship exists between Mo supply, NO_3 reductase activity (NRA), and growth. In Mo-deficient leaves, NRA is low and can be readily induced by infiltration of leaves with Mo (Witt & Jungk, 1977). Thus, "inducible" NRA can be used as an indicator for the Mo nutritional status of plants.

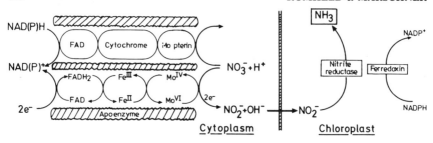

Fig. 9–5. Structural model of the nitrate reductase with its two subunits. Each subunit contains three prosthetic groups: FAD, heme-Fe, and Mo-pterin. (Based on Campbell, 1988.)

Compared with plants supplied with NO_3-N, plants with a NH_4 supply have a much lower Mo requirement, and symptoms of Mo deficiency are less severe or even absent (Table 9–7). The typical visual symptoms of Mo deficiency (whiptail) can also be prevented by substitution of Mo by tungsten, although the latter could not restore the NRA (Hewitt & Notton, 1980).

With Mo deficiency, there is an increase in concentrations of soluble N compounds such as amides, and in ribonuclease activity, whereas protein concentration and alanine aminotransferase activity decrease (Table 9–8), indicating the involvement of Mo in protein synthesis. This role of Mo in protein synthesis may explain the pronounced effect of Mo deficiency on chlorophyll concentration (Table 9–8), chloroplast structure (Hewitt & Notton, 1980), and growth (Abbott, 1967; Newmann & Steward, 1968).

Biological N_2 fixation is catalyzed by the Mo-containing enzyme, nitrogenase, which contains two metalloproteins: a Mo-Fe-S protein and a

Table 9–7. Effect of Mo and source of N on growth, deficiency symptoms, chlorophyll, and NO_3 concentrations in leaves of tomato.†

N source and Mo supply		Deficiency symptoms	Dry weight	Chlorophyll	NO_3
			g/plant	mg kg^{-1} fresh wt.	g kg^{-1} dry wt.
NO_3-N	−Mo	Severe	9.6	89	72.9
	+Mo	Absent	25.0	158	8.7
NH_4-N	−Mo	Mild	15.9	216	10.4
	+Mo	Absent	19.4	174	5.8

† Based on Hewitt and McCready (1956).

Table 9–8. Effect of Mo deficiency on growth, protein, and chlorophyll concentrations and activity of NO_3 reductase (NR), ribonuclease (RNase), and alanine aminotransferase (AAT) in corn grown in sand culture.†

Mo supply	Dry weight	Mo concentration	Protein	Chlorophyll	Enzyme activity‡		
					NR	RNase	AAT
0	8	0.1	15.5	0.2	59	179	37
0.2	22	2.2	33.5	1.2	100	100	100

† Based on Agarwala et al. (1978).
‡ Relative values expressed on protein basis.

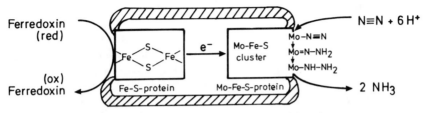

Fig. 9-6. Model of the stepwise N_2 reduction by the Mo-containing nitrogenase.

Fe-S cluster protein (Fig. 9–6). Molybdenum of the Mo-Fe-S cluster directly transfers electrons to N_2, whereas Fe acts as an electron transmitter. Because of the involvement of Mo in N_2 reduction, the Mo requirement for root nodules in legumes and nonlegumes (e.g., alder [*Alnus glutinosa* (L.) Gaertn.] is particularly high. Although the number of nodules may increase with Mo deficiency, the total nodule dry weight per plant and the N_2-fixation capacity are low, and plant growth is inhibited by a shortage of bound N (Table 9–9).

In various tropical and subtropical legumes (e.g., soybean and cowpea: *Vigna unguiculata* Walp) the ureides, allantoin and allantoic acid (allantoate), are the dominant compounds in long-distance transport of N from roots to the shoot. These ureides are formed in the cytosol of root nodules by oxidation of purine, such as xanthine, to uric acid, the precursor of allantoin and allantoic acid. The purine oxidation is catalyzed by the Mo-containing xanthine dehydrogenase, a metalloflavoprotein that contains two atoms of Mo per molecule, two molecules of FAD, and eight Fe-S groups. Therefore, with Mo deficiency, growth inhibition in legumes relying on N_2 fixation can result from low nitrogenase activity or impaired purine catabolism in the nodules, or from both these causes.

Molybdenum may also affect N metabolism indirectly via S-containing amino acids. The catabolism of amino acids (e.g., cysteine) includes the enzymatic oxidation of SO_3 to SO_4 in the mitochondria. This oxidation is catalyzed by SO_3 oxidase, a Mo-containing hemoprotein, which mediates the electron transfer between SO_3 and SO_4 (Rajagopalan, 1980).

Molybdenum also has a striking effect on pollen formation. Tasseling, anthesis, and development of anthers in corn (*Zea mays* L.) are inhibited by Mo deficiency. Poor and delayed flowering, and reduced viability of the

Table 9-9. Effect of Mo on growth, nodule formation, and N concentration in alder plants grown in a Mo-deficient soil.†

Mo supply	Dry weight, g pot^{-1}		Nodule formation		N concentration in shoot
	Shoot	Roots	Number pot^{-1}	Dry weight	
μg pot^{-1}				mg pot^{-1}	% in dry wt.
0	2.38	0.38	228–308	7	1.95
150	7.58	1.24	1–10	132	2.88

† Based on Becking (1961).

pollen grains may also explain the reduction in fruit formation in Mo-deficient melon plants (*Cucumis melon* L.) growing on acid soils (Gubler et al., 1982).

There are a number of other metabolic changes in Mo-deficient plants that are difficult to explain in terms of known functions of Mo. For example, stress resistance in Mo-deficient plants is decreased against low temperature or water logging (Vunkova-Radeva et al., 1988). Furthermore, the risk of premature sprouting of grains on corn cobs is increased when the Mo concentrations in the grains falls below 0.03 mg kg^{-1}. This premature sprouting seems to be closely related to a high NO_3 concentration in the tissue.

B. Critical Tissue Concentrations and Deficiency Symptoms

Compared with other micronutrients, the Mo requirement of plants is the lowest and depends on the form of N supply (N_2 fixation, NO_3, or NH_4). The CDC vary between 0.1 and 1.0 mg kg^{-1} in leaves (Bergmann, 1988). Due to the high Mo concentrations in root nodules of legumes (Becking, 1961), legumes relying on N_2 fixation have a higher Mo demand than other plant species.

A unique characteristic of Mo is the wide range between the CDC and CTC, which can differ within a given plant species by a factor of up to 10^4, as compared with a factor of only about 10 for B. In general, toxicity symptoms are absent in plants with tissue concentrations of up to 200 to 1000 mg kg^{-1}.

Unlike the symptoms associated with other micronutrients, Mo-deficiency symptoms are not confined to the youngest leaves because Mo is readily retranslocated in the plant (Bergmann, 1988). Symptoms of N deficiency dominate in Mo-deficient legumes relying on N_2 fixation. In plants supplied with bound N, the most characteristic Mo-deficiency symptom is reduced and irregular leaf blade formation known as whiptail. This malformation of leaves is caused by local necrosis in tissue and insufficient differentiation of vascular bundles in the early stages of development. Other symptoms of Mo deficiency are interveinal mottling and marginal chlorosis of the older leaves, followed by necrotic spots at leaf tips and margins, which are closely related to high NO_3 concentrations in the tissue.

V. ZINC

A. Physico-chemical Properties and Physiological Functions

In contrast to Fe, Mn, Cu, and Mo, the transition element Zn is not subject to valency change and exists in plants only as Zn(II). As a mineral nutrient, Zn mainly functions as a divalent cation by coupling enzymes with corresponding substrates and forming tetrahedral chelates with different organic compounds, including polypeptides.

Only a few Zn-containing enzymes, alcohol dehydrogenase, Cu-Zn-SOD, carbonic anhydrase (CA), and RNA polymerase are known in higher plants.

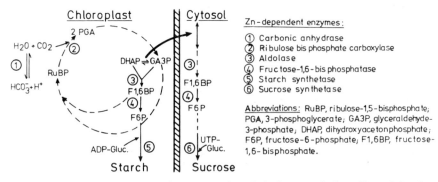

Fig. 9–7. Involvement of Zn-dependent enzymes in carbohydrate metabolism. (From Cakmak, 1988.)

However, a large number of enzymes are activated by Zn, either due to binding enzymes and substrates, or effects of Zn on conformation of enzymes or substrate, or both. In Zn-deficient plants, metabolic changes are manifold and quite complex, and include changes in metabolism of carbohydrates, proteins, and auxins, and impaired membrane integrity. A key role of Zn in gene expression and regulation has been reported recently (Klug & Rhodes, 1987).

Zinc can affect carbohydrate metabolism at various levels as summarized in Fig. 9–7. The activity of the Zn-containing enzyme CA sharply declines with Zn deficiency. Carbonic anhydrase is localized in the cytoplasm and chloroplasts, and may facilitate the transfer of CO_2/HCO_3^- for photosynthetic CO_2 fixation. Despite a close relationship between Zn nutritional status and CA activity, there is no direct relationship between CA activity and photosynthetic CO_2 fixation. Only with extreme Zn deficiency is net photosynthesis inhibited, presumably due to disturbed chloroplast structure and inhibited photosynthetic electron transfer (Sharma et al., 1982), rather than as a result of a reduction in CA activity.

Although various other enzymes involved in carbohydrate metabolism are Zn dependent (Fig. 9–7) and inhibited by Zn deficiency, and there is also a marked decline in photosynthetic electron transfer (Hill reaction; Table 9–10), the concentrations of carbohydrates in leaves of Zn-deficient plants are either unaffected or increased (Table 9–10; Marschner & Cakmak, 1989).

Table 9–10. Effect of Zn deficiency and resumption of Zn supply on Zn and carbohydrate concentration in cabbage (*Brassica oleracea* L.) leaves.†

Parameter	Zn supply, μM		
	1.0	0.001	0.001 + 2.0‡
Zn content, mg kg^{-1}	21	14	30
Hill reaction activity, relative	100	48	66
Sugars, g kg^{-1} fresh wt.	4.2	9.1	5.0
Starch, g kg^{-1} fresh wt.	7.5	24.6	19.2

† Based on Sharma et al. (1982).
‡ Twenty-four hours after resumption of 2.0 μM Zn supply.

Table 9-11. Effect of Zn supply on shoot dry weight and composition of young leaves and shoot tips of bean plants.[†]

Zn supply M	Shoot dry wt.	Concentrations in young leaves and shoot tips				
		Zn	Free amino acids	Protein	Tryptophan	IAA
	g/plant	mg kg^{-1}	μmol g^{-1} dry wt.	g kg^{-1} fresh wt.	mmol kg^{-1} dry wt.	μg kg^{-1} fresh wt.
+Zn (10^{-6})	8.24	52	82	28	0.37	240
-Zn	3.66	13	533	14	1.32	122
-Zn +Zn[‡]	4.53	141	118	30	0.27	180

[†] Cakmak et al. (1989).   [‡] 3×10^{-6} M for 3 d.

Excretion of sugars at the leaf surface can be observed with severe Zn deficiency. Thus, Zn-deficiency-induced changes in carbohydrate metabolism are not primarily responsible for either growth retardation or visible deficiency symptoms (Marschner, 1986). A particular situation might exist in the case of the Zn-containing enzyme alcohol dehydrogenase (ADH). This enzyme plays an important role in anaerobic root respiration (e.g., in the root apex of flooded rice) catalyzing the reduction of acetaldehyde to ethanol. The activity of ADH is markedly reduced with Zn deficiency, so that anaerobic root metabolism is impaired under anaerobic conditions (Moore & Patrick, 1989).

The concentrations of proteins in Zn-deficient plants are reduced and those of amino acids and amides are increased (Table 9–11). Inhibition of protein synthesis in Zn-deficient plants is mainly caused by a marked decline of ribonucleic acid (RNA), either by lower activity of the Zn-containing RNA polymerase (Soloiman & Wu, 1985), by reduced structural integrity of ribosomes (Obata & Umebayashi, 1988), or by enhanced RNA degradation (Cakmak et al., 1989).

The Zn-containing isoenzyme of SOD (Cu-Zn-SOD) plays an important role in the detoxification of superoxide radicals (O_2^-) and, thus, in the protection of membrane lipids and proteins against oxidation (Fig. 9–8). The

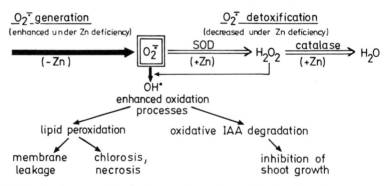

Fig. 9–8. The involvement of Zn in the generation and detoxification of superoxide radicals, and the possible effect on oxygen-free radicals on membrane function and IAA metabolism. (From Cakmak & Marschner, 1988b; Cakmak et al., 1989.)

activity of Cu-Zn-SOD is reduced with Zn deficiency (Cakmak & Marschner, 1987), but can be restored by addition of Zn. The NADPH-dependent generation of superoxide radicals also is enhanced in Zn-deficient plants, whereas the catalase activity, involved in detoxification of hydrogen peroxide (H_2O_2), is decreased (Fig. 9–8). The elevated levels of toxic oxygen-free radicals in Zn-deficient plants destruct the double bonds of polyunsaturated fatty acids and phospholipids in the membranes, and increase leakage of solutes such as K^+, sugars, and amino acids (Cakmak & Marschner, 1988a). The enhanced lipid oxidation in leaves could lead to the destruction of chlorophyll, necrosis, and stunted growth, particularly under high light intensity (Marschner & Cakmak, 1989).

Lower concentrations of phytohormones, particularly IAA, in Zn-deficient plants (Table 9–11) are either a function of enhanced oxidative degradation of IAA as a result of increased peroxidase activity and oxygen-free radicals (Cakmak, 1988), or decreased synthesis of IAA. Higher tryptophan concentrations in young leaves of Zn-deficient plants (Table 9–11) may indicate an impaired conversion of tryptophan to IAA. However, the accumulation of tryptophan is more likely an expression of an inhibited protein synthesis under Zn deficiency (Cakmak et al., 1989). Also, the gibberellic (GA) metabolism seems to be impaired in Zn-deficient plants (Suge et al., 1986).

Due to its preferential binding to SH-groups, Zn plays a key role in stabilizing and structural orientation of particular membrane proteins. Loss in membrane integrity of Zn-deficient plants certainly contributes to the increase in susceptibility to fungal diseases (Sparrow & Graham, 1988), and excessive P uptake by roots and transport into the shoots, causing P toxicity in shoots (Welch et al., 1982; Marschner & Cakmak, 1986). Additionally, retranslocation of P from shoots to roots is inhibited in Zn-deficient plants and, thus, one important component is impaired by which the shoot may control uptake and xylem loading of P in roots.

B. Critical Tissue Concentrations and Deficiency Symptoms

The CDC of Zn in leaves range from 15 to 30 mg kg^{-1} (Cakmak & Marschner, 1987; Bergmann, 1988). They depend on leaf age (Reuter et al., 1982) and may be higher with high or excessive P concentrations in the leaf tissue. Thus, water-soluble Zn instead of total Zn seems to be a better parameter for the CDC, particularly at high P supply; e.g., in cotton or citrus [*Citrus sinensis* (L.) Osbeck] leaves (Cakmak & Marschner, 1987).

The CTC of Zn in leaves of crop plants are ranged from 200 to 500 mg kg^{-1} and can reach values up to 8000 mg kg^{-1} in Zn-tolerant ecotypes of natural vegetation.

The most characteristic visible symptoms of Zn deficiency in dicotyledons are short internodes (rosetting) and a decrease in leaf expansion (little leaf). Stunted growth is often combined with chlorosis of the youngest leaves. In monocotyledons, particularly in corn, chlorotic bands occur along the midribs of leaves combined with red, spot-like discoloration. Zinc-deficiency symptoms on older leaves are mainly the result of P toxicity (Marschner & Cakmak, 1986), and are characterized by interveinal chlorosis and necrosis. Stunted growth and particular necrosis of older leaves in Zn-deficient plants are intensified with high light intensity (the sun-facing side of trees), suggesting the involvement of superoxide radicals in symptom development (Marschner & Cakmak, 1989).

VI. BORON

A. Physico-chemical Properties and Physiological Functions

Boron possesses properties intermediate between metals and electronegative nonmetals, and shows a tendency to form cationic complexes. In aqueous solutions at pH < 7, B occurs mainly as undissociated boric acid [B(OH_3)], which dissociates to $B(OH)_4^-$ + H_3O^+ at higher pH values. Only the monomeric species $B(OH)_3$ and $B(OH)_4^-$ are usually present in aqueous solutions at B concentrations <25 mM; thus, polymeric B species are most likely absent in plants.

Boron is neither an enzyme constituent nor does it directly affect enzyme activities. Boric acid forms very stable complexes with organic compounds with cis-diol configurations according to:

$$\begin{array}{c} {=}C{-}OH \\ {=}C{-}OH \end{array} + \begin{array}{c} HO \\ HO \end{array}\!\!\!>\!\!B{-}OH \rightleftharpoons \left[\begin{array}{c} {=}C{-}O \\ {=}C{-}O \end{array}\!\!\!>\!\!B\!\!<\!\!\begin{array}{c} OH \\ OH \end{array}\right]^- + H_3O^+ \qquad [2]$$

$$\left[\begin{array}{c} {=}C{-}O \\ {=}C{-}O \end{array}\!\!\!>\!\!B\!\!<\!\!\begin{array}{c} OH \\ OH \end{array}\right]^- + \begin{array}{c} HO{-}C{=} \\ HO{-}C{=} \end{array} \rightleftharpoons \left[\begin{array}{c} {=}C{-}O \\ {=}C{-}O \end{array}\!\!\!>\!\!B\!\!<\!\!\begin{array}{c} O{-}C{=} \\ O{-}C{=} \end{array}\right]^- + 2H_2O \qquad [3]$$

Compounds with these configurations include various sugars and their derivates, uronic acid, and some o-diphenols, which are abundant in cell walls. Therefore, B is strongly complexed in cell walls, and its concentrations in cell walls roughly reflect the differences in B requirement among plant species. Lewis (1980a) characterized B as an extracellular nutrient, since most functions of B are related to cell wall formation and stabilization, lignification, and xylem differentiation. More recently, functions of B at the cell wall-plasma membrane interface have attracted increasing attention. The various primary functions and the presumed secondary effects of B are summarized in Fig. 9–9.

A primary function of B is reflected in changes of the chemical composition and ultrastructure of cell walls in B-deficient tissues. Cell wall thickening in root apical meristems occurs already 3 to 6 h after interruption of B supply, and is characterized by an increase in hemicellulose and pectin, and an irregular deposition of vesicular aggregations of new cell wall material intermixed with membraneous material (Hirsch & Torrey, 1980). Furthermore, a large proportion of glucose is incorporated into β-1,3-glucan, the main component of callose. Disturbed cell wall synthesis is also indicated by a decrease in the elongation of cotton fiber suffering from B deficiency.

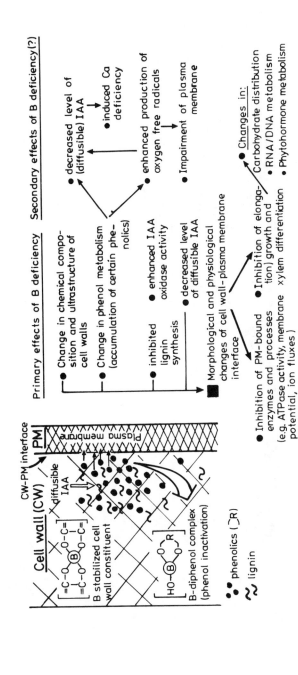

Fig. 9-9. Role of B in cell-wall metabolism, and primary and secondary effects of B deficiency.

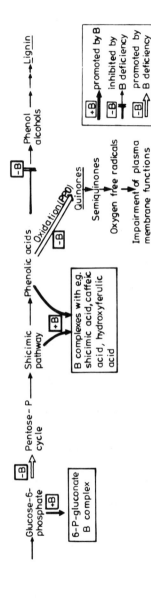

Fig. 9–10. Role of B in phenol metabolism and lignin synthesis.

The formation of B complexes with certain sugars and phenolics may explain typical shifts in metabolic pathways in B-deficient tissues, such as increased substrate flux through the pentose-phosphate cycle, enhanced formation of quinones, and inhibited lignin synthesis (Fig. 9–10).

With B deficiency, the formation of highly reactive intermediates, such as caffeic quinones, is enhanced at the expense of the precursors for lignin synthesis. There are indications that B can also affect lignin formation by regulating the conversion of phenolics to phenol alcohols (Pilbeam & Kirkby, 1983). Accumulated phenolics may also enhance production of toxic oxygen-free radicals (Fig. 9–9) via quinones and semiquinones (Fig. 9–10).

The rapid response of cell wall synthesis and phenol metabolism to B starvation may explain the fast cessation of elongation growth. Furthermore, growth inhibition with B deficiency may also be due to impairment of plasma membrane functions by reactive quinones or decreased levels of diffusible auxins (IAA), caused by enhanced IAA oxidase activity (Fig. 9–9). The latter aspects are strongly supported by the rapid responses of root elongation and IAA oxidase activity to the mode of the B supply (Fig. 9–11).

In contrast, growth inhibition with B deficiency has also been attributed to supraoptimal auxin levels in the tissue (Robertson & Loughman, 1977). This assumption is supported by similarities between B deficiency symptoms and symptoms induced by excessive IAA supply (Bohnsack & Albert, 1977). However, changes in ultrastructure at the cellular level are different between B deficiency and excessive levels of IAA (Hirsch & Torrey, 1980). Furthermore, with the onset of visual B deficiency symptoms, the IAA levels in the shoot apex are lower, rather than higher (Fackler et al., 1985). Presumably, IAA accumulation is a secondary effect and occurs in plant species that accumulate certain phenolics (e.g., caffeic acid), which are effective inhibitors of IAA oxidase.

It has also been supposed that growth inhibition with B deficiency is caused by decreased concentrations of nucleic acids (Krueger et al., 1987; Ali & Jarvis, 1988). Decrease in RNA levels precedes cessation in cell division, and could be the result of both inhibited RNA synthesis and higher RNase activity. The decrease in DNA level is a secondary effect, since DNA

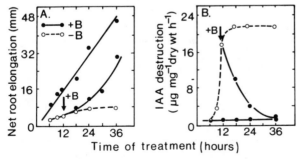

Fig. 9-11. Effect of B deficiency on elongation growth (A) and IAA oxidase activity (B) in the apical root section of squash. Resupply of B after 12 h (arrow) of B deficiency. (Redrawn from Bohnsack & Albert, 1977.)

Table 9-12. Effect of B pretreatment on the subsequent uptake of P and Rb, and the ATPase activity in root tips of corn.[†]

Pretreatment of root tips for 1 h	P uptake Preculture		Rb uptake Preculture		ATPase activity Preculture	
	−B	+B	−B	+B	−B	+B
	— nmol g^{-1} h^{-1} —				— μmol P_i mg^{-1} — protein h^{-1}	
−B	66	116	1630	2550	1.7	2.7
10^{-4} M H_3BO_3	151	177	2180	2650	2.5	nd[‡]

[†] Based on Pollard et al. (1977).   [‡] nd = not determined.

synthesis in B-deficient roots is sustained at least several hours after inhibition of root growth.

There is increasing evidence of a particular effect of B on plasma membrane functions. Activity of the plasma membrane-bound ATPase and uptake rates of ions in B-deficient roots are decreased, but can rapidly be restored by resupplying B (Table 9-12). Boron also is important for K transport into guard cells and, thus, for stomatal opening; solute leakage across the plasma membrane is increased with B deficiency (Tang & Dela Fuente, 1986). The various B deficiency-induced effects on membrane integrity and membrane potential (Blaser-Grill et al., 1989), on solute leakage and ion uptake can also be induced by certain phenolics. It might be that the effects of B deficiency on plasma membrane integrity, cell wall formation, and cell elongation are causally related to the changes in phenol metabolism in the cell walls (Fig. 9-9).

The roles of B in pollen germination and pollen tube growth are particularly important to crop production. Both processes and, also the viability of pollen grains, are severely inhibited by B deficiency (Dugger, 1983). For pollen tube growth, high B levels in the stigma and style presumably are required for physiological inactivation of callose by formation of borate-callose complexes at the pollen tube-style interface (Lewis, 1980b). As a consequence of these particular functions of B in reproductive organs, seed and grain production is much more reduced than vegetative growth with low B supply (Table 9-13).

Table 9-13. Effect of B supply on vegetative growth and various parameters of reproductive growth of red clover.[†]

B application	Shoot dry weight	Flowers	Seeds	Seed yield
mg kg^{-1} soil	g pot^{-1}	— no. pot^{-1} —		mg pot^{-1}
0	12.8	0	0	0
0.25	13.0	6	0	0
0.5	12.6	13	0	0
1.0	12.3	37	7	430
2.0	12.3	37	20	1190
4.0	8.7	34	12	740

[†] Based on Sherell (1983).

B. Critical Tissue Concentrations and Deficiency Symptoms

Plant species differ considerably in their B requirement. For example, the CDC, expressed as milligram per kilogram of B, measure about 5 to 10 mg kg $^{-1}$ in monocotyledons, 20 to 70 mg kg $^{-1}$ in dicotyledons, and 80 to 100 mg kg $^{-1}$ in latex-bearing plants, such as the poppy (*Papaver*) and dandelion (*Taraxacum*) (Bergmann, 1988). These different B requirements are most likely related to differences in cell wall composition. Within a species such as soybean, the CDC of B for young leaflets is about three to four times higher than for mature leaves (Kirk & Loneragan, 1988), reflecting the main function of B in cell growth and differentiation.

The concentration range between B deficiency and B toxicity is quite narrow, so special care is required when B fertilizers or municipal composts rich in B are applied, or when irrigation water high in B concentration is used. The CTC (mg kg $^{-1}$) in leaves differ considerably among plant species and cultivars within a species; e.g., from 100 mg kg $^{-1}$ for corn, 400 mg kg $^{-1}$ for cucumber (*Cucumis sativus* L.) and 1000 mg kg $^{-1}$ for squash (*Cucurbita pepo* L.), and between 100 and 270 mg kg $^{-1}$ in wheat genotypes (El-Sheikh et al., 1971; Paull et al., 1988).

Boron deficiency symptoms appear at the terminal buds and youngest leaves as retarded growth or necrosis. Usually, internodes are shorter, leaf blades are misshaped, and the diameters of stem and petioles are increased. The latter may lead to symptoms such as stem crack in celery (*Apium graveolens* L.). Water-soaked areas, tipburn, and brown- or blackheart in heads of vegetable crops, such as lettuce (*Lactuca sativa* L.), are common with B deficiency. In storage roots of celery or sugar beet (*Beta vulgaris* L.) necrosis of meristematic area leads to the typical heart rot. Boron deficiency-induced increases in the drop of buds, flowers, and developing fruits is widespread. In addition to the reduction or even failure of seed and fruit set, the quality of fruit often is affected by malformation (e.g., internal cork in apple [*Malus sylvestris* Mill.]) or in citrus by a decrease in the pulp/peel ratio.

VII. CHLORINE

A. Physico-chemical Properties and Physiological Functions

Chlorine is abundant in the lithosphere and atmosphere. It occurs in aqueous solutions mainly as Cl^-, which is highly mobile and easily taken up by plants. Average Cl concentrations in plants range from 1 to 20 g kg $^{-1}$ and, thus, are in the range of macronutrients. This abundance and the associated problems of avoiding Cl contamination causes particular difficulties in demonstrating the essentiality of Cl for growth of higher plants (Broyer et al., 1954). Compared with the high tissue concentrations of Cl found in most plants, the requirement for optimal growth generally is much lower (150–300 mg kg $^{-1}$).

Although various Cl-containing compounds exist in nature (Engvild, 1986), Cl exerts its functions mainly as a mobile anion (Cl^-) in processes such as osmoregulation (e.g., cell elongation, stomatal opening) and charge compensation (e.g., counter anion in cation transport) in higher plants. By specific binding to certain positively charged domains of peptides (e.g., histidyl residues), Cl can affect the reactivity of enzymes (e.g., water-splitting enzyme; Fig. 9-2). Chloride can be substituted to a large extent by other halides with similar physico-chemical properties, in particular by Br^-. Because of the much lower abundance of Br and other halides, this substitution is not of ecological relevance.

As early as 1946, Warburg and Lüttgens showed that the water-splitting system of photosystem II (PS II) requires Cl. This has been confirmed by others, including Itoh and Uwano (1986). Chloride acts as a cofactor to activate the Mn-containing water-splitting system (Fig. 9-2). The putative mechanisms involve Cl^- binding to various sites, including the Mn-active site and one of the three polypeptides of the water-splitting system. This Cl^- binding catalyzes the deprotonation of the water and H^+ export from the active Mn site (Coleman & Govindjee, 1987; Rutherford, 1989).

In contrast to photosynthetic activity in isolated chloroplasts or PSII particles, photosynthetic activity in leaves of intact plants normally is not inhibited by Cl deficiency. This is mainly due to the strict regulation of the Cl concentration at a rather constant level in the chloroplasts in vivo. Such strict regulation of compartmentation has been shown for glycophytes and halophytes. This regulation makes it experimentally very difficult to decrease the Cl concentrations in the chloroplasts of intact leaves below the critical level of about 80 mM. A decrease of photosynthetic O_2 evolution, as it occurs in isolated chloroplasts, however, also can be assumed in intact plants, provided that the Cl concentration in the chloroplasts were to fall below this critical level (Fig. 9-12).

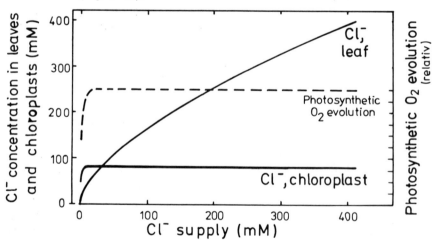

Fig. 9-12. Relationship between Cl^- concentration in the nutrient solution, leaves, and chloroplasts (based on Robinson & Downton, 1985), and the expected photosynthetic O_2 evolution capacity (schematic presentation).

Accumulation of Cl in chloroplasts is mediated by an active transport from the cytoplasm across the chloroplast envelope. With high Cl import into leaf cells, the concentrations in cytoplasm and chloroplasts are maintained at a low level by a preferential transport of Cl into the vacuole. For this preferential transport, a Cl-stimulated ATPase located in the tonoplast has been assumed (Dupont, 1987). The close relationship between stimulation of ATPase by Cl and elongation growth (Hager & Helmle, 1981) may explain why root elongation is inhibited with Cl deficiency, since there is insufficient transport of osmotically active solutes into the vacuole under such conditions.

Chloride also can affect plant growth indirectly via stomatal regulation as a mobile counter anion for K^+. This charge compensation by Cl rather than malate is of particular importance in plants in which guard cell chloroplasts are either absent or only poorly developed (e.g., onion [*Allium cepa* L.], palm trees such as coconut [*Cocos nucifera* L.]; Schnabl, 1978; Von Uexkull, 1985). In these plant species, growth inhibition with Cl deficiency is mainly the result of impaired fine regulation of stomata closing under drought stress. Compared with other plant species, palm trees have a particular high Cl demand (Von Uexkull, 1985).

Growth promotion by Cl also may be a consequence of suppressed diseases, such as grey leaf spot in coconut palms (Von Uexkull, 1985), take-all in wheat, stalk rot in corn, and downy mildew in millet [*Setaria italica* (L.) P. Beauv.] (Timm et al., 1986). Application of Cl-containing fertilizers to vegetables several days before harvest provides a possibility of lowering the NO_3-N concentration in the tissue by substitution of Cl for NO_3, and thus, increase the nutritional quality of the vegetables (Blom-Zandstra & Lampe, 1983).

B. Critical Tissue Concentrations and Deficiency Symptoms

The CDC for optimal growth varies between 70 mg kg^{-1} for tomato (*Lycopersicon esculentum* Mill.) (Ozanne et al., 1957) and 1000 mg kg^{-1} for kiwi (*Actinidia deliciosa*) (Table 9-14). The CTC is about 3 to 5 g kg^{-1} and 20 to 40 g kg^{-1} for Cl-sensitive and Cl-tolerant plant species, respectively (Bergmann, 1988).

Table 9-14. Effect of increasing concentrations in Cl$^-$ in nutrient solution on the Cl$^-$ concentration in the youngest leaf and growth (dry matter production in mean leaf area) of kiwi.

Cl$^-$ concentration in nutrient solution	Cl$^-$ concentration in youngest leaf	Total dry matter	Mean leaf area
μM	g kg^{-1} dry wt.	g plant^{-1}	m^2
0	0.7	8	0.17
350	1.5	32	0.41
700	2.1	37	0.50
1400	4.0	34	0.43

† Based on Smith et al. (1987).

Typical deficiency symptoms include wilting of leaves, curling of leaflets, bronzing and chlorosis similar to those of Mn deficiency, and severe inhibition of root growth (Ozanne et al., 1957; Smith et al., 1987; Bergmann, 1988).

VIII. SUMMARY

Since the first edition of this book, considerable progress has been made in improving our knowledge of the functions of some micronutrients (Fe, Mn, Cu, and Zn). In most instances, known functions have been more precisely defined at a cellular level. The function of various micronutrient cations in scavenger systems for toxic oxygen radicals and, thus, in protection of biomembranes it is now well established. In this context, the role of micronutrients in defense systems against pathogens deserves more attention in the future, as well as a better characterization of the "physiological active" fraction of micronutrients and the CDC in meristematic tissues (see Ch. 10). In contrast, our knowledge of the functions of Cl and of B, in particular, is still poor, and mainly descriptive or speculative. In view of the economic importance of B deficiency, the research efforts must be increased considerably to fill this gap. Although Ni has not been included in this chapter, sufficient experimental evidences of its functions in higher plants have been obtained in recent years to classify it as a micronutrient in the strict sense (see Ch. 18). Future research must show whether other candidates, in particular the "beneficial mineral elements," jump the fence and become micronutrients.

ACKNOWLEDGMENT

The authors thank Ernest A. Kirkby for his valuable suggestions and correction of the English text.

REFERENCES

Abadia, A., F. Ambard-Bretteville, R. Remy, and A. Tremolieres. 1988. Iron deficiency in pea leaves: Effect on lipid composition and synthesis. Physiol. Plant. 72:713–717.

Abbott, A.J. 1967. Physiological effects of micronutrient deficiencies in isolated roots of *Lycopersicon esculentum*. New Phytol. 66:419–437.

Agarwala, S.C., C.P. Sharma, S. Farooq, and C. Chatterjee. 1978. Effect of molybdenum deficiency on the growth and metabolism of corn plants raised in sand cultures. Can. J. Bot. 56:1905–1908.

Alcaraz, C.F.,F. Martinez-Sanchez, F. Sevilla, and E. Hellin. 1986. Influence of ferredoxin levels on nitrate reductase activity in iron deficient lemon leaves. J. Plant Nutr. 9:1405–1413.

Ali, A.H.N., and B.C. Jarvis. 1988. Effects of auxin and boron on nucleic acid metabolism and cell division during adventitious root regeneration. New Phytol. 108:383–391.

Ayala, M.B., and G. Sandmann. 1988. Activities of Cu-containing proteins in Cu-depleted pea leaves. Physiol. Plant. 72:801–806.

Becking, J.H. 1961. A requirement of molybdenum for the symbiotic nitrogen fixation in alder. Plant Soil 15:217–227.

Bergmann, W. 1988. Ernährungsstörungen bei Kulturpflanzen. Entstehung, visuelle und analytische Diagnose. Gustav Fischer Verlag, Jena, Germany.

Blaser-Grill, J., D. Knoppik, A. Amberger, and H. Goldbach. 1989. Influence of boron on the membrane potential in *Elodea densa* and *Helianthus annuus* roots and H$^+$ extrusion of suspension cultured *Daucus carota* cells. Plant Physiol. 90:280–284.

Blom-Zandstra, G., and J.E.M. Lampe. 1983. The effect of chloride and sulphate salts on the nitrate content in lettuce plants (*Lactuca sativa* L.). J. Plant Nutr. 6:611–628.

Bohnsack, C.W., and L.S. Albert. 1977. Early effects of boron deficiency on indole acetic acid oxidase levels of squash root tips. Plant Physiol. 59:1047–1050.

Botrill, D.E., J.V. Possingham, and P.E. Kriedemann. 1970. The effect of nutrient deficiencies on photosynthesis and respiration in spinach. Plant Soil 32:424–438.

Boyer, R.F., and J.R. Van der Ploeg. 1986. Iron metabolism in higher plants. The influence of nutrient iron on bean leaf lipoxygenase. J. Plant Nutr. 9:1585–1600.

Brouquisse, R., J. Gaillard, and R. Douce. 1986. Electron paramagnetic resonance characterization of membrane bound iron-sulfur clusters and aconitase in plant mitochondria. Plant Physiol. 81:247–252.

Brown, P.H., R.D. Graham, and D.J.D. Nicholas. 1984. The effect of manganese and nitrate supply on the levels of phenolics and lignin in young wheat plants. Plant Soil 81:437–440.

Broyer, T.C., A.C. Carlton, C.M. Johnson, and P.R. Stout. 1954. Chlorine—A micronutrient element for higher plants. Plant Physiol. 29:526–532.

Burnell, J.N. 1988. The biochemistry of manganese in plants. p. 125–137. *In* R.D. Graham et al. (ed.) Manganese in soils and plants. Proc. Int. Symp., Adelaide, South Australia. 22–26 Aug. 1988. Kluwer Academic Publ., Netherlands.

Bussler, W. 1981. Physiological functions and utilization of copper. p. 213–234. *In* J.F. Loneragan et al. (ed.) Copper in plants. Academic Press, Sydney, Australia.

Cakmak, I. 1988. Morphologische und physiologische Veränderungen bei Zinkmangelpflanzen. Ph.D. thesis. Universität Hohenheim, Stuttgart, Germany.

Cakmak, I., and H. Marschner. 1987. Mechanism of phosphorus-induced zinc deficiency in cotton. III. Changes in physiological availability of zinc in plants. Physiol. Plant. 70:13–20.

Cakmak, I., and H. Marschner. 1988a. Increase in membrane permeability and exudation in roots of zinc deficient plants. J. Plant Physiol. 132:356–361.

Cakmak, I., and H. Marschner. 1988b. Enhanced superoxide radical production in roots of Zn-deficient plants. J. Exp. Bot. 39:1449–1460.

Cakmak, I., H. Marschner, and F. Bangerth. 1989. Effect of Zn nutritional status on growth, protein metabolism and levels of indole-3-acetic acid and other phytohormones in bean (*Phaseolus vulgaris* L.). J. Exp. Bot. 40:405–412.

Campbell, W.H. 1988. Nitrate reductase and its role in nitrate assimilation in plants. Physiol. Plant. 74:214–219.

Coleman, W.J., and Govindjee. 1987. A model for the mechanism of chloride activation of oxygen evolution in photosystem II. Photosynth. Res. 13:199–223.

Delhaize, E., M.J. Dilworth, and J. Webb. 1986. The effect of copper nutrition and developmental state in the biosynthesis of diamine oxidase in clover leaves. Plant Physiol. 82:1126–1131.

De Vos, C.R., H.J. Lubberding, and H.F. Bienfait. 1986. Rhizosphere acidification as a response to iron deficiency in bean plants. Plant Physiol. 81:842–846.

Dugger, W.M. 1983. Boron in plant metabolism. p. 626–650. *In* A. Läuchli and R.L. Bieleski (ed.) Inorganic plant nutrition. Encycl. Plant Physiol., New Ser., Vol. 15 B, Springer Verlag New York, New York.

Dupont, F.M. 1987. Variable effects of nitrate on ATP-dependent proton transport by barley root membranes. Plant Physiol. 84:526–534.

El-Sheikh, A.M., A. Ulrich, S.K. Awad, and A.E. Nawardy. 1971. Boron tolerance of squash, melon, cucumber and corn. J. Am. Soc. Hortic. Sci. 96:536–537.

Engvild, K.C. 1986. Chlorine-containing natural compounds in higher plants. Phytochemistry 25:781–791.

Epstein, E. 1965. Mineral metabolism. p. 436–466. *In* J. Bonner and J.E. Varner (ed). Plant biochemistry. Academic Press, London.

Fackler, U., H. Goldbach, E.W. Weiler, and A. Amberger. 1985. Influence of boron deficiency on indol-3yl-acetic acid and abscisic acid levels in root and shoot tips. J. Plant Physiol. 119:295–299.

Goodman, B.A., and P.C. De Kock. 1982. Mössbauer studies of plant material. I. Duckweed, stocks, soybeans and pea. J. Plant Nutr. 5:345–353.

Graham, R.D. 1983. Effects of nutrient stress on susceptibility of plants to disease with particular reference to the trace elements. Adv. Bot. Res. 10:221–276.

Gubler, W.D., R.G. Grogan, and P.P. Osterli. 1982. Yellows of melons caused by molybdenum
deficiency in acid soil. Plant Dis. 66:449–451.

Hager, A., and M. Helmle. 1981. Properties of an ATP-fueled, Cl-dependent proton pump
localized in membranes of microsomal vesicles from maize coleoptiles. Z. Naturforsch.
36c:997–1008.

Hannam, R.J., and K. Ohki. 1988. Detection of manganese deficiency and toxicity in plants.
p. 243–259. In R.D. Graham et al. (ed.) Manganese in soils and plants. Proc. Int. Symp.,
Adelaide, South Australia. 22–26 Aug. 1988. Kluwer Academic Publ., Netherlands.

Häussling, M., V. Römheld, and H. Marschner. 1985. Relationship between chlorosis, iron
and leaf growth in grape vines growing at different locations. Vitis 24:158–168.

Herriques, F.S. 1989. Effects of copper deficiency on the photosynthetic apparatus of sugar
beet (Beta vulgaris L.). J. Plant Physiol. 135:453–458.

Hewitt, E.J. 1983. Essential and functional metals in plants. p. 277–323. In D.A. Robb and
W.S. Pierpoint (ed.) Metals and micronutrients: Uptake and utilization by plants. Academic Press, New York.

Hewitt, E.J., and C.C. McCready. 1956. Molybdenum as a plant nutrient. VII. The effect of
different molybdenum and nitrogen supplies on yields and composition of tomato plants
grown in sand culture. J. Hortic. Sci. 31:284–290.

Hewitt, E.J., and B.A. Notton. 1980. Nitrate reductase system in Eukariotic and Prokariotic
organisms. p. 273–325. In M. Coughan (ed.) Molybdenum and molybdenum-containing
enzymes. Pergamon Press, Oxford, England.

Hildebrand, D.F. 1989. Lipoxygenases. Physiol. Plant. 76:249–253.

Hirsch, A.M., and J.G. Torrey. 1980. Ultrastructural changes in sunflower root cells in relation to boron deficiency and added auxin. Can. J. Bot. 58:856–866.

Horst, W.J. 1988. The physiology of manganese toxicity. p. 175–188. In R.D. Graham et al.
(ed.) Manganese in soils and plants. Proc. Int. Symp., Adelaide, South Australia. 22–26
Aug. 1988. Kluwer Academic Publ., Netherlands.

Itoh, S., and S. Uwano. 1986. Characteristics of the Cl-action site in the O_2 evolving reaction
in PS II particles: Electrostatic interaction with ions. Plant Cell Physiol. 27:25–36.

Jewell, A.W., B.G. Murray, and B.J. Alloway. 1988. Light and electron microscope studies
on pollen development in barley (Hordeum vulgare L.) grown under copper sufficient and
deficient conditions. Plant Cell Environ. 22:273–281.

Kirk, G.J., and J.F. Loneragan. 1988. Functional boron requirement for leaf expansion and
its use as a critical value for diagnosis of boron deficiency in soybean. Agron. J. 80:758–762.

Klug, A., and D. Rhodes. 1987. "Zinc fingers": a novel protein motif for nucleic acid recognition. Trends Biochem. Sci. 12:464–469.

Kriedemann, P.E., R.D. Graham, and J.T. Wiskich. 1985. Photosynthetic dysfunction and
in vivo changes in chlorophyll a fluorescence from manganese-deficient wheat leaves. Aust.
J. Agric. Res. 36:157–169.

Krueger, R.W., C.J. Lovatt, and L.S. Albert. 1987. Metabolic requirement of Cucurbita pepo
for boron. Plant Physiol. 83:254–258.

Leidi, E.O., and M. Gomes. 1985. A role for manganese in the regulation of soybean nitrate
reductase activity? J. Plant Physiol. 118:335–342.

Leusch, H.J., and H. Buchenauer. 1988. Einfluss von Bodenbehandlungen mit siliziumreichen
Kalken und Natriumsilikat auf den Mehltaubefall von Weizen. Kali-Briefe 19:1–11.

Lewis, D.H. 1980a. Boron, lignification and the origin of vascular plants. A unified hypothesis. New Phytol. 84:209–229.

Lewis, D.H. 1980b. Are there inter-relations between the metabolic role of boron, synthesis
of phenolic phytoalexins and the germination of pollen? New Phytol. 84:261–270.

Lin, C.H., and C.R. Stocking. 1978. Influence of leaf age, light, dark and iron deficiency on
polyribosome levels in maize leaves. Plant Cell Physiol. 19:461–470.

Loneragan, J.F. 1981. Distribution and movement of copper in plants. p. 165–188. In J.F. Loneragan et al. (ed.) Copper in plants. Academic Press, Sydney, Australia.

Machold, O., W. Meisel, and H. Schnorr. 1968. Bestimmung der Bindungsform des Eisens in
Blättern durch Mössbauerspektrometrie. Naturwissenschaften 55:499–500.

Marschner, H. 1986. Mineral nutrition of higher plants. Academic Press, Orlando, FL.

Marschner, H., and I. Cakmak. 1986. Mechanism of phosphorus-induced zinc deficiency in
cotton. II. Evidence for impaired shoot control of phosphorus uptake and translocation
under zinc deficiency. Physiol. Plant. 68:491–496.

Marschner, H., and I. Cakmak. 1989. High light intensity enhances chlorosis and necrosis in leaves of zinc, potassium, and magnesium deficient bean (*Phaseolus vulgaris*) plants. J. Plant Physiol. 134:308–315.

Marziah, M., and C.H. Lam. 1987. Polyphenol oxidase from soybean (*Glycine max.* v. Palmetto) and its response to copper and other micronutrients. J. Plant Nutr. 10:2089–2094.

Mizuno, N., O. Inazu, and K. Kamada. 1982. Characteristics of concentrations of copper, iron and carbolydrates in copper deficient wheat plants. p. 396–399. *In* A. Scaife (ed.) Proc. 9th. Int. Plant Nutr. Colloq., Warwick, England. 22–27 Aug. 1982. Commonwealth Agric. Bur., Farnham House, Slough, England.

Moore, P.A., and W.H. Patrick. 1989. Effect of zinc deficiency on alcohol hydrogenase activity and nutrient uptake in rice. Agron. J. 80:882–885.

Nable, R.O., A. Bar-Akiva, and J.F. Loneragan. 1984. Functional manganese requirement and its use as a critical value for diagnosis of manganese deficiency in subterranean clover (*Trifolium subterraneum* L. cv. Seaton Park). Ann. Bot. 54:39–49.

Nambiar, E.K.S. 1976. Genetic differences in the copper nutrition of cereals. I. Differential responses of genotypes of copper. Aust. J. Agric. Res. 27:453–463.

Neumann, K.H., and F.C. Steward. 1968. Investigation on the growth and metabolism of cultured explants of *Daucus carota*. I. Effects of iron, molybdenum and manganese on growth. Planta 81:333–350.

Nishio, J.N., S.E. Taylor, and N. Terry. 1985. Changes in thylakoid galactolipids and proteins during iron nutrition-mediated chloroplast development. Plant Physiol. 77:705–711.

Obata, H., and M. Umebayashi. 1988. Effect of zinc deficiency on protein synthesis in cultured tobacco plant cells. Soil Sci. Plant Nutr. 34:351–357.

O'Hara, G.W., M.J. Dilworth, N. Boonkerd, and P. Parkpian. 1988. Iron-deficiency specifically limits nodule development in peanut inoculated with *Bradyrhizobium* sp. New Phytol. 108:51–57.

Ozanne, P.G., J.T. Woolley, and T.C. Broyer. 1957. Chlorine and bromine in the nutrition of higher plants. Aust. J. Biol. Sci. 10:66–79.

Paull, J.G., B. Cartwright, and A.J. Rathjen. 1988. Responses of wheat and barley genotypes to toxic concentrations of soil boron. Euphytica 39:137–144.

Pilbeam, D.J., and E.A. Kirkby. 1983. The physiological role of boron in plants. J. Plant Nutr. 6:563–582.

Pollard, A.S., A.J. Parr, and B.C. Loughman. 1977. Boron in relation to membrane function in higher plants. J. Exp. Bot. 28:831–841.

Pushnik, J.C., and G.W. Miller. 1989. Iron regulation of chloroplast photosynthetic function. Mediation of PS I development. J. Plant Nutr. 12:407–421.

Rajagopalan, K.V. 1980. Sulfite oxidase. p. 243–273. *In* M.P. Coughan (ed.) Molybdenum and molybdenum-containing enzymes. Pergamon Press, Oxford, England.

Reuter, D.J., J.F. Loneragan, A.D. Robson, and D. Plaskett. 1982. Zinc in subterranean clover (*Trifolium subterraneum* L. cv. Seaton Park). I. Effects of zinc supply on distribution of zinc and dry weight. Aust. J. Agric. Res. 33:989–999.

Robertson, G.A., and B.C. Loughman. 1977. Response to boron deficiency: A comparison with responses produced by chemical methods of retarding root elongation. New Phytol. 73:291–298.

Robinson, S.P., and W.J.S. Downton. 1985. Potassium, sodium and chloride ion concentration in leaves and isolated chloroplasts of the halophyte *Suaeda australis* R. Br. Aust. J. Plant Physiol. 12:471–479.

Robson, A.D., R.D. Hartley, and S.C. Jarvis. 1981. Effect of copper deficiency on phenolic and other constituents of wheat cell walls. New Phytol. 89:361–371.

Robson, A.D., and D.J. Reuter. 1981. Diagnosis of copper deficiency and toxicity. p. 287–312. *In* J.F. Loneragan et al. (ed.) Copper in plants. Academic Press, Sydney, Australia.

Römheld, V. 1987. Existence of two different strategies for the acquisition of iron in higher plants. p. 353–374. *In* G. Winkelmann et al. (ed.) Iron transport in microbes, plants and animals. VC Verlagsges, Weinheim, Germany.

Rutherford, A.W. 1989. Photosystem II, the water splitting enzyme. Trends Biochem. Sci. 14:227–232.

Schlee, D., H. Reimbothe, and W. Fritsche. 1968. Der Einfluss von Eisen auf den Purinstoffwechsel und die Riboflavinbildung von *Candida guillermondii*. Z. Allg. Mikrobiol. 8:127–158.

Schnabl, H. 1978. The effect of Cl$^-$ upon the sensitivity of starch-containing and starch-deficient stomata and guard cell protoplasts towards potassium ions, fusicoccin and abscisic acid. Planta 144:95–100.

Seckbach, J. 1982. Ferreting out the secrets of plant ferritin—A review. J. Plant Nutr. 5:369–394.

Sharma, C.P., P.N. Sharma, S.S. Bisht, and B.D. Nautiyal. 1982. Zinc deficiency induced changes in cabbage. p. 601–606. In A. Scaife (ed.) Proc. 9th Plant Nutr. Colloq., Warwick, England. 22–27 Aug. 1982. Commonwealth Agric. Bur., Farnham House, Slough, England.

Sherrell, C.G. 1983. Effect of boron application on seed production of New Zealand herbage legumes. N.Z. J. Exp. Agric. 11:113–117.

Smith, G.S., C.J. Clark, and P.T. Holland. 1987. Chloride requirement of kiwifruit (*Actinidia deliciosa*). New Phytol. 106:71–80.

Soloiman, D., and F.Y.H. Wu. 1985. Preparation and characterization of various *Escherichia coli* RNA polymerases containing one or two intrinsic metal ions. Biochemistry 24:5079–5082.

Sparrow, D.H., and R.D. Graham. 1988. Susceptibility of zinc-deficient wheat plants to colonization by *Fusarium graminearum* Schw. Group 1. Plant Soil 112:261–266.

Suge, H., H. Takahashi, S. Arita, and H. Takaki. 1986. Gibberellin relationships in zinc-deficient plants. Plant Cell Physiol. 27:1005–1012.

Tang, M.P., and R.K. Dela Fuente. 1986. The transport of indole-3-acetic acid in boron- and calcium-deficient sunflower hypocotyl segments. Plant Physiol. 81:646–650.

Terry, N., and J. Abadia. 1986. Function of iron in chloroplasts. J. Plant Nutr. 9:609–646.

Thiel, H., and A. Finck. 1973. Ermittlung von Grenzwerten optimaler Kupferversorgung für Hafer und Sommergerste. Z. Pflanzenernaehr. Bodenkd. 134:107–125.

Timm, C.A., R.J. Goos, B.E. Johnson, F.J. Siobolik, and R.W. Stack. 1986. Effect of potassium fertilizers on malting barley infected with common root rot. Agron. J. 78:197–200.

Vielemeyer, H.P., F. Fischer, and W. Bergmann. 1969. Untersuchungen über den Einfluss der Mikronährstoffe Eisen und Mangan auf den Stickstoff-Stoffwechsel landwirtschaftlicher Kulturpflanzen. 2. Mitt. Untersuchungen über die Wirkung des Mangans auf die Nitratreduktion und den Gehalt an freien Aminosäuren in jungen Buschbohnenpflanzen. Albrecht-Thaer-Arch. 13:393–404.

Von Uexkull, H.R. 1985. Chlorine in the nutrition of palm trees. Oleagineux 40:67–72.

Vunkova-Radeva, R., J. Schiemann, R.R. Mendel, G. Salcheva, and D. Georgieva. 1988. Stress and activity of molybdenum-containing complex (molybdenum cofactor) in winter wheat seeds. Plant Physiol. 87:533–535.

Warburg, O., and W. Lüttgens. 1946. Photochemical reduction of quione in green cells and granules. Biochimia 11:303–322.

Welch, R.M., M.J. Webb, and J.F. Loneragan. 1982. Zinc in membrane function and its role in phosphorus toxicity. p. 710–715. In A. Scaife (ed.) Proc. 9th Int. Plant Nutr. Colloq., Warwick, England. 22–27 Aug. 1982. Commonwealth Agric. Bur., Farnham House, Slough, England.

Wilkinson, R.E., and K. Ohki. 1988. Influence of manganese deficiency and toxicity on isoprenoid syntheses. Plant Physiol. 87:841–846.

Winkler, R.G., D.G. Blevins, J.C. Polacco, and D.D. Randall. 1988. Ureide catabolism in nitrogen-fixing legumes. Trends Biochem. Sci. 13:97–100.

Witt, H.H., and A. Jungk. 1977. Beurteilung der Molybdänversorgung von Pflanzen mit Hilfe der Mo-induzierbaren Nitratreduktase-Aktivität. Z. Pflanzenernaehr. Bodenkd. 140:209–222.

Woolhouse, H.W. 1983. Toxicity and tolerance in response of plants to metals. p. 246–300. In O.L. Lange et al. (ed.) Encycl. Plant Physiology, New Ser., Vol. 12C. Springer-Verlag New York, New York.

Chapter 10

Micronutrients and Disease Resistance and Tolerance in Plants

ROBIN D. GRAHAM AND MICHAEL J. WEBB, *University of Adelaide, Glen Osmond, Australia*

The importance of adequate nutrition to disease resistance in humans is something most people accept from personal experience. Although this vital principle is also well recognized in plant science, it is often ignored in practical agriculture. This is especially true for the micronutrients. Of many reviews dealing with plant nutrition and disease (see Graham, 1983), few have seriously considered the micronutrients. More recently, however, the role of Mn has been treated at length (Huber & Wilhelm, 1988) and the flurry of research on siderophores in disease control (Swinburne, 1986a) has brought Fe to prominence in plant pathological literature. This chapter updates the earlier, more extensive review on this subject (Graham, 1983).

I. RESISTANCE AND TOLERANCE

The terms resistance and tolerance applied to the host in a host-pathogen system relate to the growth of the pathogen and response of the host, respectively.

A. Resistance

The resistance of the host is determined by its ability to limit the penetration, development, and/or reproduction of invading pathogens. Resistance (and for that matter, tolerance) varies with genotype of the two organisms, with plant age, and with changes in the environment. In a resistant host, the development of the pathogen is slower than in a susceptible host. Resistance has been classified in various ways, such as race specific and race nonspecific (see Table 4 in Western, 1971). The former is frequently perceived to be an immune or hypersensitive response to a particular race of the pathogen involving control by one or more major genes. Nonspecific resistance is usually polygenic and involves diverse biochemical systems, and is variously described as generalized, adult-plant, or field resistance. It is this nonspecific or field resistance which is, in many cases, degraded by micronutrient deficiency in the host.

B. Tolerance

Whereas resistance in the host plant is measured in terms of its ability to inhibit the development and reproduction of the invading pathogen, tolerance in the host is measured in terms of its ability to maintain its own growth or yield in spite of the infection (Trudgill, 1986). Tolerance may be as simple as having the required vigor to quickly replace the roots or leaf surface damaged by the pathogen. Although the simple separation of resistance and tolerance in the above definition may become clouded if the pathogen produces a toxic substance which inhibits the physiological processes fundamental to regrowth (Wallace, 1987), it will serve quite adequately for the present purpose. Wallace (1987) has argued that tolerance to pathogens is not a response specific to the pathogen, but is a normal homeostatic response of the host that has been evolved to counter a wide range of environmental stresses, mostly abiotic. Thus a genetically controlled ability to tolerate a nutrient-deficient soil (nutritional stress) would, by this view, also confer tolerance to a root-rotting pathogen in a host growing in such soils, since the pathogen has the effect of reducing the nutrient absorbing surface.

A good example of tolerance conferred by a micronutrient treatment is that of Mn supplied to barley (*Hordeum vulgare* L.) in the presence of cereal cyst nematode (*Heterodera avenae*) (Wilhelm et al., 1985). In this factorial study, nematode and Mn treatments were applied to barley in a Mn-deficient sandy soil so that each factor varied from no stress to moderately severe. The results indicated that Mn had no effect on host resistance to the pathogen, since similar numbers of infections (mature females) developed irrespective of the Mn status (Fig. 10–1a). There was, however, a significant interaction on yield (Fig. 10–1b), indicating a favorable Mn effect on tolerance of barley to the nematode, possibly by offsetting the reduced absorption efficiency caused by the nematode.

C. Relationship Between Resistance and Tolerance

Resistance and tolerance are relatively independent factors in a host-pathogen relationship; it does not follow that a decrease in resistance of the host due to a change in environment, genotype or plant age (with a concomitant increase in disease incidence) will lead to a loss of yield (that is, a decrease in tolerance). A classic example is the influence of N fertilizer added to a powdery mildew-infected, N-deficient cereal crop (Last, 1962). Although resistance to the pathogen was lowered and the amount of infection increased as the plant's N status improved, the tolerance of the crop to this increased pathogen load was also increased, resulting in an increase in grain yield.

It is more than likely that all of the essential elements discussed in this book contribute to disease tolerance, wherever the soil is deficient in that

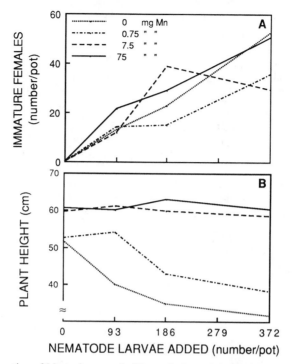

Fig. 10-1. Interaction of Mn and nematode (*Heterodera avenae*) treatments on (A) the number of infections (immature females), and (B) the height of barley plants growing in a Mn-deficient soil in pots (Wilhelm et al., 1985; reprinted with permission of Kluwer Academic Publ.).

element, by increasing the vigor of the host plant. This enhanced vigor will contribute to the yield advantage by promoting more efficient use of the limiting nutrient whether or not there is evidence of effects on resistance as well. Of course, tolerance may operate to a yield advantage even when the added element decreases resistance, as in the classic case of N and powdery mildew already mentioned (Last, 1962; Graham, 1983).

It is possible that, where a nutrient confers a growth response, the increase in, for instance, leaf area may dilute the number of lesions if expressed on a leaf-area basis, whereas the number of lesions per plant or per hectare remains unchanged. Such data may look like an increase in resistance when it is merely a form of tolerance or simply a function of (low) inoculum potential. On the other hand, since beneficial elements such as Si, Li and Cd are not known to increase yield in disease-free conditions, we presume that they are acting on resistance (or directly on the pathogen) rather than on tolerance.

II. METABOLIC PATHWAYS TO RESISTANCE

Among the various defense mechanisms available to plants (see comprehensive treatment of this subject in Horsfall & Cowling, 1980), the roles

of lignin and phenols in defense are well known and possibly the best understood biochemically. This is because, unlike phytoalexins, their synthesis occurs even in the absence of any infection. The metabolic pathways of
importance in the synthesis of phenols and lignin, and points in the pathways at which certain micronutrients may have some influence, are presented
in Fig. 10–2.

In the past, the synthesis of phenols and lignin has generally been regarded as an obligate process, occurring as a consequence of normal higher
plant growth. This synthetic process has also been implicated as a waste
removal mechanism. On the other hand, production of phytoalexins is re-

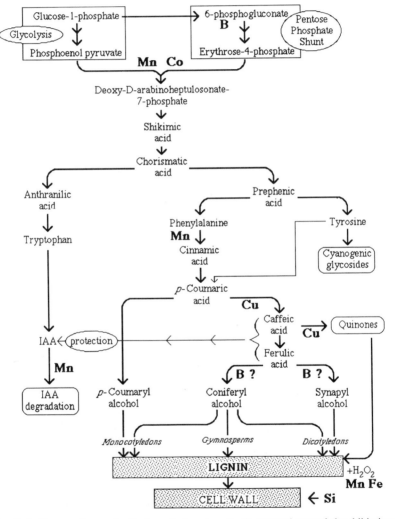

Fig. 10–2. Some pathways for lignin and phenol synthesis centered around the shikimic acid
pathway. Information presented here has been derived from Burnell (1988), Bidwell (1979),
Goodwin and Mercer (1972), Graham (1983), and Gross (1980).

garded as an elicited response to invading pathogens (Cruickshank, 1980); however, it has recently been demonstrated that localized lignin synthesis can also be induced by 'elicitors,' especially those of biotic origin (Barber & Ride, 1988). Furthermore, the differences in susceptibility to fungal attack between near-isogenic lines of cereals has been attributed to the accumulation of phenylpropanoids (for example, ferulic or *p*-coumaric acids) in the induced papillae (Aist et al., 1988), and to changes in the activity of certain key enzymes in the general phenylpropanoid pathway (Moerschbacher et al., 1988). Thus, synthesis of the above physical and chemical defense mechanisms may not always be under the banner of 'preformed barriers' but may be quite dynamic (Matern & Kneusel, 1988).

Clearly, many of the micronutrients are implicated in phenol metabolism, from control of carbohydrate movement into synthetic pathways (B) to the final polymerisation of lignin (Mn and Fe). Hence, the micronutrient status of the host plant at the time of attack by a pathogen is important to that plant's defense capabilities. Details of the involvement of some of these elements in these pathways will be covered later.

III. ROLES OF INDIVIDUAL ELEMENTS

A. Manganese

Of the micronutrients, Mn may prove to be the most important in the development of resistance in plants to both root and foliar diseases of fungal origin. The availability of Mn to plant roots and soil microorganisms varies mercurially over time, depending on many environmental and soil biotic factors. Consequently, Mn availability is subject to manipulation by both higher plants and microorganisms. As Mn is required in larger concentrations by higher plants than by fungi and bacteria, there is opportunity for the pathogen to exploit this difference in requirement.

Huber and Wilhelm (1988) have recently and comprehensively (170 references) reviewed the literature on the role of Mn in disease resistance. This section will concentrate, therefore, on the issues involved and will refer only to a selection of the published papers. Of the 82 references cited in Table 1 of Huber and Wilhelm (1988), all but four indicated that added Mn decreased disease. In two of the four reports, the Mn status of the host was in the toxic range, whereas the status in the other two was unknown. Thus, although we may accept that Mn normally contributes to suppression of fungal (and bacterial) diseases, few papers provide sufficient plant analysis data to indicate whether the effects of Mn occur over the deficiency range only or over the sufficiency range as well. Whereas the effects of nutrition on disease are normally limited to the deficiency range (Graham, 1983), there are a few indications in the literature that the suppressive effects of Mn operate well into the sufficiency range for the host plant (discussed later). This would appear to indicate either: (i) that the Mn requirement of the host plant for disease resistance is higher than for yield; or (ii) that Mn is somehow lowering the inoculum potential of soil-borne pathogens.

1. Relationship between Disease and Manganese Concentration in the Host Plant

It is often observed that as the incidence of disease increases, the Mn concentration in host tissues decreases (Huber & Wilhelm, 1988). This may be attributable to several different causes. With root pathogens, the pruning of the root system as a result of disease can lead to a smaller absorptive surface, and thereby lower concentrations in the plant (Wilhelm et al., 1985, 1988; Abia et al., 1977). Alternatively, the fungus may be able to immobilize Mn in the rhizosphere by oxidation, thereby decreasing soil Mn availability (Bromfield, 1978; Wilhelm et al., 1990). With both aboveground and below-ground pathogens, the correlation may also arise because Mn affects host plant resistance directly, as will be discussed later. While the average Mn concentration may be lower in disease-affected tissue for any of the reasons above, Mn has been reported to be mobilized and concentrated around infection sites (Kunoh et al., 1975; Takanashi & Iwata, 1963).

Another view of the inverse correlation of plant Mn concentration and disease severity is the fact that a suite of environmental factors, which collectively aggravate the severity of a number of fungal diseases, also decrease the availability of soil Mn (Graham, 1983; Huber & Wilhelm, 1988). These are summarized in Table 10-1. Whereas these factors are consciously manipulated in the control of two widely occurring soil-borne diseases, common scab of potato (*Solanum tuberosum* L.) and take-all of wheat (*Triticum aestivum* L.), they also appear to influence the prevalence of blast and leaf spot of rice (*Oryza sativa* L.) (Choong-Hoe, 1986), root rot of avocado (*Persea americana*) (Falcon et al., 1984), powdery mildew of swede (*Brassica napus*) (Brain & Whittington, 1981), and powdery mildew of wheat (Colquhoun, 1940). The distribution of powdery mildew problems on wheat in South Australia (A.H. Mayfield, 1984, unpublished data) is that which is expected from the distribution of Mn-deficient soils.

Table 10-1. Soil factors affecting the availability of soil Mn.†

Factor	Mn availability
Higher pH	Decrease
Lime	Decrease
NH_4^+ forms of N	Increase
NO_3^- forms of N	Decrease
Cl^- fertilizer	Increase
Green manures	Increase
Cold (wet) soils	Decrease
Lupin in rotation	Increase‡
Irrigation	Increase

† Summarized from Graham, 1983; Huber & Wilhelm, 1988; Reprinted with permission of Kluwer Academic Publ.).
‡ From P.M. King et al., 1989, unpublished data.

2. Disease Abatement with Manganese Fertilizers

With few exceptions (Marchal, 1902; Germar, 1934; Colquhoun, 1940) reports of beneficial effects of Mn fertilizers in disease control have lagged behind the reports of direct agronomic benefits in yield. The situation for Mn contrasts with that of Cu: the usefulness of Cu against fungal pathogens was discovered long before its essentiality, which, indeed, led to that discovery. Nevertheless, there have been a number of reports of pathogenic diseases that have been successfully controlled by Mn fertilizers, including powdery mildew of cereals (Huber & Keeler, 1977; Vlamis & Yarwood, 1962; Graham, 1983), downy mildew of sorghum [*Sorghum bicolor* (L.) Moench] (Balasubramanian, 1980), *Exserohilum* on areca palm (*Chysalidocarpus lutescens*) (Chase & Poole, 1984) and take-all of wheat (see below). As mentioned in Section I, Wilhelm et al. (1985) gained better tolerance of barley to nematodes by Mn fertilization without a change in host-plant resistance. A role for Mn in control of common scab (*Streptomyces scabies*) of potato was reported by Björling (1946) and Mortvedt et al. (1961, 1963), but few of the subsequent attempts to control scab in practice by Mn fertilization have been successful (Rodger et al., 1967; Gilmour et al., 1968; Rogers, 1969; Barnes, 1972), and this approach by agronomists has generally lost favor (Graham, 1983). These failures reflect the difficulty in maintaining Mn availability after application to soil.

Despite the rapidly mounting experimental evidence of the importance of Mn in disease resistance, there are few field reports of the benefits of Mn fertilizers. The reason is linked to the relative ineffectiveness and poor residual value of Mn fertilizers on most soils that need Mn supplements (nonacid soils), and is linked to the complex soil biochemistry of Mn discussed in other chapters. Because most Mn-deficient soils are of high pH, which favors both chemical and microbial oxidation and immobilization of soluble Mn^{2+}, rapid oxidation is the fate of added fertilizer Mn, so that the very soils which most need Mn fertilizer are the most efficient at immobilizing it when it is added. This is seen in the following reaction:

$$\underset{\text{(insoluble)}}{MnO_2} + 4H^+ + 2e^- \overset{\text{microbes}}{\longleftrightarrow} \underset{\text{(soluble)}}{Mn^{2+}} + 2H_2O \qquad [1]$$

Marcar (1986) showed that 90 to 95% of added Mn in a calcareous soil was immobilized within a week. Thus, most experiments with this type of soil would have been poor tests of the hypothesis. Indeed, potato tubers, which are phloem fed, probably require the Mn in their immediate environment, since Mn has limited phloem mobility. Hence, mixing the Mn fertilizer through the tuber zone was more effective than banding in the experiments of Mortvedt et al. (1963), although higher rates may be required to offset the effects of rapid oxidation. The importance of Mn in this host-pathogen system is emphasized by the fact that conventional control of scab involves most of the factors listed in Table 10-1 which increase available soil Mn.

Further progress may await improvements in fertilizer technology which will prolong the availability of Mn. For example, Huber and Dorich (1988) co-injected Mn, NH_3 and nitrification inhibitors for effective control of take-all of wheat. This technology should also be tried in the control of common scab, especially when nitrification inhibitors that are more effective and longer lasting than nitrapyrin appear in the marketplace.

a. Common Scab of Potato. One aspect of the connection between Mn and common scab must be mentioned here: the causal organism *Streptomyces scabies* is itself a capable oxidizer of Mn (Mortvedt et al., 1963), and it has been argued that this is important to its virulence (Graham, 1983). Moreover, Bromfield (1978, 1979), in some elegant studies of a *Streptomyces*, showed that it oxidized Mn at some distance from its mycelium by excreting a non-peptide active principle large enough to be retained by a dialysis membrane. This capacity to oxidize and immobilize a soil amendment that may contribute to its control, is also found in *Gaeumannomyces graminis* var. *tritici* (the causal agent of take-all).

b. Take-all of Wheat. Take-all of wheat, caused by the ubiquitous root-attacking fungus *Gaeumannomyces graminis* var. *tritici* (*Ggt*), is considered to be the most serious root disease of the wheat crop (Asher & Shipton, 1981) (Take-all describes the disease, also known as haydie, and *Ggt* refers to the incitant organism). The *Ggt* fungus has a strong exotrophic growth habit, but finally enters the root cortex and breaches the endodermis to crush the phloem and block the xylem, thereby effectively cutting off supplies of carbohydrates to the root tip and supplies of water and minerals to the shoots. Damage varies from minor loss of grain yield to early plant death.

Although Mn and take-all had been linked in a general way by Huber (1980), it was first proposed as the key to the epidemiology of the disease by Graham (1981, 1983). All of the factors listed in Table 10-1 influence both take-all severity and Mn availability in a way consistent with the above hypothesis. Therefore, Mn availability becomes the unifying principle which makes the suite of soil factors conducive to take-all unique, and binds them together in an operational way. The Mn theory also has better predictive and explanatory value than any of the individual factors alone. For example, the seemingly anomalous observations of severe take-all on a few quite acid, sandy soils (Asher & Shipton, 1981) can be explained by their unusually low Mn content.

In recent years, several papers have demonstrated experimentally in pot and field work that, in Mn-deficient conditions, Mn fertilizer significantly decreased take-all (Graham & Rovira, 1984; Rovira et al., 1985; Wilhelm et al., 1988, 1990). Generally, the responses in infection occur over the deficiency range, although in one case (potted soil) Mn at a high rate completely inhibited the disease. It is important to note that effects of Mn on take-all are measurable before foliar symptoms of Mn deficiency are obvious in the leaves. Moreover, Mn suppression of take-all has been repeatedly observed to occur before *Ggt*, as a treatment, has had any effect on concentrations of Mn in the plant (Graham & Rovira, 1984; Wilhelm et al., 1988). This means that Mn deficiency occurred first and predisposed the plants to infection, rather than infection developing first and predisposing the plants to Mn deficiency, by virtue of its root-pruning effects. A similar finding arose from a study of the Zn-crown rot interaction (Section III.C.2).

The biology and control of take-all is inextricably linked to Mn. In the first place, *Ggt* is a powerful oxidizer of Mn, the more so when the isolate is virulent (Wilhelm et al., 1990). In fact, in a study of 13 isolates of the fungus, their capacity to oxidize Mn was highly correlated with their virulence, the regression explaining nearly 60% of variation in virulence (Fig. 10-3). This capacity to oxidize Mn^{2+} appears to be expressed in the host-pathogen relationship: Wilhelm et al. (1987) observed black nodules of Mn (presumably MnO_2) in the interstices of epidermal and superficial cortical cells of wheat roots under attack by *Ggt*, but such nodules were never found in root segments free of the fungus. Since lignin in the form of lignitubers is involved in resistance to this fungus, it has been argued that the ability to immobilize Mn in the infection court by oxidation may contribute to the virulence of the *Ggt* isolate (Graham, 1983). Further evidence along these lines is provided by the discovery that a suppressive organism, *Pseudomonas fluorescens* strain 2-79 (Weller & Cook, 1983), which, according to D.M. Huber (1988, personal communication), is a strong Mn oxidizer on Bromfield's media, was a potent Mn reducer under our conditions, reversing the effects of *Ggt*. Moreover, on agar, strain 2-79 was more suppressive against *Ggt* in the presence of added Mn (Wilhelm et al., 1987; Wilhelm, 1990). Additionally, Albert and Anderson (1987) showed that fluorescent pseudomonads increased peroxidase activity, an observation consistent with the Mn-peroxidase-lignin hypothesis of virulence (or a component of virulence). Furthermore, when wheat root segments cultured with or without Mn were placed on the edge of *Ggt* colonies growing on ± Mn agar, penetration of fungal hyphae (after 18 h) was an inverse function of both treatment and

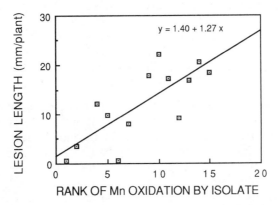

Fig. 10-3. Length of take-all lesions in wheat roots in a standard virulence test (McDonald & Rovira, 1989, unpublished data) of 13 different isolates of *Ggt* as a function of their capacity to oxidize Mn^{2+} in a Mn^{2+} agar medium. 1 represents least oxidizing ability; 15 represents greatest oxidizing ability. $R^2 = 0.59$, $P = 0.01$. (S.C. Buchhorn and R.D. Graham, 1988, unpublished data).

pretreatment Mn (Wilhelm et al., 1987). Treatment and pretreatment Mn combined successfully prevented invasion of the stele.

3. Mechanisms

Several mechanisms have been proposed for the role of Mn in disease resistance.

a. Lignification. The role of Mn in the synthesis of lignin, discussed in Section II and in more detail by Graham (1983), has been proposed as the basis of resistance to powdery mildew and to take-all. In the case of take-all, the synthesis of ligneous structures known as lignitubers occurs in response to the presence of the pathogen, but their role vis-a-vis preformed physical barriers of lignin is not agreed upon. Certainly Mn nutrition has a strong effect on the synthesis of lignin in wheat roots, maximal lignification being reached at about the same level of Mn supply as total biomass production (Brown et al., 1984). The lignin response in roots was greater than in shoots.

b. Soluble Phenols. Manganese is involved elsewhere in the biosynthetic pathway to phenols and lignin so that Mn deficiency leads to a decrease in soluble phenols as well (Brown et al., 1984); these are also frequently implicated in disease resistance (Bell, 1981).

c. Aminopeptidase. Aminopeptidase is a host enzyme activated by a pathogen, presumably to supply essential amino acids for fungal growth. The induction of this enzyme is inhibited by Mn (Huber & Keeler, 1977).

d. Pectin Methylesterase. Pectin methylesterase is a fungal exoenzyme for degrading host cell walls, which is inhibited by Mn^{2+} (Sadasivan, 1965).

e. Photosynthesis. Photosynthesis is severely inhibited by Mn deficiency. It has been argued that a decrease in root exudation of organic materials may follow and result in a weaker rhizoflora less able to compete with potential root pathogens in the rhizosphere (Graham & Rovira, 1984). However, while photosynthetic capacity in Mn-deficient leaves responds quickly to foliar-applied Mn, evidence of ineffectiveness of foliar-applied Mn in controlling take-all (Reis et al., 1982; Wilhelm et al., 1987; Huber & Wilhelm, 1988) suggests that this mechanism is not important with this disease.

f. Direct Inhibition. Direct inhibition of the pathogen is commonly suggested as a mechanism of Mn action, since, although Mn is essential to microbial growth (Bertrand & Javillier, 1912), the requirement is much less (possibly 100 times less) than in higher plant tissues. This marked difference in requirement between host and pathogen is exploited by both. The fungus may, by Mn oxidation, immobilize Mn in the infection court, and thereby induce a local Mn deficiency in the host without depriving itself of its mineral requirements, as discussed above for take-all and common scab. On the other hand, a plant capable of mobilizing high concentrations of Mn^{2+} in the rhizosphere through root exudation or encouragement of Mn-reducing fluorescent pseudomonads may possibly inhibit a potential pathogen in the rhizosphere by Mn toxicity without suffering toxicity itself. Direct control of a soil-borne pathogen by high Mn^{2+} is considered to be a mechanism of control of common scab through the standard agronomic practices (see Table 10-1); but direct toxicity to *Ggt* in soil by added Mn is not considered important since Wilhelm et al. (1987) showed that rates of Mn, which suppressed the disease in wheat, were stimulatory to saprophytic growth of the fungus in soil. Shao and Foy (1982) recommended breeding cotton (*Gossypium hirsutum* L.) cultivars that are more tolerant to Mn toxicity because the high soil Mn concentrations controlled the inoculum potential of *Verticillium alboatrum* by inhibiting sclerotial production which is essential to saprophytic survival.

B. Copper

Control of foliar pathogens by topical applications of Cu salts was so well established by the turn of the century that it was the subject of a separate treatise by Lodeman in 1902. This was almost 30 yr before Cu was recognized as essential to both higher and lower plant life. Whereas Cu is required by lower plant forms (Bortels, 1927) in minute amounts, it is particularly toxic in higher concentrations (Tomono et al., 1981, 1982; Keast et al., 1985); these concentrations can be tolerated by higher plant roots (Graham, 1979) and leaves (Bowen, 1981). It is this differential in sensitivity that is exploited in practical agriculture for protection of crop foliage, and by higher plants to protect their roots. When soil Cu is adequate, roots accumulate Cu in high concentrations, mostly in the apoplast, while transport to the shoot is under tight control (Graham, 1979). Conversely, in Cu-deficient soil, root Cu concentrations are low, and there is much evidence to indicate that such roots are vulnerable to fungal and bacterial attack. From the foregoing, we may generally expect that applied Cu will increase production when soil-available Cu is low by stimulation of growth through overcoming the host-plant deficiency, by direct toxicity to the pathogen and by stimulation of host defenses (discussed later).

1. Direct Effects on the Pathogen

Copper has been used extensively as a fungicide (Lodeman, 1902; van Alphen, 1957), but at concentrations 10 to 100 times greater than those normally needed as a foliar spray (0.1-0.2 kg ha^{-1} Cu) to cure Cu deficiency. Most of its fungicidal properties have been used against foliar pathogens, since Cu added to soil is quickly adsorbed and only a low concentration remains in the soil solution. The exception to this may be the accumuulation in the root cell walls as mentioned earlier. Copper fungicide sprays are frequently neutralized, that is, precipitated with lime, to reduce their phytotoxicity to permit the high dose rates and to make the product more rain-fast. Bordeaux mixtures and Cu oxychloride are examples. The Cu is considered to be toxic or fungistatic to the pathogen before or during the early stages of infection (Dutta & Bremner, 1981; Tomono et al., 1981). Keast et al. (1985)

found that the initial effect of Cu on *Phytophthora cinnamomi* in vitro was fungistasis with rather a long exposure (9–23 d) required for fungitoxicity. Copper was synergistic with the antifungal activity of actinomycetes against *P. cinnamomi* in this system. Tomono et al. (1981) found that, under the influence of Cu, germination-inhibited pycnospores (of *Diaporthe citri*, the stem end-rot fungus of citrus, *Citrus* spp.) contained 1.6 times as much Cu as germinating spores, whereas the corresponding factor for hyphae was 4.3. However, hyphae were inhibited at a lower Cu concentration of 10 mM Cu^{2+} (for 50% inhibition). Divalent Zn ions were also inhibitory but 30 times less toxic than Cu^{2+}; moreover, Zn^{2+} competitively inhibited the fungitoxicity of Cu^{2+} (Tomono et al., 1982). Such an interaction between micronutrients may explain some of the reports in which micronutrients appear to aggravate disease (generally those situations where the element in question is not deficient for the host plant). In another study, Tomono et al. (1983) found that the toxicity of Cu^{2+} against *Alternaria kikuchiana* was stimulated by the ligand 8-quinolinol, with a synergistic factor of ~1000. As 8-quinolinol is an uncoupler of oxidative phosphorylation and, thus, permeable to the mitochondrial membrane, the authors suggest that the synergism arises from the greater membrane permeability of the complexed Cu.

Direct fungistatic or fungicidal effects of Cu are indicated where Cu is effective in disease control, but the plants may not have been Cu-deficient; for example, *Gaeumannomyces graminis* var *tritici* on wheat (Reis et al., 1982) and *Sclerotinia* on plants (Hallock & Porter, 1981). Although Cu was effective when applied to the attacked tissues, either the roots or the leaves, it was not effective, or less effective, when applied to the unattacked tissues.

2. Effects on Resistance of the Host

Perhaps the best evidence of an effect of Cu on host-plant resistance to disease is when Cu is applied to the soil and the disease control is observed in the leaves. Invariably, these cases involve Cu-deficient soils, and the concentrations in the leaves which effectively decrease disease severity are only 1–10 mg kg^{-1} Cu (free Cu^{2+} is probably <1 μg kg^{-1}), concentrations too low to directly affect the pathogen. An example is provided in Fig. 10–4 (Graham, 1980), in which Cu fertilizer controlled powdery mildew of wheat. Copper treatment caused a marked difference in the disease index (percent leaf area affected) at 7 wk from emergence; it is evident that this change was not due to a growth-dilution effect, since the number of leaves was affected little by the Cu treatment. The lack of any difference in disease index before 7 wk is because wheat plants in this soil commonly take about 6 wk to become Cu-deficient. Consequently, Cu mainly affected disease resistance of more mature plants, when wheat normally acquires greater resistance, known as adult plant resistance (Jones & Hayes, 1971; Jenkyn & Bainbridge, 1978). It would appear, therefore, that Cu deficiency has inhibited the development of adult plant resistance in wheat to *Erysiphe graminis*. Figure 10–4 also shows a commonly observed pattern, namely that the beneficial effects of resistance from added Cu operates over the deficiency

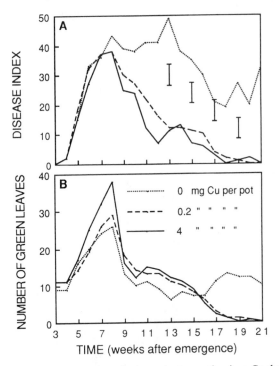

Fig. 10-4. Effect of Cu supplied to roots of wheat plants growing in a Cu-deficient soil on (A) the powdery mildew disease index per leaf and (B) the number of leaves. Vertical lines are LSD's ($P < 0.05$). There was no significant effect of Cu on number of leaves or tillers (Graham, 1980; reprinted with permission of Kluwer Academic Publ.).

range, and is much greater for the addition of 0.2 mg Cu than for a further addition of 3.8 mg. This fact also suggests that the effects of Cu act through the normal physiology of the host rather than being directly fungicidal.

Fertilization with Cu has decreased the severity of a wide range of fungal and bacterial diseases. Many reports involved control of foliar disease with soil applications; for example, mildew on wheat (Schütte, 1967), *Alternaria* on sunflower (*Helianthus annuus* L.) (W. Bussler, 1981, personal communication), *Pseudomonas cichorii* on ginseng (*Panax pseudoginseng* Wallich) (Gvozdyak & Pindus, 1988), *Puccinia triticina* on wheat (Schütte, 1964), and ergot on rye (*Secale cereale*) and barley (Tainio, 1961; Simojoki, 1969). Other reports include *Pyricularia oryzae* on rice (Primavesi & Primavesi, 1970) and *Septoria* on wheat (Toms, 1958).

Many soil-borne diseases are also suppressed by Cu supplementation. These include *Heterodera* on sugarbeet (*Beta vulgaris* L.) (Nesterov & Korol-'chuk, 1975) and *Verticillium albo-atrum* on tomato [*Lycopersicon esculentum* (L.)] (Dutta & Bremner, 1981), *Verticillium dahliae* on cotton (Miller & Becker, 1983), *Streptomyces scabies* on potato (Basu Chaudhary, 1967; Mortvedt et al., 1963), *Phytophthora cinnamomi* on *Eucalyptus marginata* (Keast et al., 1985) and *Gaeumannomyces graminis* var. *tritici* (*Ggt*) on wheat

Table 10-2. Effect of Cu supply to a Cu-deficient Lancelin sand (3 kg) in pots on yield of wheat, percent of roots infected by *Gaeumannomyces graminis* var *tritici* and the number of lesions per unit weight of roots.[†]

Cu supply	Fresh weight yield[‡]	Roots infected	Lesions
μg/pot	g/plant	%	No./g fresh weight roots
0	3.1	66 ± 3	6.5 ± 4.6
50	6.6	62 ± 3	4.0 ± 2.8
400	10.0	49 ± 5	2.4 ± 1.7
800	9.7	58 ± 5	3.2 ± 2.3
1600	9.9	51 ± 4	2.2 ± 1.6

[†] From Wood and Robson, 1984; reproduced with permission of Commonwealth Scientific and Industrial Research Organization (CSIRO).
[‡] Mean of inoculated and uninoculated treatments; recalculated from their data. Figures following ± represent standard errors ($n = 6$).

(Reis et al., 1982, 1983; Wood & Robson, 1984; Gardner & Flynn, 1988). For other references, see Fuchs and Grossmann (1972) and Graham (1983).

The three reports on take-all mentioned above have certain similarities: (i) although the experimental media for these three pot studies varied widely from nil or marginal to severe Cu deficiency, better control was achieved by soil applications than by foliar sprays; and (ii) all showed great variability which taxed the statistical power of their designs (exceptionally high variability is usually observed in studies involving both nutrient and pathogenic stresses). The data of Wood and Robson (1984) in Table 10–2 show that the disease decreased with added Cu in the deficiency range only. Since there was little difference between inoculated and uninoculated plants in their Cu concentrations, it cannot be argued that root pruning by the fungus caused the Cu deficiency, but rather than Cu deficiency promoted infection by the fungus. The data of Gardner and Flynn (1988) are interesting if one accepts the argument of the authors (unsubstantiated by plant analyses) that treatments of gypsum, which also decreased take-all, were simply releasing Cu in the soil. One treatment (Cu + gypsum) completely eliminated the disease ($P < 0.01$) and provided maximal yields. Such an extraordinary result with this ubiquitous disease deserves further study. Complete elimination of ergot was also achieved by Tainio (1961) in a field study in which the yield increased 50% (see Graham, 1983); but there are few such records, and the normal experience with any of the micronutrients and any disease is partial control only, albeit often a reduction to acceptable and manageable levels.

3. Mechanisms of Control with Copper

Copper has several possible roles in disease reduction.

a. Direct Toxicity. Copper is a toxic heavy metal with great affinity for nitrogenous organic ligands, including proteins. Its ability to denature proteins may well be fundamental to its direct toxicity to microorganisms. Microbes have a low requirement for Cu compared with higher plants, and a low tolerance of excess Cu. Copper remains an effective fungicide and evolution of resistance to it has been slow, perhaps because, as shown by Hooley and Shaw (1985), tolerant mutants are unable to transmit this character through asexual spores. Copper accumulation in the apoplast of normal roots in Cu-adequate soil may be a defense mechanism that takes advantage of the Cu sensitivity of fungal exoenzymes involved in the infection court.

b. Lignification. The indirect effects of Cu on host-plant resistance are almost certainly much more important than direct toxicity, especially in its vital role in the synthesis of lignin (Gross, 1980; Graham, 1983; Section II). Lignin is recognized as a partial barrier to the penetration of many pathogens (Beckman, 1980) including powdery mildews (Friend, 1977) and *Ggt* (Skou, 1981), two fungal groups for which there have been repeated records of the inhibitory effects of lignin. Lignin synthesis may well be the basis of the effect of Cu on adult plant resistance to powdery mildew of wheat (Graham, 1980).

c. Polyphenol Oxidase. As a component of the suite of enzymes known as polyphenol oxidase (PPO) or phenolase, Cu also is involved in the synthesis of soluble phenols and in their oxidation to the more toxic quinones (Walker & Webb, 1981). A rise in level and activity of PPO is a frequently measured plant response to invasion of pathogens (Horsfall & Cowling, 1980). A concomitant rise in toxic oxidized phenolics in the infected tissues results from enzymatic oxidation of reduced phenols stored in the cell vacuole (Beckman, 1980). Toxic quinones may kill not only the invading microorganism, but also the surrounding cells of the host and give rise to a local lesion, an important auto-immune response which constrains infections by obligate parasites such as powdery mildews and rusts. With Cu deficiency, these soluble phenols remain in the reduced state (Robson et al., 1981; Adams et al., 1975) owing to inactivation of PPO.

C. Zinc

Zinc has variously decreased, increased and had no effect on plant susceptibility to disease, although reports of decreases dominate. In some of the experiments in which Zn has decreased resistance (Dubey & Dwivedi, 1985; Spinks, 1913), the Zn treatment may have depressed the inhibitory effect of some other element. Many of these complicating aspects have been covered by Graham (1983). Discussion in this section will focus on those aspects of Zn nutrition thought to be beneficial to the plant with regard to disease control, with some speculation on the possible mechanisms of control.

1. Direct Effect of Zinc on Pathogens

Many of the studies showing that Zn reduced disease can probably be related to toxic effects of Zn directly on the pathogen, rather than through the plant's metabolism. Thus, studies on artificial media (usually agar) in the absence of host plants have shown that high concentrations of Zn can inhibit growth or development of microorganisms. For example, Wilkinson and Millar (1981) suggested that 1 to 4 mg L^{-1} Zn inhibited sporangium and zoospore formation by *Phytophthora megasperma*. Somashekar et al. (1983) demonstrated that 50 mg L^{-1} Zn resulted in growth reduction of *Penicillium citrinum* by 28%, *Cochliobolus miyabeanus* by 89%, and *Cladosporium cladosporoides* by 12%. Cripps et al. (1983) showed that 3 g L^{-1} ZnSO$_4$ inhibited growth of *Trametes versicolor* and *Stereum strigosazonatum* by 100%, *Trichoderma* and *Alternaria* by 64%, *Epicoccum* by 43%, but did not inhibit the growth of *Curvularia* or *Penicillium*. Hooley and Shaw (1985) have determined that >7.5 mM Zn was required to inhibit one strain (6500P) of *Phytophthora dreschsleri* by 50%, but only 5.5 mM Zn was required to inhibit strain 6503IMI by the same degree.

In practice, high concentrations of Zn are successful in treating some diseases. For example, the number of dead cotton plants resulting from *Fusarium* wilt decreased from 43 to 30% when the soil was pretreated with ZnSO$_4$ (Mustakimova & Muratmukhamedov, 1982). The incidence of brown-rot disease (*Phytophthora nicotianae*) of mandarin fell from 99 to 6% when fruit was sprayed with 1% Bordeaux mixture plus 0.5% ZnSO$_4$, and some of the depression was attributed to the Zn (Raghavendra Rao, 1985). The incidence of black-scurf (*Rhizoctonia solani*) of potato was depressed from an average of 97% to an average of 12% by dipping the tubers in 0.05% ZnSO$_4$ plus 1% acetic acid for 15 min before planting (Somani, 1986). Incidence of *Verticillium* wilt was depressed by spraying cotton bolls with 1% ZnSO$_4$ (Savov, 1986). Even nematode (*Rotylenchulus reniformis*) populations have been depressed to 14% of the control by a soil drench of 200 mg kg^{-1} Zn added to potted tomato plants (Haque & Mukhopadhyaya, 1983). Thus, although nutritional data are not available, it appears that these effects are more likely attributable to a direct and toxic effect of Zn on the pathogen rather than an effect through plant metabolism.

2. Effect of Soil Zinc

In recent surveys, the level of Zn in the soil was lower in soils conducive to root rot (*Phymatotrichopsis omnivorum*) of cotton (Smith & Hallmark, 1987) or to infection of ginseng by *Pseudomonas cichorii* (Gvozdyak & Pindus, 1988). Although these reports are correlative, the interpretation that Zn is important in reducing disease is supported by a decrease in *Fusarium* root rot of chickpea (*Cicer arietinum* L.) (Gaur & Vaidya, 1983) and some control of *Rhizoctonia bataticola* rot of groundnut (*Arachis hypogea*) by Zn application (Murugesan & Mahadevan, 1987).

When Zn is applied to soil, it is not always clear whether it has a direct toxic effect on the pathogen, or whether it acts through plant metabolism or physiology. However, Gildon and Tinker (1983), using a split-root technique, have shown that Zn supplied by translocation was just as effective as Zn supplied in the soil (100 mg Zn kg^{-1} soil) in suppressing the length of onion (*Allium cepa* L.) root infected by a vesicular-arbuscular mycorrhizal fungus (VAM) (*Glomus mosseae*), when compared with the control with no added Zn. Although VAMs are usually regarded as beneficial infections, these results indicate that Zn plays a role in the control of fungal growth within the plant that does not involve direct toxicity to the soil-borne organism.

3. Effect of Zinc Through Physiology

Although Zn has been known to be essential for plant growth since the 1920s, there has been surprisingly little work on the effects of Zn on disease at or near conditions of Zn deficiency. One of the earliest reports is that by Millikan (1938) who observed that root-rot diseases of wheat, in an area responsive to Zn fertilization, were greatest on plants grown without added Zn compared with those grown with 35 kg ha^{-1} ZnSO$_4$.

Possibly the first definitive experiment that produced effects in the deficiency vs. sufficiency range was that of Bolle-Jones and Hilton (1956). They produced Zn-deficient rubber (*Hevea brasiliensis*) trees and showed that infection by *Oidium heveae* was much greater on the Zn-deficient plants than on the Zn-supplied plants. Indeed, in Zn-deficient plants, infection was more severe on leaves that developed after Zn deficiency was induced than on those that had developed earlier. In 1982, Reis et al. showed that addition of Zn to the culture solution of wheat plants could suppress infection by take-all (*Gaeumannomyces graminis* var. *tritici*); however, it is not clear to what extent the plants not supplied with additional Zn were Zn deficient. The only report since that time (Sparrow & Graham, 1988) that specifically addresses the question of Zn deficiency and disease, demonstrated that progression of *Fusarium graminearum* upward through the stele of wheat was substantially depressed by the application of as little as 0.2 mg Zn/3.3 kg soil (0.06 mg kg^{-1}). This was enough Zn to increase vegetative plant yield four-fold, even though it only increased the tissue Zn concentration from 7.8 to 8.6 mg kg^{-1} dry matter. The addition of more Zn further suppressed upward movement of the pathogen, but had little effect on vegetative yield. That this further addition of Zn resulted in a substantial increase in Zn concentration indicates that disease control may still be responsive at levels considered supraoptimal for plant growth. The work of Reis et al. (1982) may also be a response under supraoptimal conditions.

Beneficial effects of supraoptimal Zn have also been demonstrated by the suppression of crook root (*Spongospora subterranea*) of watercress (*Rorippa nasturtium-aquaticum*) (Tomlinson, 1958). In a later study, Tomlinson and Hunt (1987) showed that supraoptimal Zn supply not only suppressed crook root but also suppressed watercress chlorotic leaf spot virus (WCLV). Control of WCLV is achieved through the control of its vector, *Spongospora subterranea*, the causal agent of crook root (Table 10–3). Since the Zn concentration in watercress samples not treated with Zn was >6 mg kg^{-1} fresh (presumably) weight, the effect of additional Zn was probably not by satisfying a Zn deficiency. Furthermore, that the solution concentration of Zn required to prevent the disease was <1.0 mg L^{-1}, suggests that the effect of Zn was not through direct toxicity. Thus, it appears that application of Zn in amounts greater than those directly required for growth, but still not directly toxic, can be beneficial for reducing disease.

Table 10-3. Effect of Zn on infection of watercress by donor plants infected with crook root (*Spongospora subterranea*) with or without watercress chlorotic leaf spot virus (WCLV).[†]

		Plants infected	
Donor plant infection	Zn treatment	With crook root	With WCLV
	mg L^{-1}	———— % ————	
Crook root	0	100	0
Crook root + WCLV	0	100	100
Crook root + WCLV	2	0	0

† From Tomlinson and Hunt, 1987.

The concept that supraoptimal Zn is beneficial is also evident in work on phyllody virus of white clover (*Trifolium* spp.) (Carr & Stoddart, 1963). The authors showed that throughout the range of Zn supply, including that which was phytotoxic, increasing Zn continued to suppress the inflorescence symptoms attributed to the virus. By showing that the virus was still present in the older vegetative parts (stolons) of clover plants devoid of inflorescence symptoms, the authors suggested that Zn did not eliminate the virus particles, but immobilized them, and thereby suppressed the inflorescence symptoms. Unlike the results of Tomlinson and Hunt (1987), the effect of Zn was direct and not via a fungal intermediate.

4. Mechanism of Control

There is no clear evidence that explains how Zn suppresses certain diseases; however, it is worthwhile presenting an hypothesis. Zinc is important in the integrity or stability of biological membranes (Chvapil, 1973, 1976; Bettger & O'Dell, 1981; O'Dell et al., 1984). In plant root membranes specifically, it has been suggested (Welch et al., 1982; Loneragan et al., 1987; Graham et al., 1987) that Zn may be important in preventing root membranes from leaking. This hypothesis has particular relevance to an experiment in which many more zoospores of *Phytophthora cinnamomi* were attracted to Zn-deficient *Eucalyptus marginata* and *E. sieberi* roots than to Zn-adequate roots (Table 10-4). The implication is that Zn-deficient roots leaked more

Table 10-4. Accumulation of *Phytophthora cinnamomi* zoospores on roots of *Eucalyptus* seedlings after 15 min contact with the zoospore bathing medium.[†]

	Species	
Zn supply	*E. marginata*[‡]	*E. sieberi*[§]
	——— Zoospores, number mm^{-2} root ———	
+	4 ± 1	89 ± 13
−	44 ± 8	489 ± 48

† From B. Dell and J. Webb, 1982, unpublished data. The plants were precultured in nutrient solution with or without Zn. Seedlings grown without Zn showed mild symptoms of Zn deficiency in their leaves.
‡ 582 zoospores per milliliter in bathing medium. Figures following ± represent standard error.
§ 800 zoospores per milliliter in bathing medium. Figures following ± represent standard error.

carbohydrate and/or amino acids than Zn-adequate roots, and thus attracted more zoospores by chemotaxis. A successful invasion presumably would be more likely, simply as a result of the increased population of zoospores reaching the root surface.

The hypothesis that Zn is important in membrane integrity might also explain the possible immobilization of virus particles as a result of Zn application, as suggested by Carr and Stoddart (1963). This hypothesis could also be consistent with the suppression of the upward movement of *Fusarium graminearum* in wheat under Zn-adequate conditions (Sparrow & Graham, 1988). There is no evidence of the effect of supraoptimal Zn on membrane integrity or stability.

5. Effects on Other Organisms

Complications in interpreting the effects of Zn on disease may arise from its effect on other organisms. In studies on foot rot (*Sclerotium rolfsii*) of soybean, for example, Dutta and Deb (1986) found that high rates of $ZnSO_4$ (0.5%) decreased infection, but also increased the population of potentially antagonistic microorganisms.

6. Genetics

Although there are many reports on Zn concentrations in diseased and healthy plants, of greater interest are the comparative Zn concentrations in cultivars differing in susceptibility, but in the absence of disease. Thus, Sindhan and Parashar (1984) have found that pea (*Pisum sativum* L.) varieties susceptible to powdery mildew have lower Zn concentrations than resistant varieties, in the absence of disease as well as when mildew is present. Also, there is a strong positive correlation between tolerance of wheat varieties to *Fusarium* (Burgess et al., 1984) and tolerance of these varieties to Zn deficiency (Graham, 1988). One interpretation of this correlation is that Zn efficiency is the factor responsible for tolerance to disease.

D. Boron

Boron has been reported to have beneficial effects in reducing disease, although its role in plants is probably the least understood of all the micronutrients. Many of these effects have previously been reported by Graham (1983), as have the lack of effects. Since that time, B has also been shown to reduce diseases such as clubroot (*Plasmodiophora brassicae*) in swedes (Vladimirskaya et al., 1982) and other crucifers (Dixon & Webster, 1988); *Fusarium solani* in bean (*Phaseolus vulgaris* L.) (Guerra & Anderson, 1985); *Verticillium albo-atrum* in tomato (Dutta & Bremner, 1981) and cotton (Savov, 1986); *Rhizoctonia solani* in mungbean [*Vigna radiata* (L.)], pea, and cowpea (*Vigna unguiculata*) (Kataria, 1982; Kataria & Grover, 1987); *Rhizoctonia bataticola* in groundnut (Murugesan & Mahadevan, 1987); tobacco mosaic virus in bean (Shimomura, 1982); and tomato yellow leaf curl virus in tomato (Zaher, 1985). It had little or no effect on *Leptosphaeria maculans* in oil-seed rape (*Brassica napus* var. *oleifera*) (Krüger, 1982). Application of B to soil has also reduced mite (*Petrobia latens*) populations on wheat (Singh, 1986).

Although the exact role of B in plants is far from clear (Shkolnik, 1984; Marschner, 1986), it has been implicated in many physiological and biochemical functions (Lewis, 1980; Dugger, 1983; Shkolnik, 1984; Marschner, 1986). There is little argument over the general effects of B deficiency in plants, but three schools of thought have evolved regarding the primary role of B. These are: (i) its role in formation of carbohydrate-borate complexes controlling carbohydrate transport and cell wall protein metabolism (Dugger, 1983); (ii) its function in cell membrane permeability or stability (Pollard et al., 1977; Pilbeam & Kirkby, 1983); and (iii) its role in metabolism of phenolics, with its primary role in the synthesis of lignin (Lewis, 1980).

Although it is beyond the scope of this review to consider arguments for each hypothesis, it is probably pertinent to mention that two of the most recent reviews on B in plants (Shkolnik, 1984; Marschner, 1986) favor the involvement of B in phenolic/lignin metabolism as the primary role; the other effects being secondary in time, but not necessarily in importance. This view is also favored by our interpretation of the response of disease to B nutrition of host plants.

With regard to the role of B in protecting plants from diseases, it is important to separate those pathogens that do not invade the stele (for example, *Synchytrium endobioticum* and *Plasmodiophora brassicae*) from those that do (for example, *Fusarium* and *Verticillium* species).

1. Pathogens That Do Not Invade Vascular Tissue

Boron has been shown to decrease the expression of potato wart disease (*Synchytrium endobioticum*) of potato (Hampson, 1980) and club root (*Plasmodiophora brassicae*) of crucifers (Dixon & Webster, 1988). In both cases, disease is expressed by the formation of a tumor or a gall; and in both reports, B decreased the severity of this expression of disease. Boron did not, however, diminish the initial infection of the host. Thus, with *Plasmodiophora* infection, it has been suggested that B acted during the secondary stage of cortical infection and proliferation of the gall (Dixon & Webster, 1988). Proliferation of gall or tumor tissue under low B conditions is consistent with the hypothesis (but not dependent upon it) that B plays a role in metabolism of phenolics as outlined below.

2. Defense Against Nonvascular Pathogens

One consequence of B deficiency is an increase in indoleacetic acid (IAA) concentration because of an inhibition of IAA oxidase activity (Coke & Wittington, 1968), presumably by the accumulation of phenolics. However, Shkolnik (1984) argues that the phenolics per se are the causal agents of IAA-like reactions. Irrespective of the mechanisms involved, similar conditions may occur in tumors and galls. That is, potato wart tumors have elevated levels of auxin-like substances (Reingard & Pashkar, 1959). This increase in auxin (or auxin-like) activity has been explained by an increase in auxin protectors (Haard, 1978; Tandon, 1985). It is worthwhile to note that, in a variety of tomato in which tumors were not found following successful infection, tomatine, an auxin antagonist, was present (Hampson & Haard, 1980). The auxin protectors from potato wart have been isolated, and shown to contain ferulic acid and caffeic acids covalently bound to a protein, and chlorogenic acid (Haard, 1978). Interestingly, both chlorogenic and caffeic acid have been identified in the necrotic areas of B-deficient celery (*Apium graveolens* L.) (Perkins & Aronoff, 1956), and ferulic and vanillic acid in B-deficient oil-palm (*Elaeis guineensis*) (Rajaratnam & Lowry, 1974). In addition, it is common to use borate as a buffer during plant tissue extractions to prevent conjugation of phenolics with proteins (Haard, 1978). These observations suggest that B may suppress gall or tumor formation by suppressing high concentrations of auxin or auxin-like substances. Gall formation itself is not a defense mechanism of the plant. That is, galls are incited by the pathogen (Dixon, 1984). Thus B, by suppressing high levels of auxin or auxin-like substances, may also suppress gall formation.

It may seem somewhat anomalous that high levels of phenolics be associated with high levels of disease, since phenolics traditionally have been implicated in protection from disease. In the case of galls and tumors, however, it may be the influence of high levels of phenolics on host metabolism or physiology that is necessary for expression of the symptoms; i.e., production of galls. Indeed, in the crown gall disease (caused by *Agrobacterium tumefaciens*) gall formation is autonomous after the initial infection; i.e., it can proceed even when the pathogen is absent (Dixon, 1984; Kosuge & Sanger, 1986). Thus, an increase in phenolics as a result of B deficiency would be ineffective in controlling this disease after the initial stages of infection.

3. Pathogens That Invade Vascular Tissue

Fusarium oxysporum and *Verticillium*, which are not capable of penetrating several layers of cortical cells and the epidermis, invade just behind the root cap (Mai & Abawi, 1987). In this manner, they avoid lignified tissues. Following successful invasion, both pathogens (Talboys, 1983; Mai & Abawi, 1987) are generally confined to the xylem until the later stages of the disease.

Although B has been shown to reduce the severity of disease by *Fusarium oxysporum* and *Verticillium* (Keane & Sackston, 1970; Dutta & Bremner, 1981; Guerra & Anderson, 1985; Savov, 1986), few experiments have been designed to determine at which point in pathogenesis B has an effect. No general conclusion on the effect of B could be ascertained from an experiment designed to measure the effect of B on the movement of *Fusarium* up the stem of flax (Keane & Sackston, 1970). In another experiment, Guerra and Anderson (1985) found that B depressed the total length of lesions caused by *Fusarium solani* in bean. Unfortunately it is not clear from the data whether the increase in total length of lesion under low B is a result of more lesions or longer lesions.

4. Defense Against Vascular Pathogens

There is no conclusive evidence that explains how B decreases disease caused by vascular pathogens. The association of B with lignin synthesis (Lewis, 1980) makes it tempting to suggest that B may suppress infection of the stele by a lignified physical barrier at the endodermis. It may be argued that this barrier would be of little consequence if, as suggested by Mai and Abawi (1987), *Fusarium* enters just behind the root cap, a region of the root with little lignification. However, if B deficiency weakens the lignification of other parts of the root system, successful infection may be more likely at other locations on the root axis. Indeed, Dutta and Bremner (1981) observed that B depressed the symptoms of *Verticillium* wilt in tomato, and the roots of B-supplied plants showed no vascular discoloration. This suggests that B inhibited the invasion of xylem by the pathogen.

5. Other Pathways of Pathogenesis

Boron could also conceivably play a role in retarding the movement of fungal hyphae through the cortex. Alekseya (1971 [photograph reproduced in Shkolnik, 1984]) has demonstrated that B deficiency results in cell walls that swell and split at the middle lamella. This effect most probably results from poor pectin synthesis or stabilization due to B deficiency (Shkolnik, 1984; Marschner, 1986). A weakened middle lamella is conducive to hyphal penetration especially as many root-infecting fungi synthesize pectinases (Collmer & Keen, 1986). Invading hyphae may also elicit the formation of papillae by the host (Cadena-Gomez & Nicholson, 1987). As the papillae often contain lignin and callose, and as B has been implicated in the synthesis of both lignin (Lewis, 1980; Shkolnik, 1984; Marschner, 1986) and callose (Shimomura, 1982), B deficiency could have marked effects on the host response to invasion.

As damage caused by vascular pathogens may release stored phenols and polyphenol oxidases from cells in vascular tissues (Talboys, 1984), presumably as a defense mechanism, it seems anomalous that B deficiency may result in both an increased concentration of phenolics and increased disease. However, it is probably pertinent that this accumulation of hydrophobic oxidized phenols may restrict water movement in the xylem (Talboys, 1984). In the case of wilt diseases, this effect of phenolics on water movement in the xylem, irrespective of its effect on the pathogen, may result in an even stronger expression of the disease symptoms. It may be that phenol release and xylem occlusion are general responses to any sort of damage, rather than a specific response to a pathogen, in much the same way as that which has been suggested for nematodes (Wallace, 1987).

In an experiment with another disease, take-all of wheat, preliminary results suggest that B decreased the severity of root symptoms (R.O. Nable, 1988, personal communication). This response has already been reported for Mn (Section III.A), and implicates lignin synthesis.

Thus, although the primary role of B in plants may not be agreed upon, it is clear that it reduces some diseases in plants and that this effect may be a result of its possible role in phenolic/lignin metabolism. Further evidence is the differential role of B in lignin composition and accumulation (Fig. 10-2). Finally, although there are some opposing views (Chahal & Rawla, 1984), B is generally regarded as nonessential for fungi (Lewis, 1980; Shkolnik, 1984; Marschner, 1986). Thus, under conditions of B deficiency, the host is at a metabolic disadvantage, whereas the pathogen may not be.

E. Iron

Competition between host and parasite for Fe is regarded as an important defense mechanism in animals and humans (Weinberg, 1978), self-induced anemia being a component of that defense. Similar ideas have attracted plant pathologists over the last decade or so, but intense research has so far revealed increasing complexity rather than unifying principles (Swinburne, 1986a). It appears that competition for Fe is common among soil, rhizosphere and phyllosphere organisms (Leong, 1986), but it is not yet clear whether the host actually can starve its would-be pathogens of Fe.

1. Variable Effects of Iron on Disease

Older literature sheds little light on the role of Fe in disease resistance, since it is relatively sparse compared with that on Cu, Mn and B. However, the sophistication of microbial Fe-acquisition systems suggests that they have a high requirement compared with higher plants (*Fusarium*, for example, in Jones & Woltz, 1981) or a higher utilization efficiency. In this respect, Fe appears to stand in contrast to Cu, Mn and B, for which microbial requirements are relatively low. Whether or not these differences in requirement are mechanistically important, additions of Cu, Mn and B to deficient soils generally benefit the host, whereas the effect of Fe fertilization in disease resistance cannot be predicted. Copper was antagonistic to Fe in the in vitro stimulation of lycomarismin, a phytotoxin produced by *Fusarium oxysporum* f. sp. *lycopersici*, although lycomarismin has no known function in *Fusarium* wilt disease. Tolerance of *Fusarium* wilt in tomato was decreased by Fe without affecting development of the fungus (Waggoner & Dimond, 1953). Iron stimulated and Cu inhibited spore germination (Strakhov & Yaroshenko, 1959; Halsall & Forrester, 1977; Vedie & Le Normand, 1984).

At high concentrations, Fe killed rust infections on wheat leaves (Forsyth, 1957), controlled smut on wheat (Yaroshenko, 1959) and reduced *Colletotrichum musae* on banana (*Musa bananas*) (Swinburne, 1986b). Foliar sprays of Fe increased resistance in apple (*Malus pumila*) and pear (*Pyrus communis* L.) to *Sphaeropsis malorum* (Butler and Jones, 1955), and increased the tolerance of cabbage (*Brassica oleracea*) to *Olpidium brassicae*. In cabbage, the addition of Fe overcame the fungus-induced Fe deficiency in the host, although it had no effect on the extent of infection (Clarkson et al., 1974).

Table 10–5. Effect of FeEDTA and siderophore-producing fluorescent *Pseudomonas* sp. on the survival of barley seedlings in a suppressive and a conducive soil infested with the take-all fungus, *Gaeumannomyces graminis* var *tritici.*†

Treatment	Seedling survival, %	
	Suppressive soil	Conducive soil
Control (H$_2$O)	83	27
FeEDTA (50 μM)	38	25
FeEDTA (no take-all fungus)	85	87
Pseudomonas (Strain B10)	--	88
Pseudomonas B10 + FeEDTA	--	25

† From Kloepper et al., 1980a.

However, Fe in nutrient solution suppressed neither take-all of wheat in the studies of Reis et al. (1982) nor *Colletotrichum* on bean (Drobny et al., 1984). Iron added to disease-suppressive soils counteracted the suppression and enhanced take-all of barley, whereas in a conducive soil with a high disease score, Fe had no effect (Table 10–5). Other examples of this effect have been reported by Leong (1986). The role of Fe in these systems involving soil-borne pathogens and rhizosphere bacteria is complex, but has been the subject of extensive research in recent years because of the potential of Fe-binding rhizobacteria and fungi as biological control agents. The current views of the mechanisms involving Fe are discussed in the next section.

2. Iron Mechanisms

Adding Fe to a host-fungal pathogen system may promote antimycosis, as suggested by Hemming et al. (1982) and Swinburne (1986b), or interfere with it, as suggested by Leong (1986). Obviously, the mechanisms must be diverse and dependent on the organisms and their environmental conditions, and relate to the following.

a. Lignin Synthesis. Unlike Cu, Mn and B, which have a major influence on this vital pathway in defense, effects of Fe deficiency on lignin synthesis have not been reported (Barber & Ride, 1988), even though Fe is a component of peroxidase and stimulates other enzymes involved in the biosynthetic pathway (Fig. 10–2).

b. Phytoalexin Synthesis. Through its key roles in oxidative phosphorylation, Fe is directly or indirectly involved in all plant syntheses but an especially high Fe requirement for synthesis of the phytoalexin, wyerone (Swinburne, 1986b), is of interest in the present context.

c. Enzyme Activation. Iron is essential for the production of host-attacking exoenzymes of fungi, such as pectin methylesterase of *Fusarium oxysporum* (Sadasivan, 1965) and endo- and exo-glucanase by *Phoma herbarum*, a leaf spot pathogen of peanuts (Shinde & Gangawane, 1987), a stimulation opposed by Cu. If these processes were limiting in a host-pathogen system under Fe stress, then we would expect an addition of Fe to lead to an increase in disease, which is not observed with *Fusarium* wilt (see previous sections).

   d. Synthesis of Antibiotics. Hemming et al. (1982) demonstrated production of fungal antibiotics by several classes of soil bacteria, which was strongly promoted by Fe. Some of these bacterial groups are themselves pathogens, so we have a situation in which the course of infection depends on which organisms control the availability of Fe, the host, the pathogen or the rhizosphere (or phyllosphere) bacteria.

   e. Synthesis of Siderophores. The Gramineae synthesize unique phytosiderophores (Fe-binding molecules) for which they have specific receptor molecules in the membrane (Marschner et al., 1986), but these sites do not transport other chelates such as FeEDDHA or microbial hydroxymate siderophores. Whether these phytosiderophores, which are produced only under conditions of Fe stress, are capable of suppressing potential root pathogens in the rhizosphere under these conditions by starving them of Fe, needs to be explored. This could happen if pathogens were unable to use Fe phytosiderophores and the latter were the stronger complexes, thereby dominating the available Fe. If this were the case, treatment of the soil with available Fe should favor the pathogen rather than the host. There is some speculation of this effect on Fe (Table 10–5; Kloepper et al., 1980a; Leong, 1986), but it has not been verified and is not considered a viable mechanism of disease resistance. The evidence involves the use of a suppressive soil, that is, a soil in which competitive (suppressive) microorganisms quickly dominate the rhizosphere. It has been speculated that rhizosphere microorganisms, which synthesize siderophores, are responsible for lowering Fe availability in these systems.

   Simeoni et al. (1987) reported that siderophore production by *Pseudomonas putida* was essential to suppress germination of clamydospores of *Fusarium oxysporum* f. sp. *cucumerinum* in vitro. Moreover, their experiments indicated that germination was optimally suppressed when Fe^{3+} activities ranged from 10^{-22} to 10^{-27} M. However, a nonsiderophore-producing mutant did not suppress germination even though Fe^{3+} activity was otherwise controlled in the optimal range, indicating that control of Fe^{3+} activity is not of itself the suppressive mechanism. This suppression of disease by such microorganisms (especially siderophore-producing fluorescent pseudomonads) also occurs with dicotyledonous host plants which do not themselves synthesize specific phytosiderophores for release to the rhizosphere, although they can use microbial siderophores to facilitate absorption (Becker et al., 1986). In a conducive rather than suppressive soil (Kloepper et al., 1980a), take-all was severe and there were few competitive rhizosphere organisms. In this soil, the low survival rate of barley from take-all was not changed by the addition of Fe; but where the addition of a siderophore-producing fluorescent pseudomonad (B10) had increased survival more than three times, the simultaneous addition of FeEDTA counteracted the bacterial suppression of take-all (Table 10–5).

The effect of Strain B10 (and its reversal by FeEDTA) can be mimicked by the purified fluorescent siderophore (pseudobactin) isolated from it, and has been presented as strong evidence that control of Fe availability is the antimicrobial mechanism involved in suppression of disease by this organism, which was isolated from a disease (take-all) suppressive soil. Several other examples of disease suppression by rhizosphere bacterial isolates and by their purified siderophores have been studied in detail, including soft rot of potato, *Erwinia carotovora* (Kloepper et al., 1980b), flax (*Linum usitatissumum*) wilt, *Fusarium oxysporum* f. sp. *lini* (Kloepper et al., 1980a), take-all of wheat, *Ggt* (Wong & Baker, 1984; Weller & Cook, 1983), *Pythium* on wheat (Becker & Cook, 1984), and *Fusarium wilts of carnation (Dianthus caryophyllus)* (Yuen & Schroth, 1986), cucumber (*Cucumis sativus* L.) and radish (*Raphanus sativus* L.) (Scher & Baker, 1982), and pea (Elad & Baker, 1985).

In contrast to these results, the suppressive mechanism of a fluorescent siderophore-producing *Pseudomonas* Strain 2-79 (Weller & Cook, 1983) against take-all of wheat was shown not to depend on the siderophore, but on an antibiotic, phenazine-1-carboxylic acid (Brisbane & Rovira, 1988). Surprisingly, in vitro this antibiotic is most inhibitory at low pH at which take-all is rarely a problem (and availability of Fe in soils is generally quite high). This isolate (2-79) can act either as a powerful reducer or oxidizer of Mn, which may account for its variable suppression of take-all.

Exceptions to the theory of disease suppression through Fe competition are emphasized by Lemanceau et al. (1988) who found that populations of fluorescent pseudomonads isolated from a *Fusarium*-wilt-suppressive soil were significantly more sensitive to Fe deficiency than those isolated from a conducive soil. They concluded, therefore, that the participation of these organisms in competition for Fe in the suppressiveness of this soil seems unlikely. It may be, however, that organisms other than these pseudomonads are Fe competitive. They previously attributed a role in *Fusarium*-wilt suppression to other organisms (Lemanceau et al., 1987). The picture is further complicated since 18 out of 19 strains of four *pathogenic* bacterial species produced catechol-containing siderophores in low Fe culture (Leong & Neilands, 1982). The catechol siderophore produced by *Agrobacterium tumefaciens* B6, agrobactin, does not participate in virulence and may function simply to improve survival in soil (Leong & Neilands, 1981). In other cases, siderophores are considered as virulence factors in infection (Crosa, 1984; Weinberg, 1984). If siderophores of *A. tumefaciens* increase Fe availability to the plant, they could be important factors in tumor induction, since high Fe levels are required (D.M. Huber, 1989, personal communication).

F. Molybdenum

There have been few reports associating Mo with the response of plants to disease (Graham, 1983) and no reports have been found that specifically address the effects of Mo deficiency. However, Dutta and Bremner (1981) demonstrated that Mo applied to tomato roots reduced the symptoms of *Ver-*

ticillium wilt. Miller and Becker (1983) also reported that Mo suppressed *Verticillium* wilt in tomato. Molybdenum had a direct effect by reducing the production of the Roridin E, a toxin produced by *Myrothecium roridum* (Fernando et al., 1986), and in slightly inhibiting zoosporangia formation by *Phytophthora cinnamomi* and *P. dreschleri* (Halsall, 1977). Soil application of Mo decreased nematode populations (Haque & Mukhopadhyaya, 1983).

It is not known whether Mo within the host plays any specific role in protecting plants from disease and, because of the requirement for Mo by the enzymes nitrogenase and nitrate reductase (Shkolnik, 1984; Marschner, 1986), any effect of Mo deficiency on pathogenesis may be indirect through an effect on N metabolism.

G. Chlorine

Chlorine exists in soil-plant systems mostly as the stable Cl^- anion. We must exclude, as beyond the scope of this book, the vast literature on Cl^- in its role as a major component of salinity stress which, like any other stress on plants, can be expected to lower their tolerance to pathogens, if not to affect their resistance directly. There remains, however, a small but intriguing literature on Cl^- enhancing the host plants' resistance to disease in which fairly large amounts of Cl^- are required. These amounts are far greater than those required to fulfil its role as a micronutrient, but far less than those required to induce effects of salinity. Thus, it is probably interacting with other nutrients such as Mn.

Chloride fertilizers in macronutrient amounts have partially controlled a number of diseases: corn (*Zea mays* L.) stalk rot, *Gibberella zeae* (Warren et al., 1975) or *G. fujikuroi* (Younts & Musgrave, 1958); stripe rust on wheat, *Puccinia striiformis* West (Russell, 1978; Christensen et al., 1982); take-all of wheat (Powelson & Jackson, 1978; Christensen et al., 1981, 1982, 1987; Taylor et al., 1983); northern corn leaf blight, *Exserohilum* (*Helminthosporium*) *turcicum* (Huber & Arny, 1985) and downy mildew (*Sclerophthora macrospora*) of millet (*Pennisetum typhoides* L.) (Hedge & Karande, 1978). Chloride may also suppress *Septoria* in wheat, either directly or indirectly through its effects on take-all (Christensen et al., 1982). A number of these studies have clearly distinguished the effects of Cl^- from those of its accompanying cation (Table 10-6). Others have also made this distinction (for example, Powelson & Jackson, 1978, with take-all; Younts & Musgrave, 1958, with *Gibberella*), whereas many papers studying the recognized effects of K on disease (Graham, 1983; Huber & Arny, 1985) have used KCl because it is generally more readily available or cheaper than K_2SO_4, and naturally ascribed the effects on disease to the macronutrient component which is generally more likely to be deficient than the micronutrient Cl^-. An example of this may be the study of Goss and Gould (1967) who found that KCl suppressed *Ophiobolus* patch in turf grass, a disease closely related to the take-all fungus.

The mechanism of the Cl^- effect on resistance is intriguing. Chloride appears to have an effect distinct from that of its accompanying cation, ap-

Table 10-6. Effect of Cl⁻ fertilizer on stripe rust and take-all of wheat.†

Fertilizer	Stripe rust score			Take-all score
	Experiment 1	Experiment 2	Experiment 3	Experiment 4
None	5.2	2.6	19.2	62
NaCl	0.4		9.2	
NaCl foliar	5.2			
NaCl + KCl		0.6	7.2	
NH_4NO_3		2.7		
Na phosphate		2.4		
NH_4Cl				17
$(NH_4)_2SO_4$				45

† Experiments 1 and 2 were conducted in pots, and 3 and 4 in the field, using different scoring systems.

‡ Drawn from the data of Russell (1978) and Christensen et al. (1982), respectively.

pears to be relatively nontoxic in vitro (Whitmore et al., 1983), and does not stimulate lignin synthesis in wounded wheat leaves as do Hg^{4+} and Cd^{2+} ions and many organic and microbial elicitors (Barber & Ride, 1988). The earlier-reported effects of Cl⁻ on stalk rot were explained by Huber and Watson (1974) as a competitive effect of Cl⁻ on NO_3^- absorption, and thus, on the form of N assimilated by the plant, which in turn influences rhizosphere pH. However, Graham (1983) argued that this competitive effect should not materially change the rhizosphere pH since one rapidly absorbed anion is substituted for another.

An important effect of Cl⁻ added in sufficient quantity is the suppression of nitrification (Golden et al., 1981), an effect that has repeatedly been linked to disease suppression (see reviews by Huber & Watson, 1974; Huber & Wilhelm, 1988). Huber and Wilhelm (1988) argue that inhibition of nitrification suppresses take-all and other diseases by a decrease in rhizosphere pH (greater uptake of N as NH_4^+ and less as NO_3^-), which in turn increases the availability and uptake of Mn, a beneficial effect discussed in Section III.A. Moreover, NH_4^+ may have other effects on host physiology leading to disease resistance (Huber & Watson, 1974). Clear evidence of a change in soil $NH_4^+:NO_3^-$ ratio induced by Cl⁻ and linked to suppression of take-all was published by Christensen et al. (1987).

An even more intriguing mechanistic possibility is the direct Cl⁻-mediated reduction of $Mn^{III,IV}$ oxides. A causal link between Cl⁻ application and Mn solubilization (reduction) has recently been reported (Kattak & Jarrell, 1988), but whereas Br⁻ and I⁻ may readily reduce MnO_2, the thermodynamics of Cl⁻ as the reductant are unfavorable at any but the most acid soil pH's (Norvell, 1988; Bartlett, 1988). However, microbial intervention could easily make this process occur, and increases in available Mn with Cl⁻ salts have been measured by several workers (see Norvell, 1988). Enhancement by Cl⁻ of the rhizosphere populations of fluorescent pseudomonads, potential Mn-reducing organisms, has been observed by Halsey and Powelson (reported by Christensen et al., 1981). No doubt any free Cl_2 produced by such a reaction would not last long in soils, so the involve-

Table 10-7. Suppression of *Uromyces phaseoli* on cowpea leaves by traces of Ni supplied to the roots in a filtered, controlled-environment chamber in which Ni deficiency symptoms developed in the control (−Ni) plants.[†]

Ni treatment	Rust	Leaf Ni concentration
µg/L	pustules/leaf[‡]	mg kg^{-1} dry weight
0	904 ± 112	0.03
3.3	422 ± 70	1.04

† From Graham et al., 1985.   ‡ Figures following ± represent standard errors.

ment of Cl$^-$ would, in effect, be catalytic, although the amounts required are not small. There are many implications for improvements in fertilizer technology which could flow from an understanding of how this Cl$^-$ effect leads to better disease control.

H. Nickel

Recent reports indicate that for a heavy metal, Ni is not especially toxic to microorganisms in vitro (Whitmore et al., 1983; Lakshmi et al., 1984; Gildon & Tinker, 1983; Isaeva, 1969; Romanova & Gibadullin, 1980); yet, Ni salts are particularly effective fungicides against rusts. Forsyth and Peturson (1959) showed that foliar sprays of Ni(NO$_3$)$_2$ at 70 mg L^{-1} Ni could decrease leaf rust on wheat from 77 to 0.1 pustules per leaf, and entirely prevent stem rust infections, which rated 19 pustules per leaf on control plants. The anion carrier is not particularly important, but amine chelates are more rain-fast than simple salts. Nickel has both eradicative and protective action after contact times as short as a few minutes. Bachchhav et al. (1978) improved the effectiveness of conventional organic fungicides by combining them with Ni salts.

1. Nickel Mechanisms

The relatively low concentrations, the short contact times, and the protective effects of Ni suggest physiological mechanisms in the host leading to resistance. This is supported by studies showing that Ni is effective when supplied via the roots (Sempio, 1936; Graham et al., 1985), whereby epiphytotic effects are avoided. In the study of Graham et al. (1985), Ni was supplied to cowpea roots at only 3.3 µg L^{-1}, resulting in a Ni concentration in leaves of only 1 mg kg^{-1}; yet rust pustule numbers were more than halved over control plants with only 30 µg kg^{-1} of Ni in their tissues (Table 10-7). Since these low concentrations are unlikely to be directly toxic to the pathogen, a reasonable conclusion is that Ni is involved in some biochemical pathway that leads to resistance.

Nickel may be regarded as an essential ultramicronutrient (nanonutrient) since it plays a vital role in the N metabolism of plants (Eskew et al., 1984). Between 10–100 µg kg^{-1} on a dry weight basis is the minimum requirement in tissues for normal growth; however, although 1 mg kg^{-1} Ni in the tissue (10–100 fold greater than the critical concentration) did not eliminate leaf rust entirely (Table 10–7), complete eradication, on occasion is possible (Forsyth & Peturson, 1959). Therefore, the resistance pathway may have a higher requirement for Ni than growth itself. Alternatively, foliar treatment may have an additional direct effect on the pathogen. Smirnov (1978) observed that Ni stimulated polyphenol oxidase activity, focusing attention on phenol synthesis; but Perrin and Cruikshank (1965) linked Ni to isoflavonoid biosynthesis, and stimulated production of the phytoalexin, pisatin. In rice leaves, Ni was a particularly effective metal elicitor of ill-defined fungitoxic diffusates, providing protection against *Cochliobolus miyabeanus*, brown spot on rice (Sinha & Giri, 1979).

I. Silicon

Although Si is not regarded as a fully fledged essential element for growth of higher plants, it is from recent work, now clearly essential to biochemical pathways leading to resistance to certain pathogens. Rice agronomists know the protection silicates provide against the rice blast fungus (*Piricularia oryzae*) and brown spot (*Cochliobolus miyabeanus*). Consequently, in certain soils of tropical origin that are low in silica, the application of silicate in the presence of inocula of these pathogens can suppress the severity of infection and increase yield.

A suite of common leaf pathogens accounts for most of the literature on the effects of Si on host plant resistance to powdery mildew, rusts, and rice blast (Graham, 1983). These leaf pathogens attack through the epidermis or stomata. The traditional view of the function of Si has been one of enhancement of preformed physical barriers of the host cell wall by simple evaporative deposition of Si from the transpiration stream. Preformed physical barriers reinforced by Si also are thought to contribute to plant resistance to insects such as stem borers (Ukwungwu & Odebiyi, 1985). Kunoh et al. (1975) indicated a more dynamic role of Si when they reported concentric rings of, firstly, Ca, then Si, and finally Mn around the infection peg of *Erysiphe graminis* on barley. The extent of biochemical control over the movement and distribution of Si, in contrast to the earlier perception of a passive physical barrier, emerged with the elegant studies of Heath and colleagues over the past 15 yr (Wood & Heath, 1986 and earlier papers referred to therein; see also a brief review of earlier papers by Graham, 1983). In her earlier studies, Heath (1979, 1981) developed evidence of a tug-of-war between host and pathogen for the control of the deposition of SiO_2. This clearly required metabolic intervention on the part of the host, since deposition was blocked by inhibitors such as actinomycin D, cycloheximide and blastocidin S (Heath, 1979). Virulent strains of bean rust, *Uromyces phaseoli*, were capable of dissolving host deposits adjacent to the infection peg, and extracts from leaves infected with a virulent strain mobilized SiO_2 and promoted infection by a nonvirulent strain incapable of such mobilization. Indeed, the presence of nonvirulent strains actually may stimulate the deposition of SiO_2 in the bean leaf (Heath, 1981).

More recently, this response system in French bean (*Phaseolus vulgaris*) has been studied for its activity to rusts of other species (i.e., *Uromyces vignae* and *Puccinia helianthi*) to which it is a nonhost (Wood & Heath, 1986; Stumpf & Heath, 1985; Heath & Stumpf, 1986). From these studies, SiO_2 appeared to function as previously indicated but when the bean plant was deprived of Si, other components of the host cell interaction were still able to successfully inhibit infection. There is even the suggestion (Heath & Stumpf, 1986) that, while SiO_2 normally functions positively in resistance to these rusts on French bean, it may also decrease the flow of materials between host and fungus (including phytoalexins). Indeed, with *Uromyces vignae*, this may even be to the temporary benefit of the fungus.

While the deposition of SiO_2 in the leaves of plants resisting these leaf parasitic fungi has been extensively studied histochemically (*Erysiphe*: Lowig, 1933; Germar, 1934; Grosse-Brauckmann, 1957; *Piricularia*: Volk et al., 1958; Yoshida et al., 1962; Matsubayashi et al., 1963; *Uromyces*: Stumpf & Heath, 1985), the use of energy-dispersive X-ray analysis has added new dimensions to the picture (Kunoh et al., 1975; Kunoh & Ishizaki, 1976; Zeyen et al., 1983; Carver et al., 1987). In particular, Carver et al. (1987) have shown apparently greater deposition (three to four times) of SiO_2 around unsuccessful infection sites of *Erysiphe graminis* on barley than around successful infections. The value of this new tehcnique became clear when they were able to show that these differences, established 20 h after inoculation, had disappeared 4 h later, even though the proportion of unsuccessful infections remained. Thus, the dynamic view of the function of SiO_2 presented by Heath and collegeues has been extended by Carver et al. (1987) and appears to be intensely variable in both space and time.

Stumpf and Heath (1985) showed that plants low in Si responded to the presence of the rust fungus with much stronger development of callosic papillae around infection sites than did high Si plants, whereas Buchenauer and Borghoff (1982), working with powdery mildew on cereals, found that Si in various forms suppressed disease and stimulated intense papillae formation. Since Wissemeier and Horst (1988) have observed excessive callose deposits in Mn-toxic plants, and since the severity of Mn toxicity is a function of Si supply (Williams & Vlamis, 1957; Horst & Marschner, 1978), it seems likely that Si, Mn and callose are inextricably linked in disease resistance, a view reinforced by the earlier mentioned spatial distribution of these elements around infection sites. The exact nature of the link between Si and callose formation will depend on the Mn status of the tissue and vice versa. Silicon and Mn also appear to interact in the resistance of wheat roots to take-all, as both are deposited on the inner tangential and radial walls of the endodermis (Bennett, 1982; Clarkson et al., 1975).

J. Other Trace Elements

Of the many other elements that occur in plant tissue in trace amounts (Li, Na, Be, Al, Ge, F, Br, I, Co, Cr, Cd, Pb, and Hg) and which have occasionally been linked with host-pathogen relationships, Li and Cd, through their marked suppressive effects on powdery mildews, are the most note-worthy. The literature on these elements was reviewed by Graham (1983). Cadmium is inhibitory to spore germination as well as to further development, when present in the medium at only 3 mg kg^{-1}. At this level it is not directly toxic but somehow elicits a response to infection in the host. Recently Barber and Ride (1988) reported that Cd and Hg were two abiotic agents among a range of biological factors that elicit an enhanced synthesis of lignin in wheat. This stimulation may explain the earlier observations. The mechanism of Li action is unknown, but it is quite possible that it catalyzes a metabolic pathway which functions normally in defense. Any such putative requirement for Li remains obscure because the required amounts are so small and Li deficiency in plants has not been looked for in purified cultures in the presence of the pathogen.

IV. SUMMARY AND CONCLUSIONS

In the great majority of studies reported here, the addition of micronutrients has decreased the incidence of disease in crop plants. Effects on host plant tolerance and resistance are involved. The response is greatest over the deficiency range for the element concerned, although further suppression of disease by supraoptimal rates of micronutrients has been reported in a number of cases. Iron is the exception, for which as many reports indicate no effect or an increase in disease severity as indicate a decrease, depending on the system involved. The early views of the importance of siderophores in disease control in plants appears to be losing some credibility. Of the few reports (other than with Fe) in which addition of a micronutrient has exacerbated the disease, some are cases of toxicity rather than deficiency and others may involve an interaction: for example, the addition of a nutrient that aggravates the primary deficiency. It is concluded that adequate micronutrient nutrition should be viewed as an essential component of any integrated crop protection program because, by virtue of the small amounts needed and (for some) their long residual value, micronutrients are the cheapest agricultural chemicals on the market. Although disease remission is rarely complete, micronutrient fertilization may reduce the disease to an acceptable level, or at least to a level at which further control by other cultural practices or conventional organic biocides are more successful and less expensive. For Mn deficiency, because the current fertilizers are inefficient (owing to poor residual value), there appears to be considerable scope for technology to improve this situation and eliminate chronic Mn deficiency, as well as achieve better control of certain soil-borne diseases.

Besides practical considerations, this subject is also of interest from a biochemical viewpoint, as these micronutrients can often be linked to specific steps in the biochemical pathways involved in defense against plant pathogens. Although each micronutrient has several functions, mild deficiency can usually be linked to one or two processes that are most sensitive. It is consistent with conservation in biology that the first processes disrupted are those nonessential to immediate survival—the secondary metabolism. These are the pathways fundamental to defense against pathogens and predators. Some of these roles are well understood; others are inferred from the experimental evidence and remain to be elucidated, a task made easier by the evidence of micronutrient involvement. On the other hand, the evidence of a role in defense mechanisms for other trace elements not yet regarded as essential to higher plants could lead to recognition of their essentiality. This may require a modification of the criteria of essentiality to cover the situation in which yield increases, and indeed survival, due to the element in question is manifested only in the presence of the pathogen. Indeed, since higher plants and their pathogens have survived together on earth for millions of years, such a definition seems more natural and appropriate. This means that such essential elements would not be recognized in disease-free laboratory conditions. The requirement for a key biochemical role would remain; the obvious candidate for promotion to essential element by this definition is Si, assuming Ni is already so regarded. With further evidence, Li and Cd are probably next in line.

REFERENCES

Abia, J.A., W.M. Hess, and B.N. Smith. 1977. Mn reduced susceptiblity of pumpkin seedlings to *Sclerotinia sclerotiorum*. Naturwissenschaften 64:437–438.

Adams, P., C.J. Graves, and G.W. Winsor. 1975. Some effects of copper and boron deficiencies on the growth and flowering of *Chrysanthemum moriflorum* cv. Hurricane. J. Sci. Food Agric. 26:899–901.

Aist, J.R., R.E. Gold, C.J. Bayles, G.H. Morrison, S. Chandra, and H.W. Israel. 1988. Evidence that molecular components of papillae may be involved in ml-o resistance to barley powdery mildew. Physiol. Mol. Plant Pathol. 33:17–32.

Albert, F., and A.J. Anderson. 1987. The effect of *Pseudomonas putida* colonization on root surface peroxidase. Plant Physiol. 85:537–541.

Asher, M.J.C., and P.J. Shipton. 1981. Biology and control of take-all. Academic Press, London.

Bachchhav, M.B., D.G. Hapase, A.O. Patil, and T.K. Ghure. 1978. Chemical control of sugarcane rust. Sugarcane Pathol. Newsl. 20:33–35.

Balasubramanian, K.A. 1980. Factors affecting sorghum downy mildew development. p. 207–208. *In* Proc. Int. Workshop on Sorghum Diseases, Hyderabad, India. 11–15 Dec. 1978. Int. Crops Res. Inst. Semi-arid Tropics, Hyderabad, India.

Barber, M.S., and J.P. Ride. 1988. A quantitative assay for induced lignification in wounded wheat leaves and its use to survey potential elicitors of the response. Physiol. Mol. Plant Pathol. 32:185–198.

Barnes, E.D. 1972. The effects of irrigation, manganese sulphate and sulphur applications on common scab of potato. Rec. Agric. Res. 20:35–44.

Bartlett, R.J. 1988. Manganese redox reactions and organic interactions in soils. p. 59–73. *In* R.D. Graham et al. (ed.) Manganese in soils and plants. Kluwer Academic Publ., Dordrecht, Netherlands.

Basu Chaudhary, K.C. 1967. Influence of copper and zinc on the incidence of potato scab. Neth. J. Plant Pathol. 73:49–51.

Becker, J.O., and R.J. Cook. 1984. *Pythium* control by siderophore-producing bacteria on roots of wheat. Phytopathology 74:806.

Becker, J.O., R.W. Hedges, and E. Messens. 1986. Diverse effects of some bacterial siderophores on the uptake of iron by plants. p. 61–70. *In* T.R. Swinburne (ed.) Iron, siderophores and plant disease. Plenum Press, New York.

Beckman, C.H. 1980. Defenses triggered by the invader: physical defenses. p. 222–245. *In* J.G. Horsfall and E.B. Cowling (ed.) Plant disease: An advanced treatise: How plants defend themselves. Vol. V. Academic Press, New York.

Bell, A.A. 1981. Biochemical mechanisms of disease resistance. Annu. Rev. Plant Physiol. 32:21–81.

Bennett, D.M. 1982. Silicon deposition in the roots of *Hordeum sativum* Jess, *Avena sativa* L. and *Triticum aestivum* L. Ann. Bot. (London) 50:239–245.

Bertrand, G., and M. Javillier. 1912. Action of manganese and the development of *Aspergillus niger*. Bull. Soc. Chim. Fr. 4(XI):212–221.

Bettger, W.J., and B.L. O'Dell. 1981. A critical physiological role of zinc in the structure and function of biomembranes. Life Sci. 28:1425–1438.

Bidwell, R.G.S. 1979. Plant physiology. Macmillan Publishing Co., Inc., New York.

Björling, K. 1946. List of plant diseases in plantings of factory potatoes. Medd. Vaextskydd-sanst. Stockh. 47:1–16.

Bolle-Jones, E.W., and R.N. Hilton. 1956. Zinc-deficiency of *Hevea brasiliensis* as a predisposing factor to *Oidium* infection. Nature (London) 177:619–620.

Bortels, H. 1927. Uber die bedeutung von Eisen, Zink und Kupfer fur Micro-organismen. Biochem. Z. 182:301–358.

Bowen, J.E. 1981. Kinetics of active uptake of boron, zinc, copper and manganese in barley and sugarcane. J. Plant Nutr. 3:215–223.

Brain, P.J., and W.J. Whittington. 1981. The influence of soil pH on the severity of swede powdery mildew *Erysiphe cruciferarum* infection. Plant Pathol. 30:105–110.

Brisbane, P.G., and A.D. Rovira. 1988. Mechanisms of inhibition of *Gaeumannomyces graminis* var. *tritici* by fluorescent pseudomonads. Plant Pathol. 57:104–111.

Bromfield, S.M. 1978. The oxidation of manganous ions under acid conditions by an acidophilous actinomycete from acid soil. Aust. J. Soil Res. 16:91–100.

Bromfield, S.M. 1979. Manganous ion oxidation at pH values below 5.0 by cell-free substances from *Streptomyces* sp. cultures. Soil Biol. Biochem. 11:115–118.

Brown, P.H., R.D. Graham, and D.J.D. Nicholas. 1984. The effects of manganese and nitrate supply on the levels of phenolics and lignin in young wheat plants. Plant Soil 81:437–440.

Buchenauer, H., and F. Borghoff. 1982. Effect of silicate compounds and borax on mildew infections of barley and wheat seedlings. Meded. Fac. Landbouwwet. Rijksuniv. Gent. 47:875–886.

Burgess, L.W., T. Klein, and C.M. Liddell. 1984. Crown rot of wheat. p. 62–65. *In* Research on root and crown rots of wheat in australia. Proc. workshop, Adelaide, South Australia, 14–15 Feb. 1984. Australian Wheat Ind. Res. Council, Canberra, Australia.

Burnell, J.N. 1988. The biochemistry of manganese in plants. p. 125–137. *In* R.D. Graham et al. (ed.) Manganese in soils and plants. Kluwer Academic Publ., Dordrecht, Netherlands.

Butler, E.J., and S.G. Jones. 1955. Plant pathology. Macmillian, London.

Cadena-Gomez, G., and R.L. Nicholson. 1987. Papilla formation and associated peroxidase activity: a non-specific response to attempted fungal penetration of maize. Physiol. Mol. Plant Pathol. 31:51–67.

Carr, A.J.H., and J.L. Stoddart. 1963. The ameliorating effect of zinc on symptoms of phyllo-dy virus (strawberry green-petal) in white clover. Ann. Appl. Biol. 51:259–268.

Carver, T.L.W., R.J. Zeyen, and G.G. Ahlstrand. 1987. The relationship between insoluble silicon and success or failure of attempted primary penetration by powdery mildew (*Erysiphe graminis*) germlings on barley. Physiol. Mol. Plant Pathol. 31:133–148.

Chahal, S.S., and G.S. Rawla. 1984. Boron requirement of *Curvularia lunata* and *Phyllosticta mortoni*. Indian J. Mycol. Plant Pathol. 14:301–302.

Chase, A.R., and R.T. Poole. 1984. Influence of foliar applications of micronutrients and fungicides on foliar necrosis and leaf spot disease of *Chrysalidocarpus lutescens*. Plant Dis. 68:195–197.

Choong-Hoe, K. 1986. Effect of water management on the etiology and epidemiology of rice blast caused by *Pyricularia oryzae* Cav. Ph.D. diss. Louisiana State Univ., Baton Rouge.

Christensen, N.W., T.L. Jackson, and R.L. Powelson. 1982. Suppression of take-all root rot and stripe rust diseases of wheat with chloride fertilizer. p. 111–116. *In* Plant Nutrition 1982. Proc. Ninth Int. Plant Nutr. Colloq., Warwick, England. Commonwealth Agric. Bur., Slough, England.

Christensen, N.W., R.L. Powelson, and M. Brett. 1987. Epidemiology of wheat take-all as influenced by soil pH and temporal changes in inorganic soil N. Plant Soil 98:221–230.

Christensen, N.W., R.G. Taylor, R.L. Jackson, and B.L. Mitchell. 1981. Chloride effects on water potentials and yield of winter wheat infected with take-all root rot. Agron. J. 73:1053–1058.

Chvapil, M. 1973. New aspects of biological role of zinc: A stabilizer of macromolecules and biological membranes. Life Sci. 13:1041–1049.

Chvapil, M. 1976. Effect of zinc on cells and biomembranes. Med. Clin. N. Am. 60:799–812.

Clarkson, D.T., M.C. Drew, I.B. Ferguson, and J. Sanderson. 1975. The effect of the take-all fungus *Gaeumannomyces graminis* on the transport of ions by wheat plants. Physiol. Plant Pathol. 6:75–84.

Clarkson, D.T., I.B. Ferguson, D. Hornby, and I. McFarlane. 1974. Interactions between soil-borne pathogenic fungi and root function. p. 28–30. *In* Ann. Rep. Agric. Res. Council, Letcombe Lab., Wantage (1973), Wantage, England.

Coke, L., and W.J. Wittington. 1968. The role of boron in plant growth. IV. Interrelationships between boron and indol-3yl-acetic acid in the metabolism of bean radicles. J. Exp. Bot. 19:295–308.

Collmer, A., and N.T. Keen. 1986. The role of pectic enzymes in plant pathogenesis. Annu. Rev. Phytopathol. 24:383–409.

Colquhoun, T.T. 1940. Effect of manganese on powdery mildew of wheat. Aust. Inst. Agric. Sci. J. 6:54.

Cripps, J.E.L., R.F. Doepel, and G.D. McLean. 1983. Canning peach decline in Western Australia. II. Methods of prevention. Aust. J. Agric. Res. 34:517–526.

Crosa, J.H. 1984. The relationship of plasmid-mediated iron transport and bacterial virulence. Annu. Rev. Microbiol. 38:69–89.

Cruickshank, I.A.M. 1980. Defenses triggered by the invader: chemical defenses. p. 247–267. *In* J.G. Horsfall and E.B. Cowling (ed.) Plant disease: An advanced treatise: How plants defend themselves. Vol. V. Academic Press, New York.

Dixon, G.R. 1984. Galls caused by fungi and bacteria. p. 189–197. *In* R.K.S. Wood and G.J. Jellis (ed.) Plant diseases: Infection damage and loss. Blackwell Scientific Publ., Oxford, England.

Dixon, G.R., and M.A. Webster. 1988. Antagonistic effects of boron, calcium and pH on pathogenesis caused by *Plasmodiophora brassicae* Woronin (clubroot)—A review of recent work. Crop Res. 28:83–95.

Drobny, H.G., G.M. Hoffmann, and A. Amberger. 1984. Influence of mineral nutrition on the predisposition of *Phaseolus vulgaris* against *Colletotrichum lindemuthianum*. 1. Effects of different mineral nutrients and leaf age on the disease severity. Z. Pflanzenernaehr. Bodenkd. 147:242–254.

Dubey, R.C., and R.S. Dwivedi. 1985. Toxicity of cadmium on the growth of *Macrophomina phaseolina* causing charcoal rot of soybean as influenced by kaolinite, pH zinc and manganese. Proc. Indian Natl. Sci. Acad. Part B. Biol. Sci. 51:259–264.

Dugger, W.M. 1983. Boron in plant metabolism. p. 626–650. *In* A. Läuchli and R.L. Bieleski (ed.) Encyclopedia of plant nutrition. Vol. 15B. Inorganic plant nutrition. Springer-Verlag, Berlin.

Dutta, B.K., and E. Bremner. 1981. Trace elements as plant chemotherapeutants to control *Verticillium* wilt. Z. Pflanzenkrankh. Pflanzenschutz 88:405–412.

Dutta, B.K., and P.R. Deb. 1986. Effect of organic and inorganic amendments on the soil and rhizosphere microflora in relation to the biology and control of *Sclerotium rolfsii* causing foot rot of soybean. Z. Pflanzenkrankh. Pflanzenschutz 93:163–171.

Elad, Y., and R. Baker. 1985. The role of competition for iron and carbon in suppression of chlamydospore germination of *Fusarium* spp by *Pseudomonas* spp. Phytopathology 75:1053–1059.

Eskew, D.L., R.M. Welch, and W.A. Norvell. 1984. Nickel in higher plants. Further evidence for an essential role. Plant Physiol. 76:691–693.

Falcon, M.F., R.L. Fox, and E.E. Trujillo. 1984. Interactions of soil pH, nutrients and moisture in *Phytophthora* root rot of avocado (*Persea americana*). Plant Soil 81:165–176.

Fernando, T., B.B. Jarvis, and G. Bean. 1986. Effects of micro-elements on production of Roridin E by *Myrothecium roridum*, a strain pathogenic to muskmelon (*Cucumis melo*). Trans. Br. Mycol. Soc. 86:273–277.

Forsyth, F.R. 1957. Effect of ions of certain metals on the development of stem rust in the wheat plant. Nature (London) 179:217–218.

Forsyth, F.R., and B. Peturson. 1959. Chemical control of cereal rust. IV. The influence of nickel compounds on wheat, oat and sunflower rusts in the greenhouse. Phytopathology 49:1–3.

Friend, J. 1977. Biochemistry of plant pathogens. p. 141–182. *In* D.H. Northcote (ed.) International review of biochemistry, plant biochemistry III. Vol. 13. Univ. Park Press, Baltimore, MD.

Fuchs, W.H., and F. Grossmann. 1972. Ernahrung und Resistanz von Kulturpflanzen gegenuber Krankheitserregern und Schadlingen. p. 1007–1107. *In* H. Linser (ed.) Handbuch der Pflanzenernahrung und Dungung. Vol. 1. Pt. 2. Springer-Verlag, Berlin.

Gardner, W.K., and A. Flynn. 1988. The effect of gypsum on copper nutrition of wheat grown in marginally deficient soil. J. Plant Nutr. 11:475–493.

Gaur, R.B., and P.K. Vaidya. 1983. Reduction of root rot of chickpea by soil application of phosphorus and zinc. Int. Chickpea Newsl. 9:17–18.

Germar, B. 1934. On the function of silicic acid in cereal plants, especially on their resistance to mildew. Z. Pflanzenernaehr. Dueng. Bodenkd. 35:102–115.

Gildon, A., and P.B. Tinker. 1983. Interactions of vesicular-arbuscular mycorrhizal infection and heavy metals in plants. I. The effects of heavy metals on the development of vesicular-arbuscular mycorrhizas. New Phytol. 95:247–261.

Gilmour, J., P. Crooks, J.B.A. Rodger, A. Wynd, and A.J.M. McKay. 1968. Manganese soil treatment for the control of common scab of potatoes. p. 36–37. *In* Edinburgh School Agric. Exp. Work.

Golden, D.C., S. Sivasubramanian, S. Sanderman, and M.A. Wijedasa. 1981. Inhibitory effects of commercial potassium chloride on the nitrification rates of added ammonium sulphate in an acid red-yellow podzolic soil. Plant Soil 59:147–151.

Goodwin, T.W., and E.I. Mercer. 1972. Introduction to plant biochemistry. Permagon Press, Oxford, England.

Goss, R.L., and C.J. Gould. 1967. Some inter-relationships between fertility levels and *Ophiobolus* patch disease in turf grasses. Agron. J. 59:149–151.

Graham, R.D. 1979. Transport of copper and manganese to the xylem exudate of sunflower. Plant Cell Environ. 2:139–143.

Graham, R.D. 1980. Susceptibility to powdery mildew of wheat plants deficient in copper. Plant Soil 56:181–185.

Graham, R.D. 1981. Effects of trace element stress on the susceptibility of higher plants to pathogenic organisms. Symposium Section 5. *In* Proc. XIII Int. Bot. Congr., Sydney, Australia. 21–28 Aug. 1981. B. Scheltema and H.W. Junk, Utrecht, Germany.

Graham, R.D. 1983. Effect of nutrient stress on susceptibility of plants to disease with particular reference to the trace elements. Adv. Bot. Res. 10:221–276.

Graham, R.D. 1988. Development of wheats with enhanced nutrient efficiency: progress and potential. p. 305–320. *In* A.R. Klett (ed.) Wheat production constraints in tropical environments. CIMMYT, Mexico, D.F.

Graham, R.D., and A.D. Rovira. 1984. A role for manganese in the resistance of wheat plants to take-all. Plant Soil 78:441–444.

Graham, R.D., R.M. Welch, D.L. Grunes, E.E. Cary, and W.A. Norvell. 1987. Effect of zinc deficiency on the accumulation of boron and other mineral nutrients in barley. Soil Sci. Soc. Am. J. 51:652–657.

Graham, R.D., R.M. Welch, and C.D. Walker. 1985. A role for nickel in the resistance of plants to rust. Proc. Third Aust. Agron. Conf., Hobart Tasmania, Australia. 30 Jan.–1 Feb. 1985. Australian Society of Agronomy, Hobart, Australia.

Gross, G.G. 1980. The biochemistry of lignification. Adv. Bot. Res. 8:25–63.

Grosse-Brauckmann, E. 1957. The influence of silicic acid on mildew infection of cereals with different nitrogen fertilizers. Phytopathol. Z. 30:112–115.

Guerra, D., and A.J. Anderson. 1985. The effect of iron and boron amendments on infection of bean by *Fusarium solani*. Phytopathology 75:989–991.

Gvozdyak, R.I., and N.I. Pindus. 1988. Bacterial diseases of ginseng leaves in the Ukraine. Mikrobiol. Zh. (Kiev) 50:52–55.

Haard, N.F. 1978. Isolation and partial characterization of auxin protectors from *Synchytrium endobioticum* incited tumors in potato. Physiol. Plant Pathol. 13:223–232.

Hallock, D.L., and D.M. Porter. 1981. Effects of applied plant nutrients on *Sclerotinia* blight incidence in peanuts. Peanut Sci. 8:48–52.

Halsall, D.M. 1977. Effects of certain cations on the formation and infectivity of *Phytophthora* zoospores. 2. Effects of copper, boron, cobalt, manganese, molybdenum, and zinc ions. Can. J. Microbiol. 23:1002–1010.

Halsall, D.M., and R.I. Forrester. 1977. Effects of certain cations on the formation and infectivity of *Phytophthora* zoospores. 1. Effects of calcium, magnesium, potassium and iron ions. Can. J. Microbiol. 23:994–1001.

Hampson, M.C. 1980. Pathogenesis of *Synchytrium endobioticum*: 2. Effect of soil amendments and fertilization. Can. J. Plant Pathol. 2:148–151.

Hampson, M.C., and N.F. Haard. 1980. Pathogenesis of *Synchytrium endobioticum*: 1. Infection responses in potato and tomato. Can. J. Plant Pathol. 2:143–147.

Haque, M.S., and M.C. Mukhopadhyaya. 1983. Influence of some micro-nutrients on *Rotylenchulus reniformis*. Indian J. Nematol. 13:115–116.

Heath, M.C. 1979. Effects of heat shock, actinomycin D, cycloheximide and blastocidin S on nonhost interactions with rust fungi. Physiol. Plant Pathol. 15:211–218.

Heath, M.C. 1981. The suppression of the development of silicon containing deposits in French bean leaves by exudates of the bean rust fungus and extracts from bean rust-infected tissue. Physiol. Plant Pathol. 18:149–155.

Heath, M.C., and M.A. Stumpf. 1986. Ultrastructural observations of penetration sites of the cowpea rust fungus in untreated and silicon-depleted French bean cells. Physiol. Mol. Plant Pathol. 29:27–39.

Hedge, B.A., and S.M. Karande. 1978. Effect of presowing treatment of sodium chloride on the incidence of green ear disease of *Pennisetum typhoides* (Burm) Stapf and Hubb. var. HBs. Plant Soil 49:551–559.

Hemming, B.C., C. Orser, D.L. Jacobs, D.C. Sands, and G.A. Strobel. 1982. The effects of iron on microbial antagonism by fluorescent pseudomonads. J. Plant Nutr. 5:683–702.

Hooley, P., and D.S. Shaw. 1985. Inheritance of sensitivity to heavy metals in *Phytophthora drechsleri*. Trans. Br. Mycol. Soc. 85:677–682.

Horsfall, J.G., and E.B. Cowling (ed.). 1980. Plant disease: An advanced treatise: How plants defend themselves. Academic Press, New York.

Horst, W.J., and H. Marschner. 1978. Effect of silicon on manganese tolerance of bean plants *Phaseolus vulgaris*. Plant Soil 50:287–303.

Huber, D.M. 1980. The role of nutrition in defense. p. 381–406. *In* J.G. Horsfall and E.B. Cowling (ed.) Plant disease—An advanced treatise: How plants defend themselves. Vol. V. Academic Press, New York.

Huber, D.M., and D.C. Arny. 1985. Interaction of potassium with plant disease. p. 467–488. *In* R.D. Munson (ed.) Potassium in agriculture. ASA, CSSA, and SSSA, Madison, WI.

Huber, D.M., and R.A. Dorich. 1988. Effect of nitrogen fertility on the take-all disease of wheat. Down Earth 44(3):12–17.

Huber, D.M., and R.R. Keeler. 1977. Alteration of wheat peptidase activity after infection with powdery mildew. Proc. Am. Phytopathol. Soc. 4:163.

Huber, D.M., and R.D. Watson. 1974. Nitrogen form and plant disease. Annu. Rev. Phytopathol. 12:139–165.

Huber, D.M., and N.S. Wilhelm. 1988. The role of manganese in resistance to plant diseases. p. 155–173. *In* R.D. Graham et al. (ed.) Manganese in soils and plants. Kluwer Academic Publ., Dordrecht, Netherlands.

Isaeva, G.Y. 1969. Influence of nickel and cobalt on the resistance of potato to diseases. Nauk. Pr. Zhytomyr. Sil's'kohosp. Inst. (Referat. Zh. Rasten. 4:963(1970)). 16:110–112.

Jenkyn, J.F., and A. Bainbridge. 1978. Biology and pathology of cereal powdery mildews. p. 283–321. *In* D.M. Spencer (ed.) The powdery mildews. Academic Press, London.

Jones, I.T., and J.D. Hayes. 1971. The effect of sowing date on adult plant resistance to *Erysiphe graminis* f. sp. *avenae* in oats. Ann. Appl. Biol. 68:31–39.

Jones, J.P., and S.S. Woltz. 1981. *Fusarium*-incited diseases of tomato and potato and their control. p. 157–168. *In* P.E. Nelson et al. (ed.) *Fusarium*: Diseases, biology and taxonomy. Pennsylvania State Univ. Press, University Park, PA.

Kataria, H.R. 1982. Pathogenesis of *Rhizoctonia solani* on legume crops as influenced by soil conditions and fertility level. Indian J. Mycol. Plant Pathol. 12:125–126.

Kataria, H.R., and R.K. Grover. 1987. Influence of soil factors, fertilizers and manures on pathogenicity of *Rhizoctonia solani* on *Vigna* species. Plant Soil 103:57–66.

Kattak, R.A., and W.M. Jarrell. 1988. Salt-induced manganese solubilization in California soils. Soil Sci. Soc. Am. J. 52:1606–1611.

Keane, E.M., and W.E. Sackston. 1970. Effects of boron and calcium nutrition of flax on *Fusarium* wilt. Can. J. Plant Sci. 50:415–422.

Keast, D., C. Tonkin, and L. Sanfelieu. 1985. Effects of copper salts on growth and survival of *Phytophthora cinnamomi* in vitro and on the antifungal activity of actinomycete populations from the roots of *Eucalyptus marginata* and *Banksia grandis*. Aust. J. Bot. 33:115–130.

Kloepper, J.W., J. Leong, M. Teintze, and M.N. Schroth. 1980a. Disease-suppressive soils. Curr. Microbiol. 4:317–320.

Kloepper, J.W., J. Leong, M. Teintze, and M.N. Schroth. 1980b. Enhanced plant growth by siderophores produced by plant growth-promoting rhizobacteria. Nature (London) 286:885–886.

Kosuge, T., and M. Sanger. 1986. Indoleacetic acid, its synthesis and regulation: A basis for tumorigenicity in plant disease. p. 147–161. *In* E.E. Conn (ed.) Recent advances in phytochemistry: The shikimic acid pathway. Vol. 20. Plenum Press, New York.

Krüger, W. 1982. The root collar and stem rot of oil-seed rape caused by *Phoma lingam* (stat. gen. *Leptosphaeria maculans*), a disease difficult to control. Z. Pflanzenkrankh. Pflanzenschutz 89:498–507.

Kunoh, H., and H. Ishizaki. 1976. Accumulation of chemical elements around the penetration sites of *Erysiphe graminis hordei* on barley leaf epidermis. III. Micromanipulation and Xray microanalysis of silicon. Physiol. Plant Pathol. 8:91–96.

Kunoh, H., H. Ishizaki, and F. Kondo. 1975. Composition analysis of 'halo' area of barley leaf epidermis incited by powdery mildew infection. Ann. Phytopath. Soc. Jpn. 41:33–39.

Lakshmi, M., G. Chandra, and R.A. Rai. 1984. Herbicidal and fungicidal activities of some transition metal complexes with benzoyl hydrazide and salicyl hydrazide. Pesticides (Bombay) 18:22–25.

Last, F.T. 1962. Effects of nutrition on the incidence of barley powdery mildew. Plant Pathol. 11:133–135.

Lemanceau, P., R. Samson, and C. Alabouvette. 1988. Studies on the disease suppressiveness of soils. XV. Comparison of the fluorescent *Pseudomonas* population in a wilt-suppressive and a wilt-conducive soil. Agronomie (Paris) 8:243–250.

Lemanceau, P., R. Samson, L.M. Rivière, and C. Alabouvette. 1987. Effect de la 8-hydroxyquinoleine sur la crossance, in vitro, de populations telluriques de *Pseudomonas fluorescens*. p. 244–245. *In* J.M. Legay (ed.) Biologie des populations. Coll. Nat. CNRS-IASBE, University Claude Bernard, Lyon, France.

Leong, S.A. 1986. Siderophores: their biochemistry and possible role in the biocontrol of plant pathogens. Annu. Rev. Phytopathol. 24:187–209.

Leong, S.A., and J.B. Neilands. 1981. Relationship of siderophore mediated iron assimilation to virulence in crown gall disease. J. Bacteriol. 147:482–491.

Leong, S.A., and J.B. Neilands. 1982. Siderophore production by phytopathogenic microbial species. Arch. Biochem. Biophys. 218:351–359.

Lewis, D.H. 1980. Boron, lignification and the origin of vascular plants—a unified hyptothesis. New Phytol. 84:209–229.

Lodeman, E.G. 1902. The spraying of plants. Macmillan, New York.

Loneragan, J.F., G.J. Kirk, and M.J. Webb. 1987. Translocation and function of zinc in roots. J. Plant Nutr. 10:1247–1254.

Lowig, E. 1933. On the influence of K$^+$ and accompanying anions on the resistance of various cereals to infection by *Erysiphe graminis*. Ernaehr. Pflanze. 29:161–167.

Mai, W.F., and G.S. Abawi. 1987. Interactions among root-knot nematodes and *Fusarium* wilt fungi on host plants. Annu. Rev. Phytopathol. 25:317–338.

Marcar, N.E. 1986. Genotypic variation for manganese efficiency in cereals. Ph.D. diss. Univ. of Adelaide, South Australia.

Marchal, E. 1902. De l'immunization de la laitue contre le meunier. C.R. Hebd. Seances Acad. Sci. 135:1067–1068.

Marschner, H. 1986. Mineral nutrition of higher plants. Academic Press, London.

Marschner, H., V. Römheld, and M. Kissel. 1986. Different strategies in higher plants in mobilization and uptake of iron. J. Plant Nutr. 9:695–713.

Matern, U., and R.E. Kneusel. 1988. Phenolic compounds in plant disease resistance. Phytoparasitica 16:153–170.

Matsubayashi, M., R. Ito, T. Nomoto, T. Takase, and N. Yamada. 1963. Theory and practice of growing rice, Fuji Publ. Co., Tokyo.

Miller, V.R., and Z.E. Becker. 1983. The role of microelements in cotton resistance to *Verticillium* wilt. Sel'skokhoz. Biol. (11):54–56.

Millikan, C.R. 1938. A preliminary note on the relation of zinc to disease in cereals. J. Agric. (Victoria Aust.) 409–416.

Moerschbacher, B.M., U.M. Noll, B.E. Flott, and H.J. Reisener. 1988. Lignin biosynthetic enzymes in stem rust infected, resistant and susceptible near-isogenic wheat lines. Physiol. Mol. Plant Pathol. 33:33–46.

Mortvedt, J.J., K.C. Berger, and H.M. Darling. 1963. Effect of manganese and copper on the growth of *Streptomyces scabies* and the incidence of potato scab. Am. Potato J. 40:96–102.

Mortvedt, J.J., M.H. Fleishfresser, K.C. Berger, and H.M. Darling. 1961. The relation of soluble manganese to the incidence of common scab of potatoes. Am. Potato J. 38:95–100.

Murugesan, K., and A. Mahadevan. 1987. Control of *Rhizoctonia bataticola* of groundnut by trace elements. Int. J. Trop. Plant Dis. 5:43–57.

Mustakimova, F., and K.H. Muratmukhamedov. 1982. Increasing cotton wilt resistance due to the effect of zinc sulfate and hairy vetch. Izv. Akad. Nauk Turkm. SSR Ser. Biol. Nauk. 67–70.

Nesterov, P.I., and V.V. Korol'chuk. 1975. Foliar feeding with trace elements of sugarbeet infected with *Heterodera*. p. 61–63. *In* Probl. paraz. Mat. VIII nauch. konf. parazitol. Uk. SSR Chast'2, Kiev, USSR.

Norvell, W.A. 1988. Inorganic reactions of manganese in soils. p. 37–58. *In* R.D. Graham et al. (ed.) Manganese in soils and plants. Kluwer Academic Publ., Dordrecht, The Netherlands.

O'Dell, B.L., J.D. Browning, and P.G. Reeves. 1984. Interaction of zinc and major nutrients in the stability of rat erythrocytes. p. 75–79. *In* C.F. Mills et al. (ed.) Trace elements in man and animals. Proc. Fifth Int. Symp. Trace Elements in Man and Animals. Commonwealth Agric. Bur., Slough, England.

Perkins, H., and S. Aronoff. 1956. Identification of blue-fluorescent compounds in boron-deficient plants. Arch. Biochem. Biophys. 64:506–516.

Perrin, D.R., and I.A.M. Cruikshank. 1965. Studies on phytoalexins. VII. Chemical simulation of pisatin formation in *Pisum sativum* L. Aust. J. Biol. Sci. 18:803–816.

Pilbeam, D.J., and E.A. Kirkby. 1983. The physiological role of boron in plants. J. Plant Nutr. 6:563–582.

Pollard, A.S., A.J. Parr, and B.C. Loughman. 1977. Boron in relation to membrane function in higher plants. J. Exp. Bot. 28:831–841.

Powelson, R.L., and T.L. Jackson. 1978. Suppression of take-all (*Gaeumannomyces graminis*) root rot of wheat with fall applied chloride fertilizers. p. 175–182. Proc. 29th Annu. Northwest Fert. Conf., Beaverton, OR. 11–13 July 1978.

Primavesi, A., and A.M. Primavesi. 1970. Relationship between plant nutrition and plant disease. Z. Pflanzenernaehr. Dueng. Bodenkd. 105:22–27.

Raghavendra Rao, N.N. 1985. Relative efficacy of a single pre-monsoon spray of some fungicides for the control of brown fruit-rot of citrus. Indian J. Agric. Sci. 55:189–192.

Rajaratnam, J.A., and J.B. Lowry. 1974. Role of boron in the oil-palm (*Elaeis guineensis*). Ann. Bot. (London) 38:193–200.

Reingard, T.A., and S.I. Pashkar. 1959. Potato wart. Ukranian Academy of Sci., Kiev.

Reis, E.M., R.J. Cook, and B.L. McNeal. 1982. Effect of mineral nutrition on take-all of wheat. Phytopathology 72:224–229.

Reis, E.M., R.J. Cook, and B.L. McNeal. 1983. Elevated pH and associated reduced trace-nutrient availability as factors contributing to take-all of wheat upon soil liming. Phytopathology 73:411–413.

Robson, A.D., R.D. Hartley, and S.C. Jarvis. 1981. Effect of copper deficiency on phenolic and other constituents of wheat cell walls. New Phytol. 89:361–373.

Rodger, J.B.A., A. Wynd, and J. Gilmour. 1967. Manganese and sulphur treatments for the control of common scab of potatoes. Edinburgh School Agric. Exp. Work. 24–25.

Rogers, P.F. 1969. Organic manuring for potato scab and its relation to soil manganese. Ann. Appl. Biol. 63:371–378.

Romanova, A.M., and M.G. Gibadullin. 1980. Results of treatment with microelements. Zashch. Rast. (Kiev) 9:23.

Rovira, A.D., R.D. Graham, and J.S. Ascher. 1985. Reduction in infection of wheat roots by *Gaeumannomyces graminis* var. *tritici* with application of manganese to soil. p. 212–214. *In* C.A. Parker et al. (ed.) Ecology and management of soilborne plant pathogens. Am. Phytopathol. Soc., St. Paul, Minnesota.

Russell, G.E. 1978. Some effects of applied sodium and potassium chloride on yellow rust in winter wheat. Ann. Appl. Biol. 90:163–168.

Sadasivan, T.S. 1965. Effect of mineral nutrients on soil micro-organisms and plant disease. p. 460–470. *In* K.F. Baker and W.C. Snyder (ed.) Ecology of soil-borne pathogens. Proc. Int. Symp., Berkeley, CA. 1963. Univ. California Press, Berkeley, CA.

Savov, S.G. 1986. Effectiveness of some trace elements in the control of cotton *Verticillium* wilt. Rast. Nauki. 23:68–71.

Scher, F.M., and R. Baker. 1982. Effect of *Pseudomonas putida* and a synthetic iron chelator on induction of soil suppressiveness to *Fusarium* wilt pathogens. Phytopathology 72:1567–1574.

Schütte, K.H. 1964. The biology of the trace elements. Crosley Lockwood, London.

Schütte, K.H. 1967. The influence of boron and copper deficiency upon infection by *Erysiphe graminis* D.C., the powdery mildew of wheat var. Kenya. Plant Soil 27:450–452.

Sempio, C. 1936. The influence of various substances on parasitism: Bean rust, wheat rust and mildew. Riv. Patol. Veg. 26:201–278.

Shao, F.M., and C.D. Foy. 1982. Interaction of soil manganese and reaction of cotton to *Verticillium* wilt and *Rhizoctonia* root rot. Commun. Soil Sci. Plant Anal. 13:21–38.

Shimomura, T. 1982. Effects of boron on the formation of local lesions and accumulation of callose in French bean and Samsun NN tobacco leaves inoculated with tobacco mosaic virus. Physiol. Plant Pathol. 20:257–261.

Shinde, S.R., and L.V. Gangawane. 1987. Role of trace elements in the production of cellulases by *Phoma herbarum* causing leaf spot of groundnut. Indian Bot. Rep. 6:99–100.

Shkolnik, M.Ya. 1984. Trace elements in plants. Elsevier, Amsterdam.

Simeoni, L.A., W.L. Lindsay, and R. Baker. 1987. Critical iron level associated with biological control of *Fusarium* wilt. Phytopathology 77:1057–1061.

Simojoki, P. 1969. Ergot, barley and boron. *In* Boron and Ergot. Borax Consolidated Ltd, London.

Sindhan, G.S., and R.D. Parashar. 1984. A comparative study of pea varieties resistant and susceptible to powdery mildew disease. Prog. Hortic. 16:137–139.

Singh, A.P. 1986. Effect of soil nutrients and varietal reaction to the population build-up of brown wheat mite, *Petrobia latens* (Muller) on wheat. Entomon 11:115–120.

Sinha, A.K., and D.N. Giri. 1979. An approach to control brown spot of rice with chemicals known as phytoalexin inducers. Curr. Sci. 48:782–784.

Skou, J.P. 1981. Morphology and cytology of the infection process. p. 175–197. *In* M.J.C. Asher and P.J. Shipton (ed.) Biology and control of take-all. Academic Press, London.

Smirnov, Yu.S. 1978. The activity of polyphenol oxidase in *Helianthus annuus* grown in an environment enriched with trace elements. Bot. Zh. (Leningrad) 63:1636–1639.

Smith, R.B., and C.T. Hallmark. 1987. Selected chemical and physical properties of soils manifesting cotton root rot. Agron. J. 79:155–159.

Somani, A.K. 1986. Non-hazardous chemical control of black-scurf of potato. Indian J. Agric. Sci. 56:366–369.

Somashekar, R.K., M.D. Kulashekaran, and M. Satishchandra Prabhu. 1983. Toxicity of heavy metals to some fungi. Int. J. Environ. Stud. 21:277–280.

Sparrow, D.H., and R.D. Graham. 1988. Susceptibility of zinc-deficient wheat plants to colonization by *Fusarium graminearum* Schw. Group 1. Plant Soil 112:261–266.

Spinks, G.T. 1913. Factors affecting susceptibility to disease in plants. J. Agric. Sci. (Cambridge) 5:231–247.

Strakhov, T., and T.V. Yaroshenko. 1959. Effect of trace elements on the relation between smut-producing agents and the host plant. Primen. Mikroelem. Sel'sk. Khoz. Med. Bakv. (1958):373–380.

Stumpf, M.A., and M.C. Heath. 1985. Cytological studies of the interactions between the cowpea rust fungus and silicon-depleted French bean plants. Physiol. Plant Pathol. 27:369–385.

Swinburne, T.R. 1986a. Iron, siderophores and plant disease. Plenum Press, New York.

Swinburne, T.R. 1986b. Stimulation of disease development by siderophores and inhibition by chelated iron. p. 217–226. *In* T.R. Swinburne (ed.) Iron, siderophores and plant disease. Plenum Press, New York.

Tainio, A. 1961. Can ergot be controlled by trace element fertilization? Boron and Ergot. Borax Consolidated Ltd, London.

Takanashi, K., and Y. Iwata. 1963. Microautoradiographic studies on the accumulation of radioactive calcium (^{45}Ca) and strontium (^{89}Sr) in the lesions of barley powdery mildew (*Erysiphe graminis hordei*). Bull. Natl. Inst. Agric. Sci. Ser. C (Plant Pathol. Entomol.) 15:83–94.

Talboys, P.W. 1984. Damage, symptoms and crop loss caused by vascular pathogens. p. 171–187. *In* R.K.S. Wood and G.J. Jellis (ed.) Plant diseases: infection, damage and loss. Blackwell Scientific Publ., Oxford.

Tandon, P. 1985. Peroxidase-catalyzed IAA oxidation in presence of cofactors and auxin protectors isolated from *Eriophyes* incited *Zizyphus* gall tissue. Cecidol. Int. 6:69–82.

Taylor, R.G., T.L. Jackson, R.L. Powelson, and N.W. Christensen. 1983. Chloride, nitrogen form, lime and planting date effects on take-all root rot of winter wheat. Plant Dis. 67:1116–1120.

Tomlinson, J.A. 1958. Crook root of watercress. II. The control of the disease with zinc-fritted glass and the mechanism of its action. Ann. Appl. Biol. 46:608–621.

Tomlinson, J.A., and J. Hunt. 1987. Studies on watercress chlorotic leaf spot virus and on the control of the fungus vector (*Spongospora subterranea*) with zinc. Ann. Appl. Biol. 110:75–88.

Tomono, K., Y. Arimoto, Y. Homma, and T. Misato. 1981. The relationship between Ca^{2+} absorption in each organ of *Diaporthe citri* and the inhibitory effect on pycnospore germination or hyphal penetration. J. Pestic. Sci. 6:337–340.

Tomono, K., M. Kawai, H. Sasaki, Y. Homma, and T. Misato. 1982. The influence of zinc, magnesium and calcium ions on the inhibitory effect of copper (II) ion against *Diaporthe citri*. J. Pestic. Sci. 7:329–334.

Tomono, K., N. Kumazawa, Y. Homma, and T. Misato. 1983. Mode of action of copper 8-quinolinolate on *Alternaria kikuchiana*. J. Pestic. Sci. 8:277–282.

Toms, J. 1958. The use of copper and zinc in the cereal-growing districts of Western Australia. J. Agric. West. Aust. 7:197–203.

Trudgill, D.L. 1986. Concepts of resistance, tolerance and susceptibility in relation to cyst nematodes. p. 179–187. *In* F. Lamberti and C.E. Taylor (ed.) Cyst nematodes. Plenum Press, New York.

Ukwungwu, M.N., and J.A. Odebiyi. 1985. Incidence of *Chilo zacconius* Bleszynski on some rice varieties in relation to plant characters. Insect Sci. Appl. 6:653–656.

van Alphen. Th.G. 1957. Spraying crops with copper. Lit. Rev. 20. Centre Agric. Document, Wageningen, Netherlands.

Vedie, R., and M. Le Normand. 1984. Modulation of the pathogenicity of *Botrytis fabae* and *Botrytis cinerea* by bacteria in the phylloplane of *Vicia faba*. Agronomie (Paris). 4:721–728.

Vladimirskaya, M.E., N.I. Utkina, V.A. Vytskii, T.N. Danilova, and E. Kusenkova. 1982. Effects of environmental conditions on clubroot susceptibility and yield of swede. Mikol. Fitopatol. 16:429–433.

Vlamis, J., and C.E. Yarwood. 1962. Effect of liming of soil on barley powdery mildew. Plant Dis. Rep. 46:886–887.

Volk, J.R., R.P. Kahn, and R.L. Weintraub. 1958. Silicon content of rice plants as a factor influencing the resistance to infection by the blast fungus *Piricularia oryzae*. Phytopathology 48:179–184.

Waggoner, P.E., and A.E. Dimond. 1953. Role of chelation in causing and inhibiting the toxicity of lycomarismin. Phytopathology 43:281–284.

Walker, C.D., and J. Webb. 1981. Copper in plants: forms and behaviour. p. 189–212. *In* J.F. Loneragan et al. (ed.) Copper in soils and plants. Academic Press, Sydney, Australia.

Wallace, H.R. 1987. A perception of tolerance. Nematologica 33:419–432.

Warren, H.L., D.M. Huber, D.W. Nelson, and O.W. Mann. 1975. Stalk rot incidence and yield of corn as affected by inhibiting nitrification of fall-applied ammonium. Agron. J. 67:655–660.

Weinberg, E.D. 1978. Iron and infection. Microbiol. Rev. 42:45–66.

Weinberg, E.D. 1984. Iron withholding: a defense against infection and neoplasia. Physiol. Rev. 64:65–102.

Welch, R.M., M.J. Webb, and J.F. Loneragan. 1982. Zinc in membrane function and its role in phosphorus toxicity. p. 710–715. *In* A. Scaife (ed.) Plant nutrition 1982. Proc. Ninth Int. Plant Nutr. Colloq., Commonwealth Agric. Bur., Slough, England.

Weller, D.M., and R.J. Cook. 1983. Suppression of take-all of wheat by seed treatments of fluorescent pseudomonads. Phytopathology 73:463–469.

Western, J.H. 1971. Diseases of crop plants. Macmillan, London.

Whitmore, S.C., J.F. Rissler, and R.E. Davis. 1983. In vitro susceptibility of spiroplasmas to heavy-metal salts. Antimicrob. Agents Chemother. 23:22–25.

Wilhelm, N.S. 1990. Investigations into *Gaeumannomyces graminis* var. *tritici* infection of manganese-deficient wheat. Ph.D. diss. Univ. Adelaide, South Australia.

Wilhelm, N.S., J.M. Fisher, and R.D. Graham. 1985. The effect of manganese deficiency and cereal cyst nematode infection on the growth of barley. Plant Soil 85:23–32.

Wilhelm, N.S., R.D. Graham, and A.D. Rovira. 1987. Manganese suppresses the take-all disease of wheat by increasing the plant's internal resistance to the penetration of the fungal hyphae into the root. Symposium Section 24. Proc. XIV Int. Bot. Congr., Berlin. 26 July–1 Aug. 1987. Koeltz Sci. Books, Konigstein, Germany.

Wilhelm, N.S., R.D. Graham, and A.D. Rovira. 1988. Application of different sources of manganese sulphate decreases take-all (*Gaeumannomyces graminis* var. *tritici*) of wheat grown in a manganese deficient soil. Aust. J. Agric. Res. 39:1-10.

Wilhelm, N.S., R.D. Graham, and A.D. Rovira. 1990. Control of Mn status and infection rate by genotype of both host and pathogen in the wheat take-all interaction. p. 413-421. *In* N.L. Bassam et al. (ed.) Genetic aspects of plant mineral nutrition. Kluwer Academic Publ., Dordrecht, Netherlands.

Wilkinson, H.T., and R.L. Millar. 1981. Effects of specific ions on growth and reproduction of *Phytophthora megasperma* var *megasperma*. Phytopathology 71:265.

Williams, D.E., and J. Vlamis. 1957. The effect of silicon on yield and manganese-54 uptake and distribution in the leaves of barley plants grown in culture solutions. Plant Physiol. 32:404-409.

Wissemeier, A.H., and W.J. Horst. 1988. Callose deposits as novel manganese toxicity symptom. p. 61-62. *In* M.J. Webb et al. (ed.) Int. Symp. Manganese in Soils and Plants: Contributed Papers. Manganese Symposium 1988 Inc., Adelaide, South Australia, Australia.

Wong, P.T.W., and R. Baker. 1984. Suppression of wheat take-all *Gaeumannomyces graminis* var *tritici* and *Ophiobolus* patch *Gaeumannomyces graminis* var *avenae* by fluorescent pseudomonads from a *Fusarium*-suppressive soil. Soil Biol. Biochem. 16:397-404.

Wood, L.A., and M.C. Heath. 1986. Light and electron microscopy of the interaction between the sunflower rust fungus (*Puccinia helianthi*) and leaves of the nonhost plant, French bean (*Phaseolus vulgaris*). Can. J. Bot. 64:2476-2486.

Wood, M.J., and A.D. Robson. 1984. Effect of copper deficiency in wheat on the infection of roots by *Gaeumannomyces graminis* var *tritici*. Aust. J. Agric. Res. 35:735-742.

Yaroshenko, T.V. 1959. Effect of trace elements in granules of superphosphate on the yield and disease resistance of wheat. p. 441-446. Primen. Mikroelem. Se. Khoz. Medits. Bakv. (1958).

Yoshida, S., Y. Ohnishi, and K. Kitagishi. 1962. Histochemistry of the rice plant. III. The presence of cuticle-silica double layer in epidermal tissue. Soil Sci. Plant Nutr. 8(2):1-5.

Younts, S.E., and R.B. Musgrave. 1958. Chemical composition, nutrient absorption and stalk rot incidence of corn as affected by chloride in potassium fertilizer. Agron. J. 50:426-429.

Yuen, G.Y., and M.N. Schroth. 1986. Inhibition of *Fusarium oxysporum* f. sp. *dianthi* by iron competition with an *Alcaligenes* sp. Phytopathology 76:171-176.

Zaher, N.A.M. 1985. Response of tomato yellow leaf curl virus diseased plants to spraying with some microelements. Egypt. J. Phytopathol. 17:73-82.

Zeyen, R.J., T.L.W. Carver, and G.G. Ahlstrand. 1983. Relating cytoplasmic detail of powdery mildew infection to presence of insoluble silicon by sequential use of light microscopy, SEM and X-ray microanalysis. Physiol. Plant Pathol. 22:101-108.

Environmental and Soil Factors Affecting Micronutrient Deficiencies and Toxicities

J. T. MORAGHAN, *North Dakota State University, Fargo, North Dakota*

H. J. MASCAGNI, JR., *University of Arkansas, Keiser, Arkansas*

The availability of the essential micronutrients B, Cu, Fe, Mn, Mo, and Zn to plants is often poorly related to the total quantity of the particular element in the soil. Soil properties such as pH, redox potential, organic matter content, nutrient interactions, the type of plant or variety, and environmental factors, such as soil water content, temperature and light, greatly influence the likelihood that a plant will exhibit micronutrient-deficiency or -toxicity symptoms. Changes in the environment often have a greater effect on micronutrient than on macronutrient nutrition of plants.

This chapter emphasizes advances in knowledge since Lucas and Knezek's (1972) review in the first edition of this book. In addition, greater emphasis than is customary will be placed on the role of the environment on micronutrient nutrition. Other general references that contain material on this topic are available (Adriano, 1986; Bergmann, 1988; Marschner, 1986; Mengel & Kirkby, 1987; Weber, 1971; and Wild, 1988). Some excellent reference sources include the specific contributions of Keren and Bingham (1985) and Fleming (1980) on B, of Loneragan et al. (1981) on Cu, of Jones (1982, 1984, 1986, and 1988) on Fe, of Graham et al. (1988) on Mn, of Gupta and Lipsett (1981) on Mo, and of Adriano (1986) on Zn. The comprehensive study of Sillanpaa (1982) provides much useful information concerning micronutrient uptake by plants and selected soil properties.

I. ENVIRONMENTAL FACTORS

This section will examine the specific effects of environmental factors on the solubility of the micronutrients in soil. In addition, it will focus on the effects of temperature, light, and soil moisture content on the uptake, translocation, and metabolism of these micronutrients. Little attention will be paid to nutrient dilution effects resulting from the environmental influence on dry matter accumulation, nor will focus be placed on how precipitation can influence micronutrient availability through leaching or changes in soil pH.

A. Boron

Boron deficiency is unusual in that its incidence is higher under low topsoil moisture conditions. Soil moisture status is the chief environmental factor affecting the availability of B to plants. Batey (1971) concluded that B deficiency is more prevalent during a dry summer, particularly one following a wet winter or spring.

1. Temperature

Although the theory is controversial (Mengel & Kirkby, 1987), there is considerable evidence that B uptake is largely a physical process involving, in most soil-plant systems, the absorption of un-ionized H_3BO_3 and subsequent passive movement of B in the transpiration stream (Kohl & Oertli, 1961; Oertli, 1963; Lovatt, 1985). Consequently, the relation between temperature and B uptake is likely to be complex and influenced by the effect of root and aerial temperatures on the rate of transpiration.

Increased temperature in a nutrient-solution study did not increase B concentrations in barley (*Hordeum vulgare* L.) roots, but resulted in higher B concentrations in plant tops (Vlamis & Williams, 1970). This shoot response was associated with the effect of temperature on the rate of transpiration. In another nutrient-solution study, B uptake by barley was affected more by aerial temperature than by root temperature (Oertli, 1963).

Walker (1969) found that B uptake by corn (*Zea mays* L.) shoots in a soil study changed little as soil temperature was increased from 12 to 20 °C, despite a nearly sevenfold increase in dry matter yield and a nearly ninefold increase in evapotranspiration (Table 11–1). In marked contrast, B uptake increased from 192 to 1867 mg/pot as dry matter yield and evapotranspiration increased approximately twofold between 20 and 31 °C. These data are difficult to explain from a simple, passive, uptake-transpiration theory of B uptake; the availability of organically bound soil B was possibly limited between 12 and 20 °C. Walker (1969) also reported that the B uptake-soil temperature relationship was uniquely different from that for 16 other elements, including Fe, Mn, Cu, and Zn.

Table 11–1. Influence of soil temperature on growth, water use, and B uptake by corn.[†]

Soil temperature	Root + shoot dry weight	Total water used	Boron in shoots
°C	g pot^{-1}		μg pot^{-1}
12	1.53	95	166
20	10.67	845	192
31	14.41	1635	1867

† Selected data from Walker (1969).

2. Soil Water Content

In Europe, heart rot of fodder beet and sugar beet (*Beta vulgaris* L.) was, for many years, a serious disease, which was known to be accentuated by drought stress (Anonymous, 1936). The association of drought stress in sugar beet with B deficiency was quickly recognized when Brandenburg (1931) showed that heart rot was due to lack of this element. Drought stress or, perhaps more accurately, moisture stress in the surface soil accentuates B deficiency in many other crops including alfalfa (*Medicago sativa* L.) (Barber, 1957), apple (*Malus domestica* Borkh.) (Faust & Shear, 1968), and cotton (*Gossypium hirsutum* L.) (Miley & Woodall, 1967). Boron deficiency restricts root growth (Bouma, 1969), which would intensify any drought stress effect.

Indeed, drought stress affects the incidence and severity of B deficiency more than that of any other micronutrient. According to Batey (1971), turnip (*Brassica rapa*) in Wales normally became B deficient on soils with <0.3 mg kg^{-1} of extractable B. However, deficiency in a dry summer was observed in fields with extractable B levels of 0.5 to 0.6 mg kg^{-1}.

The efficacy of analyzing surface soils for predicting B deficiency (Berger & Truog, 1944) indicates that available soil B is often concentrated in this zone. Thus, drying of surface layers should restrict water and B uptake from this zone, and consequently, restrict the supply of B to plant meristems. Movement of B in the phloem is limited. Thus, the plant has little opportunity to adjust to curtailment of the external supply through mobilization of previously accumulated B.

Another theory concerning the cause of drought-induced B deficiency involves moisture stress that restricts the mineralization and availability to plants of organically bound B in soil (Berger, 1962; Evans & Sparks, 1983; Flannery, 1985). Although considerable research indicates that soil organic matter contains B, little is known about the availability of this form of B to plants (Keren & Bingham, 1985).

Boron toxicity in plants is chiefly affected by the concentration of B in soil water (Keren & Bingham, 1985). Since the distribution of B in plants is related to transpiration patterns, tips and margins of older leaves are first affected (Marschner, 1986). Thus, environmental factors that influence the rate of transpiration will influence the B-toxicity syndrome (Lovatt, 1985). Increasing transpiration as a consequence of high temperatures and low humidities probably accentuates the occurrence of B toxicity in irrigated areas.

3. Light

Much research on the influence of light intensity on plant B nutrition was conducted prior to 1946 (see Hewitt, 1966 for a review). In general, high light intensity accentuated B deficiency and reduced the severity of B toxicity; long-day conditions also intensified B deficiency. Oertli (1963) reported that the total uptake of B by barley was stimulated by extended photoperiods and by high light intensities, due presumably to increased transpiration.

Through a possible effect on IAA-oxidase activity, a low B supply may cause hyperauxiny, the symptoms of which resemble B deficiency to some extent (Hewitt, 1984a; Lovatt, 1985). Light quality affects auxin activity (Skoog, 1940).

B. Copper

The severity of Cu deficiency in plants growing on organic soils is strongly influenced by climate (Caldwell, 1971). The problem is often very severe in dry sunny seasons, less pronounced or absent in "dull", moist seasons, and decreased by rising water tables. The causes of these effects have received little study.

1. Temperature

The absorption of Cu by plants is probably metabolically controlled (Bowen, 1987; Mengel & Kirkby, 1987). However, Graham (1981) considered that much relevant research is difficult to interpret because of the failure to separate Cu adsorbed in the root-free space from root-absorbed Cu. Soil temperature may also influence Cu uptake by plants by affecting availability of organically bound Cu. Organically bound Cu in soil is present both in soluble and insoluble forms (Stevenson & Fitch, 1981). Mobilization-immobilization reactions are undoubtedly temperature dependent and affect the solubility of soil Cu, but are not understood.

The uptake of both native and added Cu by carrot (*Daucus carota* L.), growing on an acid organic soil under greenhouse conditions, was increased when the soil temperature was increased from 8 to 20 °C (MacMillan & Hamilton, 1971). Changes in temperature in a phytotron experiment had little effect on the accumulation of Cu in tops of lettuce (*Lactuca sativa* L.) grown on soil treated with the equivalent of 60 t ha^{-1} of sewage sludge on a dry matter basis containing 572 mg Cu kg^{-1} (Siriratpiriya et al., 1985). Dowdy and Larson (1975) showed that sludge-applied Cu was not appreciably absorbed by barley grown on acid and calcareous soils in a greenhouse experiment. Copper concentration of corn tissue in a field experiment was not consistently affected by an increase of soil temperature from 16 to 35 °C (Sheaffer et al., 1979). Extractable Cu levels from incubated soils were affected by incubation temperature in an Australian study (Alston et al., 1981); the effect was complex, and differed according to soil type and to Cu treatment.

Copper and Zn apparently are absorbed through common carrier sites (Bowen, 1987). Preferential accumulation of Cu in roots at low temperatures, as has been commonly reported for Zn, does not appear to be important; however, few definitive studies are available on this subject. Roots bind Cu strongly under some conditions (Brams & Fiskell, 1971).

2. Soil Moisture Content

Kubota et al. (1963) found soil moisture to have no consistent effect on the Cu concentration of the soil solution or on the Cu concentration of alsike clover (*Trifolium hybridum* L.) grown on several soils in the green-

Table 11-2. Influence of period of submergence on the concentrations of water-soluble Cu, Mo, and Zn in a Maahas clay.[†]

Element	Submergence, weeks		
	1	2	6
	concentration, mg L^{-1}		
Cu	1.80	1.01	1.18
Mo	0.04	0.09	0.12
Zn	0.18	0.08	0.03

[†] From Ponnamperuma (1985).

house. However, the data in Table 11-2 show that complete flooding of soils reduces the water-soluble Cu levels, presumably due to intense reduction and S^{2-} formation (Ponnamperuma, 1985). Copper availability to rice (*Oryza sativa* L.) decreased with soil flooding (Beckwith et al., 1975).

Ryegrass (*Lolium multiflorum* Lam.) absorbed significant amounts of Cu from nearly air-dry soil when the roots had access to subsoil water (Nambiar, 1977). A similar effect was also observed for Zn.

3. Light

Light does not seem to have major effects on the frequency of Cu deficiency under field conditions. However, Graves and Sutcliffe (1974) showed that Cu deficiency slowed the rate of flower initiation and development in chrysanthemum (*Chrysanthemum* × *morifolium* Ramat.), which required a short photoperiod for flowerbud initiation. Copper-deficient plants grown under a short photoperiod resembled long-photoperiod plants relative to flowerbud initiation. The severity of Cu deficiency, unlike that of Zn deficiency, in subterranean clover (*Trifolium subterraneum* L.) was unaffected by reduction in light intensity under greenhouse conditions (Millikan, 1953).

C. Iron

Climatic factors greatly affect the occurrence of Fe deficiency in plants under field conditions. Classification of plants for susceptibility to Fe deficiency is sometimes conducted under growth chamber conditions because varying environmental conditions from year-to-year make precise field classification difficult (Byron & Lambert, 1983). The complexity of the climatic effect is illustrated by reports that the severity of Fe chlorosis is increased both by a combination of high soil moisture and cool temperatures (Burtch et al., 1948), and by hot, dry summers (Little, 1971).

Different species and even cultivars of species vary in their susceptibility to Fe deficiency. Plants resistant and susceptible to Fe-deficiency chlorosis when grown on alkaline soils are referred to as Fe-efficient and Fe-inefficient plants, respectively. Much research during the past two decades has shown that variations in root activity generally account for genotypic differences in Fe efficiency. Marschner (1986) has divided plants into two categories based on such root-induced effects. Plants with Strategy I-type responses are mostly dicotyledonous species, and resistance to Fe deficiency is associated with enhancement of the release of H^+ and phenolic compounds, and increased Fe^{3+} reduction at the plasma membrane. Most of the plants with Strategy II-type responses are members of the *Gramineae*, and resistance to Fe deficiency is associated primarily with increased release of nonproteinogenic amino acids (phytosiderophores) from roots.

1. Temperature

Since Fe absorption is an active process and metabolic activity is required for the transport of Fe from roots to shoots (Branton & Jacobson, 1962), temperature should influence the occurrence of Fe deficiency. Temperature changes may either enhance or suppress Fe deficiency, depending on their effects on rate of growth, plant metabolism, and the status of other elements in the soil associated with the problem (Brown, 1956). In general, soil temperature has less effect on Fe chlorosis in plants possessing the Strategy II type of Fe-stress response than in those possessing the Strategy I type (Romheld & Marschner, 1986).

Iron-deficiency chlorosis in grapes (*Vitis* spp.) growing in parts of Europe is accentuated by wet, cold conditions early in the growing season. The primary causal factor is inhibited root growth and reduced root activity at low soil temperatures (Romheld, 1985). Accumulation of CO_2 in wet soil apparently intensifies soil temperature effects.

Inskeep and Bloom (1986) found that: (i) the effect of soil temperature on chlorosis in soybean [*Glycine max* (L.) Merr.] was influenced by the air-filled porosity; (ii) the soil temperature-porosity interaction was influenced by soil type; and (iii) the observed differences apparently were not related to solution HCO_3 levels (Table 11-3). The chlorosis was less severe at 19 °C than at 12 or 26 °C. Increased Fe-deficiency chlorosis at elevated tempera-

Table 11-3. Influence of soil temperature and air-filled porosity (fa) on leaf chlorosis in Anoka soybean grown on two soils under controlled conditions.†

Treatment		Soil 1			Soil 2		
Soil temperature	fa	Chlorosis ranking‡	Chloro-phyll	Solution HCO_3	Chlorosis ranking‡	Chloro-phyll	Solution HCO_3
°C			mg cm^{-2}	mM		mg cm^{-2}	mM
12	0.21	3.8	15.1	5.2	2.3	26.7	4.8
	0.14	5.0	2.9	5.6	3.8	19.2	6.4
	0.07	5.0	1.8	8.9	1.2	40.2	9.7
19	0.21	2.6	23.5	6.9	1.0	50.4	5.7
	0.14	5.0	3.0	5.9	1.0	49.3	6.8
	0.07	4.8	7.7	8.8	1.0	51.8	8.6
26	0.21	4.7	5.9	5.2	3.4	17.8	5.3
	0.14	5.0	2.8	6.2	1.7	38.1	6.1
	0.07	5.0	3.7	9.2	1.0	49.4	9.3

† From Inskeep and Bloom (1986).
‡ 1 indicates no leaf chlorosis on a scale of 1 to 5; higher values indicate progressively more severe chlorosis.

tures may result from increased respiration rates and restricted supplies of photoassimilates for energy-dependent physiological functions in the roots (Bennett et al., 1988).

Temperature could influence the severity of Fe-deficiency chlorosis in plants growing in soils in the following ways: (i) low soil temperature, apart from reducing root growth, could reduce root metabolic activity and the Fe-stress response in nongraminaceous plants (Marschner et al., 1986b); (ii) low soil temperature could reduce the production of phytosiderophores, and the resultant mobilization and uptake of soil Fe by members of the *Gramineae*; (iii) high soil temperature could decrease Fe uptake by members of the *Gramineae* by increasing the microbial decomposition of phytosiderophores (Awad et al., 1988); (iv) low soil temperature could increase HCO_3 levels in the soil solution and the severity of Fe deficiency by increasing the solubility of CO_2 in the soil solution (Inskeep & Bloom, 1986); (v) high soil temperature could increase HCO_3 levels and Fe deficiency by stimulating microbial activity and CO_2 production (Inskeep & Bloom, 1986); (vi) high soil temperature could increase the uptake of P by plants and the severity of P-induced Fe deficiency (Riekels & Lingle, 1966; Moraghan, 1987); and (vii) high soil or aerial temperatures could stimulate relative growth rates and induce Fe deficiency (Inskeep & Bloom, 1986; Brown, 1956).

2. Soil Moisture Content

Soil moisture status through its effects on plant metabolism, the status of soil Fe, and the HCO_3 concentration in the soil solution affect the availability of Fe to certain plants (Brown, 1956). Increased Fe-deficiency chlorosis in plants subsequent to irrigation is sometimes due to high levels of HCO_3 in the added water (Harley & Lindner, 1945). However, many reports indicate that excess irrigation or prolonged wet periods can also result in chlorosis-susceptible plants, mainly dicots with Strategy I-type, Fe-stress responses, apparently developing Fe-deficiency chlorosis as a result of a build-up of HCO_3 in calcareous soils (Chaney, 1984). In addition, poorly aerated conditions caused by excess soil water destroy many of the smaller roots and reduce the absorptive capacity of the whole root system (Lindsay, 1984). Soil moisture variability does not greatly influence the severity of Fe-deficiency chlorosis in plants exhibiting the Strategy II type of Fe-stress response, presumably due to the minor effect of HCO_3 on this type of response (Romheld & Marschner, 1986; Yen et al., 1988).

Inskeep and Bloom (1986) found that decreases in leaf chlorophyll in 'Anoka' soybean, a 'Wayne' type, were consistently related to decreasing soil-water potential in three Calciaquolls high in extractable P. They concluded that increased HCO_3 was the chief causal factor for the accentuated chlorosis, but considered that other soil variables, such as clay-sized $CaCO_3$, P, and Mg, may have influenced the severity of the problem.

Geiger and Loeppert (1988) recently studied the effect of pCO_2 and HCO_3 on leaf chlorosis in soybean (cv. Coker 338) grown in three calcareous soils at moderate (67% of field capacity) soil moisture levels. There was no relationship between soil-solution-HCO_3 level and the degree of chlorosis, presumably due to CO_2 decreasing the soil solution pH. These researchers considered that, under high soil moisture conditions, factors such as O_2 deficiency and low rooting volume complemented any detrimental effect of high HCO_3 concentrations on the Fe-stress response. Excess water results in increased accumulation of ethylene in soil (Smith & Restall, 1971); accumulation of this gas sometimes detrimentally affects root growth and may increase the severity of Fe-deficiency chlorosis (Perrett & Koblet, 1984).

Absorption of Fe by plant roots is largely restricted to actively growing root tips (Clarkson & Sanderson, 1978). Therefore, restricted root growth in dry surface layers, the soil zone with the largest amount of available Fe, may partially explain the occurrence of Fe deficiency under hot, dry conditions.

Soil water status, through its effect on pH and Fe reduction, greatly influences the availability of Fe to rice plants. While many rice cultivars frequently display Fe-deficiency chlorosis under upland conditions (Reddy & Siva Prasad, 1986), the occurrence of such a problem under lowland conditions is rare, and is restricted to rice growing on alkaline soils low in organic matter (Ponnamperuma, 1985). Rice grown on Histosols in Florida sometimes develop a leaf chlorosis associated with Fe deficiency during the preflooding, seedling-establishment stage (Snyder & Jones, 1988), but the problem is ameliorated when the fields are flooded.

Enhanced reduction of soil Fe under waterlogged conditions can result in the accumulation of large quantities of soluble Fe^{2+} in certain acid soils. Lowland rice growing on such soils, especially acid sulfate soils, can develop an abnormality due to Fe toxicity (Tanaka & Yoshida, 1970). The reason that excess plant Fe sometimes, but not always, reduces rice yields is not fully understood (van Mensvoort et al., 1985). Moore and Patrick (1989) concluded that the ratio of $Fe^{2+}/(Fe^{2+} + Mn^{2+} + Ca^{2+} + Mg^{2+})$ in the soil solution (E^1-Fe), rather than the activity of Fe^{2+}, controlled Fe uptake by flooded rice grown in some acid sulfate soils from Thailand. High levels of E^1-Fe apparently stimulated Fe uptake and the likelihood of Fe toxicity. Drying and reflooding acid sulfate soils increase the risk of Fe toxicity (Sahrawat, 1979). Iron toxicity reportedly affects the distribution of certain native plants in waterlogged environments (Jones & Etherington, 1970).

3. Light

The type of light used for studying Fe-deficiency chlorosis under controlled condition may be significant for some Strategy I plants. Brown et al. (1979) concluded that the higher chlorophyll concentration in cotton and lettuce grown under cool-white fluorescent lamps (CWF), compared with that in those grown under low-pressure Na lamps (LPS), was due to greater reduction of Fe^{3+} associated with the lower wavelengths of the CWF source. Iron-deficient M8-cotton plants released protons from their roots with both CWF and LPS lamps; however, Fe-deficient plants grown under LPS lamps released much less reductant from their roots, and reduced less Fe^{3+} to Fe^{2+}

in their roots than comparably treated plants grown with a CWF source (Jolley et al., 1987). Burtch et al. (1948) found that the effect of light variability on the severity of lime-induced chlorosis was less than either soil water status or temperature.

D. Manganese

Temperature, soil water status, and light affect the incidence and severity of both Mn deficiency and toxicity in plants. A complete understanding of the role of temperature and soil water status on the availability of Mn to plants grown in well-drained soils awaits a better comprehension of the Mn cycle, particularly with regard to Mn fixation, the role of microbial activity, the significance of organic Mn complexes, and elucidation of factors affecting Mn valency states.

Manganese deficiency in field crops often is more severe in the spring than later in the summer; cold, wet weather aggravates the problem (Mederski & Wilson, 1955; Batey, 1971). Manganese availability is lowest in cold soils, but increases rapidly as the soil warms, and passes through several wetting and drying cycles (Graham et al., 1985). Mederski and Wilson (1955) demonstrated that Mn deficiency of soybean was more severe and Mn uptake was reduced when affected by a combination of a low soil temperature and a high soil-water status (Table 11-4).

1. Temperature

Manganese uptake is generally considered to be under metabolic control (Moore, 1972). Thus, Mn uptake should be reduced at low root temperatures. This probably partially accounts for the increased incidence of Mn deficiency under low soil-temperature conditions. However, temperature may also influence the solubility of soil Mn and indirectly affect plant Mn uptake.

Reid and Racz (1985) found that an increase in soil temperature from 10 to 25 °C approximately tripled Mn accumulation by tops of barley grown on an organic soil. Of particular significance were the facts that temperature influenced DTPA-extractable Mn and that plant-Mn accumulation was strongly correlated with soil temperature.

The effects of temperature on soil Mn are likely to be complex. For instance, soil microbial activity, which is markedly affected by temperature,

Table 11-4. Influence of soil temperature and moisture on the incidence of chlorotic Mn-deficient soybean leaves and Mn concentration of plant tops.[†]

Soil temperature	Chlorotic leaves[‡]		Leaf Mn	
	High soil moisture	Low soil moisture	High soil moisture	Low soil moisture
°C	—— % of leaves ——		—— mg kg^{-1} ——	
15	35	21	9	10
27	27	2	15	22

† From Mederski and Wilson (1955).   ‡ Leaves afflicted with Mn deficiency.

is known to both mobilize and immobilize soil Mn (Marschner, 1988). In addition, the release into the soil of root exudates, which are also known to solubilize MnO_2 (Bromfield, 1958a), is probably temperature dependent.

Soil temperature can also affect the enhanced solubilization and uptake of Mn, which is often associated with plant species that have Strategy I-type response patterns associated with Fe deficiency (Marschner, 1986; Marschner et al., 1986a; Moraghan, 1979). The Mn concentration of Anoka soybean grown on a calcareous soil treated with 0.2 mg kg^{-1} of FeEDDHA-Fe increased from 59 to 126 mg kg^{-1} when the soil temperature was increased from 15 to 24 °C (Moraghan, 1985). The corresponding Mn concentrations of soybean treated with 2 mg kg^{-1} of the chelated Fe were 8 and 20 mg kg^{-1}; the 15 °C, but not the 24 °C plants, were Mn deficient. However, cultivar can affect this type of temperature response (Moraghan, 1987).

Ghazali and Cox (1981) reported that a combination of low root-zone and air temperatures increased the severity of Mn deficiency in soybean, even though plant Mn concentration increased at low temperatures. This increased Mn concentration apparently resulted from a situation in which growth increased more than plant-Mn accumulation as the temperature was raised. Ghazali and Cox (1981) concluded that the functional requirement of Mn decreased with increasing temperature.

Temperature also affects plant Mn toxicity. Increasing the Mn concentration in a solution study from 0.1 to 15 mg L^{-1} decreased dry matter yields in two soybean cultivars at day/night temperatures of 22/18 °C, but not at day/night temperatures of 33/28 °C (Heenan & Carter, 1977). Higher temperatures also decreased the severity of Mn-toxicity symptoms in tobacco (*Nicotiana tabacum* L.) (Rufty et al., 1979). Other researchers reported that higher temperatures aggravated or had little effect on Mn toxicity in alfalfa (Sutton & Hallsworth, 1958) and barley (Williams & Vlamis, 1957a). Epstein (1971) speculated that potato (*Solanum tuberosum* L.) in Maine is relatively free of Mn toxicity because low soil temperatures retard Mn uptake. Manganese toxicity of potato in a controlled experiment was more severe in 30 °C than at 20 °C (Marsh et al., 1989). The growth rate was faster at 20 °C, and the authors concluded that plant growth rate must be considered in Mn toxicity-temperature studies.

Soybean (cv. Bragg) grown on a calcareous soil developed severe Mn toxicity symptoms at a soil temperature of 16 °C, but not at 24 °C (Moraghan et al., 1986). The excessive Mn accumulation was apparently associated with a Strategy I-type response at low levels of available Fe (Marschner et al., 1986a). Soybean grown at 16 °C contained higher concentrations of plant Mn, but the total uptake of Mn was less at 16 °C than at 24 °C. It is important in toxicity studies to differentiate clearly between effects of temperature on growth and on Mn uptake. Consideration of only Mn concentration data may result in misleading conclusions.

2. Soil Moisture Content

Excess soil moisture restricts the diffusion of O_2 within soils and favors the reduction of compounds containing Mn(IV). Consequently, Mn deficiency is rarely seen in a crop such as rice, which is adapted to flooded conditions. However, Mn may occasionally be deficient in certain degraded, light-textured paddy soils from which soluble Mn has been eluviated over time (Mitsui, 1955). Manganese deficiency may also occur in upland crops growing in spots that fluctuate between well-drained and waterlogged conditions, a situation that favors Mn reduction and its eluviation (Labanauskas, 1966).

Although available soil Mn often increases under impeded-drainage conditions, Mn deficiency reportedly may occur in plants unadapted to such conditions, especially at low temperatures (Batey, 1971). Restricted root activity and growth apparently suppress Mn uptake in such cases. Soil waterlogging prior to planting increased the availability of Mn for subsequently planted crops and decreased the incidence of Mn deficiency (Piper, 1931). These short-term waterlogging effects can have long-lasting effects on the incidence of Mn deficiency in susceptible crops. For example, Leeper (1947) indicated that the beneficial effect of a 4-wk waterlogging period on the growth of oat (*Avena sativa* L.) on a Mn-deficient soil lasted for at least 11 yr.

Rice normally accumulates much more Mn under waterlogged than under well-drained conditions (Clark et al., 1957). Nevertheless, Mn toxicity apparently has seldom been observed in paddy rice (Ponnamperuma, 1985), presumably because rice is relatively tolerant of this abnormality (Vlamis & Williams, 1964), and possibly due to Mn precipitation in the rhizosphere. Clark et al. (1957) found that added organic matter reduced Mn accumulation, but increased Fe accumulation by submerged rice. This reduced Mn accumulation probably was associated with lower redox potentials in the amended soil, with resulting higher soil-Fe(II) levels, and with the influence of the well-known Fe-Mn antagonism on Mn uptake (Vlamis & Williams, 1962, 1964). Large quantities of Fe and Mn can accumulate on the roots of lowland rice (van der Vorm and van Diest, 1979).

Waterlogging for even relatively short periods can cause Mn toxicity in crops less tolerant of the problem than rice (Graven et al., 1965; Grasmanis & Leeper, 1966; Siman et al., 1974). Graven et al. (1965) reported that flooding of alfalfa grown on an acid soil (pH = 4.7) in greenhouse pots resulted in lower yields, in markedly higher Mn concentrations, and in a higher incidence of Mn-toxicity symptoms (Table 11-5). Waterlogging or extended wet

Table 11-5. Effect of a 72-h flooding period on dry matter yield and accumulation of Mn by greenhouse alfalfa plants grown on an acid soil.[†]

Flooding period	Crops after flooding			
	Cut 1	Cut 2	Cut 3	Cut 4
h	Dry matter, g pot^{-1}			
0	3.1	2.3	1.5	2.4
72	1.2	0.6	0.9	1.6
	Mn, mg kg^{-1}			
0	426	643	821	602
72	6067	2621	2137	1168

† From Graven et al. (1965).

periods under field conditions caused Mn toxicity in apples (Grasmanis & Leeper, 1966) and in alfalfa (Siman et al., 1974) at soil pH values > 5.5; a value normally considered to be a limit for acidity-induced Mn toxicity (Foy, 1983).

Accumulation of plant Mn and plant Fe-Mn interactions should be considered when investigating the growth of plants on waterlogged soils. Flax (*Linum usitatissimum* L.) developed a chlorosis similar to that caused by Fe deficiency, and accumulated relatively large quantities of Mn when grown on waterlogged, calcareous soils (Olomu & Racz, 1974). The Mn-toxicity-resistant subterranean clover cultivar Geralton tolerated waterlogging better than two Mn-toxicity-susceptible medics, *Medicago truncatula* and *M. littoralis* (Robson & Loneragan, 1970).

Many field observations indicate that soil drying, often combined with high temperature, affects the incidence of Mn deficiencies and toxicities in plants. Manganese deficiency in various crops in Sweden disappeared after a heavy rainfall following a dry period (Stahlberg & Sombatpanit, 1974). Manganese deficiency of oat in Michigan was also less intense during hot, dry, summer months (Fujimoto & Sherman, 1945). Manganese toxicity of macadamia nut (*Macadamia ternifolia*) in Hawaii was aggravated by hot, dry summers (Fujimoto & Sherman, 1945), and intensified in alfalfa in Australia by hot, dry conditions (Siman et al., 1974)

Much research has shown that the concentration of exchangeable or easily extractable soil Mn increased during air-drying, often in an unpredictable manner (Nelson, 1977; Khan & Soltanpour, 1978; Stahlberg & Sombatpanit, 1974), and during air-dried storage (Boken, 1952). In view of the importance of the Fe-Mn interaction in plant nutrition (Vlamis & Williams, 1962), the finding by Khan and Soltanpour (1978) that soil air-drying affected DTPA-extractable Fe and Mn differentially may be of importance in Mn-nutrition studies. The air-drying effect associated with extraction of Mn by $NH_4H_2PO_4$ and H_3PO_4 apparently required the absorption of O_2 during the drying process (Hammes & Berger, 1960). The role of soil organic matter in drying-induced Mn effects is controversial (Boken, 1952; Hammes & Berger, 1960; Khanna & Mishra, 1978) and requires additional study.

Freezing and thawing of soils, possibly in a manner analogous to the drying effect, also influence exchangeable Mn levels. Cheng and Ouellette (1971) reported that freezing and thawing under flooded conditions, which exist during the winter in some regions, caused soil-exchangeable Mn levels to increase. Air drying and freeze drying of soils release much less DTPA-extractable Mn than does oven drying at 100 °C (Leggett & Argyle, 1983).

Knowledge of factors that influence valency states and the solubility of Mn in well-drained soils has increased relatively little since the development of the models of Dion and Mann (1946) and Mann and Quastel (1946). A complete understanding of air-drying/heating effects and plant Mn availability must await additional insight into the chemistry of soil Mn.

3. Light

The influence of light on plant Mn nutrition has received relatively little attention. Some data indicate that Mn toxicity and Mn deficiency are intensified under high and low light conditions, respectively (Mulder & Gerretsen, 1952; Hewitt, 1966). Shading reduced the concentration of Mn and decreased the incidence of Mn toxicity in bean (*Phaseolus vulgaris* L.) plants (McCool, 1935). Horiguchi (1989) confirmed that shading reduced the concentration of Mn in corn and bean plants. However, Mn toxicity symptoms in both species were more severe at high light intensities, even when leaf Mn concentrations were similar to those in plants grown under lower light intensities, but with higher solution Mn levels. In contrast, rice reportedly accumulated more Mn under shaded than under full-light conditions (Fujiwara & Ishida, 1964).

The function of Mn in plant nutrition appears to be associated with the evolution of O_2 by Photosystem II, with superoxide metabolism, and with auxin oxidation, particularly through its effect on peroxidase activity (Marschner, 1986). Consequently, the interaction of light and Mn in plant nutrition is likely to be complex. Hewitt (1984a) suggested that the dark brown pigments and cell damage associated with Mn excess may be caused by the photochemical oxidation of Mn^{2+} to Mn^{4+}, and production of a very positive potential oxidant. Kriedemann et al. (1985) speculated that the reduction of the chlorophyll a/b ratio of Mn-deficient leaves would predispose Mn-deficient leaves to photoinhibitory damage.

E. Molybdenum

Environmental factors apparently have a relatively small direct role on the incidence of Mo deficiency. Molybdenum deficiency is most pronounced in high rainfall areas, but the effect is generally related to adsorption of MoO_4 by soil constituents under acid conditions (Johansen et al., 1977). Millikan (1951) reported that a lower leaf scorch of flax, believed to be caused by Mo deficiency and to be acute under Australian winter conditions, became less severe in the spring.

1. Temperature

Although there is some evidence that Mo uptake is metabolically controlled (Moore, 1972), soil temperature seems to have little effect on the incidence or severity of Mo deficiency. High temperatures accentuate the fixation of MoO_4 in acid soils, and this may affect the long-term effectiveness of added Mo fertilizers (Barrow & Shaw, 1974).

When legumes respond to Mo fertilizer under field conditions, the beneficial effect is usually associated with increased N_2 fixation in the belowground nodules (Anderson, 1956). Low soil temperatures would possibly suppress this fixation and lower the resultant Mo requirement. Wheat (*Triticum aestivum* L.) grown in soil required more Mo when NO_3-N levels were excessive (Freney & Lipsett, 1965). Since NO_3-N absorption is suppressed by low soil temperatures (Williams & Vlamis, 1962), temperature should influence this interaction.

2. Soil Moisture Content

As shown in Table 11–2, the soluble Mo fraction of submerged acid soils generally increases, presumably as a result of decreased adsorption of MoO_4 under the higher pH conditions associated with waterlogging (Ponnamperuma, 1985). The Mo concentration of alsike clover (Kubota et al., 1963) and alfalfa (Dionne & Pesant, 1986) grown on acid soils was increased under wet conditions. Such increased accumulations could be significant in molybdenosis studies. Molybdenum availability to plants was decreased under drier soil conditions (Gupta & Sutcliffe, 1968).

3. Light

Light quantity and quality, as well as photoperiodic duration, are factors affecting N_2 fixation by legumes (Gibson, 1987). Therefore, light variability should be important in legume studies involving Mo.

F. Zinc

Temperature and light affect the incidence and severity of Zn deficiency in crop plants. In contrast, soil moisture, apart from its indirect effect on general growth and nutrient requirement, probably does not have a major effect on Zn deficiency in nonflooded crops grown in the field.

Zinc deficiency symptoms in annual crops normally are more severe when plants are young and temperatures are relatively cool. Spring-seeded crops like corn, edible bean, and potato in the western USA, may show early season Zn deficiency symptoms, which are absent from newer growth later in the season (Viets, 1967). Zinc deficiency observed in flax and subterranean clover during relatively mild Australian winters disappeared with the arrival of warmer spring temperatures (Millikan, 1951). Zinc deficiency of flax is most pronounced in the spring in North America (Moraghan, 1978).

1. Temperature

Although the evidence is conflicting, Moore (1972) and Mengel and Kirkby (1987) concluded that absorption of Zn is probably metabolically controlled. Consequently, Zn absorption should be increased as root temperatures increase. Failure to separate Zn adsorption onto root or cell surfaces from true Zn absorption may affect Zn-uptake studies (Schmid et al., 1965; Chaudhry & Loneragan, 1972). The nature of root-Zn accumulation is important in Zn-root temperature studies.

Much research under controlled temperature conditions has shown that Zn deficiency in crops like corn (Giordano & Mortvedt, 1978), tomato (*Lycopersicon esculentum* Mill.) (Martin et al., 1965), and flax (Moraghan,

Table 11-6. Response of tomato to P and Zn fertilizers at two soil temperatures.[†]

Treatment		Dry matter[‡]		Zn (Tops)	
P	Zn	10.0 °C	26.7 °C	10.0 °C	26.7 °C
—— mg kg^{-1} ——		—— g pot^{-1} ——		—— mg kg^{-1} ——	
0	0	0.06b	1.51b	10.7	16.9
200	0	0.08a	7.25b	5.1	12.4
0	10	0.04b	1.07b	28.3	54.8
200	10	0.40b	8.59b	11.9	16.4
	LSD (0.05)	0.18	3.72		

[†] From Martin et al. (1965).
[‡] a and b indicate the presence and absence of Zn-deficiency symptoms, respectively.

1980) is more severe under low soil-temperature conditions. Data of Martin et al. (1965) illustrate the following general findings from such work: (i) Zn-deficiency symptoms are more severe at a low soil temperature; (ii) plants are less likely to respond to Zn fertilizer at a high soil temperature even though the yield potential is higher at the elevated temperature; (iii) added P is more likely to induce Zn deficiency at a low soil temperature; and (iv) both Zn concentration and Zn uptake usually are increased at a high soil temperature (Table 11-6).

Edwards and Kamprath (1974) concluded that the detrimental effect of low root temperature on Zn accumulation by corn in a nutrient-solution study was partially due to lowered translocation from roots to tops. This accumulation of adsorbed or absorbed Zn in the root system at lower temperatures was also found to occur in barley (Schwartz et al., 1987).

Bauer and Lindsay (1965) found that soil incubation at low temperature increased the severity of Zn deficiency in subsequently planted corn. This indicated that the availability of soil Zn per se is less at lower soil temperatures. Reduced root growth at lower soil temperature would also restrict Zn uptake (Burleson et al., 1961).

Sutcliffe (1971) concluded that, since air temperature rather than soil temperature controls foliar absorption, foliar fertilization is especially efficacious for crops growing in cold climates. However, soil-applied Zn fertilizers normally prevent early season Zn deficiency in susceptible crops.

Mycorrhizas associated with roots are believed to enhance the uptake of Zn and other elements (Bowen et al., 1974; Gerdemann, 1975). Vesicular-arbuscular (VA) mycorrhizal infection is severely reduced at low soil temperatures (Hayman, 1974). Therefore, reduced VA mycorrhizal infection may be involved in low soil-temperature-induced Zn deficiencies. Any relationship is likely to be complex, since high soil P levels reduce VA mycorrhizal development (Tinker, 1980). Singh et al. (1986) found that field-grown wheat plants afflicted with P-induced Zn deficiency had reduced mycorrhizal infection and involvement of mycorrhizas in the P-Zn interaction was suspected. Additional research concerning soil temperature effects on the symbiotic fungi-root relationships and their association with Zn deficiency is needed.

Phytochelatins (derivatives of glutathione, which can chelate heavy metals, including Zn) have been found in the roots of angiosperms (Grill et al., 1985; Robinson & Jackson, 1986). The influence of environmental factors, especially temperature, on the production of these binding agents is needed. Likewise, the influence of temperature on the production of phytosiderophores by members of the *Gramineae* (Takagi et al., 1984) deserves additional study. These compounds, of particular importance in the uptake of Fe (Romheld, 1987), also complex Zn.

2. Soil Moisture Content

In some dryland situations, the topsoil, the zone with usually the largest quantity of available Zn (Follett & Lindsay, 1970), is dry for much of the growing season. Plants do not often show an increased incidence of Zn deficiency in such cases, even when subsoil moisture is adequate to support growth. Since Zn reaches plant roots mainly by diffusion, and since tortuosity of the diffusion paths would be increased at decreased soil moisture levels (Warncke & Barber, 1972), greater frequency of Zn deficiency in susceptible crops would be expected by this water-use pattern. However, Nambiar (1976) found that significant amounts of ^{65}Zn were absorbed from dry zones even when the soil-water suction exceeded 1.5 MPa (15 bar). Nambiar speculated that mucilage permeating the rhizosphere provided sufficient liquid continuity between the solution in fine soil pores and within root cells to permit Zn absorption.

There is some evidence that Zn deficiency in rice is accentuated by flooding (Mikkelsen & Brandon, 1975). This increased susceptibility to Zn deficiency may sometimes be due to increased pH values resulting from the use of high HCO_3 water (Cox & Wear, 1977). However, the problem is more complex, since Zn uptake by rice at comparable pH values was always lower under anaerobic conditions in a controlled aerobic-anaerobic pH experiment (Jugsujinda & Patrick, 1977).

Ponnamperuma (1972) speculated that the reduced availability of Zn under flooded conditions was due to precipitation of ZnS or possibly the formation of organic-Zn complexes. The significance of ZnS formation has been questioned (Sajwan & Lindsay, 1986). Sajwan and Lindsay (1986) concluded that increased Zn deficiency in flooded rice was due to higher levels of available Fe^{2+} and Mn^{2+} suppressing the uptake of Zn, and to precipitation of Zn as $ZnFe_2O_4$ or a similar franklinite-like solid material.

Application of cellulose to flooded soils aggravated Zn deficiency (Yoshida & Tanaka, 1969). Added organic matter would intensify soil reduction processes and the buildup of Fe^{2+}, which can suppress Zn uptake (Giordano et al., 1974). In addition, increased organic-matter decomposition should increase solution HCO_3 concentrations, which detrimentally affect translocation of Zn from the roots to tops of rice plants (Forno et al., 1975).

3. Light

Variations in light quality, light intensity, and photoperiod may be associated with the seasonal nature of certain Zn-deficiency problems. Reduced or intermediate light intensities increased the severity of Zn deficiency in subterranean clover (Ozanne, 1955) and corn (Edwards & Kamprath, 1974). Edwards and Kamprath (1974) found that the total Zn content of the seed was especially important for early growth of corn under low light conditions. This greater dependence on seed Zn was thought to be due to reduced root growth and restricted uptake of soil Zn under conditions of low light intensity.

Zinc deficiency is sometimes less severe under low light intensity or winter conditions (Chapman et al., 1937; Reed, 1946; Hoagland, 1944). Chapman et al. (1937) postulated that the increased incidence of Zn deficiency in citrus (*Citrus* spp.) leaves on the south side of trees in California was associated with higher light intensity. Trumble and Ferres (1946) concluded that short daylength and low temperatures increased the severity of Zn deficiency under Australian winter conditions. Subterranean clover grown under long days (11.8 h) demonstrated a much greater response to added Zn, absorbed more Zn, but translocated a relatively smaller proportion of root Zn to tops than did similarly treated short-day (7.5 h) plants (Ozanne, 1955). According to Hewitt (1984b), photoperiod and light intensity need to be considered in plant-Zn studies.

II. SOIL FACTORS

Various soil properties affect the availability of the essential soil micronutrients. The concentration of micronutrients in the soil solution generally is so low that the total quantity present at any one time would sustain relatively little plant growth (Loneragan, 1975). To permit optimal growth, micronutrients normally need to be rapidly replenished from the solid phase as they are depleted from the soil solution. The influence of parent material, pH, organic matter, redox potential, and nutrient interactions on soil micronutrient availability will be discussed in this section.

A. Boron

Boron deficiency in susceptible crops is a widespread problem in many countries (Gupta, 1978). Since the element is normally present in the soil as an un-ionized molecule, B is very mobile. Consequently, it is supplied to roots primarily by mass flow. Parent material, pH, and organic matter influence the availability of B to plants. Sillanpaa (1982) concluded from a comprehensive, multi-soil greenhouse study that B uptake by wheat was more closely related to a soil-test parameter (hot-water soluble B) than was uptake of Cu, Fe, Mn, Mo, and Zn to various chemically extractable forms of the relevant element.

1. Parent Material

Tourmaline is a B-containing mineral that is present in soils formed from acidic rocks and metamorphic sediments (Gupta, 1978). However, B from this source is not readily available for plant growth. Soils derived from granite and other igneous rocks are often poor in B (Liu et al., 1983). Boron deficiency is rarely observed in plants grown on soils derived from marine sediments.

Once B is released from soil minerals it can be leached from the soil rapidly because of its nonionic nature. Hence, coarse-textured soils vulnerable to leaching may contain low amounts of available B. Plant availability of B is also reduced on soils derived from volcanic ash (Sillanpaa & Vlek, 1985) and on soils rich in Al oxides (Bingham et al., 1971).

Excess B may be more of a problem than B deficiency in arid and semiarid areas (Gupta, 1978). In many cases, plant B toxicity results from the use of irrigation water that is high in B. Some of the main areas of high-B water in the USA are along the western side of the San Joaquin Valley in California (Branson, 1976).

2. Soil pH

Boron deficiency occurs most commonly when susceptible crops are grown on freshly limed soils with pH levels >6.5 (Batey, 1971). Peterson and Newman (1976) showed that the uptake of B by tall fescue (*Festuca arundinacea* Schreb.) grown on soil limed to various pH levels was unaffected between pH 4.3 and 6.3, but was drastically reduced at pH 7.4. Decreased availability at pH levels in excess of approximately 6.5 probably is associated with decreased B activity in the soil solution as a consequence of adsorption onto clay and hydroxy-Al surfaces (Keren & Bingham, 1985). Boron is present in the soil below pH 7 primarily as $B(OH)_3$, which is not adsorbed very extensively by the colloidal fraction. As soil pH rises, the concentration of $B(OH)_4^-$ increases.

Boron toxicity also affects plant growth. Bartlett and Picarelli (1973) reported that relatively high rates of B increased yield and B uptake by alfalfa, but caused increasing toxicity symptoms in corn, which disappeared at pH levels >6.0. Boron toxicity also develops in some crops grown on calcareous soils irrigated with water containing high levels of B. In assessing the quality of high-B water for plant growth, Keren et al. (1985) concluded that physiochemical properties of the soils, such as clay content, which affects B activity, must be considered.

3. Organic Matter

Many researchers have suggested that soil organic matter influences the availability of B to plants. However, little information has been reported that unequivocally demonstrates the role of organic matter in B nutrition. The strongest evidence that organic matter affects the availability of soil B is derived from studies that demonstrate a positive correlation between organic matter and hot-water-soluble B (Gupta, 1968).

Boron associated with soil organic matter reportedly originates from B assimilation in microbial biomass (Gupta et al., 1985). Boron adsorption on organic matter is negligible (Mezuman & Keren, 1981). Although B in soil organic matter is not immediately available to plants, it is considered to be a main source of available B when released through mineralization (Gupta et al., 1985).

The necessity of applying B to certain peat soils is well recognized (Prasad & Byrne, 1975). Results indicate that the reduced B uptake at high pH is partially due to a chemical reaction between limed peat and applied B. Crops grown on peats generally do not show symptoms of B toxicity when B fertilizer is applied at rates that usually produce toxicity on mineral soils (Gupta, 1978). No B toxicity was reported in sweet corn grown on a peat soil even when the hot-water-soluble B concentration was as high as 10 mg kg^{-1} (Prasad & Byrne, 1975).

4. Redox Potential

Ponnamperuma (1985) reported that B concentrations were not appreciably affected when a soil was flooded. Boron does not undergo oxidation-reduction reactions.

5. Nutrient Interactions

The Ca/B ratio in the plant has been used to delineate B deficiency. However, Gupta (1978) concluded that the ratio should not be given the same importance as levels of the individual elements. Gupta and MacLeod (1977) found that in the absence of added B, decreased B uptake appeared to be related to increasing soil pH, rather than to the availability of Ca or Mg. This effect was not evident in the presence of added B.

Applied B may enhance the utilization of applied N in cotton by increasing the translocation of N compounds into the boll (Miley et al., 1969). Smithson and Heathcote (1976) found that when B deficiency occurred in cotton, the application of 250 kg N ha^{-1} depressed yield. However, this rate of N produced a yield increase when B was applied.

Significant positive relationships have been found between K and B fertilizers (Hill & Morrill, 1975). Woodruff et al. (1987) showed that B fertilization may be necessary to prevent reduction in corn yield when heavy K fertilization and intensified production practices are used.

Graham et al. (1987) found that B uptake by barley was lower in the presence than in the absence of applied Zn. Further studies showed that both low Zn and high P increased the B accumulation. Therefore, Zn fertilization may decrease B accumulation and lessen the risk of toxicity in plants.

B. Copper

Copper probably is the most immobile micronutrient in soil. Since Cu is relatively immobile, the largest proportion of plant Cu is derived through root interception (Oliver & Barber, 1966). Fertilizer studies have revealed that movement of Cu into the plant depends to a large extent on the exploitation of soil by roots (Jarvis & Whitehead, 1981). Therefore, soil factors affecting root development should influence availability of Cu to plants.

1. Parent Material

Copper deficiencies are common in organic soils, peats, and mucks, which generally have low amounts of labile Cu (Oplinger & Ohlrogge, 1974). Copper deficiency also occurs in soils developed from sands, sandstones, and acid igneous rocks, but not generally from shales, clays, and basic rocks (Jarvis, 1981a).

Copper is translocated with clay and tends to be most abundant when clay content is high (Fagbami et al., 1985). Fractionation (Shuman, 1979) and sorption studies (McBride, 1981) have shown that Cu may be tightly adsorbed on Al, Mn, and Fe oxides. Soils derived from volcanic ash and pumice may also be deficient in plant-available Cu (Nyandat & Ochiing, 1976).

2. Soil pH

Adsorption of Cu increases appreciably as soil pH is increased from 4 to 7 (Cavallaro & McBride, 1984). Nevertheless, uptake of plant Cu is often poorly related to soil pH at moderate levels of soil Cu (Martens, 1968; Sims, 1986). Loneragan (1975) concluded that formation of soluble Cu-organic complexes may explain the insensitivity to Cu deficiency of plants grown on calcareous soils.

The incidence of Cu toxicity in tomato was greatly affected by soil pH, even though Cu concentrations in plant tops were little affected by the soil parameter (Rhoads et al., 1989). Plant growth was reduced with soil-Cu concentrations >150 mg kg^{-1} and with soil pH <6.5. However, soil-Cu concentrations >330 mg kg^{-1} were necessary to reduce plant growth with soil pH >6.5. Copper tends to accumulate in roots as a result of Cu toxicity (Brams & Fiskell, 1971).

3. Organic Matter

Plants susceptible to Cu deficiency often develop Cu-deficiency symptoms when grown on soils high in organic matter, because of low levels of Cu in the soil or of the complexing of Cu in insoluble organic forms unavailable to plants (Goodman & Cheshire, 1976). However, the role of organic matter is not clearly understood since complexation of Cu by soluble ligands, especially in calcareous soils, is believed to maintain the elements in forms available to plants (Stevenson & Fitch, 1981). Most of the available Cu reserves in soil are in the organic-bound fraction (Jarvis, 1981a), with the proportion of soluble, complexed Cu increasing as pH increases (Jeffrey & Uren, 1983).

Soluble Cu may be decreased through complexation to clay-humus particles or through the formation of insoluble humic complexes (Stevenson & Fitch, 1981). A key role is played by humic and fulvic acids, which probably form highly stable complexes with Cu, especially in Cu-deficient soils. The strength of Cu binding by humic acids decreases as the amount of applied Cu is increased (Goodman & Cheshire, 1976), and increases as the degree of humification is increased (Stevenson & Fitch, 1981).

Plant-available Cu in the soil solution is replenished from weakly, but specifically, adsorbed forms associated with organic matter (McLaren & Crawford, 1973). Even though the sorption isotherm gradient increases with increasing soil pH, there may be a concurrent increase in the complexing ability of the soil solution, which results in a greater equilibrium concentration of Cu in solution (Jarvis, 1981b). Minnich et al. (1987) reported that snapbean (*Phaseolus vulgaris* L.) accumulated higher root Cu levels at lower soil solution Cu^{2+} activities when sludge was applied. This probably reflected the superior ability of the sludge to replenish and maintain Cu supplies in the soil solution.

Natural complexing substances produced during microbial breakdown of organic matter have the ability to complex Cu into soluble, plant-available forms (Stevenson & Fitch, 1981). The plant root also may increase soluble Cu concentrations through an increase in soluble organic matter in the soil resulting from the release of root exudates (Nielson, 1976). Since the dissociation of Cu^{2+} from the organic ligand apparently must occur prior to plant uptake (Goodman & Linehan, 1979), the ease with which the dissociation and subsequent absorption of Cu by roots take place depends on the complexing ligand and the soil (Jarvis, 1981a).

Decomposition of crop residues and organic wastes by microorganisms may lead to the release of significant quantities of Cu. Complexation may reduce the concentration of Cu^{2+} to a nontoxic level when excess Cu^{2+} is present (Stevenson & Fitch, 1981).

Sillanpaa (1982) found that the Cu concentration of wheat grown in the greenhouse on more than 3000 soils was little affected by soil organic C < 12 g C kg^{-1}, but gradually decreased for wheat grown on soils with organic C concentrations between 12 and 64 g C kg^{-1}. In contrast, NH_4OAc-EDTA-extractable Cu concentrations increased greatly with increases in soil organic C for soils with < 12 g C kg^{-1}.

4. Redox Potential

Copper does not undergo valence changes in flooded soils. As indicated previously, Cu availability to plants may be decreased under such conditions. This decrease in Cu in waterlogged soil may result from the reduction of Mn and Fe oxides, which provide surfaces for Cu adsorption (Iu et al., 1981). Haldar and Mandal (1979) suggested that microbial immobilization and the antagonistic effect of increased concentrations of Fe, Mn, and P reduced plant-available Cu. After reduction, mobilized Cu also may be associated with the organic fraction of the soil (Sims & Patrick, 1978).

5. Nutrient Interactions

High Zn concentrations in the soil accentuate Cu deficiency (Haldar & Mandal, 1981). The effect is not primarily due to dilution effects or reduced translocation of Cu from roots to tops. Since Cu and Zn seem to be absorbed through the same mechanism, each competitively inhibits uptake of the other (Giordano et al., 1974). This increases the risk of Zn and Cu deficiencies in crops growing on soils marginally deficient in Zn and Cu, respectively (Kausar et al., 1976).

Application of N is known to accentuate Cu deficiency. In Western Australia, Cu deficiency on initially infertile soils was enhanced after the soil N supply was elevated by leguminous pastures (Gartrell, 1981). This effect may be partially related to increased growth due to applied N (Hill et al., 1978); however, high levels of N markedly reduced the rate of retranslocation of Cu from older leaves to meristems. The coupling of Cu movement from leaves to N movement may account for relatively high critical concentrations of Cu in tops of plants given high rates of N fertilizers (Loneragan et al., 1980). The combined effects of Zn and N fertilizers induced such severe Cu deficiency in wheat plants that grain yield was almost eliminated (Chaudhry & Loneragan, 1970). Other researchers have shown that the transport of Cu was related to the supply and transport of N, with Cu translocation increasing with N supply (Jarvis, 1981b).

Soil P may also reduce the concentration of plant Cu. This may sometimes be due to plant dilution effects as a result of added P increasing plant growth without a consequent increase in Cu uptake (Robson & Reuter, 1981). However, others have found that reduced plant Cu was caused by factors other than growth dilution (Haldar & Mandal, 1981; Touchton et al., 1980). Timmer and Leyden (1980) concluded that the reduction of plant Cu concentration at high P levels resulted from a reduced exploitation of the soil by mycorrhizas.

Wallace (1984) demonstrated that Cu toxicity can be enhanced in the presence of P deficiency. Copper toxicity also is more likely to occur in plants growing on coarse-textured soils low in available Fe, but high in Cu, than on comparable high-Fe soils (Walsh et al., 1972; Reuter et al., 1953). This condition may be corrected by applying Fe chelates (Leonard & Stewart, 1952). Crop cultivars that show differences in Fe efficiency responded differently to excess Cu (Brown & Ambler, 1973); Cu toxicity was more prevalent in Fe-efficient soybean (Wallace & Cha, 1986).

C. Iron

Iron availability depends to a large extent on soil pH and redox potential. Proper soil management may reduce soil pH and redox potential, and thereby increase Fe availability. Plants have also evolved various mechanisms to enhance Fe uptake (Marschner, 1986). The interaction between soil and plant genotype is very important in Fe nutrition.

1. Parent Material

Most of the Fe in the earth's crust is in the form of ferromagnesium silicates. Iron released by weathering is precipitated as oxides or hydroxides with only a small part of the Fe incorporated into secondary silicate materials (Schwertmann & Taylor, 1977). Although most soils contain adequate

Fe, amounts that are available to the plant are dependent on factors such as Fe species in the soil and plant genotype (Miller et al., 1984).

Iron deficiency may occur on noncalcareous, coarse-textured soils (Chesney, 1972), but Fe deficiencies are more common on calcareous soils (Miller et al., 1984). The equilibrium concentration of solution-phase Fe in a calcareous system is very low. The dissolution of Fe-containing minerals apparently occurs as a surface reaction with the rate of dissolution of Fe oxides decreasing in the following order: ferrihydrite > lepidocrocite > magnetite > hematite > goethite (Loeppert & Clark, 1984).

2. Soil pH

The solubility of inorganic Fe in well-aerated soils is controlled by the dissolution and precipitation of Fe^{3+} oxides. The concentration of Fe^{3+} is related to pH, declining from 10^{-8} to 10^{-20} M as pH increased from 4 to 8 (Romheld & Marschner, 1986). High HCO_3 concentrations decrease the availability of Fe in calcareous soils (Bloom & Inskeep, 1988).

The Fe demand of plants is higher than that supplied by the Fe concentrations of the bulk solution in most well-aerated soils between pH 5 and 8 (Romheld & Marschner, 1986). Plants may enhance the availability of Fe by various nonspecific mechanisms. For example, N applied as NH_4 vs. NO_3 (Wallace, 1982), and K^+ applied as KCl or K_2SO_4 vs. KNO_3 or K_2HPO_4 (Barak & Chen, 1984) were more effective in decreasing the rhizosphere pH as a result of differential cation-anion uptake. The availability of Fe may also be increased by acidulating the soil (Frank & Fehr, 1983) and/or applying Fe fertilizers (Parkpian & Anderson, 1988). Since broadcast applications of acidifying materials such as H_2SO_4 must be excessive to be effective, band or spot placement application has proven to be effective and more economical in alleviating Fe chlorosis (Kalbasi et al., 1988). Mortvedt and Kelsoe (1988a) improved grain-sorghum forage yields and Fe uptake when $FeSO_4$ was applied with an acid-forming fertilizer.

Plants have evolved various specific mechanisms to enhance mobilization and uptake of Fe in the root rhizosphere once an Fe deficiency occurs (Romheld & Marschner, 1986). However, soil factors may affect the ability of the plant to respond to an Fe deficiency (Table 11-7). The inhibitory effect of high HCO_3 concentration on the uptake of Fe by plant species with the Strategy-I Fe-response mechanism is primarily a pH effect, with high pH depressing the reduction mechanism as well as the release of phenolics (Romheld & Marschner, 1986). Bicarbonate also acts as a buffer, maintaining a relatively high pH in the free space and rhizosphere (Romheld & Marschner, 1986).

3. Organic Matter

The formation of soluble Fe complexes by naturally occurring chelating ligands may enhance the solubility of Fe (Olomu et al., 1973). Humic and fulvic ligands form the most stable complexes with Fe of all the transition metals, and their effectiveness increases with increasing pH, due to en-

Table 11-7. Influence of selected soil factors on plant strategies for the enhancement of Fe uptake.[†]

Soil factors	Sensitivity	
	Strategy I[‡]	Strategy II[§]
High bicarbonate and high pH	High	Low
High soil moisture levels and poor aeration	High	Low
High soil organic matter content in calcareous soils at high moisture levels	High	Low
High P supply	Low	High
High concentration of heavy metals	High	--
High ionic strength of the soil solution	High	Low
Low soil temperature	High	Low

[†] From Romheld and Marschner (1986).
[‡] For example, soybean and peanut.
[§] For example, sorghum, maize, and wheat.

hanced dispersion and ionization of the surface ligands (Stevenson & Ardakani, 1972). Levesque and Mathur (1988) concluded that the immediately plant-available forms of Fe, the water-soluble and Ca-extractable fractions, were replenished by the strongly complexed and S^{2-}-associated forms. Therefore, the likelihood of Fe deficiency is reduced in soils with high organic matter contents.

Plant refuse, manures, sewage sludges, peats, charcoal, byproducts of forest-product manufacturing (polyflavonoids and lignosulfonates), and even coal have been shown to be effective in alleviating Fe chlorosis (Chen & Barak, 1982). Various plant species sprayed with Fe and subsequently applied to problem soils were effective in supplying Fe to plants (Matocha, 1984; Matocha & Pennington, 1982). Iron-organic compounds in manure were also effective in maintaining Fe in an available form (Parsa et al., 1979).

4. Redox Potential

The major cause of Fe deficiency in plants on well-aerated soils is the insolubility of Fe^{3+} oxides. As the redox potential and/or soil pH increases, plant availability of Fe decreases. The critical redox potential for Fe^{3+} reduction is between $+300$ mV and $+100$ mV at pH 6 and 7, and -100 mV at pH 8 (Gotoh & Patrick, 1974).

After submergence, levels of Fe in soil solutions are affected by acidity, redox potential, and complexing ligands (Beckwith et al., 1975). Excess soil moisture increases the availability and uptake of Fe (Bjerre & Schierup, 1985), with waterlogging resulting in a decrease in redox potential, and an increase in water-soluble and exchangeable Fe (Sonar & Ghugare, 1982). Sonar and Ghugare (1982) saturated soil (two irrigations daily) for 15 d prior to planting, and increased the supply of Fe as a result of a reduction in soil pH and Eh. However, as discussed earlier, excess moisture may intensify Fe deficiency in calcareous soils, probably due to the effect of a buildup in HCO_3 concentration in the soil solution.

Table 11-8. Effect of genotype and planting method (nonridged control vs. ridged) on grain yield of rice afflicted with Fe toxicity.†

Genotype	1985			1986		
	Control	Ridge	Mean	Control	Ridge	Mean
	$g\ m^{-2}$					
ITA 212	76	79	77	78	254	165
ITA 247	186	252	219	145	512	328
Mean	130	165		111	383	
LSD (0.05) for yield between:						
Planting method means		42			59	
Genotype means		40			56	
Genotype means for the same planting period		57			79	

† From Winslow et al. (1989).

Reduction processes near respiring roots may increase Fe^{3+} reduction and the subsequent disassociation of Fe^{3+} chelates. This is particularly so for plants that use the Strategy-I Fe-response mechanism (Romheld & Marschner, 1986).

Certain management practices, such as periodic soil drainage to allow oxidation of the soluble Fe and the use of resistant cultivars (Gunawardena et al., 1982), can reduce Fe toxicity in rice. Winslow et al. (1989) planted rice on ridges to aerate the upper root zone. They found that ridging and resistant genotypes, especially when used in combination, appeared to be effective management strategies for reducing yield losses in Fe-toxic soils (Table 11-8). Roots of plants growing in soils high in soluble Fe may be coated with oxidized Fe (Howeler, 1973), which may reduce the uptake of other nutrients.

5. Nutrient Interactions

The form of N applied may affect the availability of soil Fe. Increasing NO_3-N uptake may cause an imbalance in the cation/anion ratio, resulting in exudation of HCO_3 into the rhizosphere with a subsequent reduction in Fe uptake (Chen & Barak, 1982). Aktaks and van Egmond (1979) found that NO_3-N increased dry matter production of the Fe-efficient Hawkeye soybean cultivar and decreased that of the Fe-inefficient T-203 cultivar.

High soil P levels may decrease plant Fe concentration. Proposed mechanisms include the immobilization of soil Fe (Brown, 1972; Mandal & Haldar, 1980), inhibition of Fe absorption by roots and of Fe transport from roots to shoots (Elliott & Lauchli, 1985), and inactivation of plant Fe (DeKock et al., 1979).

Azarbadi and Marschner (1979) reported that when P was depleted in the rhizosphere, corn roots were able to use Fe from $Fe(OH)_3$ without decreasing the pH or redox potential. This depletion of P may enable some Fe-inefficient plant species to use inorganic Fe^{3+} compounds.

Zinc deficiency increases Fe uptake in certain plant species (Francois & Goodin, 1972), sometimes to a toxic level (Adams & Pearson, 1967). Brown and Jones (1977) reported that, when the pH of a selected soil was increased from 5.2 to 7.1 by addition of lime, cotton became Zn deficient and accumulated higher levels of Fe. Haldar and Mandal (1981) found that applied Zn decreased Fe concentration in rice shoots and roots. This decrease in the concentration in the shoots was not due to a dilution effect or to a reduced rate of translocation from root to tops.

The Fe-Mn interaction is well documented (Brown, 1956). Although the Fe-Mn interaction has been extensively studied, it is not fully understood. However, the importance of this interaction is evident from the finding that application of MnEDTA induced Mn deficiency in bean plants, apparently because the ligand increased soil-Fe availability (Knezek & Greinert, 1971). Zaharieva et al. (1988) recently suggested that: (i) Fe hampers Mn uptake; and (ii) Mn decreases plant Fe^{2+} and adversely affects Fe metabolism. Kuo and Mikkelsen (1981) reported that the translocation of Fe in rice from roots to shoots was hindered at high Mn levels. Since coatings occurred on root surfaces and intensified with increasing Mn concentrations, part of the reduced Fe levels in shoots was attributed to the formation of insoluble Mn oxides on the roots.

An Fe-efficient tomato and the soybean cultivar, A7, were unable to respond to Fe-deficiency stress in the absence of K in nutrient solutions (Jolley et al., 1988). The lack of a Fe-deficiency stress response in the absence of K resulted in reduced levels of leaf Fe and greater chlorosis in both species. Potassium seems to play a very specific role in the plant for maximum utilization of Fe.

Olsen and Watanabe (1979) reported that an increase in Mo decreased Fe uptake. This interaction may be important in alkaline soils in which Fe availability may be low and soluble MoO_4^{2-} concentration high.

D. Manganese

Manganese is similar to Fe in that soil pH and redox potential determine, to a large extent, its availability. In most cases, adequate soil Mn is present in the soil. However, much of the soil Mn, depending on soil properties, may not be available to the plant. Availability may be increased through effective soil management, but poor soil management can increase available soil Mn to a toxic level.

1. Parent Material

Various soil Mn fractions are in dynamic equilibrium in the soil, with the amount available to the plant depending on the quantity present, and soil, plant, and climatic factors. Lowest concentrations of easily reducible Mn have been found in soils derived from crystalline shale and acid igneous rocks. In contrast, the highest levels have been found in soils derived from basalt, limestone, and shales formed from clay (Glinski & Thai, 1971). More Mn minerals generally occur in limestone than in shale or sandstone (Krauskopf, 1972).

Lombin (1983) reported that extractable-Mn levels were highest in Inceptisols and Vertisols, and lowest in Ultisols and Oxisols. Soil Mn tends to increase with increasing clay content (Mokma et al., 1979). Manganese deficiency commonly occurs on poorly drained sandy-textured soils in the Atlantic Coastal Plain region (Alley et al., 1978; Mascagni & Cox, 1985), and on soils that fluctuate between a well-drained and a waterlogged condition (Labanauskas, 1966). The first-mentioned soils usually have low extractable and total Mn levels with pH levels >6.0. Manganese deficiencies may also occur on calcareous soils low in reducible Mn (Liu et al., 1983).

Manganese toxicities may occur in soils with large quantities of easily reducible Mn. Ayanlaja (1984) evaluated Mn fractions in 10 soil profiles and found that easily reducible Mn was the dominant form, at 80 to 100% of the total Mn. He concluded that, as a result of the high active Mn concentrations, care should be taken in the management of these soils to prevent Mn toxicity problems.

2. Soil pH

The activity of Mn in solution is largely determined by pH and redox potential (Leeper, 1947). High soil pH and Eh favor the insoluble oxide forms of Mn, whereas low pH levels and redox potentials favor the divalent water-soluble species (Sparrow & Uren, 1987).

Addition of lime to certain acid soils decreases Mn availability (Dahiya & Singh, 1977). Parker and Walker (1986) reported that Mn deficiency in peanut (*Arachis hypogaea* L.) and responses to applied Mn occurred only on certain soils with pH levels near 6.8. In contrast, maintenance of soil pH near 6.0 provided a desirable medium for production without the need for Mn fertilizers. Application of acid-forming fertilizers decreases pH and increases Mn availability (Jackson & Carter, 1976; Miner et al., 1986). Petrie and Jackson (1984a) reported that band application in the seed row of $(NH_4)_2SO_4$ at rates of 22 and 45 kg N ha^{-1} increased both barley yield and leaf Mn concentration, whereas urea applications decreased yields (Table 11-9). The soil solution pH in the fertilizer band 7 d after fertilization was decreased from 8.1 to 7.3 by $(NH_4)_2SO_4$ (Petrie & Jackson, 1984b). In contrast, urea fertilizer increased the soil solution pH from 7.7 to 8.0.

Table 11-9. Effects of N source and added Mn on leaf Mn concentration and yield of barley.†

Treatment		1978		1980	
N	Mn	Leaf Mn	Yield	Leaf Mn	Yield
———kg ha^{-1}———		mg kg^{-1}	t ha^{-1}	mg kg^{-1}	t ha^{-1}
0	0.0	11	3.24	16	2.70
22 $(NH_4)_2SO_4$	0.0	19	5.42	25	5.88
22 Urea	0.0	12	3.52	17	4.84
22 $(NH_4)_2SO_4$	5.6	17	5.28	31	6.38
22 Urea	5.6	17	5.06	25	5.77
LSD (0.05)		3	1.34	8	0.67

† From Petrie and Jackson (1984a).

The amount of Mn solubilized in the rhizosphere is much greater than that in the bulk solution (Godo & Reisenauer, 1980). These researchers concluded that soil Mn availability is neither controlled by soil nor by plant characteristics per se, but by the combined effects of soil properties, plant characteristics, and the interaction of plant roots with the surrounding soil. Nonspecific and specific mechanisms of Fe mobilization also may enhance the availability of Mn by Strategy I-type plants (Moraghan, 1979; Marschner, 1986). Release of H^+ and reducing and complexing compounds by the roots should increase soluble Mn.

Highly acid soils with pH values < 5.5 usually have increased Mn availability, which may limit yields (Reid, 1976). Manganese toxicity may occur at higher pH levels in poorly drained or compacted soils if such soils contain sufficient total Mn (Reid, 1976). Knowledge of soil pH and extractable Mn, and some estimate of the pH likely to occur during the growth period, seems necessary for predicting Mn toxicity on acid soils (White, 1970). Soil pH was the best measure of predicting Mn status of soybean growing on acid soils (Anderson & Mortvedt, 1982). Toxic concentrations of Mn did not accumulate in soil or in leaf tissue at pH levels > 5.5.

The effects of fertilizer on soil pH and Mn availability emphasize the need for identification of potentially Mn-toxic soils, especially with rotations requiring heavy fertilization and restricted lime applications (White, 1970). For example, soils in rice rotations in Arkansas usually are not limed to avoid Zn deficiency in rice. Thus, the potential for Mn toxicity is enhanced in soybean following rice. Sims and Atkinson (1974) reported that addition of NH_4NO_3 decreased soil pH, increased exchangeable Mn, and decreased early growth of tobacco.

Application of lime will increase soil pH, decrease available Mn, and lessen the risk of Mn toxicity (Helyar & Anderson, 1974). Proper selection of cultivars may prevent yield reduction from Mn toxicity, since cultivars respond differently to Mn-toxicity conditions (Reddy & Dunn, 1987).

3. Organic Matter

Organic compounds resulting from the breakdown of soil organic matter may complex Mn. The plant root also may directly enhance soil Mn availability by releasing organic compounds, such as hydroxy-carboxylates, which reduce Mn^{4+} oxides and complex Mn^{2+} (Godo & Reisenauer, 1980). This effect is particularly marked in soils with pH values < 5.5.

Complexed organic Mn along with easily reducible Mn oxides are in equilibrium with water-soluble and exchangeable forms, which influence plant growth (Levesque & Mathur, 1988). The stability of Mn complexes and their plant availability is related to soil pH, soil type, and concentrations of other elements. Manganese organic-matter complexes possess a limited stability, which increases with increasing pH; the stability of organic matter complexes follows the order $Mn^{2+} < Zn^{2+} < Cu^{2+} < Fe^{3+}$ (Khan, 1969).

Some forms of organic matter, such as humic acid, may fix Mn in unavailable forms (Pavanasasivam, 1973). McBride (1982) reported that exchangeability of Mn^{2+} from organic solids was strongly pH dependent. Strong bonding of Mn^{2+} was induced by increasing pH.

Organic matter provides a needed energy source for microbial reductions to occur in soils. Meek et al. (1968) reported that flooding soil without additional organic matter increased extractable Mn^{2+} to a maximum of 3.7 mg kg^{-1}. The combination of flooding, organic matter, and high temperatures increased Mn^{2+} to 46 mg kg^{-1}.

A potential for soluble Mn accumulation and Mn toxicity may occur where large amounts of plant residue are incorporated into a normally well-drained soil (Elliott & Blaylock, 1975). Hue (1988) reported that Mn toxicity occurred in lettuce in sludge-amended Oxisols. The excessive Mn accumulation was not explained by soil pH, redox conditions, or the direct Mn contribution from sludge. In contrast, Mn complexation by organic ligands from sludge accounted for 76 to 99% of the soluble Mn, and apparently caused the high concentrations of Mn in the soil solution.

4. Redox Potential

Manganese availability is controlled to a great extent by the pH and redox status of soils. Oxidation and reduction of soil Mn may occur simultaneously, but independently, at sites in close proximity (Sparrow & Uren, 1987). Therefore, the dominant process will result in a net increase or decrease in available Mn.

Rapid oxidation of Mn^{2+} in soils occurred with pH levels >5.5 (Bromfield, 1958b). Ross and Bartlett (1981) found that oxidation of added Mn^{2+} was proportional to the level of existing reactive Mn oxides. Oxidation apparently was an autocatalytic nonbiological process, rather than a biological process (Bromfield, 1958b), and involved specific adsorption of Mn^{2+} onto existing Mn oxide surfaces.

The conversion of insoluble soil Mn to the water-soluble and extractable forms was dependent upon both pH and Eh between pH 6 and 8 (Gotoh & Patrick, 1972). The effect of acidity was so marked at pH 5 that changes in redox potential had little effect on Mn solubility. The critical potential for Mn reduction occurred at a much lower redox potential as pH increased.

Soil saturation decreases Eh and increases the plant availability of soil Mn (Sonar & Ghugare, 1982). Manganese is released during reduction from the organic and oxide forms, and accumulates in the more plant-available, water-soluble, and exchangeable fractions (Sims & Patrick, 1978). Sonar and Ghugare (1982) maintained a soil in a saturated condition for 15 d prior to planting and increased the availability of Mn to a subsequently planted rice crop. Manganese uptake by rice under anaerobic-soil conditions apparently was influenced by Fe uptake and soil pH (Jugsujinda & Patrick, 1977). Manganese uptake was increased when higher soil pH values restricted Fe uptake. Application of certain fertilizers such as KCl also may enhance the reduction of Mn oxides and increase the availability of soil Mn (Krishnamurti & Huang, 1988), sometimes to toxic levels (Cheng, 1982).

Plant roots excrete organic compounds, which enhance the reduction of Mn oxides (Godo & Reisenauer, 1980). Plant species with Strategy-I root-response mechanisms to Fe deficiency may also enhance solubilization and uptake of Mn (Marschner et al., 1986b).

Water-soluble Mn may increase to unusually high levels after soil sub-mergence if easily reducible Mn is present. Haby et al. (1979) reported that corn and coastal bermudagrass (*Cyndon dactylon* L.) withstood moderate to strong acidity in a normal rainfall year. However, Mn toxicity occurred in corn grown on soils with a pH of 5.2 when the soils were waterlogged in a high rainfall year.

Sonneveld and Voogt (1975) attributed the increase of soluble Mn to toxic levels during steam sterilization of greenhouse soils to the reduction of Mn oxides. The slow rate of oxidation of Mn^{2+} in steam-sterilized soils was apparently due to destruction of Mn-oxidizing bacteria during the steam-sterilization process. Oxidation of Mn^{2+} was accelerated by inoculating sterilized soils with Mn-oxidizing bacteria.

5. Nutrient Interactions

Application of Fe may reduce the concentration of Mn in plants. Baxter and Osman (1988) found that soil applications of FeEDDHA increased Fe concentration and reduced Mn concentrations in soybean. However, soil applications of FeEDDHA did not increase Fe uptake or affect Mn uptake into sorghum leaves. Since sorghum lacked the capacity to reduce Fe^{3+} from the chelate, and apparently lacked the ability to decrease rhizosphere pH in response to Fe stress, Mn availability was unaffected by the application of FeEDDHA to soil. Application of FeEDDHA to a calcareous soil eliminated Mn-toxicity symptoms in flax (Moraghan, 1979), presumably because the higher plant-Fe status reduced the Strategy-I response pattern (Romheld & Marschner, 1986) of the root system.

Romero (1988) concluded that the effect of Fe fertilization on plant-Mn response may involve the following phenomena: (i) Fe applications that increase plant growth may decrease Mn concentrations in tops to deficient levels by dilution; (ii) Fe applications that correct Fe deficiency may also lower root-to-shoot ratios; and (iii) Fe applications may decrease Mn uptake, and the resultant low-yielding, Mn-deficient plants may contain toxic concentrations of Fe. Each of these three effects of either Fe or Mn on plant growth may lead to symptoms attributed to Mn deficiency.

There are conflicting data concerning the effect of soil P on plant Mn. Haldar and Mandal (1981) attributed the reduced Mn concentration in P-fertilized rice plants to changes in uptake of these elements resulting from their availability in the soil. Increasing P levels intensified Mn toxicity in white clover (*Trifolium repens*) (Truong et al., 1971) and potato (Marsh et al., 1987). In contrast, Jones and Fox (1978) reported that apparent toxicities of Al and Mn in tomato were decreased by high levels of P. Although rates of P exceeding nutritional requirements resulted in increased growth, growth was less than that produced in soils that had been limed to eliminate the toxicity.

Therefore, they concluded that P was a poor substitute for lime in correcting Mn and Al toxicities.

Manganese uptake was reduced with application of Zn fertilizers (Haldar & Mandal, 1981). In contrast, White et al. (1979) found that Zn applications to soil increased root and plant Mn to reportedly toxic levels at both pH 5.5 and 6.5, but did not influence DTPA-extractable soil Mn. Significant cultivar differences in root and leaf Mn concentrations were observed.

Sims et al. (1975) observed that Mn concentrations were reduced in half by Mo fertilization. Since Mn toxicity of burley tobacco is common, application of Mo may decrease the toxicity. However, large applications of Mo to problem soils may detrimentally affect the nutrition of ruminants subsequently grazing on these soils.

Silicon-Mn interactions are sometimes important in plant nutrition. Addition of Si to nutrient solutions altered the distribution of Mn in leaf tissue of barley and prevented its accumulation in localized toxic concentrations (Williams & Vlamis, 1957b). Horst and Marschner (1978) showed that, in the presence of Si, a higher proportion of Mn in leaves of bean plants was located in vacuoles.

E. Molybdenum

Molybdenum is the only micronutrient in which availability normally increases with an increase in pH. Soil properties affect the availability of Mo primarily through adsorption of MoO_4 onto inorganic soil components, especially under acid conditions. Molybdenum is not particularly susceptible to leaching losses under most acid conditions. For example, marked residual effects to the application of 70 g Mo_2O_3 ha^{-1} to a subterranean clover pasture were still evident after 10 yr (Anderson, 1956). Molybdenum deficiency is rarely observed in plants growing on neutral and calcareous soils.

1. Parent Material

Shale and granite are the major rocks contributing Mo to soil parent material (Kubota, 1977); in general, soils in the eastern USA tend to have lower Mo levels than those in the western USA, possibly because of the higher incidence of sandy materials of glacial and marine origin.

The relationship between Mo concentration of soils and parent material has been extensively reviewed by Aubert and Pinta (1977). These authors concluded that pedogenic processes are more important than parent rocks in determining Mo availability. Thus, Mo deficiency in Australia has occurred in crops growing on soils derived from sedimentary rocks, basalt and granite (Anderson, 1970).

Water-soluble MoO_4 and organically complexed Mo are considered to be relatively available to plants (Gupta & Lipsett, 1981). Many peats, alkali soils, and poorly drained soils with high water tables tend to produce forages high in Mo (Allaway, 1977), which can cause molybdenosis in livestock. Little MoO_4 is adsorbed by inorganic colloids on such soils and leaching losses are minimal. Certain high-base, well-drained soils derived from serpentine in California are deficient in Mo (Johnson et al., 1952). The high-base status of these soils results in little adsorption of MoO_4, which is then susceptible to leaching losses under the given conditions.

2. Soil pH

Plant uptake of Mo increases as pH increases. The principal positively charged sites in the soil for anionic adsorption are provided by hydrous oxides of Fe (Karimian & Cox, 1979) and Al (Childs & Leslie, 1977), with adsorption decreasing as the pH increases. The adsorption maximum of MoO_4 on hematite was reduced by 80% when the pH was increased from 4.0 to 7.8 (Reyes & Jurinak, 1967). Maximum adsorption coincides with the pK_a value of H_2MoO_4, which is approximately 4 (Barrow, 1977).

Addition of lime to a soil normally increases Mo uptake by both grasses and legumes (Williams & Thornton, 1972). The relationship between liming and response to applied Mo is not always consistent. This may be partly related to the Mo content of the soil. For example, Gupta (1969) found that lime was needed for optimum alfalfa yield from three Canadian soils with a pH of 5.0. However, applied Mo did not increase yields on the soil with a relatively high Mo level, but did so on a soil with a low content of the element. Similarly, lime alone did not increase available Mo to levels adequate for optimal alfalfa production on highly oxidized soils of the Georgia Piedmont (Giddens & Perkins, 1972). Soybean grown on soils with pH values < 5.7 responded to both added Mo and lime in another southern state study (Anderson & Mortvedt, 1982). In a similar study (Mortvedt & Anderson, 1982), production of forage legumes was limited on soils with pH values < 5.5 because low levels of available Mo limited N_2 fixation. Forage yields were increased more often by liming than by application of Mo.

Much research has been conducted in Australia on lime responses and the complex roles of genotype, Ca requirement for nodulation, Ca requirement of the host plant, pH requirement for nodulation, Al toxicity, Mn toxicity, and the separate Mo requirements for host plants and N_2 fixation. Excellent reviews of these studies are available (Munns, 1977; Andrew & Kamprath, 1978).

Molybdenum toxicity in plants is rare and has been observed only under experimental conditions (Vlek & Lindsay, 1977). However, high levels of Mo in forages can induce molybdenosis in ruminants. Application of Mo to limed soils (pH > 6.5) did not increase forage yields and occasionally resulted in plant Mo concentrations that were in the hazardous range for livestock (5 to 10 mg kg^{-1}) (James et al., 1968). However, Mo fertilizers applied at recommended rates to soils with low to average Mo levels should not produce forage capable of causing molybdenosis (Hawes et al., 1976).

3. Organic Matter

Soil organic matter appears to have a much smaller effect on the availability of Mo than does soil pH. For example, soil pH was much more important than soil organic C in explaining Mo-accumulation patterns in wheat grown on diverse soils (Sillanpaa, 1982).

There is some evidence, however, that Mo is fixed by soil organic matter. Aubert and Pinta (1977) concluded that the distribution of Mo within soil profiles varies in relation to humus content. Adsorbed Mo in certain soils from the southeastern USA increased with increases in the organic matter and/or Fe oxide contents of the soils (Karimian & Cox, 1978). Gupta (1971) showed that extractable Mo levels decreased when Mo was applied to incubated soils treated with various organic materials; however, the effect was reversed in the absence of added Mo. It is important to separate organic matter effects from pH effects in such studies.

Where impeded drainage is accompanied by organic matter accumulation, available soil MoO_4 may increase. Plants grown on such soils may accumulate excessive Mo and cause molybdenosis when fed to animals (Kubota et al., 1961). Peats and mucks are associated with Mo toxicity in the soils of the California delta, the Klamath area in Oregon, and the Everglades in Florida (Kubota, 1972). Organic matter possibly increases the mobilization of Mo under conditions of impeded drainage. Additional research is needed to clearly define the role of organic matter on Mo availability.

4. Redox Potential

Molybdenum probably is not directly involved in oxidation-reduction reactions in soil (Rowell, 1981). However, increases in pH and reduction of Fe oxides at low redox values probably increase the solubility of MoO_4. Molybdenum deficiency has rarely, if ever, been observed in paddy rice production. There is some evidence that soil organic matter can convert Mo(VI) in MoO_4 to the Mo(V) and Mo(III) oxidation states (Goodman & Cheshire, 1982).

5. Nutrient Interactions

Sulfur applications may decrease Mo concentrations in plants (Gupta & MacLeod, 1975). Concentrations of tissue Mo resulting from application of 0.5 and 1.0 mg Mo kg^{-1}, which were reportedly toxic for animals, were corrected by soil applications of 50 to 200 mg S kg^{-1}.

Phosphorus generally increases the availability of Mo. Pasricha et al. (1987) found that the concentration of Mo in plants was enhanced by application of P. This increase in Mo may be due in part to the reduced adsorption of Mo by soil when P is applied (Ray et al., 1986).

Field responses of nodulated legumes to Mo fertilizers are normally associated with the activity of the enzyme nitrogenase and its requirement of Mo for N_2 fixation. Since the classical study of Anderson and Thomas (1946), many workers have demonstrated negative interactions between Mo and N fertilizers with legumes. Mortvedt (1981) found that soil application of Mo resulted in increased growth and uptake of N and Mo by several legumes at pH 5; crop response was less at pH 6 and absent at pH 7. Parker and Harris (1977) reported that seed yields of non-nodulating soybean isolines were not affected by added Mo, but added Mo increased yields in nodulating isolines in four out of five experiments.

Continued use of NH_4-containing fertilizers, especially $(NH_4)_2SO_4$, can cause Mo deficiency in crops due to: (i) an acidification effect and a decreased availability of soil Mo; and (ii) the previously discussed SO_4-Mo antagonism (Anderson, 1956). Sims and Atkinson (1974) reported that Mo concentrations of leaves of tobacco plants treated with 360 kg NH_4NO_3-N ha^{-1} were only 20 to 50% of those from plots not fertilized with N. This was due presumably to fertilizer-induced acidity effects.

A principal function of Mo in higher plants involves the activity of the enzyme NO_3 reductase. Consequently, N-Mo interactions within the plant can be important. Hewitt and Gundry (1970) found that cauliflower (*Brassica oleracea* L.) grown under sterile conditions with NH_4-N did not normally require Mo for optimal growth. Johansen (1978) reported that buffel (*Cenchrus ciliaris*), a tropical grass, did not respond to Mo when grown on a soil severely Mo deficient for tropical legumes. However, at high levels of added NO_3-N plant NO_3-N decreased from 5.2 to 0.9 g kg^{-1} with addition of Mo. Freney and Lipsett (1965) had earlier reported that high levels of NO_3 fertilizer depressed the yield of wheat, but application of Mo fertilizer overcame the yield depression. Small quantities of tungsten (W) applied to Mo-deficient nutrient cultures decreased Mo-deficiency symptoms (whiptail) in cauliflower plants (Fido et al., 1977). The effect appeared to be associated with the activity of NO_3 reductase, but the effect was not completely understood.

F. Zinc

Zinc, like Mn and Fe, moves to the plant root primarily by diffusion. Soil properties that affect the mobility of Zn obviously will affect the availability of Zn to plants. Although extensively leached, coarse-textured soils high in silica are frequently deficient in Zn for crops such as citrus, Zn deficiency is mainly found on calcareous soils, especially when plants susceptible to Zn deficiency are well supplied with P.

1. Parent Material

Total Zn concentration of soils varies greatly. Aubert and Pinta (1977) concluded that parent material has a much greater effect on soil Zn content than do pedogenic factors. These researchers indicated that: (i) basic eruptive rocks, such as basalt and gabbro, usually contain more Zn than acid eruptive rocks, metamorphic rocks, or sedimentary rocks, such as limestone or sandstone; and (ii) soil layers rich in organic matter, such as upper soil horizons, have higher Zn concentrations. However, others have found that total Zn may also be uniformly distributed in soil profiles (Follett & Lindsay, 1970) or even concentrated in the subsoil (Karim & Sedberry, 1976).

Although there is variability in the distribution of total Zn in soil profiles, most research indicates that extractable or available Zn accumulates in the topsoil (Follett & Lindsay, 1970) or upper soil horizons (Aubert & Pinta, 1977). Consequently, removal of topsoil through grading or erosion can increase the likelihood of Zn deficiency in crops (Grunes et al., 1961). Sillanpaa (1982) reported that Zn concentration of wheat plants was better correlated with soil pH and soil organic C than with CEC, soil texture, $CaCO_3$ equivalent, or electrical conductivity. Plant Zn concentration also was highly correlated with DTPA-extractable Zn ($r = 0.732$, $P = 0.001$).

2. Soil pH

Plant-available Zn decreases as soil pH increases. This decrease is due partly to increased adsorption by soil constituents (Bar-Yosef et al., 1980). As soil pH is increased above approximately 5.5, Zn is adsorbed by hydrous oxides of Al (Kalbasi et al., 1978), Fe (Kinniburgh & Jackson, 1982), and Mn (Loganathan et al., 1977). At equilibrium solution-Zn concentrations of about 10^{-1} M, adsorption increased by roughly a factor of 10 between pH 5.5 and 6.5 (Kinniburgh & Jackson, 1982). At trace concentrations of $<10^{-7}$ M, Zn adsorption was even more strongly pH dependent and increased about 45 times for each unit increase in pH. Soil Zn is adsorbed by both specific and nonspecific processes with the importance of the specific process apparently increasing with increasing pH (Kalbasi et al., 1978). The importance of Zn adsorption by soil constituents has been extensively discussed (Adriano, 1986).

Precipitation of specific Zn compounds at increasing pH values (Lindsay, 1978) could also explain the decreased availability of Zn at high pH levels, but the nature of such compounds is not known. There is the possibility that a franklinite-like material could be important in paddy-rice soils.

Transfer of Zn from the soil solution to the root surface occurs mainly by diffusion and is likely to occur close to the root. Melton et al. (1973) determined that the diffusion coefficient (D) in a calcareous loam was about 50-fold less than for an acidic soil. However, when the acidic soil was limed to about 7, the D values were similar for both soils. Thus, Zn mobility is reduced and deficiencies are more common on soils with high pH levels (Sedberry et al., 1980).

Bar-Yosef et al. (1980) concluded that excretion of H^+ and probably other means of reducing the pH near the root were more effective in enhancing Zn uptake than excretion of complexing agents. Decreased pH values due to an Fe-deficient stress response of a Strategy I-type plant (Romheld & Marschner, 1986) and rhizosphere acidification from plant uptake of NH_4-N may result in greater uptake of Zn. Certain management practices can enhance the availability of soil Zn. For example, plant availability of applied Zn was greatest when $ZnSO_4$ was banded with acid-type fertilizers (10–13–0 and 10–13–0–7S, N-P-K) than with 10–15–0, or granular triple superphosphate (TSP) and diammonium phosphate (DAP) (Mortvedt & Kelsoe, 1988b).

Melton et al. (1970) reported that pea-bean growth was reduced at both low (<20 mg Zn kg^{-1}) and high (>50 mg Zn kg^{-1}) concentrations of plant

Zn. Yields on certain acid soils generally decreased when Zn was applied. However, liming the same soils induced Zn deficiency. Keisling et al. (1977) found that liming was effective in overcoming Zn toxicity in peanut. They concluded that certain acid soils retained appreciable Zn in the plow layer, which could be potentially toxic to plants. Martens et al. (1974) reported that neither soybean growth nor seed yield was decreased when up to 11.1 kg Zn ha^{-1} was applied to soils for 6 yr. The relatively high tolerance of soybean to Zn applications was attributed partly to decreased uptake of the element at near-neutral soil pH values.

3. Organic Matter

Lindsay (1972) concluded that organic matter probably affects the availability of soil Zn in the following ways:

1. Soluble Zn-organic complexes, whether resulting from reactions with organic acids, amino acids, or fulvic acids, could increase the availability of soil Zn. Complexed Zn, presumably of organic origin, comprises an important fraction of the soluble Zn fraction of calcareous soils (Hodgson et al., 1966), and should increase diffusion of Zn to roots. This hypothesis is usually advanced to explain strong correlations of the type reported by Sillanpaa (1982) between soil organic-matter content and plant-Zn uptake. Tan et al. (1971) found that a 10-fold increase in the amounts of low molecular weight fractions complexed by Zn occurred when the pH was increased to 7.

2. Insoluble Zn-organic complexes could decrease the solubility of soil Zn and increase the likelihood of Zn deficiency. The availability of insoluble Zn-humic complexes to plants is considered to be low (Mathur & Farnham, 1985). However, little data are available indicating the importance of this effect under field or greenhouse conditions. Jahiruddin et al. (1985) concluded that Ca flocculates organic matter and usually prevents significant organic-matter solubilization. Thus, applied Zn may be strongly adsorbed by insoluble soil organic matter, especially at high pH values.

3. Root exudates may contain ligands, which could chelate Zn in the vicinity of plant roots. Release of ligands by alfalfa roots may explain why Zn deficiency in corn was reduced when alfalfa was grown with corn in the same pots in a greenhouse study (Hoagland et al., 1936).

4. Soil microbial activity could release available Zn from relatively unavailable sources. The evidence supporting this hypothesis is mostly of an indirect nature, such as the influence of preincubation of soil in decreasing the incidence of Zn deficiency in corn (Bauer & Lindsay, 1965). Soil microbial populations apparently may immobilize Zn (Ark, 1936), but such effects are not well understood.

The enigma of the old problem of Zn deficiency in crops such as edible bean and corn grown after sugar beet remains unresolved. Leggett and Westermann (1986) found that beans were Zn deficient when grown on soil previously fallowed or planted to sugar beet, but were healthy when grown on land previously cropped to corn. Proposed hypotheses to explain the data included recycling of elements through roots, chelate formation during corn root growth or decomposition, and mycorrhizal effects. Mycorrhizal plants are known to absorb more Zn than uninfected plants (Killham & Firestone, 1983); thus, VA mycorrhizas possibly need to be routinely monitored in studies involving Zn deficiency.

Zinc deficiency occurs widely in lowland rice in Asia and its incidence is positively correlated with high pH, low available soil Zn, and high organic matter contents (Yoshida et al., 1973). Forno et al. (1975) showed that readily decomposable organic matter aggravated Zn deficiency in rice. High HCO_3 concentrations resulting from the decomposition of organic matter immobilized Zn in the rice roots and reduced translocation to the shoots. Organic acids produced by anaerobic decomposition of organic matter may also have contributed to the problem. The data also indicated that products of microbial metabolism may be important in the development of Zn deficiency, even in unflooded conditions. Yoon et al. (1975) reported that HCO_3, OH, and possibly organic ligands from rice-straw addition apparently decreased solution Zn concentrations under flooded soil conditions.

Soils high in clay or organic matter have a higher adsorption capacity and bonding energy for Zn than sandy soils low in organic matter (Shuman, 1975). Rattan and Shukla (1984) reported that continued applications of Zn to alkaline sandy soils of low organic matter and clay contents in India may cause Zn toxicity. Such soils need to be monitored regularly for their Zn status. On the other hand, large applications of Zn could be made to soils high in clay or organic matter without causing Zn toxicity in plants. Zinc toxicity is relatively rare under field conditions, but the problem was observed in corn growing on Zn-rich soils adjacent to an abandoned Zn mine (Golden & Freedman, 1978).

4. Redox Potential

Zinc is not reduced under low redox conditions, but soil submergence resulted in a decrease in Zn concentration in the soil solution (Table 11–2). Concentration of Zn in rice plants decreased from 39 to 9 mg kg^{-1} when the pe + pH of the soil system was decreased from 14.99 to 4.00 (Sajwan & Lindsay, 1986). Precipitation of Zn as $ZnFe_2O_4$ or a similar franklinite-like solid material was suspected to be the causal factor for the reduced Zn concentration. Lowland rice growing on limed or calcareous soils often displays Zn deficiency (Gilmour & Kittrick, 1979; Ponnamperuma, 1972).

5. Nutrient Interactions

Many studies have shown that high soil P levels may induce Zn deficiency. In some cases, the reduction of plant-Zn concentrations with applied P was simply a dilution effect (Loneragan et al., 1979). Zinc deficiency due to dilution brought about by P-enhanced growth is certain to be a major factor where soil supplies of P and Zn are low.

Applied P tends to enhance the adsorption of Zn on certain soils (Ghanem & Mikkelsen, 1988; Saeed & Fox, 1979), and this may cause or intensify Zn deficiency. Saeed and Fox (1979) found that P additions increased Zn adsorption, especially in soils that were rich in hydrated Fe and Al oxides. Thus, the capacity of the soil to adsorb Zn is increased and Zn solubility is decreased. Some workers have found no effect of applied P on soil Zn (Pasricha et al., 1987), and others have found that P actually increased soil-Zn levels (Saeed, 1977).

Soltanpour (1969) applied Zn and P in separate bands to potato, but the P-Zn antagonism was still pronounced. Their results indicated that the effect of P in reducing Zn uptake was probably physiological rather than the result of a soil chemical reaction. Other research has indicated that P inhibited translocation of Zn from roots to tops (Terman et al., 1972). Youngdahl et al. (1977) reported that high P increased the amount of ^{65}Zn in the ethanol-soluble and pectate fractions of root cell walls. This binding of Zn to the cell wall may reduce the amount of Zn available for transport to the upper part of the plant. Phosphorus also may reduce plant Zn concentrations by reducing the Zn absorption rate by roots (Safaya, 1976).

An alternate hypothesis suggests that the P-induced Zn deficiency syndrome sometimes may involve symptoms of P toxicity in addition to the classical Zn-deficiency symptoms (Loneragan et al., 1979). Webb and Loneragan (1988) presented additional data to support the hypothesis that symptoms attributed to Zn deficiency in leaves with adequate Zn were probably due to P toxicity. They concluded that this provided a more simple interpretation for the P-induced Zn deficiency interaction within the plant than an increased physiological requirement for Zn (Cakmak & Marschner, 1987) or of the physiological inactivation of plant Zn (Leece, 1978). Safaya (1976) showed that P uptake is enhanced at low Zn levels.

Since Zn absorption by the plant root is closely related to diffusion, root volume should be directly related to Zn absorption. Friesen et al. (1980) reported increased total Zn uptake with increasing P rates. They attributed this to a larger root absorbing surface as a consequence of improved P nutrition. Application of P may reduce VA mycorrhizal infection on roots and such reduction may reduce Zn absorption (Singh et al., 1986). However, Lu and Miller (1989) found that high P levels greatly decreased VA mycorrhizal infection in both field and growth-chamber experiments, but did not affect the absorption of Zn.

Interactions involving Zn-Cu (Kausar et al., 1976), Zn-Fe (Giordano et al., 1974), Zn-Mn (Giordano eta l., 1974), Zn-K (Biswas et al., 1977), and Zn-N (Olsen, 1972) have also been reported in plant nutrition studies, but the P-Zn interaction is generally of greatest importance under most field situations.

III. CONCLUSIONS

As yield potentials increase, micronutrient nutrition, especially interactions with other elements, should become more important. Particular attention must be paid to effects of genetic diversity on micronutrient nutrition. Any newly discovered cases of micronutrient toxicity, particularly those of an anthropogenic nature, need to be studied. A recent monograph (Brooks et al., 1985) on the heavy-metal-tolerant flora of Africa raises many questions about the nature of resistance of plants to Cu and other heavy-metal toxicities.

The influence of root activity and VA-mycorrhizal infection on availability of micronutrients is receiving much needed research effort. An area that requires additional research effort concerns the possible value of cluster roots (sometimes referred to as proteoid roots) for enhancing micronutrient uptake. For example, interplanting white lupine (*Lupinus albus* L.), a plant that accumulates Mn and forms cluster roots, with wheat improved the Mn nutrition of the wheat plants (Gardner & Boundy, 1983). Cluster roots, a proliferation of bunches of small hairy rootlets on lateral roots of plants belonging to the Proteaceae and a few other genera, are believed to be important in nutrient uptake (Lamont, 1982). They are generally absent from plants of agricultural interest, but are found in some *Lupinus* species. Little is known about the mode of inheritance of the cluster-root characteristic.

Comments concerning areas of needed research for specific micronutrients are discussed in the following sections.

A. Boron

Organic matter is considered to be a major factor in B fertility, but strong research data supporting this contention is lacking. The B uptake-soil temperature data of Walker (1969) should be examined in more detail.

Additional studies involving the B nutrition of corn are warranted. Corn is unusual in that it requires a larger supply of B than most other monocotyledonous plants (Hewitt, 1984a). There is a possibility that interruption of B supply subsequent to tasseling, as a result of drought, high humidity, or heavy rainfall, could cause poor ear development (Mozafar, 1989). Such B-deficiency effects may not be evident from B analyses of soil or ear leaves. The causes and consequences of drought-induced B deficiency require additional research.

B. Copper

Knowledge concerning Cu nutrition of plants has increased greatly during the past two decades, principally because of research of Loneragan and his coworkers. However, the availability of Cu to crops susceptible to Cu deficiency, such as wheat treated with high rates of N fertilizer under potentially high yield conditions, requires further attention. The influence of Zn on such N-Cu interactions also needs to be studied. Progress is being made in Cu organic-matter research, and these studies should be continued.

C. Iron

The increased understanding of the role that plants can have on the availability of soil Fe has probably been the major achievement of micronutrient researchers since 1972. This research, particularly in relation to plants with the Strategy II-type Fe-response mechanism, should be continued. Development of Fe-efficient genotypes with useful agronomic characteristics retains high priority. Iron toxicity in rice is limiting rice production in parts of Africa, Asia, and South America, and this problem obviously requires additional research.

D. Manganese

The Mn cycle in well-drained soils is still not well understood relative to Mn fixation, the role of organic Mn complexes, and factors affecting Mn valency states. Soil drying affects the availability of Mn, but its cause still remains an enigma. Researchers studying the availability of Mn particularly need to review work from the 1936 to 1950 period and the proceedings of a recent Mn symposium (Graham et al., 1988).

The Fe-Mn interaction, although recognized as one of the most spectacular in plant nutrition, is still not understood from a physiological point of view. Major advances during the coming decade are expected in the development of Fe-efficient plants, especially of soybean. However, soybean is also susceptible to Mn deficiency, and the Mn status of highly Fe-efficient soybean genotypes should be evaluated. Additional research on Mn toxicity, and its amelioration through genetic approaches is warranted. The ability of certain plants to tolerate high Mn levels is well documented, but its relevance to most agricultural crops is mainly a matter of conjecture at this time.

E. Molybdenum

The role of Mo in plant (nonlegume) production in high-yield situations, where rather high rates of N fertilizers are frequently applied, needs to be carefully evaluated. Whether inadequate Mo levels ever limit the activity of NO_3-reductase in such situations should be determined.

Numerous, closed, drainage areas (potholes), which are grazed during dry periods or are occasionally artificially drained, occur in the northern USA and Canada. The soils in these areas are often slightly acid, neutral, or calcareous. Systematic study on the availability of Cu and Mo in these soils, and its relevance to molybdenosis, apparently has not been conducted.

F. Zinc

Most researchers who have studied Zn availability have not considered the possibility that their results were influenced by the degree of VA mycorrhizal infection or by the presence of phytosiderophores or pytochelatins.

Researchers need to determine whether soil temperature has differential effects on root and mycorrhizal development; mycorrhizal association has a significant effect on P-induced Zn deficiency; and whether mycorrhizal associations are reduced in crops growing on fallowed land and if it affects Zn deficiency.

Corn-intercropping systems are important in many tropical countries. The relevance of interactions between species on Zn availability (Hoagland et al., 1936) has received little attention.

Many questions exist about the influence of soil and added organic matter on Zn availability, but few advances have been made since Lindsay's (1972) review. The role of microbial populations on the incidence of Zn deficiency, as suggested by interesting observations from over 50 yr ago (Ark, 1936), has not been resolved. The effects of fallow and antecedent crops, such as sugar beet, on Zn deficiency are still not fully explained.

Many cases of Zn deficiency seem to involve poor translocation of Zn between roots and shoots. Some evidence is available that Zn translocation effects sometimes explains differences in Zn deficiency between cultivars of the same species. Additional physiological studies of these differences seem warranted.

Safaya's (1976) finding that Zn deficiency increased P uptake has led to a rethinking of the nature of P-induced Zn deficiency, and offers promising leads for useful research. All researchers need to consider the likelihood of P toxicity in their Zn-deficiency studies. However, the apical dieback symptom is not a typical P-toxicity symptom and, in a Zn-deficient plant such as flax, is aggravated by added P. Studies of the type conducted by Reed (1946), using modern cytological and analytical techniques, may be appropriate.

ACKNOWLEDGMENTS

The authors express their thanks to Dr. John Mortvedt of the National Fertilizer and Environmental Research Center, Muscle Shoals, Alabama, and Dr. Fred Cox of North Carolina State University for their assistance during preparation of this paper. Appreciation is also extended to two anonymous reviewers for their constructive comments on the original manuscript. Special thanks are also due to Mrs. Letha Cattanach of the Department of Soil Science, North Dakota State University for typing the manuscript.

REFERENCES

Adams, F., and R.W. Pearson. 1967. Crop response to lime in the southern United States and Puerto Rico. p. 161–206. *In* R.W. Pearson and F. Adams (ed.) Soil acidity and liming. Agron. Monogr. 12. ASA, Madison, WI.

Adriano, D.C. 1986. Trace elements in the terrestrial environment. Springer-Verlag, New York.

Aktaks, M., and F. van Egmond. 1979. Effect of nitrate nutrition and iron utilization by an Fe-efficient and an Fe-inefficient soybean cultivar. Plant Soil 51:257–274.

Allaway, W.H. 1977. Perspectives on molybdenum in soils and plants. p. 317–339. *In* W.R. Chappell and K.K. Petersen (ed.) Molybdenum in the environment. Vol. 2. Marcel Dekker, New York.

Alley, M.M., C.J. Rich, G.W. Hawkins, and D.C. Martens. 1978. Correction of Mn deficiency of soybeans. Agron. J. 70:35–38.

Alston, A.M., S.P. Harry, and G.D. Reddy. 1981. Influence of temperature on readily-extractable copper in soils. p. 357. *In* J.F. Loneragan et al. (ed.) Copper in soils and plants. Academic Press, Sydney, Australia.

Anderson, A.J. 1956. Molybdenum as a fertilizer. Adv. Agron. 8:163–202.

Anderson, A.J. 1970. Trace elements for sheep pastures and fodder crops in Australia. J. Aust. Inst. Agric. Sci. 36:15–29.

Anderson, A.J., and M.P. Thomas. 1946. Molybdenum and symbiotic nitrogen fixation. Council for Sci. and Ind. Res. (C.S.I.R.) Bull. 198. CSIR, Melbourne, Australia.

Anderson, O.E., and J.J. Mortvedt. 1982. Soybeans: diagnosis and correction of manganese and molybdenum problems. South. Coop. Ser. Bull. 281. Univ. of Georgia.

Andrew, C.S., and E.J. Kamprath (ed.). 1978. Mineral nutrition of legumes in tropical and subtropical soils. Commonwealth Sci. and Ind. Res. Org. (C.S.I.R.O.), Melbourne, Australia.

Anonymous. 1936. Boron and plant life. Spec. Publ., Boron Agric. Bur., London.

Ark, P.A. 1936. Little-leaf or rosette of fruit trees. Am. Soc. Hortic. Sci. Proc. 34:216–221.

Aubert, H., and M. Pinta. 1977. Trace elements in soils. Elsevier, Amsterdam, Netherlands.

Awad, F., V. Romheld, and H. Marschner. 1988. Mobilization of ferric iron from a calcareous soil by plant-borne chelators (phytosiderophores). J. Plant Nutr. 11:701–713.

Ayanlaja, S.A. 1984. Forms and pedogenic distribution of some extractable manganese in some soils of southern Nigeria. Commun. Soil Sci. Plant Anal. 15:65–79.

Azarbadi, S., and H. Marschner. 1979. Role of the rhizosphere in utilization of inorganic iron-III compounds by corn plants. Z. Pflanzenernaehr. Bodenkd. 142:751–764.

Barak, P., and Y. Chen. 1984. The effect of potassium on iron chlorosis in calcareous soils. J. Plant Nutr. 7:125–133.

Barber, S.A. 1957. Boron deficiency in Indiana soils. Purdue Agric. Exp. Stn. Bull. 652.

Barrow, N.J. 1977. Factors affecting the molybdenum status of soils. p. 583–595. *In* W.R. Chappell and K.K. Petersen (ed.) Molybdenum in the environment. Vol. 2. Marcel Dekker, New York.

Barrow, N.J., and T.C. Shaw. 1974. Factors affecting the long-term effectiveness of phosphate and molybdate fertilizers. Commun. Soil Sci. Plant Anal. 5:355–364.

Bartlett, R.J., and C.J. Picarelli. 1973. Availability of boron and phosphorus as affected by liming an acid potato soil. Soil Sci. 116:77–83.

Bar-Yosef, B., S. Fishman, and H. Talpaz. 1980. A model of zinc movement to single roots in soils. Soil Sci. Soc. Am. J. 44:1272–1279.

Batey, T. 1971. Manganese and boron deficiency. p. 137–149. *In* J. Webber (ed.) Trace elements in soils and crops. United Kingdom Ministry Agric., Fish., and Food Tech. Bull. 21. Her Majesty's Stationery Office, London.

Bauer, A., and W.L. Lindsay. 1965. The effect of soil temperature on the availability of indigenous soil zinc. Soil Sci. Soc. Am. Proc. 29:562–565.

Baxter, J.C., and M. Osman. 1988. Evidence for the existence of different uptake mechanisms in soybean and sorghum for iron and manganese. J. Plant Nutr. 11:51–64.

Beckwith, R.S., K.G. Tiller, and E. Suwadji. 1975. The effects of flooding on the availability of trace metals to rice in soils of differing organic matter status. p. 135–149. *In* D.C.D. Nicholas and A. Egan (ed.) Trace elements in soil-plant-animal systems. Academic Press, New York.

Bennett, J.H., N.J. Chatterton, and P.A. Harrison. 1988. Rhizosphere physiology of crested wheatgrass and legume seedlings: Root-shoot carbohydrate interactions. J. Plant Nutr. 11:1099–1116.

Berger, K.C. 1962. Micronutrient deficiencies in the United States. J. Agric. Food Chem. 10:178–181.

Berger, K.C., and E. Truog. 1944. Boron tests for soils and plants. Soil Sci. 57:25–36.

Bergmann, W. 1988. Ernährungsstörungen bei Kulturpflanzen. Gustav Fischer Verlag, Stuttgart, W. Germany.

Bingham, F.T., A.L. Page, N.T. Coleman, and K. Flach. 1971. Boron adsorption characteristics of selected amorphous soils from Mexico and Hawaii. Soil Sci. Soc. Am. J. 35:546–552.

Biswas, C.R., S. Rajinderjit, and G.S. Sekhon. 1977. Zinc availability to maize and wheat in relation to P and K status of the soil in a long-term fertility experiment. J. Indian Soc. Soil Sci. 25:414–421.

Bjerre, G.K., and H.H. Schierup. 1985. Influence of waterlogging on availability and uptake of heavy metals by oat grown in different soils. Plant Soil 88:45–56.

Bloom, P.R., and W.P. Inskeep. 1988. Factors affecting bicarbonate chemistry and iron chlorosis in soils. J. Plant Nutr. 9:215–228.

Boken, E. 1952. On the effect of storage and temperature on the exchangeable manganese in soil samples. Plant Soil 4:154–163.

Bouma, D. 1969. Effects of changes in boron nutrition on growth and development of subterranean clover. Aust. J. Biol. Sci. 22:523–533.

Bowen, G.D., M.F. Skinner, and D.I. Bevege. 1974. Zinc uptake by mycorrhizal and uninfected roots of *Pinus radiata* and *Araucaria cunninghamii*. Soil Biol. Biochem. 6:141–144.

Bowen, J.E. 1987. Physiology of genotypic differences in zinc and copper uptake in rice and tomato. Plant Soil 99:413–423.

Brams, E.A., and J.G.A. Fiskell. 1971. Copper accumulation in citrus roots and desorption with acid. Soil Sci. Soc. Am. Proc. 35:772–775.

Brandenburg, E. 1931. The heart and dry rot of beets as a symptom of boron deficiency. Phytopathol. Z. 3:499–517.

Branson, R.L. 1976. Soluble salts, exchangeable sodium, and boron in soils. p. 42–45. *In* H.M. Reisenauer (ed.) Soil and plant-tissue testing in California. Univ. California Div. of Agric. Sci. Bull. 1879, Davis, CA.

Branton, D., and L. Jacobson. 1962. Iron transport in pea plants. Plant Physiol. 37:539–545.

Bromfield, S.M. 1958a. The solution of γ-MnO_2 by substances released from soil and from the roots of oats and vetch in relation to manganese availability. Plant Soil 10:147–160.

Bromfield, S.M. 1958b. The properties of a biologically formed manganese oxide, its availability to oats and its solution by root washings. Plant Soil 9:325–337.

Brooks, R.R., F. Malaisse, and A. Empain. 1985. The heavy metal-tolerant flora of south-central Africa. A.A. Balkema, Rotterdam, Netherlands.

Brown, J.C. 1956. Iron chlorosis. Annu. Rev. Plant Physiol. 7:171–190.

Brown, J.C. 1972. Competition between phosphate and the plant for Fe from Fe^{2+} ferrozine. Agron. J. 64:240–243.

Brown, J.C., and J.E. Ambler. 1973. "Reductants" released by roots of Fe-deficient soybeans. Agron. J. 65:311–314.

Brown, J.C., H.M. Cathey, J.H. Bennett, and R.W. Thimijan. 1979. Effect of light quality and temperature on Fe^{3+} reduction, and chlorophyll concentration in plants. Agron. J. 71:1015–1021.

Brown, J.C., and W.E. Jones. 1977. Fitting plants nutritionally to soils. II. Cotton. Agron. J. 69:405–409.

Burleson, C.A., A.D. Dacus, and C.J. Gerard. 1961. The effect of phosphorus fertilization on zinc nutrition of several irrigated crops. Soil Sci. Soc. Am. Proc. 25:365–368.

Burtch, L.M., D.W. Thorne, and F.B. Wann. 1948. The effect of light, soil temperature, and soil moisture on high-lime chlorosis. Soil Sci. Soc. Am. Proc. 13:394–398.

Byron, D.F., and J.W. Lambert. 1983. Screening soybeans for iron efficiency in the growth chamber. Crop Sci. 23:885–888.

Cakmak, I., and H. Marschner. 1987. Mechanism of phosphorus-induced zinc deficiency in cotton. III. Changes in physiological availability of zinc in plants. Physiol. Plant. 70:13–20.

Caldwell, T.H. 1971. Copper deficiency in crops: II. Copper deficiency in peats and sands in East Anglia. p. 73–87. *In* J. Webber (ed.) Trace elements in soils and crops. United Kingdom Ministry Agric., Fish., and Food Tech. Bull. 21. Her Majesty's Stationery Office, London.

Cavallaro, N., and M.B. McBride. 1984. Zinc and copper status and fixation by an acid soil clay: Effect of selective dissolutions. Soil Sci. Soc. Am. J. 48:1050–1054.

Chaney, R.L. 1984. Diagnostic practices to identify iron deficiency in higher plants. J. Plant Nutr. 7:47–67.

Chapman, H.D., A.P. Vanselow, and G. Liebig. 1937. The production of citrus mottle leaf in controlled nutrient cultures. J. Agric. Res. 55:365–379.

Chaudhry, F.M., and J.F. Loneragan. 1970. Effects of nitrogen, copper, and zinc fertilizers on the copper and zinc nutrition of wheat plants. Aust. J. Agric. Res. 21:865–879.

Chaudhry, F.M., and J.F. Loneragan. 1972. Zinc absorption by wheat seedlings: I. Inhibition by macronutrient ions in short-term experiments and its relevance to long-term zinc nutrition. Soil Sci. Soc. Am. Proc. 36:323-327.

Chen, Y., and P. Barak. 1982. Iron nutrition of plants in calcareous soils. Adv. Agron. 35:217-240.

Cheng, B.T. 1982. The role of iodine, silicon and titanium on manganese toxicity in an acid soil. Agrochimica 25:258-267.

Cheng, B.T., and G.J. Ouellette. 1971. Manganese availability in soil. Soil Fert. 34:589-595.

Chesney, H.A.D. 1972. Yield response of pangolagrass grown on Tiwiwid fine sand to Mg and fritted micronutrients. Agron. J. 64:152-154.

Childs, C.W., and D.M. Leslie. 1977. Interelement relationships in iron-manganese concretions from a catenary sequence of yellow-grey earth soils in loess. Soil Sci. 123:369-376.

Clark, F.E., D.C. Nearpass, and A.W. Specht. 1957. Influence of organic additions and flooding on iron and manganese uptake by rice. Agron. J. 49:586-589.

Clarkson, D.T., and J. Sanderson. 1978. Sites of absorption and translocation of iron in barley roots. Plant Physiol. 61:731-736.

Cox, F.R., and J.I. Wear. 1977. Diagnosis and correction of zinc problems in corn and rice production. South. Coop. Ser. Bull. 222. North Carolina State Univ.

Dahiya, S.G., and M. Singh. 1977. Effect of $CaCO_3$ and iron application on the availability of manganese in light textured soils. Plant Soil 46:239-243.

DeKock, P.C., A. Hall, and R.H.E. Inkson. 1979. Active iron in plant leaves. Ann. Bot. 43:737-740.

Dion, H.G., and P.J.G. Mann. 1946. Trivalent manganese in soils. J. Agric. Sci. 36:239-245.

Dionne, J.L., and A.R. Pesant. 1986. Effets des regimes hydriques et des pH du sol sur la reponse au molybdene de la luzerne. Can. J. Soil Sci. 66:421-435.

Dowdy, R.H., and W.E. Larson. 1975. Metal uptake by barley seedlings grown on soils amended with sewage sludge. J. Environ. Qual. 4:229-233.

Edwards, J.H., and E.J. Kamprath. 1974. Zinc accumulation by corn seedlings as influenced by phosphorus, temperature and light intensity. Agron. J. 66:479-482.

Elliott, G.C., and A. Lauchli. 1985. Phosphorus efficiency and phosphate-iron interaction in maize. Agron. J. 77:399-403.

Elliott, L.F., and J.W. Blaylock. 1975. Effects of wheat straw and alfalfa amendments on solubilization of manganese and iron in soil. Soil Sci. 120:205-211.

Epstein, E. 1971. Effect of soil temperature on mineral element composition of the potato plant. Agron. J. 63:661-666.

Evans, C.M., and D.L. Sparks. 1983. On the chemistry and mineralogy of boron in pure and in mixed systems. Commun. Soil Sci. Plant Anal. 14:827-846.

Fagbami, A., S.O. Ajayi, and E.M. Ali. 1985. Nutrient distribution in the basement complex soils of the tropical, dry rainforest of southwestern Nigeria: 2. Micronutrients—zinc and copper. Soil Sci. 139:531-537.

Faust, M., and C.B. Shear. 1968. Corking disorders of apples: A physiological and biochemical review. Bot. Rev. 34:441-469.

Fido, R.J., C.S. Gundry, E.J. Hewitt, and B.A. Notton. 1977. Ultra-structural features of molybdenum deficiency and whiptail of cauliflower leaves: Effect of nitrogen source and tungsten substitution for molybdenum. Aust. J. Plant Physiol. 4:675-689.

Flannery, R.L. 1985. Understanding boron needs in crop production. Fert. Progres 16(3):41-45.

Fleming, G.A. 1980. Essential micronutrients. I. Boron and molybdenum. p. 155-197. In B.E. Davies (ed.) Applied soil trace elements. John Wiley and Sons, Chichester, England.

Follett, R.H., and W.L. Lindsay. 1970. Profile distribution of zinc, iron, manganese and copper in Colorado soils. Colorado Agric. Exp. Stn. Tech. Bull. 110.

Forno, D.A., S. Yoshida, and C.J. Asher. 1975. Zinc deficiency in rice. I. Soil factors associated with the deficiency. Plant Soil 42:537-550.

Foy, C.D. 1983. Plant adaptation to mineral stress in problem soils. Iowa State J. Res. 57:339-354.

Francois, L.E., and J.R. Goodin. 1972. Interaction of temperature and salinity on sugar beet germination. Agron. J. 64:272-273.

Frank, S.J., and W.R. Fehr. 1983. Band application of sulfuric acid or elemental sulfur for control of Fe-deficiency chlorosis of soybeans. Agron.J. 75:451-454.

Freney, J.R., and J. Lipsett. 1965. Yield depression in wheat due to nitrate application, and its alleviation by molybdenum. Nature 205:616-617.

Friesen, D.K., M.H. Miller, and A.S.O. Juo. 1980. Liming and lime-phosphorus-zinc interactions in two Nigerian Ultisols: II. Effects on maize root and shoot growth. Soil Sci. Soc. Am. J. 44:1227–1232.

Fujimoto, C.K., and G.D. Sherman. 1945. The effect of drying, heating, and wetting on the level of exchangeable manganese in Hawaiian soils. Soil Sci. Soc. Am. Proc. 10:107–112.

Fujiwara, A., and H. Ishida. 1964. Acceleration of manganese uptake by rice plant grown under unfavorable temperature or light condition. Tohoku J. Agric. Res. 14:209–215.

Gardner, W.K., and K.A. Boundy. 1983. The acquisition of phosphorus by *Lupinus albus* L. IV. The effect of interplanting wheat and white lupin on the growth and mineral composition of the two species. Plant Soil 70:391–402.

Gartrell, J.W. 1981. Distribution and correction of copper deficiency in crops and pastures. p. 313–350. *In* J.F. Loneragan et al. (ed.) Copper in soils and plants. Academic Press, Sydney, Australia.

Geiger, S.C., and R.H. Loeppert. 1988. The effect of soil gas-phase CO_2 concentration on Fe-deficiency chlorosis of soybean and sorghum grown on calcareous soils. J. Plant Nutr. 11:1394–1502.

Gerdemann, J.W. 1975. Vesicular-arbuscular mycorrhizae. *In* G.D. Torrey and D.T. Clarkson (ed.) The development and function of roots. Academic Press, London.

Ghanem, S.A., and D.S. Mikkelsen. 1988. Sorption of zinc on iron hydrous oxide. Soil Sci. 146:15–21.

Ghazali, N.J., and F.R. Cox. 1981. Effect of temperature on soybean growth and manganese accumulation. Agron. J. 73:363–367.

Gibson, A.J. 1987. Evaluation of nitrogen fixation by legumes in the greenhouse and growth chamber. p. 321–370. *In* G.H. Elkan (ed.) Symbiotic nitrogen fixation technology. Marcel Dekker, New York.

Giddens, J., and H.F. Perkins. 1972. Essentiality of molybdenum for alfalfa on highly oxidized Piedmont soils. Agron. J. 64:819–820.

Gilmour, J.T., and J.A. Kittrick. 1979. Solubility and equilibria of zinc in a flooded soil. Soil Sci. Soc. Am. J. 43:890–892.

Giordano, P.M., and J.J. Mortvedt. 1978. Response of corn to Zn in ortho- and pyrophosphate fertilizers, as affected by soil temperature and moisture. Agron. J. 70:531–534.

Giordano, P.M., J.C. Noggle, and J.J. Mortvedt. 1974. Zinc uptake by rice as affected by metabolic inhibitors and competing cations. Plant Soil 41:637–646.

Glinski, J., and V.C. Thai. 1971. Soluble trace elements (Mn, Cu, B, Zn, Mo) in the soils of North Vietnam. Pol. J. Soil Sci. 4:125–130.

Godo, G.H., and H.M. Reisenauer. 1980. Plant effects on soil manganese availability. Soil Sci. Soc. Am. J. 44:993–995.

Golden, M.L., and J. Freedman. 1978. Zinc toxicity in corn as a result of a geochemical anomaly. Plant Soil 50:151–159.

Goodman, B.A., and M.V. Cheshire. 1976. The occurrence of copper-porphyrin complexes in soil humic acids. J. Soil Sci. 27;337–347.

Goodman, B.A., and M.V. Cheshire. 1982. Reduction of molybdate by soil organic matter: EPR evidence for formation of both Mo (V) and Mo (III). Nature (London) 399:618–620.

Goodman, B.A., and D.J. Linehan. 1979. An electron paramagnetic resonance study of the uptake of Mn (II) and Cu (II) by wheat roots. p. 67–82. *In* J.L. Harley and R.S. Russell (ed.) The soil-root interface. Academic Press, London.

Gotoh, S., and W.H. Patrick, Jr. 1972. Transformation of manganese in a waterlogged soil as affected by redox potential and pH. Soil Sci. Soc. Am. Proc. 36:738–742.

Gotoh, S., and W.H. Patrick, Jr. 1974. Transformation of iron in a waterlogged soil as influenced by redox potential and pH. Soil Sci. Soc. Am. Proc. 38:66–71.

Graham, R.D. 1981. Absorption of copper by plant roots. p. 141–163. *In* J.F. Loneragan et al. (ed.) Copper in soils and plants. Academic Press, Sydney, Australia.

Graham, R.D., W.J. Davies, and J.S. Ascher. 1985. The critical concentration of manganese in field-grown wheat. Aust. J. Agric. Res. 36:145–155.

Graham, R.D., R.J. Hannam, and N.C. Uren (ed.). 1988. Manganese in soils and plants. Kluwer Academic Publ., Dordrecht, Netherlands.

Graham, R.D., R.M. Welch, D.L. Grunes, E.E. Cary, and W.A. Norvell. 1987. Effect of zinc deficiency on the accumulation of boron and other mineral nutrients in barley. Soil Sci. Soc. Am. J. 51:652–657.

Grasmanis, V.O., and G.W. Leeper. 1966. Toxic manganese in near neutral soils. Plant Soil 25:41–48.

Graven, E.H., O.J. Attoe, and D. Smith. 1965. Effect of liming and flooding on manganese toxicity in alfalfa. Soil Sci. Soc. Am. Proc. 29:702–706.

Graves, C.J., and J.F. Sutcliffe. 1974. An effect of copper deficiency on the initiation and development of flower buds of *Chrysanthemum morifolium* grown in solution culture. Ann. Bot. 38:729–738.

Grill, E., E. Winnacker, and M.H. Zenk. 1985. Phytochelatins: The principal heavy-metal complexing peptides of higher plants. Science 230:674–676.

Grunes, D.L., L.C. Boawn, C.W. Carlson, and R.G. Viets. 1961. Land-leveling may cause zinc deficiency. N.D. Farm Res. 21(11):4–7.

Gunawardena, I., S.S. Virmani, and F.J. Sumo. 1982. Breeding rice for tolerance to iron toxicity. Oryza (Cuttack, India) 19:5–12.

Gupta, U.C. 1968. Relationship of total and hot-water soluble boron, and fixation of added boron, to properties of Podzol soils. Soil Sci. Soc. Am. Proc. 32:45–48.

Gupta, U.C. 1969. Effect and interaction of molybdenum and limestone on growth and molybdenum content of cauliflower, alfalfa, and bromegrass on acid soils. Soil Sci. Soc. Am. Proc. 33:929–932.

Gupta, U.C. 1971. Influence of various organic materials on the recovery of molybdenum and copper added to a sandy clay loam soil. Plant Soil 34:249–253.

Gupta, U.C. 1978. Boron nutrition of crops. Adv. Agron. 31:273–307.

Gupta, U.C., Y.M. Jame, C.A. Campbell, A.J. Leyshon, and W. Nicholaichuk. 1985. Boron toxicity and deficiency: A review. Can. J. Soil Sci. 65:381–409.

Gupta, U.C., and J. Lipsett. 1981. Molybdenum in soils, plants, and animals. Adv. Agron. 34:73–115.

Gupta, U.C., and J.A. MacLeod. 1975. The effects of sulfur and molybdenum on the molybdenum, copper, and sulfur concentrations of forage crops. Soil Sci. 119:441–447.

Gupta, U.C., and J.A. MacLeod. 1977. Influence of calcium and magnesium sources on boron uptake and yield of alfalfa and rutabaga as related to soil pH. Soil Sci. 124:279–284.

Gupta, U.C., and J.A. Sutcliffe. 1968. Influence of phosphorus on molybdenum content of brussel sprouts under field and greenhouse conditions and on recovery of added molybdenum in soil. Can. J. Soil Sci. 48:117–123.

Haby, V.A., W.B. Anderson, and C.D. Welch. 1979. Effect of limestone variables on amendment of acid soils and production of corn and coastal bermudagrass. Soil Sci. Soc. Am. J. 43:343–347.

Haldar, H.M., and L.N. Mandal. 1979. Influence of soil moisture regimes and organic matter applications on the extractable Zn and Cu content in rice soils. Plant Soil 53:203–213.

Haldar, M., and L.N. Mandal. 1981. Effect of P and Zn on the growth and P, Zn, Cu, Fe and Mn nutrition of rice. Plant Soil 59:415–420.

Hammes, J.K., and K.C. Berger. 1960. Chemical extraction and crop removal of manganese from air-dried and moist soils. Soil Sci. Soc. Am. Proc. 24:361–364.

Harley, C.P., and R.C. Lindner. 1945. Observed responses of apple and pear trees to some irrigation waters of north central Washington. Am. Soc. Hortic. Sci. Proc. 46:35–44.

Hawes, R.L., J.L. Sims, and K.L. Wells. 1976. Molybdenum concentration of certain crop species as influenced by previous applications of molybdenum fertilizer. Agron. J. 68:217–218.

Hayman, D.S. 1974. Plant growth responses to vesicular-arbuscular mycorrhiza. VI. Effect of light and temperature. New Phytol. 73:71–80.

Heenan, D.P., and O.G. Carter. 1977. Influence of temperature on the expression of manganese toxicity by two soybean varieties. Plant Soil 47:219–227.

Helyar, K.R., and A.J. Anderson. 1974. Effects of calcium carbonate on the availability of nutrients in an acid soil. Soil Sci. Soc. Am. Proc. 38:341–346.

Hewitt, E.J. 1966. Sand and water culture methods used in the study of plant nutrition. Commonwealth Bur. Hortic. Plant. Crops Tech. Bomm. 22. East Malling, Maidstone, Kent.

Hewitt, E.J. 1984a. The essential and functional mineral elements. p. 7–53. In J.B.D. Robinson (ed.) Diagnosis of mineral disorders in plants. Vol. 1. Chemical Publ., New York.

Hewitt, E.J. 1984b. The effects of mineral deficiencies and excesses on growth and composition. p. 54–110. In J.B.D. Robinson (ed.) Diagnosis of mineral disorders in plants. Vol. 1. Chemical Publ., New York.

Hewitt, E.J., and C.S. Gundry. 1970. The molybdenum requirement of plants in relation to nitrogen supply. J. Hortic. Sci. 45:351–358.

Hill, J., A.D. Robson, and J.F. Loneragan. 1978. The effects of copper and nitrogen supply on the retranslocation of copper in four cultivars of wheat. Aust. J. Agric. Res. 29:925–939.

Hill, W.E., and L.G. Morrill. 1975. Boron, calcium and potassium interactions in Spanish peanuts. Soil Sci. Soc. Am. Proc. 39:80-83.

Hoagland, D.R. 1944. Lectures on the inorganic nutrition of plants. Chronica Botanica Co., Waltham, MA.

Hoagland, D.R., W.H. Chandler, and P.L. Hibbard. 1936. Little leaf or rosette of fruit trees. V. Effect of zinc on the growth of plants of various types in controlled soil and water culture experiments. Am. Soc. Hortic. Sci. Proc. 33:133-141.

Hodgson, J.F., W.L. Lindsay, and J.F. Trierweiler. 1966. Micronutrient cation complexing in soil solution: II. Complexing of zinc and copper in displaced solution from calcareous soils. Soil Sci. Soc. Am. Proc. 30:723-726.

Horiguchi, T. 1989. Mechanism of manganese toxicity and tolerance of plants. J. Plant Nutr. 11:235-246.

Horst, W.J., and H. Marschner. 1978. Effect of silicon on manganese tolerance of bean plants (*Phaseolus vulgaris* L.). Plant Soil 50:287-303.

Howeler, R.H. 1973. Iron-induced oranging disease of rice in relation to physico-chemical changes in a flooded Oxisol. Soil Sci. Soc. Am. Proc. 37:898-903.

Hue, N.V. 1988. A possible mechanism for manganese phytotoxicity in Hawaii soils amended with a low-manganese sewage sludge. J. Environ. Qual. 17:473-479.

Inskeep, W.P., and P.R. Bloom. 1986. Effects of soil moisture on soil pCO_2, soil solution bicarbonate, and iron chlorosis in soybeans. Soil Sci. Soc. Am. J. 50:946-952.

Iu, K.L., I.D. Pulford, and H.J. Duncan. 1981. Influence of waterlogging and lime or organic matter additions on the distribution of trace metals in an acid soil. II. Zinc and copper. Plant Soil 59:327-333.

Jackson, T.L., and G.E. Carter. 1976. Nutrient uptake by Russet Burbank potatoes as influenced by fertilization. Agron. J. 68:9-12.

Jahiruddin, M., N.T. Livesey, and M.S. Cresser. 1985. Observation on the effect of soil pH upon zinc adsorption by soils. Commun. Soil Sci. Plant Anal. 16:909-922.

James, D.W., T.L. Jackson, and M.E. Harward. 1968. Effect of molybdenum and lime on the growth and molybdenum content of alfalfa grown on acid soils. Soil Sci. 105:397-402.

Jarvis, S.C. 1981a. Copper concentrations in plants and their relationship to soil properties. p. 265-286. *In* J.F. Loneragan et al. (ed.) Copper in soils and plants. Academic Press, Sydney, Australia.

Jarvis, S.C. 1981b. The uptake and distribution of copper in some forage grasses as affected by nitrate-nitrogen supply in flowing solution culture. Ann. Bot. 48:147-157.

Jarvis, S.C., and D.W. Whitehead. 1981. The influence of some soil and plant factors on the concentration of copper in perennial ryegrass. Plant Soil 60:275-286.

Jeffrey, J.J., and N.C. Uren. 1983. Copper and zinc species in the soil solution and the effects of soil pH. Aust. J. Soil Res. 21:479-488.

Johansen, C. 1978. Response of some tropical grasses to molybdenum application. Aust. J. Exp. Agric. Anim. Husb. 18:732-736.

Johansen, C., P.C. Kerridge, P.E. Luck, B.G. Cook, and K.F. Lowe, and H. Ostrowski. 1977. The residual effect of molybdenum fertilizer on growth of tropical pasture legumes in a subtropical environment. Aust. J. Exp. Agric. Anim. Husb. 17:961-968.

Johnson, C.M., G.A. Pearson, and P.R. Stout. 1952. Molybdenum nutrition of crop plants. Plant Soil 4:178-196.

Jolley, V.D., J.C. Brown, M.J. Blaylock, and S.D. Camp. 1988. A role for potassium in the use of iron by plants. J. Plant Nutr. 11:1159-1175.

Jolley, V.D., J.C. Brown, J. Pushnick, and G. Miller. 1987. Influences of ultra-violet-blue light radiation on the growth of cotton. I. Effect on iron nutrition and iron stress response. J. Plant Nutr. 10:333-351.

Jones, H.E., and J.R. Etherington. 1970. Comparative studies of plant growth and distribution in relation to waterlogging. I. The survival of *Erica cinerea* L. and *E. tetralix* L. and its apparent relationship to iron and manganese uptake in waterlogged soil. J. Ecol. 58:487-496.

Jones, J., Jr. (ed.). 1982. Proceedings of the first international symposium on iron nutrition and interactions in plants. J. Plant Nutr. 5(4-7):229-1001.

Jones, J., Jr. (ed.). 1984. Proceedings of the second international symposium on iron nutrition and interactions in plants. J. Plant Nutr. 7(1-5):1-1774.

Jones, J., Jr. (ed.). 1986. Proceedings of the third international symposium on iron nutrition and interactions in plants. J. Plant Nutr. 9(3-7):161-1076.

Jones, J., Jr. (ed.). 1988. Proceedings of the fourth international symposium on iron nutrition and interactions in plants. J. Plant Nutr. 11(6–11):605–1621.

Jones, J.P., and R.L. Fox. 1978. Phosphorus nutrition of plants influenced by manganese and aluminum uptake from an Oxisol. Soil Sci. 126:230–236.

Jugsujinda, A., and W.H. Patrick, Jr. 1977. Growth and nutrient uptake by rice in a flooded soil under controlled aerobic-anaerobic and pH conditions. Agron.J. 69:705–710.

Kalbasi, M., F. Filsoof, and Y. Rezai-Nejad. 1988. Effect of sulfur treatments on yield and uptake of Fe, Zn and Mn by corn, sorghum and soybeans. J. Plant Nutr. 11:1353–1360.

Kalbasi, M., G.J. Racz, and L.A. Loewer-Rudgers. 1978. Mechanism of zinc adsorption by iron and aluminum oxides. Soil Sci. 125:146–150.

Karim, J., and J.E. Sedberry, Jr. 1976. The profile distribution of Zn in selected soils in Louisiana. Commun. Soil Sci. Plant Anal. 7:453–464.

Karimian, N., and F.R. Cox. 1978. Adsorption and extractability of molybdenum in relation to some chemical properties of soil. Soil Sci. Soc. Am. J. 42:757–761.

Karimian, N., and F.R. Cox. 1979. Molybdenum availability as predicted from selected soil chemical properties. Agron. J. 71:63–65.

Kausar, M.A., F.M. Chaudhry, A. Rashid, A. Latif, and S.M.Alam. 1976. Micronutrient availability to cereals from calcareous soils. I. Comparative Zn and Cu deficiency and their mutual interaction in rice and wheat. Plant Soil 45:397–410.

Keisling, T.C., D.A. Lauer, M.E. Walker, and R.J. Henning. 1977. Visual, tissue and soil factors associated with Zn toxicity of peanuts. Agron. J. 69:765–769.

Keren, R., and F.T. Bingham. 1985. Boron in water, soils, and plants. Adv. Soil Sci. 1:229–276.

Keren, R., F.T. Bingham, and J.D. Rhoades. 1985. Effect of clay content in soil on boron uptake and yield of wheat. Soil Sci. Soc. Am. J. 49:1466–1470.

Khan, A., and P.N. Soltanpour. 1978. Effect of wetting and drying on DTPA-extractable Fe, Zn, Mn, and Cu in soils. Commun. Soil Sci. Plant Anal. 9:193–202.

Khan, S.U. 1969. Interaction between the humic acid fraction of soils and certain metallic cations. Soil Sci. Soc. Am. proc. 33:851–854.

Khanna, P.K., and B. Mishra. 1978. Behavior of manganese in some acid soils in western Germany in relation to pH and air-drying. Geoderma 20:289–297.

Killham, K., and M.K. Firestone. 1983. Vesicular arbuscular mycorrhizal mediation of grass response to acidic and heavy metal deposition. Plant Soil 72:39–48.

Kinniburgh, D.G., and M.L. Jackson. 1982. Concentration and pH dependence of calcium and zinc adsorption by iron hydrous oxide gel. Soil Sci. Soc. Am. J. 46:56–61.

Knezek, B.D., and H. Greinert. 1971. Influence of soil iron and manganese chelate interactions upon the iron and manganese nutrition of bean plants (*Phaseolus vulgaris* L.). Agron. J. 63:617–619.

Kohl, H.C., and J.J. Oertli. 1961. Distribution of boron in leaves. Plant Physiol. 36:420–424.

Krauskopf, K.B. 1972. Geochemistry of micronutrients. p. 7–40. *In* J.J. Mortvedt et al. (ed.) Micronutrients in agriculture. 1st ed. SSSA, Madison, WI.

Kriedemann, P.E., R.D. Graham, and J.T. Wiskich. 1985. Photosynthetic dysfunction and in vivo changes in chlorophyll-b fluorescence from manganese-deficient wheat leaves. Aust. J. Agric. Res. 36:157–169.

Krishnamurti, G.S.R., and P.M. Huang. 1988. Kinetics of manganese released from selected manganese oxide minerals as influenced by potassium chloride. Soil Sci. 146:326–334.

Kubota, J. 1972. Sampling of soils for trace element studies. p. 105–115. *In* H.C. Hopps and H.L. Cannon (ed.) Geochemical environment in relation to health and disease. Geological Soc. Am., Boulder, CO.

Kubota, J. 1977. Molybdenum status of United States soils and plants. p. 555–581. *In* W.R. Chappell and K.K. Petersen (ed.) Molybdenum in the environment. Vol. 2. Marcel Dekker Inc., New York.

Kubota, J., E.R. Lemon, and W.H. Allaway. 1963. The effect of soil moisture content upon the uptake of molybdenum, copper and cobalt by alsike clover. Soil Sci. Soc. Am. Proc. 27:679–683.

Kubota, J., V.A. Lozar, L.N. Langan, and K.C. Beeson. 1961. The relationship of soil to molybdenum toxicity in cattle in Nevada. Soil Sci. Soc. Am. Proc. 25:227–232.

Kuo, S., and D.S. Mikkelsen. 1981. Effect of P and Mn on growth response and uptake of Fe, Mn and P by sorghum. Plant Soil 62:15–22.

Labanauskas, C.K. 1966. Manganese. p. 264–285. *In* H.D. Chapman (ed.) Diagnostic criteria for plants and soils. Univ. of California Div. Agric. Sci., Berkeley, CA.

Lamont, B. 1982. Mechanisms for enhancing nutrient uptake in plants, with particular reference to mediterranean South Africa and Western Australia. Bot. Rev. 48:597–689.

Leece, D.R. 1978. Distribution of physiologically inactive zinc in maize growing on a black earth soil. Aust. J. Agric. Res. 29:749–758.

Leeper, G.W. 1947. The forms and reactions of manganese in the soil. Soil Sci. 63:79–94.

Leggett, G.E., and D.P. Argyle. 1983. The DTPA-extractable iron, manganese, copper, and zinc from neutral and calcareous soils dried under different conditions. Soil Sci. Soc. Am. J. 47:518–522.

Leggett, G.E., and D.T. Westermann. 1986. Effect of corn, sugarbeets and fallow on zinc availability to subsequent crops. Soil Sci. Soc. Am. J. 50:963–968.

Leonard, C.D., and I. Stewart. 1952. Correction of iron chlorosis in citrus with chelated iron. Proc. Fla. State Hortic. Soc. 65:20–24.

Levesque, M., and S.P. Mathur. 1988. Soil tests for copper, iron, manganese and zinc in Histosols: 3. A comparison of eight extractants for measuring active and reserve forms of the elements. Soil Sci. 145:215–221.

Lindsay, W.L. 1972. Zinc in soils and plant nutrition. Adv. Agron. 24:147–186.

Lindsay, W.L. 1978. Chemical equilibria in soils. John Wiley and Sons, New York.

Lindsay, W.L. 1984. Soil and plant relationships associated with iron deficiency with emphasis on nutrient interactions. J. Plant Nutr. 7:489–500.

Little, R.C. 1971. The treatment of iron deficiency. p. 45–61. In J. Webber (ed.) Trace elements in soils and crops. United Kingdom Ministry Agric., Fish., and Food Tech. Bull. 21. Her Majesty's Stationery Office, London.

Liu, Z., Q.Q. Zhu, and L.H. Tang. 1983. Microelements in the main soils of China. Soil Sci. 135:40–46.

Loeppert, R.H., and E.T. Clark. 1984. Reactions of Fe^{2+} and Fe^{3+} in calcareous soils. J. Plant Nutr. 7:149–163.

Loganathan, P., R.G. Burau, and D.W. Fuerstenau. 1977. Influence of pH on Co^{2+}, Zn^{2+} and Ca^{2+} by a hydrous manganese oxide. Soil Sci. Soc. Am. J. 41:57–62.

Lombin, G. 1983. Evaluating the micronutrient fertility of Nigeria's semiarid savanna soils. 1. Copper and manganese. Soil Sci. 135:377–384.

Loneragan, J.F. 1975. The availability and absorption of trace elements in soil-plant systems and their relation to movement and concentrations of trace elements in plants. p. 109–133. In D.J.D. Nicholas and A.R. Egan (ed.) Trace elements in soil-plant-animal systems. Academic Press, New York.

Loneragan, J.F., Y.S. Grove, A.D. Robson, and K. Snowball. 1979. Phosphorus toxicity as a factor in zinc-phosphorus interactions in plants. Soil Sci. Soc. Am. J. 43:966–972.

Loneragan, J.F., A.D. Robson, and R.D. Graham (ed.). 1981. Copper in soils and plants. Academic Press, Sydney, Australia.

Loneragan, J.F., K. Snowball, and A.D. Robson. 1980. Copper supply in relation to content and redistribution of copper among organs of the wheat plant. Ann. Bot. 45:621–632.

Lovatt, C.J. 1985. Evolution of xylem resulted in a requirement for boron in the apical meristems of vascular plants. New Phytol. 99:509–522.

Lu, S., and M.H. Miller. 1989. The role of VA mycorrhizae in the absorption of P and Zn by maize in field and growth chamber experiments. Can. J. Soil Sci. 69:97–109.

Lucas, R.E., and B.D. Knezek. 1972. Climatic and soil conditions promoting micronutrient deficiencies in plants. p. 265–288. In J.J. Mortvedt et al. (ed.) Micronutrients in agriculture. 1st ed. SSSA, Madison, WI.

MacMillan, K.A., and H.A. Hamilton. 1971. Carrot response to soil temperature and copper, manganese, zinc and magnesium. Can. J. Soil Sci. 51:293–297.

Mandal, L.N., and H.M. Haldar. 1980. Influence of phosphorus and zinc application on the availability of zinc, copper, iron, manganese and phosphorus in waterlogged rice soils. Soil Sci. 130:251–257.

Mann, P.J.G., and J.H. Quastel. 1946. Manganese metabolism in soils. Nature 158:154–156.

Marschner, H. 1986. Mineral nutrition of higher plants. Academic Press, London.

Marschner, H. 1988. Mechanisms of manganese acquisition by roots from soil. p. 191–204. In R.D. Graham et al. (ed.) Manganese in soils and plants. Kluwer Academic Publ., Dordrecht, Netherlands.

Marschner, H., V. Romheld, W.J. Horst, and P. Martin. 1986a. Root-induced changes in the rhizosphere: Importance for the mineral nutrition of plants. Z. Pflanzenernaehr. Bodenk. 149:441–456.

Marschner, H., V. Romheld, and M. Kissel. 1986b. Different strategies in higher plants in mobilization and uptake of iron. J. Plant Nutr. 9:695–713.

Marsh, K.B., L.A. Peterson, and B.H. McCown. 1987. A microculture method for assessing nutrient uptake: The effect of phosphate on manganese uptake and toxicity. J. Plant Nutr. 10:1457–1469.

Marsh, K.B., L.A. Peterson, and B.H. McCown. 1989. A micronutrient method for assessing nutrient uptake. II. The effect of temperature on manganese uptake and toxicity in potato shoots. J. Plant Nutr. 12:219–232.

Martens, D.C. 1968. Plant availability of extractable boron, copper and zinc as related to selected soil properties. Soil Sci. 106:23–28.

Martens, D.C., M.T. Carter, and G.D. Jones. 1974. Response of soybeans following six annual applications of various levels of boron, copper and zinc. Agron. J. 66:82–84.

Martin, W.E., J.G. McLean, and J. Quick. 1965. Effect of temperature on the occurrence of phosphorus-induced zinc deficiency. Soil Sci. Soc. Am. Proc. 29:411–413.

Mascagni, H.J., Jr., and F.R. Cox. 1985. Calibration of a manganese availability index for soybean soil test data. Soil Sci. Soc. Am. J. 49:382–386.

Mathur, S.P., and R.S. Farnham. 1985. Geochemistry of humic substances in peatlands. p. 53–85. In G.R. Aiken et al. (ed.) Humic substances in soil, sediment, and water. John Wiley and Sons, New York.

Matocha, J.E. 1984. Grain sorghum response to plant residue-recycled iron and other iron sources. J. Plant Nutr. 7:259–270.

Matocha, J.E., and D. Pennington. 1982. Effects of plant iron recycling on iron chlorosis of grain sorghum grown on calcareous soils. J. Plant Nutr. 5:869–882.

McBride, M.B. 1981. Forms and distribution of copper in solid and solution phases of soil. p. 25–46. In J.F. Loneragan et al. (ed.) Copper in soils and plants. Academic Press, Sydney, Australia.

McBride, M.B. 1982. Electron spin resonance investigation of Mn^{2+} complexation in natural and synthetic organics. Soil Sci. Soc. Am. J. 46:1137–1143.

McCool, M.M. 1935. Effect of light intensity on the manganese content of plants. Boyce Thompson Inst. Contrib. 7:427–437.

McLaren, R.G., and D.V. Crawford. 1973. Studies on soil copper. I. The fractionation of copper in soils. J. Soil Sci. 24:172–181.

Mederski, H.J., and J.H. Wilson. 1955. Effect of soil temperature and soil moisture on manganese absorption by soybean plants. Soil Sci. Soc. Am. Proc. 19:461–464.

Meek, B.D., A.J. MacKenzie, and L.B. Grass. 1968. Effects of organic matter, flooding time and temperature on the dissolution of iron and manganese from soil in situ. Soil Sci. Soc. Am. Proc. 32:634–638.

Melton, J.R., B.G. Ellis, and E.C. Doll. 1970. Zinc, phosphorus and lime interactions with yield and zinc uptake by Phaseolus vulgaris. Soil Sci. Soc. Am. Proc. 34:91–93.

Melton, J.R., S.K. Mahtab, and A.R. Swoboda. 1973. Diffusion of zinc in soils as a function of applied zinc, phosphorus and soil pH. Soil Sci. Soc. Am. Proc. 37:379–381.

Mengel, K., and E.A. Kirkby. 1987. Principles of plant nutrition. 4th ed. Int. Potash Inst., Bern, Switzerland.

Mezuman, U., and R. Keren. 1981. Boron adsorption by soil using a phenomenological adsorption equation. Soil Sci. Soc. Am. J. 45:722–726.

Mikkelsen, D.S., and D.M. Brandon. 1975. Zinc deficiency in California rice. California Agric. 29(9):8–9.

Miley, W.N., G.W. Hardy, and M.B. Sturgis. 1969. Influence of boron, nitrogen and potassium on yield, nutrient uptake and abnormalities of cotton. Agron. J. 61:9–13.

Miley, W.N., and W.E. Woodall. 1967. Boron for cotton. Univ. Arkansas Coop. Ext. Serv. Leaflet 349.

Miller, G.W., J.C. Pushnik, and G.W. Welkie. 1984. Iron chlorosis, a world wide problem: The relation of chlorophyll biosynthesis to iron. J. Plant Nutr. 7:1–22.

Millikan, C.R. 1951. Diseases of flax and linseed. Victoria (Australia) Dep. Agric. Tech. Bull. 9.

Millikan, C.R. 1953. Relative effects of zinc and copper deficiencies on lucerne and subterranean clover. Aust. J. Biol. Sci. 6:164–177.

Miner, G.S., S. Traore, and M.R. Tucker. 1986. Corn response to starter fertilizer acidity and manganese materials varying in water solubility. Agron. J. 78:291–295.

Minnich, M.M., M.B. McBride, and R.L. Chaney. 1987. Copper activity in soil solution: II. Relation to copper accumulation in young snapbeans. Soil Sci. Soc. Am. J. 51:573–578.

Mitsui, S. 1955. Inorganic nutrition, fertilization and soil amelioration for lowland rice. Yokendo Ltd., Tokyo, Japan.

Mokma, D.L., B.D. Knezek, and L.S. Robertson. 1979. Extractable micronutrient levels in the profiles of soil used for corn production. Michigan State Univ. Agric. Exp. Stn. Res. Rep. 384.

Moore, D.P. 1972. Mechanisms of micronutrient uptake by plants. p. 171–198. *In* J.J. Mortvedt et al. (ed.) Micronutrients in agriculture. 1st ed. SSSA, Madison, WI.

Moore, P.A., and W.H. Patrick, Jr. 1989. Iron availability and uptake by rice in acid sulfate soils. Soil Sci. Soc. Am. J. 53:471–476.

Moraghan, J.T. 1978. Chlorotic dieback in flax. Agron. J. 70:501–505.

Moraghan, J.T. 1979. Manganese toxicity in flax growing on certain calcareous soils low in available iron. Soil Sci. Soc. Am. J. 43:1177–1180.

Moraghan, J.T. 1980. Effect of soil temperature on response of flax to phosphorus and zinc fertilizers. Soil Sci. 129:290–296.

Moraghan, J.T. 1985. Manganese deficiency in soybeans as affected by FeEDDHA and low soil temperature. Soil Sci. Soc. Am. J. 49:1584–1586.

Moraghan, J.T. 1987. Effects of phosphorus and iron fertilizers on the growth of two soybean varieties at two soil temperatures. Plant Soil 104:121–127.

Moraghan, J.T., T.P. Freeman, and D. Whited. 1986. Influence of FeEDDHA and soil temperature on the growth of two soybean varieties. Plant Soil 95:57–67.

Mortvedt, J.J. 1981. Nitrogen and molybdenum uptake and dry matter relationships of soybeans and forage legumes in response to applied molybdenum on acid soils. J. Plant Nutr. 3:245–256.

Mortvedt, J.J., and O.E. Anderson (ed.). 1982. Forage legumes: diagnosis and correction of molybdenum and manganese problems. South. Coop. Ser. Bull. 278. Univ. Georgia.

Mortvedt, J.J., and J.J. Kelsoe. 1988a. Grain sorghum response to banded acid-type fertilizers in iron-deficient soil. J. Plant Nutr. 11:1297–1310.

Mortvedt, J.J., and J.J. Kelsoe. 1988b. Response of corn to zinc applied with banded acid-type fertilizers and ammonium polyphosphates. J. Fert. Issues 6:83–88.

Mozafar, A. 1989. Boron effect on mineral nutrients of maize. Agron. J. 81:285–290.

Mulder, E.G., and F.C. Gerretsen. 1952. Soil manganese in relation to plant growth. Adv. Agron. 4:222–277.

Munns, D.N. 1977. Mineral nutrition and the legume symbiosis. p. 353–391. *In* R.W.F. Hardy (ed.) A treatise on dinitrogen fixation. John Wiley and Sons, New York.

Nambiar, E.K.S. 1976. The uptake of zinc-65 by oats in relation to soil water content and root growth. Aust. J. Soil Res. 14:67–74.

Nambiar, E.K.S. 1977. The effects of drying on the topsoil and of micronutrients in the subsoil on micronutrient uptake by an intermittently defoliated ryegrass. Plant Soil 46:185–193.

Nelson, L.E. 1977. Changes in water-soluble Mn due to soil sample preparation and storage. Commun. Soil Sci. Plant Anal. 8:479–487.

Nielson, N.E. 1976. A transport kinetic concept for ion uptake by plants. III. Test of the concept by results from water culture and pot experiments. Plant Soil 45:659–677.

Nyandat, N.W., and P.N. Ochiing. 1976. Copper content and availability in soils—a survey of arable and range areas of Kenya. East Afr. Agric. For. J. 42:1–7.

Oertli, J.J. 1963. The influence of certain environmental conditions on water and nutrient uptake and nutrition distribution in barley seedlings with special reference to boron. p. 55–85. *In* L. Chandra (ed.) Advancing frontiers of plant sciences. Vol. 6. Inst. Advancement Sci. and Culture, New Dehli, India.

Oliver, S., and S.A. Barber. 1966. An evaluation of the mechanisms governing the supply of Ca, Mg, K and Na to soybean roots. Soil Sci. Soc. Am. Proc. 30:82–86.

Olomu, M.O., and G.J. Racz. 1974. Effect of soil water and aeration on Fe and Mn utilization by flax. Agron. J. 66:523–526.

Olomu, M.O., G.J. Racz, and C.M. Cho. 1973. Effect of flooding on Eh, pH and concentrations of Fe and Mn in several Manitoba soils. Soil Sci. Soc. Am. Proc. 37:220–224.

Olsen, S.R. 1972. Micronutrient interactions. p. 243–264. *In* J.J. Mortvedt et al. (ed.) Micronutrients in agriculture. 1st ed. SSSA, Madison, WI.

Olsen, S.R., and F.W. Watanabe. 1979. Interaction of added gypsum in alkaline soils with uptake of iron, molybdenum, manganese and zinc by sorghum. Soil Sci. Soc. Am. J. 43:125–130.

Oplinger, E.S., and A.J. Ohlrogge. 1974. Response of corn and soybeans to field applications of copper. Agron. J. 66:568–571.

Ozanne, P.G. 1955. The effect of light on zinc deficiency in subterranean clover. Aust. J. Biol. Sci. 8:344-353.

Parker, M.B., and H.B. Harris. 1977. Yield and leaf nitrogen of nodulating and nonnodulating soybeans as affected by nitrogen and molybdenum. Agron. J. 69:551-554.

Parker, M.B., and M.E. Walker. 1986. Soil pH and manganese effects on manganese nutrition of peanuts. Agron. J. 78:614-620.

Parkpian, P., and W.B. Anderson. 1988. Iron by-product as influenced by selective dissolution techniques, acidification and soil reaction. J. Plant Nutr. 11:1321-1331.

Parsa, A.A., A. Wallace, and J.P. Martin. 1979. Enhancement of iron availability by some organic materials. J. Agric. Sci. 93:115-120.

Pasricha, N.S., H.S. Baddesha, M.S. Aulakh, and V.K. Nayyar. 1987. The zinc quantity-intensity relationship in four different soils as influenced by phosphorus. Soil Sci. 143:1-4.

Pavanasasivam, V. 1973. Manganese studies in some soils with a high organic matter content. Plant Soil 38:245-255.

Perret, P., and W. Koblet. 1984. Soil compaction induced iron chlorosis in grape vineyards: Presumed involvement of exogenous soil ethylene. J. Plant Nutr. 7:533-539.

Peterson, L.A., and R.C. Newman. 1976. Influence of soil pH on the availability of added boron. Soil Sci. Soc. Am. J. 40:280-282.

Petrie, S.E., and T.L. Jackson. 1984a. Effects of nitrogen fertilization on manganese concentration and yield of barley and oats. Soil Sci. Soc. Am. J. 48:319-322.

Petrie, S.E., and T.L. Jackson. 1984b. Effects of fertilization on soil solution pH and manganese concentration. Soil Sci. Soc. Am. J. 48:315-318.

Piper, C.S. 1931. The availability of manganese in the soil. J. Agric. Sci. 21:762-779.

Ponnamperuma, F.N. 1972. Chemistry of submerged soils. Adv. Agron. 24:29-95.

Ponnamperuma, F.N. 1985. Chemical kinetics of wetland rice soils relative to soil fertility. p. 71-89. In Wetland soils: Characterization, classification, and utilization. Int. Rice Res. Inst., Los Banos, Philippines.

Prasad, M., and E. Byrne. 1975. Boron source and lime effects on the yield of three crops grown in peat. Agron. J. 67:553-556.

Rattan, R.K., and L.M. Shukla. 1984. Critical limits of deficiency and toxicity of zinc in paddy in a Typic Ustipsamment. Commun. Soil Sci. Plant Anal. 15:1041-1051.

Ray, W.R., J.J. Hassett, and R.A. Griffin. 1986. Competitive coefficients for the adsorption of arsenate, molybdate, and phosphate mixtures by soils. Soil Sci. Soc. Am. J. 50:1176-1182.

Reddy, C.K., and G.V.S. Siva Prasad. 1986. Varietal response to iron chlorosis in upland rice. Plant Soil 94:289-292.

Reddy, M.R., and S.J. Dunn. 1987. Differential response of soybean genotypes to soil pH and manganese application. Plant Soil 101:123-126.

Reed, J. 1946. Effect of zinc deficiency on phosphate metabolism of the tomato plant. Am. J. Bot. 33:778-784.

Reid, D.A. 1976. Aluminum and manganese toxicities in the cereal grains. p. 55-64. In M.J. Wright (ed.) Plant adaptation to mineral stress in problem soils. Proc. Workshop, Beltsville, MD. 22-23 Nov. 1976. Cornell Univ., Ithaca, NY.

Reid, J.M., and G.J. Racz. 1985. Effects of soil temperature on manganese availability to plants grown on an organic soil. Can. J. Soil Sci. 65:769-775.

Reuther, W., P.F. Smith, and G.K. Scudder. 1953. Relation of pH and soil type to toxicity of copper to citrus seedlings. Fla. State Hortic. Soc. Proc. 66:73-80.

Reyes, E.D., and J.J. Jurinak. 1967. A mechanism of molybdate adsorption on α Fe_2O_3. Soil Sci. Soc. Am. Proc. 31:637-641.

Rhoads, F.M., S.M. Olson, and A. Manning. 1989. Copper toxicity in tomato plants. J. Environ. Qual. 18:195-197.

Riekels, J.W., and J.C. Lingle. 1966. Iron uptake and translocation by tomato plants as influenced by root temperature and manganese nutrition. Plant Physiol. 41:1095-1101.

Robinson, N.J., and P.J. Jackson. 1986. "Metallothionein-like" metal complexes in angiosperms: Their structure and function. Physiol. Plant 67:499-506.

Robson, A.D., and J.F. Loneragan. 1970. Sensitivity of annual Medicago species to manganese toxicity as affected by calcium and pH. Aust. J. Agric. Res. 21:223-232.

Robson, A.D., and D.J. Reuter. 1981. Diagnosis of copper deficiency and toxicity. p. 313-350. In J.F. Loneragan et al. (ed.) Copper in soils and plants. Academic Press, Sydney, Australia.

Romero, L. 1988. A new statistical approach for the interpretation of nutrient interrelationships. III. Manganese/iron. J. Plant Nutr. 11:995-1004.

Romheld, V. 1985. Bad-weather chlorosis in grapevine: Effect of bicarbonate and low soil temperature on uptake and translocation of iron and also on the incidence of chlorosis [In German, English sumary]. p. 211–217. *In* Bodenbewirtschaftung, Bodenfruchtbarkeit, Bodenschutz. Verband Deutscher Landwirtschaftlicher Untersuchungs-und Forschungsanstalten-Verlag, Darmstadt.

Romheld, V. 1987. Different strategies for iron acquisition in higher plants. Physiol. Plant 70:231–234.

Romheld, V., and H. Marschner. 1986. Mobilization of iron in the rhizosphere of different plant species. Adv. Plant Nutr. 2:155–204.

Ross, D.S., and R.J. Bartlett. 1981. Evidence for nonmicrobial oxidation of manganese in soil. Soil Sci. 132:153–160.

Rowell, D.L. 1981. Oxidation and reduction. p. 401–461. *In* D.J. Greenland and M.H.B. Hayes (ed.) The chemistry of soil processes. John Wiley and Sons, Chichester, England.

Rufty, T.W., G.S. Miner, and C.D. Raper. 1979. Temperature effects on growth and manganese tolerance in tobacco. Agron. J. 71:638–644.

Saeed, M. 1977. Phosphate fertilization reduces zinc adsorption by calcareous soils. Plant Soil 48:641–649.

Saeed, M., and R.L. Fox. 1979. Influence of phosphate fertilization on zinc adsorption by tropical soils. Soil Sci. Soc. Am. J. 43:683–686.

Safaya, N.M. 1976. Phosphorus-zinc interaction in relation to absorption rates of phosphorus, zinc, copper, manganese and iron in corn. Soil Sci. Soc. Am. J. 40:719–722.

Sahrawat, K.L. 1979. Iron toxicity to rice in an acid sulfate soil as influenced by water regimes. Plant Soil 51:143–144.

Sajwan, K.S., and W.L. Lindsay. 1986. Effects of redox on zinc deficiency in paddy rice. Soil Sci. Soc. Am. J. 50:1264–1269.

Schmid, W.E., H.P. Haag, and E. Epstein. 1965. Absorption of zinc by excised barley roots. Physiol. Plant 18:860–869.

Schwartz, S.M., R.M. Welch, D.L. Grunes, E.E. Cary, W.A. Norvell, M.D. Gilbert, M.P. Meredith, and C.A. Sanchirico. 1987. Effect of zinc, phosphorus, and root-zone temperature on nutrient uptake by barley. Soil Sci. Soc. Am. J. 51:371–375.

Schwertmann, U., and R.M. Taylor. 1977. Iron oxides. p. 145–180. *In* J.B. Dixon et al. (ed.) Minerals in soil environments. SSSA, Madison, WI.

Sedberry, J.E., F.J. Peterson, F.E. Wilson, D.B. Mengel, P.E. Schilling, and R.H. Brupbacher. 1980. Influence of soil reaction and applications of zinc on yields and zinc contents of rice plants. Commun. Soil Sci. Plant Anal. 11:283–295.

Sheaffer, C.C., A.M. Decker, R.L. Chaney, and L.W. Douglass. 1979. Soil temperature and sewage sludge effects on corn yield and macronutrient content. J. Environ. Qual. 8:450–454.

Shuman, L.M. 1975. The effect of soil properties on zinc adsorption by soils. Soil Sci. Soc. Am. Proc. 39:454–458.

Shuman, L.M. 1979. Zinc, manganese and copper in soil fractions. Soil Sci. 127:10–17.

Sillanpaa, M. 1982. Micronutrients and the nutrient status of soils: a global study. United Nations Food and Agriculture Organization (Rome) Bull. 48.

Sillanpaa, M., and P.L.G. Vlek. 1985. Micronutrients and the agroecology of tropical and Mediterranean regions. p. 151–167. *In* P.L.G. Vlek (ed.) Micronutrients in tropical food crop production. Martinus Nijhoff and W. Junk Publ., Dordrecht, Netherlands.

Siman, A., F.W. Craddock, and A.W. Hudson. 1974. The development of manganese toxicity in pasture legumes. Plant Soil 41:129–140.

Sims, J.L., and W.O. Atkinson. 1974. Soil and plant factors influencing accumulation of dry matter in burley tobacco growing in soil made acid by fertilizer. Agron. J. 66:775–778.

Sims, J.L., W.O. Atkinson, and C. Smitobol. 1975. Mo and N effects on growth, yield and Mo composition of burley tobacco. Agron. J. 67:824–828.

Sims, J.L., and W.H. Patrick, Jr. 1978. The distribution of micronutrient cations in soil under conditions of varying redox potential and pH. Soil Sci. Soc. Am. Proc. 42:258–262.

Sims, J.T. 1986. Soil pH effects on the distribution and plant availability of manganese, copper and zinc. Soil Sci. Soc. Am. J. 50:367–373.

Singh, J.P., R.E. Karamanos, and J.W.B. Stewart. 1986. Phosphorus-induced zinc deficiency in wheat on residual phosphorus plots. Agron. J. 78:668–675.

Siriratpiriya, O., E. Vigerust, and A.R. Selmer-Olsen. 1985. Effect of temperature and heavy metal application on metal content in lettuce. Agric. Univ. Norway, Dep. Soil Fert. Mgmt. Rep. 145. Agric. Univ. Norway, Hovedkontoret, Norway.

Skoog, F. 1940. Relationships between zinc and auxin in the growth of higher plants. Am. J. Bot. 27:939-951.

Smith, K.A., and S.W.F. Restall. 1971. The occurrence of ethylene in anaerobic soil. J. Soil Sci. 22:420-443.

Smithson, J.B., and R.G. Heathcote. 1976. A new recommendation for the application of boronated superphosphate to cotton in northeastern Beune Plateau States. Samarau Agric. Newsl. 18:59-63.

Snyder, G.H., and D.B. Jones. 1988. Prediction and prevention of iron-related seedling chlorosis on Everglades Histosols. Soil Sci. Soc. Am. J. 52:1043-1046.

Soltanpour, P.N. 1969. Effect of N, P and Zn placement on yield and composition of potatoes. Agron. J. 61:288-289.

Sonar, K.R., and R.V. Ghugare. 1982. Release of Fe, Mn and P in a calcareous Vertisol and yield of upland rice as influenced by presowing soil water treatments. Plant Soil 68:11-18.

Sonneveld, C., and S.J. Voogt. 1975. Studies on the manganese uptake of lettuce on steam-sterilized glasshouse soils. Plant Soil 42:49-64.

Sparrow, L.A., and N.C. Uren. 1987. Oxidation and reduction of Mn in acidic soils: Effect of temperature and soil pH. Soil Biol. Biochem. 19:143-148.

Stahlberg, S., and S. Sombatpanit. 1974. Manganese relationships of soil and plant. I. Investigation and classification of Swedish manganese-deficient soils. Acta Agric. Scand. 24:179-194.

Stevenson, F.J., and M.S. Ardakani. 1972. Organic matter reactions involving micronutrients. p. 79-114. In J.J. Mortvedt et al. (ed.) Micronutrients in agriculture. 1st ed. SSSA, Madison, WI.

Stevenson, F.J., and A. Fitch. 1981. Reactions with organic matter. p. 69-96. In J.F. Loneragan et al. (ed.) Copper in soils and plants. Academic Press, Sydney, Australia.

Sutcliffe, J.F. 1971. Trace elements in plants—uptake and translocation. p. 35-44. In J. Webber (ed.) Trace elements in soils and crops. United Kingdom Ministry Agric., Fish., and Food Tech. Bull. 21. Her Majesty's Stationery Office, London.

Sutton, C.D., and E.G. Hallsworth. 1958. Studies on the nutrition of forage legumes. I. The toxicity of low pH and high manganese supply to lucerne as affected by climatic factors and calcium supply. Plant Soil 9:305-317.

Takagi, S., K. Nomoto, and T. Takemoto. 1984. Physiological aspects of mugineic acid, a possible phytosiderophore of graminaceous plants. J. Plant Nutr. 7:469-477.

Tan, K.H., L.D. King, and H.D. Morris. 1971. Complex reactions of zinc with organic matter extracted from sewage sludge. Soil Sci. Soc. Am. Proc. 35:748-752.

Tanaka, A., and S. Yoshida. 1970. Nutritional disorders of the rice plant in Asia. Int. Rice Res. Inst. Tech. Bull. 10.

Terman, G.L., P.M. Giordano, and S.E. Allen. 1972. Relationship between dry matter yields and concentration of Zn and P in young corn plants. Agron. J. 64:686-687.

Timmer, L.W., and R.F. Leyden. 1980. The relationship of mycorrhizal infection to phosphorus-induced copper deficiency in sour orange seedlings. New Phytol. 85:15-23.

Tinker, P.B. 1980. Role of rhizosphere microorganisms in phosphorus uptake by plants. p. 617-654. In F.E. Khasawneh et al. (ed.) The role of phosphorus in agriculture. ASA, CSSA, and SSSA, Madison, WI.

Touchton, J.T., J.W. Johnson, and B.M. Cunter. 1980. The relationship between phosphorus and copper concentrations in wheat. Commun. Soil Sci. Plant Anal. 11:1051-1066.

Trumble, H.C., and H.M. Ferres. 1946. Response of herbage legumes to applied nutrients on some southern Australian soils and their dependence on external factors. J. Aust. Inst. Agric. Sci. 12:32-43.

Truong, N.V., G.L. Wilson, and C.S. Andrew. 1971. Manganese toxicity in pasture legumes. I. Effects of calcium and phosphorus levels in the substrate. Plant Soil 34:309-330.

van der Vorm, P.D.J., and A. van Diest. 1979. Aspects of the Fe- and Mn nutrition of rice plants. I. Iron- and manganese uptake by rice plants, grown under aerobic and anaerobic conditions. Plant Soil 51:233-246.

van Mensvoort, M.E., R.S. Lantin, R. Brinkman, and N. van Breemen. 1985. Toxicities of wetland soils. p. 123-138. In Wetland soils: Characterization, classification, and utilization. Int. Rice Res. Inst., Los Banos, Philippines.

Viets, F.E. 1967. Zinc deficiency of field and vegetable crops in the West. USDA Leaflet 495. U.S. Gov. Print Office, Washington, DC.

Vlamis, J., and D.E. Williams. 1962. Ion competition in manganese uptake by barley plants. Plant Physiol. 37:650-655.

Vlamis, J., and D.E. Williams. 1964. Iron and manganese relations in rice and barley. Plant Soil 20:221-231.

Vlamis, J., and D.E. Williams. 1970. Comparative accumulation of manganese and boron in barley tissues. Plant Soil 33:623-628.

Vlek, P.L.G., and W.L. Lindsay. 1977. Molybdenum contamination of Colorado pasture soils. p. 619-649. *In* W.R. Chappell and K.K. Petersen (ed.) Molybdenum in the environment. Vol. 2. Marcel Dekker, Inc., New York.

Walker, J.M. 1969. One-degree increments in soil temperatures affect maize seedling behavior. Soil Sci. Soc. Am. Proc. 33:729-736.

Wallace, A. 1982. Effect of nitrogen fertilizer and nodulation on lime-induced chlorosis in soybeans. J. Plant Nutr. 5:363-368.

Wallace, A. 1984. Effect of phosphorus deficiency and copper excess on vegetative growth of bush bean plants in solution culture at two different solution pH levels. J. Plant Nutr. 7:603-608.

Wallace, A., and J.W. Cha. 1986. Effects of bicarbonate, phosphorus, iron EDDHA and nitrogen sources on soybeans grown in calcareous soil. J. Plant Nutr. 9:251-256.

Walsh, L.M., W.H. Erhardt, and H.D. Seibel. 1972. Copper toxicity in snapbeans (*Phaseolus vulgaris* L.). J. Environ. Qual. 1:197-200.

Warncke, D.D., and S.A. Barber. 1972. Diffusion of zinc in soil: I. The influence of soil moisture. Soil Sci. Soc. Am. Proc. 36:39-42.

Webb, M.J., and J.F. Loneragan. 1988. Effect of zinc deficiency on growth, phosphorus concentration, and phosphorus toxicity of wheat plants. Soil Sci. Soc. Am. J. 52:1676-1680.

Weber, J. (ed.). 1971. Trace elements in soils and crops. United Kingdom Ministry Agriculture, Fish., and Food Tech. Bull. 21. Her Majesty's Stationery Office, London.

White, M.C., A.M. Decker, and R.L. Chaney. 1979. Differential cultivar tolerance in soybean to phytotoxic levels of soil Zn. I. Range of cultivar response. Agron. J. 71:121-126.

White, R.P. 1970. Effects of lime upon soil and plant manganese levels in an acid soil. Soil Sci. Soc. Am. Proc. 34:625-629.

Wild, A. 1988. Russell's soil conditions and plant growth. 11th ed. Longman Sci. and Techn., London.

Williams, C., and I. Thornton. 1972. The effect of soil additives on the uptake of molybdenum and selenium from soils from different environments. Plant Soil 36:395-406.

Williams, D.E., and J. Vlamis. 1957a. Manganese toxicity in standard culture solutions. Plant Soil 8:183-193.

Williams, D.E., and J. Vlamis. 1957b. The effect of silicon on yield and Mn-54 uptake and distribution in the leaves of barley plants grown in nutrient solution. Plant Physiol. 32:404-409.

Williams, D.E., and J. Vlamis. 1962. Differential cation and anion absorption as affected by climate. Plant Physiol. 37:198-202.

Winslow, M.D., M. Yamauchi, K. Alluri, and T.M. Masajo. 1989. Reducing iron toxicity in rice with resistant genotype and ridge planting. Agron. J. 81:458-460.

Woodruff, J.R., F.W. Moore, and H.L. Musen. 1987. Potassium, boron, nitrogen and lime effects on corn yield and earleaf nutrient concentrations. Agron. J. 79:520-524.

Yen, P.Y., W.P. Inskeep, and R.L. Westerman. 1988. Effect of soil moisture and phosphorus fertilization on iron chlorosis of sorghum. J. Plant Nutr. 11:1517-1531.

Yoon, S.K., J.T. Gilmour, and B.R. Wells. 1975. Micronutrient levels in the rice plant Y leaf as a function of soil solution concentration. Soil Sci. Soc. Am. Proc. 39:685-688.

Yoshida, S., and A. Tanaka. 1969. Zinc deficiency of the rice plant in calcareous soils. Soil Sci. Plant Nutr. 15:75-80.

Yoshida, S., J.S. Ahn, and D.A. Forno. 1973. Occurrence, diagnosis, and correction of zinc deficiency of lowland rice. Soil Sci. Plant Nutr. 19:83-93.

Youngdahl, L.J., L.V. Svec, W.C. Leibhardt, and M.R. Teel. 1977. Changes in the zinc-65 distribution in corn root tissue with a phosphorus variable. Crop Sci. 17:66-69.

Zaharieva, T., D. Kasabov, and V. Romheld. 1988. Response of peanuts to iron-manganese interaction in calcareous soil. J. Plant Nutr. 11:1015-1024.

Chapter 12

Micronutrient Soil Tests

J. T. SIMS, *University of Delaware, Newark, Delaware*

G. V. JOHNSON, *Oklahoma State University, Stillwater, Oklahoma*

Micronutrient soil fertility, the capacity of soil to provide those nutrient elements required by plants in minute amounts, is a chemical soil property. Consequently, aside from measured plant-response differences, micronutrient soil fertility variations can best be characterized through chemical examination of the soil. These chemical characterizations or soil tests are most apt to differentiate micronutrient availability when nutrient element chemistry is carefully considered as part of the soil test development. The reliability of crop response studies that relate the extractable portion of a micronutrient in the soil to plant uptake or yield is greatly enhanced when the soil test has evolved from a sound, theoretical basis.

Soil testing for micronutrients is, in general, a well-established practice, based on fundamental principles of soil chemistry, and verified by field and greenhouse research. There are, however, many areas that still require refinement or, in some cases, extensive research. Future efforts should consider the objectives of soil testing, the chemistry of extracting solutions, and, as much as possible, involve multi-site, multi-year, field studies with sensitive crops.

I. PRINCIPLES OF SOIL TESTING

A. Soil Test Objectives

Soil testing has evolved out of the need to produce food, feed, and fiber efficiently and economically. Conventional soil tests are used primarily as a means for predicting the soil's capacity to provide essential nutrients to a crop during its growing season. Ideally, the soil test should not only identify whether or not a micronutrient deficiency exists, but also the degree of deficiency in terms of anticipated yield loss. The quantity of micronutrient required to correct the deficiency is then determined by field calibration studies with the soil test.

As a minimum requirement and with normal analytical performance (accuracy and precision), the test should separate soils that are adequate from those deficient in nutrient supply. Test accuracy should also be able to further separate deficient soils categorically (very low, low, medium) or in terms of their responsiveness to fertilizers under field conditions.

Soil test reliability is indicated by the probability of the soil test result to correctly predict the field outcome. That is, when a reliable soil test indicates micronutrient deficiency, there should be a high probability that a loss in crop production will occur when remedial action is not taken. Soil test reliability may also encompass laboratory quality assurance and timeliness from the user's perspective.

B. Soil Test Correlation and Calibration

Extracting reagents and procedures can be used successfully for soil testing if the amount of nutrient extracted from the soil is strongly related to that absorbed by the plant. The degree to which this relationship exists may be statistically examined using correlation analysis.

There are two important aspects of the chemical extraction—plant absorption data that must be considered before statistical analysis. First, it is important to plot the soil and plant data, and to determine, generally, the form of response, and whether or not a relationship appears to exist. Biological responses to nutrient inputs are often curvilinear (quadratic, inverse, logrithimic) and seldom linear. Hence, linear correlation is usually inappropriate as a statistical test unless the data have been transformed (Johnson & Young, 1973). Secondly, it is important to exclude data outside the range of plant response. A plot of the data will help identify superfluous data points and improve the sensitivity of correlation analysis for separating potentially good extractants from poor ones. If these precautions are not taken, a strong relationship between soil test levels and plant response over a narrow concentration range may be masked by many data points outside the plant response range (Fig. 12–1).

Correlation research usually involves measuring plant response to various levels of micronutrient availability. For convenience and economics, these studies often are performed in the greenhouse. Measured parameters include yield, nutrient concentration, nutrient uptake, and color (or chlorosis) as dependent variables. The amount of nutrient extracted from each soil in the laboratory is then compared, by correlation analysis, with the plant response data. Other independent variables, such as soil pH, texture, or organic matter, may be included in the correlation analysis when there is reason to believe that these soil parameters influence micronutrient supply to the crop in question.

Correlation may be limited to one or more of a few crop species that are noticeably susceptible to deficiency of the micronutrient. The study should include soils with a wide range of properties representative of the geographic area where the soil test is expected to be used.

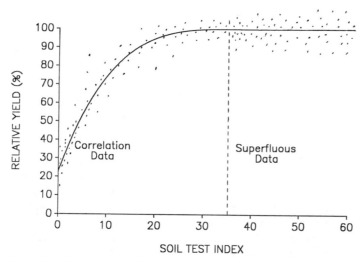

Fig. 12-1. Hypothetical plot of soil test/plant response data showing separation of useful data.

Soil test calibration is the final step in the development of soil tests for micronutrients that are not wholly present in an available form. For these elements, such as Fe, the soil test will usually extract more of this element than is available at the time of sampling. In these instances, the calibration serves as the link between chemical extraction and plant absorption. The calibration usually cannot be derived from the earlier correlation-study data, and must involve crop response data from field studies that consider factors of the normal growing environment that influence micronutrient soil fertility and plant nutrition. An example of ideal soil test calibration data is illustrated in Table 12-1.

It is important to note from Table 12-1 that the soil test value is identified as an index rather than a discrete quantity (i.e., kilograms per hectare) of the nutrient in an available form. Also of interest is the use of relative

Table 12-1. Hypothetical soil test calibration data.

Soil test index	Crop yield	Relative yield†	Fertilizer requirement
	kg ha^{-1}	%	
0	19	26	10
5	38	53	7
7	45	62	5
10	53	74	3
14	60	83	2
20	68	94	1
30	71	99	0
40	72	100	0

† Calculated by dividing each yield by the yield value when the nutrient in question is not limiting.

‡ Amount of fertilizer required to correct the deficiency. Units will usually be mass/unit land area, and will vary with nutrient and soil test.

yield, which not only allows the use of data across locations and years, but also the expression of the soil test value in terms of percent sufficiency. In other words, a soil test value of 20 is associated with 94% sufficiency (or adequacy) of the nutrient. Thus, calibration is an important part of soil test interpretation for micronutrients in situations in which only a fraction of the total quantity available during the growing season is extracted by a soil test.

C. Interpretation of Soil Test Results

Successful calibration of chemical soil extractants results in their use as soil tests that can be interpreted in relation to adequacy of the nutrient. Interpretation identifies whether or not the micronutrient in question is deficient and, if deficient, the degree of deficiency. Because the amount of fertilizer required to correct even severe deficiencies is usually small, interpretations often result in identifying a single fertilizer rate. In these instances, a critical soil test value may be identified, above which no fertilizer is recommended and below which a single rate is recommended for all soil test values. This critical level may be identified using the Cate-Nelson (Cate & Nelson, 1971) Technique for separating deficient and adequate nutrient-supplying soils (Fig. 12–2). This technique may be used instead of correlation analysis.

For micronutrients that are relatively soluble and mobile in the soil (B and Cl), the amount of added fertilizer nutrient may be determined by direct comparison of the amount extracted with the total crop requirement. The crop requirement for these most-soluble nutrients is calculated by multiplying the potential yield by an average nutrient concentration for the crop. Average concentration should be calculated using crops grown in soils that are adequately, but not excessively, fertilized with the nutrient. Adjustments may be required when excessive water movement leaches the nutrient below the root zone just prior to or during the growing season. The fertilizer requirement is the difference between the crop requirement and that extracted by the soil test (kilogram per hectare).

For some micronutrient soil tests the interpretation is complex and may consider one or more other soil chemical or physical properties (e.g., clay content, pH, organic matter) (Cox, 1987). These complexities usually arise when element availability is influenced by soil reactions such as surface adsorption, oxidation-reduction, co-precipitation, or hydration, to name a few. Because of these complexities, soil test development for some micronutrients is still in its infancy.

Finally, interpretation of a properly developed soil test should consider the user's interests. Ultimately, this involves economic considerations related to crop production and environmental concerns of society. The economics of correcting a deficiency can be estimated from relative yield and nutrient deficiency values obtained during soil test development. Using data in Table 12–1 as an example, if the soil test value is 10, then a loss of about 25% of normal (or possible) yield could be expected if the deficiency is not corrected. Fertilizing to add three increments of the nutrient must cost less than

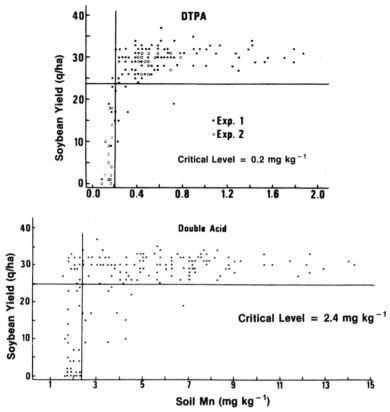

Fig. 12-2. Critical values for DTPA and Mehlich-1 (double acid) extractable Mn as estimated by the Cate-Nelson approach (Shuman et al., 1980).

the value of increased crop production (25% of normal yield) for the practice to be economical.

Interpretation of soil tests in relation to environmental impact is not always possible because cause-and-effect relationships are lacking. However, it should be obvious that when the soil test value is greater than that required to obtain 100% relative yield, adding more of the nutrient is of no agronomic benefit. Except for B, Cl, and Mo, soil test levels of essential micronutrient elements in excess of twice their adequate value will usually have no adverse environmental effect, but may prove to be unprofitable.

II. CHEMISTRY OF MICRONUTRIENT SOIL TESTING EXTRACTANTS

A. Necessary Characteristics of an Extractant

The fundamental dilemma encountered when developing a soil testing solution for any element is the need to reconcile the generally accepted criteria for an extractant, originally proposed by Bray (1948), with the scientific and agronomic realities of soil testing. Bray suggested that an ideal soil test should: (i) extract all or a proportionate part of the plant-available form or forms of a nutrient from soils with differing properties; (ii) be reasonably accurate and rapid; and (iii) correlate well with crop response to applications of the nutrient under various conditions.

Viets and Lindsay (1973) stated that a necessary corollary of these criteria was the need for a soil test to reflect changes in nutrient supply related to fertilization, plant uptake, and environmental conditions, such as soil temperature and moisture. To satisfy these goals, a soil test method must include: (i) an extracting solution with a sound theoretical relationship to the labile phases of the element; (ii) be readily adapted to use in a laboratory where convenience and speed of analysis are essential; and (iii) have a large database, covering many years and soil types, that relates extractable nutrient level in the soil to crop response, preferably under field conditions. Attainment of all of these goals is a formidable, perhaps impossible, task, but there are recent examples of successful efforts to improve soil testing methods that provide encouragement.

Devising a chemical solution that can remove immediately and potentially available levels of an element requires an understanding of the various forms in which the element exists in the soil. Viets (1962) suggested that micronutrient elements are found in five chemical pools: (i) water soluble; (ii) exchangeable; (iii) adsorbed, chelated, or complexed; (iv) secondary clay minerals and metal oxides; and (v) primary minerals. The complexity of the interactions among these pools is illustrated in Fig. 12–3 for micronutrient cations and for B, an uncharged ($H_3BO_3^0$) or anionic [$B(OH)_4^-$] micronutrient. A good soil test would extract micronutrients from both the solution phase and labile solid phases, but not from inert phases.

Initial efforts in micronutrient soil-test development were directed at preparation of solutions that simulated the extracting power of plant roots, primarily through the use of water, dilute acids or bases, or dilute salt solutions. These extractants, while similar in pH or ionic strength to the soil solution, do not dissolve sufficient quantities of an element to accurately reflect the true capacity of a soil to maintain an adequate level of a micronutrient in the soil solution. Modifications to these extracting solutions have included the addition of cations or anions to displace exchangeable micronutrients, and the use of chelating agents that enhance the dissolution of labile solid phases and/or effectively compete with organic matter for complexed micronutrients.

Intensive efforts have been directed at the development of sequential fractionation schemes that quantitatively partition the total amount of a micronutrient into soil pools that are useful for predicting bioavailability (see chapter 5 in this book). Greenhouse and field studies have been conducted that relate these chemical fractions to plant uptake and soil-test-extractable levels (Iyengar et al., 1981; LeClaire et al., 1984; Mullins et al., 1982; Rappaport et al., 1986; Shuman, 1985; Sims, 1986). Although these fractionation procedures frequently use methodological, not chemical, definitions of

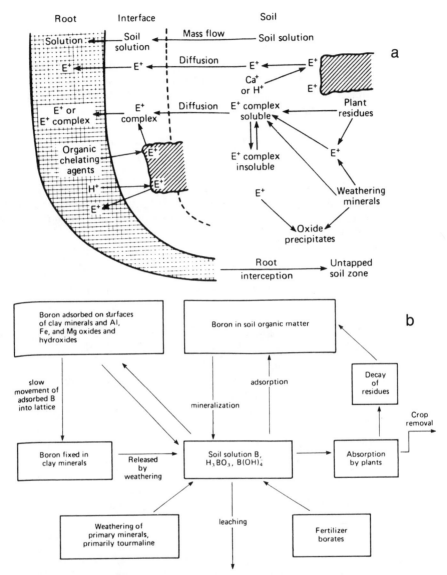

Fig. 12–3. Schematic representation of micronutrient forms in soils for (a) any trace element cation and (b) for B (Fig. 1a from Mitchell, 1972; Fig. 1b from Mengel, 1980).

soil phases, they can be useful in identifying components of an extractant that may be well correlated with plant uptake.

Lake et al. (1984) reviewed the use of fractionation schemes to determine speciation of heavy metals in sludge-amended soils. Typical pools, identified by these procedures and extracting solutions used, included: soluble ($CaCl_2$, deionized water), exchangeable (KNO_3, NaF, $CaCl_2$), adsorbed (CH_3COOH, deionized water), organically bound ($K_4P_2O_7$, NaOH,

NaOCl), available (DTPA, Na_2-EDTA), precipitated as carbonates or sulfides (HNO_3, DTPA, EDTA), bound or occluded by metal oxides ($HONH_2$-HCl, ammonium oxalate-oxalic acid), and residual (HF, concentrated HNO_3). Of the wide variety of chemical reagents used in fractionation schemes to identify micronutrients in what would be considered plant-available pools, presently only DTPA and EDTA are used as constituents of soil testing extractants.

B. Current Micronutrient Extractants

The major categories of micronutrient extractants presently in use are dilute acids, and solutions containing chelating agents, such as DTPA or EDTA. Other tests less commonly used include hot water (B), acidic ammonium or Na acetate (pH 3–4.8) (Zn), Na-citrate or Na-dithionate (Fe), and ammonium oxalate (Mo).

1. Dilute Acid Extractants

Dilute acids (0.025–0.1 M) have been used as micronutrient soil tests for many years, primarily on acidic soils. Strong acids have been avoided because they generally extract micronutrients from nonlabile solid phases (e.g., primary minerals). Dilute acid solutions should remove micronutrients from the soil solution, from exchange sites on clays and organic matter, and, through partial dissolution, from metal oxides and clays. However, their applicability is confined to acidic soils because they generally are not sufficiently buffered to extract meaningful levels of micronutrients from calcareous soils.

Acidic extractants do not have a particularly sound theoretical basis, but, due to their extensive use in field and laboratory studies, a well-developed database exists, relating acid-extractable levels of most micronutrients to crop response. The most commonly used dilute acids are Mehlich-1 (dilute double acid, 0.0125 M H_2SO_4 + 0.05 M HCl) and 0.1 M HCl. Other acidic solutions currently in use include 0.03 M H_3PO_4 (Mn), 0.05 M H_2SO_4 (Mn), 1 M HCl (Cu), and 1 M NH_4OAc (pH 3 or 4.8, Mn, Zn).

2. Extractants that use Chelating Agents

One of the major advances in micronutrient soil testing has been the development of extracting solutions that contain chelating agents, primarily DTPA and EDTA. These chelates reduce the activity of free-metal ions in solution through the formation of soluble metal-chelate complexes. Replenishment of free-ion concentration in the soil solution from solid phases occurs in response to this complexation. The quantity of micronutrient extracted by a chelate reflects both the initial concentration in the soil solution (intensity factor) and the ability of the soil to maintain this concentration (capacity factor) (Viets & Lindsay, 1973). Thus, chelating agents simulate nutrient removal by plant roots and replenishment from labile solid phases in the soil.

Chelate-based extractants are usually well buffered at a desired pH and, in some cases, contain other constituents to facilitate simultaneous extraction of macronutrient cations (K, Ca, and Mg) and anions (P). Extractant pH buffering and ionic strength are critical in calcareous soils. The solution pH is usually buffered near neutrality ($\sim$pH 7.3) to avoid dissolution of carbonate minerals that could release occluded, unavailable micronutrients, and the ionic strength is maintained near 0.01 M to promote flocculation, insure effective filtration, and regulate chelate activity in solution. Direct transfer of an extractant that is buffered at a pH appropriate for calcareous soils to acidic soils is inappropriate, and can succeed only if the pH and buffering capacity of the extractant are modified, or if sufficient calibration research is conducted.

Chelates that have been investigated include DTPA, EDTA, NTA, HEDTA, and EGTA. Initial efforts in selecting a chelate for micronutrient soil testing centered around EDTA. Cheng and Bray (1953) demonstrated that an EDTA-citrate method for assessing available Cu was as effective as 0.1 M HCl. Viro (1955) found that EDTA, buffered at pH 9.0, recovered all of the Cu and Zn added to five California podzols, while Tucker and Kurtz (1955) reported a correlation coefficient of 0.76**[1] between EDTA in 1.0 M NH_4OAc (pH 7.0) and available Zn assessed by a bioassay technique with 14 Illinois soils. Trierwiler and Lindsay (1969) developed an EDTA-$(NH_4)_2CO_3$ extractant that was highly correlated with plant available Zn in calcareous soils ($r > 0.81$**, critical value = 1.4 mg kg^{-1}).

Current extractants that incorporate EDTA are the Mehlich-3, the modified Olsen's, and acid ammonium acetate-EDTA (AAAc-EDTA). The Mehlich-3 extractant (0.20 M CH_3COOH + 0.25 M NH_4F + 0.013 M HNO_3 + 0.001 M EDTA + 0.25 M NH_4NO_3) has generated intense interest since its development by Mehlich in 1984, primarily because it allows for simultaneous extraction of all elements routinely measured in soil testing laboratories (P, K, Ca, Mg, Mn, Cu, and Zn) and because it has been shown to be well correlated with levels of these nutrients extracted by existing soil tests, such as the Mehlich-1, the Bray P1, NH_4OAc (1.0 M, pH 7), and EDTA (Hanlon & Johnson, 1984; Mehlich, 1984; Michaelson et al., 1987; Sims, 1989).

Conversion to the Mehlich-3 extractant would eliminate the need for multiple extractions for bases (K, Ca, Mg), P, and micronutrients. This is highly desirable, since, with the advent of inductively coupled plasma spectroscopy (ICP), rapid multi-element analysis of a single extract is easily accomplished. Field and greenhouse calibration studies recently conducted with the Mehlich-3 have demonstrated that it is as well correlated with plant uptake and yield response as currently used extractants (Mascagni & Cox, 1985; Junus & Cox, 1987; Sims, 1985).

Acid ammonium acetate-EDTA (1.0 M NH_4OAc + 0.02 M EDTA, pH 4.65) was used in a global study conducted by the Food and Agricultural Organization of the United Nations (FAO) and the Institute of Soil Science in Finland (Sillanpaa, 1982). This extractant had previously been compared

---

[1] In this text, *, **, *** refer to correlations or regressions that are statistically significant at probability levels of 0.05, 0.01, and 0.001, respectively.

Table 12-2. Correlations between micronutrient uptake by wheat from 3538 soils from 30 nations and extractable levels with AAAc-EDTA and DTPA, with and without correction factors.†

Element and soil property	Extractant	
	AAAc-EDTA	DTPA
	r	
Iron‡	0.325***	0.263***
Manganese	0.039***	0.552***
Manganese and soil pH	0.588***	0.713***
Zinc	0.665***	0.732***
Zinc and soil pH	0.707***	No improvement
Copper	0.664***	0.518***
Copper and organic C	0.731***	No improvement
	Hot water	AO-OA
Boron	0.741***	--
Boron and CEC	0.826***	--
Molybdenum	--	0.245***
Molybdenum and pH	--	0.696***

*** Represents significance at the 0.001 probability level.
† Equations used to determine correction factors for adjusting extractable micronutrient level prior to correlation with plant uptake are from Sillanpaa (1982).
‡ Correlation for Fe was not improved by inclusion of soil property.

with eight others by Lakanen and Ervio (1971) and identified, similarly to the Mehlich-3, as suitable for multi-element extraction (P, K, Ca, Mg, Fe, Mn, Cu, Zn, and Mo). The FAO study involved 30 nations and more than 3500 soils, and compared AAAc-EDTA (pH 4.65) and DTPA (pH 7.3) as extractants for Fe, Cu, Mn, and Zn. Extractable levels of these elements, with and without six other soil properties, were correlated with micronutrient uptake by wheat (*Triticum aestivum* L.) under greenhouse conditions. Correlation coefficients between AAAc-EDTA extractable and micronutrient concentrations in wheat tissue were 0.66, 0.33, 0.04, and 0.67 for Cu, Fe, Mn, and Zn, respectively; and for DTPA were 0.52, 0.26, 0.55, and 0.73 (Table 12-2). Inclusion of one soil property in the correlation markedly improved the correlation coefficient for AAAc-EDTA extractable Cu (organic matter), Mn, and Zn (pH), but not for Fe (Table 12-2). Improvements in correlations with DTPA, however, were noted only when extractable Mn was corrected for soil pH.

The modified Olsen's solution (0.5 M $NaHCO_3$ + 0.01 M EDTA + 0.1 g/L Superfloc 127, pH 8.6) was developed by the International Soil Fertility Evaluation and Improvement Project for use in Latin America (Hunter, 1975). Lindsay and Cox (1985) reported widespread use of this extractant in Africa, Asia, and Central and South America. However, little correlation research has been conducted with this extractant (Rohman & Cox, 1988).

In summary, use of EDTA in multi-element extractants, such as the Mehlich-3, modified Olsen's, and AAAc-EDTA, particularly in conjunction with readily measured soil properties, should result in effective prediction of micronutrient deficiencies, particularly on acidic soils. The FAO study also suggests that, even though buffered at pH 7.3, DTPA may be a good soil test for soils exhibiting wide variations in chemical and physical properties.

The DTPA soil test, developed for near-neutral and calcareous soils by Lindsay and Norvell (1978), illustrates the evolution of a soil test extractant from theoretical principles derived from soil chemistry to verification through greenhouse and field calibration studies. The extracting solution consists of 0.005 M DTPA and 0.01 M $CaCl_2$, buffered at pH 7.3 by 0.1 M triethanolamine (TEA). The DTPA extractant was selected because it offered the most favorable combination of stability constants necessary to simultaneously extract four micronutrient cations (Fe, Mn, Cu, and Zn). The buffered pH and presence of soluble Ca^{2+} prevent excessive dissolution of $CaCO_3$, avoiding the release of unavailable micronutrients occluded by this solid phase. It should be noted that at pH 7.3, 70 to 80% of the buffering capacity provided by TEA has been consumed. Therefore, using the DTPA extractant on acidic soils, will likely result in neutralization of the remaining buffer capacity and an unpredictable extraction pH (Norvell, 1984).

Results such as those obtained in the FAO study, and those reported by others on acidic soils, reduced soils, and metal-contaminated soils (Lee et al., 1978; Mandal & Haldar, 1980; Schauer et al., 1980) have intensified the interest in DTPA as a universal micronutrient extractant. O'Connor (1988) recently cautioned against misuse of the DTPA soil test, identifying four classes of misuse that, in fact, apply to all soil test extractants:

1. Method alteration. This involves varying chemical composition of extracting solution, sample preparation, extracting procedures (e.g., soil/solution ratio), or applying critical levels to crops without field calibration.

2. pH considerations. Inappropriate interpretations are made of results due to incorrect pH of extracting solution or of final soil suspension. An incorrect pH can result in exceeding the buffering capacity of the soil test solution and disruption of metal-chelate equilibria, causing shifts in metal chelating-tendencies.

3. Metal loading. Although DTPA may identify soils that have received high rates of metals (e.g., soils amended with sludges, fly ash, etc.), direct correlations between DTPA-extractable and plant-available metals are not assured, particularly at levels far in excess of established critical levels.

4. Metals other than Fe, Zn, Mn, and Cu. Many researchers have attempted to use the DTPA soil test to predict plant-available levels of nonessential heavy metals (Cd, Cr, Ni, and Pb), often with mixed or no success. Field research generally does not support the use of DTPA as a reliable predictor of metal concentrations within the plant across broad ranges of extractable metal levels in soils.

O'Connor's criticisms of DTPA misuse should not be interpreted to mean that modification of a soil test is not possible or desired; rather they indicate that extrapolation of the use of the test beyond its original intent, design, and field calibration is inappropriate. Indeed, one of the valid criticisms of the DTPA test is that it is somewhat difficult to use in a routine soil testing laboratory because it requires a 2-h shaking period, and is used only for four essential elements (Fe, Mn, Cu, and Zn).

In response to these problems, Soltanpour and Schwab (1977) modified the DTPA test by combining it with ammonium bicarbonate (AB) to extract P, K, Ca, and Mg, adjusting the pH from 7.3 to 7.6, and shortening the extraction time to 15 min. Later modifications of the AB-DTPA test have included removal of carbon black that absorbed Cu, Fe and Mn complexed by DTPA from soil extracts (Soltanpour & Workman, 1979), evaluation of the test for B (Gestring & Soltanpour, 1984; 1987) and heavy metals in sludge-amended soils (Barbarick & Workman, 1987), and development of a procedure for simultaneous multi-element analysis (except P) via an ICP (Soltanpour et al., 1979). Soil test methods should evolve, but logically and concurrent with field calibration, and should not simply become more widespread due to ease of use.

In addition to EDTA and DTPA, some research has been conducted that evaluates other chelates as micronutrient extractants. Haq et al. (1980) noted little difference in correlations between plant Zn, Cd, Ni, and Cu, and soil metals extracted by NTA, DTPA, and EDTA in a greenhouse study with 46 metal-contaminated soils (e.g., $r^2 = 0.64, 0.63,$ and 0.65, respectively, for Zn). Kennedy and Brown (1981) reported that HEDTA, $0.1\ M$ HCl, and DTPA were equally successful in identifying Zn-deficient soils.

Norvell (1984) modified the DTPA soil test to increase its applicability to acidic and metal-rich soils. Modifications included buffering to pH 5.3 and increasing the solution/soil ratio from 2:1 to 5:1 to provide greater chelating capacity and pH control. He compared the modified DTPA with 0.005 M HEDTA, NTA, and EGTA solutions also buffered to pH 5.3, original DTPA (pH 7.3), NH_4OAc (pH 5.3), and $0.1\ M$ HCl as extractants for Al, Fe, Mn, Zn, Cu, Cd, and Ni in 25 diverse soils. The most effective chelating agents were DTPA (pH 5.3) and HEDTA, followed by EDTA, NTA, and EGTA. With a 5:1 soil/solution ratio, DTPA (pH 7.3) was found to be surprisingly effective for most metals in acidic and metal-contaminated soils, indicating, as observed in the FAO study, that the alkaline nature of the extractant may not be a serious limitation to its effectiveness. It should be emphasized that Norvell (1984) evaluated only the relative effectiveness of these chelates as extractants of the metals, and did not in any way attempt to correlate the results with plant uptake.

3. Other Extractants

There are relatively few other classes of micronutrient soil test extractants currently in use. Extraction with hot water (actually $0.01\ M\ CaCl_2$ or similar dilute salt) remains the method of choice for B, primarily because of existing field calibration data. There has been a renewed interest in using other extractants for B (e.g., AB-DTPA), chiefly to eliminate the need for a separate extraction, thereby increasing laboratory efficiency. Ammonium oxalate-oxalic acid (AO-OA) has been used for Mo, but most studies have indicated that it is of little value and only a few laboratories in the world still use this approach (Lindsay & Cox, 1985). In the FAO study, correlations between plant B and Mo, and hot-water-soluble B and AO-OA extractable Mo were 0.74 and 0.25, respectively. When corrected for CEC (B) and pH (Mo), correlation coefficients were 0.83 and 0.70, respectively.

C. Analytical and Interpretive Considerations

Research has clearly shown that sample preparation, handling, and extraction method can have marked effects on the quantity of a micronutrient extracted from the soil. Several reports have discussed the advantages and disadvantages of drying soil samples prior to analysis (Bartlett & James, 1980; Leggett & Argyle, 1983; Shuman, 1980). Soltanpour et al. (1976) determined the effect of grinding, type of shaker and extraction vessel, time of filtering, and soil/solution ratio on DTPA-extractable Fe, Zn, Mn, and Cu. Since most preparatory steps were shown to significantly influence one or more of the extractable metals (Fig. 12–4), a standardized procedure was developed. The proposed method included a brief (~30 s) grinding time with minimal force, and reciprocal shaking in Erlenmeyer flasks at 180 oscillations/min, followed by filtration within 30 min. Detailed reviews of recommended methods for micronutrient analysis have been published as well (Oklahoma State Univ., 1984; Page et al., 1982).

An abundance of evidence exists that suggests that the predictive value of a micronutrient soil test can be enhanced by the use of multiple regression equations that include soil properties as well as extractable levels of the element. To be implemented successfully, multiple variable approaches must use routinely determined soil properties. Although the FAO study and other research have demonstrated the value of CEC, organic matter, percent clay, percent $CaCO_3$, and other variables in improving predictability of soil test extractants, soil pH is the only correction factor commonly used to modify soil test results. A summary of current critical-level ranges for all micronutrients and factors that are useful in interpreting these values is provided in Table 12–3.

In summary, as stated by Lindsay and Cox (1985), it seems likely that ". . .advances in soil testing may not be made by searching for the 'ideal' extractant for all soils; they may be made by carefully standardizing a procedure and improving its interpretation with the inclusion of important soil factors that affect extractability and availability of nutrients."

III. SOIL TESTS FOR MICRONUTRIENTS ESSENTIAL TO PLANT NUTRITION

A. Boron

1. Current Soil Tests

The hot-water-soluble extraction procedure proposed by Berger and Truog (1939) continues to be the basis of most B soil testing methods. Cur-

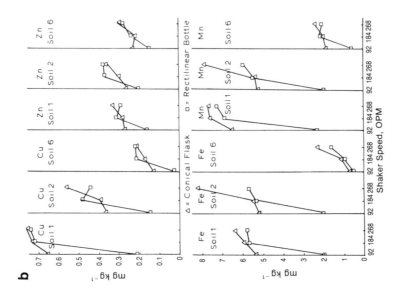

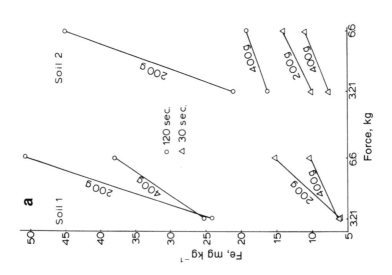

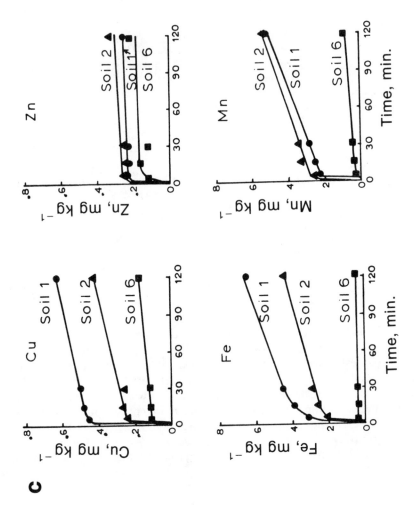

Fig. 12–4. Identification of the critical value for Cu with the DTPA soil test (Kruger et al., 1985).

Table 12-3. Soil test methods, soil factors influencing their interpretation, and typical ranges in critical levels for micronutrients.

Element	Interacting factors	Method	Range in critical level
			mg/kg
Boron	Crop yield goal, pH, soil moisture, texture, organic matter, soil type	Hot-water soluble	0.1–2.0
Copper	Crop, organic matter, pH, percent $CaCO_3$	Mehlich-1 Mehlich-3	0.1–10.0
		DTPA AB-DTPA	0.1–2.5
		0.1 M HCl	1.0–2.0
		Modified Olsen's	0.3–1.0
Iron	pH, percent $CaCO_3$, aeration, soil moisture, organic matter, CEC	DTPA	2.5–5.0
		AB-DTPA	4.0–5.0
		Modified Olsen's	10.0–16.0
Manganese	pH, texture, organic matter, percent $CaCO_3$	Mehlich-1	5.0 at pH 6, 10.0 at pH 7
		Mehlich-3	4.0 at pH 6, 8.0 at pH 7
		DTPA	1.0–5.0
		0.1 M HCl	1.0–4.0
		0.03 M H_3PO_4	10.0–20.0
		Modified Olsen's	2.0–5.0
Molybdenum	pH, crop	Ammonium Oxalate, pH 3.3	0.1–0.3
Zinc	pH, percent $CaCO_3$, P, organic matter, percent clay, CEC	Mehlich-1	0.5–3.0
		Mehlich-3	1.0–2.0
		DTPA	0.2–2.0
		AB-DTPA	0.5–1.0
		Modified Olsen's	1.5–3.0
		0.1 M HCl	1.0–5.0

rent methods typically include the use of dilute electrolyte, such as a 0.01 to 0.02 M $CaCl_2$ solution instead of water. Use of a dilute solution provides a clear, colorless extract, which eliminates the need for charcoal as a decolorizing agent. Gupta (1979) and Parker and Gardner (1981) found that this also removed a source of negative error associated with B adsorption by charcoal during extraction. Odom (1980) found more consistent results by extending the extraction time from 5 to 10 min. Keren et al. (1985), in a greenhouse study using bell peppers (*Capsicum frutescens* L.) grown in soil and soil-sand mixtures, provided convincing evidence that B in soil solution, not adsorbed B, was responsible for B uptake by plants.

Analysis of B in hot-water extracts traditionally has been performed by colorimetric procedures using either curcumin or azomethine-H. These procedures and the hot-water extraction have been described by Bingham (1982) in detail. The major drawbacks to these methods are that they are somewhat time consuming, require some specialized equipment for refluxing the sample during extraction, and that the procedure is limited to the extraction of a single element.

Gestring and Soltanpour (1981), Nilsson and Jennische (1986), and Jeffrey and McCullum (1988) have demonstrated that either ICP or direct-current-plasma (DCP) emission spectrometry analysis are acceptable alternatives to the colorimetric analysis. Analysis of filtered soil extracts without further pretreatment is possible using ICP or DCP technology. The increasing popularity of these instruments in soil testing laboratories will likely replace the use of colorimetric procedures.

Other recent advances in B soil testing methodology include the use of plastic pouches by Mahler et al. (1984) and extraction using plastic tubes in an Al-block digester by Nilsson and Jennische (1986), as alternatives to glass refluxing of the sample. These suggested improvements allow the processing of more samples in a shorter period of time and require only inexpensive or existing equipment.

2. Calibration and Correlation

In a previous review, Cox and Kamprath (1972) found the critical value for hot-water-soluble B to be influenced by soil type, plant species, climate, and soil pH. Generally, however, a value of about 0.5 mg B kg^{-1} soil may separate adequate B-supplying soils from those that may be deficient.

A. Greenhouse Studies. Parker and Gardner (1982) examined B availability in 15 western Oregon soils using New Zealand white clover (*Trifolium repens* L.) as the test crop. The soils represented a wide range of physical and chemical properties. Hot-water-soluble B ranged from 0.47 to 2.34 mg B kg^{-1} and was not well correlated with plant B concentrations ($r^2 = 0.00$, 0.17, and 0.33 for three successive harvests). The only significant effect of differential soil B levels was low yield caused by toxicity.

Gestring and Soltanpour (1987) used four alfalfa (*Medicago sativa* L.) varieties and three soils, to which 0, 10, 20, and 40 mg kg^{-1} B were added, to evaluate B soil tests. Hot-water-soluble B extracted after two harvests was well correlated ($r^2 = 0.78$ to 0.96) with plant B when pooled across varieties. However, correlations of soil B and B uptake or plant yield were poorer and sometimes not significant because some treatments caused B toxicity. Similar correlations were obtained for B extracted from soil using AB-DTPA, mannitol-CaCl$_2$, or a water saturation extract. Although hot-water-soluble B levels measured <0.2 mg B kg^{-1} soil, B deficiency in plants was not found.

Jin-Yun Jin et al. (1987) also found a good correlation between B in corn (*Zea mays* L.) 23 d after planting and B extracted by water ($r = 0.78$) or 0.02 M CaCl$_2$ ($r = 0.77$). However, they also failed to find B deficiency even when some of the 14 Virginia soils contained <0.1 mg B kg^{-1} soil using the hot-water-soluble extraction. This finding may have been caused by the short duration of the study or the release of organically bound B as a result of drying and rewetting the soil.

b. Field Studies. Chude and Obigbesan (1984) surveyed the B status of 23 cocoa (*Theobroma cacao* L.) growing areas in southwestern Nigeria and found the deficiency range for hot-water-soluble B to be 0.44 to 0.88 mg B kg^{-1} soil. Sherrell (1983) found hot-water-soluble B correlated to B in alfalfa from 91 locations in New Zealand. A critical soil test value was not identified, however, and plant B was concluded to be a more reliable means of identifying deficiency than soil tests. Khan et al. (1979) studied 33 crops and 162 soils in Lebanon and concluded that B was adequately supplied to most crops even when hot-water-soluble levels measured <0.35 mg B kg^{-1} soil. Although a critical soil test level could not be defined, plant B and soil B were significantly correlated ($r = 0.63$ to 0.96) for most crops.

3. Summary

The correlation and calibration of soil tests for B are not being actively researched. The basic tests have not changed in many years, except for modifications to improve extraction techniques and the use of emission spectrographic analysis. Critical soil test levels remain poorly defined for a variety of reasons, not the least of which is a scarcity of B-deficient soils. Greenhouse studies have limited value beyond demonstrating that B is an essential element when a small enough soil volume is used for a relatively high-yielding crop. Hot-water-soluble B continues to be the soil test of choice. New research is needed that examines the relationship of soil-extracted B and plant response, limited to a large, diverse group of soils that have all been identified with B deficiency in the field.

B. Chlorine

1. Current Soil Tests

Soil testing for Cl has only recently been initiated and appears limited to the Northern Great Plains of the USA. Because Cl$^-$ salts are highly water soluble and Cl$^-$ is not strongly adsorbed, Cl$^-$ can be extracted with water or dilute electrolyte. Fixen et al. (1988) have described, in detail, the extraction of Cl$^-$ using either 0.01 M Ca(NO$_3$)$_2$, 0.5 M K$_2$SO$_4$, or a CaO-saturated solution corresponding to analysis by colorimetric, potentiometric, or ion chromatographic procedures, respectively.

2. Calibration and Correlation

a. Greenhouse Studies. Broyer et al. (1954), while documenting the essentiality of Cl, showed that the content of Cl in early stages of deficiency in tomato (*Lycopersicum esculentum* Mill.) was about 7 mmol kg^{-1} dry leaf tissue (250 mg kg^{-1}). Although deficiency of Cl is rare, the plant requirement is higher than that for other micronutrients. Johnson et al. (1957) examined the Cl requirements for several crop species and made the general conclusion that, "From a soil fertility point of view, it is estimated that plants require 1 lb of chlorine for each 10 000 lb of dry matter produced. Hence, it would seem that, given the mobility of Cl in soil, even under intensive management for high yields, 2 to 3 kg Cl ha^{-1} would be sufficient for annual nutritional needs of most cropping systems. Greenhouse studies involving Cl have the same limitations described for studies with B because Cl^- is extremely mobile in soils.

b. Field Studies. Christensen et al. (1981) found application of Cl^- to have an apparent prophylactic effect against root rot (*Gaeumannomyces graminis* var. *tritici*) in winter wheat production. This effect and the abundance of Cl^- from extraneous sources in most geographic regions of the world will make it difficult to calibrate the soil test. Fixen et al. (1986b) found a positive response in yield of spring wheat and barley (*Hordeum vulgare* L.), but not oat (*Avena sativa* L.), to KCl fertilization of soils that tested high in K. A detailed examination of the effect of added Cl on wheat response led Fixen et al. (1986a) to conclude that increased yield was not simply a result of disease suppression. However, the conclusion that identified > 43.5 kg ha^{-1} of soil Cl^- in the top 60 cm of soil as the level adequate for near-maximum yield is inconsistent with levels suggested from greenhouse studies. Additional work will undoubtedly be necessary to partition direct nutritional effects from other plant responses to soil Cl^-. Nevertheless, for geographic areas of low Cl^-, soil testing for this micronutrient may serve as a useful guide for identifying potential economic responses.

3. Summary

Little research has been reported on the use of Cl soil tests, presumably because deficiencies of the element are rare. Suitable extraction and analytical procedures are available for routine testing. Calibration and correlation data are lacking to the degree that test interpretation is difficult at best.

C. Copper

1. Current Soil Tests for Copper

Documented plant responses to Cu are rare and occur in quite specific situations (e.g., high organic-matter soils). As a result, Cu soil tests have not received much individual effort, and extractable Cu is generally measured by the same procedures as other micronutrient cations. Methods used at present include DTPA, ammonium bicarbonate-DTPA (AB-DTPA), Mehlich-1, Mehlich-3, 0.1 M HCl, and, in some tropical countries, the modified Olsen's solution. Critical levels range from 0.12 to 0.25 mg kg^{-1} for DTPA, from 0.1 to 10 mg kg^{-1} for Mehlich-1 and Melhich-3, and from 0.4 to 1.0 for EDTA solutions.

Soil properties are often used with extractable Cu to verify the likelihood of a Cu response. The most frequently reported factors that supplement extractable Cu are organic matter, pH, soil test P, and percent $CaCO_3$. All of these factors are used qualitatively, however, as little evidence exists for useful multiple regression models that identify Cu-responsive soils.

2. Calibration and Correlation

a. Greenhouse Studies. Osiname et al. (1973), in a greenhouse study with oat grown in 28 Nigerian soils, compared EDTA, DTPA, 0.1 M HCl, 1.0 M HCl and 1.0 M NH$_4$OAc (pH 7) as extractants for available Cu. Copper uptake was significantly correlated with extractable Cu by EDTA, 1.0 M HCl, and DTPA (r = 0.62**, 0.55**, and 0.50**, respectively). Extractable Cu by all methods was highly correlated with (Fe + Al) oxide content, but not with organic matter or pH. Including these soil properties in multiple regression equations did not improve prediction of Cu uptake.

Aboul-Roos and Abdel-Wabid (1978) in a pot study with barley grown in 15 Egyptian soils obtained critical levels of 3.0 and 2.6 mg kg^{-1} and correlation coefficients of 0.85** and 0.88** for 0.1 M HCl extractable Cu + titratable alkalinity, and 0.01 M EDTA + (NH$_4$)$_2$CO$_3$, respectively.

Ponnamperuma et al. (1981) compared four extractants for Cu in a greenhouse study with 33 wetland rice (*Oryza sativa* L.) soils and obtained significant correlation coefficients between Cu uptake and extractable Cu with 0.05 M (r = 0.74**) and 0.1 M HCl (r = 0.64**), but not with (NH$_4$)$_2$CO$_3$ + EDTA or DTPA. The critical level for 0.05 M HCl extractable Cu was proposed to be 0.1 mg kg^{-1}. Based on plant correlations and laboratory considerations, such as ease of analysis, potential toxicity, and cost of reagents, 0.05 M was stated to be the best extractant for Cu.

Correlation coefficients of 0.664*** and 0.518*** were reported in the FAO study between DTPA and AAAc-EDTA extractable Cu, respectively, and Cu concentration in wheat grown in 3538 soils (Sillanpaa, 1982). Inclusion of organic C increased the correlation with AAAc-EDTA to 0.731***, but did not improve the predictive ability of DTPA. Correlations between extractable Cu, by either method, and Cu concentration in maize and wheat grown in the field were much lower, ranging from 0.114*** to 0.354***, but AAAc-EDTA was superior to DTPA.

Tiwari and Kumar (1982) compared 1 M NH$_4$OAc (pH 4.8 or 7.0), 1 M NH$_4$OAc (pH 7.0) + 0.01 M EDTA, 0.05 M EDTA, and 0.1 M HCl as Cu extractants in a greenhouse study with rice grown in peaty, red, and alluvial soils of India. Significant correlations with Cu uptake by rice seedlings were obtained only with 0.1 M HCl (r = 0.85**) and 0.05 M EDTA (r = 0.79**) extractable Cu. Copper uptake was found to be negatively correlated with soil pH (r = 0.83**), and positively correlated with soil organic matter and CEC (r = 0.79** and r = 0.66**, respectively).

Selvarajah et al. (1982) evaluated AAAc-EDTA, modified Olsen's, 0.05 M HCl, 0.01 M CaCl$_2$, and 0.2 M MgSO$_4$ as extractants for Cu in a study with rice grown under flooded conditions. Copper extracted by 0.05 M HCl and AAAc-EDTA were best correlated with total Cu uptake by two rice crops (r = 0.57* and r = 0.51*, respectively).

Tills and Alloway (1983) grew wheat in a greenhouse study with 20 soils in the United Kingdom and found that plant Cu was best correlated with Cu extracted by 0.05 M EDTA (pH 7.0, r = 0.868***). Correlations obtained with HCl, HNO$_3$, or DTPA extractants were lower (r < 0.70) and

AB-DTPA-extractable Cu was not correlated with plant Cu. Unlike Osiname et al. (1973), the authors reported that inclusion of Fe and Mn oxides, clay, pH, and organic matter significantly increased correlations of extractable Cu with plant Cu. A multiple regression equation including extractable Cu, Mn and Fe oxides, percent clay, pH, and percent organic matter accounted for 79 and 63% of the variability in Cu concentration in wheat for EDTA and DTPA, respectively.

Sedberry et al. (1988) evaluated eight extractants for Cu in a greenhouse study with rice grown under flooded conditions in 19 Louisiana soils. The extractants were 0.5 M HCl, 0.1 M HCl, 0.5 M HCl + 0.003 M AlCl$_3$, 0.5 M HCO$_3$, 0.05 M (NH$_4$)$_2$CO$_3$ + 0.01 M EDTA, 1.0 M NH$_4$OAc + 0.01 M EDTA, 1.0 M NH$_4$OAc (pH 4.8), and DTPA (pH 7.3). Extractable Cu, by any method, was not significantly correlated with soil organic matter, but plant Cu decreased by 1 mg kg^{-1} for each 1% increase in soil organic matter content. Correlations between Cu concentration and uptake in rice plants and extractable soil Cu were best for DTPA ($r = 0.56*$ and $r = 0.67**$, respectively) and 1.0 M NH$_4$OAc (pH 4.8) ($r = 0.55*$ and $r = 0.60**$, respectively). Including soil organic matter with extractable Cu in multiple regression equations resulted in highly significant R^2 values (0.58–0.70) for all extractants. Again, DTPA and 1.0 M NH$_4$OAc (pH 4.8) were found to be best related to plant Cu.

Rohman and Cox (1988) compared the modified Olsen's extractant with Mehlich-1, Mehlich-3, and AB-DTPA as a predictor of Cu availability for wheat in a greenhouse study with six soils under limed and unlimed conditions. Correlation coefficients between plant uptake and extractable Cu were rather low for all extractants ($r = 0.47**$ to $0.69**$), probably because of reduced Cu uptake under acidic (unlimed) conditions and extremely low, native soil, Cu levels. Results of this study showed that the critical level of extractable Cu by the modified Olsen's should be 0.3 mg L^{-1}, lower than the currently recommended value of 1.0 mg L^{-1}.

b. Field Studies. Field studies documenting the relationship between soil test levels of Cu and crop responses to Cu fertilization are extremely limited in number. Robertson et al. (1973) reported soybean [*Glycine max* (L.) Merr.] yield responses to Cu in a 1-yr study on a fine, sandy Spodosol, limed to pH 7.0. Mehlich-1 extractable Cu in the 0- to 15- and 15- to 30-cm depths was linearly related to soybean yield ($r = 0.63$ and $r = 0.77$, respectively), but a critical level of extractable Cu was not determined.

Gough et al. (1980) evaluated DTPA and EDTA, in conjunction with nine routinely measured soil properties (pH, organic C, particle size, CEC) as predictors of Cu uptake by native plants from A and C horizons of 21 soils of the northern Great Plains of the USA. Neither DTPA- nor EDTA-extractable Cu, either alone or in combination with any soil property, was significantly correlated with Cu uptake by any plant.

Grundon and Best (1982) evaluated DTPA as a soil test for Cu on 35 soils in Australia, and noted responses by wheat, either as grain yield or increased grain Cu, where DTPA-extractable Cu was <0.4 mg kg^{-1} for gray or gray-brown soils. Copper deficiency was not widespread and was related to soil order and pH, occurring most frequently on gray or gray-brown clays with near-neutral to alkaline pH values. For brown or red-brown soils, extractable Cu levels as low as 0.2 mg kg^{-1} did not result in wheat responses to applied Cu.

Makarim and Cox (1983), conducted field and greenhouse studies with corn, wheat, and soybean to evaluate Mehlich-1, Mehlich-3, AB-DTPA, and the Mehlich-Bowling (0.5 M HCl + 0.017 M AlCl$_3$) as Cu extractants. In the field study, yield responses to Cu fertilization were obtained at three of seven locations for wheat and two of five locations for soybean. The critical level for Cu, was determined only with the Mehlich-Bowling extractant, and was estimated to be 0.7 mg L^{-1} for wheat and soybean. A successive cropping study (soybean-corn-wheat) was conducted in the greenhouse, with 11 mineral, two mineral-organic, and two organic soils. Average critical values (across all crops) were determined by a linear plateau model to be 0.26, 0.62, 0.37, and 0.53 mg L^{-1} for Mehlich-1, Mehlich-Bowling, Mehlich-3, and AB-DTPA, respectively. These critical values compare favorably with those of Mehlich and Bowling (1975) (0.5 to 0.8 mg L^{-1}) and Soltanpour and Schwab (1977) (0.5 mg kg^{-1}).

Karamanos et al. (1986) studied the response of wheat, flax (*Linum usitatissimum* L.), barley, and canola (*Brassica napus* L.) to Cu applications for 2 yr at six locations in the sandy transitional grassland soils of Saskatchewan, Canada to compare soil and plant analysis as predictors of crop response. DTPA-extractable Cu was found to be more effective than plant analysis in diagnosis of Cu deficiency. The critical DTPA-extractable level of soil Cu was 0.4 mg kg^{-1}. This critical value for DTPA was identical to the value proposed by Kruger et al. (1985) in an earlier study in Saskatchewan involving 21 field trials with wheat, barley, rapeseed (*Brassica napus* var. annua Koch) and alfalfa and growth chamber studies with wheat grown in 11 soils (Fig. 12–5).

Martens (D. Martens, 1989, personal communication) conducted 41 Cu-response experiments with corn (33), soybean (4), and wheat (4) in Virginia from 1967 to 1983, primarily on Ultisols. Mehlich-1-extractable Cu ranged from 0.2 to 2.9 mg kg^{-1}. The only significant response to applied Cu was obtained with wheat in 1981 on an Altavista fine sandy loam with an extractable soil-Cu level of 0.7 mg kg^{-1}.

3. Summary

The most consistent success in predicting plant response to Cu has occurred with EDTA- and DTPA- based extractants. Critical values have ranged from 0.3 to 0.6 mg kg^{-1}. Additional field studies in areas of observed Cu deficiency are needed and future research should concentrate on quantification of the role of soil organic matter content in identification of Cu-responsive soils.

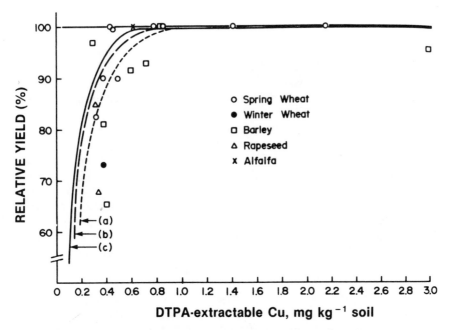

Fig. 12–5. Identification of the critical value for Cu with the DTPA soil test (Kruger et al., 1985).

D. Iron

1. Current Soil Tests for Iron

Crop responses to Fe fertilization, as with Cu, are rare and confined to specific soil-crop situations, generally occurring on alkaline soils with crops such as sorghum [*Sorghum bicolor* (L.) Moench], soybean, and certain fruits. The primary goal of the DTPA soil test developed by Lindsay and Norvell (1978) was to identify Fe- (and Zn-) responsive soils. This test was later modified to the ammonium bicarbonate-DTPA extractant(AB-DTPA) by Soltanpour and Schwab (1977) to allow for simultaneous determination of P, K, Cu, Zn, Mn, and Fe, greatly increasing its utility for soil testing laboratories. At present, however, only a few laboratories in the USA routinely test soils for Fe. Lindsay and Cox (1985), in a survey of soil testing laboratories of the tropics reported that other Fe extractants and critical levels were $1.0\ M$ NH_4OAc (pH 4.8, 0.4 mg kg^{-1}), 0.1 M HCl (0.3–0.5 mg kg^{-1}), and 0.5 M NaHCO$_3$ + 0.01 M EDTA (10–16 mg kg^{-1}). Critical levels for DTPA in the USA and tropics ranged from 2.5 to 5.0 mg kg^{-1} extractable Fe.

Iron recommendations are frequently made without soil test values for extractable Fe, based solely on crop and soil type. Soil parameters critical to accurate Fe recommendations are pH, the calcareous nature of soil, soil aeration, temperature, organic matter, and texture.

2. Calibration and Correlation

a. **Greenhouse Studies.** In their original study, Lindsay and Norvell (1978) used 77 surface soils representing the major agricultural soils of Colorado. The majority of the soils were alkaline (pH > 7.0) and low in organic matter ($< 2.0\%$). Sixty-two of the soils were calcareous. A greenhouse study was conducted with 35 of the soils, using sorghum as the test crop, to determine the need for Fe fertilization. A critical level of 4.5 mg kg^{-1} extractable Fe separated responsive from nonresponsive soils, with < 2.5 mg kg^{-1} associated with Fe-deficiency symptoms in sorghum.

Havlin and Soltanpour (1981) evaluated the AB-DTPA soil test in a greenhouse study with 40 Colorado soils. As with the study of Lindsay and Norvell (1978), the soils were generally alkaline, calcareous, and low in organic matter, and the test crop was sorghum. Mean pH, $CaCO_3$, and organic matter values of the soils were 7.7, 2.4, and 1.3%, respectively. A critical value of 4.8 mg Fe kg^{-1} was determined for both AB-DTPA and DTPA (Fig. 12–6). Havlin and Soltanpour further identified low, medium, and high categories of AB-DTPA-extractable Fe, corresponding to 0 to 3.5, 3.6 to 5.0, and > 5.0 mg kg^{-1}, respectively.

In the FAO study (Sillanpaa, 1982), neither AAAc-EDTA (pH 4.6) nor DTPA (pH 7.3) was significantly correlated with Fe content of field-grown maize or wheat. Correlation coefficients obtained in the greenhouse study with wheat were $r = 0.325***$ for EDTA and $r = 0.263***$ for DTPA. Possible causes for the poor correlations in the field were the absence of large quantities of high pH soils, and contamination of plant material from the field with soil or dust that contained large or erratic quantities of Fe. Unlike all other micronutrients, no soil property was identified that, when combined with extractable Fe, significantly improved the correlation with plant uptake in the greenhouse.

Barak and Chen (1982) proposed a bioassay test to rapidly screen soils for Fe deficiency. Three peanut (*Arachis hypogaea* L.) genotypes were grown in six soils in Israel, varying in $CaCO_3$ content from 3.6 to 63%. Iron deficiency was estimated by chlorophyll content of leaves at the end of a 5 wk pot study and was significantly correlated with percent $CaCO_3$ and active lime content.

Katyal and Sharma (1984) compared DTPA and EDTA as Fe extractants in a greenhouse study with 16 soils and upland rice as the indicator crop. No significant correlation was found between relative yield and extractable Fe by either method, but total plant Fe was significantly correlated with DTPA-Fe ($r = 0.52*$). Inclusion of pH, organic C, and percent clay did not improve the predictive ability of equations including extractable Fe. Total plant Fe was not related to yield, but a multiple regression equation between relative yield and Fe^{2+} in leaves, soil pH, and lime content had a R^2 value of 0.59*.

b. **Field Studies.** Few field studies have been reported that relate soil test Fe to crop yield or Fe content. DeBoer and Reisenauer (1973) successfully predicted Fe deficiency symptoms with DTPA in the field (11 of 13

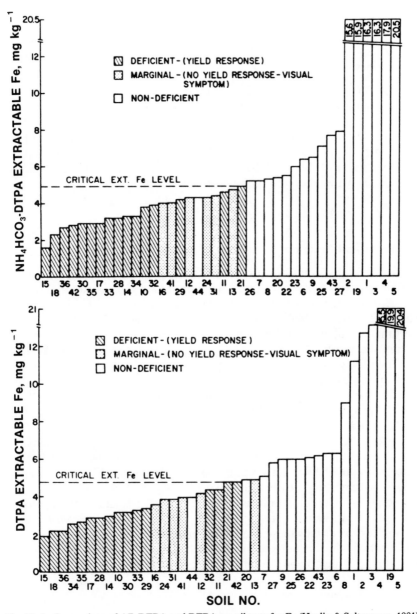

Fig. 12–6. Comparison of AB-DTPA and DTPA as soil tests for Fe (Havlin & Soltanpour, 1981).

sites, critical level of 6 mg kg^{-1}) and in a greenhouse study with sorghum (13 of 14 soils, critical level of 5 mg kg^{-1}).

Havlin and Soltanpour (1982) visually identified 23 Fe-deficient sorghum fields in eastern Colorado and obtained soil samples from deficient and non-deficient areas in each field. Based on these observations, deficient, marginal, and sufficient levels of AB-DTPA-extractable Fe were determined to be <2.0, 2.1 to 4.4, and >4.4 mg kg^{-1}, respectively, consistent with results obtained in a separate greenhouse study.

3. Summary

The DTPA and AB-DTPA extractants are based on sound theoretical principles and have been demonstrated, at least under greenhouse conditions, to separate Fe-deficient and Fe-sufficient soils. Critical levels with the two extractants are similar (4.5–5.0 mg kg^{-1}). Given the success of these two extractants, the primary research need in soil testing for Fe would appear to be expansion of the database to verify critical levels for a wider variety of crops grown in the field on Fe-responsive soils.

E. Manganese

1. Current Soil Tests for Manganese

Extractable Mn has been used successfully in many studies, particularly for soybean and small grains, to predict crop yield responses to Mn fertilization. At present, most of the soil testing laboratories in the USA use acidic extractants, such as Mehlich-1, Mehlich-3, 0.1 M HCl, or 0.03 M H_3PO_4 to estimate available Mn (Cox, 1987). Critical values reported for these extractants ranged from 4 to 20 mg kg^{-1}, relative to 1.4 mg kg^{-1} for DTPA.

The survey conducted by Lindsay and Cox (1985) of soil testing laboratories in tropical regions showed a wide range of extracting solutions used for Mn, including, in addition to those mentioned previously, 0.05 M H_2SO_4, 1.0 M NH$_4$OAc (pH 7 and 4.8), modified Olsen's, 0.05 M HCl, and water. Critical values reported in this survey generally ranged from 1.0 to 5.0 mg kg^{-1} for DTPA, modified Olsen's, and the dilute acid solutions. In most cases, the critical level for extractable Mn varies with soil pH. For instance, with the Mehlich-1 extractant the critical value used for Mn-sensitive crops is 4.0 mg kg^{-1} at pH 6.0 and 8.0 mg kg^{-1} at pH 7.0.

Soil properties commonly used to supplement extractable Mn for identification of Mn deficiencies include pH, organic matter, percent $CaCO_3$, and soil texture. Manganese availability indexes based on multiple regression equations that include soil pH and extractable Mn have shown considerable promise in identifying soils in which crop response to applied Mn is likely.

2. Calibration and Correlation

a. Greenhouse Studies. Shuman and Anderson (1974) examined the effect of soil pH on the ability of six extractants (Mehlich-1, EDDHA, DTPA, water, 1.0 M NH$_4$OAc [pH 7], and 1.0 M NH$_4$OAc + hydroquinone) to predict Mn availability to wheat and soybean grown in eight Georgia soils. Under extremely acidic conditions (pH 4.8) water-soluble Mn was the best extractant for wheat and soybean ($r = 0.85^{***}$ and $r = 0.40^{***}$, respectively), reflecting the increased solubility of solid-phase Mn at pH values <5.2.

When the soils were limed to pH 5.8 or 6.8, however, DTPA was best correlated with Mn uptake by both crops. At pH 5.8, the pH most similar to that of agricultural soils in the Southeast, the Mehlich-1 was equivalent to DTPA in predictive ability. In a subsequent study with the same soils, Shuman and Anderson (1978) reported that available soil Mn, as assessed by these soil tests, was best correlated with total soil Mn and clay content, but poorly correlated with organic matter.

Randall et al. (1976) conducted an extensive evaluation of extractants for Mn on Wisconsin soils, of which 37 were low ($<6\%$) and 20 high (4.2 to 79%) in organic matter, to determine the value of including pH and organic matter in predictive equations relating soil Mn to Mn uptake by oat and ryegrass (*Lolium multiflorum* Lam.). Eighteen extractants were used with the low organic matter soils and 13 with the high organic matter soils. The extractants included a variety of dilute acids (HCl, H_3PO_4), chelates (EDTA, DTPA) at various concentrations and pH values in combination with NH_4OAc or $(NH_4)_2CO_3$, water, salt solutions [$Mg(NO_3)_2$], and reducing agents (hydroxylamine, hydroquinone) alone or in combination with NH_4OAc (pH 7.0). The authors concluded that extractable Mn alone was not in itself a good criterion for Mn availability in high organic matter soils and that, in fact, either soil pH or organic matter content, without the use of a Mn soil test, could adequately predict Mn availability. For the low organic matter soils, $0.03 \ M \ H_3PO_4$, $0.01 \ M$ EDTA $+ \ 1.0 \ M \ NH_4OAc$, 0.05 M EDTA, and DTPA (pH 7.3) were recommended for determination of available Mn.

Singh et al. (1977) concluded that $1.0 \ M \ NH_4OAc$ (pH 4.8 or 7) was the most suitable extractant for estimating Mn availability to maize grown on 30 calcareous soils in India. Other extractants evaluated were DTPA, 0.5 M KCl, $0.02 \ M$ EDTA, $1.0 \ M \ NH_4OAc$ (pH 3.0), and $1.0 \ M \ NH_4OAc \ +$ 0.2% hydroquinone.

Salcedo et al. (1979) correlated extractable soil Mn by six methods, with Mn uptake by soybean from 12 Michigan soils and selected soil properties. Simple correlation coefficients and multiple regression models, including pH and the ratio of bases (Ca + Mg/K), identified $0.03 \ M \ H_3PO_4$ as the best extractant, with a critical level of 12 mg kg^{-1}. The soil property best correlated with Mn uptake was Mn oxide content (hydroxylamine hydrochloride extractable), suggesting that amorphous Mn oxides in mineral soils are a plant-available fraction that should be considered in development of a Mn soil test. This is consistent with the results of Randall et al. (1976) who reported a simple correlation coefficient of $r = 0.67^{***}$ between hydroxylamine hydrochloride-extractable Mn and plant uptake by oat in mineral soils.

In the FAO study (Sillanapaa, 1982), correlations between AAAc + EDTA and DTPA-extractable Mn with Mn uptake by wheat grown in the greenhouse in over 3500 soils were $r = 0.039^*$ and $r = 0.552^{***}$, respectively, and increased to $r = 0.588^{***}$ and $r = 0.713^{***}$ when a correction factor for soil pH was included in a multiple correlation. Although the correlation coefficients were quite low ($r = 0.161^{***}$ and $r = 0.119^{***}$ for maize and wheat, respectively), DTPA was also better correlated than AAAc-

EDTA with Mn concentration of maize and wheat grown in the field at the original sites.

Sheppard and Bates (1982) compared seven Mn extractants for their ability to predict Mn uptake by barley and soybean from 69 soils in Canada. Correlation coefficients obtained between extractable Mn and plant uptake were low ($r = 0.24$–0.49) and little difference in predictive ability was noted between extractants. A backward stepwise regression technique was used to develop a Mn availability index relating Mn uptake to extractable Mn and soil pH, organic matter, clay content, and extractable P. Final regression models included only extractable Mn, soil pH, and dry matter yield (assumed to represent an integration of all factors affecting crop growth under greenhouse conditions).

Based on the above variables, the general ranking of extractants was $0.005\ M$ DTPA + $0.5\ M$ NaHCO$_3$ (pH 8.5) > $0.005\ M$ DTPA + $1.0\ M$ NH$_4$HCO$_3$ (pH 7.6) > $0.3\ M$ H$_3$PO$_4$ > 0.2% hydroquinone + $1.0\ M$ NH$_4$OAc (pH 7) > $1.5\ M$ NH$_4$H$_2$PO$_4$ > $1\ M$ NH$_4$OAc (pH 7) > $0.005\ M$ DTPA + $0.001\ M$ CaCl$_2$ + $0.1\ M$ TEA (pH 7.3). Coefficients of determination for the multiple regression equations ranged from $R^2 = 0.79$ to 0.88. Manganese availability indexes developed from these equations were used with results from 11 field studies and successfully identified Mn deficient sites on coarse-textured, but not fine-textured, soils.

Sims (1985, 1986) compared the Mehlich-1 and Mehlich-3 extractants as predictors of Mn uptake by wheat grown in four Atlantic coastal plain soils amended with manures or MnSO$_4$. Mehlich-1 and Mehlich-3 extractable soil Mn were highly correlated ($r = 0.95***$), and multiple regression equations, when soil pH was included, accounted for from 57 to 77% of the variability in Mn uptake. Plant uptake of Mn and Zn was primarily related to exchangeable fractions; however, predictive models were significantly enhanced by the inclusion of soil pH ($R^2 = 0.77**$). Organically complexed Mn, Mn oxides, and Mn occluded by Fe oxides were all negatively correlated with plant uptake of Mn.

b. Field Studies. Extensive field studies have been conducted to refine the ability to predict Mn availability to sensitive crops. Three of these studies were conducted with soybean grown in the Atlantic Coastal Plain region of the USA, on coarse-textured, low organic matter soils known to be Mn responsive when overlimed.

Shuman et al. (1980) conducted two field experiments for three years to calibrate four soil-Mn extractants for soybean grown in the Coastal Plain of Georgia. Critical values of 2.6, 1.8, 0.2 and 0.4 mg kg^{-1} were determined for Mehlich-1, Mehlich-Bowling, DTPA, and AB-DTPA using the method of Cate and Nelson (1971) (Fig. 12-2). In a related laboratory study, Shuman et al. (1978) evaluated the ability of DTPA, 0.03 M H$_3$PO$_4$, and Mehlich-1 to identify changes in soil Mn availability due to soil pH, and source and rate of Mn fertilization. All extractants separated the highest Mn rates

(22 and 56 kg ha^{-1}), but only DTPA successfully identified decreases in extractable Mn as pH increased from 6.2 to 6.7.

Mascagni and Cox (1985) conducted 38 soybean experiments from 1979 to 1982 with the goal of incorporating extractable Mn (Mehlich-1 and Mehlich-3) and soil pH into a single availability index that could be used to identify Mn-deficient soils. Significant yield responses to Mn fertilization were obtained in 25 of the experiments. Regression analyses indicated that either soil pH or extractable Mn could explain <30% of the variation in yield response, but together yielded R^2 values of 0.56** and 0.59** for the Mehlich-1 and Mehlich-3 extractants, respectively. Including organic matter, CEC, and subsoil pH (20–30, and 30–40 cm) did not improve R^2 values. Critical values obtained from Mehlich-1 Mn were 4.7 and 9.7 mg L^{-1} at pH 6 and 7, respectively; and for Mehlich-3 Mn the critical values at these pH values were 3.9 and 8.0 mg L^{-1}, respectively. A Mn availability index (MnAI) was developed using the empirical relationship between yield responses, soil pH, and extractable Mn. For the Mehlich-3 extractant, the equation for the index was MnAI = 101.7 − 15.2 pH + 3.75 Mehlich-3 Mn. The critical index was set at 25, with "probable" responses for MnAI values of 20 to 25, and "likely" responses at MnAI <20 (Fig. 12–7).

Mascagni and Cox (1984) also conducted four experiments to evaluate the Mehlich-3 extractant as a predictor of Mn response by corn. As with soybean, corn yield increases were best explained by a multiple regression equation including Mehlich-3 Mn and soil pH (R^2 = 0.51***). The critical value for Mehlich-3 Mn was determined to be lower for corn than for soybean; 1.5 mg L^{-1} at pH 6 and 5.3 mg L^{-1} at pH 7, respectively.

Gettier et al. (1985), in a similar study, conducted 30 Mn fertilization experiments with eight soybean cultivars over a 7-yr period using 13 soil types in the Coastal Plain region of Virginia. A yield prediction equation, combining Mehlich-1-extractable Mn and soil pH accounted for 68% of the variation in yield (percent maximum yield = 205.7 − 24.71 pH + 7.03 Mehlich-1 Mn). As noted by Mascagni and Cox (1985), including organic matter or subsoil parameters did not improve yield prediction. Using 90% of maximum yield as a criterion, the critical levels for Mehlich-1 Mn at pH 6 and 7 were 4.6 and 8.1 mg kg^{-1}, virtually identical to the values of Mascagni and Cox (1985) (Fig. 12–8).

3. Summary

Field and greenhouse research have consistently demonstrated that the most successful approach to identification of Mn-deficient soils is the use of an availability index incorporating extractable Mn and soil pH. Manganese extracted by acidic- (Mehlich-1, 0.3 H_3PO_4) and chelate-based (Mehlich-3, DTPA, AB-DTPA) extractants can be used in multiple regression models to identify critical index values. Field evaluation of existing Mn availability equations is needed to determine appropriate modifications for various soils and crops.

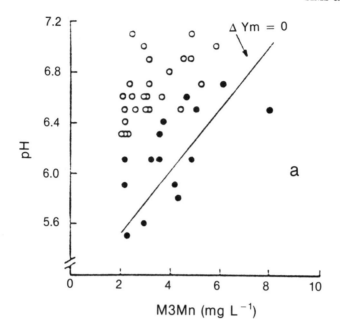

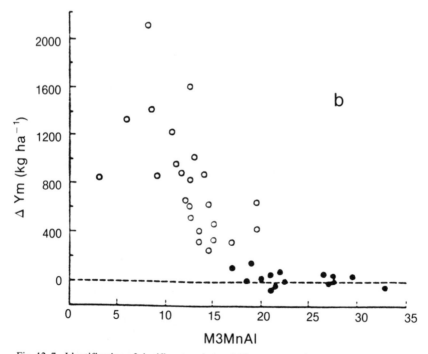

Fig. 12–7. Identification of significant soybean yield responses using (a) soil pH and Mehlich-3 Mn (open symbols indicate significant yield response to Mn fertilization); and (b) the Mehlich-3 Mn availability index (MnAI) (Mascagni & Cox, 1985).

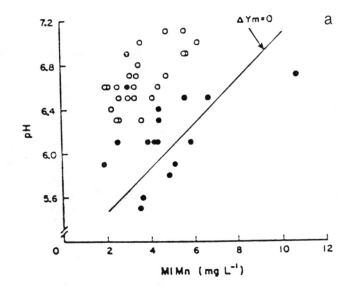

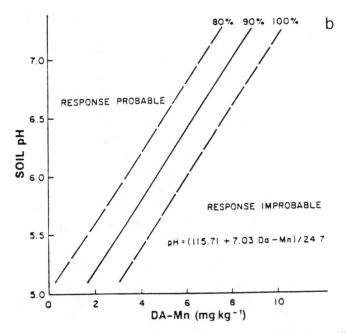

Fig. 12-8. Prediction equations for estimating yield response to Mn based on soil pH and Mehlich-1 Mn in (a) North Carolina (Mascagni & Cox, 1985) and (b) Virginia (Gettier et al., 1985).

F. Molybdenum

1. Currently Used Soil Tests

The acid ammonium oxalate (AAO) procedure first proposed by Grigg (1953) is perhaps still the most commonly used soil test extractant for Mo. Popularity of the procedure is not a result of its unerring ability to predict Mo deficiency, but rather because no better methods have been developed. Scarcity of Mo-deficient soils worldwide and the apparent influence of other soil properties, particularly soil pH, on Mo availability, contribute significantly to the problem. In an earlier review by Cox and Kamprath (1972), a level of >0.2 mg kg^{-1} AAO-extractable Mo was identified as adequate.

2. Calibration and Correlation

a. Greenhouse Studies. Bhella and Dawson (1972) extracted Mo from 30 western Oregon soils using an anion exchange resin. They found a good correlation ($r = 0.86$) between extractable Mo and Mo in subterranean clover (*Trifolium subterraneum* L.). The procedure was not compared with other extraction methods and extracted Mo was also well correlated with total plant N ($r = 0.875$) and soil pH ($r = 0.80$) from pH 5 to 7. The relationships were treated as linear across levels of 0.002 to 0.022 mg Mo kg^{-1} soil and 0.0 to 1.2 mg Mo kg^{-1} plant tissue. However, critical levels were not identified.

Karimian and Cox (1979) evaluated resin extraction of Mo in a comparison with acid ammonium oxalate in a study using cauliflower (*Brassica oleracea* var. *botrytis* L.) grown in 20 soils representative of the southeastern USA. They found no correlation between amounts of Mo extracted by the two procedures, or between soil test Mo and either yield or plant-tissue Mo. Relative yield and plant Mo were best predicted from soil pH and a ratio of amorphous to free Fe ($R^2 = 0.47$ and $R^2 = 0.61$, respectively). Responses to applied Mo were obtained, but critical soil test levels could not be identified. In a study comparing ammonium oxalate and resin extraction, Lombin (1985) found the best prediction of plant-available Mo for peanut ($R^2 = 0.64$) when soil organic matter (percent) was included as an independent variable with oxalate-extracted Mo.

b. Field Studies. Mortvedt and Anderson (1982) conducted an intensive study of six forage legumes grown at 11 sites in five states of the southern USA. Ammonium oxalate-extractable Mo ranged from 0.11 to 0.49 mg Mo kg^{-1} soil. Molybdenum fertilization increased extractable Mo, but seldom increased forage yields. Yield increases were more consistently obtained by liming than by Mo fertilization. Correlations of soil Mo and plant Mo were not statistically significant. Relative forage yield and plant Mo concentrations were, however, highly correlated to soil pH. Including soil pH in the correlation of soil Mo, and either relative yield or plant Mo, slightly improved the correlation. Resulting R^2 values of only 0.5 indicate poor predictive ability of the soil test.

Burmester et al. (1988) observed widespread Mo deficiency in northern Alabama while measuring soybean response to lime and Mo at 15 different field locations. Acid ammonium oxalate-extracted Mo was not correlated to yield increase or other plant parameter responses associated with Mo fertilization or liming. A high correlation ($R^2 = 0.88$), however, was obtained between relative yield and the ratio of Fe/Mo extracted by acid ammonium oxalate. Ratios of Fe/Mo >1540 were identified with Mo deficiency.

3. Summary

Research on Mo soil testing, although limited, continues efforts to find better extraction procedures and improve interpretation of test results with better correlation and calibration data from greenhouse and field studies. Acid ammonium oxalate extraction has received the most attention, however resin extraction has shown some benefit as a potential test method. Including other soil characteristics in prediction equations often improves their reliability for predicting Mo fertilizer response. Recent work using the Fe/Mo ratio in acid ammonium oxalate soil extracts holds promise for significant improvement in Mo soil testing.

G. Zinc

1. Current Soil Tests for Zinc

Crop responses to Zn occur less frequently than to Mn and have been documented for a wider range of crops and soil types than Cu and Fe. As with the other micronutrient cations, the most common, and certainly the most desired approach from a practical standpoint, to Zn soil testing is the use of a multi-element extractant such as Mehlich-1, Mehlich-3, or AB-DTPA. Some laboratories in the USA use 0.1 M HCl, DTPA, or acidic NH_4OAc (pH 3 or 4.8) as a single extractant for Zn. Average critical levels for the major Zn extractants are DTPA, 0.8 mg kg^{-1}; Mehlich-1, 1.1 mg kg^{-1}; and 0.1 M HCl, 5 mg kg^{-1} (Cox, 1987). Tropical soil-testing laboratories use these Zn soil tests as well as EDTA, modified Olsen's, and 1 M KCl (pH 7.0). Critical levels reported by tropical laboraties were DTPA, 0.5 to 1.0 mg kg^{-1}; 0.1 M HCl, 1.0 to 5.0 mg kg^{-1}; modified Olsen's, 1.5 to 10 mg kg^{-1}; and KCl, 0.85 mg kg^{-1} (Lindsay & Cox, 1985).

Soil properties used to improve the interpretation of Zn soil test results include pH, organic matter, CEC, soil test P, texture, percent clay, and percent $CaCO_3$. Some laboratories have developed Zn availability indexes that include pH, soil P, CEC, or clay content in the interpretation of the Zn status of soils (Alley et al., 1972; Junus & Cox, 1987).

2. Calibration and Correlation

a. Greenhouse Studies. Haq and Miller (1972) reported that the coefficient of determination between Zn extracted by EDTA + 1.0 M $(NH_4)_2CO_3$, DTPA, EDDHA, and Mehlich-1 and plant Zn uptake by corn grown in 85 soils, was increased from about 0.4 to 0.75 when soil pH was included in multiple regression equations. Plant Zn was correlated better with EDTA or DTPA ($r = 0.61**$ and $r = 0.60**$, respectively) than with Mehlich-1 or EDDHA ($r = 0.45*$ and $r = 0.48**$, respectively).

Osiname et al. (1973) found that EDTA was superior to DTPA, 0.1 M HCl, and 1.0 M HCl in predicting Zn uptake by oat grown on 28 soils of western Nigeria. Use of a multiple regression model incorporating 0.1 M HCl-extractable Zn, pH, organic matter and silt + clay was recommended, particularly for more acidic soils (pH $<$ 6.0).

Singh et al. (1977) reported correlation coefficients between extractable Zn and Zn uptake by maize grown in 30 calcareous soils in India were as follows: DTPA, 0.93***; 0.5 M KCl, 0.02[ns]; 0.02 M EDTA, 0.11[ns]; and 1.0 M NH$_4$OAc, pH 3 = 0.08[ns], pH 4.8 = 0.38**, pH 7 = 0.5[ns]). The critical value for DTPA-Zn was estimated to be 1.4 mg kg^{-1}.

Havlin and Soltanpour (1981) established a critical level of 0.9 mg kg^{-1} for AB-DTPA-extractable Zn, based on yield and plant Zn of corn grown in 40 Colorado soils. In the same study, the critical value of DTPA-extractable Zn was determined to be 0.7 mg kg^{-1}, consistent with the value of 0.8 mg kg^{-1} originally determined by Lindsay and Norvell (1978) for DTPA. Zinc uptake was highly correlated with AB-DTPA extractable Zn ($r = 0.87***$). Low, medium, and high soil test values were proposed to be 0 to 0.31, 0.32 to 0.87, and $>$0.88 mg kg^{-1}, respectively, for AB-DTPA extractable Zn. For DTPA-Zn, the same categories were 0 to 0.20, 0.21 to 0.44, and $>$0.45 mg kg^{-1}, respectively.

Gupta and Mittal (1981) determined critical values for Zn with six extractants based on plant Zn content of green gram (*Phaseolus aureus* Roxb.) grown for 6 wk in 22 noncalcareous soils in India. Critical soil Zn levels with the four best extractants were 0.48, 0.80, 0.70, and 2.2 mg kg^{-1} for DTPA, NH$_4$OAc + EDTA, AB-EDTA, and 0.1 M HCl, respectively. Correlations between relative yield and extractable Zn for these extractants ranged from $r = 0.54**$ to $0.58**$, and between yield and plant Zn concentration from $r = 0.55**$ to $0.73**$.

Sakal et al. (1981) also found that DTPA-extractable Zn was a useful extractant for predicting response of rice and wheat to Zn applications in soils of India. Correlation coefficients between DTPA Zn and plant Zn were $r = 0.72**$ for rice and $r = 0.85**$ for wheat.

Singh and Takar (1981) determined, based on Zn uptake by rice from 46 salt-affected soils representing two soil associations in India, that the critical level for extractable Zn was 0.86 mg kg^{-1} ($r^2 = 0.89$) for DTPA, 1.42 mg kg^{-1} for 0.05 M EDTA ($r^2 = 0.91$), and 1.0 mg kg^{-1} ($r^2 = 0.87$) for (NH$_4$)$_2$CO$_3$ + EDTA Zn. Critical values could not be obtained with Mehlich-1 or soil solution Zn due to lack of a significant relationship between soil and plant Zn. Prediction of yield response to applied Zn for all 46 soils was improved by including percent CaCO$_3$ and percent clay in a multiple regression equation. When examined separately, however, organic C was also found to be highly correlated with yield and Zn uptake in one of the soil associations, resulting in a significantly lower Zn critical value (0.69 mg kg^{-1}) (Fig. 12–9).

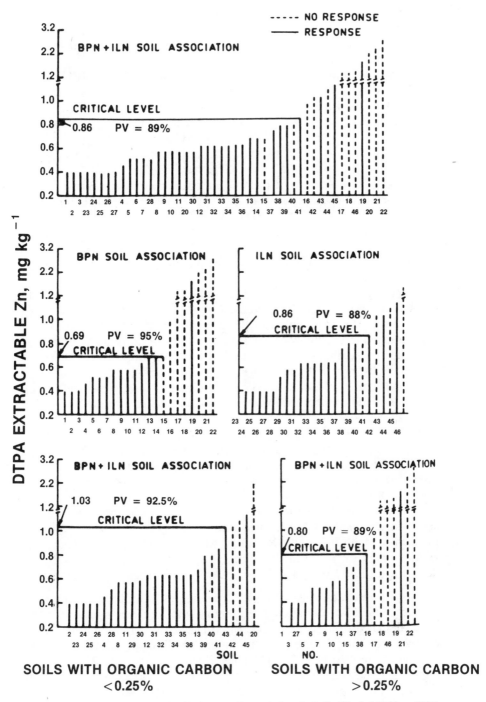

Fig. 12-9. Critical values for DTPA Zn in two soil associations in India (Singh & Takkar, 1981).

Madziva (1981) reported that for soils in Zimbabwe, critical Zn levels for five extractants, in order of efficiency of prediction of Zn uptake, were Mehlich-1, 0.50 mg kg^{-1} ($r = 0.68$); DTPA, 0.25 mg kg^{-1} ($r = 0.64$), HCl, 0.48 mg kg^{-1} ($r = 0.59$), NH$_4$OAc EDTA, 0.48 mg kg^{-1} ($r = 0.48$), and EDTA, 0.59 ($r = 0.43$).

Ponnamperuma et al. (1981) compared 0.05 M and 0.1 M HCl, EDTA, and DTPA as Zn extractants for rice grown under flooded conditions on 33 soils in India. Rice grown on 16 soils exhibited Zn deficiency symptoms at levels far in excess of critical limits for all extractants except 0.05 M HCl (critical level = 1.0 mg kg^{-1}). Zinc extracted by 0.05 M HCl, 0.1 M HCl, and EDTA, but not DTPA, were significantly correlated with plant Zn ($r = 0.88$**, $r = 0.55$**, and $r = 0.43$**, respectively).

Correlations between extractable Zn and Zn concentrations of field-grown corn and wheat reported in the FAO study (Sillanpaa, 1982) were $r = 0.38$*** and $r = 0.47$*** for DTPA, and $r = 0.39$*** and $r = 0.41$*** for AAAc-EDTA. Correlations with Zn in wheat grown in the greenhouse were $r = 0.73$*** for DTPA and $r = 0.67$*** for AAAc-EDTA. Use of soil pH as a correction factor slightly improved the correlation with AAAc-EDTA ($r = 0.71$***), but not DTPA.

Selvarajah et al. (1982) compared 0.05 M HCl, AAAc-EDTA, modified Olsen's, 0.01 M CaCl$_2$, and 0.2 M MgSO$_4$ as extractants for Zn using two varieties of rice grown under flooded conditions in four soils in India. All extractants were highly correlated with Zn concentration and uptake by 4-wk-old rice seedlings ($r = 0.73$ to 0.99), but only moderately related to Zn uptake by 8-wk-old rice plants ($r = 0.34$ to 0.50).

Singh et al. (1977) conducted a pot study with wheat grown in 21 semi-arid soils of India and determined critical values, based on a 20% reduction in yield, of 0.60, 0.80, 0.92, and 1.20 mg kg^{-1} for DTPA + CaCl$_2$, modified Olsen's, NH$_4$OAc-EDTA, and 0.1 M HCl, respectively. The DTPA + CaCl$_2$ extractant was best correlated with relative yield ($r = 0.85$).

Rohman and Cox (1988) evaluated the modified Olsen's extractant to determine if the suggested critical value for Zn by this method (2.0 mg kg^{-1}) was valid for a soils with a wide range of properties. Corn was grown under limed and nonlimed conditions on six diverse soils representing four soil orders. Plant Zn uptake was correlated with Zn extracted by modified Olsen's, Mehlich-1, Mehlich-3, and AB-DTPA. All extractants were well correlated with Zn uptake ($r > 0.80$), but the critical level for modified Olsen's Zn was determined to be 1.0 mg kg^{-1}, significantly lower than the present value.

b. Field Studies. Alley et al. (1972) conducted 10 field experiments from 1968 to 1970 in the Coastal Plain, Piedmont, and Applachian regions of Virginia, designed to evaluate Mehlich-1, 0.1 M HCl, DTPA, and EDTA as predictors of corn yield response to applied Zn. Soil pH varied from 5.4 to 7.2 and soil test extractable P (Mehlich-1) varied from 31 to 224 mg kg^{-1}. Significant yield responses to Zn occurred at five of the 10 locations. With the critical level estimated to be 0.8 mg kg^{-1}, EDTA-extractable Zn gave the best separation of sufficient and deficient soils. A multiple regression equation, using information routinely available from the soil testing laboratory, was used to define a Zn availability index (ZnAI) [ZnAI = 780.2 + 68.8 × Mehlich-1 Zn − 101.3 × pH − 0.2 × Mehlich-1 P] ($R = 0.945***$). A critical index of 135 was proposed to identify Zn-responsive sites.

Cox and Wear (1977) reported the results of a regional study in the southern USA with the goal of diagnosing Zn deficiencies in corn and rice. For low CEC soils (<7.5 cmol kg^{-1}), the predictive ability of extractable Zn was improved by incorporating CEC in a regression equation. Including clay content and soil pH in the regression equation did not improve interpretation of Zn response.

Peaslee (1980) used acid-extractable Zn (0.1 M HCl), pH, and soil test P (Bray P1) to identify Zn deficiency based on plant and soil samples collected from 54 fields in Kentucky. A multiple regression equation (leaf Zn = 37.1 + 1.51 soil test Zn − 4.04 pH − 1.79 ln [soil test P/100]) had an R value of 0.82**, relative to a simple correlation coefficient of 0.68 for soil test Zn alone.

Payne et al. (1986) compared DTPA and Mehlich-1 as predictors of Zn uptake and soybean yield with two cultivars grown at pH values of 6.5, 7.6, and 8.0 in a Georgia Ultisol. Zinc fertilization increased soybean yield, but Zn deficiency symptoms were not present. From 80 to 95% of the variability in leaf Zn concentration could be accounted for by multiple regression equations including either Mehlich-1 or DTPA-extractable Zn and soil pH.

Junus and Cox (1987) recommended the development of continuous functions, including extractable Zn, and readily measured or estimated soil properties related to Zn availability (e.g., CEC by summation, pH) as the logical approach to identification of Zn-responsive soils. They conducted a greenhouse study with eight soils using soybean and corn as the indicator crops and evaluated the Mehlich-3 extractant, soil acidity, and CEC as predictors of Zn availability. Plant Zn concentrations in field-grown soybean and corn from six locations were also compared with these soil properties.

Plant Zn, but not yield, was affected by soil Zn levels in the greenhouse study. Multiple regression equations, including Mehlich-3 Zn, pH, and CEC, as well as interaction and squared terms of these variables, could account for 76 and 66% of the variability in soybean and corn Zn concentrations, respectively. Substituting percent Zn saturation of the soil CEC for Mehlich-3 Zn increased R^2 to 0.82 for soybean and 0.71 for corn. Coefficients of determination from field studies, with equations using the same variables, ranged from $R^2 = 0.50$ to 0.57 for both crops. Critical levels for Mehlich-3 Zn and percent Zn saturation were calculated using greenhouse equations, and assuming recommended pH values and typical CEC values for the various soil groups (mineral, mineral-organic, and organic). Critical values for Mehlich-3 Zn ranged from 1.15 to 1.62 mg dm^{-3} and for percent Zn saturation ranged from 0.34 to 2.33%, and were consistently higher on mineral than organic soils.

Lins and Cox (1988) conducted field and greenhouse studies with four Oxisols to determine the influence of soil pH and clay content on the interpretation of the Mehlich-1 Zn soil test for corn. Clay contents were 21,

57, 63, and 68%, and soil pH values were 5.2, 5.7, and 6.2. Regression equations including Mehlich-1 Zn and soil pH were developed for the four soils and could account for 70, 91, 84, and 90% of the variation in yield, and 93, 89, 88, and 89% of the variation in plant Zn, respectively. Critical levels, as determined by a linear plateau technique were unaffected by clay content, but increased with pH and were 1.0, 1.4, and 2.0 mg L^{-1} for soil pH values of 5.2, 5.7, and 6.2, respectively. Critical values for Mehlich-1 Zn were also determined by a 1-yr field study and measured 0.9, 1.5, and 1.1 mg L^{-1} at pH 6.0, 6.4, and 6.7.

3. Summary

A rather narrow range exists in critical values determined for Zn in studies conducted on quite diverse soils. For instance, in the seven studies cited in this chapter on soils from Colorado, India, and Zimbabwe, the critical value for DTPA ranged from 0.3 to 1.4 mg kg^{-1}. However, research has consistently shown that, as with Mn, a multiple variable approach including soil pH and extractable Zn is preferable to extractable Zn alone, regardless of the extractant. Unlike Mn, however, other readily measured (or estimated) soil properties, such as soil test P, CEC by summation, and clay content may enhance prediction of Zn response.

IV. SOIL TEST METHODS FOR ELEMENTS OF ENVIRONMENTAL CONCERN

Soil testing laboratories face new challenges in the area of environmental quality. The traditional role of most laboratories has been to accurately and rapidly identify soils that are deficient in essential elements and to recommend corrective action based on soil, plant, and agronomic factors. Now, and undoubtedly more so in the future, one of the questions that will be posed to soil testing programs will be "Is the soil contaminated by heavy metals from sludges and manures, acid rain, toxic wastes, or other chemicals; agricultural or otherwise?" As with essential nutrients, analytical methods have been developed and extensively evaluated for many potentially toxic elements, primarily in sludges and sludge-amended soils. The greater challenge, then, is not accurately measuring the quantity of a nonessential element in the soil, but interpreting the results in terms of phytotoxicity, potential for ground- or surface-water contamination, and mammalian toxicity.

A. Selection of Soil Testing Methods for Environmental Purposes

Many nonessential elements are taken up by plants, often without any cause for concern; conversely, essential elements can exist in soils at levels that are phytotoxic (e.g., Mn). The first question that must be addressed by soil testing laboratories, then, is which additional analyses must be offered to identify and/or monitor soil quality. Frequently, the answer is provided by regulatory agencies that require certain soil analyses in situations in which impairment of soil, crop, and water quality may occur. Recent guidelines adopted by the Delaware Department of Natural Resources and Environmental Control that regulate the application of sludges and wastewaters to agricultural soils, stated that an initial soil analysis must be provided including pH, CEC, organic matter, crop "nutrient needs," and lime requirement. Monitoring must include analysis for ". . .key constituents which may accumulate in the soil and are potentially harmful. . ." (Delaware Dep. of Natural Resources and Environmental Control, 1988).

Application rates of organic wastes in most situations are based on established annual or lifetime loading rates of Cd, Cr, Ni, Pb, Cu, or Zn. Therefore, soil analyses for these metals should be the first priority for soil testing programs. Many regulatory agencies also require analyses of organic wastes. Soil testing laboratories may be requested to analyze manures and sludges for essential nutrients, heavy metals, As, Hg, cyanide, and certain organic priority pollutants. For the most part, however, the initial additional efforts of soil testing laboratories will likely involve monitoring heavy metal (essential and nonessential) levels in soils. As noted by O'Connor (1988) with regard to the DTPA soil test, methods do exist to identify metal-enriched soils, but they cannot be randomly applied to all situations without thorough consideration of the chemistry of the soil and the extractant.

Most soil testing laboratories do not presently offer routine tests for nonessential heavy metals. However, the Southern Regional Soil Testing and Plant Analysis Information Exchange Group of the USDA-CSRS has recently considered adopting the DTPA soil test as the preferred method for analysis of certain heavy metals, an indication that there is probably a general consensus that a chelate-based extractant is most suitable for heavy metal analysis (G. Lessman, 1989, personal communication). Some laboratories, however, will continue to use dilute acids (e.g., 0.1 M HCl), either to avoid the need for implementation of another test or because of access to a database relating the extractant to a level believed to be phytotoxic or excessive.

B. Problems in Soil Testing for Environmental Purposes

Routine monitoring of heavy metal levels in soils can most easily be accomplished by using current soil testing methods. Therefore, the first problem faced by soil testing laboratories in the routine screening of soils for excessive metal levels with standard extractants (e.g., Mehlich-1, Mehlich-3, AB-DTPA, 1.0 M NH$_4$OAc) is identification of critical toxic levels for each extractant-metal combination. Unfortunately, limited calibration data are available, particularly from field studies, that clearly identify soil or plant levels known to be toxic, although general guidelines for single-element toxicity have been published (Davis et al., 1978; Logan & Chaney, 1983; Melsted, 1973). Many studies have shown that soil-test-extractable elements can be correlated with heavy metal concentrations in plants. Thus, the establishment of definitive toxic levels in diagnostic tissues of crops is a prerequisite to identification of critical toxic levels in soils.

Site specific monitoring, as opposed to routine screening, may require expanded analytical efforts on the part of soil testing laboratories. A second extractant, known to be well correlated with phytotoxic effects of specific metals, may be used in conjunction with soil properties that are not routinely measured. Most soil testing laboratories now offer special tests, conducted on a limited number of samples, that provide more detailed information on soil properties. Examples would include tests to provide information on CEC, particle size analysis, organic matter, and electrical conductivity. The need and capability of laboratories to offer special tests for environmental purposes should be considered as well. Some examples would include:

1. Metal fractionation. Since extractable levels of heavy metals may not provide detailed enough information on the long-term fate of these elements, it would seem logical to develop simplified fractionation schemes that could partition metals into available, organic, and residual pools.

2. Adsorption isotherms. Standardized adsorption isotherms have been developed for P (Nair et al., 1984), and, as several authors have demonstrated the value of constants determined from these isotherms in predicting plant availability of essential and nonessential metals, these tests may be useful as well (King, 1988; McLaren et al., 1981; Shuman, 1975).

It is not the intent of this discussion to review the voluminous quantities of research relating soil levels of potentially toxic elements to plant concentrations or growth, but to briefly outline the problems in extractant selection and interpretation for environmental purposes. Several recent studies provide examples of problems likely to be faced by soil testing laboratories involved in environmental testing programs.

Greenhouse results have frequently yielded highly significant correlations between plant concentration or uptake of a heavy metal and soil-test-extractable levels. Haq et al. (1980), in a greenhouse study with swiss chard (*Beta vulgaris* L.), compared nine extractants for plant-available Zn, Cd, Ni, and Cu in 46 Ontario, Canada soils contaminated with heavy metals from sludge application, atmospheric deposition around metal smelters, and other urban activities. Of the extractants currently in use in soil testing programs, DTPA was best correlated with heavy metal uptake. When soil pH was included with DTPA in multiple regression equations, coefficients of determination obtained were $R^2 = 0.80**$, $R^2 = 0.80**$, and $R^2 = 0.81**$ for Zn, Cd, and Ni, respectively. Korcak and Fanning (1978) also reported successful use, under greenhouse conditions, of DTPA and pH in predicting plant-available Cd, Cu, Ni, and Zn in metal salt-amended Coastal Plain soils in the USA.

Barbarick and Workman (1987) compared DTPA and AB-DTPA as predictors of Cd, Cu, Ni, Pb, and Zn uptake by swiss chard from an acidic and a calcareous soil in the greenhouse, and by winter wheat grown in four eastern Colorado soils under field conditions. Highly significant linear relationships were found between DTPA- and AB-DTPA-extractable metals in soils from both greenhouse ($r^2 = 0.97$ to 0.99) and field ($r^2 = 0.90$ to 0.98) studies. The relationship between AB-DTPA-extractable metal and metal uptake by swiss chard was markedly influenced by soil pH. Separate regression equations were required for the acidic and calcareous soils (Fig. 12–10). In the field, however, significant correlations between extractable metals and plant uptake (grain or straw) were rarely found. The highest correlations obtained in this 3-yr study were between DTPA- and AB-DTPA-extractable Zn and Zn content in wheat grain ($r = 0.84**$ and $r = 0.82**$, respectively). Indicating that either extractant could be used to monitor soil accumulations of these metals, DTPA and AB-DTPA extractable Cd, Cu, Pb, and Zn were similarly correlated with total metal additions from sewage sludge ($r = 0.59**$, $r = 0.80**$, $r = 0.68**$, and $r = 0.89**$ for AB-DTPA Cd, Cu, Pb, and Zn).

Rappaport et al. (1988) evaluated the ability of DTPA to predict heavy metal (Cd, Cu, Ni, and Zn) availability to corn grown under field conditions in three diverse Virginia soils amended with sewage sludge at rates in excess of US-EPA guidelines. Corn grain and stover yields, and DTPA-extractable Cd, Cu, and Ni increased linearly with sludge rate. Poor correlations were noted between ear leaf concentrations of all metals and DTPA-extractable metals except Zn ($r = 0.65**$). Maximum levels of DTPA-extractable Cd, Cu, Ni, and Zn, reached 0.6, 150, 4.0, and 75 mg kg^{-1}, respectively. Critical levels for DTPA Cu and Zn were <2 mg kg^{-1}. This agrees with the contention of O'Connor (1988) that, although use of DTPA may help identify soils with excessive levels (Fig. 12–11), the absence of phytotoxic effects and poor correlation with plant metal content makes interpretation of "critical toxic levels" for most metals quite difficult.

In a separate field study Rappaport et al. (1986) reported that DTPA-extractable Zn was better correlated than Mehlich-1 Zn with ear leaf Zn in corn grown in 14 sludge-amended soils in Virginia ($r = 0.64*$, $r = 0.35$). Including soil pH improved the correlation with Mehlich-1 ($R^2 = 0.46*$), but not with DTPA. The predictive ability of DTPA was markedly improved by including organically complexed Zn determined by a sequential fractionation procedure ($R^2 = 0.77***$).

The consistently good correlations obtained between plant and DTPA Zn, combined with known toxic levels of Zn for certain crops (Fig. 12–12), suggest that Zn could perhaps serve as an index of heavy metal accumulation to undesirable levels in soils.

These studies illustrate some of the problems faced by soil testing laboratories involved in evaluating soils for heavy metal contamination. First, correlation and regression data obtained from greenhouse studies, although useful in ranking extractants, cannot be directly applied to field soils, and field correlations are often poor (Sommers et al., 1987). Second, soil properties (pH, organic matter, CEC) undoubtedly influence metal uptake and require the use of multiple regression equations, validated under field conditions, to include their effect. Third, since plant availability of sludge-derived metals in soil may decrease with time, soil testing must consider this time factor, information that may not be readily available (Corey et al., 1987). To be truly successful, these equations may require determination of soil properties that are not readily measured (e.g., chemical fractions of certain metals). Finally, the appropriate diagnostic tissue for use in correlating extractants and soil properties must be identified and will likely depend upon the end use of the crop.

In summary, soil test extractants can identify metal-enriched soils and predict, with moderate success, plant uptake of heavy metals. However, successful implementation of environmental monitoring programs based on extractable metal levels requires further research to quantitatively define critical toxic levels and the influence of soil properties on these values.

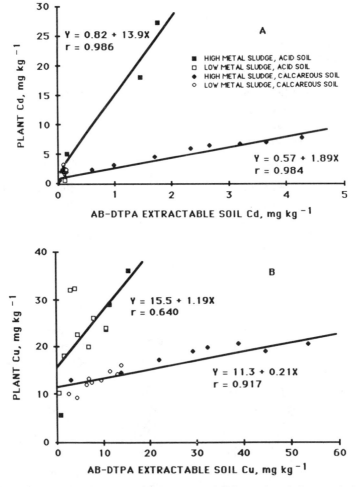

Fig. 12-10. The relationship between AB-DTPA-extractable metals and plant uptake in acidic and calcareous soils (Barbarick & Workman, 1987).

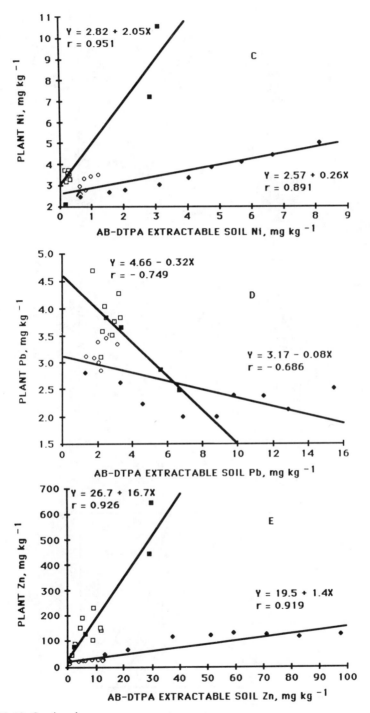

Fig. 12-10. Continued.

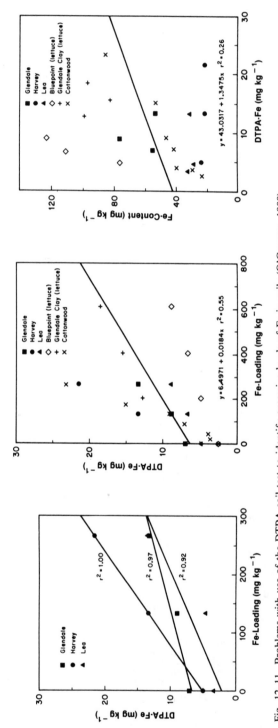

Fig. 12–11. Problems with use of the DTPA soil test to identify excessive levels of Fe in soils (O'Connor, 1988).

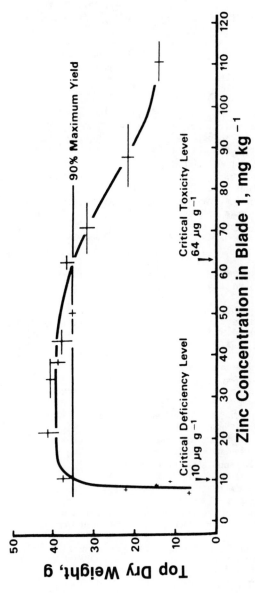

Fig. 12–12. Deficient and toxic levels of Zn for sorghum (Ohki, 1984).

REFERENCES

Aboul-Roos, S.A., and M.A. Abdel-Wabid. 1978. Evaluation of two methods of measuring available soil copper. Beitr. Trop. Landwirtsch. Veterinarmed. 16:155–162.

Alley, M.M., D.C. Martens, M.G. Schnappinger, Jr., and G.W. Hawkins. 1972. Field calibration of soil tests for available zinc. Soil Sci. Soc. Am. Proc. 36:621–624.

Barak, P., and Y. Chen. 1982. The evaluation of iron deficiency using a bioassay type test. Soil Sci. Soc. Am. J. 46:1019–1022.

Barbarick, K.A., and S.M. Workman. 1987. Ammonium bicarbonate-DTPA and DTPA extractions of sludge-amended soils. J. Environ. Qual. 16:125–130.

Bartlett, R.J., and B.L. James. 1980. Studying dried, stored soil samples—some pitfalls. Soil Sci. Soc. Am. J. 44:721–724.

Berger, K.C., and E. Truog. 1939. Boron determination in soils and plants. Ind. Eng. Chem. Anal. Ed. 11:540–545.

Bhella, H.S., and M.D. Dawson. 1972. The use of anion exchange resin for determining available soil molybdenum. Soil Sci. Soc. Am. proc. 36:177–179.

Bingham, F.T. 1982. Boron. p. 501–538. In A.L. Page (ed.) Methods of soil analysis. Part II. 2nd ed. Agron. Monogr. 9. ASA and SSSA, Madison, WI.

Bray, R.H. 1948. Requirements for successful soil tests. Soil Sci. 66:83–89.

Broyer, T.C., A.B. Carlton, C.M. Johnson, and P.R. Stout. 1954. Chlorine—A micronutrient element for higher plants. Plant Physiol. 29:526–532.

Burmester, C.H., J.F. Adams, and J.W. Odom. 1988. Response of soybean to lime and molybdenum on ultisols in northern Alabama. Soil Sci. Soc. Am. J. 52:1391–1394.

Cate, R.B., Jr., and L.A. Nelson. 1971. A simple statistical procedure for partitioning soil test correlation data into two classes. Soil Sci. Soc. Am. Proc. 36:658–660.

Cheng, K.L., and R.H. Bray. 1953. Two specific methods of determining copper in soil and plant material. Anal. Chem. 25:655–659.

Christensen, N.W., R.G. Taylor, T.L. Jackson, and B.L. Mitchell. 1981. Chloride effects on water potential and yield of winter wheat infected with take-all root rot. Agron. J. 73:1053–1058.

Chude, V.O., and G.O. Obigbesan. 1984. A comparison of soil test methods for estimating available soil boron in cocoa growing areas of southwestern Nigeria. Beitr. Trop. Landwirtsch. Veterinaermed. 22:245–254.

Corey, R.B., L.D. King, C. Lue-Jing, D.S. Fanning, J.J. Street, and J.M. Walker. 1987. Effects of sludge properties on accumulated trace elements by crops. p. 25–51. In A.L. Page et al. (ed.) Land application of sludge. Lewis Publ., Chelsea, MI.

Cox, F.R. 1987. Micronutrient soil tests: correlation and calibration. p. 97–117. In J.R. Brown (ed.) Soil testing: sampling, correlation, calibration, and interpretation. SSSA Spec. Publ. 21. ASA, CSSA, and SSSA, Madison, WI.

Cox, F.R., and E.J. Kamprath. 1972. Micronutrient soil tests. p. 289–317. In J.J. Mortvedt et al. (ed.) Micronutrients in agriculture. SSSA, Madison, WI.

Cox, F.R., and J.I. Wear. 1977. Diagnosis and correction of zinc problems in corn and rice production. South Coop. Ser. Bull. 222. North Carolina State Univ., Raleigh.

Davis, R.D., P.H.T. Beckett, and E. Wollan. 1978. Critical levels of twenty potentially toxic elements in young spring barley. Plant Soil 49:395–408.

DeBoer, G.J., and H.M. Reisenauer. 1973. DTPA as an extractant for available soil iron. Commun. Soil Sci. Plant Anal. 4:121–128.

Delaware Department of Natural Resources and Environmental Control. 1988. Guidance and regulations governing the land treatment of wastes. Delaware Dep. Natural Resour. Environ. Control, Dover.

Fixen, P.E., G.W. Buchenau, R.H. Gelderman, T.E. Schumacher, J.R. Gerwing, F.A. Cholick, and B.G. Farber. 1986a. Influence of soil and applied chloride on several wheat parameters. Agron. J. 78:736–740.

Fixen, P.E., R.H. Gelderman, and J.L. Denning. 1988. Chloride tests. p. 26–29. In W. Dahnke (ed.) Recommended chemical soil test procedures for the North Central Region. North Dakota Agric. Exp. Stn., North Central Reg. Publ. 221 (Revised).

Fixen, P.E., R.H. Gelderman, J. Gerwing, and F.A. Cholick. 1986b. Response of spring wheat, barley, and oats to chloride in potassium chloride fertilizer. Agron. J. 78:664–668.

Gestring, W.D., and P.N. Soltanpour. 1981. Boron analysis in soil extracts and plant tissue by plasma emission spectroscopy. Commun. Soil Sci. Plant Anal. 12:733–742.

Gestring, W.D., and P.N. Soltanpour. 1984. Evaluation of the ammonium bicarbonate-DTPA soil test for assessing boron availability to alfalfa. Soil Sci. Soc. Am. J. 48:96–100.

Gestring, W.D., and P.N. Soltanpour. 1987. Comparison of soil tests for assessing boron toxicity to alfalfa. Soil Sci. Soc. Am. J. 51:1214–1219.

Gettier, S.W., D.C. Martens, and S.J. Donahue. 1985. Soybean yield response prediction from soil test and manganese levels. Agron. J. 77:63–67.

Gough, L.P., J.M. McNeal, and R.C. Severson. 1980. Predicting native plant copper, iron, manganese, and zinc levels using DTPA and EDTA soil extractants, Northern Great Plains. Soil Sci. Soc. Am. J. 44:1030–1036.

Grigg, J.L. 1953. Determination of the available molybdenum of soils. N.Z. J. Sci. Technol. 34:405–414.

Grundon, N.J., and E.K. Best. 1982. Survey of the extent of copper deficiency of wheat on the Western Downs, Queensland. Queensl. J. Agric. Anim. Sci. 39:41–46.

Gupta, U.C. 1979. Some factors affecting the determination of hot water-soluble boron from Podzol soils using azomethione-H. Can. J. Soil Sci. 59:241–247.

Gupta, V.K., and S.B. Mittal. 1981. Evaluation of chemical methods for estimating available zinc and response of green gram (*Phaseolus aureus* Roxb.) to applied zinc in noncalcareous soils. Plant Soil 63:477–484.

Hanlon, E.A., and G.V. Johnson. 1984. Bray/Kurtz, Mehlich III, AB/D and ammonium acetate extractions of P, K, and Mg in four Oklahoma soils. Commun. Soil Sci. Plant Anal. 15:277–294.

Haq, A.U., and M.H. Miller. 1972. Prediction of available soil Zn, Cu and Mn using chemical extractants. Agron. J. 64:779–782.

Haq, A.U., T.E. Bates, and Y.K. Soon. 1980. Comparison of extractants for plant-available zinc, cadmium, nickel and copper in contaminated soils. Soil Sci. Soc. Am. J. 44:772–777.

Havlin, J.L., and P.N. Soltanpour. 1981. Evaluation of the NH_4HCO_3-DTPA soil test for iron and zinc. Soil Sci. Soc. Am. J. 45:70–75.

Havlin, J.L., and P.N. Soltanpour. 1982. Greenhouse and field evaluation of the NH_4HCO_3-DTPA soil test for Fe. J. Plant Nutr. 5:769–783.

Hunter, A.H. 1975. New techniques and equipment for routine plant analytical procedure. p. 467–483. *In* E. Bornemisza and A. Alvarado (ed.) Soil management in tropical America. North Carolina State University, Raleigh.

Iyengar, S.S., D.C. Martens, and W.P. Miller. 1981. Distribution and plant availability of soil zinc fractions. Soil Sci. Soc. Am. J. 45:735–739.

Jeffrey, A.J., and L.E. McCallum. 1988. Investigation of a hot 0.01 M calcium chloride soil boron extraction procedure followed by ICP-AES analysis. Commun. Soil Sci. Plant Anal. 19:663–673.

Jin-Yun, Jin, D.C. Martens, and L.W. Zelazny. 1987. Distribution and plant availability of soil boron fractions. Soil Sci. Soc. Am. J. 51:1228–1231.

Johnson, C.M., P.R. Stout, T.C. Broyer, and A.B. Carlton. 1957. Comparative chlorine requirements of different plant species. Plant Soil 8:337–353.

Johnson, G.V., and R.A. Young. 1973. Evaluation of EDDHA as an extraction and analytical reagent for assessing the iron status of soils. Soil Sci. 115:11–17.

Junus, M.A., and F.R. Cox. 1987. A zinc soil test calibration based upon Mehlich 3 extractable zinc, pH and cation exchange capacity. Soil Sci. Soc. Am. J. 51:678–683.

Karamanos, R.E., G.A. Kruger, and J.W.B. Stewart. 1986. Copper deficiency in cereal and oilseed crops in Northern Canadian prairie soils. Agron. J. 78:317–323.

Karimian, N., and F.R. Cox. 1979. Molybdenum availability as predicted from selected soil chemical properties. Agron. J. 71:63–65.

Katyal, J.C., and B.D. Sharma. 1984. Association of soil properties and soil and plant iron to iron deficiency response in rice (*Oryza sativa* L.). Commun. Soil Sci. Plant Anal. 15:1065–1081.

Kennedy, A.C., and J.R. Brown. 1981. A comparison of three extractants for soil zinc. Soil Sci. Soc. Am. J. 45:1000–1002.

Keren, R., F.T. Bingham, and J.D. Rhoads. 1985. Plant uptake of boron as affected by boron distribution between liquid and solid phases in soil. Soil Sci. Soc. Am. J. 49:297–302.

Khan, Z.D., J. Ryan, and K.C. Berger. 1979. Available boron in calcareous soils of Lebanon. Agron. J. 71:688–690.

King, L.D. 1988. Retention of cadmium by several soils of the southeastern United States. J. Environ. Qual. 17:246–250.

Korcak, R.F., and D.S. Fanning. 1978. Extractability of cadmium, copper, nickel and zinc by double acid versus DTPA and plant content at excessive soil levels. J. Environ. Qual. 7:506–512.

Kruger, G.A., R.E. Karamanos, and J.P. Singh. 1985. The copper fertility of Saskatchewan soils. Can. J. Soil Sci. 65:89–99.

Lakanen, E., and R. Ervio. 1971. A comparison of eight extractants for the determination of plant available micronutrients in soils. Suom. Maataloustiet. Seuran Julk. 123:232–233.

Lake, D.L., P.W.W. Kirk, and J.N. Lester. 1984. Fractionation, characterization and speciation of heavy metals in sewage sludge and sludge-amended soils: A review. J. Environ. Qual. 13:175–183.

LeClaire, J.P., A.C. Chang, C.S. Levesque, and G. Sposito. 1984. Trace metal chemistry in arid-zone field soils amended with sewage sludge: IV. Correlations between zinc uptake and extracted soil zinc fractions. Soil Sci. Soc. Am. J. 48:509–513.

Lee, C.R., R.M. Smart, T.C. Sturgis, R.N. Gordon, Sr., and M.C. Landin. 1978. Prediction of heavy metal uptake by marsh plants based on chemical extraction from dredged material. U.S. Army Corps of Eng. Tech. Rep. D-78-6.

Leggett, G.E., and D.P. Argyle. 1983. The DTPA-extractable iron, manganese, copper and zinc from neutral and calcareous soils dried under different conditions. Soil Sci. Soc. Am. J. 47:518–522.

Lindsay, W.L., and F.R. Cox. 1985. Micronutrient soil testing for the tropics. In P.L.G. Vlek (ed.) Micronutrients in tropical food crop production. Fert. Res. 7:169–200.

Lindsay, W.L., and W.A. Norvell. 1978. Development of a DTPA soil test for zinc, iron, manganese and copper. Soil Sci. Soc. Am. J. 42:421–428.

Lins, I.D.G., and F.R. Cox. 1988. Effect of soil pH and clay content on the zinc soil test interpretation for corn. Soil Sci. Soc. Am. J. 52:1681–1685.

Logan, T.J., and R.L. Chaney. 1983. Metals. p. 235–328. In A.L. Page et al. (ed.) Proc. of the 1983 Workshop on Utilization of municipal wastewater and sludge on land. Denver, CO. 23–25 Feb. 1983. Univ. of California, Riverside.

Lombin, G. 1985. Micronutrient soil tests for the semi-arid savannah of Nigeria: Boron and molybdenum. Soil Sci. Plant Nutr. 31:1–11.

Madziva, T.J.T. 1981. Methods of measuring available zinc in Zimbabwean soil. Zimbabwe J. Agric. Res. 19:83–90.

Mahler, R.L., D.V. Naylor, and M.K. Fredrickson. 1984. Hot water extraction of boron from soils using sealed plastic pouches. Commun. Soil Sci. Plant Anal. 15:479–492.

Makarim, A.K., and F.R. Cox. 1983. Evaluation of the need for copper with several soil extractants. Agron. J. 75:493–496.

Mandal, L.N., and M. Haldar. 1980. Influence of phosphorus and zinc application on the availability of zinc, copper, iron, manganese and phosphorus in waterlogged soils. Soil Sci. 130:251–257.

Mascagni, H.J., Jr., and F.R. Cox. 1984. Diagnosis and correction of manganese deficiency in corn. Commun. Soil Sci. Plant Anal. 15:1323–1333.

Mascagni, H.J., Jr., and F.R. Box. 1985. Calibration of a manganese availability index for soybean soil test data. Soil Sci. Soc. Am. J. 49:382–386.

McLaren, R.G., R.S. Swift, and J.G. Williams. 1981. The adsorption of copper by soil materials at low equilibrium solution concentrations. J. Soil Sci. 32:247–256.

Mehlich, A. 1984. Mehlich 3 soil test extractant. A modification of the Mehlich-2 extractant. Commun. Soil Sci. Plant Anal. 15:1409–1416.

Mehlich, A., and S.S. Bowling. 1975. Advances in soil test methods for copper by atomic absorption spectrophotometry. Commun. Soil Sci. Plant Anal. 6:113–128.

Melsted, S.W. 1973. Soil-plant relationships—some practical considerations in waste management. p. 121–128. In Recycling municipal sludges and effluents on land. Natl. Assoc. State Univ. Land Grant Colleges, Washington, DC.

Mengel, D.B. 1980. Boron in soils and plant nutrition. U.S. Borax Plant Food Borate Meet., Lafayette, IN.

Michaelson, G.J., C.L. Ping, and C.A. Mitchell. 1987. Correlation of Mehlich 3, Bray 1 and ammonium acetate extractable P, K, Ca, and Mg for Alaska soils. Commun. Soil Sci. Plant Anal. 18:1003–1015.

Mitchell. 1972. Trace elements in soils and factors that affect their availability. Geol. Soc. Am. Bull. 83:1069.

Mortvedt, J.J., and O.E. Anderson. 1982. Forage legumes: Diagnosis and correction of molybdenum and manganese problems. South. Coop. Ser. Bull. 178. University of Georgia, Athens.

Mullins, G.L., D.C. Martens, W.P. Miller, E.T. Kornegay, and D.L. Hallock. 1982. Copper availability, form and mobility in soils from three annual copper-enriched hog manure applications. J. Environ. Qual. 11:316–320.

Nair, P.S., T.J. Logan, A.N. Sharpley, L.E. Sommers, M.A. Tabatabai, and T.L. Yuan. 1984. Interlaboratory comparisons of a standardized phosphorus adsorption procedure. J. Environ. Qual. 13:591–595.

Nilsson, L.G., and P. Jennische. 1986. Determination of boron in soils and plants. Chemical methods and biological evaluation. Swed. J. Agric. Res. 16:97–103.

Norvell, W.A. 1984. Comparison of chelating agents as extractants for metals in diverse soil materials. Soil Sci. Soc. Am. J. 48:1285–1292.

O'Connor, G.A. 1988. Use and misuse of the DTPA soil test. J. Environ. Qual. 17:715–718.

Odom, J.W. 1980. Kinetics of the hot water soluble boron soil test. Commun. Soil Sci. Plant Anal. 11:759–765.

Ohki, K. 1984. Zinc nutrition related to critical deficiency and toxicity levels for sorghum. Agron. J. 76:253–256.

Oklahoma State University. 1984. Procedures used by state soil testing laboratories in the southern region of the United States. South. Coop. Ser. Bull. 190. Oklahoma State Univ., Stillwater, OK.

Osiname, O.A., E.E. Schulte, and R.B. Corey. 1973. Soil tests for available copper and zinc in soils of western Nigeria. J. Sci. Food Agric. 24:1341–1349.

Page, A.L. (ed.). 1982. Methods of soil analysis. Part 2. 2nd ed. Agron. Monogr. 9. ASA, Madison, WI.

Parker, D.R., and E.H. Gardner. 1981. The determination of hot-water-soluble boron in some acid Oregon soils using a modified azomethine-H procedure. Commun. Soil Sci. Plant Anal. 12:1311–1322.

Parker, D.R., and E.H. Gardner. 1982. Factors affecting the mobility and plant availability of boron in some western Oregon soils. Soil Sci. Soc. Am. J. 46:573–578.

Payne, G.G., M.E. Sumner, and C.O. Plank. 1986. Yield and composition of soybeans as influenced by soil pH, phosphorus, zinc and copper. Commun. Soil Sci. Plant Anal. 17:257–273.

Peaslee, D.E. 1980. Effect of extractable zinc, phosphorus, and soil pH values on zinc concentration in leaves of field-grown corn. Commun. Soil Sci. Plant. Anal. 11:417–425.

Ponnamperuma, F.N., M.T. Clayton, and R.S. Lantin. 1981. Dilute hydrochloric acid as an extractant for available zinc, copper and boron in rice soils. Plant Soil 61:297–310.

Randall, G.W., E.E. Schulte, and R.B. Corey. 1976. Correlation of plant manganese with extractable soil manganese and soil factors. Soil Sci. Soc. Am. J. 40:282–287.

Rappaport, B.D., D.C. Martens, R.B. Reneau, Jr., and T.W. Simpson. 1988. Metal availability in sludge-amended soils with elevated metal levels. J. Environ. Qual. 17:42–47.

Rappaport, B.D., D.C. Martens, T.W. Simpson, and R.B. Reneau, Jr. 1986. Prediction of available zinc in sewage sludge-amended soils. J. Environ. Qual. 15:133–136.

Robertson, W.K., L.G. Thompson, and F.G. Martin. 1973. Manganese and copper requirements of soybeans. Agron. J. 65:641–644.

Rohman, P.C., and F.R. Cox. 1988. Evaluation of the modified Olsen extracting reagent for copper, zinc and manganese. Commun. Soil Sci. Plant Anal. 19:1859–1870.

Sakal, R., A.P. Singh, H. Sinha, and K.N. Thakur. 1981. Evaluation of critical concentration of zinc in rice and wheat grown in Tarai soils. J. Indian Soc. Soil Sci. 29:107–109.

Salcedo, I.H., B.G. Ellis, and R.E. Lucas. 1979. Studies in soil manganese: II. Extractable manganese and plant uptake. Soil Sci. Soc. Am. J. 43:138–141.

Schauer, P.S., W.R. Wright, and J. Pelchat. 1980. Sludge-borne heavy metal availability and uptake by vegetable crops under field conditions. J. Environ. Qual. 9:69–73.

Sedberry, J.E., Jr., D.P. Bligh, and M.Y. Eun. 1988. An evaluation of chemical methods for extracting copper from rice soils. Commun. Soil Sci. Plant Anal. 19:1841–1857.

Selvarajah, N., V. Pavanasasivan, and K.A. Nandasena. 1982. Evaluation of extractants for zinc and copper in paddy soils. Plant Soil 68:309–320.

Sheppard, S.C., and T.E. Bates. 1982. Selection of a soil extraction and a multiple regression model to predict plant available manganese. Commun. Soil Sci. Plant Anal. 13:1095–1111.

Sherrell, C.G. 1983. Plant and soil boron in relation to boron deficiency in lucerne. N.Z. J. Agric. Res. 26:209–214.

Shuman, L.M. 1975. The effect of soil properties on zinc adsorption by soils. Soil Sci. Soc. Am. Proc. 39:454–458.

Shuman, L.M. 1980. Effects of soil temperature, moisture and air-drying on extractable manganese, iron, copper and zinc. Soil Sci. 130:336–343.

Shuman, L.M. 1985. Fractionation method for soil micronutrients. Soil Sci. 140:11–22.

Shuman, L.M., and O.E. Anderson. 1974. Evaluation of six extractants for their ability to predict manganese concentrations in wheat and soybeans. Soil Sci. Soc. Am. Proc. 38:788–790.

Shuman, L.M., and O.E. Anderson. 1978. Relationship of extractable soil manganese to soil properties. Soil Sci. Soc. Am. J. 42:666–667.

Shuman, L.M., F.C. Boswell, K. Ohki, M.B. Parker, and D.O. Wilson. 1980. Critical soil manganese deficiency levels for four extractants for soybeans grown in sandy soil. Soil Sci. Soc. Am. J. 44:1021–1025.

Shuman, L.M., D.O. Wilson, F.C. Boswell, M.B. Parker, and K. Ohki. 1978. Applied Mn extracted by four methods correlated with Mn concentrations in soybean leaf tissue on a southeastern soil. Commun. Soil Sci. Plant Anal. 9:317–333.

Sillanpaa, M. 1982. Micronutrients and the nutrient status of soils: A global study. Food and Agriculture Organization of the United Nations Soils Bull. 48.

Sims, J.T. 1985. A comparison of Mehlich I and Mehlich III extractants as predictors of manganese, copper and zinc availability in four Delaware soils. Commun. Soil Sci. Plant Anal. 16:1039–1052.

Sims, J.T. 1986. Soil pH effects on the distribution and plant availability of manganese, copper and zinc. Soil Sci. Soc. Am. J. 50:367–373.

Sims, J.T. 1989. Comparison of Mehlich 1 and Mehlich 3 extractants for P, K, Ca, Mg, Mn, Cu and Zn in Atlantic Coastal Plain soils. Commun. Soil Sci. Plant Anal. 20:1707–1728.

Singh, C.P., N. Prasad, H. Sinba, and B. Kranke. 1977. Evaluation of the critical limit and extractants for the determination of available copper, manganese, and iron in calcareous soils. Beitr. Trop. Landsirtsch. Veterinarmed. 15:69–72.

Singh, H.J., and P.N. Takkar. 1981. Evaluation of efficient soil test methods for Zn and their critical values in salt-affected soils for rice. Commun. Soil Sci. Plant. Anal. 12:383–406.

Soltanpour, P.N., A. Khan, and W.L. Lindsay. 1976. Factors affecting DTPA-extractable Zn, Fe, Mn and Cu from soils. Commun. Soil Sci. Plant. Anal. 7:797–821.

Soltanpour, P.N., and A.P. Schwab. 1977. A new soil test for simultaneous extraction of macro and micronutrients in soils. Commun. Soil Sci. Plant. Anal. 3:195–207.

Soltanpour, P.N., and S.M. Workman. 1979. Modification of the NH_4HCO_3-DTPA soil test to omit carbon black. Commun. Soil Sci. Plant. Anal. 10:1411–1420.

Soltanpour, P.N., S.M. Workman, and A.P. Schwab. 1979. Use of inductively coupled plasma spectrometry for the simultaneous determination of macro and micronutrients in ammonium bicarbonate-DTPA extracts of soils. Soil Sci. Soc. Am. J. 43:75–78.

Sommers, L.E., V.V. Volk, P.M. Giordano, W.E. Sopper, and R. Bastain. 1987. Effects of soil properties on accumulation of trace metals by crops. p. 5–24. In A.L. Page et al. (ed.) Land application of sludge. Lewis Publ., Chelsea, MI.

Tills, A.R., and B.J. Alloway. 1983. An appraisal of currently used soil tests for available copper with reference to deficiencies in English soils. J. Sci. Food Agric. 34:1190–1196.

Tiwari, R.C., and M.B. Kumar. 1982. A suitable extractant for assessing plant-available copper in different soils (peaty, red, and alluvial). Plant Soil 68:131–134.

Trierweiler, J.F., and W.L. Lindsay. 1969. EDTA-ammonium carbonate soil test for zinc. Soil Sci. Soc. Am. Proc. 33:49–54.

Tucker, T.C., and L.T. Kurtz. 1955. A comparison of several chemical methods for extracting zinc from soils. Soil Sci. Soc. Am. Proc. 19:477–481.

Viets, F.G. 1962. Chemistry and availability of micronutrients. J. Agric. Food Chem. 10:174–177.

Viets, F.G., and W.L. Lindsay. 1973. Testing soils for zinc, copper, manganese and iron. p. 153–172. In L.M. Walsh and J.D. Beaton (ed.) Soil testing and plant analysis. SSSA, Madison, WI.

Viro, P.J. 1955. Use of ethylene diamine tetra acetic acid in soil analysis. I. Exp. Soil Sci. 79:459–465.

Chapter 13

Plant Tissue Analysis in Micronutrients

J. BENTON JONES, JR., *Micro-Macro International, Athens, Georgia*

Surveys conducted in the United States since the early 1960s show that between 300 000 and 400 000 plant tissue samples are analyzed for farmers and growers each year by state and commercial plant analysis laboratories (Jones, 1985). This number of samples is slightly more than one-tenth the number of soil samples analyzed for many of the same farmers and growers, indicating a substantial underutilization of a very useful procedure for evaluating the soil/plant nutritional status and for prescribing fertilizer need. This is particularly true for the micronutrients, since many of the soil testing procedures for these elements are quite poor.

The plant analysis technique is not new. One could say that von Liebig (1840) introduced the concept of plant analysis as a means of determining the nutrient element needs of soils by means of determining element removal by plants. A short time later, Weinhold (1862) conceived the idea of using plant analysis as an index of available nutrient element supply. Goodall and Gregory (1947) reviewed much of this early research, concluding that much of the work done prior to 1947 could be grouped into one of four categories: "(i) investigations of nutritional disorders made manifest by definite symptoms; (ii) interpretation of the results of field trials; (iii) development of rapid testing methods for use in advisory work; and (iv) use of plant analysis as a method of nutritional survey." These categories are still applicable today in terms of research as well as plant analysis utilization in crop-production decision making.

Two excellent reviews on plant analysis have been published (Ulrich, 1952; Smith, 1962), but there have not been any recent reviews of a similar nature. One of the first comprehensive books on plant analysis was edited by Chapman (1966), followed by another edited by Walsh and Beaton (1972). Two new books on plant analysis have recently been published (Reuter & Robinson, 1986; Martin-Prevel et al., 1987). With particular reference to the micronutrients, frequently referred to as trace elements, recent publications (Robb & Pierpoint, 1983; Shkolnik, 1984; Kabata-Pendias & Pendias, 1984; Adriano, 1986) provide a wealth of information on the micronutrient content of plants.

The designation micronutrient refers to the seven elements, B, Cl, Cu, Fe, Mn, Mo, and Zn, that have been determined to be essential for plants based on the criteria of essentiality established by Arnon and Stout (1939), and whose sufficiency concentrations are <0.005% of the plant's dry matter. My discussion will address these seven elements, although the reader should be aware that plants contain other elements whose presence may be either beneficial or detrimental to their growth and development at similar low concentrations. Three elements, Ni, Si, and V, have been shown to beneficially affect plants, with the suggestion that they partially meet the requirements of essentiality (Arnon & Stout, 1939). These and other elements are discussed in greater detail in chapter 18 of this book.

Much of the current interest in the micronutrients is due to the increased recognition of their need for successful crop production, and significant analytical developments that have greatly simplified their determination in plant tissue. In reference to analytical procedures, a very significant development involved atomic absorption spectroscopy (Christian & Feldman, 1970), which provides a very sensitive and easy method for the determination of Cu, Fe, Mn, Mo, and Zn in plant tissue digests using a moderately priced instrument. There followed two simultaneous multielement procedures; first, spark emission spectrometry (Jones, 1976), and, more recently, plasma emission spectrometry (Montaser & Golightly, 1987). Therefore, those who have the need to assay plant tissues for their micronutrient (except Cl) content can do so quickly and easily by any one of these three instrumental procedures. Assay procedures for Cl will be discussed in detail later.

The micronutrient content of a plant, or one of its parts, is a reflection of the soil's available micronutrient status, a status that is not always easily determined with a soil test. Soil tests for most of the micronutrients are highly specific in terms of soil properties, such as pH, organic matter, clay content, etc., and, therefore, are not adapted for wide and general use. Although this point may be argued by some, the author believes that soil tests for the micronutrients are not always effective in diagnostic situations. However, the value of a soil test result should not be underestimated when interpretating a plant analysis result. The two techniques used together can effectively evaluate the soil-plant micronutrient status, and thereby confirm a sufficiency or insufficiency for any one of the micronutrients (Jones, 1983).

I. PROCEDURES FOR PLANT ANALYSIS

The plant analysis technique involves a series of steps from sampling to sample preparation and laboratory analysis, and then to interpretation as shown in Fig. 13–1. Each step in the process requires precise execution on the part of the user. The proper plant part must be identified, collected, decontaminated, if necessary, and prepared for laboratory analysis without altering its elemental composition. A plant analysis interpretation is essentially based on the comparison of the obtained test result with known interpretative values, although considerable skill and experience is required on

PLANT ANALYSIS

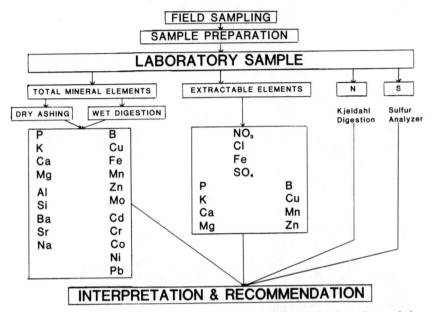

Fig. 13-1. The sequence of procedures from field sampling to interpretation for a plant analysis.

the part of the interpreter in order to properly describe the plant's elemental status and make corrective recommendations. This paper is a review of the current state of the art of assaying plant tissue and interpreting the obtained result for micronutrients.

A. Sampling

The most extensive compilation of sampling procedures has been given by Chapman (1964), who attempted to standardize methods for sampling through his review. Jones et al.(1971) published suggested sampling procedures for field and vegetable crops, fruits and nuts, and ornamentals.

Sampling is partially a statistical problem, a process of collecting sufficient numbers of individual tissue samples to minimize the variance. Since plants are made up of complex structures that lack homogeneity in elemental concentration, specific plant parts are normally designated for sampling rather than whole plants. The distribution of a number of elements even in plant leaves is not homogeneous as has been determined by Sayre (1952) in corn (*Zea mays* L.) leaves. Jones (1970), as well as others, have found that B and Mn accumulate in the margins of leaves. The removal of leaf puncheons from the leaf blade would minimize the effect of this uneven distribution. But the task of removing these puncheons would significantly increase the time and effort required to collect a tissue sample for analysis. In addition, current sampling instructions call for the whole plant part to be collected, not just a portion of it. This lack of elemental homogeneity, even in the leaves of plants, may partially explain why Steyn (1961) and Colonna (1970) found it necessary to take fairly large numbers of replicate leaves in order to obtain high levels of precision. Therefore, those using plant analysis need to be certain that their sampling technique is sufficient to bring the variance in elemental content within acceptable limits.

Deciding which plant part to collect is based on two considerations: (i) the best correlation between plant appearance or performance and elemental content; and (ii) the ease of identification and collection. Therefore, most sampling procedures call for the collection of mid-shoot leaves from woody perennial plants and trees, and recently mature leaves from annual plants. These leaves reflect the plant's current nutritional status, and are relatively easy to identify and collect.

Time of sampling is equally important and varies considerably depending on the plant species and current physical appearance. As a general rule, sampling is recommended either when the plant is in its mid-growth cycle, or when it is approaching or entering its reproductive stage.

When using the plant analysis technique for diagnostic purposes, it is useful to obtain tissue from sets of plants that represent a range in physical appearance when visual symptoms are evident (Munson & Nelson, 1973). However, this can be difficult to accomplish if there is a substantial growth difference among the plants to be sampled. Sufficient differences may exist that will affect the plant's dry matter content as well as the growth stage, factors that will invalidate the attempted comparison (Jarrell & Beverly, 1981). Therefore, comparisons are only valid if the sampled plants are relatively similar in appearance and stage of growth. This means that sampling must be done at the initial stages of differentiation and not after a long period of stress. Sampling at initiation of symptoms is particularly important for Fe deficiency diagnosis, which is discussed in greater detail later.

Which plants should not be sampled is as equally important a consideration as which should be sampled. Plants or a particular part should not be sampled if they are dust covered, unless the dust can be easily and completely removed without affecting the elemental concentration in the tissue. Plants should not be selected for sampling if they have been either mechanically damaged, or are infested with insects or disease. Plants that have been under stress for a long time should not be selected for sampling. Dead plant tissue should not be collected or be included as a part of the collected sample. Seed and plant parts that are senescent are not normally suitable tissue for diagnostic use.

The importance of proper sampling and following specific directions cannot be overemphasized, as exemplified by the detailed sampling procedures described by Steyn (1961) for citrus (*Citrus* spp.) and pineapple (*Ananas comosus*). As with soil testing, the analysis and interpretation of the results are no better than the sample collected (Sabbe & Max, 1987).

B. Sample Preparation and Storage

1. Transport to the Laboratory

Fresh plant tissue is perishable and must be kept cool and/or in a dry atmosphere while in transit to the laboratory. Transporting plant tissue in clean paper or cloth bags, and not in air tight containers or plastic bags unless refrigerated, is recommended. If possible, fresh tissue should be air dried before shipment, particularly if the time in transit is going to be >24 h. Storing tissue at a reduced temperature (<10 °C) will also prevent decay. Any deterioration will result in reduced dry weight (Lockman, 1970), which in turn will affect the analysis result. Therefore, maintaining the integrity of the sample is essential during its transit to the laboratory.

2. Decontamination

Fresh plant tissue that is covered with dust, soil particles, or applied spray materials may require decontamination prior to drying. Normally, washing to decontaminate is not recommended unless absolutely necessary, owing to the potential loss of soluble elements, such as K and Cl (Bhan et al., 1959), and possible further contamination of the sample (Piper, 1942). However, numerous studies have shown that failing to decontaminate tissue, even if visual signs of dust or soil accumulation are not apparent, will invalidate the assay for Fe. Therefore, if an accurate determination of Fe is to be made, washing the tissue in a mild (0.1–0.3%) detergent solution is absolutely necessary (Wallace et al., 1980; Sonneveld & van Dijk, 1982; Wallace et al., 1982).

Washing in water or dilute acid is not as effective as in a detergent solution. Long exposure to the washing solution should be avoided in order to minimize loss of the soluble elements. The presence of dust or soil contamination can be easily determined by including Al and Si in the elemental determination. If Fe, Al, and Si are all found in fairly high concentrations (>100 mg kg^{-1}), and/or their concentrations in tissue are observed to move in concert with each other, the tissue is contaminated and the analysis result invalid for these three elements. Cherney and Robinson (1983) have suggested that the analysis of plant tissue should use the element Ti to indicate the presence of soil or dust in the assayed tissue sample. The effect of washing on the micronutrient concentration of several different leaf tissues is shown in Table 13–1.

The ease with which plant tissue can be decontaminated is determined to a considerable degree by the surface characteristics of the tissue. Rough and pubescent tissue surfaces are almost impossible to thoroughly decontaminate. Also, some types of foliar spray materials may be difficult to remove from tissue surfaces (Arkley et al., 1970).

3. Oven Drying

The moisture content in most plant tissue is removed by drying at temperatures between 60 and 80 °C. Unfortunately, regardless of the tempera-

Table 13-1. Micronutrient concentration found in orange, soybean, and other leaves as affected by washing to decontaminate.

Micro-nutrient	Orange leaves[†]		Soybean leaves[‡]		Other leaves[§]	
	Unwashed	Washed	Unwashed	Washed	Unwashed	Washed
			$mg\ kg^{-1}$			
B	367	368	--	--	--	--
Cu	5.6	5.1	8.5	8.0	--	--
Fe	186	61	147	67	236	110
Mn	182	94	37	33	--	--
Zn	123	68	--	--	84	64

† From Labanauskas (1968).
‡ From Wallace et al. (1982).
§ Mean of tomato, cucumber, and eggplant (Sonneveld & van Dijk, 1982).

ture, moisture cannot be completely removed. Moisture may remain if the drying temperature is $<60\,°C$, and thermal decomposition can occur if the drying temperature is $>80\,°C$ (Grant & Macnaughlain, 1968). If the drying process is too slow or tissue is packed tightly in the drying container or oven, decay can occur, resulting in a significant loss of dry weight (Lockman, 1970). Hygroscopic plant tissues are best dried by either freeze-drying or vacuum-oven drying (Horwitz, 1980).

4. Particle Size Reduction

Particle size reduction homogenizes the tissue and prepares it for ease of handling in the laboratory. The reduction may be performed by cutting in a moving-fixed blade mill (Wiley type), by crushing in a ball mill, or by abrasion in a cyclone (UDY) mill. During the milling process, some portions of the mill components will be added to the tissue sample. For instance, steel components can add Fe to the sample, brass components add Cu and Zn (Hood et al., 1944), Al fittings add Al, and rubber fittings add Zn. Therefore, test samples should be run through the mill to determine if elements included in the assay are being added to the tissue during the particle-size reduction process.

Particle size becomes important depending on the aliquot of plant tissue to be assayed. If the aliquot is to be ≤ 0.50 g, then the fineness, particularly when using a Wiley-type mill, should be <0.84 mm (20-mesh). Plant tissue that has been reduced in size using either ball or UDY mills will consist of particle sizes considerably <0.85 mm (20-mesh).

During the cutting process in Wiley-type mills, separation of tissue particles into various size fractions will occur (Nelson & Boodley, 1965), fractions which can vary in their elemental concentrations (Jones, 1963; Smith et al., 1968). In order to minimize this segregation effect, sufficient time must be provided to allow the entire sample to pass through the mill (Graham, 1972; Ulrich, 1984). Also, static electricity should be controlled (Nelson & Boodley, 1965; Smith et al., 1968). After milling, thorough and careful mixing of the ground sample without segregation is best performed in the storage sample container. After milling, most tissues are sensitive to thermal decom-

Table 13-2. Organic matter destruction in plant tissue by high-temperature oxidation (dry ashing).

Dry ashing procedure:
  1. Weigh 0.5 g dried (80 °C) −0.84 mm (20-mesh) plant tissue into a 30 mL high form procelain and/or quartz crucible.†
  2. Place crucible in a rack, and the rack in a cool muffle furnace.
  3. Set furnace temperature to reach set temperature (500 °C) in about 2 h.
  4. After 4 to 8 h of muffling at 500 °C, remove the crucible rack from the furnace and let cool.
  5. Add 10 mL dilute acid (300 mL HCl and 100 mL HNO_3 in 1 L pure water) to dissolve the ash. Crucible and contents may be heated to assist in solubilization of ash by weighing crucible, heating to acid fumes, cooling, and adding pure water to original weight.
  6. Allow suspended material to settle to the bottom of the crucible. Clear solution is ready for elemental analysis.

---

† If an ashing aid is needed, add either 5 mL HNO_3, or 5 mL 7% $Mg(NO_3)_2 \cdot 6H_2O$. Dry on a hot plate and then return to Step 2 above.

position at temperatures > 80 °C (Steyn, 1961) and, therefore, a drying temperature not be exceeded prior to weighing and analysis. For long-term storage, milled tissue should be kept in an air-tight container and stored in a cool (< 10 °C), dark environment (Steyn, 1961).

5. Methods of Organic Matter Destruction

Organic matter destruction can be accomplished by either high temperature thermal oxidation or acid digestion; the former is frequently referred to as dry ashing, and the latter as wet digestion or wet ashing. There continues to be considerable controversy between advocates of either method in terms of ease of execution, elemental losses and/or additions during the ashing process, and suitability of use with some types of tissues. Major works on this subject are authored by Gorsuch (1970), Bock (1978), Tolg (1974), and Gorsuch (1976). The number of papers written about both methods of organic matter destruction is considerable. Therefore, only a few selected articles are referenced that relate to the preparation of plant tissue for micronutrient determinations.

Dry ashing is best done in a muffle furnace at a maximum temperature of 500 °C. An ashing temperature < 500 °C can result in incomplete organic matter destruction, while temperatures > 500 °C can result in elemental losses (Isaac & Jones, 1972). The extent of losses occurring at temperatures > 500 °C may be significantly less for tissues relatively high (> 1.0%) in Ca. Quartz crucibles are the best ashing vessels, although acid-washed, well-glazed, porcelain crucibles and pyrex beakers can be satisfactorily used. Munter et al. (1984) found small additions of B, Cu, Fe, and Mn to corn leaf tissue when procelain crucibles were used as the ashing vessel as compared with those made of quartz.

After placing ashing vessels in a cool muffle furnace, the furnace is slowly brought to 500 °C in about 1 to 1.5 h. The minimum ashing time at 500 °C is 4 h, although an overnight ash of 6 to 8 h is preferred. A dry ashing procedure is described in Table 13-2.

Ashing aids are not normally needed unless for very carbonaceous tissues. Gorsuch (1970) recommends 10 mL of 10% H_2SO_4 or 10 mL of 7% $Mg(NO_3)_2 \cdot 6H_2O$ per 5 g sample. The procedure using HNO_3 is described in the 1980 *Association of Official Analytical Chemists (AOAC) Manual* (Horwitz, 1980).

After muffling the plant tissue at 500 °C, the remaining ash is dissolved in either $3M$ HNO_3 or HCl, or $2M$ *aqua regia*. Acid dissolution at room temperature may not completely release all the elements in the ash. Munter and Grande (1981) and Munter et al. (1984) suggest that the mixture of ash and dissolving acid be heated until acid fumes appear. Then, after cooling, the original volume is restored by adding pure water.

For tissues high in Si, such as rice (*Oryza sativa* L.) leaves and stems, Zn can be trapped in the Si particles (as SiO_2) formed during dry ashing. Therefore, for high-Si-content tissues, acid digestion is recommended as the technique for organic matter destruction.

Numerous wet (digestion) ashing procedures have been proposed, but they all make use of some combination of HNO_3, H_2SO_4, and $HClO_4$ acids with or without 30% H_2O_2, as described by Tolg (1974). The use of $HClO_4$ requires special precautions as described by Horwitz (1980). The digestion can be carried out in beakers on a hot plate, in digestion tubes placed in a port of a digestion block (Zasoski & Burau, 1977; Halvin & Soltanpour, 1980; Adler & Wilcox, 1985; Zarcinas et al., 1987), in an enclosed container under pressure (Vigler et al., 1980; Sung et al., 1984; Knapp, 1985), or in vessels placed in a microwave oven (White & Douthit, 1985).

The inclusion of H_2SO_4 in the digestion mixture is limited to tissues low ($<1.0\%$) in Ca, since $CaSO_4$ can be formed during the digestion step, trapping elements within the formed precipitate. Parkinson and Allen (1975), and Wolf (1982) have successfully used a mixture of H_2SO_4 and 30% H_2O_2 as the digestion mixture for the determination of N as well as other major elements and micronutrients in plant tissue.

If B is a determined element, it is recommended that organic matter destruction be performed by dry ashing (Wikner, 1986), since B can be lost during the wet-digestion procedure. However, the extent of loss will vary with tissue type and Ca tissue content (Feldman, 1961). van der Lee et al. (1987) found that wet ashing in a mixture of HCl and HF gave similar B results to those obtained when using dry ashing as the organic destruction procedure. Gestring and Soltanpour (1981) obtained certified B concentrations by wet digesting plant tissue in nalgene bottles with concentrated HNO_3.

Since there are conflicting published results as well as considerable disagreement on how best to destroy plant tissue organic matter, the analyst should carefully verify the results obtained by the ashing procedure using reference standards of verified elemental concentration, such as those available from the National Institute of Standards and Technology (N.I.S.T.) (Alvarez, 1980). Several wet-digestion procedures are described in Table 13–3.

Table 3-3. Acid digestion procedures for organic matter destruction of plant tissue.

Acid digestion in HNO_3 and $HClO_4$:
1. Weight 0.5 g dried (80 °C) − 0.84 min (20-mesh) plant tissue into a beaker or digestion tube.
2. Add 2.5 mL concentrated HNO_3. Cover the beaker with a watch glass or place a funnel into the mouth of the digestion tube. Let stand overnight.
3. Place covered beaker on a hot plate or digestion tube into a port of a digestion block and digest at 80 °C for 1 h. Remove beaker or digestion tube from hot plate or block, and let cool.
4. Add 2.5 mL $HClO_4$, replace watch glass or funnel, and heat at 180–200 °C for 2 to 3 h, or until digest is clear.
5. Remove watch glass or funnel, lower heat to 100 °C until fumes of $HClO_4$ dissipate. If digest is not colorless at this point, repeat Step 4.
6. Remove from hot plate or digestion block and let cool.
7. Add pure water to digest to bring to 10 mL or other appropriate volume. Digest is ready for elemental assay.

Acid digestion in HNO_3 and 30% H_2O_2:
1. Weigh 0.5 g dried (80 °C) −0.84 mm (20-mesh) plant tissue into a beaker or digestion tube.
2. Add 5.0 mL concentrated HNO_3. Cover with watch glass, or place funnel into mouth of the digestion tube. Let stand overnight.
3. Place covered beaker on a hot plate or digestion tube into a port of a digestion block, and digest at 125 °C for 1 h. Remove beaker or digestion tube from plate or block and let cool.
4. Add 3 mL 30% H_2O_2 to the beaker or digestion tube and digest at 125 °C. Repeat additions of 30% H_2O_2 until digest is clear. Add HNO_3 as needed to keep digest from going dry.
5. When the digest is clear, remove the watch glass or funnel, and reduce temperature of hot plate or block to 80 °C. Take nearly to dryness. Residue should be colorless. If not, repeat Step 4.
6. Add 1:10 HNO_3 or HCl to bring to final volume of 10 mL. Clear solution is ready for elemental assay.

Acid digestion in H_2SO_4 and 30% H_2O_2:
1. Weigh 0.5 g dried (80 °C) −0.84 mm (20-mesh) plant tissue into a beaker or digestion tube.
2. Add 3.5 mL concentrated H_2SO_4, and let stand for 30 min.
3. Add 3.5 mL 30% H_2O_2.
4. Cover the beaker or place a funnel into the mouth of the digestion tube. Place beaker on a hot plate or digestion tube into a port of a digestion block. Heat at 350 °C for 30 min.
5. Remove beaker or digestion tube from hot plate or digestion block, and let cool.
6. Add 2 mL aliquots of 30% H_2O_2 and repeat digestion step until cool digest is clear.
7. Once the digest is clear, dilute to 20 mL with pure water. Digest is ready for elemental assay.

C. Analytical Procedures

1. Methods of Analysis

Piper (1942) described in detail many of the classical colorimetric procedures for elemental content determination in plant tissue. Jackson (1958), Johnson and Ulrich (1959), and Chapman and Pratt (1982) described various colorimetric and instrumental methods of plant tissue analysis for the micronutrients. The Official *AOAC Manual* (Williams, 1984) also contains assay procedures specific for plant tissue. Emission spectrometry, a method for elemental determination in plant tissue ash, has had a long history of use that still continues today.

Mitchell (1956, 1964) prepared two extensive reviews on spectrographic and spectrochemical procedures. There have been continual advancements in these procedures from photographic (Chloak & Story, 1941) to photo-electric, normally referred to as direct reading, detection of the produced spectrum (Carpenter, 1964; Christian et al., 1968; Chaplin & Dixon, 1974; Gabriels & Cottenie, 1976). Changes in the method of excitation from AC (Conner & Bass, 1959) and DC arcs (Thompson & Bankston, 1969) have been made to AC spark (Mathis, 1953; Jones, 1976), and then to DC (Skogerboe et al., 1976) and inductively coupled (Scott et al., 1974) plasmas.

A number of authors have described the elemental assay of plant tissue ash by AC spark emission spectrometry (Baker et al., 1964; Carpenter, 1964; Christensen et al., 1968; Jones & Warner, 1969; Jones, 1976), a method of excitation that is being replaced by plasmas. The advantages for plasma excitation are considerable in terms of minimal matrix and spectral interferences, excellent sensitivity (frequently < 0.1 mg kg^{-1}), and dynamic reading range (usually three to five decades). These characteristics of the plasma make it an ideal source for micronutrient determination in plant tissue ash. Inductively coupled Ar plasma-emission spectrometry, frequently referred to by the acronym ICP or ICAP, is a procedure that has been described by Jones (1977), Dalquist and Knoll (1978), Munter and Grande (1981), Soltanpour et al. (1982), Munter et al. (1984), Zarcinas (1984), and Zarcinas et al. (1987). Two recent books have been published on the ICP analytical technique (Walsh, 1983; Montaser & Golightly, 1987).

The other plasma excitation source is the DC plasma. Debolt (1980) has described this method of excitation for the assay of plant tissue ash.

The spectrometer receiving and recording a plasma-generated emission can have either an air or vacuum light path. Evacuated spectrometers can detect emission lines in the ultraviolet region of the spectrum, which is most useful for B determination as well as two major elements P and S. The spectrometer design may be either a sequential monochromator, which records one emission line at a time in a programmed sequence, or a polychromator, which has an individual detector at each emission line position for simultaneous determination (Nygaard & Sofera, 1988). The advantages of the polychromator over the sequential spectrometer can be considerable when five or more elemental determinations are being made repetitively in terms of shorter time for analysis, less use of Ar, and improved precision. All of the micronutrients except Cl can be determined by ICP spectrometry.

The other major instrumental method for the determination of the micronutrients Cu, Fe, Mn, and Zn is flame atomic absorption spectrometry (AA or AAS). The micronutrients B and Cl are not determinable by AAS, whereas Mo can be determined only by flameless AAS (Wilson, 1979). Introduced in the late 1950s, flame AAS (Christian & Feldman, 1970) was rapidly adopted and is still in wide use today. Although it is a method with excellent sensitivity and relatively easy to use, considerable sample manipulation is required prior to analysis and only one element can be determined at a time. Therefore, the technique is time consuming and costly when compared with the ICP technique. Atomic absorption methods of analysis have been described by Greweling (1976), Isaac (1980), Baker and Suhr (1982), and Ure (1983).

Another instrumental method for the determination of Fe, Mn, and Zn in plant tissue is x-ray fluorescence (Alexander, 1965; Kubota & Lazar, 1971). This method is matrix sensitive and is in little use today for routine assay of plant tissue.

There are other analytical procedures that can be used to assay plant tissue ash and digests for their micronutrient content. However, most are highly specialized methods designed for unique applications and, therefore, are beyond the scope of this review.

2. Selection of Analytical Method

It is difficult to specifically select any one method or technique as being superior to another, although studies conducted by Kenworthy et al. (1956), Bowen (1967), Brech (1968), Jones (1969), and Jones and Isaac (1969) have tried to make that distinction. Baker et al. (1964), Carpenter et al. (1968), Jones and Warner (1969), and Munter et al. (1984) also studied the variance associated with various methods of plant ash analysis. Of these authors, only Bowen (1967) recommended that a particular instrumental technique be specifically designated for each element. Unfortunately, in many instances method selection is based on what instrumentation and facilities are available rather than on the best method for the element(s) determined, and the form and composition of the prepared sample that constitutes the matrix.

For the micronutrients, precision of the determination may be more a factor associated with sampling and sample preparation rather than determination of the elemental concentration of the prepared digest or ash, a factor discovered by Munter et al. (1984). In an interlaboratory study, Watson (1981) found that the micronutrients B and Fe were the most variable among the 10 elements determined in nine different plant tissues. For most instrumental procedures, coefficients of variability are usually <5%, although they increase as the detection limit of the analytical procedure is approached, as well as at high concentrations (Horwitz, 1982).

Horwitz (1982), based on his many years with the AOAC, has discussed the practical limits of acceptable variability for methods of analysis, focusing on the important aspects of reliability, reproducibility, repeatability, systematic error of bias, specificity, and limit of reliable measurement. The impact of these aspects on any analytical procedure varies considerably in terms of sample size, determinations made, concentration of the determined element, and the characteristics of the analytical instrument used. An additional criterion is the ruggedness factor, which sets the limits for each step in the analytical procedure that, if exceeded, will invalidate the obtained result. Unfortunately, most plant analysis procedures have not been so described. Examples would include limit criteria for sample preparation proce-

Table 13-4. Analytical criteria for selection technique of analysis (Hislop, 1980).

Accuracy	Elemental coverage
Precision	Single or multielement
Limit of detection	Determine chemical form

dures, such as moisture removal technique, ashing and digestion temperatures, length of time, etc. These procedures have been described earlier in this paper, but with few specifically defined limits.

The analyst today has a wide range of instrumentation from which to choose. Some factors that affect the choice are described by McLaughlin et al. (1979). A similar evaluation of analytical techniques has been developed by Hislop (1980) as shown in Table 13-4. Those in search of a suitable analytical procedure may find the articles by Morrison (1979), and Stika and Morrison (1981) helpful as they compare the relative sensitivity and precision of various analytical procedures. In those instances in which the micronutrient concentration in plant tissue is high (> 100 mg kg^{-1}), detection limit considerations are of less significance than those factors that affect precision.

3. Quality Assurance

Quality assurance is a management tool designed to ensure reliable performance for most types of testing laboratories (Aldehoff & Ernest, 1983). Criteria for implementation of a quality assurance program have been established by the AOAC (Garfield, 1984). The elements of a quality assurance program include: (i) administration; (ii) personnel management; (iii) management of equipment and supplies; (iv) records maintenance; (v) sample analysis; (vi) proficiency testing; (vii) audit procedures; and (viii) design and safety of facilities. Application of quality assurance criteria on an actual analytical procedure are discussed in detail by Dux (1986) and Taylor (1987).

The basis for reliable preformance in an analytical laboratory has been titled "Good Laboratory Practices," the subject of a Federal Register entry in 1979 (Anonymous, 1979), and is described in some detail by Fischbeck (1980). The Council of Independent Laboratories (ACIL, 1976), the U.S. EPA (Booth, 1979), and the N.I.S.T. (Berman, 1980) have published proceedings on symposia on the subject of laboratory performance.

The issues of sensitivity, accuracy, and precision are important considerations for the analyst and should be significant determining factors in method selection. These issues are particularly important for micronutrient determinations since critical levels can be close to detection limits of most analytical procedures, such as that for Mo, whereas relatively small changes in concentration for the micronutrients, such as for Cu and Zn, can mean the difference between deficiency and sufficiency. Sensitivity has been variously defined as two parameters; the minimum level of detectability and the ability to significantly distinguish between two analytical values. The detection limit is defined as the smallest concentration that can be identified as being greater than zero and is usually defined as either two or three standard deviations above a background determination. Sensitivity in terms of level distinction is confounded with precision.

Accuracy is the ability of the method to obtain the true value and is dependent on the use of reliable standards and matrix matching. Several kinds of standards are needed in the laboratory; one set to monitor analytical procedures, and another set to calibrate instruments and standardize reagents. Prepared and certified standard solutions and reagents can be obtained from many chemical supply houses. Standard Reference Materials, referred to as SRMs (Uriano, 1979), are available from the U.S. N.I.S.T. (Alvares, 1980). Unfortunately, not every element of interest to the plant nutritionist is certified in every SRM, which can limit its usefulness. However, SRMs should be used whenever possible for verification of accuracy, as has been described by Taylor (1985).

Precision is a measure of the degree of variability associated with an obtained analytical result that is determined by repeated assays of the same sample carried through all the steps, from sample preparation to the final assay result. Poor precision may be the compound result of accumulated errors made across the entire analytical procedure and, therefore, not the result of a single factor. Hislop (1980) has written an excellent article on the requirements for obtaining accurate and precise analytical results. Horwitz (1982) also has evaluated various analytical procedures by assigning levels of performance by analytical technique, basing this judgement on years of experience in the determination of elements and substances in various materials. Dux (1986) describes how precision determinations can be included in a quality assurance program.

In the normal laboratory routine, a standard can be used not only to monitor an analytical procedure, but when placed into a sequence of unknowns, it serves the dual purpose as marker and standard. By noting the position and value of the marker-standard at the end of an analytical run, the analyst can determine if an unknown had been skipped or duplicated, as well as being able to determine if a shift in the calibration has occurred. Therefore, an evaluated calibration shift may serve as the basis for adjustment of those results obtained between each marker-standard.

These, as well as other factors, form the basis for an established quality assurance program as has been defined by Garfield (1984), Dux (1986), and Taylor (1987). Without such a program of laboratory and analytical management, performance in terms of reliable analytical results cannot be obtained. A recent collaborative study reported by Munter et al. (1984) points to certain areas that should be of concern when conducting an elemental assay of plant tissue. They found that both preparation procedures and instrumental calibration techniques must be standardized in order to minimize variation. In a similar collaborative study, Sterrett et al. (1987) found a wide variance in the determination of B, Cu, and Fe in plant tissue, and recommended a closer scrutiny of both the analysis procedure as well as the use of the obtained assay results for these elements. Both of these studies emphasize the need for careful evaluation of each step in the analytical process on the basis of quality assurance criteria.

II. MICRONUTRIENT CONCENTRATIONS IN PLANTS

Micronutrient concentration data published in much of the literature prior to the mid 1980s are frequently expressed as parts per million (ppm), although much of the very early results were expressed as percent. Today, concentration results are reported using the SI (le Système International d'Unites) system as milligrams per kilogram or as micrograms per gram. Some have preferred to express concentrations in moles per kilogram, although this means of expression is not as widely used. In this discussion, concentrations will be expressed as mg kg^{-1}, which is the same numerical value as when expressed in ppm.

Weight of element is usually expressed on a dry weight basis, frequently designated in the literature as DW or d.w. of tissue. Therefore, some prefer to make the concentration expression as mg kg^{-1} DW, or mg kg^{-1} d.w. In this discussion, results will be on the dry weight basis without providing the dry weight designation.

There has never been an established convention for designating the number of significant figures for expressing micronutrient concentrations. In terms of biological significance, the author suggests that concentrations >10 mg kg^{-1} be expressed as a whole number, while concentrations <10, but >1 mg kg^{-1} be expressed to the nearest 0.1 mg kg^{-1}. For concentrations <1 mg kg^{-1}, the concentration should be expressed to the nearest 0.01 mg kg^{-1}. This system of expression will be followed in this presentation.

Over the years there has developed a jargon of specific terms used to define the biological impact that a particular elemental concentration, primarily in leaves, has on plant growth or yield. For most of the micronutrients, leaf concentration, rather than that in the whole plant or other plant part, is the usual measuring criteria for defining the micronutrient status of the plant. Leaf micronutrient concentration then, is defined in terms of plant performance or status as either being deficient, sufficient, or as excessive or toxic.

Much of the published plant analysis interpretative concentrations are defined as either being a critical level, standard value, or sufficiency range. Ohki and Ulrich (1977) used the terms critical deficiency level (CDL) and critical toxicity level (CTL) to define the concentration point at which a 10% reduction in growth occurred. The critical level is that elemental concentration that is at the dividing point between deficiency and sufficiency, normally chosen at the 10% yield or growth-reduction point.

The terms used to define the relationship between elemental concentration, and yield or growth vary considerably in the literature. For example, Prevot and Ollagnier (1961) identified part D in Fig. 13–2 as the luxury range, which today is defined as the sufficiency range. The standard value concept of interpretation for fruit trees was established by Kenworthy (1961), whose standard values were derived from mean concentrations of a large number of assay results of leaves taken from normal-appearing grower orchards. Sufficiency range defines the adequate range in concentration for normal

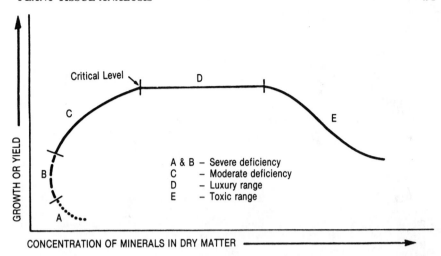

Fig. 13-2. General relationship between plant growth or yield and elemental content of the plant (Prevot & Ollagnier, 1961).

growth. Micronutrient concentrations outside the sufficiency range will either result in deficiency or toxicity.

Most of the interpretative tabular data provided in the following sections for each micronutrient are provided as either critical levels or sufficiency ranges. For some, the use of the words value and level to mean concentration is an unfortunate circumstance, words that are widely used in the past and current literature. In this discussion, concentration will be the term used, unless referencing published data that uses a term other than concentration.

The concentration of several micronutrients in plants is determined to some degree by their bioaccumulation characteristics. Kabata-Pendias and Pendias (1984) determined the bioaccumulation index for a number of trace elements, which included several of the micronutrients. According to their categorization, the approximate bioaccumulation index for B is 8; Zn, 0.9; Mo, 0.8; Cu, 0.7; Mn, 0.09; and Fe, 0.08; therefore B is the highest bioaccumulator for these six micronutrients and Fe the lowest.

The average concentration of micronutrients in plants, including the relative number of atoms compared to Mo, has been estimated by Epstein (1972), as shown in Table 13-5. The approximate concentrations of micronutrients in plant leaves associated with the general health of the plant, sensitivity in terms of plant species, and symptoms of deficiency and toxicity, are listed in Tables 13-6, 13-7, and 13-8, respectively.

A. Boron

In general, the B concentration in the plant reflects, to a considerable degree, the plant's B requirement. For example, monocotyledons contain less B than do dicotyledons, which agrees with their requirement for this element.

Table 13-5. Average concentrations of micronutrients in plants (Epstein, 1972).

Micro-nutrient	Proportion according to dry weight		Relative number of atoms compared to Mo
	mol g^{-1}	mg kg^{-1}	
Mo	0.001	0.1	1
Cu	0.10	6.0	100
Zn	0.30	20	300
Mn	1.0	50	1000
B	2.0	20	2000
Fe	2.0	100	2000
Cl	3.0	100	3000

Table 13-6. Approximate concentration of micronutrients in mature-leaf tissue generalized for various plant species (Kabata-Pendias & Pendias, 1984; and author).

Micronutrient	Deficient	Sufficient or normal	Excessive or toxic
		mg kg^{-1}	
B	5–30	10–200	50–200
Cl	<100	100–500	500†–1000
Cu	2–5	5–30	20–100
Fe	<50	100–500	>500
Mn	15–25	20–300	300–500
Mo	0.03–0.15	0.1–2.0	>100
Zn	10–20	27–150	100–400

† Toxic for sensitive plants (see Table 7).

Table 13-7. Crop species sensitive to either deficient or excessive levels of the micronutrients (Kabata-Pendias & Pendias, 1984, and author).

Micro-nutrient	Species sensitive to deficiency†	Species sensitive to excess†
B	Alfalfa, *Brassica* (cabbage and relatives), beet, celery, grape, apple, pear, cotton, sugar beet, and sunflower	Cereals, potato, tomato, cucumber, soybean, and mustard
Cl	Cereals, celery, potato, coconut palm, sugar beet, lettuce, carrot, and cabbage	Strawberry, navy bean, fruit trees, pea, and onion
Cu	Cereals (oat), sunflower, spinach, alfalfa, onion, and watermelon	Cereals and legumes, spinach, citrus seedlings, and gladiolus
Fe	Citrus, grape, several calcifuge species, pecan, sorghum, soybean, and clover	Rice and tobacco
Mn	Cereals (oat), legumes, apple, cherry, citrus, onion, lettuce, pea, soybean, and sugar beet	Cereals, legumes, potato, and cabbage
Mo	*Brassica* (cabbage and relatives) and legumes	Cereals, pea, and greenbean
Zn	Cereals (corn), legumes, grasses, hops, flax, grape, citrus, soybean, field bean, and pecan	Cereals, spinach, and peanut

† Scientific names are given in the Glossary.

Table 13–8. Generalized deficiency symptoms and toxicity effect for the micronutrients (Kabata-Pendias & Pendias, 1984).

Micro-nutrient	Deficiency symptoms	Toxicity effects
B	Chlorosis and browning of young leaves; dead growing points; distorted blossom development; lesions in pith and roots, and multiplication of cell division.	Margin or leaf tip chlorosis, browning of leaf points, and wilting and drying-off of older leaves.
Cl	Wilting, restricted and highly branched root system, often with stubby tips.	Marginal leaf scorch, abscission.
Cu	Wilting, melanism, white twisted tips, reduction in panicle formation, and disturbance of lignification.	Dark green leaves followed by induced Fe chlorosis, thick, short, or barbed-wire looking roots, depressed tillering.
Fe	Interveinal chlorosis of young organs.	Dark green foliage, stunted growth of tops and roots, dark brown to purple leaves of some plants (e.g., bronzing disease of rice).
Mn	Interveinal chlorosis with dark green major veins, chlorotic spots or lesions, necrosis of young leaves, grey speck, and yellow disease.	Chlorosis and necrotic lesions on old leaves, blackish-brown or red necrotic spots, accumulation of MnO_2 particles in epidermal cells, drying tips of leaves, and stunted roots.
Mo	Chlorosis of leaf margins whiptail of leaves and distorted curding of cauliflower, fired margin and deformation of leaves due to NO_3 excess, and destruction of embryonic tissues.	Yellowing or browning of leaves, depressed tillering.
Zn	Interveinal chlorosis (mainly of monocots), stunted growth, little-leaf rosette of trees, and violet-red points on leaves.	Chlorotic and necrotic leaf tips, interveinal chlorosis in new leaves, retarded growth of entire plant, and injured roots resemble barbed wire.

Members of the *Papilionaceae* and *Cruciferae* families have relatively high B requirements and, therefore, generally contain fairly high (>25 mg kg^{-1}) B concentrations in their leaves. This is not to say that plant and soil B are not correlated, for indeed they are (Keren & Bingham, 1985), as the relative species difference remains about the same with a change in soil B concentration.

Boron deficiency occurs in many plants when the concentration in fully mature leaves if <15 mg kg^{-1} and the B sufficiency range is between 20 and 100 mg kg^{-1} (Gupta, 1979; Adriano, 1986). It is the leaf concentration at toxicity that varies considerably, since some plants are particularly sensitive to B, making their sufficiency range between deficiency and toxicity <25 mg B kg^{-1}. A summary of B concentrations in leaves when deficient, sufficient, and toxic is provided in Table 13–9. Additional and recent interpretative B levels for a large number of crops may be found in Reuter and Robinson (1986) and Martin-Prevel et al. (1987). Boron critical concentrations for corn,

Table 13-9. Deficient, sufficient, and toxic levels of B in plants (Adriano, 1986).

Plant species§	Plant part	Deficient	Sufficient	Toxic
		—— mg B kg^{-1} in dry matter ——		
Alfalfa	Whole tops at early bloom	<15	20–40¶	200
	Top ⅓ of plant shortly before flowering	<20	31–80	>100
	Upper stem cuttings in early flower stage		30†	
Broccoli	Leaves		70	
	Leaf tissue when 5% heads formed	2–9	10–71	
Brussels sprout	Leaf tissue when sprouts begin to form	6–10	13–101	
Carrot	Mature leaf lamina	<16	32–103	175–307
	Leaves	18		
Cauliflower	Whole tops before the appearance of curd	3	12–23	
	Leaves	23	36	
	Leaf tissue when 5% heads formed	4–9	11–97	
Celery	Petioles	16	28–75	
	Leaflets	20	68–432	720
Corn	Leaf at or opposite and below ear leaf at tassel stage		10†	
	Total aboveground plant material at vegetative stage until ear formation	<9	15–90	>100
Cucumber	Mature leaves from center of stem 2 wk after first picking	<20	40–120	>300
Dwarf kidney bean	Leaves and stem (plants cut 50 cm above the soil)		40	132
	Pods		28	43
Oats	47-d old plants			>105
	Boot stage tissue		15–50	44–400
	Boot stage tissue	<1	8–30	>30‡
	Boot stage tissue	1.1–3.5	6–15	>35
	Straw	3.5–5.6	10	>20
Pasture grasses	Aboveground part at first bloom at first cut		10–50	>800
Potato	32-d old plants		12	>180
	Fully developed first leaf at 75 d after planting	<15	21–50	>50‡
Red clover	Whole tops at bud stage	12–20	21–45	>59
	Top ⅓ of platn at bloom		20–60	>60‡
Rutabaga	Leaf tissue at harvest	20–38#	38–140	>250
	Leaf tissue when roots begin to swell	32–40††	40	
	Roots	8‡‡	13	
Spanish peanut	Young leaf tissue from 30-d old plants		54–65§§	>250

(continued on next page)

Table 13-9. Continued.

Plant species§	Plant part	Deficient	Sufficient	Toxic
		— mg B kg^{-1} in dry matter —		
Sugar beet	Blades or recently matured leaves	12–40	35–200	
	Middle fully developed leaf without stem taken at end of June or early July	<20	31–200	>800
Timothy	Whole plants at heading stage		3–93	>102
Tomato	Plants	14–32	34–96	91–415
	Mature young leaves from top of the plant	<10	30–75	>200
	63-d old plants			>125
Wheat	Boot stage tissue	2.1–5.0	8	>16
	Straw	4.6–6.0	17	>34
White pea bean	Aerial portion of plants 30 d after planting		36–94	144
Winter wheat	Aboveground vegetative plant tissue when plants 40 cm high	<0.3	2.1–10.1	>10‡

† Considered critical.
‡ Considered high.
§ Scientific names are given in the Glossary.
¶ 15–20 mg B kg^{-1} considered critical.
# Less than 12 mg B kg^{-1} severely deficient.
†† Moderately deficiency, less than 12 mg B kg^{-1} severely deficient.
‡‡ Severely deficient.
§§ 15–20 mg B kg^{-1} considered critical.

soybean [*Glycine max* (L.) Merr.], alfalfa (*Medicago sativa* L.), and wheat (*Triticum* spp.) have been set by Melsted et al. (1969) and are given in Table 13–10.

Many important food crops have been classified in terms of their sensitivity and/or tolerance to B concentrations in soil or applied irrigation water (Keren & Bingham, 1985; Adriano, 1986). Hot-water-extractable (Berger & Truog, 1940) soil B concentrations <0.009 mol B mg^{-1} have been classed as potentially deficient, while those >0.046 mol B mg^{-1} are potentially toxic. Boron concentrations at 0.50 μg mL^{-1} in the soil solution are probably safe for many species, but when they are >0.50 μg mL^{-1}, many plants can be adversely affected (Wilcox, 1960). Irrigation water B concentrations <0.046 mol m^{-3} would be considered safe in terms of potential crop damage, while concentrations >0.19 mol m^{-3} are potentially damaging to B-sensitive crops. The degree of sensitivity for B concentrations either in soil or applied irrigation waters varies considerably among crop species (Keren & Bingham, 1985).

Boron uptake and leaf B concentrations may be genetically controlled, as has been suggested by Gorsline et al. (1968) for corn. The B concentration in the corn plant decreases with age, with B concentration in leaves higher than they are in the stalk, and with upper leaves higher in B than are the

Table 13-10. Critical micronutrient concentration for corn, soybean, wheat, and alfalfa for diagnostic interpretations of total plant analyses (Melsted et al., 1969).

Micronutrient	Corn†	Soybean‡	Wheat§	Alfalfa¶
			mg kg^{-1}	
B	10	25	15	30
Cu	5	5	5	7
Fe	25	30	25	30
Mn	15	20	30	25
Mo	0.2	0.5	0.3	0.5
Zn	15	15	15	15

† Leaf at or opposite and below ear level at tasseling.
‡ Youngest mature leaves and petioles after first pod formation.
§ Whole plant at the boot stage.
¶ Upper stem cuttings in early flower stage.

lower leaves (Gorsline et al., 1965). Also, is not evenly distributed within the corn leaf, as the B concentration in the margins is usually four to five times that in the leaf blade alone (Sayre, 1958; Kohl & Oertli, 1961; Jones, 1970). This accumulation occurs in most leaves as B is carried in the transpiration stream and deposited at the leaf margins as water is transpired. Such an uneven B leaf distribution may result in highly variable results if the relative weight ratio between margin and leaf blade does not remain constant.

Boron in plant tissue is best determined following organic matter destruction by dry ashing, since B can be lost during the wet acid digestion procedure. However, van der Lee et al. (1987) were able to determine B accurately following wet digestion in a mixture of HCl and HF, whereas Gestring and Soltanpour (1981) digested samples in Nalgene bottles using concentrated HNO_3 followed by analysis using ICP spectrometry. In order to prevent possible contamination, contact with pyrex glassware should be avoided during preparation and analysis. The B content of the prepared tissue digest can be determined by several analytical procedures: colorimetrically using azomethine-H (Wolf, 1974; Lohse, 1982); AC spark (Jones, 1976); ICP (Munter & Grande, 1981); or DC plasma (DeBolt, 1980) emission spectrometry.

B. Chlorine

Chlorine was the last of the micronutrients to be determined as essential for plants, a determination that was unique because of the ubiquitous nature of Cl in the environment (Broyer et al., 1954). The critical concentration for this element may be as low as 35 mg kg^{-1} to as high as several thousand milligrams per kilogram. Therefore, the determination must be carefully performed in order to cope with the varying range in Cl concentration that might occur in plant tissues as well as the considerable potential that exists for contamination.

A number of studies have been conducted to determine the need for Cl for several crops (Jackson, 1986). Fixen et al. (1986b) obtained yield responses to applied Cl for spring wheat, barley (*Hordeum vulgaris* L.), and oat (*Avena sativa* L.). In a similar study with wheat, Fixen et al. (1986a) determined the critical Cl concentration for the aboveground plant at head emergence to be 1.5 g kg^{-1}. Ulrich and Ohki (1956) found that the critical Cl concentration for sugarbeet (*Beta vulgaris* L.) was about 1.4 g kg^{-1} in leaves and 5.7 g kg^{-1} in the petiole. Therefore, Cl is not evenly distributed in the plant. Also, Cl tends to accumulate with age.

Chlorine deficiency is considered a minor problem in selected soils and for particular crops (see Table 13-7), whereas Cl excess and toxicity are more frequently occurring problems. Much of the older literature has been reviewed by Eaton (1966). Reisenauer et al. (1973) associated yield reductions due to excess Cl in plant tissue with concentrations from 5.0 to 20 g kg^{-1} for sensitive crops, whereas Cl concentrations >40 g kg^{-1} would be toxic for the more tolerant species.

The determination of Cl in plant tissue can be done by a number of methods, the more classic procedures have been described by Williams (1979). A gravimetric and two volumetric procedures are provided in the *AOAC Manual* (Williams, 1984). More recently, Cl-specific, ion-electrode procedures, as described by LaCroix et al. (1970), and Krieg and Sung (1977), or with a solid state Cl electrode (Islam et al., 1983), are being used in place of the gravimetric and volumetric methods. In order to minimize interferences with either electrode method, Cl is determined in either an 0.5 M HNO_3 extract of the plant tissue, or the determination is made after the tissue is dry ashed and the ash solubilized in dilute HNO_3. The latest innovation is ion chromatography, a procedure described by Kalbasi and Tabatabai (1985) as well as Grunau and Swiader (1986) for the determination of Cl in plant tissue.

C. Copper

The normal Cu concentration in plant tissues ranges from 5 to 20 mg kg^{-1}. For some plants, the critical concentration in leaves as the indicator plant part is 5 mg kg^{-1}, although in some instances deficiency symptoms will not appear until the Cu concentration in leaves is <5 mg kg^{-1}. Melsted et al. (1969) have established critical Cu concentrations for four crops as given in Table 13-10. Plant Cu concentrations that are toxic vary considerably according to species, with some becoming Cu toxic with concentrations <10 mg kg^{-1} and others when concentrations exceed 20 mg kg^{-1}. Table 13-11 lists deficient, sufficient, and toxic concentrations of Cu for a number of plant species.

Unlike B, Gorsline et al. (1965) observed that Cu levels in the corn plant remain fairly constant over its growth period. In addition, Jones (1970) found Cu evenly distributed in corn leaves. However, Cu concentrations in various plant parts may be quite different, with leaves being higher in Cu than either petioles, stems, or fruit.

In many parts of the world, Cu deficiency has been described physiologically as reclamation disease, yellow-tip, and die-back (Adriano, 1986). Deficiency is more likely to occur on peat and muck soils, alkaline and cal-

Table 13–11. Deficient, sufficient, and toxic levels of Cu in various crops (Adriano, 1980).

Plant species†	Part or tissue sampled	Deficient	Sufficient	Toxic
		— mg Cu kg^{-1} in dry matter —		
Alfalfa	Upper stem cuttings in early flower stage	7	--	--
	Top 15 cm of plant sampled before bloom	<5	11–30	>50
	Top ⅓ plant shortly before flowering	<2	8–30	>60
Barley	Boot stage tissue	2.3	4.8	--
	Kernels	0.5	2.0	--
	Straw	1.5	3.0	
	Top four leaves at bloom		6–12	>12
Corn	Leaf at or opposite and below ear level at tassel stage	5		
	Ear leaf sampled when in initial silk	<2	6–20	>50
	Middle of first ear leaf at tasseling	<2	6–50	>70
Cucumber	Mature leaves from center of stem 2 wk after picking	<2	7–10	>10
Oat	Boot stage tissue	2.3	3.3	
	Kernels	0.7	1.8	
	Straw	1.2	2.3	
	Leaf lamina	<4	6.8–16.5	
Pasture grasses	Aboveground part at first cut	<5	5–12	>12
Potato	Aboveground part 75 d from planting	<8	11–20	>20
Red clover	Tops		7–16.4	
	Top of plant at bloom	<3	8–17	>17
	Top of plant at bloom		9.8–11.5	
Soybean	Upper fully mature trifoliate leaves before pod set	<4	10–30	>50
Spring wheat	Boot stage tissue	1.9	3.2	
	Kernels	0.8	2.3	
	Straw	2.4	3.9	
	Grain	2.5		
Timothy	Tops		5.7–11.7	
Tomato	Mature leaves from top of plant	<5	8–15	>15
	Mature leaves		3.1–12.3	
Winter wheat	Aboveground vegetative plant tissue		5–10	>10

† Scientific names are given in the Glossary.

careous soils, and highly leached, sandy soils. Copper toxicity most frequently occurs where Cu-containing fungicides have long been in use. Plants affected by Cu toxicity are slow growing and they frequently exhibit symptoms typical of Fe deficiency (Hewitt, 1953). In most instances, soil tests for Cu have been useful indicators of a potential Cu-toxicity problem (Baker, 1974).

Copper in plant tissue can be determined following organic matter destruction by either dry ashing or wet-acid digestion. The determination of Cu in the prepared digest can either be by AAS (Isaac, 1980), spark (Jones, 1976), ICP (Munter & Grande, 1981), or DC plasma (DeBolt, 1980) emission spectrometry.

D. Iron

The determination of the Fe status of the plant by assaying tissue for its Fe content is a highly questionable procedure (Chaney, 1984). Tissue Fe concentration may or may not be related to the appearance of Fe-deficiency symptoms. Frequently, chlorotic plants have an equal or higher total Fe concentration in their leaves than nonchlorotic plants. Plants grown in the open environment, no matter how clean the air, are usually coated with dust, although not always clearly visible. Unless the assayed tissue is carefully and thoroughly decontaminated, the determined, tissue, Fe concentration result is highly questionable in terms of defining the Fe status of plants (Wallace et al., 1982). If an Fe determination is made on plants growing in a very clean environment and the assayed tissue is removed at the time of initial Fe-deficiency symptom appearance, then a valid critical Fe concentration value can be determined. If these conditions are not met, then the determined Fe concentration will have little relevance to the Fe status of the plant.

Loop and Fink (1984) found that total plant Fe could be a valid indicator of the Fe status for oat and rape (*Brassica rapa* L.) when determined under the following conditions: (i) the tissue was carefully decontaminated; and (ii) the assayed tissue was removed from non-Fe-stressed plants that were under a high N fertilization regime growing on noncalcareous soils in a humid climate. Wallihan (1978) has found that the determination of total Fe in carefully washed leaves can be an effective means of determining the Fe status of plants. He assembled a list of interpretative concentration ranges as given in Table 13–12. Melsted et al. (1969) have listed critical Fe concentrations for four crops (Table 13–10).

Some researchers have suggested that a measure of the active Fe (generally the ferrous [Fe^{2+}] form is so considered) in plant tissue would be a better measure of the Fe status than total Fe. Various extraction procedures have been proposed as reviewed by Chaney (1984), but none have proven infalliable when universally applied. Katyal and Sharma (1980) used 1,10 o-phenanthroline (o-Ph) as an extractant for Fe in order to distinguish between chlorotic (suspected to be Fe deficient) and nonchlorotic plants. The author was unable to distinguish normal from Fe-deficient peach (*Prunus persica* L.) tree leaves using this method. Mehrotra et al. (1985) extracted chlorotic (Fe-deficient) and nonchlorotic (Fe-sufficient) corn leaf tissue using 14 different extractants. They found that the amount of Fe extracted by $1M$ $HC_2H_3O_2$ from chlorotic leaves was <20 mg kg^{-1}, whereas the normal green leaves had extractable levels >30 mg kg^{-1}. None of the other 13 extraction reagents, including 1,10 o-phenanthroline, produced as consistent results as the $1M$ $HC_2H_3O_2$ extractant.

Table 13-12. Leaf analysis data useful as reference concentrations for diagnosis of Fe status in various plants (Wallihan, 1978).

Plant species[†]	Tissue sampled	Age, stage, or date of sample	Measure of plant performance	Deficient	Sufficient
				mg Fe kg^{-1} in dry matter	
Acacia	Phyllodia	September	Leaf symptoms	50	90
Avocado	Leaves	Recently matured	Chlorosis	30–69	44–86
	Leaves	Recently matured	Chlorophyll concentrated	12–40	
Cotton	Leaf blades	60-d-old plants mature leaves	Plant growth	25–100	100–150
Cottonwood	Leaves	Mature	Leaf symptoms	33	90
	Stems		Leaf symptoms	11	24
Corn	Leaves (middle portion minus mid-rib)	Recently matured	Chlorophyll concentrated	24–100	
Eucalyptus	Leaves	September	Leaf symptoms	51	60
Geranium	Leaves	Middle or upper	Leaf symptoms	33–60	60
Lemon	Leaves	All	Leaf symptoms	20	77
	Stems			35	40
Locust, black	Leaves	Mature	Leaf symptoms	93	135
Orange	Leaves	Spring cycle-180 d	Fruit production	10–30	30–60
	Leaves	Recently matured	Leaf symptoms	11–36	40–52
Pea	Leaves	Recently matured	Chlorophyll concentrated	14–76	100
	Leaves	Recently matured	Plant growth	14–100	

† Scientific names are given in the Glossary.

Bar-Akiva et al. (1978) used peroxidase activity as a measure of plant Fe status, a procedure that was later modified by Bar-Akiva (1984). Chaney (1984) suggests spotting a suspected Fe-deficient leaf with an Fe chelate or $FeSO_4$ solution, and then, after 24 or 48 h, observing the change in leaf color (chlorotic to green) at the point of contact. All of these procedures are useful only in distinguishing between suspected Fe-deficient (chlorotic) and normal-appearing (nonchlorotic) plants, and therefore, are not methods for assessing the Fe status of a plant without symptoms. Therefore, the ability to assess the Fe status of plants by means of a plant analysis is still a highly questionable procedure.

Iron toxicity has also been observed, mainly in rice (Ottow et al., 1982). It results in a physiological problem called bronzing or yellowing, but it is not defined in terms of Fe concentration in the plant itself (Benckiser et al., 1984). Iron deficiency is also described in terms of its interaction with other elements (Brown & Jolley, 1986) as well as having a genetic component (Ross, 1986). There is much that is not known about Fe; for instance, how it is taken up by plants and utilized. The concepts of Fe plant nutrition have recently been reviewed by Vose (1982), Brown and Jolley (1986), and Wallace (1986).

The method of organic matter destruction can affect the Fe concentration that is determined. Wet-acid digestion of tissue frequently results in a higher Fe concentration than that obtained when tissue is dry ashed. The author believes this difference is due to the formation of insoluble Fe compounds (from unremoved dust as well as in the tissue) formed during the high-temperature (500 °C), dry-ashing process. During wet-acid digestion, most of the Fe in both dust and plant material is solubilized. Therefore, if the plant tissue is not decontaminated, Fe concentrations after dry ashing may be more representative of the plant status than those obtained by wet acid digestion of the tissue. The author has observed that the difference in Fe concentration between methods of organic matter destruction is frequently less for washed (decontaminated) tissue than for unwashed.

The Fe content in plant digests can be determined by colorimetric procedures (Chapman & Pratt, 1982), AAS (Isaac & Kerber, 1971), AC spark (Jones, 1976), ICP (Munter & Grande, 1981), or DC (DeBolt, 1980) emission spectrometry.

E. Manganese

Manganese deficiency occurs in many plant species when leaf concentrations are < 20 mg kg^{-1}. Melsted et al. (1969) determined that 15 mg kg^{-1} was the critical concentration in corn for the leaf opposite or below the ear leaf at tassel, 20 mg kg^{-1} for the youngest mature leaves and petioles after pod formation in soybean, and 30 mg kg^{-1} for the whole wheat plant at the boot stage in field studies (Table 13–10). Mascagni and Cox (1984) determined the critical Mn concentration in the corn ear leaf at initial tasseling to be 11 mg kg^{-1} in field experiments. Ohki et al. (1977) determined the critical Mn concentration in the upper, mature leaves of soybean at the mid-bloom stage (R2) to be only 10 mg kg^{-1}. In hydroponic studies Ohki

Table 13-13. Effect of sampling time on critical Mn concentration related to bean yield under field conditions (Ohki et al., 1977).

Sampling period after planting	Tissue sampled†	Growth stage	Critical Mn concentration
week			mg kg^{-1}
4	Blade two	Five-leaf	8
6	Blade two	Seven-leaf	7
9	Blade two	Mid-bloom	10
12	Blade one	Late bloom and early pod development	20
16	Blade one	Late pod-filling	22

† Most recently matured trifoliate leaf on the main plant axis. Blade numbers begin from the top with Leaf 1 as the youngest leaf.

(1984a) also found the critical deficiency concentration in Blade 1 of wheat to be only 13 mg Mn kg^{-1}. The larger differences among reported concentrations are probably due to the techniques used to grow the plants.

Ohki (1975b) established the Mn critical concentration in grain sorghum (*Sorghum vulgare* L.) to be 15 mg kg^{-1} for the third leaf blade, with the critical Mn cocnentrations for leaf Blades 4 and 5 as 32 and 60 mg kg^{-1}, respectively. However, he recommended that the 1st leaf blade be sampled at the boot stage, with its critical concentration being 10 mg kg^{-1}. Ohki (1984a) also found that, with wheat, the critical deficiency concentration for leaf Blades 1, 2, and 3 were 13, 39, and 83 mg kg^{-1}, respectively, and the critical deficiency concentration of the stem was 12 mg kg^{-1}. Ohki et al. (1977) found that the critical Mn concentration in soybean leaves increased with age (Table 13-13). These observations clearly established that leaf position and time of sampling can significantly affect the critical concentration. The sampling technique must be specific if the proper critical concentration is to be applied to the interpretation.

Ohki (1981) studied the relationship between plant Mn concentration and various physiological processes (respiration, photosynthesis, transpiration, etc.), and found that the critical Mn concentration differed slightly for each function. Similarly, Hannam et al. (1987) set the critical Mn concentration for the youngest emerged leaf blade of barley at 12 mg kg^{-1}, although slightly higher critical concentrations were found to be associated with various physiological functions in the plant. Both of these studies suggest that the critical concentration for appearance of visual deficiency symptoms and/or a 10% reduction in growth may not correspond to the same critical concentration, based on a change in some physiological function.

The sufficiency range for most plant species ranges between 20 and 500 mg kg^{-1}, although Mn-sensitive crops are affected when Mn leaf concentrations are >200 mg kg^{-1}. In general, species that are sensitive to Mn have a relatively narrow sufficiency range, usually <200 mg kg^{-1}. Manganese sufficiency ranges by plant species are listed in Table 13-14.

Manganese deficiency is frequently described in terms of various physiological disorders, such as grey speck in oats, yellow disease in spinach (*Spinacea oleracea*); etc. (Adriano, 1986). In addition, the Mn status of the

Table 13-14. Deficient, sufficient, and toxic Mn concentrations in plants (Adriano, 1986).

Plant species†	Plant part	Deficient	Sufficient	Toxic
		—— mg Mn kg^{-1} in dry matter ——		
Alfalfa	Tops			477–1083
	Tops		65–240	651–1970
Apple	Leaves	15	30	
	Leaves (interveinal bark necrosis)			>400
Apricot	Leaves	10	86–94	
Avocado	Leaves		1300	
	Leaves (Sept.)		366–655	
Banana	Leaves	<10		
Barley	Old leaves (moderate to severe necrosis)			305–410
	Tops		14–76	
Bean	Tops		40–940	1104–4201
Brussels sprout	Leaves plus petioles, youngest fully expanded		78–148	760–2035
Carrot	Tops			7100–9600
Corn	Ear leaf		116–214	
	Whole leaf		76–213	
Cotton	Tops		196–924	
	Leaves and petioles		58–238	
Cowpea	Tops (toxicity symptoms)			1224
Lespedeza	Tops			>570
Lima bean	Tops	32–68	207–1340	
Onion	Tops (maturity)		34	
Orange	Leaves (7-month bloom cycle; leaves from nonfruiting terminals	<19	20–90	>100
Oat	Tops		14–76	
	Tops	8–12	30–43	
Pea	Leaves			550
Peanut	Leaves		110–440	890–10900
Potato	Leaves	7	40	
Spinach	Plant	23	34–60	
Soybean	Uppermost fully developed leaf	<20		
	Leaves (30 d)	2–3	14–102	173–199
Sugar beet	Leaves	5–30	7–1700	1250–3020
Sweet clover	Tops (toxic symptoms)			321–754
Tobacco	Upper leaf	10	45	
Tomato	Leaves	5–6	70–398	
Turnip	Leaves		75	
Rice	Single leaf			4000–8000
Rye	Mature tops		10–50	
	Old leaves			1400
Ryegrass	Old leaves			800
Vetch	Tops			500–1117
Wheat	Plants	4–10	75	
	Tops		108–113	356–432
	Tops		181–621	396–2561
White clover	Tops			650

† Scientific names are given in the Glossary.

plant may also relate to its ability to resist disease infestations, such as take-all in wheat (Graham & Rovira, 1984). Manganese toxicity has also been described in terms of a physiological disorder, such as measles in apple (*Malus sylvestris* Mill.) (Shear & Foust, 1980), a symptom that appears before a significant yield reduction occurs. However, in potato (*Solanum tuberosum* L.), Mn toxicity produces stem streak necrosis and significantly reduces tuber yield (Berger & Gerloff, 1948). As with most of the other micronutrients, the critical toxicity level (CTL) is not as clearly defined for most crops. Ohki (1984a) found the CTL in wheat to be 380, 900, 1100, and 200 mg Mn kg^{-1}, respectively, for leaf Blades 1, 2, and 3, and the stem.

Gorsline et al. (1965) found that the Mn concentration in the corn plant tends to decrease with development, with Mn concentration increasing from lower to upper leaves. Manganese accumulates in the margins of corn leaves to a level about twice that in the leaf blade (Jones, 1970), with similar accumulation occurring in leaves of other plant species. Therefore, the time and plant part taken for a plant analysis must be specific in order to minimize the lack of homogeneity in Mn concentration among plant parts and with growth stage.

Manganese can be determined in plant ash and digests by either AAS (Isaac, 1980), AC spark (Jones, 1976), ICP (Munter & Grande, 1981), or DC plasma (DeBolt, 1980) emission spectrometry.

F. Molybdenum

Among the micronutrients, Mo is the least required for plants (Table 13-6), the critical concentration being ≤ 0.1 mg kg^{-1} for many crops (Anderson, 1956). However, the Mo requirement does vary considerably among various species, being the least (0.03 to 0.07 mg kg^{-1}) required micronutrient for some grain crops (barley, corn, oat, and wheat) and highest (>0.2 mg kg^{-1}) for most small seeded legumes (Anderson & Mortvedt, 1982). Crops like tomato (*Lycopersicon esculentum* Mill.), sugarbeet, squash (*Cucurbita* spp.), and spinach fall somewhere between, with requirements in the 0.1 to 0.2 mg kg^{-1} range. Cauliflower (*Brassica oleracea botrytis* L.), broccoli (*Brassica oleracea botrytis*), cabbage (*Brassica oleracea capitata* L.), lettuce (*Lactuca* sp.), tomato, and citrus in the tropics are considered good indicator crops for Mo (Adriano, 1986). Two physiological disorders due to Mo deficiency are whiptail in the *Brassica* family, and yellow spot disease in citrus. Critical Mo concentrations for four crops are given in Table 13–10 and sufficiency range data are provided for a number of crops in Table 13–15.

Molybdenum toxicity is not generally observed in the field, although it has been created in hydroponic studies. Toxicity has been obtained in barley when plant concentrations exceeded 135 mg kg^{-1}, whereas toxicities did not occur in some other plant species until Mo plant concentrations exceeded 500 mg kg^{-1} (Adriano, 1986). However, Mo concentrations in excess of 15 mg kg^{-1} in pasture plants can be toxic to cattle (Barshad, 1948) if the Cu concentration in the diet is not adjusted as well.

Table 13-15. Deficient and sufficient levels of Mo in plants (Adriano, 1986).

Plant species†	Plant part	Deficient	Sufficient
		mg Mo kg^{-1} in dry matter	
Alfalfa	Leaves at 10% bloom	0.26-0.38	0.34
	Whole plant at harvest	0.55-1.15	
	Top 15.2 cm of plant prior to bloom	<0.4	1.5
	Upper stem cutting at early flowering stage		0.5†
	Shortly before flowering (top ⅓ of plants)	<0.2	0.5-5.0
	Whole tops at 10% bloom		0.12-1.29
Barley	Blades 8 wk old		0.03-0.07
	Whole tops at boot stage		0.09-0.18
	Grain		0.26-0.32
Bean	Tops 8 wk old		0.4
Beet	Tops 8 wk old	0.05	0.62
Broccoli	Tops 8 wk old	0.04	
Brussels sprout	Whole plants when sprouts begin to form	<0.08	0.16
	Leaves	0.09	0.61
Cabbage	Leaves	0.09	0.42
	Aboveground plants at the first signs of curding	<0.26	0.68-1.49
Cauliflower	Whole plants before curding	<0.11	0.56
	Young leaves showing whiptail	0.07	
	Leaves	0.02-0.07	0.19-0.25
Corn	Roots	0.023-0.3	2.8-11.9
	Stems	0.013-0.11	1.4-7.0
	At tassel middle of the first leaf opposite and below the lower ear	<0.1	>0.2‡
Lettuce	Leaves	0.06	0.08-0.14
Pasture grass	First cut at first bloom		0.2-0.7
Red clover	Total aboveground plants at bloom	<0.15	0.3-1.59
	First cut at flowering		0.26
	Plant at 10% bloom	<0.22	
	Whole plants at the bud stage	0.1-0.2	0.45
Soybean	Plants 26-28 cm high	0.19	
Spinach	Leaves 8 wk old	0.1	1.61
	Whole tops at normal maturity		0.15-1.09
Sugar beet	Blades shortly after symptoms appear	0.01-0.15	0.2-2.0
	Fully developed stemless leaf; late June or early July	<0.1	0.2-2.0§
Temperate pasture legumes	Plant shoots		>0.1
Timothy	Whole tops at prebloom: out of the panicle	0.11	
Tobacco	Leaves 8 wk old		1.08
Tomato	Leaves 8 wk old	0.13	0.68

(continued on next page)

Table 13-15. Continued.

Plant species†	Plant part	Deficient	Sufficient
		mg Mo kg^{-1} in dry matter	
Tropical pasture legumes	Plant shoots		>0.02
Wheat	Whole tops; boot stage		0.09-0.18
	Grain		0.16-0.20
Winter wheat	Aboveground plants at ear emergence, 40 cm high		>0.3

† Scientific names are given in the Glossary.
‡ Considered critical.
§ Greater than 20 mg Mo kg^{-1} considered toxic.

Molybdenum is found to accumulate in the interveinal areas of leaves (Stout & Meagher, 1948). Jones (1970) found Mo to be higher in the corn leaf blade than in either the margin or midrib. Reisenauer (1956) found that Mo concentrations in alfalfa leaves were four times those in the stems. Similar differences in Mo concentrations among various plant parts have been observed by Barshad (1951) and Gupta and Lipsett (1981), with Mo levels in leaves being higher than in petioles, stems, seed, and fruit.

The determination of Mo in plant tissue at the critical concentration of 0.1 mg kg^{-1} is best performed by colorimetric procedures described by Chapman and Pratt (1982) and Williams (1979). An automated colorimetric method has been described by Eivazi et al. (1982), which is sensitive below the 0.1 mg kg^{-1} critical concentration. Molybenum can also be determined by flameless AAS (Wilson, 1979) and X-ray fluorescence (Kubota & Lazar, 1971). Because of relatively weak emission lines, Mo is difficult to determine at low concentrations (<0.5 mg kg^{-1}) in plant tissue by either AC spark (Jones, 1976) or ICP plasma (Munter & Grande, 1981) emission spectrometry.

G. Zinc

The critical Zn concentration in mature leaves for many crops is around 15 mg kg^{-1}, which is unique since, for the other micronutrients, critical concentrations vary considerably with species. Normally, a Zn deficiency is likely when leaf and/or plant contents are <20 mg kg^{-1} (Table 13-6). Much of the older (prior to 1957) literature on plant Zn concentrations associated with deficiency has been reviewed by Thorne (1957) and a brief review of the more current literature has been made by Adriano (1986).

Viets et al. (1954) described Zn deficiency symptoms and provided Zn plant concentrations for 12 crops growing on a Zn-deficient soil. Average leaf concentration for the 12 crops in the Zn-deficient area was 15.44 mg kg^{-1}, whereas average leaf Zn for those same crops growing in the Zn-sufficient area was 16.82 mg kg^{-1}. This illustrates another aspect of the relationship between Zn plant concentration and deficiency, showing that a very small change in concentration (usually only 1 or 2 mg kg^{-1}) can mean the difference between deficiency and sufficient. This is illustrated in Fig. 13-3 by the very steep slope of the left hand portion of the response curve.

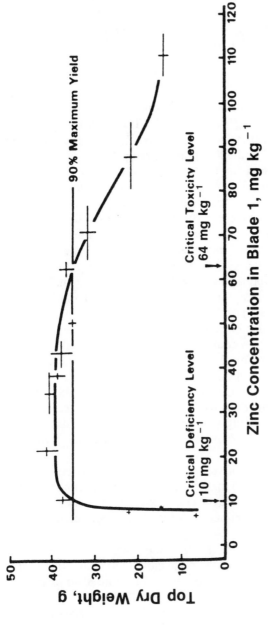

Fig. 13-3. Relationship between Zn content in Blade 1 of grain sorghum and top dry weight (Ohki, 1984b).

This observation is not unique to Zn alone, but relates to most of the other micronutrients as well.

In a hydroponic study, Ohki (1984b) determined the critical deficiency level (CDL) in sorghum to be 10, 10, 9, 13, and 24 mg kg^{-1} for Blades 1 (top), 2, 3, 4, and 5 (bottom), respectively. The critical toxicity levels (CTL) for the same blades were 64, 68, 80, 100, and 195 mg kg^{-1}, respectively. These CDL and CTL concentrations are similar to those set by Lockman (1972). Ohki (1984b) recommended sampling Blade 1 near the maximum vegetative growth stage (Stage 2) with 10 mg kg^{-1} as the CDL, whereas the CTL was 64 mg kg^{-1}. In a similar study with cotton (*Gossypium hirsutum* L.) Ohki (1975a) found the CDL and CTL concentrations for Blade 3 to be 11 and 200 mg kg^{-1}, respectively. There was no significant effect of time of sampling on these concentrations, although the CTLs for leaf Blades 1 and 5 were 110 and 300 mg kg^{-1}, respectively. No similar differences for CDLs were found for Blades 1, 3, and 5.

For lowland rice, Yoshida et al. (1973) established the following criteria for diagnosing Zn deficiency based on whole-shoot analysis: <10 mg kg^{-1}, definite deficiency; 10–15 mg kg^{-1}, very likely deficiency; 15–20 mg kg^{-1}, likely deficiency; and >20 mg kg^{-1}, unlikely deficiency.

As with most of the other micronutrients, the plant Zn concentration at which toxicity occurs is not well known. For many species, Zn leaf concentrations >100 mg kg^{-1} will result in either significant yield reductions and/or toxicity symptoms, symptoms not too dissimilar from Fe deficiency. Ruano et al. (1987) observed a 10% reduction in bush bean (*Phaseolus vulgaris*) growth when Zn concentrations in the roots, stems, and mature primary and trifoliate leaves contained >486, 242, 95, and 134 mg Zn kg^{-1}, respectively. However, for some plants, Zn levels must be >200 mg kg^{-1} before toxicity occurs, such as 485 mg kg^{-1} for tung (*Aleurites* spp.), 526 mg kg^{-1} for tomato, and 1700 mg kg^{-1} for oat (Adriano, 1986). MacLean (1974) observed yield reductions when Zn levels in corn, lettuce, and alfalfa reached 792, 523, and 702 mg kg^{-1}, respectively, and as did Keisling et al. (1977) for peanut (*Arachis hypogaea* L.) when leaf concentrations were >220 mg kg^{-1}.

The sensitivity of various cultivars to Zn toxicity has been investigated by White et al. (1979) for soybean, and by Safaya and Gupta (1979) for corn. Both studies emphasize the complexity of interactions observed between Zn and the uptake and utilization of P, Fe, and Mn for various cultivars of these two species.

There has been much research on the P-Zn interaction, a phenomenon that has produced a considerable number of conflicting results and opinions (Adriano, 1986). The use of the P/Zn ratio as an interpretative value has also been controversial.

Zinc can be determined in plant ash or digests by either AAS (Isaac, 1980), or by AC spark (Jones, 1976), ICP (Munter & Grande, 1981), or DC plasma (DeBolt, 1980) emission spectrometry.

III. INTERPRETATION OF THE RESULTS

Difficulties have been encountered in the use and interpretation of plant analyses, although the quantitative association between absorbed micronutrients and growth has been the subject of many studies. Questions raised at the 1959 Plant Analysis and Fertilizer Problems Colloquium (Reuther, 1961) regarding the limitations of the plant analysis technique are still applicable today, such as the reliability of interpretative data, utilization of ratio and balance concepts, hybrid influences, and changing physiological processes occurring at varying elemental concentrations. In addition, reliable interpretative data are lacking for Cl, for all micronutrients for use with most ornamental plants, for all plants during their early growth stages, and for identification of those concentrations considered excessive and/or toxic. It is also questionable whether the determination of the Fe concentration in a particular tissue can be used to establish the degree of Fe sufficiency (Chaney, 1984).

Initially, single concentration values, such as critical (Macy, 1936; Ulrich, 1952; Smith, 1962) or standard (Kenworthy, 1961) concentrations, were sought. But today, those who interpret plant analysis results for diagnostic purposes prefer working with the full range in concentration, from deficiency to excess. Such interpretative data are obtained from response curves such as that described by Prevot and Ollagnier (1961) (Fig. 13-2). Others have drawn similar response curves with varying slopes within the deficiency range, such as that obtained by Ohki (1984b) as shown in Fig. 13-3. The slope and general configuration shown in Fig. 13-2 are typical for dscribing the association between yield or plant response and macronutrient concentration in the leaf or plant, whereas Fig. 13-3 better typifies the association between yield and the micronutrient concentration.

The C-shape of the left hand portion of Fig. 13-2 has been coined the Steenbjerg Effect, and is the result of a combination of either elemental concentration or dilution, effects which have been discussed in some detail by Jarrell and Beverly (1981). Therefore, a misinterpretation of a plant analysis result can occur if the interpreter is not familiar with the interactive relationship between element concentration and dry matter accumulation.

The steep left-hand slope shown in Fig. 13-3 poses a significant sampling and analytical problem since a very small change in concentration results in a significant change in plant growth and/or yield. This is particularly true for Mn and Zn, where a concentration change of only 1 or 2 mg kg^{-1} in the leaf tissue can define the difference between deficiency and sufficiency (Viets et al., 1954; Ohki, 1975b, 1981).

In an ever-increasing number of instances, identifying at what concentration a micronutrient becomes excessive or toxic is becoming of equal importance as the determination of that concentration considered deficient. Unfortunately, very little detailed information has been obtained on the full range of response from deficiency to toxicity as has been done for sorghum with Mn (Ohki, 1975b) and Zn (Ohki, 1984b), and for soybean with Mn (Ohki, 1981) and Zn (Ohki, 1978).

A critical value is that concentration below which deficiency occurs. Being a single value, it is difficult to use when interpreting a plant analysis result if the assay concentration is considerably higher or lower than the critical value. Ulrich and Hill (1973) have suggested the interpretative use of the transition zone, the range in elemental concentration that exists between deficiency and sufficiency. Similarily, Dow and Roberts (1982) have proposed using critical nutrient ranges (CNR), which is the same as the Ulrich and Hill (1973) transition zone concept. The concentration range that lies within the transition zone is the range in which a 0 to 10% reduction in yield occurs, with the critical value at the 10% yield reduction point. Ohki (1987) has used this same concept to define critical nutrient levels, the point at which a 10% yield reduction occurs, as the CDL, and at the point of toxicity, as the CTL. Since the terminology proposed is new, it has yet to be accepted.

Diagnosing a plant analysis result based on either critical or standard values, or sufficiency ranges requires that the elemental plant part and time of sampling be identical for the diagnosed tissue as that for the source of the interpretative data. Because micronutrient concentrations in the plant can vary depending on plant part, stage of growth, genotype, and geographical location, these traditional techniques of plant analysis interpretation have their limitations.

Now there is a different and fairly new concept of plant analysis interpretation called the Diagnosis and Recommendation Integrated System (DRIS), which was proposed by Beaufils (1971, 1973). The DRIS technique of interpretation is based on a comparison of calculated elemental ratio indices with established norms. The DRIS approach was designed to: (i) provide a valid diagnosis irrespective of plant age or tissue origin; (ii) rank nutrients in their limiting order; and (iii) stress the importance of nutrient balance.

DRIS is based on the principle of elemental interrelationships by determining, in descending order, those elements from the most to the least limiting. Beaufils (1973) used the survey approach by using the world's published literature to obtain a plot of elemental leaf concentration versus yield, a distribution that is normally skewed. In order to normalize the distribution curve, the yield component is divided into low- and high-yield groups. Walworth et al. (1986) suggested that the data bank for determining DRIS norms have at least several thousand entries, be randomly selected, and that at least 10% of the population be in the high-yield subgroup. It is also important that the cutoff value used to divide the low- from the high-yielding subgroups be such that the high-yield data subgroup remains normally distributed. Selecting the elemental concentration mean, the ratio and product of elemental means are determined. The ratio or product selected for calculating DRIS norms is the one with the largest variance. This maximizes the diagnostic sensitivity.

Although the DRIS method has been applied primarily for interpretation based on the major elements, DRIS indices have been generated that include B, Cu, Fe, Mn, and Zn. The emphasis on the major elements is based on the fact that the database for the major elements is considerably larger than that for the micronutrients. Therefore, the reliability of a micronutrient DRIS index would be less than that for a major element.

The DRIS concept of plant analysis interpretation has been compared to the more traditional techniques based primarily on sufficiency range interpretative values in established plant analysis programs for corn (Kelling & Schulte, 1986), sweet cherry (*Prunus avium*) (Davee et al., 1986), and hazelnut (*Corylus avellana*) (Alkoshab et al., 1988). In these studies, it was found that a DRIS-based interpretation was no better than that based on sufficiency range values. All agreed that both methods of interpretation have their advantages, but they seem to work best when used together.

Jones and Bowen (1981) compared a DRIS interpretation with that obtained by means of a Crop Log diagnosis of sugarcane (*Saccharum officinarum* L.) tissue. They found that the DRIS approach produced slightly more accurate diagnoses of nutrient deficiencies than the Crop Log approach. This is in stark contrast to the remark that appears in Reuter and Robinson's book (1986) that "in view of the apparent lack of physiological bases for a number of the key ratios and balances it (DRIS) uses, the current form of DRIS cannot be recommended for use in Australia."

It seems that DRIS works best at the extremes of the sufficiency range by pinpointing that element or balance of elements that is insufficient, and is the least useful when plant nutrient levels are well within the sufficiency range. In most studies that have been designed to test the DRIS concept, users have found that DRIS is not entirely independent of either location or time of sampling, and that DRIS diagnosis can frequently be misleading and incorrect.

It is doubtful that the DRIS method of plant analysis interpretation will ever be exclusively used in lieu of the more traditional critical value or sufficiency range techniques. In addition to factors discussed earlier in this chapter, it is also partially due to the lack of an adequate quantity of micronutrient concentration data in the literature needed to calculate DRIS norms, as well as the questionable quality of a significant portion of published micronutrient concentrations. In addition, there are only 16 crop species with established DRIS norms as shown in Table 13-16 (Walworth & Sumner, 1978 and author).

None of the various interpretative procedures discussed are infallible and they are best used when in the hands of the most experienced. The interpretation of a plant analysis is still an art in which the interpreter must use all the resources available, including a soil test result, to determine the nutrient element status of the plant in order to advise on treatments to correct uncovered insufficiencies.

IV. PRACTICAL APPLICATION AND FUTURE

The adaptation of the plant analysis technique to solve micronutrient problems in the field is considerably underutilized by farmers. However, the

Table 13-16. Sources for published DRIS norms (Walworth & Sumner, 1987 and author).

Plant species†	Source
Alfalfa	Kelling et al. (1983); Walworth et al. (1986)
Corn	Sumner (1981); Escano et al. (1981); Elwali et al. (1985)
Citrus	Beverly et al. (1984); Sumner (1985); Beverly (1987)
Hazelnut	Alkoshab et al. (1988)
Oat	Chojnacki (1984)
Peach	Sumner (1985)
Pineapple	Langenegger & Smith (1978)
Poplar	Leech & Kim (1981)
Potato	Meldal-Johnsen & Sumner (1980)
Rubber	Beaufils (1957)
Soybean	Sumner (1977); Hallmark et al. (1984, 1985)
Sugarcane	Beaufils & Sumner (1976); Elwali & Gascho (1983, 1984)
Sunflower	Grove & Sumner (1982)
Sweet cherry	Davee et al. (1986)
Tea	Lee (1980)
Wheat	Sumner (1981)

† Scientific names are given in the Glossary.

numbers of plant tissue samples being assayed by plant analysis laboratories in the USA for farmers, has been increasing from 200 000 in the early 1970s to 450 000 in the late 1980s. These numbers compare with the three to four million soil samples assayed each year for farmers by many of these same laboratories. Significant advances have been made in the methods for assaying plant tissue for its micronutrient content, although some laboratories have yet to switch from the more traditional wet chemistry, and flame and atomic absorption spectrophotometry procedures to plasma emission spectrometry, which is a faster and more efficient analytical technique.

Cost and lack of understanding of the value of a plant analysis result may be the major factors that still limit wider use of the plant analysis technique for diagnostic and monitoring purposes. Farmers need to be made more fully aware of the value by monitoring the nutrient element status of their soils and crops by means of soil tests and plant analyses, which provides a means for ensuring micronutrient sufficiency.

Although considerable strides have been made to expand the reserve of plant analysis interpretative data, better, more reliable, and more specific data are still needed for most of the micronutrients. How best to determine the Fe status of a plant is still an unanswered question. For all micronutrients, basing an interpretation on changing physiological function may eventually be a more reliable criteria for evaluation than one based on either a 10% loss in yield, or the appearance of visual deficiency and/or toxicity symptoms.

There is growing interest in the effect of micronutrient content of plants and food products directly consumed from plants on animal and human health. Therefore, the purpose of applying micronutrients in the future may be to influence their concentration for consumption considerations rather than for the health of the plant itself.

REFERENCES

Adler, P.R., and G. Wilcox. 1985. Rapid perchloric acid methods for analysis of major elements in plant tissue. Commun. Soil Sci. Plant Anal. 16:1153–1163.

Adriano, D. 1986. Trace elements in the terrestrial environment. Springer-Verlag New York, New York.

Aldehnoff, G.A., and L.A. Ernest. 1983. Quality assurance program at a municipal wastewater treatment plant laboratory. J. Water Pollut. Control Fed. 55:1132–1137.

Alexander, G.V. 1965. An X-ray fluorescence method for the determination of calcium, potassium, chlorine, sulfur, and phosphorus in biological tissues. Anal. Chem. 37:1671–1674.

Alkoshab, O., T.L. Righetti, and A.R. Dixon. 1988. Evaluation of DRIS for judging the nutritional status of Hazelnuts. J. Am. Soc. Hortic. Sci. 113:643–647.

Alvarez, R. 1980. NBS plant tissue standard reference materials. J. Assoc. Off. Anal. Chem. 63:806–808.

American Council Independent Laboratories (ACIL). 1976. Quality control systems-requirements for a testing laboratory. American Council Independent Laboratories, Washington, DC.

Anderson, A.J. 1956. Molybdenum as a fertilizer. Adv. Agron. 8:164–202.

Anderson, O.E., and J.J. Mortvedt. 1982. Soybeans: Diagnosis and correction of manganese and molybdenum problems. Southern Coop. Ser. Bull. 281, Univ. of Georgia, Athens, GA.

Anonymous. 1979. Nonclinical laboratory studies, good laboratory practices. Register, Part II, vol. 43, No. 247. Dep. Health Educ. Welfare, U.S. Food and Drug Admin., Washington, DC.

Arkley, T.H., D.N. Munns, and C.M. Johnson. 1970. Preparation of plant tissues for micronutrient analysis. Removal of dust and spray materials. J. Agric. Food Chem. 8:318–321.

Arnon, D.I., and P.R. Stout. 1939. The essentiality of certain elements in minute quantity for plants with special reference to copper. Plant Physiol. 14:371–375.

Baker, D.E. 1974. Copper: Soil, water, plant relationships. Proc. Fed. Am. Exp. Biol. 33:1188–1193.

Baker, D.E., G.W. Gorsline, C.G. Smith, W.I. Thomas, W.E. Grube, and J.L. Ragland. 1964. Technique for rapid analyses of corn leaves for eleven elements. Agron. J. 56:133–136.

Baker, D.E., and N.H. Suhr. 1982. Atomic absorption and flame emission spectrometry. p. 13–28. In A.L. Page et al. (ed.) Methods of soil analysis, Part 2. 2nd ed. Agron. Monogr. 9. ASA and SSSA, Madison, WI.

Bar-Akiva, A. 1984. Substitutes for benzidine as H-donors in the peroxidase assay for rapid diagnosis of iron in plants. Commun. Soil Sci. Plant Anal. 15:929–934.

Bar-Akiva, A.,D.N. Maynard, and J.E. English. 1978. A rapid tissue test for diagnosis of iron deficiencies in vegetable crops. Hortic. Sci. 13:284–285.

Barshad, I. 1948. Molybdenum content of pasture plants in relation to toxicity to cattle. Soil Sci. 66:187–195.

Barshad, I. 1951. Factors affecting the molybdenum content of pasture plants. I. Nature of soil molybdenum, growth of plants, and soil pH. Soil Sci. 71:297–313.

Beaufils, E.R. 1957. Research for rational exploitation of Hevea using a physiological diagnosis based on the mineral analysis of various parts of plants. Fertilite 3:27–38.

Beaufils, E.R. 1971. Physiological diagnosis—A guide for improving maize production based on principles developed for rubber trees. Fert. Soc. S. Agr. J. 1:1–28.

Beaufils, E.R. 1973. Diagnosis and recommendation integrated system (DRIS). Soil Sci. Bull. 1, Univ. of Natal, Natal, South Africa.

Beaufils, E.R., and M.E. Sumner. 1976. Application of DRIS approach for calibrating soil, plant yield and plant quality factors of sugarcane. Proc. S. Agr. Sugar Technol. Assoc. 50:118–124.

Benckiser, G., J.C.G. Ottow, I. Watanabe, and S. Santiago. 1984. The mechanism of excessive iron-uptake (iron toxicity) of wetland rice. J. Plant Nutr. 7:177–185.

Berger, K.C., and E. Truog. 1940. Boron deficiencies as revealed by plant and soil tests. J. Am. Soc. Agron. 32:297–301.

Berger, K.C., and G.C. Gerloff. 1948. Manganese toxicity of potatoes in relation to strong soil acidity. Soil Sci. Soc. Am. Proc. 12:310–314.

Berman, G.A. 1980. Testing laboratory performance: Evaluation and accreditation. Natl. Bureau of Standards, Washington, DC.

Beverly, R.D. 1984. Modified DRIS method for simplified nutrient diagnosis of 'Valencia' oranges. J. Plant Nutr. 10:1401–1408.

Beverly, R.B. 1987. Modified DRIS method for simplified nutrient diagnosis of 'Valencia' oranges. J. Plant Nutr. 10:1401–1408.

Beverly, R.B., J.C. Stark, J.C. Ojala, and T.W. Embleton. 1984. Nutrient diagnosis of 'Valencia' oranges by DRIS. J. Am. Soc. Hortic. Sci. 109:649–654.

Bhan, K.C., A. Wallace, and D.R. Hunt. 1959. Some mineral losses from leaves by leaching. Proc. Am. Soc. Hortic. Sci. 73:289–293.

Bock, R. 1978. Handbook of decomposition methods in analytical chemistry. Int. Textbook Co., Glasgow, Scotland.

Booth, R.L. 1979. Handbook for analytical quality control in water and wastewater laboratories. Analytical Quality Control Lab., Natl. Environ. Res. Ctr., Cincinnati, OH.

Bowen, H.J.M. 1967. Comparative elemental analyses of a standard plant material. Analyst 92:124–131.

Brech, F. 1968. Comparison of optical emission and atomic absorption methods for the analysis of plant tissue. J. Assoc. Off. Anal. Chem. 51:132–136.

Brown, J.C., and V.D. Jolley. 1986. An evaluation of concepts related to iron-deficiency chlorosis. J. Plant Nutr. 9:175–186.

Broyer, T.C., A.B. Carlton, C.M. Johnson, and P.R. Stout. 1954. Chlorine—a micronutrient element for higher plants. Plant Physiol. 29:526–532.

Carpenter, P.N. 1964. Spectrographic analysis of plant tissue. Maine Agric. Exp. Stn. Misc. Publ. 666.

Carpenter, P.N., A. Ellis, H.E. Young, and T.E. Byther. 1968. A critical evaluation of results from spectrographic analysis of plant tissue. Maine Agric. Exp. Stn. Tech. Bull. 30.

Chaney, R.L. 1984. Diagnostic practices to identify iron deficiency in higher plants. J. Plant Nutr. 7:47–67.

Chaplin, M.H., and A.R. Dixon. 1974. A method for analysis of plant tissue by direct reading emission spectroscopy. Appl. Spectrosc. 28:5–8.

Chapman, H.D. 1964. Foliar sampling for determining the nutrient status of crops. World Crops 16:35–46.

Chapman, H.D. 1966. Diagnostic criteria for plants and soils. Div. Agric. Sci., Univ. California, Riverside.

Chapman, H.D., and P.F. Pratt. 1982. Methods of analysis for soils, plants, and waters. Priced Publ. 4034. Div. Agric. Sci., Univ. California, Berkeley.

Cherney, J.H., and D.L. Robinson. 1983. A comparison of plant digestion methods for identifying soil contamination of plant tissue by Ti analysis. Agron. J. 75:145–147.

Chloak, J., and R.V. Story. 1941. Spectrochemical determination of trace metals in biological material. J. Opt. Soc. Am. 31:730–738.

Chojnacki, A. 1984. The evaluation of the nutritional status of oats by the DRIS method. Proc. Int. Colloq. Opt. Plant Nutr., 6th 1:139–148.

Christensen, R.E., R.M. Beckman, and J.J. Birdsall. 1968. Some mineral elements of commercial spices and herbs as determined by direct reading emission spectroscopy. J. Assoc. Off. Anal. Chem. 51:1003–1010.

Christian, G.D., and F.J. Feldman. 1970. Atomic absorption spectroscopy applications in agriculture, biology and medicine. Wiley-Interscience, New York.

Colonna, J.P. 1970. The mineral diet of excelsior coffee plants. Natural variability of the mineral foliar composition on a homogeneous plantation. Cashiers Off. Res. Sci. Tech. Outre-Mer Ser. Biol. 13:67–80.

Conner, J., and S.T. Bass. 1959. The determination of suitable circuit parameters for a high voltage spark discharge source in the spectrochemical analysis of plant materials. Appl. Spectrosc. 16:150–155.

Dalquist, R.L., and J.W. Knoll. 1978. Inductively coupled plasma emission spectroscopy; analysis of biological materials and soil for major, trace, and ultra-trace elements. Appl. Spectrosc. 32:1–30.

Davee, D.E., T.L. Righetti, E. Fallahi, and S. Robbins. 1986. An evaluation of the DRIS approach for identifying mineral limitations on yield in 'Napolean' sweet cherry. J. Am. Soc. Hortic. Sci. 111:988–993.

DeBolt, D.C. 1980. Multielement emission spectroscopic analysis of plant tissue using DC agron plasma source. J. Assoc. Off. Anal. Chem. 63:802–805.

Dow, A.T., and S. Roberts. 1982. Proposal: Critical nutrient ranges for crop diagnoses. Agron. J. 74:401–403.

Dux, J.P. 1986. Handbook of quality assurance for the analytical chemistry laboratory. van Nostrand Reinhold Co., New York.

Eaton, F.M. 1966. Chlorine. p. 98–138. *In* C.D. Chapman (ed.) Diagnostic criteria for plants and soils. Div. Agric. Sci., Univ. California, Riverside, CA.

Eivazi, F., J.L. Sims, and J. Crutchfield. 1982. Determination of molybdenum in plant materials using a rapid, automated method. Commun. Soil Sci. Plant Anal. 13:135–150.

Elwali, A.M.O., and G.J. Gascho. 1983. Sugarcane response to P, K and DRIS corrective treatments on Florida Histosols. Agron. J. 75:79–83.

Elwali, A.M.O., and G.J. Gascho. 1984. Soil testing, foliar analysis, and DRIS as guides for sugarcane fertilization. Agron. J. 76:466–470.

Elwali, A.M.O., G.J. Gascho, and M.E. Sumner. 1985. Sufficiency levels and DRIS norms for 11 nutrients in corn. Agron. J. 77:506–508.

Epstein, E. 1972. Mineral nutrition of plant: Principles and perspectives. John Wiley and Sons, New York.

Escano, C.R., C.A. Jones, and G. Uehara. 1981. Nutrient diagnosis in corn grown on Hydric Dystrandepts: II. Comparison of two systems of tissue diagnosis. Soil Sci. Soc. Am. J. 45:1140–1144.

Feldman, C. 1961. Evaporation of boron from acid solutions and residues. Anal. Chem. 33:1916–1920.

Fischbeck, R.D. 1980. Good laboratory practices. Am. Lab. 12:125–130.

Fixen, P.E., G.W. Buchenau, R.H. Gelderman, T.E. Schumacher, J.R. Gerwing, F.A. Cholick, and B.G. Farber. 1986a. Influence of soil and applied chloride on several wheat parameters. Agron. J. 78:736–740.

Fixen, P.E., R.H. Gelderman, J. Gerwing, and F.A. Cholick. 1986b. Response of spring wheat, barley and oats to chloride in potassium chloride fertilizers. Agron. J. 78:664–668.

Gabriels, R., and A. Cottenie. 1976. Direct reading emission spectrometric determination of major and trace elements in plants, soils and soil extracts. Lab. Pract. 25:835–838.

Garfield, F.M. 1984. Quality assurance principles for analytical laboratories. Assoc. Off. Anal. Chem., Arlington, VA.

Gestring, W.D., and P.N. Soltanpour. 1981. Evaluation of wet and dry digestion methods for boron determination in plant samples by ICP-AES. Commun. Soil Sci. Plant Anal. 12:743–753.

Goodall, D.W., and F.G. Gregory. 1947. Chemical composition of plants as an index to their nutritional status. Tech. Comm. 17. Imperial Bureau Hortic. and Plantation Crops, East Malling, Kent, England.

Gorsline, G.W., D.E. Baker, and W.I. Thomas. 1965. Accumulation of eleven elements by field corn (*Zea mays* L.). Pennsylvania State Exp. Stn. Bull. 725.

Gorsline, G.W., W.I. Thomas, and D.E. Baker. 1968. Major gene inheritance of Sr-Ca, Mg, K, P, Zn, Cu, B, Al-Fe, and Mn concentration in corn (*Zea mays* L.). Pennsylvania State Exp. Stn. Bull. 746.

Gorsuch, T.T. 1970. Destruction of organic matter. Int. Ser. Monogr. Anal. Chem., Vol. 39. Perganon Press, New York.

Gorsuch, T.T. 1976. Dissolution of organic matter. p. 491–508. *In* P.D. LaFluer (ed.) Accuracy in trace analysis: Sampling, sample handling, analysis, Vol. 1. Natl. Bureau of Standards Spec. Publ. 422, Washington, DC.

Graham, R.D. 1972. Vacuum attachment for grinding mills. Commun. Soil Sci. Plant Anal. 3:167–173.

Graham, R.D., and A.D. Rovira. 1984. A role for manganese in the resistance of wheat to take-all. Plant Soil 84:441–444.

Grant, C.L., and D.J. Macnaughlain, Jr. 1968. Preparation of biological samples and standards for spectrochemical analysis. Appl. Spectrosc. Abstr. 22(4):365.

Greweling, T. 1976. Chemical analysis of plant tissue. Search Agron. 6. No. 8, Cornell Univ., Ithaca, NY.

Grove, J.H., and M.E. Sumner. 1982. Yield and leaf composition of sunflower in relation to N, P, K and lime treatments. Fert. Res. 3:367–378.

Grunau, J.A., and J.M. Swiader. 1986. Application of ion chromatography to anion analysis in vegetable leaf extracts. Commun. Soil Sci. Plant Anal. 17:321–335.

Gupta, U.C. 1979. Boron nutrition of crops. Adv. Agron. 31:273–307.

Gupta, U.C., and J. Lipsett. 1981. Molybdenum in soils, plants, and animals. Adv. Agron. 34:73–117.

Hallmark, W.B., J.F. Adams, and H.F. Morris. 1984. Detection of zinc deficiency in soybeans by the Diagnosis and Recommendation Integrated System. J. Fert. Issues 1:104–109.

Hallmark, W.B., J.F. Adams, and H.F. Morris. 1985. The use of plant analysis to diagnose nutrients limiting soybean yield for the subsequent year. J. Fert. Issues 2:66–73.

Halvin, J.L., and P.N. Soltanpour. 1980. A nitric acid plant tissue digest method for use with inductively-coupled plasma spectrometry. Commun. Soil Sci. Plant Anal. 11:969–980.

Hannam, R.J., J.L. Riggs, and R.D. Graham. 1987. The critical concentrations of manganese in barley. J. Plant Nutr. 10:2039–2048.

Hislop, J.S. 1980. Choice of the analytical method. p. 747–767. In P. Bratter and P. Schramel (ed.) Trace element analytical chemistry in medicine and biology. DeGruyter, Berlin.

Hood, S.L., R.Q. Parks, and C. Hurwitz. 1944. Mineral contamination resulting from grinding plant samples. Ind. Eng. Chem. 16:202–205.

Horwitz, W. 1980. Official methods of analysis of the Association of Official Analytical Chemists. 13th ed. Assoc. Off. Anal. Chem., Arlington, VA.

Horwitz, W. 1982. Evaluation of analytical methods used for regulation of foods and drugs. Anal. Chem. 54:67A–76A.

Isaac, R.A. 1980. Atomic absorption methods for analysis of soil extracts and plant tissue digests. J. Assoc. Off. Anal. Chem. 63:788–796.

Isaac, R.A., and J.B. Jones, Jr. 1972. Effects of various drying temperatures on the determination of 13 nutrient elements in five plant tissues. Commun. Soil Sci. Plant Anal. 3:261–269.

Isaac, R.A., and J.D. Kerber. 1971. Atomic absorption and flame photometry: Techniques and uses in soil, plant, and water analysis. p. 17–37. In L.M. Walsh (ed.) Instrumental methods for analysis of soils and plant tissue. SSSA, Madison, WI.

Islam, A.K.M.S., G.L. Kerven, and C.J. Asher. 1983. Chloride determination in plant tissue using solid state chloride ion specific electrode. Commun. Soil Sci. Plant Anal. 14:645–653.

Jackson, M.L. 1958. Soil chemical analysis. Prentice-Hall, Inc., Englewood Cliffs, NJ.

Jackson, T.L. 1986. Chloride and crop production. Spec. Bull. 2. Potash and Phosphate Inst., Atlanta, GA.

Jarrell, W.M., and R.B. Beverly. 1981. The dilution effect in plant nutrition studies. Adv. Agron. 34:197–224.

Johnson, C.M., and A. Ulrich. 1959. II. Analytical methods used in plant analysis. California Agric. Exp. Stn. Bull. 766.

Jones, C.A. 1981. Proposed modification of the Diagnosis and Recommendation Integrated System (DRIS) for interpreting plant analyses. Commun. Soil Sci. Plant Anal. 12:785–794.

Jones, C.A., and J.E. Bowen. 1981. Comparative DRIS and crop log diagnosis of sugarcane tissue. Agron. J. 73:941–944.

Jones, J.B., Jr. 1963. Effect of drying on ion accumulation in corn leaf margins. Agron. J. 55:579–580.

Jones, J.B., Jr. 1969. Elemental analysis of plant tissue by several laboratories. J. Assoc. Off. Anal. Chem. 59:900–903.

Jones, J.B., Jr. 1970. Distribution of 15 elements in corn leaves. Commun. Soil Sci. Plant Anal. 1:27–34.

Jones, J.B., Jr. 1976. Elemental analysis of biological substances by direct reading spark emission spectroscopy. Am. Lab. 8:15–18.

Jones, J.B., Jr. 1977. Elemental analysis of soil extracts and plant tissue ash by plasma emission spectroscopy. Commun. Soil Sci. Plant Anal. 8:345–365.

Jones, J.B., Jr. 1983. Soil test works when used right, part II. Solutions (St. Louis) 27(3):61–70.

Jones, J.B., Jr. 1985. Recent survey of number of soil and plant tissue samples tested for growers in the United States. In J.R. Brown (ed.) Tenth soil-plant analysts workshop, St. Louis, MO. 3-4 Nov. Counc. Soil Test. Plant Anal., Athens, GA.

Jones, J.B., Jr., and R.A. Isaac. 1969. Comparative elemental analyses of plant tissue by spark emission and atomic absorption spectroscopy. Agron. J. 61:393–394.

Jones, J.B., Jr., R.L. Large, D.B. Pfeiderer, and H.S. Klosky. 1971. How to properly sample for a plant analysis. Crops Soils 23(8):15–18.

Jones, J.B., Jr., and M.H. Warner. 1969. Analysis of plant-ash solutions by spark-emission spectroscopy. p. 152–160. In E.L. Grove and H.D. Perkins (ed.) Developments in applied spectroscopy. Vol. 7A. Plenum Press, New York.

Kabata-Pendias, A., and H. Pendias. 1984. Trace elements in soils and plants. CRC Press, Boca Raton, FL.

Kalbasi, M., and M.A. Tabatabai. 1985. Simultaneous determination of nitrate, chloride, sulfate, and phosphate in plant materials by ion chromatography. Commun. Soil Sci. Plant Anal. 16:787–800.

Katyal, J.C., and B.D. Sharma. 1980. A new technique of plant analysis to resolve iron chlorosis. Plant Soil 55:105–119.

Keisling, T.C., D.A. Lauer, M.E. Walker, and R.J. Henning. 1977. Visual, tissue, and soil factors associated with Zn toxicity of peanuts. Agron. J. 69:765–769.

Kelling, K.A., and E.E. Schultee. 1986. DRIS as a part of a routine plant analysis program. J. Fert. Issues 3:107–112.

Kelling, K.A., E.E. Shulte, and T. Kaehler. 1983. Use of DRIS in routine plant analysis. Proc. Wisconsin Agric. Lime Pest Mgmt. Conf. 22:239–243.

Kenworthy, A.L. 1961. Interpreting the balance of nutrient elements in leaves of fruit trees. p. 28–34. *In* W. Reuther (ed.) Plant analysis and fertilizer problems. Publ. 8, Am. Inst. Biol. Sci., Washington, DC.

Kenworthy, A.L., E.J. Miller, and W.T. Mathis. 1956. Nutrient-element analysis of fruit tree leaf samples by several laboratories. Proc. Am. Soc. Hortic. Sci. 67:16–21.

Keren, R., and F.T. Bingham. 1985. Boron in water, soils, and plants. p. 229–276. *In* B.A. Stewart (ed.) Adv. Soil Sci. Vol. 1. Springer-Verlag New York, New York.

Knapp, G. 1985. Sample preparation techniques—an important part in trace element analysis for environmental research and monitoring. Int. J. Environ. Anal. Chem. 22:71–83.

Kohl, H.C., and J.J. Oertli. 1961. Distribution of boron in leaves. Plant Physiol. 36:420–424.

Krieg, D.R., and D. Sung. 1977. Interferences in chloride determinations using the specific ion electrode. Commun. Soil Sci. Plant Anal. 8:109–114.

Kubota, J., and V.A. Lazar. 1971. X-ray emission spectrograph: Techniques and uses for plant and soil studies. p. 67–83. *In* L.M. Walsh (ed.) Instrumental methods for analysis of soils and plant tissue. SSSA, Madison, WI.

Labanauskas, C.K. 1968. Washing citrus leaves for leaf analysis. Calif. Agric. 22:12–14.

LaCroix, R.L., D.R. Keeney, and L.M. Walsh. 1970. Potentiometric titration of chloride in plant tissue extracts using the chloride ion electrode. Commun. Soil Sci. Plant Anal. 1:1–6.

Langeneger, W., and B.L. Smith. 1978. An evaluation of the DRIS system as applied to pineapple leaf analysis. p. 263–273. *In* Proc. 8th Int. Colloq. Plant Anal. Fertil. Prob., Aukland, New Zealand. 28 Aug.-1 Sept. DSIR Info. Ser. 134, New Zealand Dep. Sci. Ind. Res., Willington, New Zealand.

Lee, P.F.W. 1980. Initial observations on the application of the DRIS approach to tea (*Camellia sinensis* L.): Foliar analysis results in South Africa. Crop Prod. 9:207–209.

Leech, R.H., and Y.T. Kim. 1981. Foliar analysis and DRIS as a guide to fertilizer amendments in poplar plantations. For. Chron. 17–21.

Lockman, R.B. 1970. Plant sample analysis as affected by sample decomposition prior to laboratory processing. Commun. Soil Sci. Plant Anal. 1:13–19.

Lockman, R.B. 1972. Mineral composition of grain plant samples. III. Suggested nutrient sufficiency limits at various stages of growth. Commun. Soil Sci. Plant Anal. 3:295–303.

Lohse, G. 1982. Micro analytical Azomethine-H method for boron determination in plant tissue. Commun. Soil Sci. Plant Anal. 13:127–134.

Loop, E.A., and A. Fink. 1984. Total iron as a useful index of the Fe-status of crops. J. Plant Nutr. 7:69–79.

MacLean, A.J. 1974. Effect of soil properties and admendments on the availability of zinc in soils. Can. J. Soil Sci. 54:369–378.

Martin-Prevel, P., J. Gagnard, and P. Gautier. 1987. Plant analysis as a guide to the nutrient requirements of temperate and tropical crops. Lavosier Publ., New York.

Macy, P. 1936. The quantitative mineral nutrient requirements of plants. Plant Physiol. 11:749–764.

Mascagni, H.J., Jr., and F.R. Cox. 1984. Diagnosis and correction of manganese deficiency in corn. Commun. Soil Sci. Plant Anal. 15:1323–1333.

Mathis, W.T. 1953. Spectrochemical analysis of plant material using spark excitation. Anal. Chem. 25:943–950.

McLaughlin, R.D., M.S. Hunt, D.L. Murphy, and C.R. Chen. 1979. Instrumentation in environmental monitoring. p. 224–245. *In* D.L. Hemphill (ed.) Trace elements in environmental health—XIII. Univ. Missouri, Columbia.

Mehrotra, S.C., C.P. Sharma, and S.C. Agarwala. 1985. A search for extractants to evaluate the iron status of plants. Soil Sci. Plant Nutr. 31:155–162.

Meldal-Johnson, A., and M.E. Sumner. 1980. Foliar diagnostic norms for potatoes. J. Plant Nutr. 2:569–576.

Melsted, S.W., H.L. Motto, and T.R. Peck. 1969. Critical plant nutrient composition values useful in interpreting plant analysis data. Agron. J. 61:17–20.

Mitchell, R.L. 1956. The spectrographic analysis of soils, plants, and related materials. Tech. Comm. 44. Commonwealth Bureaux of Soils, Harpenden, Herts, England.

Mitchell, R.L. 1964. The spectrographic analysis of soils, plants, and related materials. Tech. Comm. 44A. Commonwealth Bureaux, Franham Royal, Bucks, England.

Montaser, A., and D.W. Golightly (ed.). 1987. Inductively coupled plasmas in analytical atomic spectrometry. VCH Publ., Inc., New York.

Morrison, G.H. 1979. Elemental trace analysis of biological materials. Crit. Rev. Anal. Chem. 8:287–320.

Munson, R.D., and W.L. Nelson. 1973. Principles and practices in plant analysis. p. 223–248. In L.M. Walsh and J.D. Beaton (ed.) Soil testing and plant analysis (rev. ed.). SSSA, Madison, WI.

Munter, R.C., and R.A. Grande. 1981. Plant analysis and soil extract analysis by ICP-atomic emission spectrometry. p. 653–672. In R.M. Barnes (ed.) Developments in atomic plasma spectrochemical analysis. Heyden and Son, Ltd, London.

Munter, R.C., T.L. Halverson, and R.D. Anderson. 1984. Quality assurance of plant tissue analysis by ICP-AES. Commun. Soil Sci. Plant Anal. 15:1285–1322.

Nelson, P.B., and J.W. Boodley. 1965. An error involved in the preparation of plant tissue for analysis. Proc. Am. Soc. Hortic. Sci. 86:712–716.

Nygaard, D.D., and J.J. Sofera. 1988. New developments in polychromator plasma emission spectrometers. Am. Lab. 20:30–36.

Ohki, K. 1975a. Lower and upper critical zinc levels in relation to cotton growth and development. Physiol. Plant 35:96–110.

Ohki, K. 1975b. Manganese supply, growth, and micronutrient concentration in grain sorghum. Agron. J. 67:30–32.

Ohki, K. 1978. Zinc concentration in soybean as related to growth, photosynthesis, and carbonic anhydrase activity. Crop Sci. 18:79–82.

Ohki, K. 1981. Manganese critical levels for soybean growth and physiological processes. J. Plant Nutr. 3:271–284.

Ohki, K. 1984a. Manganese deficiency and toxicity effects on growth, development, and nutrient composition in wheat. Agron. J. 76:213–218.

Ohki, K. 1984b. Zinc nutrition related to critical deficiency and toxicity levels for sorghum. Agron. J. 76:253–256.

Okhi, K. 1987. Critical nutrient levels related to plant growth and some physiological processes. J. Plant Nutr. 10:1583–1590.

Ohki, K., and A. Ulrich. 1977. Manganese and zinc appraisal of selected crops by plant analysis. Commun. Soil Sci. Plant Anal. 8:297–312.

Ohki, K., D.O. Wilson, F.C. Boswell, M.B. Parker, and L.M. Shuman. 1977. Mn concentration in soybean leaf related to bean yields. Agron. J. 69:597–600.

Ottow, J.C.G., G. Benckiser, S. Santiago, and I. Watanbe. 1982. Iron toxicity of wetland rice (Oryza sativa L.) as a multiple nutritional stress. p. 454–460. In A. Scaife (ed.) Plant nutrition 1982. Proc. Ninth Int. Plant Nutr. Colloq., Coventry, England. 22–27 Aug. 1982. Commonwealth Agric. Bureaux, Slough, England.

Parkinson, J.A., and S.E. Allen. 1975. A wet oxidation procedure suitable for the determination of nitrogen and mineral nutrients in biological material. Commun. Soil Sci. Plant Anal. 6:1–11.

Piper, C.S. 1942. Soil and plant analysis. Hassell Press, Adelaide, Australia.

Prevot, P., and M. Ollagnier. 1961. Law of the minimum and balanced nutrition. p. 257–277. In W. Reuther (ed.) Plant analysis and fertilizer problems. Publ. 8, Am. Inst. Biol. Sci., Washington, DC.

Reisenauer, H.H. 1956. Molybdenum content of alfalfa in relation to deficiency symptoms and response to molybdenum fertilization. Soil Sci. 81:237–242.

Reisenauer, H.M., L.M. Walsh, and R.G. Hoeft. 1973. Testing soils for sulphur, boron, molybdenum and chlorine. p. 173–200. In L.M. Walsh and J.D. Beaton (ed.) Soil testing and plant analysis (rev. ed.). SSSA, Madison, WI.

Reuter, D.J., and J.B. Robinson. 1986. Plant analysis: An interpretation manual. Inkata Press, Ltd., Melbourne, Australia.

Reuther, W. 1961. Limitations of plant analysis as a research diagnostic tool. p. 443–454. *In* W. Reuther (ed.) Plant analysis and fertilizer problems. Publ. 8, Am. Inst. Biol. Sci., Washington, DC.

Robb, D.A., and W.S. Pierpoint. 1983. Metals and micronutrients: Uptake and utilization by plants. Academic Press, New York.

Ross, W.M. 1986. Improving plants for tolerance to iron deficiency and other mineral nutrition problems: Breeding and genetic points of view. J. Plant Nutr. 9:309–333.

Ruano, A., J. Barcelo, and C. Poschenrieder. 1987. Zinc toxicity-induced variation of mineral element composition in hydroponically grown bush bean plants. J. Plant Nutr. 10:373–384.

Sabbe, W.E., and D.B. Max. 1987. Soil sampling: Spatial and temperal variability. p. 1–14. *In* J.R. Brown (ed.) Soil testing: Sampling, correlation, calibration, and interpretation. SSSA, Madison, WI.

Safaya, N.M., and A.P. Gupta. 1979. Differential susceptibility of corn cultivars to zinc deficiency. Agron. J. 71:132–136.

Sayre, J.D. 1952. Accumulation of radio isotopes in corn leaves. Ohio Agric. Exp. Stn. Bull. 723.

Sayre, J.D. 1958. The accumulation of boron in margins of corn leaves. p. 245–250. *In* C.B. Lamb (ed.) Trace elements. Academic Press, New York.

Scott, R.N., V.A. Fassel, R.N. Kniseley, and D.E. Dixon. 1974. Inductively coupled plasma-optical emission spectroscopy. Anal. Chem. 46:75–80.

Shear, C.B., and M. Faust. 1980. Nutritional ranges in deciduous tree fruits and nuts. p. 142–163. *In* J. Janick (ed.) Horticultural reviews. Vol. 2. AVI Publ. Co., Westport, CT.

Shkolnik, A.Y. 1984. Trace elements in plants. Elsevier Sci. Publ., Amsterdam, Netherlands.

Skogerboe, R.K., I.T. Urasa, and G.N. Coleman. 1976. Characterization of a DC plasma as an excitation source for multielement analysis. Appl. Spectrosc. 30:500–507.

Smith, P.F. 1962. Mineral analysis of plant tissues. Annu. Rev. Plant Physiol. 13:81–108.

Smith, J.H., D.L. Carter, M.J. Brown, and C.L. Parks. 1968. Differences in chemical composition of plant sample fractions resulting from grinding and screening. Agron. J. 60:149–151.

Soltanpour, P.N., J.B. Jones, Jr., and S.M. Workman. 1982. Optical emission spectroscopy. p. 29–66. *In* A.L. Page et al. (ed.) Methods of soil analysis. Part 2. 2nd ed. Agron. Monogr. 9. ASA, Madison, WI.

Sonneveld, C., and P.A. van Dijk. 1982. The effectiveness of some washing procedures on the removal of contaminates from plant tissues of glasshouse crops. Commun. Soil Sci. Plant Anal. 13:487–496.

Sterrett, S.B., C.B. Smith, M.P. Mascianica, and K.T. Demchek. 1987. Comparison of analytical results from plant analysis laboratories. Commun. Soil Sci. Plant Anal. 18:287–299.

Steyn, J.W.A. 1961. Sampling errors in citrus and pineapple leaf analysis. p. 409–430. *In* W. Reuther (ed.) Plant analysis and fertilizer problems. Publ. 8, Am. Inst. Biol. Sci., Washington, DC.

Stika, K.M., and G.H. Morrison. 1981. Analytical methods for mineral content of human tissues. Fed. Proc. 40:2115–2120.

Stout, P.R., and W.R. Meagher. 1948. Studies of the molybdenum nutrition of plants with radioactive molybdenum. Science 108:471–473.

Sumner, M.E. 1977. Preliminary N, P, and K foliar diagnostic norms for soybeans. Agron. J. 69:226–230.

Sumner, M.E. 1981. Diagnosing the sulfur requirements of corn and wheat using foliar analysis. Soil Sci. Soc. Am. J. 45:87–90.

Sumner, M.E. 1985. The diagnosis and recommendation integrated system (DRIS) as a guide to orchard fertilization. Food Fert. Tech. Ctr. Ext. Bull. 231. FFTC/ASPAC, Taipei, Taiwan.

Sung, J.F.C., A.E. Nevussu, and F.B. Dewalle. 1984. Simple sample digestion of sewage and sludge for multielement analysis. J. Environ. Sci. Health A19:959–972.

Taylor, J.K. 1985. Handbook for SRM users. Spec. Publ. 260-100. U.S. Dep. Commerce, Nat. Bureau of Standards, Gaithersburg, MD.

Taylor, J.K. 1987. Quality assurance of chemical measurements. Lewis Publ., Chelsea, MI.

Thompson, G., and D. Bankston. 1969. A technique for trace element analysis of powdered material using d.c. arc and photoelectric spectrometry. Spectrochim. Acta 24B:335–350.

Thorne, W. 1957. Zinc deficiency and its control. Adv. Agron. 9:31–67.

Tolg, G. 1974. The basis of trace analysis. p. 698–710. *In* E. Korte (ed.) Methodium chimicum. Vol. 1, Analytical methods. Part B. Micromethods, biological methods, quality control, automation. Academic Press, New York.

Ulrich, A. 1952. Physiological bases for assessing the nutritional requirements of plants. Annu. Rev. Plant Physiol. 3:207–228.

Ulrich, A., and F.J. Hill. 1973. Plant analysis as an aid in fertilizing sugar crops: Part I. Sugar beets. p. 71–88. *In* L.M. Walsh and J.D. Beaton (ed.) Soil testing and plant analysis. (rev. ed.). SSSA, Madison, WI.

Ulrich, A., and K. Ohki. 1956. Chlorine, bromine and sodium as nutrients for sugar beets. Plant Physiol. 31:171–181.

Ulrich, J.M. 1984. Pulsing air enhances Wiley mill utility. Commun. Soil Sci. Plant Anal. 15:189–190.

Ure, A.M. 1983. Atomic absorption and flame emission spectrometry. p. 1–54. *In* K. Smith (ed.) Soil analysis. Marcel Dekker, Inc., New York.

Uriano, G.A. 1979. The NBS standard reference materials program: SRM's today and tomorrow. ASTM Stand. Newsl. 7:8–13.

van der Lee, J.J., I. Walinga, P.K. Mangeki, V.J.G. Houba, and I. Novozamsky. 1987. Determination of boron in fresh and dried plant material by plasma emission spectrometry after extraction with HF-HCl. Commun. Soil Sci. Plant Anal. 18:789–802.

Viets, F.G., Jr., L.C. Boawn, and C.L. Crawford. 1954. Zinc contents and deficiency symptoms of 26 crops grown on a zinc deficient soil. Soil Sci. 78:305–316.

Vigler, M.S., A.W. Varnes, and H.A. Strecker. 1980. Sample preparation techniques for AA and ICP spectroscopy. Am. Lab. 12:31–34.

Von Liebig, J. 1840. Organic chemistry in its applications to agriculture and physiology (edited from notes to the author by Lynn Play Fair) Taylor and Walton, London. p. XVI–387.

Vose, P.B. 1982. Iron nutrition in plants: A world overview. J. Plant Nutr. 5:233–249.

Wallace, A. 1986. Definition of stress in crop production—Iron, plant nutrient, and non-nutrient stress interactions. J. Plant Nutr. 9:187–192.

Wallace, A., J. Kinnear, J.W. Cha, and E.M. Romney. 1980. Effect of washing procedures on mineral analyses and their cluster analysis for orange leaves. J. Plant Nutr. 2:1–9.

Wallace, A., R.T. Mueller, J.W. Cha, and E.M. Rommey. 1982. Influence of washing of soybean leaves on identification of iron deficiency by leaf analysis. J. Plant Nutr. 5:805–810.

Wallihan, E.F. 1978. Tissue tests for iron. p. 32–34. *In* H.M. Reisenauer (ed.) Soil and plant-tissue testing in California. Bull. 1879. Div. Agric. Sci., Univ. California, Berkeley.

Walsh, J.M., and J.D. Beaton. 1973. Soil testing and plant analysis (rev. ed.). SSSA, Madison, WI.

Walworth, J.L., and M.E. Sumner. 1987. The diagnosis and recommendation integrated system. p. 149–188. *In* B.A. Stewart (ed.) Advances in soil science. Springer-Verlag New York, New York.

Walworth, J.L., M.E. Sumner, R.A. Isaac, and C.O. Plank. 1986. Preliminary DRIS norms for alfalfa. Agron. J. 78:1046–1052.

Watson, M.E. 1981. Interlaboratory comparison in the determination of nutrient concentration of plant tissue. Commun. Soil Sci. Plant Anal. 12:601–617.

Weinhold, A. 1862. Analyse von unkiauterm des bodens der versuchsstation chemnitz. Landeo. Vers Stn. 4:188–193.

White, M.C., R.L. Chaney, and A.M. Decker. 1979. Differential cultivar tolerance in soybean to phytotoxic levels of soil Zn. II. Range of Zn additions and the uptake and translocation of Zn, Mn, Fe, and P. Agron. J. 71:126–131.

White, R.T., Jr., and G.E. Douthit. 1985. Use of microwave oven and nitric acid-hydrogen peroxide digestion to prepare botanical materials for elemental analysis by inductively coupled agron plasma emission spectroscopy. J. Assoc. Off. Anal. Chem. 68:766–769.

Wikner, B. 1986. Pretreatment of plant and soil samples. A problem in boron analysis. Part I: Plants. Commun. Soil Sci. Plant Anal. 17:1–25.

Wilcox, L.V. 1960. Boron injury to plants. USDA Info. Bull. 211, U.S. Dep. Agric., Washington, DC.

Williams, S. 1984. Official methods of analysis of the association of official analytical chemists. Assoc. Off. Anal. Chem., Arlington, VA.

Williams, W.J. 1979. Handbook of anion determination. Butterworths and Co., London.

Wilson, D.O. 1979. Determination of molybdenum in wet-ashed digests of plant material using flameless atomic absorption. Commun. Soil Sci. Plant Anal. 10:1319–1330.

Wolf, B. 1974. Improvements in the azomethine-H method for the determination of boron. Commun. Soil Sci. Plant Anal. 5:39–44.

Wolf, B. 1982. A comprehensive system of leaf analysis and its use for diagnosing crop nutrient status. Commun. Soil Sci. Plant Anal. 13:1035–1059.

Yoshida, S., J.S. Ahn, and D.A. Forno. 1973. Occurrence diagnosis, and correction of zinc deficiency of lowland rice. Soil Sci. Plant Nutr. 19:83–93.

Zarcinas, B.A. 1984. Analysis of soil and plant material by inductively coupled plasma-optical emission spectrometry. CSIRO Div. Rep. 70. Commonwealth Sci. Industrial Res. Org. (CSIRO), Glen Osmond, Australia.

Zarcinas, B.A., B. Cartwright, and L.P. Spouncer. 1987. Nitric acid digestion and multi-element analysis of plant material by inductively coupled plasma spectrometry. Commun. Soil Sci. Plant Anal. 18:131–147.

Zasoski, R.J., and R.G. Burau. 1977. A rapid nitric-perchloric acid digestion method for multi-element tissue analysis. Commun. Soil Sci. Plant Anal. 8:425–436.

Chapter 14

Micronutrient Fertilizer Technology

JOHN J. MORTVEDT, *Tennessee Valley Authority, Muscle Shoals, Alabama*

Micronutrient deficiencies are often corrected by application of micronutrient fertilizers to soil. Because recommended application rates are much lower for micronutrients than for N-P-K fertilizers, most micronutrient sources are applied with N-P-K fertilizers rather than alone. Applying micronutrients with N-P-K fertilizers results in more uniform distribution in the field, which is especially important for B, whose range between toxicity and deficiency is narrow. Combining materials also reduces spreading costs to the grower.

Applying micronutrients with N-P-K fertilizers may result in problems due to chemical reactions between some components of the N-P-K fertilizers and the micronutrient sources. Studies of these reactions have resulted in improved procedures for preparing, handling, and applying micronutrients.

In the first edition of this book, separate chapters covered trends in the use of micronutrients (Cunningham, 1972), preparation of fertilizers containing micronutrients (Silverberg et al., 1972), chemical reactions of micronutrients in fertilizers (Lehr, 1972), and agronomic effectiveness of micronutrients in macronutrient fertilizers (Giordano & Mortvedt, 1972). Much of this information in the first edition will not be discussed in this chapter, so the above references should be consulted for further information. Production, marketing, and use of micronutrient fertilizers also was reviewed by Mortvedt and Cox (1985).

I. MICRONUTRIENT SOURCES

Micronutrient sources vary considerably in physical state, chemical reactivity, cost, and availability to plants. There are three main classes of micronutrient sources—inorganic, synthetic chelates, and natural organic complexes.

Fritted glass products (frits) also have been considered as a class of micronutrients, but they are not as important now as they once were. To produce frits, powdered raw materials are mixed with silicates and melted in a furnace. More than one micronutrient can be included in fritted products. The molten mix is quenched, dried, and ground to a powder. Micronutrient solubility is controlled by particle size and matrix composition (Holden, 1959). However, micronutrient availability to crops is decreased when frits are incorporated with granular N-P-K products because of a decrease in the number of application sites. Some fritted products are still marketed, but mainly for maintenance of micronutrient supplies in the soil rather than for correcting deficiencies.

A. Inorganic Sources

Oxides, carbonates, and metallic salts, such as sulfates, chlorides, and nitrates, are the sources of inorganic products. Oxides of Mn and Zn are commonly used, and are marketed as fine powders and in granular form. Because oxides such as MnO and ZnO are water insoluble, their immediate effectiveness for crops is low when applied in granular form since their specific surface is greatly decreased.

Naturally occurring sphalerite (ZnS) is roasted to form ZnO, which is available to plants. Naturally occurring MnO_2 must be reduced to the plant-available divalent Mn form (MnO) prior to its use for crops. Divalent Mn in MnO and $MnSO_4$ may oxidize to the unavailable tetravalent form after soil application, reducing the residual availability of Mn fertilizers. Ferric oxide (Fe_2O_3) also is unavailable for crops because of its low solubility and the oxidized state of Fe in this compound.

The sulfates of Cu, Fe, Mn, and Zn are the most common of the metallic salts and are marketed in crystalline or granular form. Their physical properties make them suitable for fertilizer use. Sulfates are water soluble and dissolve quickly after soil application. This is especially important when micronutrient sulfates are granulated for application with bulk-blended N-P-K fertilizers. Whereas these products also add plant-available S to soils, the amount of S applied at most recommended micronutrient rates is low and may not supply recommended S rates.

Oxysulfates are oxides that are partially acidulated with H_2SO_4. The percentage of water-soluble micronutrient in these products is directly related to the degree of acidulation. Results of unpublished TVA greenhouse experiments (J.J. Mortvedt, 1985, unpublished data) have shown that about 35 to 50% of the Zn in granular Zn oxysulfate should be in water-soluble form to be effective for crops. Similar results would be expected for Mn oxysulfate products.

Inorganic sources usually are the least costly sources per unit of micronutrient, but they are not always the most effective for crops. Therefore, cost is only one criterion to consider when selecting micronutrient sources. Some common inorganic compounds used as micronutrient sources are listed in Table 14-1.

Metal-ammonia complexes also are used as micronutrient sources. The most common inorganic complex is ammoniated $ZnSO_4$ solution. Ammo-

Table 14-1. Inorganic compunds commonly used as micronutrient sources.

Micronutrient source	Solubility in H_2O	Percent element
B		
$Na_2B_4O_7$ (anhydrous borax)	Soluble	20
$Na_2B_4O_7 \cdot 5H_2O$ (fertilizer borate)	Soluble	14
$Na_2B_4O_7 \cdot 10H_2O$ (borax)	Soluble	11
H_3BO_3	Soluble	17
$Ca_2B_6O_{11} \cdot 5H_2O$ (colemanite)	Slightly soluble	10
Cu		
$CuSO_4 \cdot H_2O$	Soluble	35
$CuSO_4 \cdot 5H_2O$	Soluble	25
$CuSO_4 \cdot 3Cu(OH)_2 \cdot H_2O$	Insoluble	37
CuO	Insoluble	75
Fe		
$FeSO_4 \cdot H_2O$	Soluble	33
$FeSO_4 \cdot 7H_2O$	Soluble	20
$Fe_2(SO_4)_3 \cdot 9H_2O$	Soluble	20
$FeSO_4 \cdot (NH_4)_2SO_4$	Soluble	22
Mn		
$MnSO_4 \cdot xH_2O$	Soluble	24–30
$MnCl_2 \cdot 4H_2O$	Soluble	28
$MnCO_3$	Insoluble	31
MnO	Insoluble	41–68
Mn oxysulfate	Variable	30–50
Mo		
Na_2MoO_4 (anhydrous)	Soluble	47
$Na_2MoO_4 \cdot 2H_2O$	Soluble	39
$(NH_4)_2MoO_4$	Soluble	49
MoO_3	Slightly soluble	66
$CaMoO_4$	Insoluble	48
Zn		
$ZnSO_4 \cdot H_2O$	Soluble	36
$ZnSO_4 \cdot 7H_2O$	Soluble	22
$ZnCl_2$	Soluble	47
$ZnSO_4 \cdot 4Zn(OH)_2$	Slightly soluble	55
$ZnCO_3$	Insoluble	52
ZnO	Insoluble	60–78
Zn oxysulfate	Variable	25–60

nia is coordinately bonded with divalent Zn to form the complex. This product has somewhat different chemical properties than divalent Zn, but it is assumed that this complex decomposes after soil application to form Zn^{2+} ions again. The most common commercial product contains 10% N, 10% Zn, and 5% S. It is easily mixed with ammonium polyphosphate solution, 10-15-0 (10-34-0 oxide basis), to provide Zn in starter fertilizers for crops.

B. Synthetic Chelates

Chelates are formed by combining a chelating agent with a metal cation through coordinate bonds, although some ionic bonding also is present. Chelates can be synthetic (manufactured) or natural (from sugars such as glucoheptonic acid and from other products such as citric acid), but they all must contain known coordinate bonds. The descriptive word chelate, derived from the Greek work "chela" or "claw," was proposed for this type of molecular structure in 1920 (McCrary & Howard, 1979).

The stability of the metal-chelate bond is indicated by the stability constant of the chelated micronutrient. Stability constants are measured values ($\log_{10}$) for the forward reaction of the equation:

$$M + L = ML \qquad [1]$$

where M is a metal cation and L is a chelate ligand. Larger log K values indicate that more of the metal is chelated at equilibrium, so the chelated metal would be more stable in chemical reactions. Stability constants of micronutrient chelates are further discussed in Ch. 4 and 7 of this book.

The most common chelating agent used for micronutrient chelates is EDTA (ethylenediamine tetraacetic acid). Two additional chelating agents commonly used for Fe are HEDTA (N-hydroxyethyl-ethylenediamine triacetic acid) and EDDHA [ethylenediamine di(o-hydroxyphenylacetic acid)]. The stability constant of FeEDDHA is estimated at 35 to 39, and Fe in this product will remain in chelated form in soil until the chelate molecule is decomposed by microorganisms. Whereas this Fe source is very effective, it also is rather costly per unit of Fe, so it is used mainly for high-value crops.

Stability constants can be used to predict the stability of chelates when mixed with fluid fertilizers. In a laboratory study, seven Zn sources were each mixed with an ammonium polyphosphate 10–15–0 fluid fertilizer to contain 1% Zn. The percentage of Zn remaining as each Zn source was determined after 4 min (Picanso, 1984). It was shown that 100% of the Zn remained chelated as ZnEDTA, whereas only 19 and 8% of the Zn remained chelated as ZnHEDTA and Zn citrate, respectively (Table 14–2). Less than 15% of the Zn remained as each of the other four Zn sources. The stability constants ($\log_{10}$ values) for ZnEDTA, ZnHEDTA, and Zn citrate are 17.2, 15.2, and 5.5, respectively, as compared with 8.0 for Zn pyrophosphate, the competing "chelate" in the 10–15–0 fertilizer solution (Norvell, 1972). Conversion of Zn from each Zn source to a different form in 10–15–0 does not necessarily mean that agronomic effectiveness will be changed. Such comparative effects must be determined in multiple-rate field experiments such as those conducted by Hergert et al. (1984).

Many of the chelated micronutrients are sold in liquid form in the USA because production costs per unit of micronutrient are lower than those in powder form. Liquid chelates are sold mainly for mixing with fluid fertilizers, although some also are used as foliar sprays. Dry chelates are mixed with solid fertilizers mainly as specialty products for turf, ornamentals, fruits, and vegetables.

Table 14-2. Percentage of Zn remaining as each original Zn source 4 min after mixing with a 10-15-0 fertilizer solution (Picanso, 1984).

Zn source	Percent remaining as original source
ZnEDTA	100
ZnHEDTA	19
$Zn(NO_3)_2$-UAN	15
Zn-Phenolic acid	11
Zn-Citrate	8
$ZnSO_4$-NH_3 complex	8
$ZnSO_4$	4

C. Natural Organic Complexes

Natural organic micronutrient sources are produced by reacting metal-lic salts with organic by-products, mainly those of the wood pulp industry. Several groups of these compounds are the lignosulfonates, phenols, and poly-flavonoids. These by-products are rather diverse, depending on the chemi-cal process and type of wood. Some of the bonds with metallic salts may be similar to those in chelates, but the remainder are not well defined; hence, the term complexes. Therefore, these products are placed in a separate class from the chelates.

Digest liquors from the wood pulp industry containing the organic com-plexes in the Ca or Na form are reacted with a micronutrient source to form a metal complex. Oxides may be used, but sulfates are preferred because they are soluble. Digest liquors from the Sulfite process of wood pulp produc-tion contain lignosulfonates that complex metals. However, digest liquors from the more widely used Kraft process of wood pulp production must be sulfonated to improve their complexing capacity.

The most popular micronutrient natural organic complexes contain Zn or Fe, with lesser quantities of complexes containing Cu or Mn. Products containing more than one of the above micronutrients also have been deve-loped. Stability constants for metals in these complexes are not available, mainly because most of the products are rather variable in composition for the reasons described earlier. However, it may be presumed that values of such constants would be lower than those for analogous micronutrient chelates.

D. Comparisons of Sources

There are few published reports that discuss direct comparisons of agro-nomic effectiveness of micronutrient chelates and natural organic complexes. Response of corn (*Zea mays* L.) to Zn in a Zn-lignosulfonate product was less than half that to similar rates of Zn in ZnEDTA applied to a Zn-deficient soil (Mortvedt, 1979).

Agronomic effectiveness of a micronutrient source is defined as the degree of crop response per unit of applied micronutrient. Lower rates of more effective sources are needed to produce maximum responses. Field ex-

Table 14–3. Response of corn to Zn sources band applied with a 10–15–0 starter fertilizer (Hergert et al., 1984).

Zn source	Zn applied, kg ha^{-1}				
	0	0.11	0.33	1.12	3.36
	grain yield, t ha^{-1}				
--	3.9				
ZnEDTA		8.6	8.7	9.5	8.8
ZnO		8.2	8.2	8.6	9.1
ZnSO$_4$		8.3	8.9	8.7	9.1
ZnSO$_4$-NH$_3$ complex		7.8	8.6	8.5	8.8
Zn(NO$_3$)$_2$-UAN		8.2	8.2	8.9	8.8

periments using two or more non-zero rates of each micronutrient source are needed to best determine the relative agronomic effectiveness of several sources of a given micronutrient.

An excellent example of such an experiment is summarized in Table 14–3. Five Zn sources were each banded with a 10–15–0 starter fertilizer (112 kg ha^{-1} of product) at Zn rates up to 3.3 kg ha^{-1} for corn on a calcareous (pH 7.6) Zn-deficient soil in Nebraska. Results in Table 14–3 show that ZnEDTA was more effective than the ZnSO$_4$-NH$_3$ complex at the lowest Zn rate, but all sources were about equally effective at the higher Zn rates (Hergert et al., 1984). Relative agronomic effectiveness varied with rate, which emphasizes the need for including multiple rates.

Cost per unit of micronutrient also must be considered when selecting micronutrient sources. In the above example, Zn sources other than ZnEDTA might be more economical to apply even if higher Zn rates were required to obtain maximum crop response because ZnEDTA is more costly per unit of Zn. Compatibility with the N-P-K fertilizer, convenience in application, agronomic effectiveness, and cost per unit of micronutrient are factors that must be considered in selecting micronutrient sources.

II. INDUSTRIAL BY-PRODUCTS AS MICRONUTRIENT FERTILIZERS

A. Methods of Preparation

Many industrial by-products containing micronutrients are being marketed as fertilizers in the USA. Such use constitutes resource recovery instead of costly disposal as may be required by regulations. Most of these by-products are Zn or Mn sources, although there are also some by-products that contain other micronutrients. For many years, one of the main industrial by-products used in the USA as a micronutrient fertilizer was MnSO$_4$, a by-product of the manufacture of hydroquinone. This by-product constituted a major fraction of the MnSO$_4$ fertilizers sold in the USA. The hydroquinone manufacturing process was changed in 1986 so fertilizer MnSO$_4$ had to be obtained elsewhere, although by-product MnSO$_4$ is still available from the earlier hydroquinone process in Mexico.

Sources of by-product Zn include spent acids from the galvanizing industry and other industries, flue dusts, baghouse dusts, and other products from Zn smelters, pigment, battery, rubber, and other industries. Leaching processes are needed to remove impurities from these products, but some by-products are used without purification. Some spent acids also contain Fe, which can be precipitated as $FeSO_4$. Resulting precipitates from spent acids of the galvanizing industry contain both $ZnSO_4$ and $FeSO_4$. Whereas Zn in these products is available to plants, these products may not be effective Fe fertilizers with soil application. More research is needed to determine effectiveness of Fe in most fertilizers made from industrial by-products.

B. Heavy Metal Contaminants

Some industrial by-products also may contain heavy metal contaminants such as Cd, Cr, Ni, and Pb. Concentrations of these heavy metals in the by-products are highly variable. Because micronutrient application rates are low, the heavy metal application rates would be correspondingly lower. For example, application of 10 kg of ZnO ha^{-1} that contains 10 mg Cd kg^{-1} would result in a Cd application rate of 0.1 g ha^{-1}.

Heavy metal uptake by plants has been studied more closely in recent years than previously. Most field crops do not absorb appreciable quantities of heavy metals, but some leafy vegetables such as spinach (*Spinacea oleracea*) are known to accumulate heavy metals. Several Zn fertilizers made from industrial by-products were compared with reagent-grade $ZnSO_4$ in a greenhouse pot study (Mortvedt, 1985). Concentrations of Cd in corn forage were not affected by Zn fertilizers containing from 1 to 2165 mg Cd kg^{-1}. However, Cd uptake by Swiss chard (*Beta vulgaris* L.) increased with Cd concentration in these fertilizers applied to an acid soil (pH 5.8), but not to an alkaline soil (pH 7.4). Uptake of Pb and Ni by both crops at either soil pH was not affected even though these Zn sources contained up to 52 000 mg Pb kg^{-1} and 8950 mg Ni kg^{-1}.

These data suggest that plant uptake of heavy metals from industrial by-products used as micronutrient fertilizers is rather low. Because Mn and Zn fertilizers are mainly applied to soils of pH > 6.0, heavy metal uptake also is restricted. Studies of long-term use of such fertilizers containing heavy metal contaminants are needed. Efforts should be made to minimize the concentrations of these contaminants in such products to be used as fertilizers. This may require chemical engineering research on processes such as differential precipitation and physical separation techniques.

III. METHODS OF APPLYING MICRONUTRIENTS WITH N-P-K FERTILIZERS

Most micronutrients are applied directly to the soil, but some are sprayed onto plant foliage. Because recommended rates usually are < 10 kg ha^{-1}, uniform application to the soil of micronutrient fertilizers alone is difficult.

Both granular and fluid N-P-K fertilizers are used as carriers of micronutrients. Conventional application equipment can then be used and application costs are reduced by combining micronutrients with N-P-K fertilizers.

Chemical reactions between micronutrient fertilizers and one or more components of the N-P-K fertilizer can occur during manufacture, in storage, or after soil application. Reaction products differ markedly, depending on fertilizer sources, pH of the mixture, and processing temperature (Lehr et al., 1967). Therefore, care must be taken to select those micronutrient sources that, when combined with N-P-K fertilizers, will supply micronutrients in a plant-available form.

Micronutrient sources can be combined with N-P-K fertilizers by incorporation during the manufacture of granular fertilizers, bulk blending with granular fertilizers, coating onto granular fertilizers, or mixing with fluid fertilizers. Advantages and disadvantages of each method are discussed in the following sections.

A. Incorporation During Manufacture

Optimum incorporation distributes micronutrients uniformly throughout N-P-K fertilizers. During manufacture, the micronutrient source is in intimate contact with components of the N-P-K fertilizer under conditions of high temperature and moisture. This enhances the rate of chemical reactions that may affect the plant availability of the added micronutrient. For example, when ZnEDTA was mixed with H_3PO_4 before ammoniation, acid decomposition of the organic chelate ligand resulted in decreased availability of the applied Zn (Ellis et al., 1965). When this process was changed by adding the ZnEDTA with the ammoniating solution, the EDTA ligand was not decomposed by the acid and plant availability of the incorporated ZnEDTA was greater (Brinkerhoff et al., 1966).

Incorporation of either $ZnSO_4$ or ZnO with ammoniated orthophosphate fertilizers resulted in fertilizers with low immediate availability of Zn to plants, but proper incorporation of ZnEDTA in the same fertilizer did not affect its availability to plants (Mortvedt & Giordano, 1969). Incorporating $ZnSO_4$ with superphosphates prior to ammoniation resulted in decreased water solubility of Zn (Jackson et al., 1962), probably due to the formation of water-insoluble $ZnNH_4PO_4$ (Lehr, 1972). Immediate plant availability of applied Zn decreased with the level of water-soluble Zn in ammoniated phosphates (Mortvedt, 1968a).

While immediate availability of applied Zn was decreased by incorporation with ammoniated fertilizers, the residual effects of this Zn appeared to be similar to those of other more soluble Zn products. Soil test levels of available Zn generally have increased with repeated annual Zn applications due to residual effects of applied Zn, and recommended Zn application rates have decreased. Incorporating ZnO with a granular N-P-K fertilizer (1% Zn) was more effective for corn than incorporation with a granular dolomite product to supply 4.4 kg of Zn ha^{-1} (Tanner & Grant, 1974).

Effects of chemical reactions between a micronutrient source with components of a granular N–P–K fertilizer on subsequent reactions after soil application are shown in Fig. 14-1, using $ZnSO_4$ in DAP as an example. After application, soil water moves to the granule site due to a high salt concentration gradient. The soluble fertilizers dissolve and salts move in solution away from the granule site. Zinc is immobilized by the formation of insoluble reaction products with the P fertilizer, such as $ZnNH_4PO_4$ and $Zn_3(PO_4)_2$, and by reactions with soil organic matter and clay colloids. The distance that Zn diffuses from the granule site depends on the extent of these reactions as well as on other soil parameters. If there is greater Zn movement from the granule site, more soil will be affected and more plant roots can absorb the applied Zn, which will increase its agronomic effectiveness.

Release patterns of Zn and Cu incorporated with ordinary superphosphate (OSP) were studied by Gilkes and Sadleir (1981). About 90 and 50% of the incorporated Zn and Cu, respectively, were in water-soluble form and dissolved within 7 d after soil application. Most of the remaining fractions of both Zn and Cu were found in the OSP granules after 1 yr.

Application of Zn sources with NH_4-N fertilizers is effective due to the acidifying effect of these fertilizers on soil, but varies according to the fertilizer pH. Uptake of Zn by grain sorghum [*Sorghum bicolor* (L.) Moench] and ladino clover (*Trifolium repens* L.) from $ZnSO_4$ applied with N fertilizers decreased in the order: $(NH_4)_2SO_4$, NH_4NO_3, and $NaNO_3$ (Viets et al., 1957). The resulting soil pH with these fertilizers was 5.0, 6.0, and 7.3, respectively, as compared with pH 7.2 for the unfertilized soil. Forage yields and Zn uptake by corn also were higher with $(NH_4)_2SO_4$ than with anhydrous NH_3 or urea whether $ZnSO_4$ was omitted, mixed, or spot-placed in a Zn-deficient soil, again due to the fertilizer effect on soil pH (Giordano et al., 1966). Zincated urea (containing 2–3% Zn as $ZnSO_4$) broadcast and incor-

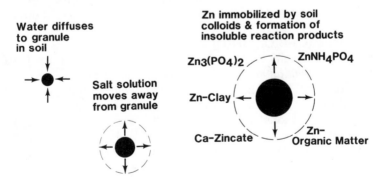

Dissolution & Movement of Zn from a DAP Granule Containing ZnSO4 in a Calcareous Soil

Water diffuses to granule in soil

Salt solution moves away from granule

Zn immobilized by soil colloids & formation of insoluble reaction products

$Zn_3(PO_4)_2$ $ZnNH_4PO_4$

Zn–Clay

Ca-Zincate   Zn-Organic Matter

Fig. 14-1. Example of possible chemical reactions after soil application of granular $(NH_4)_2HPO_4$ containing incorporated $ZnSO_4$ (Mortvedt, 1984a).

porated with soil was equally effective as broadcast $ZnSO_4$ for wheat (*Triticum aestivum* L.) (Mutatkar et al., 1977).

Band application of Mn sources with acid-forming fertilizers, such as superphosphate, is a recommended practice. The applied Mn remains available to plants for a longer period of time in the acidic band before it oxidizes to unavailable forms. Effects of P source on Mn uptake are related to fertilizer pH (Hossner & Richards, 1968). Uptake of Mn by soybean [*Glycine max* (L.) Merr.] increased as fertilizer pH increased from 1.2 with $Ca(H_2PO_4)_2$ to 3.7 with MAP, but decreased as fertilizer pH increased further to 7.2 with DAP. In the above study, movement of Mn in soil away from the fertilizer band also decreased with increasing pH. No Mn movement in soil was detected above pH 5.8. Response of corn to Mn fertilizers also increased with increasing acidity of starter N–P fertilizers in the order: $NaNO_3$ + TSP, DAP, and $(NH_4)_2SO_4$ + TSP (Miner et al., 1986).

Effects of the incorporation of Cu and Fe sources with N–P–K fertilizers have been less well studied. However, reactions of Cu fertilizers would be expected to be similar to those of Zn fertilizers. Reactions of Fe sources should be similar to those of Mn sources, because the plant-available divalent forms of both Fe and Mn may be oxidized to less available forms. Both Fe^{2+} and Mn^{2+} salts do not appear to oxidize readily in N–P–K fertilizers under the usual manufacturing conditions of fertilizer composition, pH, and temperature (Lehr, 1972). Therefore, such oxidation must occur after initial dissolution of these products when applied to soil.

Incorporation of B sources with N–P–K fertilizers also is commonly practiced. Plant availability of incorporated B was not affected by method of incorporation (Mortvedt, 1968b), apparently because the B compounds did not react chemically with components of most N–P–K fertilizers. However, plant uptake of B was closely correlated with the level of water-soluble B in these fertilizers. Application of B with N–P–K fertilizers is a widely recommended practice since the more uniform application decreases distribution problems in the field, thus minimizing overapplication or underapplication. The range between B deficiency or toxicity for many crops is narrow. Many plant species are sensitive to B, so fertilizers containing B (boronated fertilizers) must be clearly marked so they are not applied to the B-sensitive crops. Some fertilizer regulations require special warning tags for boronated fertilizers.

Colemanite ($Ca_2B_6O_{11} \cdot 5H_2O$) and fertilizer borate ($Na_2B_4O_7 \cdot 5H_2O$) were found to be equally effective for cotton (*Gossypium hirsutum* L.) and sunflower (*Helianthus annuus* Mill.) when incorporated with N–P–K fertilizers (Rowell & Grant, 1975). Both colemanite (moderate solubility) and B frits (low solubility) were superior to $Na_2B_4O_7 \cdot 5H_2O$ (completely water soluble) for cotton on sandy soils under high rainfall conditions (Page, 1956).

Incorporating Mo sources in P or N–P–K fertilizers is a routine practice, especially since the recommended Mo application rates are so low (30–200 g ha^{-1}). There is little evidence to show that Mo sources react with components of N–P–K fertilizers to affect plant availability of Mo. However, inclusion of Mo with fertilizers containing $(NH_4)_2SO_4$ or other soluble sulfates appears to reduce Mo availability (Sauchelli, 1969). This may be due to the acidic nature of sulfates and also to the antagonistic effects of sulfates on Mo in plant nutrition.

The main disadvantage of incorporating micronutrients with N–P–K fertilizers during manufacture involves the special handling and storage of these special fertilizers, which increases distribution costs. Large tonnages of such products are required to reduce the relative losses of off-grade products resulting from start-up and shut-down during manufacture. Therefore, this method usually is limited to fertilizers that can be applied to crops on large land areas. In addition, micronutrient concentrations in such fertilizers cannot be changed to meet individual needs. Other problems encountered during the incorporation of micronutrients with these fertilizers were discussed by Achorn and Mortvedt (1977).

B. Bulk Blending

Blending granular fertilizers together to obtain fertilizer grades that meet recommendations for specific fields is becoming more popular in the USA and elsewhere. The fertilizer dealer purchases bulk supplies of products such as urea, DAP, TSP, and KCl and blends them together in the desired proportions. The main advantage of bulk blending is in its flexibility to produce small batches of specific grades. Micronutrient sources can be blended with the N, P, and K products to produce grades that will provide the recommended N, P, K, and micronutrient rates for a given field.

Blending of these products should be performed just prior to application so there is less chance for chemical reactions that could alter the plant availability of micronutrients. Special procedures may be required to place the proper amount of micronutrient into each batch and a longer mixing time should be used to ensure that a uniform mixture is obtained. The need for extra bin space is eliminated if these micronutrient-containing batches are prepared just before field application.

Blending micronutrients with other fertilizers has increased dramatically in the USA over the past 20 yr. Results of a 1987–1988 survey conducted by the Tennessee Valley Authority (TVA) and the Association of American Plant Food Control Officials (AAPFCO) showed that there were more than 6000 bulk blending plants in the USA, with a total annual production of about 18 million metric tons of fertilizer (Hargett & Berry, 1988). Micronutrients were being added to bulk blends at 79% of these blending facilities in 1988 as compared with 45% in 1974.

The main problem encountered with applying micronutrients in bulk blends is that segregation of nutrients can occur during blending, and in subsequent handling and application. Studies have shown that the main cause of segregation is differences in particle size, although particle shape and density also may have an effect (Silverberg et al., 1972). Mechanical devices that minimize coning and segregation of materials during handling and storage were described by Achorn and Mortvedt (1977).

Bulk blended fertilizers will remain blended with well granulated, closely sized products that do not deteriorate in storage. Particle size is especially important in reducing segregation of components of bulk blends. Most problems with segregation of micronutrients result with the use of B fertilizers because $Na_2B_4O_7 \cdot 5H_2O$ is crystalline in nature. A granulation method patented by Harrison (1981) produces a granular B product with very satisfactory physical and chemical properties for blending and storage. It is now estimated that about 80% of the B fertilizer used in the USA is granulated by this process.

Incorporating a micronutrient source with one compound of a bulk blend also is practiced. This requires a higher micronutrient concentration in that particular component than is needed in the final product, however. A comparison of micronutrient distribution in bags with ZnO incorporated with MAP and then bulk blended with powdered MnO is shown in Table 14-4. Concentrations of incorporated Zn were uniform in all bags, but those of blended Mn varied considerably. Obviously, fine MnO had segregated from the granular fertilizer during blending and bagging operations. Blending granular $MnSO_4$ that matched the particle size range of the MAP and KCl would have resulted in more uniform Mn concentrations.

Solubility of micronutrient sources must be considered in selecting granular sources needed for bulk blending. Availability to plants of water-insoluble oxides is decreased with an increase in particle size because of decreasing specific surface. Crop response to insoluble ZnO and to water-soluble $ZnSO_4$ was similar when each powdered source was mixed with soil (Allen & Terman, 1966). Whereas granular ZnO was completely ineffective, granular $ZnSO_4$ was satisfactory as a Zn source for corn. Field results with pea beans (*Phaseolus vulgaris* L.) also showed that granular ZnO was ineffective (Judy et al., 1964). Granular MnO also has been shown to be ineffective for oat (*Avena sativa* L.) (Mortvedt, 1984a), corn (Miner et al., 1986), and soybean (Mascagni & Cox, 1985). Use of granular oxysulfates with bulk blends will require that close attention be given to the level of water-soluble micronutrients in these by-products to ensure that sufficient amounts of micronutrients are immediately available to plants.

Table 14-4. Micronutrient concentrations in four bags of fertilizer, as affected by incorporating ZnO in granular MAP and blending this product with granular KCl and powdered MnO (Hignett, 1964).

Bag identification	Test 1		Test 2	
	Mn	Zn	Mn	Zn
			%	
A	3.0	0.7	2.9	1.4
B	0.7	0.6	0.9	1.6
C	2.9	0.6	9.8	1.1
D	0.6	0.6	4.9	1.4
Intended concentration	(3.0)	(0.5)	(3.0)	(1.2)

C. Coating onto Granular Fertilizers

Coating micronutrient sources onto granular N–P–K fertilizers can improve uniformity of field application. Theoretically, each N–P–K granule would have a thin micronutrient coating, so distribution in the field would be directly related to N–P–K application rate. In practice, care must be taken to obtain a uniform coating and then to ensure that the binding agent sustains the micronutrient coating.

The coating procedure devised by the TVA is rather simple and can be performed with the mixing equipment used in most bulk blend plants. Rotary drum mixers are considered most satisfactory and ribbon-type mixers also have been used effectively, but gravity-type mixers such as blending towers are not suitable for coating micronutrients onto N–P–K fertilizers. The procedure consists of dry mixing a finely ground (-100 mesh, <0.15 mm) micronutrient source with the granular fertilizer. A liquid binding agent is then sprayed onto the granules as they are mixing. The liquid material promotes formation of reaction products on the surface of the fertilizer granule or serves as a mechanical binder. The total mixing cycle takes 3 to 5 min in small rotary blenders and somewhat longer in larger mixers.

The binding agent must be inexpensive, must adhere to the granular fertilizer during handling, and must not cause undesirable physical properties. Water, oils, waxes, and APP and UAN solutions have been used as binding agents. Water may be used in situations in which an increase in granule surface moisture does not promote caking. If such products are to be stored in piles or bags, anticaking agents may be needed. Oil should not be added to mixtures containing NH_4NO_3 because of the explosion hazard. Less than 1% by weight of oil should be used with other mixtures to prevent lighter oils from seeping through the fertilizer bags. Fertilizer solutions are preferred as binding agents because the fertilizer grade would not be decreased appreciably. Care must be taken in selecting binding agents because some do not retain micronutrient coatings during bagging, storage, and handling operations. Then, segregation of the finely ground micronutrient sources from the granular N–P–K fertilizers will occur, resulting in nonuniform micronutrient application in the field.

The required amount of binding agent ranges from 1 to 3%, and varies with intended micronutrient concentration and with the physical state of the micronutrient source and the granular fertilizer. Water and fertilizer solutions provide chemical bonding, whereas oils and waxes provide mechanical adherence. Fertilizer solutions may promote caking after the coating procedure, so conditioning agents may be needed to prevent caking.

Relative agronomic effectiveness of micronutrients coated onto soluble granular fertilizers is similar to that with incorporation during manufacture. Chemical reactions after dissolution of the fertilizers in soil and the distribution of applied micronutrients in soil would be similar with both methods. Ellis et al. (1965) reported that pea bean yields were similar with either $ZnSO_4$ or ZnO incorporated during manufacture or coated onto a granular N–P–K fertilizer, but Zn concentrations in plant tissue were higher with

Table 14-5. Yield and Zn concentrations in pea beans, as affected by Zn sources and methods of application with a granular N-P-K fertilizer (Ellis et al., 1965).

Zn source	Method of application	Yield	Zn concentration
		kg ha^{-1}	mg kg^{-1}
--	--	1230	20
$ZnSO_4$	Blended	1660	40
$ZnSO_4$	Incorporated	1640	31
$ZnSO_4$	Coated	1670	34
ZnO	Incorporated	1620	30
ZnO	Coated	1670	26
LSD (0.05)		170	3

$ZnSO_4$ (Table 14-5). Zinc concentrations in plant tissue were highest with granular $ZnSO_4$ bulk blended with the same fertilizer. This indicates greater plant availability, probably due to a reduced rate of chemical reactions of granular $ZnSO_4$ with the N-P-K fertilizer. Ellis et al. (1965) also reported that ZnEDTA remained completely water soluble when coated onto the N-P-K fertilizer along with $MnSO_4$, but Zn was only 42% water soluble when ZnEDTA was coated with MnO onto the same fertilizer. Bean yields also were lower with the latter product.

Tanner and Grant (1973) compared several methods of applying Zn sources with a granular N-P-K fertilizer for corn in Zimbabwe. The relative agronomic effectiveness of Zn sources decreased in the order: ZnO coated, $ZnSO_4$ incorporated, and ZnO incorporated. Fine $ZnSO_4$ coated onto the N-P-K fertilizer was not included in this study.

The nature of the binding agent does not appear to affect micronutrient availability to plants. Water was used as the binding agent for $ZnSO_4$ or ZnO in the results by Ellis et al. (1965) discussed earlier. Uptake of Mn or Zn by corn or soybean was not affected by the oil binding agent used to coat MnO or ZnO onto a N-P-K fertilizer (Jones, 1969).

One of the main disadvantages of the coating method is the extra production costs associated with batch processing. Another disadvantage results when segregation of the micronutrient occurs due to failure of the binding agent. Coating micronutrients provides more flexibility than incorporation in obtaining the desired grades to meet recommended rates for specific fields. It also results in better micronutrient distribution than with bulk blending granular micronutrients while providing the same flexibility. Because of the extra production costs, the coating procedure is mainly used to add micronutrients to specialty fertilizers.

D. Mixing with Fluid Fertilizers

Micronutrients are applied with fluid N, N-P, or N-P-K fertilizers because of convenience as well as the resulting uniform application. This method is popular in supplying micronutrients, especially Zn sources with starter fertilizers. However, care must be taken to select the correct micronutrient sources that can be easily applied with fluid fertilizers.

Table 14-6. Solubility of some micronutrient sources in ammonium orthophosphate or polyphosphate fertilizer solutions (Silverberg et al., 1972).

Micronutrient source	In 8–11–0 (orthophosphate)	In 11–16–0 (polyphosphate)
	solubility, % by weight	
$Na_2B_4O_7 \cdot 10H_2O$	0.9	0.9
CuO	0.03	0.7
$CuSO_4 \cdot 5H_2O$	0.13	1.5
$Fe_2(SO_4)_3 \cdot 9H_2O$	0.08	1.0
MnO	<0.02	0.2†
$MnSO_4 \cdot H_2O$	<0.02	0.2†
$Na_2MoO_4 \cdot 2H_2O$	0.5‡	0.5‡
ZnO	0.05	3.0
$ZnSO_4 \cdot H_2O$	--	3.0§

† Largest amount tested.
‡ Precipitates formed after several days.
§ pH of 6 was maintained by adding NH_3.

Solubility of Cu, Fe, Mn, and Zn sources is greater in polyphosphates than in orthophosphate clear liquids (Table 14-6). Solubility is higher in 11–16–0 (11–37–0 oxide basis) produced from electric furnace superphosphoric acid than in 10–15–0 produced from wet-process superphosphoric acid. Solubility of these micronutrient sources is related to pH and polyphosphate content; thus, it may not be possible to achieve the desired micronutrient concentrations in fluids with low polyphosphate contents or at certain pH levels (Table 14-7).

Effectiveness of $ZnSO_4$, ZnO, or ZnEDTA for corn in orthophosphate or low (16–40%) polyphosphate suspensions has been found to be similar to that of each source applied alone to soil (Mortvedt, 1979). This suggests that these Zn sources do not react with these phosphate suspensions to form unavailable reaction products. However, agronomic effectiveness of either $ZnSO_4$ or ZnO was greater in a high (75%) polyphosphate suspension than in an orthophosphate suspension, indicating increased availability of Zn in high polyphosphate fertilizers.

Polyphosphates sequester metallic micronutrients so they can maintain higher concentrations of these cations in solution than can orthophosphates.

Table 14-7. Solubility of ZnO in ammonium polyphosphate fertilizer solutions, as affected by pH and polyphosphate contents (TVA, 1972).

Polyphosphate content	Fertilizer solution pH		
	5.0	6.0	7.0
% of total P	% Zn		
40	0.6	1.3	1.6
50	0.7	1.6	1.9
60	0.7	1.7	2.0
70	0.7	1.7	1.6
80	0.7	1.4	2.6

Sequestration is the suppression of a property or reaction of a given metal without removal of that metal from the system or phase (Smith, 1959). Sequestration by polyphosphates is accomplished mainly by bidentate or polydentate structural groups for coordination. Polyphosphates are unstable in soil and hydrolyze to orthophosphates, thus losing their sequestering properties.

In laboratory experiments, concentrations of Cu, Fe, Mn, and Zn in solutions expressed from acid soils were temporarily increased more by polyphosphates than orthophosphates applied at a rate of 112 kg of P ha^{-1} (Mortvedt & Osborn, 1977). Hydrolysis of polyphosphates was rapid; less than 25% of the applied P remained in the polyphosphate form 2 wk after soil application. Increases in micronutrient solubility were related in part to solubilization of soil organic matter by these fertilizers. Micronutrient concentrations in soil solutions of acid soils were highest after 1 wk and decreased to those of the untreated soils after 4 wk. Soluble micronutrient concentrations in neutral or calcareous soils were not affected by P applications even after 1 d. Apparently, micronutrient solubilization by polyphosphates decreased with increased soil pH. Therefore, solubilization of soil micronutrients by polyphosphates does not appear to play an important role in micronutrient nutrition of crops, since most micronutrient deficiencies occur on soils with pH levels >6.0.

Formation of reaction products due to inclusion of metallic micronutrients in polyphosphate fertilizers is related to pH and percent polyphosphate in the system as well as to properties of the metal. The ionic radii and coordination properties of the divalent cations of Cu, Fe, Mn, and Zn are similar. Their reaction products with polyphosphates are also similar. Knowledge gained in chemical studies with one metal should enable prediction of behavior with other metals, as illustrated by similar behavior of divalent Zn and Mn in Fig. 14–2.

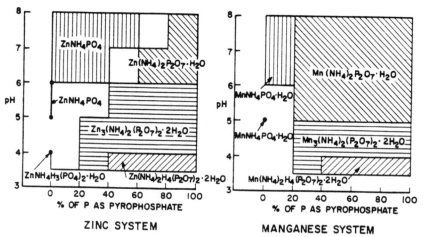

ZINC SYSTEM   MANGANESE SYSTEM

Fig. 14–2. Comparison of the reaction products formed by various Zn-ammonium polyphosphate (APP) and Mn-APP mixtures after soil application, as affected by pH and pyrophosphate content of the APP (Hossner & Blanchar, 1969, 1970).

Solubility of most micronutrient sources is low in UAN (28% N) solutions. For example, solubility of $ZnSO_4 \cdot H_2O$ was 0.5% Zn and that of $Fe(NO_3)_3 \cdot 9H_2O$ was 0.5% Fe (Silverberg et al., 1972). The resulting pH of the fertilizer solution was 3.0. When the pH was increased to between 7 and 8 by addition of NH_3, the solubility of $ZnSO_4$ and ZnO was 2% Zn, and that of three Cu sources was 0.5% Cu (Table 14-8). The solution salt-out temperature was not changed by adding either Zn source, but it was increased by including the Cu sources.

Because of their high solubilities and lower application rates, enough B or Mo can be included with fluid fertilizers to correct deficiencies at usual fertilizer application rates. Whereas most synthetic chelates are compatible with fluid fertilizers, natural organic complexes of Cu, Fe, Mn, or Zn may not be compatible with all fluid fertilizers. A jar test using the desired proportions of fluid fertilizer and intended micronutrient source should be made to determine compatibility before any micronutrient source is mixed with a fluid fertilizer for field application.

The amounts of some micronutrients that can be applied with clear liquids at the desired N-P-K rates are limited by the solubility of each micronutrient source in a given fertilizer solution. Suspension fertilizers may be used if greater amounts of micronutrients are desired. Suspensions have an advantage over clear liquids because complete solution of the micronutrient source is not needed. Micronutrient oxides may be used in suspensions at much higher concentrations than in clear liquids. Boron sources in dry form can be mixed in solution or suspension fertilizers, although the methods of incorporation are different. Storage characteristics of B-containing solutions and suspensions should be evaluated before large amounts are produced (Cole & Turner, 1986).

Micronutrient incorporation in suspensions should be performed just before application to the field. Powdered sources (-60 mesh, <0.25 mm) are suggested for incorporation with suspensions so the particles do not clog screens and also so they will remain in suspension (Mortvedt, 1984b). Incorporating micronutrients with suspensions must be performed in a manner that prevents the formation of aggregates, which are very difficult to disperse. One recommended method to incorporate dry powders directly into

Table 14-8. Solubility of Cu and Zn sources in urea-NH_4NO_3 (UAN) solution (Silverberg et al., 1972).

Micronutrient source	NH_3/Cu or Zn†	Cu or Zn	Salting-out temperature
	mol	% by wt.	°C
--	--	--	-20
Cu_2O	2.5	0.5	19
$Cu(NO_3)_2 \cdot 3H_2O$	5.0	0.5	14
$CuSO_4 \cdot 5H_2O$	4.8	0.5	17
ZnO	2.3	2.0	-21
$ZnSO_4 \cdot H_2O$	4.3	2.0	-21

† NH_3 added to maintain pH of solutions at 7 to 8.

suspension fertilizers is through use of an injector or eductor (Silverberg et al., 1972). Another method is to prewet the dry powder and mix the resulting suspension with the fluid fertilizer. Clearly, care must be taken when incorporating micronutrients into fluid fertilizers.

IV. MICRONUTRIENT MARKETING AND USE

Micronutrient use is low in comparison with amounts of N, P, and K fertilizers applied for crops annually, accounting for <1% of the total fertilizer sales in the USA (Hargett et al., 1987). Most micronutrient deficiencies are not as widespread as those of N, P, and K. Crop demands also are much lower with micronutrients. Therefore, micronutrient marketing practices may differ from those of the primary and secondary nutrients.

Many fertilizer dealers take soil and possibly plant tissue samples for their customers and send these samples to commercial or government testing laboratories. The dealer then should discuss the analytical results and fertilizer recommendations with the grower and together they should develop a fertilizer plan, including micronutrients if needed. Results of several surveys in the USA have shown that most growers depend heavily on recommendations made by their local fertilizer dealer. Therefore, the fertilizer dealer should know the most effective and economical fertilizers and methods of application for each situation to be of most help to the grower.

A. Fertilization Practices

There are two philosophies of micronutrient fertilization—insurance applications and prescription applications. The insurance or "shotgun" philosophy is to add low amounts of more than one, and sometimes all, micronutrients either to the soil or as foliar sprays. This method is designed to supply all micronutrients removed by the crop, regardless of whether micronutrient deficiencies may occur. This practice may be considered as a maintenance program.

Premium fertilizers are those that contain all micronutrients in low concentrations and are designed for the maintenance philosophy. Usually this program does not consider the specific needs of a given crop nor the existing available micronutrient levels in soil. Because some of the added micronutrients may not be required by the growing crop, this method may be wasteful.

Maintenance applications are used most often on high-value crops such as coffee (*Coffea arabica* L.), vegetables, and some fruit and nut crops. Fertilizer costs for high-value crops usually are low in comparison with the cost of other inputs, as well as the expected gross income per hectare. Micronutrient fertilizer costs also may be low in comparison with the possible loss of income due to decreased yields and/or quality of those high-value crops caused by a micronutrient deficiency.

The insurance philosophy also has been used where the micronutrient status of the soil and the nutrient needs of the crops have not yet been determined. After soil tests have assessed the nutrient status of the soil and crop needs have been determined, the growers should use the prescription philosophy for micronutrient fertilization. Now that soil and plant analyses can be used to more accurately assess micronutrient status of soils and crops, it is preferable to use these diagnostic tools as much as possible for micronutrient fertilization programs as well as those for the primary and secondary plant nutrients.

Premium fertilizers used for the insurance or maintenance philosophy generally contain micronutrients incorporated during manufacture. Sometimes these fertilizers contain low amounts of all micronutrients. However, the trend in recent years has been to produce premium fertilizers for specific crops over a wide geographic area. These products contain the desired N–P–K grade along with appreciable concentrations (0.5–2%) of one or two micronutrients for which the given crop has a higher requirement. For example, a premium fertilizer for corn may contain 2% Zn, 0.5% Mn, and lower concentrations of the other micronutrients. Premium fertilizers for soybean will contain more Mn than Zn, those for cotton contain mainly B and Mn, and those for alfalfa (*Medicago sativa* L.) contain mainly B. Because rather large tonnages of a specific grade are needed for profitable factory production, the market demand for the specific grade must be closely estimated before production.

The prescription philosophy uses results of soil tests and plant analyses as well as other information to help determine which micronutrients are in short supply. Only needed micronutrients are applied to the soil or as foliar sprays, depending on the crop and soil situation. It is recommended that only the required nutrients be applied at rates necessary to obtain a specific yield goal for the crop in a given field. This helps prevent application of excessive amounts of micronutrients and omits the application of those micronutrients already present at adequate levels. These more precise recommendations also reduce the possibility of nutrient antagonisms in plant nutrition due to unbalanced ratios of micronutrients in the soil.

Ideally, the prescription philosophy should be used for most field crops, especially those of lower value per hectare. Economic returns are lower for these crops, so fertilizer costs should be minimized, but still provide sufficient micronutrients for maximum economic yields. This can best be done by determining the micronutrient status of the soil before application, and then applying only those micronutrients needed by the crop. Therefore, use of the prescription philosophy requires soil testing, plant analyses, and other knowledge of crop needs and responses on a given soil. It is a much more intense program than that needed with the insurance or maintenance philosophy, but it is also more economical.

The prescription philosophy requires formulation of different fertilizer grades for almost every field. Such formulations may be possible with bulk-blended granular fertilizers and with most fluid fertilizers, but not with granular fertilizers containing incorporated micronutrients. Granular fertilizers con-

taining coated micronutrients also may fit this philosophy, although costs
to change formulations and produce these fertilizers generally restrict their
use to specialty fertilizers for high-value crops. Because of costs associated
with extra handling for the above methods of providing micronutrients, a
compromise method involves using those premium fertilizers formulated for
specific crops even though they may contain low concentrations of unneed-
ed micronutrients.

B. Fertilizer Regulations

Regulations concerning handling and sale of micronutrients vary considerably. Each state in the USA is responsible for such regulations. In 1963,
the AAPFCO, which includes members from the appropriate regulatory
bodies in each state, formulated a general proposal for micronutrient labeling. A uniform state fertilizer bill listed the minimum percentages of each
micronutrient that could be accepted for registration. The bill also suggested the allowable deficiencies of each micronutrient from those guaranteed
by the manufacturer on the fertilizer label. This bill was proposed to help
standardize regulations to simplify interstate shipping of these fertilizers.

After numerous revisions, the AAPFCO published the uniform state
fertilizer bill, which suggested regulations for all plant nutrients in 1968. Since
then, over 38 states have adopted this bill. Increasing numbers of fertilizers
that contain micronutrients are being registered. Many N–P–K fertilizers contain one or more micronutrients incorporated during manufacture. Frequency
in the number of deficiencies below guaranteed micronutrient levels appears
to be similar to the number of deficiencies reported for the other nutrients.

The suggested minimum percentages of micronutrients that are acceptable for registration on fertilizer labels are shown in Table 14–9. These percentages are not to be considered as recommended levels; rather, they are
simply concentrations that can be determined in the government control and
inspection laboratories. One of the problems encountered when these low
levels are allowed to be listed on fertilizer labels is that these amounts applied to soils at the usual N–P–K rates are too low to supply the recommended
micronutrient rates to crops if there are micronutrient deficiencies, as shown
in Table 14–9.

The uniform state fertilizer bill requires only that the total amount of
micronutrient be guaranteed. This total amount may not be completely available to plants because of chemical reactions with various components of the
N–P–K fertilizer, as discussed in Section III-A of this chapter. Therefore,
further information about the micronutrient source and method of manufacture may be needed to predict the effect of a given product in supplying available micronutrients for a specific crop.

Many micronutrient sources are sold separately for application in foliar
sprays, bulk blending or coating onto granular fertilizers, or mixing with fluid
fertilizers. The fertilizers obviously will contain much higher concentrations
than the minimum levels listed in Table 14-9. However, the guaranteed
amount on the label again provides only the total amount, which may not

Table 14-9. Suggested minimum percentages that can be guaranteed on a fertilizer label and their amounts applied with N-P-K fertilizers as related to recommended rates.

Micronutrient	Minimum guarantee[†]	Micronutrient rate when N-P-K fertilizer applied at 500 kg ha^{-1}	Range of recommended rates[‡]
	%	kg ha^{-1}	
B	0.02	0.1	0.5-4
Cu	0.05	0.25	5-20
Fe	0.10	0.5	--
Mn	0.05	0.25	5-20
Mo	0.0005	0.0025	0.03-0.20
Zn	0.05	0.25	1-10

† From Association of American Plant Food Control Officials (1968).
‡ From inorganic sources; soil applications of Fe are not recommended.

be directly related to plant availability. Some states are considering inclusion of a second requirement on the label, percent water-soluble micronutrient, in addition to total amount (Warren, 1988). This would give the user some knowledge of the micronutrient source and method of processing. It may be especially important in labeling of micronutrient oxysulfates, such as Mn-oxysulfates and Zn-oxysulfates.

As discussed in Section I-A of this chapter, the level of water-soluble Mn or Zn increases directly with degree of acidulation of the respective oxides with H_2SO_4. Agronomic results generally have shown that immediate availability to plants is directly related to percentage of water-soluble micronutrient in the fertilizer. Uptake of Mn by corn increased with the percentage of water-soluble Mn in seven Mn sources (Miner et al., 1986). Corn forage yields and Zn uptake also increased with level of water-soluble Zn (up to 50% of the total Zn) in NH_4NO_3, MAP, or APP fertilizers containing varying proportions of $ZnSO_4$ and ZnO (Giordano & Mortvedt, 1969).

Because agronomic effectiveness of B and Mo sources is not affected by inclusion with other fertilizers, the total concentration of these micronutrients in fertilizers should provide sufficient information to the user.

Reporting chelated micronutrients on fertilizer labels also has caused some concern. Many micronutrient chelates are more costly and may be more effective per unit of micronutrient; therefore, lower amounts of these sources may supply the needed micronutrient. Relative agronomic effectiveness of synthetic chelates, natural organic complexes, and inorganic sources was discussed in Section I of this chapter. Because there are conditions in which chelates are considered the most effective sources, it has become popular to include the phrase "contains chelated micronutrients" on the fertilizer label. This phrase may imply that all of the micronutrient is in chelate form when, in fact, only a small portion may be chelated. Chelates also may react with other components of N-P-K fertilizers to change the amount of micronutrient remaining in chelate form. Some states are considering legislation that requires that the label include the fraction of the total micronutrient which is in chelated form, and also that it list the type of chelate and/or natural organic complex. Inclusion of such requirements in regulations requires that appropriate analytical methods be developed for use by the fertilizer control laboratories.

The uniform state fertilizer bill also suggests that fertilizers containing >0.03% B or >0.001% Mo in water-soluble form should include a warning or caution statement on the label. This is done to help prevent toxicities to B-sensitive plants through misuse of boronated fertilizers and to act as a safeguard against Mo toxicity to animals resulting from consumption of forage with high Mo concentrations.

C. Consumption Data

Data on micronutrient use has not been as carefully recorded as that for the primary nutrients. There may be numerous reasons for this paucity of data, but the main reason appears related to the relatively larger number of micronutrient producers per unit of production. Many of these companies may produce only one micronutrient source and sell their entire supply to one dealer. Another reason concerns the increased use of industrial by-products that contain micronutrients; companies may sell these by-products to wholesalers or directly to fertilizer dealers. A third reason may be that governmental organizations have concentrated their efforts on collecting N-P-K consumption data, which is >95% of the total fertilizer volume in most countries.

In 1967, the Crop Reporting Board of the Statistical Reporting Service, USDA, began collecting information on micronutrient use on a state-by-state basis. Data were obtained from known producers of Cu, Fe, Mn, Mo, and Zn sources for application with N-P-K fertilizers and for direct application to soil or by foliar sprays. Boron use data were not included since there were so few producers. However, B use in the USA was estimated at 4250 metric tons in 1986 (Lyday, 1988).

The first USDA data in the 1967–1968 reporting year showed that use of Zn and Mn was much higher than that of Cu, Fe, and Mo (Table 14–10). Highest use of Zn and Mn would be expected because these micronutrients are mainly applied to corn, wheat, soybean, cotton, and rice (*Oryza sativa* L.), which are grown over the largest area in the USA. Amounts of Cu and Fe used in the USA decreased from 1968 to 1972 and increased thereafter. However, the amount of Cu sold in 1984 was still lower than in 1967–1968.

Table 14-10. Amounts of micronutrients sold in the USA (USDA, 1968, 1972, 1976, 1980, 1984).

Year	Cu	Fe	Mn	Mo	Zn
			1000 metric t†		
1967–1968	2.2	3.1	10.5	0.07	13.1
1971–1972	0.6	1.2	11.2	0.09	14.4
1975–1976	0.5	2.3	8.1	0.10	14.7
1979–1980	1.5	5.1	13.2	0.12	40.2
1983–1984	1.1	5.9	15.1	‡	37.3

† Amounts expressed on elemental basis.   ‡ Not reported.

Decreased use of Cu after 1967–1968 was related to lower consumption in Florida where recommended Cu application rates were decreased. Marked residual effects of applied Cu in soils may result in toxicities if annual application rates are too high; toxicities of Cu may be especially prevalent on acid, sandy soils. Consumption of Mo is very low because of the low recommended rates (30–200 g ha^{-1}) and relatively sparse areas of Mo deficiencies in the USA.

Data in Table 14–10 shows a dramatic increase in Zn consumption from 1976 to 1980. While actual Zn usage did increase during this period, the major reason for this increase was a change in reporting procedure, which included more producers of Zn sources, especially some industrial by-products. The relatively smaller increase in Mn use mainly resulted from including more industrial by-products as Mn sources.

The data in Table 14–10 are reported on an elemental basis, so the actual amount of micronutrient fertilizer use is much higher. This method of reporting is necessary since micronutrient concentrations in all of these fertilizers vary considerably. Questions concerning the relative amounts of micronutrients sold in each class are frequently asked. This type of information was not requested in the reporting procedures used by the USDA. However, most micronutrient fertilizers are inorganic sources, mainly oxides and sulfates, as discussed earlier.

In 1984, the USDA ceased collecting all fertilizer consumption data, and this function was assumed by the National Fertilizer Development Center of the TVA. With the change in responsibility, collection of micronutrient use data was discontinued.

Few micronutrient consumption data have been collected in other countries, probably for the same reasons given earlier in this section. Such data would be valuable to draw attention to micronutrient needs in countries where such deficiencies have been confirmed.

V. SUMMARY

Micronutrient deficiencies are widespread because of increased nutrient demands due to more intense cropping practices and also to farming of marginal lands. Sources of micronutrients are classified as inorganic, synthetic chelates, and natural organic complexes. Fritted micronutrients are less commonly used now than 25 yr ago. Micronutrient sources vary considerably in physical state, chemical reactivity, cost per unit of micronutrient, and relative availability to plants. Some industrial by-products also are used as micronutrient fertilizers because of their lower costs.

Because of the relatively low recommended rates (< 10 kg ha^{-1}), micronutrient sources often are applied with N–P–K fertilizers. This practice assures more uniform micronutrient application in the field. Methods of application include incorporation of micronutrients during the manufacture of N–P–K fertilizers, bulk blending with or coating onto granular fertilizers, or mixing micronutrients with fluid fertilizers. Chemical reactions between the micronutrient source and one or more components of the N–P–K fertilizer may occur during mixing or after application to the soil. Plant availability of the micronutrient source may be affected by these reactions. Therefore, care must be taken to select the most effective and economical micronutrient sources for each intended method of application.

Whereas micronutrient fertilizer technology is well defined, it is not wide-ly understood. It is important for dealers and others involved in advising growers about micronutrient fertilization to understand the importance of supplying micronutrients in forms that are available to plants at the time they are needed for optimum crop production. This requires continued studies on comparisons of the available sources and methods of application for crops under various soil-climate conditions, and the transfer of this technology to the fertilizer dealers and growers.

REFERENCES

Achorn, F.P., and J.J. Mortvedt. 1977. Addition of secondary and micronutrients to granular fertilizers. p. 304–332. *In* Proc. Int. Conf. on Granular Fertilizers and Their Production, London, England. 13–15 Nov. British Sulfur Corp., London.

Allen, S.E., and G.L. Terman. 1966. Response of maize and sudangrass to zinc in granular micronutrients. p. 255–266. *In* G.V. Lacks (ed.) Soil chemistry and fertility. Trans. Joint Meet. Commissions II and IV. Int. Soc. Soil Sci., Aberdeen, Scotland.

Association of American Plant Food Control Officials. 1968. Uniform state fertilizer bill. AAPFCO Publ. 31 (Available from H.P. Moore [Treas.], 8995 E. Main Street, Reynolds-burg, OH 43068.)

Brinkerhoff, F., B.G. Ellis, J.F. Davis, and J. Melton. 1966. Field and laboratory studies with zinc fertilization of pea beans and corn in 1965. Michigan Agric. Exp. Stn. Q. Bull. 48:344–356.

Cole, C.A., Jr., and J.R. Turner. 1986. Incorporating boron in fluid fertilizers. Abstracts, 192nd Meeting of Am. Chem. Soc., Anaheim, CA. Am. Chem. Soc., Washington, DC.

Cunningham, H.G. 1972. Trends in the use of micronutrients. p. 419–430. *In* J.J. Mortvedt et al. (ed.) Micronutrients in agriculture. 1st ed. SSSA, Madison, WI.

Ellis, B.G., J.F. Davis, and W.H. Judy. 1965. Effect of method of incorporation of zinc in fertilizer on zinc uptake and yield of pea beans (*Phaseolus vulgaris*). Soil Sci. Soc. Am. Proc. 29:635–636.

Gilkes, R.J., and S.B. Sadleir. 1981. Dissolution of granulated CuZn-superphosphate in soils. Fert. Res. 2:147–157.

Giordano, P.M., and J.J. Mortvedt. 1969. Response of several corn hybrids to level of water-soluble Zn in fertilizers. Soil Sci. Soc. Am. Proc. 33:145–148.

Giordano, P.M., and J.J. Mortvedt. 1972. Agronomic effectiveness of micronutrients in macro-nutrient fertilizers. p. 505–524. *In* J.J. Mortvedt et al. (ed.) Micronutrients in agriculture. 1st ed. SSSA, Madison, WI.

Giordano, P.M., J.J. Mortvedt, and R.I. Papendick. 1966. Response of corn (*Zea mays* L.) to zinc, as affected by placement and nitrogen source. Soil Sci. Soc. Am. Proc. 30:767–770.

Hargett, N.L., and J.T. Berry. 1988. Today's retail fertilizer industry. Tennessee Valley Authority, Natl. Fertilizer Development Ctr. Cir. Z-239, TVA, Muscle Shoals, AL.

Hargett, N.L., J.T. Berry, and S.L. McKinney. 1987. Commercial fertilizers. Tennessee Valley Authority Bull. Y-199, TVA, Muscle Shoals, AL.

Harrison, C.P. 1981. Granulation of fertilizer borate. U.S. Patent 4 256 489. Date issued: 17 March.

Hergert, G.W., G.W. Rehm, and R.A. Wiese. 1984. Field evaluation of zinc sources band ap-plied in ammonium polyphosphate suspension. Soil Sci. Soc. Am. J. 48:1190–1193.

Hignett, T.P. 1964. Supplying micronutrients in solid bulk-blended fertilizers. Commer. Fert. Plant Food Ind. 108(1):23–25.

Holden, E.R. 1959. Glass as a boron source. Relationship of surface area and particle-size distribution of borosilicate glasses to boron status in alfalfa. J. Agric. Food Chem. 7:756–762.

Hossner, L.R., and R.W. Blanchar. 1969. The utilization of applied zinc as affected by pH and pyrophosphate content of ammonium phosphates. Soil Sci. Soc. Am. Proc. 33:618–621.

Hossner, L.R., and R.W. Blanchar. 1970. Manganese reactions and availability as influenced by pH and pyrophosphate content of ammonium polyphosphate fertilizers. Soil Sci. Soc. Am. Proc. 34:509–512.

Hossner, L.R., and G.E. Richards. 1968. The effect of phosphorus source on the movement and uptake of band-applied manganese. Soil Sci. Soc. Am. Proc. 32:83–85.

Jackson, W.A., N.A. Heinly, and J.H. Caro. 1962. Solubility status of zinc carriers intermixed with N-P-K fertilizers. J. Agric. Food Chem. 10:361–364.

Jones, J.B., Jr. 1969. Effect of oil coating a fertilizer on yield and the uptake of manganese and zinc by corn and soybeans. Agron. J. 61:476–477.

Judy, W., G. Lessman, T. Rozycka, L. Robertson, and B.G. Ellis. 1964. Field and laboratory studies with zinc fertilization of pea beans. Michigan Agric. Exp. Stn. Q. Bull. 46:386–400.

Lehr, J.R. 1972. Chemical reactions of micronutrients in fertilizers. p. 459–503. In J.J. Mortvedt et al. (ed.) Micronutrients in agriculture. 1st ed. SSSA, Madison, WI.

Lehr, J.R., E.H. Brown, A.W. Frazier, J.P. Smith, and R.D. Thrasher. 1967. Crystallographic properties of fertilizer compounds. Tennessee Valley Authority Bull. 6. TVA, Muscle Shoals, AL.

Lyday, P.A. 1988. Boron. p. 167–175. In 1986 minerals yearbook. Vol. 1. Bureau of Mines, U.S. Dep. of Interior, U.S. Gov. Print. Office, Washington, DC.

Mascagni, H.J., Jr., and F.R. Cox. 1985. Evaluation of inorganic and organic manganese fertilizer sources. Soil Sci. Soc. Am. J. 49:458–461.

McCrary, A.L., and W.L. Howard. 1979. Chelating agents. p. 339–368. In Kirk-Othmer encyclopedia of chemical technology. Vol. 5. 3rd ed. John Wiley and Sons, New York.

Miner, G.S., S. Traore, and M.R. Tucker. 1986. Crop response to starter fertilizer acidity and manganese materials varying in water solubility. Agron. J. 78:291–295.

Mortvedt, J.J. 1968a. Crop response to zinc in ammoniated phosphate fertilizers. J. Agric. Food Chem. 16:241–245.

Mortvedt, J.J. 1968b. Availability of boron in various boronated fertilizers. Soil Sci. Soc. Am. Proc. 32:433–437.

Mortvedt, J.J. 1979. Crop response to zinc sources applied alone or with suspensions. Fert. Solutions 23(3):64, 66, 70, 75–79.

Mortvedt, J.J. 1984a. Micronutrients with granular fertilizer. Custom. Applic. 14(3):46–48, 50, 59–60.

Mortvedt, J.J. 1984b. Suspensions as a micronutrient carrier. Custom. Applic. 14(3):70, 72, 74, 76, 80, 82.

Mortvedt, J.J. 1985. Plant uptake of heavy metals in zinc fertilizers made from industrial by-products. J. Environ. Qual. 14:424–427.

Mortvedt, J.J., and F.R. Cox. 1985. Production, marketing, and use of calcium, magnesium, and micronutrient fertilizers. p. 455–481. In O.P. Engelstad (ed.) Fertilizer technology and use. 3rd ed. SSSA, Madison, WI.

Mortvedt, J.J., and P.M. Giordano. 1969. Availability to corn of zinc applied with various macronutrient fertilizers. Soil Sci. 108:180–187.

Mortvedt, J.J., and G. Osborn. 1977. Micronutrient concentrations in soil solution after ammonium phosphate applications. Soil Sci. Soc. Am. J. 41:1004–1009.

Mutatkar, V.K., B.L. Parcik, R.N. Sahay, and S.P. Dhua. 1977. Efficiency of zinc incorporated urea on wheat in two Bihar soils. J. Nucl. Agric. Biol. 6(4):148–152.

Norvell, W.A. 1972. Equilibria of metal chelates in soil solution. p. 115–138. In J.J. Mortvedt et al. (ed.) Micronutrients in agriculture. 1st ed. SSSA, Madison, WI.

Page, N.R. 1956. Minor elements for field crops. South Carolina Agric. Exp. Stn. Cir. 104.

Picanso, D. 1984. Chelated micronutrients: Why, when, and how to use them. Farm Chem. 147(5):38–41.

Rowell, A.W.G., and P.M. Grant. 1975. A comparison of fertilizer borate and colemanite incorporated in granular fertilizers. Rhod. J. Agric. Res. 13:63–66.

Sauchelli, V. 1969. Trace elements in agriculture. Van Nostrand Reinhold Co., New York.

Silverberg, J., R.D. Young, and G. Hoffmeister, Jr. 1972. Preparation of fertilizers containing micronutrients. p. 431–458. In J.J. Mortvedt et al. (ed.) Micronutrients in agriculture. 1st ed. SSSA, Madison, WI.

Smith, R.L. 1959. The sequestration of metals. The Macmillan Co., New York.

Tanner, P.D., and P.M. Grant. 1973. Effectiveness of zincated fertilizers for young maize as influenced by fertilizer pH and method of applying zinc. Rhod. J. Agric. Res. 11:69–75.

Tanner, P.D., and P.M. Grant. 1974. The effectiveness of NPK fertilizer as carriers of zinc for maize under field conditions. Rhod. J. Agric. Res. 12:163–168.

Tennessee Valley Authority. 1972. Solubility of zinc in ammonium polyphosphate liquid fertilizers. p. 6–7. In Proc. Ninth TVA Fert. Tech. Demonstration, Muscle Shoals, AL. 17–18 Oct. Tennessee Valley Authority, Muscle Shoals, AL.

United States Department of Agriculture, Crop Reporting Board, Statistical Reporting Service. 1968. Commercial fertilizers: Consumption for year ended June 30, 1968. U.S. Gov. Print. Office, Washington, DC.

United States Department of Agriculture, Crop Reporting Board, Statistical Reporting Service. 1972. Commercial fertilizers: Consumption for year ended June 30, 1972. U.S. Gov. Print. Office, Washington, DC.

United States Department of Agriculture, Crop Reporting Board, Statistical Reporting Service. 1976. Commercial fertilizers: Consumption for year ended June 30, 1976. U.S. Gov. Print. Office, Washington, DC.

United States Department of Agriculture, Crop Reporting Board, Statistical Reporting Service. 1980. Commercial fertilizers: Consumption for year ended June 30, 1980. U.S. Gov. Print. Office, Washington, DC.

United States Department of Agriculture, Crop Reporting Board, Statistical Reporting Service. 1984. Commercial fertilizers: Consumption for year ended June 30, 1984. U.S. Gov. Print. Office, Washington, DC.

Viets, F.G., Jr., L.C. Brown, and C.L. Crawford. 1957. The effect of nitrogen and types of nitrogen carriers on plant uptake of indigenous and applied zinc. Soil Sci. Soc. Am. Proc. 21:197–201.

Warren, J.D. 1988. Basis for Florida fertilizer rule change. Proc. Soil Crop Sci. Soc. Fla. 47:1–4.

Chapter 15

Fertilizer Applications for Correcting Micronutrient Deficiencies

D. C. MARTENS, *Virginia Polytechnic Institute and State University, Blacksburg, Virginia*

D. T. WESTERMANN, *Snake River Conservation Research Center, Kimberly, Idaho*

Increases in crop yields from application of B, Cu, Fe, Mn, Mo, and/or Zn occur in many parts of the world including numerous regions of the USA. There is growing awareness that micronutrient deficiencies may limit crop yields even though exceedingly small amounts are required by plants (Table 15-1). Various reasons can be provided to account for the current increased recognition of micronutrient needs in crop production. These include (i) improved soil test and tissue analysis methods for diagnosis of micronutrient deficiencies; (ii) accumulated data on crop responses to micronutrient applications on diverse soil types; (iii) micronutrient removal from long-term crop production; (iv) increased use of high-analysis fertilizers with low amounts of micronutrient impurities; (v) higher micronutrient requirements accompanying higher crop yields; (vi) less use of animal manures in crop production; and (vii) induction of micronutrient deficiencies by high P concentrations from long-term applications (Berger, 1962; Vitosh et al., 1981). Attention will be directed in this chapter toward correction of B, Cu, Fe, Mn, Mo, and Zn deficiencies in plants grown under diverse management regimes. Literature on Cl, Co, and Ni deficiencies also will be discussed.

I. BORON

Soil and environmental factors influencing B availability to plants are discussed in Ch. 11 of this book and in other reviews (Keren & Bingham, 1985; Gupta, 1972a; Gupta et al., 1985). Boron deficiencies in the USA occur on low-organic-matter, acid, sandy and silt loam soils, particularly in the South Atlantic and Pacific area states, although B deficencies were report-

Table 15-1. Approximate micronutrient uptake for the production of high yields of alfalfa, corn, and soybean (Mengel, 1980).

Micronutrient	Nutrient uptake by		
	13.4 t alfalfa	9.4 t corn	4.0 t soybean
	kg ha^{-1}		
B	0.33	0.18	0.11
Cu	0.07	0.11	0.11
Fe	2.02	2.13	1.90
Mn	0.67	0.33	0.67
Mo	0.02	0.01	0.01
Zn	0.27	0.30	0.22

ed in 43 states (Sparr, 1970). Deficiencies are more prevalent during drouth and availabilities generally decrease when acid soils are limed. Most dicotyledons require more B than do monocotyledons. Vegetables of the *Cruciferous* and *Umbelliferous* families have a high B requirement and tolerate high B concentrations that are toxic to some other crops (Table 15-2). Crop yield and quality responses to B fertilization may not be consistent because of soil and other environmental interactions affecting B availability and plant growth.

A. Sources

The B concentrations of the common sources of B fertilizers are provided in Table 15-3. The Na borates are generally used for soil application, except Solubor® which is used for both soil and foliar applications because of its solubility. Boric acid has only received limited use. Borax is a popular water-soluble B fertilizer, but it readily leaches in sandy soils. Colemanite and B frits may be used successfully on soils subject to leaching losses if their particle size is small enough. Manures, sewage sludges, composts, waste effluents, and fly ash materials are also readily available B sources for plants, but B toxicity can be a problem at high application rates (Adriano et al., 1980; Kardos et al., 1977).

B. Application Methods and Rates

Soil applications and foliar spraying are the two principal methods of applying B. Boron fertilizers are mixed and applied with other fertilizer materials to correct potential B deficiencies for cultivated annual crops. Foliar sprays are used after these crops are established and for several perennial agricultural crops.

1. Soil Application

Selected field experiments in which different B rates were used are summarized in Table 15-4. Legumes and certain root crops required 2 to 4 kg B ha^{-1}, while lower rates were necessary for maximum yields in other crops to avoid toxicity problems.

Table 15-2. Relative sensitivities of selected crops to micronutrient deficiencies.

Crop‡	Sensitivity to micronutrient deficiency†					
	B	Cu	Fe	Mn	Mo	Zn
Alfalfa	High	High	Medium	Medium	Medium	Low
Asparagus	Low	Low	Medium	Low	Low	Low
Barley	Low	Medium	High	Medium	Low	Medium
Bean	Low	Low	High	High	Medium	High
Blueberry	Low	Medium	--§	Low	--	--
Broccoli	Medium	Medium	High	Medium	High	--
Cabbage	Medium	Medium	Medium	Medium	Medium	--
Carrot	Medium	Medium	--	Medium	Low	Low
Cauliflower	High	Medium	High	Medium	High	--
Celery	High	Medium	--	Medium	Low	--
Clover	Medium	Medium	--	Medium	Medium	Low
Cucumber	Low	Medium	--	Medium	--	--
Corn	Low	Medium	Medium	Medium	Low	High
Grass	Low	Low	High	Medium	Low	Low
Lettuce	Medium	High	--	High	High	Medium
Oat	Low	High	Medium	High	Low	Low
Onion	Low	High	--	High	High	High
Parsnip	Medium	Medium	--	Medium	--	--
Pea	Low	Low	--	High	Medium	Low
Peppermint	Low	Low	Low	Medium	Low	Low
Potato	Low	Low	--	High	Low	Medium
Radish	Medium	Medium	--	High	Medium	--
Rye	Low	Low	--	Low	Low	Low
Sorghum	Low	Medium	High	High	Low	High
Spearmint	Low	Low	--	Medium	Low	Low
Soybean	Low	Low	High	High	Medium	Medium
Spinach	Medium	High	High	High	High	--
Sudan grass	Low	High	High	High	Low	Medium
Sugar beet	High	Medium	High	Medium	Medium	Medium
Sweet corn	Medium	Medium	Medium	Medium	Low	High
Table beet	High	High	High	High	High	Medium
Tomato	Medium	Medium	High	Medium	Medium	Medium
Turnip	High	Medium	--	Medium	Medium	--
Wheat	Low	High	Low	High	Low	Low

† Based on data from Robertson et al. (1981), Robertson and Lucas (1981), Vitosh et al. (1981), Alloway and Tills (1984), and Fenster et al. (1984).

‡ Asparagus (*Asparagus officinalis*); blueberry (*Vaccinium corymbosum*); broccoli (*Brassica oleracea botrytis*); parsnip (*Pastinaca sativa*); peppermint (*Mentha piperita*); radish (*Raphanus sativa*); rye (*Secale cereale*); spearmint (*Mentha spicata*); sudan grass (*Sorghum vulgare sudanese*); turnip (*Brassica rapa* var. *rapa*).

§ Inadequate available data to categorize into low, medium, or high sensitivity groups.

Boron fertilizers are generally broadcast and incorporated prior to seeding crops not planted in rows; e.g., legumes, rape (*Brassica napus*), and grasses (Gupta, 1984; Plank & Martens, 1974; Nuttall et al., 1987; Monson & Gaines, 1986). Once established, broadcast applications are also recommended for these crops (Rehm et al., 1987; Gerwing et al., 1988). Broadcast applications are particularly effective around trees and grapevines (*Vitis vinifera* L.) on coarser-textured soils (Boswell et al., 1980; Hopmans & Flinn, 1984).

Table 15-3. Boron sources used for correcting B deficiencies in plants.†

Source	Formula	B, $g\ kg^{-1}$‡
Boric acid	H_3BO_3	170
Boron frits	Fritted glass	20–60
Borax	$Na_2B_4O_7 \cdot 10H_2O$	110
Colemanite	$CaB_6O_{11} \cdot 5H_2O$	100
Sodium pentaborate	$Na_2B_{10}O_{16} \cdot 10H_2O$	180
Sodium tetraborate: Borate-45	$Na_2B_4O_7 \cdot 5H_2O$	140
Borate-65	$Na_2B_4O_7$	200
Solubor® §	$Na_2B_4O_7 \cdot 5H_2O$ $+ Na_2B_{10}O_{16} \cdot 10H_2O$	200

† Data from Murphy and Walsh (1972), Keren and Bingham (1985), Gupta (1979a), and Gupta et al. (1985).
‡ Approximate concentration.
§ Solubor is partially dehydrated borax.

Boron concentrations in rutabaga (*Brassica napobrassica*) leaf tissue were greater when B was applied in fertilizer bands compared with similar B rates broadcast (Gupta & Cutcliffe, 1978). Banding 1.12 kg B ha^{-1} resulted in higher B concentrations than broadcasting 2.24 kg B ha^{-1}. Similar results are reported by Touchton and Boswell (1975a, b) for corn (*Zea mays* L.) and soybean [*Glycine max* (L.) Merr.]. Boron application sometimes improve crop quality and economic yields, but not total yields (Gupta & Cutcliffe, 1978; Hemphill et al., 1982; Morrill et al., 1977). Boron should neither be placed in contact with the seed nor should broadcast rates be used when banding because of potential toxicity problems.

The B contained in fly ash, scrubber and sewage sludges, municipal composts, and wastewater effluents is readily available to plants (Plank & Martens, 1974; Adriano et al., 1980; Kardos et al., 1977). A wide range of B concentrations exists among, as well as within, these materials. The B availability from these materials when broadcast is similar to that from traditional

Table 15-4. Rates of B application for correction of B deficiencies of various crops.

Crop	B source	B rate, kg ha^{-1} Range	Optimum	Application method	Reference
Alfalfa	$Na_2B_4O_7$	1.12–4.48	2.24	Broadcast	Gupta, 1984
Alfalfa	Fly ash	1.7–3.4	1.7	Broadcast	Plank & Martens, 1974
Cole crops	$Na_2B_4O_7$	--	0.45	Banded	Gupta & Cutcliffe, 1975
Grape	Solubor	0.38–3.05	0.76	Broadcast	Boswell et al., 1980
Pine tree†	$Na_2B_4O_7 \cdot 10H_2O$	5.7–17.0	5.7	Broadcast	Hopmans & Flinn, 1984
Rapeseed	H_3BO_3	0–2.8	1.4	Broadcast	Nuttall et al., 1987
Soybean	$Na_2B_4O_7 \cdot 5H_2O$	0.28–2.24	1.12	Broadcast	Touchton & Boswell, 1975b
Strawberry†	$Na_2B_4O_7$	0.56–2.24	1.12	Broadcast	Blatt, 1982
Sugarbeet	Solubor	2.2–6.6	2.2	Banded	Voth et al., 1979
Table beet	Solubor	3.4–6.7	3.4	Broadcast	Hemphill et al., 1982

† Pine tree (*Pinus radiata* D. Don); strawberry (*Fragaria ananassa*).

B fertilizer materials (Table 15-3). Boron toxicity and crop yield reductions can occur at B application rates greater than those recommended (Walker & Dowdy, 1980; Purves & Mackenzie, 1973; Ransome & Dowdy, 1987).

2. Foliar Application

Foliar sprays are widely used on perennial crops such as nuts, vines, and fruit orchards because they have consistently produced better results than soil applications. Hanson and Breen (1985) and Shrestha et al. (1987) found that spring spray applications of 300 to 600 mg B L^{-1} on hazelnut (*Corylus americana* Marshall) and prune (*Prunus domestica*) trees increased fruit set and B concentrations in plant tissues. Environmental conditions appear to have more influence on a spring application than on a fall application after petal fall.

Foliar applications of B to annual crops are superior to broadcast applications, and equivalent or slightly more effective than banded applications (Touchton & Boswell, 1975a, b; Gupta & Cutcliffe, 1978). A general foliar spray with B is recommended on peanut (*Arachis hypogaea* L.) at early bloom (Hill & Morrill, 1974; Donohue et al., 1979). Effective foliar application rates are 10 to 50% of that required by the broadcasting method, although repeated applications may be necessary because of B immobility. Phytotoxicity may be a problem at higher application rates.

C. Residual Effects of Boron Application

Boron fertilizers have a longer residual effect on high silt and clay soils compared with that on sandy soils. Lower solubility materials also have more residual effects. Foliar-applied materials on perennial crops usually show no residual effects during the year following applications, whereas soil applications do. A broadcast application of 2 kg B ha^{-1} as Borate-65 on a loam soil provided sufficient B for 2 yr of alfalfa (*Medicago sativa* L.) and red clover (*Trifolium pratense* L.) (Gupta, 1984). High application rates, 4 to 8 kg B ha^{-1}, on soils susceptible to leaching losses were not toxic to later cereal and bean (*Phaseolus vulgaris* L.) crops (Gupta & Cutcliffe, 1982, 1984). Annual applications of 1.2 to 3.6 kg B ha^{-1} on crimson clover (*Trifolium incarnatum* L.) for 4 yr did not adversely affect subsequent B-sensitive crops, even though B had accumulated in the profiles of the heavier-textured soils (Wear, 1957).

D. Toxicity Effects of Boron

Indigenous concentrations of B in virgin soils are generally not sufficient to cause B toxicity, except in arid and semiarid regions where salts accumulate. Boron toxicity from irrigation waters is usually caused by B salts concentrating in the soil via evapotranspiration processes. Some wastewater effluents contain sufficient B to be toxic when applied to satisfy evapotranspiration demand (Kardos et al., 1977).

Potential B toxicity exists when fertilizer application rates are >3 to 4 kg B ha^{-1} for annual crops (Touchton & Boswell, 1975a, b) and perennial crops (Gupta, 1984; Blatt, 1982). This is a particular problem with high application rates of scrubber sludge, fly ash (Walker & Dowdy, 1980; Plank & Martens, 1974; Ransome & Dowdy, 1987; Adriano et al., 1980), municipal compost (Purves & Mackenzie, 1973), and certain waste effluents (Kardos et al., 1977). Banding B fertilizers has greater potential to result in B toxicity than broadcasting and at lower application rates. In general, most B toxicity problems occur from distribution and overfertilization problems. Under these conditions, tolerant crops should be planted if possible (Gupta, 1979a; Gupta et al., 1985).

II. COPPER

Copper deficiencies are most prevalent in organic soils, but also occur in sandy-textured soils, in mineral soils with high organic matter contents, and in calcareous mineral soils (Mortvedt, 1982a; Markarim & Cox, 1983). Complexation reactions between Cu^{2+} and functional groups of organic matter cause Cu deficiencies in peats and mucks even at pH $\leq$ 5.5 (Powell, 1975). Low Cu concentrations in parent material, such as quartz, lead to low amounts of available Cu in some sandy-textured soils (Alloway & Tills, 1984). Soils that developed from limestone often contain inadequate Cu due to a low total Cu content coupled with an alkaline pH (Gartrell, 1981; Alloway & Tills, 1984).

Occurrences of Cu deficiencies frequently reflect the management practices used during crop production. Overliming acid soils may cause Cu deficiencies by increasing the amount of Cu complexed by soil organic matter, adsorbed on surfaces of inorganic soil components, and occluded by soil hydroxides and oxides. Application of N fertilizers may cause rapid plant growth rates and accentuate Cu deficiencies by exhausting the Cu in soil solution (Alloway & Tills, 1984). Higher yields from N and P applications increase the crop demand for Cu and, hence, induce Cu deficiency on some soils (DeKock et al., 1971; Robson & Reuter, 1981; Vitosh et al., 1981). Induction of Cu deficiency from N and P fertilization is most severe on soils with an inherently low ability to supply Cu. Plants differ widely in susceptibility to Cu deficiency (Table 15-2). Copper deficiency may occur in wheat (*Triticum aestivum* L.), a highly sensitive plant, but not in soybean, a very insensitive plant, when these plants are used in a crop rotation on the same soil.

A. Sources of Copper

Numerous inorganic compounds, natural organic complexes like Cu lignosulfonate, and synthetic chelates such as CuEDTA and CuHEDTA are used to correct Cu deficiencies (Table 15-5). Cupric sulfate is the most common Cu compound used for correction of Cu deficiencies. The general use

Table 15-5. Copper sources used for correcting Cu deficiencies in plants.†

Source	Formula	Cu, g kg^{-1}‡
Inorganic compounds		
Basic copper (ic) sulfates	$CuSO_4 \cdot 3Cu(OH)_2$	130–530
Copper (ic) chloride	$CuCl_2$	470
Copper (ic) sulfate monohydrate	$CuSO_4 \cdot H_2O$	350
Copper (ic) sulfate pentahydrate	$CuSO_4 \cdot 5H_2O$	250
Cuprous oxide	Cu_2O	890
Cupric oxide	CuO	750
Organic compounds		
Copper chelate	$Na_2CuEDTA$	130
Copper chelate	$NaCuHEDTA$	90
Copper lignosulfonate	--	50–80
Copper polyflavonoid	--	50–70

† Data from Murphy and Walsh (1972), Robertson et al. (1981), Mortvedt (1982a), and Alloway and Tills (1984).
‡ Approximate concentration.

of $CuSO_4$ reflects its high water solubility, relatively low cost, and wide availability (Alloway & Tills, 1984; Varvel et al., 1983; Karamanos et al., 1986). Since $CuSO_4$ is hygroscopic it does not blend well with macronutrient fertilizers (Karamanos et al., 1986) and it may react with P in macronutrient fertilizers to form insoluble compounds with low Cu availability (Gilkes, 1977; Mortvedt, 1982a). The application of some sewage sludges and animal manures containing sufficient Cu will correct deficiencies (ASCE, 1987; Payne et al., 1988a). Indiscriminate use of either animal manure or sewage sludge containing high Cu concentrations is to be avoided due to the pollution potential from their application.

B. Application Methods and Rates

Copper deficiencies can be corrected by applying Cu to plant foliage, or to soil by either band or broadcast application procedures. Broadcast Cu must be tilled into soil to attain maximum effectiveness. Soil application can be completed in a convenient manner before or during planting and, therefore, is often favored by producers over foliar Cu procedures. Foliar application of Cu compounds is considered an emergency method for correction of Cu deficiency, which was not identified by preplant soil tests. Use of soil application procedures for correction of Cu deficiency usually is further justified on the basis of the relative high residual value of soil-incorporated Cu (Gartrell, 1980).

1. Soil Applications

Murphy and Walsh (1972) indicated from a review of literature through 1971 that Cu deficiencies are most frequently corrected by soil application of Cu rather than by foliar application. Their interpretation is still valid based on our review of literature.

a. Inorganic Sources. Copper deficiencies are generally corrected by applying 3.3 to 14.5 kg Cu ha^{-1} as broadcast $CuSO_4$ (Table 15–6). Differences in broadcast rates of Cu required for correcting Cu deficiency reflect variations in soil properties, plant requirements, and concentrations of extractable soil Cu. Powell (1975) recommended broadcasting 4.5 and 13.4 kg Cu ha^{-1} as $CuSO_4$ for correcting Cu deficiency of crops on sands and mucks, respectively. A higher broadcast $CuSO_4$ rate was recommended for crops with a high sensitivity to Cu deficiency than for those with a medium sensitivity on sandy-textured soils; i.e., 11 kg Cu ha^{-1} for lettuce (*Lactuca sativa* L.), onion (*Allium cepa* L.), and spinach (*Spinacea oleracea* L.) and 4.5 kg Cu ha^{-1} for carrots (*Daucus carota* L.), cauliflower (*Brassica oleracea* L.), and celery (*Apium graveolens* L.), respectively. Varvel et al. (1983) suggested broadcasting 6.7 to 13.4 kg Cu ha^{-1} for correcting Cu deficiencies in alfalfa, barley (*Hordeum vulgare* L.), flax (*Linum usitatissimum* L.), lettuce, oat (*Avena sativa* L.), onion, spinach, table beets (*Beta vulgaris* L.), and wheat if the DTPA-extractable soil Cu concentration was < 2.6 mg kg^{-1}. Broadcasting $CuSO_4$ at 6.7 kg Cu ha^{-1} was suggested for correcting Cu deficiency in these crops if the soil contained a higher concentration of DTPA-extractable Cu; i.e., 2.6 to 5.0 mg kg^{-1}.

Lower rates of Cu application are required for correcting Cu deficiency with banded than with broadcast $CuSO_4$ (Table 15–6). Rates of band-placed $CuSO_4$ required for correcting Cu deficiency are as low as 1.1 kg Cu ha^{-1} for vegetables (Walsh & Schulte, 1970) and as high as 6.6 kg Cu ha^{-1} for highly sensitive crops (Vitosh et al., 1981). The 6.6 kg Cu ha^{-1} is needed for highly sensitive crops grown on organic soils with a 1.0 M HCl-extractable Cu concentration of < 9 mg kg^{-1} (Vitosh et al., 1981). Organic soils that contain 1.0 M HCl-extractable Cu concentrations between 10 and 20 mg kg^{-1} should be provided with 3.3 kg Cu ha^{-1}.

The same rates of $CuSO_4$ and CuO were recommended for correcting Cu deficiency by either band or broadcast Cu application (Walsh & Shulte, 1970; Powell, 1975; Mengel, 1980; Vitosh et al., 1981). The suitability of broadcast CuO for correcting Cu deficiencies depends on particle size. For example, CuO broadcast on the soil surface at 5 kg Cu ha^{-1} and worked into the soil did not correct Cu deficiencies in canola (*Brassica napus* L.), barley, or wheat during the year of application, but corrected these deficiencies the following year (Karamanos et al., 1986). The lack of Cu response during the initial year was mainly due to the low water solubility of the coarse, granular CuO, which ranged in particle diameter from < 0.2 (powder) to 3.0 mm. Coarse Cu carriers also are ineffective where inadequate contact occurs between the plant root and applied Cu (Gartrell, 1981).

Broadcast $CuSO_4$ application at rates up to 10 kg Cu ha^{-1} did not increase seed yield of dryland wheat under conditions of severe Cu deficiency (Grundon, 1980). Low uptake of applied Cu was attributed to lack of moisture content in the zone of Cu application. The plants were able to absorb adequate Cu for vegetative growth early in the growing season when the soil was wet. As the soil dried later in the growing season, the plants were unable to absorb sufficient Cu for vegetative and reproductive growth.

Table 15-6. Rates of CuSO$_4$ for correction of Cu deficiencies in various crops.

Crop	Cu rate, kg ha^{-1}	Application method	Remarks	Reference
Citrus, tung	7	Broadcast	Every 5 yr.	Fiskel & Younts, 1963
Citrus	0.09	Foliar	Annual application using 100 L H$_2$O ha^{-1}.	Leonard, 1967
Vegetables	1.1–4.5 4.5–14.5	Band Broadcast	Maximum accumulative application ≤68 kg ha^{-1}.	Walsh & Schulte, 1970
Carrot, cauliflower, celery, clover alfalfa, corn, oat, potato, radish, Sudangrass, wheat	13.4	Broadcast	Recommendation for mucks; use 4 kg Cu ha^{-1} for sand.	Powell, 1975
	3.4	Band	Recommendation for mucks; use 1 kg Cu ha^{-1} for sand.	
Dryland wheat	4.0	Foliar	Two sprays of 2 kg Cu ha^{-1} at Feekes Growth Stages 1 and 10.	Grundon, 1980
Corn, soybean, wheat	2.2–3.3 3.3–6.6 2.2	Band Broadcast Foliar	Band with row fertilizer. Use basic CuSO$_4$.	Mengel, 1980
Highly sensitive crops (Table 15–2)	6.6	Band	Soils with 1.0 M HCl extractable Cu, <9 mg kg^{-1}.	Vitosh et al., 1981
	3.3	Band	Soils with 1.0 M HCl extractable Cu, 10 to 20 mg kg^{-1}.	
Barley, flax, oat, wheat	0.3	Foliar	Organic soils with DTPA extractable Cu, <2.5 mg kg^{-1}.	Varvel et al., 1983
Alfalfa, barley, flax, lettuce, oat, onion, spinach, table beet, wheat	6.7–13.4	Broadcast	Organic soils with DTPA extractable Cu, <2.6 mg kg^{-1}.	Varvel et al., 1983
	6.7	Broadcast	Organic soils with DTPA extractable Cu, 2.6 to 5.0 mg kg^{-1}.	

Foliar application of Cu was effective in alleviating Cu deficiency in the dryland wheat.

b. Organic Sources. The majority of the research directed toward correcting Cu deficiencies since 1950 has been with inorganic sources. There are also several organic Cu sources used to correct Cu deficiencies (Table 15-5). Usually lower Cu application rates are required with organic than inorganic carriers to correct Cu deficiencies by either a band or broadcast application (Walsh & Shulte, 1970).

2. Foliar Applications

Copper deficiencies are corrected during the growing season by foliar application of 0.09 to 4.0 kg Cu ha^{-1} as $CuSO_4$ (Table 15-6). Leonard (1967) sprayed 0.09 kg Cu as $CuSO_4$ in 100 L H_2O ha^{-1} on foliage for correcting Cu deficiency in citrus (*Citrus* spp.). Mengel (1980) recommended foliar application of 2.2 kg Cu as $CuSO_4$ in 280 L water ha^{-1} for correcting Cu deficiencies in corn, soybean, and wheat. Robertson et al. (1981) reported that Cu deficiencies could be controlled by foliar application of 0.6 to 1.1 kg Cu as either $CuSO_4$ or CuO in 280 L water ha^{-1}. Copper sulfate solutions frequently are made basic by adding $CaCO_3$ prior to a foliar application to prevent toxicity to leaves (Benson, 1967; Graham, 1976; Grundon, 1980; Mengel, 1980). Usually, lower levels of foliar Cu are applied as chelates than as inorganic compounds for correcting Cu deficiencies (Murphy & Walsh, 1972; Varvel et al., 1983). The cost and local availability generally dictate the selection of organic or inorganic carriers for correcting Cu deficiencies by foliar applications.

The effectiveness of foliar $CuSO_4$ application for correcting Cu deficiency in wheat is related to time of application. Grundon (1980) reported that under conditions of severe Cu deficiency in wheat a single foliar spray of 2 kg Cu ha^{-1} as $CuSO_4$ at mid-tillering (Feekes Growth Stage 3) increased grain yield only slightly. In contrast, a double spray of 2 kg Cu ha^{-1} at both mid-tillering and just before booting (Feekes Growth Stage 10) was effective in controlling Cu deficiency in the wheat. Under conditions of less severe Cu deficiency, 0.3 kg Cu ha^{-1} applied as foliar $CuSO_4$ at early tillering was effective for small grains (Varvel et al., 1983). Foliar Cu application may be ineffective in correcting Cu deficiency in young wheat plants owing to insufficient leaf area to intercept adequate Cu (Graham, 1976). To overcome this leaf area effect under conditions of severe Cu deficiency, Varvel et al. (1983) suggested two foliar applications of 0.3 kg Cu ha^{-1} as $CuSO_4$, the first when symptoms initially appear and the second about 2 wk later.

C. Residual Effects

Knowledge of the residual availability of applied Cu is needed to determine when reapplication of Cu is necessary. There is evidence of a very slow reversion of applied Cu to plant-unavailable forms. Gartrell (1980) found that 1.1 kg Cu ha^{-1} as $CuSO_4$ increased wheat yield 9 yr after initial application and, in a study on a second soil, 5.5 kg Cu ha^{-1} as $CuSO_4$ increased wheat yield 12 yr after initial application. Others also have shown that one soil application of Cu corrects the deficiency for several years (Murphy & Walsh, 1972).

Recommendations for correcting Cu deficiency reflect the relatively high residual availability of applied Cu. Fiskel and Younts (1963) suggested reapplication of Cu every 5 yr for correcting Cu deficiency in citrus. Powell (1975) recommended an interval of 5 to 8 yr for Cu application depending on the sensitivity of the crop to Cu deficiency and on its severity. Research completed in Michigan indicated that Cu addition to organic soils was not necessary after a total of 22 and 45 kg Cu ha^{-1} was applied for responsive and highly responsive crops, respectively, or after 1.0 M HCl-extractable soil Cu exceeded 20 mg kg^{-1} (Robertson et al., 1981).

D. Toxicity Effects

A potential for Cu phytotoxicity from excess Cu application exists because very small amounts of Cu leach, and because reversion of applied Cu to unavailable forms is relatively slow in soils (Murphy & Walsh, 1972; Vitosh et al., 1981; Gartrell, 1980; Varvel et al., 1983). Copper phytotoxicities are undesirable because of decreased crop yield and quality, and because of the difficulties encountered in correction (Varvel et al., 1983). Vitosh et al. (1981) reported that cucumber (*Cucumis sativis* L.) and snapbean (*Phaseolus vulgaris* L.) yields decreased on a sandy-textured soil from an application of 112 kg Cu ha^{-1}. Rates of Cu application up to 54 kg ha^{-1} $CuSO_4$ were not toxic to snapbean on Plainfield loamy sand (mixed, mesic Typic Udipsamment) with a pH of 6.7 (Walsh et al., 1972a). Snapbean yields decreased in both years of this study in which 486 kg Cu ha^{-1} as $CuSO_4$ was applied.

The total cumulative Cu application recommended for correcting Cu deficiencies ranges from 33.6 (Powell, 1975) to 45 kg Cu ha^{-1} (Varvel et al., 1983). These recommendations appear sufficiently conservative when compared with the guidelines for sewage sludge utilization provided by the USEPA (1983). Based on these guidelines, the recommended cumulative limits for Cu application to cropland are 140, 280, and 560 kg Cu ha^{-1} for soils with CEC of <5, 5 to 15, and >15 cmol$_c$ kg^{-1}, respectively. A pH of 6.5 or above must be maintained where sewage sludge is incorporated into soil in order to decrease Cu availability.

III. IRON

Iron deficiency in plants occurs mainly on alkaline and calcareous soils, particularly under high soil moisture conditions, although the deficiency also exists in some acid soils. In calcareous soils, it is sometimes referred to as Fe chlorosis or lime-induced chlorosis. Large differences exist among plant species as well as within species in their relative susceptibility to Fe deficiency (Table 15–2). Differences among plant species and genotypes, and soil conditions conducive to Fe deficiency are discussed in other chapters of this book. The prevention and correction of Fe deficiency by soil management practices generally has had limited success (Anderson, 1982; Hagstrom, 1984; Chen & Barak, 1982; Mortvedt, 1986; Murphy & Walsh, 1972).

A. Sources of Iron

Inorganic sources and acids, synthetic chelates, natural organic complexes, frits, mine and industrial wastes, jarosites, pyrites, and crop residues have all been used in attempts to eliminate or correct Fe deficiencies in crops (Table 15-7). Inorganic sources include Fe chloride, oxides, and sulfates. Inorganic acids are used to increase the solubility of indigenous and added Fe materials, particularly in calcareous soils. Synthetic chelates are generally the most effective Fe sources for soil and foliar applications, but their cost may be prohibitive at the rates necessary for correction. The organic complexes, lignosulfonates, and polyflavonoids are generally less effective and costly than the synthetic chelates. Fritted materials are mainly used on acid soils in maintenance programs. Their effectiveness depends on particle size and matrix composition. The mine and industrial wastes are generally acidified and applied in pelleted form, but relatively high rates of some of these materials may be necessary. Animal wastes, municipal composts, and sewage sludges provide available Fe and other micronutrients for plants and may improve the soil structure of exposed subsoils. Potential heavy-metal toxicities are a problem with some compost and sewage sludge materials. Organic soils and plant residues enriched with Fe salts and sprays are more effective than the Fe salts alone, and may be equivalent to synthetic chelates in effectiveness under some conditions.

Table 15-7. Iron sources used for correcting Fe deficiencies in plants.[†]

Source	Formula	Fe, g kg^{-1}[‡]
	Inorganic compounds	
Ferrous sulfate	$FeSO_4 \cdot 7H_2O$	190
Ferric sulfate	$Fe_2(SO_4)_3 \cdot 4H_2O$	230
Ferrous ammonium sulfate	$(NH_4)_2SO_4 \cdot FeSO_4 \cdot 6H_2O$	140
Iron frits	Fritted glass	200–400
	Organic compounds	
Iron chelate	NaFeEDTA	50–140
Iron chelate	NaFeHEDTA	50–90
Iron chelate	NaFeEDDHA	60
Iron chelate	NaFeDTPA	100
Iron lignosulfonate	--	50–80
Iron polyflavonoid	--	90–100
Iron methoxyphenylpropane	FeMPP	50

[†] Data from Murphy and Walsh (1972), Chen and Barak (1982), Mortvedt (1986), Kardos et al. (1977), and Tindall (1984).
[‡] Approximate concentration.

B. Application Methods and Rates

1. Soil Applications

Soil applications of inorganic Fe sources are ineffective for controlling Fe chlorosis except at very high rates. These sources are either too insoluble to be effective at low to moderate application rates or they become unavailable because of insoluble reaction products formed in soils. The effectiveness of synthetic chelates is usually greater than inorganic Fe sources, and is related to the stability of the Fe chelate in soil-plant systems. Their cost restricts their use to high-cash-value crops, lawns, and ornamentals.

a. Inorganic Sources. Field applications of $FeSO_4 \cdot 7H_2O$ at rates up to 100 kg Fe ha^{-1} to a calcareous soil did not increase peanut or rice (*Oryza sativa* L.) yields (Anderson, 1982). Banding 72 mg Fe kg^{-1} as $FeSO_4$ increased sorghum [*Sorghum bicolor* (L.) Moench] yields on two calcareous soils in the greenhouse, but not as much as did FeEDDHA (Mortvedt, 1982b). Broadcast applications of $FeSO_4$ are not recommended (Knudsen & Frank, 1977; Johnson & Tucker, 1982). Relatively large applications (1000 mg kg^{-1}) to Fe-deficient calcareous soils were required to alleviate Fe chlorosis and increase sorghum and bermudagrass [*Cynodon dactylon* (L.) Pers.] yields in the greenhouse (Ryan et al., 1975; Ryan & Stroehlein, 1976). Iron chlorosis in peach (*Prunus persica* L.) and apple (*Malus sylvestris* Mill.) trees was reduced when 2 to 8 kg Fe as $FeSO_4$ was placed in the root zone at several locations around the crown of each tree, whereas surface broadcasting dry or placement under a drip irrigation system was not effective (Razeto, 1982; Zheng-ging & Chang-zhen, 1982). Rice yields increased after correcting Fe chlorosis by banding 30 kg Fe ha^{-1} as $FeSO_4$ next to the seed on Histosols (Snyder & Jones, 1988). A broadcast application of 24 kg Fe ha^{-1} as $FeSO_4$ increased alfalfa yields 21% on a poorly buffered, calcareous sandy soil (Rammah et al., 1984). The $Fe(NH_4)_2(SO_4)_2$ by-product of the P fertilizer industry was a more effective Fe source than $FeSO_4$ at the 12 mg kg^{-1} rate (Mortvedt, 1982b).

Waste and by-product materials from mining and industrial operations have been used in attempts to alleviate Fe chlorosis. In general their effective rates approach those used for other soil amendments. The effectiveness of Fe dust products from the steel industry increased as particle size decreased, when acidified with H_2SO_4, and as the levels of application increased (Mortvedt, 1982b; Parkpian & Anderson, 1986). Mining residues (containing jarosite) and low grade pyrites were evaluated as Fe sources in several studies on calcareous soils. Effectiveness was increased by acidification (Ryan et al., 1975), band applications (Marsolek & Hagstrom, 1982), increasing application rates (Barak et al., 1983), and decreasing the particle size (Vlek & Lindsay, 1978). Elemental S and other S compounds may also increase their effectiveness (Olsen & Watanabe, 1979; Wallace, 1988). Surface broadcast applications of these materials under drip-irrigation emitters have not been effective (Nelson & Jolley, 1984).

A spot or band application of H_2SO_4 effectively reduced Fe chlorosis at relatively low application rates (Ryan & Stroehlein, 1976; Frank & Fehr, 1983). Application method was not significant at higher application rates (Nefae & O'Conner, 1978). Irrigation water containing 3 g H_2SO_4 L^{-1} was also effective in alleviating Fe chlorosis in bermudagrass (Ryan & Stroehlein, 1976) and in peach trees watered with a drip-irrigation system (Razeto, 1982).

Iron chlorosis in trees may also be controlled by the injection of $FeSO_4$ or $FeNH_4C_6H_4O_7$ solutions (Tindall, 1984; Wallace & Wallace, 1986; Yoshikawa, 1988). Greening usually occurs within a few days; however, there may be some tissue injury at the injection points and it is a labor-intensive practice.

Inorganic Fe sources are somewhat more effective when applied with fluid or suspension fertilizers. Effectiveness decreased in this order: APP suspension, AOP suspension, UAN solution (Mortvedt & Giordano, 1971; Mortvedt, 1982b). Including $(NH_4)_2S_2O_3$ further increased Fe effectiveness in APP suspension (Mortvedt & Giordano, 1973). Banding acid-type fertilizers (e.g., urea-phosphate) increased Fe uptake by sorghum (Mortvedt & Kelsoe, 1988). These effects would be more pronounced on acid and neutral soils than on calcareous soils. The effectiveness of Fe sources applied with various fertilizer materials depended on the contaminants in the fertilizer, the chemical processes during manufacture, and the subsequent reactions with soil (Mortvedt, 1982b). The complexity of these reactions is shown by the correction of Fe chlorosis in peanut by the application of $(NH_4)_2SO_4$ with a nitrification inhibitor (Kafkafir & Neumann, 1985).

b. Organic Sources. Iron chelates were first shown to be effective Fe sources in the early 1950s. Their effectiveness in soils is related to their stabilities at various pH levels. At most soil pH levels FeEDDHA is effective, whereas FeEDTA is effective only in acid soils. The FeDTPA chelate is less effective than FeEDDHA. The FeHBED chelate provided an available source of Fe in nutrient solutions, but is yet to be tested in soils (Chaney, 1988). The relative theoretical effectiveness of the chelates was substantiated in soil systems (Mortvedt, 1982b; Lindsay & Schwab, 1982; Murphy & Walsh, 1972; Wallace & Wallace, 1983). Experimental results demonstrate the greater effectiveness of synthetic chelates compared with inorganic Fe sources. However, the chelates are not widely used on most field crops because of their relative costs, except for high-value crops or where low rates are effective (Hagstrom, 1984; Chen & Barak, 1982).

A soil application of 0.25 kg Fe ha^{-1} as FeEDDHA gave equivalent unshelled peanut yields as 50 kg Fe ha^{-1} as $FeSO_4$. Maximum peanut yields occurred at 10 kg Fe ha^{-1} as FeEDDHA, which alleviated visual Fe chlorosis under field conditions (Anderson, 1982). The largest sorghum yields on a calcareous soil in the greenhouse resulted from mixing 20 mg Fe kg^{-1} as FeEDDHA. An 80 mg Fe kg^{-1} rate caused some phytotoxicity (Salardini & Murphy, 1978). Soil injection of Fe chelates, especially FeEDDHA, proved to be an effective method of correcting Fe chlorosis in trees (Kadman & Lahav, 1982; Rogers, 1975; Kochan, 1962; Reed et al., 1988). These same materials can also be successfully applied in drip-irrigation systems at lower Fe application rates (Razeto, 1982; Kadman & Lahav, 1982).

Soil applications of Fe-polyflavonoids and Fe-lignosulfonates were not as effective as synthetic chelates, but were more effective than similar Fe rates applied as $FeSO_4$ (Anderson, 1982; Mortvedt, 1982b). A 3-yr field study of four Fe sources showed that an Fe-lignosulfonate was the most economical source of Fe when placed in the seed furrow at planting (Cihacek, 1984). A greenhouse study with grain sorghum showed that effectiveness for dry matter production was: lignosulfonate > EDDHA > polyflavonoid, whereas for Fe uptake it was EDDHA > lignosulfonate > polyflavonoid on an Fe-deficient subsoil. Iron chlorosis was largely alleviated by FeEDDHA (Salardini & Murphy, 1978).

It is a well-established practice in irrigated areas to apply farmyard manure on exposed subsoil areas after land leveling. This practice provides needed micronutrients (Wallingford et al., 1975) and may improve soil structure. An 11-t ha^{-1} application of farmyard manure produced larger grain sorghum yields than a similar application of Fe from $FeSO_4$ (Mathers et al., 1980). Municipal sewage sludges and composts are suitable sources of available Fe as well as other micronutrients (Abdou & El-Nennah, 1980; Kardos et al., 1977; Chen & Barak, 1982), provided other heavy metals do not become phytotoxic (Chaney & Giordano, 1977). A 5-yr field study that compared municipal sewage sludge with dairy manure to correct Fe chlorosis on a calcareous soil showed that a manure treatment (89.6 t ha^{-1}) was only effective for 1 yr, while a similar sewage sludge application was effective for 5 yr. A lower sewage sludge rate (33.6 t ha^{-1}) was effective for at least 3 yr. The sewage sludge and dairy manure contained 9934 and 30 mg Fe kg^{-1}, respectively (McCaslin et al., 1987). Approximately 0.5 kg Cd was contained in the 33.6 t of sewage sludge.

A wide band of an Fe-enriched muck (3.7 mg Fe kg^{-1}) applied to a calcareous soil increased peanut pod yields 185 and 76% of the control and FeEDDHA foliar spray treatments, respectively (Chen et al., 1982). Approximately 56 kg total Fe ha^{-1} was supplied by the muck. Matocha (1984) showed that the residue of the *Amaranthus albus* (pigweed) plant species treated with $FeSO_4$ was a more effective Fe source than FeEDDHA for field-grown grain sorghum. Highest grain yields occurred in the foliar-applied $FeSO_4$ and acidified mine residue treatments (Table 15–8). The amount of Fe supplied by the Fe-enriched *Amaranthus* was equivalent to that in the FeEDDHA treatment. The plants with the untreated *Amaranthus* resembled those of the control treatment on 3 June. In a greenhouse study, the effectiveness of several plant materials after treatment with $FeSO_4$ was: sunflower (*Helianthus annus*) > pigweed > guar (*Cyamopsis psoralides*) > clover > wheat. Iron chlorosis increased as the application rate of all untreated plant materials increased (Mostaghimi & Matocha, 1988). These data suggest that some of the Fe compounds formed when plant materials are sprayed with $FeSO_4$ and soil incorporated are more effective than the Fe sources applied alone. Adding an organic material with $FeSO_4$ also reduced the phytotoxic

Table 15-8. Effects of Fe treatments on dry matter (DM), grain yield, and Fe uptake by grain sorghum (Matocha, 1984).

Treatment	6 April		3 June	Grain yield
	DM	Fe uptake	DM	
	kg ha^{-1}	mg ha^{-1}	—— kg ha^{-1} ——	
Control	19.5	3454	0	0
FeEDDHA (2.2 kg Fe ha^{-1})	25.3	4774	567	43
Manure (33.6 t ha^{-1})	29.5	4433	540	102
Acidified mining residue (4.48 t ha^{-1})	39.2	5171	2421	821
Amaranthus + Fe	34.6	5816	4092	548
Amaranthus − Fe	26.9	4764	0	0
Foliar FeSO$_4$†	25.0	4260	4094	1531
LSD (0.05)	0.05	NS‡	0.05	0.05

† Foliar spray (25 g FeSO$_4$ L^{-1}) applied four times.
‡ NS represents not significant.

effects from FeSO$_4$ applied in holes around apple trees (Zheng-ging & Chang-zhen, 1982).

2. Foliar Applications

Foliar spray applications of soluble Fe compounds can generally correct Fe chlorosis in plants, although repeated applications are necessary since translocation of the absorbed Fe is not sufficient for new plant growth. The effective vegetative coverage by the spray can be improved by including a surfactant (Chen & Barak, 1982). Low concentrations of urea and NH$_4$NO$_3$ increased Fe absorption from FeSO$_4$, but not from an Fe-amino acid complex (Hsu & Ashmead, 1984).

Near-maximum grain sorghum and peanut yields occurred with two to three foliar sprays of a 2 to 3% FeSO$_4$ solution (Anderson, 1982; Matocha, 1984). A single foliar spray of 0.9 kg Fe ha^{-1} as FeSO$_4$ increased pea (*Pisum sativum* L.) yields, while an additional foliar spray application 2 wk later further increased yields 23% (Seeliger & Moss, 1976). A comparison of FeSO$_4$ and FeEDDHA to correct Fe chlorosis on Kentucky bluegrass (*Poa pratensis* L.) showed that 2.2 kg Fe ha^{-1} from FeEDDHA was more effective than FeSO$_4$. A single application of 4.5 kg Fe ha^{-1} from either source caused some phytotoxicity (Yust et al., 1984). A comparison of several foliar spray Fe compounds applied on pear (*Pyrus communis* L.) trees showed that the least amount of phytotoxicity to the fruit was from an Fe-lignosulfonate material. All Fe materials increased the Fe concentration in the leaves and reduced Fe chlorosis symptoms (Raese & Staiff, 1988). The correction of Fe chlorosis by foliar sprays is not generally recommended for perennial crops (Reed et al., 1988; Kochan, 1962), whereas it is recommended for annual row crops (Johnson & Tucker, 1982; Fehr & Trimble, 1982; Knudsen & Frank, 1977).

C. Residual Effects

Soil applications of Fe sources have very little residual effect because the Fe^{2+} ion is rapidly converted to Fe^{3+} in aerated soils. Band applications at relatively high rates may be effective for more than 1 yr provided tillage operations do not mix the fertilizer band with the surrounding soil. A band application of an acidified mining residue had some residual visual effect the second yr (Marsolek & Hagstrom, 1982). A similar material broadcast on turfgrass was more effective than chelates or inorganic Fe salts 1 yr after its application (Minner & Butler, 1984). A complete mixing of 3 t ha^{-1} of several Fe sources was only effective for two cuttings of common bermudagrass in the greenhouse (Ryan et al., 1975). The application of acidified mining residues (4.48 t ha^{-1}) increased the DTPA-extractable Fe concentration in the seedbed nearly 300% over the control after 2 yr of cropping (Matocha, 1984). Soil injections of both FeEDDHA and $FeSO_4$ sources under fruit trees were effective for 2 or 3 yr (Razeto, 1982; Kochan, 1962; Zheng-ging & Chang-zhen, 1982). Even injections of $FeSO_4$ into peach trees were effective for 2 yr (Yoshikawa, 1988). In contrast, large application rates of municipal sewage sludges containing 9934 mg Fe kg^{-1} alleviated Fe chlorosis in grain sorghum for 3 to 5 yr (McCaslin et al., 1987). Similar residual effects might be expected from farmyard manure at equivalent Fe application rates.

D. Toxicity Effects

A direct Fe toxicity from a general soil application of Fe fertilizers would not be expected because of the relatively rapid conversion of soluble Fe to insoluble Fe compounds in soil systems. Some phytotoxic effects on young apple trees have been reported from the placement of 8 kg of $FeSO_4$ in 10 holes under the crown of the tree. These effects were alleviated by mixing the $FeSO_4$ with organic materials (Zheng-ging & Chang-zhen, 1982). High rates of foliar Fe sprays may also cause some phytotoxicity effects to be expressed as plant tissue necrosis, particularly on tree fruits (Raese & Staiff, 1988; Yust et al., 1984). Injecting Fe solutions into tree trunks and limbs may also cause some injury at the injection point (Wallace & Wallace, 1986). An application of 80 mg Fe kg^{-1} as FeEDDHA or Fe-polyflavonoid caused a yield reduction in grain sorghum in the greenhouse (Salardini & Murphy, 1978). Municipal sewage sludges and composts may also contain sufficient concentrations of other heavy metals that become toxic at high application rates (Chaney & Giordano, 1977).

IV. MANGANESE

Manganese deficiencies occur in organic soils, in alkaline and calcareous soils, and in poorly drained, slightly acid soils with sandy textures (Rich, 1956; Berger, 1962; Reuter et al., 1973b; Mortvedt, 1982a). The presence of Mn in higher oxidation states as very insoluble hydroxides and oxides accounts for low Mn availability in well-drained alkaline and calcareous soils (McKenzie, 1989). The common occurrence of Mn deficiencies on the poorly drained soils reflects Mn solubilization during periods of low aeration and then leaching of Mn^{2+} below the root zone (Robertson & Lucas, 1981; Mortvedt, 1982a). Lack of root proliferation and extension into subsoils during periods of low aeration aggravates Mn deficiencies in these soils (Robertson & Lucas, 1981).

Overliming is the principle management practice that induces Mn deficiencies (Rich, 1956; Holmes et al., 1983; Parker & Walker, 1986). Manganese deficiencies occur in crops with high sensitivity to Mn deficiency (Table 15-2) on some limed soils with a pH below 6.5. For example, Mn deficiencies are common in sensitive crops like soybean and medium-sensitive crops like corn when grown on poorly drained, sandy-textured soils with a low Mn content, and limed to a pH > 6.2 (Mehlich, 1957; Boswell et al., 1981; Uribe et al., 1988). Manganese deficiencies in peanut, which is highly sensitive to Mn deficiency, occur in poorly drained, sandy-textured soils with pH levels as low as 5.8 (Rich, 1956).

A. Sources of Manganese

Both inorganic and organic Mn compounds are used for correcting Mn deficiencies (Table 15-9). Manganese sulfate is used more as a Mn fertilizer than other Mn compounds. Use of $MnSO_4$ is so common that it is usually included as the standard in research to determine the efficacy of other Mn sources. Finely ground MnO was used more than $MnCl_2$, frits, or oxysulfate as a Mn source. In recent years, research has centered on determination of the appropriate rates and placements of Mn chelates, MnO, and $MnSO_4$ for correcting Mn deficiencies.

Table 15-9. Manganese sources used for correcting Mn deficiencies in plants.[†]

Source	Formula	Mn, g kg^{-1}[‡]
Inorganic compounds		
Manganese chloride	$MnCl_2$	170
Manganese frits	Fritted glass	100–350
Manganous oxide	MnO	400
Manganese oxysulfate	--	280
Manganese sulfate	$MnSO_4$	230–280
Organic compounds		
Manganese chelate	$Na_2MnEDTA$	50–120
Manganese lignosulfonate	--	50
Manganese polyflavonoid	--	50–70

[†] Data from Murphy and Walsh (1972), Robertson and Lucas (1981), Mortvedt (1982a), and Mascagni and Cox (1985b).
[‡] Approximate concentration.

B. Application Methods and Rates

Manganese deficiencies usually are corrected by foliar application of Mn or by banding Mn with an acid-forming starter fertilizer. Broadcast Mn may undergo rapid oxidation, forming insoluble hydroxides and oxides of low plant availability. Therefore, high rates of broadcast Mn may be required to correct Mn deficiency during the year of application, and yet have low residual value during subsequent years (Vitosh et al., 1981; Mortvedt, 1982a). Recent improvements in foliar Mn application procedures, considering stage of plant growth and number of sprays, has led to more frequent us of foliar Mn for correcting Mn deficiencies (Gettier et al., 1985).

1. Soil Applications

Research completed through the early 1970s indicated that high rates of broadcast-applied $MnSO_4$, from 22 to 134 kg Mn ha^{-1}, were required for optimum vegetable and soybean yields (Murphy & Walsh, 1972). A need for high levels of broadcast $MnSO_4$ also was shown for correcting Mn deficiencies in barley, peanut, and soybean by field research from 1978 through 1984 (Table 15-10). Generally, higher Mn rates are required to correct Mn deficiencies by broadcast than by band application (Mortvedt & Giordano, 1975; Randall et al., 1975a; Mascagni & Cox, 1984).

Various rates and sources of banded Mn are used for correcting Mn deficiencies. In a series of studies, Mascagni and Cox (1984, 1985a, b) found that $MnSO_4$ banded with acid-forming starter fertilizer was more effective in correcting Mn deficiency of corn than broadcasting an equal rate of the fertilizer mixture. Banding 3 kg Mn ha^{-1} as $MnSO_4$ without the acid-forming fertilizer corrected a Mn deficiency in soybean; while banding 1 kg Mn ha^{-1} as Mn-lignosulfonate, MnDTPA, MnEDTA, or $MnSO_4$ without a starter fertilizer was ineffective in increasing soybean yields. Randall et al. (1975a) alleviated Mn deficiency in soybean by banding 5 to 22 kg Mn ha^{-1} as $MnSO_4$ with the starter fertilizer. The wide variation in amount of banded

Table 15-10. Rates of soil-applied $MnSO_4$ for correcting Mn deficiencies in various crops.

Crop	Rate	Application method	Comment	Reference
	kg Mn ha^{-1}			
Barley	6	Broadcast	Foliar Mn was also needed for optimum yield.	Reuter et al., 1973a
Soybean	5–22	Band	Applied with starter fertilizer.	Randall et al., 1975a
Soybean	45	Broadcast	--	Alley et al., 1978
Peanut	45	Broadcast	--	Hallock, 1979
Soybean	20–40	Broadcast	--	Gettier et al., 1984
Corn	5	Band	Applied with 170 kg diammonium phosphate ha^{-1}.	Mascagni & Cox, 1985a
Soybean	14	Broadcast	--	Mascagni & Cox, 1985a
	3	Band	Applied without starter fertilizer.	

Mn required for correcting Mn deficiency probably reflects the severity of the deficiency on diverse soils.

Soybean seed yield decreased where 0.56 kg Mn ha^{-1} was banded as MnEDTA in the row with a starter fertilizer (Randall et al., 1975a; Alley et al., 1978). This intensification of Mn deficiency is attributable to displacement of Mn from MnEDTA by Fe, with a concomitant increase in Fe uptake and decrease in Mn uptake (Randall & Schulte, 1971). Alley et al. (1978) reported that banding 16.8 kg Mn ha^{-1} as $MnSO_4$ with the seed corrected Mn deficiency of soybean under adequate soil moisture; under drought conditions, this treatment decreased seed yield by stand reduction.

The most effective soil application procedure for correcting Mn deficiencies is band-placement of a mixture of Mn and acid-forming fertilizer near the seed at planting time (Robertson & Lucas, 1981; Vitosh et al., 1981). Acid from the fertilizer retards the oxidation of Mn^{2+} and thereby slows the reversion of the Mn to plant-unavailable forms (Mortvedt, 1982a). Acidity from banded starter fertilizer corrected Mn deficiency without any Mn application on some soils (Randall et al., 1975b; Kroetz et al., 1977a, b; Jackson & Carter, 1976).

Suggested rates of banded Mn for correcting Mn deficiencies vary with soil properties and extractable Mn concentrations. For example, applying 18 kg Mn ha^{-1} in a band as either $MnSO_4$ or finely ground MnO is suggested for correcting Mn deficiencies on organic soils with < 5 mg kg^{-1} of 0.1 M HCl-extractable Mn and a pH $\geq$ 6.5. One-half as much banded Mn is suggested for correcting Mn deficiencies on mineral soils with equivalent pH and extractable Mn levels. Manganese application is unnecessary in either organic or mineral soils with a pH $\geq$ 6.5 and a 0.1 M HCl extractable Mn > 40 mg kg^{-1} (Robertson & Lucas, 1981; Vitosh et al., 1981). Finely ground MnO banded with starter fertilizer is less effective than $MnSO_4$, but acceptable for correcting Mn deficiencies. Broadcast MnO was also ineffective in correcting Mn deficiency in soybean (Mascagni & Cox, 1985b).

2. Foliar Applications

Foliar Mn is effective for correcting Mn deficiencies of barley, corn, fruit trees, oat, onion, peanut, safflower (*Carthamus tinctorius* L.), and soybean (Table 15–11) (Murphy & Walsh, 1972). Rates of foliar Mn from 0.3 to 5.4 kg in 31 to 230 L H_2O ha^{-1} were used to correct the Mn deficiencies. Manganese sulfate was used as the Mn source for foliar application on barley, corn, fruit trees, peanut, safflower, and soybean. Compounds other than $MnSO_4$ that were used to correct Mn deficiencies in soybean include $MnCl_2$, MnEDTA, MnDTPA, Mn-lignosulfonate, and $Mn(NO_3)_2$.

Field research by Cox (1968) indicated that multiple applications of foliar Mn as $MnSO_4$ are superior to a single application for correcting Mn deficiency in soybean. Multiple foliar Mn applications also are necessary for correcting Mn deficiency in barley (Reuter et al., 1973a), peanut (Hallock, 1979), and wheat (Nayyar et al., 1985). Parker and Walker (1986) indicated that foliar application of fungicide is initiated 4 to 7 wk after peanut is planted

Table 15-11. Rates of foliar Mn for correcting Mn deficiencies of various crops.

Crop	Mn sources	Total applied, kg Mn ha^{-1}	Volume, L ha^{-1}	Comment	Reference
Barley	MnSO$_4$	3.9–5.4	56–225	Three sprays of 1.3 to 1.8 kg Mn ha^{-1} each at tillering, stem elongation, and after ear emergence.	Reuter et al., 1973a
Soybean	MnSO$_4$	0.34	230	Two sprays of 0.17 kg Mn ha^{-1} at early blossom and early pod set growth stages.	Randall et al., 1975a
Soybean	MnSO$_4$	4.4	187	Two sprays of 2.2 kg Mn ha^{-1} at the 2–3 and 5–6 trifoliolate leaf growth stages.	Kroetz et al., 1977b
Soybean	MnSO$_4$	2.2	--	Two sprays of 1.1 kg Mn ha^{-1}, the first at pre-bloom.	Alley et al., 1978
Peanut	MnSO$_4$	4.5	140	2.3 kg Mn ha^{-1} in mid June, and 1.1 kg Mn ha^{-1} in mid July and late August.	Hallock, 1979
Corn	MnSO$_4$	1.2–2.2	150	Two sprays of 0.6 to 1.1 kg Mn ha^{-1} at the four- and eight-leaf growth stage.	Mascagni & Cox, 1984
Soybean	MnSO$_4$ MnCl$_2$ MnEDTA MnDTPA Mn-lignosulfonate	0.3	150	Three sprays of 0.1 kg Mn ha^{-1}, the first at the V4 growth stage and then when symptoms reappear.	Mascagni & Cox, 1985b
Safflower	MnSO$_4$	0.5	200	One spray at the rosette to end of stem elongation growth period.	Lewis & McFarlane, 1986
Soybean	MnSO$_4$ MnEDTA	1.1 0.4	31 31	First application at the V5 growth stage; 3 additional applications at 2 wk interals.	Ohki et al., 1987

Table 15–12. Influence of foliar Mn applications on soybean yield, single seed weight, and seed number on three soils (Gettier et al., 1985).

Foliar Mn application†	Soil			Mean
	Myatt‡	Dragston 1	Dragston 2	
	Seed yield, kg ha^{-1}			
Control	2863a*	1308a	950a	1707a
Early	3402a	2969b	2703c	3025c
Late	2985a	2694b	1670b	2450b
Early + late	3488a	3826c	2940c	3418d
	Single seed wt., mg seed^{-1}			
Control	205a	113a	104a	141a
Early	208a	171c	140b	173b
Late	206a	158b	143b	169b
Early + late	209a	188d	170c	189c
	Seed number, seeds m^{-2}			
Control	1403a	1139a	903a	1148a
Early	1633a	1737b	1937b	1769c
Late	1453a	1705b	1174a	1444b
Early + late	1669a	2033b	1735b	1812c

* Within a column, means followed by different letters are significantly different at the 0.05 probability level.
† Mn applications: early = 1.12 kg ha^{-1} applied at Stage V6; late = 1.12 kg ha^{-1} applied at Stage R1; early + late = 1.12 kg ha^{-1} applied at Stage V6 and 1.12 kg ha^{-1} applied at Stage R1.
‡ Fine-loamy, siliceous, thermic Typic Ochraquults.

and continued on 2- to 3-wk intervals for control of leafspot. They suggested including a soluble Mn source in the tank with the fungicide to decrease the number of trips over the field.

Recent field research was designed to identify the appropriate time of foliar Mn application. Foliar applications of 0.17 kg Mn ha^{-1} as MnEDTA were most effective in increasing soybean yield when applied at the early bloom or ear pod set growth stages, or in multiple applications at these growth stages (Randall et al., 1975a). In field experiments on three soils, a single foliar application of 1.1 kg Mn ha^{-1} as $MnSO_4$ at the V6 and R1 growth stages was less effective in increasing soybean yields than equivalent foliar Mn treatments applied at both growth stages (Table 15–12). The increases in soybean yield from the foliar Mn resulted from increases in both seed weight and set. Higher corn yields were obtained from foliar application of 0.6 and 1.1 kg Mn ha^{-1} as $MnSO_4$ at the four- and eight-leaf stages than from one, equal, foliar Mn treatment at either of the growth stages (Mascagni & Cox, 1984). Research by Lewis and McFarlane (1986) indicated that timing of foliar Mn application was critical for correcting Mn deficiency of safflower and showed that 0.5 kg Mn ha^{-1} as foliar $MnSO_4$ was required between the rosette stage and the end of the stem elongation, but before branching.

Research has been completed to compare the efficiency of foliar Mn sources for correcting Mn deficiency of soybean. Foliar application of 2.2

kg Mn ha^{-1} as MnSO$_4$ at the two- to three- and the five- to six-trifoliolate-leaf growth stages increased soybean yields more than did two foliar applications of 0.15 kg Mn ha^{-1} as MnEDTA at the two growth stages (Kroetz et al., 1977a). A lower rate of foliar Mn as MnEDTA than as MnSO$_4$ was required (Ohki et al., 1987). Maximum yield was obtained from 1.1 and 0.4 kg Mn ha^{-1} applied in four equal applications as MnSO$_4$ and MnEDTA, respectively. Equivalent increases in soybean yield were obtained from MnCl$_2$, MnEDTA, Mn-lignosulfonate, Mn(NO$_3$)$_2$, and MnSO$_4$ applied three times during the growing season at a rate of 0.1 kg Mn ha^{-1} (Mascagni & Cox, 1985b). The first application was at the V4 growth stage and the other two when deficiency symptoms became evident. Low rates of foliar Mn application, such as applied by Mascagni and Cox (1985a, b), are desirable for preventing leaf burn (Randall et al., 1975a; Mengel, 1980).

C. Residual Effects

Maximum soybean seed yields occurred on Dragston fine sandy loam (coarse-loamy, mixed, thermic Aeric Ochraquults) from 20 to 40 kg Mn ha^{-1} as broadcasted MnSO$_4$ during the first year of application, but the residual effect from 60 kg Mn ha^{-1} as MnSO$_4$ was inadequate to correct Mn deficiency of soybean during the second year (Gettier et al., 1984). Optimum soybean yields still occurred on a Lenoir loam (clayey, mixed, thermic Aeric Paleaquults) 2 yr after broadcasting 30 kg Mn ha^{-1} as MnSO$_4$ and Mn-oxysulfate (Mascagni & Cox, 1985b). Experimental findings from the field research on the Dragston and Lenoir soils, as well as laboratory research (Mascagni & Cox, 1988), support the conclusion by Murphy and Walsh (1972) that there is some residual Mn availability from large amounts of applied Mn. Furthermore, these experimental findings support the recommendation that band and foliar Mn application procedures, rather than broadcast methods, should be used for correcting Mn deficiencies (Robertson & Lucas, 1981; Vitosh et al., 1981; Parker & Walker, 1986).

D. Toxicity Effects

Manganese toxicity occurs in strongly acid agricultural soils (Murphy & Walsh, 1972; Stivers, 1974; Vitosh et al., 1981). Plants that are sensitive to Mn toxicity include alfalfa, cabbage (*Brassica oleracea* var. *capitata*), cauliflower, clover, cotton (*Gossypium hirsutum* L.), field bean, flax, pineapple (*Ananas comosus*), small grain, sugar beet (*Beta saccharifera* L.), tobacco (*Nicotiana tabacum* L.), and tomato (*Lycopersicon esculentum* Mill.) (Vitosh et al., 1981; Mortvedt, 1982a; Moraghan, 1985; Ohki, 1985). Manganese toxicity can be remedied by liming (Murphy & Walsh, 1972; Stivers, 1974; Mortvedt, 1982a). Mortvedt (1982a) indicated that liming a soil to pH 6.0 generally reduces Mn availability to a normal level and alleviates Mn phytotoxicity.

V. MOLYBDENUM

Molybdenum is required by plants for NO_3-N reduction and for symbiotic N_2-fixation. Legumes, cruciferous crops, grasses, and several vegetable crops have responded to Mo fertilization. Deficiencies in the USA occur on the acid, sandy soils of the Atlantic, Gulf, and Pacific Coasts, and in those states surrounding the Great Lakes. Large areas of New Zealand and Australia are also reportedly Mo deficient. Information on the interactions of various factors in soils and plants, and fertilization practices are given in previous reviews (Gupta & Lipsett, 1981; Murphy & Walsh, 1972).

A. Sources of Molybdenum

Ammonium and Na molybdates are soluble compounds used as sources of Mo fertilizers (Table 15-13); the MoO_3 and Mo frits are almost as effective, but MoS_2 is not as satisfactory. The soluble materials are sometimes mixed with other fertilizers, and are also applied as foliar sprays. Molybdenum is also contained in some sewage sludges and fly ash materials.

B. Application Methods and Rates

Molybdenum deficiencies may be corrected by soil and foliar applications, and by seed treatments. Application rates of 0.01 to 0.5 kg ha^{-1} of Mo will generally correct Mo deficiencies. Since the availability of Mo increases as soil pH increases, liming of acid soils will frequently prevent or correct a Mo deficiency, but liming to increase soil pH is not always desirable. Molybdenum fertilization may increase Mo concentrations in forages enough to cause molybdenosis in ruminant animals.

1. Soil Applications

The quantity of Mo needed for optimum yields is small compared with other micronutrients and is dependent on soils, crops, application methods, and the other fertilizer nutrients being applied. Molybdenum was readily available to bean plants when applied in combination with superphosphate on several New Zealand soils (Widdowson, 1966), although the concentration of Mo may vary according to fertilizer particle size (Lipsett & David, 1977).

Table 15-13. Molybdenum sources used for correcting Mo deficiencies in plants.[†]

Source	Formula	Mo, g kg^{-1}[‡]
Sodium molybdate	$Na_2MoO_4 \cdot 2H_2O$	390
Ammonium molybdate	$(NH_4)_6Mo_7O_{24} \cdot 4H_2O$	540
Molybdenum trioxide	MoO_3	660
Molybdenum frits	Fritted glass	20–30
Molybdic acid	$H_2MoO_4 \cdot H_2O$	530

[†] Data from Murphy and Walsh (1972), Kardos et al. (1977), Adriano et al. (1980), and Gupta and Lipsett (1981).
[‡] Approximate concentration.

Phosphorus may also enhance the uptake of Mo under some environmental conditions, whereas SO_4-S applications depressed Mo concentrations and uptake (Jones & Ruckman, 1973; Petrie & Jackson, 1982; Gupta & MacLeod, 1975). Forage yields of subterranean clover (*Trifolium subterraneum* L.) were increased by the application of 0.282 kg Mo ha^{-1} as H_2MoO_4 sprayed on the soil surface and incorporated into the seedbed (Jones & Ruckman, 1973). Soybean responded to Mo applications when the soil pH measured between 4.9 to 6.0. Soil (226 g Mo ha^{-1}) and foliar (85 g Mo ha^{-1}) applications, and seed treatments (7 g Mo ha^{-1}) were all effective (Sedberry et al., 1973; Franco & Day, 1980). Sufficient Mo may sometimes be available for NO_3-N reduction, but not for the N_2-fixation symbosis in soybean (Parker & Harris, 1977). A significant difference in the ability to obtain Mo from an acid soil was identified between two corn inbred lines (Brown & Clark, 1974).

The effect of soil pH, and application of Mo and P on Mo uptake by subclover is illustrated in Table 15-14. Liming increased the pH of the soil (Typic Haploxeralf) from 5.3 to 6.2, and increased the Mo concentration in the subterranean clover when either P or Mo was applied. Molybdenum fertilization effects were also larger where lime was applied. No significant yield increases occurred in this study (Petrie & Jackson, 1982).

The Mo concentration in sewage sludges (2 to 1000 mg Mo kg^{-1}) and fly ash materials (8 to 33 mg Mo kg^{-1}) is substantially lower than that found in the more traditional fertilizer materials (Table 15-13); nevertheless, their applications increase the Mo concentrations in plants (Elseewi & Page, 1984; Pierzynski & Jacobs, 1986). This effect occurs because the application rates of these materials are relatively large (tons per hectare) and many also increase soil pH. Molybdenum application rates by these materials also exceed recommended rates used for the other Mo fertilizer materials (Thom, 1985).

Table 15-14. Effect of lime, P, and Mo applications on the Mo and Cu concentrations in subterranean clover-grass mixture (Petrie & Jackson, 1982).

Lime rate	Fertilization rates		Forage concentrations		
	P	Mo	Mo	Cu	Cu/Mo
t ha^{-1}	—— kg ha^{-1} ——		————mg kg^{-1}————		
0	0	0.5	1.5	9.5	6.3
0	57	0	0.5	7.7	15.4
0	57	0.5	2.7	10.9	4.0
4.5	0	0.5	3.5	7.3	2.1
4.5	57	0	1.3	6.8	5.2
4.5	57	0.5	7.1	11.8	1.6
9.0	0	0.5	3.1	7.3	2.3
9.0	57	0	2.1	7.3	3.5
9.0	57	0.5	5.2	8.1	1.6
LSD 0.05			1.7	NS†	4.0

† NS represents not significant.

2. Foliar Applications

Foliar application of Mo is an accepted practice for correcting Mo deficiency on many crops. Highest soybean yields were obtained when applied to young plants at bloom or later (Parker & Harris, 1962; Boswell & Anderson, 1969). Molybdenum sprayed (100 g ha^{-1}) over the row 2 wk after plant emergence increased soybean yields on 12 out of 15 experimental sites on Ultisols (Burmester et al., 1988). Foliar sprays may also be more effective than soil applications under dry conditions (Gupta, 1979b). The relative effective application rate of foliar sprays was about one-third of the soil application rate (Sedberry et al., 1973).

3. Seed Concentrations and Applications

Treating seeds with Mo fertilizers is an effective method to prevent Mo deficiencies; however, the Mo concentration and content of the seed will affect the Mo response (Sherrell, 1984). Large seeded plants, such as pea, responded to Mo when their seeds contained <0.2 mg Mo kg^{-1}, but not when they contained 0.5 to 0.7 mg Mo kg^{-1} when planted on a Mo-deficient soil. Seed-applied Mo was as effective as foliar sprays for soybean (Boswell & Anderson, 1969; Parker & Harris, 1962) and cowpea (*Vigna unguiculata* L.) (Rodes & Kpaka, 1982). Relatively high Mo application rates may be detrimental to *Rhizobia* in seed inoculum by some pelleting procedures or cause seedling injury under certain growing conditions (Sedberry et al., 1973).

C. Residual Effects

The residual effects of Mo fertilization depend on the reactions of MoO_4^{2-} with soil constituents, the amount of Mo leached, and the removal by cropping and by grazing animals. An application of 0.11 kg Mo ha^{-1} on an acidic sandy loam soil in Australia was effective for 15 yr, whereas 0.14 kg Mo ha^{-1} applied on another soil lasted only 1 yr (Riley, 1987). Other studies showed that effectiveness decreased at approximately 50% per year on selected soils (Barrow et al., 1985). An application of 0.4 kg Mo ha^{-1} alleviated Mo deficiency up to 3 yr on a podzolic soil (Gupta, 1979b), whereas 0.28 kg Mo ha^{-1} continued to increase Mo concentration and uptake by subterranean clover after 8 yr (Jones & Ruckman, 1973).

D. Toxicity

Molybdenum toxicity in plants rarely occurs under field conditions. Soybean seedling injury was observed from Mo seed treatments (Sedberry et al., 1973). The yields of some forage species were reduced when grown on soils that received 1.32 and 2.64 kg Mo ha^{-1} 1 yr earlier (Hawes et al., 1976). Relatively high Mo application rates (300 kg Mo ha^{-1}) from some sewage sludges did not reduce forage yields (Pierzynski & Jacobs, 1986). High concentrations of Mo in forages may induce Cu deficiencies in animals, referred to as molybdenosis. A Cu/Mo ratio of <2 is expected to induce Cu deficiency (Miltmore & Mason, 1971). Even moderate Mo application rates may produce forages in this category (Table 15-14). Dietary intake levels of SO_4-S also affect this relationship.

VI. ZINC

Zinc deficiencies are more likely to occur in sands, sandy loams, loams, and organic soils than in silty or clayey soils (Schulte & Walsh, 1982). Low Zn concentrations in parent material, such as quartz, account for the low amount of total and available Zn in some sandy-textured soils (Krauskopf, 1972). Organic soils also often have low total Zn concentrations, which lead to low Zn availabilities (Schulte & Walsh, 1982). Zinc availability decreases with an increase in soil pH (Frye et al., 1978; Sedberry et al., 1980; Wells, 1980; Rehm & Penas, 1982). The frequent occurrence of Zn deficiencies during cool, wet springs is attributed to slow microbial temperature-dependent release of Zn from soil organic matter (Gray et al., 1974) and to restricted root growth with low capacity for Zn absorption (Robertson & Lucas, 1976; Vitosh et al., 1981).

Overliming, as well as other management practices, can cause Zn deficiencies (Rehm & Penas, 1982). High available soil P concentrations from either repeated applications or from parent material can induce Zn deficiency. Phosphorus-induced Zn deficiency occurs where sensitive crops (Table 15-2) are grown on soils with marginal amounts of available Zn and with high pH levels (Murphy et al., 1981; Mikkelsen & Kuo, 1977; Rehm & Penas, 1982). Zinc deficiencies may be intense where sensitive crops are grown on areas where topsoil was removed by erosion, land leveling, or terracing (Frye et al., 1978; Gerwing et al., 1982). Occurrences of Zn deficiencies on exposed subsoil are caused by removal of much of the available Zn, which is either complexed by organic matter (Frye et al., 1978) or bonded by mineral surfaces in topsoil (Iyengar et al., 1981). The occurrence of Zn deficiency on a particular soil also depends on differences in plant species (Table 15-2) and variety susceptibilities (Knudsen & Frank, 1977; Mikkelsen & Kuo, 1977; Graves et al., 1980, 1981).

A. Sources of Zinc

Many inorganic compounds, natural organic complexes such as the Zn lignosulfonate, and synthetic chelates are used to correct Zn deficiencies (Table 15-15). Zinc sulfate is used more than other inorganic compounds for correcting Zn deficiency. High water solubility, relatively low cost, and wide availability of $ZnSO_4$ account for its frequent use as a Zn fertilizer (Schulte & Walsh, 1982). High rates of either animal manure or sewage sludge can be used to correct Zn deficiencies (Robertson & Lucas, 1976; Fenster et al., 1984). Animal manures and sewage sludges vary widely in Zn concentrations and other potentially phytotoxic metals (Robertson & Lucas, 1976; Payne et al., 1988a). Concentrations of macronutrients and potentially phyto-

Table 15-15. Zinc sources used for correcting Zn deficiencies in plants.†

Source	Formula	Zn, g kg^{-1}‡
	Inorganic compounds	
Zinc ammonia complex	Zn-NH$_3$	100
Zinc carbonate	ZnCO$_3$	520–560
Zinc chloride	ZnCl$_2$	480–500
Zinc frits	Fritted glass	100–300
Zinc nitrate	Zn(NO$_3$)$_2$·6H$_2$O	220
Zinc oxide	ZnO	500–800
Zinc oxysulfate	ZnO + ZnSO$_4$	400–550
Zinc sulfate monohydrate	ZnSO$_4$·H$_2$O	360
Zinc sulfate heptahydrate	ZnSO$_4$·7H$_2$O	230
Basic zinc sulfate	ZnSO$_4$·4Zn(OH)$_2$	550
	Organic compounds	
Zinc chelate	Na$_2$ZnEDTA	140
Zinc chelate	NaZnHEDTA	90
Zinc chelate	NaZnNTA	90
Zinc lignosulfonate	--	50–80
Zinc polyflavonoid	--	50–100

† Data from Murphy and Walsh (1972), Mortvedt (1982a), Fenster et al. (1984), and Killorn (1984).
‡ Approximate concentration.

toxic metals, including Zn, require consideration when determining the amount of animal manure or sewage sludge to apply for correcting Zn deficiency.

B. Application Methods and Rates

Zinc deficiencies can be corrected by applying Zn to plant foliage or to soil by either band or broadcast procedures. Foliar Zn application often is considered an emergency procedure for salvaging a crop when unexpected Zn deficiency occurs during a growing season (Mengel, 1980; Schulte & Walsh, 1982; Moraghan, 1983). Use of foliar Zn application for correcting Zn deficiencies in fruit trees has been discussed by Murphy & Walsh (1972). Zinc deficiency was alleviated in pecan (*Carya illinoensis* Wang.) by injecting 1 g ZnSO$_4$ per 2.5 cm of trunk circumference with 8 L H$_2$O tree^{-1} (Worley et al., 1980). Application of 750 g of ZnSO$_4$ in each of six soil holes 30- to 60-cm from the trunk, when the apical buds were bursting, corrected Zn deficiency in apple trees (Orphanos, 1982). The root must be cut in the zone of Zn application and the area must be irrigated soon after because Zn enters into the apple tree by mass flow through the cut roots. Band or broadcast application of Zn is used to correct Zn deficiencies in many crops when the problem is recognized before planting (Frye et al., 1978; Fenster et al., 1984; Killorn, 1984). Frequent use of broadcast Zn probably reflects the relatively high carryover value of soil-incorporated Zn. Banding of Zn is often used where fields are periodically planted to a row-crop such as corn (Frye et al., 1978).

1. Soil Applications

Murphy and Walsh (1972) concluded, from a review of literature through 1971, that Zn deficiencies are most frequently and effectively corrected by soil application of Zn. Their conclusion is valid still, based on our review of literature.

a. Inorganic Sources. Broadcast applications of 4.5 to 34 kg Zn ha^{-1} as $ZnSO_4$ are used for correcting Zn deficiencies (Table 15-16). Differences in rates of broadcast Zn required for correcting the deficiency reflect variations in soil properties, plant requirements, and concentrations of extractable soil Zn. The highest rate of broadcast $ZnSO_4$ was needed for correcting Zn deficiency of corn, a crop that is highly sensitive to the deficiency (Table 15-2), on silt loam soils with very high available P contents and slightly acid to alkaline pH levels (Frye et al., 1978). More broadcast Zn as $ZnSO_4$ is required to correct Zn deficiencies of corn on calcareous than on noncalcareous soils; i.e., from 11 to 17 kg Zn ha^{-1} are needed for calcareous soils and from 6 to 9 kg Zn ha^{-1} for noncalcareous soils (Wiese & Penas, 1979). Larger amounts of broadcast Zn as $ZnSO_4$ are required for correcting Zn deficiencies in soils with lower concentrations of extractable Zn; i.e., 11 kg Zn ha^{-1} as $ZnSO_4$ should be applied for soils with <0.4 mg DTPA-extractable Zn kg^{-1} and one-half of this amount should be applied for soils with 0.41 to 0.80 mg DTPA-extractable Zn kg^{-1} (Killorn, 1984).

Incorporation of broadcast Zn into the soil provides the mixing that usually is necessary to attain maximum uptake of applied Zn by most crops (Boawn, 1973; Moraghan, 1973; Killorn, 1984). However, Mikkelson and Brandon (1975) reported that broadcast Zn as $ZnSO_4$ was more effective in correcting Zn deficiency of water-sown rice when it was incorporated after flooding than before flooding. They pointed out that applied Zn must be located on the soil surface in the area of initial root activity for effective control of Zn deficiency in rice. Immobilization of Zn at the soil surface above the zone of root development necessitates incorporation of Zn into the soil for most crops (Boawn, 1973).

Lower rates of band than broadcast application of $ZnSO_4$ can be used to correct Zn deficiencies (Table 15-16). The greater efficiency of the banded $ZnSO_4$ is due to the lower amount of Zn-soil contact and, hence, to slower reversion of the applied Zn^{2+} to unavailable forms. Higher rates of banded $ZnSO_4$ are required under conditions of severe than of mild Zn deficiency and, therefore, application rates have been based on extractable Zn concentrations and soil pH. For example, 5.6, 3.3, and 2.2 kg Zn ha^{-1} as banded $ZnSO_4$ are needed for soils with <2 mg 0.1 M HCl-extractable Zn kg^{-1} at pH levels of >7.5, 7.4 to 6.7, and <6.7, respectively (Vitosh et al., 1981). Less banded $ZnSO_4$, 3.3 kg Zn ha^{-1}, is needed for soils with higher 0.1 M HCl-extractable Zn concentrations, between 3 to 5 mg kg^{-1}, and with pH levels of ≥6.7.

Schulte and Walsh (1982) indicated that Zn frits, ZnO, and $ZnSO_4$ were equally effective for correcting Zn deficiencies of corn, snapbean, and vegetables by band or broadcast application procedures. About twice as much

Table 15-16. Band and broadcast procedures for correcting Zn deficiencies in various plants.

Crop	Zn source	Zn rate, kg ha^{-1}	Application method	Comment	Reference
Red Mexican bean, sweet corn	Na$_2$ZnEDTA	0.9-1.8	Broadcast	Apply with macronutrient fertilizer and plow in.	Boawn, 1973
Rice	ZnSO$_4$, ZnO	9.0	Broadcast	Surface apply before flooding	Mikkelson & Brandon, 1975
Corn	ZnSO$_4$	34.0 6.6	Broadcast Band	Reapply every 4 to 5 yr.	Frye et al., 1978
Corn	ZnSO$_4$, ZnO Zn chelate	11.0 2.2-3.3	Broadcast Broadcast	Use finely divided ZnO.	Mengel, 1980
Corn	ZnSO$_4$, ZnO Zn chelate	3.3 0.6-1.1	Band Band	Band with starter fertilizer; use finely divided ZnO.	Mengel, 1980
Corn, snapbean, vegetables	ZnSO$_4$ ZnEDTA	4.5-9.0 1.1-2.2	Broadcast Broadcast	Apply with N, P, and K fertilizer.	Schulte & Walsh, 1982
Corn, snapbean, vegetables	ZnSO$_4$ ZnEDTA	2.2-4.5 0.6-1.1	Band Band	Band with N, P, and K fertilizer.	Schulte & Walsh, 1982
Flax	ZnSO$_4$	11.0	Broadcast	Incorporate by plowing.	Moraghan, 1983
Corn, bean, grain, sorghum, sweet corn	ZnSO$_4$	11.0-17.0 5.6-11.0	Broadcast Broadcast	DTPA extractable Zn, <0.5 mg kg^{-1} DTPA extractable Zn, 0.5 to 1.0 mg kg^{-1}	Fenster et al., 1984
Corn, bean, grain, sorghum, sweet corn	ZnSO$_4$ Na$_2$ZnEDTA	1.1-2.2 <1.1	Band Band	DTPA extractable Zn, <0.5 mg kg^{-1}; band with starter fertilizer.	Fenster et al., 1984
Corn, sorghum	ZnSO$_4$	11.0 5.5	Broadcast Broadcast	DTPA extractable Zn, <0.40 mg kg^{-1}. DTPA extractable Zn, 0.41 to 0.81 mg kg^{-1}	Killorn, 1984
Corn, bean, flax, potato, sorghum, soybean	ZnSO$_4$	5.6-11.0 1.0-5.5	Broadcast Band	Reapply every 2 to 4 yr.	Gerwing et al., 1988

broadcast as banded Zn was needed for correcting these deficiencies (Schulte & Walsh, 1982). Banding Zn carriers with N, P, and K fertilizer ensures maximum effectiveness of the applied Zn (Table 15–16). Mikkleson and Brandon (1975) indicated that broadcasting $ZnCl_2$, $Zn(NO_3)_2$, or $ZnSO_4$ before flooding was equally effective in correcting Zn deficiency in water-sown rice, but that ZnO was slightly less effective. Zinc oxide must be finely divided to serve as an effective source for correcting Zn deficiency (Mengel, 1980).

b. **Organic Sources.** Lower rates of broadcast Zn as organic than as inorganic sources can generally be used to correct Zn deficiencies (Table 15–16) (Moraghan, 1983). Boawn (1973) compared the effectiveness of broadcast, plowed down ZnEDTA and $ZnSO_4$ applied with P and K fertilizer for correcting Zn deficiencies in Red Mexican bean (*Phaseolus vulgaris* L.) and sweet corn (*Zea saccharata* L.) on noncalcareous, but alkaline, silt loam soils. The ZnEDTA was 2.0 to 2.5 times more effective than $ZnSO_4$ in increasing Zn uptake by the two crops, and the minimum amount of the chelate required to correct these Zn deficiencies was from 0.9 to 1.8 kg Zn ha^{-1}. Surface-applied Zn as $ZnSO_4$ at rates up to 10.7 kg ha^{-1} was ineffective in correcting Zn deficiencies of irrigated Red Mexican bean and sweet corn unless plowed into soil to a depth of 25 cm (Boawn, 1973). In contrast, surface-applied Zn as ZnEDTA followed by irrigation was as effective as the broadcast, plowed down application for correcting these Zn deficiencies. The greater effectiveness of the ZnEDTA in comparison with $ZnSO_4$ was attributed to its deeper movement into the soil with irrigation water. A Zn chelate would be more effective than an inorganic Zn compound for use in no-till systems in which the Zn carrier would not be incorporated into the soil (Killorn, 1984).

Lower rates of Zn are used as chelates than as inorganic compounds when banding to correct Zn deficiencies (Table 15–16) (Robertson & Lucas, 1976; Moraghan, 1983; Fenster et al., 1984). Hergert et al. (1984) determined the effect of five Zn sources banded with 224 kg fluid fertilizer (97.5% fertilizer and 2.5% Na bentonite) ha^{-1} on Zn uptake and growth of irrigated corn on sandy soils. Up to 3.36 kg Zn ha^{-1} as ZnEDTA was more effective in increasing Zn uptake, but not grain yield, compared with equal Zn rates as a Zn-NH_3 complex, ZnO, $ZnSO_4$, and $Zn(NO_3)_2$ on a calcareous soil. Where rainfall caused leaching of ZnEDTA, this organic source was less effective in increasing Zn uptake in comparison with the four inorganic sources. Osiname et al. (1973) reported that from 1.1 to 2.2 kg Zn ha^{-1} as banded ZnEDTA were adequate to obtain optimum corn grain yields on sandy Inceptisols located in the savannah area of Nigeria. Lower rates of Zn as a banded chelate than as a broadcast inorganic or organic Zn source are recommended for correcting Zn deficiencies (Table 15–16).

2. Foliar Applications

Inorganic and organic Zn sources can be used to alleviate Zn deficiencies by spray application of Zn on plant foliage. Schulte and Walsh (1982) indicated that 0.7 kg Zn ha^{-1} as $ZnSO_4$ or 0.17 kg Zn ha^{-1} as ZnEDTA should be applied with 187 L H_2O ha^{-1} for correcting Zn deficiency. They pointed out that either broadcast or banded Zn usually was more effective than foliar Zn. Mengel (1980) suggested that foliar application of 1.4 kg Zn ha^{-1} as $ZnSO_4$ would improve crop yields. Fenster et al. (1984) recommended a foliar application of 0.56 to 1.1 kg Zn ha^{-1} as $ZnSO_4$ or 0.17 kg Zn ha^{-1} as ZnEDTA in 187 L H_2O ha^{-1} for correcting Zn deficiencies. They cautioned that foliar Zn should be applied in the morning or evening to prevent leaf injury.

Usually one foliar application of Zn is not adequate for correcting moderate to severe Zn deficiencies (Frye et al., 1978; Schulte & Walsh, 1982; Fenster et al., 1984). Moraghan (1983) reported that foliar Zn was less effective than soil-applied Zn in correcting Zn deficiency of flax because of inadequate interception of foliar Zn by the undeveloped leaf canopy. Dryland pinto bean yields were increased from 18 to 92% by three foliar applications of 1% $ZnSO_4 \cdot 7H_2O$ in 280 L H_2O ha^{-1} (Khan & Soltanpour, 1978). The foliar applications were completed 1 wk before bloom, and 1 and 2 wk after bloom.

3. Seed Applications

Seed treatment procedures have been tried in an attempt to correct Zn deficiencies. Neither use of seed from a Zn-fertilized crop nor application of $ZnSO_4$ to seed was as satisfactory in correcting Zn deficiency in linseed (*Linum usitatissimum* L.) plants as was foliar or soil Zn applications (Whitehouse, 1973). Vitosh et al. (1981) reported that treatment of bean seed with 1.1 kg Zn ha^{-1} as ZnO reduced emergence and yields in many locations. Fenster et al. (1984) suggested that a maximum of 0.22 kg Zn ha^{-1} could be banded in direct contact with seed. Mikkelson and Brandon (1975) indicated that coating 1 kg of seed with 20 g of Zn from either $ZnSO_4$ or ZnO satisfactorily corrected Zn deficiency in water-sown rice.

C. Residual Effects

Relatively large application rates of broadcast Zn correct Zn deficiencies for several years (Mikkelsen & Kuo, 1977) because of the relatively slow reversion of applied Zn to plant-unavailable forms (ASCE, 1987; Bidwell & Dowdy, 1987; Payne et al., 1988b). Robertson and Lucas (1976) indicated that, under conditions of severe deficiencies, broadcasting 28 kg Zn ha^{-1} as $ZnSO_4$ was effective in correcting Zn deficiencies for 7 yr. Frye et al. (1978) reported that residual Zn from broadcast application of 34 kg Zn ha^{-1} as $ZnSO_4$ was adequate to correct the deficiency for 4 to 5 yr. In contrast, banded Zn must be applied at a rate of 6.6 kg ha^{-1} for about 5 yr to assure adequate availability of residual Zn to correct Zn deficiencies (Frye et al., 1978). Vitosh et al. (1981) pointed out that, after applying 28 kg Zn ha^{-1} by banding annually, further application of Zn is unnecessary for correcting Zn deficiencies. Foliar Zn usually is applied at such a low rate that it has little residual value.

D. Toxicity Effects

Potential Zn phytotoxicity from excess Zn application exists because only small amounts of Zn leach, and because reversion of applied Zn to unavailable forms is relatively slow in soils (ASCE, 1987; Bidwell & Dowdy, 1987; Payne et al., 1988b). Zinc phytotoxicities are undesirable because of (i) decreased crop yield and quality; (ii) problems in correcting Zn phytotoxicities; and (iii) possible entrance of excess Zn into the food chain (ASCE, 1987).

Plants differ widely in sensitivity to Zn toxicity (ASCE, 1987). For example, normal growth of corn, a tolerant crop, may occur on a soil where Zn phytotoxicity limits growth of sensitive crops such as Sanilac white and Charlevoix red kidney beans (*Phaseolus vulgaris* L.) (Vitosh et al., 1981). From 7.1 to 10.7 kg Zn ha^{-1} as broadcasted ZnEDTA caused severe leaf scorching and reduced yields of irrigated bean plants (Boawn, 1973). Walsh et al. (1972b) found that a single application of 363 kg Zn ha^{-1} as $ZnSO_4$ decreased snapbean yield on a Plainfield loamy sand (Typic Udipsamment) during the first growing season, but did not affect yield during the second year.

Zinc phytotoxicity from excess application should be considered when making recommendations for correcting Zn deficiencies. The USEPA (1983) has prepared guidelines for maximum tolerable levels of Zn applied by incorporating sewage sludge into soil. Based on these guidelines, the recommended cumulative limits for Zn application to cropland are 280, 560, and 1120 kg Zn ha^{-1} for soils with CEC levels of <5, 5 to 15, and >15 cmol$_c$ kg^{-1}, respectively. A pH of 6.5 or above must be maintained where sewage sludge is incorporated into soil in order to decrease Zn availability.

VII. OTHER MICRONUTRIENTS

A. Chlorine

Chloride deficiency has been observed under greenhouse or laboratory conditions for several different crops. The critical Cl concentration is about 70 to 200 mg kg^{-1} in the dry matter for most plants (Eaton, 1966; Whitehead, 1985). The amount of Cl in the atmosphere or rainwater has been considered sufficient to meet crop demands, although the quantities in these sources are influenced by the distance from the source; e.g., salt water bodies. Significant amounts of Cl are also found in some irrigation waters (Eaton, 1966) and municipal effluents (Kardos et al., 1977). Fertilizer sources of Cl include KCl, $CaCl_2$, NH_4Cl, and NaCl. Yield increases from Cl fertilization have also been associated with suppression of foliar or root diseases (Christensen et al., 1987; Timm et al., 1986).

Chlorine deficiencies under field conditions are reported for potato (*Solanum tuberosum* L.) in Maine (Gausmann et al., 1959), oil palm (*Elaeis guinenis* J.) in Peru (Daniel & Ochs, 1975), sugarcane (*Saccharum officinarum* L.) in Hawaii (Bowen, 1972), and hard red spring wheat in South Dakota

(Fixen et al., 1986a). The critical Cl concentration in the wheat plant was about 1.5 g Cl kg^{-1}. No yield response to Cl fertilization occurred when the Cl content was ≥ 70 kg ha^{-1} in the top 12 cm of soil (Fixen et al., 1986a, 1987). Responses to Cl were also obtained in spring barley and oat crops (Fixen et al., 1986b). These data may suggest that Cl should be considered as a macronutrient rather than a micronutrient for selected crops.

Crops grown on salt-affected soils often show symptoms of toxicity. Chloride 'toxicity' from KCl applications was reported for soybean grown on Atlantic Coastal Plain soils (Parker et al., 1983). Sensitivity to high Cl concentrations varies widely between plant species and cultivars (Eaton, 1966).

B. Cobalt

Cobalt is essential for microorganisms that fix molecular N_2. It is required by *Rhizobia* in symbiosis with legumes, as well as by free-living bacteria and blue-green algae. The actual Co requirement is very low; about 0.3% of the requirement for Mo. Deficiencies may occur in highly leached, sandy soils derived from acid igneous rocks in calcareous soils or peaty soils. Legumes grown on some soils in the lower Atlantic Coastal Plain and in Australia, New Zealand, Scotland, and India have responded to Co applications.

Both the SO_4^{2-} and NO_3^- salts of Co are used as fertilizers (Gladstones et al., 1977; Raj, 1987). Application rates range from 0.4 to 6 kg Co ha^{-1} broadcast (Gladstones et al., 1977; McLaren et al., 1979), 500 mg Co L^{-1} foliar, and 500 mg Co kg^{-1} as a seed treatment (Raj, 1987; Reddy & Raj, 1975). Deficiencies are generally corrected by broadcasting 1 to 2 kg Co ha^{-1} (McLaren et al., 1979; Gladstone et al., 1977). Higher rates may be required on soils that contain Mn minerals that are capable of immobilizing Co (McKenzie, 1978). Cobalt concentrations in municipal wastes are generally similar to those of B and Mo (Kardos et al., 1977). Cobalt toxicity in plants is often expressed as deficiencies of other heavy metals (e.g., Fe or Mn) and it is generally not a problem for most agronomic crops, unless the soils contain cobaltiferous ores. These areas are identified by the presence of plants that accumulate Co in their tissues in excess of 1 g kg^{-1} (Adriano, 1986).

C. Nickel

Beneficial effects of Ni on plant growth are reported for some plant species (Welch, 1981). It has been proposed as an essential element for legumes (Eskew et al., 1983). Oat grown in nutrient solutions at very low Ni concentrations accumulated urea when provided with a urea-N source, whereas added Ni increased shoot and root growth, and plant maturity (Brown et al., 1987). Nickel also increased the activity of the nodule hydrogenase enzyme in symbiotic legumes (Welch, 1981; Dalton et al., 1985). Nickel fertilization of soybean in the greenhouse did not affect yields, but did increase leaf urease and nodule hydrogenase activity in a low Ni, non-serpentine soil (Dalton et al., 1985). Soil urease activity increased in three out of ten soils to which purified $CaCO_3$ was added to increase soil pH to 6.8.

Nickel is ubiquitous in the environment. It is a component of most P fertilizers. Coal and fly ash materials, and sewage sludges contain significant quantities of Ni, which increase Ni uptake by plants, but usually do not cause Ni toxicity when land applied (Kardos et al., 1977; Kelling et al., 1977). Foliar applications may correct Ni deficiencies (Chamel & Newmann, 1987). Additional information on Ni in the environment may be found in a recent review by Adriano (1986).

VIII. SUMMARY

Considerable progress is being made on the development of procedures to correct micronutrient deficiencies in diverse cropping systems under various management regimes. Reliable data have been obtained on residual availabilities and toxicities of applied micronutrients. Logical scientific explanations are proposed to explain reasons for successful as well as unsuccessful procedures used to correct micronutrient deficiencies. Nevertheless, improved methods and explanations are still needed.

The correction of micronutrient deficiencies depends on the availability of the micronutrient when applied by band, broadcast, or foliar application procedures. In addition, the residual availability may depend on the application procedure, but there is a lack of micronutrient carryover data from long-term experiments. It would be appropriate to initiate field research on diverse soils to determine interactions between soil properties and the long-term availability of applied micronutrients. Foliar procedures have been developed to correct Mn deficiency in soybean because of ineffectiveness of soil-applied Mn. Similar research is needed to devise effective foliar application methods to correct micronutrient deficiencies in other crops.

Both inorganic and organic sources are used for correcting micronutrient deficiencies. There is a lack of experimental data to compare the efficacy of inorganic and organic carriers by band, broadcast, or foliar procedures. Research is also needed to evaluate the effect of other fertilizers on the availability of micronutrients. Much of the research reported in the literature does not allow an evaluation of any interactions between and among macronutrient fertilizers and each of the micronutrients. Interactions with other environmental factors also need better documentation and characterization to increase our understanding of micronutrient responses and to aid modeling efforts. Efforts to find and develop improved agronomic micronutrient sources and application methods under field conditions should continue. These include the organic decomposition product approach for Fe and the general role of organic-micronutrient complexes on plant availability. Studies on the role of micronutrients on the plant's susceptibility to diseases may allow us to separate disease and nutritional relationships.

Potential phytotoxicity from misapplications of most micronutrients exists because very small amounts are leached (except B) or needed by plants, and because reversion to unavailable forms is relatively slow. Phytotoxicities are undesirable because of decreased crop yields and quality, because correction may be difficult, and because of possible entrance into the food chain. Increasing soil pH will generally reduce most micronutrient availabilities; however, Mo availability increases. Soil pH and CEC levels are considered in the USEPA guidelines for maximum application rates of waste products to soils. Fertilization rates needed to correct deficiencies will generally be much lower than those rates. Phytotoxicity is potentially greater with a chelated material compared with an inorganic material, and decreases in the order of foliar, band, and broadcast application of chelates, respectively. A reliable preplant soil test will generally identify a potential phytotoxic situation.

Knowing the sensitivities of various plants to micronutrient deficiencies will allow the substitution of one crop for another where there is high potential for a micronutrient deficiency or toxicity. This approach may not be suitable where the crop to be produced is determined from economic considerations. This problem could be overcome by developing varieties that are less susceptible. A goal in this research would involve tailoring a plant for maximum productivity on a specific soil.

REFERENCES

Abdou, F.M., and M. El-Nennah. 1980. Effect of irrigating loamy sand soil by liquid sewage sludge on its content of some micronutrients. Plant Soil 56:53–57.

Adriano, D.C. 1986. Trace elements in the terrestrial environment. Springer-Verlag New York, New York.

Adriano, D.C., A.L. Page, A.A. Elseewi, A.C. Chang, and I. Staugham. 1980. Utilization and disposal of fly ash and other coal residues in terrestrial ecosystems: A review. J. Environ. Qual. 9:333–334.

Alley, M.M., C.I. Rich, G.W. Hawkins, and D.C. Martens. 1978. Correction of Mn deficiency of soybeans. Agron. J. 70:35–38.

Alloway, B.J., and A.R. Tills. 1984. Copper deficiency in world crops. Outlook Agric. 13:32–42.

American Society of Civil Engineers (ASCE). 1987. Role of trace elements. p. 30–39. *In* T.M. Younos (ed.) Land application of wastewater sludge. American Society of Civil Engineers, New York.

Anderson, W.B. 1982. Diagnosis and correction of iron deficiency in field crop—an overview. J. Plant Nutr. 5:785–795.

Barak, P., Y. Chen, and A. Singer. 1983. Ground basalt and tuff as iron fertilizers for calcareous soils. Plant Soil 73:155–158.

Barrow, N.J., P.J. Leaky, I.N. Soutkey, and D.B. Purser. 1985. Initial and residual effectiveness of molybdate fertilizer in two areas of southwestern Australia. Aust. J. Agric. Res. 36:579–587.

Benson, N.R. 1967. Deciduous fruit. The micronutrient manual. Farm Tech. 23(6).

Berger, K.C. 1962. Micronutrient deficiencies in the United States. J. Agric. Food Chem. 10:178–181.

Bidwell, A.M., and R.H. Dowdy. 1987. Cadmium and zinc availability to corn following termination of sewage sludge applications. J. Environ. Qual. 16:438–442.

Blatt, C.R. 1982. Effects of two boron sources each applied at three rates to the strawberry cv. Midway on soil and leaf boron levels and fruit yields. Commun. Soil Sci. Plant Anal. 13:39–47.

Boawn, L.C. 1973. Comparison of zinc sulfate and zinc EDTA as zinc fertilizer sources. Soil Sci. Soc. Am. Proc. 37:111–115.

Boswell, F.C., and O.E. Anderson. 1969. Effect of time of molybdenum application on soybean yield, and nitrogen, oil, and molybdenum contents. Agron. J. 61:58–60.

Boswell, F.C., R.P. Lane, and K. Ohki. 1980. Field studies with boron on Muscadine grapes. Commun. Soil Sci. Plant Anal. 11:201–207.

Boswell, F.C., K. Ohki, M.B. Parker, and L.M. Shuman, and D.O. Wilson. 1981. Methods and rates of applied manganese for soybeans. Agron. J. 73:909–912.

Bowen, J.E. 1972. Essentiality of chlorine for optimum growth of sugarcane. p. 1102–1112. *In* Proc. 14th Congress Int. Soc. Sugar Cane Technol., New Orleans, LA. October 1971. Int. Soc. Sugar Cane Technol.

Brown, J.C., and R.B. Clark. 1974. Differential response of two maize inbreeds to molybdenum stress. Soil Sci. Soc. Am. Proc. 38:331–333.

Brown, P.H., R.M. Welch, E.E. Cary, and R.T. Checkai. 1987. Beneficial effects of nickel on plant growth. J. Plant Nutr. 10:2125–2135.

Burmester, C.H., J.F. Adams, and J.W. Odom. 1988. Response of soybean to lime and molybdenum on Ultisols in northern Alabama. Soil Sci. Soc. Am. J. 52:1391–1394.

Chamel, A., and P. Neumann. 1987. Foliar absorption of nickel: Determination of its cuticular behavior using isolated cuticles. J. Plant Nutr. 10:99–111.

Chaney, R.L. 1988. Plants can utilize iron from Fe-N,N '-DI-(2-hydroxybenozyl)-ethylenediamine-N,N '-diacetic acid, a ferric chelate with 10^6 greater formation constant than Fe-EDDHA. J. Plant Nutr. 11:1033–1050.

Chaney, R.L., and P.M. Giordano. 1977. Microelements as related to plant deficiencies and toxicities. p. 233–298. *In* L. Elliott and F.J. Stevenson (ed.) Soils for management of organic wastes and waste waters. ASA, CSSA, and SSSA, Madison, WI.

Chen, Y., and P. Barak. 1982. Iron nutrition of plants in calcareous soils. Adv. Agron. 35:217–240.

Chen, Y., J. Navrot, and P. Barak. 1982. Remedy of lime-induced chlorosis with iron-enriched muck. J. Plant Nutr. 5:927–940.

Christensen, N.W., R.G. Taylor, T.L. Jackson, and B.L. Mitchell. 1987. Chloride effects on water potentials and yield of wheat infected with take-all root rot. Agron. J. 73:1053–1058.

Cihacek, L.J. 1984. Economic soil treatment of iron chlorosis in grain sorghum grown on a gypsum affected soil. J. Plant Nutr. 7:329–340.

Cox, F.R. 1968. Development of a yield response prediction and manganese soil test interpretation for soybeans. Agron. J. 60:521–524.

Dalton, D.A., H.J. Evans, and F.J. Hanus. 1985. Effects of nickel fertilization on soybeans. Plant Soil 88:245–258.

Daniel, C., and R. Ochs. 1975. Improvement of production of young oil palms in Peru by chloride fertilizer application. Oliagineux 30:295–298.

DeKock, P.C., M.V. Cheshire, and A. Hall. 1971. Comparison of the effect of phosphorus and nitrogen on copper-deficient and -sufficient oats. J. Sci. Food Agric. 22:437–440.

Donohue, S.J., G.W. Hawkins, and A.H. Allison. 1979. Trace element applications—Soil Test Note 4. Virginia Polytechnic Inst. and State Univ. Ext. Div. Publ. 452-234.

Eaton, F.M. 1966. Chlorine. p. 98–135. *In* H.D. Chapman (ed.) Diagnostic criteria for plants and soils. Div. Agric. Sci., Univ. of California, Berkeley, CA.

Elseewi, A.A., and A.L. Page. 1984. Molybdenum enrichment of plants grown on fly-ash-treated soils. J. Environ. Qual. 13:394–398.

Eskew, D.L., R.M. Welch, and E.E. Cary. 1983. Nickel: An essential micronutrient for legumes and possibly all higher plants. Science 222:621–623.

Fehr, W.R., and M.W. Trimble. 1982. Minimizing soybean yield losses from iron deficiency chlorosis. Iowa State Univ. Coop. Ext. Serv. PM 1059.

Fenster, W.E., G.W. Rehm, and J. Grava. 1984. Zinc for Minnesota soils. Minnesota Agric. Ext. Serv. AG-FS-0720.

Fiskel, J.G., and S.E. Younts. 1963. Copper status and needs in the southern region. Plant Food Rev. 9:6–10.

Fixen, P.E., G.W. Buckenau, R.H. Gelderman, T.E. Schumacher, J.R. Gerwing, F.A. Cholick, and G. Farber. 1986a. Influence of soil and applied Cl on several wheat parameters. Agron. J. 78:736–740.

Fixen, P.E., R.H. Gelderman, J. Gerwing, and F.A. Cholick. 1986b. Response of spring wheat, barley, and oats to chloride in KCl fertilizers. Agron. J. 78:664–668.

Fixen, P.E., R.H. Gelderman, J.R. Gerwing, and B.G. Farber. 1987. Calibration and implementation of a soil Cl test. J. Fert. Issues 4:91–97.

Franco, A.A., and J.M. Day. 1980. Effects of lime and molybdenum on nodulation and nitrogen fixation of *Phaseolus vulgaris* L. in acid soils of Brazil. Turrialba 30:90–105.

Frank, S.J., and W.R. Fehr. 1983. Band application of sulfuric acid or elemental sulfur for control of Fe-deficiency chlorosis of soybeans. Agron. J. 75:451–454.

Frye, W.W., H.F. Miller, L.W. Murdock, and D.E. Peaslee. 1978. Zinc fertilization of corn in Kentucky. Kentucky Coop. Ext. Serv. Agron. Notes 11:1–4.

Gartrell, J.W. 1980. Residual effectiveness of copper fertilizer for wheat in Western Australia. Aust. J. Exp. Agric. Anim. Husb. 20:370–376.

Gartrell, J.W. 1981. Distribution and correction of copper deficiency in crops and pastures. p. 313–349. *In* J.F. Loneragon et al. (ed.) Copper in soils and plants. Academic Press, New York.

Gausmann, H.W., G.O. Estes, and A. Burns. 1959. Chloride deficiency on potatoes under field conditions. Maine Farm Res. October, p. 21–22.

Gerwing, J., P. Fixen, and R. Gelderman. 1982. Zinc rate and source studies. South Dakota Exp. Stn. Prog. Rep. 13.

Gerwing, J., R. Gelderman, and P. Fixen. 1988. Fertilizer recommendations guide. South Dakota Coop. Ext. Serv. EC 750.

Gettier, S.W., D.C. Martens, and T.B. Brumback, Jr. 1985. Timing of foliar manganese application for correction of manganese deficiency in soybeans. Agron. J. 77:627–630.

Gettier, S.W., D.C. Martens, D.L. Hallock, and M.J. Stewart. 1984. Residual Mn and associated soybean yield response from $MnSO_4$ application on a sandy loam soil. Plant Soil 81:101–110.

Gilkes, R.J. 1977. Factors influencing the release of copper and zinc additives from grandulated superphosphate. J. Soil Sci. 28:103–111.

Gladstones, J.S., J.F. Loneragan, and N.A. Goodchild. 1977. Field responses to cobalt and molybdenum by different legume species, with inferences on the role of cobalt in plant growth. Aust. J. Agric. Res. 28:619–628.

Graham, R.D. 1976. Physiological aspects of time of application of copper to wheat plants. J. Exp. Bot. 27:717–724.

Graves, C.R., J. Jared, W.A. Warren, and G.M. Lessman. 1980. Forrest soybeans respond to zinc at soil pH values above 7. Tenn. Farm Home Sci. 114:2–3.

Graves, C.R., J. Jared, W.A. Warren, and G.M. Lessman. 1981. Soybean varieties respond to zinc at soil pH values above 7. Tenn. Farm Home Sci. 118:22.

Gray, C., W.B. Anderson, and C.D. Welch. 1974. Iron and zinc deficiencies in field crops. Texas Agric. Ext. Serv. L-891.

Grundon, N.J. 1980. Effectiveness of soil dressings and foliar sprays of copper sulphate in correcting copper deficiency of wheat (*Triticum aestivum*) in Queensland. Aust. J. Exp. Agric. Anim. Husb. 20:717–723.

Gupta, U.C. 1979a. Boron nutrition of crops. Adv. Agron. 31:273–307.

Gupta, U.C. 1979b. Effect of methods of application and residual effect of molybdenum on the molybdenum concentration and yield of forages on podzol soils. Can. J. Soil Sci. 59:183–189.

Gupta, U.C. 1984. Boron nutrition of alfalfa, red clover, and timothy grown on podzol soils of Eastsern Canada. Soil Sci. 137:16–22.

Gupta, U.C., and J.A. Cutcliffe. 1975. Boron deficiency in cole crops under field and greenhouse conditions. Commun. Soil Sci. Plant Anal. 6:181–188.

Gupta, U.C., and J.A. Cutcliffe. 1978. Effects of method of boron application on leaf tissue concentration of boron and control of brown-heart in rutabaga. Can. J. Plant Sci. 58:63–68.

Gupta, U.C., and J.A. Cutcliffe. 1982. Residual effect of boron applied to rutabaga on subsequent cereal crops. Soil Sci. 133:155–159.

Gupta, U.C., and J.A. Cutcliffe. 1984. Effects of applied and residual boron on the nutrition of cabbage and field beans. Can. J. Soil Sci. 64:571–576.

Gupta, U.C., Y.W. Jame, C.A. Campbell, A.J. Leyshon, and W. Nicholaichuk. 1985. Boron toxicity and deficiency: A review. Can. J. Soil Sci. 65:381–409.

Gupta, U.C., and J. Lipsett. 1981. Molybdenum in soils, plants, and animals. Adv. Agron. 34:73–115.

Gupta, U.C., and L.B. MacLeod. 1975. Effects of sulfur and molybdenum on the molybdenum, copper, and sulfur concentrations of forage crops. Soil Sci. 119:441–447.

Hagstrom, G.R. 1984. Current management practices for correcting iron deficiency in plants with emphasis on soil management. J. Plant Nutr. 7:23–46.

Hallock, D.L. 1979. Relative effectiveness of several Mn sources on Virginia-type peanuts. Agron. J. 71:685–688.

Hanson, E.J., and P.J. Breen. 1985. Effects of fall boron sprays and environmental factors on fruit set and boron accumulation in "Italian" prune flowers. J. Am. Soc. Hortic. Sci. 110:389–392.

Hawes, R.L., J.L. Sims, and K.L. Wells. 1976. Molybdenum concentration of certain forage crop species as influenced by previous applications of molybdenum fertilizer. Agron. J. 68:217–218.

Hemphill, D.D., Jr., M.S. Weber, and T.L. Jackson. 1982. Table beet yield and boron deficiency as influenced by lime, nitrogen, and boron. Soil Sci. Soc. Am. J. 46:1190–1192.

Hergert, G.W., G.W. Rehm, and R.A. Wiese. 1984. Field evaluations of zinc sources band applied in ammonium polyphosphate suspension. Soil Sci. Soc. Am. Proc. 48:1190–1193.

Hill, W.E., and L.G. Morrill. 1974. Assessing boron needs for improving peanut yields and quality. Agron. J. 38:791–794.

Holmes, J.C., A.H. Donald, W. Chapman, R.W. Lang, K.A. Smith, and M.F. Franklin. 1983. Effects of soil compaction, seed depth, form of nitrogen fertilizer, fertilizer placement and manganese availability on barley. J. Sci. Food Agric. 34:671–684.

Hopmans, P., and D.W. Flinn. 1984. Boron deficiency in *Pinus radiata* D. Don and the effect of applied boron on height, growth and nutrient uptake. Plant Soil 79:295–298.

Hsu, H.H., and H.D. Ashmead. 1984. Effect of urea and ammonium nitrate on the uptake of iron through leaves. J. Plant Nutr. 7:291–299.

Iyengar, S.S., D.C. Martens, and W.P. Miller. 1981. Distribution and plant availability of soil zinc fractions. Soil Sci. Soc. Am. J. 45:735–739.

Jackson, T.L., and G.E. Carter. 1976. Nutrient uptake by Russet Burbank potatoes as influenced by fertilization. Agron. J. 68:9–12.

Johnson, G., and B. Tucker. 1982. Oklahoma State Univ. soil test calibrations. Oklahoma State Univ. Ext. Facts 2225.

Jones, M.B., and J.E. Ruckman. 1973. Long-term effects of phosphorus, sulfur, and molybdenum on a subterranean clover pasture. Soil Sci. 115:343–348.

Kadman, A., and E. Lahav. 1982. Experiments to correct iron deficiency in avocado trees. J. Plant Nutr. 5:961–966.

Kafkafir, U., and R.G. Neumann. 1985. Correction of iron chlorosis in peanut (*Arachis hypogaea shulamit*) by ammonium sulfate and nitrification inhibitor. J. Plant Nutr. 8:303–309.

Karamanos, R.E., G.A. Kruger, and J.W.B. Stewart. 1986. Copper deficiency in cereal and oilseed crops in northern Canadian prairie soils. Agron. J. 78:317–323.

Kardos, L.T., C.E. Scarsbrook, and V.V. Volk. 1977. Recycling elements in wastes through soil-plant systems. p. 299–324. *In* L.F. Elliott and F.J. Stevenson (ed.) Soils for management of organic wastes and waste waters. ASA, CSSA, and SSSA, Madison, WI.

Kelling, K.A., D.R. Keeney, L.W. Walsh, and J.A. Ryan. 1977. A field study of the agricultrual use of sewage sludge. III. Effect of uptake and extractability of sludge-borne metals. J. Environ. Qual. 6:352–358.

Keren, R., and F.T. Bingham. 1985. Boron in water, soils, and plants. Adv. Soil Sci. 1:229–276.

Khan, A., and P.N. Soltanpour. 1978. Factors associated with Zn chlorosis in dryland beans. Agron. J. 70:1022–1026.

Killorn, R. 1984. Zinc—an essential nutrient. Iowa Coop. Ext. Serv. Pm-1129.

Knudsen, D., and K.D. Frank. 1977. Understand your soil test zinc, iron and sulfur. Nebraska Coop. Ext. Serv. NebGuide G74-126.

Kochan, W.J. 1962. Iron chelate control of chlorosis in peach trees. Idaho Agric. Exp. Stn. Bull. 384.

Krauskopf, K.B. 1972. Geochemistry of micronutrients. p. 7–40. *In* J.J. Mortvedt et al. (ed.) Micronutrients in agriculture. SSSA, Madison, WI.

Kroetz, M.E., W.H. Schmidt, J.E. Beuerlein, and G.L. Ryder. 1977a. Correcting manganese deficiency increases soybean yields. Ohio Rep. 62:51–53.

Kroetz, M.E., W.H. Schmidt, J.E. Beuerlein, and G.L. Ryder. 1977b. Prevent manganese deficiency in soybeans. Better Crops Plant Food LXI(2):26–28.

Leonard, C.D. 1967. Citrus. The micronutrient manual. Farm Tech. 23(6).

Lewis, D.C., and J.D. McFarlane. 1986. Effect of foliar applied manganese on the growth of safflower (*Carthamus tinctorius* L.) and the diagnosis of manganese deficiency by plant tissue and seed analysis. Aust. J. Agric. Res. 37:567–572.

Lindsay, W.L., and A.P. Schwab. 1982. The chemistry of iron and its availability to plants. J. Plant Nutr. 5:821–840.

Lipsett, J., and D.J. David. 1977. Amount and distribution of molybdenum in a bag of molybdenized superphosphate. J. Aust. Inst. Agric. Sci. 43:149–151.

Markarim, A.K., and F.R. Cox. 1983. Evaluation of the need for copper with several soil extractants. Agron. J. 75:493–496.

Marsolek, M.D., and G.R. Hagstrom. 1982. Acidified mining residue for correction of iron chlorosis on calcareous soils. J. Plant Nutr. 5:941–948.

Mascagni, H.J., Jr., and F.R. Cox. 1984. Diagnosis and correction of manganese deficiency in corn. Commun. Soil Sci. Plant Anal. 15:1323–1333.

Mascagni, H.J., Jr., and F.R. Cox. 1985a. Effective rates of fertilization for correcting manganese deficiency in soybeans. Agron. J. 77:363–366.

Mascagni, H.J., Jr., and F.R. Cox. 1985b. Evaluation of inorganic and organic manganese fertilizer sources. Soil Sci. Soc. Am. J. 49:458–461.

Mascagni, H.J., Jr., and F.R. Cox. 1988. Residual effect of manganese fertilization. Soil Sci. Soc. Am. J. 52:434–438.

Mathers, A.C., J.D. Thomas, B.A. Stewart, and J.E. Herring. 1980. Manure and inorganic fertilizer effects on sorghum and sunflower growth on iron-deficient soil. Agron. J. 72:1025–1029.

Matocha, J.E. 1984. Grain sorghum response to plant residue-recycled iron, and other iron sources. J. Plant Nutr. 7:259–270.

McCaslin, B.D., J.G. Davis, J. Cihacek, and L.A. Schluter. 1987. Sorghum yield and soil analysis from sludge-amended calcareous iron-deficient soil. Agron. J. 79:204–209.

McKenzie, R.M. 1978. The effect of two manganese dioxides on the uptake of lead, cobalt, nickel, copper, and zinc by subterranean clover. Aust. J. Soil Res. 16:209–214.

McKenzie, R.M. 1989. Manganese oxides and hydroxides. p. 439–466. In J.B. Dixon and S.B. Weed (ed.) Minerals in soil environments. 2nd ed. SSSA, Madison, WI.

McLaren, R.G., D. Purves, E.J. Mackenzie, and C.G. Mackenzie. 1979. The residual effect of pasture cobalt applications on some soils in southeast Scotland. J. Agric. Sci. 93:509–511.

Mehlich, A. 1957. Aluminum, iron, and pH in relation to lime induced manganese deficiencies. Soil Sci. Soc. Am. Proc. 21:625–628.

Mengel, D.B. 1980. Role of micronutrients in efficient crop production. Indiana Coop. Ext. Serv. AY-239.

Mikkelson, D.S., and D.M. Brandon. 1975. Zinc deficiency in California rice. Calif. Agric. 29(9):8–9.

Mikkelsen, D.S., and S. Kuo. 1977. Zinc fertilization and behavior in flooded soils. Special Publ. 5, Commonwealth Agric. Bureaux, Farnham Royal, England.

Miltmore, J.E., and J.L. Mason. 1971. Copper to molybdenum ratios and molybdenum and copper concentrations in ruminant feeds. Can. J. Anim. Sci. 51:193–200.

Minner, D.D., and J.D. Butler. 1984. Correcting iron deficiency of Kentucky Bluegrass. Hort-Science 19:109–110.

Monson, W.G., and T. Powell Gaines. 1986. Supplemental B effects on yield and quality of seven Bermudagrasses. Agron. J. 78:522–523.

Moraghan, J.T. 1983. Zinc deficiency of flax in North Dakota. North Dakota Farm Res. 40:23–26.

Moraghan, J.T. 1985. Manganese deficiency in soybeans as affected by FeEDDHA and low soil temperature. Soil Sci. Soc. Am. J. 49:1584–1586.

Morrill, L.G., W.E. Hill, W.W. Chrudimsky, L.O. Ashluck, L.D. Tripp, B.B. Tucker, and L. Weatherly. 1977. Boron requirements of Spanish peanuts in Oklahoma: Effects on yield and quality and interaction with other nutrients. Oklahoma State Agric. Exp. Stn. Bull. MP-99.

Mortvedt, J.J. 1982a. Calcium, magnesium, sulfur, and the micronutrients. p. 91–110. In W.C. White and D.N. Collins (ed.) The fertilizer handbook. The Fertilizer Institute, Washington, DC.

Mortvedt, J.J. 1982b. Grain sorghum response to iron sources applied alone or with fertilizers. J. Plant Nutr. 5:859–868.

Mortvedt, J.J. 1986. Iron sources and management practices for correcting iron chlorosis problems. J. Plant Nutr. 9:961–974.

Mortvedt, J.J., and P.M. Giordano. 1971. Response of grain sorghum to iron sources applied alone or with fertilizers. Agron. J. 63:758–761.

Mortvedt, J.J., and P.M. Giordano. 1973. Grain sorghum response to iron in a ferrous sulfate-ammonium thiosulfate-ammonium polyphosphate suspension. Soil Sci. Soc. Am. Proc. 37:951–955.

Mortvedt, J.J., and P.M. Giordano. 1975. Crop response to manganese sources applied with ortho- and polyphosphate fertilizers. Soil Sci. Soc. Am. Proc. 39:782–787.

Mortvedt, J.J., and J.J. Kelsoe. 1988. Grain sorghum response to banded acid-type fertilizers in iron deficient soil. J. Plant Nutr. 11:1297–1310.

Mostaghimi, S., and J.E. Matocha. 1988. Effects of normal and Fe-treated organic matter on Fe chlorosis and yields of grain sorghum. Commun. Soil Sci. Plant Anal. 19:1415–1428.

Murphy, L.S., R. Ellis, Jr., and D.C. Adriano. 1981. Phosphorus-micronutrient interaction effects on crop production. J. Plant Nutr. 3:593–613.

Murphy, L.S., and L.M. Walsh. 1972. Correction of micronutrient deficiencies with fertilizers. p. 347–388. *In* J.J. Morvedt et al. (ed.) Micronutrients in agriculture. SSSA, Madison, WI.

Nayyar, V.K., U.S. Sadana, and T.N. Takkar. 1985. Methods and rates of application of Mn and its critical levels for wheat following rice on coarse textured soils. Fert. Res. 8:173–178.

Nefae, R., and G.A. O'Conner. 1978. Effect of sulfuric acid on iron availability in New Mexico soils. New Mexico State Univ. Agric. Exp. Stn. Res. Rep. 362.

Nelson, S.D., and V.D. Jolley. 1984. Effect of an acidified iron-sulfur-rich mining residue (Iron-Sul) on soil and plant nutrient relationships in drip-irrigated raspberry and strawberry. J. Plant Nutr. 7:251–257.

Nuttall, W.F., H. Ukrainetz, J.W.B. Stewart, and D.T. Spurr. 1987. The effect of nitrogen, sulphur and boron on yield and quality of rapeseed (*Brassica napus* L. and *B. compestris* L.). Can. J. Soil Sci. 67:545–559.

Ohki, K. 1985. Manganese deficiency and toxicity effects on photosynthesis, chlorophyll, and transpiration in wheat. Crop Sci. 25:187–190.

Ohki, K., F.C. Boswell, M.B. Parker, L.M. Shuman, and D.O. Wilson. 1987. Foliar manganese application to soybeans. Commun. Soil Sci. Plant Anal. 18:243–253.

Olsen, S.R., and F.S. Watanabe. 1979. Interaction of added gypsum in alkaline soils with uptake of iron, molybdenum, manganese, and zinc by sorghum. Soil Sci. Soc. Am. J. 43:125–130.

Orphanos, P.I. 1982. Spray and soil application of zinc to apples. J. Hortic. Sci. 57:259–266.

Osiname, O.A., B.T. Kang, E.E. Schulte, and R.B. Corey. 1973. Zinc response of maize (*Zea mays* L.) grown on sandy Inceptisols in Western Nigeria. Agron. J. 65:875–877.

Parker, M.B., G.J. Gascho, and T.P. Gaines. 1983. Chloride toxicity of soybeans grown on Atlantic Coast flatwood soils. Agron. J. 75:439–443.

Parker, M.B., and H.B. Harris. 1962. Soybean response to molybdenum and lime and the relationship between yield and chemical composition. Agron. J. 54:480–483.

Parker, M.B., and H.B. Harris. 1977. Yield and leaf nitrogen of nodulating and non-nodulating soybeans as affected by nitrogen and molybdenum. Agron. J. 69:551–554.

Parker, M.B., and M.E. Walker. 1986. Soil pH and manganese effects on manganese nutrition of peanut. Agron. J. 78:614–620.

Parkpian, P., and W.B. Anderson. 1986. Iron availability from a steel industry by-product. J. Plant Nutr. 9:1027–1038.

Payne, G.G., D.C. Martens, E.T. Kornegay, and M.D. Lindemann. 1988a. Availability and form of copper in three soils following eight annual applications of copper-enriched swine manure. J. Environ. Qual. 17:740–746.

Payne, G.G., D.C. Martens, C. Winarko, and N.F. Perera. 1988b. Form and availability of copper and zinc following long-term copper sulfate and zinc sulfate applications. J. Environ. Qual. 17:707–711.

Petrie, S.E., and T.L. Jackson. 1982. Effects of lime, P, and Mo application on Mo concentrations in seedclover. Agron. J. 74:1077–1081.

Pierzynski, G.M., and L.W. Jacobs. 1986. Molybdenum accumulation by corn and soybeans from a molybdenum-rich sewage sludge. J. Environ. Qual. 15:394–398.

Plank, C.O., and D.C. Martens. 1974. Boron availability as influenced by application of fly ash to soil. Soil Sci. Soc. Am. Proc. 38:974–977.

Powell, R.D. 1975. Soil and applied copper. Univ. of Wisconsin Coop. Ext. Publ. A2527.

Purves, D., and E.J. Mackenzie. 1973. Effect of applications of municipal compost on uptake of copper, zinc, and boron by garden vegetables. Plant Soil 39:361–371.

Raese, J.T., and D.C. Staiff. 1988. Chlorosis of "Anjou" pear trees reduced with foliar sprays of iron compounds. J. Plant Nutr. 11:1379–1385.

Raj, A.S. 1987. Cobalt nutrition of pigeonpea and peanut in relation to growth and yield. J. Plant Nutr. 10:2137–2145.

Rammah, A.M., M.S. Khedr, M. Th-Hassen, and M. Nasr. 1984. Response of alfalfa to iron and boron in some Egyptian soils. J. Plant Nutr. 7:235–242.

Randall, G.W., and E.E. Schulte. 1971. Manganese fertilization of soybeans in Wisconsin. Proc. Wis. Fert. Aglime Conf. 10:4–10.

Randall, G.W., E.E. Schulte, and R.B. Corey. 1975a. Effect of soil and foliar-applied manganese on the micronutrient content and yield of soybeans. Agron. J. 67:502–507.

Randall, G.W., E.E. Schulte, and R.B. Corey. 1975b. Soil Mn availability to soybeans as affected by mono and diammonium phosphate. Agron. J. 67:705–709.

Ransome, C.S., and R.H. Dowdy. 1987. Soybean growth and B distribution in a sand soil amended with scrubber sludge. J. Environ. Qual. 16:171–175.

Razeto, B. 1982. Treatments for iron chlorosis in peach trees. J. Plant Nutr. 5:917–922.

Reddy, D.T., and A.S. Raj. 1975. Cobalt nutrition of groundnut in relation to growth and yield. Plant Soil 42:145–152.

Reed, D.W., G.G. Lyors, Jr., and G.R. McEachern. 1988. Field evaluation of inorganic and chelated iron fertilizer on foliar sprays and soil application. J. Plant Nutr. 11:1369–1378.

Rehm, G.W., W.E. Fenster, and C.J. Overdahl. 1987. Boron for Minnesota soils. Univ. of Minnesota Ext. Serv. Bull. AG-FO-0723.

Rehm, G.W., and E.J. Penas. 1982. Use and management of micronutrient fertilizers in Nebraska. Nebraska Coop. Exp. Serv. NebGuide G82-596.

Reuter, D.J., T.G. Heard, and A.M. Alston. 1973a. Correction of manganese deficiency in barley crops on calcareous soils. 1. Manganous sulphate applied at sowing and as foliar sprays. Aust. J. Exp. Agric. Anim. Husb. 13:434–439.

Reuter, D.J., T.G. Heard, and A.M. Alston. 1973b. Correction of manganese deficiency in barley crops on calcareous soils. 2. Comparison of mixed and compound fertilizers. Aust. J. Exp. Agric. Anim. Husb. 13:440–445.

Rich, C.I. 1956. Manganese content of peanut leaves as related to soil factors. Soil Sci. 82:353–363.

Riley, M.M. 1987. Molybdenum deficiency in wheat in western Australia. J. Plant Nutr. 10:2117–2123.

Robertson, L.S., and R.E. Lucas. 1976. Essential micronutrients: Zinc. Michigan Coop. Ext. Serv. Bull. E-1012.

Robertson, L.S., and R.E. Lucas. 1981. Manganese: An essential plant micronutrient. Michigan Coop. Ext. Serv. Bull. E-1031.

Robertson, L.S., D.D. Warncke, and B.D. Knezek. 1981. Copper: An essential plant micronutrient. Michigan Coop. Ext. Serv. Bull. E-1519.

Robson, A.D., and D.J. Reuter. 1981. Diagnosis of copper deficiency and toxicity. p. 287–312. In J.F. Loneragan et al. (ed.) Copper in soils and plants. Academic Press, New York.

Rodes, E.R., and M. Kpaka. 1982. Effects of nitrogen, molybdenum, and cultivar on cowpea growth and yield on an Oxisol. Commun. Soil Sci. Plant Anal. 13:279–283.

Rogers, E. 1975. Effects of nitrogen, and different rates and sources of iron on iron chlorosis in Sungold peach trees. Colorado State Univ. Exp. Stn. Tech. Bull. 124.

Ryan, J., and J.L. Stroehlein. 1976. Copper industrial byproducts for improving iron deficient calcareous soils. Agron. J. 68:79–82.

Ryan, J., J.L. Stroehlein, and S. Miyamoto. 1975. Sulfuric acid applications to calcareous soils: Effects on growth and chlorophyll content of common bermudagrass in the greenhouse. Agron. J. 67:633–637.

Salardini, A.A., and L.S. Murphy. 1978. Grain sorghum (*Sorghum bicolor* Pers.) responses to organic iron on calcareous soils. Plant Soil 49:57–70.

Schulte, E.E., and L.M. Walsh. 1982. Soil and applied zinc. Univ. Wisconsin Coop. Ext. Serv. A2528.

Sedberry, J.E., Jr., F.J. Peterson, F.E. Wilson, D.B. Mengel, S.D. Maika, P.E. Schilling, and R.H. Brupbacher, 1980. Influence of soil reaction and zinc applications on yields and zinc contents of rice plants. Louisiana Agric. Exp. Stn. Bull. 724.

Sedberry, J.E., Jr., T.S. Sharmaputra, R.H. Brupbacher, S. Phillips, J.G. Marshall, L.W. Slvane, D.R. Melville, J.I. Ralb, and J. Davis. 1973. Molybdenum investigations with soybeans in Louisiana. Louisiana Agric. Exp. Stn. Bull. 670.

Seeliger, M.T., and D.E. Moss. 1976. Correction of iron deficiency in peas by foliar sprays. Aust. J. Exp. Agric. Anim. Husb. 16:758–760.

Sherrell, C.G. 1984. Effect of molybdenum concentration in the seed on the response of pasture legumes to molybdenum. N.Z. J. Agric. Res. 27:417–423.

Shrestha, G.K., M.M. Thompson, and T.L. Righetti. 1987. Foliar-applied boron increases fruit set in "Barcelona" hazelnut. J. Am. Soc. Hortic. Sci. 112:412–416.

Snyder, G.H., and D.B. Jones. 1988. Prediction and prevention of iron-related "rice seedling chlorosis" on Everglades Histosols. Soil Sci. Soc. Am. J. 52:1043–1046.

Sparr, M.C. 1970. Micronutrient needs—which, where, on what—in the United States. Commun. Soil Sci. Plant Anal. 1:241–262.

Stivers, R.K. 1974. Micronutrients for field crops in Indiana. Indiana Coop. Ext. Serv. AY-203.

Thom, W.O. 1985. Micronutrients in Kentucky. Soil Sci. News and Views 6(7). Univ. of Kentucky, College of Agric., Lexington, KY.

Timm, C.A., R.J. Goos, B.E. Johnson, F.J. Sobolite, and R.W. Stack. 1986. Effect of K fertilizers on malting barley infected with common root rot. Agron. J. 78:197–200.

Tindall, T.A. 1984. Control of iron chlorosis in Utah. Utah State Univ. Coop. Ext. Serv. EC-408.

Touchton, J.T., and F.C. Boswell. 1975a. Boron application for corn grown on selected southeastern soils. Agron. J. 67:197–200.

Touchton, J.T., and F.C. Boswell. 1975b. Effects of B application on soybean yield, chemical composition, and related characteristics. Agron. J. 67:417–420.

U.S. Environmental Protection Agency. 1983. Process design manual for land application of municipal sludge. USEPA Rep. 625/1-83-016. USEPA, Cincinnati, OH.

Uribe, E., D.C. Martens, and D.E. Brann. 1988. Response of corn (*Zea mays* L.) to manganese application on Atlantic Coastal Plain soils. Plant Soil 112:83–88.

Varvel, G.E., W.E. Fenster, and J. Grava. 1983. Copper for organic soils. Minnesota Agric. Ext. Serv. Folder 347.

Vitosh, M.L., D.D. Warncke, B.D. Knezek, and R.E. Lucas. 1981. Secondary and micronutrients for vegetables and field crops. Michigan Coop. Ext. Serv. Bull. E-486.

Vlek, P.L.G., and W.L. Lindsay. 1978. Potential use of finely disintegrated iron pyrite in sodic and iron-deficient soils. J. Environ. Qual. 7:111–114.

Voth, R.D., J. Reisen, and D.R. Christenson. 1979. Effect of applied boron on yield of sugarbeets. Michigan Sate Univ. Agric. Exp. Stn. Res. Rep. 376.

Walker, W.J., and R.H. Dowdy. 1980. Elemental composition of barley and ryegrass grown on acid soils amended with scrubber sludge. J. Environ. Qual. 9:27–30.

Wallace, A. 1988. Acid and acid-iron fertilizers for iron-deficiency control in plants. J. Plant Nutr. 11:1311–1319.

Wallace, A., and G.A. Wallace. 1983. DTPA as a source of Zn, Mn, Cu, and Fe in calcareous soil. J. Plant Nutr. 6:451–455.

Wallace, G.A., and A. Wallace. 1986. Correction of iron deficiency in trees by injection with ferric ammonium citrate solution. J. Plant Nutr. 9:981–986.

Wallingford, G.W., L.S. Murphy, W.L. Powers, and H.L. Manges. 1975. Effects of beef-feedlot manure and lagoon water on iron, zinc, manganese and copper content in corn and in DTPA soil extracts. Soil Sci. Soc. Am. Proc. 39:482–487.

Walsh, L.M., W.H. Erhardt, and H.D. Seibel. 1972a. Copper toxicity in snapbeans (*Phaseolus vulgaris* L.). J. Environ. Qual. 1:197–200.

Walsh, L.M., and E.E. Schulte. 1970. Computer-programmed soil test recommendations for field and vegetable crops. Wisconsin Agric. Exp. Stn. Soil Fertility Ser. Bull. 5.

Walsh, L.M., D.R. Stevens, H.D. Seibel, and G.G. Weis. 1972b. Effect of high rates of zinc on several crops grown on an irrigated Plainfield sand. Commun. Soil Sci. Plant Anal. 3:187–195.

Wear, J.J. 1957. Boron requirements of some crops in Alabama. Alabama Agric. Exp. Stn. Bull. 305.

Welch, R.M. 1981. The biological significance of nickel. J. Plant Nutr. 3:345–356.

Wells, B.R. 1980. Zinc nutrition of rice growing on Arkansas soils. Arkansas Agric. Exp. Stn. Bull. 848.

Whitehead, D.C. 1985. Chlorine deficiency in red clover grown in solution culture. J. Plant Nutr. 8:193–198.

Whitehouse, M.J. 1973. Effect of seed source and treatment on the control of zinc deficiency in linseed. Queensl. J. Agric. Anim. Sci. 30:311–313.

Widdowson, J.P. 1966. Molybdenum uptake by French beans on two recent soils. N.Z. J. Agric. Res. 9:59–67.

Wiese, R.A., and E.J. Penas. 1979. Fertilizer suggestions for corn. Nebraska Coop. Ext. Serv. NebGuide G74-174.

Worley, R.E., R.L. Littrell, and J.D. Dutcher. 1980. A comparison of tree trunk injection and implantation of zinc capsules for correction of zinc deficiency. J. Arboric. 6:253–257.

Yoshikawa, F.T. 1988. Correcting iron deficiency of peach trees. J. Plant Nutr. 11:1387–1396.

Yust, A.K., D.J. Wehner, and T.W. Fermanian. 1984. Foliar application of N and Fe to Kentucky Bluegrass. Agron. J. 76:934–938.

Zheng-ging, Z., and L. Chang-zhen. 1982. Studies on the application of ferrous sulfate for controlling chlorosis of apple trees on calcareous soils. J. Plant Nutr. 5:883–896.

Chapter 16

Trace Elements in Animal Nutrition

ELWYN R. MILLER, *Michigan State University, East Lansing, Michigan*

XINGEN LEI, *Sichuan Agricultural University, Yaan, Sichuan, China*

DUANE E. ULLREY, *Michigan State University, East Lansing, Michigan*

I. ESSENTIAL TRACE ELEMENTS

Trace elements that are essential for the nutrition of animals are usually required in amounts ≤ 100 mg/kg in dietary dry matter. These elements include Fe, Zn, Cu, Mn, Se, I, Co, and Mo. All but Mo have been shown to be deficient in some natural feed ingredients, necessitating the use of supplements to make the diet nutritionally complete.

Molybdenum has essential metabolic functions, but an excess in the diets of ruminants, rather than a deficiency, is of greater practical consequence. A specific metabolic function for F has not been identified, but certain minimum levels in the diet or drinking water aid in the prevention of tooth decay and inhibit demineralization of the skeleton of elderly humans. Excesses of F, particularly from certain P supplements, can cause undesirable changes in bones and teeth.

All of the above elements are discussed in this chapter, using the information assembled by Scott (1972) in the previous edition of this book as a base. Research published since 1971 has been emphasized in updating Dr. Scott's review. Magnesium is not included as a trace element in our review, since its requirement in the diet is generally > 400 mg/kg.

Other trace elements for which nutritional requirements have been proposed include Cr, Si, Ni, V, Sn, As, B, and Pb (Mertz, 1987). Studies demonstrating these requirements generally have been conducted with rats (*Rattus norvegicus*), mice (*Mus musculus*), or chicks (*Gallus domesticus*) fed purified diets in plastic isolators supplied with filtered air. Whereas animals of importance to agriculture probably have physiological requirements for these elements, it is unlikely that livestock diets would be deficient. Thus, these elements have not been reviewed. Likewise, Cd and Hg, which may be present

Table 16-1. Trace element and composition of animals.†

Animal and age	Body weight	Water	N	Fe	Zn	Cu	I	Se
	kg	— g kg^{-1} —			mg kg^{-1}			
Adult								
Chicken	2.0	760	31.0	40	35	1.3	0.4	0.25
Human	65.0	720	34.0	74	28	1.7	0.7	0.2
Pig	125.0	750	31.5	90	25	2.5	--	0.2
Cat	4.0	740	33.6	60	23	1.5	--	--
Rabbit	2.6	730	37.0	60	50	1.5	--	--
Rat	0.35	720	35.0	60	30	2.0	--	--
Steer	500.0	550	27.2	168	--	--	0.1	0.1
Newborn								
Chicken	0.04	830	20.8	40	--	1.3	--	0.20
Human	3.56	823	22.6	94	19.2	4.7	--	--
Pig	1.26	820	18.0	29	10.1	3.2	--	0.15
Cat	1.18	822	24.4	55	28.7	2.9	--	--
Rabbit	0.54	865	18.1	135	22.5	4.0	--	--
Rat	0.006	862	15.6	59	24.4	4.3	--	--

† Data from Scott (1972).

in trace amounts, but have no known essential function, and may be toxic at low dietary levels, are not discussed in this review.

Concentrations of some of the trace elements in the body of newborn and mature humans, and several of the important agricultural and experimental animals are presented in Table 16-1. In general, mean body concentrations of all of these trace elements (Fe, Zn, Cu, I, and Se) measure < 100 mg/kg and concentrations of I and Se may be as low as 0.1 mg/kg in some adequately fed animals. Also, on a dry, fat-free tissue basis, body concentrations of trace elements of newborn and mature animals are quite similar.

Trace element concentrations of common feedstuffs are listed in Table 16-2. Large differences exist between certain feedstuffs in some of the trace element concentrations. Blood meal, of course, has a high concentration of Fe, whereas milk and milk byproducts (dried skim milk and dried whey) are quite low in Fe. Fish by-product feedstuffs have a high concentration of Se. Variation within a feedstuff may be considerable from soil element concentration variation, such as with Se concentrations of crops grown on seleniferous versus nonseleniferous soils.

II. IRON

A. Distibution in the Animal Body

Iron occurs in the body of higher animals in conjunction with various proteins that serve unique functions (Underwood, 1981; Miller, 1981; Morris, 1987). Iron exists as a component of the heme of hemoglobin in erythrocytes and of myoglobin in muscle. In serum, Fe is bound to transferrin and transported to other tissues in this form. Iron is stored as ferritin and

Table 16-2. Trace element concentrations of common feedstuffs.†

Feedstuffs‡	Fe	Zn	Mn	Cu	I	Co	Se
				mg kg^{-1}			
Alfalfa meal, 17% protein	200	35	43	10	0.5	0.18	0.05–0.45
Barley	50	17	16	8	0.05	0.1	0.1–0.3
Beet pulp	300	1	35	12.5	--	0.1	--
Blood meal (flash dried)	3800	--	5	9	--	0.1	0.07
Bone meal (steamed)	800	425	30	16	--	0.1	--
Citrus pulp, dried	200	14	7	6	--	--	--
Coconut oil meal	680	--	55	19	--	0.2	--
Corn, dent, yellow	35	10	5	4.5	0.05	0.1	0.03–0.38
Corn gluten feed	500	--	25	50	--	0.1	0.2
Corn gluten meal	400	--	7	30	--	0.1	1.15
Cottonseed meal	100	--	20	20	0.12	0.1	0.06
Distillers dried corn grains	200	--	19	45	--	0.1	--
Distillers dried corn solubles	600	85	74	80	--	--	0.50
Fish meal, menhaden	270	150	36	8	--	--	1.7
Fish meal, herring	300	110	10	20	1.0	--	1.5–2.45
Fish solubles (30%)	300	38	25	48	--	--	1.0
Hominy feed	10	--	14	2	--	0.1	0.1
Linseed meal	300	--	37	25	0.07	0.2	1.1
Meat and bone meal, 50% protein	500	100	19	12	1.3	0.1	0.1–0.8
Milk, cow's	2	4	0.06	0.3	0.04	--	0.04
Molasses, beet	100	--	5	18	1.6	0.4	--
Molasses, cane	100	--	42	60	1.6	0.9	--
Oat grain	70	--	38	6	0.06	0.06	0.05–0.02
Oystershell, ground	2900	--	130	--	--	--	0.01
Peanut meal	20	20	24	30	--	--	0.28
Rice bran	190	30	200	13	--	--	--
Rye grain	45	35	35	6	0.05	--	0.2
Sesame meal	--	100	48	--	--	--	--
Skim milk, dried	8	40	2	3	--	--	0.08–0.15
Sorghum grain	50	17	13	14	0.02	0.1	--
Soybean meal, 44% protein	150	27	35	20	0.13	0.1	0.05–0.10
Soybean meal, dehulled	150	45	40	20	0.1	0.1	0.05–0.10
Wheat bran	150	80	115	12	0.07	0.1	0.6
Wheat grain	50	5	20	7	0.04	0.08	0.05–0.8
Wheat standard middlings	100	150	118	22	0.1	0.1	0.28–0.88
Whey, dried	7	3	5	45	--	0.1	0.008
Yeast, dried, brewer's	50	40	6	30	0.01	0.2	0.11–1.1
Yeast, dried, torula	90	100	13	13	--	0.04	0.03–0.05

† Data from Scott (1972).

‡ Alfalfa (*Medicago sativa*)
  Barley (*Hordeum vulgare*)
  Beet (*Beta vulgaris*)
  Citrus (*Citrus* spp.)
  Coconut (*Cocos nucifera*)
  Corn (*Zea mays* L.)
  Cotton (*Gossypium hirsutum*)
  Flax (*Linum usitatissimum*) linseed meal
  Molasses, cane (*Saccharum officinarum*)

Oat (*Avena sativa*)
Peanut (*Arachis hypogaea*)
Rice (*Oryza sativa*)
Rye (*Secale cereale*)
Sesame (*Sesamum indicum*)
Sorghum (*Sorghum vulgare*)
Soybean [*Glycine max* (L.) Merr.]
Wheat (*Triticum* spp.)

hemosiderin in all tissues, with the highest concentrations in liver, spleen, and bone marrow. Iron also serves as a cofactor of a number of metabolic enzymes such as cytochrome oxidase. In addition, a small amount of Fe is located in wool and feathers. The uteroplacental Fe is bound in uteroferrin.

The total body Fe content of the newborn pig (*Sus scrofa*) measures about 50 mg and rises to 125 mg at weaning in those pigs fed on concrete and to 417 mg in those pigs fed on soil (Venn et al., 1947; McCance & Widdowson, 1951). Four-week-old New Hampshire chickens (*Gallus domesticus*) contain 110 to 140 mg Fe kg^{-1} body weight. Body Fe concentration progressively decreases more than 60% by the time the chicken reaches 18 wk (Marti et al., 1989). The total body Fe contents of the calf (*Bos taurus*), dog (*Canis familiaris*), horse (*Equus caballus*), and rat have been reviewed by Church and Pond (1988).

Hemoglobin Fe occupies a dominant position in all healthy higher animals (Church & Pond, 1988). The normal ranges of blood hemoglobin in the adults of various species are as follows: pig, sheep (*Ovis aries*), goat (*Capra hircus*), and horse, 10–11 g dL^{-1}; cattle and rabbit (*Lepus cuniculus*), 11–12 g dL^{-1}; dog, 13–14 g dL^{-1}; and human and rat, 13–17 g dL^{-1} (Morris, 1978). Generally, hemoglobin comprises about 0.5 to 1.0% of body weight of animals. Hemoglobin contains about 0.35% Fe. Thus, in an animal such as a 500 kg horse, there is about 2.5 to 5.0 kg of hemoglobin in its body, which would contain about 9 to 18 g of Fe. Hemoglobin Fe accounts for approximately 65% of the total body Fe (Church & Pond, 1988). Myoglobin Fe represents about 5% of total body Fe or even more in myoglobin-rich species, such as the horse and dog (Church & Pond, 1988).

Ferritin and hemosiderin Fe represent about 25% of total body Fe (Church & Pond, 1988; Furugouri, 1978). These two Fe storage compounds are chemically dissimilar and differ in Fe content, although they are intimately related in function. Ferritin is water soluble and contains 20% Fe, whereas hemosiderin is water insoluble and contains 35% Fe (Morris, 1987).

Serum Fe, largely bound to transferrin, ranges from 100 to 180 μg dL^{-1} for farm animals (Morris, 1987; Garcia et al., 1987; Ku et al., 1983; Miller et al., 1982; Furugouri, 1971; Calvo & Allue, 1986). Transferrin is a glycoprotein with a molecular weight of 73 000 to 90 000 (Bezkorovaing, 1980), and serves as the principal carrier of Fe in the plasma. Usually, only 30–50% of the transferrin is bound by Fe (Furugouri, 1978; Morris, 1987; Garcia et al., 1987; Calvo & Allue, 1986). The unsaturated remainder is designated as latent-binding capacity. Furthermore, ferritin has also been found in serum and has been demonstrated to be a reliable index of the status of Fe in the storage sites of animals (Smith et al., 1984a, b; Furugouri et al., 1983; Calvo & Allue, 1986). The average Fe content of cleaned wool is 50 mg kg^{-1} (Burns et al., 1964). The feather Fe content of 4-wk-old chickens is about 80 mg kg^{-1} for males and 120 mg kg^{-1} for females, and progressively decreases with age in both sexes (Marti et al., 1989).

The distribution of Fe in the animal body varies with species, physiological condition, nutrition, sex, and other factors (Morris, 1987; Marti et al., 1989; Garcia et al., 1987; Calvo & Allue, 1986). In addition, Caperna et al. (1989) recently reported that exogenous porcine growth-hormone administration reduced hematocrit, and serum and hepatic Fe content. The mechanism remains to be determined.

B. Absorption, Storage, and Excretion

Iron absorption is well established as the key regulatory step in body Fe homeostasis because animals have a limited capacity to excrete Fe (Morris, 1987; Underwood, 1981; Miller et al., 1981). Generally, absorption of Fe is affected by: (i) age, Fe status, and health of the animal; (ii) conditions within the gastrointestinal tract; (iii) amount and chemical form of Fe ingested; and (iv) amounts and proportions of various other components of the diet with which Fe interacts. Iron absorption is greater in young than in mature animals and greater in Fe-deficient than in Fe-sufficient animals (Garcia et al., 1986, 1987; Saiz et al., 1980; Furugouri, 1981). Heme forms of Fe and ferrous forms are often thought to be absorbed better than non-heme Fe complexes and ferric salts (Underwood, 1981; Morris, 1987).

Normal gastric secretion is necessary for optimal absorption of Fe (Murray & Stein, 1970). Dietary ascorbic acid and certain amino acids may enhance Fe absorption by reducing Fe^{3+} and chelating Fe (Morris, 1987; El-Hawary et al., 1975; Gipp et al., 1974; Miski & Kratzer, 1976, 1977; Monsen & Page, 1978). Some divalent metals, notably Cu, Mn, Zn, Co, and Cd, which are believed to compete with Fe for binding sites in the intestinal mucosa, reduce Fe absorption (Gipp et al., 1973; ARC, 1981). Inorganic phosphates and phytate may reduce Fe absorption by forming insoluble salts (Rose & Ammerman, 1982; O'Donovan et al., 1963; Standish et al., 1969; Frolich, 1986).

Iron absorption takes place exclusively in the small intestine, with the greatest activity occurring in the proximal portion (Furugouri, 1981; Furugouri & Kawabata, 1976). The transfer of Fe from the lumen of the intestine to the portal blood involves two active phases: (i) the initial passage of Fe across the brush border into the mucosal cell; and (ii) the subsequent transfer of some of this iron across the serosal surface of the cell into the blood (Furugouri, 1981). Topham et al. (1981) have shown that xanthine oxidase in intestinal mucosa promotes incorporation of Fe into transferrin for transport in blood. Iron in the mucosal cell that is not transported to plasma is stored in the cell as ferritin until it is sloughed off at the top of the villus and lost in the feces (Furugouri, 1981). Iron absorption in newborn pigs has been shown to be related to developmental changes in neonatal intestinal function (Furugouri, 1981). However, the control mechanism of Fe absorption is still unclear (Morris, 1987).

Body Fe is retained tenaciously. Fecal Fe is mainly unabsorbed dietary Fe, and a small amount of Fe from that which is lost through bile and sloughed intestinal mucosal cells (Miller et al., 1981; Morris, 1987). The amount of Fe lost daily through the pig's urine is about 0.1 mg, and is independent of the dietary supplemental Fe level and form (Miller et al., 1981).

Lactation Fe loss is of some significance despite the low Fe content of milk. The average milk Fe content measured 0.5 mg L^{-1} in cattle, 1.0 mg L^{-1} in sow, and 0.8 mg L^{-1} in human (Brady et al., 1978; Morris, 1987). Rat and Australian marsupial (*Setonix brachyurus*) milk is extremely rich in Fe (Morris, 1987; Kaldor & Morgan, 1986). Milk Fe occurs in combination with lactoferrin and transferrin (Morris, 1987). Other forms of Fe have also been found (Richardson & Guss, 1965; Loh & Kaldor, 1973, 1974). More importantly, milk Fe is resistant to changes in the level of dietary Fe (NRC, 1988b).

Laying chickens and quail (*Colinus virginianus*) lose 7 to 8 mg Fe and 1.8 to 2.0 mg Fe weekly, respectively, through egg production (Ramsay & Campbell, 1954; Garcia et al., 1986). An average hen's egg contains about 1 mg Fe and an average quail's egg contains 0.3 mg Fe (Morgan, 1975; Garcia et al., 1986). Egg Fe is present mainly as an Fe-phosvitin complex in the yolk (Morgan, 1975). The edible portion of an egg contains approximately 20 mg of Fe kg^{-1} (Tolan et al., 1974).

C. Essential Functions in Metabolism

The essential functions of Fe and the history of the discovery of its functions have been well reviewed (Underwood, 1981; Miller, 1981; Scott, 1972). Briefly, Fe serves in the body as a component of hemoglobin and myoglobin, and of the enzymes catalase, peroxidase, cytochrome oxidase, succinic dehydrogenase, aconitase and xanthine oxidase. In these various protein forms, Fe influences O_2 and CO_2 transport or electron transfer, all of which is involved in cellular and whole-body energetics. In addition, Fe has been shown to participate in the defense mechanisms of the body against infections (Bullen et al., 1972; Furugouri, 1978; Osborn & Davis, 1968; Parsons et al., 1977; Nalder et al., 1972). Finally, dietary Fe is effective in detoxifying diets containing gossypol (Smith, 1966).

D. Deficiency and Excess

Iron deficiency anemia is of universal concern in suckling animals, particularly in newborn pigs reared in modern confinement facilities (Miller, 1981). There are several features of the nutritional physiology of Fe peculiar to pigs that combine to make the piglet particularly susceptible to Fe-deficiency anemia. Pigs are born with unusually low body-Fe stores and they grow very rapidly. It has been estimated that 21 mg of Fe are needed for each kilogram of body weight gain in baby pigs (ARC, 1981). The pigs require a retention of 7 to 11 mg Fe d^{-1}, whereas only about 1 mg of Fe d^{-1} is obtained from milk alone because sow's milk contains low levels of Fe (Veen et al., 1947). Other young animals reared largely on a milk or milk product diet may also suffer from Fe deficiency (Blaxter et al., 1957; Bremner & Dalgarno, 1973; Bernier et al., 1984). Some intensive feeding programs used in modern animal production, such as replacing natural protein N by urea in cattle diets and adding high levels of Cu as a growth stimulant to swine diets, may induce Fe deficiency (Underwood, 1981; Gipp et al., 1974). Iron deficiency occurs rarely in grazing animals because of the normally high Fe content of pasture and forage (Underwood, 1981). However, a parasitic infestation or blood loss may produce secondary Fe deficiency (Kolb, 1963; Lumsden et al., 1975). Heavy egg production in poultry may be accompanied by anemia (Underwood, 1981).

Other Fe-containing functional compounds in tissues may also change in concentration during certain times of the three stages of Fe deficiency. But the nature and magnitude of the changes vary with species, and severity and duration of the Fe deficiency (Underwood, 1981; Furugouri, 1978).

The blood hemoglobin concentration has been considered as a simple and reliable index of pig Fe status (NRC, 1988b). A concentration of 10 g hemoglobin dL^{-1} of whole blood is considered adequate, and a level <7 is considered frank anemia (Zimmerman, 1980). Plasma ferritin level has been shown to correlate with the amount of Fe deposited and is established as a simple, modern, and reliable means of evaluating storage Fe status (Smith et al., 1984a, b; Furugouri et al., 1983). Moreover, serum Fe and serum total Fe-binding capacity (TIBC) are often used as well. Recently, Calvo and Allue (1986) suggested that the coefficiency of utilization, expressed as the quotient between plasma Fe and total iron-binding capacity (TIBC) may be another valuable parameter in piglets. Numerous studies have shown that anemia may be prevented in piglets by intramuscular injection of 100 to 200 mg of Fe in the form of Fe dextran, Fe dextrin, or gleptoferrin provided in the first 3 d after birth (NRC, 1988b).

Characteristic signs of chronic Fe toxicosis for most species are reduced growth rate, and reduced feed intake and efficiency (NRC, 1980). The clinical signs of acute toxicosis of Fe include anorexia, oliguria, diarrhea, hypothermia, diphasic shock, metabolic acidosis, and death (Boyd & Shanas, 1963). High levels of Fe in the diet reduce plasma Cu in lambs and produce P deficiency (Standish & Ammerman, 1971; Debald & Elvehjem, 1935; O'Donovan et al., 1963' Furugouri, 1972). In addition, an excessively high level of supplemental Fe may elevate serum-unbound Fe, which encourages bacterial growth and results in increased susceptibility to infection and diarrhea (Weinberg, 1978; Klasing et al., 1980; Knight et al., 1983; Kadis et al., 1984).

Pigs are more tolerant of excess Fe than cattle, sheep, or poultry. The maximum tolerable levels of dietary Fe are 3000 mg kg^{-1} for swine, 1000 mg kg^{-1} for cattle and poultry, and 500 mg kg^{-1} for sheep (NRC, 1980). Many factors that can affect Fe absorption may in turn affect Fe toxicity in animals because the toxicity of Fe is governed largely by its absorption (NRC, 1980).

E. Interactions with Other Nutrients

Iron can interact with other nutrients at both absorption and utilization levels. However, since the influences of other nutrients on Fe absorption have been discussed in a previous section, only the interactions concerning utilization of absorbed Fe are presented here.

It is well known that Cu plays a vital role in Fe utilization through ceruloplasmin, the principal form of Cu in plasma. Ceruloplasmin has ferroxidase activity, which is necessary for the movement of Fe out of liver storage (ferritin or hemosiderin) to the transport form (transferrin) and on to the reticulocyte for hemoglobin synthesis (Frieden, 1971; Frieden & Hsieh,

1976; Miller, 1981). This interaction of Cu and Fe has been verified by the fact that Cu deficiency also produces anemia (Hill et al., 1983a). Thus, adequate Cu is necessary for Fe to serve its functions in the body. However, high levels of Cu may also produce anemia by reducing Fe absorption, as cited previously. Therefore, an appropriate ratio of Fe to Cu (about 10:1) is desirable in the diet. McNaughton and Day (1979) reported that a 10:1 dietary Fe/Cu ratio appeared to maximize hemoglobin level and packed red cell volume of 21-d-old broiler chicks, whereas a 5:1 dietary Fe/Cu ratio tended to maximize the body weight gain of the chicks.

F. Requirements, Feed Sources, and Availability

The net dietary requirements of Fe of growing animals consist of the amounts of Fe accretion in the body tissues in the processes of growth, and the amounts of Fe lost in the feces, urine, sweat, and/or products.

The Fe requirement of young pigs fed milk or purified liquid diets is 50 to 150 mg kg^{-1} (Matrone et al., 1960; Ullrey et al., 1960; Harmon et al., 1967; Hitchcock et al., 1974). Miller et al. (1982) suggested a requirement of 100 mg kg^{-1} of Fe for pigs raised in a conventional or germ-free environment. The postweaning dietary-Fe requirement of pigs is about 80 mg kg^{-1}, but decreases to 60 or 50 mg kg^{-1} in later stages (NRC, 1988b). Pigs fed a dry casein-basal diet required about 50% more Fe than those fed a similar diet in liquid form (Hitchcock et al., 1974). Pigs fed a 250 mg kg^{-1} Cu diet needed 150 mg kg^{-1} Fe (Suttle & Mills, 1966).

The dietary Fe requirement of Leghorn-type chickens is 80 mg kg^{-1} during the first 8 wk of life, but then drops to 60 mg kg^{-1} from 8 to 20 wk of age. Broiler-type chicks require 80 mg kg^{-1} of dietary Fe to market weight. The dietary Fe requirement for laying and breeding hens is 50 and 60 mg kg^{-1}, respectively. Chio et al. (1976) reported that a dystrophic strain of New Hampshire chickens had a higher Fe requirement than the normal birds of this breed. Morck and Austic (1981) demonstrated that the Fe requirement for maintenance of hematocrit in white Leghorn hens was lower than that for maximum hatchability of fertile eggs (40 vs. 55 mg kg^{-1}). Garcia et al. (1986) showed that quails fed an Fe-deficient diet used Fe preferentially for hematopoiesis at the expense of Fe content of the eggs.

The Fe requirements of ruminants are not well established. It is generally accepted that the Fe requirements of young animals are higher than those of mature ruminants and are thought to be about 100 mg kg^{-1} (NRC, 1988a). Most common natural dry feedstuffs contain an adequate amount of Fe. Cereal grains and oil seed meals commonly contain 30 to 60 mg kg^{-1} and 100 to 200 mg kg^{-1} Fe, respectively. Pasture Fe contents vary with plant species and generally are around 300 mg kg^{-1} on a dry matter basis. Feeds of animal origin, other than milk and milk products, are rich sources of Fe, with blood meals at about 3000 mg kg^{-1}, fish meal at about 400 mg kg^{-1}, and dried skimmed milk at about 50 mg kg^{-1} (Underwood, 1981).

Availability of Fe from various sources varies greatly (Zimmerman, 1980; Miller, 1981; NRC, 1988a, b). Iron in legumes and grass is generally less available than that of most inorganic Fe forms for ruminants (Ammerman & Miller, 1972; Bremner & Dalgarno, 1973). Ferrous sulfate, $FeCl_3$, $FeC_6H_5O_7$, $FeC_{11}H_{24}O_{11}$, and $Fe(NH_4)_3(C_6H_5O_7)_2$ are well utilized by both ruminants and swine (NRC, 1988a, b; Miller et al., 1981; Ullrey et al., 1973; Ammerman & Miller, 1972; Harmon et al., 1967). The Fe in Fe_2O_3 is essentially unavailable, whereas that in $FeCO_3$ is intermediate in availability, although the crystalline structure of $FeCO_3$ influences the availability of Fe in this compound (Ammerman & Miller, 1972; Ammerman et al., 1967; McGuire et al., 1985).

III. ZINC

A. Distribution in the Animal Body

The whole-body concentration of Zn, on a fresh, fat-free basis, is in the range of 20 to 30 mg kg^{-1} in rats, cats (*Felinus catus*), pigs (Spray & Widdowson, 1950), cows (Miller et al., 1974), and sheep (Grace, 1983). Compared with most other trace minerals, Zn is much more uniformly distributed throughout the animal body. Most mammalian tissues contain 10 to 100 mg kg^{-1} Zn (wet basis), or 20 to 250 mg kg^{-1} (dry basis), with the exception of some specialized tissues, such as the choroid of the eye of some species, that may have a much higher level (Hambidge et al., 1987; O'Dell, 1979; Hill et al., 1983c, d; Prabowo et al., 1988; Neathery et al., 1973b). Values for tissue Zn of various species have been presented previously (Underwood, 1977; O'Dell, 1979; Hill et al., 1983a, c, d; Neathery et al., 1973b; Hambidge et al., 1987).

Generally, the highest concentrations of Zn occur in bone followed by liver, pancreas, kidney, muscle, and heart. However, muscle contains the largest amount of total Zn because of its large weight. About 50 to 60% of total-body Zn is present in skeletal muscle of lactating cows (Neathery et al., 1973b). It is also estimated that approximately 20 to 30% of total-body Zn resides in bone and teeth of cows and sheep (Neathery et al., 1973b; Hambidge et al., 1987). Total Zn in the integument varies greatly among species. About 2 to 3% of total-body Zn in humans and cattle is situated in skin and hair (NRC, 1978; Neathery et al., 1973b), but in smaller animals covered with hair or wool, a much higher proportion is present in these tissues. No less than 38% of the total-body Zn is found in skin and hair, or skin and bristles of rats and hedgehogs (*Erinaceus europaeus*) (Spray & Widdowson, 1950). Blood Zn represents less than 0.5% of total-body Zn (Grace, 1983a).

Hill et al. (1983c, d) reported that the Zn concentration of liver was 60 and 100 mg kg^{-1} (wet basis) for sows and their offspring at normal Zn intake, respectively. Prabowo et al. (1988) reported that lamb liver contained 100 mg kg^{-1} Zn (dry basis). In the liver cells, Zn is found in the nuclear, mitochondrial, and supernatant fractions, with the highest levels per unit of protein found in the supernatant and microsomes (Miller et al., 1978). Kidney Zn concentration was reported to be 30 mg kg^{-1} (wet basis) in sows and 50% lower in their offspring (Hill et al., 1983c, d). In lambs, kidney Zn concentration is slightly lower than that of the liver (Prabowo et al., 1988). In rats, kidney cortex contains five times more Zn than the medulla, with the highest level occurring in the cytoplasm of cells of the juxtaglomerular apparatus (NRC, 1978). There is little difference in the pancreas Zn concentration of sows and young pigs (Hill et al., 1983c, d). Pancreas Zn is found mainly in the cytoplasm of the alpha and beta cells of the islets of Langerhans (NRC, 1978).

Muscle Zn concentration varies with color and functional activity (Hambidge et al., 1987; O'Dell, 1979). The red muscle of the thigh contains approximately three times the Zn concentration found in breast muscle (O'Dell, 1979). The concentrations of Zn in the diaphysis of the tibia and the boney portion of the mandible in rats are higher than those in the epiphysis and condyle, respectively (Hambidge et al., 1987). Zinc can be identified in growing compact bone at the border between the uncalcified and calcifying tissue where a high level of Zn-containing enzyme alkaline phosphatase is found (Hambidge et al., 1987). The Zn concentration of testes of young pigs is about 10 mg kg^{-1} (wet basis) (Hill et al., 1983d). Female sex organs and secretions generally contain lower Zn than other body tissues (Hambidge et al., 1987). But a level of 100 mg kg^{-1} of Zn (dry basis) has been reported for adult chicken ovaries (O'Dell, 1979). The total body concentration of Zn in the fetus of several species at term is in the range of 20 to 30 mg kg^{-1} body weight and is affected by the maternal Zn intake (Hambidge et al., 1987).

Dietary Zn intake can influence Zn concentrations of hair, bone, testes, liver, and other internal organs, but it has little effect on that of tissues such as muscle, heart, and brain (Miller et al., 1979; Hambidge et al., 1987; Hill et al., 1983c). Sex has an effect on the Zn content of some chicken tissues; adult males have a lower concentration in femur, brain, and skin, and a higher concentration in thigh muscle (Turk, 1964).

Of the total Zn in blood, 80% is found in the erythrocytes, 12 to 22% is in the plasma, and 1 to 3% is in the leukocytes and platelets (Hambidge et al., 1987). Much of the Zn in erythrocytes is accounted for as carbonic anhydrase. In human serum, Zn is distributed in three pools; 80% is loosely associated with albumin, 18% is tightly bound to a$_2$-macroglobulin, and the rest is bound to other proteins, with a minor amount of free Zn (Hambidge et al., 1987). In pig serum much smaller proportions of Zn are bound to albumin since 30% of serum Zn is bound to a globulin-like protein of molecular weight 100 000 to 140 000 (Chesters & Will, 1981). Serum Zn concentrations of pigs are about 60 μg dL^{-1} (Hill et al., 1983c; Miller et al., 1979). A similar level has been found in lambs (Prabowo et al., 1988), whereas steers appear to have higher serum Zn concentrations (150 μg dL^{-1}) (Greene et al., 1988). It has been noted in a number of studies that age, dietary Zn intake, pregnancy, stress, disease, sex, and hormones may alter Zn concentrations and distribution in plasma or serum (Miller et al., 1979; Hambidge et al., 1987).

B. Absorption, Storage, and Excretion

Zinc is absorbed principally throughout the small intestine of most non-ruminants and, to a limited extent, from the stomach of rats (Van Campen & Mitchell, 1965), about one-third from the abomasum of cattle (Miller & Cragle, 1965), and a greater proportion from the proventriculus of chicks (Miller & Jensen, 1966). By using fistulas and jejunectomy, Kruse-Jarres et al. (1988) have shown that the essential site of Zn absorption is the proximal intestine, and no absorption was observed from the stomach or lower intestine of pigs. In contrast, Hill et al. (1987) demonstrated no differences in Zn absorption among four segments of gut from duodenum to jejunum in weanling pigs, using noneverted intestinal sacs and continuous-flow perfusion in vitro.

Intestinal absorption of Zn has been proposed to occur in four phases: (i) uptake by the intestinal cell, (ii) movement through the mucosal cell, (iii) transfer to the portal circulation, and (iv) secretion of endogenous Zn back to the intestinal cell (Cousins, 1982). The first step involves the transport of Zn across brush border and appears to be a carrier-mediated process that is probably associated with a Zn-binding ligand (Solomons & Cousins, 1984; Miller et al., 1979). A large number of low-molecular-weight binding ligands have been shown to enhance mucosal uptake and absorption of Zn, including citrate, picolinate, EDTA, and certain amino acids such as histidine and glutamate (Hambidge et al., 1987). However, Hill et al. (1987) reported that addition of picolinic acid (a low-molecular-weight, Zn-binding ligand isolated from human milk) depressed Zn uptake by intestinal cells. In addition, Zn absorption from Zn-methionine was shown to be similar to that from $ZnCl_2$.

The Zn in the mucosal cells includes both that entering from the lumen and that resecreted into the cell from the serosal surface. Within the mucosal cells, the transfer of Zn between the intestinal lumen and portal circulation is thought to be regulated by the metal-binding protein, metallothionein. This protein has a molecular weight of 10 000 and exists in liver as well as in the cytosol of intestinal mucosal cells (Richards & Cousins, 1977). Dietary Zn levels can influence metallothionein mRNA activity and its synthesis (Richards & Cousins, 1976; Menard et al., 1981; Cousins et al., 1988). When the rate of metallothionein synthesis is at a maximum, net Zn absorption is lowest (Menard et al., 1981). The transfer of Zn from the mucosal cell to the portal circulation is slower than uptake and accumulation within the cell, and appears to be the rate-limiting step in absorption (Smith & Cousins, 1980; Miller, 1969). Moreover, transfer of Zn across the serosal surface into the blood seems to depend on albumin, which carries newly absorbed Zn in blood (Smith et al., 1979).

Zinc absorption is affected by dietary level of Zn, with an elevated dietary level resulting in a reduction of the percent absorbed (Neathery et al., 1973a, b; Weigand & Kirchgessner, 1978; Chavez & Kalinowski, 1988). There are also age and sex effects upon absorption, with Zn being more efficiently absorbed by the young and by females (Strain et al., 1978). Pregnancy and lactation may also influence the level of Zn absorption (Davis & Williams, 1977; Stake et al., 1975).

Many other dietary components can influence Zn absorption. These include dietary phytate, Ca, fiber, P, Cu, Cd, Cr, EDTA, and vitamin D. The interactions of these factors with Zn absorption have been reviewed extensively by Miller et al. (1979) and O'Dell (1979).

Zinc absorption is also influenced by the chemical form used in the diet. Zinc from ZnO, $ZnCO_3$, $ZnSO_4$, $ZnCl_2$, $Zn(NO_3)_2$ and $Zn(C_2H_3O_2)_2$ or Zn metal is well absorbed, whereas Zn in sphalerite (ZnS) and franklinite $[Zn(FeO_2)_2]$ is largely unabsorbed (Miller et al., 1979).

Currently, there is little information on Zn storage form and amount in the animal body. Metallothionein is considered a major storage form of Zn in the liver, and in other tissues as well, because most of the additional cytosolic Zn is found in the metallothionein fraction of these tissues when dietary Zn intake is increased (Oh et al., 1979; Wanger et al., 1981). Metallothionein-Zn may be mobilized during a metabolic need for Zn (Bremner & Davis, 1975; Feldman & Cousins, 1976; Richards & Cousins, 1976). The superoxide dismutase fraction of liver also has been proposed as a storage form of Zn in the animal body (Bremner & Davis, 1975; Richards & Cousins, 1976; Frieden, 1978).

Zinc is excreted primarily in the feces, with a smaller proportion eliminated in the urine (Miller et al., 1979; Miller, 1979; Hambidge et al., 1987). Fecal Zn includes unabsorbed dietary Zn and reexcreted endogenous Zn from gastrointestinal, pancreatic, and biliary secretions (Miller et al., 1979). Fecal endogenous Zn increases with increased Zn intake, whereas urinary Zn does not vary appreciably with changes in dietary Zn concentration (Miller et al., 1979; Miller, 1979; Weigand & Kirchgessner, 1978).

Lactation is another route of Zn excretion. The Zn content of milk varies with species and stage of lactation (Hambidge et al., 1987). The Zn concentrations of colostrum and mature milk, respectively, are 7.2 and 3–5 μg mL^{-1} for cows, and 13–16 and 4–8 μg mL^{-1} for sows (Miller, 1979; Hill et al., 1983b, Hambidge et al., 1987). Bovine milk Zn is largely (over 75%) precipitated with casein, with 15% in the aqueous layer (whey) and little in fat (1%).

Unlike milk Fe, milk Zn can be increased by increasing dietary Zn levels of the dam (Hill et al., 1983b; Miller, 1979). Reducing dietary Zn from 40 to 17 mg kg^{-1} caused a 23% reduction in cattle milk Zn concentration (Neathery et al., 1973b). The reductions in milk Zn concentration occur rapidly and are accompanied by changes in Zn absorption and metabolism (Miller, 1979; Neathery et al., 1973b). Therefore, lactation represents one of the major factors in Zn metabolism and homeostasis (Miller, 1979; Stake et al., 1975; Neathery et al., 1973a).

Laying hens may excrete Zn partly through formation of eggs. The total Zn content of eggs is 0.5 to 1.0 mg, and more than 99% of this Zn resides in yolk, where it is associated with the lipoprotein lipovitelin (Tupper et al., 1954; O'Dell, 1979; Hambidge et al., 1987).

There is also a minor amount of Zn lost from the body through sweat and dermal exfoliation (Hambidge et al., 1987).

C. Essential Functions in Metabolism

Zinc was first shown to be needed by mice and rats by Todd et al. (1934) and to be a component of carbonic anhydrase by Hove et al. (1940). Since 1955, when Tucker and Salmon (1955) discovered that Zn deficiency caused parakeratosis in swine, much research has been conducted with this element. Nevertheless, it is still difficult to relate Zn deficiency signs and the biochemical roles of Zn in the body, particularly at the molecular level.

The metabolic functions of Zn have been well reviewed by Miller et al. (1979), O'Dell (1979), and Hambidge et al. (1987). Here the topic will be only briefly described.

Zinc is an indispensible component of over 200 enzymes or other proteins (Hambidge et al., 1987). Zinc functions in these enzymes in five ways. In Zn-deficient animals, activity of the following enzymes may be decreased: (i) plasma alkaline phosphatase; (ii) liver, retina, and testes alcohol dehydrogenase; and (iii) connective tissue thymidine kinase, pancreatic carboxypeptidase A, and liver nuclear DNA-dependent RNA-polymerase (Hambidge et al., 1987; Miller et al., 1979). Zinc is involved extensively in nucleic acid and protein metabolism and, hence, in the fundamental processes of cell differentiation and, especially, replication. Zinc is also related to glucose, lipid, and vitamin A metabolism. Zinc is chemically bound in crystalline insulin. Zinc has been recognized to play a role in the production, storage, and release of several other hormones as well as in the effectiveness of receptor sites and end-organ responsiveness (Hambidge et al., 1987). Zinc is essential for maintaining normal growth, reproduction, and lactation performance (Miller et al., 1979). Zinc is associated with taste and smell acuity, and wound and burn healing. Moreover, Zn is essential to the integrity of the immune system. Zinc has also been proposed to play a role in stabilization of cell membranes and microtubule polymerization (Hambidge et al., 1987).

D. Deficiency and Excess

Zinc deficiency is likely to present a practical problem with nonruminant animals fed diets in which protein is mainly derived from plant sources and contains a high level of Ca (Miller et al., 1979; Underwood, 1981). Marginal Zn deficiency may also occur in grazing sheep and cattle in certain areas of the world (Underwood, 1981).

In all species, Zn deficiency is characterized clinically by inappetance, retardation, or cessation of growth, and lesions of the integument and its outgrowths; hair, wool, or feathers. Spermatogenesis and the development of the primary and secondary sex organs in the male, and all phases of the reproductive process in the female can be adversely affected (Underwood, 1981).

The classic sign of Zn deficiency in growing pigs is parakeratosis (Tucker & Salmon, 1955). Zinc deficiency significantly reduces feed intake, growth rate and efficiency, and serum levels of Zn, alkaline phosphatase, and albumin (Hoekstra et al., 1956, 1967; Luecke et al., 1957; Miller et al., 1968, 1970; Prasad et al., 1969; Ku et al., 1970). Gilts fed Zn-deficient diets during gestation and lactation produce fewer and smaller pigs, which have reduced serum and tissue Zn levels (Pond & Jones, 1964; Hoekstra et al., 1967; Hill et al., 1983a, b, c). In addition, Zn deficiency retards testicular development of boars and thymic development of pigs (Miller et al., 1968; Liptrap et al., 1970). A twofold increase in the wet weight of the adrenal glands has been observed in Zn-deficient pigs (Miller et al., 1968). Zinc deficiency in calves is identified by decreased feed consumption and efficiency, subnormal growth, reduced testicular growth, listlessness, the development of swollen feet with open, scaly lesions, alopecia, a general dermatitis, particularly on the legs, neck, and head, and around the nostrils, and other parakeratotic lesions (Miller & Miller, 1962; Ott et al., 1965). Zinc deficiency signs in dairy cows and lambs are more or less comparable to those described in calves (Underwood, 1981; NRC, 1988a). In addition, sheep wool and horns are particularly influenced by Zn deficiency (Underwood, 1981). Zinc deficiency also has been shown to affect vitamin A metabolism in lambs (Saraswat & Arora, 1972).

Zinc deficiency in the chick is characterized by poor growth and feed efficiency and severe dermatitis, especially of the feet. Feather growth also is poor, respiration is abnormal, and the long bones are thickened and shortened. Decreased hatchability and disturbance of embryonic development may result when hens are subjected to Zn deficiency (O'Dell & Savage, 1957; O'Dell et al., 1958; Underwood, 1981).

Detection of mild Zn deficiency appears much more difficult than detection of severe Zn deficiency (Hambidge et al., 1987; Underwood, 1981; Solomons, 1988). The Zn concentration of blood plasma or serum is often used to evaluate Zn status. But it is still an unsatisfactory criterion because of its variability (Hambidge et al., 1987; Underwood, 1981). Hair and wool Zn concentrations may reflect dietary Zn intake (Miller et al., 1965; Hidiroglou & Spurr, 1975), but pelage Zn concentrations vary greatly with age, season, and sampling procedures (Underwood, 1981). Therefore, it may be necessary to examine several functional and static indices of Zn in the body, simultaneously, to correctly assess Zn status (Solomons, 1988).

Animals can tolerate high intakes of Zn. The maximum tolerable levels of Zn for animals are largely influenced by the nature of the diets, especially the relative levels of Ca, Cu, Fe, and Cd (NRC, 1980; Underwood, 1981). High dietary Ca reduces the severity of Zn toxicity in weanling pigs (Hsu et al., 1975) and, hence, may increase the maximum tolerable level of Zn. On a natural-ingredient diet with many nutrients above required levels, the maximum tolerable levels of Zn for various species have been proposed as follows: sheep, 300 mg kg^{-1}; cattle, 500 mg kg^{-1}; and swine, turkeys, and chickens, 1000 mg kg^{-1} (NRC, 1980). Zinc toxicosis is manifest as gastrointestinal distress, emesis, decreased food consumption, pica, decreased growth, anemia, poor bone mineralization, damage to the pancreas, arthritis, internal hemorrhaging and nonviable newborn (NRC, 1980). Sows fed a 5000-mg kg^{-1} Zn diet (Zn from ZnO) for two parities have small litters, lighter pigs at weaning, and a higher incidence of osteochondrosis. Moreover, the offspring of these sows have reduced tissue levels of Cu and rapidly develop anemia when given a low-Cu diet (Hill & Miller, 1983; Hill et al., 1983a, c, d).

E. Interactions with other Nutrients

Zinc can interact with a number of nutrients, especially calcium. Antagonism of Ca to Zn was recognized in early studies of parakeratosis (Miller et al., 1979). Dietary Ca tended to react with Zn in the presence of phytate in the intestinal tract, resulting in formation of an insoluble complex (O'Dell et al., 1964). High dietary Ca can significantly increase the incidence and severity of Zn deficiency or ameliorate the toxicity of excess Zn, depending on dietary Zn level (Hsu et al., 1975; Miller et al., 1979). High inorganic phosphate also depresses Zn utilization (Cabell & Earle, 1965). Kiely et al. (1988) and Singh et al. (1988) reported that the binding of 60 to 70% of the Zn in bovine casein micelles to colloidal Ca phosphate reduces the bioavailability of Zn in cow's milk. Moreover, the antagonistic action of Ca and Zn also has been shown intracellularly. Zinc can inhibit both Ca-activated calmodulin and calmodulin-stimulated enzyme activity (Brewer et al., 1979). Calmodulin concentrations in muscle, testis, and brain are elevated during Zn deficiency in rats (Roth & Kirchgessner, 1988).

There is also a Zn-Cu antagonism (Miller et al., 1979). Copper depresses Zn absorption and utilization, and vice versa (Miller et al., 1979). Sows fed a 5000-mg kg^{-1} Zn diet for two parities had significantly reduced Cu concentrations in their own livers and milk as well as in the tissues of their offspring (Hill & Miller, 1983; Hill et al., 1983a, b, c, d). Contrary to the early assumption that Zn causes displacement of Cu from some transport protein, Zn stimulates the intestinal synthesis of metallothionein, which in turn induces a reduction in Cu transfer across the serosal membrane into the plasma, because Cu binds preferentially to the mucosal metallothionein (Bremner, 1988).

Similarly, Zn interacts with Fe (Fairweather-Tait & Southon, 1988; Gordon & Ellersieck, 1988; Miller et al., 1979). Greger et al. (1988) reported that ingestion of excess Zn (2000–2400 mg kg^{-1}) induced anemia in weanling rats and chicks without altering Fe levels of the soft tissues. The data suggest that the gut may not be the only site of Zn-Fe interaction. In contrast, Prabowo et al. (1988) reported that Zn status of lambs, based on plasma Zn, serum alkaline phosphatase activity, and tissue Zn concentration, was not affected by supplemental dietary Fe from 0 to 1200 mg kg^{-1}.

The metabolic antagonism of Cd and Zn metabolism has been well established (Miller et al., 1979). Now, the interactions of these two elements are often discussed with Cu because the interactions of these three elements have been shown to be of environmental and clinical significance for both humans and grazing animals (Bremner, 1988). The absorption and distribution of Cd can be modified by changes in Cu and Zn status. On the other hand, increased Cd intakes can result in disturbances in Cu and Zn metabolism (Bremner, 1988). Furthermore, Hamilton et al. (1978) reported that Cd-induced inhibition of Zn uptake and transfer by the intestinal mucosa could only be shown in Fe-deficient mice. No inhibition occurred in Fe-replete mice. This reflects the complexity of the interaction of these elements.

The interaction between Zn and Se has been demonstrated by an increased incidence of acute Se deficiency diseases when chicks on a low-Se diet are fed supplemental Zn (Jensen, 1975). Further work has shown that additional Zn significantly enhances the elimination of ^{75}Se in Se-deficient rats, and that Se-adequate rats retain more ^{65}Zn than Se-deficient rats (Zinn & Morris, 1988). In another study, Zn deficiency was found to accelerate lipoperoxidation and oxidation of reduced glutathione to its oxidized form. Supplementary Se fails to prevent this oxidation, despite an increase in the activity of glutathione peroxidase (Dreosti & Partick, 1988).

Chromium and Pb have also been shown to interact with Zn (Hsu et al., 1975; Hahn & Evans, 1975; Miller et al., 1979). As mentioned previously, Zn deficiency has been reported to have a strong adverse effect on vitamin A status in rats, pigs, lambs, and goats (Saraswat & Arora, 1972; Underwood, 1981). However, this Zn-deficiency effect on vitamin A status could not be confirmed in rats and swine by Kirchgessner et al. (1988). They found that the mobilization of vitamin A from the liver to the plasma was not disturbed by Zn deficiency. Vitamin A supplementation tends to elevate serum Zn concentration and alkaline phosphatase activity when dietary Zn is not sufficient. Supplemental vitamin A may elevate Zn absorption by a vitamin A-dependent Zn-binding protein in the intestinal mucosa (Berzin & Bauman, 1987).

F. Requirements, Sources, and Availability

The minimum Zn requirement of animals depends on species, breed, age, and physiological state. The composition of the diet, particularly the levels and proportions of the many factors discussed in previous sections greatly influences Zn requirement of animals (Miller et al., 1979; NRC, 1988a, b).

The Zn requirement of young pigs fed semipurified diets or corn (Zea mays L.)-soybean [Glycine max (L.) Merr.] meal diets is about 50 mg kg^{-1} (Miller et al., 1970; NRC, 1988b). The NRC (1988b) recommends 100, 60 to 80, and 50 mg kg^{-1} in the diet for pigs at nursing, growing, and finishing stages, respectively. The Zn requirements of breeding animals are less well established, although boars have a higher Zn requirement than gilts, and gilts require more than barrows (Liptrap et al., 1970; Miller et al., 1970). The NRC (1988b) recommends 50 mg kg^{-1} Zn in the diet for all breeding swine.

Proposed minimum dietary Zn level for poultry are estimated as follows: starting chickens (0–8 wk), 40 mg kg^{-1}; growing chickens (8–18 wk), 35 mg kg^{-1}; laying hens, 50 mg kg^{-1}; and breeding hens, 65 mg kg^{-1} (NRC, 1984).

The Zn requirement of cattle is less well studied than that of non-ruminants (Underwood, 1981; NRC, 1988a; Hambidge et al., 1987). A Zn level of 40 mg kg^{-1} has been suggested for the diets of calves, dairy cows, and bulls (NRC, 1988a).

Zinc concentrations and availability from different Zn sources has been summarized by Miller et al. (1979), O'Dell (1979), and Underwood (1981). Zinc concentrations in pasture herbage range from 17 to 60 mg kg^{-1} on a dry basis, with most values falling between 20 and 30 mg kg^{-1} (Underwood, 1981). Cereal grains typically contain 20 to 30 mg kg^{-1} Zn, whereas soybean, peanut (*Arachus hypogaea* L.), and linseed meal (*Linum usitatissimum*) contain 50 to 70 mg kg^{-1}. Fish meal, whale meal (*Odontoceti* spp.), and meat meal may contain 80 to 120 mg kg^{-1} Zn (Miller et al., 1979).

Industrial pollution or other sources of contamination, may increase Zn concentrations in feed and water (Mills & Dalgarno, 1972). Crude inorganic sources of Zn should be checked for Cd and Pb (NRC, 1980).

IV. COPPER

A. Distribution in the Animal Body

Generally, Cu occurs in relatively high concentrations in liver, brain, heart, and hair (Burns et al., 1964; Woolliams et al., 1983a, b; Hill et al., 1983a; O'Dell, 1979), but is low in concentration in pituitary, thyroid, thymus, prostate, ovary, and testes (Davis & Mertz, 1987; McCormick, 1985). Other tissues, including pancreas, skin, muscles, spleen, and bones, contain intermediate Cu concentrations (Davis & Mertz, 1987; Hill et al., 1983a; O'Dell, 1979). In cattle, Cu concentrations in the liver may be very high. The total-body Cu of adult sheep has been found to be distributed as follows: liver, 72 to 79%; muscle, 8 to 12%; skin and wool, 9%, and skeleton, 2% (Davis & Mertz, 1987). The liver Cu values for chickens, turkeys (*Meleagris gallopavo*), swine, and most other nonruminants are found to be 15 to 30 mg kg^{-1} on a dry basis; only about one tenth of those found in cattle and sheep (O'Dell, 1979; Hill et al., 1983a; Davis & Mertz, 1987; McHowell et al., 1988; Anke et al., 1988a). In swine, other tissues contain 0.6 to 8.0 mg kg^{-1} (wet basis), with the highest concentration found in hair and kidney, and the lowest in muscle (Hill et al., 1983a; Okonkwo et al., 1979).

The distribution of total-body Cu varies with species, age, and Cu status. Ruminants have a higher Cu concentration in liver than nonruminants. For most species, newborn and very young animals are normally richer in Cu per unit of body and liver weight than adults of the same species, but this is not true for sheep and cattle (Davis & Mertz, 1987; Srai et al., 1988). In sheep, newborn liver Cu values are lower than in adults, and Cu levels continue to increase throughout life. The liver Cu concentrations of newborn calves are comparable to those found in adult cattle (Davis & Mertz, 1987). Dietary Cu intake affects Cu distribution in tissues. In swine, the liver, heart, hair, kidney, spleen, pancreas, and bone are fairly responsive to variations in dietary Cu levels (Hill et al., 1983a; Okonkwo et al., 1979). To some extent, the Cu status of the dam influences the tissue Cu levels of the newborn (Hill et al., 1983a; Davis & Mertz, 1987; Bingley & Dufty, 1972; Gooneratne & Christensen, 1985). Tissue Cu is also influenced by the level of Mo, SO_4-S, Zn, Cd, $CaCO_3$, and Fe in the diet (Davis & Mertz, 1987; Bremner et al., 1987; Bremner, 1988; Humphries et al., 1988; Grace et al., 1988; Gooneratne et al., 1988; Allen & Gawthorne, 1988; Anke et al., 1988b; Van Ryssen & Barrowman, 1988).

The subcellular distribution of Cu is found to change with age. In rats, at birth, more than 80% of the total Cu is present in the nuclear and mitochondrial fractions, whereas in the adult, the supernatant contains about 50% of the total Cu (Saylor & Leach, 1980; Kelleher & Ivan, 1985). In adult animals, a major portion of the liver Cu is in the cytosol, where the Cu is bound to the enzyme superoxide dismutase and a low-molecular-weight protein similar to metallothionein (Evans, 1971).

The normal range of Cu in the blood of healthy sheep is 0.7 to 1.2 μg mL^{-1} (Thompson & Todd, 1974). The whole-blood Cu values for chicken, turkey, and duck (*Anas* spp.) is expressed as 0.23 to 0.35 mg kg^{-1} (O'Dell, 1979). In normal mammalian blood, approximately 50% of the Cu is located in the erythrocytes. Much smaller amounts are present in white blood cells and platelets (Davis & Mertz, 1987). The plasma or serum Cu concentrations are about 2 μg mL^{-1} for pigs that are older than 2 wk and adequately fed (Hill et al., 1983a; Okonkwo et al., 1979), and <1 μg mL^{-1} for grazing sheep (Yu et al., 1988). In plasma or serum, about 20 to 30% of the Cu is about equally associated with albumin and transcuprein, a newly discovered plasma protein (Weiss & Linder, 1985), about 10% is associated with low-molecular-weight components, and the remainder is firmly bound to ceruloplasmin (Linder et al., 1988). In the erythrocytes, Cu is present both as a labile pool, much like that in the plasma (40%), and in a more firmly bound form, superoxide dismutase (SOD) (60%). The Cu in the labile pool is complexed with amino acids. The Cu bound in the enzyme SOD provides a good measure of Cu status in several species (Davis & Mertz, 1987). Subnormal levels of dietary Cu and excessive Zn, Cd, Fe, and Mo plus SO_4-S under certain conditions may depress plasma Cu concentration. In addition, plasma Cu and ceruloplasmin concentrations change with age in cattle and pigs (Gooneratne & Christensen, 1985; Chang et al., 1975). A polymorphism of plasma ceruloplasmin has been reported in calves (Wegger, 1988).

B. Absorption, Storage, and Excretion

Copper absorption takes place mainly in the small intestine (Miller et al., 1979), but absorption at other sites is possible and the magnitude of absorption at these sites varies with species. In sheep, there is substantial absorption of Cu in the large intestine (Grace, 1975). In chicks, an appreciable amount of Cu is absorbed from the proventriculus (Starcher, 1969). The absorption efficiency of Cu is about 7 to 27% in rats (Johnson & Murphy, 1988).

In pigs, the values are inconsistent. Menten (1988) reported that the absorption efficiency of dietary Cu was about 20% for weanling pigs fed diets containing either low Cu levels or 250 mg Cu per kilogram of diet. However, Cu absorption efficiency found for the same age pig by Okonkwo et al. (1979) was more than twice that found by Menten (1988). The reason for this difference is unclear, although Okonkwo et al. (1979) used a more highly purified diet than Menten (1988).

Copper absorption is thought to be regulated by Cu status, but it is also influenced by the form of Cu ingested, and the presence of other dietary compounds that tend to interact with Cu. The relative rates of absorption of Cu from various Cu sources administered orally to beef cattle were found to be in the following order: $CuCO_3 > Cu(NO_3)_2 > CuSO_4 > CuCl_2 > Cu_2O > Cu_2O$ (powder) $> CuO$ (crystals) $> Cu$ (wire) (Chapman & Bell, 1963). The dietary factors that tend to depress Cu absorbability include phytates, ascorbic acid, Ca, Zn, Fe, Pb, Ag, Mo, and S (O'Dell, 1979; Miller et al., 1979; Davis & Mertz, 1987; Bremner, 1988). Of great practical importance are Cu-thiomolybdate interactions in ruminants (Miller, 1979; Underwood, 1981). There is convincing evidence for the formation of thiomolybdates in the gastrointestinal tract of sheep from SO_4-S and Mo, which decreases Cu absorption and promotes the development of Cu deficiency (Bremner, 1988). In addition, it has been shown that young suckling lambs absorb Cu at a much higher rate than do mature sheep (Suttle, 1973), although this difference might be explained by differences in diet composition rather than by age.

The regulation mechanism of Cu absorption is not well understood. Copper appears to be absorbed by both active transport and simple diffusion (Bronner & Yost, 1985). Metallothionein has been proposed as a regulator of Cu absorption and as the intestinal compound involved in the interaction between Cu and Zn (Cousins, 1985). The involvement of metallothionein in the Cu-Zn interaction has been well studied and is becoming generally accepted. However, a role for metallothionein as a Cu absorption regulator remains to be defined. Two forms of metallothionein, differing in Cu binding, have been shown in studies of Cu loading of chick liver (McCormick & Lin, 1988). Moreover, genes for metallothionein synthesis have been studied in mice, rats, hamsters (*Cricetus cricetus*), humans, and sheep (Danks & Mercer, 1988). Prenatal and postnatal changes in hepatic metallothionein mRNA have been shown in rats and sheep (Mercer et al., 1988).

Newly absorbed Cu is transported from the intestine loosely bound to albumin or to certain amino acids (Weiner & Cousins, 1980). Using ^{67}Cu, Weiss and Linder (1985) have demonstrated that Cu immediately binds to plasma albumin and another plasma protein transcuprein, after entering the blood from the intestine or directly by intravenous injection. The liver is the central organ of Cu metabolism. The uptake of Cu by liver is rapid and preferential (Waldrop et al., 1988). Ceruloplasmin serves as the carrier for the tissue-specific export of Cu from the liver to the extrahepatic target tissues (Van den Hamer, 1988; Davis & Mertz, 1987). Within the hepatocyte of adult animals, a major portion of Cu is found in the cytosol (Davis & Mertz, 1987).

Excess Cu, or a combination of Mo and S in the diet, enhances biliary Cu excretion in cattle. Intravenous injection of thiomolybdates results in a similar, but a more rapid and marked, increase in biliary Cu excretion (Gooneratne et al., 1988). Glutathione depletion reduced biliary Cu excretion in rats (Nederbragt, 1988). Bile Cu excretion was higher in Simmental than in Angus cattle (Goonerate et al., 1988). Young pigs excreted less Cu in bile than adult swine (Srai et al., 1988).

Lactation represents another excretion route. In all species, colostrum is substantially higher in Cu than is milk, and the level tends to decline throughout lactation. The milk Cu level of normal ewes declines from 0.06 to 0.2 μg mL^{-1} in early lactation to 0.04 to 0.16 μg mL^{-1} several months later. The Cu level in mare's milk falls from a mean of 0.36 μg mL^{-1} in the first week of lactation to 0.17 μg mL^{-1} several weeks later. Cow's milk contains 0.09 μg mL^{-1} of Cu, and the proportion of Cu associated with fat increases as lactation proceeds. Adding Cu to diets already adequate in Cu has little effect on the concentration of Cu in the milk of ruminants (Davis & Mertz, 1987).

Copper concentrations in hen's eggs ranges from 0.68 to 0.73 mg kg^{-1} fresh weight. About two-thirds of total egg Cu is located in the yolk, with the remaining one-third found in the egg white (Davis & Mertz, 1987).

C. Essential Functions in Metabolism

Copper performs a variety of physiological functions. At the cellular level, Cu is primarily involved with Cu proteins, many of which are enzymes with oxidative functions. Enzymes containing Cu include: ferroxidase, monoamine oxidase, lysyl oxidase, cytochrome C oxidase, superoxide dismutase, tyrosinase, lactate dehydrogenase, ascorbic acid oxidase, uricase, and dopamine-β-hydroxylase (Underwood, 1977). The relationships between some of these enzymes and signs of Cu deficiency have been elucidated (O'Dell, 1984; Davis & Mertz, 1987).

Copper, in the form of ceruloplasmin, is vital in facilitating Fe absorption and mobilization (O'Dell, 1984). Copper is a cofactor of lysyl oxidase participates in catalyzing the oxidation of specific lysyl and hydroxylysyl residues in soluble collagen and elastin, which is essential to establish cross-linkages in collagen and elastin (Davis & Mertz, 1987). If the formation of cross-linkages is impaired due to Cu deficiency or depressed lysyl oxidase activity, fragile bones, aortic ruptures, and other connective tissue abnormalities result (Miller et al., 1979). Copper is involved in the formation of at least two brain neurotransmitters, dopamine and norepinephrine, and the myelination of the dopaminergic system through the function of dopamine-β-hydroxylase (O'Dell, 1984). Copper may participate in the desaturation of fatty acids and in other processes of lipid metabolism (Davis & Mertz, 1987).

Copper plays several roles in pigmentation and keratinization of hair and wool, including the conversion of tyrosine to melanin by Cu-containing polyphenyloxidase, the formation or incorporation of disulfide groups in keratin synthesis, and the tertiary arrangement of the polypeptide chain in keratin synthesis (Davis & Mertz, 1987). Copper appears essential for normal reproduction since Cu deficiency results in fetal death and resorption in rats and guinea pigs, reduced egg production and hatchability in chickens, depressed estrus in cattle, and abortion in sheep (Underwood, 1981). Copper possesses a strong anti-inflammatory action (Davis & Mertz, 1987). In addition, Cu in superoxide dismutase is important in the microbiocidal systems of phagocytes (Miller et al., 1979). Recent studies on Cu and the immune system have been reviewed by Gershwin et al. (1988). Copper may play a role in the maintenance of intestinal integrity (Miller, 1979).

D. Deficiency and Excess

Copper deficiency occurs naturally in grazing livestock, but not in poultry or pigs fed typical corn-soybean meal diets. In many parts of the world, under a wide range of soil and climatic conditions, the occurrence of Cu deficiency in grazing animals may be attributed to: (i) inherently low soil and herbage Cu concentrations, such as in the area of falling disease of cattle and neonatal ataxia of lambs in western Australia; (ii) dual deficiency of Cu and Co on coastal calcareous-leached soils of granitic origin, such as in Florida and southern Australia; and (iii) conditioned deficiency from high intake of antagonists of Cu metabolism, such as $CaCO_3$ and Mo in the peat soil areas of New Zealand and the humic peat soils of Europe (Underwood, 1981). Copper deficiency in pigs leads to poor Fe mobilization, abnormal hematopoiesis, and poor keratinization and synthesis of collagen, elastin, and myelin. The deficiency signs include a microcytic hypochromic anemia, bowing of the legs, spontaneous fractures, cardiac hypertrophy and aortic rupture (NRC, 1988b).

With a severe Cu deficiency in cattle, several symptoms may be observed, including: severe diarrhea, rapid weight loss, cessation of growth, a rough hair coat, loss of hair color, a change in hair texture, swelling at the ends of the long bones (especially above the pasterns), fragile bones, stiff joints that may result in a pacing gait in old cattle, depressed or delayed estrus and reduced reproduction, difficulty in calving and retention of the placenta, birth of calves with congenital rickets, falling disease or sudden death due to acute heart failure, and anemia (NRC, 1988a).

Neonatal ataxia, a nervous disorder characterized by incoordinated movements of the hind limbs, a stiff and staggering gait, swaying of the hind quarters and/or paralysis, and high mortality, often occurs in lambs of Cu-deficient ewes at birth or several weeks later (Underwood, 1981).

An explanation of the development of these signs has been proposed as follows. At the critical period in late gestation when myelin is being deposited most rapidly in the fetal lamb, Cu deficiency causes a depression in cytochrome oxidase activity, leading to inhibition of aerobic metabolism and impaired phospholipid synthesis. Thus, myelin synthesis is impaired, since myelin is composed largely of phospholipids (Davis & Mertz, 1987). Other signs of Cu deficiency in sheep are similar to those in cattle.

The signs of Cu deficiency in poultry are similar to those in pigs except that poultry do not exhibit achromotricia (O'Dell, 1979). Although all Cu-deficient species manifest anemia, the relative susceptibility to other Cu-dependent processes varies with species. Neonatal ataxia has never been reported in Cu-deficient puppies (*Canis familaris*), although it readily arises in some areas in lambs and kids from deficient ewes and goats. The cardio-vascular lesions of the major blood vessels, characteristic of Cu deficiency in pigs and chicks, have not been observed in deficient cattle under natural conditions (Underwood, 1981).

As mentioned previously, liver and blood Cu concentrations can be used as criteria to assess Cu status and then to diagnose Cu deficiency in animals. However, serum ceruloplasmin and superoxide dismutase may be more sensitive indicators and offer some technical convenience (Underwood, 1981). In lambs, weight gains and blood hemoglobin are correlated with plasma Cu concentrations and superoxide dismutase activities (Suttle et al., 1988a, b).

Species vary widely in susceptibility to Cu toxicity, in part due to differences in S metabolism, as well as to differences in concurrent dietary levels of S, Mo, Zn, and Fe. When these elements are present at normal levels the maximum tolerable levels of dietary Cu during growth of various species approximate the following: sheep, 25 mg kg^{-1}; cattle, 100 mg kg^{-1}; swine, 250 mg kg^{-1}; horses, 800 mg kg^{-1}; chickens, 300 mg kg^{-1}; and rabbits, 200 mg kg^{-1} (NRC, 1980). Adult animals may tolerate higher levels of Cu than the young. Overt manifestations of Cu toxicosis in ruminants are secondary to a hemolytic crisis triggered by severely elevated hepatic Cu levels. In other animals, Cu toxicosis is less dramatic and includes growth inhibition, anemia, muscular dystrophy, impaired reproduction, and decreased longevity (NRC, 1980). Recently, metallothionein has been shown to be involved in Cu tolerance and toxicosis (Elmes et al., 1988; Nederbragt et al., 1988).

E. Interactions with other Nutrients

Three types of interactions between Cu and other elements have been recognized as practically significant (Bremner, 1988). The first is between Cu and Zn, which has been summarized in the previous section on Zn. The second is between Cu and Fe, which has also been mentioned previously. The third, and most conspicuous, is among Cu, Mo, and S. The following discussion will focus on the effects of Mo and Fe on Cu metabolism. The interactions of Cu with nutrients other than those mentioned above have been well presented elsewhere (Miller et al., 1979; O'Dell, 1979; Davis & Mertz, 1987).

The importance of Fe as a Cu antagonist has only recently become apparent. Slight increases in dietary Fe content from 100 to 250 mg kg^{-1} are sufficient to significantly reduce liver and plasma Cu concentrations (Bremner et al., 1987). Dietary Fe of over 500 mg kg^{-1} induces the same changes in tissue Cu levels and in activities of Cu-dependent enzymes of 5 mg kg^{-1} of Mo does (Humphries et al., 1983). Such Fe levels are typical of those found in many feedstuffs. Therefore, this interaction is of great importance in ruminant nutrition. More importantly, there is an additive action of Fe and Mo, at levels of 150 mg kg^{-1} Fe and 2 mg kg^{-1} Mo on Cu utilization (Humphries et al., 1988).

The antagonism between Mo and Cu in ruminants has been extensively studied for many years (Miller, 1979; Underwood, 1981). It is well established that high Mo intake results in Cu deficiency. However, the mechanism of the interaction involving Mo and Cu is not fully understood. The paradoxical finding that dietary SO$_4$-S potentiates the toxic effect of Mo in ruminants, whereas in nonruminants, sulfur alleviates Mo toxicity, makes the picture even more complicated (Davis & Mertz, 1987). Currently, the thiomolybdate hypothesis is used to explain this interaction. The principal features of the hypothesis are as follows (Davis & Mertz, 1987): (i) sulfide (S^{2-}) or hydrosulfide (HS$^-$) ions are generated within the rumen both by microbial reduction of ingested SO$_4$-S and partial degradation of S-amino acids derived from dietary or rumen bacterial proteins; (ii) this reactive S progressively displaces O from ingested MoO$_4$ ions to yield oxythio- or tetrathiomolybdate(s) as follows: MoO$_4^{2-}$ $\rightarrow$ MoO$_3$S^{2-} $\rightarrow$ MoO$_2$S$_2^{2-}$ $\rightarrow$ MoOS$_3^{2-}$ $\rightarrow$ MoS$_4^{2-}$; and (iii) subsequent reaction of the thio- or oxythiomolybdates with Cu yields products from which Cu is physiologically unavailable.

Considerable evidence has been obtained in recent years to prove that thiomolybdates form in the gastrointestinal tract and its subsequent effect on the development of Cu deficiency (Bremner, 1988). In contrast, there is also evidence opposing this hypothesis (Allen & Gasthorne, 1988). Molybdenum appears to have effects independent of Cu deficiency, and does not influence Cu metabolism, although Cu can influence Mo metabolism (Bremner, 1988; Chen et al., 1988).

F. Requirements, Feed Sources, and Availability

As Cu requirements of animals are powerfully influenced by the interactions between this metal and other dietary components, it is necessary to specify the conditions under which the requirements are to apply. In ruminants, the Mo content of the diet, and sometimes S, should be considered. Although 4 mg kg^{-1} of dietary Cu will meet the requirement of cattle under certain conditions, 10 mg kg^{-1} is a more practical minimum requirement. More than 10 mg kg^{-1} of Cu may be required, however, for cattle grazing pastures or consuming feedstuffs that contain high levels of Mo or other interfering substances (NRC, 1988a). The Cu requirement of sheep also depends on dietary Mo content and other factors. When the Mo concentrations of pastures were < 1.5 mg kg^{-1} (dry basis), 6 mg kg^{-1} of Cu was found adequate. When Mo in the herbage was of the order of 2 to 5 mg kg^{-1} (dry basis), sheep needed approximately 10 mg kg^{-1} dietary Cu (Underwood, 1981). A level of 5 to 6 mg kg^{-1} Cu in the diet is adequate for the neonatal pig (Okonkwo et al., 1979; Hill et al., 1983a). The requirement is probably no greater for later stages of growth. The Cu requirement of sows is not well defined (NRC, 1988b). Diets containing 4 to 5 mg kg^{-1} of Cu can be considered adequate for poultry (O'Dell, 1979). High levels (250 mg kg^{-1}) of Cu in diets of young pigs have been shown to stimulate growth and to increase feed conversion efficiency. This effect seems to be pharmacological, with a response analagous to low-level feeding of antibiotics, but the mechanism is not completely understood (Miller et al., 1979; NRC, 1988b).

In young lambs fed milk or milk substitutes, apparent Cu availability values as high as 47 to 71% have been reported (Suttle, 1975). Whole-body analyses of carcass indicated that veal calves retained an average of 20 to 22% of the Cu consumed (Kirchgessner & Neese, 1976). In pig balance studies, 20 to 50% of Cu ingested was retained (Okonkwo et al., 1979; Menten, 1988). The bioavailability of the main sources of supplemental Cu is in the following order: $CuSO_4 > CuCO_3 > CuCl_2 > CuO > CuS$ (NRC, 1988a, b). Intramuscular or subcutaneous injections of Cu glycinate or Cu-Ca EDTA have been found satisfactory in sheep and cattle. Recent years have witnessed the development of glass pellets that contain Cu or Cu plus other trace elements. These pellets can be administered orally and will slowly release Cu into the gastrointestinal tract (NRC, 1988a).

V. MANGANESE

A. Distribution in the Animal Body

Manganese is fairly uniformly distributed throughout the tissues and fluids relative to other essential trace elements, with comparatively little variation among species or at different ages (Hurley & Keen, 1987). Typically, Mn in brain, heart, lung, and muscle is <1 mg kg^{-1} fresh tissue. Bone, liver, and kidney contain 1 to 3 mg kg^{-1} fresh tissue (Keen & Graham, 1989). The concentrations of Mn in various tissues of humans, cattle, rabbits, and rats have been listed by Scott (1972), Underwood (1977) and Hurley and Keen (1987). Values for pigs and poultry have been presented by other researchers (Leibholz et al., 1962; Kayongo-Male et al., 1977). Skeletal Mn can amount to about 25% of total-body Mn, but does not constitute an important mobilizable store of the element (Black et al., 1984; Howes & Dyer, 1971). It has been demonstrated in various animals that the concentration of Mn in bones can be raised or lowered by substantially varying Mn intakes of animals (Hurley & Keen, 1987). This is also true for the concentrations of Mn in liver, kidney, and heart (Leibholz et al., 1962; Kayongo-Male et al., 1977; Ammerman et al., 1988; Masters & Paynter, 1988). Ammerman et al. (1988) have shown linear increases in bone, kidney, and liver Mn, with bone and kidney providing the greater sensitivity when 0 to 4000 mg kg^{-1} Mn is incorporated into practical diets. Changes in bone Mn concentrations have been used as a measure of dietary Mn bioavailability in chicks (Black et al., 1984; Ammerman et al., 1988).

Manganese was previously thought to be more concentrated in the mitochondria than in the cytoplasm or other organelles of the cell (Hurley & Keen, 1987). But, Brandt et al. (1988) reported that approximately 40% of total hepatocyte Mn is associated with cytosolic components. In contrast to several of the other essential trace elements, the fetus does not normally accumulate liver Mn before birth (Hurley & Keen, 1987). However, higher liver Mn in the newborn of Mn-supplemented mothers has been demonstrated in rats and mice (Britton & Cotzias, 1966). Likewise, the concentration of Mn was significantly higher in the fetuses from sows on a diet with 100 mg kg^{-1} Mn than those from sows on a diet with 6 mg kg^{-1} Mn on the 60th, 80th, and 110th d of gestation (Newland & Davis, 1961).

The concentration of Mn in hair varies with species, individual, season, color, and, less certainly, with the Mn status of the diet (Hurley & Keen, 1987). O'Mary et al. (1969) observed a range of 26 to 104 mg kg^{-1} Mn in hair of Hereford cattle and calves. Manganese concentrations in wool and feathers vary significantly with dietary Mn intakes. Lassiter and Morton (1968) reported a mean of 6.1 mg kg^{-1} in the wool of lambs fed a low Mn diet for 22 wk, compared with 18.7 mg kg^{-1} in the wool of control lambs. Mathers and Hill (1968) found the skin and feathers of pullets fed a low Mn diet for several months contained 1.2, as opposed to 11.4 mg kg^{-1} Mn in pullets fed a high Mn diet.

Keen and Graham (1989) generalized that whole blood and serum Mn concentrations are about 0.01 and 0.001 $\mu g\ mL^{-1}$, respectively. These values are much lower than those observed in pigs. Kayongo-Male et al. (1977) found that the serum Mn of growing pigs was about 0.02 $\mu g\ mL^{-1}$. Newland and Davis (1961) found blood serum contained 0.28 to 0.45 μg Mn mL^{-1}, and blood cells contained 0.18 to 0.24 μg Mn ml^{-1}. The Mn concentration in the blood plasma of pullets increases markedly with the onset of egg laying (Hill, 1974), suggesting an influence of estrogen on plasma Mn concentrations (Panic et al., 1974).

B. Absorption, Storage, and Excretion

Absorption of Mn was reported to occur throughout the small intestine (Thomson et al., 1971a, b). But Kayongo-Male (1976) found net absorption of Mn in the stomach and cecum, and net secretion of Mn in the cranial and caudal small intestine, colon, and rectum of growing pigs. The efficiency of Mn absorption is quite low. In cattle, approximately 1 to 4% of dietary Mn is absorbed (Sullivan et al., 1979; Van Bruwaene et al., 1984). Excessive dietary Ca, P, and phytate may reduce Mn absorption and increase requirements for Mn in several species (Keen & Graham, 1989). Likewise, Fe can interfere with Mn absorption. Manganese absorption and retention are higher in neonates than in adults (Keen et al., 1986). Observations on the effect of dietary Mn level on Mn absorption are inconclusive. Numerous reports show highest absorption and retention of Mn at lower dietary Mn levels (Carter et al., 1974; Settle et al., 1969; Watson et al., 1973; Miller et al., 1973a).

On the other hand, Sullivan et al. (1979) and Van Bruwaene et al., 1984) reported that the absorption of Mn was independent of dietary concentration in cattle. Keen et al. (1987) reported that Mn absorption did not appear to be increased under conditions of Mn deficiency in rats. Weigand and Kirchgessner (1985) found that percent Mn retention did not differ in rats fed diets containing 35, 65, and 100 mg kg^{-1} Mn.

The mode and control of Mn absorption are poorly understood. Bell et al. (1989) reported that Mn absorption in the small intestine occurs primarily by simple diffusion, whereas Garcia-Aranda et al. (1983) indicated that low-molecular-weight ligands in the intestine may facilitate the uptake of Mn. When entering the portal blood, Mn may remain free or rapidly become bound to alpha$_2$-macroglobulin. After reaching the liver, Mn is removed by hepatocytes by a unidirectional, saturable process with the properties of passive-mediated transport (Keen & Graham, 1989). Five cellular pools of Mn have been identifiedd for newly absorbed Mn entering the hepatocyte. These pools include lysosome, mitochondria, nucleus, newly synthesized Mn proteins and free Mn pools (Keen & Graham, 1989).

Little is known about the storage of Mn. No specific Mn storage protein has been identified. In calves given a single dose of Mn intravenously, highest Mn levels were found in the pancreas, liver, kidney, gall bladder, bile, and spleen 1 d after dosing. The fastest decline was in bile, liver, spleen, and gastrointestinal tract tissues, with the slowest decline in bone, muscle, skin, heart, and testicles. The ^{54}Mn turnover rate was much more rapid than that of ^{65}Zn, but there is a similar relative order of rates among various tissues (Miller et al., 1973).

Absorbed stable Mn or ^{54}Mn is predominantly excreted by way of the feces regardless of dietary Mn level or pathway of isotope administration (Miller et al., 1973; Watson et al., 1973; Carter et al., 1974). Miller et al. (1973) reported that calves fed a practical diet, with or without 21 mg kg^{-1} of supplemented Mn, excreted 40% of ^{54}Mn within 2 d and 73% within 21 d via feces after a single trace ^{54}Mn dose. Under ordinary conditions, bile is the main route of excretion. Carter et al. (1974) reported that supplements of 15 mg kg^{-1} Mn to young calves fed whole milk caused a two-fold increase in liver Mn (11 vs. 22 mg kg^{-1}) and gall bladder Mn (6 vs. 11 mg kg^{-1}), but a 30-fold increase in bile Mn (1.3 vs. 39 mg kg^{-1}), with no significant increase in other tissues. Excretion of Mn also occurs via pancreatic juice (Hurley & Keen, 1987).

The homeostatic control of Mn is not well understood. Some researchers have proposed that both variable excretion and absorption play important roles in Mn homeostasis (Carter et al., 1974; Watson et al., 1973; King et al., 1980). However, others support only variable excretion as the regulator of Mn homeostasis (Settle et al., 1969). Normal mature ruminant milk contains 20 to 50 μg Mn L^{-1} (Hurley & Keen, 1987). Sow's milk has been reported to contain 0.02 to 0.04 mg kg^{-1} Mn (Leibholz et al., 1962). The level of egg Mn varies widely with dietary Mn intake (Hurley & Keen, 1987).

C. Essential Functions in Metabolism

Manganese plays its role in metabolism both as a constituent of metaloenzymes and in enzyme activation. The Mn-containing enzymes include arginase, pyruvate carboxylase, Mn-superoxide dismutase, and glutamine synthetase. The activities of the first three enzymes appear to be reduced by Mn deficiency. The large number of Mn-activated enzymes includes hydrolyases, kinases, decarboxylases, and transferases (Keen & Graham, 1989). In these reactions, Mn can act by binding either to the substrate (such as ATP) or to the protein directly, with induction of subsequent conformational changes. Although other metal ions, particularly Mg, can replace Mn in these reactions, there are three enzymes that require Mn specifically: glycosyltransferases, xylosyltransferase, and phosphoenolpyruvate carboxykinase (Leach, 1986; McNatt et al., 1976; Baly et al., 1986). The activities of these enzymes tend to be low in Mn deficiency, and the reductions can account for some of the pathological defects (Keen & Graham, 1989).

In addition, Mn is required for insulin synthesis and release (Gershwin et al., 1988). Manganese may participate in the regulation of pancreatic exocrine function (Korc & Brannon, 1988), and Mn deficiency has a pronounced effect on glucose transport in adipose cells (Baly, 1988). Manganese supplementation has been reported to elevate antibody titers and to maintain these elevated antibody titers over extended periods, to increase levels of other nonspecific resistance factors, and to stimulate natural killer cell activity (Gershwin et al., 1988). Manganese is essential for normal brain function (Hurley & Keen, 1987).

In summary, Mn appears to play a critical role in at least three basic aspects of metabolism: (i) glycosaminoglycan synthesis, (ii) carbohydrate metabolism, and (iii) lipid metabolism (Scott, 1972; Gershwin et al., 1988). The role of Mn in immunological function is little understood.

D. Deficiency and Excess

In all animals, Mn deficiency is manifested clinically by impaired growth, skeletal abnormalities, ataxia of the newborn, disturbed or depressed reproductive function, and defects in lipid and carbohydrate metabolism (Underwood, 1981; Hurley & Keen, 1987). Growth impairment can be explained by reduced feed consumption and efficiency of feed use (Underwood, 1981).

In Mn-deficient pigs, the skeletal abnormalities are characterized by lameness and enlarged hock joints with crooked and shortened legs; in calves and sheep by difficulty in standing, and joint pain with poor locomotion and balance; in chicks, poults, and ducklings by perosis or slipped tendon; and in chick embryos by chondrodystrophy. Perosis is characterized by enlargement and malformation of the tibiometatarsal joint, twisting and bending of the tibia, thickening and shortening of the long bones, and slipping of the gastrocnemius tendon from its chondyles. Nutritional chondrodystrophy is characterized by shortened and thickened wings and legs of the embryo

(Underwood, 1981). The basic biochemical lesion underlying the development of bone defects in Mn deficiency is a reduction in protoglycan biosynthesis, which is secondary to a reduction in the activities of glycosyltransferases. As mentioned above, these enzymes are specifically activated by Mn and are needed for the synthesis of chondroitin sulfate side chains of proteoglycan molecules (Keen & Graham, 1989).

Ataxia is the result of impaired vestibular function induced by impaired otolith development in centricular and saccular maculae (Keen & Graham, 1989). Thus, this ataxia is secondary to skeletal defects and differs from that of Cu deficiency, which is due to defective myelin synthesis (Underwood, 1981). The precise biochemical lesion underlying the block in otolith development has not been identified, although it is thought to involve a defect in proteoglycan biosynthesis (Keen & Graham, 1989).

Reproductive disorders caused by Mn deficiency include depressed or delayed estrus and conception, as well as increased abortion and stillbirths, and lowered birth weights (Hurley & Keen, 1987). The biochemical role of Mn in reproduction is unclear. Doisey (1973) suggested that the lack of Mn inhibited the synthesis of cholesterol and its precursors, and in turn the synthesis of sex hormones and possibly other steroids. Hidiroglou (1975) suggested that Mn may have a role in the functioning of the corpus luteum.

Defects in carbohydrate metabolism in Mn-deficient animals may result from a Mn requirement for: (i) pyruvate carboxylase and phosphoenolpyruvate carboxykinase, thus regulating gluconeogenesis by cellular Mn concentrations; (ii) insulin synthesis and release, with Mn deficiency resulting in a diabetic-type condition; (iii) glucose transport in the isolated adipose cell, with Mn deficiency most likely reducing production of transport protein (Baly, 1988); and (iv) the regulation of pancreatic amlyase, and in adaptation of lipase production to high fat diets (Korc & Brannon, 1988).

Abnormal lipid metabolism caused by Mn deficiency has been shown to reduce fat deposition in pigs and kids of goats (Underwood, 1981). The defect in lipid metabolism from Mn deficiency may be ascribed to: (i) ultrastructural abnormalities of tissues, particularly alterations in the integrity of cell membranes associated with decreased activity of Mn-superoxide dismustase; (ii) Mn requirements for farnesyl pyrophosphate synthase, an enzyme of cholesterol synthesis; and (iii) abnormal lipoprotein metabolism (Keen & Graham, 1989). It is interesting to note that the activity of Mn-superoxide dismutase in the heart of sheep is more sensitive to dietary Mn intake than that in the liver. Dietary Mn may be an additional factor involved in the etiology of nutritional muscular dystrophy of the sheep, since Cu superoxide dismutase is relatively low in the heart of this animal (Masters & Paynter, 1988).

Currently there are no satisfactory measures for evaluation of Mn status in animals. Manganese concentrations in blood, bones, and liver decline in animals deprived of Mn, but they do not provide diagnostic criteria that are as useful as measures of other elements, such as Cu (Underwood, 1981). The measurement of hair Mn has been used as an indicator of Mn status, but the diagnostic value of this measure is doubtful (Hurley & Keen, 1987).

In general, adverse health effects have not been seen in most species with dietary concentrations up to 1000 mg kg^{-1} Mn. Swine appear to be more sensitive to excessive Mn than cattle, sheep, or poultry. The maximum tolerable level of Mn is 1000 mg kg^{-1} for cattle and sheep, 2000 mg kg^{-1} for poultry, and 400 mg kg^{-1} for swine (NRC, 1980). These values are based on use of well-balanced, adequate diets for a relatively short term (NRC, 1980). The maximum tolerable level of Mn for animals is inversely correlated with dietary Fe intake. Signs of Mn toxicosis include growth retardation, anemia, gastrointestinal lesions, and, sometimes, neurological signs (NRC, 1980).

E. Interactions with Other Nutrients

The antagonism of Mn and Fe is of primary importance in Mn nutrition. Excess Mn feeding has been shown in several animals to reduce hemoglobin concentration, accompanied by low levels of tissue Fe and elevated levels of Cu (Hartman et al., 1955). Matrone et al. (1959) showed that excess Mn interfered with hemoglobin regeneration in baby pigs and rabbits, presumably by decreasing Fe absorption. Reduced Fe absorption with high dietary Mn has also been reported in cattle and chickens (Ho et al., 1984; Wilgus & Patton, 1939). Likewise, oral or parenteral Fe can reduce Mn absorption in rats (Gruden, 1988a, b). Manganese absorption has been shown to be elevated under conditions of Fe deficiency (NRC, 1980; Keen & Graham, 1989). Moreover, Gruden (1988b) found that the inhibitory effect of Fe on Mn absorption was significant only in the proximal part of the small intestine, and the inhibition was more pronounced in the young and in females than in the old and in males, respectively. Besides the interaction of Mn with Fe absorption, there is also evidence that Mn can be incorporated in vivo into the porphyrin of red blood cells under conditions of Fe deficiency (Borg & Cotzias, 1958).

As mentioned in section B, excess dietary Ca and P can reduce Mn absorption. In birds, the effect of high dietary levels of Ca phosphate in aggravating Mn deficiency is believed to be due to a reduction in soluble Mn through adsorption by solid mineral (Hurley & Keen, 1987). Using a factorial feeding trial with two ratios of Ca and P, two levels of Ca and P, and two levels of Mn in growing pigs, Kayongo-Male et al. (1977) have shown that there is a significant interaction between dietary Ca and P levels and ratios, and levels of Mn in serum, liver, pancreas, and metacarpals. They have also demonstrated that Mn supplementation significantly decreases rib Ca and Mg levels, and results in less compact bone in the diaphysis.

F. Requirements, Feed Sources, and Availability

The Mn requirements of domestic animals are less well defined than those of other trace elements. But there is evidence to show that (i) poultry have a higher requirement for Mn than do mammals because of lower absorption efficiency; (ii) the requirement for optimal reproductive performance is higher than that for growth; and (iii) the requirement for Mn is higher when dietary Ca and P levels are higher.

The minimum dietary Mn requirements of poultry for the growth of chicks, and for normal egg production and hatchability are approximately 40 mg kg^{-1} under normal dietary conditions, and a dietary concentration of 50 mg kg^{-1} is recommended to provide a margin of safety (Underwood, 1981). The Mn requirement of pigs is about one-tenth that of poultry. The NRC (1988b) recommends 4 mg kg^{-1} for baby pigs, 3 mg kg^{-1} for growing pigs, and 2 mg kg^{-1} for finishing pigs. It is clear that a dam's Mn status affects her neonatal pig's requirement because Mn readily crosses the placenta (NRC, 1988b). It has also been shown that the Mn requirement of pregnant sows is 25 mg kg^{-1}, based on Mn retention (Kirchgessner et al., 1981). The minimum dietary Mn requirements of ruminants cannot be given with any certainty. The recommended level is 40 mg kg^{-1} (NRC, 1988a).

The sources and availability of Mn have been reviewed by Ammerman and Miller (1972), Underwood (1981), and Hurley and Keen (1987). Typical values for whole cereal grains were 30 to 50 mg kg^{-1}, and 30 to 40 mg kg^{-1} for soybean meal. Protein supplements obtained from animal sources are generally low in Mn, approximately 5 to 15 mg kg^{-1}.

Early research indicated that most chemical forms of Mn were of equal value to the chick, whereas a recent study by Ammerman et al. (1988) showed differences in Mn bioavailability among $MnSO_4$, MnO, and $MnCO_3$, when evaluated on the basis of tissue Mn uptake from supplemental levels of either 40 to 120 mg kg^{-1} Mn or 1000 to 4000 mg kg^{-1} Mn in practical diets. When a purified diet (5 mg kg^{-1} Mn) was used and Mn sources were added at 10 mg kg^{-1} Mn, no differences in bioavailability were detected. The most commonly used forms in animal feeds are $MnSO_4$ and MnO.

VI. SELENIUM

A. Distribution in the Animal Body

Selenium occurs in all cells and tissues of the body in various concentrations. In all species studied, kidney has the highest Se concentration followed by liver, spleen, pancreas, testis, heart, skeletal muscle, lungs, and brain (Ullrey, 1987). Adipose tissue is very low because Se tends to be associated with protein. Muscle has the largest proportion of total body Se. About 40, 12, 10, 7, and 6% of the total, fleece-free, empty-body Se in grazing sheep is associated with skeletal muscle, digestive tract, bone, kidney, and liver, respectively. The relationship between the total Se content of the fleece-free empty body (Y) and the fleece-free empty body weight (X) has been described by the equation $Y = 672 + 50.8 X$ ($r = 0.96$, $P < 0.01$) (Grace & Watkinson, 1985). Studies with swine, cattle and sheep have demonstrated that the Se concentration (miligrams per kilogram, wet basis) is about 1 to 3 for kidney, 0.2 to 0.9 for liver, 0.1 to 0.7 for heart, and 0.1 to 0.2 for skeletal muscle (Ullrey, 1987). It should be noted that these values vary somewhat with species or breeds, and substantially with the amount and chemical form of Se in the diet (Levander, 1987). Ku et al. (1972) found a linear correlation ($r = 0.95$, $P < 0.01$) between Se in the longissimus muscle of pigs from 13 locations in the USA and natural dietary Se concentrations ranging from 0.027 to 0.493 mg kg^{-1}. Addition of Se from Na_2SeO_3 to swine diets low in natural Se increased Se concentrations of tissues, but not to the extent produced by organic Se forms (Groce et al., 1973b, Ku et al., 1973). Similar observations have been made in cattle and sheep (Ullrey et al., 1977) and poultry (Scott & Thompson, 1971).

The concentration of Se in blood is highly responsive to changes in the diet over a wide range. The serum Se of pigs receiving an unsupplemented natural diet (0.04 mg kg^{-1} Se) or this diet supplemented with 0.05, 0.1, or 0.2 mg kg^{-1} Se from Na_2SeO_3 was 0.046, 0.150, 0.164, and 0.168 mg kg^{-1}, respectively (Groce et al., 1973b). Also, Meyer et al. (1981) found a very strong relationship ($r = 0.70$, $P < 0.01$) between plasma Se and tissue Se in weanling swine fed diets (0.05–0.08 mg kg^{-1} Se) supplemented with SeO_3-Se from 0.1 to 2.0 mg kg^{-1}. Erythrocytes have a higher concentration of Se than plasma on a weight basis (Groce et al., 1973b).

Hair from cattle on normal range has 1 to 4 mg kg^{-1} Se, whereas yearling cattle grazing on seleniferous range have mean hair Se concentrations > 10 mg kg^{-1} (Olson et al., 1954). Cows with hair Se levels between 0.06 and 0.23 mg kg^{-1} produced calves with white muscle disease, but no lesions were seen in calves from dams with hair Se levels > 0.25 mg kg^{-1} (Hidiroglou et al., 1965). In addition to dietary Se intake, other factors also affect hair Se level in animals. Wahlstrom et al. (1984) reported that black hair of pigs contained higher Se than white hair, and both were higher than red hair.

The forms of Se in animal tissues are not completely understood, but some is bound to protein, perhaps by a Se-sulfide linkage, and some is incorporated into proteins (Ullrey, 1987; Levander, 1987). The only essential form known, and perhaps the most important function of Se in tissues, is as a component of glutathione peroxidase (GSH-Px).

B. Absorption, Storage, and Excretion

Absorption of Se occurs mainly in the duodenum, with essentially no uptake in the rumen or abomasum of ruminants and the stomach of pigs (Wright & Bell, 1966; Levander, 1987). In nonruminants, absorption of soluble forms of Se is significantly higher than that in ruminants (Brown et al., 1972; Stewart et al., 1978; NRC, 1983; Swanson et al., 1983; Harrison & Conrad, 1984a), presumably because of the reduction of SeO_3-Se to insoluble forms of Se in the rumen (Butler & Peterson, 1961). The extent of Se absorption also depends on the form of the element. The apparent absorption and retention of Se from selenomethionine is higher than that from SeO_3-Se (Norheim & Moksnes, 1985; Peter et al., 1985). Monensin and narasin have been shown to increase Se absorption in steers (Costa et al., 1985), and the same is true for cysteine in sheep (Wolffram et al., 1988).

In chicks, the presence of 1 mM As in the dose significantly reduced the total absorption of SeO_3-Se and enhanced accumulation of the label in intestinal tissue, whereas the same dose of As had different effects on these measures when SE from SeO_4 or selenomethionine were studied (Mykkanen, 1988). In addition, Ca, Co, and S also may decrease the absorption of Se (NRC, 1980; Peter et al., 1981; Harrison & Conrad, 1984b).

After entering the circulation, water-soluble Se appears to distribute rapidly among most organs. However, exact mechanisms for transport and intracellular processing of Se are poorly understood (Levander, 1987). Placental transfer of Se is limited (Bopp et al., 1982). Excretion of Se occurs primarily via the urine and appears to be dependent on a renal threshold (Burk et al., 1973; Groce et al., 1973a; Robinson et al., 1985). Selenium is also lost through feces and exhalation. In ruminants, fecal excretion of Se assumes greater importance than in nonruminants because of poorer absorption rather than from higher endogenous secretion. Exhalation becomes an important route of excretion only at high dietary intake (Handreck & Godwin, 1970) or at subacute doses of soluble Se salts injected (Olson et al., 1963). Milk Se levels are readily influenced by dietary Se intake of animals (Ullrey, 1987). Hojo (1982) reported an average Se concentration in cow's milk of 24 ng mL^{-1}. However, a range of 2.9 to 1270 ng Se mL^{-1} milk has been presented (Underwood, 1977). Miller et al. (1985) found that sows fed normal diets produced colostrum containing 0.15 mg kg^{-1} Se and 2-d milk containing 0.06 mg kg^{-1} Se. Whole-egg Se levels on an adequate diet measure about 0.3 mg kg^{-1} and can be changed by dietary Se concentration (Latshaw, 1975).

C. Essential Functions in Metabolism

Selenium was regarded as a toxic element until 1957. At that time, Se was found to prevent liver necrosis in rats (Schwarz & Foltz, 1957), exudative diathesis in chicks (Patterson et al., 1957), and hepatosis dietetica in swine (Eggert et al., 1957). Later, Rotruck et al. (1973) discovered that glutathione peroxidase (GSHPx; EC1.11.1.9) is a selenoprotein, and Flohe et al. (1973) concurrently found that GSH-Px contains four atoms of Se per molecule. Thus, the essentiality of Se was established. There is another form of GSH-Px that is Se-independent and is referred to as GSH S-transferase (Burk, 1983). Glutathione peroxidase detoxifies lipid peroxides, and protects cellular and subcellular membranes against peroxide damage, in conjunction with vitamin E and other antioxidants (Levander, 1987). In addition to the Se-dependent GSH-Px enzyme, a number of other mammalian selenoproteins have been studied, but their functions and metabolism remain undetermined (Keen & Graham, 1989).

D. Deficiency and Excess

Soils in a number of areas of the world are low in available Se. When diets consist exclusively of ingredients grown in such regions, Se deficiency in animals may occur if supplemental Se is not provided. Moreover, modern animal production facilities may create environmental stress, which increases the incidence and degree of Se deficiency (Mahan et al., 1975).

A major sign of Se deficiency, which has been seen in all livestock, especially the young, is white muscle disease or nutritional muscular dystrophy (NRC, 1988a, b; Underwood, 1981; Keen & Graham, 1989). This myopathy is typically associated with excessive peroxidation of lipids, resulting in chalky white striations, degeneration, necrosis, and subsequent fibrosis of myofibrils. In chicks, Se deficiency results in exudative diathesis and pancreatic atrophy (Underwood, 1981). The former is characterized by a generalized edema, which first appears on the breast, wing, and neck, and which arises from abnormal permeability of the capillary walls, resulting in accumulation of fluid throughout the tissue. Pancreatic fibrosis was originally thought to be a specific Se-responsive disorder (Thompson & Scott, 1970), and is apparently related to a severe alteration of the pancreatic endoplasmic reticulum (Root & Combs, 1988). More recently, pancreatic atrophy in chicks also has been produced by vitamin E deficiency.

In swine, signs of Se deficiency include hepatosis dietetica and mulberry heart disease (Underwood, 1981). Hepatosis dietetica involves massive intralobular hemorrhage and hepatic necrosis, and mulberry heart disease is characterized by mottling and dystrophy of the myocardium. Both lesions result in sudden death of pigs. Reproductive disorders are also common signs of Se deficiency (Underwood, 1981). These defects include testicular degeneration, impaired spermatogenesis, infertility, abortion, weak and stillborn young, and retained placentas (Keen & Graham, 1989). The mastitis, metritis, and agalactia syndrome in swine and mastitis in cattle have been shown to be associated with Se deficiency (Martin et al., 1967; Erskin et al., 1987). In addition, Se deficiency alters immunocompetence in several species (Moksnes et al., 1988; Levander, 1987; Keen & Graham, 1989), and induces unthriftiness in sheep and cattle (Underwood, 1981).

The primary biochemical change in Se deficiency is a decline in GSH-Px activity and Se concentration in tissues and blood (Levander, 1987; NRC, 1988a, b). Hence, plasma GSH-Px activity and plasma Se have been used to evaluate the Se status of animals (Keen & Graham, 1989). This method is not useful when Se intakes range from deficient to just adequate. Measures of urinary Se, Se balance, or Se in other tissues also may be helpful (Ullrey, 1987).

Selenium poisoning is a practical problem in the many seleniferous areas around the world (Underwood, 1981; Keen & Graham, 1989). Plants grown in these areas, particularly Se accumulator plants, contain very high levels of Se. Animals may consume a toxic amount of Se by consuming these plants when more desirable forage plants are scarce (Underwood, 1981).

Selenium toxicity can be classified into three types: acute, chronic blind staggers, and chronic alkali disease (NRC, 1980). Acute Se toxicity results from consumption of large amounts of accumulator plants by grazing animals or from accidental provision of excess supplemental Se. This type of toxicity is characterized by abnormal movement and posture, breathing difficulties, diarrhea, and rapid death (NRC, 1988a; Keen & Graham, 1989). Blind staggers results from consumption of limited amounts of Se accumulator plants over several weeks or months, and is manifest as blindness, slight ataxia, severe abdominal pain, paralysis, and death due to respiratory failure. Alkali disease results from consuming feeds containing 5 to 40 mg kg^{-1} Se over weeks or months. Signs include lameness; loss of vitality; loss of appetite; emaciation; sore feet; deformed, cracked, and enlongated hoofs; loss of hair from body, mane, and tail; liver cirrhosis, and anemia (NRC, 1980). Serum biochemical alterations during intoxication by Se in pigs have been reported, but these changes tended to be due to hepatic dysfunction, muscular degeneration, or, in part, to reduced feed intake rather than being pathognomonic for Se intoxication (Baker et al., 1988).

The maximum tolerable dietary level of Se has been proposed as 2 mg kg^{-1} for all species (NRC, 1980). However, a recent study with sheep indicated this level was too high in terms of immune response and, perhaps, should be < 1 mg kg^{-1} (Moksnes et al., 1988). Pigs may tolerate a bit higher Se, but a level of 5 mg kg^{-1} has been shown to produce toxicity (Mahan & Moxon, 1984).

E. Interaction with other Nutrients

Selenium has been shown to interact with many other nutrients, and the interaction between Se and vitamin E is very important. Selenium, as a component of GSH-Px, serves to detoxify lipid peroxides and to provide protection against damage to vital components of cells. Actually, GSH-Px is only a part of the protective system. Other important parts include vitamin E, catalase, and superoxide dismutase. These are compartmentalized and complement one another. Vitamin E scavenges free radicals and possibly singlet oxygen before they can attack membranes. Glutathione peroxidase destroys H_2O_2 and hydroperoxides in the cytosol and mitochondrial matrix. Calatase degrades H_2O_2 in the peroxisome. Superoxide dismutase detoxifies superoxide in the cytosol and mitochondria before superoxide can react with H_2O_2 to form hydroxy radical (NRC, 1983).

Since Se shares antioxidant functions with vitamin E, signs of Se deficiency often are identified as those of vitamin E deficiency as well (NRC, 1983, 1988a, b). There is a mutual sparing effect of Se and vitamin E. However, high levels of one do not completely eliminate the need for the other (Cantor et al., 1975; NRC, 1983; Hakkarainen et al., 1978). Addition of polyunsaturated fatty acids to diets tends to exacerbate Se and vitamin E deficiency, whereas synthetic antioxidants, in many cases, alleviate the deficiency (NRC, 1983). The addition of S-amino acids to the diets also alleviates Se and vitamin E deficiency, presumably by improving Se availability and sparing seleno methionine (NRC, 1983). In addition, the tissue activities of GSH-Px can be depressed by a deficiency of Fe (Rodvien et al., 1974), riboflavin (Brady et al., 1978), vitamin B_6 (Yasumoto et al., 1979), and Cu (Jenkinson et al., 1980). Selenium has been shown to reduce the toxicity of Cd, inorganic and methyl Hg, Ti, and Ag (NRC, 1983). The interactions of Se and other nutrients at the level of absorption have been documented in section B.

F. Requirements, Feed Sources, and Availability

The minimum Se requirements of animals vary with the chemical form of the element ingested; the previous Se and vitamin E status of the animal; the amounts of interfering or enhancing factors in the diet, such as vitamin E, S, lipids, proteins, amino acids, Cu, As, and Cd; viral, bacterial, or parasitic challenge; and oxidative stress from various physical causes (Ammerman & Miller, 1975; NRC, 1983; Masters et al., 1985).

Although it is not well defined, the requirement for Se by ruminants is approximately 0.1 to 0.3 mg kg^{-1} (NRC, 1988a). The dietary requirement for Se by swine is also between 0.1 and 0.3 mg kg^{-1} (Groce et al., 1973a, b; Ku et al., 1973; Meyer et al., 1981). The U.S. Food and Drug Administration approved the addition of 0.1 mg kg^{-1} Se to all swine diets in 1974 and up to 0.3 mg kg^{-1} recently (NRC, 1988b). The recommended dietary Se level for poultry is 0.15 to 0.2 mg kg^{-1} (NRC, 1984).

Selenium concentrations in feedstuffs vary widely with plant species and geographical area of production. Accumulator plants frequently have Se concentrations between 1000 and 3000 mg kg^{-1} (dry basis), whereas pastures and forages in areas without Se deficiency contain up to 0.2 mg kg^{-1} Se (Levander, 1987). In areas with Se deficiency, Se concentrations are generally below 0.05 mg kg^{-1} (Underwood, 1981). The cereal grains and other seeds exhibit a similar variation in Se content in different areas. Fish meal contains as much as 1 to 5 mg kg^{-1} Se, and can be used to improve substantially the Se concentration of cereal-based pig and poultry diets (NRC, 1983).

The availability of Se in different feedstuffs depends on its form as well as its concentration. Much of the Se in wheat, and probably other grains and alfalfa, is thought to be in the form of selenomethionine (Levander, 1987). Reports on the difference in the availability of Se between plant and animal sources are inconsistent (Levander, 1987). The usual supplemental forms of Se include Na_2SeO_3, Na_2SeO_4, and selenomethionine. The availability of Se in these forms varies with the criteria chosen (NRC, 1983).

VII. IODINE

A. Distribution in the Animal Body

The thyroid gland contains about 70 to 80% of the total-body I. The concentration of I in the thyroid of healthy mammals ranges from 0.2 to 0.5% of dry weight (Hetzel & Maberly, 1987). On a fresh basis, Groppel et al. (1988) reported 170 mg I kg^{-1} of thyroid for adult goats and sheep, and fattening bulls with a sufficient I status. Downer et al. (1981) reported that thyroid I concentration was about 400 mg kg^{-1} for 17-mo-old Holstein steers. The I concentration of the thyroid gland varies with I intake and age of the animal as well as the activity of the gland. Young animals have a higher concentration than adults (Groppel et al., 1988). Iodine-deficient or supplemented animals may have a lower or higher concentration than control animals (Downer et al., 1981; Hetzel & Maberley, 1987). However, there is little difference among species (Groppel et al., 1988; Hetzel & Maberly, 1987). Iodine exists in the gland as organic iodine, monoiodotyrosine (MIT), diiodotyrosine (DIT), 3,5,3′,5′-tetraiodothyronine (T_4), 3,5,3′-triiodothyronine (T_3), and probably other iodinated compounds (Underwood, 1977).

Other tissues or organs contain about 0.1 to 0.3 mg kg^{-1} I, dry basis (Groppel et al., 1985, 1988; Hetzel & Maberly, 1987). Unlike other trace elements, I is not concentrated in liver. Moreover, the I concentration of liver is lower than that of other tissues (Groppel et al., 1985, 1988; Downer et al., 1981). It appears that the distribution of I in the tissues varies somewhat with age and species (Groppel et al., 1985, 1988). However, dietary I intake is the strongest factor in altering the I concentration of tissues, regardless of species (Groppel et al., 1985; Downer et al., 1981). Interestingly, a significant difference in I concentration of individual muscles appeared when 400 mg, rather than 50 mg or no ethylene-diamine dihydriodide head^{-1} d^{-1}, was given to yearling Holstein steers (Downer et al., 1981). Iodine in the tissues occurs mainly as organically bound forms, with very little in inorganic form (Underwood, 1977). In addition, I has been found to be preferentially concentrated in the stomach (or abomasum), small intestine, salivary glands, mammary gland, ovary, and placenta (Church & Pond, 1988). More I is incorporated into black than into white hair (Groppel et al., 1985, 1988). The I content of hair and wool is suited for the assessment of long-term I intake (Groppel et al., 1985).

There is a wide range of blood serum I concentrations because they can be increased from several-fold to a hundred-fold times initial values, depending on dietary I intake. Normal blood serum I concentrations for cattle, sheep, and swine are about 5–15 μg/dL (Newton & Clawson, 1974; Newton et al., 1974; Downer et al., 1981; Groppel et al., 1985). Iodine exists in blood in inorganic and organic forms. The organic form is present mainly as T_4 bound to plasma proteins. Up to 10% of the organic I of plasma consists of other iodinated substances, including T_3 and DIT (Hetzel & Maberly, 1987). Concentrations of several different I-containing components of blood serum have been estimated while researchers have attempted to develop convenient and satisfactory indices of thyroid function. These include T_4, protein-bound iodine (PBI), and butanol extractable iodine (BEI). Values reflecting a sufficient I status for goats, calves, cows, and bulls have been proposed by Groppel et al. (1988). Yen and Pond (1985) reported that genetically obese pigs have a lower circulating plasma T_3 concentration than lean pigs.

B. Absorption, Storage, and Excretion

Iodine can be absorbed in any of its soluble chemical forms from all levels of the gastrointestinal tract (Hetzel & Maberly, 1987). In the intestine,

I is usually in the form of iodides (I^-), iodates (IO_4^-), or in hormonal forms (Kaneko, 1989). In ruminants, 70 to 80% of I is absorbed directly from the rumen, and another 10% is absorbed from the omasum (Miller et al., 1975). Net absorption also occurs from the small intestine and from the remainder of the gastrointestinal tract (Miller et al., 1974). The abomasum of ruminants is the major site of endogenous secretion (Barua et al., 1964). The absorption of I can be affected by the presence of goitrogens (Underwood, 1977), soil factors (Healy et al., 1972; Horn et al., 1974), or forms of I (Miller & Swanson, 1973).

The I^- in the circulation is trapped almost exclusively by the thyroid gland, with small amounts being trapped by the salivary gland, stomach, skin hair, mammary gland, placenta, and ovary (Gross, 1962; Miller et al., 1973b). The I^- trapped by the thyroid is rapidly oxidized and converted to organic iodine by combination with tyrosine. This process also occurs in the lactating mammary gland and to a very small extent in the ovum within the ovary. In other sites, the element remains in the form of I^- (NRC, 1980).

The main route I^{-1} excretion is by the kidneys, through which almost all of the I^- that was not trapped by the thyroid is lost in the urine (Hetzel & Maberly, 1987). A small, but significant, amount is lost in the saliva, and minimal amounts are lost in tears, feces, and sweat. In dairy cows, about 10% of I intake is normally excreted in the milk (NRC, 1988a). Milk I is increased dramatically by feeding dairy cows high levels of dietary I or by using I as a sanitizing agent (NRC, 1980; Groppel et al., 1985; Caple et al., 1985). Therefore, milk is an important route of excretion at high I intake. Usually, colostrum is richer than mature milk in I (Groppel et al., 1985). Goat's milk accumulates more I than cow's milk (Groppel et al., 1988).

C. Essential Functions in Metabolism

The only known function of I is as a chemical component of thyroid hormones. The process of thyroid hormonogenesis and release, the action and mechanism(s) of thyroid hormones, and their regulation have been well described in many biochemistry books (Kaneko, 1989). Briefly, there are three steps in the synthesis of thyroid hormones: (i) the I^- in the general circulation is taken up by the thyroid follicular cells by a highly efficient trapping and concentrating mechanism; (ii) the trapped I^- is then oxidized to a highly active form, I^*, by a peroxidase, and the I^* almost instantaneously binds to the phenyl groups of the tyrosine moieties of thyroglobulin at the 3 and/or 5 position to form MIT or DIT; (iii) the iodinated phenyl groups of tyrosine are coupled by the oxidative condensation of an iodinated phenyl group of one DIT to another DIT to form T_4 or of an MIT group to a DIT to form T_3. Many factors can interfere with these steps. Goitrogenic agents such as thiocyanate and perchlorate and large amounts of I^- can block Step 1. Thyrotoxic agents such as the thiouracils or thioureas can inhibit Step 2, and sulfa drugs, thiourea, and para-aminobenzoic acid (PABA) can block Step 3. The practical significance of these interferences will be discussed below.

The synthesis and release of the thyroid hormones is under the control of the thyroid stimulating hormone (TSH), which is secreted by the anterior pituitary gland, which in turn is mediated through the hypothalamus and its thyrotropin-releasing factor (TRF). Thyroid hormones are known to play a role in thermoregulation, intermediary metabolism, reproduction, growth and development, hematopoiesis and circulation, and neuromusclar functioning. The molecular basis for these thyroid hormone actions is unclear. However, uncoupling of oxidative phosphorylation in mitochondria, stimulating the Na pump ($^+$Na, K$^+$-ATPase) in cell membranes, and stimulating cellular protein synthesis have been suggested (Kaneko, 1989).

D. Deficiency and Excess

Iodine deficiency occurs when animals consume feeds and water with a subnormal amount of I or if feeds contain goitrogenic agents (Underwood, 1981).

A severe iodine deficiency causes pigs to be stunted and lethargic, and to have an enlarged thyroid (Sihombing et al., 1974). Sows fed I-deficient, goitrogenic diets farrow weak or dead pigs that are hairless, show signs of myxedema, and have an enlarged, hemorrhagic thyroid (NRC, 1988b). The first sign of I deficiency in cattle is an enlargement of the thyroid gland (goiter) noted in slaughtered cattle or newborn calves. The birth of goitrous calves is a sign of borderline or definite dietary I deficiency even though the cows may appear to be normal (Hemken et al., 1971). Deficiency signs may not be noticed for more than a year on low I diets (Hemken et al., 1971; Swanson, 1972). Long-term deficiencies may result in depressed milk yield and some signs of hypothyroidism (Hemken et al., 1971). The reduction of growth and productive performance by I deficiency result from reduced metabolic rate, and reduced cell differentation and growth (Underwood, 1981). Iodine deficiency can be detected by measuring I, PBI, BEI, and T_4 concentration of blood serum, milk, hair (or wool), and other organs in animals (Groppel et al., 1985, 1988; Caple et al., 1985; Underwood, 1981; NRC, 1988a).

Iodine toxicity can occur in animals fed excessive dietary I or treated with organic I for an extended period in an attempt to overcome health problems, such as foot rot. Species differ widely in their susceptibility to I toxicity, but all animals can tolerate I levels far in excess of their requirements.

The maximum tolerable level of I proposed for cattle and sheep is 50 mg kg^{-1} (NRC, 1980). Newton et al. (1974) showed that 50 mg kg^{-1} I significantly reduced growth rate and feed intake of calves weighing about 100 kg. Lactating cows apparently have a higher tolerance than calves, but the elevation of milk I is undesirable for human consumption (Hemken, 1978). Signs of toxicity in cattle include excessive lacrimation and salivation, a watery nasal discharge, and tracheal congestion that causes coughing (Newton et al., 1974; NRC, 1988a).

Swine and poultry appear to be tolerant of higher levels of I than cattle. Between 400 and 800 mg kg^{-1} were needed to depress feed intake and growth rate in growing-finishing pigs (Newton & Clawson, 1974). The maximum tolerable level for I in poultry diets is 300 mg kg^{-1}. Toxic effects of higher I include reduced egg production and hatchability (NRC, 1980). The horse apparently is the least tolerant animal, with a proposed maximum tolerable level of 5 mg kg^{-1} of I (NRC, 1980).

E. Interactions with Other Nutrients

Two types of inteactions between I and other nutrients or factors have been demonstrated. The first is the relationship between high dietary I, and Fe and Ca. The second is the interference of goitrogenic substances with I uptake by the thyroid. In calves, high dietary I intake significantly decreased hemoglobin and blood serum Ca concentration (Newton et al., 1974). In pigs, high dietary I intake significantly decreased hemoglobin and liver Fe concentration, which could be offset by Fe supplementation (Newton & Clawson, 1974). Likewise, excess Ca intake has been shown to have an antithyroid effect (Taylor, 1954).

Many plants and plant products used for animal feeds are known to contain goitrogenic substances that can induce goiter in animals. Among the naturally occurring goitrogens, the best characterized are the glucosinolate derivatives isolated from the *Brassica* species (Underwood, 1981). The conversion of hydrogen cyanide (HCN) into thiocyanate is the key step in exerting the goitrogenic effect, because thiocyanate inhibits the selective concentration of I by the thyroid, as described above. *Brassica* species also contain an active substance, 1-5-vinyl-2-thio-oxazolidone, called goitrin, that seems to interfere with the binding of I by the thyroid gland. The goitrin actions cannot be reversed completely by increasing the level of I in the diet.

Other feeds such as soybean, cottonseed (*Gossypium hirsutum* L.) and linseed meals, lentils (*Lens culinaris*), and peanuts also contain goitrogenic substances (NRC, 1988b). Moreover, perchlorates and Rb salts are known to interfere with I uptake by the thyroid (Underwood, 1977). Bromide, F, Co, Mn, and NO_3-N may also inhibit normal I uptake (Talbot et al., 1976).

F. Requirements, Feed Sources, and Availability

The dietary I requirements for farm animals have not been well established. The criteria of adequacy employed, the adaptive capacity of the thyroid gland to various dietary I supplies, the efficiency of the gland in reutilizing I, and the presence of goitrogens in feeds can significantly influence the needs of I by animals (Underwood, 1981).

The incorporation of iodized salt (0.007% I) at a level of 0.2% of the diet provides sufficient I (0.14 mg kg^{-1}) to meet the needs of growing pigs fed grain-soybean meal diets (NRC, 1988b). The same level of I (0.14 mg kg^{-1}) is also recommended for breeding swine. A diet concentration of 0.6 mg kg^{-1} of I has been suggested for lactating cows and 0.25 mg kg^{-1} for other classes of cattle (NRC, 1988a). However, if as much as one-quarter of the feed is derived from strongly goitrogenic crops, especially *Brassica* forages, the recommended dietary I is 0.5 mg kg^{-1} for growing and nonlactating cattle, and 1.0 mg kg^{-1} for cows in late gestation or lactation (NRC, 1988a). The requirement for I by poultry is set at 0.30 to 0.35 mg kg^{-1} (NRC, 1984).

In most instances the I requirements can be met with the use of iodized salt along with the I present in the natural feedstuffs. Calcium iodate, KIO_3, and $Ca_5(IO_6)_2$ are nutritionally available forms and are more stable in salt mixtures than NaI or KI (Kuhajek & Andelfinger, 1970). There are a number of other forms of I permitted as feed additives (NRC, 1980). Plants vary widely in I content, depending on the species and the I content of the soil. Hemken et al. (1972) reported that samples of hay from a Maryland farm contained 1.31 to 2.54 mg kg^{-1} I, while those from Illinois contained 0.62 to 1.02 mg kg^{-1}. The Chilean Iodine Education Bureau (1952) reported the following typical I concentrations in: cereal grains, 0.04 to 0.09 mg kg^{-1}; oilseed meals and meat meals, 0.1 to 0.2 mg kg^{-1}; and milk and milk products, 0.2 to 0.4 mg kg^{-1}. Protein supplements of animal origin, other than fish meal, which contains 0.8 to 8.0 mg I kg^{-1} dry weight (sea fish), are not rich in I if the animals have not been fed large amounts of I (Underwood, 1981). Dried seaweeds, such as kelp, may contain 0.4 to 0.6% I and could be potentially toxic to animals, at least to ruminants and horses, if fed at more than 1% of the diet (Underwood, 1977).

VIII. COBALT

A. Distribution in the Animal Body

Tissue levels of Co are very low in comparison with other essential metals, and measurements are often performed by neutron activation analysis rather than atomic absorption spectrophotometry. Cobalt in most tissues measures < 0.2 mg kg^{-1} (dry basis). Accumulation of Co does not occur in any particular organ or tissue, although liver, heart, and bone contain the highest concentrations (Smith, 1987). Cobalt does not accumulate with fetal age (Keen & Graham, 1989), but Co status of the dam has a significant impact on the level of Co in newborns (Smith, 1987). In addition, the level of Co in the liver and kidney of adults can be influenced by Co deficiency or supplementation. Cobalt is normally associated with vitamin B_{12}, or cobalamin, and the proportion of liver Co that occurs as vitamin B_{12} decreases greatly in Co-deficient animals (Smith, 1987). A level of 60 to 80 ng Co mL^{-1} plasma has been reported for unsupplemented lactating dairy cows by McAdam and O'Dell (1984). In most reports, the concentration of vitamin B_{12} in blood or plasma has been reported, rather than the concentration of Co itself. The serum vitamin B_{12} level for the ewe is about 400 to 1000 ng L^{-1} (MacPherson et al., 1988; Driver et al., 1988; Zervas, 1988), and about 200 ng L^{-1} for calves (MacPherson & Chalmers, 1985; MacPherson et al., 1988). In both species, Co supplementation can increase the serum vitamin B_{12} level appreciably (MacPherson et al., 1988; Driver et al., 1988; Zervas, 1988; MacPherson & Chalmers, 1985).

B. Absorption, Storage, and Excretion

Cobalt is not well absorbed by ruminants. Following oral or intraruminal administration of labelled Co to sheep and cattle, 84 to 98% appeared in the feces within 5 to 14 d. The poor Co absorption may be related to the rapid binding of Co by rumen microorganisms (Looney et al., 1976; Rothery et al., 1953; Smith & Marston, 1970). Increased Fe can depress Co absorption and vice versa (Smith, 1987). In simple-stomached animals, Co is essential as a component of vitamin B_{12}. Absorption of vitamin B_{12} is dependent on normal gastric parietal cell synthesis of intrinsic factor and a healthy illeal mucosa for the binding and transport of the vitamin B_{12}-intrinsic factor complex (Keen & Graham, 1989).

In most experimental animals, the tissue distribution of injected ^{60}Co is similar, with initial rapid uptake by liver and kidney, and, to a lesser extent, by the spleen, pancreas, and parts of the gastrointestinal tract (Smith, 1987). In chicks, following intravenous injection of ^{60}Co, the wall of the large intestine was found to be especially radioactive, and it was concluded that ^{60}Co was actively secreted there (Lee & Wolterink, 1955). The majority of Co is eliminated via the urine, but small amounts of Co are also lost by way of the feces, sweat, and hair (Smith, 1987). Normal cow's milk contains about 0.5 μg Co L^{-1}, and colostrum contains 4 to 10 times more than does milk (NRC, 1988a).

C. Essential Functions in Metabolism

The only established function of Co in animal metabolism is thought to be as a component of vitamin B_{12} and, thus, Co is indirectly associated with erythropoiesis, granulopoiesis, and glucose homeostasis. Vitamin B_{12} acts as the catalytic site of intramolecular mutations and single carbon transfer reactions, and serves as a cofactor of two important enzymes, methylmalonyl CoA mutase and 5-methyltetrahydrofolate-homocysteine methyltransferase (Keen & Graham, 1989). The former enzyme catalyzes the molecular rearrangement of methylmalonyl-CoA to succinyl CoA, a critical reaction for glucose homeostasis in ruminants because a primary gluconeogenic precursor for these animals is propionic acid. The latter enzyme demethylates 5-methyltetrahydrofolate, and regenerates methionine and tetrahydrofolate, two essential compounds for the synthesis of S-adenosylmethionine and nucleic acids. The serum level of vitamin B_{12} has been reported to be related to the immune function of ruminants (MacPherson et al., 1988).

It is interesting to note that Co can substitute for Zn in the enzyme carboxypeptidase and for part of the Zn in the enzyme alkaline phosphatase (NRC, 1988b). Hoekstra (1970) and Chung et al. (1976) have shown that supplemental Co prevents lesions associated with a Zn deficiency.

D. Deficiency and Excess

Both severe and mild Co deficiency occurs in grazing ruminants in particular areas of many countries. The severe forms of Co deficiency in sheep and cattle have been known as "bush-sickness" in New Zealand, "coast disease" in South Australia, "wasting disease" in West Australia, "Nakumitis" in Kenya, "Pining" in Great Britian, "Lecksucht" in the Netherlands and Germany, and "Grand Traverse disease" in Michigan (Underwood, 1981). Subclinical Co deficiency is of considerable economic importance because it occurs in much larger areas than clinically detectable Co deficiency, and is hard to diagnose (Underwood, 1981).

Ruminants grazing in Co-deficient areas, or consuming diets containing Co <0.07 to 0.11 mg kg^{-1} of dry matter, show loss of appetite, reduced growth, or loss in body weight followed by extreme emaciation, listlessness, normocytic normochromic anemia, and, eventually, death. Fatty degeneration of the liver and hemosiderosis of the spleen occur (Underwood, 1977). Microbial synthesis of vitamin B_{12} in the rumen of deficient ruminants is depressed (McDonald & Suttle, 1986).

As discussed above, Co plays a role as a component of vitamin B_{12}. The deficiency signs of Co are identical to those of vitamin B_{12}. The hepatic lipidosis and megaloblastic anemia in Co-deficient animals can be attributed to a reduction in activity of 5-methyltetrahydrofolate-homocysteine methyltransferase and, in turn, a reduction in regeneration of methionine and tetrahydrofolic acid. Reduction of methionine may impair choline synthesis and, consequently, the transport of hepatic lipid to extra-hepatic tissues, and finally may induce hepatic lipidosis. Reduced tetrahydrofolate production will reduce the available methyl donors, and, therefore, reduce purine biosynthesis and slow cell division, resulting in megalobastic anemia (Fell et al., 1985; Keen & Graham, 1989). The reduction in activity of another vitamin B_{12}-requiring enzyme, methylmalonyl CoA mutase, a key enzyme in gluconeogenesis from propionate in ruminants, may account for the reduction in blood glucose, increased plasma pyruvate and methylmalonate, and increased urinary methylmalonate. Elevated blood pyruvate and methylmalonate suppress the appetite control center in the hypothalamus, resulting in anorexia and extreme emaciation (Smith, 1987).

Recently, MacPherson et al. (1988) have reported that Co deficiency decreases serum vitamin B_{12}, and adversely affects immune function of both sheep and cattle, with particularly severe consequences for lamb viability. Cobalt repletion restores neutrophil function in both species.

Response to therapy and a diet containing <0.08 mg Co kg^{-1} of dry matter are diagnostic of Co deficiency in ruminants (Smith, 1987). The first notable response to Co feeding is an improved appetite followed by increased blood hemoglobin concentration (Church & Pond, 1988). Hepatic and plasma vitamin B_{12} levels have been used extensively to assess Co status of sheep and cattle (Keen & Graham, 1989; Suttle et al., 1988b), but considerable confusion has a risen regarding the interpretation of the levels found (McMurray et al., 1985; Halpin et al., 1984). Therefore, the measurement of plasma methylmalonate levels has been proposed as an indicator of the functional cobalamin status of the animal (McMurray et al., 1985). A regression equation of plasma methylmalonate against plasma vitamin B_{12} in lambs has been developed by Suttle et al. (1988b).

Cobalt toxicosis is less likely to occur than deficiency, and toxic levels appear to be at least 3000 times greater than the requirement in most species (NRC, 1980). Cases of toxicity are often the result of accidental oversupplementation to prevent deficiency. Daily Co doses in excess of 4 mg and 1 mg kg^{-1} body weight can be toxic for sheep and cattle, respectively, but dietary concentrations of 10 mg kg^{-1} appear safe (NRC, 1980; Young, 1984). No signs of toxicosis were observed in chicks fed diets with 4.7 mg kg^{-1} Co, but severe toxicosis was observed at 50 mg kg^{-1} (Turk & Kratzer, 1960). In swine, 200 mg kg^{-1} Co produced no aderse effect (Huck & Clawson, 1976). It appears that swine and poultry should be able to tolerate 10 mg kg^{-1} Co in diets (NRC, 1980). Signs of toxicosis include polycythemia in simple-stomached animals, and reduced feed intake and body weight, emaciation, anemia, debility, increased hemoglobin and packed red cell volume, and elevated liver Co in ruminants (NRC, 1980). Increased protein or methionine administration appear to alleviate Co toxicosis (Huck & Clawson, 1976), as do Se and vitamin E (Van Vleet et al., 1977).

E. Interactions with Other Nutrients

As mentioned above, Co interferes with the absorption of Fe and vice versa (Smith, 1987). These findings imply that Co may share a common intestinal mucosal transport pathway with Fe in which acceleration of transport of both elements is governed by the same mechanism, although this has not been resolved (Valberg, 1971). It has been noted that Co can substitute for Zn in the enzyme carboxypeptidase and for part of the Zn in the enzyme alkaline phosphatase (Piras & Vallee, 1967; NRC, 1988b). Consistently, supplemental Co prevents lesions associated with a Zn deficiency in swine (Hoekstra, 1970; Chung et al., 1976; ARC, 1981). In addition, Co also has been reported to interact with amino acids. Feeding 0.5 to 1% methionine alleviated the toxicosis caused by feeding 600 mg kg^{-1} Co in pigs (Huck & Clawson, 1976). Likewise, 500 mg methionine administered intravenously to calves prior to injection with 50 or 75 mg Co (0.64–0.85 mg kg^{-1}) prevented or decreased the severity of Co toxicosis signs (Ely et al., 1953). It is surprising to note that the toxicosis of Co in swine is not affected by Fe alone, but a combination of 200 mg kg^{-1} Fe, 400 mg kg Mn^{-1}, and 400 mg kg^{-1} Zn alleviates the growth depression in these animals caused by adding 400 mg kg^{-1} Co, and partially restores feed intake and growth from feeding 600 mg kg^{-1} Co (Huck & Clawson, 1976).

F. Requirements, Sources, and Availability

Field experience suggests that differences among ruminant species in Co requirement are small, and a level of 0.1 mg kg^{-1} of Co in dietary dry matter has been recommended (Smith, 1987; NRC, 1988a). Young (1984) indicated that between 2 and 5 mg d^{-1} of CoCl$_2$ for sheep and 20 to 30 mg d^{-1} for cattle were required for normal vitamin B$_{12}$ production. Nonruminants require preformed vitamin B$_{12}$, and must either ingest animal tissues or obtain their vitamin B_{12} from microorganisms in the intestinal tract or by coprophagy. The intestinal flora of pigs and poultry can synthesize vitamin B_{12}, but the amount is inadequate to meet the needs of these animals (Underwood, 1981). Overall, pigs and poultry have much lower dietary requirements for Co than have ruminants because the former probably have a lower requirement for vitamin B_{12} and have a higher vitamin B_{12} absorption efficiency (Underwood, 1981).

Forages in many areas of the world contain < 0.10 mg kg^{-1} Co in the dry matter. Cobalt sulfate and $CoCO_3$ have been used as effective sources of supplemental Co for ruminants. A heavy pellet (bullet) containing CoO and finely divided Fe, which, upon oral administration, remains in the reticulorumen, has prevented Co deficiency for extended periods in cattle that graze Co-deficient pastures (NRC, 1988a). Two problems have arisen from use of the bullets; regurgitation by the animal and coating of the pellets inside the rumen with Ca phosphate, which inhibits bioavailability of Co (NRC, 1980). Recently, soluble glass boluses containing Co and other essential trace elements have been used successfully in providing these elements in sheep and cattle (Knott et al., 1985; Driver et al., 1988; Zervas, 1988).

IX. MOLYBDENUM

A. Distribution in the Animal Body

A total of 0.85 mg and 1.27 mg of Mo has been found in the fleece-free, empty bodies of sheep (less the digesta), aged 153 and 405 d, respectively (Grace & Martinson, 1985). The concentration of Mo in the fleece-free, empty body is about 30 μg kg^{-1} and does not vary with age (Grace & Martinson, 1985). Liver has the highest concentration; about 1 mg kg^{-1} of fresh tissue (Grace & Martinson, 1985) or 2 to 8 mg kg^{-1} of dry tissue (Anke et al., 1985; NRC, 1980; Mills & Davis, 1987). Kidney is second to liver in Mo concentration followed by lung, omasum, pancreas, spleen, reticulorumen, bone, skin, and muscle (Grace & Martinson, 1985). Although the concentrations of Mo in skin and muscle are much lower than those in other tissues, the total content of Mo in these tissues is second only to that in liver. Grace and Martinson (1985) reported that about 55, 12, and 10% of total fleece-free body Mo were associated with the liver, skeleton, and muscle, respectively. This is in sharp contrast to an earlier detailed study by Dick (1956a) in which sheep were found to have about 2 and 55% of their total-body Mo in the liver and skeleton, respectively. The difference between the two studies cannot be satisfactorily explained, but variations in previous Mo, Cu, S, and protein nutritional history has been shown to significantly influence the distribution and metabolism of Mo in tissues (Hidiroglou et al., 1982; Lesperance et al., 1985; Mills & Davis, 1987).

In contrast to Mn, species difference in Mo concentrations in tissues appears to exist. Anke et al. (1985) reported that horses have the highest Mo concentrations in liver (8 mg kg^{-1} on dry basis), roe deer (*Capreolus capreo-*

lus) have the lowest concentration (0.6 mg kg^{-1}), and species such as pigs and cows have liver Mo concentrations (1-3 mg kg^{-1}) between those of horses and roe deer. Moreover, species differ in the response of liver Mo concentration to variations in dietary Mo and S (Mills & Davis, 1987). However, there are no significant sex and age differences in tissue Mo concentrations (Grace & Martinson, 1985).

Fetal liver is a major storage organ for both Mo and Cu, as about 70% of fetal content of these elements is associated with the liver at Day 62 and 40% at Day 143 of gestation of ewes (Grace et al., 1988). As pregnancy progresses, increasing amounts of Mo and Cu are taken up by the developing fetus. Just prior to parturition, about 90% of the Cu and 38% of the Mo found in the conceptus is associated with the fetus. For most of gestation, the rate of Cu and Mo uptake into the conceptus is greater in the twin-bearing ewe compared with the single bearing ewe (Grace et al., 1988). Molybdenum can cross the placental barrier, resulting in high levels of the element in the diet of the dam making less Cu and more Mo available to the conceptus and fetus (Mills & Davis, 1987; Grace et al., 1988).

The Mo levels of whole blood of sheep and cattle on low Mo diets can range from 1 to 6 μg dL^{-1} (Underwood, 1977), and are very sensitive to oral Mo intake (Lesperance et al., 1985; Mills & Davis, 1987) or parenteral Mo administration (Allen & Gawthorne, 1985). The wool contains 35 μg Mo kg^{-1} fresh tissue (Grace & Martinson, 1985).

B. Absorption, Storage, and Excretion

Many forms of Mo are readily absorbed from the gastrointestinal tract by all species (Mills & Davis, 1987). Not only di- or tri-thiomolybdate, but even tetrathiomolybdate can be absorbed to some extent (Price et al., 1988). It has been proposed that Mo is transported by a carrier-mediated process and that SO_4-S and Mo may compete for the same carrier or inhibit membrane transport in the intestine and renal tubules (Dick, 1956b), with heme impairing Mo absorption and retention. An alternate postulate is that formation of insoluble thiomolybdates precludes absorption (Mills & Davis, 1987). Specific Mo transport proteins have not been identified, although it has been reported that, at low Mo and S intakes, most of the Mo is associated with red cells and, at high levels, with plasma protein (Keen & Graham, 1989). The rates of absorption and routes of excretion differ with species. In swine, peak blood levels of Mo occur within 4 h after an oral dose of ^{99}Mo, and the urinary tract is the main excretory route for absorbed Mo (Bell et al., 1964; Robinson et al., 1973). In cattle, peak blood levels from an equivalent dose of ^{99}Mo are not reached until 96 h postadministration, and the main route of Mo excretion is via the feces (Bell et al., 1964). Absorbed Mo is also excreted via the milk from cattle and sheep in proportion to the levels of orally or parenterally administered Mo (Mills & Davis, 1987). The concentration of Mo in milk of cattle fed standard diets ranges from 18 to 120 μg L^{-1} (Archibald, 1951; Anke et al., 1985).

The rates of absorption, retention, and excretion are strongly influenced by the level of dietary inorganic SO_4. In addition, dietary levels of Mn, Zn, Fe, Pb, WO_4, ascorbic acid, methionine, cysteine, and protein affect these processes (NRC, 1980). Winston et al. (1985) found that the patterns of absorption and excretion of dietary Mo from water and food were different in rats, but the bioavailability of Mo was essentially the same.

C. Essential Functions in Metabolism

The biological significance of Mo to animals has been recognized since the discovery that excess Mo causes severe diarrhea of cattle (teart scours) in England and that Mo supplements could be used to alleviate chronic Cu toxicosis of sheep in Australia (NRC, 1980). More recently, several important enzymes have been found to require Mo as part of a functional cofactor consisting of a molybdopterine (Rajagopalan, 1987). These enzymes include xanthine oxidase (xanthine dehydrogenase), aldehyde oxidase, and sulfite oxidase. Xanthine oxidase catalyzes the oxidation of purines, pyrimidines, pteridines, and pyridines. Superoxide radicals are released in these reactions. Aldehyde oxidase shares many common substrates with xanthine oxidase. Both are similarly distributed between tissues, but these two enzymes are distinguishable from each other on the basis of their sensitivity to a range of enzyme inhibitors. Sulfite oxidase is a mitochondrial enzyme that catalyses the oxidation or detoxication of SO_3-S to SO_4-S during the degradation of S-amino acids (Mills & Davis, 1987). In addition, there are reports that Mo improves growth, egg hatchability and viability in chicks, and increases the rate of gain and cellulose degradation in sheep under certain conditions (Payne, 1977; Reid et al., 1957; Ellis et al., 1958).

Phillips et al. (1985) reported that a diet containing 5 mg Mo kg^{-1} dry matter can delay the time of onset of first estrus at least 6 wk and reduce fertility in cattle. Molybdenum seems to alter the secretion of luteinizing hormone (LH) directly or to affect estrogen receptor activity rather than to reduce Cu status. This occurs before growth is reduced. Anke et al. (1985) reported that goats fed a diet with 24 μg kg^{-1} Mo had a slower growth rate, lower insemination rate, higher abortion rate, and higher mortality of both mothers and kids than goats fed the same diet with 533 μg kg^{-1} Mo. Fungwe et al. (1988) found that Mo supplementation at 10–100 mg kg^{-1} did not affect fertility, but could prolong the estrus cycle as well as modulate fetal growth during gestation. Hepatic xanthine oxidase and sulfite oxidase activities were increased in mated and nonmated rats by Mo supplementation, but sulfite oxidase activity eventually declined in gestating animals.

Another exciting discovery is the finding that Mo supplementation at 10 mg kg^{-1} in drinking water exerts an inhibitory effect on mammary carcinogenesis (Yang et al., 1985). Further work indicates that the Mo enzymes and superoxide dismutase appear not to play roles in anticarcinogenic activity of Mo and implies that there are other important functions of Mo that need study (Yang & Yang, 1988).

D. Deficiency and Excess

Molybdenum deficiency is apparently relatively rare, and is usually produced by feeding its antagonist, tungsten, in amounts 1000-fold greater than Mo (Rajagopalan, 1984, 1987; Abumrad et al., 1981). However, Mo deficiency does occur occasionally in animals. Anke et al. (1985) reported that Mo-deficiency experiments were repeated ten times with six each of growing, gravid, and lactating control, and Mo-deficient goats between 1973 and 1982. As mentioned in the section above, goats fed diets with 24 μg kg^{-1} Mo had decreased growth, impaired fetal development, reduced insemination rate, and elevated abortion rate and mortality of mothers and their kids. Moreover, other research has also shown that Mo deficiency impairs growth and production in poultry (Payne, 1977), goats (Anke et al., 1978), and sheep (Ellis et al., 1958). It has been postulated that, in ruminants, there is a depression in microbial nitrate reductase in Mo deficiency, allowing for an increase in nitrite levels within the animal (Geurink et al., 1982; Korzeniowski et al., 1981). In induced Mo deficiency in chicks, tissue Mo and xanthine oxidase activity were reduced (Higgins et al., 1956; Johnson et al., 1974).

Molybdenum toxicosis is an important practical problem in grazing ruminants in some areas of the world where the soils and resulting herbage have relatively high Mo levels. The Mo content of typical teart pastures may range from 20 to 100 mg kg^{-1} (dry basis) (Underwood, 1977). The Mo content of forage is likely to be higher on poorly drained soils, and especially on soils such as granite alluviums and black shales, or highly organic soils such as peats and mucks (Underwood, 1977). Higher soil pH increases Mo availability to plants while decreasing Cu uptake.

Molybdenosis in livestock is essentially a secondary Cu deficiency manifested by diarrhea, anorexia, depigmentation of hair or wool, neurological disturbances, and premature death. The maximum tolerable levels of Mo vary widely among species. A range of 5 to 10 mg kg^{-1} Mo has been suggested for cattle and horses, whereas 1000 mg kg^{-1} has been proposed for swine. The maximum tolerable level of Mo can be increased substantially by increased amounts of Cu and inorganic SO_4, and is influenced by other factors such as Zn, Ag, Cd, and S-amino acids (NRC, 1980).

E. Interactions with Other Nutrients

The most conspicuous interaction between Mo and other nutrients is the three-way interaction of Mo, Cu, and S. The characteristics of this interaction have been described in the section on Cu. With respect to preventing molybdenosis or hypocupremia, the critical Cu-Mo ratio in cattle diets used in western Canada was 2:1 (Miltmore & Mason, 1971). Alloway (1973) suggested that a Cu/Mo ratio nearer to 4:1 was required on some pastures in England to prevent Cu deficiency in sheep. Finally, there are the interactions of Mo with Zn, Mn, Fe, Pb, WO_4, ascorbic acid, methionine, cysteine, and alkalinity of soils, but the basis for these interactions are, as yet, unexplained (NRC, 1980).

F. Requirements, Sources, and Availability

The Mo requirements of animals are extremely low and can be met by most natural dietary ingredients. Chicks grow normally, reproduce, and oxidize xanthine satisfactorily on diets containing only 0.2 mg kg Mo^{-1} (Higgins et al., 1956). Goats consuming a semipurified diet with 0.533 mg kg^{-1} Mo performed normally but 0.024 mg kg^{-1} Mo was insufficient (Anke et al., 1985). A significant growth response to added Mo, and an improvement in cellulose digestibility has been reported in lambs fed a semipurified diet containing 0.36 mg kg^{-1} Mo, but sheep and cattle have performed normally when they grazed pastures containing <0.36 mg kg^{-1} Mo (Underwood, 1981).

Concentrations of Mo in normal herbage often range from 0.1 to 0.3 mg kg^{-1} on a dry basis (Underwood, 1977). The Mo in herbage is present as watersoluble Na_2MoO_4 and $(NH_4)_2MoO_4$, and as insoluble MoS_2. Only MoS_2 appears to be very poorly absorbed. Plants growing on soils industrially contaminated with Mo contain up to 231 mg kg^{-1} Mo (Gardner & Hall-Patch, 1962).

X. FLUORINE

A. Distribution in the Animal Body

An extremely high proportion of total-body F is present in the skeleton because bone has great affinity for F and incorporates it into hydroxyapatite, forming fluorapatite (NRC, 1974). In normal adult farm animals not unduly exposed to F, the concentration of F in whole, dry, fat-free bones usually ranges from 300 to 600 mg kg^{-1} (Underwood, 1977). Various types or portions of bones contain various levels of F. Cancellous bones, such as the frontal, ribs, vertebrae, and ilium, have a higher F concentration than the more compact metacarpals and metatarsals, and the diaphyseal portion of the metacarpals and metatarsals has a lower F concentration than the metaphyseal portion (NRC, 1980).

Skeletal F concentrations can be increased dramatically if the animals are exposed to supplemental F. Forsyth et al. (1972b) reported that pigs, weighing from 33.6 to 98.3 kg, fed diets containing 150 mg kg^{-1} F as NaF had a concentration of F in the humerus metaphysis of 5000 to 6300 mg kg^{-1}, while pigs on the unsupplemented diet had F concentrations of 300 to 350 mg kg^{-1}. A similar, but greater, response of bone F to dietary F intake has also been observed in pigs by Burnell et al. (1986). Chan et al. (1973) reported that Japanese quail fed a diet with 750 mg kg^{-1} F as NaF for 35 d had a concentration of F in the tibia of 2000 to 2200 mg kg^{-1}, whereas the control had 13 to 14 mg kg^{-1}. Flourine concentrations of normal teeth parallel those of long bones, but usually at lower levels. Normal enamel is reported to contain 100 to 270 mg kg^{-1}, normal dentine 240 to 625 mg kg^{-1}, and normal molars 200 to 537 mg kg^{-1} F on a dry, fat-free basis

(Underwood, 1977). However, the F content of teeth is extremely sensitive to changes in F intake (Harkins et al., 1963; NRC, 1980).

Soft tissues do not appear to accumulate F under normal conditions since insignificant amounts of F in these tissues have been reported in cattle receiving up to 93 mg kg^{-1} F for more than 7 yr (Hoogstratten et al., 1965; NRC, 1974). The normal level of F in soft tissues of ruminants is about 204 mg kg^{-1} (dry basis) (Underwood, 1977). The kidney has the highest concentration of all soft tissues because F is lost mainly via urine. In addition, tendon, aorta, and placenta have higher F concentrations than do most soft tissues (NRC, 1974). Fluorine can cross the placenta (Cerklewski & Ridlington, 1988). The average F levels of fetuses from rats fed 50, 100, and 200 mg kg^{-1} F diets ranged from 0.6 to 0.9, 1.1 to 2.0 and 3.0 to 4.0 mg kg^{-1} F, respectively (Theurer et al., 1971). It appears that the degree of placental transfer of F varies with the maternal nutritional status (Cerklewski & Ridlington, 1988) and the form of F (Theurer et al., 1971).

About 75% of the total F of blood is in the plasma (Carlson et al., 1960). Plasma F exists in both ionic and bound forms, with the proportion of each varying with total plasma levels and species (Underwood, 1977). In a long-term study of dairy cows continuously or periodically exposed to high F intakes, plasma F concentrations were related to the current level of ingestion, and 0.2 mg kg^{-1} F could be regarded as a critical plasma concentration in cattle because dental lesions appeared if plasma F was above this level (Underwood, 1977). Plasma F concentrations are thought to be maintained within narrow limits by regulatory mechanisms that involve, principally, the skeletal and renal tissues (NRC, 1974). However, Burnell et al. (1986) found that serum F concentrations in swine increased linearly with increasing dietary F levels from 7 to 632 mg kg^{-1}. In addition, a marked diurnal variation and a considerable effect of the method of F administration on plasma F levels of sheep have been reported (Simon & Suttie, 1968a, b).

B. Absorption, Storage, and Excretion

Fluorine is presumed to be readily absorbed by a passive process (NRC, 1974). Sites of absorption include the stomach in nonruminants and the rumen in ruminants (NRC, 1980). The speed and extent of F absorption varies with the physical and chemical form of the compound. Soluble fluorides, such as NaF administered in solution, are rapidly absorbed (79%) (Harkins et al., 1963). When CaF$_2$ in solid form was administered, about 60 to 70% of the F was absorbed. Fluorine absorption from dietary bone meal ranged from 37 to 54%; 50% of the F in rock phosphate was absorbed (NRC, 1980). For lambs, the relative availability of F in P sources, compared with NaF as measured by bone F uptake, was: CaHPO$_4$, 50%; defluorinated phosphate, 20%; and rock phosphate, 65% (Clay & Suttie, 1985).

Several dietary factors can influence the absorption of F. Among these, Ca is well known to reduce F deposition in bones and other tissues (Forsyth et al., 1972a, b; Chan et al., 1973), probably by decreasing F absorption and retention (Krishnamachari, 1987). Increased dietary Mg levels from 200 to

1000 mg kg^{-1} resulted in about a 10% reduction of F absorption in rats regardless of differences in dietary F levels (Cerklewski & Ridlington, 1988). Other elements or compounds, such as P, Al, or S also affect F absorption in a manner similar to Ca (NRC, 1980). Dietary fat seems to enhance F absorption (McGown & Suttie, 1974).

Absorbed F is distributed rapidly throughout the body, particularly in the hard tissues. The removal rate of intravenously injected F from the blood of ruminants is about 30 to 40% min^{-1} (Kirshnamachari, 1987). A positive correlation between urinary F excretion and intake of F has been demonstrated in several species. The urinary F concentration of sheep and cattle, not exposed to excess F, rarely exceeds 10 μg mL^{-1}, and usually is closer to 5 μg mL^{-1} (Krishnamachari, 1987). Urinary F excretion occurs by glomerular filtration, with variable amounts of tubular reabsorption (NRC, 1974). Urinary F may be derived from the release of the element from previously deposited skeleton, as well as from the current food and water supply. Thus, a high urinary F level does not necessarily reflect current high ingestion of the element.

Urinary excretion of F also has been shown to be affected by the method of F administration (Simon & Suttie, 1968a). Two groups of sheep were given 2 mg F kg^{-1} body weight, either as a single oral dose or as a continuous intrarumenal infusion for a 13-wk period, and a balance study was conducted during Days 38 to 42 of the experiment. Apparently, there was a higher amount of F absorbed by the infused group than by the orally dosed group (72.3 vs. 67.7%). However, F retention was statistically the same for the two groups because the ruminally infused animals had an increase in urinary F and a decrease in fecal F excretion compared with the orally dosed animals. Moreover the infused group excreted F constantly in the urine (50 mg kg^{-1}), while the orally administered group excreted urine containing about 49 mg kg^{-1} F during the day and only 14 mg kg^{-1} during the night.

Fluorine does not readily pass the mammary barrier. Thus, dietary F intake has a minimal effect on milk F concentration. Milk from cows that were fed 10, 19, 55, and 109 mg kg^{-1} of F from 3 mo. of age to 7.5 yr averaged 0.06, 0.10, 0.14, and 0.20 mg kg^{-1} of F, respectively (Greenwood et al., 1964).

C. Essential Functions in Metabolism

The essentiality of F for animals and humans is still questionable because it has been possible for most investigators, until recently, to prepare nutritionally adequate diets that are either wholly devoid of F or sufficiently low to demonstrate that it is or is not required (NRC, 1974).

Currently, both positive and negative reports for the essentiality of F are available, but none of them seems unequivocal. The evidence supporting F as an essential element includes: (i) F is a constituent of bone and teeth, and trace amounts have been shown to be beneficial to development of caries-resistant teeth, and may also be beneficial in preventing excessive demineralization of bone in aged individuals (NRC, 1980); (ii) F was reported to stimulate the growth of rats fed on a specially purified diet (containing <0.04 mg kg^{-1} F) and/or housed in a plastic isolator or environment designed to eliminate atmospheric contamination (Schwarz & Milne, 1972; Milne & Schwarz, 1974); and (iii) female mice fed a diet containing 0.1 to 0.2 mg kg^{-1} F developed a progressive infertility in two successive generations, and a severe anemia during pregnancy and in the offspring before weaning (Messer et al., 1974). Unfortunately, these results have not been confirmed in other studies. Maurer and Day (1957) and Doberenz et al. (1964) failed to observe an effect of added F on growth of rats fed a basic diet even lower in F than that of Schwarz's study. Furthermore, two groups of workers reported no effect of F on fertility or growth in mice fed a low F diet through six generations (Weber & Reid, 1974) or three generations (Tao & Suttie, 1976). The latter workers suggested that the apparent essentiality observed by Messer et al. (1974) could be due to a pharmacological effect of F in improving Fe utilization in a marginally Fe-sufficient basal diet. In summary, the essentiality of F remains open to question.

D. Deficiency and Excess

Fluorine deficiency, if it exists, has never been documented unequivocally, since the essentiality of the element has not been established with certainty. However, excess F intake is a potential practical problem for many species.

Animals may ingest excessive amounts of F from contaminated surface water, deep well percolating through fluorapatite, forages contaminated by F-bearing dusts, fumes, or water, animal by-products containing bone high in F, and a variety of inorganic P supplements. Primarily, excess F intake affects teeth and bone (NRC, 1974, 1980). The severity of such effects depends on amount of intake, length of exposure, age at exposure, solubility of the source, general nutritional status, and other dietary components (NRC, 1988a). Developing teeth and bone are particularly sensitive, and excessive exposure in early life is especially damaging (Shupe, 1980). The teeth changes that may occur include mottling, staining, excessive wear, erosion, or pitting of enamel, depending on the degree of fluorosis. Bone lesions are manifest as exostoses, with enlarged rough, porous areas, and a chalky white surface. Consequently, the effects on bones and teeth can result in leg stiffness, lameness, reduced feed and water intake, a decline in general health, and lower weight gain and milk production (NRC, 1980; Crissman et al., 1980).

The maximum tolerable dietary F level (from NaF) for both young and mature dairy cattle has been set at 40 mg kg^{-1} (NRC, 1980). Finishing cattle can tolerate 100 mg kg^{-1} of F in the diet because of the shorter feeding period (NRC, 1988a). There is limited information on the maximum tolerable levels of other species. However, it is known that lifetime exposure to F of sheep, swine, and poultry is less than for cattle, and poultry are relatively less sensitive to F (NRC, 1980). The maximum tolerable F levels of breeding sheep and finishing sheep have been set at 60 and 150 mg kg^{-1}, respectively. Maximum tolerable F levels are 150 to 200 mg kg $^{-1}$ for turkey and chickens, respectively. The maximum tolerable F level for swine has been set at 150 mg kg $^{-1}$ (NRC, 1980). However, recent work by Burnell et al. (1986) showed that growing-finishing pigs were able to tolerate approximately 132 mg kg $^{-1}$ F (from NaF) for growth, but F levels up to 7 mg kg $^{-1}$ (from NaF) affected bone integrity. In all species, a proportional reduction should be made in the suggested maximum tolerable dietary F level if the water ingested by the animals contains elevated levels of F.

E. Interactions with Other Nutrients

Several dietary components have been shown to alleviate F toxicosis by reducing F deposition in bone and teeth. These components include Ca salts, NaCl, Mg salts, Al salts, and P (NRC, 1980). The effectiveness of these compounds may be dependent on their simultaneous ingestion with F (NRC, 1980). Intakes of total digestible nutrients (TDN) that were 60% of recommended allowances resulted in greater incisor damage over 4.5-yr in Holstein heifers from amounts of F less than or equal to those consumed by heifers fed the recommended TDN allowances (Suttie & Faltin, 1973). Dietary fat has been shown to enhance F toxicity, presumably by delaying gastric emptying and, hence, increasing F absorption (McGown & Suttie, 1974). Recently, Nielsen (1985) reported an interaction between F and B in rats.

F. Requirements, Feed Sources, and Availability

There is no need to discuss the requirements of F by animals fed practical diets because only fluorosis, not F deficiency, occurs. The most common source of F in animal diets is phosphates, especially the undefluorinated fertilizer-grade phosphates that contain 2 to 5% F. When feed-grade phosphates are processed sufficiently to qualify as defluorinated, they should contain <1 part of F to 100 parts of P (AAFCO, 1986). Most plants, except for tea (*Camellia sinensis*) and camellia (*Camellia japonica*), have a limited capacity to absorb F from the soil, and uncontaminated forages and grains generally contain from 0.5 to about 6 mg kg $^{-1}$ F (Ammerman & Henry, 1983). Animal by-products containing bone may contribute significant amounts of F to animals. Bone ash normally contains <1500 mg kg $^{-1}$ F. This level could be increased to 10 000 mg kg $^{-1}$ if the animals continuously ingest large amounts of F (NRC, 1980). Water is another important source of F. Uncontaminated surface water generally contains less F than water derived from springs or wells. Much of the northeastern USA water is supplied with natural F concentrations that range from 0.02 to 0.1 mg kg $^{-1}$. Further west and south, concentrations tend to be higher, but seldom >1 mg kg $^{-1}$. In endemic fluorosis areas, deep water may percolate through fluorapatite and frequently contains 3 to 5 mg kg $^{-1}$ F, sometimes 10 to 15 mg kg $^{-1}$, and even as much as 40 mg kg $^{-1}$ (NRC, 1980; Underwood, 1981).

XI. PROSPECTUS

While much progress has been made in the role of trace elements in animal nutrition since the first edition of *Micronutrients in Agriculture* (Scott, 1972), much remains to be learned in this important area of science. Further research with trace elements in the nutrition of animals that produce food for the diet of humans needs to be directed toward achieving the following objectives:

1. to define dietary requirements of trace elements by food producing animals to realize maximum conversion of feed to lean tissue;
2. to elucidate factors influencing enzyme systems in which trace elements are a vital component;
3. to determine if trace elements such as Cr, Ni, Sn, Si, V, and B are required by food-producing animals and, if so, determine the dietary requirements; and
4. to determine the role that the trace elements have in immunocompetence of animals.

REFERENCES

Abumrad, N.N., A.J. Schneider, D. Steel, and L.S. Rogers. 1981. Amino acid intolerance during prolonged total parenteral nutrition reversed by molybdate therapy. Am. J. Clin. Nutr. 34:2551–2559.

Agricultural Research Council (ARC). 1981. The nutrient requirements of pigs. Commonwealth Agric. Bureaux, Slough, England.

Allen, J.D., and J.M. Gawthorne. 1985. Changes in copper metabolism following intravenous administration of organic and inorganic molybdenum-sulphur compounds. p. 361–363. *In* C.F. Mills et al. (ed.) Trace elements in man and animals—TEMA 5. Commonwealth Agric. Bureaux, Farnham Royal, England.

Allen, J.D., and J.M. Gawthorne. 1988. Interactions between proteins, thiomolybdates and copper. p. 325–316. *In* L.S. Hurley et al. (ed.) Trace elements in man and animals—TEMA 6. Plenum Press, New York.

Alloway, B.J. 1973. Copper and molybdenum in swayback pastures. J. Agric. Sci. (Cambridge) 80:521–524.

Ammerman, C.B., J.R. Black, P.R. Henry, and R.D. Miles. 1988. Tissue uptake of manganese as a measure of its bioavailability for chicks. p. 515–516. *In* L.S. Hurley et al. (ed.) Trace elements in man and animals—TEMA 6. Plenum Press, New York.

Ammerman, C.B., and P.R. Henry. 1983. Effects of fluorides on animals: Dietary and mineral supplement considerations. p. 281–290. *In* J.L. Shupe et al. (ed.) Fluorides: Effects on vegetation, animals and humans. Paragon Press, Salt Lake City, Utah.

Ammerman, C.B., and S.M. Miller. 1972. Biological availability of minor mineral ions: A review. J. Anim. Sci. 35:681–694.

Ammerman, C.B., and S.M. Miller. 1975. Selenium in ruminant nutrition: A review. J. Dairy Sci. 58:1561–1577.

Ammerman, C.B., J.M. Wing, D.C. Dunavant, W.K. Robertson, J.P. Feaster, and L.R. Arrington. 1967. Utilization of inorganic iron by ruminants as influenced by form of iron and iron status of the animal. J. Anim. Sci. 26:404–409.

Anke, M., B. Groppel, U. Krause, L. Angelow, W. Arnhold, T. Masaoka, S. Barhoum, and G. Zervas. 1988a. Normal manganese, zinc, copper, iron, iodine, molybdenum, nickel, arsenic, lithium and cadmium supply dependent on the geological origin of the site and its effects on the status of these elements in wild and domestic ruminants. p. 663–665. *In* L.S. Hurley et al. (ed.) Trace elements in man and animals—TEMA 6. Plenum Press, New York.

Anke, M., B. Groppel, and M. Grun. 1985. Essentiality, toxicity, requirement and supply of molybdenum in humans and animals. p. 154–157. *In* C.F. Mills et al. (ed.) Trace elements in man and animals—TEMA 5. Commonwealth Agric. Bureaux, Farnham Royal, England.

Anke, M., M. Grun, M. Partschefeld, and B. Groppel. 1978. Molybdenum deficiency in ruminants. p. 230–233. *In* M. Kirchgessner (ed.) Trace element metabolism in man and animals—TEMA 3. Institut fur Ernahrungsphysiologie, Technische Universitat, Munchen, Freising, Weihenstephan, Federal Republic of Germany

Anke, M., T. Masaoka, A. Henig, and W. Arnold. 1988b. Antagonistic effect of a high sulphur, molybdenum and cadmium content of diets on copper metabolism and deficiency symptoms in cattle and pigs. p. 317–318. *In* L.S. Hurley et al. (ed.) Trace elements in man and animals—TEMA 6. Plenum Press, New York.

Archibald, J.G. 1951. Molybdenum in cow's milk. J. Dairy Sci. 34:1026–1029.

Association of American Feed Control Officials (AAFCO). 1986. Official publication of AAFCO. Assoc. Am. Feed Control Officials, Baton Rouge, LA.

Baker, D., L. James, K. Panter, H. Mayland, and J. Pfister. 1988. Toxicosis of developing pigs fed selenium from various sources. Clinical Pathology. p. 701–702. *In* L.S. Hurley et al. (ed.) Trace elements in man and animals—TEMA 6. Plenum Press, New York.

Baly, D.L. 1988. Effect of manganese deficiency on glucose transport and insulin binding in rat adipocytes. p. 49–50. *In* L.S. Hurley et al. (ed.) Trace elements in man and animals—TEMA 6. Plenum Press, New York.

Baly, D.L., C.L. Keen, and L.S. Hurley. 1986. Effects of manganese deficiency on pyruvate carboxylase and phosphenol pyruvate carboxykinase activity and carbohydrate homeostasis in adult rats. Biol. Trace Elem. Res. 11:201–212.

Barua, J., R.G. Gragle, and J.K. Miller. 1964. Sites of gastrointestinal blood passage of iodide and thyroxine in young cattle. J. Dairy Sci. 47:539–541.

Bell, M.D., G.D. Diggs, R.S. Lowrey, and P.L. Wright. 1964. Comparison of ^{99}Mo metabolism in swine and cattle as affected by stable molybdate. J. Nutr. 84:367–372.

Bell, J.G., C.K. Keen, and B. Lonnerdal. 1989. Higher retention of manganese in suckling than in adult rats is not due to maturational differences in manganese uptake by rat small intestine. J. Toxicol. Environ. Health 26:387–398.

Bernier, J.F., F.J. Fillion, and G.B. Brisson. 1984. Dietary fibers and supplementary iron in a milk replacer for veal calves. J. Dairy Sci. 67:2369–2379.

Berzin, N.J., and V.K. Bauman. 1987. Vitamin A-dependent zinc-binding protein and intestinal absorption of zinc in chicks. Br. J. Nutr. 57:255–268.

Bezkorovaing, A. 1980. Biochemistry of nonheme iron. Plenum Press, New York.

Bingley, J.B., and J.H. Dufty. 1972. Distribution of copper in the tissues of the bovine neonate and dam. Res. Vet. Sci. 13:8–14.

Black, J.R., C.B. Ammerman, P.R. Henry, and R.D. Miles. 1984. Tissue manganese uptake as a measure of manganese availability. Nutr. Rep. Int. 39:807–814.

Blaxter, K.L., G.A.M. Sharman, and A.M. MacDonald. 1957. Iron-deficiency anemia in calves. Br. J. Nutr. 11:234–246.

Bopp, B.A., R.C. Sonders, and J.W. Kesterson. 1982. Metabolic fate of selected selenium compounds in laboratory animals and man. Drug Metab. Rev. 13:271–318.

Borg, D.C., and G.C. Cotzias. 1958. Incorporation of manganese into erythrocytes as evidence for a manganese porphyrin in man. Nature (London). 182:1677–1678.

Boyd, E.M., and S.N. Shanas. 1963. The acute oral toxicity of reduced iron. Can. Med. Assoc. J. 89:171–175.

Brady, P.S., P.K. Ku, D.E. Ullrey, and E.R. Miller. 1978. Evaluation of an amino acid-iron chelate hematinic for the baby pig. J. Anim. Sci. 47:1135–1140.

Brandt, M., C.L. Keen, D.E. Ash, and U.L. Schramm. 1988. Transport, subcellular distribution and export of Mn(II) in rat liver and hepatocytes. p. 125–128. *In* L.S. Hurley et al. (ed.) Trace elements in man and animals—TEMA 6. Plenum Press, New York.

Bremner, I. 1988. Mechanisms and nutritional importance of trace element interactions. p. 303–307. *In* L.S. Hurley et al. (ed.) Trace elements in man and animals—TEMA 6. Plenum Press, New York.

Bremner, I., and A.C. Dalgarno. 1973. Iron metabolism in the veal calf. 2. Iron requirements and the effect of copper supplementation. Br. J. Nutr. 30:61–76.

Bremner, I., and N.T. Davis. 1975. The induction of metallothionein in rat liver by injection and restriction of food intake. Biochem. J. 149:733–738.

Bremner, I., W.R. Humphries, M. Phillippo, M.J. Walker, and P.C. Morrice. 1987. Iron-induced copper deficiency in calves: dose-response relationships and interactions with molybdenum and sulphur. Anim. Prod. 45:403-414.

Brewer, G.L., J.C. Aster, C.A. Knutsen, and W.C. Kruckeberg. 1979. Zinc inhibition of calmodulin: A proposed molecular mechanism of zinc action on cellular functions. Am. J. Hematol. 7:53-60.

Britton, A.A., and G.C. Cotzias. 1966. Dependence of manganese turnover on intake. Am. J. Physiol. 211:203-206.

Bronner, F., and J.H. Yost. 1985. Saturable and nonsaturable copper and calcium transport in mouse duodenum. Am. J. Physiol. 249:G108-G112.

Brown, D.G., R.F. Burk, R.J. Seely, and K.W. Kiker. 1972. Effect of dietary selenium on the gastrointestinal absorption of $^{75}SeO_3^{2-}$ in the rat. Int. J. Vitam. Nutr. Res. 42:588-591.

Bullen, J.J., H.J. Rogers, and E. Griffiths. 1972. Iron binding proteins and infection. Br. J. Haematol. 23:389-392.

Burk, R.F. 1983. Biological activity of selenium. Ann. Rev. Nutr. 3:53-70.

Burk, R.F., R.J. Seely, and K.W. Kiker. 1973. Selenium: Dietary threshold for urinary excretion in the rat. Proc. Soc. Exp. Biol. Med. 142:214-216.

Burnell, T.W., E.R. Peo, Jr., A.J. Lewis, and J.D. Crenshaw. 1986. Effect of dietary fluorine on growth, blood and bone characteristics of growing-finishing pigs. J. Anim. Sci. 63:2053-2063.

Burns, RH., A. Johnston, J.W. Hamilton, R.J. McColloch, W.E. Duncan, and H.G. Fisk. 1964. Minerals in domestic wools. J. Anim. Sci. 23:5-11.

Butler, G.W., and P.F. Peterson. 1961. Aspects of the faecal excretion of selenium by sheep. N.Z. J. Agric. Res. 4:484-491.

Cabell, C.A., and I.P. Earle. 1965. Additive effect of calcium and phosphorus on utilization of dietary zinc. J. Anim. Sci. 24:800-804.

Calvo, J.J., and J.R. Allue. 1986. Plasma ferritin and other parameters related to iron metabolism in piglets. Comp. Biochem. Physiol. A 85:471-476.

Cantor, A.M., M.L. Langevin, T. Noguchi, and M.L. Scott. 1975. Efficacy of selenium in selenium compounds and feedstuffs for prevention of pancreatic fibrosis in chicks. J. Nutr. 105:106-111.

Caperna, T.J., R.G. Campbell, and N.C. Steele. 1989. Interrelationship of exogenous porcine growth hormone administration and feed intake level affecting various tissue levels of iron, copper, zinc and bone calcium of growing pigs. J. Anim. Sci. 67:654-663.

Caple, I.U., J.K. Azuolas, and G.F. Nugent. 1985. Assessment of iodine status and thyroid function of sheep and goats kept under pastoral conditions. p. 609-613. In C.F. Mills et al. (ed.) Trace elements in man and animals—TEMA 5. Commonwealth Agric. Bureaux, Farnham Royal, England.

Carlson, C.H., W.D. Armstrong, and L. Singer. 1960. Distribution, migration and binding of whole blood fluoride evaluated with radiofluoride. Am. J. Physiol. 199:187-189.

Carter, J.C., W.J. Miller, M.W. Neathery, R.P. Gentry, P.E. Stake, and D.M. Blackman. 1974. Manganese metabolism with oral and intravenous ^{54}Mn in young calves as influenced by supplemental manganese. J. Anim. Sci. 38:1284-1290.

Cerklewski, F.L., and J.W. Ridlington. 1988. Enhanced maternal transfer of fluoride in the magnesium-deficient rat. p. 273-274. In L.S. Hurley et al. (ed.) Trace elements in man and animals—TEMA 6. Plenum Press, New York.

Chan, M.M., R.B. Rucker, F. Zerman, and R.S. Riggins. 1973. Effect of fluoride on bone formation and strength in Japanese quail. J. Nutr. 103:1431-1440.

Chang, I.C., T.P. Lee, and G. Matrone. 1975. Development of ceruloplasmin in pigs during the neonatal period. J. Nutr. 105:624-630.

Chapman, H.C., and M.C. Bell. 1963. Relative absorption and excretion by beef cattle of copper from various sources. J. Anim. Sci. 22:82-85.

Chavez, E.R., and J. Kalinowski. 1988. Metabolic adaptation of gilts on trace-minerals in response to pregnancy and low dietary zinc. p. 695-696. In L.S. Hurley et al. (ed.) Trace elements in man and animals—TEMA 6. Plenum Press, New York.

Chen, J.J., M.T. Yang, and S.P. Yang. 1988. Interrelationships between molybdenum and copper in female rats. p. 321-322. In L.S. Hurley et al. (ed.) Trace elements in man and animals—TEMA 6. Plenum Press, New York.

Chesters, J.K., and M. Will. 1981. Zinc transport proteins in plasma. Br. J. Nutr. 46:111-118.

Chilean Iodine Educational Bureau. 1952. Iodine content of foods. p. 183. Chilean Iodine Educational Bureau, London.

Chio, L.F., K. Bunden, P. Vohra, and F.H. Kratzer. 1976. An abnormal requirement for iron in dystrophic chickens. Poult. Sci. 55:808-813.

Chung, A.S., W.G. Hoekstra, and R.H. Grummer. 1976. Supplemental cobalt or nickel for zinc-deficient GH pigs. J. Anim. Sci. 42:1352.

Church, D.C., and W.G. Pond. 1988. Basic animal nutrition and feeding. 3rd ed. John Wiley and Sons, New York.

Clay, A.B., and J.W. Suttie. 1985. The availability of fluoride from NaF and phosphorus supplements. Vet. Hum. Toxicol. 27:3-6.

Costa, N.D., P.T. Gleed, B.F. Sanson, H.W. Symonds, and W.M. Allen. 1985. Monensin and narasin increase selenium and zinc absorption in steers. p. 472-474. In C.F. Mills et al. (ed.) Trace elements in man and animals—TEMA 5. Commonwealth Agric. Bureaux, Farnham Royal, England.

Cousins, R.J. 1982. Mechanisms of zinc absorption. p. 117-128. In A.S. Prasad (ed.) Clinical, biochemical and nutritional aspects of trace elements. Alan R. Liss, Inc., New York.

Cousins, R.J. 1985. Absorption, transport, and hepatic metabolism of copper and zinc: special reference to metallothionein and ceruloplasmin. Physiol. Rev. 65:238-309.

Cousins, R.J., M.A. Dunn, T.L. Blalock, and A.S. Leinart. 1988. Coordinate regulation of zinc metabolism and metallothionein gene expression by cAMP, interleukin-1 and dietary copper and zinc. p. 281-285. In L.S. Hurley et al. (ed.) Trace elements in man and animals—TEMA 6. Plenum Press, New York.

Crissman, J.W., G.A. Maylin, and L. Krook. 1980. New York State and U.S. federal fluoride pollution standards do not protect cattle health. Cornell Vet. 70:183-192.

Danks, D.M., and F.B. Mercer. 1988. Metallothionein and ceruloplasmin genes. p. 287-291. In L.S. Hurley et al. (ed.) Trace elements in man and animals—TEMA 6. Plenum Press, New York.

Davis, G.K., and W. Mertz. 1987. Copper. p. 301-364. In W. Mertz (ed.) Trace elements in humans and animal nutrition. Vol. 1. 5th ed. Academic Press, New York.

Davis, N.T., and R.B. Williams. 1977. The effect of pregnancy and lactation on the absorption of zinc and lysine by the rat in situ. Br. J. Nutr. 38:417-423.

Debald, H.J., and C.A. Elvehjem. 1935. The effect of feeding high amounts of soluble iron and aluminum salts. Am. J. Physiol. 111:118-123.

Dick, A.T. 1956a. Molybdenum in animal nutrition. Soil Sci. 81:229-236.

Dick, A.T. 1956b. Molybdenum and copper relationships in animal nutrition. p. 445-473. In W.D. McElroy and B. Glass (ed.) A symposium on inorganic nitrogen metabolism: Function of metallo-flavoproteins. The John's Hopkins Press, Baltimore, Maryland.

Doberenz, A.R., A.A. Kurmick, E.B. Kurtz, A.R. Bemmerer, and B.L. Reid. 1964. Effect of a minimal fluoride diet on rats. Proc. Soc. Exp. Biol. Med. 117:689-693.

Doisey, E.R., Jr. 1973. Micronutrient controls on biosynthesis of clotting proteins and cholesterol. p. 193. In D.D. Hemphill (ed.) Trace substances in environmental health. Vol. 6. Univ. of Missouri, Columbia, MO.

Downer, J.U., R.W. Hemken, J.D. Fox, and L.S. Bull. 1981. Effect of dietary iodine on tissue iodine content in the bovine. J. Anim. Sci. 52:413-417.

Dreosti, I.E., and E.J. Partick. 1988. Trace elements, free radicals, and lipoperoxidation in rats. p. 253-254. In L.S. Hurley et al. (ed.) Trace elements in man and animals. Vol. 6. Plenum Press, New York.

Driver, P.M., C. Eames, and S.B. Telfer. 1988. The effects of differing compositions of soluble phosphate glass boluses on the copper, cobalt and selenium status of swaledale ewes. p. 637-638. In L.S. Hurley et al. (ed.) Trace elements in man and animals—TEMA 6. Plenum Press, New York.

Eggert, R.G., E. Patterson, W.T. Akers, and E.L.R. Stokstad. 1957. The role of vitamin E and selenium in the nutrition of the pig. J. Anim. Sci. 16:1307.

Ellis, W.C., W.H. Pfander, M.E. Muhrer, and E.E. Pickett. 1958. Molybdenum as a dietary essential for lambs. J. Anim. Sci. 17:180-188.

Elmes, M., S. Haywood, J.P. Clarkson, I.C. Fuentealba, and B. Jasami. 1988. Copper tolerance in rats—a histochemical and immunocytochemical study. p. 699-700. In L.S. Hurley et al. (ed.) Trace elements in man and animals—TEMA 6. Plenum Press, New York.

El-Hawary, M.F.S., F.A. El-Shobaki, T. Kholeif, R. Sahr, and M. El-Bassoussy. 1975. The absorption of iron, with or without supplements of single amino acids and of ascorbic acid, in healthy and Fe-deficient children. Br. J. Nutr. 33:351-355.

Ely, R.E., K.M. Dunn, C.F. Huffman, C.L. Comar, and G.K. Davis. 1953. The effect of methionine on the tissue distribution of radioactive cobalt injected intravenously into dairy calves. J. Anim. Sci. 12:394-401.

Erskin, R.J., R.S. Eberhart, L.J. Hutchinson, and R.W. Scholz. 1987. Blood selenium concentrations and glutathione peroxidase activities in dairy herds with high and low somatic cell counts. J. Am. Vet. Med. Assoc. 190:1417-1421.

Evans, G.W. 1971. Function and nomenclature for two mammalian copper proteins. Nutr. Rev. 29:195-197.

Fairweather-Tait, S.J., and S. Southon. 1988. Iron-zinc interactions in relation to infant weaning foods. p. 567-569. In L.S. Hurley et al. (ed.) Trace elements in man and animals—TEMA 6. Plenum Press, New York.

Feldman, S.L., and RJ. Cousins. 1976. Degradation of hepatic zinc-thionein after parenteral zinc administrations. Biochem. J. 160:583-588.

Fell, B.F., J.E. Hesketh, A.K. Lough, W.R.H. Duncan, and W.S. Mackie. 1985. Observations of the central nervous system of sheep deficient in cobalt (Vitamin B_{12}). p. 263-267. In C.F. Mills et al. (ed.) Trace elements in man and animals—TEMA 5. Commonwealth Agric. Bureaux, Farnham Royal, England.

Flohe, L., W.A. Gunzler, and H.H. Schock. 1973. Glutathione peroxidase: A selenoenzyme. FEBS Lett. 32:132-134.

Forsyth, D.M., W.G. Pond, and L. Krook. 1972a. Dietary calcium and fluoride interactions in swine: In utero and neonatal effects. J. Nutr. 102:1639-1646.

Forsyth, D.M., W.G. Pond, R.H. Wasserman, and L. Krook. 1972b. Dietary calcium and fluoride interactions in swine: Effects of physical and chemical bone characteristics, calcium binding protein and histology of adults. J. Nutr. 102:1623-1638.

Frieden, E. 1971. Ceruloplasmin, a link between copper and iron metabolism. Adv. Chem. Ser. 100:292-331.

Frieden, E. 1978. Model of metal metabolism in mammals. p. 8-14. In M. Kirchgessner (ed.) Trace element metabolism in man and animals—TEMA 3. Institut fur Ernahrungsphysiologie, Technische Universitat, Munchen, Freising, Weihenstephan, Federal Republic of Germany.

Frieden, E., and H.S. Hsieh. 1976. Ceruloplasmin: the copper transport protein with essential oxidase activity. p. 187. In A. Meister (ed.) Advances in enzymology and related areas of molecular biology. Vol. 44. Wiley, New York.

Frolich, W. 1986. Bioavailability of minerals from cereals. p. 173. In G.A. Spiller (ed.) Handbook of dietary fiber in human nutrition. CRC Press, Boca Raton, FL.

Fuentealba, I.C., and S. Haywood. 1988. Subcellular changes and metal metabolism in the livers of copper loaded rats. p. 179-180. In L.S. Hurley et al. (ed.) Trace elements in man and animals—TEMA 6. Plenum Press, New York.

Fungwe, T.U., F. Buddingh, M.T. Yang, and S.P. Yang. 1988. Effects of molybdenum on reproduction and molybdenum/copper enzyme activity in the female rat. p. 619-620. In L.S. Hurley et al. (ed.) Trace elements in man and animals—TEMA 6. Plenum Press, New York.

Furugouri, K. 1971. Normal values and physiological variation of plasma iron and total iron binding capacity in pigs. J. Anim. Sci. 32:667-672.

Furugouri, K. 1972. Effect of elevated dietary levels of iron on iron stores in liver, some blood constituents and phosphorus deficiency in young swine. J. Anim. Sci. 34:573-577.

Furugouri, K. 1978. Effect of nutrient deficiency in animals: Iron. p. 265-294. In M. Recheigl, Jr. (ed.) CRC Handbook series in nutrition and food. Section E: Nutritional disorders. Vol. II. CRC Press, Boca Raton, FL.

Furugouri, K. 1981. Iron absorption and its application to piglet anemia. Pig News Inform. 2:279-285.

Furugouri, K., and A. Kawabata. 1976. Iron absorption by neonatal pig intestine in vivo. J. Anim. Sci. 42:1460-1464.

Furugouri, K., Y. Migata, K. Shijimaya, and N. Naraski. 1983. Developmental changes in serum ferritin of piglets. J. Anim. Sci. 57:960-965.

Garcia, F., J. Sanchez, and J. Planas. 1986. The influence of laying on iron metabolism in quail. Br. Poult. Sci. 27:585-592.

Garcia, F., J. Sanchez, and J. Planas. 1987. Iron metabolism in iron deficient male quail. Comp. Biochem. Physiol. 87A:947-950.

Garcia-Aranda, J.A., R.A. Wapnir, and F. Lifshitz. 1983. In vivo intestinal absorption of manganese in the rat. J. Nutr. 113:2601-2607.

Gardner, A.W., and P.K. Hall-Patch. 1962. An outbreak of industrial molybdenosis. Vet. Rec. 74:113–115.

Gershwin, M.E., C.L. Keen, M.P. Fletcher, and L.S. Hurley. 1988. Trace element deficiencies and immune responsiveness. p. 85–90. *In* L.S. Hurley et al. (ed.) Trace elements in man and animals—TEMA 6. Plenum Press, New York.

Geurink, J.H., A. Malestein, A. Kemp, A. Korzeniowski, and A.T. Vant Klooster. 1982. Nitrate poisoning in cattle. 7. Prevention. Neth. J. Agric. Sci. 30:105–113.

Gipp, W.F., W.G. Pond, F.A. Kallfelz, J.B. Basker, D.R. van Campen, L. Krook, and W.J. Visek. 1974. Effect of dietary copper, iron and ascorbic acid levels on hematology, blood and tissue copper, iron and zinc concentration, and ^{64}Cu and ^{59}Fe metabolism in young pigs. J. Nutr. 104:532–541.

Gipp, W.F., W.G. Pond, J. Tasker, D.R. van Campen, L. Krook, and W.J. Visek. 1973. Influence of level of dietary copper on weight gain, hematology and liver copper and iron storage of young pigs. J. Nutr. 103:713–719.

Gooneratne, R., and D. Christensen. 1985. Gestation age and maternal-fetal liver copper levels in the bovine. p. 334–336. *In* C.F. Mills et al. (ed.) Trace elements in man and animals—TEMA 5. Commonwealth Agric. Bureaux, Farnham Royal, England.

Gooneratne, S.R., D.A. Christensen, J.V. Bailey, and H.W. Symonds. 1988. Influence of breed and dietary Cu, Mo and S levels in biliary Cu excretion in cattle. p. 313–314. *In* L.S. Hurley et al. (ed.) Trace elements in man and animals—TEMA 6. Plenum Press, New York.

Gordon, D.T., and M. Ellersieck. 1988. The interactions among Fe, Zn and Cu affecting liver Cu and femur Zn concentrations in the rat. p. 181–182. *In* L.S. Hurley et al. (ed.) Trace elements in man and animals—TEMA 6. Plenum Press, New York.

Grace, N.D. 1975. Studies on the flow of zinc, cobalt, copper and manganese along the digestive tract of sheep given fresh perennial rye grass, or white or red clover. Br. J. Nutr. 34:73–82.

Grace, N.D. 1983. Amounts of distribution of mineral elements associated with fleece-free empty body weight gains in grazing sheep. N.Z. J. Agric. Res. 26:59–70.

Grace, N.D., J. Lee, and P.L. Martinson. 1988. Accumulation of Cu and Mo by the foetus and conceptus of single and twin bearing ewes. p. 311–312. *In* L.S. Hurley et al. (ed.) Trace elements in man and animals—TEMA 6. Plenum Press, New York.

Grace, N.D., and P.L. Martinson. 1985. The distribution of Mo between the liver and other organs and tissues of sheep grazing a ryegrass white clover pasture. p. 534–536. *In* C.F. Mills et al. (ed.) Trace elements in man and animals—TEMA 5. Commonwealth Agric. Bureaux, Farnham Royal, England.

Grace, N.D., and J.H. Watkinson. 1985. The distribution and the amounts of Se associated with various tissue and liveweight gains of grazing sheep. p. 490–493. *In* C.F. Mills et al. (ed.) Trace elements in man and animals—TEMA 5. Commonwealth Agric. Bureaux, Farnham Royal, England.

Greene, L.W., D.K. Lunt, F.M. Byers, N.K. Shirase, C.E. Richmond, R.E. Knutson, and G.T. Schelling. 1988. Performance and carcass quality of steers supplemented with zinc oxide or zinc methionine. J. Anim. Sci. 66:1818–1823.

Greenwood, D.A., J.L. Shupe, G.E. Stoddard, L.E. Harris, H.M. Nielsen, and L.E. Olson. 1964. Fluorosis in cattle. p. 36. *In* Utah State Univ. Agric. Exp. Stn. Spec. Rep. 17. Logan, UT.

Greger, J.L., M.L. Storey, J.L. Stahl, M.E. Cook, S.E. Gentry-Roberts, and J.C. Lynds. 1988. Zinc, iron and copper interactions in humans, rats and chicks. p. 231–232. *In* L.S. Hurley et al. (ed.) Trace elements in man and animals—TEMA 6. Plenum Press, New York.

Groce, A.W., E.R. Miller, J.P. Hitchcock, D.E. Ullrey, and W.T. Magee. 1973a. Selenium balance in the pig as affected by selenium source and vitamin E. J. Anim. Sci. 37:942–947.

Groce, A.W., E.R. Miller, D.E. Ullrey, P.K. Ku, K.K. Keahey, and D.J. Ellis. 1973b. Selenium requirements in corn-soy diets for growing-finishing swine. J. Anim. Sci. 37:948–956.

Groppel, B., M. Anke, and A. Hennig. 1988. Possibilities of diagnosing iodine deficiency in ruminants. p. 661–662. *In* L.S. Hurley et al. (ed.) Trace elements in man and animals—TEMA 6. Plenum Press, New York.

Groppel, B., M. Anke, and H. Kronemann. 1985. Influence of iodine supply on reproduction and iodine content of milk, blood, hair and several other organs of ruminants. p. 279–282. *In* C.F. Mills et al. (ed.) Trace elements in man and animals—TEMA 5. Commonwealth Agric. Bureaux, Farnham Royal, England.

Gross, J. 1962. Iodine and bromine. p. 221–285. *In* C.L. Comar and F. Bronner (ed.) Mineral metabolism. Vol. 2. Academic Press, New York.

Gruden, N. 1988a. The effect of parenteral iron administration upon manganese metabolism. p. 555–556. *In* L.S. Hurley et al. (ed.) Trace elements in man and animals—TEMA 6. Plenum Press, New York.

Gruden, N. 1988b. The effect of age and sex upon iron-manganese interaction in different segments of the rats intestine. p. 557–558. *In* L.S. Hurley et al. (ed.) Trace elements in man and animals—TEMA 6. Plenum Press, New York.

Hahn, C.J., and G.W. Evans. 1975. Absorption of trace metals in the zinc-deficient rat. Am. J. Physiol. 228:1020–1023.

Hakkarainen, J., P. Lindberg, G. Bengtsson, L.J. Jonsson, and N. Lannek. 1978. Requirement for selenium (as selenite) and vitamin E (as alpha-tocopherol) in weaned pigs. III. The effect on the development of VESD syndrome of varying selenium levels with a low-tocopherol diet. J. Anim. Sci. 46:1001–1008.

Halpin, C.G., D.J. Harris, and F.W. Caple. 1984. Contribution of cobalamin analogues to plasma vitamin B_{12} concentrations in cattle. Res. Vet. Sci. 37:249–251.

Hambidge, K.M., C.W. Casey, and N.F. Krebs. 1987. Zinc. p. 1–137. *In* W. Mertz (ed.) Trace elements in human and animal nutrition. Vol. 2, 5th ed. Academic Press, New York.

Hamilton, D.L., J.E.C. Bellamy, J.D. Valberg, and L.S. Balbert. 1978. Zinc, cadmium and iron interaction during intestinal absorption in iron-deficient mice. Can. J. Physiol. Pharmacol. 56:384–388.

Handreck, K.A., and K.D. Godwin. 1970. Distribution in sheep of selenium derived from ^{75}Se-labelled ruminal pellets. Aust. J. Agric. Res. 21:71–84.

Harkins, R.W., J.B. Longenecker, and H.P. Sarett. 1963. Effect of NaF on the growth of rats and varying vitamin and calcium intakes. J. Nutr. 81:81–86.

Harmon, B.G., D.E. Becker, and A.H. Jensen. 1967. Efficacy of ferric ammonium citrate in preventing anemia in young swine. J. Anim. Sci. 26:1051–1053.

Harrison, J.H., and H.R. Conrad. 1984a. Effect of selenium intake on selenium utilization by the nonlactating dairy cow. J. Dairy Sci. 67:219–223.

Harrison, J.H., and H.R. Conrad. 1984b. Effect of dietary calcium on selenium absorption by the nonlactating dairy cows. J. Dairy Sci. 67:1860–1864.

Hartman, R.H., G. Matrone, and G.H. Wise. 1955. Effects of high dietary manganese on hemoglobin formation. J. Nutr. 51:429–439.

Healy, W.G., G. Crowhley, R.L. Gillett, P.C. Rankin, and H.M. Watts. 1972. Ingested soil and iodine deficiency in lambs. N.Z. J. Agric. Res. 15:778–782.

Hemken, R.W. 1978. Factors that influence the iodine content of milk and meat: A review. J. Anim. Sci. 48:981–985.

Hemken, R.W., J.H. Vandersall, M.A. Oskarsson, and L.R. Fryman. 1972. Iodine intake related to milk iodine and performance of dairy cattle. J. Dairy Sci. 55:931–934.

Hemken, R.W., J.H. Vandersall, B.A. Sass, and J.W. Hibbs. 1971. Goitrogenic effects of a corn silage-soybean meal supplemented ration. J. Dairy Sci. 54:85–88.

Hetzel, B.S., and G.F. Maberly. 1987. Iodine. p. 139–208. *In* W. Mertz (ed.) Trace elements in human and animal nutrition. Vol. 2. 5th ed. Academic Press, New York.

Hidiroglou, M. 1975. Mn uptake by the ovaries and reproductive tract of cycling and anestrous ewes. Can. J. Physiol. Pharmacol. 53:969–972.

Hidiroglou, M., R.B. Carson, and G.A. Brossard. 1965. Influence of selenium on the selenium contents of hair and on the incidence of nutritional muscular disease in beef cattle. Can. J. Anim. Sci. 45:197–202.

Hidiroglou, M., G. Morris, and M. Ivan. 1982. Chemical composition of sheep bones as influenced by molybdenum supplementation. J. Dairy Sci. 65:619–624.

Hidiroglou, M., and D.T. Spurr. 1975. Influence of cold exposure and diet change on the trace element composition of hair from short horn cattle. Can. J. Anim. Sci. 55:231–238.

Higgins, E.S., D.A. Richert, and W.W. Westerfeld. 1956. Effect of reducing agents on copper deficiency and tungstate inhibition studies. J. Nutr. 59:539–559.

Hill, D.A., E.R. Peo, Jr., and A.J. Lewis. 1987. Effect of zinc source and picolinic acid on [65]Zn uptake in an in vitro continuous-flow perfusion system for pig and poultry intestinal segments. J. Nutr. 117:1704–1707.

Hill, G.M., P.K. Ku, E.R. Miller, D.E. Ullrey, T.A. Losty, and B.L. O'Dell. 1983a. A copper deficiency in neonatal pigs induced by a high zinc maternal diet. J. Nutr. 113:867–872.

Hill, G.M., and E.R. Miller. 1983. Effect of dietary zinc level on the growth and development of the gilt. J. Anim. Sci. 57:106–113.

Hill, G.M., E.R. Miller, and P.K. Ku. 1983b. Effect of dietary zinc levels on mineral concentration in milk. J. Anim. Sci. 57:123–129.

Hill, G.M., E.R. Miller, and H.D. Stowe. 1983c. Effect of dietary zinc levels on health and productivity of gilts and sows through two parities. J. Anim. Sci. 57:114–122.

Hill, G.M., E.R. Miller, P.A. Whetter, and D.E. Ullrey. 1983d. Concentration of minerals in tissues of pigs from dams fed different levels of dietary zinc. J. Anim. Sci. 57:130–138.

Hill, R. 1974. Changes in circulating copper, manganese and zinc with the onset of lay in the pullet. p. 632–634. *In* W.G. Hoekstra et al. (ed.) Trace element metabolism in animals—TEMA 2. University Park Press, Baltimore, MD.

Hitchcock, J.P., P.K. Ku, and E.R. Miller. 1974. Factors influencing iron utilization by the baby pig. p. 598–600. *In* W.G. Hoekstra et al. (ed.) Trace element metabolism in animals—TEMA 2. University Park Press, Baltimore, MD.

Ho, S.Y., W.J. Miller, R.P. Gentry, N.W. Neathery, and D.M. Blackman. 1984. Effects of high but nontoxic dietary manganese and iron on their metabolism by calves. J. Dairy Sci. 67:1489–1495.

Hoekstra, W.G. 1970. The complexity of dietary factors affecting zinc nutrition and metabolism in chicks and swine. p. 347–353. *In* C.F. Mills (ed.) Trace element metabolism in animals—TEMA 1. E. & S. Livingstone, Edinburgh and London, England.

Hoekstra, W.G., E.C. Faltin, C.W. Lin, H.F. Roberts, and R.H. Grummer. 1967. Zinc deficiency in reproducing gilts fed a diet high in calcium and its effects on tissue zinc and blood serum alkaline phosphatase. J. Anim. Sci. 26:1348–1357.

Hoekstra, W.G., P.K. Lewis, P.H. Phillips, and R.H. Grummer. 1956. The relationship of zinc parakeratosis, supplemental calcium and zinc to the zinc content of certain body components of swine. J. Anim. Sci. 15:752–764.

Hojo, Y. 1982. Selenium concentration and glutathione peroxidase activity in cow's milk. Biol. Trace Elem. Res. 4:233–239.

Hoogstratten, B., N.C. Leone, J.L. Shupe, D.A. Greenwood, and J.L. Lieberman. 1965. Effect of fluorides on the hematopoietic system, liver and thyroid gland in cattle. J. Anim. Med. Assoc. 192:26–32.

Horn, F.P., R.L. Reid, and G.A. Jung. 1974. Iodine nutrition and thyroid function of ewes and lambs on orchardgrass under different levels of nitrogen and micro-element fertilization. J. Anim. Sci. 38:968–974.

Hove, E., C.A. Elvehjem, and E.B. Hart. 1940. The relation of zinc to carbonic anhydrase. J. Biol. Chem. 136:425–434.

Howes, A.D., and I.A. Dyer. 1971. Diet and supplemental mineral effects on manganese metabolism in newborn calves. J. Anim. Sci. 32:144–145.

Hsu, F.S., L. Krook, W.G. Pond, and J.R. Duncan. 1975. Interactions of dietary calcium with toxic levels of lead and zinc in pigs. J. Nutr. 105:112–118.

Huck, P.W., and A.J. Clawson. 1976. Excess dietary cobalt in pigs. J. Anim. Sci. 43:1231–1246.

Humphries, W.R., M. Phillips, B.W. Young, and I. Bremner. 1983. The influence of dietary iron and molybdenum on copper metabolism in calves. Br. J. Nutr. 49:77–86.

Humphries, W.R., M.J. Walker, P.C. Morrice, and I. Bremner. 1988. Effects of dietary molybdenum and iron on copper metabolism in calves. p. 309–310. *In* L.S. Hurley et al. (ed.) Trace elements in man and animals—TEMA 6. Plenum Press, New York.

Hurley, L.S., and C.L. Keen. 1987. Manganese. p. 185–224. *In* W. Mertz (ed.) Trace elements in human and animal nutrition. Vol. 1, 5th ed. Academic Press, New York.

Jenkinson, S.G., D.M. Williams, R.A. Lawrence, and R.F. Burk. 1980. Effects of copper deficiency on superoxide dismutase (SOD) and glutathione peroxidase (GSH-Px) activities in rat lung and liver. Fed. Proc. 39:555.

Jensen, L.S. 1975. Precipitation of a selenium deficiency by high dietary levels of copper and zinc. Proc. Soc. Exp. Biol. Med. 149:113–116.

Johnson, J.L., K.U. Rajagopalan, and H.J. Cohen. 1974. Effect of tungsten on xanthine oxidase and sulfite oxidase in the rat. J. Biol. Chem. 249:859–866.

Johnson, M.A., and C.L. Murphy. 1988. Effect of high dietary iron and ascorbic acid on copper and iron utilization during copper deficiency. p. 545–546. *In* L.S. Hurley et al. (ed.) Trace elements in man and animals—TEMA 6. Plenum Press, New York.

Kadis, S., F.A. Udeze, J. Polanco, and D.W. Dreesen. 1984. Relationship of iron administration to susceptibility of newborn pigs to enterotoxic colibacillosis. Am. J. Vet. Res. 45:255–259.

Kaldor, I., and E.H. Morgan. 1986. Iron metabolism during lactation and suckling in a marsupial, the quokka (*Steomix brachyurus*). Comp. Biochem. Physiol. A 84:691–694.

Kaneko, J.J. 1989. Thyroid function. p. 630–649. *In* J.J. Kaneko (ed.) Clinical biochemistry of domestic animals. 4th ed. Academic Press, San Diego, CA.

Kayongo-Male, H. 1976. Manganese (Mn) nutrition of the pig the flux patterns of Mn from different sources in the gastrointestinal tract of the growing pig. Bull. Anim. Health Prod. Afr. 26:207–214.

Kayongo-Male, H., D.E. Ullrey, E.R. Miller, and K.K. Keahey. 1977. Manganese, calcium and phosphorus interactions in the diet of the growing pig. Ghana J. Agric. Sci. 10:39–46.

Keen, C.L., J. Bell, and B. Lonnerdal. 1986. The effect of age on manganese uptake and retention from milk and infant formulas in rats. J. Nutr. 116:395–402.

Keen, C.L., and T.W. Graham. 1989. Trace elements. p. 753–795. *In* J.J. Kaneko (ed.) Clinical biochemistry of domestic animals. 4th ed. Academic Press, San Diego, CA.

Kelleher, C.A., and M. Ivan. 1985. Hepatic subcellular distribution of copper and molybdenum-99 in sheep following intravenous administration of copper and [^{99}Mo]-tetrathiomolybdate. p. 364–367. *In* C.F. Mills et al. (ed.) Trace elements in man and animals—TEMA 5. Commonwealth Agric. Bureaux, Farnham Royal, England.

Kiely, J., A. Flynn, H. Singh, and P.F. Fox. 1988. Improved zinc bioavailability from colloidal calcium phosphate-free cows milk. p. 499–500. *In* L.S. Hurley et al. (ed.) Trace elements in man and animals—TEMA 6. Plenum Press, New York.

King, B.D., J.W. Lassiter, M.N. Neathery, W.J. Miller, and R.P. Gentry. 1980. Effect of lactose, copper and iron on manganese retention and tissue distribution in rats fed dextrose-casein diets. J. Anim. Sci. 50:452–458.

Kirchgessner, M., and K.R. Neese. 1976. Copper, manganese and zinc contents in the whole body and in individual parts of veal calves at different weights. Z. Lebensm. Unters. Forsch. 161:1–6.

Kirchgessner, M., F.X. Roth, and H.R. Roth. 1988. Interactions between zinc and vitamin A metabolism in rats and swine. p. 183–184. *In* L.S. Hurley et al. (ed.) Trace elements in man and animals—TEMA 6. Plenum Press, New York.

Kirchgessner, M., D.A. Roth-Maier, and S. Sporl. 1981. Untersuchungen zum Trachtigkeitsanabolismus der spurenelumente kupfer, zink, nickel und mangan bei zuchtsauer. Arch. Tierernaehr. 31:21.

Klasing, K.C., C.D. Knight, and D.M. Forsyth. 1980. Effects of iron on the anti-coli capacity of sow's milk in vitro and in ligated intestinal segments. J. Nutr. 110:1914–1921.

Knight, D.D., K.C. Klasing, and D.M. Forsyth. 1983. *E. Coli* growth in serum of iron dextran-supplemented pigs. J. Anim. Sci. 57:387–395.

Knott, P., B. Algar, G. Zervas, and S.B. Telfer. 1985. Glass—A medium for providing animals with supplementary trace elements. p. 708–714. *In* C.F. Mills et al. (ed.) Trace elements in man and animals—TEMA 5. Commonwealth Agric. Bureaux, Farnham Royal, England.

Kolb, E. 1963. The metabolism of iron in farm animals under normal and pathological condition. Adv. Vet. Sci. Comp. Med. 8:49–114.

Korc, M., and P.M. Brannon. 1988. Regulation of pancreatic exocrine function by manganese. p. 43–47. *In* L.S. Hurley et al. (ed.) Trace elements in man and animals—TEMA 6. Plenum Press, New York.

Korzeniowski, A., J.H. Geurink, and A. Kemp. 1981. Nitrate poisoning in cattle. 6. Tungsten (Wolfram) as a prophylactic against nitrate-nitrite intoxication in ruminants. Neth. J. Agric. Sci. 29:37–47.

Krishnamachari, K.A.U.R. 1987. Fluorine. p. 265–416. *In* W. Mertz (ed.) Trace elements in human and animal nutrition. Vol. 1. 5th ed. Academic Press, San Diego, CA.

Kruse-Jarres, J.D., E.M. Hecht, and W. Hecht. 1988. Pathobiochemical aspects to the mechanism of zinc absorption. p. 409–411. *In* L.S. Hurley et al. (ed.) Trace elements in man and animals—TEMA 6. Plenum Press, New York.

Ku, P.K., W.T. Ely, A.W. Groce, and D.E. Ullrey. 1972. Natural dietary selenium, tocopherol and effect on tissue selenium. J. Anim. Sci. 34:208–211.

Ku, P.K., E.R. Miller, and D.E. Ullrey. 1983. Effect of parenteral iron on serum electrolytes of the baby pig. J. Anim. Sci. 51:638–644.

Ku, P.K., E.R. Miller, R.C. Wahlstrom, A.W. Groce, J.P. Hitchcock, and D.E. Ullrey. 1973. Selenium supplementation of naturally high selenium diets for swine. J. Anim. Sci. 37:501–505.

Ku, P.K., D.E. Ullrey, and E.R. Miller. 1970. Zinc deficiency and tissue nucleic acid and protein concentration. p. 158–164. *In* C.F. Mills (ed.) Trace element metabolism in animals—TEMA 1. E. & S. Livingstone, Edinburgh and London, England.

Kuhajek, E.J., and G.F. Andelfinger. 1970. A new source of iodine for salt blocks. J. Anim. Sci. 31:51–58.

Lassiter, J.W., and J.D. Morton. 1968. Effects of a low manganese diet on certain ovine characteristics. J. Anim. Sci. 27:776–779.

Latshaw, J.D. 1975. Natural and selenite selenium in the hen and egg. J. Nutr. 105:32–37.

Leach, R.M., Jr. 1986. Mn (II) and glycosyltransferase essential for skeletal development. p. 81–89. *In* V.L. Schramm and F.C. Wedler (ed.) Manganese in metabolism and enzyme function. Academic Press, Orlando, FL.

Lee, C.C., and L.F. Wolterink. 1955. Metabolism of cobalt 60 in chickens. Poult. Sci. 34:764–776.

Leibholz, J.M., V.C. Speer, and V.W. Hays. 1962. Effects of dietary manganese on baby pig performance and tissue manganese levels. J. Anim. Sci. 21:772–776.

Lesperance, A.L., V.R. Bohman, and J.E. Oldfield. 1985. Interaction of molybdenum, sulfate and alfalfa in the bovine. J. Anim. Sci. 60:791–802.

Levander, O.A. 1987. Selenium. p. 209–280. *In* W. Mertz (ed.) Trace elements in human and animal nutrition. Vol. 2. 5th ed. Academic Press, New York.

Linder, M.C., K.C. Weiss, and Y.M. Hai. 1988. Structure and function of transcuprein, in transport of copper by mammalian blood plasma. p. 141–144. *In* L.S. Hurley et al. (ed.) Trace elements in man and animals—TEMA 6. Plenum Press, New York.

Liptrap, D.O., E.R. Miller, D.E. Ullrey, D.L. Whitenack, B.L. Schoepke, and R.W. Luecke. 1970. Sex influence on the zinc requirement of developing swine. J. Anim. Sci. 30:736–741.

Loh, T.T., and I. Kaldor. 1973. Iron in milk and milk fractions of lactating rats, rabbits and quokkas. Comp. Biochem. Physiol. 44B:337–346.

Loh, T.T., and I. Kaldor. 1974. Iron in rat milk: distribution between centrifugally separated phases. J. Dairy Sci. 57:339–340.

Looney, J.W., G. Gille, R.L. Preston, E.R. Graham, and W.H. Pfander. 1976. Effects of plant species and cobalt intake upon cobalt utilization and ration digestibility. J. Anim. Sci. 42:693–698.

Luecke, R.W., J.A. Hoefer, W.S. Brammell, and D.A. Schmidt. 1957. Calcium and zinc in parakeratosis of swine. J. Anim. Sci. 16:3–11.

Lumsden, H.H., V.E. Valli, B.J. McSherry, G.A. Robinson, and C. Laxton. 1975. The kinetics of hematopoiesis in the light horse. II. The hematological response to hemorrhagic anemia. Can. J. Comp. Med. 39:324–331.

MacPherson, A., and J.S. Chalmers. 1985. Effect of dietary energy concentration on the cobalt vitamin B_{12} requirement of growing calves. p. 145–167. *In* C.F. Mills et al. (ed.) Trace elements in man and animals—TEMA 5. Commonwealth Agric. Bureaux, Farnham Royal, England.

MacPherson, A., G. Fisher, and J.E. Paterson. 1988. Effect of cobalt deficiency on the immune function of ruminants. p. 397–398. *In* L.S. Hurley et al. (ed.) Trace elements in man and animals—TEMA 6. Plenum Press, New York.

Mahan, D.C., and A.L. Moxon. 1984. Effect of inorganic selenium supplementation on selenosis in postweaning swine. J. Anim. Sci. 58:1216–1221.

Mahan, D.C., A.L. Moxon, and J.H. Cline. 1975. Efficacy of supplemental selenium in reproductive diets on sow and progeny serum and tissue selenium values. J. Anim. Sci. 40:624–631.

Marti, M.T., M.P. Saiz, M.T. Mitjavila, and J. Planas. 1989. Body iron content in Shaver and New Hampshire chickens. Comp. Biochem. Physiol. 92A:211–213.

Martin, C.E., B.E. Hopper, C.H. Armstrong, and H.E. Amstutz. 1967. A clinical and pathological study of the mastitis-metritis-agalactia syndrome of sows. J. Am. Vet. Med. Assoc. 151:1629–1634.

Masters, D.G., and D.I. Paynter. 1988. The relationship between manganese intake and the activity of manganese superoxidase dismutase in tissues of sheep. p. 247–248. *In* L.S. Hurley et al. (ed.) Trace elements in man and animals—TEMA 6. Plenum Press, New York.

Masters, H.G., R.H. Cosey, P.D. Jelinek, R.K. Mitchell, P.E. Wilson, and D.S. Petterson. 1985. Lack of response to Se supplementation in calves with low Se status. p. 248–250. *In* C.F. Mills et al. (ed.) Trace elements in man and animals—TEMA 5. Commonwealth Agric. Bureaux, Farnham Royal, England.

Mathers, J.W., and R. Hill. 1968. Manganese in the nutrition and metabolism of the pullet. 2. The manganese contents of the tissues of pullets given diets of high or low manganese content. Br. J. Nutr. 22:635–643.

Matrone, G., R.H. Hartman, and A.J. Clawson. 1959. Studies of a manganese-iron antagonism in the nutrition of rabbits and baby pigs. J. Nutr. 67:309–317.

Matrone, G., E.L. Thomason, Jr., and C.R. Bunn. 1960. Requirement and utilization of iron by the baby pig. J. Nutr. 72:459–465.

Maurer, R.L., and H.G. Day. 1957. The non-essentiality of fluorine in nutrition. J. Nutr. 62:561–573.

McAdam, P.A., and G.D. O'Dell. 1982. Mineral profile of blood plasma of lactating dairy cows. J. Dairy Sci. 65:1219–1226.

McCance, R.A., and E.M. Widdowson. 1951. The metabolism of iron during suckling. J. Physiol. 112:450–458.

McCormick, C.C., and L.Y. Lin. 1988. Accumulation of hepatic Zn and Zn/Cu metallothionein in copper-loaded chicks: Isolation and characterization. p. 39–40. In L.S. Hurley et al. (ed.) Trace elements in man and animals—TEMA 6. Plenum Press, New York.

McCormick, L.D. 1985. Bound trace element content of bovine retinal disk membranes as determined by particle-induced x-ray emission. Biophys. J. 47:381–385.

McDonald, P., and N.F. Suttle. 1986. Abnormal fermentations in continuous cultures of rumen microorganisms given cobalt-deficient hay or barley as the food stubstrate. Br. J. Nutr. 56:369–378.

McGown, E.L., and J.W. Suttie. 1974. Influence of fat and fluoride on gastric emptying time. J. Nutr. 104:909–915.

McGuire, S.O., W.J. Miller, R.D. Gentry, M.W. Neathery, S.Y. Ho, and D.M. Blackman. 1985. Influence of high dietary iron as ferrous carbonate and ferrous sulfate on iron metabolism in young calves. J. Dairy Sci. 68:2621–2628.

McHowell, J., H. Patel, and P. Dorling. 1988. Heliotrope alkaloids and copper. p. 319–320. In L.S. Hurley et al. (ed.) Trace elements in man and animals—TEMA 6. Plenum Press, New York.

McMurray, C.H., D.A. Rice, M. McLoughlin, and W.J. Blanchflower. 1985. Cobalt deficiency and the potential of using methylmalonic acid as a diagnostic and prognostic indicator. p. 603–608. In C.F. Mills et al. (ed.) Trace elements in man and animals—TEMA 5. Commonwealth Agric. Bureaux, Farnham Royal, England.

McNatt, M.L., F.M. Fisher, M.J. Elders, B.S. Kilgore, W.G. Smith, and E.F. Hughes. 1976. Uridine diphosphate xylosyltransferase activity in cartilage from manganese-deficient chicks. Biochem. J. 160:211–216.

McNaughton, J.L., and E.J. Day. 1979. Effect of dietary Fe to Cu ratio on hematological and growth responses of broiler chickens. J. Nutr. 109:559–564.

Menard, M.P., C.C. McCormick, and R.J. Cousins. 1981. Regulation of intestinal metallothionein biosynthesis in rats by dietary zinc. J. Nutr. 111:1353–1361.

Menten, J.F.M. 1988. Effects of high dietary copper on the utilization of nutrients and on blood and intestinal variables of starter pigs. Ph.D. diss. Michigan State Univ., East Lansing.

Mercer, J.F.B., J. Smith, A. Grimes, J. MacHowell, P. Gill, and D.M. Danks. 1988. Zinc, copper and metallothionein mRNA in sheep liver during development. p. 679–680. In L.S. Hurley et al. (ed.) Trace elements in man and animals—TEMA 6. Plenum Press, New York.

Mertz, W. 1987. Trace elements in human and animal nutrition. Vol. 1, 2. 5th ed. Academic Press, New York.

Messer, H.H., W.D. Armstrong, and L. Singer. 1974. Essentiality and function of fluoride. p. 425–437. In W.G. Hoekstra et al. (ed.) Trace element metabolism in animals—TEMA 2. University Park Press, Baltimore, MD.

Meyer, W.R., D.C. Mahan, and A.L. Moxon. 1981. Value of dietary selenium and vitamin E for weanling swine as measured by performance and tissue selenium and glutathione peroxidase activities. J. Anim. Sci. 52:302–311.

Miller, E.R. 1981. Iron. Anim. Nutr. Health. 36:14–16.

Miller, E.R., D.O. Liptrap, and D.E. Ullrey. 1970. Sex influence on zinc requirement of swine. p. 377–379. In C.F. Mills (ed.) Trace element metabolism in animals—TEMA 1. E. & S. Livingstone, Edinburgh and London, England.

Miller, E.R., M.S. Loudenslager, P.K. Ku, P.A. Whetter, C.K. Whitehair, and D.E. Ullrey. 1985. Importance of dam's diet and colostrum for the biological antioxidant status of the young pig. p. 118–120. In C.F. Mills et al. (ed.) Trace elements in man and animals—TEMA 5. Commonwealth Agric. Bureaux, Farnham Royal, England.

Miller, E.R., R.W. Luecke, D.E. Ullrey, B.V. Baltzer, B.L. Bradley, and J.A. Hoefer. 1968. Biochemical skeletal and allometric changes due to zinc deficiency in the baby pig. J. Nutr. 95:278–286.

Miller, E.R., M.J. Parsons, D.E. Ullrey, and P.K. Ku. 1981. Bioavailability of iron from ferric choline citrate and a ferric copper cobalt choline citrate complex for young pigs. J. Anim. Sci. 52:783–787.

Miller, E.R., H.D. Stowe, P.K. Ku, and G.M. Hill. 1979. Copper and zinc in swine nutrition. p. 1–139. In National Feed Ingredients Association literature review on copper and zinc in animal nutrition. Natl. Feed Ingredient Assoc., West Des Moines, IA.

Miller, E.R., G.L. Waxler, P.K. Ku, D.E. Ullrey, and C.K. Whitehair. 1982. Iron requirements of baby pigs reared in germ-free or conventional environments on a condensed milk diet. J. Anim. Sci. 54:106-115.

Miller, J.K., and W.J. Miller. 1962. Experimental zinc deficiency and recovery in calves. J. Nutr. 76:467-474.

Miller, J.K., and R.G. Cragle. 1965. Gastrointestinal sites of absorption and endogenous excretion of zinc in dairy cattle. J. Dairy Sci. 48:370-373.

Miller, J.K., and L.S. Jensen. 1966. Effect of protein source on zinc absorption and excretion along the alimentary tracts of chicks. Poult. Sci. 45:1051-1053.

Miller, J.K., and E.W. Swanson. 1973. Metabolism of ethylenediaminedihydiodide and sodium or potassium iodide by dairy cows. J. Dairy Sci. 56:378-384.

Miller, J.K., E.W. Swanson, and W.A. Lyke. 1973b. Iodine concentration in nonthyroid tissues of cows. J. Dairy Sci. 56:1344-1346.

Miller, J.K., E.W. Swanson, W.A. Lyke, B.R. Moss, and W.F. Byrne. 1974. Effect of thyroid status on digestive tract fill and flow rate of undigested residues in cattle. J. Dairy Sci. 57:193-197.

Miller, J.K., E.W. Swanson, and G.E. Spalding. 1975. Iodine absorption, excretion, recycling and tissue distribution in the dairy cow. J. Dairy Sci. 58:1578-1593.

Miller, W.J. 1969. Absorption, tissue distribution, endogenous excretion and homeostatic control of zinc in ruminants. Am. J. Clin. Nutr. 22:1323-1331.

Miller, W.J. 1979. Copper and zinc in ruminant nutrition. p. 1-72. *In* National Feed Ingredients Association literature reviews on copper and zinc in animal nutrition. Natl. Feeding Ingredient Assoc., West Des Moines, IA.

Miller, W.J., R.L. Kincaid, M.W. Neathery, R.P. Gentry, M.S. Ansari, and J.W. Lassiter. 1978. Zinc metabolism in calves, cows, rats and chicks fed high dietary zinc. p. 175-178. *In* M. Kirchgessner (ed.) Trace element metabolism in man and animals—TEMA 3. Institut fur Ernahrungsphysiologie, Technische Universitat, Munchen, Freising, Weihenstephan, Federal Republic of Germany.

Miller, W.J., M.W. Neathery, R.P. Gentry, D.M. Blackman, and J.W. Lassiter. 1973a. Fecal excretion, tissue accumulation and turnover of ^{54} manganese after intravenous dosing in Holstein calves fed a practical-type diet. J. Anim. Sci. 37:827-832.

Miller, W.J., M.W. Neathery, R.P. Gentry, D.M. Blackman, and P.E. Stake. 1974. Adaptations in zinc metabolism by lactating cows fed a low-zinc practical-type diet. p. 550-552. *In* W.G. Hoekstra et al. (ed.) Trace element metabolism in animals—TEMA 2. University Park Press, Baltimore, MD.

Miller, W.J., G.W. Powell, W.J. Pitts, and H.F. Perkins. 1965. Factors affecting zinc content of bovine hair. J. Dairy Sci. 48:1091-1095.

Mills, C.F., and A.C. Dalgarno. 1972. Copper and zinc status of ewes and lambs receiving increased dietary concentrations of cadmium. Nature (London) 239:171-173.

Mills, C.F., and G.K. Davis. 1987. Molybdenum. p. 429-463. *In* W. Mertz (ed.) Trace elements in human and animal nutrition. Vol. 1. 5th ed. Academic Press, San Diego, CA.

Milne, D.B., and K. Schwarz. 1974. Effect of different fluorine compounds on growth and bone fluoride levels in rats. p. 710-714. *In* W.G. Hoekstra et al. (ed.) Trace element metabolism in animals—TEMA 2. University Park Press, Baltimore, MD.

Miltimore, J.E., and J.L. Mason. 1971. Copper to molybdenum ratio and molybdenum and copper concentrations in ruminant feeds. Can. J. Anim. Sci. 51:193-200.

Miski, A.M.-A., and F.H. Kratzer. 1976. Effect of dietary ascorbic acid on iron utilization in the growing chick. Poult. Sci. 55:454-456.

Miski, A.M.-A., and F.H. Kratzer. 1977. Effects of dietary protein, glycine and tryptophan on iron metabolism in the growing chicks. J. Nutr. 107:24-34.

Moksnes, K., H.J. Larsen, and G. Overnes. 1988. Immune responses as parameters for selenium tolerance determination in sheep. p. 91-93. *In* L.S. Hurley et al. (ed.) Trace elements in man and animals—TEMA 6. Plenum Press, New York.

Monsen, E.R., and J.F. Page. 1978. Effects of EDTA and ascorbic acid on the absorption of iron from an isolated rat intestinal loop. J. Agric. Food. Chem. 26:223-226.

Morck, T.A., and R.E. Austic. 1981. Iron requirement of white leghorn hens. Poult. Sci. 60:1497-1503.

Morgan, E.H. 1975. Plasma iron transport during egg-laying and after oestrogen administration in the domestic fowl (*Gallus domesticus*). Q. J. Exp. Physiol. 60:233-247.

Morris, E.R. 1987. Iron. p. 79-142. *In* W. Mertz (ed.) Trace elements in human and animal nutrition. Vol. 1. 5th ed. Academic Press, San Diego, CA.

Murray, J., and N. Stein. 1970. Gastric secretions and iron absorption in rats. p. 321–324. *In* C.F. Mills (ed.) Trace element metabolism in animals—TEMA 1. E. & S. Livingstone, Edinburgh and London, England.

Mykkanen, H. 1988. Effects of arsenic on the intestinal absorption of ^{75}Se compounds in chicks. p. 551–552. *In* L.S. Hurley et al. (ed.) Trace elements in man and animals—TEMA 6. Plenum Press, New York.

Nalder, B.N., A.W. Mahoney, R. Ramakrishman, and D.G. Hendricks. 1972. Sensitivity of the immunological response to the nutritional status of rats. J. Nutr. 102:535–542.

National Research Council (NRC). 1974. Effects of fluorides in animals. Natl. Acad. Sci. Press, Washington, DC.

National Research Council (NRC). 1978. Zinc Committee on medical and biological effects of environmental pollutants. Natl. Academy of Sci., Washington, DC, Univ. Park Press, Baltimore, MD.

National Research Council (NRC). 1980. Mineral tolerance of domestic animals. Natl. Academy of Sci., Washington, DC.

National Research Council (NRC). 1983. Selenium in nutrition. Rev. ed. Natl. Academy of Sci., Washington, DC.

National Research Council (NRC). 1984. Nutrient requirements of poultry. 8th ed. Natl. Acad. Sci., Washington, DC.

National Research Council (NRC). 1988a. Nutrient requirements of dairy cattle. 6th ed. Natl. Acad. Sci., Washington, DC.

National Research Council (NRC). 1988b. Nutrient requirements of swine. 9th ed. Natl. Acad. Sci., Washington, DC.

Neathery, M.W., W.J. Miller, D.M. Blackman, and R.P. Gentry. 1973a. ^{65}Zinc metabolism, secretion into milk and biological half-life in lactating cows. J. Dairy Sci. 56:1526–1530.

Neathery, M.W., W.J. Miller, D.M. Blackman, R.P. Gentry, and J.B. Jones. 1973b. Absorption and tissue zinc content in lactating dairy cows as affected by low dietary zinc. J. Anim. Sci. 37:848–852.

Nederbragt, H. 1988. Influence of glutathione depletion on hepatic copper uptake and biliary excretion in the rat. p. 361–362. *In* L.S. Hurley et al. (ed.) Trace elements in man and animals—TEMA 6. Plenum Press, New York.

Nederbragt, H., A.J. Lagerwerf, and T.S.G.A.M. van den Ingh. 1988. Instability of low pH of copper-thionein-protein from livers of bedlington terriers with copper toxicosis. p. 677–678. *In* L.S. Hurley et al. (ed.) Trace elements in man and animals—TEMA 6. Plenum Press, New York.

Newland, H.W., and G.K. Davis. 1961. Placental transfer of manganese in swine. J. Anim. Sci. 20:15–17.

Newton, G.L., E.R. Barrick, R.W. Harvey, and M.G. Wise. 1974. Iodine toxicity: physiological effects of elevated dietary iodine on calves. J. Anim. Sci. 38:449–455.

Newton, G.L., and A.J. Clawson. 1974. Iodine toxicity: physiological effects of elevated dietary iodine on pigs. J. Anim. Sci. 39:879–884.

Nielsen, F.H. 1985. Effects in rats of boron deprivation and of interactions between boron and fluoride, aluminum, magnesium, or calcium. p. 271–275. *In* C.F. Mills et al. (ed.) Trace elements in man and animals—TEMA 5. Commonwealth Agric. Bureaux, Farnham Royal, England.

Norheim, G., and K. Moksnes. 1985. Distribution and elimination of selenium and glutathione peroxidase (GSH-Px) in chickens after supplementation with sodium selenite or selenomethione. p. 493–495. *In* C.F. Mills et al. (ed.) Trace elements in man and animals—TEMA 5. Commonwealth Agric. Bureaux, Farnham Royal, England.

O'Dell, B.L. 1979. Copper and zinc in poultry nutrition. p. 1–62. *In* National Feed Ingredients Association literature review on copper and zinc in animal nutrition. Natl. Feed Ingredients Assoc., West Des Moines, IA.

O'Dell, B.L. 1984. Copper. p. 506–518. *In* Present knowledge in nutrition. Nutrition Reviews. 5th ed. The Nutrition Found., Inc., Washington, DC.

O'Dell, B.L., P.M. Newberne, and J.E. Savage. 1958. Significance of dietary zinc for the growing chicken. J. Nutr. 65:503–518.

O'Dell, B.L., and J.E. Savage. 1957. Symptoms of zinc deficiency in chicks. Fed. Proc. 16:394.

O'Dell, B.L., J.M. Yohe, and J.E. Savage. 1964. Zinc availability in the chick as affected by phytate, calcium and ethylenediaminetetraacetate. Poult. Sci. 43:415–419.

O'Donovan, P.B., R.A. Pickett, M.P. Plumlee, and W.M. Beeson. 1963. Iron toxicity in the young pig. J. Anim. Sci. 22:1075–1080.

Oh, S.H., H. Nakaue, J.T. Deagen, P.D. Whanger, and G.H. Arscott. 1979. Accumulation and depletion of zinc in chick tissue metallothioneins. J. Nutr. 109:1720-1729.

Okonkwo, A.C., P.K. Ku, E.R. Miller, K.K. Keahey, and D.E. Ullrey. 1979. Copper requirement of baby pigs fed purified diets. J. Nutr. 109:939-948.

Olson, O.E., C.A. Dinkel, and L.D. Kamstra. 1954. A new aid in diagnosing selenium poisoning. S.D. Farm Home Res. 6:12.

Olson, O.E., B.M. Schulte, E.I. Whitehead, and A.W. Halverson. 1963. Effect of arsenic on selenium metabolism in rats. J. Agric. Food Chem. 11:531-534.

O'Mary, C.C., W.T. Butts, R.A. Reynolds, and M.C. Bell. 1969. Effects of irradiation, age, season and color on mineral composition of Hereford cattle hair. J. Anim. Sci. 28:268-271.

Osborne, J.C., and J.W. Davis. 1968. Increased susceptibility to bacterial endotoxin of pigs with iron-deficiency anemia. J. Am. Vet. Med. Assoc. 152:1630-1632.

Ott, E.A., W.H. Smith, M. Stob, H.E. Parker, R.B. Harrington, and W.M. Beeson. 1965. Zinc requirement of the growing lamb fed a purified diet. J. Nutr. 87:459-463.

Panic, B., L.J. Bezbradica, N. Nedeljkou, and A.G. Istwani. 1974. Some characteristics of trace element metabolism in poultry. p. 635-637. In W.G. Hoekstra et al. (ed.) Trace element metabolism in animals—TEMA 2. University Park Press, Baltimore, MD.

Parsons, M.J., E.R. Miller, D.M. Bebiak, J.P. Erickson, M.G. Hogberg, D.J. Ellis, and D.E. Ullrey. 1977. Influence of iron status of weanling pigs when exposed to TGE. Mich. Agric. Exp. Stn. Res. Rep. 343:10-12.

Patterson, E.L., R. Milstrey, and E.L.R. Stokstad. 1957. Effect of selenium in preventing exudative diathesis in chicks. Proc. Soc. Exp. Biol. Med. 95:617-620.

Payne, C.G. 1977. Involvement of molybdenum in feather growth. Br. Poult. Sci. 18:427-432.

Peter, D.W., A.W. Mann, and R.A. Hunter. 1981. Effect of Zn containing pellets on selenium pellet function. p. 199-201. In J. McHowell et al. (ed.) Trace elements in metabolism in man and animals—TEMA 4. Canberra, Australian Academy of Science, Canberra, Australia.

Peter, D.W., P. Young, D.J. Buscall, and P.D. Whanger. 1985. Selenium retention and concentrations in sheep given selenite or selenomethionine-anomalies, an apparent explanation and implications. p. 484-487. In C.F. Mills et al. (ed.) Trace elements in man and animals—TEMA 5. Commonwealth Agric. Bureaux, Farnham Royal, England.

Phillippo, M.,W.R. Humphries, I. Bremner, T. Atkinson, and G. Henderson. 1985. Molybdenum-induced infertility in cattle. p. 176-180. In C.F. Mills et al. (ed.) Trace elements in man and animals—TEMA 5. Commonwealth Agric. Bureaux, Farnham Royal, England.

Piras, R., and L. Vallee. 1967. Procarboxypeptidase A-carboxypeptidase A interrelationships. Metal and substrate binding. Biochemistry 6:348-357.

Pond, W.G., and J.R. Jones. 1964. Effect of level of zinc in high-calcium diets on pigs from weaning through one reproductive cycle and on subsequent growth of their offspring. J. Anim. Sci. 23:1057-1060.

Prabowo, A., J.W. Spears, and L. Goode. 1988. Effect of dietary iron on performance and mineral utilization in lambs fed a forage based diet. J. Anim. Sci. 66:2028-2035.

Prasad, A.S., D. Oberleas, R. Wolf, J.P. Horwitz, E.R. Miller, and R.W. Leucke. 1969. Changes in trace elements and enzyme activities in tissues of zinc-deficient pigs. Am. J. Clin. Nutr. 22:628-637.

Price, J., A.M. Will, G. Paschaleris, and J.K. Chesters. 1988. Demonstration of ruminal synthesis of thiomolybdates and their subsequent absorption in sheep. p. 589-590. In L.S. Hurley et al. (ed.) Trace elements in man and animals—TEMA 6. Plenum Press, New York.

Rajagopalan, K.V. 1984. Molybdenum. p. 149-174. In E. Frieden (ed.) Biochemistry of the essential ultra-trace elements. Plenum Press, New York.

Rajagopalan, K.V. 1987. Molybdenum—An essential trace element. Nutr. Rev. 45:321-328.

Ramsay, W.N.M., and E.A. Campbell. 1954. Iron metabolism in the laying hen. Biochem. J. 58:313-317.

Reid, B.L., A.A. Kurnick, R.N. Burroughs, R.L. Suacha, and J.R. Couch. 1957. Molybdenum in poult nutrition. Proc. Soc. Exp. Biol. Med. 94:737-740.

Richards, M.P., and R.J. Cousins. 1976. Zinc-binding protein relationship to short term changes in zinc metabolism. Proc. Soc. Exp. Biol. Med. 153:52-56.

Richards, M.P., and R.J. Cousins. 1977. Isolation of an intestinal metallothionein induced by parenteral zinc. Biochem. Biophys. Res. Comm. 75:286-294.

Richardson, T., and P.L. Guss. 1965. Lipids and metals in fat globule membrane fractions. J. Dairy Sci. 48:523-530.

Robinson, J.R., M.T. Robinson, O.A. Levander, and C.D. Thomson. 1985. Urinary excretion of selenium by New Zealand and North American human subjects on differing intakes. Am. J. Clin. Nutr. 41:1023-1031.

Robinson, M.F., J.M. McKenzie, C.D. Thomson, and A.L. Van Rij. 1973. Metabolic balance of zinc, copper, cadmium, iron, molybdenum and selenium in young New Zealand women. Br. J. Nutr. 30:195-205.

Rodvien, R., A. Gillum, and L.R. Weintraub. 1974. Decreased glutathione peroxidase activity secondary to severe iron deficiency: A possible mechanism responsible for the shortened life span of the iron-deficient cell. Blood 43:281-289.

Root, E.J., and C.F. Combs, Jr. 1988. Disruption of endoplasmic reticulum is the primary ultrastructural lesion of the pancreas in the selenium-deficient chick. Proc. Soc. Exp. Biol. Med. 187:513-521.

Rose, I.V., and C.A. Ammerman. 1982. Interrelationship of dietary phosphorus, aluminum and iron on performance and tissue mineral composition in lambs. J. Anim. Sci. 55:1231-1240.

Roth, H.P., and M. Kirchgessner. 1988. Calmodulin concentration in tissue of zinc and calcium deficient rats. p. 119-120. In L.S. Hurley et al. (ed.) Trace elements in man and animals—TEMA 6. Plenum Press, New York.

Rothery, P., J.M. Bell, and J.W.T. Spinks. 1953. Cobalt and vitamin B_{12} in sheep. 1. Distribution of radiocobalt in tissues and ingesta. J. Nutr. 49:173-181.

Rotruck, J.T., A.L. Pope, H.E. Ganther, A.B. Swanson, D.G. Haferman, and W.G. Hoekstra. 1973. Selenium: biochemical role as a component of glutathione peroxidase. Science 179:588-590.

Saiz, M.P., M.T. Marti, M.T. Mitjavila, and J. Planas. 1980. Intestinal absorption in chickens. II. Effect of sex. Biol. Trace Element Res. 2:255-267.

Saraswat, R.C., and S.P. Arora. 1972. Effect of dietary zinc on the vitamin A level and alkaline phosphatase activity in blood sera of lambs. India J. Anim. Sci. 42:358-362.

Saylor, W.W., and R.M. Leach, Jr. 1980. Intracellular distribution of copper and zinc in sheep: Effect of age and dietary levels of the metals. J. Nutr. 110:448-459.

Schwarz, K., and C.M. Foltz. 1957. Selenium as an integral part of factor 3 against dietary necrotic liver degeneration. J. Am. Chem. Soc. 79:3292-3293.

Schwarz, K., and D.B. Milne. 1972. Fluorine requirement for growth in the rat. Bioinorg. Chem. 1:331-338.

Scott, M.L. 1972. Trace elements in animal nutrition. p. 555-591. In J.J. Mortvedt et al. (ed.) Micronutrients in agriculture. SSSA, Madison, WI.

Scott, M.L., and J.N. Thompson. 1971. Selenium content of feedstuffs and effects of dietary selenium levels upon tissue selenium in chick and poults. Poult. Sci. 50:1742-1748.

Settle, E.A., F.R. Mraz, C.R. Douglas, and J.K. Bletner. 1969. Effect of diet and manganese level on growth, perosis and ^{54}Mn uptake in chicks. J. Nutr. 97:141-146.

Shupe, J.L. 1980. Clinicopathologic features of fluoride toxicosis in cattle. J. Anim. Sci. 51:746-758.

Sihombing, D.T.H., G.L. Cromwell, and V.W. Hays. 1974. Effects of protein source, goitrogens and iodine levels on performance and thyroid status of pigs. J. Anim. Sci. 39:1106-1112.

Simon, G., and J.W. Suttie. 1968a. Effect of method of fluoride administration on plasma fluoride concentrations. J. Nutr. 94:511-515.

Simon, G., and J.W. Suttie. 1968b. Effect of dietary fluoride on food intake and plasma fluoride concentration in the rat. J. Nutr. 96:152-156.

Singh, H., A. Flynn, and P.F. Fox. 1988. Binding of zinc to colloidal calcium phosphate in human and cow's milks. p. 565-566. In L.S. Hurley et al. (ed.) Trace elements in man and animals—TEMA 6. Plenum Press, New York.

Smith, J.E., K. Moore, D. Boyington, D.S. Pollman, and D. Schoneweis. 1984a. Serum ferritin and total iron binding capacity to estimate iron storage in pigs. Vet. Pathol. 21:597-600.

Smith, J.E., K. Moore, J.E. Cipriano, and P.G. Morris. 1984b. Serum ferritin as a measure of stored iron in horses. J. Nutr. 114:677-681.

Smith, K. 1966. Interaction of gossypol with mineral salts. Natl. Cottonseed Production Assoc., Memphis, TN.

Smith, K.T., and R.J. Cousins. 1980. Quantitative aspects of zinc absorption by isolated, vascularly perfused rat intestine. J. Nutr. 110:316-323.

Smith, K.T., M.L. Failla, and R.J. Cousins. 1979. Identification of albumin as the plasma carrier for zinc absorption by perfused rat intestine. Biochem. J. 184:627-633.

Smith, R.M. 1987. Cobalt. p. 143-183. In W. Mertz (ed.) Trace elements in human and animal nutrition. Vol. 1. 5th ed. San Diego, CA.

Smith, R.M., and H.R. Marstn. 1970. Production, absorption, distribution and excretion of vitamin B_{12} in sheep. Br. J. Nutr. 24:857–877.

Solomons, N.W. 1988. Zinc and copper. p. 238–262. In M.E. Shils and V.R. Young (ed.) Modern nutrition in health and disease. 7th ed. Lea and Febiger, Philadelphia.

Solomons, N.W., and R.J. Cousins. 1984. Zinc. p. 125–197. In N.W. Solomons and I.H. Rosenberg (ed.) Absorption and malabsorption of mineral nutrients. Alan R. Liss, New York.

Spray, C.M., and E.M. Widdowson. 1950. The effect of growth and development on the composition of mammals. Br. J. Nutr. 4:332–353.

Srai, S.K.S., C. Bingle, and O. Epstein. 1988. Neonatal and adult [64]copper metabolism in the pig and its relationship to copper metabolism in Wilson's disease. p. 147–148. In L.S. Hurley et al. (ed.) Trace elements in man and animals—TEMA 6. Plenum Press, New York.

Stake, P.E., W.J. Miller, N.W. Neathery, and R.P. Gentry. 1975. [65]Zinc absorption and tissue distribution in two- and six-month-old Holstein calves and lactating cows. J. Dairy Sci. 58:78–81.

Standish, J.F., and C.B. Ammerman. 1971. Effect of excess dietary iron as ferrous sulfate and ferric citrate on tissue mineral composition of sheep. J. Anim. Sci. 33:481–484.

Standish, J.F., C.B. Ammerman, C.F. Simpson, F.C. Neal, and A.Z. Palmer. 1969. Influence of graded levels of dietary iron, as ferrous sulfate, on performance and tissue mineral composition of steers. J. Anim. Sci. 29:496–503.

Starcher, B. 1969. Studies on the mechanism of copper absorption in the chick. J. Nutr. 97:321–326.

Stewart, R.D.H., N.M. Griffiths, C.D. Thomson, and M.F. Robinson. 1978. Quantitative selenium metabolism in normal New Zealand women. Br. J. Nutr. 40:45–54.

Strain, W.H., W.J. Pories, E. Michael, R.M. Peer, and S.A. Zaresky. 1978. Age and sex effects on trace element absorption from the alimentary tract. p. 132–135. In M. Kirchgessner (ed.) Trace element metabolism in man and animals—TEMA 3. Institut fur Ernahrungsphysiologie, Technische Universitat, Munchen, Freising, Weihenstephan, Federal Republic of Germany.

Sullivan, J.F., A.T. Blotcky, M.M. Jetton, H.K. Hahn, and R.E. Burch. 1979. Serum levels of selenium, calcium, copper, magnesium, manganese and zinc in various human diseases. J. Nutr. 109:1432–1437.

Suttie, J.W., and E.C. Faltin. 1973. Effects of sodium fluoride on dairy cattle: influence on nutritional state. Am. J. Vet. Res. 34:479–483.

Suttle, N.F. 1973. Effects of age and weaning on the apparent availability of dietary copper to young lambs. Proc. Nutr. Soc. 32:24A–25A.

Suttle, N.F. 1975. Changes in the availability of dietary copper to young lambs associated with age and weaning. J. Agric. Sci. (Cambridge) 84:255–261.

Suttle, N.F., D.G. Jones, J.A. Woolliams, and C. Woolliams. 1988a. Predication of disorder in Cu-deficient lambs from different genotypes. p. 435–437. In L.S. Hurley et al. (ed.) Trace elements in man and animals—TEMA 6. Plenum Press, New York.

Suttle, N.F., and C.F. Mills. 1966. Studies of the toxicity of copper to pigs. 1. Effect of oral supplements of zinc and iron salts on the development of copper toxicosis. Br. J. Nutr. 20:135–148.

Suttle, N.F., C. Wright, A. MacPherson, R. Harkess, G. Halliday, K. Miller, P. Phillips, C. Evans, and D. Rice. 1988b. The predication of impaired growth due to Cu, Co and Se deficiencies in lambs on improved hill pastures in Scotland. p. 473–474. In L.S. Hurley et al. (ed.) Trace elements in man and animals—TEMA 6. Plenum Press, New York.

Swanson, C.A., D.C. Reamer, C. Veillon, J.C. King, and O.A. Levander. 1983. Quantitative and qualitative aspects of selenium utilization in pregnant and nonpregnant women: an application of stable isotope methodology. Am. J. Clin. Nutr. 38:169–180.

Swanson, E.W. 1972. Effect of dietary iodine on thyroxine secretion in rate of lactating cows. J. Dairy Sci. 55:1763–1767.

Talbot, J.M., K.D. Fisher, and C.J. Carr. 1976. A review of the effects of dietary iodine on certain thyroid disorders. Life Sci. Res. Office, Fed. of Am. Soc. for Exp. Biol., Bethesda, MD.

Tao, S., and J.W. Suttie. 1976. Evidence for a lack of an effect of dietary fluoride level on reproduction in mice. J. Nutr. 106:1115–1122.

Taylor, S. 1954. Calcium as a goitrogen. J. Clin. Endocrinol. Metab. 14:1412–1422.

Theurer, R.C., A.W. Mahoney, and H.P. Sarett. 1971. Placental transfer of fluoride and tin in rats given various fluoride and tin salts. J. Nutr. 101:525–532.

Thompson, J.N., and M.L. Scott. 1970. Impaired lipid and vitamin E absorption related to atrophy of the pancreas in selenium-deficient chicks. J. Nutr. 100:797–809.

Thompson, R.H., and J.R. Todd. 1974. Muscle damage in chronic copper poisoning of sheep. Res. Vet. Sci. 16:97–99.

Thomson, A.B.R., D. Olatunbosun, and L.S. Valberg. 1971a. Interrelation of intestinal transport system for manganese and iron. J. Lab. Clin. Med. 78:642–655.

Thomson, A.B.R., L.S. Valberg, and D.C. Sinclair. 1971b. Competitive nature of the intestinal transport mechanism for cobalt and iron in the rat. J. Clin. Invest. 50:2384–2394.

Todd, W.R., C.A. Elvehjem, and E.B. Hart. 1934. Zinc in the nutrition of the rat. Am. J. Physiol. 107:146–155.

Tolan, A., J. Robertson, C.R. Orton, M.J. Head, A.A. Christie, and B.A. Millburn. 1974. Studies on the composition of food. 5. The chemical composition of eggs produced under battery, deep litter and free range conditions. Br. J. Nutr. 31:185–200.

Topham, R.W., H. Woodruff, and M.C. Walker. 1981. Purification and characterization of the intestinal promoter of iron (3+-transferrin) formation. Biochemistry 20:319–324.

Turk, D.E. 1964. Effect of sex upon the distribution of zinc in the adult foul. Poult. Sci. 43:1472–1474.

Tucker, H.F., and W.D. Salmon. 1955. Parakeratosis or zinc deficiency disease in the pig. Proc. Soc. Exp. Biol. Med. 88:613–616.

Tupper, R., R.W.E. Watts, and A. Wormall. 1954. The incorporation of ^{65}Zn into avian eggs. Biochem. J. 57:245–255.

Turk, J.L., Jr., and F.H. Kratzer. 1960. The effects of cobalt in the diet of the chicks. Poult. Sci. 39:1302.

Ullrey, D.E. 1987. Biochemical and physiological indicators of selenium status in animals. J. Anim. Sci. 65:1712–1726.

Ullrey, D.E., P.S. Brady, P.A. Whetter, P.K. Ku, and W.T. Magee. 1977. Selenium supplementation of diets for sheep and beef cattle. J. Anim. Sci. 46:559–565.

Ullrey, D.E., E.R. Miller, J.P. Hitchcock, P.K. Ku, R.L. Lovert, J. Hegenauer, and P. Saltman. 1973. Oral ferric citrate vs. ferrous sulfate for prevention of baby pig anemia. Mich. Agric. Exp. Stn. Res. Rep. 232:34–38.

Ullrey, D.E., E.R. Miller, O.A. Thompson, I.M. Ackermann, D.A. Schmidt, J.A. Hoefer, and R.W. Luecke. 1960. The requirement of the baby pig for orally administered iron. J. Nutr. 70:187–192.

Underwood, E.J. 1977. Trace elements in human and animal nutrition. 4th ed. Academic Press, New York.

Underwood, E.J. 1981. The mineral nutrition of livestock. 2nd ed. Commonwealth Agric. Bureaux, Slough, England.

Valberg, L.S. 1971. Cobalt. p. 257. In S.C. Skoryna and D. Waldron-Edwards (ed.) Intestinal absorption of metal ions, trace elements and radionuclides. Pergamon, Oxford, England.

Van Bruwaene, R., G.B. Gerber, R. Kirchmann, J. Coland, and J. VanKerkom. 1984. Metabolism of ^{51}Cr, ^{54}Mn, ^{59}Fe and ^{60}Co in lactating dairy cows. Health Phys. 46:1069–1082.

Van Campen, D.R., and E.A. Mitchell. 1965. Absorption of ^{64}Cu, ^{65}Zn, ^{99}Mo and ^{59}Fe from ligated segments of rat gastrointestinal tract. J. Nutr. 86:120–124.

Van den Hamer, C.J.A. 1988. Extracellular transport of trace elements. p. 129–133. In L.S. Hurley et al. (ed.) Trace elements in man and animals—TEMA 6. Plenum Press, New York.

Van Ryssen, J.B.J., and P.R. Barrowman. 1988. Copper and molybdenum levels in tissues of hypercuprotic sheep during and after being fed different levels of molybdenum. p. 541–542. In L.S. Hurley et al. (ed.) Trace elements in man and animals—TEMA 6. Plenum Press, New York.

Van Vleet, J.F., A.H. Rebar, and V.J. Ferrans. 1977. Acute cobalt and isoproterenol cardiotoxicity in swine: protection by selenium-vitamin E supplementation and potentiation by stress-susceptible phenotype. Am. J. Vet. Res. 38:991–1002.

Venn, J.A., R.A. McCance, and E.M. Widdowson. 1947. Iron metabolism in piglet anemia. J. Comp. Pathol. Ther. 57:314–325.

Wahlstrom, R.C., T.B. Goehring, D.D. Johnson, G.W. Libal, O.E. Olson, I.S. Palmer, and R.C. Thaler. 1984. The relationship of hair color to selenium content of hair and selenosis in swine. Nutr. Rep. Int. 29:143–147.

Waldrop, G.L., F. Palida, M. Hadi, P. Longergan, and M. Ettinger. 1988. Differences in Cu-transport by hepatocytes and fibroblasts. p. 145–146. In L.S. Hurley et al. (ed.) Trace elements in man and animals—TEMA 6. Plenum Press, New York.

Wanger, P.D., S.H. Oh, and J.T. Deagen. 1981. Ovine and bovine metallothioneins: Accumulation and depletion of zinc in various tissues. J. Nutr. 111:1196–1206.

Watson, L.T., C.B. Ammerman, J.P. Feaster, and C.E. Roessler. 1973. Influence of manganese intake on metabolism of manganese and other minerals in sheep. J. Anim. Sci. 36:131-136.

Weber, C.W., and B.L. Reid. 1974. Effect of low-fluoride diets fed to mice for six generations. p. 707-709. In W.G. Hoekstra et al. (ed.) Trace element metabolism in animals—TEMA 2. University Park Press, Baltimore, MD.

Wegger, I. 1988. Copper and iron status of calves in relation to plasma protein polymorphism. p. 463-465. In L.S. Hurley et al. (ed.) Trace elements in man and animals—TEMA 6. Plenum Press, New York.

Weigand, E., and M. Kirchgessner. 1978. Homeostatic adaptation of Zn absorption and endogenous Zn excretion over a wide range of dietary Zn supply. p. 106-109. In M. Kirchgessner (ed.) Trace element metabolism in man and animals—TEMA 3. Institut fur Ernahrungsphysiologie, Technische Universitat, Munchen, Freising, Weihenstephan, Federal Republic of Germany.

Weigand, E., and M. Kirchgessner. 1985. Radioisotope studies on true absorption of manganese. p. 506-509. In C.F. Mills et al. (ed.) Trace elements in man and animals—TEMA 5. Commonwealth Agric. Bureaux, Farnham Royal, England.

Weinberg, E.D. 1978. Iron and infection. Microbiol. Rev. 42:45-66.

Weiner, A.C., and R.J. Cousins. 1980. Copper accumulation and metabolism in primary monolayer cultures of rat liver parenchymal cells. Biochim. Biophys. Acta. 629:113-125.

Weiss, K.C., and M.C. Linder. 1985. Copper transport in rats involving a new plasma protein. Am. J. Physiol. 249:E77-E88.

Wilgus, H.R., Jr., and A.R. Patton. 1939. Factors affecting manganese utilization in the chicken. J. Nutr. 18:35-45.

Winston, P.W., D.K. Franzen, S.L. Wimberg, and E.H. Reid. 1985. Comparison of absorption patterns of dietary molybdenum in different forms. p. 531-533. In C.F. Mills et al. (ed.) Trace elements in man and animals—TEMA 5. Commonwealth Agric. Bureaux, Farnham Royal, England.

Wolffram, S., R. Wurmli, and E. Scharrer. 1988. Influence of cysteine on mucosal uptake of 75-Se-selenite by sheep jejunum. p. 353-354. In L.S. Hurley et al. (ed.) Trace elements in man and animals—TEMA 6. Plenum Press, New York.

Woolliams, J.A., N.F. Suttle, G. Wiener, A.C. Field, and C. Woolliams. 1983a. The long-term accumulation and depletion of copper in the liver of diffeent breeds of sheep fed diets of differing copper content. J. Agric. Sci. 100:441-449.

Woolliams, J.A., G. Wiener, N.F. Suttle, and A.C. Field. 1983b. The copper content of wool in relation to breed and the concentration of copper in the liver and plasma. J. Agric. Sci. 100:505-507.

Wright, P.L., and M.C. Bell. 1966. Comparative metabolism of selenium and tellurium in sheep and swine. Am. J. Physiol. 211:6-10.

Yang, M.T., and S.P. Yang. 1988. Effect of molybdenum on hepatic enzymes and minerals of female rats. p. 583-584. In L.S. Hurley et al. (ed.) Trace elements in man and animals—TEMA 6. Plenum Press, New York.

Yang, S.P., M.M. Luo, and H.J. Wei. 1985. Effect of molybdenum and tungsten on carcinogenesis. p. 160-161. In C.F. Mills et al. (ed.) Trace elements in man and animals—TEMA 5. Commonwealth Agric. Bureaux, Farnham Royal, England.

Yasumoto, K., K. Iwami, and M. Yoshida. 1979. Vitamin B_6 dependence on selenomethionine and selenite utilization for glutathione peroxidase in the rat. J. Nutr. 109:760-766.

Yen, J.T., and W.G. Pond. 1985. Plasma thyroid hormones, growth and carcass measurements of genetically obese and lean pigs as influenced by thyroprotein supplementation. J. Anim. Sci. 61:566-572.

Young, R.S. 1984. Cobalt. p. 133-147. In E. Frieden (ed.) Biochemistry of the essential ultratrace elements. Plenum Press, New York.

Yu, S.X., D.G. Masters, Q. Su, Z.S. Wang, Y.Q. Duang, and D.B. Purser. 1988. Mineral and trace element nutrition of sheep in Gansu province, Northern China. p. 171-172. In L.S. Hurley et al. (ed.) Trace elements in man and animals—TEMA 6. Plenum Press, New York.

Zervas, G. 1988. Treatment of dairy sheep with soluble glass boluses. p. 669-670. In L.S. Hurley et al. (ed.) Trace elements in man and animals—TEMA 6. Plenum Press, New York.

Zimmerman, D.R. 1980. Iron in swine nutrition. In National Feed Ingredient Association literature review on iron in animal and poultry nutrition. Natl. Feed Ingredient Assoc., West Des Moines, IA.

Zinn, K.R., and J.S. Morris. 1988. High resolution gamm-ray spectroscopy as an in vitro tool for following the zinc-selenium interaction. p. 591-592. In L.S. Hurley et al. (ed.) Trace elements in man and animals—TEMA 6. Plenum Press, New York.

Chapter 17

Trace Elements in Human Nutrition

DARRELL R. VAN CAMPEN, *USDA-ARS, Ithaca, New York*

The first edition of this book (Mortvedt et al., 1972) did not include a chapter devoted to trace elements in human nutrition, thus some pre-1972 references are included in this chapter. In addition to 11 major elements (C, H, O, N, S, Na, K, Ca, Mg, P, and Cl), the trace elements (Fe, Zn, Cu, Mn, Se, Cr, Mo, and I) are considered essential for humans. Fluoride is generally considered beneficial for maintaining healthy teeth and bones, but has not been shown to be essential for life. Cobalt is considered essential for ruminants because rumen microflora can synthesize sufficient vitamin B_{12} to meet the animal's needs; however, monogastric species require that B_{12} be supplied directly. The newer or ultra trace elements (As, B, Br, Cd, Pb, Li, Ni, Si, Sn, and V) have been shown to be beneficial to some species, under carefully controlled conditions. Generally, deficiencies of these newer trace elements have not been demonstrated in humans; however, B was recently shown to protect against losses of Ca and Mg by postmenopausal women (Nielsen et al., 1987). This chapter will emphasize those elements for which human studies are available. For readers interested in more detail than can be provided here, two books edited by Mertz (1986b, 1987) are recommended.

I. IRON

A. Body Content and Distribution

Iron content averages about 4 to 5 g (60–70 mg kg^{-1}) for a 70-kg male with normal stores (Bothwell et al., 1979), but varies greatly, depending on body size and Fe status. Beutler (1980) estimated total body Fe at <2 g for a 45-kg female with a hemoglobin concentration of 12 g dL^{-1}, and at >6 g for a 100-kg male with a hemoglobin concentration of 18 g dL^{-1}. Approximately 60% of body Fe is found in hemoglobin and 8 to 9% is found in myoglobin. Hemoglobin and myoglobin are responsible for transport and tissue storage of O_2, respectively. Iron in plasma is predominantly bound to transferrin, a transport glycoprotein with two Fe-binding sites and a molecular weight of approximately 76 000 (Schade & Caroline, 1946; Laurell, 1947; Feeney & Allison, 1969). The stability constant for Fe^{3+} is estimated at approximately 10^{24} M^{-1} under physiological conditions (Aisen & Liebman, 1968), and it is normally about 30 to 40% saturated with Fe (Cartwright & Wintrobe, 1949).

About two-thirds of storage Fe is found in ferritin and the remainder is stored as hemosiderin. Ferritin consists of a protein shell of 24 subunits that contain an Fe core. The apoprotein has a moelcular weight of about 450 000 and, when fully saturated with Fe, it has a molecular weight of about 900 000 (Harrison et al., 1974). Small amounts of ferritin circulate in plasma and plasma ferritin concentration is an indicator of Fe stores (Lipschitz et al., 1974).

About 3% of body Fe is found in heme enzymes (cytochromes, catalase), and a similar amount is contained in nonheme enzymes (xanthine oxidase, aconitase, amino acid hydroxylases, and Fe-S proteins).

B. Balance

Iron balance is maintained almost exclusively by changes in absorption; i.e., Fe-depleted individuals absorb more and Fe-sated individuals absorb less Fe than Fe-adequate individuals. Differences in Fe excretion among these groups are small (McCance & Widdowson, 1937). More detailed reviews include: Conrad (1987), Lynch (1984), Charlton and Bothwell (1983), Linder and Munro (1977), and Van Campen (1974).

1. Regulation of Absorption

Edible animal, poultry, and fish tissues average about 40% heme and 60% nonheme Fe, whereas nearly all Fe in plant foods is nonheme. Heme Fe absorption by human subjects averages 20 to 25%, whereas nonheme Fe absorption is usually ≤ 10%. Heme and nonheme Fe are absorbed by different mechanisms; i.e. there are specific heme-receptor sites on the brush border membrane of intestinal mucosal cells (Tenhunen et al., 1980). Once heme enters the mucosal cell, Fe is released by heme oxygenase and, thereafter, is indistinguishable from nonheme Fe (Weintraub et al., 1968).

Nonheme Fe is absorbed primarily from the small intestine (Charlton & Bothwell, 1983) and the rate appears to be highest in the duodenum (Van Campen & Mitchell, 1964). Absorption of nonheme Fe increases in response to increased demand; i.e., Fe deficiency, pregnancy, and moves to higher altitudes generally result in increased Fe absorption. Mucosal epithelial cells are thought to be the primary control point; however, mechanisms for regulation of Fe absorption are poorly understood and none that have been proposed is completely satisfactory. Most proposed mechanisms involve either intracellular or cell-membrane controls. Evidence for intracellular control theories includes the following hypotheses: (i) Fe absorption is blocked when certain intracellular Fe acceptors (mucosal ferritin?) are saturated with Fe (Granick, 1946); or (ii) absorption is enhanced by intracellular Fe acceptors (mucosal transferrin or unsaturated ferritin?) that are released or synthesized in response to Fe deficiency (Heubers et al., 1983; Van Campen, 1974; Heubers et al.,1971).

Evidence for control at the cell membrane includes the following hypotheses: (i) receptor-mediated endocytosis of transferrin-bound Fe has been demonstrated in hepatocytes, reticulocytes, and certain other cell types, and Fe deficiency results in increased numbers of transferrin receptors and increased rates of endocytosis (Holmes & Morgan, 1989); (ii) in hepatocytes, Fe uptake parallels NADH-ferricyanide oxidoreductase activity in the plasma membrane. Presumably, transferrin-bound Fe^{3+} is reduced to Fe^{2+} at the plasma membrane and is transferred across the cell membrane by nonendocytotic processes (Sun et al., 1987). Both hypotheses involve transferrin binding to the plasma membrane by specific receptors. In regard to intestinal absorption, transferrin receptors have been found only on basal and lateral membranes of intestinal epithelial cells; i.e., apparently, there are no transferrin receptors on the apical (lumenal) membrane (Parmley et al., 1985; Banerjee et al., 1986). Thus, these mechanisms may be involved in Fe transport out of the mucosal cell, but probably are not involved in absorption from the lumen. There is no a priori reason to expect Fe in the gut to be transferrin-bound, and, perhaps, it should not be surprising that there are no transferrin receptors on the apical membrane. Various hypotheses regarding regulation of Fe absorption and transport are not mutually exclusive and all of them could play a role.

2. Effects of Diet on Absorption/Bioavailability

Low bioavailability often makes it difficult to meet the Fe needs of people, since both Fe intake and bioavailability are critical. While there is no universally accepted definition of bioavailability, it generally refers to that fraction of a nutrient that is available for absorption and is in a form that is physiologically useful.

Both in vivo and in vitro techniques are used to estimate bioavailability (Van Campen, 1983). In vivo techniques include balance studies, radioactive or stable isotope balance, changes in plasma Fe concentrations, hemoglobin repletion, incorporation of an isotope into hemoglobin, isotope dilution, and whole-body counting. In vitro techniques generally involve a simulated digestion followed by a determination of soluble or dialyzable Fe. All of these techniques are useful, but none is accepted as a universal procedure for determining bioavailability.

Isotopic methods use either intrinsic or extrinsic labeling. Intrinsic labeling provides the isotope to a plant or an animal so that it is incorporated into the food in its naturally occurring form(s). Early studies, using this technique, demonstrated that, in general, Fe from animal food was more available than that from plants (Layrisse et al., 1969). A disadvantage of the intrinsic labeling technique, in addition to time and cost, is that foods are rarely eaten singly and meal composition affects bioavailability. Extrinsic labeling involves in vitro addition of the isotope to a meal or a major component of a meal. The underlying assumptions for interpreting results from studies using extrinsic labeling are that: (i) nonheme Fe consists of a single exchangeable pool; (ii) isotopic Fe added to the meal will equilibrate completely with the pool; and (iii) uptake of the isotope will represent total Fe absorption (Hallberg, 1974). The advantages of extrinsic labeling are reduced time and cost, and the ability to label complete meals. The primary disadvantage is that, in some cases, not all of the meal Fe is exchangeable; thus, the availability of the total-food Fe may be overestimated.

The following discussion of bioavailability is a synopsis of material taken from several reviews including Thompson (1988), Morris (1983, 1987), Kies (1982), and Morck and Cook (1981). Some foods contain Fe absorption enhancers; the two most effective are ascorbic acid and animal tissue. Estimates of nonheme Fe absorption, by individuals with normal Fe stores, range from 3% for meals containing small amounts of ascorbic acid (<25 mg) and meat (<30 g) to 8% for meals containing >75 mg of ascorbate and 90 g of meat (Food and Nutrition Board, 1980). Ascorbic acid is both a reducing agent and an Fe chelator, and either property could enhance Fe absorption. Animal tissue provides heme Fe, which is well used (20–25%) and also enhances absorption of nonheme Fe from other components of the meal. The mechanism for the meat effect is not known, but it has been suggested that amino acids or products of digestion are the enhancers. Individual digestion products that enhance nonheme Fe absorption include cysteine, valine, histidine, fructose, lactate, citrate, malate, tartrate, pyruvate, and succinate.

A number of compounds inhibit Fe absorption. Phytate (inositol hexaphosphate) has received much attention. Generally, addition of Na or K salts of phytate inhibits Fe uptake and insoluble Fe-phytate complexes are poor sources of Fe. Effects of the phytates, which occur naturally in plants, are less consistent, possibly because of the various forms of phytate encountered. Monoferric phytate, a major Fe component in wheat, is well used by rats (*Rattus norvegicus*), dogs (*Canis familiaris*), and humans, whereas Fe from diferric or tetraferric phytate is not. With intrinsically labeled soybean [*Glycine max* (L.) Merr.] there is no correlation between phytate content and Fe utilization by rats and, in some cases, dephytinizing soy flour does not ameliorate its inhibitory effect on Fe absorption. To summarize, the practical role of phytate as an inhibitor of Fe absorption by humans is still in question. Inorganic phosphate can inhibit Fe absorption and may be of practical importance in diets that contain large proportions of grains and seeds. Tannins and other polyphenolics can be inhibitory; e.g., tea (*Camellia sinensis* L.) is a potent inhibitor of Fe absorption. High dietary intakes of either Ca or Zn inhibit Fe utilization. Calcium could be a practical problem for Fe absorption by humans, particularly for those taking Ca supplements; however, the dietary intakes of Zn required to inhibit Fe utilization in experimental animals are much higher than those found in normal human diets.

3. Excretion

Fecal Fe consists mostly of unabsorbed Fe, with endogenous Fe generally accounting for 1 mg d^{-1} or less. About two-thirds of endogenous losses

Table 17-1. Recommended dietary allowances for Fe.†

Category	Age, yr	Fe, mg d^{-1}
Infants	0.0–0.5	6
	0.5–1.0	10
Children	1.0–10	10
Males	11–18	12
	19+	10
Females	11–50	15
	51+	10
Pregnant		30
Lactating		15

† Food and Nutrition Board (1989).

are fecal from desquamated intestinal epithelial cells, bile secretions, and small GI tract blood losses; the remainder is lost in urine, sweat, and sloughed skin tissue. In women of reproductive age, menstrual losses averaged over an entire cycle approximate 0.5 mg d^{-1}; however, this varies widely and approximately 10% of menstruating women lose an average of ≥ 2 mg d^{-1} (Hallbert et al., 1966). During pregnancy, losses to the fetus generally exceed those of menstruation, i.e., about 2 mg d^{-1} averaged over the gestation period. Losses in milk approximate those lost in menstrual blood (0.5–1 mg d^{-1}) (Bothwell et al., 1979).

C. Requirements

Recommended Dietary Allowances (RDA's) are designed to meet the needs of practically all individuals and may exceed actual requirements of much of the population. In establishing RDAs, 10% absorption of dietary Fe is assumed; therefore, a normal adult male, with obligatory losses of 1 mg d^{-1} has an RDA of 10 mg of Fe d^{-1}. Pregnant women generally cannot meet their Fe needs by diet alone and daily supplements are usually recommended. For lactating women, Fe loss in milk is usually less than that of menstrual loss. Menstruation often is absent during lactation; thus, no additional Fe allowance is recommended for this group. The RDA's of Fe for various age and sex groups are summarized in Table 17-1.

D. Deficiency

Iron deficiency is one of the most common nutritional deficiencies in the world. The most susceptible groups are infants, young children, adolescents, menstruating women, and pregnant or lactating women. In one USA study, 20% of women and 3% of men had low or no Fe stores, and 8.4% of women and 1.2% of men were anemic (Cook et al., 1976). Developing countries often have a higher incidence of Fe deficiency, which is often more severe than that in developed countries. Iron deficiency develops sequentially. Depletion of Fe stores, without anemia, is best detected by low plasma or serum ferritin concentrations (Lipschitz et al., 1974; Walters et al., 1973). The second stage usually results in a decrease in transferrin saturation and an increase in free erythrocyte protoporphyrin (FEP) concentrations (Dallman et al., 1984).

Severe Fe deficiency, or anemia, is most commonly diagnosed by low hemoglobin and/or hematocrit values. Estimates of the prevalence of Fe deficiency depend on the measurements used; however, by any criterion, significant numbers of people are affected. Routine clinical use of serum ferritin, transferrin saturation, and FEP, in addition to hemoglobin or hematocrit, would allow earlier diagnosis and intervention. In addition to anemia, consequences of severe Fe deficiency include: decreased immuno-competence and resistance to infection; disorders of the gastrointestinal system, including hypochlorhydria or achlorhydria, and malabsorption of certain nutrients; decreased ability to maintain core body temperature; decreased capacity for physical work; and, possibly, changes in cognitive behavior (Vyas & Chandra, 1984).

E. Toxicity

Reports of chronic Fe poisoning in adults are generally limited to unusual circumstances such as Bantu siderosis, which results from consumption of beer that is home brewed in Fe kettles and is very high in Fe (Bothwell et al., 1979). Iron overload is also encountered in certain metabolic disorders including idiopathic hemochromatosis, transfusional siderosis, and cirrhosis. Acute Fe poisoning generally results either from ingestion during suicide attempts in adults or accidental ingestion of Fe supplements by young children. Accidental ingestion by children accounts for several hundred hospital admissions each year (Bothwell et al., 1979).

F. Sources

Iron bioavailability data are often presented as percent absorption, which can mask the importance of total-Fe intake. For example, Hallberg and Rossander (1982) found that replacing meat with soy products in a hamburger meal significantly decreased percent absorption of nonheme Fe. However, the total amount of Fe absorbed was not significantly affected because soy has a higher Fe content than meat.

1. Native Iron

A joint report by the U.S. Department of Health and Human Services and the USDA (1986) summarized contributions of various food groups to dietary Fe intake in the USA. These were: grain products, 35%; meat, poultry, and fish, 32%; vegetables, 12%; other protein foods (meat, poultry, and fish mixtures, eggs, beans, and nuts), 8%; fruit, 5%; sugar and sweets, 3%; milk, cream, and cheese, 2%; miscellaneous, 2%; fats and oils, <1%. Many Western diets contain a relatively constant 6 to 7 mg of Fe per 1000 kcal, making it difficult for some population groups to meet the RDA without becoming obese. Foods with a good Fe/calorie ratio (>20 mg/1000 kcal) include asparagus (*Asparagus officinales* L.), green bean (*Phaseolus vulgaris* L.), broccoli (*Brassica oleracea* var. *Botrytis* L.), lettuce (*Latuca sativa* L.), liver, spinach (*Spinacea oleracea* L.), and wheat (*Triticum aestivum* L.) bran. Intermediate sources 7–19 mg/1000 kcal) include ground or round beef, enriched white bread, whole wheat bread, chicken (*Gallus domesticus*), and egg. Poor sources (<7 mg per 1000 kcal) include apple (*Mallus sylvestris* Mill.) bologna, frankfurters, unenriched bread, milk, potato (*Solanum tuberosum* L.) chips, rice (*Oryza sativa* L.), white sugar, and unenriched white flour (Thompson, 1988).

2. Fortification

Iron-fortified formulas and Fe-fortified cereals are often recommended for infants and young children. White flour has been enriched in the USA since 1945 at a concentration of 33 mg kg^{-1}, which provides about 22 mg Fe kg^{-1} for bread and other products made with enriched flour. There is little evidence that this level of fortification has reduced the incidence of anemia, perhaps because of the low bioavailability of some products used for fortification. Proposals to increase Fe fortification levels have generated considerable opposition, generally on the basis that this could exacerbate Fe-overload disorders or delay diagnosis of disorders for which anemia is an early clinical sign.

3. Contamination

Many soils contain high concentrations of Fe (>20 000 mg kg^{-1}), and contamination of food with soil or dust can contribute substantially to Fe intake. Hallberg et al. (1983) reported that 4 to 50% of the Fe in Asian meals was from contamination, even with carefully washed foods. Cary et al. (1986) used Ti content of plant samples to correct for soil or dust contamination (little or no Ti is taken up by plants; thus, any Ti in the sample is the result of contamination). Using this procedure, Van Buren et al. (1989) reported that correction of the outer peel of beet roots for contamination reduced average Fe concentrations from 203 to 81 mg kg^{-1}. Cary (E. Cary, 1989, personal communication) has found that leafy vegetables may contain large quantities of contamination Fe, even after vigorous washes with dilute acid or chelating solutions. Contamination Fe is poorly available, contributes substantial amounts of Fe to some foods, and is not completely removed by vigorous washing, consequently it should be taken into account when assessing Fe intake.

II. ZINC

Recent reviews of Zn nutrition include those of Smith (1988), Hambidge et al. (1986), Cousins (1985), Sandstead and Evans (1984), and Inglett (1983).

A. Body Content and Distribution

Total-body Zn for a 70-kg male approximates 1.5 to 2.5 g, with about 30% in bone, 60% in muscle, and the remainder distributed among other tissues. The average concentration is about 30 mg kg^{-1} of fat-free tissue, with individual tissues ranging from 10 to 100 mg kg^{-1}. The concentrations of Zn in bones and teeth are generally higher (100–150 mg kg^{-1}), but are not readily mobilized. Zinc concentrations of blood, hair, bone, testes, and liver may reflect Zn intake; however, Zn concentrations of soft tissues generally are not significantly affected by Zn status, since deficiency usually results in overall growth retardation, rather than declines in tissue Zn concentrations.

Zinc in human blood generally is in the range of 4 to 8 mg L^{-1}. Plasma accounts for about 15 to 20% of whole-blood Zn and concentrations usually range from 70 to 100 μg dL^{-1}, with serum being about 10% higher. About 75 to 80% of whole-blood Zn is found in erythrocytes, primarily as the enzyme carbonic anhydrase. White cells account for 3 to 4% of whole blood Zn and, on a per cell basis, contain 5 to 10 times as much Zn as red cells. For more detail, see Hambidge et al. (1986).

B. Balance

1. Absorption

Zinc absorption is generally estimated at 30 to 40%, but is affected both by diet and homeostatic controls. Zinc, presumably, is absorbed as Zn^{2+} along the entire small intestine. The exact mechanism(s) have not been delineated, but there is evidence that it is an active process requiring oxygen (Kowarski et al., 1974) and is a homeostatically controlled, carrier-mediated process (Solomons & Cousins, 1984) with both saturable and nonsaturable components (Oestreicher & Cousins, 1989). Metallothionein influences Zn absorption, perhaps by sequestering Zn in intestinal mucosal cells (Cousins, 1985), and thereby controls the amount of Zn available for transport. Transport of Zn in plasma is thought to be mediated by binding to albumin.

A number of dietary factors affect Zn absorption. Several amino acids (methionine, histidine, and cysteine) and other low-molecular-weight compounds (glutathione, citrate, and picolinate) facilitate absorption. Proposed roles of citrate and picolinate in Zn absorption are controversial and stem primarily from efforts to explain why Zn in human milk is more readily available than that from cow (*Bos taurus*) milk (Evans & Johnson, 1980; Lonnerdal et al., 1981). No consensus regarding the practical roles of these and other low-molecular-weight ligands has been reached.

2. Bioavailability

Zinc from animal foods is thought to be more available than that from plant foods. Efforts to explain these differences have resulted in extensive, and sometimes confusing, literature on the effects of phytate, fiber, and protein on Zn utilization. Addition of soluble phytate salts reduces utilization of Zn. In contrast, studies with naturally occurring phytate are inconclusive; in some cases Zn absorption and utilization were reduced, and, in others, there was little or no effect. Similarly, literature on fiber and protein ranges from significant changes in Zn absorption to no effect. In part, these discrepancies may be a result either of differences in the fibers and proteins that have been studied or of differences in other dietary components. The complete literature on factors affecting absorption and/or availability of Zn is too extensive to cover in detail and readers are referred to Hambidge et al. (1986), House and Welch (1984), and Inglett (1983).

Mineral/mineral interactions are also confounded by diet, species, etc. For example, increased dietary Ca exacerbated negative effects of phytate on Zn absorption by rats (Morris & Ellis, 1980), but Ca supplements, in the absence of phytate, had no effect on Zn utilization by humans (Dawson-Hughes et al., 1986). Concerns have been raised regarding the effects of Fe supplements on Zn utilization (Solomons et al., 1983); however, it seems unlikely that the Fe content of normal, unsupplemented diets presents a problem. Experimentally, either high dietary Cu or Cd depress Zn absorption (Van Campen, 1969), but it is unlikely that normal diets contain sufficient amounts of these elements to significantly affect Zn absorption (Valberg et al., 1984).

3. Excretion

Zinc is primarily excreted via the feces (McCance & Widdowson, 1942). Fecal Zn includes both unabsorbed Zn and endogenous Zn, which has re-entered the gastrointestinal tract via bile, pancreatic, salivary, and mucosal cell secretions, and sloughing of mucosal epithelial cells. Endogenous fecal excretion can account for 1/3 or more of total fecal Zn (House et al., 1982). In humans, losses in urine usually range from 300 to 600 μg d^{-1} (Sandstead & Evans, 1984) and losses in sweat account for about 500 μg d^{-1} in temperate climates (Jacob et al., 1979).

C. Requirements

There are no sensitive indicators for Zn status; thus, the Zn RDA's are based primarily on balance studies. For adult males, these studies indicate a requirement for absorbed Zn of about 2.5 mg d^{-1}. Assuming 20% absorption yields an estimated daily requirement of 12.5 mg. To meet the needs of practically all healthy individuals, including those who consume diets of low Zn bioavailability, 2.5 mg d^{-1} is added as a safety factor, resulting in an RDA of 15 mg d^{-1} for adult males. Because of their lower body weight the RDA for women is set at 12 mg d^{-1}. The RDA's for pregnant and lactating women include an allowance to meet the needs of the fetus and to compensate for zinc losses in milk, respectively. For infants and children, RDA's are adjusted to provide the Zn required for growth. The Zn RDA's for various age and sex groups are summarized in Table 17-2.

Table 17-2. Recommended dietary allowances for Zn.†

Category	Age, yr	Zn, mg d^{-1}
Infants	0.0-1.0	5
Children	1.0-10	10
Males	11+	15
Females	11+	12
Pregnant		15
Lactating		
1st 6 mo		19
2nd 6 mo		16

† Food and Nutrition Board (1989).

D. Deficiency

Readily available stores of Zn are limited. Animal studies suggest that exchangeable Zn accounts for only about 11% of total-body Zn (House et al., 1982). Consequently, Zn deficiency develops rapidly compared with deficiencies of most other elements. More than 200 Zn enzymes and proteins have been identified (Hambidge et al., 1986). Severe Zn deficiency depresses activities of several important enzymes including alkaline phosphatase, alcohol dehydrogenase, thymidine kinase, carboxypeptidase A, and DNA and RNA polymerases (Sandstead & Evans, 1984). Zinc may also play a role in maintaining a secondary structure of nucleic acids and nucleoproteins, and plays a role in maintaining the integrity of cell membranes (Bettger & O'Dell, 1981). The multiplicity of Zn functions results in nonspecific, and often confusing, symptoms of Zn deficiency, particularly in mild deficiencies.

Signs of Zn deficiency in humans were first reported by Prasad et al. (1963); adolescent males in the Middle East displayed growth failure and sexual immaturity. Sandstead and Evans (1984) suggest that, in the USA, diets of poor children from the southeastern region, certain institutionalized children, and teenage and college-age women may be marginal with respect to Zn. Also, there is considerable evidence for Zn deficiency in some populations of infants and young children (Hambidge et al., 1986). Finally, pregnancy results in increased Zn requirements; thus, some pregnant women may be at risk for Zn deficiency (Jameson, 1976).

The assessment of Zn deficiency, particularly marginal deficiency, is difficult. Clinical signs include dermatitis, poor wound healing, impaired immunity, growth failure, hypogonadism, oligospermia, impotence, hypogeusia, poor dark adaptation, and neuropsychological dysfunction (Sandstead & Evans, 1984). The wide range of symptoms is not surprising as Zn metalloenzymes are involved in lipid, protein, carbohydrate, and nucleic acid metabolism. Unfortunately, none of the clinical signs are specific to Zn. Plasma and hair are the tissues most commonly used to assess Zn status, although they are not reliable indicators. In some cases, diagnosis of Zn deficiency can be confirmed only by a measurable response to Zn supplementation.

E. Toxicity

Zinc toxicity generally is limited to cases of accidental overdose or to therapeutic use of high doses of Zn. However, lower doses are not without effect, particularly in regard to Cu. Balance studies suggest that Zn/Cu ratios of 10:1 may depress Cu utilization (Solomons, 1983). Sickle cell anemia patients receiving 150 mg Zn d^{-1} (10 times the RDA) developed signs of Cu deficiency (Prasad et al., 1978), and young men receiving 160 mg Zn d^{-1} experienced substantial declines in plasma high-density lipoproteins (Hooper et al., 1980). Animal and epidemiological studies suggest that high intakes of Zn, combined with low intakes of Cu, adversely affect cholesterol metabolism (Klevay, 1980); however, the impact on human health is difficult to assess.

F. Sources

Generally, the best sources of Zn are red meat and seafoods, and the worst sources are fruits and fats. Whole cereal grains are relatively rich in Zn, but milling often removes 75 to 80% of the whole-grain Zn. Legume seeds such as pea (*Pisum sativum* L.), lentil (*Lens culinaris* Medic), and soybean contain substantial amounts of Zn; however, it generally seems to be less available than that from animal sources. Phytate and fiber are often blamed for low availability of Zn from legume seeds, but experimental results are not consistent. Data on the Zn composition of foods is extensive and much of it is summarized in the USDA's Handbook 8 (Consumer Nutrition Center, 1976).

1. Effect of Agronomic Practices

In contrast to some trace elements, including Fe, Mn, and Cr, the Zn content of some plant foods can be increased by increasing the Zn supply to the plants (Welch & House, 1984). Zinc fertilization, possibly in excess of the needs of the plant, could increase Zn intake with little or no effect on bioavailability (Welch & House, 1982; Welch et al., 1974).

III. COPPER

Reviews of Cu in human nutrition include those of Davis and Mertz (1987), O'Dell (1984), Owen (1981–82), and the National Research Council (1977).

A. Body Content and Distribution

Total-body Cu of a 70-kg male is about 75 mg or an average fat-free tissue concentration of approximately 1 mg kg^{-1}. The young of most species are born with 3 to 5 times more Cu per unit of body weight than adults (Underwood, 1977). Adult, whole blood contains about 1 μg mL^{-1}, which is equally distributed between plasma and erythrocytes. Serum or plasma Cu concentrations increase two- to threefold during pregnancy, but return to normal during the first few weeks postpartum. About 90% of plasma Cu is bound to the metalloprotein, ceruloplasmin, and the remainder is loosely bound to albumen and, perhaps, amino acids (Neumann & Sass-Kortsak, 1967). About 40% of erythrocyte Cu is loosely bound to amino acids and nonspecific proteins. The remaining 60% is in the Cu protein, erythrocuprein, now known to be the enzyme, superoxide dismutase. Apparently, the liver protein is identical to cerebrocuprein and hepatocuprein found in brain and liver, respectively (Carrico & Deutsch, 1970).

The liver is the primary storage organ for Cu, and concentrations depend upon species, age, and diet. Normal, adult concentrations range from 10 to 50 mg kg^{-1} on a dry weight basis (Underwood, 1977). Full-term infants have much higher concentrations (200–300 mg kg^{-1}).

B. Balance

1. Absorption/Bioavailability

Approximately 2% of body Cu is lost daily (Cartwright & Wintrobe, 1964); thus, a 70-kg male needs to absorb about 1.0 to 1.5 mg d^{-1} to stay in balance. Absorption occurs by both saturable and unsaturable pathways, with the former predominating at low Cu concentrations. Absorption is regulated, in part, by the S-containing protein, metallothionein. Cousins (1985) proposed that excess Cu induces synthesis of thionein, which sequesters Cu in the intestinal mucosa, thereby preventing further absorption. Absorption ranges from 30 to 50% (Sternlieb, 1967), but is affected by many dietary and physiological factors (Van Campen, 1970). High dietary intakes of ascorbic acid depress bioavailability of Cu to rats (Van Campen & Gross, 1968), guinea pigs (*Cavia cobaya*) (Smith & Bidlack, 1980), and, possibly, humans (Finley & Cerklewski, 1983; Jacob et al., 1987). Zinc interference with Cu absorption has been demonstrated in animals (Van Campen & Scaife, 1967) and Cu deficiency has been observed in human subjects receiving Zn supplements (Prasad et al., 1978). Effects of fructose on Cu utilization are puzzling in that male rats are affected more than females (Fields et al., 1984). A number of other dietary components, including Ca, Fe, fiber, organic acids, and amino acids, have been shown, experimentally, to influence Cu utilization (Davis & Mertz, 1987). The practical importance of these factors in human nutrition is uncertain.

2. Transport and Storage

Copper is transported to the liver as albumin or, possibly, amino acid complexes (Neumann & Sass-Kortsak, 1967), incorporated into ceruloplasmin and released back into the plasma. The role of ceruloplasmin in Cu transport is not fully understood, although it has been shown to be more efficient than other Cu compounds in restoring cytochrome C oxidase in Cu-depleted animals (Hsieh & Frieden, 1975). The mechanism by which Cu transfer takes place is not known; apparently, Cu^{2+} must be reduced to Cu^+ to be released and transferred (Owen, 1975). Hepatic Cu is found primarily as superoxide dismutase, metallothionein and cytochrome C oxidase, and as unidentified species bound to lysosomes and nuclei.

3. Excretion

The primary excretory route for Cu is fecal. Biliary excretion accounts for 0.5 to 1.0 mg of Cu d^{-1} (Sternlieb et al., 1961); direct secretion of ceruloplasmin into the intestine amounts to about 0.1 mg d^{-1} (Waldmann et al., 1967). The remaining endogenous fecal Cu is contributed by saliva, gastric, and pancreatic secretions. Urinary losses generally are about 0.05 mg d^{-1}; e.g., a recent study reported daily urinary excretion of 0.025 to 0.074 mg, depending on diet and season (Iyengar, 1989). Biliary Cu is protein bound and reabsorption is limited (Gollan & Deller, 1973).

C. Requirements

Previous recommendations for Cu were based primarily on balance studies (Robinson et al., 1973; Butler & Daniel, 1973; Engel et al., 1967). Some of the earlier studies suggested requirements of ≥ 2 mg d^{-1} for adults. However, Klevay et al. (1980) reported that adult men could replace urinary and fecal losses when consuming a diet providing 1.3 mg d^{-1}, and recent studies using the stable ^{65}Cu isotope also suggest adult requirements of <2 mg d^{-1}. Women with an intake of 1.25 mg d^{-1} were essentially in balance (Johnson et al., 1988), and, in young men, ^{65}Cu balance was achieved at 0.8 mg d^{-1} (Turnlund et al., 1989). For other age and sex groups, even fewer human data are available. Butte et al. (1987) reported that Cu intake of breast-fed infants averaged 0.23 mg d^{-1}, or approximately 40 μg kg^{-1} d^{-1}, for the first 4 mo. and, presumably, this was adequate. Positive Cu balance has been observed in children from 3 mo. to 8 yr of age with Cu intakes as low as 35 μg kg^{-1} d^{-1} (Alexander et al., 1974). Because of uncertainty about human requirements for Cu, and certain other nutrients, the Food and Nutrition Board (1989) provides "Estimated Safe and Adequate Daily Dietary Intakes (ESADDI's)" in lieu of RDA's. These ESADDIS for Cu are summarized in Table 17-3.

Table 17-3. Estimated safe and adequate daily dietary intakes of Cu.†

Category	Age, yr	Cu, mg d^{-1}
Infants	0.0-0.5	0.4-0.6
	0.5-1	0.6-0.7
Children and	1-3	0.7-1.0
adolescents	4-6	1.0-1.5
	7-10	1.0-2.0
Adults	11+	1.5-2.5
		1.5-3.0

† Food and Nutrition Board (1989).

D. Deficiency

Overt Cu deficiency in adult humans is rare. Most observed cases are associated with prolonged parenteral nutrition (Vilter et al., 1974), administration of Cu-chelators (Henkin et al., 1967), malabsorption disorders (Sternlieb & Janowitz, 1964), or protein-losing disorders (Waldmann et al., 1967). Copper deficiency in infants and young children is usually associated either with long-term intake of cow's milk or with severe malnutrition (Al-Rashid & Spangler, 1971; Graham & Cordano, 1969, Cordano & Graham, 1966).

Copper-dependent metalloenzymes include: (i) ceruloplasmin (ferroxidase I) and ferroxidase II, a nonceruloplasmin oxidase, both of which catalyze oxidation of Fe^{2+} to Fe^{3+}; (ii) cytochrome C oxidase, the terminal oxidase in the respiratory chain; (iii) dopamine beta-hydroxylase, which catalyzes conversion of dopamine to norepinephrine; (iv) lysyl oxidase, an enzyme involved in synthesis of collagen and elastic proteins; (v) monoamine oxidase, which catalyzes oxidation of epinephrine and serotonin; (vi) superoxide disumutases, which catalyzes conversion of superoxide into O_2 and H_2O_2; (vii) tyrosinase, which is involved in converting tyrosine to melanin pigment; and (viii) peptidyl glycine alpha-amidating monooxygenase, which is required for post-translational maturation of several neuropeptides. For more detail on Cu proteins and enzymes, see Davis and Mertz (1987).

Consequences of Cu deficiency discussed by Davis and Mertz (1987) include: (i) anemia associated with impaired Fe absorption and utilization, apparently a result of decreased activities of ferroxidase I and ferroxidase II. These Cu metalloenzymes catalyze oxidation of Fe^{2+} to Fe^{3+}, a necessary step for Fe mobilization and transport (Frieden & Hsieh, 1976); (ii) bone and cardiovascular disorders, which can be explained, in part, by reduced lysyl oxidase, an enzyme required for the synthesis of desmosine and isodesmosine, the cross-links in bone collagen and in elastic proteins (O'Dell et al., 1966); (iii) Mental and/or nervous system deterioration and defective keratinization of hair, which are features of the severe Cu deficiency observed in Menke's syndrome, a genetic disorder with defective Cu utilization. The specific role of Cu in these defects is not known, however deficiency results in reduction in levels of the neurotransmitters, dopamine and norepinephrine (Morgan & O'Dell, 1977), and in defective myelination in the brain stem and spinal cord (Underwood, 1977). Defective keratinization is thought to be a result of impaired formation or incorporation of S^{2-} groups during keratin synthesis; and (iv) other Cu-deficiency disorders including: depigmentation of hair and wool (possibly a result of decreased tyrosinase activity), decreased immunocompetence, decreased resistance to oxidative stress, increased serum cholesterol, infertility, and abnormal carbohydrate metabolism.

E. Toxicity

Acute Cu toxicity in humans is rare and is usually associated with consumption of acidic food or drink that has had prolonged contact with Cu containers or with ingestion of gram quantities of Cu salts in suicide attempts.

Acute poisoning causes ulcerations of gastrointestinal mucosa, hemolysis, hepatic necrosis, and renal damage. Chronic Cu poisoning also is rare and prolonged intakes of 0.5 mg kg^{-1} body weight (10–20 times normal) are thought to be safe for monogastric species. Much information on consequences of chronic toxicity is derived from studies of patients with Wilson's Disease, a genetic disorder with low or undetectable levels of serum ceruloplasmin and high tissue concentrations of Cu. These consequences include liver necrosis and cirrhosis, nervous system disorders, kidney failure, and, if untreated, death.

F. Sources

Oysters (*Ostrea* spp.), liver and other organ meats, mushrooms (*Agaricus campestris*), nuts, and dried legumes are generally considered good dietary sources of Cu. Copper content of plant foods is influenced by soil type and pH, fertilizer, fungicides, season, weather, contamination with soil or airborne particles, and contamination during harvesting, storage, or processing. Copper in animal foods varies with species, diet, age, and tissue or organ. Several publications (Davis & Mertz, 1987; Owen, 1981–82; National Research Council, 1977) provide representative ranges of food Cu content.

IV. MANGANESE

Manganese was recognized as essential for animals in 1931, and effects of deficiency in animals have been well characterized (Hurley & Keen, 1987; Kies, 1987; Hurley, 1984; Underwood, 1977). However, information from human studies is limited. By inference, one would expect roles for Mn in humans to parallel those in animals; however, the practical significance of Mn in human nutrition is not well defined.

A. Body Content and Distribution

The adult human body contains about 10 to 20 mg of Mn (Schroeder et al., 1966). Compared with most trace elements, concentration differences between organs, and between infants and adults are small (Casey & Robinson, 1978; Widdowson et al., 1972). Whole blood contains about 0.01 μg mL^{-1}, most of which is in the erythrocytes. Manganese content tends to be highest (1.0–1.5 mg kg^{-1} fresh weight) in tissues rich in mitochondria, such as liver, intestine, and kidney. It is deposited in bone, but bone Mn is not readily mobilized (Hurley & Keen, 1987).

B. Balance

Data on Mn absorption and utilization by humans are limited. Estimates of 3 to 5% absorption are often cited, but are based primarily on animal studies. In a recent human study using radioactive Mn, average Mn retention was 14% at 5 d after dosing and 5% at 10 d after dosing; however, absorption was not estimated (Davidsson et al., 1988). Balance studies (Johnson et al., 1982; Spencer et al., 1979; Greger et al., 1978; McLeod & Robinson, 1972) generally demonstrated either slightly positive or slightly negative balances at intakes of 2.5 mg d^{-1} or greater. Feces contain both unabsorbed and endogenously secreted Mn, and the amounts are small. Therefore, apparent absorption is difficult to determine and to interpret.

Mechanisms for Mn absorption are not known. However, recent studies with membrane vesicles demonstrated both saturable and nonsaturable components, suggesting that there are specific Mn-binding sites on intestinal brush border membranes (Kabata et al., 1989). In animal studies, Mn from milk is well utilized (Carter et al., 1974), and utilization is depressed by phytate (Davies & Nightingale, 1975) or by high Fe intakes (Gruden, 1977). Conversely, Mn absorption is increased by anemia (Chandra & Shukla, 1976). From human balance studies, Kies et al. (1987) suggest that, at low intakes, Mn bioavailability is enhanced by ascorbic acid and by meat-containing diets, but is depressed by Fe and certain dietary fibers. The effects of Fe are consistent with recent studies, suggesting that plasma Mn is predominantly transferrin bound (Davidsson et al., 1989). It has generally been accepted that biliary excretion was the primary mechanism for maintaining Mn balance (Papavasiliou et al., 1966). However, a recent paper suggests that, for rats, both absorption and excretion are important in maintaining balance (Lee & Johnson, 1988). Recent reviews of Mn absorption and excretion include those of Hurley and Keen (1987), and Kies (1987).

C. Requirements

Human data on Mn requirements are limited primarily to balance studies, a number of which have been summarized by Freeland-Graves et al. (1987). The effects of Mn status on endogenous Mn losses makes interpretation of balance studies very difficult. There is little evidence for Mn deficiency in people consuming normal diets; thus, it seems that the estimated current dietary intakes of 2 to 5 mg d^{-1} are adequate. For infants and children, the average daily intake from human milk has been estimated at only 2 μg d^{-1} for the first month after birth (Casey et al., 1985). This low intake has not been associated with Mn deficiency, but probably results in depletion of tissue reserves in young infants. Gibson and De Wolfe (1980) estimated that the introduction of other foods results in an average intake of 0.4 mg d^{-1}

Table 17-4. Estimated safe and adequate daily dietary intakes of Mn.†

Category	Age, yr	Mn, mg d^{-1}
Infants	0.0–0.5	0.3–0.6
	0.5–1.0	0.6–1.0
Children	1–3	1.0–1.5
	4–6	1.5–2.0
	7–10	2.0–3.0
Others	11+	2.0–5.0

† Food and Nutrition Board (1989).

for infants up to 0.5 yr, and 0.7 mg d^{-1} between 0.5 and 1 yr. Provisional recommendations are based on these values. Ranges for children and adolescents are obtained by extrapolation. No increased allowances are suggested for pregnancy and lactation since increased needs are probably modest. The ESADDIs for Mn are summarized in Table 17–4.

D. Deficiency

Manganese functions as a cofactor for a number of hydrolases, kinases, decarboxylases, and transferases, and in several metalloenzymes. The Mn-activated glycotransferases are of particular interest. In Mn deficiency, glycotransferase activity is depressed, resulting in reduced synthesis of mucopolysaccharides of the glucoseaminoglycan family. This leads to defects in cartilage or bone matrix formation, which is manifested in a number of ways, particularly by abnormal skeletal development (Leach & Liburn, 1978). Also, offspring of Mn-deficient mothers exhibit poor balance and coordination. In these offspring, the otoliths (calcified structures in the inner ear that are essential to normal balance) are defective, presumably the result of depressed mucopolysaccharide synthesis (Shrader et al., 1973).

Manganese metalloenzymes include arginase, pyruvate carboxylase, and Mn-dependent superoxide dismutase. Manganese superoxide dismutase is found in mitochondria and is of special interest because it catalyzes dismutation of superoxide radicals, thereby protecting vital cellular components from free radical damage (McCord et al., 1971). Manganese deficiency is also associated with abnormal lipid and carbohydrate metabolism in animals, but the specific biochemical lesions are not known. For recent reviews, see Zidenberg-Cherr and Keen (1987) or Hurley and Keen (1987).

Manganese deficiency has not been clinically diagnosed in otherwise normal humans. Signs of experimentally induced Mn deficiency may include rashes or dermatitis, hypocholesterolemia, and elevated concentrations of Ca and P (Freeland-Graves et al., 1987). Low Mn has been associated with galactosemia, epilepsy, phenylketonuria, and pancreatic insufficiency (Freeland-Graves et al., 1987), but cause/effect relationships have not been demonstrated. In the absence of widespread Mn deficiencies in normal human populations, its practical significance in human nutrition is difficult to assess.

E. Toxicity

Manganese toxicity produces psychiatric disorders resembling schizophrenia, followed by permanent neurological disorders resembling Parkinson's disease. Cases of Mn toxicity in humans generally are the result of chronic inhalation of airborne Mn in mines or factories (Ulrich et al., 1979). Orally ingested Mn is relatively nontoxic; rats can tolerate dietary intakes of 1000 mg kg^{-1} of body weight (25 to 50 times normal) with no depression of growth (Hurley & Keen, 1987).

F. Sources

Nuts and whole grains are the richest sources of Mn, followed by fruits and vegetables. Dairy products, meats, and seafoods contain only small amounts (Food and Nutrition Board, 1980). Hurley and Keen (1987) report the following mean concentrations of Mn: cereals, 6.77 mg kg^{-1}; vegetables, 1.34 to 1.67 mg kg^{-1}; meat, 0.59 mg kg^{-1}; fish, 0.85 mg kg^{-1}; and milk, <0.10 mg kg^{-1}. For more complete information on Mn in foods and meals, see Kies et al. (1987) or Freeland-Graves et al. (1987).

V. CHROMIUM

Chromium is necessary for normal glucose metabolism in animals. Responses to Cr supplementation have been demonstrated in some human trials. Recent reviews include those of Anderson (1987, 1988), Borel and Anderson (1984), Pi-Sunyer and Offenbacher (1984), Saner (1980), and Mertz (1969).

A. Body Content and Distribution

Chromium is present in all body tissues, is not concentrated in any particular organ or tissue, and, with the exception of lung tissue, tissue concentrations tend to decline with age (Anderson, 1987). In contrast to some pre-1970 estimates, which exceeded 1000 μg L^{-1}, normal serum Cr concentrations are now thought to range from 0.1 to 0.3 μg L^{-1}. This change is, primarily, a result of improved methodology and, particularly, improved control of Cr contamination. Similarly, estimates of normal, daily, urinary Cr excretion have declined over the past two decades and are now thought to be <1 μg d^{-1} (Anderson, 1987). Urinary Cr is considered a reliable indicator of Cr intake with intakes >40 μg d^{-1}, but tends to be relatively constant at intakes <40 μg d^{-1} (Anderson & Koslovsky, 1985).

B. Balance

The mechanisms for Cr absorption are not known. Absorption of Cr from inorganic, trivalent compounds declines with increasing intake and is generally $<3\%$ (Anderson & Koslovsky, 1985). Chromium competes with Fe for binding to transferrin, suggesting the possibility of parallel transport mechanisms (Sargent et al., 1979). It is stored in a mobilizeable pool and is released, as is insulin, in response to a glucose challenge (Liu & Abernathy, 1982; Glinsmann et al., 1966). Virtually all endogenous Cr is excreted in the urine (Doisy et al., 1971; Mertz, 1969) and approximates 0.5 μg d^{-1} (Anderson et al., 1983). Excretion can be increased by high sugar diets, diabetes, strenuous exercise, and trauma (Anderson, 1988).

Table 17-5. Estimated safe and adequate daily dietary intakes of Cr.†

Category	Age, yr	Cr, μg d^{-1}
Infants	0.0–0.5	10–40
	0.5–1.0	20–60
Children	1–3	20–80
	4–6	30–120
Others	7+	50–200

† Food and Nutrition Board (1989).

C. Requirements

Urine is the primary route of Cr excretion and minimum requirements for absorbed Cr can be estimated from daily urinary losses. In adults, mean urinary losses are usually in the range of 0.5 to 1.5 μg d^{-1}; i.e., about 1 μg d^{-1} of Cr must be absorbed to meet minimal requirements. In contrast to older estimates of daily Cr intakes of 100 to 200 μg d^{-1}, more recent studies suggest daily intakes ≤ 50 μg for developed countries (Finland, Canada, England, USA) (Anderson, 1988). In the USA, there is no indication of Cr deficiency in the adult population, which consumes an average of 50 μg d^{-1}. Also, there is no evidence for adverse effects at intakes of 200 μg d^{-1}. Based primarily on these observations and an estimated bioavailability of 0.5 to 1% from mixed diets, adult intakes of 50 to 200 μg d^{-1} of Cr are tentatively recommended. The ESADDIs for other age groups are obtained by extrapolation from adult levels. The ESADDIs for Cr are summarized in Table 17-5. A recent study, with 10 men and 22 women consuming self-selected diets, indicated that more than 90% were consuming less than the recommended amount of Cr (Anderson, 1988). However, there is little to suggest that 90% of the population is actually suffering from Cr deficiency.

D. Deficiency

Early animal studies indicated that an organic Cr-containing compound, glucose tolerance factor (GTF), was essential to maintain normal glucose tolerance (Schwartz & Mertz, 1959). Evans et al. (1973) suggested that GTF potentiates the action of insulin. The exact structure of GTF is not known. It has generally been thought to be a nicotinic acid-Cr complex with ligands of glutamic acid, glycine, and cysteine. Synthetic complexes containing these components display GTF activity. Yamamoto et al. (1988) recently isolated a low-molecular-weight, Cr-binding substance from bovine colostrum that has properties similar to GTF. This material contained aspartic acid, glutamic acid, glycine, and cysteine, but the researchers were not able to positively identify nicotinic acid; thus, the structure of GTF is still in question.

Although the incidence of Cr deficiency in the human population of the USA cannot be estimated with any precision, there is evidence to suggest suboptimal Cr status in some groups of people. Of the trace elements generally considered essential for humans, Cr is the only one for which tissue concentrations decline throughout adult life, suggesting less than optimal intake

(Schroeder et al., 1970). Other evidence for human Cr deficiency comes primarily from Cr supplementation studies. In studies using subjects with impaired glucose tolerance, about half responded to long-term (4–5 mo) supplementation with inorganic Cr (Glinsmann & Mertz, 1966). Also, Cr supplementation increased both insulin sensitivity and high-density, lipoprotein cholesterol concentrations in young men (Riales & Albrink, 1981). Supplementation with brewers yeast, which contains organically bound Cr, generally has been more effective than supplementation with inorganic forms of Cr, and has been shown to improve glucose tolerance, insulin sensitivity, and cholesterol concentrations in elderly subjects (Offenbacher & Pi-Sunyer, 1980). Chromium deficiency signs in humans have been summarized by Anderson (1987) and, in addition to glucose intolerance, elevated serum cholesterol, and elevated serum triglycerides include elevated blood insulin concentrations, glycosuria, fasting hyperglycemia, neuropathy, and encephalopathy. Although acute, life-threatening deficiencies of Cr have not been reported, some population groups apparently would benefit from increased Cr intake.

E. Toxicity

Trivalent Cr at the dietary intake levels normally encountered is not likely to be toxic. In human studies, long-term supplementation with 150 μg d^{-1} of Cr did not produce any ill effects (Glinsmann & Mertz, 1966). A number of animal studies suggest that even pharmacologic doses of Cr have few, if any, long-term effects (Pi-Sunyer & Offenbacher, 1984).

F. Sources

Brewer's yeast, meat, cheese, whole grains, and certain condiments are good sources of Cr. Leafy vegetables contain moderate amounts of Cr, but it is thought to be in a poorly available form. Anderson (1988) lists mushrooms, brewer's yeast, black pepper (*Piper nigrum*), prune (*Prunus domestica*), raisin (*Vitis vinifera* L.), nuts, asparagus, beer, and wine as foods high in Cr. Based on a daily intake totaling 29.1 μg, he estimated the contributions of various food groups at: cereal products, 3.7 μg d^{-1}; meat, 5.2 μg d^{-1}; fish and seafoods, 0.6 μg d^{-1}; fruits, vegetables, mushrooms, and nuts, 6.8 μg d^{-1}; dairy products, eggs, and margarine, 6.2 μg d^{-1}; beverages, confectioneries, sugar, and condiments, 6.6 μg d^{-1}.

VI. SELENIUM

Prevention of liver necrosis in rats was the first evidence for the essentiality of Se (Schwartz & Foltz, 1957), but Se-responsive disorders were soon identified in other species. Selenium is a constituent of the enzyme, Se-dependent glutathione peroxidase (GPX) (Rotruck et al., 1973), and has been shown to be effective in preventing and treating Keshan Disease, a cardiomyopathy found in the Keshan region of China (Keshan Disease Research Group, 1979). Reviews of Se include those of Mason (1988), Combs et al. (1987), Levander (1986), Burk (1984), Combs and Combs (1984), National Research Council (1983), and Burk (1983).

A. Body Content and Distribution

The adult human body contains about 20 mg of Se. The highest tissue concentrations are in the liver and kidneys, and the largest total amount is in the muscle mass (Levander, 1986). Blood concentrations of Se generally reflect dietary intake. Data summarized by Burk (1984) indicated that USA dietary intakes ranged from 60 to 216 μg d^{-1} and blood Se concentrations ranged from 19 to 25 μg dL^{-1}; corresponding values for New Zealand were 28 to 56 μg d^{-1} and 5 to 10 μg dL^{-1}, respectively; and, in the low-Se areas of China, values were <30 μg d^{-1} and <1 μg dL^{-1}, respectively.

Blood glutathione peroxidase activity sometimes corresponds to Se intake, but may be a useful indicator of Se status only for populations with low intakes (Whanger et al., 1988; Burk, 1984). In one USA study, neither whole blood Se nor GPX were significantly affected by supplementation with 19 to 24 μg d^{-1} of Se for 6 wk (Levander et al., 1981); however, longer term supplementation (several months) of New Zealand subjects, whose Se intakes are lower than those in the USA, did increase blood concentrations (Thomson & Robinson, 1980). In recent studies in the People's Republic of China, both plasma Se and GPX activity of subjects with low to marginal Se status were increased by supplementation (Xia et al., 1989).

Selenium contents of other tissues also tend to reflect intake. Selenium concentrations of liver tissue from New Zealand subjects ranged from 0.72 to 1.03 mg kg^{-1} dry weight compared with 2.14 to 2.34 mg kg^{-1} for USA subjects; corresponding values for muscle were 0.29 vs. 1.24 to 1.90 mg kg^{-1}, respectively, (Masironi et al., 1987). In China, major differences were seen in hair from people in Se-deficient and Se-toxic regions; i.e., mean concentrations of 0.16 and 32.2 mg kg^{-1}, respectively (Levander, 1986). However, it is uncertain whether marginal Se deficiencies could be detected by hair-Se concentrations.

B. Balance

Both anionic (SeO_3^{2-}, SeO_4^{2-}) and naturally occurring Se compounds (selenocystine, selenocysteine, selenomethionine, and Se-methyl-selenomethionine) are efficiently absorbed. Levander (1986) summarized several human studies that suggest that absorption generally ranges from 55–70%. Generally, Se from selenomethionine is utilized better than that from selenite. In one study using ^{75}Se, absorption from selenite ranged from 44 to 70% (Thomson & Stewart, 1974), whereas in a second similar study, absorption from selenomethionine approximated 94 to 97% (Griffiths et al., 1976). Efficiency of Se absorption from mixed diets appears to be comparable. Apparent absorption from diets providing 166 to 260 μg d^{-1} averaged

67% (Greger, 1987). The efficiency with which dietary Se is incorporated into GPX depends on the chemical form. For most trace elements, it is assumed that if they get into the general circulation, they can be used; this apparently does not hold for Se. Levander (1987) summarized several studies comparing the ability of various sources of Se to increase liver GPX activity. Compared with the SeO_3^{2-} reference source (100%), these sources ranged from 4% for mushrooms to 142% for whole wheat bread. The reasons for these differences are not well understood.

Differences in absorption of Se from selenomethionine and SeO_3^{2-} probably are the result of different absorption mechanisms. In one study, selenomethionine was transported against a concentration gradient and methionine acted as a competitive inhibitor. In contrast, neither SeO_3^{2-} nor selenocysteine was transported against a gradient and neither SO_3^{2-} nor cysteine, respectively, inhibited their absorption (McConnell & Cho, 1965). Apparently, Se is transported in protein-bound form and, in humans, is bound, predominantly, to the very low-density lipoprotein fraction (Burk, 1974). In humans, approximately 1.5% of plasma Se and about 10% of erythrocyte Se is accounted for by Se-dependent GPX. These percentages generally are lower than those of most other species (Levander, 1986).

Excretion of endogenous Se occurs by both urinary and fecal routes, with trimethyl selenonium ions accounting for much of the urinary Se (Palmer et al., 1969). Levander (1986) summarized a number of experiments that indicated that: (i) urinary excretion accounts for 50 to 60% of total endogenous excretion; (ii) fecal excretion accounts for a relatively constant fraction of total excretion over a wide range of intakes (8.8–226 μg d^{-1}); (iii) approximately half of total fecal Se is of endogenous origin; and (iv) both urinary and fecal excretion are controlled homeostatically.

C. Requirements

In the 9th edition of *Recommended Dietary Allowances* (Food and Nutrition Board, 1980), the ESADDI's provided for Se were based, in part, on extrapolation from animal studies and on the observation that no detrimental human health effects had been observed in New Zealand, where daily intakes were estimated at 28 to 56 μg d^{-1} (Burk, 1984). Since 1980, results from several human studies have become available. Mason (1988) summarized a number of these studies and, generally, intakes were within the range reported by Burk (1984). Yang et al. (1987) reported that average Se intakes of adults in endemic Keshan Disease regions of China were 7.2 μg d^{-1} compared with 16.2 μg d^{-1} in nonendemic areas. Although Keshan Disease may not be due solely to Se deficiency, one would expect intakes of 16.2 μg d^{-1} to be close to the absolute minimum requirement. For the 10th edition of *Recommended Dietary Allowances* (Food and Nutrition Board, 1989), sufficient human data were available to replace the ESADDI's with RDA's, and intakes of 55 μg d^{-1} for adult women and 70 μg d^{-1} for adult men were recommended. The average intake by adults, estimated at 60 to 216 μg d^{-1}, generally meets these standards (Burk, 1984). Recommendations for infants

Table 17-6. Recommended dietary allowances for Se.[†]

Category	Age, yr	Se, μg d^{-1}
Infants	0.0–0.5	10
	0.5–1.0	15
Children	1–6	20
	7–10	30
Males	11–14	40
	15–18	50
	19+	70
Females	11–14	45
	15–18	50
	19+	55
Pregnant		65
Lactating		75

[†] Food and Nutrition Board (1989).

and children were obtained by extrapolating from adult values and adding an allowance for growth. For pregnant and lactating women, allowances are made for accretion of selenium by the fetus and for secretion into milk, respectively. The RDA's for Se for various age and sex groups are summarized in Table 17-6.

D. Deficiency

The only well-documented enzymatic function for Se is in GPX (Rotruck et al., 1973), which reduces H_2O_2, lipid peroxides, and sterol peroxides by using reducing equivalents of reduced glutathione. The GPX functions as part of a multicomponent system, which protects critical cell components from free radical and peroxide damage. The GPX functions as a cytoplasmic complement to vitamin E, which protects cell membranes and fat-soluble cell components from peroxidation (Combs & Combs, 1984). In addition to GPX, two other forms of Se are present in plasma. The methionine analog, selenomethionine, circulates in plasma and can be incorporated into protein in place of methionine. Plasma Se is also found in a protein-designated selenoprotein P, which may serve a transport function in the rat (Yang et al., 1987). A similar protein in humans may account for more of the plasma Se than GPX (Avissar et al., 1989), but little is known of its function. Although specific enzymatic roles, other than GPX, have not been positively identified, Se protects against certain toxic chemicals, chemically induced carcinogenesis, and Hg poisoning (Burk, 1983). One might expect that additional biochemical functions will be discovered.

Selenium-deficiency disorders and signs in animals have been well documented, but deficiency in humans has not been well characterized. On the basis of epidemiological evidence, a role for Se in preventing some human cancers has been proposed (Schrauzer et al., 1977; Shamberger & Frost, 1969). Also, a proposed role for Se in preventing cardiovascular disease has been dramatically strengthened by studies of the endemic cardiac myopathies observed in the Keshan region of China (Chen et al., 1980). This Se-responsive disorder primarily affects infants, children, and women of reproductive age, affects up to 11% of the susceptible groups in the endemic areas, and produces mortality rates of up to 80% (Combs & Combs, 1984). Although other factors are involved, Keshan Disease apparently is, primarily, the consequence of severe Se deficiency.

E. Toxicity

Both naturally occurring and experimental cases of selenosis have been observed in animals consuming feeds that contain ≥ 5 mg kg^{-1} of Se. Seleniferous areas have been identified in the USA, Ireland, Israel, Australia, the Soviet Union, Venezuela, China, and South Africa. Animals consuming toxic amounts of Se suffer emaciation, loss of hair, malformations, sloughing of hooves, erosion of joints, and atrophy of heart muscle (Levander, 1986).

Selenosis in humans is not nearly as well defined. Early studies in the high-Se areas of the USA did not reveal any problems that could be attributed specifically to high-Se intakes (Levander, 1986). Similarly, overt Se toxicity was neither observed in studies in Caracas, Venezuela, where daily intakes of Se have been estimated at 325 μg d^{-1} (Mondragon & Jaffe, 1976), nor in Japan, with intakes up to 500 μg d^{-1} (Sakurai & Tsuchiya, 1975). An outbreak of Se toxicity apparently occurred in China from 1961 to 1964, with the most common indicators being loss of hair and nail deformities. Samples taken several years afterward revealed high concentrations of Se in food, hair, blood, and urine (Yang, 1987). After visiting the affected areas, Whanger (1989) attributed high intakes to a number of factors, all, primarily, the result of the use of high Se-coal. Burnt coal was used as a fertilizer, which greatly increased soil Se and the Se content of plant foods grown on the contaminated soil. Use of the same coal for cooking added Se to the diet and breathing of the coal smoke may have contributed to the body burden. Selenium content of corn (*Zea mays* L.) grain was as high as 40 mg kg^{-1}, and dietary intakes of up to 38 mg d^{-1} were possible (Yang, 1987). Yang (1987) summarized a number of studies, reported that 750 μg d^{-1} of Se from a vegetable diet did not produce any signs of toxicity, and proposed that consumption of up to 500 μg d^{-1} was safe.

F. Sources

The Se content of plants is highly correlated with the availability of Se from the soil on which the plant is grown (Kubota et al., 1967). Given regional variations, seafoods, organ meats, and muscle meats are generally good sources of Se (>0.2 mg kg^{-1}), whereas fruits and vegetables generally provide <0.01 mg kg^{-1} wet weight, and are considered poor sources (Morris & Levander, 1970). Levander (1986) summarized a number of studies that demonstrated the dependence of intake on the origin of foodstuffs: (i) intakes in Finland and New Zealand, which have low Se soils approximated 30 μg d^{-1}, (ii) intakes in high-Se areas in Venezuela and South Dakota exceeded 200 μg d^{-1}; and (iii) national food surveys in the USA indicated mean daily intakes of 108 μg d^{-1}, with a range from 83 to 129 μg d^{-1}, with approximately 56% coming from grain products, 38% from meat, fish, and poultry, and 6% from dairy products.

VII. IODINE

Iodine is an essential component of the thyroid hormones, 3,5,3′,5′-tetraiodothyronine (thyroxine or T_4) and 3,5,3′-triiodothyronine (T_3), and is essential to both humans and animals. Recent reviews include those of Hetzel and Dunn (1989), Hetzel and Maberly (1986), Hetzel and Mano (1989), Matovinovic (1984), Pennington (1988), and Underwood (1977).

A. Body Content and Distribution

Total body content of I is estimated at 10 to 50 mg for an adult (Pennington, 1988). It is present in all body tissues and fluids, but 70 to 90% is located in the thyroid gland, which has I concentrations of about 0.4 to 1.0 g kg^{-1} wet weight. Iodine exists in blood in both inorganic and organic forms. Normal plasma concentrations of inorganic I range from 0.08 to 0.60 μg dL^{-1}, with values < 0.08 μg dL^{-1}, suggesting I deficiency (Hetzel & Maberly, 1986). Iodine concentrations of most other tissues do not exceed 0.2 mg kg^{-1}; i.e., approximately a thousandfold less than thyroid tissue (Hetzel & Maberly, 1986).

B. Balance

Iodine in foods is present primarily as inorganic I$^-$, which is rapidly and almost completely absorbed. Approximately 30% of absorbed I is removed by the thyroid, with the remainder excreted in the urine (Pennington, 1988). Urinary I is a good indicator of I status, as this is the primary excretory route. Iodine is actively transported from plasma to the thyroid gland with transport regulated by thyrotropin, a pituitary hormone. The thyroid hormones are stored as the glycoprotein, thyroglobulin. Release of T_4 and T_3 is mediated by proteases released from lysozomes, and the free hormones diffuse into the capillaries. Approximately 80 to 90 μg of T_4 and 10 to 20 μg of T_3 are secreted daily with normal serum concentrations averaging 8.6 μg dL^{-1} and 128 ng dL^{-1}, respectively (Matovinovic, 1984). A large proportion of the I released by metabolic degradation is reused by the thyroid.

C. Requirements

The daily adult requirement for I is 1 to 2 μg kg^{-1} of body weight; daily intakes of 50 to 1000 μg are considered safe (Food and Nutrition Board, 1970). Urinary I excretion is often used as an indicator of I status. Excretion

Table 17-7. Recommended dietary allowances for I.[†]

Category	Age, yr	I, μg d^{-1}
Infants	0.0–0.5	40
	0.5–1.0	50
Children	1–3	70
	4–6	90
	7–10	120
Others	11 +	150
Pregnant		175
Lactating		200

† Food and Nutrition Board (1989).

of 50 mg of I kg^{-1} of creatinine is indicative of adequate I status; excretion of 25 to 50 mg kg^{-1} is marginal and excretion of < 25 mg kg^{-1} is indicative of serious risk for I deficiency (Querido et al., 1974). Iodine is well absorbed; thus, an intake of 50 to 75 μg d^{-1} will generally maintain urinary excretion at normal levels. The recommended adult allowance of 150 μg d^{-1} for both sexes provides a margin of safety. An additional allowance of 25 μg d^{-1} is recommended during pregnancy to meet the needs of the fetus and an additional 50 μg d^{-1} are recommended during lactation to meet the needs of the infant. For children and adolescents, values are obtained by extrapolation from adult recommendations. The RDAs for various age and sex groups are summarized in Table 17-7.

D. Deficiency

Iodine deficiency is the primary cause of goiter and cretinism. Large numbers of people are at risk for I deficiency because they live in regions of the world where soil I is low because of glaciation, high rainfall, or flooding (Hetzel et al., 1987). Food grown in these soils is low in I, and, unless food is imported from I-adequate areas or I supplementation is initiated, deficiencies develop. Estimates of the numbers of people at risk vary from 200 million (Matovinovic, 1984) to 800 million (Hetzel & Dunn, 1989).

In adults, I deficiency is suspected if daily urinary output is < 50 μg, with goiter as a primary external sign. As thyroid I stores are depleted, blood concentrations of T_4 and T_3 are reduced. This triggers secretion of thyroid-stimulating hormone, which results in hyperplasia and enlargement of the thyroid. Signs of I deficiency include reduced metabolic rate, lower energy levels, depressed appetite, cold intolerance, and weight gain (Pennington, 1988).

Children born of mothers who consume < 25 μg d^{-1} of I are often afflicted with cretinism as a result of in utero I deficiency. Two types of cretinism can result; the neurologic form is characterized by mental deficiency and deaf-mutism, whereas the myxedematous type is characterized by hypothyroidism and dwarfism (Hetzel & Dunn, 1989). Iodine deficiency can also cause miscarriages, stillbirths, and congenital abnormalities (Hetzel & Mano, 1989).

E. Toxicity

For adults, I intakes up to 1000 $\mu g\ d^{-1}$ are generally considered safe (Food and Nutrition Board, 1970), whereas intakes >2000 $\mu g\ d^{-1}$ are potentially harmful (Hetzel & Maberly, 1986). Perversely, I excess can result in either hypo- or hyperthyroidism. In individuals susceptible to the Wolff-Chaikoff effect, high I intakes inhibit binding of I to tyrosine, which depresses circulating T_4 and T_3. This, in turn, increases a thyroid stimulating hormone, which leads to hypertrophy and goiter. In most individuals, high I intakes result in hyperthyroidism; excess I causes overstimulation of the thyroid gland resulting in overproduction of thyroid hormones. Signs of hyperthyroidism include nervousness, fatigue, bulging eyes, weakness, increased appetite, and goiter (Pennington, 1988).

F. Sources

In countries where iodized salt is used, it is a major source of I. A little more than half of the table salt that is consumed in the USA is iodized at a level that provides 76 mg of I kg^{-1} of salt (Food and Nutrition Board, 1980). The I content of plant foods reflects the I content of the soil in which the foods are grown, and reflects any additions through fertilizers or irrigation water. Meat, poultry, egg, and milk products generally reflect the I intake of the animals, including that contained in feed supplements or salt. The I content of seafood is higher than other foods as a result of the concentration of I from seawater. Some processed foods contain I additives, such as KIO_3, which is added to breads to strengthen the dough.

The chapter by Pennington (1988) has an excellent summary of the I content of foods in the USA, with the average intake of I from various food groups estimated at (micrograms per serving): beverages, fats and sauces, nuts, fruits, fruit juices and drinks and sweets, ≤ 3; vegetables, 6; breakfast or luncheon meats, 7; soups, 12; grain-based desserts, 13; cheese, 14; ready to eat breakfast cereals, 19; grain products, 20; meat and poultry, 20; eggs, 32; cooked grains, 45; legumes, 58; fluid milk, 60; and cottage cheese and fish, 72.

Pennington's (1988) summary of total diet studies demonstrates that the primary sources of I for all groups are: grains and grain products; milk and milk products; and meat, fish, poultry, and eggs. Further, these studies indicated that, in the USA, all age/sex groups from infants to 65 yr had average daily intake levels that exceeded the RDA's. These ranged from 167% RDA for older females to 657% RDA for 2-yr-old children.

VIII. OTHER TRACE ELEMENTS

A. Fluoride

The literature on F is extensive; some recent reviews include those of Spencer and Kramer (1988), Krishnamachari (1987), Singer and Ophaug

Table 17-8. Estimated safe and adequate daily dietary intakes of F.†

Category	Age, yr	F, mg d^{-1}
Infants	0.0–0.5	0.1–0.5
	0.5–1.0	0.2–1.0
Children and	1–3	0.5–1.5
adolescents	4–6	1.0–2.5
	7+	1.5–2.5
Adults		1.5–4.0

† Food and Nutrition Board (1989).

(1984), and Rao (1984). Although F has not been shown to be absolutely essential for life, it provides increased resistance to dental caries. It has been estimated that fluoridation of community water supplies has reduced dental caries by 50 to 60% over the last 30 to 40 yr (Leverett, 1982). There is some evidence that appropriate F intakes also provide protection against periodontal disease and osteoporosis in older people. The effects of mild excesses of F are generally limited to mottling of the teeth. However, the advent of fluoridated toothpastes and mouthwashes has caused some concerns about excess F intake. One study indicated that 7 to 13-yr-old children retained 0.4 to 1.2 mg of F after brushing with a fluoridated toothpaste, and 0.2 to 0.4 mg after using a fluoridated mouthwash (Bell et al., 1982). Large excesses of F result in general skeletal deterioration (Krishnamachari, 1987).

The estimated safe and adequate range of F intake levels for adults is 1.5 to 4.0 mg d^{-1}, and includes both food and water sources. For younger age groups, the maximum suggested intake is set at 2.5 mg d^{-1} to avoid mottling of teeth. The American Dental Association (1982) recommends F supplements for children who consume low-F water. These recommendations are (milligrams F per day): for areas with <0.3 µg mL^{-1} in water, 0.25, 0.50, and 1.0 for age groups 0 to 2, 2 to 3, and 3 to 13 yr, respectively; for areas with 0.3 to 0.7 µg mL^{-1} in water, 0.24 and 0.50 for age groups 2 to 3 and 3 to 13, respectively; for areas with >0.7 µg mL^{-1} in water, no supplement is recommended for any age group. The Food and Nutrition Board (1989) recommends fluoridation of public water supplies if the natural F concentrations are substantially <0.7 mg L^{-1}. The ESADDI's for various age and sex groups are summarized in Table 17-8.

In areas with fluoridated water, foods contribute about 22% of total F intake (Taves, 1983). Of that amount, grain and cereal products provide about 60%, with 11% derived from meat, fish, and poultry. Leafy vegetables and dairy products contribute 7 and 3%, respectively. Fluoride from NaF is essentially 100% available (Ekstrand et al., 1978), with bioavailability of F from foods somewhat less (Rao, 1984) and influenced by other dietary ingredients. Aluminum-containing antacids are particularly effective in inhibiting intestinal absorption of F (Spencer & Kramer, 1988).

B. Molybdenum

Reviews of Mo in human and animal nutrition include those of Nielsen (1988), Mills and Davis (1987), and Nielsen and Mertz (1984). Molybdenum

Table 17-9. Estimated safe and adequate daily dietary intakes of Mo.†

Category	Age, yr	Mo, $\mu g\ d^{-1}$
Infants	0.0–0.5	15–30
	0.5–1.0	20–40
Children	1–3	25–50
	4–6	30–75
	7–10	50–150
Others	11 +	75–250

† Food and Nutrition Board (1989).

deficiency has not been observed in humans and is difficult to produce in experimental animals. Much of the interest in Mo stems from its being an essential component of the enzymes, xanthine oxidase, aldehyde oxidase, and SO_3^{2-} oxidase, and from observations of Mo toxicity in animals (Kubota et al., 1961).

Observed effects in the human population have been limited to correlations; direct cause/effect relations have not been established. High intake levels of Mo have been correlated with low incidence of dental caries in children (Healy et al., 1961; Anderson, 1966). However, high dietary intake levels may be harmful. A Soviet population exposed to a high-Mo environment presented increased blood xanthine oxidase, increased concentrations of uric acid in blood and urine, and a high incidence of gout (Kovalskiy et al., 1961 as cited in Nielsen and Mertz, 1984). Low Mo, as well as low Se, was found in grains growing in the Keshan region of China (Jian-An et al., 1987), but its relationship to Keshan Disease, if any, is not clear. In the absence of human deficiencies, the Food and Nutrition Board (1989) has suggested ESADDI's based on average reported intake levels. These are summarized in Table 17-9.

Food is the major source of Mo for humans. Milk and milk products, legume seeds, organ meats, cereal grains, and baked goods are the primary contributors (Tsongas et al., 1980). Daily intake levels in the adult population of the USA are estimated at 80 to 350 $\mu g\ d^{-1}$ (Tsongas et al., 1980), which is well within the safe and adequate range.

C. Other Elements

Recent reviews of the newer or ultra trace elements include those of Carlisle (1986), Mertz (1986a), Nielsen (1984, 1986, 1987a, b, 1988), and Nielsen and Mertz (1984). Nielsen (1984) critically reviewed evidence for essentiality of 11 trace elements that, since 1970, have been proposed as beneficial to animals. These were As, B, Br, Cd, F, Pb, Li, Ni, Si, Sn, and V. An excellent summary in this paper suggested that: (i) evidence for essentiality of Br, Cd, Pb, and Sn was weak, and that these elements should not be considered essential; (ii) evidence for essentiality of F was weak, but it should be considered an element with beneficial pharmacologic properties; (iii) B, Li, and V require further study, but are probably essential; and (iv) evidence for As, Ni, and Si is sufficiently strong to consider them essential for animals.

Subsequent to this 1984 review, evidence for B essentiality has been strengthened considerably. Nielsen et al. (1987) demonstrated that B supplementation of postmenopausal women who consumed a low-B diet markedly reduced urinary excretion of Ca and Mg, and markedly increased serum concentrations of 17 beta-estradiol and testosterone. However, the situation for the other elements remains much the same as in 1984. In addition to these elements, Co is an essential component of vitamin B_{12}. Cobalt is considered essential for ruminants because rumen microflora can synthesize sufficient B_{12} to meet the needs of the animal; however, nonruminants, including humans, do not have a Co requirement, instead they require preformed vitamin B_{12}.

IX. RESEARCH NEEDS

About 60% of the food consumed in the USA is from plant foods; a little more than half of which is derived from seeds and grains. Thus, for people, plant foods are a critical source of nutrients, including the trace elements, and there are many areas where improvement is possible. Progress through agronomic practices, plant breeding, or genetic engineering will require a much better understanding of the relationships among soils, plants, and humans.

If soil and plant scientists are to improve plant foods as sources of nutrients for people, human nutritionists need to provide appropriate information. For example, if one could increase either the amount or bioavailability of trace elements in plant foods, which ones should be increased, which decreased, and by how much would need to be determined. Satisfactory answers are not available for most trace elements. Human nutritionists need to continue to refine dietary intake recommendations and to develop better recommendations for individuals. Practically all current recommendations are made for population groups and, often, have little relevance to a particular individual. To better meet the basic requirements of groups and/or individuals, there is a need to develop improved approaches to: (i) determine total amounts of trace elements in foods; (ii) determine chemical forms in foods, as produced and as consumed; (iii) determine effects of interactions with other nutrients and/or antinutrients; (iv) assess bioavailability from different foods or from different chemical forms, and determine the underlying reasons for differences; and (v) determine the most promising methods of intervention.

If soil and plant scientists were provided clear goals regarding improvements in plant foods as sources of trace elements, there are still barriers to the desired change. Among others, more information is needed on: (i) processes that limit solubility of trace elements in soils; (ii) physical, chemical, and biological barriers to the movement of trace elements through the soil to root surfaces; (iii) interactions at the root/soil interface; (iv) mechanisms of trace element absorption by root cells; and (v) mechanisms for and controls on the translocation of trace elements to the edible part of plants.

The needs listed are far from all inclusive; nevertheless each presents a unique challenge, and finding appropriate answers will require the coordinated efforts of soil scientists, plant scientists, and nutritionists.

REFERENCES

Aisen, P., and A. Liebman. 1968. The stability constants of the Fe^{3+} conalbumin complexes. Biochem. Biophys. Res. Commun. 3:407–413.

Alexander, F.W., B.E. Clayton, and H.T. Delves. 1974. Mineral and trace-metal balances in children receiving normal and synthetic diets. Q. J. Med. 43:89–111.

Al-Rashid, R.A., and J. Spangler. 1971. Neonatal copper deficiency. New Eng. J. Med. 285:841–843.

American Dental Association. 1982. Accepted dental therapeutics. 39th ed. Am. Dent. Assoc., Chicago, IL.

Anderson, R.A. 1987. Chromium, p. 225–244. In W. Mertz (ed.) Trace elements in human and animal nutrition. 5th ed. Vol. 1. Academic Press, San Diego, CA.

Anderson, R.A. 1988. Chromium. p. 231–247. In K.T. Smith (ed.) Trace minerals in foods. Marcell Dekker Inc., New York.

Anderson, R.A., and A. Koslovsky. 1985. Chromium intake, absorption and excretion of subjects consuming self-selected diets. Am. J. Clin. Nutr. 41:1177–1183.

Anderson, R.A., M.M. Polansky, N.A. Bryden, K.Y. Patterson, C. Veillon, and W.H. Glinsmann. 1983. Effect of chromium supplementation on urinary Cr excretion of human subjects and correlation of Cr excretion with selected clinical parameters. J. Nutr. 113:276–281.

Anderson, R.J. 1966. Dental caries prevention in relation to trace elements. Br. Dent. J. 120:271–275.

Avissar, N., J.C. Whitin, P.Z. Allen, I.S. Palmer, and H.J. Cohen. 1989. Antihuman plasma glutathione peroxidase antibodies. Immunologic investigations to determine plasma glutathione peroxidase protein and selenium content in plasma. Blood 73:318–323.

Banerjee, D.B., P.R. Flanagan, J. Cluett, and L.S. Valberg. 1986. Transferrin receptors in the human gastrointestinal tract. Gastroenterologia 91:861–869.

Bell, R.A., J.T. Barenie, and G.M. Whitford. 1982. Fluoride retention in children using self-administered fluoride products. J. Dent. Res. 61:235.

Bettger, W.J., and B.L. O'Dell. 1981. A critical physiological role of zinc in the structure and function of biomembranes. Life Sci. 28:1425–1438.

Beutler, E. 1980. Iron. p. 324–354. In R.S. Goodhart, and M.E. Shils (ed.) Modern nutrition in health and disease. Vol. 6. Lea and Febiger, Philadelphia, PA.

Borel, J., and R. Anderson. 1984. Chromium. p. 175–190. In E. Frieden (ed.) Biochemistry of the essential ultratrace elements. Plenum Publ. Co., New York.

Bothwell, T.H., R.W. Charlton, J.D. Cook, and C.A. Finch. 1979. Iron metabolism in man. Blackwell Sci. Publ., London.

Burk, R.F. 1974. In vivo ^{75}Se binding to human plasma proteins after administration of ^{75}Se-O_3^{2-}. Biochim. Biophys. Acta 372:255–265.

Burk, R.F. 1983. Biological activity of selenium. Annu. Rev. Nutr. 3:53–70.

Burk, R.F. 1984. Selenium. p. 519–527. In Present knowledge of nutrition. 5th ed. The Nutrition Foundation, Washington, DC.

Butler, L.C., and J.M. Daniel. 1973. Copper metabolism in young women fed two levels of copper and two protein sources. Am. J. Clin. Nutr. 26:744–749.

Butte, N.F., C. Garza, E.O. Smith, C. Wills, and B.L. Nichols. 1987. Macro- and trace-mineral intakes of exclusively breast-fed infants. Am. J. Clin. Nutr. 45:42–48.

Carlisle, E.M. 1986. Silicon. p. 373–390. In W. Mertz (ed.) Trace elements in human and animal nutrition. Vol. 2. Academic Press, Orlando, FL.

Carrico, R., and H. Deutsch. 1970. Isolation of human hepatocuprein and cerebrocuprein. Their identity with erythrocuprein. J. Biol. Chem. 244:6087–6093.

Carter, J., W. Miller, M. Neathery, R. Gentry, P. Stake, and D. Blackmon. 1974. Manganese metabolism with oral and intravenous ^{54}Mn in young calves as influenced by supplemental manganese. J. Anim. Sci. 38:1284–1290.

Cartwright, G.E., and M.M. Wintrobe. 1949. Chemical, clinical and immunological studies on the products of human plasma fractionation. XXXIX. The anemia of infection. Studies on the iron-binding capacity of serum. J. Clin. Invest. 28:86–98.

Cartwright, G.E., and M.M. Wintrobe. 1964. Copper metabolism in normal subjects. Am. J. Clin. Nutr. 14:224–232.

Cary, E., D. Grunes, V. Bohman, and C. Sanchirico. 1986. Titanium determination for correction of plant sample contamination by soil. Agron. J. 78:933–936.

Casey, C.E., K.M. Hambidge, and M.C. Neville. 1985. Studies in human lactation: zinc, copper, manganese and chromium in human milk in the first month of lactation. Am. J. Clin. Nutr. 41:1193–1200.

Casey, C.E., and M.F. Robinson. 1978. Copper, manganese, zinc, nickel, cadmium and lead in human foetal tissues. Br. J. Nutr. 39:639–646.

Chandra, S.V., and G.S. Shukla. 1976. Role of iron deficiency in inducing susceptibility of manganese toxicity. Arch. Toxicol. 35:319–325.

Charlton, R., and T. Bothwell. 1983. Iron absorption. Annu. Rev. Med. 34:55–68.

Chen, X., G. Yang, J. Chen, X. Chen, Z. Wen, and K. Ge. 1980. Studies on the relations of selenium and Keshan disease. Biol. Trace Elem. Res. 2:91–100.

Combs, G.F., Jr., and S.B. Combs. 1984. The nutritional biochemistry of selenium. Ann. Rev. Nutr. 4:257–280.

Combs, G., Jr., J. Spallholz, O. Levander, and J. Oldfield (ed.). 1987. Selenium in biology and medicine. Parts A and B. Van Nostrand Reinhold Co., Inc., New York.

Conrad, M.E., 1987. Iron absorption. p. 1437–1453. In L.R. Johnson (ed.) Physiology of the gastrointestinal tract. Raven Press, New York.

Consumer Nutrition Center. 1976. Composition of foods, raw, processed, prepared. USDA Handb. 8. U.S. Gov. Print. Office, Washington, DC.

Cook, J.D., C.A. Finch, and N.J. Smith. 1976. Evaluation of the iron status of a population. Blood 48:449–455.

Cordano, A., and G.G. Graham. 1966. Copper deficiency complicating severe chronic intestinal malabsorption. Pediatrics 38:596–604.

Cousins, R.J. 1985. Absorption, transport and hepatic metabolism of copper and zinc: Special reference to metallothionein and ceruloplasmin. Physiol. Rev. 65:238–309.

Dallman, P., R. Yip, and C. Johnson. 1984. Prevalence and causes of anemia in the United States, 1976 to 1980. Am. J. Clin. Nutr. 39:437–445.

Davidsson, L., A. Cederblad, E. Hagebo, B. Lonnerdal, and B. Sandstrom. 1988. Intrinsic and extrinsic labeling for studies of manganese absorption in humans. J. Nutr. 118:1517–1521.

Davidsson, L., B. Lonnerdal, B. Sandstrom, C. Kunz, and C.L. Keen. 1989. Identification of transferrin as the major plasma carrier protein for manganese introduced orally or intravenously or after in vitro addition in the rat. J. Nutr. 119:1461–1464.

Davies, N.T., and R. Nightingale. 1975. The effects of phytate on intestinal absorption and secretion of zinc and whole-body retention of zinc, copper, iron and manganese in rats. Bt. J. Nutr. 34:1298–1305.

Davis, G., and W. Mertz. 1987. Copper. p. 301–354. In W. Mertz (ed.) Trace elements in human and animal nutrition. 5th ed. Vol. 1. Academic Press, San Diego, CA.

Dawson-Hughes, B., F.H. Seligson, and V.A. Hughs. 1986. Effects of calcium carbonate and hydroxyapatite on zinc and iron retention in postmenopausal women. Am. J. Clin. Nutr. 44:83–88.

Doisy, R., D. Streeten, M. Souma, M. Kalafer, S. Rekant, and T. Dalakos. 1971. Metabolism of ^{51}chromium in human subjects: Normal, elderly and diabetic subjects. p. 155–168. In W. Mertz and E. Cornatzer (ed.) Newer trace elements in nutrition. Marcell Dekker, New York.

Ekstrand, J., M. Ehrnebo, and L. Boreus. 1978. Fluoride bioavailability after intravenous and oral administration. Importance of renal clearance and urine flow. Clin. Pharmacol. Ther. 23:329–341.

Engel, R.W., N.O. Price, and R.F. Miller. 1967. Copper, manganese, cobalt and molybdenum balance in pre-adolescent girls. J. Nutr. 92:197–204.

Evans, G.W., and P.E. Johnson. 1980. Characterization and quantitation of a zinc binding ligand in human milk. Pediatr. Res. 14:876–880.

Evans, G.W., E.E. Roginski, and W. Mertz. 1973. Interaction of the glucose tolerance factor with insulin. Biochem. Biophys. Res. Commun. 50:718–722.

Feeney, R.E., and R.G. Allison. 1969. Evolutionary biochemistry of proteins. Wiley Interscience, New York.

Fields, M., J. Ferretti, and J.C. Smith, Jr. 1984. The interaction of type of dietary carbohydrate with copper deficiency. Am. J. Clin. Nutr. 39:289–295.

Finley, E., and F. Cerklewski. 1983. Influence of ascorbic acid supplementation on copper status in young adult men. Am. J. Clin. Nutr. 37:553–556.

Food and Nutrition Board. 1970. Subcommittee on iodine. National Research Council. Iodine nutriture in the United States. Natl. Acad. Press, Washington, DC.

Food and Nutrition Board. 1980. Subcommittee on the ninth edition of the RDAs. National Research Council. Recommended dietary allowances. 9th ed. Natl. Acad. Press, Washington, DC.

Food and Nutrition Board. 1989. Subcommittee on the tenth edition of the RDAs. National Research Council. Recommended dietary allowances. 10th ed. Natl. Acad. Press, Washington, DC.

Freeland-Graves, J.H., C.W. Bales, and F. Behmardi. 1987. Manganese requirements of humans. p. 90–104. In C. Kies (ed.) Nutritional bioavailability of manganese. Am. Chem. Soc., Washington, DC.

Frieden, E., and H.S. Hsieh. 1976. Ceruloplasmin: The copper transport protein with essential oxidase activity. Adv. Enzymol. 44:187–236.

Gibson, R.S., and M.S. De Wolfe. 1980. The dietary trace metal intake of some Canadian full-term and low birthweight infants during the first twelve months of infancy. J. Can. Diet. Assoc. 41:206–215.

Glinsmann, W.H., F.J. Feldman, and W. Mertz. 1966. Plasma chromium after glucose administration. Science 152:1243–1245.

Glinsmann, W.H., and W. Mertz. 1966. Effect of trivalent chromium on glucose tolerance. Metabolism 15:510–520.

Gollan, J.L., and D.J. Deller. 1973. Studies on the nature and excretion of biliary copper in man. Clin. Sci. 44:9–15.

Graham, G.G., and A. Cordano. 1969. Copper depletion and deficiency in the malnourished infant. Johns Hopkins Med. J. 124:139–150.

Granick, S. 1946. Ferritin. IX. Increase of the protein apoferritin in the gastrointestinal mucosa as a direct response to iron feeding. The function of ferritin in the regulation of iron absorption. J. Biol. Chem. 164:737–746.

Greger, J.L. 1987. Factors affecting selenium absorption, excretion and retention by human subjects. p. 419–425. In G. Combs, Jr. et al. (ed.) Selenium in biology and medicine. Part A. Van Nostrand Reinhold Co., New York.

Greger, J.L., S.C. Zahie, R.P. Abernathy, O.H. Bennett, and J. Huffman. 1978. Zinc, nitrogen, copper, iron and manganese balance in adolescent females fed two levels of zinc. J. Nutr. 108:1449–1456.

Griffiths, N.M., R.D.H. Stewart, and M.F. Robinson. 1976. The metabolism of (^{75}Se)selenomethionine in four women. Br. J. Nutr. 35:373–382.

Gruden, N. 1977. Suppression of transduodenal manganese transport by milk diet supplemented with iron. Nutr. Metab. 21:305–309.

Hallberg, L. 1974. The pool concept in food iron absorption and some of its implications. Proc. Nutr. Soc. 33:285–291.

Hallberg, L., E. Bjorn-Rasmussen, L. Rossander, R. Suwanik, R. Pleehachinda, and M. Tuntawiroon. 1983. Iron absorption from some Asian meals containing contamination iron. Am. J. Clin. Nutr. 37:272–277.

Hallberg, L., A. Hogdahl, L. Nilsson, and G. Rybo. 1966. Menstrual blood loss. A population study. Variation at different ages and attempts to define normality. Acta Obstet. Gynecol. Scand. 45:320–351.

Hallberg, L., and L. Rossander. 1982. Effect of soy protein on nonheme iron absorption in man. Am. J. Clin. Nutr. 36:514–520.

Hambidge, K.M., C.E. Casey, and N.F. Krebs. 1986. Zinc. p. 1–137. In W. Mertz (ed.) Trace elements in human and animal nutrition. 5th ed. Vol. 2. Academic Press, Orlando, FL.

Harrison, P.M., R.J. Hoare, T.G. Hoy, and I.G. Macara. 1974. Ferritin and hemosiderin. p. 73–114. In A. Jacobs and M. Worwood (ed.) Iron in biochemistry and medicine. Academic Press, Orlando, FL.

Healy, W.B., T.G. Ludwig, and F.L. Losee. 1961. Soils and dental caries in Hawkes Bay, New Zealand. Soil Sci. 92:359–366.

Henkin, R.L., H.R. Keiser, I.A. Jaffe, I. Sternlieb, and I.H. Sheinberg. 1967. Decreased taste sensitivity after D-penicillamine, reversed by copper administration. Lancet 2:1268–1271.

Hetzel, B.S., and J.T. Dunn. 1989. The iodine deficiency disorders: Their nature and prevention. Ann. Rev. Nutr. 9:21–38.

Hetzel, B.S., J.T. Dunn, and J.B. Stanbury. 1987. The prevention and control of iodine deficiency disorders. Elsevier, Amsterdam.

Hetzel, B.S., and G.F. Maberly. 1986. Iodine. p. 139–208. In W. Mertz (ed.) Trace elements in human and animal nutrition. 5th ed. Vol. 2. Academic Press, Orlando, FL.

Hetzel, B.S., and M.T. Mano. 1989. A review of experimental studies of iodine deficiency during fetal development. J. Nutr. 119:145–151.

Heubers, H., E. Heubers, E. Csiba, W. Rummel, and C. Finch. 1983. The significance of transferrin for intestinal iron absorption. Blood 61:283–290.

Heubers, H., E. Heubers, W. Forth, and W. Rummel. 1971. Binding of iron to a non-ferritin protein in the mucosal cells of normal and iron-deficient rats during absorption. Life Sci. 10:1141–1148.

Holmes, J., and E. Morgan. 1989. Uptake and distribution of transferrin and iron in perfused iron-deficient rat liver. Am. J. Physiol. 19:G1022–G1027.

Hooper, P., L. Visconti, P. Garry, and G. Johnson. 1980. Zinc lowers high-density lipoprotein cholesterol levels. J. Am. Med. Assoc. 244:1960–1961.

House, W.A., and R.M. Welch. 1984. Effects of naturally occurring antinutrients on the nutritive value of cereal grain, potato tubers and legume seeds. p. 9–36. In R.M. Welch and W.H. Gabelman (ed.) Crops as sources of nutrients for humans. ASA Spec. Publ. 48. ASA, CSSA, and SSSA, Madison, WI.

House, W.A., R.M. Welch, and D.R. Van Campen. 1982. Effect of phytic acid on the absorption, distribution, and endogenous excretion of zinc in rats. J. Nutr. 112:941–953.

Hsieh, H.W., and E. Friedan. 1975. Evidence for ceruloplasmin as a copper transport protein. Biochem. Biophys. Res. Commun. 67:1326–1331.

Hurley, L.S. 1984. Manganese. p. 558–570. In Present knowledge in nutrition. 5th ed. The Nutrition Foundation Inc., Washington, DC.

Hurley, L.S., and C. Keen. 1987. Manganese. p. 185–223. In W. Mertz (ed.) Trace elements in human and animal nutrition. 5th ed. Vol. 1. Academic Press, San Diego, CA.

Inglett, G.E. 1983. Nutritional bioavailability of zinc. Am. Chem. Soc., Washington, DC.

Iyengar, V. 1989. Variations in urinary excretion of zinc and copper in normal female human subjects: A long-term follow-up in the same subjects. Trace Elem. Med. 6:47–49.

Jacob, R.A., H.H. Sandstead, J.M. Munoz, and L.M. Klevay. 1979. Whole body surface loss of trace metals in normal males. Fed. Proc. 38:552.

Jacob, R.A., J.H. Skala, S.T. Omaye, and J.R. Turnlund. 1987. Effect of varying ascorbic acid intakes on copper absorption and ceruloplasmin levels of young men. J. Nutr. 117:2109–2115.

Jameson, S. 1976. Effects of zinc deficiency in human reproduction. Acta Med. Scand. 593:4–89.

Jian-An, T., Z. Da-Xian, H. Shao-Fan, Z. Wen-Yu, L. Ri-Bang, Z. Zhen-Yuan, and W. Wu-Yi. 1987. Selenium ecological chemicogeography and endemic Keshan Disease and Kaschin-Beck Disease in China. p. 859–876. In G. Combs, Jr. et al. (ed.) Selenium in biology and medicine. Part B. Van Nostrand Reinhold Co., Inc., New York.

Johnson, M.A., M.J. Baier, and J.L. Greger. 1982. Effect of dietary tin on zinc, copper, iron, manganese, and magnesium metabolism of adult males. Am. J. Clin. Nutr. 35:1332–1338.

Johnson, P., M. Stuart, J. Hunt, L. Mullen, and T. Starks. 1988. [65]Copper absorption by women fed intrinsically and extrinsically labeled goose meat, goose liver, peanut butter and sunflower butter. J. Nutr. 118:1522–1528.

Kabata, H., K. Inui, and Y. Itokawa. 1989. The binding of manganese to the brush border membrane vesicles of rat small intestine. Nutr. Res. 9:791–799.

Keshan Disease Research Group. 1979. Observations on effect of sodium selenite in prevention of Keshan disease. Chin. Med. J. 92:471–476.

Kies, C. (ed.). 1982. Nutritional bioavailability of iron. Am. Chem. Soc., Washington, DC.

Kies, C. (ed.). 1987. Nutritional bioavailability of manganese. Am. Chem. Soc., Washington, DC.

Kies, C., K.D. Aldrich, J.M. Johnson, C. Creps, C. Kowalski, and R.H. Wang. 1987. Manganese availability for humans: Effect of selected dietary factors. p. 136–145. In C. Kies (ed.) Nutritional bioavailability of manganese. Am. Chem. Soc., Washington, DC.

Klevay, L.M. 1980. Interactions of copper and zinc in cardiovascular disease. Ann. N.Y. Acad. Sci. 355:140–151.

Klevay, L.M., S.J. Reck, R.A. Jacob, F.M. Logan, Jr., J.M. Munoz, and H.H. Sandstead. 1980. The human requirement for copper. I. Healthy men fed conventional American diets. Am. J. Clin. Nutr. 33:45–50.

Kowarski, S., C.S. Blair-Stanek, and D. Schachter. 1974. Active transport of zinc and identification of zinc-binding protein in rat jejunal mucosa. Am. J. Physiol. 226:401–407.

Krishnamachari, K. 1987. Fluorine. p. 365–415. In W. Mertz (ed.) Trace elements in human and animal nutrition. 5th ed. Vol. 1. Academic Press, San Diego, CA.

Kubota, J., W.H. Allaway, D.L. Carter, E.E. Cary, and V.A. Lazar. 1967. Selenium in crops in the United States in relation to selenium-responsive diseases of animals. Agric. Food Chem. 15:448–453.

Kubota, J., V. Lazar, L. Langan, and K. Beeson. 1961. The relationship of soils to Mo toxicity in cattle in Nevada. Soil Sci. Soc. Am. Proc. 25:227–232.

Laurell, C.B. 1947. Studies on the transportation and metabolism of iron in the body. Acta Physiol. Scand. 14:1–129.

Layrisse, M., J.D. Cook, C. Martinez, M. Roche, I. Kuhn, R. Walker, and C. Finch. 1969. Food iron absorption: A comparison of vegetable and animal foods. Blood. 33:430–443.

Leach, R.M., and M.S. Liburn. 1978. Manganese metabolism and its function. World Rev. Nutr. Diet. 32:123–134.

Lee, D., and P.E. Johnson. 1988. Factors affecting absorption and excretion of ^{54}Mn in rats. J. Nutr. 118:1509–1516.

Levander, O.A. 1986. Selenium. p. 209–279. In W. Mertz (ed.) Trace elements in human and animal nutrition. 5th ed. Vol. 2. Academic Press, Orlando, FL.

Levander, O.A. 1987. Assessing the bioavailability of selenium in foods. p. 403–412. In G. Combs et al. (ed.) Selenium in biology and medicine. Part A. Van Nostrand Reinhold Co., New York.

Levander, O.A., B. Sutherland, V.C. Morris, and J.C. King. 1981. Selenium balance in young men during selenium depletion and repletion. Am. J. Clin. Nutr. 34:2662–2669.

Leverett, D.H. 1982. Fluorides and changing prevalence of dental caries. Science 217:26–30.

Linder, M.C., and H.N. Munro. 1977. The mechanism of iron absorption and its regulation. Fed. Proc. 36:2017–2023.

Lipschitz, D.A., J.D. Cook, and C.A. Finch. 1974. A clinical evaluation of serum ferritin. New Engl. J. Med. 290:1213–1216.

Liu, V.S.K., and R.P. Abernathy. 1982. Chromium and insulin in young subjects with normal glucose tolerance. Am. J. Clin. Nutr. 35:661–667.

Lonnerdal, B., C.L. Keen, and L.S. Hurley. 1981. Iron, copper, zinc and manganese in milk. Ann. Rev. Nutr. 1:149–174.

Lynch, S.R. 1984. Iron. p. 89–124. In N.W. Solomons and I.H. Rosenberg (ed.) Absorption and malabsorption of mineral nutrients. Alan R. Liss, Inc., New York.

Masironi, R., R. Parr, and M. Perry. 1987. Selenium and cardiovascular diseases: Preliminary results of the WHO/IAEA joint research program. p. 905–910. In G. Combs et al. (ed.) Selenium in biology and medicine. Part B. Van Nostrand Reinhold Co., New York.

Mason, A.C. 1988. Selenium. p. 325–355. In K.T. Smith (ed.) Trace minerals in foods. Marcel Dekker, Inc., New York.

Matovinovic, J. 1984. Iodine. p. 587–606. In Present knowledge in nutrition. 5th ed. The Nutrition Foundation, Inc., Washington, DC.

McCance, R.A., and E.M. Widdowson. 1937. Absorption and excretion of iron. Lancet 2:680–684.

McCance, R.A., and E.M. Widdowson. 1942. The absorption and excretion of zinc. Biochem. J. 36:692–696.

McConnell, K.P., and G.J. Cho. 1965. Transmucosal movement of selenium. Am. J. Physiol. 208:1191–1195.

McCord, J.M., B.B. Keele, Jr., and I. Fridovich. 1971. An enzyme-based theory of obligate anaerobiosis: The physiological function of superoxide dismutase. Proc. Natl. Acad. Sci. 68:1024–1027.

McLeod, B.E., and M.F. Robinson. 1972. Metabolic balance of manganese in women. Br. J. Nutr. 27:221–227.

Mertz, W. 1969. Chromium occurrence and function in biological systems. Physiol. Rev. 49:163–239.

Mertz, W. 1986a. Lithium. p. 391–397. In W. Mertz (ed.) Trace elements in human and animal nutrition. 5th ed. Vol. 2. Academic Press, Orlando, FL.

Mertz, W. (e.d). 1986b. Trace elements in human and animal nutrition. 5th ed. Vol. 2. Academic Press, Orlando, FL.

Mertz, W. (ed.). 1987. Trace elements in human and animal nutrition. 5th ed. Vol. 1. Academic Press, San Diego, CA.

Mills, C., and G. Davis. 1987. Molybdenum. p. 429–463. In W. Mertz (ed.) Trace elements in human and animal nutrition. 5th ed. Vol. 1. Academic Press, San Diego, CA.

Mondragon, M., and W. Jaffe. 1976. The ingestion of selenium in Caracas compared with some other cities of the world. Arch. Latinoam. Nutr. 26:341–352.

Morck, T., and J. Cook. 1981. Factors affecting the bioavailability of dietary iron. Cereal Foods World 26:667–672.

Morgan, R.F., and B.L. O'Dell. 1977. Effect of copper deficiency on the concentration of catecholamines and related enzyme activities in the rat brain. J. Neurochem. 28:207–213.

Morris, E. 1983. An overview of current information on bioavailability of dietary iron to humans. Fed. Proc. 42:1716–1720.

Morris, E. 1987. Iron. p. 79–142. In W. Mertz (ed.) Trace elements in human and animal nutrition. 5th ed. Vol. 1. Academic Press, San Diego, CA.

Morris, E., and R. Ellis. 1980. Bioavailability to rats of iron and zinc in wheat bran: Response to low-phytate/zinc molar ratios. J. Nutr. 110:2000–2010.

Morris, V.C., and O.A. Levander. 1970. Selenium content of foods. J. Nutr. 100:1383–1388.

Mortvedt, J.J., P.M. Giordano, and W.L. Lindsay (ed.). 1972. Micronutrients in agriculture. SSSA, Madison, WI.

National Research Council. 1977. Medical and biological effects of environmental pollutants: Copper. Natl. Acad. Sci., Washington, DC.

National Research Council. 1983. Selenium in nutrition. Natl. Acad. Press, Washington, DC.

Neumann, P.Z., and A. Sass-Kortsak. 1967. The state of copper in human serum: Evidence for an amino acid-bound fraction. J. Clin. Invest. 46:646–658.

Nielsen, FH. 1984. Ultratrace elements in nutrition. Annu. Rev. Nutr. 4:21–41.

Nielsen, F.H. 1986. Other elements: Sb, Ba, B, Br, Cs, Ge, Rb, Ag, Sr, Sn, Ti, Zr, Be, Bi, Ga, Au, In, Nb, Sc, Te, Tl, W. p. 415–463. In W. Mertz (ed.) Trace elements in human and animal nutrition. 5th ed. Vol. 2. Academic Press, Orlando, FL.

Nielsen, F.H. 1987a. Nickel. p. 245–273. In W. Mertz (ed.) Trace elements in human and animal nutrition. 5th ed. Vol. 1. Academic Press, San Diego, CA.

Nielsen, F.H. 1987b. Vanadium. p. 275–300. In W. Mertz (ed.) Trace elements in human and animal nutrition. 5th ed. Vol. 1. Academic Press, San Diego, CA.

Nielsen, F.H. 1988. The ultratrace elements. p. 357–428. In K.T. Smith (ed.) Trace minerals in foods. Marcel Dekker, New York.

Nielsen, F.H., C.D. Hunt, L.M. Mullen, and J.R. Hunt. 1987. Effect of dietary boron on mineral, estrogen and testosterone metabolism in postmenopausal women. FASEB J. 1:394–397.

Nielsen, F.H., and W. Mertz. 1984. Other trace elements. p. 607–618. In Present knowledge of nutrition. 5th ed. The Nutrition Foundation, Washington, DC.

O'Dell, B.L. 1984. Copper. p. 506–518. In Present knowledge of nutrition. 5th ed. The Nutrition Foundation, Washington, DC.

O'Dell, B.L., D.F. Elsden, J. Thomas, S.M. Partridge, R.H. Smith, and R. Palmer. 1966. Inhibition of the biosynthesis of the crosslinks in elastin by a lathyrogen. Nature 209:401–402.

Oestreicher, P., and R.J. Cousins. 1989. Zinc uptake by basolateral membrane vesicles from rat small intestine. J. Nutr. 119:639–646.

Offenbacher, E., and F. Pi-Sunyer. 1980. Beneficial effects of chromium-rich yeast on glucose tolerance and blood lipids in elderly subjects. Diabetes 29:919–925.

Owen, C.A., Jr. 1975. Uptake of Cu^{67} by ceruloplasmin in vitro. Proc. Soc. Exp. Biol. Med. 149:681–682.

Owen, C.A., Jr. 1981–82. Copper in biology and medicine series. In 5 volumes: Copper Deficiency and Toxicity; Wilson's Disease; Biochemical Aspects of Copper; Physiological Aspects of Copper; Biological Aspects of Copper. Noyes Publ., Park Ridge, NJ.

Palmer, I.S., D.D. Fischer, A.W. Halverson, and O.E. Olson. 1969. Identification of a major selenium excretory product in rat urine. Biochim. Biophys. Acta 177:336–342.

Parmley, R.T., J.C. Barton, and M.E. Conrad. 1985. Ultrastructural localization of transferrin, transferrin receptor and iron-binding sites on human placental and duodenal microvilli. Br. J. Haematol. 60:81–89.

Papavasiliou, P., S. Miller, and G. Cotzias. 1966. Role of liver in regulating distribution and excretion of manganese. Am. J. Physiol. 211:211–216.

Pennington, J.A.T. 1988. Iodine. p. 249–289. *In* K.T. Smith (ed.) Trace minerals in foods. Marcel Dekker, Inc., New York.

Pi-Sunyer, F.X., and E.G. Offenbacher. 1984. Chromium. p. 571–586. *In* Present knowledge in nutrition. 5th ed. The Nutrition Foundation, Washington, DC.

Prasad, A.S., G. Brewer, E. Schoomaker, and P. Rabbani. 1978. Hypocupremia induced by zinc therapy in adults. J. Am. Med. Assoc. 240:2166–2168.

Prasad, A.S., A. Miale, Jr., Z. Farid, H.H. Sandstead, A.R. Schulert, and W.J. Darby. 1963. Biochemical studies on dwarfism, hypogonadism and anemia. Arch. Int. Med. 111:407–428.

Querido, A., F. Delange, J.T. Dunn, R. Fierro-Benitez, H.K. Ibbertson, D.A. Koutras, and H. Perinetti. 1974. Definitions of endemic goiter and cretinism, classification of goiter size and severity of endemias, and survey techniques. p. 267–272. *In* J.T. Dunn and G.A. Medeiros-Neto (ed.) Endemic goiter and cretinism: Continuing threats to world health. Sci. Publ. 292. Pan American Health Org., Washington, DC.

Rao, G.S. 1984. Dietary intake and bioavailability of fluoride. Ann. Rev. Nutr. 4:115–136.

Riales, R., and M.J. Albrink. 1981. Effects of chromium chloride supplementation on glucose tolerance and serum lipids including high-density lipoprotein of adult men. Am. J. Clin. Nutr. 34:2670–2678.

Robinson, M.F., J.M. McKenzie, C.D. Thomson, and A.L. Van Rij. 1973. Metabolic balance of zinc, copper, cadmium, iron, molybdenum and selenium in young New Zealand women Br. J. Nutr. 30:195–205.

Rotruck, J.T., A.L. Pope, H.E. Ganther, A.B. Swanson, D.G. Hafeman, and W.G. Hoekstra. 1973. Selenium: Biochemical role as a component of glutathione peroxidase. Science 179:585–590.

Sakurai, H., and K. Tsuchiya. 1975. A tentative recommendation for the maximum daily intake of selenium. Environ. Physiol. Biochem. 5:107–118.

Sandstead, H.H., and G.W. Evans. 1984. Zinc. p. 479–505. *In* Present knowledge in nutrition. 5th ed. The Nutrition Foundation, Washington, DC.

Saner, G. 1980. Chromium in nutrition and disease. Alan R. Liss, Inc., New York.

Sargent, T., T.H. Lim, and R.L. Gensen. 1979. Reduced chromium retention in patients with hemochromatosis, a possible basis for hemochromatotic diabetes. Metabolism 28:70–79.

Schade, A.L., and L. Caroline. 1946. An iron-binding component in human blood plasma. Science 100:340–341.

Schrauzer, G.N., D.A. White, and CJ. Schneider. 1977. Cancer mortality correlation studies. III. Statistical associations with dietary selenium intakes. Bioinorg. Chem. 7:23–34.

Schroeder, H.A., J.J. Balassa, and I.H. Tipton. 1966. Essential trace metals in man: Manganese, a study in homeostasis. J. Chronic Dis. 19:545–571.

Schroeder, H.A., A.P. Nason, and I.H. Tipton. 1970. Chromium deficiency as a factor in atherosclerosis. J. Chron. Dis. 23:123–142.

Schwartz, K., and C. Foltz. 1957. Selenium as an integral part of factor 3 against dietary necrotic liver degeneration. J. Am. Chem. Soc. 79:3292–3293.

Schwartz, K., and W. Mertz. 1959. Chromium (III) and the glucose tolerance factor. Arch. Biochem. Biophys. 85:292–295.

Shamberger, R.J., and D.V. Frost. 1969. Possible protective effect of selenium against human cancer. Can. Med. Assoc. J. 104:682.

Shrader, R.E., L.C. Erway, and L.S. Hurley. 1973. Mucopolysaccharide synthesis in the developing inner ear of manganese-deficient and pallid mutant mice. Teratology 8:257–266.

Singer, L., and R.H. Ophaug. 1984. Fluoride. p. 538–547. *In* Present knowledge in nutrition. 5th ed. The Nutrition Foundation, Washington, DC.

Smith, K.T. 1988. Zinc. p. 209–229. *In* K.T. Smith (ed.) Trace minerals in foods. Marcel Dekker, New York.

Smith, C.H., and W.R. Bidlack. 1980. Interrelationships of dietary ascorbic acid and iron on the tissue distribution of ascorbic acid, iron and copper in female guinea pigs. J. Nutr. 110:1398–1408.

Solomons, N.W. 1983. Competitive mineral-mineral interaction in the intestine. p. 147–271. *In* G.E. Inglett (ed.) Nutritional bioavailability of zinc. Am. Chem. Soc., Washington, DC.

Solomons, N.W., and R. Cousins. 1984. Zinc. p. 125–197. *In* N. Solomons and I. Rosenberg (ed.) Absorption and malabsorption of mineral nutrients. Alan R. Liss, New York.

Solomons, N.W., O. Pineda, F.E. Viteri, and H.H. Sandstead. 1983. Studies on the bioavailability of zinc in humans: Mechanisms of the intestinal interaction of non-heme iron and zinc. J. Nutr. 113:337–349.

Spencer, H., C. Asmussen, R. Holtzman, and L. Kramer. 1979. Metabolic balance of cadmium, copper, manganese and zinc in man. Am. J. Clin. Nutr. 32:1867–1875.

Spencer, H., and L. Kramer. 1988. Calcium, phosphorus and fluoride. p. 95–115. In K.T. Smith (ed.) Trace minerals in foods. Marcel Dekker, New York.

Sternlieb, I. 1967. Gastrointestinal copper absorption in man. Gastroenterology 52:1038–1041.

Sternlieb, I., and H.D. Janowitz. 1964. Absorption of copper in malabsorption syndromes. J. Clin. Invest. 43:1049–1055.

Sternlieb, I., A.G. Morell, W.D. Tucker, M.W. Greene, and I.H. Sheinberg. 1961. The incorporation of copper into ceruloplasmin in vivo: Studies with copper[64] and copper[67]. J. Clin. Invest. 40:1834–1840.

Sun, I., P. Navas, F. Crane, D. Morre, and H. Low. 1987. NADH diferric transferrin reductase in liver plasma membrane. J. Biol. chem. 262:15915–15921.

Taves, D.R. 1983. Dietary intake of fluoride: Ashed (total fluoride) vs. unashed (inorganic fluoride) analysis of individual foods. Br. J. Nutr. 49:295–302.

Tenhunen, R., R. Grasbeck, I. Kuovonen, and M. Lundberg. 1980. An intestinal receptor for heme: its partial characterization. J. Biochem. 12:713–716.

Thompson, D. 1988. Iron. p. 157–208. In K.T. Smith (ed.) Trace minerals in foods. Marcel Dekker, New York.

Thomsen, D.D., and R.D.H. Stewart. 1974. The metabolism of (^{75}Se)selenite in young women. Br. J. Nutr. 32:47–57.

Thomson, C.D., and M.F. Robinson. 1980. Selenium in human health and disease with emphasis on those aspects peculiar to New Zealand. Am. J. Clin. Nutr. 33:303–323.

Tsongas, T., R. Meglen, P. Walravens, and W. Chappell. 1980. Molybdenum in the diet: An estimate of average daily intake in the U.S. Am. J. Clin. Nutr. 33:1103–1107.

Turnlund, J.R., W.R. Keyes, H.L. Anderson, and L.L. Accord. 1989. Copper absorption and retention in young men at three levels of dietary copper by use of the stable isotope ^{65}Cu. Am. J. Clin. Nutr. 49:870–878.

Ulrich, C.E., W. Rinehart, and W. Busey. 1979. Evaluation of the chronic inhalation toxicity of manganese oxide aerosol. 1. Introduction, experimental design and aerosol generation methods. Am. Ind. Hyg. Assoc. J. 40:238–244.

Underwood, E.J. (ed.). 1977. Trace elements in human and animal nutrition. 4th ed. Academic Press, New York.

U.S. Department of Health and Human Services and U.S. Department of Agriculture. 1986. Nutrition Monitoring in the United States. A Report from the Joint Nutrition Monitoring Evaluation Committee. DHHS Publ. (PSH) 86-1255. Public Health Serv., Washington, DC.

Valberg, L.S., P.R. Flanagan, and M.J. Chamberlain. 1984. Effects of iron, tin and copper on zinc absorption in humans. Am. J. Clin. Nutr. 40:536–541.

Van Buren, J.P., N.H. Peck, G.E. MacDonald, and E.E. Cary. 1989. Element concentration in layers of table beet roots and in various beet cultivars. Hortic. Sci. 24:338–340.

Van Campen, D. 1969. Copper interference with the intestinal absorption of zinc-65 in rats. J. Nutr. 97:104–108.

Van Campen, D. 1970. Absorption of copper from the gastrointestinal tract. p. 211–227. In S.C. Skoryna and D. Waldron-Edward (ed.) Intestinal absorption of metal ions, trace elements and radionuclides. Pergamon Press, New York.

Van Campen, D. 1974. Regulation of iron absorption. Fed. Proc. 33:100–105.

Van Campen, D. 1983. Iron bioavailability techniques: An overview. Food Technol. October, p. 127–132.

Van Campen, D., and E. Gross. 1968. Influence of ascorbic acid on the absorption of copper by rats. J. Nutr. 95:617–622.

Van Campen, D., and E. Mitchell. 1964. Absorption of Cu^{64}, Zn^{65}, Mo^{99}, and Fe^{59} from ligated segments of the rat gastrointestinal tract. J. Nutr. 86:120–124.

Van Campen, D., and P. Scaife. 1967. Zinc interference with copper absorption in rats. J. Nutr. 91:473–476.

Vilter, R.W., R.C. Bozian, E.V. Hess, D.C. Zellner, and H.G. Petering. 1974. Manifestations of copper deficiency in a patient with systemic sclerosis of intravenous hyperalimentation. New Eng. J. Med. 291:188–191.

Vyas, D., and R. Chandra. 1984. Functional implications of iron deficiency. p. 45–49. In A. Stekel (ed.) Iron nutrition in infancy and childhood. Raven Press, New York.

Waldmann, T.A., A.G. Morell, R.D. Wochner, W. Strober, and I. Sternlieb. 1967. Measurement of gastrointestinal protein loss using ceruloplasmin labeled with copper[67]. J. Clin. Invest. 46:10–20.

Walters, G., F. Miller, and M. Worwood. 1973. Serum ferritin concentration and iron stores in normal subjects. J. Clin. Pathol. 26:770–772.

Weintraub, L.R., M.B. Weinstein, H.J. Huser, and S. Rafal. 1968. Absorption of hemoglobin iron: the role of a heme-splitting substance in the intestinal mucosa. J. Clin. Invest. 47:531–539.

Welch, R.M., and W.A. House. 1982. Availability to rats of iron from soybean seeds as affected by maturity of seed, source of dietary protein and soluble phytate. J. Nutr. 112:879–885.

Welch, R., and W. House. 1984. Factors affecting the bioavailability of mineral nutrients in plant foods. p. 37–54. In R. Welch and W. Gabelman (ed.) Crops as sources of nutrients for humans. ASA Spec. Publ. 48. ASA, CSSA, and SSSA, Madison, WI.

Welch, R.M., W.A. House, and W.H. Allaway. 1974. Availability of zinc from pea seeds to rats. J. Nutr. 104:733–740.

Whanger, P.D. 1989. China, a country with both selenium deficiency and toxicity: Some thoughts and impressions. J. Nutr. 119:1236–1239.

Whanger, P.D., M.A. Beilstein, C.D. Thomson, M.F. Robinson, and M. Howe. 1988. Blood selenium and glutathione peroxidase activity of populations in New Zealand, Oregon and South Dakota. FASEB J. 2:2996–3002.

Widdowson, E., H. Chan, G. Harrison, and R. Miner. 1972. Accumulation of Cu, Zn, Mn, Cr and Co in human liver before birth. Biol. Neonat. 20:360–367.

Xia, Y., K. Hill, and R. Burk. 1989. Biochemical studies of a selenium-deficient population in China: Measurement of selenium, glutathione peroxidase and other oxidant defense indices in blood. J. Nutr. 119:1318–1326.

Yamamoto, A., O. Wada, and H. Suzuki. 1988. Purification and properties of biologically active chromium complex from bovine colostrum. J. Nutr. 118:39–45.

Yang, G. 1987. Research on selenium-related problems in human health in China. p. 8–32. In G. Combs et al. (ed.) Selenium in biology and medicine. Part A. Van Nostrand Reinhold Co., New York.

Yang, G., J. Morrison-Plummer, and R.F. Burk. 1987. Purification and quantitation of a rat plasma selenoprotein distinct from glutathione peroxidase using monoclonal antibodies. J. Biol. Chem. 262:13372–13375.

Yang, G., L. Zhu, S. Liu, L. Gu, P. Quian, J. Huang, and M. Lu. 1987. Human selenium requirements in China. p. 589–607. In G. Combs et al. (ed.) Selenium in biology and medicine. Part B. Van Nostrand Reinhold Co., New York.

Zidenberg-Cherr, S., and C.L. Keen. 1987. Enhanced tissue lipid peroxidation: Mechanisms underlying pathologies associated with dietary manganese deficiency. p. 56–66. In C. Kies (ed.) Nutritional bioavailability of manganese. Am. Chem. Soc., Washington, DC.

Chapter 18

Beneficial Elements, Functional Nutrients, and Possible New Essential Elements

COLIN J. ASHER, *The University of Queensland, Queensland, 4072, Australia*

I. CONCEPTS AND DEFINITIONS

More than half of the elements in the Periodic Table are known to occur in plant tissues, and it seems likely that, with further improvements in procedures for plant chemical analysis, most of the remaining elements will be found there also. However, at present, only 17 are regarded as essential for all higher plants. These include the nine macronutrients, C, H, O, N, K, Ca, Mg, P, and S, which typically occur in the plant dry matter at concentrations $\geq 0.1\%$, and the seven micronutrients, Cl, Fe, B, Mn, Zn, Cu, and Mo. In addition, Co is essential for symbiotic N fixation in legumes and some other species. The term ultra-micronutrient has been proposed (Nicholas, 1961) for elements such as Mo and Co, which are needed in particularly small quantities.

However, positive effects of many other elements on plant growth have been reported over the years. This prompts researchers to question what constitutes essentiality (and nonessentiality), whether all the essential elements have been discovered, and how elements that appear to have beneficial effects on plant growth, yet have not been shown to conform with our definition of an essential element should be regarded. This chapter is intended to explore these questions and to comment on some of the elements in the latter category.

A. The Concept of Essentiality

Arnon and Stout (1939) proposed that for an element to be considered essential, it should satisfy three criteria: (i) it must be present for completion of the plant's life cycle; (ii) its action must be specific, and unable to be replaced by any other element; and (iii) its action must be direct.

Although these criteria initially met with general acceptance, with time it became apparent that they were rather too rigid. For example, the action of several essential elements is not completely specific. Thus, Br can take over the function of Cl in some species, and Rb and Na can take over some of the functions of K. Again, the first criterion cannot be tested in any absolute sense, since even the most efficient purification procedures for water and nutrient salts are unlikely to remove the final traces of any element under investigation. This means that while essentiality may be proved by failure of the plant to complete its lifecycle when the level of contamination is sufficiently low, nonessentiality cannot be proved. It follows that all elements present in plant tissues, but not yet shown to be essential, must be regarded as potential candidates for inclusion on the essential list.

Nicholas (1961) introduced the term functional (or metabolism) nutrient to describe an element that plays a role in plant metabolism, whether or not that role is specific or indispensable. For example, the role of Ni in urease activity in plants (Section V) would justify the classification of Ni as a functional nutrient. Subsequently, Epstein (1965) proposed that an element be regarded as essential if it was a constituent of a molecule known to be an essential metabolite, even though compliance with the criteria of Arnon and Stout (1939) could not be demonstrated. The establishment of essentiality for ultramicronutrients poses formidable problems in purification and the control of contamination because of the very low quantitative requirements involved.

More recently, the term beneficial element has been introduced to include elements that have been found to stimulate plant growth, but that have not been shown, so far, to be essential, or have been found to be essential only under certain conditions or only for certain species. As pointed out by Marschner (1986), with improvements in experimental technique, elements currently classified as beneficial may later be shown to satisfy Arnon's criteria and, hence, be added to the essential list. A case can be made for also including those elements that have positive effects on plant growth by improving resistance to pests and diseases in the beneficial category, although these elements may not otherwise be required. The role of micronutrients (and beneficial elements) in disease resistance is discussed in Ch. 10 of this book (Graham & Webb, 1990), and will not be considered in any detail here.

B. Comparisons between Plants and Other Organisms

All living things appear to have many biochemical processes in common, and so, some commonality of mineral nutrient requirements across phylogenetic boundaries might be expected. Indeed, the history of nutrient essentiality research up to the late 1950s tended to suggest that the discovery of an element requirement in one type of organism would usually lead to similar discoveries in other types of organisms. There were exceptions, such as the apparent lack of a B requirement in animals and microorganisms, and the apparent restriction of I requirements to animals and some algae. However, since nonessentiality is virtually impossible to prove, the expectation remained that further research might remove some of these anomalies. Indeed, recent work on animals (Nielsen, 1986) indicates that there is an essential function of B in the regulation of parathormone activity, and, although essentiality is not yet proven, it is suggested that diets for rats (*Rattus norvegicus*) and chicks (*Gallus domesticus*), should contain B at ≥ 0.3 to 0.4 mg kg^{-1}. Other research (Nielsen et al., 1987) strongly suggests that B may play a role in the prevention of Ca loss and bone demineralization in postmenopausal women.

Since the late 1950s, there has been considerably more research on nutrient essentiality in animals than in plants. Schwarz (1974) stated that the essentiality of seven new trace elements for warm blooded animals was established between 1957 and 1973 (F, Si, V, Cr, Ni, Se, and Sn), and that additional discoveries were likely. He indicated that 19 other elements were under special consideration by animal scientists, or elicited special effects. Another 32 elements were regarded as having possible roles in animal nutrition, whereas only 16 elements in the Periodic Table were considered unlikely to have any role. Later work suggests that As should be added to the essential list for animals, but it also calls into question the essentiality of V and Sn (Nielsen & Mertz, 1984; Nielsen, 1986). From the foregoing, it is apparent that the list of known essential elements for animals is now appreciably longer than that for plants.

The agricultural significance of the more recent trace element discoveries for animals remains to be determined. To the extent that animals derive these elements from plants and plant products, it is important that plants absorb them in adequate quantities, whether they are required for plant growth or not. However, elements such as B, for which plant requirements are high relative to those of animals (e.g., typically ≥ 15 mg kg^{-1} compared with a tentative value of ≥ 0.3 to 0.4 mg kg^{-1}), are unlikely to become deficient in animals fed plant-based diets.

C. Scope of the Present Review

Throughout the history of plant nutrition, there have been claims of beneficial effects of many elements. In this review, space precludes a detailed examination of a majority of these claims. Instead, a small number of elements of contemporary interest (Table 18-1) will be discussed.

Table 18-1. Characteristics of some of the beneficial elements.

Element	Symbol	Atomic mass	Oxidation states	Position in periodic table
Sodium	Na	22.99	$+1$	Group IA (alkali metals)
Aluminum	Al	26.98	$+3$	Group IIIA
Silicon	Si	28.09	$-4, +2, +4$	Group IVA
Nickel	Ni	58.71	$+2, +3$	Group VIII (transition elements)
Cobalt	Co	58.93	$+2, +3$	
Lanthanum	La	138.9	$+3$	Group IIIB (rare earths)
Cerium	Ce	140.1	$+3, +4$	

II. SODIUM

Sodium is the sixth most abundant element on earth (about 2.6% of the earth's crust), and is the most abundant of the alkali metals (Weast, 1969). Over large areas of the earth, agricultural production is impeded or prevented by excessive accumulations of Na salts in the soil. Nevertheless, Na is essential for the growth of animals and some plant species. In addition, it has been shown to have beneficial effects on the growth of some plant species for which it has not been shown to be essential. The wide variety of effects of Na on individual plant species makes generalization about these effects difficult (Brownell, 1979).

A. Essentiality

The essentiality of Na for plants with the C_4 photosynthetic pathway (and under some conditions those with the CAM pathway), some blue-green algae, and some bacteria and fungi has been established. External Na concentrations $\leq 100 \, \mu M$ have been shown to be required for maximum growth of C_4 plants, whereas C_3 plants have been shown to grow normally in highly purified nutrient solutions in which the Na concentration has been reduced to 0.07 μM (Brownell, 1968). Hence, if C_3 plants do have a Na requirement, it must be very small indeed.

B. Functions of Sodium

In C_4 plants, recent research indicates that Na is required for the conversion of pyruvate to phosphoenolpyruvate in the mesophyll cells (Nable & Brownell, 1984; Johnson et al., 1988), but the exact nature of this requirement is not known. In the blue-green alga *Anabaena cylindrica*, Na is required for the normal assimilation of NO_3 via NO_2^- and other intermediates into protein. In cultures supplied with NO_3, toxic accumulations of NO_2^- may occur in the cells under conditions of Na deficiency. In cultures dependent on symbiotic N_2 fixation, growth and nitrogenase activity are reduced by withholding Na, but the Na requirement is lower than for NO_3 cultures (Brownell, 1979).

C. Partial Substitution of Sodium for Other Elements

In cotton (*Gossypium* spp.) partial substitution of Na for Ca has been reported for the growth of excised roots (Johanson & Joham, 1971), and Na has been found to overcome the impairment of carbohydrate transport associated with Ca deficiency (Joham & Johanson, 1973).

There are many reports in the literature of partial substitution of Na for K in plants. A good example is provided by an experiment of Smith (1974) in which Rhodes grass (*Chloris gayana* Kunth) was grown in a K-deficient soil with various combinations of Na and K. The results showed a progressive decrease in both the external and internal K requirements as the Na level was increased (Fig. 18–1).

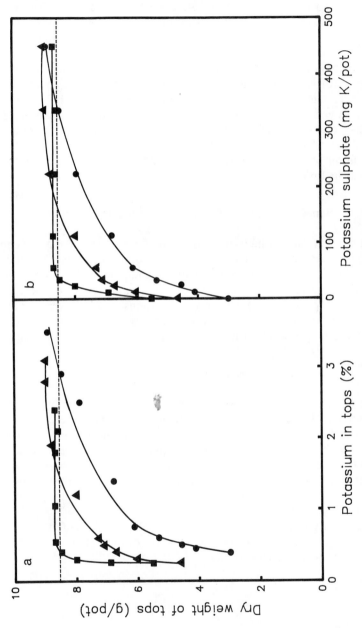

Fig. 18-1. Relationships between dry weight of tops of Rhodes grass plants and (a) K concentration in the tops, and (b) amount of K supplied, when Na_2SO_4 was added at 0 (●), 67 (▲), or 400 (■) mg pot^{-1}. The broken line indicates 95% of maximal yield. Note the decrease in critical internal and external K concentrations with the increase in Na supply (redrawn after Smith, 1974).

The precise nature of the partial substitution of Na for K in plants is not well understood, and it is possible that different mechanisms may be operating in different species. Substitution for K at sites of action of enzymes requiring a monovalent ion for maximum activity seems an unlikely explanation, because of the rather low effectiveness of Na for activation of those enzymes that have been studied (Evans & Sorger, 1966; Nitsos & Evans, 1969). Sodium is able to substitute for K in stomatal opening in some species. In *Commelina bengalensis*, full opening was achieved with Na, but 40 m*M* Na was required in the incubation medium for maximum opening, compared with 20 m*M* for K (Raghavendra et al., 1976). However, Na appears to be the preferred ion in the halophyte, *Cakile maritima* (Eshel et al., 1974). Hence, some of the beneficial effects of Na under conditions of suboptimal K supply could be due to improved stomatal function. In other cases it could be that beneficial effects of Na under conditions of restricted K supply are due to substitution of Na for K in the osmotic and electrical balance of cells, rather than in functions with a specific K requirement.

D. Beneficial Effects of High Sodium Concentrations

Addition of relatively high concentrations of Na salts (≥ 10 m*M*) to complete culture media containing adequate K has often increased the growth of halophytes. This effect has been attributed to increased turgor (Flowers et al., 1977). However, these effects may not be specific to Na. Indeed, Flowers et al. (1977) provide examples in which responses to KCl were equal to or greater than those to NaCl. Some glycophytes and, notably, sugarbeet (*Beta vulgaris* L.) respond positively to Na in the presence of adequate K.

E. Agricultural Significance

Lehr (1953) produced a classification of crop plants according to their responses to Na (Table 18–2). In addition to effects on dry matter, there have been reports of positive effects of Na on sugar concentration in sugarbeet (El-Sheikh & Ulrich, 1970), and in the fiber quality of flax (*Linum usitatissimum* L.) (Lehr & Wybenga, 1955). Sodium concentration in herbage is an important quality factor in relation to animal nutrition, as evidenced by the Na deficiency of grazing cattle that has been reported from many parts of the world (Playne, 1970).

Whether or not it is advantageous to apply Na-containing fertilizers will depend on the cost of the fertilizer, the Na status of the soil, and the responsiveness of the plant species to Na.

III. ALUMINUM

Aluminum is among the most abundant elements on earth, representing about 8% by weight of the earth's crust. Main interest in this element

Table 18-2. Response of some plant species† to Na (Lehr, 1953).

Species benefited by Na when K is deficient		
(i) Little or no benefit		
Buckwheat	Parsley	Spearmint
Red clover	Parsnip	Spinach
Cucumber	Peppermint	Squash
Lettuce	Potato	Strawberry
Maize	Rye	Sunflower
Onion	Soybean	White bean
(ii) Slight to medium benefit		
Asparagus	Chicory	Oat
Barley	Ladino clover	Pea
Broccoli	Cotton	Salsify
Brussels sprouts	Flax	Swede
Caraway	Lucerne	Tomato
Carrot	Millet	Vetch

Species benefited by Na when K is adequately supplied		
(i) Slight to medium benefit		
Cabbage	Kale	Radish
Celeriac	Kohlrabi	Rape
Horseradish	Mustard	Wheat
(ii) Large benefit		
Celery	Red beet	Swiss chard
Mangold	Sugarbeet	Turnip

† Scientific names are listed in the Glossary.

has been concerned with (i) the ability of some plant species (accumulators) to tolerate very high Al concentrations (up to several percent) in their tissues; and (ii) the toxic effects on plant growth of free Al ions in the soil solutions of acid soils (Bell & Edwards, 1987). In the latter case, both direct toxic effects and Al-induced deficiencies of essential elements may be involved.

No convincing evidence of essentiality has been provided, but Al has long been known to be a constituent of a blue pigment in *Hydrangea* (Chenery, 1948). There have also been many examples reported in the literature over the past 50 yr of stimulation of plant growth by subtoxic concentrations of Al. Stimulatory effects have been observed both in accumulators (e.g., tea, *Camellia sinensis* (L.) Kuntze, [Matsumoto et al., 1976]), and in crop and pasture species that do not accumulate high concentrations of Al in their tissues. As an example of the latter, Bertrand and de Wolf (1968) showed that raising the concentration of Al in purified nutrient solutions from 2.2 to 7.4 μM resulted in a four-fold increase in the yield of corn (*Zea mays* L.) seedlings. The nature of these beneficial effects on plant growth is, at present, not well understood.

In some cases, reported beneficial effects of Al may relate to a reduction, by Al, of the uptake of a second element present in the root environment at potentially toxic concentrations. Thus, Liebig et al. (1942) showed that Cu toxicity in citrus (*Citrus* spp.) plants grown in solution culture could be overcome to a substantial degree by small additions of Al to the nutrient solution. Later work by Hiat et al. (1963) showed that Cu uptake by wheat

Table 18-3. Effects of Al activity (sum activities Al monomers in solution) on yields of
tops and roots, and on Zn concentration in the youngest, fully expanded leaf blades
(YEB) of Red Spanish peanut (*Arachis hypogaea*) in flowing solution culture.†

	Al activity, μM				
	0	4.9	10.2	20.4	39.0
Zn in YEB, mg kg^{-1}‡	332	201	185	117	80
Yield of tops, g plant^{-1}	1.05	1.45	1.36	1.17	0.68
Yield of roots, g plant^{-1}	0.36	0.54	0.50	0.46	0.27

† All values significantly different at $P = 0.05$; data from Suthipradit, 1988.
‡ Critical tissue concentrations for Zn toxicity (10% reduction) under the conditions of
this study estimated at 204 mg kg^{-1} for yield of tops and 190 mg kg^{-1} for nodulation (Suthipradit, 1988).

(*Triticum aestivum* L.) plants was appreciably reduced by Al concentrations
$\geq 3.7 \mu M$. In other studies, beneficial effects have been observed in solution
culture experiments at potentially toxic P concentrations, suggesting that P
may have been precipitated or P uptake otherwise reduced. In an experiment
with dilute, continuously flowing, nutrient solutions maintained at pH 4.5
and 0.5 μM Zn, Suthipradit (1988) found that Zn uptake was excessive in
peanut (*Arachis hypogaea* L.) in the absence of added Al, but that the Zn
toxicity was overcome, and the yields of tops and roots significantly increased
at Al activities of 4.9 to 20.4 μM (Table 18-3). Raising the Al level above
20.4 μM significantly depressed yields because of Al toxicity.

In most cases in which positive effects of Al on plant growth have been
reported, there has been insufficient supporting information to establish
whether or not they were indirect effects mediated through alleviation of toxicity of another element. Further studies are warranted to establish whether
or not Al stimulation can occur under conditions of optimum nutrition.

Most positive responses to Al have been observed at nominal Al concentrations $\leq 37 \mu M$. However, because of the ease with which free Al ions
are lost from solution by complexation, polymerization, and precipitation
reactions, the actual Al concentrations in solution have probably been much
lower. Indeed, several workers have given critical Al activities for toxicity
in the range of 1 to 5 μM for well-controlled solution culture systems (Alva
et al., 1986; Hetherington et al., 1988) or acid soil solutions (Bruce et al.,
1988). Hence, future work on the possible essentiality of Al will need to be
conducted at much lower Al levels; thus necessitating careful purification
of media and strict control of Al contamination.

IV. SILICON

Silicon is the second most abundant element in the lithosphere, accounting for about 26% by weight (Weast, 1969). There is an extensive literature
on the biological roles of Si. The earlier work was reviewed by Jones and
Handreck (1967) and Lewin and Reimann (1969), and much of the more recent material by Werner and Roth (1983), Raven (1983), Carlisle (1984), and
Takahashi et al. (1990).

Essentiality studies require special precautions to avoid Si contamination, particularly arising from contact of water and nutrient solutions with glass surfaces. Preferred procedures involve solution culture in plastic pots, use of plastic rather than glass laboratory ware in the preparation and purification of stock solutions, and water purification by distillation in a still with a polyethylene condenser or an all-metal still, followed by demineralization to remove the traces of metal (Woolley, 1957; Miyake & Takahashi, 1983).

Essentiality has long been established in diatoms in which active accumulation of $Si(OH)_4$ across the plasma membrane has been demonstrated, possibly involving cotransport with Na (Raven, 1983). Silicon also is regarded as an essential trace element for normal growth and development in higher animals where it is involved in the formation of bone and cartilage (Carlisle, 1984).

Vascular land plants differ widely in the amounts of Si absorbed from the soil solution. Thus, members of the Cyperaceae (e.g., *Equisetum arvense*) and wetland members of the Gramineae, (e.g., rice [*Oryza sativa* L.]) commonly accumulate >4% Si in the dry matter of their tops compared with <0.5% in dicotyledons. Dryland Graminaceae form an intermediate group. The available evidence suggests that plant species with the highest tissue Si concentrations actively accumulate Si, whereas those with the lowest tissue Si concentrations possess mechanisms by which they exclude the element. In the intermediate group, Si and water enter in an approximately constant ratio.

A wide variety of beneficial effects of Si has been demonstrated in agricultural plant species. These include improved resistance to fungus diseases (Ch. 10), to insect attack, and to Mn toxicity. In addition, deposition of SiO_2 in cell walls of the leaf and stem may be expected to confer considerable structural rigidity. In rice and sorghum [*Sorghum bicolor* (L.) Moench], silica is deposited in the inner tangential wall of the endodermis (Parry & Sony, 1972; Sangster & Parry, 1976). In some woody perennials, xylem vessels and fibers may be lined with, or the lumina filled with, SiO_2 (Scurfield & Anderson, 1974). With soil-grown plants, the addition of silicate materials may benefit plant growth by increasing P availability (Suehisa et al., 1963), and by decreasing the solubility of Al and heavy metals, which may be otherwise present at toxic levels (Clements et al., 1967). However, unequivocal evidence of essentiality has not yet been obtained.

In rice and *Equisetum*, growth reductions and specific leaf symptoms have been demonstrated in plants in low-Si solution cultures. In sugarcane (*Saccharum officinarum* L.), growth reductions and leaf freckle have been associated with highly weathered soils that are low in extractable Si (<20 mg kg^{-1} extractable, with 0.1M HOAc), low Si concentrations in the irrigation water (<0.9 mg L^{-1}), and low Si concentrations in leaf sheathes (<0.5% dry weight) (Fox et al., 1967). In rice and sugarcane, the amendment of soils with silicate materials has entered commercial practice. Sometimes the resultant yield increases have been quite large; e.g., from 21 to 23 t sugar ha^{-1} without silicate addition to 32 to 33 t ha^{-1} with 4.5 t ha^{-1} $CaSiO_3$ in the study by Fox et al. (1967).

Table 18-4. Effects of Si supply on grain-yield components in lowland rice (after Okuda & Takahashi, 1964).

Treatment	Panicles per pot	Spikelets per panicle	Fully ripened grains, %	Weight mature grains per pot, g
−Si−Si	9.5	49	55	5.3
+Si−Si†	10.3	47	67	6.6
−Si+Si†	10.0	65	78	10.3
+Si+Si	11.0	63	76	10.8

† Plants transferred to + or − Si solutions at beginning of the ear-forming stage.

In solution culture studies (reviewed by Okuda & Takahashi, 1965) grain yield of rice was markedly reduced by withholding Si during the ear-forming stage (Table 18-4). These observations are consistent with the notion that Si may be essential for the growth of these species, but failure to complete the lifecycle has not yet been demonstrated.

Research on dicotyledenous species has yielded conflicting results. In carefully conducted experiments with tomato (*Lycopersicon esculentum* Mill.), Woolley (1957) could find no evidence of a Si requirement. He concluded that, if this species does have a Si requirement, it must be very low (<6 mg kg^{-1} dry plant material). However, Miyake and Takahashi (1978) found that withholding Si up to the first flower bud stage reduced fruit yield to zero, whether Si was later supplied or not. Transfer of +Si plants to −Si cultures at the first flower bud stage led to the rapid onset of leaf symptoms on the young growth and a substantial (58%) reduction in fruit yield (Table 18-5). In these tomato experiments, plants from which Si was withheld at the bloom stage exhibited reduced pollen viability by the acetocarmine test (64% viable compared with 91% in +Si controls), abnormalities of pollen color and form, and in about 10% of the flowers, signs of degeneration of the anthers.

Reduced pollen viability (and fruit or pod production) was observed also in −Si cultures of cucumber (*Cucumis sativus* L.), soybean [*Glycine max* (L.) Merr.], and strawberry (*Fragaria* × *ananassa* Duchesne) (Miyake & Takahashi, 1983, 1985, 1986). However, Marschner et al. (1989) have drawn attention to the high P and low Zn concentrations in the nutrient solutions used in these studies. They have produced experimental evidence showing that, in cucumber, the alleviation of leaf symptoms by adding Si to such nutrient solutions is associated with an increase in the water-soluble Zn concentration and a very large decrease in P concentration in the leaves. They

Table 18-5. Effects of Si supply on the growth of tomato (after Miyake & Takahashi, 1978).

Treatment	Dry weight of tops + roots	Number of fruit per plant	Fresh weight of fruit, g per plant
−Si−Si	27.8	0	0
−Si+Si†	36.2	0	0
+Si−Si†	45.3	3	70
+Si+Si	52.9	4	168

† Plants transferred to + or − Si solutions at the first flower bud stage.

concluded that the observed beneficial effect of Si on cucumber was a result of alleviation of P toxicity induced by Zn deficiency.

Further careful research on the effects of Si on plant growth and reproduction is needed. Although beneficial effects are well established in some species, on the basis of present evidence Si cannot be added to the list of elements known to be essential for agricultural plant species.

V. NICKEL

Until comparatively recently, the main interest in Ni concerned its toxic effects on plant growth, first demonstrated by Wolff (1913) in a solution-culture experiment with barley (*Hordeum vulgare* L.). However, recent research has demonstrated Ni requirements in both plants and animals. Much of the earlier work on plants was reviewed by Vanselow (1966), and Mishra and Kar (1974), while Hewitt (1979) and Welch (1981) deal with more recent developments, particularly those relating to possible biochemical roles of Ni. The role of Ni in animal nutrition has been reviewed by Nielsen and Mertz (1984).

A. Toxic Effects on Plants

Soils vary widely in total Ni content, but commonly fall within the range of 5 to 500 mg kg^{-1} (Swaine, 1955). However, soils derived from serpentine may contain up to 5000 mg kg^{-1} total Ni and provide a toxic substrate for most plant species. These soils often carry a distinct flora, including Ni hyperaccumulators, in which tissue Ni concentrations may exceed 1000 mg kg^{-1}. Such species are of special interest in relation to biogeochemical mineral exploration (Jaffre et al., 1979).

In agricultural species, a range of symptoms has been reported to be associated with excess Ni. Often symptoms similar to Fe deficiency have been observed. However, a characteristic feature of Ni toxicity in cereals and grasses is a variation in intensity of the chlorosis along the length of the leaf, yielding a series of transverse bands (Anderson et al., 1973). Substantial differences in Ni tolerance exist among species (Table 18-6).

Table 18-6. Critical Ni concentrations for toxicity (10% yield reduction) in soil and plant tops for six tropical grasses grown in soil to which graded amounts of NiSO$_4$ had been added in a greenhouse pot experiment (M.R. Brown & L.C. Bell, 1984, unpublished data).

	Critical Ni concentration	
Grass species[†]	Soil[‡]	Plant
	——— mg kg^{-1} ———	
Pangola grass	112	56
Signal grass	60	27
Sabi grass	46	10
Rhodes grass	24	12
Bambatsi grass cv. Bambatsi	19	14
Bermuda grass	6	7

[†] Scientific names are listed in the Glossary.
[‡] Extractable with DTPA.

B. Beneficial Effects on Plants

Since McHargue (1925) showed Ni to be a trace constituent of plants, there have been periodic reports of beneficial effects of the element on plant growth. Notable among these were the reports of Roach and Barklay (1946) on potato (*Solanum tuberosum* L.), Dobrolyubskii and Slavvo (1957) on grape (*Vitus vinifera* L.), and Bertrand and de Wolf (1973) on soybean. Although Trelease and Trelease (1933) included Ni among the micronutrients in their culture solution, proof of essentiality for plants was not obtained for another 54 yr. However, work in the 1960s demonstrated Ni requirements for some bacteria (Bartha & Ordal, 1965) and algae (Bertrand & de Wolf, 1967).

Metabolically mediated accumulation of Ni by barley roots was demonstrated by Colclaisure and Schmid (1974). Enzyme kinetic analysis suggested a common transport mechanism for Co and Ni. Later work by Cataldo et al. (1978) with intact soybean seedlings showed inhibition of Ni uptake by Fe, Zn, and Cu, as well as Co. They concluded that Ni was absorbed via the same mechanism as Cu and Zn. Further research in this area is warranted.

A key development that stimulated much interest in Ni was the discovery by Dixon et al. (1975) that the urease from jackbean [*Canavalia ensiformis* (L.) DC] is a Ni metalloenzyme. Thus, the status of Ni was elevated to that of a functional nutrient. Later research demonstrated a Ni requirement for the growth of soybean tissue cultures, *Lemna, Spirodella*, and *Wolffia* when supplied with urea as the sole source of N (Polacco, 1976; Gordon et al., 1978). Shimada and Ando (1980) found that low-Ni plants of tomato and soybean accumulated urea in the tissues and developed a leaf-tip necrosis. Eskew et al. (1983, 1984) also demonstrated leaf-tip necroses and high tissue urea concentrations (e.g., 2.5%) in low-Ni soybean dependent on symbiotic N_2 fixation or supplied with a mixture of NO_3- and NH_4-N. These symptoms were associated with the onset of the reproductive phase and could be prevented by addition of Ni, but not by addition of Al, Cd, Sn, or V. Walker et al. (1985) reviewed earlier work on the role of Ni in urea metabolism of plants, and showed similar effects in cowpea [*Vigna unguiculata* (L.) Walp]. In none of these experiments was there any evidence that a shortage of Ni reduced seed production or viability. Hence, essentiality had not been established.

The vital confirmation of essentiality was provided by Brown et al. (1987a) who showed that Ni was essential for grain viability in barley. At grain Ni concentrations < 100 μg kg^{-1}, the germination percentage decreased linearly with decreasing Ni concentration (Fig. 18–2). In associated work (Brown et al., 1987b), symptoms of Ni deficiency in wheat, oat (*Avena sativa* L.), and barley were described briefly. These symptoms included an interveinal chlorosis showing similarities with deficiencies of Fe, Mn, Zn, and Cu. In oat, in which particularly low Ni concentrations were achieved (down to 17 μg kg^{-1}), the terminal 2 cm of the leaves failed to unfold completely, and the plants underwent premature senescence. The criti-

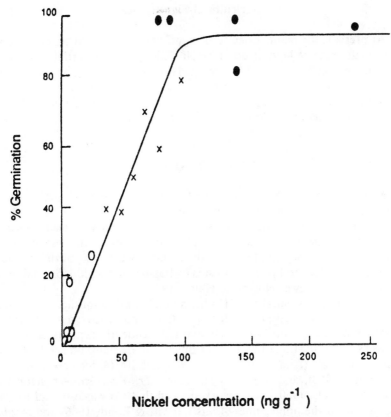

Fig. 18-2. Relationship between grain Ni concentration and germination percentage in barley. Maternal plants received 0 (O), 0.6 (x), or 1.0 (●) μM Ni (reproduced from Brown et al., 1987a).

cal tissue concentration for growth in barley was established at approximately $100 \ \mu g \ kg^{-1}$.

C. Role in Animal Nutrition

The first indications that Ni might be essential for animals were obtained in the early 1970s, but the conditions of these experiments did not permit optimal growth of the experimental animals when Ni was supplied. However, more recent work has clearly established Ni as a micronutrient for animals (Nielsen, 1984). Symptoms of Ni deprivation have been described both for ruminants (sheep [*Ovis aries*], goat [*Capra hircus*], and cow) and non-ruminants (chick, rat, and minipig [*Sus scrofa*]). Dietary requirements appear to be of the order of $50 \ \mu g \ kg^{-1}$ for rats and chicks, and $> 100 \ \mu g \ kg^{-1}$ for ruminants (Nielsen, 1984).

D. Agricultural Significance

At present, the main agricultural significance of Ni still concerns relatively small areas of land affected by Ni toxicity, where partial control of the problem may be obtained by liming. However, now that its essentiality for both plants and animals has been demonstrated, one may expect a considerable increase in research on the element. Hence, it is likely that naturally occurring areas of Ni deficiency will be discovered.

VI. COBALT

Most interest in Co relates to the health of ruminant animals, which require Co for the synthesis of vitamin B_{12} by their rumen microflora (Underwood, 1984). For these animals, inadequate dietary Co leads to wasting diseases characterized by anemia and loss of appetite. In the case of breeding ewes Co deficiency can lead to reduced lamb weights at birth, elevated neonatal mortality, and poor lamb survival associated with depressed milk production by the ewe (Norton & Hales, 1976).

Although the essentiality of Co for animals was established in the mid 1930s (Lee, 1975), an essential role in plants was not discovered until 1960. In that year, three groups separately and independently demonstrated that Co was essential for the growth of various legumes reliant on symbiotic N_2 fixation: soybean (Ahmed & Evans, 1960), alfalfa (*Medicago sativa* L.) (Reisenauer, 1960), and subterranean clover (*Trifolium subterraneum* L.) (Hallsworth et al., 1960). Later work showed that Co was essential for N_2 fixation also in the nonlegumes *Alnus* (Hewitt & Bond, 1966) and *Azolla* (Johnson et al., 1966).

Essentiality of Co for plants not dependent on symbiotic N_2 fixation has not been established. However, beneficial effects on growth have been reported in *Hevea* (Bolle-Jones & Mallikarjuneswara, 1957), wheat (Wilson & Nicholas, 1967), and nonnodulated subterranean clover (Hallsworth et al., 1965; Wilson & Hallsworth, 1965; Wilson & Nicholas, 1967). More research is needed to provide a basis for understanding these beneficial effects.

A. Agricultural Significance

Cobalt absorption by plant roots is metabolically mediated, probably by the same transport mechanism as for Ni (Colclaisure & Schmid, 1974). Hence, it is possible to prevent Co deficiency of livestock by the use of Co-containing fertilizers on the pasture (Adams et al., 1969). However, in many situations, it is more practical to supply the Co directly to the animal via a Co bullet administered orally to the young animal.

Field responses of subterranean clover to Co fertilizer were demonstrated on poor siliceous sands in South Australia and Western Australia soon after the discovery of Co essentiality for nodulated legumes (Powrie, 1960; Ozanne et al., 1963). Later work on narrow-leafed lupins (*Lupinus angustifolius* L.)

showed that seed yield of plants grown on a deep yellow sand without deliberate additions of Co was only 40% of that on plus-Co plots (Gartrell, 1974). Narrow-leafed lupins may be particularly sensitive to Co deficiency, as Gladstones et al. (1977) demonstrated a 50% response in vegetative yield in this species at a site where *L. cosentinii, L. luteus,* and subterranean clover showed no significant response to Co. The effects of Co on the growth of narrow-leafed lupin have been associated with the delayed onset of nitrogenase activity, and marked depression of specific nitrogenase activity (only 5 to 13% of that of plus Co controls) (Dilworth et al., 1979).

Samples of seed of narrow-leafed lupin may vary widely in Co status (4–730 μg kg^{-1}) (Robson & Mead, 1980; Robson & Snowball, 1987), and the magnitude of the response to fertilizer Co has been shown to be strongly affected by Co status. Robson and Snowball (1987) concluded that yield responses to fertilizer Co are likely to be small if the seed contains >128 μg kg^{-1} Co. Further work is needed to establish the extent to which fertilization of the seed crop can be used to overcome the need for more widespread fertilization of production crops, as has been done for Mo in corn (Weir & Hudson, 1966). However, in the study by Chatel et al. (1978), fertilization of a Co-deficient sand with $CoSO_4 \cdot 7H_2O$ at 420 g ha^{-1} resulted in seed containing only a relatively low Co concentration (19–24 μg kg^{-1}).

VII. LANTHANUM AND CERIUM

The rare earths constitute a group of 14 elements (the lanthanide series of the Periodic Table) with atomic numbers ranging from 57 for La to 71 for Lu. All have chemical properties and ionic radii similar to Ca. Most agricultural and biological interest centers on La and Ce, the two lightest members of the series (Brown et al., 1990). Because of its higher charge, La^{3+} tends to replace Ca^{2+} in many biological systems.

Chinese scientists have produced a fertilizer Nongle ("happy farmer") consisting of a mixture of La and Ce nitrates, which has been applied to large (>500 000 ha in 1986) and rapidly increasing areas of land in China (Guo, 1987). Recommended rates of application as a foliar spray or seed treatment (400–700 g ha^{-1}) are in the micronutrient range. Yield responses, typically of the order of 5 to 15%, and improvements in product quality have been claimed for a wide range of annual and perennial crops (Guo, 1987). Chinese workers consider soils containing <10 or <5 mg kg^{-1} NaOAc/HOAc (pH 8.0)-extractable rare earths to be low or very low, respectively (Zhu & Liu, 1985), and presumably likely to be responsive to rare earth fertilization. Unfortunately, most of the published information, at present, comes from sources that are difficult to assess because of lack of detail concerning experimental methods and the absence of statistical treatment of the data.

No evidence for essentiality of any of the rare earths for any organism appears to have been produced so far, although there are some well-documented effects on physiological processes in both plants and animals. Detailed chemical analysis of Nongle (Table 18–7) shows that the material

Table 18-7. Chemical composition of Nongle rare earth fertilizer. (Means for two samples of fertilizer; from G.L. Kerven, 1987, unpublished data).

Component	Percent by weight
NO_3	48.7
Water of crystallization	17.2
Ce	15.4
La	9.3
Cl	5.0
Ca	2.2
Insoluble matter	0.11
Mg	0.049
Mn	0.048
Mo	0.021
Zn	0.012
B	0.008
P	≤ 0.002
S	≤ 0.002
Fe	≤ 0.002
Cu	≤ 0.002
Ni	≤ 0.002
Co	≤ 0.002
Sr	≤ 0.002

contains traces of several essential elements, but, at the recommended rates of application, it is doubtful whether any of these could be responsible for the reported beneficial effects. Hence, there is a need to examine further how these effects might come about if indeed they are real.

Wu et al. (1985) reported that addition of a rare earth Cl solution to the soil increased nodule number by 46 to 57%, acetylene reduction activity by 10 to 25%, and shoot growth of soybean plants by 32%. Similarly, Wang et al. (1985) reported that La concentrations in the range of 30 to 120 μM stimulated photosynthesis and photofixation of N by *Anabaena azotica*. Wu et al. (1985) cite earlier work in which rare earths increased uptake of ^{32}P by plant roots and affected its distribution in the leaves. Ning (1985) also referred to the stimulation of P uptake by 8 to 60% in rice and by 5 to 23% in peanut. However the results were not reported in detail.

In well-controlled experiments with corn roots, Leonard et al. (1975) found that short-term (10 min) uptake of ^{32}P was strongly stimulated by La^{3+} concentrations up to 100 μM; however, they cited unpublished information indicating that the stimulation was limited to the first 3 min of the uptake period. They concluded that the phenomenon involved nonmetabolic accumulation of a La–P complex in the apoplasm. Effects of La on K uptake were similar to the effects of Ca. In recent work at this laboratory (Weggler & Asher, 1989, unpublished data), no significant effects of low concentrations (1–10 μM) of La or Ce were found on ^{32}P uptake and transport to the tops in soybean or corn over 10 h uptake periods. Lanthanum at higher concentrations appeared phytotoxic in root elongation tests with these species.

In view of the apparently large-scale use of rare earth fertilizers in China and uncertainty about the true nature of the apparent beneficial effects, there is a need for further well-controlled and carefully documented experiments on these elements.

VIII. NEED FOR FURTHER RESEARCH

There are many questions left unanswered in relation to the precise mode of action of each of the elements discussed briefly in this chapter. In addition, there are a number of other elements not included in the review, but deserving of attention. Among these are Cr, As, Se, and the halides I and F, all of which have been shown to be required by various organisms, but, so far, not by higher plants.

REFERENCES

Adams, S.N., J.L. Honeysett, K.G. Tiller, and K. Norrish. 1969. Factors controlling the increase of cobalt in plants following the addition of a cobalt fertilizer. Aust. J. Soil Res. 7:29–42.

Ahmed, S., and H.J. Evans. 1960. Cobalt: A micronutrient element for the growth of soybean plants under symbiotic conditions. Soil Sci. 90:205–210.

Alva, A.K., F.P.C. Blamey, D.G. Edwards, and C.J. Asher. 1986. An evaluation of aluminum indices to predict aluminum toxicity to plants grown in nutrient solutions. Commun. Soil Sci. Plant Anal. 17:1271–1280.

Anderson, A.J., D.R. Meyer, and F.K. Mayer. 1973. Heavy metal toxicities: Levels of nickel, cobalt, and chromium in the soil and plants associated with visual symptoms and variation in growth of an oat crop. Aust. J. Agric. Res. 24:557–571.

Arnon, D.I., and P.R. Stout. 1939. The essentiality of certain elements in minute quantity for plants with special reference to copper. Plant Physiol. 14:371–375.

Bartha, R., and E.J. Ordal. 1965. Nickel-dependent chemolithotropic growth of two *Hydrogenomonas* strains. J. Bacteriol. 89:1015–1019.

Bell, L.C., and D.G. Edwards. 1987. The role of aluminum in acid soil infertility. p. 201–223. *In* M. Latham (ed.) Soil management under humid conditions in Asia (ASIALAND). Proc. 1st Regional Seminar Soil Management under Humid Conditions in Asia and the Pacific, Khon Kaen, Thailand. October 1986. IBSRAM Inc., Bangkok.

Bertrand, D., and A. de Wolf. 1967. Le nickel, oligo-element dynamique pour les vegetaux superieurs. C.R. Sci. Ser. A 265:1053–1055.

Bertrand, D., and A. de Wolf. 1968. Physiologie vegetale. L'aluminium, oligo-element necessaire au mais. C.R. Acad. Sci. Ser. 2 267:2325–2326.

Bertrand, D., and A. de Wolf. 1973. Importance du nickel, comme oligo-element, pour les Rhizobium des nodosites des legumineuses. C.R. Acad. Sci. Ser. A 276:1855–1858.

Bolle-Jones, E.W., and V.R. Mallikarjuneswara. 1957. Cobalt: Effects on the growth and composition of *Hevea*. J. Rubber Res. Inst. Malays. 15:128–140.

Brown, P.H., A.H. Rathgen, R.D. Graham, and D.E. Tribe. 1990. Rare earth elements in biological systems. p. 423–452. *In* K.A. Gschneider Jr. and L. Eyring (ed.) Handbook on the physics and chemistry of rare earths. Vol. 13. North Holland, Amsterdam.

Brown, P.H., R.M. Welch, and E.E. Cary. 1987a. Nickel: A micronutrient essential for higher plants. Plant Physiol. 85:801–803.

Brown, P.H., R.M. Welch, E.E. Cary, and R.T. Checkai. 1987b. Beneficial effects of nickel on plant growth. J. Plant Nutr. 10:2125–2135.

Brownell, P.F. 1968. Sodium as an essential micronutrient element for some higher plants. Plant Soil 28:161–164.

Brownell, P.F. 1979. Sodium as an essential micronutrient element for plants and its possible role in metabolism. Adv. Bot. Res. 7:117–224.

Bruce, R.C., L.A. Warrell, D.G. Edwards, and L.C. Bell. 1988. Effects of aluminium and calcium in the soil solution of acid soils on root elongation of *Glycine max* cv. Forrest. Aust. J. Agric. Res. 39:319–338.

Carlisle, E.M. 1984. Silicon. p. 548–557. *In* R.E. Olson (ed.) Nutrition review's present knowledge in nutrition. 5th ed. Nutrition Foundation Inc., Washington, DC.

Cataldo, D.A., T.R. Garland, and R.E. Wildung. 1978. Nickel in plants. 1. Uptake kinetics using intact soybean seedlings. Plant Physiol. 62:563–565.

Chatel, D.L., A.D. Robson, J.W. Gartrell, and MJ. Dilworth. 1978. The effect of inoculation and cobalt application on the growth of and nitrogen fixation by sweet lupins. Aust. J. Agric. Res. 29:1191–1202.

Chenery, E.M. 1948. Aluminum in plants and its relation to plant pigments. Ann. Bot. 12:121–136.

Clements, H.F., E.W. Putman, and J.R. Wilson. 1967. Eliminating soil toxicities with calcium metasilicate. p. 43–54. *In* Hawaiian Sugar Technol. 1967 Reports.

Colclasure, G.C., and W.E. Schmid. 1974. Absorption of cobalt by excised barley roots. Plant Cell Physiol. 15:273–279.

Dilworth, M.J., M.J. Robson, and D.L. Chatel. 1979. Cobalt and nitrogen fixation in *Lupinus angustifolius* L. II. Nodule formation and function. New Phytol. 83:63–79.

Dixon, N.E., C. Gazzola, R.L. Blakeley, and B. Zerner. 1975. Jack bean urease (EC3.5.1.5). A Metalloenzyme. A simple biological role for nickel. J. Am. Chem. Soc. 97:4131–4133.

Dobrolyubskii, O.K., and A.V. Slavvo. 1957. Use of trace element nickel for the nutrition of grapes. Dokl. Akad. Nauk. SSSR. 112:347–349.

El-Sheikh, A.M., and A. Ulrich. 1970. Interactions of rubidium, sodium, and potassium on the nutrition of sugar beet plants. Plant Physiol. 46:645–649.

Epstein, E. 1965. Mineral metabolism. p. 438–466. *In* J. Bonner and J.E. Varner (ed.) Plant biochemistry. Academic Press, New York.

Eshel, A., Y. Waisel, and A. Ramati. 1974. The role of sodium in stomatal movements in a halophyte: A study by x-ray microanalysis. p. 1–9. *In* J. Wehrmann (ed.) 7th Int. Colloq. Plant Anal. Fertilizer Problems, Hannover, FRG. September, 1974. German Soc. Plant Nutr.

Eskew, D.L., R.M. Welch, and E.E. Cary. 1983. Nickel: An essential micronutrient for legumes and possibly all higher plants. Science 222:621–623.

Eskew, D.L., R.M. Welch, and W.A. Norvell. 1984. Nickel in higher plants: Further evidence for an essential role. Plant Physiol. 76:691–693.

Evans, F.W., and F.J. Sorger. 1969. Role of mineral elements with emphasis on the univalent cations. Ann. Rev. Plant Physiol. 17:47–76.

Flowers, T.J., P.F. Troke, and A.R. Yeo. 1977. The mechanism of salt tolerance in halophytes. Ann. Rev. Plant Physiol. 28:89–121.

Fox, R.L., J.A. Silva, O.R. Younge, D.L. Plunknett, and G.D. Sherman. 1967. Soil and plant silicon and silicate response by sugar cane. Soil Sci. Soc. Am. Proc. 31:775–779.

Gartrell, J.W. 1974. Annual Report of Western Australian Department of Agriculture 1973–74.

Gladstones, J.S., J.F. Loneragan, and N.A. Goodchild. 1977. Field responses to cobalt and molybdenum by different legume species, with inferences on the role of cobalt in legume growth. Aust. J. Agric. Res. 28:619–628.

Gordon, W.R., S.S. Schwemmer, and W.S. Hillman. 1978. Nickel and the metabolism of urea by *Lemna paucicostata* Hegelm. 6746. Planta 140:265–268.

Graham, R.D., and M.J. Webb. 1990. Micronutrients and disease resistance and tolerance in plants. p. 329–370. *In* J.J. Mortvedt et al. (ed.) Micronutrients in agriculture. 2nd ed. SSSA Book Ser. 4. SSSA, Madison, WI.

Guo, BoSheng. 1987. A new application for rare earth—agriculture. p. 237–246. *In* Rare earth horizons. Aust. Dep. Industry and Commerce, Canberra, Australia.

Hallsworth, E.G., S.B. Wilson, and W.A. Adams. 1965. Effect of cobalt on the non-nodulated legume. Nature (London) 205:307–308.

Hallsworth, E.G., S.B. Wilson, and E.A.N. Greenwood. 1960. Copper and cobalt in nitrogen fixation. Nature (London) 187:79–80.

Hetherington, S.J., C.J. Asher, and F.P.C. Blamey. 1988. Comparative tolerance of sugarcane, navybean, soybean and maize to aluminium toxicity. Aust. J. Agric. Res. 38:171–176.

Hewitt, E.J. 1979. Essential and functional aspects of trace elements. p. 91–127. *In* Chemistry and agriculture. Ann. Chem. Congr. Spec. Publ. 36, Bristol, England. 3–5 April 1979. The Chemical Society, London.

Hewitt, E.J., and G. Bond. 1966. The cobalt requirement of non-legume root nodule plants. J. Exp. Bot. 17:480–491.

Hiatt, A.J., D.F. Amos, and H.F. Massey. 1963. Effect of aluminum on copper sorption by wheat. Agron. J. 55:242–287.

Jaffre, T., R.R. Brooks, and J.M. Trow. 1979. Hyperaccumulation of nickel by *Geissois* species. Plant Soil 51:157–162.

Joham, H.E., and L. Johanson. 1973. The effects of sodium and calcium on the translocation of ^{14}C-sucrose in excised cotton roots. Physiol. Plant. 28:121–126.

Johanson, L., and H.E. Joham. 1971. The influence of sodium on the calcium nutrition of excised cotton roots. Plant Soil 35:323–336.

Johnson, G.V., P.A. Mayeux, and H.J. Evans. 1966. A cobalt requirement for symbiotic growth of *Azolla fibiculoides* in the absence of combined nitrogen. Plant Physiol. 41:852–855.

Johnson, M., C.P.L. Graf, and P.F. Brownell. 1988. The effect of sodium nutrition on the pool sizes of intermediates of the C_4 pathway. Aust. J. Plant Physiol. 15:749–760.

Jones, L.H.P., and K.A. Handreck. 1967. Silica in soils, plants, and animals. Adv. Agron. 19:107–149.

Lee, H.J. 1975. Trace elements in animal production. p. 39–54. *In* D.J.D. Nicholas and A.R. Egan (ed.) Trace elements in soil-plant-animal systems. Academic Press, New York.

Lehr, J.J. 1953. Sodium as a plant nutrient. J. Sci. Food Agric. 4:460–471.

Lehr, J.J., and J.M. Wybenga. 1955. Exploratory pot experiments on sensitiveness of different crops to sodium: C. flax. Plant Soil 6:251–261.

Leonard, R.T., G. Nagahashi, and W.W. Thomson. 1975. Effect of lanthanum on ion absorption in corn roots. Plant Physiol. 55:542–546.

Lewin, J., and B.E.F. Reimann. 1969. Silicon and plant growth. Ann. Rev. Plant Physiol. 20:289–304.

Liebig, G.F., Jr., A.P. Vanselow, and H.D. Chapman. 1942. Effects of aluminum on copper toxicity, as revealed by solution-culture and spectrographic studies of citrus. Soil Sci. 53:341–351.

McHargue, J.S. 1925. The occurrence of copper, manganese, nickel and cobalt in soils, plants, and animals, and their possible function as vital factors. J. Agric. Res. 30:193–196.

Marschner, H. 1986. Mineral nutrition of higher plants. Academic Press, London.

Marschner, H., H. Oberle, I. Cakmak, and V. Romheld. 1989. Silicon prevents phosphorus toxicity in zinc deficient cucumber plants. *In* Plant Nutrition—Physiology and Applications. Proc. XI Int. Colloq. Plant Nutr. Wageningen, The Netherlands. 30 July–4 Aug. 1989. Kluwer Acad. Publ., Dordrecht, The Netherlands.

Matsumoto, H., E. Hirarsawa, M. Seiichiro, and E. Takahashi. 1976. Localization of aluminum in tea leaves. Plant Cell Physiol. 17:627–631.

Mishra, D., and M. Kar. 1974. Nickel in plant growth and metabolism. Bot. Rev. 40:395–449.

Miyake, Y., and E. Takahashi. 1978. Silicon deficiency of tomato plant. Soil Sci. Plant Nutr. 24:175–178.

Miyake, Y., and E. Takahashi. 1983. Effect of silicon on the growth of solution-cultured cucumber plant. Soil Sci. Plant Nutr. 29:71–83.

Miyake, Y., and E. Takahashi. 1985. Effect of silicon on the growth of soybean plants in a solution culture. Soil Sci. Plant Nutr. 31:625–636.

Miyake, Y., and E. Takahashi. 1986. Effect of silicon on the growth and fruit production of strawberry plants in a solution culture. Soil Sci. Plant Nutr. 32:321–326.

Nable, R.O., and P.F. Brownell. 1984. Effect of sodium and light upon the concentrations of alanine in leaves of C4 plants. Aust. J. Plant Physiol. 11:314–324.

Nicholas, D.J.D. 1961. Minor mineral nutrients. Ann. Rev. Plant Physiol. 12:63–90.

Nielsen, F.H. 1984. Ultratrace elements in nutrition. Ann. Rev. Nutr. 4:21–41.

Nielsen, F.H. 1986. Other elements: Sb, Ba, B, Br, Cs, Ge, Rb, Ag, Sv, Sr, Ti, Zr, Be, Bi, Ga, Au, In, Nb, Sc, Te, Tl, W. p. 415–463. *In* W. Mertz (ed.) Trace elements in human and animal nutrition. 5th ed. Academic Press, New York.

Nielsen, FH., C.D. Hunt, L.M. Mullen, and J.R. Hunt. 1987. Effect of dietary boron on mineral, estrogen, and testosterone metabolism in postmenopausal women. FASEB J. 1:394–397.

Nielsen, F.H., and W. Mertz. 1984. Other trace elements. 5th ed. p. 607–618. *In* R.E. Olson (ed.) Nutrition review's present knowledge in nutrition. The Nutrition Foundation, Washington, DC.

Ning Jiaben. 1985. The results of applying rare earth elements to rice and other crops. p. 1518–1521. *In* Xu Guangxian and Xiao Jimei (ed.) New frontiers in rare earth science and applications. Proc. Int. Conf. Rare Earth Devel. and Appl., Beijing, China 10–14 Sept. 1985. Science Press, Beijing, China.

Nitsos, R.E., and H.J. Evans. 1969. Effects of univalent cations on the activity of particulate starch synthetase. Plant Physiol. 44:1260–1266.

Norton, B.W., and J.W. Hales. 1976. A response of sheep to cobalt supplementation in southeastern Queensland. Proc. Aust. Soc. Anim. Prod. 11:393–396.

Okuda, A., and E. Takahashi. 1965. The role of silicon. p. 123–146. *In* The mineral nutrition of the rice plant. Proc. Symp. Int. Rice Res. Inst., Los Banos. February, 1964. Johns Hopkins, Baltimore, MD.

Ozanne, P.G., E.A.N. Greenwood, and T.C. Shaw. 1963. The cobalt requirement of subterranean clover in the field. Aust. J. Agric. Res. 14:39–50.

Parry, D.W., and S.L. Sony. 1972. Electron-probe microanalysis of silicon in the roots of *Oryza sativa* L. Ann. Bot. 36:781–783.

Playne, M.J. 1970. The sodium concentration in some tropical pasture species with reference to animal requirements. Aust. J. Exp. Agric. Anim. Husb. 10:32–35.

Polacco, J.C. 1976. Nitrogen metabolism in soybean tissue culture. Plant Physiol. 58:350–357.

Powrie, J.K. 1960. A field response by subterranean clover to cobalt fertilizer. Aust. J. Sci. 23:198–199.

Raghavendra, A.S., I.M. Rao, and V.S.R. Das. 1976. Replacibility of potassium by sodium for stomatal opening in epidermal strips of *Commelina benghalensis*. Z. Pflanzenphysiol. 80:36–42.

Raven, J.A. 1983. The transport and functions of silicon in plants. Bot. Rev. 58:179–207.

Reisenauer, H.M. 1960. Cobalt in nitrogen fixation by a legume. Nature (London) 186:375–376.

Roach, W.A., and C. Barclay. 1946. Nickel and multiple trace-element deficiencies in agricultural crops. Nature (London) 157:696.

Robson, A.D., and G.R. Mead. 1980. Seed cobalt in *Lupins angustifolius*. Aust. J. Agric. Res. 31:109–116.

Robson, A.D., and K. Snowball. 1987. Response of narrow-leafed lupins to cobalt concentration in seed. Aust. J. Exp. Agric. 27:657–660.

Sangster, A.G., and D.W. Parry. 1976. The ultrastructure and electron-probe microassay of silicon deposits in the endodermis of the seminal roots of *Sorghum bicolor* (L.) Moench. Ann. Bot. 40:447–459.

Schwarz, K. 1974. Recent dietary trace element research, exemplified by tin, fluorine, and silicon. Fed. Proc. 33:1748–1757.

Scurfield, G., and C.A. Anderson. 1974. Silica in woody stems. Aust. J. Bot. 22:211–229.

Shimada, N., and T. Ando. 1980. Nippon dojo hiryogaku zasshi. 51:493.

Smith, F.W. 1974. The effect of sodium on potassium nutrition and ionic relations in Rhodes grass. Aust. J. Agric. Res. 25:407–414.

Suehisa, R.H., O.R. Young, and D.G. Sherman. 1963. Effects of silicates on phosphorus availability to Sudangrass grown on Hawaiian soils. Hawaii Agric. Exp. Stn. Tech. Bull. 51.

Suthipradit, S. 1988. Effects of aluminium on growth and nodulation of some tropical crop legumes. Ph.D. thesis. University of Queensland, Australia.

Swaine, D.J. 1955. The trace element content of soils. Commonwealth Bur. Soil Sci. Tech. Comm. 48. Herald Print. Works, York, England.

Takahashi, E., J.F. Ma, and Y. Miyake. 1990. The possibility of silicon as an essential element for higher plants. p. 99–122. *In* Comments on Agriculture and Food Chemistry. Gordon and Breach Sci. Publ., Great Britain.

Trelease, S.F., and H.M. Trelease. 1933. Physiologically balanced culture solutions with stable hydrogen-ion concentration. Science 78:438–439.

Underwood, E.J. 1984. Cobalt. p. 528–537. *In* R.E. Olson (ed.) Nutrition review's present knowledge in nutrition. 5th ed. The Nutrition Foundation, Washington, DC.

Vanselow, A.P. 1966. Nickel. p. 302–309. *In* H.D. Chapman (ed.) Diagnostic criteria for plants and soils. Univ. California Citrus Res. Ctr. Agric. Exp. Stn., Riverside, CA.

Walker, C.D., R.D. Graham, J.T. Madison, E.E. Cary, and R.M. Welch. 1985. Effects of Ni deficiency on some nitrogen metabolites in cowpeas (*Vigna unguiculata* L. Walp). Plant Physiol. 79:474–479.

Wang Lanxiam, Zhong Xu, Xiangyu Wu, and Tang Renhuan. 1985. Effects of rare earth elements on photosynthesis and photofixation of nitrogen in *Anabaena azotica*. p. 1527–1529. *In* Xu Guangxian and Xiao Jimei (ed.) New frontiers in rare earth science and applications. Proc. Int. Conf. Rare Earth Develop. Appl., Beijing, China. 10–14 Sept. 1985. Science Press, Beijing, China.

Weast, R.C. 1969. Handbook of physics and chemistry. Chemical Rubber Co., Cleveland, OH.

Weir, R.G., and A. Hudson. 1966. Molybdenum deficiency in maize in relation to seed reserves. Aust. J. Exp. Agric. Anim. Husb. 6:35–41.

Welch, R.M. 1981. The biological significance of nickel. J. Plant Nutr. 3:345–356.

Werner, D., and R. Roth. 1983. Silica metabolism. p. 682–692. *In* A. Lauchli and Bieleski (ed.) Inorganic plant nutrition. Encyclopedia of plant physiol. New Ser. 15. Springer Verlag, Berlin.

Wilson, S.B., and E.G. Hallsworth. 1965. Studies on the nutrition of forage legumes. IV. The effect of cobalt on the growth of nodulated and non-nodulated *Trifolium subterraneum* L. Plant Soil 22:260–279.

Wilson, S.B., and D.J.D. Nicholas. 1967. A cobalt requirement for non-nodulated legumes and wheat. Phytochemistry 6:1057–1060.

Wolff, J. 1913. The influence of iron in the development of barley, and the nature of its action. C. R. Acad. Sci. Ser. 2 157:1022–1024.

Woolley, J.T. 1957. Sodium and silicon as nutrients for the tomato plant. Plant Physiol. 32:317–321.

Wu Zhaoming, Li Jiage, Xu Ji, and Xin Shuying. 1985. The effect of rare earth elements on nodulation and nitrogen fixation of soybean plants. p. 1515–1517. *In* Xu Guangxian and Xiao Jimei (ed.) New frontiers in rare earth science and applications. Proc. Int. Conf. Rare Earth Develop. Appl., Beijing, China. 10–14 Sept. 1985. Science Press, Beijing, China.

Zhu Quiqing, and Liu Zheng. 1985. Soluble rare earth elements in soils. p. 1511–1514. *In* Xu Guangxian and Xiao Jimei (ed.) New frontiers in rare earth science and applications. Proc. Int. Conf. Rare Earth Develop. Appl., Beijing, China. Science Press, Beijing, China.

GLOSSARY

Botanical Names of Plants

Common name	Scientific name
Acacia	*Robinia* spp.
African oil palm	*Elaeis guineensis* Jacq.
Alder (black)	*Alnus glutinosa* (L.) Gaertn.
Alfalfa	*Medicago sativa* L.
Alkali princesplume	*Stanleya bipinnata* (Pursh.) Britt.
Almond	*Prunus dulcus*
Apple	*Malus domestica* Borkh.
Apricot	*Prunus armeniaca* L.
Areca palm	*Areca catechu* L.
Asparagus	*Asparagus officinalis* L.
Avocado	*Persea americana*
Bambatsi grass	*Panicum coloratum* L. var. *makarikariense* Goosens
Banana	*Musa* spp.
Barley	*Hordeum vulgare* L.
Bean	*Phaseolus vulgaris* L.
Beet (sugar)	*Beta vulgaris* L.
(fodder)	*Beta vulgaris* L.
Bell pepper	*Capsicum frutescens* L.
Bermuda grass	*Cynodon dactylon* (L.) Pers.
Black gum	*Nyassa sylvatica*
Black pepper	*Piper nigrum*
Blueberry	*Vaccinium corymbosum*
Bluegrass	*Poa pratensis* L.
Broccoli	*Brassica oleracea* L. Botrytis Group
Brussels sprouts	*Brassica oleracea* L. Gemmifera Group
Buckwheat	*Fagopyrum esculentum* Moench.
Buffel grass	*Cenchrus ciliaris*
Cabbage	*Brassica oleracea* L. Capitata Group
Camellia	*Camellia japonica*
Canola	*Brassica napus* L.
Caraway	*Carum carvi* L.
Carnation	*Dianthus caryophyllus* L.
Carrot	*Daucus carota* L.
Castor bean	*Ricinus communis* L.
Cauliflower	*Brassica oleracea* L. Botrytis Group
Celery	*Apium graveolens* (Miller) Pers.
Cherry	*Prunus cerasus* L.
Chicory	*Chichorium intybus* L.
Chickpea	*Cicer arietinum* L.
Chrysanthemum	*Chrysanthemum morifolium*
Citrus	*Citrus sinensis* (L.) Osbeck
Clover (alsike)	*Trifolium hybridum* L.
(crimson)	*Trifolium incarnatum* L.
(ladino)	*Trifolium repens* f. *lodigense* Gams

(continued on next page)

Common name	Scientific name
Clover (red)	*Trifolium pratense* L.
(subterranean)	*Trifolium subterraneum* L.
(white)	*Trifolium repens* L.
Cocklebur	*Xanthium pensylvanicum* Wallr.
Cocoa	*Theobroma cacao* L.
Coconut	*Cocos nucifera* L.
Coffee	*Coffea arabica* L.
Corn	*Zea mays* L.
Cotton	*Gossypium* spp.
Cottonwood	*Populus* spp.
Cowpea	*Vigna unguiculata* (L.) Walp
Cucumber	*Cucumis sativa* L.
Dandelion	*Taraxacum* spp.
Duckweed	*Lemna minor*
Eggplant	*Solanum melongena* L.
Eucalyptus	*Eucalyptus* spp.
Fescue	*Festuca arundinacea* Schreb.
Flax	*Linum usitatissimum* L.
Geranium	*Pelargonium zonale*
Ginseng	*Aralia* spp.
Gladiolus	*Gladiolus* spp.
Grape	*Vitis vinifera* L.
Grapefruit	*Citrus paradisi* L.
Green gram	*Phaseolus aureus* Roxb.
Groundnut	*Arachis hypogaea* L.
Guar	*Cyamopsis psoralides*
Hazelnut	*Corylus americana* Walt.
Hops	*Humulus* spp.
Horseradish	*Armoracia rusticana* P. Gaertner, Meyer & Scherb.
Jackbean	*Canavalia ensiforms* (L.) DC
Kale	*Brassica oleracea* L. Acephala Group
Kidney bean	*Phaseolus vulgaris* L.
Kiwi fruit	*Actinidia deliciosa*
Kohlrabi	*Brassica oleracea* L. Gongylodes Group
Lemon	*Citrus limon* Burmif.
Lentil	*Lens culinaris* Medic
Lespedeza	*Lespedeza* spp.
Lettuce	*Lactuca sativa* L.
Lima bean	*Phaseolus humilis* Alef.
Linseed	*Linum usitatissimum* L.
Locust (black)	*Robina pseudoacacia* L.
Lucerne	*Medicago sativa* L.
Lupin (narrow-leafed)	*Lupinus angustifolius* L.
(white)	*Lupinus albus* L.
Macadamia	*Macadamia ternifolia*
Maize	*Zea mays* L.
Mandarin	*Citrus reticulata*
Mangold	*Beta vulgaris* subsp. *vulgaris*

(continued on next page)

Common name	Scientific name
Medic	*Medicago* spp.
Melon	*Cucumis melon* L.
Millet	*Panicum miliaceum* L.
Mungbean	*Phaseolus aureus* Roxb.
Mushroom	*Agaricus campestris*
Mustard	*Brassica nigra* (L.) Koch
Oat	*Avena sativa* L.
Onion	*Allium cepa* L.
Orange (sweet)	*Citrus sinensis* L.
Pangola grass	*Digitaria decumbens* Stent
Parsley	*Petroselinum crispum* (Miller) A. W. Hill
Parsnip	*Pastinaca sativa* L.
Pea	*Pisum sativum* L.
Pea bean	*Phaseolus vulgaris* L.
Peach	*Prunus persica* L.
Peanut	*Arachis hypogaea* L.
Pear	*Pyrus communis* L.
Pecan	*Carya ilinoensis* Wang.
Peppermint	*Mentha* × *piperita* L.
Pigweed	*Amaranthus* spp.
Pine	*Pinus radiata*
Pineapple	*Ananas comosus*
Poplar	*Populus* spp.
Poppy	*Papaver* spp.
Potato	*Solanum tuberosum* L.
Prune	*Prunus domestica*
Radish	*Raphanus sativus* L.
Rape	*Brassica napus* L.
Red beet	*Beta vulgaris* subsp. *vulgaris*
Rhodes grass	*Chloris gayana* Kunth
Rice	*Oryza sativa* L.
Rubber	*Hevea brasiliensis*
Rutabaga	*Brassica napobrassica* L.
Rye	*Secale cereale* L.
Ryegrass (annual)	*Lolium multiflorum* Lam.
(perennial)	*Lolium perenne* L.
Sabi grass	*Urochloa mosambicensis* (Hack.) Dandy
Safflower	*Carthamus tinctorius* L.
Signal grass	*Brachiaria decumbens* Stapf.
Silver maple	*Acer saccharinum*
Snapbean	*Phaseolus vulgaris* L.
Sorghum	*Sorghum bicolor* (L.) Moench.
Soybean	*Glycine max* (L.) Merr.
Spearmint	*Mentha spicata* L.
Spinach	*Spinacia oleracea* L.
Squash	*Cucurbita* spp.
Strawberry	*Fragaria ananassa* Duchesne
Sudangrass	*Sorghum vulgare sudanese*

(continued on next page)

Common name	Scientific name
Sugarcane	*Saccharum officinarum* L.
Sunflower	*Helianthus annuus* Mill.
Swede	*Brassica napus* L. Napobrassica Group
Sweet cherry	*Prunus avium* L.
Sweet corn	*Zea saccharata* L.
Swiss chard	*Beta vulgaris* subsp. cicla (L.) Koch
Tea	*Camellia sinensis* (L.) Kuntze
Timothy	*Phleum pratense* L.
Tobacco	*Nicotiana tabacum* L.
Tomato	*Lycopersicon esculentum* Mill.
Twogrooved loco weed	*Astragalus bisulcatus* Hook.
Tung	*Aleurites* spp.
Turnip	*Brassica rapa* L. Rapifera Group
Vetch	*Vicia sativa* L.
Watercress	*Nasturtium officinale* R. Br.
Watermelon	*Citrullus vulgaris* Schrad.
Wheat	*Triticum aestivum* L.
White bean	*Phaseolus coccineus* cv. Albus
Yucca	*Manihot esculenta* Crantz

Scientific Names of Plant Pathogens

Pathogen	Common name	Crop affected
Agrobacterium tumefaciens	Crown gall	
Alternaria		Sunflower
Alternaria kikuchiana		
Cladosporium cladosporoides		
Cochliobolus miyabeanus	Brown spot	Rice
Colletotrichum		Bean
Colletotrichum musae		Banana
Curvularia		
Diaporthe citri	Stem end-rot	Citrus
Epicoccum		
Erwinia carotovora	Wilt	Flax
Erysiphe graminis	Powdery mildew	Barley, wheat
Exserohilum		Areca palm
Exserohilum	Northern leaf blight	Corn
Fusarium		Flax
Fusarium	Wilt	Carnation, cotton, cucumber, pea, radish, tomato
Fusarium	Root rot	Chickpea
Fusarium graminearum		Wheat
Fusarium oxysporum		
Fusarium solani		Bean
Gaeumannomyces graminis	Take-all, haydie	Wheat

(continued on next page)

Pathogen	Common name	Crop affected
Gibberella fujikuroi	Stalk rot	Corn
Gibberella zeae	Stalk rot	Corn
Heterodera		Sugarbeet
Heterodera avenae	Cereal cyst nematode	Barley
Leptosphaeria maculans		Rape
Myrothecium roridum		
Oidium heveae		Rubber
Olpidium brassicae		Cabbage
Ophiobolus		Turf grass
Penicillium		
Penicillium citrinum		
Petrobia latens	Mite	Wheat
Phoma herbarum	Leaf spot	Peanut
Phymatotrichopsis omnivorum	Root rot	Cotton
Phytophthora cinnamomi		Eucalyptus
Phytophthora dreschsleri		
Phytophthora megasperma		
Phytophthora nicotianae	Brown-rot	Mandarin
Piricularia oryzae	Brown spot	Rice
Plasmodiophora brassicae	Clubroot	Swede
Pseudomonas cichorii		Ginseng
Pseudomonas putida		
Puccinia helianthi		
Puccinia striiformis	Stripe rust	Wheat
Puccinia triticina		Wheat
Pyricularia oryzae		Rice
Pythium		Wheat
Rhizoctonia bataticola		Groundnut
Rhizoctonia solani	Black-scurf	Cowpea, mungbean, pea, potato
Rotylenchulus reniformis	Nematode	Tomato
Sclerophthora macrospora	Downy mildew	Millet
Sclerotina		
Sclerotium rolfsii	Foot rot	Soybean
Septoria	Wheat	
Sphaeropsis malorum		Apple, pear
Spongospora subterranea	Crook rot	Watercress
Stereum strigosazonatum		
Streptomyces scabies	Common scab	Potato
Synchytrium endobioticum	Wart disease	Potato
Trametes versicolor		
Trichoderma		
Uromyces phaseoli	Rust	Bean, cowpea
Uromyces vigna		Bean
Verticillium albo-atrum	Wilt	Cotton, tomato

Scientific Names of Animals

Common name	Scientific name
Cat	*Felinus catus*
Chicken	*Gallus domesticus*
Cow	*Bos taurus*
Dog	*Canis familiaris*
Duck	*Anas* spp.
Goat	*Capra hircus*
Guinea pig	*Cavia cobaya*
Hamster	*Cricetus cricetus*
Hedgehog	*Erinaceus europaeus*
Horse	*Equus caballus*
Minipig	*Sus scrofa*
Mouse	*Mus musculus*
Oyster	*Ostrea* spp.
Pig	*Sus* spp.
Quail	*Colinus virginianus*
Quokka	*Setonix brachyurus*
Rabbit	*Lepus cuniculus*
Rat	*Rattus norvegicus*
Roe deer	*Capreolus capreolus*
Sheep	*Ovis aries*
Turkey	*Meleagris gallopavo*
Whale	*Odontoceti* spp.

Fertilizers and Chelates

Fertilizers	Abbreviation
Ammonium orthophosphate	AOP
Ammonium polyphosphate	APP
Nitric phosphate	NP
Ordinary superphosphate	OSP
Triple superphosphate	TSP
Urea ammonium nitrate	UAN
Urea phosphate	UP
Chelates (see also Table 7-1, page 188)	
Citrate	CIT
Cyclohexanediaminetetraacetic acid	CDTA
Diethylenetriaminepentaacetic acid	DTPA
Ethylenediamine di(o-hydroxyphenylacetic acid)	EDDHA
Ethylenediaminetetraacetic acid	EDTA
Ethylene glycol-bis(2-aminoethylether)tetraacetic acid	EGTA
N-hydroxyethylethylenediaminetriacetic acid	HEDTA
Nitrilotriacetic acid	NTA

SUBJECT INDEX

Refer to the Glossary preceding this index for a listing of common and scientific names of plants, animals, and plant pathogens. The abbreviations for fertilizers and chelates are also listed.